HERMAN MELVILLE

LIBRARY OF ESSENTIAL WRITERS

HERMAN MELVILLE

◆

SEVEN NOVELS

◆

COMPLETE AND UNABRIDGED

Typee • Omoo • Mardi • Redburn •

White-Jacket • Moby-Dick • Billy Budd, Sailor

BARNES & NOBLE
NEW YORK

Barnes & Noble, Inc.
122 Fifth Avenue
New York, NY 10011

ISBN-13: 978-0-7607-9021-2

Printed and bound in China

1 3 5 7 9 10 8 6 4 2

Contents

Introduction

At his death in 1891 Herman Melville was a nearly forgotten author, remembered vaguely perhaps as a writer of sea adventures. The renown he enjoyed from the success of his first two books, *Typee* and *Omoo,* had dwindled over the decades since he burst onto the American literary landscape. Almost thirty years before his death, Melville had essentially given up writing fiction and turned to poetry. For the last years of his life, this giant of American letters worked as a deputy inspector at the Customs House in New York City and published small volumes of verse. *Moby-Dick,* perhaps the most studied book in the history of American literature, had been a failure during Melville's lifetime, and had become merely a line in the bibliography of a once popular novelist. All of this would change in the early decades of the twentieth century when Melville was "rediscovered" by American academics. Since that time, his exalted stature in American literature has been assured. A brilliant and enormously influential novel, *Moby-Dick* is the work of a confident writer grappling with weighty philosophical issues and experimenting with narrative form. A clear line of artistic progress can be traced in Melville's work up through the novel. Like most good writers, he improved at his craft over time. As his ambitions for what he could achieve through the novel expanded, his writing skills evolved commensurately. Unfortunately for his financial well-being, the reading public did catch up to him in his lifetime.

Herman Melville was born in New York City on August 1, 1819, into a family with ties to America's aristocracy. His paternal grandfather had participated in the Boston Tea Party, and his maternal grandfather had served as a general in the Revolutionary War. His distinguished lineage notwithstanding, Melville's childhood was hard. His father's business went bankrupt in 1830, after which the family moved to Albany, New York seeking better financial prospects. Apparently, the financial failure caused something to snap in Melville's father. He suffered a breakdown and died only two years after the bankruptcy. Melville and his brother began working to help support the family, and he soon acquired a lengthy resume that included positions as bank clerk, surveyor, and schoolteacher. A strong desire, to support himself independently, perhaps owing to the memory of his father's breakdown, was a motivating force throughout his life.

Melville's most important early vocation was serving as a sailor. His brother got him a job as a cabin boy on a ship sailing for Liverpool in 1839. Less than two years later he took to the sea again, as a hand aboard a whaling ship. Melville deserted from that ship in the Marquesas Islands and lived among the locals there for a time. Eventually, he got passage to Honolulu where he worked as a clerk for several months before placing himself on the frigate, *United States,* and returning home. These voyages contained the seeds of all that he was to write about for the next decade of his life: life on a ship, whaling, and brushes with authoritarian figures.

Melville's experiences in the Marquesas became the basis for his first book, *Typee,* published in 1846. *Typee* is narrated by Tommo, a sailor aboard *The Dolly* who abandons ship for the nearby by islands to escape the harshness and cruelty of life aboard ship. For all of his love of the sea, Melville frequently depicted the sailor's life as difficult and oppressive. In *Typee,* the society of the ship serves as a metaphor for society as a whole, and Melville establishes a clear dichotomy between Western and non-Western culture. The novel promotes the ideal of the "noble savage" and depicts the fearsome cannibals known as the Typee as more civilized than their Western counterparts. The strict regimen of shipboard life mirrors the constraints and restrictions of "civilized" life in the West, which contrasts sharply with the idyllic, natural life of the Typee.

In Melville's time, travel literature that offered a look at an alien and mysterious land that "civilized" folk could enjoy from the safety of their own homes was popular, and *Typee* proved a huge success. Marketed as a factual travelogue, the book sold well and immediately established Melville's literary reputation. Although the book found an audience, there was some controversy at publication as to whether the book was entirely factual or not. The debate over this became a critical point of contention, one that Melville argued. The argument was settled when Melville's former shipmate and fellow-deserter, Richard Tobias Greene, on whom Melville had modeled Tommo's friend, Toby, came to Melville's defense. Of course, we know today that while *Typee* has some basis in events that happened in Melville's life, it is a work of fiction.

The debate over the reality of the adventures described in *Typee* is of little consequence today. The novel is the work of a very skilled writer and the original debate sprung, in part, from how well it was written. Some argued that a sailor could not such an account so articulately. *Typee* clearly demonstrates Melville's descriptive skill, his ability to chronicle the natural world and to bring to glorious life the minutiae of a ship. In his first book, Melville showed a talent for fashioning a believable world, rich in detail, where living and breathing men struggle and sweat. The story also touches on themes that Melville would explore more deeply in later works. *Typee* is not as psychologically complex a tale as *Moby-Dick,* yet one sees in its telling the same struggle between light and dark that is the foundation of Melville's mature work. Tommo fears the Typee at first, but comes to understand and admire them. Nevertheless, the Typee are not idealized humans; their cannibalism prevents so facile a distinction. The grayness , the shading of dark into light, is a part of *Typee,* just as it is in Melville's masterpiece, *Moby-Dick.*

Omoo, published in 1847, was also marketed as a travel book. It is a sequel to *Typee* and tells of Tommo's adventure after leaving the Marquesas for Tahiti. Again, Melville captured the local life of the islands in vivid detail. Also again, Melville portrays the natives as people of some complexity who are a contrast to the world which Tommo knows. Like *Typee, Omoo* was a success and as a result Melville was able to devote himself solely to writing. In 1847 he married Elizabeth Shaw, the daughter of Lemuel Shaw, the Chief Justice of the Massachusetts Supreme Court. Herman and Elizabeth moved to New York City in 1847 and stayed there until 1850.

Melville's ambitions as a writer were changing. Both *Typee* and *Omoo* were proof that he had talent, both proved he could weave an engaging narrative, and both demonstrated a desire to touch on, however briefly, themes of struggle and the vagaries of the human heart. Melville, however, hoped to go farther afield thematically. *Mardi,* his next book, veered from the previous two in its more philosophical tone and in measuring the moral compass of individual lives. Though clearly rooted in Melville's own experiences as a seaman, *Mardi* was more clearly a work of fiction than either *Typee* or *Omoo.* Like those books, *Mardi* features sailing and adventures in the South Seas, yet it reads less like a travelogue and more like a novel of ideas.

Mardi, published in 1849, was apparently written to be a more conventional adventure narrative, intended as an answer of sorts to the attacks on the veracity of *Typee* and *Omoo.* In his preface to the book, Melville writes, "Not long ago, having published two narratives of voyages in the Pacific, which, in many quarters, were received with incredulity, the thought occurred to me, of indeed writing a romance of Polynesian adventure . . ." Melville seemed to be saying to his critics "if you want a pure adventure story, then I'll give you one." But he could not, given his increasingly metaphysical speculation, follow through completely.

Mardi abounds with conversations between characters that reflect on the nature of man, nobility, even morality. The "adventure" of the narrative is merely a jumping off point for many of their philosophical reflections. The book delves into the underpinnings of what makes us human, touching on the darker places in the soul. Melville again portrays exotic native peoples and contrasts their lives with those of westerners, but here the characters take in what they experience and offer commentary on what it means to them. In this novel, Melville attempts to uncover the heart of good and evil in its complex forms.

Reading Melville's novels in chronological order one can trace his evolution as a literary artist, and see his confidence grow not only in terms of his craft, but in his tackling of weighty themes. *Mardi* marks a critical point in Melville's development because it anticipates his masterworks to come. Another great benefit to reading Melville's works in chronological order is to see how his real-life experience informs his art. By the time of *Mardi's* publication, Melville was a family man, supporting not only his immediate family but also, after the death of his brother, his extended family. His father gone, his older brother gone, Melville became the man of two houses. *Typee* and *Omoo* were popular successes that had afforded Melville the opportunity to write full time. The more thematically complex *Mardi* did not find the same favor with the public, and as a result Melville was faced with something of a dilemma. He craved the freedom to pursue his ambitions as a writer, but he needed money to care for his family and thus needed to sell books to be able to continue working solely as a writer.

Melville wrote his next two novels largely with an eye toward making money. He completed *Redburn,* published in 1849, in ten weeks. Possibly hoping to experience the same success he enjoyed with *Typee* and *Omoo,* Melville drew on his first voyage at sea, when he served as a cabin boy on a vessel bound for England. *Redburn* tells the story of Wellingborough Redburn, a young man from a once well-off family who must go to sea to earn money. Perhaps Melville intended his novel to be a fairly straightforward coming-of-age tale with some adventure thrown in. However, a trip to England was not nearly as enticing to the public as a voyage to the South Seas and the book did not sell particularly well.

Reading the book now, it is possible to see why it did not find favor with the public. Redburn is relatively naïve and innocent, and somewhat racist in how he views people different from himself: he can't understand them, yet to make his way in the world he must. The book also gives a rather startling portrait of industrialized England and the squalor in which many lived at that time. Once again, Melville could not merely write a straight narrative, despite his best intentions. It should have been fairly evident to almost anyone that this odd book, with its chapters on England, would not garner a huge following.

The hard-working Melville ventured on to his next project, *White-Jacket,* published in 1850. He also wrote this novel quickly, reportedly in two months, and drew his subject matter from another early experience, sailing on the Navy frigate *United States.* The novel explores life aboard a Navy ship in such great detail that the reader can easily sense the monotony of shipboard routine while reading the book.

All Melville protagonists are marked as outsiders in some way. Through the circumstances of their voyages, owing to their backgrounds, or because of their temperaments, these characters do not fit in easily among peers. Although all are hard-working and able to pull their own weight aboard ship, they are rarely comfortable with their fellow sailors. The eponymous narrator of *White-Jacket* is perhaps the best example of this quality in Melville's writing up to that point in his career. He creates the garment of the title at the beginning of the book, an odd coat, brightly white, made piecemeal from other scraps of clothing and intended as protection against the cold weather. It immediately sets him apart from his fellow sailors. He is among them, but not of them, the white garment a continuous reminder of his inability to completely conform. White-Jacket, as the narrator is known, is an obvious precursor to Ishmael, the narrator of *Moby-Dick.*

White-Jacket did not prove to be a strong seller and Melville was forced to struggle on, weighing the merits of his literary ambitions against the fickleness of a reading public that again and again had shown itself to be not overly fond of his books any more. In 1850, Melville bought a farm in Pittsfield, Massachusetts. He lived there for the next thirteen years, writing and working the farm. The move proved most fruitful, for with it he became friends with Nathaniel Hawthorne. Hawthorne's own ideas of literature and his artistic inquiries into humanity's sinful nature inspired Melville to attempt increasingly complex explorations of good and evil. Melville dedicated his next novel, *Moby-Dick,* to Hawthorne.

Moby-Dick remains as vibrant, as strikingly original today as it did when first published in 1851. It is one of those timeless novels that each generation can approach and relish, not as a monument to the past, but as a work that speaks anew with each reading. The remarkable opening of the novel is a perfect introduction for what is to come. It begins easily enough, with the narrator's invitation to "Call me Ishmael," but then in a few sentences Melville reveals Ishmael to be a complex man struggling with the meaning of his own existence. "Whenever I find myself growing grim about the mouth; whenever it is a damp, drizzly November in my soul; whenever I find myself involuntarily pausing before coffin warehouses . . . I account it high time to get to sea as soon as I can."

That opening is a marvel with which Melville makes his case in a confident, remarkable style. This will be no simple adventure story, no travelogue; it will be a work of art that wrestles with serious questions, that shines a light on the darkness in man's heart. Ostensibly, it is the story of Ishmael's time aboard the whaling ship *Pequod,* but of course the voyage is anything but simple. Ishmael and the other sailors, especially his friend Queequeg, are caught in a battle of natural wills between the evil represented by the white whale Moby-Dick and the evil of the mad Ahab. There is no escape from these two extremes; they define the world aboard ship and outside it, with the result that the men are inexorably caught in a battle of wills beyond their control. It is a novel full of exciting characters: the thoughtful Ishmael, the noble Queequeg, and towering over them all the driven, monomaniacal Ahab. Perhaps the most memorable character in the history of American literature, Ahab dominates the book. He is man's will corroded by blind revenge. *Moby-Dick* is one of those truly rare literary feats, a book that can be almost all things to all people: a meditation on evil, a journey into the heart of sin, a metaphor for the darkness in all men's hearts. It is a book that changed American literature.

Moby-Dick, however, was not a financial success. In fact, it was badly reviewed and largely ignored. The mature Melville went on to write other master works, the short stories "Bartleby the Scrivener" and "Benito Cereno," and the short novel *Billy Budd* which was found incomplete among his papers at his death and published posthumously in 1924. These works, too, explore the moral dilemmas facing humanity, but Melville never again experienced any notoriety for examining them in his lifetime. He went on to take the job in the Customs House so that he could provide for his family and then died without fanfare in 1891. The world was still not quite ready to accept the brilliance of Herman Melville at the time of his death. Fortunately, his genius persisted through his enduring works until the rest of the world caught up to him.

TOMMY JENKINS

Tommy Jenkins is a published author and has taught creative writing for several years. He studied at the University of North Carolina as an undergraduate and holds a master's degree from Columbia University. He is currently studying and teaching creative writing at North Carolina State University.

TYPEE

A ROMANCE OF THE SOUTH SEAS

TO

LEMUEL SHAW,

CHIEF JUSTICE OF THE COMMONWEALTH OF MASSACHUSETTS,

THIS LITTLE WORK IS GRATEFULLY INSCRIBED

BY THE AUTHOR.

Contents

Preface

More than three years have elapsed since the occurrence of the events recorded in this volume. The interval, with the exception of the last few months, has been chiefly spent by the author tossing about on the wide ocean. Sailors are the only class of men who now-a-days see anything like stirring adventure; and many things which to fireside people appear strange and romantic, to them seem as common-place as a jacket out at elbows. Yet, notwithstanding the familiarity of sailors with all sorts of curious adventure, the incidents recorded in the following pages have often served, when "spun as a yarn," not only to relieve the weariness of many a night-watch at sea, but to excite the warmest sympathies of the author's shipmates. He has been, therefore, led to think that his story could scarcely fail to interest those who are less familiar than the sailor with a life of adventure.

In his account of the singular and interesting people among whom he was thrown, it will be observed that he chiefly treats of their more obvious peculiarities; and, in describing their customs, refrains in most cases from entering into explanations concerning their origin and purposes. As writers of travels among barbarous communities are generally very diffuse on these subjects, he deems it right to advert to what may be considered a culpable omission. No one can be more sensible than the author of his deficiencies in this and many other respects; but when the very peculiar circumstances in which he was placed are understood, he feels assured that all these omissions will be excused.

In very many published narratives no little degree of attention is bestowed upon dates; but as the author lost all knowledge of the days of the week, during the occurrence of the scenes herein related, he hopes that the reader will charitably pass over his shortcomings in this particular.

In the Polynesian words used in this volume—except in those cases where the spelling has been previously determined by others—that form of orthography has been employed, which might be supposed most easily to convey their sound to a stranger. In several works descriptive of the islands in the Pacific, many of the most beautiful combinations of vocal sounds have been altogether lost to the ear of the reader by an over-attention to the ordinary rules of spelling.

There are a few passages in the ensuing chapters which may be thought to bear rather hard upon a reverend order of men, the account of whose proceedings in different quarters of the globe—transmitted to us through their own hands—very generally, and often very deservedly, receives high commendation. Such passages will be found, however, to be based upon facts admitting of no contradiction, and which have come immediately under the writer's cognizance. The conclusions deduced from these facts are unavoidable, and in stating them the author has been influenced by no feeling of animosity, either to the individuals themselves, or to that glorious cause which has not always been served by the proceedings of some of its advocates.

The great interest with which the important events lately occurring at the Sandwich, Marquesas, and Society Islands, have been regarded in America and England, and indeed throughout the world, will, he trusts, justify a few otherwise unwarrantable digressions.

There are some things related in the narrative which will be sure to appear strange, or perhaps entirely incomprehensible, to the reader; but they cannot appear more so to him than they did to the author at the time. He has stated such matters just as they occurred, and leaves everyone to form his own opinion concerning them; trusting that his anxious desire to speak the unvarnished truth will gain for him the confidence of his readers.

PREFACE

Chapter I

The Sea—Longings for Shore—A Land-sick Ship—Destination of the Voyagers—The Marquesas—Adventure of a Missionary's Wife Among the Savages—Characteristic Anecdote of the Queen of Nukuheva

Six months at sea! Yes, reader, as I live, six months out of sight of land; cruising after the sperm-whale beneath the scorching sun of the Line, and tossed on the billows of the wide-rolling Pacific—the sky above, the sea around, and nothing else! Weeks and weeks ago our fresh provisions were all exhausted. There is not a sweet potato left; not a single yam. Those glorious bunches of bananas which once decorated our stern and quarter-deck have, alas, disappeared! and the delicious oranges which hung suspended from our tops and stays—they, too, are gone! Yes, they are all departed, and there is nothing left us but salt-horse and sea-biscuit. Oh! ye state-room sailors, who make so much ado about a fourteen-days' passage across the Atlantic; who so pathetically relate the privations and hardships of the sea, where, after a day of breakfasting, lunching, dining off five courses, chatting, playing whist, and drinking champagne-punch, it was your hard lot to be shut up in little cabinets of mahogany and maple, and sleep for ten hours, with nothing to disturb you but "those good-for-nothing tars, shouting and tramping overhead"—what would you say to our six months out of sight of land?

Oh! for a refreshing glimpse of one blade of grass—for a snuff at the fragrance of a handful of the loamy earth! Is there nothing fresh around us? Is there no green thing to be seen? Yes, the inside of our bulwarks is painted green; but what a vile and sickly hue it is, as if nothing bearing even the semblance of verdure could flourish this weary way from land. Even the bark that once clung to the wood we use for fuel has been gnawed off and devoured by the captain's pig; and so long ago, too, that the pig himself has in turn been devoured.

There is but one solitary tenant in the chicken-coop, once a gay and dapper young cock, bearing him so bravely among the coy hens. But look at him now; there he stands, moping all the day long on that everlasting one leg of his. He turns with disgust from the moldy corn before him, and the brackish water in his trough. He mourns no doubt his lost companions, literally snatched from him one by one, and never seen again. But his days of mourning will be few; for Mungo, our black cook, told me yesterday that the word had at last gone forth, and poor Pedro's fate was sealed. His attenuated body will be laid out upon the captain's table next Sunday, and long before night will be buried, with all the usual ceremonies, beneath that worthy individual's vest. Who would believe that there could be anyone so cruel as to long for the decapitation of the luckless Pedro; yet the sailors pray every minute, selfish fellows, that the miserable fowl may be brought to his end. They say the captain will never point the ship for the land so long as he has in anticipation a mess of fresh meat. This unhappy bird can alone furnish it; and when he is once devoured, the captain will at once come to his senses. I wish thee no harm, Peter; but as thou art doomed, sooner or later, to meet the fate of all thy race; and if putting a period to thy existence is to be the signal for our deliverance, why—truth to speak—I wish thy throat cut this very moment; for, oh! how I wish to see the living earth again! The old ship herself longs to look out upon the land from her hawse-holes once more, and Jack Lewis said right the other day when the captain found fault with his steering.

"Why, d'ye see, Captain Vangs," says bold Jack, "I'm as good a helmsman as ever put hand to spoke; but none of us can steer the old lady now. We can't keep her full and bye, sir; watch her ever so close, she will fall off; and then, sir, when I put the helm down so gently, and try like to coax her to the work, she won't take it kindly, but will fall round off again; and it's all because she knows the land is under the lee, sir, and she won't go any more to windward." Ay, and why should she, Jack? didn't every one of her stout timbers grow on shore, and hasn't she sensibilities as well as we?

Poor old ship! Her very looks denote her desires! how deplorably she appears! The paint on her sides, burned up by the scorching sun, is puffed out and cracked. See the weeds she trails along with her, and what an unsightly bunch of those horrid barnacles has formed about her stern-piece; and every time she rises on a sea, she shows her copper torn away, or hanging in jagged strips.

Poor old ship! I say again: for six months she has been rolling and pitching about, never for one moment at rest. But courage, old lass, I hope to see thee soon within a biscuit's toss of the merry land, riding snugly at anchor in some green cove, and sheltered from the boisterous winds.

"Hurra, my lads! It's a settled thing; next week we shape our course to the Marquesas!" The Marquesas! What strange visions of outlandish things does the very name spirit up! Naked houris—cannibal banquets—groves of cocoanut—coral reefs—tattooed chiefs—and bamboo temples; sunny valleys planted with bread-fruit-trees—carved canoes dancing on the flashing blue waters—savage woodlands guarded by horrible idols—*heathenish rites and human sacrifices.*

Such were the strangely jumbled anticipations that haunted me during our passage from the cruising-ground. I felt an irresistible curiosity to see those islands which the olden voyagers had so glowingly described.

The group for which we were now steering (although among the earliest of European discoveries in the South Seas, having been first visited in the year 1595) still continues to be tenanted by beings as strange and barbarous as ever. The missionaries, sent on a heavenly errand, had sailed by their lovely shores, and had abandoned them to their idols of wood and stone. How interesting the circumstances under which they were discovered! In the watery path of Mendaña, cruising in quest of some region of gold, these isles had sprung up like a scene of enchantment, and for a moment the Spaniard believed his bright dream was realized. In honor of the Marquess de Mendoza, then viceroy of Peru—under whose auspices the navigator sailed—he bestowed upon them the name which denoted the rank of his patron, and gave to the world on his return a vague and magnificent account of their beauty. But these islands, undisturbed for years, relapsed into their previous obscurity; and it is only recently that anything has been known concerning them. Once in the course of a half-century, to be sure, some adventurous rover would break in upon their peaceful repose, and, astonished at the unusual scene, would be almost tempted to claim the merit of a new discovery.

Of this interesting group, but little account has ever been given, if we except the slight mention made of them in the sketches of South Sea voyages. Cook, in his repeated circumnavigations of the globe, barely touched at their shores; and all that we know about them is from a few general narratives. Among these, there are two that claim particular notice. Porter's *Journal of the Cruise of the U.S. Frigate Essex, in the Pacific, during the late War,* is said to contain some interesting particulars concerning the islanders. This is a work, however, which I have never happened to meet with; and Stewart, the chaplain of the American sloop of war Vincennes, has likewise devoted a portion of his book, entitled "A Visit to the South Seas," to the same subject.

Within the last few years American and English vessels engaged in the extensive whale fisheries of the Pacific have occasionally, when short of provisions, put into the commodious harbor which there is in one of the islands; but a fear of the natives, founded on a recollection of the dreadful fate which many white men have received at their hands, has deterred their crews from intermixing with the population sufficiently to gain any insight into their peculiar customs and manners.

The Protestant Missions appear to have despaired of reclaiming these islands from heathenism. The usage they have in every case received from the natives has been such as to intimidate the boldest of their number. Ellis, in his *Polynesian Researches,* gives some interesting accounts of the abortive attempts made by the Tahiti Mission to establish a branch Mission upon certain islands of the group. A short time before my visit to the Marquesas, a somewhat amusing incident took place in connection with these efforts which I cannot avoid relating.

An intrepid missionary, undaunted by the ill-success that had attended all previous endeavors to conciliate the savages, and believing much in the efficacy of female influence, introduced among them his young and beautiful wife, the first white woman who had ever visited their shores. The islanders at first gazed in mute admiration at so unusual a prodigy, and seemed inclined to regard it as some new divinity. But after a short time, becoming familiar with its charming aspect, and jealous of the folds which encircled its form, they sought to pierce the sacred veil of calico in which it was enshrined, and in the gratification of their curiosity so far overstepped the limits of good breeding, as deeply to offend the lady's sense of decorum. Her sex once ascertained, their idolatry was changed into contempt; and there was no end to the contumely showered upon her by the savages, who were exasperated at the deception which they conceived had been practiced upon them. To the horror of her affectionate spouse, she was stripped of her garments, and given to understand that she could no longer carry on her deceits with impunity. The gentle dame was not sufficiently evangelized to endure this, and, fearful of further improprieties, she forced her husband to relinquish his undertaking, and together they returned to Tahiti.

Not thus shy of exhibiting her charms was the Island Queen herself, the beauteous wife of Mowanna, the king of Nukuheva. Between two and three years after the adventures recorded in this volume, I chanced, while aboard of a man-of-war, to touch at these islands. The French had then held possession of the Marquesas some time, and already prided themselves upon the beneficial effects of their jurisdiction, as discernible in the deportment of the natives. To be sure, in one of their efforts at reform they had slaughtered about a hundred and fifty of them at Whitihoo—but let that pass. At the time I mention, the French squadron was *rendezvousing* in the bay of Nukuheva, and during an interview between one of their captains and our worthy Commodore, it was suggested by the former, that we, as the flag-ship of the American squadron, should receive, in state a visit from the royal pair. The French officer likewise represented, with evident satisfaction, that under their tuition the king and queen had imbibed proper notions of their elevated station, and on all ceremonious occasions conducted themselves with suitable dignity. Accordingly, preparations were made to give their majesties a reception on board in a style corresponding with their rank.

One bright afternoon a gig, gaily bedizened with streamers, was observed to shove off from the side of one of the French frigates, and pull directly for our gangway. In the stern sheets reclined Mowanna and his consort. As they approached, we paid them all the honors due to royalty;—manning our yards, firing a salute, and making a prodigious hubbub.

They ascended the accommodation ladder, were greeted by the Commodore, hat in hand, and passing along the quarter-deck, the marine guard presented arms, while the band struck up "The King of the Cannibal Islands." So far all went well. The French officers grimaced and smiled in exceedingly high spirits, wonderfully pleased with the discreet manner in which these distinguished personages behaved themselves.

Their appearance was certainly calculated to produce an effect. His majesty was arrayed in a magnificent military uniform, stiff with gold lace and embroidery, while his shaven crown was concealed by a huge *chapeau bras,* waving with ostrich plumes. There was one slight blemish, however, in his appearance. A broad patch of tattooing stretched completely across his face, in a line with his eyes, making him look as if he wore a huge pair of goggles; and royalty in goggles suggested some ludicrous ideas. But it was in the adornment of the fair person of his dark-complexioned spouse that the tailors of the fleet had evinced the gaiety of their national taste. She was habited in a gaudy tissue of scarlet cloth, trimmed with yellow silk, which, descending a little below the knees, exposed to view her bare legs, embellished with spiral tattooing, and somewhat resembling two miniature

Trajan's columns. Upon her head was a fanciful turban of purple velvet, figured with silver sprigs, and surmounted by a tuft of variegated feathers.

The ship's company, crowding into the gangway to view the sight, soon arrested her majesty's attention. She singled out from their number an old *salt,* whose bare arms and feet, and exposed breast were covered with as many inscriptions in India ink as the lid of an Egyptian sarcophagus. Notwithstanding all the sly hints and remonstrances of the French officers, she immediately approached the man, and pulling further open the bosom of his duck frock, and rolling up the leg of his wide trousers, she gazed in admiration at the bright blue and vermilion pricking thus disclosed to view. She hung over the fellow, caressing him, and expressing her delight in a variety of wild exclamations and gestures. The embarrassment of the polite Gauls at such an unlooked-for occurrence may be easily imagined but picture their consternation, when all at once the royal lady, eager to display the hieroglyphics on her own sweet form, bent forward for a moment, and turning sharply round, threw up the skirts of her mantle, and revealed a sight from which the aghast Frenchmen retreated precipitately, and tumbling into their boat, fled the scene of so shocking a catastrophe.

Chapter II

PASSAGE FROM THE CRUISING-GROUND TO THE MARQUESAS—SLEEPY TIMES ABOARD SHIP—SOUTH SEA SCENERY—LAND HO!—THE FRENCH SQUADRON DISCOVERED AT ANCHOR IN THE BAY OF NUKUHEVA—STRANGE PILOT—ESCORT OF CANOES—A FLOTILLA OF COCOANUTS—SWIMMING VISITORS—THE DOLLY BOARDED BY THEM—STATE OF AFFAIRS THAT ENSUE

I CAN NEVER FORGET THE EIGHTEEN OR TWENTY DAYS DURING WHICH THE LIGHT TRADE-WINDS were silently sweeping us towards the islands. In pursuit of the sperm-whale, we had been cruising on the line some twenty degrees to the westward of the Gallipagos; and all that we had to do, when our course was determined on, was to square in the yards and keep the vessel before the breeze, and then the good ship and the steady gale did the rest between them. The man at the wheel never vexed the old lady with any superfluous steering, but comfortably adjusting his limbs at the tiller, would doze away by the hour. True to her work, the *Dolly* headed to her course, and like one of those characters who always do the best when let alone, she jogged on her way like a veteran old sea-pacer as she was.

What a delightful, lazy, languid time we had whilst we were thus gliding along! There was nothing to be done; a circumstance that happily suited our disinclination to do anything. We abandoned the fore-peak altogether, and spreading an awning over the forecastle, slept, ate, and lounged under it the live-long day. Everyone seemed to be under the influence of some narcotic. Even the officers aft, whose duty required them never to be seated while keeping a deck watch, vainly endeavored to keep on their pins; and were obliged invariably to compromise the matter by leaning up against the bulwarks, and gazing abstractedly over the side. Reading was out of the question; take a book in your hand, and you were asleep in an instant.

Although I could not avoid yielding in a great measure to the general languor, still at times I contrived to shake off the spell, and to appreciate the beauty of the scene around me. The sky presented a clear expanse of the most delicate blue, except along the skirts of the horizon, where you might see a thin drapery of pale clouds which never varied their form or color. The long, measured, dirge-like well of the Pacific came rolling along, with its surface broken by little tiny waves, sparkling in the sunshine. Every now and then a shoal of flying-fish, scared from the water under the bows, would leap into the air, and fall the next moment like a shower of silver into the sea. Then you would see the superb albacore, with his glittering sides, sailing aloft, and often describing an arc in his descent, disappear on the surface of the water. Far off, the lofty jet of the whale might be seen, and nearer at hand the prowling shark, that villainous foot-pad of the seas, would come skulking along, and, at a wary distance, regard us with his evil eye. At times, some shapeless monster of the deep, floating on the surface, would, as we approached, sink slowly into the blue waters, and fade away from the sight. But the most impressive feature of the scene was the almost unbroken silence that reigned over sky and water. Scarcely a sound could be heard but the occasional breathing of the grampus, and the rippling at the cut-water.

As we drew nearer the land, I hailed with delight the appearance of innumerable sea-fowl. Screaming and whirling in spiral tracks, they would accompany the vessel, and at times alight on our yards and stays. That piratical-looking fellow, appropriately named the man-of-war's hawk, with his blood-red bill and raven plumage, would come sweeping round us in gradually diminishing circles, till you could distinctly mark the strange flashings of his eye; and then, as if satisfied with his observation, would sail up into the air and disappear from the view. Soon, other evidences of our vicinity to the land were apparent, and it was not long before the glad announcement of its being in sight was heard from aloft—given with that peculiar prolongation of sound that a sailor loves—"Land ho!"

The captain, darting on deck from the cabin, bawled lustily for his spy-glass; the mate in still louder accents hailed the mast-head with a tremendous "Where-away?" The black cook thrust his woolly head from the galley, and Boatswain, the dog, leaped up between the knight-heads, and barked most furiously. Land ho! Ay, there it was. A hardly perceptible blue irregular outline, indicating the bold contour of the lofty heights of Nukuheva.

This island, although generally called one of the Marquesas, is by some navigators considered as forming one of a distinct cluster, comprising the islands of Ruhooka, Ropo, and Nukuheva; upon which three the appellation of the Washington Group has been bestowed. They form a triangle, and lie within the parallels of 8° 38" and 9° 32" South latitude, and 139° 20' and 140° 10' West longitude from Greenwich. With how little propriety they are to be regarded as forming a separate group will be at once apparent, when it is considered that they lie in the immediate vicinity of the other islands, that is to say, less than a degree to the north-west of them; that their inhabitants speak the Marquesan dialect, and that their laws, religion, and general customs are identical. The only reason why they were ever thus arbitrarily distinguished may be attributed to the singular fact that their existence was altogether unknown to the world until the year 1791, when they were discovered by Captain Ingraham, of Boston, Massachusetts, nearly two centuries after the discovery of the adjacent islands by the agent of the Spanish Viceroy. Notwithstanding this, I shall follow the example of most voyagers, and treat of them as forming part and parcel of the Marquesas.

Nukuheva is the most important of these islands, being the only one at which ships are much in the habit of touching, and is celebrated as being the place where the adventurous Captain Porter refitted his ships during the late war between England and the United States, and whence he sallied out upon the large whaling-fleet then sailing under the enemy's flag in the surrounding seas. This island is about twenty miles in length, and nearly as many in breadth. It has three good harbors on its coast; the largest and best of which is called by the people living in its vicinity "Taiohae," and by Captain Porter was denominated Massachusetts Bay. Among the adverse tribes dwelling about the shores of the other bays, and by all voyagers, it is generally known by the name bestowed upon the island itself—Nukuheva. Its inhabitants have become somewhat corrupted, owing to their recent commerce with Europeans; but so far as regards their peculiar customs and general mode of life, they retain their original primitive character, remaining very nearly in the same state of nature in which they were first beheld by white men. The hostile clans, residing in the more remote sections of the island, and very seldom holding any communication with foreigners, are in every respect unchanged from their earliest known condition.

In the bay of Nukuheva was the anchorage we desired to reach. We had perceived the loom of the mountains about sunset; so that after running all night with a very light breeze, we found ourselves close in with the island the next morning; but as the bay we sought lay on its farther side, we were obliged to sail some distance along the shore, catching, as we proceeded, short glimpses of blooming valleys, deep glens, waterfalls, and waving groves, hidden here and there by projecting and rocky headlands, every moment opening to the view some new and startling scene of beauty.

Those who for the first time visit the South Seas, generally are surprised at the appearance of the islands when beheld from the sea. From the vague accounts we sometimes have of their beauty, many people are apt to picture to themselves enamelled and softly swelling plains, shaded over with delicious groves, and watered by purling brooks, and the entire country but little elevated above the surrounding ocean. The reality is very different; bold rock-bound coasts, with the surf beating high against the lofty cliffs, and broken here and there into deep inlets, which open to the view thickly wooded valleys, separated by the spurs of mountains clothed with tufted grass, and sweeping down towards the sea from an elevated and furrowed interior, form the principal features of these islands.

Towards noon we drew abreast the entrance to the harbor, and at last we slowly swept by the intervening promontory, and entered the bay of Nukuheva. No description can do justice to its beauty; but that beauty was lost to me then, and I saw nothing but the tri-colored flag of France trailing over the stern of six vessels, whose black hulls and bristling broadsides proclaimed their war-like character. There they were, floating in that lovely bay, the green eminences of the shore looking down so tranquilly upon them, as if rebuking the sternness of their aspect. To my eye nothing could be more out of keeping than the presence of these vessels; but we soon learned what brought them there. The whole group of islands had just been taken possession of by Rear-Admiral Du Petit Thouars, in the name of the invincible French nation.

This item of information was imparted to us by a most extraordinary individual, a genuine South Sea vagabond, who came alongside of us in a whale-boat as soon as we entered the bay, and by the aid of some benevolent persons at the gangway was assisted on board; for our visitor was in that interesting stage of intoxication when a man is amiable and helpless. Although he was utterly unable to stand erect, or to navigate his body across the deck, he still magnanimously proffered his services to pilot the ship to a good and secure anchorage. Our captain, however, rather distrusted his ability in this respect, and refused to recognize his claim to the character he assumed; but our gentleman was determined to play his part, for by dint of much scrambling, he succeeded in getting into the weather-quarter boat, where he steadied himself by holding on to a shroud, and then commenced issuing his commands with amazing volubility and very peculiar gestures. Of course no one obeyed his orders; but as it was impossible to quiet him, we swept by the ships of the squadron with this strange fellow performing his antics in full view of all the French officers.

We afterwards learned that our eccentric friend had been a lieutenant in the English navy; but having disgraced his flag by some criminal conduct in one of the principal ports on the main, he had deserted his ship, and spent many years wandering among the islands of the Pacific, until accidentally being at Nukuheva when the French took possession of the place, he had been appointed pilot of the harbor by the newly constituted authorities.

As we slowly advanced up the bay, numerous canoes pushed off from the surrounding shores, and we were soon in the midst of quite a flotilla of them, their savage occupants struggling to get aboard of us, and jostling one another in their ineffectual attempts. Occasionally the projecting outriggers of their slight shallops running foul of one another, would become entangled beneath the water, threatening to capsize the canoes, when a scene of confusion would ensue that baffles description. Such strange outcries and passionate gesticulations I never certainly heard or saw before. You would have thought the islanders were on the point of flying at one another's throats, whereas they were only amicably engaged in disentangling their boats.

Scattered here and there among the canoes might be seen numbers of cocoanuts floating closely together in circular groups, and bobbing up and down with every wave. By some inexplicable means these cocoanuts were all steadily approaching towards the ship. As I leaned curiously over the side, endeavoring to solve their mysterious movements, one mass far in advance of the rest attracted my attention. In its center was something I could take for nothing else than a cocoanut, but which I certainly considered one of the most extraordinary specimens of the fruit I had ever seen. It kept twirling and dancing about among the rest in the most singular manner, and as it drew nearer, I thought it bore a remarkable resemblance to the brown shaven skull of one of the savages. Presently it betrayed a pair of eyes, and soon I became aware that what I had supposed to have been one of the fruit was nothing else than the head of an islander, who had adopted this singular method of bringing his produce to market. The cocoanuts were all attached to one another by strips of the husk, partly torn from the shell, and rudely fastened together. Their proprietor, inserting his head into the midst of them, impelled his necklace of cocoanuts through the water by striking out beneath the surface with his feet.

I was somewhat astonished to perceive that among the number of natives that surrounded us, not a single female was to be seen. At that time I was ignorant of the fact that, by the operation of the "taboo," the use of canoes in all parts of the island is rigorously prohibited to the entire sex, for whom it is death even to be seen entering one when hauled on shore; consequently, whenever a Marquesan lady voyages by water, she puts in requisition the paddles of her own fair body.

We had approached within a mile and a half, perhaps, of the foot of the bay, when some of the islanders, who by this time had managed to scramble aboard of us at the risk of swamping their canoes, directed our attention to a singular commotion in the water ahead of the vessel. At first I imagined it to be produced by a shoal of fish sporting on the surface, but our savage friends assured us that it was caused by a shoal of "whinhenies" (young girls), who in this manner were coming off from the shore to welcome us. As they drew nearer, and I watched the rising and sinking of their forms, and beheld the uplifted right arm bearing above the water the girdle of tappa, and their long dark hair trailing beside them as they swam, I almost fancied they could be nothing else than so many mermaids—and very like mermaids they behaved too.

We were still some distance from the beach, and under slow headway, when we sailed right into the midst of these swimming nymphs, and they boarded us at every quarter; many seizing hold of the chain-plates and springing into the chains; others, at the peril of being run over by the vessel in her course, catching at the bob-stays, and wreathing their slender forms about the ropes, hung suspended in the air. All of them at length succeeded in getting up the ship's side, where they clung dripping with the brine, and glowing from the bath, their jet-black tresses streaming over their shoulders, and half enveloping their otherwise naked forms. There they hung, sparkling with savage vivacity, laughing gaily at one another, and chattering away with infinite glee. Nor were they idle the while, for each one performed the simple offices of the toilette for the other. Their luxuriant locks, wound up and twisted into the smallest possible compass, were freed from the briny element; the whole person carefully dried, and from a little round shell that passed from hand to hand, anointed with a fragrant oil: their adornments were completed by passing a few loose folds of white tappa, in a modest cincture, around the waist. Thus arrayed, they no longer hesitated, but flung themselves lightly over the bulwarks, and were quickly frolicking about the decks. Many of them went forward, perching upon the head-rails, or running out upon the bowsprit, while others seated themselves upon the taffrail, or reclined at full length upon the boats. What a sight for us bachelor sailors! How avoid so dire a temptation? For who could think of tumbling these artless creatures overboard, when they had swam miles to welcome us?

Their appearance perfectly amazed me; their extreme youth, the light clear brown of their complexions, their delicate features, and inexpressibly graceful figures, their softly molded limbs, and free unstudied action, seemed as strange as beautiful.

The *Dolly* was fairly captured; and never I will say was vessel carried before by such a dashing and irresistible party of boarders! The ship taken, we could not do otherwise than yield ourselves prisoners, and for the whole period that she remained in the bay, the *Dolly*, as well as her crew, were completely in the hands of the mermaids.

In the evening after we had come to an anchor the deck was illuminated with lanterns, and this picturesque band of sylphs, tricked out with flowers, and dressed in robes of variegated tappa, got up a ball in great style. These females are passionately fond of dancing, and in the wild grace and spirit of their style excel everything I have ever seen. The varied dances of the Marquesan girls are beautiful in the extreme, but there is an abandoned voluptuousness in their character which I dare not attempt to describe.

Chapter III

Some Account of the Late Operations of the French at the Marquesas—Prudent Conduct of the Admiral—Sensation Produced by the Arrival of the Strangers—The First Horse Seen by the Islanders—Reflections—Miserable Subterfuge of the French—Digression Concerning Tahiti—Seizure of the Island by the Admiral—Spirited Conduct of an English Lady

It was in the summer of 1842 that we arrived at the islands; the French had then held possession of them for several weeks. During this time they had visited some of the principal places in the group, and had disembarked at various points about five hundred troops. These were employed in constructing works of defense, and otherwise providing against the attacks of the natives, who at any moment might be expected to break out in open hostility. The islanders looked upon the people who made this cavalier appropriation of their shores with mingled feelings of fear and detestation. They cordially hated them; but the impulses of their resentment were neutralized by their dread of the floating batteries, which lay with their fatal tubes ostentatiously pointed, not at fortifications and redoubts, but at a handful of bamboo sheds, sheltered in a grove of cocoanuts! A valiant warrior, doubtless, but a prudent one too, was this same Rear Admiral Du Petit Thouars. Four heavy, double-banked frigates and three corvettes to frighten a parcel of naked heathen into subjection! Sixty-eight pounders to demolish huts of cocoanut boughs, and Congreve rockets to set on fire a few canoe sheds!

At Nukuheva, there were about one hundred soldiers ashore. They were encamped in tents, constructed of the old sails and spare spars of the squadron, within the limits of a redoubt mounted with a few nine-pounders, and surrounded with a fosse. Every other day, these troops were marched out in martial array, to a level piece of ground in the vicinity, and there for hours went through all sorts of military evolutions, surrounded by flocks of the natives, who looked on with savage admiration at the show, and as savage a hatred of the actors. A regiment of the Old Guard, reviewed on a summer's day in the Champs Elysées, could not have made a more critically correct appearance. The officers' regimentals, resplendent with gold lace and embroidery, as if purposely calculated to dazzle the islanders, looked as if just unpacked from their Parisian cases.

The sensation produced by the presence of the strangers had not in the least subsided at the period of our arrival at the islands. The natives still flocked in numbers about the encampment, and watched with the liveliest curiosity everything that was going forward. A blacksmith's forge, which had been set up in the shelter of a grove near the beach, attracted so great a crowd, that it required the utmost efforts of the sentries posted around to keep the inquisitive multitude at a sufficient distance to allow the workmen to ply their vocation. But nothing gained so large a share of admiration as a horse, which had been brought from Valparaiso by the Achille, one of the vessels of the squadron. The animal, a remarkably fine one, had been taken ashore and stabled in a hut of cocoanut boughs within the fortified enclosure. Occasionally it was brought out, and, being gaily caparisoned, was ridden by one of the officers at full speed over the hard sand beach. This performance was sure to be hailed with loud plaudits, and the "puarkee nuee" (big hog) was unanimously pronounced by the islanders to be the most extraordinary specimen of zoology that had ever come under their observation.

The expedition for the occupation of the Marquesas had sailed from Brest in the spring of 1842, and the secret of its destination was solely in the possession of its commander. No wonder that those who contemplated such a signal infraction of the rights of humanity should have sought to veil the enormity from the eyes of the world. And yet, notwithstanding their iniquitous conduct in this and in other matters, the French have ever plumed themselves upon being the most humane and polished of nations. A high degree of refinement, however, does not seem to subdue our wicked propensities so much after all; and were civilization itself to be estimated by some of its results, it would seem perhaps better for what we call the barbarous part of the world to remain unchanged.

One example of the shameless subterfuges under which the French stand prepared to defend whatever cruelties they may hereafter think fit to commit in bringing the Marquesan natives into subjection is well worthy of being recorded. On some flimsy pretext or other, Mowanna, the king of Nukuheva, whom the invaders by extravagant presents had cajoled over to their interests, and move about like a mere puppet, has been set up as the rightful sovereign of the entire island—the alleged ruler by prescriptions of various clans who for ages perhaps have treated with each other as separate nations. To reinstate this much-injured prince in the assumed dignities of his ancestors, the disinterested strangers have come all the way from France: they are determined that his title shall be acknowledged. If any tribe shall refuse to recognize the authority of the French, by bowing down to the laced *chapeau* of Mowanna, let them abide the consequences of their obstinacy. Under cover of a similar pretense, have the outrages and massacres at Tahiti the beautiful, the queen of the South Seas, been perpetrated.

On this buccaneering expedition, Rear Admiral Du Petit Thouars, leaving the rest of his squadron at the Marquesas—which had then been occupied by his forces about five months—set sail for the doomed island in the Reine Blanche frigate. On his arrival, as an indemnity for alleged insults offered to the flag of his country, he demanded some twenty or thirty thousand dollars to be placed in his hands forth with, and in default of payment, threatened to land and take possession of the place.

The frigate, immediately upon coming to an anchor, got springs on her cables, and with her guns cast loose, and her men at their quarters, lay in the circular basin of Papeete, with her broadside bearing upon the devoted town; while her numerous cutters, hauled in order alongside, were ready to effect a landing under cover of her batteries. She maintained this belligerent attitude for several days, during which time a series of informal negotiations were pending, and wide alarm spread over the island. Many of the Tahitians were at first disposed to resort to arms, and drive the invaders from their shores; but more pacific and feebler counsels ultimately prevailed. The unfortunate queen, Pomare, incapable of averting the impending calamity, terrified at the arrogance of the insolent Frenchman, and driven at last to despair, fled by night in a canoe to Emio.

During the continuance of the panic there occurred an instance of feminine heroism that I cannot omit to record.

In the grounds of the famous missionary consul, Pritchard, then absent in London, the consular flag of Britain waved as usual during the day, from a lofty staff planted within a few yards of the beach, and in full view of the frigate. One morning an officer, at the head of a party of men, presented himself at the verandah of Mr. Pritchard's house, and inquired in broken English for the lady, his wife. The matron soon made her appearance; and the polite Frenchman, making one of his best bows, and playing gracefully with the aiguillettes that danced upon his breast, proceeded in courteous accents to deliver his mission. "The admiral desired the flag to be hauled down—hoped it would be perfectly agreeable—and his men stood ready to perform the duty."—"Tell the pirate, your master," replied the spirited Englishwoman, pointing to the staff, "that if he wishes to strike those colors, he must come and perform the act himself; I will suffer no one else to do it." The lady then bowed haughtily, and withdrew into the house. As the discomfited officer slowly walked away, he looked up at the flag, and perceived that the cord by which it was elevated to its place led from the top of the staff, across the lawn, to an open upper window of the mansion, where sat the lady from whom he had just parted, tranquilly engaged in knitting. Was that flag hauled down? Mrs. Pritchard thinks not; and Rear Admiral Du Petit Thouars is believed to be of the same opinion.

Chapter IV

State of Affairs Aboard the Ship—Contents of Her Larder—Length of South Seamen's Voyages—Account of a Flying Whale-man—Determination to Leave the Vessel—The Bay of Nukuheva—The Typees—Invasion of Their Valley by Porter—Reflections—Glen of Tior—Interview Between the Old King and the French Admiral

OUR SHIP HAD NOT BEEN MANY DAYS IN THE HARBOR OF NUKUHEVA BEFORE I CAME TO THE DEtermination of leaving her. That my reasons for resolving to take this step were numerous and weighty, may be inferred from the fact that I chose rather to risk my fortunes among the savages of the island, than to endure another voyage on board the *Dolly*. To use the concise, point-blank phrase of the sailors, I had made up my mind to "run away." Now, as a meaning is generally attached to these two words no way flattering to the individual to whom they are applied, it behooves me, for the sake of my own character, to offer some explanation of my conduct.

When I entered on board the *Dolly*, I signed, as a matter of course, the ship's articles, thereby voluntarily engaging, and legally binding myself to serve in a certain capacity for the period of the voyage; and, special considerations apart, I was of course bound to fulfill the agreement. But in all contracts, if one party fail to perform his share of the compact, is not the other virtually absolved from his liability? Who is there who will not answer in the affirmative?

Having settled the principle, then, let me apply it to the particular case in question. In numberless instances had not only the implied but the specified conditions of the articles been violated on the part of the ship in which I served. The usage on board of her was tyrannical; the sick had been inhumanly neglected; the provisions had been doled out in scanty allowance; and her cruises were unreasonably protracted. The captain was the author of these abuses; it was in vain to think that he would either remedy them, or alter his conduct, which was arbitrary and violent in the extreme. His prompt reply to all complaints and remonstrances was—the but-end of a handspike, so convincingly administered as effectually to silence the aggrieved party.

To whom could we apply for redress? We had left both law and equity on the other side of the Cape; and unfortunately, with a very few exceptions, our crew was composed of a parcel of dastardly and mean-spirited wretches, divided among themselves, and only united in enduring without resistance the unmitigated tyranny of the captain. It would have been mere madness for any two or three of the number, unassisted by the rest, to attempt making a stand against his ill-usage. They would only have called down upon themselves the particular vengeance of this "Lord of the Plank," and subjected their shipmates to additional hardships.

But, after all, these things could have been endured awhile, had we entertained the hope of being speedily delivered from them by the due completion of the term of our servitude. But what a dismal prospect awaited us in this quarter! The longevity of Cape Horn whaling voyages is proverbial, frequently extending over a period of four or five years.

Some long-haired, bare-necked youths, who, forced by the united influences of Captain Marryatt and hard times, embark at Nantucket for a pleasure excursion to the Pacific, and whose anxious mothers provide them with bottled milk for the occasion, oftentimes return very respectable middle-aged gentlemen.

The very preparations made for one of these expeditions are enough to frighten one. As the vessel carries out no cargo, her hold is filled with provisions for her own consumption. The owners, who officiate as caterers for the voyage, supply the larder with an abundance of dainties. Delicate morsels of beef and pork, cut on scientific principles from every part of the animal, and of all conceivable shapes and sizes, are carefully packed in salt, and stored away in barrels; affording a never-ending variety in their different degrees of toughness, and in the peculiarities of their saline properties. Choice old water too, decanted into stout six-barrel-casks, and two pints of which are allowed every day to each soul on board; together with ample store of sea-bread, previously reduced to a state of petrifaction, with a view to preserve it either from decay or consumption in the ordinary mode, are likewise provided for the nourishment and gastronomic enjoyment of the crew.

But not to speak of the quality of these articles of sailors' fare, the abundance in which they are put on board a whaling vessel is almost incredible. Oftentimes, when we had occasion to break out in the hold, and I beheld the successive tiers of casks and barrels, whose contents were all destined to be consumed in due course by the ship's company, my heart sank within me.

Although, as a general case, a ship unlucky in falling in with whales continues to cruise after them until she has barely sufficient provisions remaining to take her home, turning round then quietly and making the best of her way to her friends, yet there are instances when even this natural obstacle to the further prosecution of the voyage is overcome by headstrong captains, who, bartering the fruits of their hard-earned toils for a new supply of provisions in some of the ports of Chile or Peru, begin the voyage afresh, with unabated zeal and perseverance. It is in vain that the owners write urgent letters to him to sail for home, and for their sake to bring back the ship, since it appears he can put nothing in her. Not he. He has registered a vow: he will fill his vessel with good sperm oil, or failing to do so, never again strike Yankee soundings.

I heard of one whaler, which after many years' absence was given up for lost. The last that had been heard of her was a shadowy report of her having touched at some of those unstable islands in the far Pacific, whose eccentric wanderings are carefully noted in each new edition of the South Sea charts. After a long interval, however, the Perseverance—for that was her name—was spoken somewhere in the vicinity of the ends of the earth, cruising along as leisurely as ever, her sails all bepatched and bequilted with rope-yarns, her spars fished with old pipe stores, and her rigging knotted and spliced in every possible direction. Her crew was composed of some twenty venerable Greenwich-pensioner-looking old salts, who just managed to hobble about deck. The ends of all the running ropes, with the exception of the signal halyards and poop-down-haul, were rove through snatch-blocks, and led to the capstan or windlass, so that not a yard was braced or a sail set without the assistance of machinery.

Her hull was encrusted with barnacles, which completely encased her. Three pet sharks followed in her wake, and every day came alongside to regale themselves from the contents of the cook's bucket, which were pitched over to them. A vast shoal of bonetas and albacores always kept her company.

Such was the account I heard of this vessel, and the remembrance of it always haunted me; what eventually became of her I never learned; at any rate she never reached home, and I suppose she is still regularly tacking twice in the twenty-four hours somewhere off Desolate Island, or the Devil's-Tail Peak.

Having said thus much touching the usual length of these voyages, when I inform the reader that ours had as it were just commenced, we being only fifteen months out, and even at that time hailed as a late arrival, and boarded for news, he will readily perceive that there was little to encourage one in looking forward to the future, especially as I had always had a presentiment that we should make an unfortunate voyage, and our experience so far had justified the expectation.

I may here state, and on my faith as an honest man, that though more than three years have elapsed since I left this same identical vessel, she still continues in the Pacific; and but a few days since I saw her reported in the papers as having touched at the Sandwich Islands, previous to going on the coast of Japan.

But to return to my narrative. Placed in these circumstances then, with no prospect of matters mending if I remained aboard the *Dolly*, I at once made up my mind to leave her: to be sure it was rather an inglorious thing to steal away privily from those at whose hands I had received wrongs and outrages that I could not resent; but how was such a course to be avoided when it was the only alternative left me? Having made up my mind, I proceeded to acquire all the information I could obtain relating to the island and its inhabitants, with a view of shaping my plans of escape accordingly. The result of these inquiries I will now state, in order that the ensuing narrative may be the better understood.

The bay of Nukuheva, in which we were then lying, is an expanse of water not unlike in figure the space included within the limits of a horse-shoe. It is, perhaps, nine miles in circumference. You approach it from the sea by a narrow entrance, flanked on either side by two small twin islets which soar conically to the height of some five hundred feet. From these the shore recedes on both hands, and describes a deep semicircle.

From the verge of the water the land rises uniformly on all sides, with green and sloping acclivities, until from gently rolling hill-sides and moderate elevations it insensibly swells into lofty and majestic heights, whose blue outlines, ranged all around, close in the view. The beautiful aspect of the shore is heightened by deep and romantic glens, which come down to it at almost equal distances, all apparently radiating from a common center, and the upper extremities of which are lost to the eye beneath the shadow of the mountains. Down each of these little valleys flows a clear stream, here and there assuming the form of a slender cascade, then stealing invisibly along until it bursts upon the sight again in larger and more noisy waterfalls, and at last demurely wanders along to the sea.

The houses of the natives, constructed of the yellow bamboo, tastefully twisted together in a kind of wicker-work, and thatched with the long tapering leaves of the palmetto, are scattered irregularly along these valleys beneath the shady branches of the cocoanut-trees.

Nothing can exceed the imposing scenery of this bay. Viewed from our ship as she lay at anchor in the middle of the harbor, it presented the appearance of a vast natural amphitheater in decay, and overgrown with vines, the deep glens that furrowed its sides appearing like enormous fissures caused by the ravages of time. Very often when lost in admiration at its beauty, I have experienced a pang of regret that a scene so enchanting should be hidden from the world in these remote seas, and seldom meet the eyes of devoted lovers of nature.

Besides this bay the shores of the island are indented by several other extensive inlets, into which descend broad and verdant valleys. These are inhabited by as many distinct tribes of savages, who, although speaking kindred dialects of a common language, and having the same religion and laws, have from time immemorial waged hereditary warfare against each other. The intervening mountains, generally two or three thousand feet above the level of the sea, geographically define the territories of each of these hostile tribes, who never cross them, save on some expedition of war or plunder. Immediately adjacent to Nukuheva, and only separated from it by the mountains seen from the harbor, lies the lovely valley of Happar, whose inmates cherish the most friendly relations with the inhabitants of Nukuheva. On the other side of Happar, and closely adjoining it, is the magnificent valley of the dreaded Typees, the unappeasable enemies of both these tribes.

These celebrated warriors appear to inspire the other islanders with unspeakable terrors. Their very name is a frightful one; for the word "Typee" in the Marquesan dialect signifies a lover of human flesh. It is rather singular that the title should have been bestowed upon them exclusively, inasmuch as the natives of all this group are irreclaimable cannibals. The name may, perhaps, have been given to denote the peculiar ferocity of this clan, and to convey a special stigma along with it.

These same Typees enjoy a prodigious notoriety all over the islands. The natives of Nukuheva would frequently recount in pantomime to our ship's company their terrible feats, and would show the marks of wounds they had received in desperate encounters with them. When ashore they would try to frighten us by pointing to one of their own number, and calling him a Typee, manifesting no little surprise that we did not take to our heels at so terrible an announcement. It was quite amusing, too, to see with what earnestness they disclaimed all cannibal propensities on their own part, while they denounced their enemies—the Typees—as inveterate gourmandizers of human flesh; but this is a peculiarity to which I shall hereafter have occasion to allude.

Although I was convinced that the inhabitants of our bay were as arrant cannibals as any of the other tribes on the island, still I could not but feel a particular and most unqualified repugnance to the aforesaid Typees. Even before visiting the Marquesas, I had heard from men who had touched at the group on former voyages some revolting stories in connection with these savages; and fresh in my remembrance was the adventure of the master of the Katherine, who only a few months previous, imprudently venturing into this bay in an armed boat for the purpose of barter, was seized by the natives, carried back a little distance into this valley, and was only saved from a cruel death by the intervention of a young girl, who facilitated his escape by night, along the beach to Nukuheva.

I had heard too, of an English vessel that many years ago, after a weary cruise, sought to enter the bay of Nukuheva, and arriving within two or three miles of the land, was met by a large canoe filled with natives, who offered to lead the way to the place of their destination. The captain, unacquainted with the localities of the island, joyfully acceded to the proposition—the canoe paddled on, and the ship followed. She was soon conducted to a beautiful inlet, and dropped her anchor in its waters, beneath the shadows of the lofty shore. That same night the perfidious Typees, who had thus inveigled her into their fatal bay, flocked aboard the doomed vessel by hundreds, and at a given signal murdered every soul on board.

I shall never forget the observation of one of our crew as we were passing slowly by the entrance of this bay on our way to Nukuheva. As we stood gazing over the side at the verdant headlands, Ned, pointing with his hand in the direction of the treacherous valley, exclaimed, "There—there's Typee. Oh, the bloody cannibals, what a meal they'd make of us if we were to take it into our heads to land! but they say they don't like sailor's flesh, it's too salt. I say, maty, how should you like to be shoved ashore there, eh?" I little thought, as I shuddered at the question, that in the space of a few weeks I should actually be a captive in that self-same valley.

The French, although they had gone through the ceremony of hoisting their colors for a few hours at all the principal places of the group, had not as yet visited the bay of Typee, anticipating a fierce resistance on the part of the savages there, which for the present at least they wished to avoid. Perhaps they were not a little influenced in the adoption of this unusual policy from a recollection of the war-like reception given by the Typees to the forces of Captain Porter, about the year 1814, when that brave and accomplished officer endeavored to subjugate the clan merely to gratify the mortal hatred of his allies the Nukuhevas and Happars.

On that occasion I have been told that a considerable detachment of sailors and marines from the frigate *Essex,* accompanied by at least two thousand warriors of Happar and Nukuheva, landed in boats and canoes at the head of the bay, and after penetrating a little distance into the valley, met with the stoutest resistance from its inmates. Valiantly, although with much loss, the Typees disputed every inch of ground, and after some hard fighting obliged their assailants to retreat and abandon their design of conquest.

The invaders, on their march back to the sea, consoled themselves for their repulse by setting fire to every house and temple on their route; and a long line of smoking ruins defaced the once-smiling bosom of the valley, and proclaimed to its pagan inhabitants the spirit that reigned in the breasts of Christian soldiers. Who can wonder at the deadly hatred of the Typees to all foreigners after such unprovoked atrocities?

Thus it is that they whom we denominate "savages" are made to deserve the title. When the inhabitants of some sequestered island first descry the "big canoe" of the European rolling through the blue waters towards their shores, they rush down to the beach in crowds, and with open arms stand ready to embrace the strangers. Fatal embrace! They fold to their bosoms the vipers whose sting is destined to poison all their joys; and the instinctive feeling of love within their breasts is soon converted into the bitterest hate.

The enormities perpetrated in the South Seas upon some of the inoffensive islanders well-nigh pass belief. These things are seldom proclaimed at home; they happen at the very ends of the earth; they are done in a corner, and there are none to reveal them. But there is, nevertheless, many a petty trader that has navigated the Pacific, whose course from island to island might be traced by a series of cold-blooded robberies, kidnappings, and murders, the iniquity of which might be considered almost sufficient to sink her guilty timbers to the bottom of the sea.

Sometimes vague accounts of such things reach our firesides, and we coolly censure them as wrong, impolitic, needlessly severe, and dangerous to the crews of other vessels. How different is our tone when we read the highly wrought description of the massacre of the crew of the Hobomak by the Fijis! how we sympathize for the unhappy victims, and with what horror do we regard the diabolical heathens, who, after all, have but avenged the unprovoked injuries which they have received! We breathe nothing but vengeance, and equip armed vessels to traverse thousands of miles of ocean in order to execute summary punishment upon the offenders. On arriving at their destination, they burn, slaughter, and destroy, according to the tenor of written instructions, and sailing away from the scene of devastation, call upon all Christendom to applaud their courage and their justice.

How often is the term "savages" incorrectly applied! None really deserving of it were ever yet discovered by voyagers or by travelers. They have discovered heathens and barbarians, whom by horrible cruelties they have exasperated into savages. It may be asserted, without fear of contradiction, that in all the cases of outrages committed by Polynesians, Europeans have at some time or other been the aggressors, and that the cruel and blood-thirsty disposition of some of the islanders is mainly to be ascribed to the influence of such examples.

But to return. Owing to the mutual hostilities of the different tribes I have mentioned, the mountainous tracts which separate their respective territories remain altogether uninhabited; the natives invariably dwelling in the depths of the valleys, with a view of securing themselves from the predatory incursions of their enemies, who often lurk along their borders, ready to cut off any imprudent straggler, or make a descent upon the inmates of some sequestered habitation. I several times met with very aged men, who from this cause had never passed the confines of their native vale, some of them having never even ascended midway up the mountains in the whole course of their lives, and who, accordingly, had little idea of the appearance of any other part of the island, the whole of which is not perhaps more than sixty miles in circuit. The little space in which some of these clans pass away their days would seem almost incredible.

The glen of the Tior will furnish a curious illustration of this. The inhabited part is not more than four miles in length, and varies in breadth from half a mile to less than a quarter. The rocky vine-clad cliffs on one side tower almost perpendicularly from their base to the height of at least fifteen hundred feet; while across the vale—in striking contrast to the scenery opposite—grass-grown elevations rise one above another in blooming terraces. Hemmed in by these stupendous barriers, the valley would be altogether shut out from the rest of the world, were it not that it is accessible from the sea at one end, and by a narrow defile at the other.

The impression produced upon my mind, when I first visited this beautiful glen, will never be obliterated.

I had come from Nukuheva by water in the ship's boat, and when we entered the bay of Tior it was high noon. The heat had been intense, as we had been floating upon the long smooth swell of the ocean, for there was but little wind. The sun's rays had expended all their fury upon us; and to add to our discomfort, we had omitted to supply ourselves with water previous to starting. What with heat and thirst together, I became so impatient to get ashore, that when at last we glided towards it, I stood up in the bow of the boat ready for a spring. As she shot two-thirds of her length high upon the beach, propelled by three or four strong strokes of the oars, I leaped among a parcel of juvenile savages, who stood prepared to give us a kind reception; and with them at my heels, yelling like so many imps, I rushed forward across the open ground in the vicinity of the sea, and plunged, diver fashion, into the recesses of the first grove that offered.

What a delightful sensation did I experience! I felt as if floating in some new element, while all sort of gurgling, trickling, liquid sounds fell upon my ear. People may say what they will about the refreshing influences of a cold-water bath, but commend me when in a perspiration to the shade baths of Tior, beneath the cocoanut-trees, and amidst the cool delightful atmosphere which surrounds them.

How shall I describe the scenery that met my eye, as I looked out from this verdant recess! The narrow valley, with its steep and close adjoining sides draperied with vines, and arched overhead with a fret-work of interlacing boughs, nearly hidden from view by masses of leafy verdure, seemed from where I stood like an immense arbor disclosing its vista to the eye, whilst as I advanced it insensibly widened into the loveliest vale eye ever beheld.

It so happened that the very day I was in Tior the French admiral, attended by all the boats of his squadron, came down in state from Nukuheva to take formal possession of the place. He remained in the valley about two hours, during which time he had a ceremonious interview with the king. The patriarch-sovereign of Tior was a man very far advanced in years; but though age had bowed his form and rendered him almost decrepit, his gigantic frame retained all its original magnitude and grandeur of appearance. He advanced slowly and with evident pain, assisting his tottering steps with the heavy war-spear he held in his hand, and attended by a group of gray-bearded chiefs, on one of whom he occasionally leaned for support. The admiral came forward with head uncovered and extended hand, while the old king saluted him by a stately flourish of his weapon. The next moment they stood side by side, these two extremes in the social scale—the polished, splendid Frenchman, and the poor tattooed savage. They were both tall and noble-looking men; but in other respects how strikingly contrasted! Du Petit Thouars exhibited upon his person all the paraphernalia of his naval rank. He wore a richly decorated admiral's frock-coat, a laced *chapeau bras,* and upon his breast were a variety of ribbons and orders; while the simple islander, with the exception of a slight cincture about his loins, appeared in all the nakedness of nature.

At what an immeasurable distance, thought I, are these two beings removed from eachother. In the one is shown the result of long centuries of progressive civilization and refinement, which have gradually converted the mere creature into the semblance of all that is elevated and grand; while the other, after the lapse of the same period, has not advanced one step in the career of improvement. "Yet, after all," quoth I to myself, "insensible as he is to a thousand wants, and removed from harassing cares, may not the savage be the happier man of the two?" Such were the thoughts that arose in my mind as I gazed upon the novel spectacle before me. In truth it was an impressive one, and little likely to be effaced. I can recall even now with vivid distinctness every feature of the scene. The umbrageous shades where the interview took place, the glorious tropical vegetation around, the picturesque grouping of the mingled throng of soldiery and natives, and even the golden-hued bunch of bananas that I held in my hand at the time, and of which I occasionally partook while making the aforesaid philosophical reflections.

Chapter V

Thoughts Previous to Attempting an Escape—Toby, a Fellow-Sailor, Agrees to Share the Adventure—Last Night Aboard the Ship

Having fully resolved to leave the vessel clandestinely, and having acquired all the knowledge concerning the bay that I could obtain under the circumstances in which I was placed, I now deliberately turned over in my mind every plan of escape that suggested itself, being determined to act with all possible prudence in an attempt where failure would be attended with so many disagreeable consequences. The idea of being taken and brought back ignominiously to the ship was so inexpressibly repulsive to me, that I was determined by no hasty and imprudent measures to render such an event probable.

I knew that our worthy captain, who felt such a paternal solicitude for the welfare of his crew, would not willingly consent that one of his best hands should encounter the perils of a sojourn among the natives of a barbarous island; and I was certain that in the event of my disappearance, his fatherly anxiety would prompt him to offer, by way of a reward, yard upon yard of gaily printed calico for my apprehension. He might even have appreciated my services at the value of a musket, in which case I felt perfectly certain that the whole population of the bay would be immediately upon my track, incited by the prospect of so magnificent a bounty.

Having ascertained the fact before alluded to, that the islanders, from motives of precaution, dwelt altogether in the depths of the valleys, and avoided wandering about the more elevated portions of the shore, unless bound on some expedition of war or plunder, I concluded that if I could effect unperceived a passage to the mountains, I might easily remain among them, supporting myself by such fruits as came in my way until the sailing of the ship, an event of which I could not fail to be immediately apprised, as from my lofty position I should command a view of the entire harbor.

The idea pleased me greatly. It seemed to combine a great deal of practicability with no inconsiderable enjoyment in a quiet way; for how delightful it would be to look down upon the detested old vessel from the height of some thousand feet, and contrast the verdant scenery about me with the recollection of her narrow decks and gloomy forecastle! Why, it was really refreshing even to think of it; and so I straightway fell to picturing myself seated beneath a cocoanut-tree on the brow of the mountain, with a cluster of plantains within easy reach, criticizing her nautical evolutions as she was working her way out of the harbor.

To be sure there was one rather unpleasant drawback to these agreeable anticipations—the possibility of falling in with a foraging party of these same bloody-minded Typees, whose appetites, edged perhaps by the air of so elevated a region, might prompt them to devour one. This, I must confess, was a most disagreeable view of the matter.

Just to think of a party of these unnatural gourmands taking it into their heads to make a convivial meal of a poor devil, who would have no means of escape or defense: however, there was no help for it. I was willing to encounter some risks in order to accomplish my object, and counted much upon my ability to elude these prowling cannibals amongst the many coverts which the mountains afforded. Besides, the chances were ten to one in my favor that they would none of them quit their own fastnesses.

I had determined not to communicate my design of withdrawing from the vessel to any of my shipmates, and least of all to solicit anyone to accompany me in my flight. But it so happened one night, that being upon deck, revolving over in my mind various plans of escape, I perceived one of the ship's company leaning over the bulwarks, apparently plunged in a profound reverie. He was a young fellow about my own age, for whom I had all along entertained a great regard; and Toby, such was the name by which he went among us, for his real name he would never tell us, was every way worthy of it. He was active, ready, and obliging, of dauntless courage, and singularly open and fearless in the expression of his feelings. I had on more than one occasion got him out of scrapes into which this had led him; and I know not whether it was from this cause, or a certain congeniality of sentiment between us, that he had always shown a partiality for my society. We had battled out many a long watch together, beguiling the weary hours with chat, song, and story, mingled with a good many imprecations upon the hard destiny it seemed our common fortune to encounter.

Toby, like myself, had evidently moved in a different sphere of life, and his conversation at times betrayed this, although he was anxious to conceal it. He was one of that class of rovers you sometimes meet at sea, who never reveal their origin, never allude to home, and go rambling over the world as if pursued by some mysterious fate they cannot possibly elude.

There was much even in the appearance of Toby calculated to draw me towards him, for while the greater part of the crew were as coarse in person as in mind, Toby was endowed with a remarkably prepossessing exterior. Arrayed in his blue frock and duck trousers, he was as smart a looking sailor as ever stepped upon a deck; he was singularly small and slightly made, with great flexibility of limb. His naturally dark complexion had been deepened by exposure to the tropical sun, and a mass of jetty locks clustered about his temples, and threw a darker shade into his large black eyes. He was a strange wayward being, moody, fitful, and melancholy—at times almost morose. He had a quick and fiery temper too, which, when thoroughly roused, transported him into a state bordering on delirium.

It is strange the power that a mind of deep passion has over feebler natures. I have seen a brawny fellow, with no lack of ordinary courage, fairly quail before this slender stripling, when in one of his furious fits. But these paroxysms seldom occurred, and in them my big-hearted shipmate vented the bile which more calm-tempered individuals get rid of by a continual pettishness at trivial annoyances.

No one ever saw Toby laugh; I mean in the hearty abandonment of broad-mouthed mirth. He did smile sometimes, it is true; and there was a good deal of dry, sarcastic humor about him, which told the more from the imperturbable gravity of his tone and manner.

Latterly I had observed that Toby's melancholy had greatly increased, and I had frequently seen him since our arrival at the island gazing wistfully upon the shore, when the remainder of the crew would be rioting below. I was aware that he entertained a cordial detestation of the ship, and believed that, should a fair chance of escape present itself, he would embrace it willingly. But the attempt was so perilous in the place where we then lay, that I supposed myself the only individual on board the ship who was sufficiently reckless to think of it. In this, however, I was mistaken.

When I perceived Toby leaning, as I have mentioned, against the bulwarks and buried in thought, it struck me at once that the subject of his meditations might be the same as my own. And if it be so, thought I, is he not the very one of all my shipmates whom I would choose for the partner of my adventure? and why should I not have some comrade with me to divide its dangers and alleviate its hardships? Perhaps I might be obliged to lie concealed among the mountains for weeks. In such an event what a solace would a companion be!

These thoughts passed rapidly through my mind, and I wondered why I had not before considered the matter in this light. But it was not too late. A tap upon the shoulder served to rouse Toby from his reverie; I found him ripe for the enterprise, and a very few words sufficed for a mutual understanding between us. In an hour's time we had arranged all the preliminaries, and decided upon our plan of action. We then ratified our engagement with an affectionate wedding of palms, and to elude suspicion repaired each to his hammock, to spend the last night on board the *Dolly*.

The next day the starboard watch, to which we both belonged, was to be sent ashore on liberty; and, availing ourselves of this opportunity, we determined, as soon after landing as possible, to separate ourselves from the rest of the men without exciting their suspicions, and strike back at once for the mountains. Seen from the ship, their summits appeared inaccessible, but here and there sloping spurs extended from them almost into the sea, buttressing the lofty elevations with which they were connected, and forming those radiating valleys I have before described. One of these ridges, which appeared more practicable than the rest, we determined to climb, convinced that it would conduct us to the heights beyond. Accordingly, we carefully observed its bearings and locality from the ship, so that when ashore we should run no chance of missing it.

In all this the leading object we had in view was to seclude ourselves from sight until the departure of the vessel; then to take our chance as to the reception the Nukuheva natives might give us; and after remaining upon the island as long as we found our stay agreeable, to leave it the first favorable opportunity that offered.

Chapter VI

A Specimen of Nautical Oratory—Criticism of the Sailors—The Starboard Watch are Given a Holiday—The Escape to the Mountains

EARLY THE NEXT MORNING THE STARBOARD WATCH WERE MUSTERED UPON THE QUARTER-DECK, and our worthy captain, standing in the cabin gangway, harangued us as follows—

"Now, men, as we are just off a six months' cruise, and have got through most all our work in port here, I suppose you want to go ashore. Well, I mean to give your watch liberty to-day, so you may get ready as soon as you please, and go; but understand this, I am going to give you liberty because I suppose you would growl like so many old quarter gunners if I didn't; at the same time, if you'll take my advice, every mother's son of you will stay aboard, and keep out of the way of the bloody cannibals altogether. Ten to one, men, if you go ashore, you will get into some infernal row, and that will be the end of you; for if those tattooed scoundrels get you a little ways back into their valleys, they'll nab you—that you may be certain of. Plenty of white men have gone ashore here and never been seen anymore. There was the old *Dido*, she put in here about two years ago, and sent one watch off on liberty; they never were heard of again for a week—the natives swore they didn't know where they were—and only three of them ever got back to the ship again, and one with his face damaged for life, for the cursed heathens tattooed a broad patch clean across his figure-head. But it will be no use talking to you, for go you will, that I see plainly; so all I have to say is, that you need not blame me if the islanders make a meal of you. You may stand some chance of escaping them though, if you keep close about the French encampment, and are back to the ship again before sunset. Keep that much in your mind, if you forget all the rest I've been saying to you. There, go forward; bear a hand and rig yourselves, and stand by for a call. At two bells the boat will be manned to take you off, and the Lord have mercy on you!"

Various were the emotions depicted upon the countenances of the starboard watch whilst listening to this address; but on its conclusion there was a general move towards the forecastle, and we soon were all busily engaged in getting ready for the holiday so auspiciously announced by the skipper. During these preparations his harangue was commented upon in no very measured terms; and one of the party, after denouncing him as a lying old son of a sea-cook who begrudged a fellow a few hours' liberty, exclaimed with an oath, "But you don't bounce me out of my liberty, old chap, for all your yarns; for I would go ashore if every pebble on the beach was a live coal, and every stick a gridiron, and the cannibals stood ready to broil me on landing."

The spirit of this sentiment was responded to by all hands, and we resolved that in spite of the captain's croakings we would make a glorious day of it.

But Toby and I had our own game to play, and we availed ourselves of the confusion which always reigns among a ship's company preparatory to going ashore, to confer together and complete our arrangements. As our object was to effect as rapid a flight as possible to the mountains, we determined not to encumber ourselves with any superfluous apparel; and accordingly, while the rest were rigging themselves out with some idea of making a display, we were content to put on new stout duck trousers, serviceable pumps, and heavy Havre-frocks, which with a Payta hat completed our equipment.

When our shipmates wondered at this, Toby exclaimed in his odd, grave way that the rest might do as they liked, but that he for one preserved his go-ashore traps for the Spanish Main, where the tie of a sailor's neckerchief might make some difference; but as for a parcel of unbreeched heathen, he wouldn't go to the bottom of his chest for any of them, and was half disposed to appear among them in buff himself. The men laughed at what they thought was one of his strange conceits, and so we escaped suspicion.

It may appear singular that we should have been thus on our guard with our own shipmates; but there were some among us who, had they possessed the least inkling of our project, would, for a paltry hope of reward, have immediately communicated it to the captain.

As soon as two bells were struck, the word was passed for the liberty-men to get into the boat. I lingered behind in the forecastle a moment, to take a parting glance at its familiar features, and just as I was about to ascend to the deck, my eye happened to light on the bread-barge and beef-kid, which contained the remnants of our last hasty meal. Although I had never before thought of providing anything in the way of food for our expedition, as I fully relied upon the fruits of the island to sustain us wherever we might wander, yet I could not resist the inclination I felt to provide luncheon from the relics before me. Accordingly I took a double handful of those small, broken, flinty bits of biscuit, which generally go by the name of "midshipmen's nuts," and thrust them into the bosom of my frock; in which same ample receptacle I had previously stowed away several pounds of tobacco and a few yards of cotton cloth—articles with which I intended to purchase the good-will of the natives, as soon as we should appear among them after the departure of our vessel.

This last addition to my stock caused a considerable protuberance in front, which I abated in a measure by shaking the bits of bread around my waist, and distributing the plugs of tobacco among the folds of the garment.

Hardly had I completed these arrangements when my name was sung out by a dozen voices, and I sprung upon the deck, where I found all the party in the boat, and impatient to shove off. I dropped over the side, and seated myself with the rest of the watch in the stern sheets, while the poor larboarders shipped their oars, and commenced pulling us ashore.

This happened to be the rainy season at the islands, and the heavens had nearly the whole morning betokened one of those heavy showers which during this period so frequently occur. The large drops fell bubbling into the water shortly after our leaving the ship, and by the time we had affected a landing it poured down in torrents. We fled for shelter under cover of an immense canoe-house which stood hard by the beach, and waited for the first fury of the storm to pass.

It continued, however, without cessation; and the monotonous beating of the rain over head began to exert a drowsy influence upon the men, who, throwing themselves here and there upon the large war-canoes, after chatting awhile, all fell asleep.

This was the opportunity we desired, and Toby and I availed ourselves of it at once by stealing out of the canoe-house and plunging into the depths of an extensive grove that was in its rear. After ten minutes' rapid progress we gained an open space from which we could just descry the ridge we intended to mount looming dimly through the mists of the tropical shower, and distant from us, as we estimated, something more than a mile. Our direct course towards it lay through a rather populous part of the bay; but desirous as we were of evading the natives and securing an unmolested retreat to the mountains, we determined, by taking a circuit through some extensive thickets, to avoid their vicinity altogether.

The heavy rain that still continued to fall without intermission favored our enterprise, as it drove the islanders into their houses, and prevented any casual meeting with them. Our heavy frocks soon became completely saturated with water, and by their weight, and that of the articles we had concealed beneath them, not a little impeded our progress. But it was no time to pause when at any moment we might be surprised by a body of the savages, and forced at the very outset to relinquish our undertaking.

Since leaving the canoe-house we had scarcely exchanged a single syllable with one another; but when we entered a second narrow opening in the wood, and again caught sight of the ridge before us, I took Toby by the arm, and pointing along its sloping outline to the lofty heights at its extremity, said in a low tone, "Now Toby, not a word, nor a glance backward, till we stand on the summit of yonder mountain—so no more lingering, but let us shove ahead while we can, and in a few hours' time we may laugh aloud. You are the lightest and the nimblest, so lead on, and I will follow."

"All right, brother," said Toby, "quick's our play; only lets keep close together, that's all"; and so saying with a bound like a young roe, he cleared a brook which ran across our path, and rushed forward with a quick step.

When we arrived within a short distance of the ridge, we were stopped by a mass of tall yellow reeds, growing together as thickly as they could stand, and as tough and stubborn as so many rods of steel; and we perceived, to our chagrin, that they extended midway up the elevation we purposed to ascend.

For a moment we gazed about us in quest of a more practicable route; it was, however, at once apparent that there was no resource but to pierce this thicket of canes at all hazards. We now reversed our order of march, I, being the heaviest, taking the lead, with a view of breaking a path through the obstruction, while Toby fell into the rear.

Two or three times I endeavored to insinuate myself between the canes, and by dint of coaxing and bending them to make some progress; but a bull-frog might as well have tried to work a passage through the teeth of a comb, and I gave up the attempt in despair.

Half wild with meeting an obstacle we had so little anticipated, I threw myself desperately against it, crushing to the ground the canes with which I came in contact; and, rising to my feet again, repeated the action with like effect. Twenty minutes of this violent exercise almost exhausted me, but it carried us some way into the thicket; when Toby, who had been reaping the benefit of my labors by following close at my heels, proposed to become pioneer in turn, and accordingly passed ahead with a view of affording me a respite from my exertions. As however with his slight frame he made but bad work of it, I was soon obliged to resume my old place again.

On we toiled, the perspiration starting from our bodies in floods, our limbs torn and lacerated with the splintered fragments of the broken canes, until we had proceeded perhaps as far as the middle of the brake, when suddenly it ceased raining, and the atmosphere around us became close and sultry beyond expression. The elasticity of the reeds, quickly recovering from the temporary pressure of our bodies, caused them to spring back to their original position; so that they closed in upon us as we advanced, and prevented the circulation of the little air which might otherwise have reached us. Besides this, their great height completely shut us out from the view of surrounding objects, and we were not certain but that we might have been going all the time in a wrong direction.

Fatigued with my long-continued efforts, and panting for breath, I felt myself completely incapacitated for any further exertion. I rolled up the sleeve of my frock, and squeezed the moisture it contained into my parched mouth. But the few drops I managed to obtain gave me little relief, and I sunk down for a moment with a sort of dogged apathy, from which I was aroused by Toby, who had devised a plan to free us from the net in which we had become entangled.

He was laying about him lustily with his sheath-knife, lopping the canes right and left, like a reaper, and soon made quite a clearing around us. This sight reanimated me, and seizing my own knife, I hacked and hewed away without mercy. But alas! the farther we advanced, the thicker and taller, and apparently the more interminable, the reeds became.

I began to think we were fairly snared, and had almost made up my mind that without a pair of wings we should never be able to escape from the toils; when all at once I discerned a peep of daylight through the canes on my right, and, communicating the joyful tidings to Toby, we both fell to with fresh spirit, and speedily opening a passage towards it, we found ourselves clear of perplexities, and in the near vicinity of the ridge.

After resting for a few moments we began the ascent, and after a little vigorous climbing found ourselves close to its summit. Instead however of walking along its ridge, where we should have been in full view of the natives in the vales beneath, and at a point where they could easily intercept us were they so inclined, we cautiously advanced on one side, crawling on our hands and knees, and screened from observation by the grass through which we glided, much in the fashion of a couple of serpents. After an hour employed in this unpleasant kind of locomotion, we started to our feet again and pursued our way boldly along the crest of the ridge.

This salient spur of the lofty elevations that encompassed the bay, rose with a sharp angle from the valleys at its base, and presented, with the exception of a few steep acclivities, the appearance of a vast inclined plane, sweeping down towards the sea from the heights in the distance. We had ascended it near the place of its termination and at its lowest point, and now saw our route to the mountains distinctly defined along its narrow crest, which was covered with a soft carpet of verdure, and was in many parts only a few feet wide.

Elated with the success which had so far attended our enterprise, and invigorated by the refreshing atmosphere we now inhaled, Toby and I in high spirits were making our way rapidly along the ridge, when suddenly from the valleys below which lay on either side of us, we heard the distant shouts of the natives, who had just descried us, and to whom our figures, brought in bold relief against the sky, were plainly revealed.

Glancing our eyes into these valleys, we perceived their savage inhabitants hurrying to and fro, seemingly under the influence of some sudden alarm, and appearing to the eye scarcely bigger than so many pigmies; while their white thatched dwellings, dwarfed by the distance, looked like baby-houses. As we looked down upon the islanders from our lofty elevation, we experienced a sense of security; feeling confident that, should they undertake a pursuit, it would, from the start we now had, prove entirely fruitless, unless they followed us into the mountains, where we knew they cared not to venture.

However, we thought it as well to make the most of our time; and accordingly, where the ground would admit of it, we ran swiftly along the summit of the ridge, until we were brought to a stand by a steep cliff, which at first seemed to interpose an effectual barrier to our further advance. By dint of much hard scrambling however, and at some risk to our necks, we at last surmounted it, and continued our flight with unabated celerity.

We had left the beach early in the morning, and after an uninterrupted, though at times difficult and dangerous ascent, during which we had never once turned our faces to the sea, we found ourselves, about three hours before sunset, standing on the top of what seemed to be the highest land on the island, an immense overhanging cliff, composed of basaltic rocks, hung round with parasitical plants. We must have been more than three thousand feet above the level of the sea, and the scenery viewed from this height was magnificent.

The lonely bay of Nukuheva, dotted here and there with the black hulls of the vessels composing the French squadron, lay reposing at the base of a circular range of elevations, whose verdant sides, perforated with deep glens or diversified with smiling valleys, formed altogether the loveliest view I ever beheld, and were I to live a hundred years, I shall never forget the feeling of admiration which I then experienced.

Chapter VII

The Other Side of the Mountain—Disappointment—Inventory of Articles Brought from the Ship—Division of the Stock of Bread—Appearance of the Interior of the Island—A Discovery—A Ravine and Waterfalls—A Sleepless Night—Further Discoveries—My Illness—A Marquesan Landscape

My curiosity had been not a little raised with regard to the description of country we should meet on the other side of the mountains; and I had supposed, with Toby, that immediately on gaining the heights we should be enabled to view the large bays of Happar and Typee reposing at our feet on one side, in the same way that Nukuheva lay spread out below on the other. But here we were disappointed. Instead of finding the mountain we had ascended sweeping down in the opposite direction into broad and capacious valleys, the land appeared to retain its general elevation, only broken into a series of ridges and intervales, which as far as the eye could reach stretched away from us, with their precipitous sides covered with the brightest verdure, and waving here and there with the foliage of clumps of woodland; among which, however, we perceived none of those trees upon whose fruit we had relied with such certainty.

This was a most unlooked-for discovery, and one that promised to defeat our plans altogether, for we could not think of descending the mountain on the Nukuheva side in quest of food. Should we for this purpose be induced to retrace our steps, we should run no small chance of encountering the natives, who in that case, if they did nothing worse to us, would be certain to convey us back to the ship for the sake of the reward in calico and trinkets, which we had no doubt our skipper would hold out to them as an inducement to our capture.

What was to be done? The *Dolly* would not sail perhaps for ten days, and how were we to sustain life during this period? I bitterly repented our improvidence in not providing ourselves, as we easily might have done, with a supply of biscuit. With a rueful visage I now bethought me of the scanty handful of bread I had stuffed into the bosom of my frock, and felt somewhat desirous to ascertain what part of it had weathered the rather rough usage it had experienced in ascending the mountain. I accordingly proposed to Toby that we should enter into a joint examination of the various articles we had brought from the ship. With this intent we seated ourselves upon the grass; and a little curious to see with what kind of judgment my companion had filled his frock—which I remarked seemed about as well lined as my own—I requested him to commence operations by spreading out its contents.

Thrusting his hand, then, into the bosom of this capacious receptacle, he first brought to light about a pound of tobacco, whose component parts still adhered together, the whole outside being covered with soft particles of sea-bread. Wet and dripping, it had the appearance of having been just recovered from the bottom of the sea. But I paid slight attention to a substance of so little value to us in our present situation, as soon as I perceived the indications it gave of Toby's foresight in laying in a supply of food for the expedition.

I eagerly inquired what quantity he had brought with him, when, rummaging once more beneath his garment, he produced a small handful of something so soft, pulpy, and discolored, that for a few moments he was as much puzzled as myself to tell by what possible instrumentality such a villainous compound had become engendered in his bosom. I can only describe it as a hash of soaked bread and bits of tobacco, brought to a doughy consistency by the united agency of perspiration and rain. But repulsive as it might otherwise have been, I now regarded it as an invaluable treasure, and proceeded with great care to transfer this paste-like mass to a large leaf which I had plucked from a bush beside me. Toby informed me that in the morning he had placed two whole biscuits in his bosom, with a view of munching them, should he feel so inclined, during our flight. These were now reduced to the equivocal substance which I had just placed on the leaf.

Another dive into the frock brought to view some four or five yards of calico print, whose tasteful pattern was rather disfigured by the yellow stains of the tobacco with which it had been brought in contact. In drawing this calico slowly from his bosom inch by inch, Toby reminded me of a juggler performing the feat of the endless ribbon. The next cast was a small one, being a sailor's little "ditty-bag," containing needles, thread, and other sewing utensils; then came a razor-case, followed by two or three separate plugs of negro-head, which were fished up from the bottom of the now empty receptacle. These various matters being inspected, I produced the few things which I had myself brought.

As might have been anticipated from the state of my companion's edible supplies, I found my own in a deplorable condition, and diminished to a quantity that would not have formed half a dozen mouthfuls for a hungry man who was partial enough to tobacco not to mind swallowing it. A few morsels of bread, with a fathom or two of white cotton cloth, and several pounds of choice pigtail, composed the extent of my possessions.

Our joint stock of miscellaneous articles was now made up into a compact bundle, which it was agreed we should carry alternately. But the sorry remains of the biscuit were not to be disposed of so summarily: the precarious circumstances in which we were placed made us regard them as something on which very probably depended the fate of our adventure. After a brief discussion, in which we both of us expressed our resolution of not descending into the bay until the ship's departure, I suggested to my companion that little of it as there was, we should divide the bread into six equal portions, each of which should be a day's allowance for both of us. This proposition he assented to;

so I took the silk kerchief from my neck, and cutting it with my knife into half a dozen equal pieces, proceeded to make an exact division.

At first, Toby, with a degree of fastidiousness that seemed to me ill-timed, was for picking out the minute particles of tobacco with which the spongy mass was mixed; but against this proceeding I protested, as by such an operation we must have greatly diminished its quantity.

When the division was accomplished, we found that a day's allowance for the two was not a great deal more than what a table-spoon might hold. Each separate portion we immediately rolled up in the bit of silk prepared for it, and joining them all together into a small package, I committed them, with solemn injunctions of fidelity, to the custody of Toby. For the remainder of that day we resolved to fast, as we had been fortified by a breakfast in the morning; and now starting again to our feet, we looked about us for a shelter during the night, which, from the appearance of the heavens, promised to be a dark and tempestuous one.

There was no place near us which would in any way answer our purpose; so turning our backs upon Nukuheva, we commenced exploring the unknown regions which lay upon the other side of the mountain.

In this direction, as far as our vision extended, not a sign of life, nor anything that denoted even the transient residence of man, could be seen. The whole landscape seemed one unbroken solitude, the interior of the island having apparently been untenanted since the morning of the creation; and as we advanced through this wilderness, our voices sounded strangely in our ears, as though human accents had never before disturbed the fearful silence of the place, interrupted only by the low murmurings of distant waterfalls.

Our disappointment, however, in not finding the various fruits with which we had intended to regale ourselves during our stay in these wilds, was a good deal lessened by the consideration that from this very circumstance we should be much less exposed to a casual meeting with the savage tribes about us, who we knew always dwelt beneath the shadows of those trees which supplied them with food.

We wandered along, casting eager glances into every bush we passed, until just as we had succeeded in mounting one of the many ridges that intersected the ground, I saw in the grass before me something like an indistinctly traced footpath, which appeared to lead along the top of the ridge, and to descend with it into a deep ravine about half a mile in advance of us.

Robinson Crusoe could not have been more startled at the footprint in the sand than we were at this unwelcome discovery. My first impulse was to make as rapid a retreat as possible, and bend our steps in some other direction; but our curiosity to see whither this path might lead, prompted us to pursue it. So on we went, the track becoming more and more visible the farther we proceeded, until it conducted us to the verge of the ravine, where it abruptly terminated.

"And so," said Toby, peering down into the chasm, "everyone that travels this path takes a jump here, eh?"

"Not so," said I, "for I think they might manage to descend without it; what say you—shall we attempt the feat?"

"And what, in the name of caves and coal-holes, do you expect to find at the bottom of that gulf but a broken neck—why it looks blacker than our ship's hold, and the roar of those waterfalls down there would batter one's brains to pieces."

"Oh, no, Toby," I exclaimed, laughing; "but there's something to be seen here, that's plain, or there would have been no path, and I am resolved to find out what it is."

"I will tell you what, my pleasant fellow," rejoined Toby quickly, "if you are going to pry into everything you meet with here that excites your curiosity, you will marvelously soon get knocked on the head; to a dead certainty you will come bang upon a party of these savages in the midst of your discovery-makings, and I doubt whether such an event would particularly delight you. Just take my advice for once, and let us 'bout ship and steer in some other direction; besides, it's getting late and we ought to be mooring ourselves for the night."

"That is just the thing I have been driving at," replied I; "and I am thinking that this ravine will exactly answer our purpose, for it is roomy, secluded, well watered, and may shelter us from the weather."

"Ay, and from sleep too, and by the same token will give us sore throats and rheumatisms into the bargain," cried Toby with evident dislike at the idea.

"Oh, very well then, my lad," said I, "since you will not accompany me, here I go alone. You will see me in the morning"; and advancing to the edge of the cliff upon which we had been standing, I proceeded to lower myself down by the tangled roots which clustered about all the crevices of the rock. As I had anticipated, Toby, in spite of his previous remonstrances, followed my example, and dropping himself with the activity of a squirrel from point to point, he quickly outstripped me and effected a landing at the bottom before I had accomplished two-thirds of the descent.

The sight that now greeted us was one that will ever be vividly impressed upon my mind. Five foaming streams, rushing through as many gorges, and swelled and turbid by the recent rains, united together in one mad plunge of nearly eighty feet, and fell with wild uproar into a deep black pool scooped out of the gloomy looking rocks that lay piled around, and thence in one collected body dashed down a narrow sloping channel which seemed to penetrate into the very bowels of the earth. Overhead, vast roots of trees hung down from the sides of the ravine dripping with moisture, and trembling with the concussions produced by the fall. It was now sunset, and the feeble uncertain light that found its way into these caverns and woody depths heightened their strange appearance, and reminded us that in a short time we should find ourselves in utter darkness.

As soon as I had satisfied my curiosity by gazing at this scene, I fell to wondering how it was that what we had taken for a path should have conducted us to so singular a place, and began to suspect that after all I might have been deceived in supposing it to have been a track formed by the islanders. This was rather an agreeable reflection than otherwise, for it diminished our dread of accidentally meeting with any of them, and I came to the conclusion that perhaps we could not have selected a more secure hiding-place than this very spot we had so accidentally hit upon. Toby agreed with me in this view of the matter, and we immediately began gathering together the limbs of trees which lay scattered about, with the view of constructing a temporary hut for the night. This we were obliged to build close to the foot of the cataract, for the current of water extended very nearly to the sides of the gorge. The few moments of light that remained we employed in covering our hut with a species of broad-bladed grass that grew in every fissure of the ravine. Our hut, if it deserved to be called one, consisted of six or eight of the straightest branches we could find laid obliquely against the steep wall of rock, with their lower ends within a foot of the stream. Into the space thus covered over we managed to crawl, and dispose our wearied bodies as best we could.

Shall I ever forget that horrid night? As for poor Toby, I could scarcely get a word out of him. It would have been some consolation to have heard his voice, but he lay shivering the livelong night like a man afflicted with the palsy, with his knees drawn up to his head, while his back was supported against the dripping side of the rock. During this wretched night there seemed nothing wanting to complete the perfect misery of our condition. The rain descended in such torrents that our poor shelter proved a mere mockery. In vain did I try to elude the incessant streams that poured upon me; by protecting one part I only exposed another, and the water was continually finding some new opening through which to drench us.

I have had many a ducking in the course of my life, and in general cared little about it; but the accumulated horrors of that night, the death-like coldness of the place, the appalling darkness and the dismal sense of our forlorn condition, almost unmanned me.

It will not be doubted that the next morning we were early risers, and as soon as I could catch the faintest glimpse of anything like daylight I shook my companion by the arm, and told him it was sunrise. Poor Toby lifted up his head, and after a moment's pause said, in a husky voice, "Then, shipmate, my toplights have gone out, for it appears darker now with my eyes open than it did when they were shut."

"Nonsense!" exclaimed I; "You are not awake yet."

"Awake!" roared Toby in a rage, "awake! You mean to insinuate I've been asleep, do you? It is an insult to a man to suppose he could sleep in such an infernal place as this."

By the time I had apologized to my friend for having misconstrued his silence, it had become somewhat more light, and we crawled out of our lair. The rain had ceased, but everything around us was dripping with moisture. We stripped off our saturated garments, and wrung them as dry as we could. We contrived to make the blood circulate in our benumbed limbs by rubbing them vigorously with our hands; and after performing our ablutions in the stream, and putting on our still wet clothes, we began to think it advisable to break our long fast, it being now twenty-four hours since we had tasted food.

Accordingly our day's ration was brought out, and seating ourselves on a detached fragment of rock, we proceeded to discuss it. First we divided it into two equal portions, and carefully rolling one of them up for our evening's repast, divided the remainder again as equally as possible, and then drew lots for the first choice. I could have placed the morsel that fell to my share upon the tip of my finger; but notwithstanding this I took care that it should be full ten minutes before I had swallowed the last crumb. What a true saying it is that "appetite furnishes the best sauce." There was a flavor and a relish to this small particle of food that under other circumstances it would have been impossible for the most delicate viands to have imparted. A copious draft of the pure water which flowed at our feet served to complete the meal, and after it we rose sensibly refreshed, and prepared for whatever might befall us.

We now carefully examined the chasm in which we had passed the night.. We crossed the stream, and gaining the further side of the pool I have mentioned, discovered proofs that the spot must have been visited by someone but a short time previous to our arrival. Further observation convinced us that it had been regularly frequented, and, as we afterwards conjectured from particular indications, for the purpose of obtaining a certain root, from which the natives obtain a kind of ointment.

These discoveries immediately determined us to abandon a place which had presented no inducement for us to remain, except the promise of security; and as we looked about us for the means of ascending again into the upper regions, we at last found a practicable part of the rock, and half an hour's toil carried us to the summit of the same cliff from which the preceding evening we had descended.

I now proposed to Toby that instead of rambling about the island, exposing ourselves to discovery at every turn, we should select some place as our fixed abode for as long a period as our food should hold out, build ourselves a comfortable hut, and be as prudent and circumspect as possible. To all this my companion assented, and we at once set about carrying the plan into execution.

With this view, after exploring without success a little glen near us, we crossed several of the ridges of which I have before spoken; and about noon found ourselves ascending a long and gradually rising slope, but still without having discovered any place adapted to our purpose. Low and heavy clouds betokened an approaching storm, and we hurried on to gain a covert in a clump of thick bushes which appeared to terminate the long ascent. We threw ourselves under the lee of these bushes, and pulling up the long grass that grew around, covered ourselves completely with it, and awaited the shower.

But it did not come as soon as we had expected, and before many minutes my companion was fast asleep, and I was rapidly falling into the same state of happy forgetfulness. Just at this juncture, however, down came the rain with the violence that put all thoughts of slumber to flight. Although in some measure sheltered, our clothes soon became as wet as ever: this, after all the trouble we had taken to dry them, was provoking enough: but there was no help for it; and I recommend all adventurous youths who abandon vessels in romantic islands during the rainy season to provide themselves with umbrellas.

After an hour or so the shower passed away. My companion slept through it all, or at least appeared so to do; and now that it was over I had not the heart to awaken him. As I lay on my back completely shrouded with verdure, the leafy branches drooping over me, my limbs buried in grass, I could not avoid comparing our situation with that of the interesting babes in the wood. Poor little sufferers!—no wonder their constitutions broke down under the hardships to which they were exposed.

During the hour or two spent under the shelter of these bushes, I began to feel symptoms which I at once attributed to the exposure of the preceding night. Cold shiverings and a burning fever succeeded one another at intervals, while one of my legs was swelled to such a degree, and pained me so acutely, that I half suspected I had been bitten by some venomous reptile, the congenial inhabitant of the chasm from which we had lately emerged. I may here remark by the way—what I subsequently learned—that all the islands of Polynesia enjoy the reputation, in common with the Hibernian isle, of being free from the presence of any vipers; though whether Saint Patrick ever visited them, is a question I shall not attempt to decide.

As the feverish sensation increased upon me, I tossed about, still unwilling to disturb my slumbering companion, from whose side I removed two or three yards. I chanced to push aside a branch, and by so doing suddenly disclosed to my view a scene which even now I can recall with all the vividness of the first impression. Had a glimpse of the gardens of Paradise been revealed to me I could scarcely have been more ravished with the sight.

From the spot where I lay transfixed with surprise and delight, I looked straight down into the bosom of a valley, which swept away in long wavy undulations to the blue waters in the distance. Midway towards the sea, and peering here and there amidst the foliage, might be seen the palmetto-thatched houses of its inhabitants glistening in the sun that had bleached them to a dazzling whiteness. The vale was more than three leagues in length, and about a mile across at its greatest width.

On either side it appeared hemmed in by steep and green acclivities, which, uniting near the spot where I lay, formed an abrupt and semicircular termination of grassy cliffs and precipices hundreds of feet in height, over which flowed numberless small cascades. But the crowning beauty of the prospect was its universal verdure; and in this indeed consists, I believe, the peculiar charm of every Polynesian landscape. Everywhere below me, from the base of the precipice upon whose very verge I had been unconsciously reposing, the surface of the vale presented a mass of foliage, spread with such rich profusion that it was impossible to determine of what description of trees it consisted.

But perhaps there was nothing about the scenery I beheld more impressive than those silent cascades, whose slender threads of water, after leaping down the steep cliffs, were lost amidst the rich herbage of the valley.

Over all the landscape there reigned the most hushed repose, which I almost feared to break lest, like the enchanted gardens in the fairy tale, a single syllable might dissolve the spell. For a long time, forgetful alike of my own situation, and the vicinity of my still slumbering companion, I remained gazing around me, hardly able to comprehend by what means I had thus suddenly been made a spectator of such a scene.

Chapter VIII

The Important Question, Typee or Happar?—A Wild-Goose Chase—My Sufferings—Disheartening Situation—A Night in a Ravine—Morning Meal—Happy Idea of Toby—Journey Towards the Valley

Recovering from my astonishment at the beautiful scene before me, I quickly awakened Toby, and informed him of the discovery I had made. Together we now repaired to the border of the precipice, and my companion's admiration was equal to my own. A little reflection, however, abated our surprise at coming so unexpectedly upon this valley, since the large vales of Happar and Typee, lying upon this side of Nukuheva, and extending a considerable distance from the sea towards the interior, must necessarily terminate somewhere about this point.

The question now was as to which of those two places we were looking down upon. Toby insisted that it was the abode of the Happars, and I that it was tenanted by their enemies the ferocious Typees. To be sure I was not entirely convinced by my own arguments, but Toby's proposition to descend at once into the valley, and partake of the hospitality of its inmates, seemed to me to be risking so much upon the strength of a mere supposition, that I resolved to oppose it until we had more evidence to proceed upon.

The point was one of vital importance, as the natives of Happar were not only at peace with Nukuheva, but cultivated with its inhabitants the most friendly relations, and enjoyed besides a reputation for gentleness and humanity which led us to expect from them, if not a cordial reception, at least a shelter during the short period we should remain in their territory.

On the other hand, the very name of Typee struck a panic into my heart which I did not attempt to disguise. The thought of voluntarily throwing ourselves into the hands of these cruel savages, seemed to me an act of mere madness; and almost equally so the idea of venturing into the valley, uncertain by which of these two tribes it was inhabited. That the vale at our feet was tenanted by one of them, was a point that appeared to us past all doubt, since we knew that they resided in this quarter, although our information did not enlighten us further.

My companion, however, incapable of resisting the tempting prospect which the place held out of an abundant supply of food and other means of enjoyment, still clung to his own inconsiderate view of the subject, nor could all my reasoning shake it. When I reminded him that it was impossible for either of us to know anything with certainty, and when I dwelt upon the horrible fate we should encounter were we rashly to descend into the valley, and discover too late the error we had committed, he replied by detailing all the evils of our present condition, and the sufferings we must undergo should we continue to remain where we then were.

Anxious to draw him away from the subject, if possible—for I saw that it would be in vain to attempt changing his mind—I directed his attention to a long bright unwooded tract of land which, sweeping down from the elevations in the interior, descended into the valley before us. I then suggested to him that beyond this ridge might lie a capacious and untenanted valley, abounding with all manner of delicious fruits; for I had heard that there were several such upon the island, and proposed that we should endeavor to reach it, and if we found our expectations realized we should at once take refuge in it and remain there as long as we pleased.

He acquiesced in the suggestion; and we immediately, therefore, began surveying the country lying before us, with a view of determining upon the best route for us to pursue; but it presented little choice, the whole interval being broken into steep ridges, divided by dark ravines, extending in parallel lines at right angles to our direct course. All these we would be obliged to cross before we could hope to arrive at our destination.

A weary journey! But we decided to undertake it, though, for my own part, I felt little prepared to encounter its fatigues, shivering and burning by turns with the ague and fever; for I know not how else to describe the alternate sensations I experienced, and suffering not a little from the lameness which afflicted me. Added to this was the faintness consequent on our meager diet—a calamity in which Toby participated to the same extent as myself.

These circumstances, however, only augmented my anxiety to reach a place which promised us plenty and repose, before I should be reduced to a state which would render me altogether unable to perform the journey. Accordingly we now commenced it by descending the almost perpendicular side of a steep and narrow gorge, bristling with a thick growth of reeds. Here there was but one mode for us to adopt. We seated ourselves upon the ground, and guided our descent by catching at the canes in our path. The velocity with which we thus slid down the side of the ravine soon brought us to a point where we could use our feet, and in a short time we arrived at the edge of the torrent, which rolled impetuously along the bed of the chasm.

After taking a refreshing draft from the water of the stream, we addressed ourselves to a much more difficult undertaking than the last. Every foot of our late descent had to be regained in ascending the opposite side of the gorge—an operation rendered the less agreeable from the consideration that in these perpendicular episodes we did not progress a hundred yards on our journey. But, ungrateful as the task was, we set about it with exemplary patience, and after a snail-like progress of an hour or more, had scaled perhaps one-half of the distance, when the fever which had left me for a while returned with such violence, and accompanied by so raging a thirst, that it required all the entreaties of Toby to prevent me from losing all the fruits of my late exertion, by precipitating myself madly down the cliffs we had just climbed, in quest of the water which flowed so temptingly at their base. At the moment all my hopes and fears appeared to be merged in this one desire, careless of the consequences that might result from its gratification. I am aware of no feeling, either of pleasure or of pain, that so completely deprives one of all power to resist its impulses, as this same raging thirst.

Toby earnestly conjured me to continue the ascent, assuring me that a little more exertion would bring us to the summit, and that then in less than five minutes we should find ourselves at the brink of the stream, which must necessarily flow on the other side of the ridge.

"Do not," he exclaimed, "turn back, now that we have proceeded thus far; for I tell you that neither of us will have the courage to repeat the attempt, if once more we find ourselves looking up to where we now are from the bottom of these rocks!"

I was not yet so perfectly beside myself as to be heedless of these representations, and therefore toiled on, ineffectually endeavoring to appease the thirst which consumed me, by thinking that in a short time I should be able to gratify it to my heart's content.

At last we gained the top of the second elevation, the loftiest of those I have described as extending in parallel lines between us and the valley we desired to reach. It commanded a view of the whole intervening distance; and, discouraged as I was by other circumstances, this prospect plunged me into the very depths of despair. Nothing but dark and fearful chasms, separated by sharp-crested and perpendicular ridges as far as the eye could reach. Could we have stepped from summit to summit of these steep but narrow elevations we could easily have accomplished the distance; but we must penetrate to the bottom of every yawning gulf, and scale in succession every one of the eminences before us. Even Toby, although not suffering as I did, was not proof against the disheartening influences of the sight.

But we did not long stand to contemplate it, impatient as I was to reach the waters of the torrent which flowed beneath us. With an insensibility to danger which I cannot call to mind without shuddering, we threw ourselves down the depths of the ravine, startling its savage solitudes with the echoes produced by the falling fragments of rock we every moment dislodged from their places, careless of the insecurity of our footing, and reckless whether the slight roots and twigs we clutched at sustained us for the while, or treacherously yielded to our grasp. For my own part, I scarcely knew whether I was helplessly falling from the heights above, or whether the fearful rapidity with which I descended was an act of my own volition.

In a few minutes we reached the foot of the gorge, and kneeling upon a small ledge of dripping rocks, I bent over to the stream. What a delicious sensation was I now to experience! I paused for a second to concentrate all my capabilities of enjoyment, and then immerged my lips in the clear element before me. Had the apples of Sodom turned to ashes in my mouth, I could not have felt a more startling revulsion. A single drop of the cold fluid seemed to freeze every drop of blood in my body; the fever that had been burning in my veins gave place on the instant to death-like chills, which shook me one after another like so many shocks of electricity, while the perspiration produced by my late violent exertions congealed in icy beads upon my forehead. My thirst was gone, and I fairly loathed the water. Starting to my feet, the sight of those dank rocks, oozing forth moisture at every crevice, and the dark stream shooting along its dismal channel, sent fresh chills through my shivering frame, and I felt as uncontrollable a desire to climb up towards the genial sunlight as I before had to descend the ravine.

After two hours' perilous exertions we stood upon the summit of another ridge, and it was with difficulty I could bring myself to believe that we had ever penetrated the black and yawning chasm which then gaped at our feet. Again we gazed upon the prospect which the height commanded, but it was just as depressing as the one which had before met our eyes. I now felt that in our present situation it was in vain for us to think of ever overcoming the obstacles in our way, and I gave up all thoughts of reaching the vale which lay beyond this series of impediments; while at the same time I could not devise any scheme to extricate ourselves from the difficulties in which we were involved.

The remotest idea of returning to Nukuheva, unless assured of our vessel's departure, never once entered my mind, and indeed it was questionable whether we could have succeeded in reaching it, divided as we were from the bay by a distance we could not compute, and perplexed too in our remembrance of localities by our recent wanderings. Besides, it was unendurable the thought of retracing our steps and rendering all our painful exertions of no avail.

There is scarcely anything when a man is in difficulties that he is more disposed to look upon with abhorrence than a right-about retrograde movement—a systematic going-over of the already trodden ground; and especially if he has a love of adventure, such a course appears indescribably repulsive, so long as there remains the least hope to be derived from braving untried difficulties.

It was this feeling that prompted us to descend the opposite side of the elevation we had just scaled, although with what definite object in view it would have been impossible for either of us to tell.

Without exchanging a syllable upon the subject, Toby and myself simultaneously renounced the design which had lured us thus far—perceiving in each other's countenances that desponding expression which speaks more eloquently than words.

Together we stood towards the close of this weary day in the cavity of the third gorge we had entered, wholly incapacitated for any further exertion, until restored to some degree of strength by food and repose.

We seated ourselves upon the least uncomfortable spot we could select, and Toby produced from the bosom of his frock the sacred package. In silence we partook of the small morsel of refreshment that had been left from the morning's repast, and without once proposing to violate the sanctity of our engagement with respect to the remainder, we rose to our feet, and proceeded to construct some sort of shelter under which we might obtain the sleep we so greatly needed.

Fortunately the spot was better adapted to our purpose than the one in which we had passed the last wretched night. We cleared away the tall reeds from a small but almost level bit of ground, and twisted them into a low basket-like hut, which we covered with a profusion of long thick leaves, gathered from a tree near at hand. We disposed them thickly all around, reserving only a slight opening that barely permitted us to crawl under the shelter we had thus obtained.

These deep recesses, though protected from the winds that assail the summits of their lofty sides, are damp and chill to a degree that one would hardly anticipate in such a climate; and being unprovided with anything but our woolen frocks and thin duck trousers to resist the cold of the place, we were the more solicitous to render our habitation for the night as comfortable as we could. Accordingly, in addition to what we had already done, we plucked down all the leaves within our reach and threw them in a heap over our little hut, into which we now crept, raking after us a reserved supply to form our couch.

That night nothing but the pain I suffered prevented me from sleeping most refreshingly. As it was, I caught two or three naps, while Toby slept away at my side as soundly as though he had been sandwiched between two Holland sheets. Luckily it did not rain, and we were preserved from the misery which a heavy shower would have occasioned us.

In the morning I was awakened by the sonorous voice of my companion ringing in my ears and bidding me rise. I crawled out from our heap of leaves, and was astonished at the change which a good night's rest had wrought in his appearance. He was as blithe and joyous as a young bird, and was staying the keenness of his morning's appetite by chewing the soft bark of a delicate branch he held in his hand, and he recommended the like to me as an admirable antidote against the gnawings of hunger.

For my own part, though feeling materially better than I had done the preceding evening, I could not look at the limb that had pained me so violently at intervals during the last twenty-four hours, without experiencing a sense of alarm that I strove in vain to shake off. Unwilling to disturb the flow of my comrade's spirits, I managed to stifle the complaints to which I might otherwise have given vent, and calling upon him good-humoredly to speed our banquet, I prepared myself for it by washing in the stream. This operation concluded, we swallowed, or rather absorbed, by a peculiar kind of slow sucking process, our respective morsels of nourishment, and then entered into a discussion as to the steps is was necessary for us to pursue.

"What's to be done now?" inquired I, rather dolefully.

"Descend into that same valley we descried yesterday," rejoined Toby, with a rapidity and loudness of utterance that almost led me to suspect he had been slyly devouring the broadside of an ox in some of the adjoining thickets. "What else," he continued, "remains for us to do but that, to be sure? Why, we shall both starve to a certainty if we remain here; and as to your fears of those Typees—depend upon it, it is all nonsense."

"It is impossible that the inhabitants of such a lovely place as we saw can be anything else but good fellows; and if you choose rather to perish with hunger in one of these soppy caverns, I for one prefer to chance a bold descent into the valley, and risk the consequences."

"And who is to pilot us thither," I asked, "even if we should decide upon the measure you propose? Are we to go again up and down those precipices that we crossed yesterday, until we reach the place we started from, and then take a flying leap from the cliffs to the valley?"

" 'Faith, I didn't think of that," said Toby; "sure enough, both sides of the valley appeared to be hemmed in by precipices, didn't they?"

"Yes," answered I, "as steep as the sides of a line-of-battle-ship, and about a hundred times as high." My companion sank his head upon his breast and remained for a while in deep thought. Suddenly he sprang to his feet, while his eyes lighted up with that gleam of intelligence that marks the presence of some bright idea.

"Yes, yes," he exclaimed; "the streams all run in the same direction, and must necessarily flow into the valley before they reach the sea; all we have to do is just to follow this stream, and sooner or later it will lead us into the vale."

"You are right, Toby," I exclaimed, "you are right; it must conduct us thither, and quickly too; for, see with what a steep inclination the water descends."

"It does, indeed," burst forth my companion, overjoyed at my verification of his theory, "it does indeed; why, it is as plain as a pike-staff. Let us proceed at once, come, throw away all those stupid ideas about the Typees, and hurrah for the lovely valley of the Happars!"

"You will have it to be Happar, I see, my dear fellow; pray Heaven you may not find yourself deceived," observed I, with a shake of my head.

"Amen to all that, and much more," shouted Toby, rushing forward; "but Happar it is, for nothing else than Happar can it be. So glorious a valley—such forests of bread-fruit trees—such groves of cocoanut—such wilderness of guava-bushes! Ah, shipmate! don't linger behind: in the name of all delightful fruits, I am dying to be at them. Come on, come on; shove ahead, there's a lively lad; never mind the rocks; kick them out of the way, as I do; and to-morrow, old fellow, take my word for it, we shall be in clover. Come on"; and so saying, he dashed along the ravine like a mad man, forgetting my inability to keep up with him. In a few minutes, however, the exuberance of his spirits abated, and, pausing for a while, he permitted me to overtake him.

Chapter IX

Perilous Passage of the Ravine—Descent into the Valley

THE FEARLESS CONFIDENCE OF TOBY WAS CONTAGIOUS, AND I BEGAN TO ADOPT THE HAPPAR side of the question. I could not, however, overcome a certain feeling of trepidation as we made our way along these gloomy solitudes. Our progress, at first comparatively easy, became more and more difficult. The bed of the watercourse was covered with fragments of broken rocks, which had fallen from above, offering so many obstructions to the course of the rapid stream, which vexed and fretted about them—forming at intervals small waterfalls, pouring over into deep basins, or splashing wildly upon heaps of stones.

From the narrowness of the gorge, and the steepness of its sides, there was no mode of advancing but by wading through the water; stumbling every moment over the impediments which lay hidden under its surface, or tripping against the huge roots of trees. But the most annoying hindrance we encountered was from a multitude of crooked boughs, which, shooting out almost horizontally from the sides of the chasm, twisted themselves together in fantastic masses almost to the surface of the stream, affording us no passage except under the low arches which they formed. Under these we were obliged to crawl on our hands and feet, sliding along the oozy surface of the rocks, or slipping into the deep pools, and with scarce light enough to guide us. Occasionally we would strike our heads against some projecting limb of a tree; and while imprudently engaged in rubbing the injured part, would fall sprawling amongst flinty fragments, cutting and bruising ourselves, whilst the unpitying waters flowed over our prostrate bodies. Belzoni, worming himself through the subterranean passages of the Egyptian catacombs, could not have met with greater impediments than those we here encountered. But we struggled against them manfully, well knowing our only hope lay in advancing.

Towards sunset we halted at a spot where we made preparations for passing the night. Here we constructed a hut, in much the same way as before, and crawling into it, endeavored to forget our sufferings. My companion, I believe, slept pretty soundly; but at daybreak, when we rolled out of our dwelling, I felt nearly disqualified for any further efforts. Toby prescribed as a remedy for my illness the contents of one of our little silk packages, to be taken at once in a single dose. To this species of medical treatment, however, I would by no means accede, much as he insisted upon it; and so we partook of our usual morsel, and silently resumed our journey. It was now the fourth day since we left Nukuheva, and the gnawings of hunger became painfully acute. We were fain to pacify them by chewing the tender bark of roots and twigs, which, if they did not afford us nourishment, were at least sweet and pleasant to the taste.

Our progress along the steep watercourse was necessarily slow, and by noon we had not advanced more than a mile. It was somewhere near this part of the day that the noise of falling waters, which we had faintly caught in the early morning, became more distinct; and it was not long before we were arrested by a rocky precipice of nearly a hundred feet in depth, that extended all across the channel, and over which the wild stream poured in an unbroken leap. On either hand the walls of the ravine presented their overhanging sides both above and below the fall, affording no means whatever of avoiding the cataract by taking a circuit round it.

"What's to be done now, Toby?" said I.

"Why," rejoined he, "as we cannot retreat, I suppose we must keep shoving along."

"Very true, my dear Toby; but how do you purpose accomplishing that desirable object?"

"By jumping from the top of the fall, if there be no other way," unhesitatingly replied my companion: "it will be much the quickest way of descent; but as you are not quite as active as I am, we will try some other way."

And, so saying, he crept cautiously along and peered over into the abyss, while I remained wondering by what possible means we could overcome this apparently insuperable obstruction. As soon as my companion had completed his survey, I eagerly inquired the result.

"The result of my observations you wish to know, do you?" began Toby, deliberately, with one of his odd looks: "well, my lad, the result of my observations is very quickly imparted. It is at present uncertain which of our two necks will have the honor to be broken first; but about a hundred to one would be a fair bet in favor of the man who takes the first jump."

"Then it is an impossible thing, is it?" inquired I gloomily.

"No, shipmate; on the contrary, it is the easiest thing in life: the only awkward point is the sort of usage which our unhappy limbs may receive when we arrive at the bottom, and what sort of traveling trim we shall be in afterwards. But follow me now, and I will show you the only chance we have."

With this he conducted me to the verge of the cataract, and pointed along the side of the ravine to a number of curious looking roots, some three or four inches in thickness, and several feet long, which after twisting among the fissures of the rock, shot perpendicularly from it and ran tapering to a point in the air, hanging over the gulf like so many dark icicles. They covered nearly the entire surface of one side of the gorge, the lowest of them reaching even to the water. Many were moss-grown and decayed, with their extremities snapped short off, and those in the immediate vicinity of the fall were slippery with moisture.

Toby's scheme, and it was a desperate one, was to entrust ourselves to these treacherous-looking roots, and by slipping down from one to another to gain the bottom.

"Are you ready to venture it?" asked Toby, looking at me earnestly but without saying a word as to the practicability of the plan.

"I am," was my reply; for I saw it was our only resource if we wished to advance, and as for retreating, all thoughts of that sort had been long abandoned.

After I had signified my assent, Toby, without uttering a a single word, crawled along the dripping ledge until he gained a point from whence he could just reach one of the largest of the pendant roots; he shook it—it quivered in his grasp, and when he let it go it twanged in the air like a strong wire sharply struck. Satisfied by his scrutiny, my light-limbed companion swung himself nimbly upon it, and twisting his legs round it in sailor fashion, slipped down eight or ten feet, where his weight gave it a motion not unlike that of a pendulum. He could not venture to descend any further; so holding on with one hand, he with the other shook one by one all the slender roots around him, and at last, finding one which he thought trustworthy, shifted himself to it and continued his downward progress.

So far so well; but I could not avoid comparing my heavier frame and disabled condition with his light figure and remarkable activity; but there was no help for it, and in less than a minute's time I was swinging directly over his head. As soon as his upturned eyes caught a glimpse of me, he exclaimed in his usual dry tone, for the danger did not seem to daunt him in the least, "Mate, do me the kindness not to fall until I get out of your way"; and then swinging himself more on one side, he continued his descent. In the mean time I cautiously transferred myself from the limb down which I had been slipping to a couple of others that were near it, deeming two strings to my bow better than one, and taking care to test their strength before I trusted my weight to them.

On arriving towards the end of the second stage in this vertical journey, and shaking the long roots which were round me, to my consternation they snapped off one after another like so many pipe stems, and fell in fragments against the side of the gulf, splashing at last into the waters beneath.

As one after another the treacherous roots yielded to my grasp, and fell into the torrent, my heart sunk within me. The branches on which I was suspended over the yawning chasm swang to and fro in the air, and I expected them every moment to snap in twain. Appalled at the dreadful fate that menaced me, I clutched frantically at the only large root which remained near me, but in vain; I could not reach it, though my fingers were within a few inches of it. Again and again I tried to reach it, until at length, maddened with the thought of my situation, I swayed myself violently by striking my foot against the side of the rock, and at the instant that I approached the large root caught desperately at it, and transferred myself to it. It vibrated violently under the sudden weight, but fortunately did not give way.

My brain grew dizzy with the idea of the frightful risk I had just run, and I involuntarily closed my eyes to shut out the view of the depth beneath me. For the instant I was safe, and I uttered a devout ejaculation of thanksgiving for my escape.

"Pretty well done," shouted Toby underneath me; "you are nimbler than I thought you to be—hopping about up there from root to root like any young squirrel. As soon as you have diverted yourself sufficiently, I would advise you to proceed."

"Ay, ay, Toby, all in good time: two or three more such famous roots as this, and I shall be with you."

The residue of my downward progress was comparatively easy; the roots were in greater abundance, and in one or two places jutting out points of rock assisted me greatly. In a few moments I was standing by the side of my companion.

Substituting a stout stick for the one I had thrown aside at the top of the precipice, we now continued our course along the bed of the ravine. Soon we were saluted by a sound in advance, that grew by degrees louder and louder, as the noise of the cataract we were leaving behind gradually died on our ears.

"Another precipice for us, Toby."

"Very good; we can descend them, you know—come on."

Nothing indeed appeared to depress or intimidate this intrepid fellow. Typees or Niagaras, he was as ready to engage one as the other, and I could not avoid a thousand times congratulating myself upon having such a companion in an enterprise like the present.

After an hour's painful progress, we reached the verge of another fall, still loftier than the preceding, and flanked both above and below with the same steep masses of rock, presenting, however, here and there narrow irregular ledges, supporting a shallow soil, on which grew a variety of bushes and trees, whose bright verdure contrasted beautifully with the foamy waters that flowed between them.

Toby, who invariably acted as pioneer, now proceeded to reconnoiter. On his return, he reported that the shelves of rock on our right would enable us to gain with little risk the bottom of the cataract. Accordingly, leaving the bed of the stream at the very point where it thundered down, we began crawling along one of these sloping ledges until it carried us to within a few feet of another that inclined downwards at a still sharper angle, and upon which, by assisting each other, we managed to alight in safety. We warily crept along this, steadying ourselves by the naked roots of the shrubs that clung to every fissure. As we proceeded, the narrow path became still more contracted, rendering it difficult for us to maintain our footing, until suddenly, as we reached an angle of the wall of rock where we had expected it to widen, we perceived to our consternation that a yard or two farther on it abruptly terminated at a place we could not possibly hope to pass.

Toby as usual led the van, and in silence I waited to learn from him how he proposed to extricate us from this new difficulty.

"Well, my boy," I exclaimed, after the expiration of several minutes, during which time my companion had not uttered a word; "what's to be done now?"

He replied in a tranquil tone, that probably the best thing we could do in our present strait was to get out of it as soon as possible.

"Yes, my dear Toby, but tell me *how* we are to get out of it."

"Something in this sort of style," he replied; and at the same moment to my horror he slipped sideways off the rock, and as I then thought, by good fortune merely alighted among the spreading branches of a species of palm-tree, that shooting its hardy roots along a ledge below, curved its trunk upwards into the air, and presented a thick mass of foliage about twenty feet below the spot where we had thus suddenly been brought to a stand still. I involuntarily held my breath, expecting to see the form of my companion, after being sustained for a moment by the branches of the tree, sink through their frail support, and fall headlong to the bottom. To my surprise and joy, however, he recovered himself, and disentangling his limbs from the fractured branches, he peered out from his leafy bed, and shouted lustily, "Come on, my hearty, there is no other alternative!" and with this he ducked beneath the foliage, and slipping down the trunk, stood in a moment at least fifty feet beneath me, upon the broad shelf of rock from which sprung the tree he had descended.

What would I not have given at that moment to have been by his side! The feat he had just accomplished seemed little less than miraculous, and I could hardly credit the evidence of my senses when I saw the wide distance that a single daring act had so suddenly placed between us.

Toby's animating "Come on!" again sounded in my ears, and dreading to lose all confidence in myself if I remained meditating upon the step, I once more gazed down to assure myself of the relative bearing of the tree and my own position, and then closing my eyes and uttering one comprehensive ejaculation of prayer, I inclined myself over towards the abyss, and after one breathless instant fell with a crash into the tree, the branches snapping and crackling with my weight, as I sunk lower and lower among them, until I was stopped by coming in contact with a sturdy limb.

In a few moments I was standing at the foot of the tree manipulating myself all over with a view of ascertaining the extent of the injuries I had received. To my surprise the only effects of my feat were a few slight contusions too trifling to care about. The rest of our descent was easily accomplished, and in half an hour after regaining the ravine we had partaken of our evening morsel, built our hut as usual, and crawled under its shelter.

The next morning, in spite of our debility and the agony of hunger under which we were now suffering, though neither of us confessed to the fact, we struggled along our dismal and still difficult and dangerous path, cheered by the hope of soon catching a glimpse of the valley before us, and towards evening the voice of a cataract which had for some time sounded like a low deep bass to the music of the smaller waterfalls, broke upon our ears in still louder tones, and assured us that we were approaching its vicinity.

That evening we stood on the brink of a precipice, over which the dark stream bounded in one final leap of full three hundred feet. The sheer descent terminated in the region we so long had sought. On each side of the fall, two lofty and perpendicular bluffs buttressed the sides of the enormous cliff, and projected into the sea of verdure with which the valley waved, and a range of similar projecting eminences stood disposed in a half circle about the head of the vale. A thick canopy of trees hung over the very verge of the fall, leaving an arched aperture for the passage of the waters, which imparted a strange picturesqueness to the scene.

The valley was now before us; but instead of being conducted into its smiling bosom by the gradual descent of the deep watercourse we had thus far pursued, all our labors now appeared to have been rendered futile by its abrupt termination. But, bitterly disappointed, we did not entirely despair.

As it was now near sunset we determined to pass the night where we were, and on the morrow, refreshed by sleep and by eating at one meal all our stock of food, to accomplish a descent into the valley, or perish in the attempt.

We laid ourselves down that night on a spot, the recollection of which still makes me shudder. A small table of rock which projected over the precipice on one side of the stream, and was drenched by the spray of the fall, sustained a huge trunk of a tree which must have been deposited there by some heavy freshet. It lay obliquely, with one end resting on the rock and the other supported by the side of the ravine. Against it we placed in a sloping direction a number of the half decayed boughs that were strewn about, and covering the whole with twigs and leaves, awaited the morning's light beneath such shelter as it afforded.

During the whole of this night the continual roaring of the cataract—the dismal moaning of the gale through the trees—the pattering of the rain, and the profound darkness, affected my spirits to a degree which nothing had ever before produced. Wet, half famished, and chilled to the heart with the dampness of the place, and nearly wild with the pain I endured, I fairly cowered down to the earth under this multiplication of hardships, and abandoned myself to frightful anticipations of evil; and my companion, whose spirit at last was a good deal broken, scarcely uttered a word during the whole night.

At length the day dawned upon us, and rising from our miserable pallet, we stretched our stiffened joints, and after eating all that remained of our bread, prepared for the last stage of our journey.

I will not recount every hair-breadth escape, and every fearful difficulty that occurred before we succeeded in reaching the bosom of the valley. As I have already described similar scenes, it will be sufficient to say that at length, after great toil and great dangers, we both stood with no limbs broken at the head of that magnificent vale which five days before had so suddenly burst upon my sight, and almost beneath the shadow of those very cliffs from whose summits we had gazed upon the prospect.

Chapter X

THE HEAD OF THE VALLEY—CAUTIOUS ADVANCE—A PATH—FRUIT—DISCOVERY OF TWO OF THE NATIVES—THEIR SINGULAR CONDUCT—APPROACH TOWARDS THE INHABITED PARTS OF THE VALE—SENSATION PRODUCED BY OUR APPEARANCE—RECEPTION AT THE HOUSE OF ONE OF THE NATIVES

HOW TO OBTAIN THE FRUIT WHICH WE FELT CONVINCED MUST GROW NEAR AT HAND WAS OUR first thought.

Typee or Happar? A frightful death at the hands of the fiercest of cannibals, or a kindly reception from a gentler race of savages? Which? But it was too late now to discuss a question which would so soon be answered.

The part of the valley in which we found ourselves appeared to be altogether uninhabited. An almost impenetrable thicket extended from side to side, without presenting a single plant affording the nourishment we had confidently calculated upon; and with this object, we followed the course of the stream, casting quick glances as we proceeded into the thick jungles on either hand.

My companion—to whose solicitations I had yielded in descending into the valley—now that the step was taken, began to manifest a degree of caution I had little expected from him. He proposed that, in the event of our finding an adequate supply of fruit, we should remain in this unfrequented portion of the country—where we should run little chance of being surprised by its occupants, whoever they might be—until sufficiently recruited to resume our journey, when laying in a store of food equal to our wants, we might easily regain the bay of Nukuheva, after the lapse of a sufficient interval to ensure the departure of our vessel.

I objected strongly to this proposition, plausible as it was, as the difficulties of the route would be almost insurmountable, unacquainted as we were with the general bearings of the country, and I reminded my companion of the hardships which we had already encountered in our uncertain wanderings; in a word, I said that since we had deemed it advisable to enter the valley, we ought manfully to face the consequences, whatever they might be; the more especially as I was convinced there was no alternative left us but to fall in with the natives at once, and boldly risk the reception they might give us; and that as to myself, I felt the necessity of rest and shelter, and that until I had obtained them I should be wholly unable to encounter such sufferings as we had lately passed through. To the justice of these observations Toby somewhat reluctantly assented.

We were surprised that, after moving as far as we had along the valley, we should still meet with the same impervious thickets, and thinking that although the borders of the stream might be lined for some distance with them, yet beyond there might be more open ground, I requested Toby to keep a bright look-out upon one side, while I did the same on the other, in order to discover some opening in the bushes, and especially to watch for the slightest appearance of a path or anything else that might indicate the vicinity of the islanders.

What furtive and anxious glances we cast into those dim-looking shades! With what apprehensions we proceeded, ignorant at what moment we might be greeted by the javelin of some ambushed savage! At last my companion paused, and directed my attention to a narrow opening in the foliage. We struck into it and it soon brought us, by an indistinctly traced path, to a comparatively clear space, at the further end of which we descried a number of the trees, the native name of which is "annuee," and which bear a most delicious fruit.

What a race! I hobbling over the ground like some decrepit wretch, and Toby leaping forward like a greyhound. He quickly cleared one of the trees on which there were two or three of the fruit, but to our chagrin they proved to be much decayed; the rinds partly opened by the birds, and their hearts half devoured. However, we quickly dispatched them, and no ambrosia could have been more delicious.

We looked about us, uncertain whither to direct our steps, since the path we had so far followed appeared to be lost in the open space around us. At last we resolved to enter a grove near at hand, and had advanced a few rods when, just upon its skirts, I picked up a slender bread-fruit shoot, perfectly green, and with the tender bark freshly stripped from it. It was still slippery with moisture, and appeared as if it had been but that moment thrown aside. I said nothing, but merely held it up to Toby, who started at this undeniable evidence of the vicinity of the savages.

The plot was now thickening. A short distance further lay a little faggot of the same shoots bound together with a strip of bark. Could it have been thrown down by some solitary native who, alarmed at seeing us, had hurried forward to carry the tidings of our approach to his countrymen? Typee or Happar? But it was too late to recede, so we moved on slowly, my companion in advance casting eager glances under the trees on either side, until all at once I saw him recoil as if stung by an adder. Sinking on his knee, he waved me off with one hand, while with the other he held aside some intervening leaves, and gazed intently at some object.

Disregarding his injunction, I quickly approached him, and caught a glimpse of two figures partly hidden by the dense foliage; they were standing close together, and were perfectly motionless. They must have previously perceived us, and withdrawn into the depths of the wood to elude our observation.

My mind was at once made up. Dropping my staff, and tearing open the package of things we had brought from the ship, I unrolled the cotton cloth, and holding it in one hand, plucked with the other a twig from the bushes beside me, and telling Toby to follow my example, I broke through the covert and advanced, waving the branch in token of peace, towards the shrinking forms before me.

They were a boy and a girl, slender and graceful, and completely naked, with the exception of a slight girdle of bark, from which depended at opposite points two of the russet leaves of the bread-fruit tree. An arm of the boy, half screened from sight by her wild tresses, was thrown about the neck of the girl, while with the other he held one of her hands in his; and thus they stood together, their heads inclined forward, catching the faint noise we made in our progress, and with one foot in advance, as if half inclined to fly from our presence.

As we drew near their alarm evidently increased. Apprehensive that they might fly from us altogether, I stopped short and motioned them to advance and receive the gift I extended towards them, but they would not; I then uttered a few words of their language with which I was acquainted, scarcely expecting that they would understand me, but to show that we had not dropped from the clouds upon them. This appeared to give them a little confidence, so I approached nearer, presenting the cloth with one hand and holding the bough with the other, while they slowly retreated. At last they suffered us to approach so near to them that we were enabled to throw the cotton cloth across their shoulders, giving them to understand that it was theirs, and by a variety of gestures endeavoring to make them understand that we entertained the highest possible regard for them.

The frightened pair now stood still, whilst we endeavored to make them comprehend the nature of our wants. In doing this Toby went through with a complete series of pantomimic illustrations—opening his mouth from ear to ear, and thrusting his fingers down his throat, gnashing his teeth and rolling his eyes about, till I verily believe the poor creatures took us for a couple of white cannibals who were about to make a meal of them. When, however, they understood us, they showed no inclination to relieve our wants. At this juncture it began to rain violently, and we motioned them to lead us to some place of shelter. With this request they appeared willing to comply, but nothing could evince more strongly the apprehension with which they regarded us, than the way in which, whilst walking before us, they kept their eyes constantly turned back to watch every movement we made, and even our very looks.

"Typee or Happar, Toby?" asked I as we walked after them.

"Of course Happar," he replied with a show of confidence which was intended to disguise his doubts.

"We shall soon know," I exclaimed; and at the same moment I stepped forward towards our guides, and pronouncing the two names interrogatively and pointing to the lowest part of the valley, endeavored to come to the point at once. They repeated the words after me again and again, but without giving any peculiar emphasis to either, so that I was completely at a loss to understand them; for a couple of wilier young things than we afterwards found them to have been on this particular occasion never probably fell in any traveler's way.

More and more curious to ascertain our fate, I now threw together in the form of a question the words "Happar" and "Motarkee," the latter being equivalent to the word "good." The two natives interchanged glances of peculiar meaning with one another at this, and manifested no little surprise; but on the repetition of the question, after some consultation together, to the great joy of Toby, they answered in the affirmative. Toby was now in ecstasies, especially as the young savages continued to reiterate their answer with great energy, as though desirous of impressing us with the idea that being among the Happars, we ought to consider ourselves perfectly secure.

Although I had some lingering doubts, I feigned great delight with Toby at this announcement, while my companion broke out into a pantomimic abhorrence of Typee, and immeasurable love for the particular valley in which we were; our guides all the while gazing uneasily at one another as if at a loss to account for our conduct.

They hurried on, and we followed them; until suddenly they set up a strange halloo, which was answered from beyond the grove through which we were passing, and the next moment we entered upon some open ground, at the extremity of which we descried a long, low hut, and in front of it were several young girls. As soon as they perceived us they fled with wild screams into the adjoining thickets, like so many startled fawns. A few moments after the whole valley resounded with savage outcries, and the natives came running towards us from every direction.

Had an army of invaders made an irruption into their territory they could not have evinced greater excitement. We were soon completely encircled by a dense throng, and in their eager desire to behold us they almost arrested our progress; an equal number surrounding our youthful guides, who with amazing volubility appeared to be detailing the circumstances which had attended their meeting with us. Every item of intelligence appeared to redouble the astonishment of the islanders, and they gazed at us with inquiring looks.

At last we reached a large and handsome building of bamboos, and were by signs told to enter it, the natives opening a lane for us through which to pass; on entering without ceremony, we threw our exhausted frames upon the mats that covered the floor. In a moment the slight tenement was completely full of people, whilst those who were unable to obtain admittance gazed at us through its open cane-work.

It was now evening, and by the dim light we could just discern the savage countenances around us, gleaming with wild curiosity and wonder; the naked forms and tattooed limbs of brawny warriors, with here and there the slighter figures of young girls, all engaged in a perfect storm of conversation, of which we were of course the one only theme; whilst our recent guides were fully occupied in answering the innumerable questions which everyone put to them. Nothing can exceed the fierce gesticulation of these people when animated in conversation, and on this occasion they gave loose to all their natural vivacity, shouting and dancing about in a manner that well-nigh intimidated us.

Close to where we lay, squatting upon their haunches, were some eight or ten noble-looking chiefs—for such they subsequently proved to be—who, more reserved than the rest, regarded us with a fixed and stern attention, which not a little discomposed our equanimity. One of them in particular, who appeared to be the highest in rank, placed himself directly facing me; looking at me with a rigidity of aspect under which I absolutely quailed. He never once opened his lips, but maintained his severe expression of countenance, without turning his face aside for a single moment. Never before had I been subjected to so strange and steady a glance; it revealed nothing of the mind of the savage, but it appeared to be reading my own.

After undergoing this scrutiny till I grew absolutely nervous, with a view of diverting it if possible, and conciliating the good opinion of the warrior, I took some tobacco from the bosom of my frock and offered it to him. He quietly rejected the proffered gift, and, without speaking, motioned me to return it to its place.

In my previous intercourse with the natives of Nukuheva and Tior, I had found that the present of a small piece of tobacco would have rendered any of them devoted to my service. Was this act of the chief a token of his enmity? Typee or Happar? I asked within myself. I started, for at the same moment this identical question was asked by the strange being before me. I turned to Toby; the flickering light of a native taper showed me his countenance pale with trepidation at this fatal question. I paused for a second, and I know not by what impulse it was that I answered "Typee." The piece of dusky statuary nodded in approval, and then murmured "Motarkee!"—"Motarkee," said I, without further hesitation—"Typee motarkee."

What a transition! The dark figures around us leaped to their feet, clapped their hands in transport, and shouted again and again the talismanic syllables, the utterance of which appeared to have settled everything.

When this commotion had a little subsided, the principal chief squatted once more before me, and throwing himself into a sudden rage, poured forth a string of philippics, which I was at no loss to understand, from the frequent recurrence of the word Happar, as being directed against the natives of the adjoining valley. In all these denunciations my companion and I acquiesced, while we extolled the character of the war-like Typees. To be sure our panegyrics were somewhat laconic, consisting in the repetition of that name, united with the potent adjective "motarkee." But this was sufficient, and served to conciliate the good will of the natives, with whom our congeniality of sentiment on this point did more towards inspiring a friendly feeling than anything else that could have happened.

At last the wrath of the chief evaporated, and in a few moments he was as placid as ever. Laying his hand upon his breast, he now gave me to understand that his name was "Mehevi," and that, in return, he wished me to communicate my appellation. I hesitated for an instant, thinking that it might be difficult for him to pronounce my real name, and then with the most praiseworthy intentions intimated that I was known as "Tom." But I could not have made a worse selection; the chief could not master it; "Tommo," "Tomma," "Tommee," everything but plain "Tom." As he persisted in garnishing the word with an additional syllable, I compromised the matter with him at the word "Tommo," and by that name I went during the entire period of my stay in the valley. The same proceeding was gone through with Toby, whose mellifluous appellation was more easily caught.

An exchange of names is equivalent to a ratification of good will and amity among these simple people; and as we were aware of this fact, we were delighted that it had taken place on the present occasion.

Reclining upon our mats, we now held a kind of levee, giving audience to successive troops of the natives, who introduced themselves to us by pronouncing their respective names, and retired in high good humor on receiving ours in return. During this ceremony the greatest merriment prevailed, nearly every announcement on the part of the islanders being followed by a fresh sally of gaiety, which induced me to believe that some of them at least were innocently diverting the company at our expense, by bestowing upon themselves a string of absurd titles, of the humor of which we were of course entirely ignorant.

All this occupied about an hour, when the throng having a little diminished, I turned to Mehevi and gave him to understand that we were in need of food and sleep. Immediately the attentive chief addressed a few words to one of the crowd, who disappeared, and returned in a few moments with a calabash of "poee-poee," and two or three young cocoanuts stripped of their husks, and with their shells partly broken. We both of us forthwith placed one of these natural goblets to our lips, and drained it in a moment of the refreshing draft it contained. The poee-poee was then placed before us, and even famished as I was, I paused to consider in what manner to convey it to my mouth.

This staple article of food among the Marquese islanders is manufactured from the produce of the bread-fruit tree. It somewhat resembles in its plastic nature our bookbinders' paste, is of a yellow color, and somewhat tart to the taste.

Such was the dish, the merits of which I was now eager to discuss. I eyed it wistfully for a moment, and then, unable any longer to stand on ceremony, plunged my hand into the yielding mass, and to the boisterous mirth of the natives drew it forth laden with the poee-poee, which adhered in lengthy strings to every finger. So stubborn was its consistency, that in conveying my heavily freighted hand to my mouth, the connecting links almost raised the calabash from the mats on which it had been placed. This display of awkwardness—in which, by the by, Toby kept me company—convulsed the bystanders with uncontrollable laughter.

As soon as their merriment had somewhat subsided, Mehevi, motioning us to be attentive, dipped the forefinger of his right hand in the dish, and giving it a rapid and scientific twirl, drew it out coated smoothly with the preparation. With a second peculiar flourish he prevented the poee-poee from dropping to the ground as he raised it to his mouth, into which the finger was inserted and drawn forth perfectly free from any adhesive matter. This performance was evidently intended for our instruction; so I again essayed the feat on the principles inculcated, but with very ill success.

A starving man, however, little heeds conventional proprieties, especially on a South-Sea Island, and accordingly Toby and I partook of the dish after our own clumsy fashion, beplastering our faces all over with the glutinous compound, and daubing our hands nearly to the wrist. This kind of food is by no means disagreeable to the palate of a European, though at first the mode of eating it may be. For my own part, after the lapse of a few days I became accustomed to its singular flavor, and I grew remarkably fond of it.

So much for the first course; several other dishes followed it, some of which were positively delicious. We concluded our banquet by tossing off the contents of two more young cocoanuts, after which we regaled ourselves with the soothing fumes of tobacco, inhaled from a quaintly carved pipe which passed round the circle.

During the repast, the natives eyed us with intense curiosity, observing our minutest motions, and appearing to discover abundant matter for comment in the most trifling occurrence. Their surprise mounted the highest, when we began to remove our uncomfortable garments, which were saturated with rain. They scanned the whiteness of our limbs, and seemed utterly unable to account for the contrast they presented to the swarthy hue of our faces, embrowned from a six months' exposure to the scorching sun of the Line. They felt our skin, much in the same way that a silk mercer would handle a remarkably fine piece of satin; and some of them went so far in their investigation as to apply the olfactory organ.

Their singular behavior almost led me to imagine that they never before had beheld a white man; but a few moments' reflection convinced me that this could not have been the case; and a more satisfactory reason for their conduct has since suggested itself to my mind.

Deterred by the frightful stories related of its inhabitants, ships never enter this bay, while their hostile relations with the tribes in the adjoining valleys prevent the Typees from visiting that section of the island where vessels occasionally lie. At long intervals, however, some intrepid captain will touch on the skirts of the bay, with two or three armed boats' crews and accompanied by an interpreter. The natives who live near the sea descry the strangers long before they reach their waters, and aware of the purpose for which they come, proclaim loudly the news of their approach. By a species of vocal telegraph the intelligence reaches the inmost recesses of the vale in an inconceivably short space of time, drawing nearly its whole population down to the beach laden with every variety of fruit. The interpreter, who is invariably a "tabooed kanaka,"[1] leaps ashore with the goods intended for barter, while the boats, with their oars shipped, and every man on his thwart, lie just outside the surf, heading off from the shore, in readiness at the first untoward event to escape to the open sea. As soon as the traffic is concluded, one of the boats pulls in under cover of the muskets of the others, the fruit is quickly thrown into her, and the transient visitors precipitately retire from what they justly consider so dangerous a vicinity.

The intercourse occurring with Europeans being so restricted, no wonder that the inhabitants of the valley manifested so much curiosity with regard to us, appearing as we did among them under such singular circumstances. I have no doubt that we were the first white men who ever penetrated thus far back into their territories, or at least the first who had ever descended from the head of the vale. What had brought us thither must have appeared a complete mystery to them, and from our ignorance of the language it was impossible for us to enlighten them. In answer to inquiries which the eloquence of their gestures enabled us to comprehend, all that we could reply was, that we had come from Nukuheva, a place, be it remembered, with which they were at open war. This intelligence appeared to affect them with the most lively emotions. "Nukuheva motarkee?" they asked. Of course we replied most energetically in the negative.

They then plied us with a thousand questions, of which we could understand nothing more than that they had reference to the recent movements of the French, against whom they seemed to cherish the most fierce hatred. So eager were they to obtain information on this point, that they still continued to propound their queries long after we had shown that we were utterly unable to answer them. Occasionally we caught some indistinct idea of their meaning, when we would endeavor by every method in our power to communicate the desired intelligence. At such times their gratification was boundless, and they would redouble their efforts to make us comprehend them more perfectly. But all in vain; and in the end they looked at us despairingly, as if we were the receptacles of invaluable information; but how to come at it they knew not.

After a while the group around us gradually dispersed, and we were left about midnight (as we conjectured) with those who appeared to be permanent residents of the house. These individuals now provided us with fresh mats to lie upon, covered us with several folds of tappa, and then extinguishing the tapers that had been burning, threw themselves down beside us, and after a little desultory conversation were soon sound asleep.

1. The word "kanaka" is at the present day universally used in the South Seas by Europeans to designate the Islanders. In the various dialects of the principal groups it is simply a sexual designation applied to the males; but it is now used by the natives in their intercourse with foreigners in the same sense in which the latter employ it.

A "Tabooed kanaka" is an islander whose person has been made to a certain extent sacred by the operation of a singular custom hereafter to be explained.

Chapter XI

Midnight Reflections—Morning Visitors—A Warrior in Costume—A Savage Æsculapius—Practice of the Healing Art—Body Servant—A Dwelling-house of the Valley Described—Portraits of its Inmates

Various and conflicting were the thoughts which oppressed me during the silent hours that followed the events related in the preceding chapter. Toby, wearied with the fatigues of the day, slumbered heavily by my side; but the pain under which I was suffering effectually prevented my sleeping, and I remained distressingly alive to all the fearful circumstances of our present situation. Was it possible that, after all our vicissitudes, we were really in the terrible valley of Typee, and at the mercy of its inmates, fierce and unrelenting tribe of savages?

Typee or Happar? I shuddered when I reflected that there was no longer any room for doubt; and that, beyond all hope of escape, we were now placed in those very circumstances from the bare thought of which I had recoiled with such abhorrence but a few days before. What might not be our fearful destiny? To be sure, as yet we had been treated with no violence; nay, had been even kindly and hospitably entertained. But what dependence could be placed upon the fickle passions which sway the bosom of a savage? His inconstancy and treachery are proverbial. Might it not be that beneath these fair appearances the islanders covered some perfidious design, and that their friendly reception of us might only precede some horrible catastrophe? How strongly did these forebodings spring up in my mind as I lay restlessly upon a couch of mats, surrounded by the dimly revealed forms of those whom I so greatly dreaded!

From the excitement of these fearful thoughts I sank towards morning into an uneasy slumber; and on awaking, with a start, in the midst of an appalling dream, looked up into the eager countenances of a number of the natives, who were bending over me.

It was broad day; and the house was nearly filled with young females, fancifully decorated with flowers, who gazed upon me as I rose with faces in which childish delight and curiosity were vividly portrayed. After waking Toby, they seated themselves round us on the mats, and gave full play to that prying inquisitiveness which time out of mind has been attributed to the adorable sex.

As these unsophisticated young creatures were attended by no jealous duennas, their proceedings were altogether informal, and void of artificial restraint. Long and minute was the investigation with which they honored us, and so uproarious their mirth, that I felt infinitely sheepish; and Toby was immeasurably outraged at their familiarity.

These lively young ladies were at the same time wonderfully polite and humane; fanning aside the insects that occasionally lighted on our brows; presenting us with food; and compassionately regarding me in the midst of my afflictions. But in spite of all their blandishments, my feelings of propriety were exceedingly shocked, for I could but consider them as having overstepped the due limits of female decorum.

Having diverted themselves to their hearts' content, our young visitants now withdrew, and gave place to successive troops of the other sex, who continued flocking towards the house until near noon; by which time I have no doubt that the greater part of the inhabitants of the valley had bathed themselves in the light of our benignant countenances.

At last, when their numbers began to diminish, a superb-looking warrior stooped the towering plumes of his head-dress beneath the low portal, and entered the house. I saw at once that he was some distinguished personage, the natives regarding him with the utmost deference, and making room for him as he approached. His aspect was imposing. The splendid long drooping tail-feathers of the tropical bird, thickly interspersed with the gaudy plumage of the cock, were disposed in an immense upright semicircle upon his head, their lower extremities being fixed in a crescent of guinea-beads which spanned the forehead. Around his neck were several enormous necklaces of boars' tusks, polished like ivory, and disposed in such a manner as that the longest and largest were upon his capacious chest. Thrust forward through the large apertures in his ears were two small and finely-shaped sperm-whale teeth, presenting their cavities in front, stuffed with freshly plucked leaves, and curiously wrought at the other end into strange little images and devices. These barbaric trinkets, garnished in this manner at their open extremities, and tapering and curving round to a point behind the ear, resembled not a little a pair of cornucopias.

The loins of the warrior were girt about with heavy folds of a dark-colored tappa, hanging before and behind in clusters of braided tassels, while anklets and bracelets of curling human hair completed his unique costume. In his right hand he grasped a beautifully carved paddle-spear, nearly fifteen feet in length, made of the bright koar-wood, one end sharply pointed, and the other flattened like an oar-blade. Hanging obliquely from his girdle by a loop of sinnate was a richly decorated pipe, the slender reed forming its stem was colored with a red pigment, and round it, as well as the idol-bowl, fluttered little streamers of the thinnest tappa.

But that which was most remarkable in the appearance of the splendid islander was the elaborate tattooing displayed on every noble limb. All imaginable lines and curves and figures were delineated over his whole body, and in their grotesque variety and infinite profusion I could only compare them to the crowded groupings of quaint patterns we sometimes see in costly pieces of lace-work. The most simple and remarkable of all these ornaments was that which decorated the countenance of the chief. Two broad stripes of tattooing, diverging from the center of his shaven crown, obliquely crossed both eyes—staining the lids—to a little below either ear, where they united with another stripe which swept in a straight line along the lips and formed the base of the triangle. The warrior, from the excellence of his physical proportions, might certainly have been regarded as one of Nature's noblemen, and the lines drawn upon his face may possibly have denoted his exalted rank.

This warlike personage, upon entering the house, seated himself at some distance from the spot where Toby and myself reposed; while the rest of the savages looked alternately from us to him, as if in expectation of something they were disappointed in not perceiving. Regarding the chief attentively, I thought his lineaments appeared familiar to me. As soon as his full face was turned upon me, and I again beheld its extraordinary embellishment, and met the strange gaze to which I had been subjected the preceding night, I immediately, in spite of the alteration in his appearance, recognized the noble Mehevi. On addressing him, he advanced at once in the most cordial manner, and greeting me warmly, seemed to enjoy not a little the effect his barbaric costume had produced upon me.

I forthwith determined to secure, if possible, the good-will of this individual, as I easily perceived he was a man of great authority in his tribe, and one who might exert a powerful influence upon our subsequent fate. In the endeavor I was not repulsed; for nothing could surpass the friendliness he manifested towards both my companion and myself. He extended his sturdy limbs by our side, and endeavored to make us comprehend the full extent of the kindly feelings by which he was actuated. The almost insuperable difficulty in communicating to one another our ideas affected the chief with no little mortification. He evinced a great desire to be enlightened with regard to the customs and peculiarities of the far-off country we had left behind us, and to which under the name of Maneeka he frequently alluded.

But that which more than any other subject engaged his attention was the late proceedings of the "Franee," as he called the French, in the neighboring bay of Nukuheva. This seemed a never-ending theme with him, and one concerning which he was never weary of interrogating us. All the information we succeeded in imparting to him on this subject was little more than that we had seen six men-of-war lying in the hostile bay at the time we had left it. When he received this intelligence, Mehevi, by the aid of his fingers, went through a long numerical calculation, as if estimating the number of Frenchmen the squadron might contain.

It was just after employing his faculties in this way that he happened to notice the swelling in my limb. He immediately examined it with the utmost attention, and after doing so dispatched a boy who happened to be standing by with some message.

After the lapse of a few moments the stripling re-entered the house with an aged islander, who might have been taken for old Hippocrates himself. His head was as bald as the polished surface of a cocoanut shell, which article it precisely resembled in smoothness and color, while a long silvery beard swept almost to his girdle of bark. Encircling his temples was a bandeau of the twisted leaves of the Omoo-tree, pressed closely over the brows to shield his feeble vision from the glare of the sun. His tottering steps were supported by a long slim staff, resembling the wand with which a theatrical magician appears on the stage, and in one hand he carried a freshly plaited fan of the green leaflets of the cocoanut-tree. A flowing robe of tappa, knotted over the shoulder, hung loosely round his stooping form, and heightened the venerableness of his aspect.

Mehevi, saluting this old gentleman, motioned him to a seat between us, and then uncovering my limb, desired him to examine it. The leech gazed intently from me to Toby, and then proceeded to business. After diligently observing the ailing member, he commenced manipulating it; and on the supposition probably that the complaint had deprived the leg of all sensation, began to pinch and hammer it in such a manner that I absolutely roared with one pain. Thinking that I was as capable of making an application of thumps and pinches to the part as anyone else, I endeavored to resist this species of medical treatment. But it was not so easy a matter to get out of the clutches of the old wizard; he fastened on the unfortunate limb as if it were something for which he had been long seeking, and muttering some kind of incantation continued his discipline, pounding it after a fashion that set me well-nigh crazy; while Mehevi, upon the same principle which prompts an affectionate mother to hold a struggling child in a dentist's chair, restrained me in his powerful grasp, and actually encouraged the wretch in this infliction of torture.

Almost frantic with rage and pain, I yelled like a bedlamite; while Toby, throwing himself into all the attitudes of a posture-master, vainly endeavored to expostulate with the natives by signs and gestures. To have looked at my companion, as, sympathizing with my sufferings, he strove to put an end to them, one would have thought that he was the deaf and dumb alphabet incarnated. Whether my tormentor yielded to Toby's entreaties, or paused from sheer exhaustion, I do not know; but all at once he ceased his operations, and at the same time the chief relinquishing his hold upon me, I fell back, faint and breathless, with the agony I had endured.

My unfortunate limb was now left much in the same condition as a rump-steak after undergoing the castigating process which precedes cooking. My physician, having recovered from the fatigues of his exertions, as if anxious to make amends for the pain to which he had subjected me, now took some herbs out of a little wallet that was suspended from his waist, and moistening them in water, applied them to the inflamed part, stooping over it at the same time, and either whispering a spell, or having a little confidential chat with some imaginary demon located in the calf of my leg. My limb was now swathed in leafy bandages, and, grateful to Providence for the cessation of hostilities, I was suffered to rest.

Mehevi shortly after rose to depart; but before he went he spoke authoritatively to one of the natives whom he addressed as Kory-Kory; and from the little I could understand of what took place, pointed him out to me as a man whose peculiar business thenceforth would be to attend upon my person. I am not certain that I comprehended as much as this at the time, but the subsequent conduct of my trusty body-servant fully assured me that such must have been the case.

I could not but be amused at the manner in which the chief addressed me upon this occasion, talking to me for at least fifteen or twenty minutes as calmly as if I could understand every word that he said. I remarked this peculiarity very often afterwards in many other of the islanders.

Mehevi having now departed, and the family physician having likewise made his exit, we were left about sunset with ten or twelve natives, who by this time I had ascertained composed the household of which Toby and I were members. As the dwelling to which we had been first introduced was the place of my permanent abode while I remained in the valley, and as I was necessarily placed upon the most intimate footing with its occupants, I may as well here enter into a little description of it and its inhabitants. This description will apply also to nearly all the other dwelling-places in the vale, and will furnish some idea of the generality of the natives.

Near one side of the valley, and about midway up the ascent of a rather abrupt rise of ground waving with the richest verdure, a number of large stones were laid in successive courses, to the height of nearly eight feet, and disposed in such a manner that their level surface corresponded in shape with the habitation which was perched upon it. A narrow space, however, was reserved in front of the dwelling, upon the summit of this pile of stones (called by the natives a "pi-pi"), which being enclosed by a little pocket of canes, gave it somewhat the appearance of a verandah. The frame of the house was constructed of large bamboos planted uprightly, and secured together at intervals by transverse stalks of the light wood of the hibiscus, lashed with thongs of bark. The rear of the tenement—built up with successive ranges of cocoanut boughs bound one upon another, with their leaflets cunningly woven together—inclined a little from the vertical, and extended from the extreme edge of the "pi-pi" to about twenty feet from its surface; whence the shelving roof—thatched with the long tapering leaves of the palmetto—sloped steeply off to within about five feet of the floor; leaving the eaves drooping with tassel-like appendages over the front of the habitation. This was constructed of light and elegant canes, in a kind of open screen work, tastefully adorned with bindings of variegated sinnate, which served to hold together its various parts. The sides of the house were similarly built; thus presenting three quarters for the circulation of the air, while the whole was impervious to the rain.

In length this picturesque building was perhaps twelve yards, while in breadth it could not have exceeded as many feet. So much for the exterior; which with its wire-like reed-twisted sides, not a little reminded me of an immense aviary.

Stooping a little, you passed through a narrow aperture in its front; and facing you, on entering, lay two long, perfectly straight, and well-polished trunks of the cocoanut-tree, extending the full length of the dwelling; one of them placed closely against the rear, and the other lying parallel with it some two yards distant, the interval between them being spread with a multitude of gaily-worked mats, nearly all of a different pattern. This space formed the common couch and lounging place of the natives, answering the purpose of a divan in Oriental countries. Here would they slumber through the hours of the night, and recline luxuriously during the greater part of the day. The remainder of the floor presented only the cool shining surfaces of the large stones of which the "pi-pi" was composed.

From the ridge-pole of the house hung suspended a number of large packages enveloped in coarse tappa; some of which contained festival dresses, and various other matters of the wardrobe, held in high estimation. These were easily accessible by means of a line, which, passing over the ridge-pole, had one end attached to a bundle, while with the other, which led to the side of the dwelling and was there secured, the package could be lowered or elevated at pleasure.

Against the farther wall of the house were arranged in tasteful figures a variety of spears and javelins, and other implements of savage warfare. Outside of the habitation, and built upon the piazza-like area in its front, was a little shed used as a sort of larder or pantry, and in which were stored various articles of domestic use and convenience. A few yards from the pi-pi was a large shed built of cocoanut boughs, where the process of preparing the "poee-poee" was carried on and all culinary operations attended to.

Thus much for the house, and its appurtenances; and it will be readily acknowledged that a more commodious and appropriate dwelling for the climate and the people could not possibly be devised. It was cool, free to admit the air, scrupulously clean, and elevated above the dampness and impurities of the ground.

But now to sketch the inmates; and here I claim for my tried servitor and faithful valet Kory-Kory the precedence of a first description. As his character will be gradually unfolded in the course of my narrative, I shall for the present content myself with delineating his personal appearance. Kory-Kory, though the most devoted and best natured serving-man in the world, was, alas! a hideous object to look upon. He was some twenty-five years of age, and about six feet in height, robust and well made, and of the most extraordinary aspect. His head was carefully shaven, with the exception of two circular spots, about the size of a dollar, near the top of the cranium, where the hair, permitted to grow of an amazing length, was twisted up in two prominent knots, that gave him the appearance of being decorated with a pair of horns. His beard, plucked out by the roots from every other part of his face, was suffered to droop in hairy pendants, two of which garnished his upper lip, and an equal number hung from the extremity of his chin.

Kory-Kory, with a view of improving the handiwork of nature, and perhaps prompted by a desire to add to the engaging expression of his countenance, had seen fit to embellish his face with three broad longitudinal stripes of tattooing, which, like those country roads that go straight forward in defiance of all obstacles, crossed his nasal organ, descended into the hollow of his eyes, and even skirted the borders of his mouth. Each completely spanned his physiognomy; one extending in a line with his eyes, another crossing the face in the vicinity of the nose, and the third sweeping along his lips from ear to ear. His countenance thus triply hooped, as it were, with tattooing, always reminded me of those unhappy wretches whom I have sometimes observed gazing out sentimentally from behind the grated bars of a prison window; whilst the entire body of my savage valet, covered all over with representations of birds and fishes, and a variety of most unaccountable-looking creatures, suggested to me the idea of a pictorial museum of natural history, or an illustrated copy of Goldsmith's *Animated Nature*.

But it seems really heartless in me to write thus of the poor islander, when I owe perhaps to his unremitting attentions the very existence I now enjoy. Kory-Kory, I mean thee no harm in what I say in regard to thy outward adornings; but they were a little curious to my unaccustomed sight, and therefore I dilate upon them. But to underrate or forget thy faithful services is something I could never be guilty of, even in the giddiest moment of my life.

The father of my attached follower was a native of gigantic frame, and had once possessed prodigious physical powers; but the lofty form was now yielding to the inroads of time, though the hand of disease seemed never to have been laid upon the aged warrior. Marheyo—for such was his name—appeared to have retired from all active participation in the affairs of the valley, seldom or never accompanying the natives in their various expeditions; and employing the greater part of his time in throwing up a little shed just outside the house, upon which he was engaged to my certain knowledge for four months, without appearing to make any sensible advance. I suppose the old gentleman was in his dotage, for he manifested in various ways the characteristics which mark this particular stage of life.

I remember in particular his having a choice pair of ear-ornaments, fabricated from the teeth of some sea-monster. These he would alternately wear and take off at least fifty times in the course of the day, going and coming from his little hut on each occasion with all the tranquility imaginable. Sometimes slipping them through the slits in his ears, he would seize his spear—which in length and slightness resembled a fishing pole—and go stalking beneath the shadows of the neighboring groves, as if about to give a hostile meeting to some cannibal knight. But he would soon return again, and hiding his weapon under the projecting eaves of the house and rolling his clumsy trinkets carefully in a piece of tappa, would resume his more pacific operations as quietly as if he had never interrupted them.

But despite his eccentricities, Marheyo was a most paternal and warm-hearted old fellow, and in this particular not a little resembled his son Kory-Kory. The mother of the latter was the mistress of the family, and a notable housewife, and a most industrious old lady she was. If she did not understand the art of making jellies, jams, custard, tea-cakes, and such like trashy affairs, she was profoundly skilled in the mysteries of preparing "amar," "poee-poee," and "kokoo," with other substantial matters. She was a genuine busy-body; bustling about the house like a country landlady at an unexpected arrival; forever giving the young girls tasks to perform, which the little hussies as often neglected; poking into every corner, and rummaging over bundles of old tappa, or making a prodigious clatter among the calabashes. Sometimes she might have been seen squatting upon her haunches in front of a huge wooden basin, and kneading poee-poee with terrific vehemence, dashing the stone pestle about as if she would shiver the vessel into fragments; on other occasions, galloping about the valley in search of a particular kind of leaf, used in some of her recondite operations, and returning home, toiling and sweating, with a bundle of it, under which most women would have sunk.

To tell the truth, Kory-Kory's mother was the only industrious person in all the valley of Typee; and she could not have employed herself more actively had she been left an exceedingly muscular and destitute widow with an inordinate supply of young children, in the bleakest part of the civilized world. There was not the slightest necessity for the greater portion of the labor performed by the old lady; but she seemed to work from some irresistible impulse; her limbs continually swaying to and fro, as if there were some indefatigable engine concealed within her body which kept her in perpetual motion.

Never suppose that she was a termagant or a shrew for all this; she had the kindliest heart in the world, and acted towards me in particular in a truly maternal manner, occasionally putting some little morsel of choice food into my hand, some outlandish kind of savage sweetmeat or pastry, like a doting mother petting a sickly urchin with tarts and sugar-plums. Warm indeed are my remembrances of the dear, good, affectionate old Tinor!

Besides the individuals I have mentioned, there belonged to the household three young men, dissipated, good-for-nothing, roystering blades of savages, who were either employed in prosecuting love-affairs with the maidens of the tribe, or grew boozy on "arva" and tobacco in the company of congenial spirits, the scape-graces of the valley.

Among the permanent inmates of the house were likewise several lovely damsels, who instead of thrumming pianos and reading novels, like more enlightened young ladies, substituted for these employments the manufacture of a fine species of tappa; but for the greater portion of the time were skipping from house to house, gadding and gossiping with their acquaintances.

From the rest of these, however, I must except the beauteous nymph Fayaway, who was my peculiar favorite. Her free pliant figure was the very perfection of female grace and beauty. Her complexion was a rich and mantling olive, and when watching the glow upon her cheeks I could almost swear that beneath the transparent medium there lurked the blushes of a faint vermilion. The face of this girl was a rounded oval, and each feature as perfectly formed as the heart or imagination of man could desire. Her full lips, when parted with a smile, disclosed teeth of a dazzling whiteness; and when her rosy mouth opened with a burst of merriment, they looked like the milk-white seeds of the "arta," a fruit of the valley, which, when cleft in twain, shows them reposing in rows on each side, imbedded in the rich and juicy pulp. Her hair of the deepest brown, parted irregularly in the middle, flowed in natural ringlets over her shoulders, and whenever she chanced to stoop, fell over and hid from view her lovely bosom. Gazing into the depths of her strange blue eyes, when she was in a contemplative mood, they seemed most placid yet unfathomable; but when illuminated by some lively emotion, they beamed upon the beholder like stars. The hands of Fayaway were as soft and delicate as those of any countess; for an entire exemption from rude labor marks the girlhood and even prime of a Typee woman's life. Her feet, though wholly exposed, were as diminutive and fairly shaped as those which peep from beneath the skirts of a Lima lady's dress. The skin of this young creature, from continual ablutions and the use of mollifying ointments, was inconceivably smooth and soft.

I may succeed, perhaps, in particularizing some of the individual features of Fayaway's beauty, but that general loveliness of appearance which they all contributed to produce I will not attempt to describe. The easy unstudied graces of a child of nature like this, breathing from infancy an atmosphere of perpetual summer, and nurtured by the simple fruits of the earth; enjoying a perfect freedom from care and anxiety, and removed effectually from all injurious tendencies, strike the eye in a manner which cannot be portrayed. This picture is no fancy sketch; it is drawn from the most vivid recollections of the person delineated.

Were I asked if the beauteous form of Fayaway was altogether free from the hideous blemish of tattooing, I should be constrained to answer that it was not. But the practitioners of the barbarous art, so remorseless in their inflictions upon the brawny limbs of the warriors of the tribe, seem to be conscious that it needs not the resources of their profession to augment the charms of the maidens of the vale.

The females are very little embellished in this way, and Fayaway, and all the other young girls of her age, were even less so than those of their sex more advanced in years. The reason of this peculiarity will be alluded to hereafter. All the tattooing that the nymph in question exhibited upon her person may be easily described. Three minute dots, no bigger than pinheads, decorated either lip, and at a little distance were not at all discernible. Just upon the fall of the shoulder were drawn two parallel lines half an inch apart, and perhaps three inches in length, the interval being filled with delicately executed figures. These narrow bands of tattooing, thus placed, always reminded me of those stripes of gold lace worn by officers in undress, and which were lieu of epaulettes to denote their rank.

Thus much was Fayaway tattooed—the audacious hand which had gone so far in its desecrating work stopping short, apparently wanting the heart to proceed.

But I have omitted to describe the dress worn by this nymph of the valley.

Fayaway—I must avow the fact—for the most part clung to the primitive and summer garb of Eden. But how becoming the costume! It showed her fine figure to the best possible advantage; and nothing could have been better adapted to her peculiar style of beauty. On ordinary occasions she was habited precisely as I have described the two youthful savages whom we had met on first entering the valley. At other times, when rambling among the groves, or visiting at the houses of her acquaintances, she wore a tunic of white tappa, reaching from her waist to a little below the knees; and when exposed for any length of time to the sun, she invariably protected herself from its rays by a floating mantle of the same material, loosely gathered about the person. Her gala dress will be described hereafter.

As the beauties of our own land delight in bedecking themselves with fanciful articles of jewelery, suspending them from their ears, hanging them about their necks, and clasping them around their wrists; so Fayaway and her companions were in the habit of ornamenting themselves with similar appendages.

Flora was their jeweler. Sometimes they wore necklaces of small carnation flowers, strung like rubies upon a fiber of tappa, or displayed in their ears a single white bud, the stem thrust backward through the aperture, and showing in front the delicate petals folded together in a beautiful sphere, and looking like a drop of the purest pearl. Chaplets too, resembling in their arrangement the strawberry coronal worn by an English peeress, and composed of intertwined leaves and blossoms, often crowned their temples; and bracelets and anklets of the same tasteful pattern were frequently to be seen. Indeed, the maidens of the island were passionately fond of flowers, and never wearied of decorating their persons with them; a lovely trait in their character, and one that ere long will be more fully alluded to.

Though in my eyes, at least, Fayaway was indisputably the loveliest female I saw in Typee, yet the description I have given of her will in some measure apply to nearly all the youthful portion of her sex in the valley. Judge ye then, reader, what beautiful creatures they must have been.

Chapter XII

Officiousness of Kory-Kory—His Devotion—A Bath in the Stream—Want of Refinement of the Typee Damsels—Stroll with Mehevi—A Typee Highway—The Taboo Groves—The Hoolah Hoolah Ground—The Ti—Time-worn Savages—Hospitality of Mehevi—Midnight Misgivings—Adventure in the Dark—Distinguished Honors Paid to the Visitors—Strange Procession and Return to the House of Marheyo

When Mehevi had departed from the house, as related in the preceding chapter, Kory-Kory commenced the functions of the post assigned him. He brought us various kinds of food; and, as if I were an infant, insisted upon feeding me with his own hands. To this procedure I, of course, most earnestly objected, but in vain; and having laid a calabash of kokoo before me, he washed his fingers in a vessel of water, and then putting his hand into the dish and rolling the food into little balls, put them one after another into my mouth. All my remonstrances against this measure only provoked so great a clamor on his part, that I was obliged to acquiesce; and the operation of feeding being thus facilitated, the meal was quickly dispatched. As for Toby, he was allowed to help himself after his own fashion.

The repast over, my attendant arranged the mats for repose, and, bidding me lie down, covered me with a large robe of tappa, at the same time looking approvingly upon me, and exclaiming "Ki-Ki, muee muee, ah! moee moee motarkee" (eat plenty, ah! sleep very good). The philosophy of this sentiment I did not pretend to question; for deprived of sleep for several preceding nights, and the pain of my limb having much abated, I now felt inclined to avail myself of the opportunity afforded me.

The next morning, on waking, I found Kory-Kory stretched out on one side of me, while my companion lay upon the other. I felt sensibly refreshed after a night of sound repose, and immediately agreed to the proposition of my valet that I should repair to the water and wash, although dreading the suffering that the exertion might produce. From this apprehension, however, I was quickly relieved; for Kory-Kory, leaping from the pi-pi, and then backing himself up against it, like a porter in readiness to shoulder a trunk, with loud vociferations and a superabundance of gestures, gave me to understand that I was to mount upon his back and be thus transported to the stream, which flowed perhaps two hundred yards from the house.

Our appearance upon the verandah in front of the habitation drew together quite a crowd, who stood looking on and conversing with one another in the most animated manner. They reminded one of a group of idlers gathered about the door of a village tavern when the equipage of some distinguished traveler is brought round previously to his departure. As soon as I clasped my arms about the neck of the devoted fellow, and he jogged off with me, the crowd—composed chiefly of young girls and boys—followed after, shouting and capering with infinite glee, and accompanied us to the banks of the stream.

On gaining it, Kory-Kory, wading up to his hips in the water, carried me half-way across, and deposited me on a smooth black stone which rose a few inches above the surface. The amphibious rabble at our heels plunged in after us, and, climbing to the summit of the grass-grown rocks with which the bed of the brook was here and there broken, waited curiously to witness our morning ablutions.

Somewhat embarrassed by the presence of the female portion of the company, and feeling my cheeks burning with bashful timidity, I formed a primitive basin by joining my hands together, and cooled my blushes in the water it contained; then removing my frock, bent over and washed myself down to my waist in the stream. As soon as Kory-Kory comprehended from my motions that this was to be the extent of my performance, he appeared perfectly aghast with astonishment, and rushing towards me, poured out a torrent of words in eager deprecation of so limited an operation, enjoining me by unmistakable signs to immerse my whole body. To this I was forced to consent; and the honest fellow regarding me as a froward, inexperienced child, whom it was his duty to serve at the risk of offending, lifted me from the rock, and tenderly bathed my limbs. This over, and resuming my seat, I could not avoid bursting into admiration of the scene around me.

From the verdant surfaces of the large stones that lay scattered about, the natives were now sliding off into the water, diving and ducking beneath the surface in all directions—the young girls springing buoyantly into the air, and revealing their naked forms to the waist, with their long tresses dancing about their shoulders, their eyes sparkling like drops of dew in the sun, and their gay laughter pealing forth at every frolicsome incident.

On the afternoon of the day that I took my first bath in the valley, we received another visit from Mehevi. The noble savage seemed to be in the same pleasant mood, and was quite as cordial in his manner as before. After remaining about an hour, he rose from the mats, and motioning to leave the house, invited Toby and myself to accompany him. I pointed to my leg; but Mehevi in his turn pointed to Kory-Kory, and removed that objection; so, mounting upon the faithful fellow's shoulders again—like the old man of the sea astride of Sindbad—I followed after the chief.

The nature of the route we now pursued struck me more forcibly than anything I had yet seen, as illustrating the indolent disposition of the islanders. The path was obviously the most beaten one in the valley, several others leading from either side into it, and perhaps for successive generations it had formed the principal avenue of the place. And yet, until I grew more familiar with its impediments, it seemed as difficult to travel as the recesses of a wilderness. Part of it swept around an abrupt rise of ground, the surface of which was broken by frequent inequalities, and thickly strewn with projecting masses of rocks, whose summits were often hidden from view by the drooping foliage of the luxurious vegetation. Sometimes directly over, sometimes evading these obstacles with a wide circuit, the path wound along;—one moment climbing over a sudden eminence smooth with continued wear, then descending on the other side into a steep glen, and crossing the flinty channel of a brook. Here it pursued the depths of a glade, occasionally obliging you to stoop beneath vast horizontal branches; and now you stepped over huge trunks and boughs that lay rotting across the track.

Such was the grand thoroughfare of Typee. After proceeding a little distance along it—Kory-Kory panting and blowing with the weight of his burden—I dismounted from his back, and grasping the long spear of Mehevi in my hand, assisted my steps over the numerous obstacles of the road; preferring this mode of advance to one which, from the difficulties of the way, was equally painful to myself and my wearied servitor.

Our journey was soon at an end: for, scaling a sudden height, we came abruptly upon the place of our destination. I wish that it were possible to sketch in words this spot as vividly as I recollect it.

Here were situated the Taboo groves of the valley—the scene of many a prolonged feast, of many a horrid rite. Beneath the dark shadows of the consecrated bread-fruit trees there reigned a solemn twilight—a cathedral-like gloom. The frightful genius of pagan worship seemed to brood in silence over the place, breathing its spell upon every object around. Here and there, in the depths of these awful shades, half screened from sight by masses of overhanging foliage, rose the idolatrous altars of the savages, built of enormous blocks of black and polished stone, placed one upon another, without cement, to the height of twelve or fifteen feet, and surmounted by a rustic open temple, enclosed with a low picket of canes, within which might be seen, in various stages of decay, offerings of bread-fruit and cocoanuts, and the putrefying relics of some recent sacrifice.

In the midst of the wood was the hallowed "hoolah hoolah" ground—set apart for the celebration of the fantastical religious ritual of these people—comprising an extensive oblong pi-pi, terminating at either end in a lofty terraced altar, guarded by ranks of hideous wooden idols, and with the two remaining sides flanked by ranges of bamboo sheds, opening towards the interior of the quadrangle thus formed. Vast trees, standing in the middle of this space, and throwing over it an umbrageous shade, had their massive trunks built round with slight stages, elevated a few feet above the ground, and railed in with canes, forming so many rustic pulpits, from which the priests harangued their devotees.

This holiest of spots was defended from profanation by the strictest edicts of the all-pervading "taboo," which condemned to instant death the sacrilegious female who should enter or touch its sacred precincts, or even so much as press with her feet the ground made holy by the shadows that it cast.

Access was had to the enclosure through an embowered entrance on one side, facing a number of towering cocoanut-trees, planted at intervals along a level area of a hundred yards. At the further extremity of this space was to be seen a building of considerable size, reserved for the habitation of the priests and religious attendants of the groves.

In its vicinity was another remarkable edifice, built as usual upon the summit of a pi-pi, and at least two hundred feet in length, though not more than twenty in breadth. The whole front of this latter structure was completely open, and from one end to the other ran a narrow verandah, fenced in on the edge of the pi-pi with a picket of canes. Its interior presented the appearance of an immense lounging-place, the entire floor being strewn with successive layers of mats, lying between parallel trunks of cocoanut-trees, selected for the purpose from the straightest and most symmetrical the vale afforded.

To this building, denominated in the language of the natives the "Ti," Mehevi now conducted us. Thus far we had been accompanied by a troop of the natives of both sexes; but as soon as we approached its vicinity, the females gradually separated themselves from the crowd, and standing aloof, permitted us to pass on. The merciless prohibitions of the taboo extended likewise to this edifice, and were enforced by the same dreadful penalty that secured the Hoolah Hoolah ground from the imaginary pollution of a woman's presence.

On entering the house, I was surprised to see six muskets ranged against the bamboo on one side, from the barrels of which depended as many small canvas pouches, partly filled with powder. Disposed about these muskets, like the cutlasses that decorate the bulkhead of a man-of-war's cabin, were a great variety of rude spears and paddles, javelins, and war-clubs. This then, said I to Toby, must be the armory of the tribe.

As we advanced further along the building, we were struck with the aspect of four or five hideous old wretches, on whose decrepit forms time and tattooing seemed to have obliterated every trace of humanity. Owing to the continued operation of this latter process, which only terminates among the warriors of the island after all the figures skretched upon their limbs in youth have been blended together—an effect, however, produced only in cases of extreme longevity—the bodies of these men were of a uniform dull green color—the hue which the tattooing gradually assumes as the individual advances in age. Their skin had a frightful scaly appearance, which, united with its singular color, made their limbs not a little resemble dusty specimens of verde-antique. Their flesh, in parts, hung upon them in huge folds, like the overlapping plaits on the flank of a rhinoceros. Their heads were completely bald, whilst their faces were puckered into a thousand wrinkles, and they presented no vestige of a beard. But the most remarkable peculiarity about them was the appearance of their feet; the toes, like the radiating lines of the mariner's compass, pointed to every quarter of the horizon. This was doubtless attributable to the fact, that during nearly a hundred years of existence the said toes never had been subjected to any artificial confinement, and in their old age, being averse to close neighborhood, bid one another keep open order.

These repulsive-looking creatures appeared to have lost the use of their lower limbs altogether; sitting upon the floor cross-legged in a state of torpor. They never heeded us in the least, scarcely looking conscious of our presence, while Mehevi seated us upon the mats, and Kory-Kory gave utterance to some unintelligible gibberish.

In a few moments a boy entered with a wooden trencher of poee-poee; and in regaling myself with its contents I was obliged again to submit to the officious intervention of my indefatigable servitor. Various other dishes followed, the chief manifesting the most hospitable importunity in pressing us to partake, and to remove all bashfulness on our part, set us no despicable example in his own person.

The repast concluded, a pipe was lighted, which passed from mouth to mouth, and yielding to its soporific influence, the quiet of the place, and the deepening shadows of approaching night, my companion and I sank into a kind of drowsy repose, while the chief and Kory-Kory seemed to be slumbering beside us.

I awoke from an uneasy nap, about midnight, as I supposed; and, raising myself partly from the mat, became sensible that we were enveloped in utter darkness. Toby lay still asleep, but our late companions had disappeared. The only sound that interrupted the silence of the place was the asthmatic breathing of the old men I have mentioned, who reposed at a little distance from us. Besides them, as well as I could judge, there was no one else in the house.

Apprehensive of some evil, I roused my comrade, and we were engaged in a whispered conference concerning the unexpected withdrawal of the natives, when all at once, from the depths of the grove, in full view of us where we lay, shoots of flame were seen to rise, and in a few moments illuminated the surrounding trees, casting, by contrast, into still deeper gloom the darkness around us.

While we continued gazing at this sight, dark figures appeared moving to and fro before the flames; while others, dancing and capering about, looked like so many demons.

Regarding this new phenomenon with no small degree of trepidation, I said to my companion, "What can all this mean, Toby?"

"Oh, nothing," replied he; "getting the fire ready, I suppose."

"Fire!" exclaimed I, while my heart took to beating like a trip-hammer, "what fire?"

"Why, the fire to cook us, to be sure, what else would the cannibals be kicking up such a row about if it were not for that?"

"Oh, Toby! have done with your jokes; this is no time for them; something is about to happen, I feel confident."

"Jokes, indeed!" exclaimed Toby indignantly. "Did you ever hear me joke? Why, for what do you suppose the devils have been feeding us up in this kind of style during the last three days, unless it were for something that you are too much frightened at to talk about? Look at that Kory-Kory there!—has he not been stuffing you with his confounded mushes, just in the way they treat swine before they kill them? Depend upon it, we will be eaten this blessed night, and there is the fire we shall be roasted by."

This view of the matter was not at all calculated to allay my apprehensions, and I shuddered when I reflected that we were indeed at the mercy of a tribe of cannibals, and that the dreadful contingency to which Toby had alluded was by no means removed beyond the bounds of possibility.

"There! I told you so! they are coming for us!" exclaimed my companion the next moment, as the forms of four of the islanders were seen in bold relief against the illuminated background, mounting the pi-pi and approaching towards us.

They came on noiselessly, nay stealthily, and glided along through the gloom that surrounded us as if about to spring upon some object they were fearful of disturbing before they should make sure of it.—Gracious heaven! the horrible reflections which crowded upon me that moment. A cold sweat stood upon my brow, and spellbound with terror I awaited my fate!

Suddenly the silence was broken by the well-remembered tones of Mehevi, and at the kindly accents of his voice my fears were immediately dissipated. "Tommo, Toby, ki ki!" (eat).—He had waited to address us until he had assured himself that we were both awake, at which he seemed somewhat surprised.

"Ki ki! is it?" said Toby in his gruff tones; "well, cook us first, will you?—but what's this?" he added, as another savage appeared, bearing before him a large trencher of wood containing some kind of steaming meat as appeared from the odors it diffused, and which he deposited at the feet of Mehevi. "A baked baby, I dare-say! but I will have none of it, never mind what it is.—A pretty fool I should make of myself, indeed, waked up here in the middle of the night, stuffing and guzzling, and all to make a fat meal for a parcel of bloody-minded cannibals one of these mornings!—No, I see what they are at very plainly, so I am resolved to starve myself into a bunch of bones and gristle, and then, if they serve me up, they are welcome! But I say, Tommo, you are not going to eat any of that mess there, in the dark, are you? Why, how can you tell what it is?"

"By tasting it, to be sure," said I, masticating a morsel that Kory-Kory had just put in my mouth; "and excellently good it is, too, very much like veal."

"A baked baby, by the soul of Captain Cook!" burst forth Toby, with amazing vehemence: "Veal? why there never was a calf on the island till you landed. I tell you you are bolting down mouthfuls from a dead Happar's carcass, as sure as you live, and no mistake!"

Emetics and lukewarm water! What a sensation in the abdominal region! Sure enough, where could the fiends incarnate have obtained meat? But I resolved to satisfy myself at all hazards; and turning to Mehevi, I soon made the ready chief understand that I wished a light to be brought. When the taper came, I gazed eagerly into the vessel, and recognized the mutilated remains of a juvenile porker! "Puarkee!" exclaimed Kory-Kory, looking complacently at the dish; and from that day to this I have never forgotten that such is the designation of a pig in the Typee lingo.

The next morning, after being again abundantly feasted by the hospitable Mehevi, Toby and myself arose to depart. But the chief requested us to postpone our intention. "Abo, abo," (Wait, wait,) he said, and accordingly we resumed our seats, while, assisted by the zealous Kory-Kory, he appeared to be engaged in giving directions to a number of the natives outside, who were busily employed in making arrangements, the nature of which we could not comprehend. But we were not left long in our ignorance, for a few moments only had elapsed, when the chief beckoned us to approach, and we perceived that he had been marshaling a kind of guard of honor to escort us on our return to the house of Marheyo.

The procession was led off by two venerable-looking savages, each provided with a spear, from the end of which streamed a pennon of milk-white tappa. After them went several youths, bearing aloft calabashes of poee-poee; and followed in their turn by four stalwart fellows, sustaining long bamboos, from the tops of which hung suspended, at least twenty feet from the ground, large baskets of green bread-fruits. Then came a troop of boys, carrying bunches of ripe bananas, and baskets made of the woven leaflets of cocoanut boughs, filled with the young fruit of the tree, the naked shells stripped of their husks peeping forth from the verdant wicker-work that surrounded them. Last of all came a burly islander, holding over his head a wooden trencher, in which lay disposed the remnants of our midnight feast, hidden from view, however, by a covering of bread-fruit leaves.

Astonished as I was at this exhibition, I could not avoid smiling at its grotesque appearance, and the associations it naturally called up. Mehevi, it seemed, was bent on replenishing old Marheyo's larder, fearful perhaps that without this precaution his guests might not fare as well as they could desire.

As soon as I descended from the pi-pi, the procession formed anew, enclosing us in its center; where I remained part of the time, carried by Kory-Kory, and occasionally relieving him from his burden by limping along with a spear. When we moved off in this order, the natives struck up a musical recitative, which, with various alternations, they continued until we arrived at the place of our destination.

As we proceeded on our way, bands of young girls, darting from the surrounding groves, hung upon our skirts, and accompanied us with shouts of merriment and delight, which almost drowned the deep notes of the recitative. On approaching old Marheyo's domicile, its inmates rushed out to receive us; and while the gifts of Mehevi were being disposed of, the superannuated warrior did the honors of his mansion with all the warmth of hospitality evinced by an English squire when he regales his friends at some fine old patrimonial mansion.

Chapter XIII

Attempt to Procure Relief from Nukuheva—Perilous Adventure of Toby in the Happar Mountains—Eloquence of Kory-Kory

Amidst these novel scenes a week passed away almost imperceptibly. The natives, actuated by some mysterious impulse, day after day redoubled their attentions to us. Their manner towards us was unaccountable. Surely, thought I, they would not act thus if they meant us any harm. But why this excess of deferential kindness, or what equivalent can they imagine us capable of rendering them for it?

We were fairly puzzled. But despite the apprehensions I could not dispel, the horrible character imputed to these Typees appeared to be wholly undeserved.

"Why, they are cannibals!" said Toby on one occasion when I eulogized the tribe. "Granted," I replied, "but a more humane, gentlemanly, and amiable set of epicures do not probably exist in the Pacific."

But, notwithstanding the kind treatment we received, I was too familiar with the fickle disposition of savages not to feel anxious to withdraw from the valley, and put myself beyond the reach of that fearful death which, under all these smiling appearances, might yet menace us. But here there was an obstacle in the way of doing so. It was idle for me to think of moving from the place until I should have recovered from the severe lameness that afflicted me; indeed my malady began seriously to alarm me; for, despite the herbal remedies of the natives, it continued to grow worse and worse. Their mild applications, though they soothed the pain, did not remove the disorder, and I felt convinced that without better aid I might anticipate long and acute suffering.

But how was this aid to be procured? From the surgeons of the French fleet, which probably still lay in the bay of Nukuheva, it might easily have been obtained, could I have made my case known to them. But how could that be effected?

At last, in the exigency to which I was reduced, I proposed to Toby that he should endeavor to go round to Nukuheva, and if he could not succeed in returning to the valley by water, in one of the boats of the squadron, and taking me off, he might at least procure me some proper medicines, and effect his return overland.

My companion listened to me in silence, and at first did not appear to relish the idea. The truth was, he felt impatient to escape from the place, and wished to avail himself of our present high favor with the natives to make good our retreat, before we should experience some sudden alteration in their behavior. As he could not think of leaving me in my helpless condition, he implored me to be of good cheer, assured me that I should soon be better, and enabled in a few days to return with him to Nukuheva.

Added to this, he could not bear the idea of again returning to this dangerous place; and as for the expectation of persuading the Frenchmen to detach a boat's crew for the purpose of rescuing me from the Typees, he looked upon it as idle; and with arguments that I could not answer, urged the improbability of their provoking the hostilities of the clan by any such measure; especially as, for the purpose of quieting its apprehensions, they had as yet refrained from making any visit to the bay. "And even should they consent," said Toby, "they would only produce a commotion in the valley, in which we might both be sacrificed by these ferocious islanders." This was unanswerable; but still I clung to the belief that he might succeed in accomplishing the other part of my plan; and at last I overcame his scruples, and he agreed to make the attempt.

As soon as we succeeded in making the natives understand our intention, they broke out into the most vehement opposition to the measure, and for a while I almost despaired of obtaining their consent. At the bare thought of one of us leaving them, they manifested the most lively concern. The grief and consternation of Kory-Kory, in particular, was unbounded; he threw himself into a perfect paroxysm of gestures, which were intended to convey to us not only his abhorrence of Nukuheva and its uncivilized inhabitants, but also his astonishment that after becoming acquainted with the enlightened Typees, we should evince the least desire to withdraw, even for a time, from their agreeable society.

However, I overbore his objections by appealing to my lameness; from which I assured the natives I should speedily recover, if Toby were permitted to obtain the supplies I needed.

It was agreed that on the following morning my companion should depart, accompanied by some one or two of the household, who should point out to him an easy route, by which the bay might be reached before sunset.

At early dawn of the next day, our habitation was astir. One of the young men mounted into an adjoining cocoanut-tree, and threw down a number of the young fruit, which old Marheyo quickly stripped of the green husks, and strung together upon a short pole. These were intended to refresh Toby on his route.

The preparations being completed, with no little emotion I bade my companion adieu. He promised to return in three days at farthest; and, bidding me keep up my spirits in the interval, turned round the corner of the pi-pi, and, under the guidance of the venerable Marheyo, was soon out of sight. His departure oppressed me with melancholy, and, re-entering the dwelling, I threw myself almost in despair upon the matting of the floor.

In two hours' time the old warrior returned, and gave me to understand that after accompanying my companion a little distance, and showing him the route, he had left him journeying on his way.

It was about noon of this same day, a season which these people are wont to pass in sleep, that I lay in the house, surrounded by its slumbering inmates, and painfully affected by the strange silence which prevailed. All at once I thought I heard a faint shout, as if proceeding from some persons in the depth of the grove which extended in front of our habitation.

The sounds grew louder and nearer, and gradually the whole valley rang with wild outcries. The sleepers around me started to their feet in alarm, and hurried outside to discover the cause of the commotion. Kory-Kory, who had been the first to spring up, soon returned almost breathless, and nearly frantic with the excitement under which he seemed to be laboring. All that I could understand from him was that some accident had happened to Toby. Apprehensive of some dreadful calamity, I rushed out of the house, and caught sight of a tumultuous crowd, who, with shrieks and lamentations, were just emerging from the grove bearing in their arms some object, the sight of which produced all this transport of sorrow. As they drew near, the men redoubled their cries, while the girls, tossing their bare arms in the air, exclaimed plaintively, "Awha! awha! Toby mukee moee!"—Alas! alas! Toby is killed!

In a moment the crowd opened, and disclosed the apparently lifeless body of my companion borne between two men, the head hanging heavily against the breast of the foremost. The whole face, neck, back, and bosom were covered with blood, which still trickled slowly from a wound behind the temple. In the midst of the greatest uproar and confusion the body was carried into the house and laid on a mat. Waving the natives off to give room and air, I bent eagerly over Toby, and, laying my hand upon the breast, ascertained that the heart still beat. Overjoyed at this, I seized a calabash of water, and dashed its contents upon his face, then wiping away the blood, anxiously examined the wound.

It was about three inches long, and on removing the clotted hair from about it, showed the skull laid completely bare. Immediately with my knife I cut away the heavy locks, and bathed the part repeatedly in water.

In a few moments Toby revived, and opening his eyes for a second, closed them again without speaking. Kory-Kory, who had been kneeling beside me, now chafed his limbs gently with the palms of his hands, while a young girl at his head kept fanning him, and I still continued to moisten his lips and brow. Soon my poor comrade showed signs of animation, and I succeeded in making him swallow from a cocoanut shell a few mouthfuls of water.

Old Tinor now appeared, holding in her hand some simples she had gathered, the juice of which she by signs besought me to squeeze into the wound. Having done so, I thought it best to leave Toby undisturbed until he should have had time to rally his faculties. Several times he opened his lips, but fearful for his safety I enjoined silence. In the course of two or three hours, however, he sat up, and was sufficiently recovered to tell me what had occurred.

"After leaving the house with Marheyo," said Toby, "we struck across the valley, and ascended the opposite heights. Just beyond them, my guide informed me, lay the valley of Happar, while along their summits, and skirting the head of the vale, was my route to Nukuheva.

"After mounting a little way up the elevation my guide paused, and gave me to understand that he could not accompany me any farther, and by various signs intimated that he was afraid to approach any nearer the territories of the enemies of his tribe. He, however, pointed out my path, which now lay clearly before me, and bidding me farewell, hastily descended the mountain.

"Quite elated at being so near the Happars, I pushed up the acclivity, and soon gained its summit. It tapered to a sharp ridge, from whence I beheld both the hostile valleys. Here I sat down and rested for a moment, refreshing myself with my cocoanuts. I was soon again pursuing my way along the height, when suddenly I saw three of the islanders, who must have just come out of Happar valley, standing in the path ahead of me. They were each armed with a heavy spear, and one from his appearance I took to be a chief. They sung out something, I could not understand what, and beckoned me to come on.

"Without the least hesitation I advanced towards them, and had approached within about a yard of the foremost, when, pointing angrily into the Typee valley, and uttering some savage exclamation, he wheeled round his weapon like lightning, and struck me in a moment to the ground. The blow inflicted this wound, and took away my senses. As soon as I came to myself, I perceived the three islanders standing a little distance off, and apparently engaged in some violent altercation respecting me.

"My first impulse was to run for it; but, in endeavoring to rise, I fell back, and rolled down a little grassy precipice. The shock seemed to rally my faculties; so, starting to my feet, I fled down the path I had just ascended. I had no need to look behind me, for, from the yells I heard, I knew that my enemies were in full pursuit. Urged on by their fearful outcries, and heedless of the injury I had received—though the blood flowing from the wound trickled over into my eyes and almost blinded me—I rushed down the mountain-side with the speed of the wind. In a short time I had descended nearly a third of the distance, and the savages had ceased their cries, when suddenly a terrific howl burst upon my ear, and at the same moment a heavy javelin darted past me as I fled, and stuck quivering in a tree close to me. Another yell followed, and a second spear and a third shot through the air within a few feet of my body, both of them piercing the ground obliquely in advance of me. The fellows gave a roar of rage and disappointment; but they were afraid, I suppose, of coming down further into the Typee valley, and so abandoned the chase. I saw them recover their weapons and turn back; and I continued my descent as fast as I could.

"What could have caused this ferocious attack on the part of these Happars I could not imagine, unless it were that they had seen me ascending the mountain with Marheyo, and that the mere fact of coming from the Typee valley was sufficient to provoke them.

"As long as I was in danger I scarcely felt the wound I had received; but when the chase was over I began to suffer from it. I had lost my hat in my flight, and the sun scorched my bare head. I felt faint and giddy; but, fearful of falling to the ground beyond the reach of assistance, I staggered on as well as I could, and at last gained the level of the valley, and then down I sunk; and I knew nothing more until I found myself lying upon these mats, and you stooping over me with the calabash of water."

Such was Toby's account of this sad affair. I afterwards learned that fortunately he had fallen close to a spot where the natives go for fuel. A party of them caught sight of him as he fell, and sounding the alarm, had lifted him up; and after ineffectually endeavoring to restore him at the brook, had hurried forward with him to the house.

This incident threw a dark cloud over our prospects. It reminded us that we were hemmed in by hostile tribes, whose territories we could not hope to pass, on our route to Nukuheva, without encountering the effects of their savage resentment. There appeared to be no avenue opened to our escape but the sea, which washed the lower extremity of the vale.

Our Typee friends availed themselves of the recent disaster of Toby to exhort us to a due appreciation of the blessings we enjoyed among them; contrasting their own generous reception of us with the animosity of their neighbors. They likewise dwelt upon the cannibal propensities of the Happars, a subject which they were perfectly aware could not fail to alarm us; while at the same time they earnestly disclaimed all participation in so horrid a custom. Nor did they omit to call upon us to admire the natural loveliness of their own abode, and the lavish abundance with which it produced all manner of luxuriant fruits: exalting it in this particular above any of the surrounding valleys.

Kory-Kory seemed to experience so heartfelt a desire to infuse into our minds proper views on these subjects, that, assisted in his endeavors by the little knowledge of the language we had acquired, he actually succeeded in making us comprehend a considerable part of what he said. To facilitate our correct apprehension of his meaning, he at first condensed his ideas into the smallest possible compass.

"Happar keekeeno nuee," he exclaimed: "nuee, nuee, ki ki kannaka!—ah! owle motarkee!" which signifies, "Terrible fellows those Happars!—devour an amazing quantity of men!—ah, shocking bad!" Thus far he explained himself by a variety of gestures, during the performance of which he would dart out of the house, and point abhorrently towards the Happar valley; running in to us again with a rapidity that showed he was fearful he would lose one part of his meaning before he could complete the other; and continuing his illustrations by seizing the fleshy part of my arm in his teeth, intimating by the operation that the people who lived over in that direction would like nothing better than to treat me in that manner.

Having assured himself that we were fully enlightened on this point, he proceeded to another branch of his subject. "Ah! Typee mortakee!—nuee, nuee mioree—nuee, nuee, wai—nuee, nuee poee-poee—nuee, nuee kokoo—ah! nuee, nuee kiki—ah! nuee, nuee, nuee!" Which, literally interpreted as before, would imply, "Ah, Typee! isn't it a fine place though!—no danger of starving here, I tell you!—plenty of bread-fruit—plenty of water—plenty of pudding—ah! plenty of everything! ah! heaps, heaps, heaps!" All this was accompanied by a running commentary of signs and gestures which it was impossible not to comprehend.

As he continued his harangue, however, Kory-Kory, in emulation of our more polished orators, began to launch out rather diffusely into other branches of his subject, enlarging, probably, upon the moral reflections it suggested; and proceeded in such a strain of unintelligible and stunning gibberish, that he actually gave me the headache for the rest of the day.

Chapter XIV

A Great Event Happens in the Valley—The Island Telegraph—Something Befalls Toby—Fayaway Displays a Tender Heart—Melancholy Reflections—Mysterious Conduct of the Islanders—Devotion of Kory-Kory—A Rural Couch—A Luxury—Kory-Kory Strikes a Light à la Typee

In the course of a few days Toby had recovered from the effects of his adventure with the Happar warriors; the wound on his head rapidly healing under the vegetable treatment of the good Tinor. Less fortunate than my companion however, I still continued to languish under a complaint, the origin and nature of which were still a mystery. Cut off as I was from all intercourse with the civilized world, and feeling the inefficacy of anything the natives could do to relieve me; knowing, too, that so long as I remained in my present condition, it would be impossible for me to leave the valley, whatever opportunity might present itself; and apprehensive that ere long we might be exposed to some caprice on the part of the Islanders, I now gave up all hopes of recovery, and became a prey to the most gloomy thoughts. A deep dejection fell upon me, which neither the friendly remonstrances of my companion, the devoted attentions of Kory-Kory, nor all the soothing influences of Fayaway could remove.

One morning as I lay on the mats in the house, plunged in melancholy reverie, and regardless of everything around me, Toby, who had left me about an hour, returned in haste, and with great glee told me to cheer up and be of good heart; for he believed, from what was going on among the natives, that there were boats approaching the bay.

These tidings operated upon me like magic. The hour of our deliverance was at hand, and starting up, I was soon convinced that something unusual was about to occur. The word "botee! botee!" was vociferated in all directions; and shouts were heard in the distance, at first feebly and faintly; but growing louder and nearer at each successive repetition, until they were caught up by a fellow in a cocoanut-tree a few yards off, who sounding them in turn, they were reiterated from a neighboring grove, and so died away gradually from point to point, as the intelligence penetrated into the farthest recess of the valley. This was the vocal telegraph of the islanders; by means of which condensed items of information could be carried in a very few minutes from the sea to their remotest habitation, a distance of at least eight or nine miles. On the present occasion it was in active operation; one piece of information following another with inconceivable rapidity.

The greatest commotion now appeared to prevail. At every fresh item of intelligence the natives betrayed the liveliest interest, and redoubled the energy with which they employed themselves in collecting fruit to sell to the expected visitors. Some were tearing off the husks from cocoanuts; some perched in the trees were throwing down bread-fruit to their companions, who gathered them into heaps as they fell; while others were plying their fingers rapidly in weaving leafen baskets in which to carry the fruit.

There were other matters too going on at the same time. Here you would see a stout warrior polishing his spear with a bit of old tappa, or adjusting the folds of the girdle about his waist; and there you might descry a young damsel decorating herself with flowers, as if having in her eye some maidenly conquest; while, as in all cases of hurry and confusion in every part of the world, a number of individuals kept hurrying to and fro, with amazing vigor and perseverance, doing nothing themselves, and hindering others.

Never before had we seen the islanders in such a state of bustle and excitement; and the scene furnished abundant evidence of the fact—that it was only at long intervals any such events occur.

When I thought of the length of time that might intervene before a similar chance of escape would be presented, I bitterly lamented that I had not the power of availing myself effectually of the present opportunity.

From all that we could gather, it appeared that the natives were fearful of arriving too late upon the beach, unless they made extraordinary exertions. Sick and lame as I was, I would have started with Toby at once, had not Kory-Kory not only refused to carry me, but manifested the most invincible repugnance to our leaving the neighborhood of the house. The rest of the savages were equally opposed to our wishes, and seemed grieved and astonished at the earnestness of my solicitations. I clearly perceived that while my attendant avoided all appearance of constraining my movements, he was nevertheless determined to thwart my wish. He seemed to me on this particular occasion, as well as often afterwards, to be executing the orders of some other person with regard to me, though at the same time feeling towards me the most lively affection.

Toby, who had made up his mind to accompany the islanders if possible, as soon as they were in readiness to depart, and who for that reason had refrained from showing the same anxiety that I had done, now represented to me that it was idle for me to entertain the hope of reaching the beach in time to profit by any opportunity that might then be presented.

"Do you not see," said he, "the savages themselves are fearful of being too late, and I should hurry forward myself at once did I not think that if I showed too much eagerness I should destroy all our hopes of reaping any benefit from this fortunate event. If you will only endeavor to appear tranquil or unconcerned, you will quiet their suspicions, and I have no doubt they will then let me go with them to the beach, supposing that I merely go out of curiosity. Should I succeed in getting down to the boats, I will make known the condition in which I have left you, and measures may then be taken to secure our escape."

In the expediency of this I could not but acquiesce; and as the natives had now completed their preparations, I watched with the liveliest interest the reception that Toby's application might meet with. As soon as they understood from my companion that I intended to remain, they appeared to make no objection to his proposition, and even hailed it with pleasure. Their singular conduct on this occasion not a little puzzled me at the time, and imparted to subsequent events an additional mystery.

The islanders were now to be seen hurrying along the path which led to the sea. I shook Toby warmly by the hand, and gave him my Payta hat to shield his wounded head from the sun, as he had lost his own. He cordially returned the pressure of my hand, and solemnly promising to return as soon as the boats should leave the shore, sprang from my side, and the next minute disappeared in a turn of the grove.

In spite of the unpleasant reflections that crowded upon my mind, I could not but be entertained by the novel and animated sight which by now met my view. One after another the natives crowded along the narrow path, laden with every variety of fruit. Here, you might have seen one, who, after ineffectually endeavoring to persuade a surly porker to be conducted in leading strings, was obliged at last to seize the perverse animal in his arms, and carry him struggling against his naked breast, and squealing without intermission. There went two, who at a little distance might have been taken for the Hebrew spies, on their return to Moses with the goodly bunch of grapes. One trotted before the other at a distance of a couple of yards, while between them, from a pole resting on the shoulders, was suspended a huge cluster of bananas, which swayed to and fro with the rocking gait at which they proceeded. Here ran another, perspiring with his exertions, and bearing before him a quantity of cocoanuts, who, fearful of being too late, heeded not the fruit that dropped from his basket, and appeared solely intent upon reaching his destination, careless how many of his cocoanuts kept company with him.

In a short time the last straggler was seen hurrying on his way, and the faint shouts of those in advance died insensibly upon the ear. Our part of the valley now appeared nearly deserted by its inhabitants, Kory-Kory, his aged father, and a few decrepit old people being all that were left.

Towards sunset the islanders in small parties began to return from the beach, and among them, as they drew near to the house, I sought to descry the form of my companion. But one after another they passed the dwelling, and I caught no glimpse of him. Supposing, however, that he would soon appear with some of the members of the household, I quieted my apprehensions, and waited patiently to see him advancing in company with the beautiful Fayaway. At last, I perceived Tinor coming forward, followed by the girls and young men who usually resided in the house of Marheyo; but with them came not my comrade, and, filled with a thousand alarms, I eagerly sought to discover the cause of his delay.

My earnest questions appeared to embarrass the natives greatly. All their accounts were contradictory: one giving me to understand that Toby would be with me in a very short time; another that he did not know where he was; while a third, violently inveighing against him, assured me that he had stolen away, and would never come back. It appeared to me, at the time, that in making these various statements they endeavored to conceal from me some terrible disaster, lest the knowledge of it should overpower me.

Fearful lest some fatal calamity had overtaken him, I sought out young Fayaway, and endeavored to learn from her, if possible, the truth.

This gentle being had early attracted my regard, not only from her extraordinary beauty, but from the attractive cast of her countenance, singularly expressive of intelligence and humanity. Of all the natives she alone seemed to appreciate the effect which the peculiarity of the circumstances in which we were placed had produced upon the minds of my companion and myself. In addressing me—especially when I lay reclining upon the mats suffering from pain—there was a tenderness in her manner which it was impossible to misunderstand or resist. Whenever she entered the house, the expression of her face indicated the liveliest sympathy for me; and moving towards the place where I lay, with one arm slightly elevated in a gesture of pity, and her large glistening eyes gazing intently into mine, she would murmur plaintively, "Awha! awha! Tommo," and seat herself mournfully beside me.

Her manner convinced me that she deeply compassionated my situation, as being removed from my country and friends, and placed beyond the reach of all relief. Indeed, at times I was almost led to believe that her mind was swayed by gentle impulses hardly to be anticipated from one in her condition; that she appeared to be conscious there were ties rudely severed, which had once bound us to our homes; that there were sisters and brothers anxiously looking forward to our return, who were, perhaps, never more to behold us.

In this amiable light did Fayaway appear in my eyes; and reposing full confidence in her candor and intelligence, I now had recourse to her, in the midst of my alarm, with regard to my companion.

My questions evidently distressed her. She looked round from one to another of the bystanders, as if hardly knowing what answer to give me. At last, yielding to my importunities, she overcame her scruples, and gave me to understand that Toby had gone away with the boats which had visited the bay, but had promised to return at the expiration of three days. At first I accused him of perfidiously deserting me; but as I grew more composed, I upbraided myself for imputing so cowardly an action to him, and tranquillized myself with the belief that he had availed himself of the opportunity to go round to Nukuheva, in order to make some arrangement by which I could be removed from the valley. At any rate, thought I, he will return with the medicines I require, and then, as soon as I recover, there will be no difficulty in the way of our departure.

Consoling myself with these reflections, I lay down that night in a happier frame of mind than I had done for some time. The next day passed without any allusion to Toby on the part of the natives, who seemed desirous of avoiding all reference to the subject. This raised some apprehensions in my breast; but when night came, I congratulated myself that the second day had now gone by, and that on the morrow Toby would again be with me. But the morrow came and went, and my companion did not appear. Ah! thought I, he reckons three days from the morning of his departure—to-morrow he will arrive. But that weary day also closed upon me, without his return. Even yet I would not despair; I thought that something detained him—that he was waiting for the sailing of a boat, at Nukuheva, and that in a day or two at farthest I should see him again. But day after day of renewed disappointment passed by; at last hope deserted me, and I fell a victim to despair.

Yes, thought I, gloomily, he has secured his own escape, and cares not what calamity may befall his unfortunate comrade. Fool that I was, to suppose that anyone would willingly encounter the perils of this valley, after having once got beyond its limits! He has gone, and has left me to combat alone all the dangers by which I am surrounded. Thus would I sometimes seek to derive a desperate consolation from dwelling upon the perfidity of Toby: whilst at other times I sunk under the bitter remorse which I felt as having by my own imprudence brought upon myself the fate which I was sure awaited me.

At other times I thought that perhaps after all these treacherous savages had made away with him, and thence the confusion into which they were thrown by my questions, and their contradictory answers, or he might be a captive in some other part of the valley; or, more dreadful still, might have met with that fate at which my very soul shuddered. But all these speculations were vain; no tidings of Toby ever reached me; he had gone never to return.

The conduct of the islanders appeared inexplicable. All reference to my lost comrade was carefully evaded, and if at any time they were forced to make some reply to my frequent inquiries on the subject, they would uniformly denounce him as an ungrateful runaway, who had deserted his friend, and taken himself off to that vile and detestable place, Nukuheva.

But whatever might have been his fate, now that he was gone, the natives multiplied their acts of kindness and attention towards myself, treating me with a degree of deference which could hardly have been surpassed had I been some celestial visitant. Kory-Kory never for one moment left my side, unless it were to execute my wishes. The faithful fellow, twice every day, in the cool of the morning and in the evening, insisted upon carrying me to the stream, and bathing me in its refreshing water.

Frequently in the afternoon he would carry me to a particular part of the stream, where the beauty of the scene produced a soothing influence upon my mind. At this place the waters flowed between grassy banks, planted with enormous bread-fruit trees, whose vast branches interlacing overhead, formed a leafy canopy. Near the stream were several smooth black rocks. One of these, projecting several feet above the surface of the water, had upon its summit a shallow cavity, which, filled with freshly-gathered leaves, formed a delightful couch.

Here I often lay for hours, covered with a gauze-like veil of tappa, while Fayaway, seated beside me, and holding in her hand a fan woven from the leaflets of a young cocoanut bough, brushed aside the insects that occasionally lighted on my face, and Kory-Kory, with a view of chasing away my melancholy, performed a thousand antics in the water before us.

As my eye wandered along this romantic stream, it would fall upon the half-immersed figure of a beautiful girl, standing in the transparent water, and catching in a little net a species of diminutive shell-fish, of which these people are extraordinarily fond. Sometimes a chattering group would be seated upon the edge of a low rock in the midst of the brook, busily engaged in thinning and polishing the shells of cocoanuts, by rubbing them briskly with a small stone in the water, an operation which soon converts them into a light and elegant drinking vessel, somewhat resembling goblets made of tortoise shell.

But the tranquillizing influences of beautiful scenery, and the exhibition of human life under so novel and charming an aspect were not my only sources of consolation.

Every evening the girls of the house gathered about me on the mats, and after chasing away Kory-Kory from my side—who, nevertheless, retired only to a little distance and watched their proceedings with the most jealous attention—would anoint my whole body with a fragrant oil, squeezed from a yellow root, previously pounded between a couple of stones, and which in their language is denominated "aka." And most refreshing and agreeable are the juices of the "aka," when applied to one's limbs by the soft palms of sweet nymphs, whose bright eyes are beaming upon you with kindness; and I used to hail with delight the daily recurrence of this luxurious operation, in which I forgot all my troubles, and buried for the time every feeling of sorrow.

Sometimes in the cool of the evening my devoted servitor would lead me out upon the pi-pi in front of the house, and seating me near its edge, protect my body from the annoyance of the insects which occasionally hovered in the air, by wrapping me round with a large roll of tappa. He then bustled about, and employed himself at least twenty minutes in adjusting everything to secure my personal comfort.

Having perfected his arrangements, he would get my pipe, and, lighting it, would hand it to me. Often he was obliged to strike a light for the occasion, and as the mode he adopted was entirely different from what I had ever seen or heard of before, I will describe it.

A straight, dry, and partly decayed stick of the Hibiscus, about six feet in length, and half as many inches in diameter, with a smaller bit of wood not more than a foot long, and scarcely an inch wide, is as invariably to be met with in every house in Typee as a box of lucifer matches in the corner of a kitchen cupboard at home.

The islander, placing the larger stick obliquely against some object, with one end elevated at an angle of forty-five degrees, mounts astride of it like an urchin about to gallop off upon a cane, and then grasping the smaller one firmly in both hands, he rubs its pointed end slowly up and down the extent of a few inches on the principal stick, until at last he makes a narrow groove in the wood, with an abrupt termination at the point furthest from him, where all the dusty particles which the friction creates are accumulated in a little heap.

At first Kory-Kory goes to work quite leisurely, but gradually quickens his pace, and waxing warm in the employment, drives the stick furiously along the smoking channel, plying his hands to and fro with amazing rapidity, the perspiration starting from every pore. As he approaches the climax of his effort, he pants and gasps for breath, and his eyes almost start from their sockets with the violence of his exertions. This is the critical stage of the operation; all his previous labors are vain if he cannot sustain the rapidity of the movement until the reluctant spark is produced. Suddenly he stops, becoming perfectly motionless. His hands still retain their hold of the smaller stick, which is pressed convulsively against the further end of the channel among the fine powder there accumulated, as if he had just pierced through and through some little viper that was wriggling and struggling to escape from his clutches. The next moment a delicate wreath of smoke curls spirally into the air, the heap of dusty particles glows with fire, and Kory-Kory, almost breathless, dismounts from his steed.

This operation appeared to me to be the most laborious species of work performed in Typee; and had I possessed a sufficient intimacy with the language to have conveyed my ideas upon the subject, I should certainly have suggested to the most influential of the natives the expediency of establishing a college of vestals to be centrally located in the valley, for the purpose of keeping alive the indispensable article of fire; so as to supersede the necessity of such a vast outlay of strength and good temper, as were usually squandered on these occasions. There might, however, be special difficulties in carrying this plan into execution.

What a striking evidence does this operation furnish of the wide difference between the extreme of savage and civilized life. A gentleman of Typee can bring up a numerous family of children and give them all a highly respectable cannibal education, with infinitely less toil and anxiety than he expends in the simple process of striking a light; whilst a poor European artisan, who through the instrumentality of a lucifer performs the same operation in one second, is put to his wit's end to provide for his starving offspring that food which the children of a Polynesian father, without troubling their parents, pluck from the branches of every tree round them.

Chapter XV

Kindness of Marheyo and the Rest of the Islanders—A Full Description of the Bread-fruit Tree—Different Modes of Preparing the Fruit

All the inhabitants of the valley treated me with great kindness; but as to the household of Marheyo, with whom I was now permanently domiciled, nothing could surpass their efforts to minister to my comfort. To the gratification of my palate they paid the most unwearied attention. They continually invited me to partake of food, and when after eating heartily I declined the viands they continued to offer me, they seemed to think that my appetite stood in need of some piquant stimulant to excite its activity.

In pursuance of this idea, old Marheyo himself would hie him away to the sea-shore by the break of day, for the purpose of collecting various species of rare sea-weed; some of which among these people are considered a great luxury. After a whole day spent in this employment, he would return about nightfall with several cocoanut shells filled with different descriptions of kelp. In preparing these for use he manifested all the ostentation of a professed cook, although the chief mystery of the affair appeared to consist in pouring water in judicious quantities upon the slimy contents of his cocoanut shells.

The first time he submitted one of these saline salads to my critical attention I naturally thought that anything collected at such pains must possess peculiar merits; but a mouthful was a complete dose; and great was the consternation of the old warrior at the rapidity with which I ejected his Epicurean treat.

How true it is, that the rarity of any particular article enhances its value amazingly. In some part of the valley—I know not where, but probably in the neighborhood of the sea—the girls were sometimes in the habit of procuring small quantities of salt, a thimbleful or so being the result of the united labors of a party of five or six employed for the greater part of the day. This precious commodity they brought to the house, enveloped in multitudinous folds of leaves; and as a special mark of the esteem in which they held me, would spread an immense leaf on the ground, and dropping one by one a few minute particles of the salt upon it, invite me to taste them.

From the extravagant value placed upon the article, I verily believe, that with a bushel of common Liverpool salt all the real estate in Typee might have been purchased. With a small pinch of it in one hand, and a quarter section of a bread-fruit in the other, the greatest chief in the valley would have laughed at all luxuries of a Parisian table.

The celebrity of the bread-fruit tree, and the conspicuous place it occupies in a Typee bill of fare, induce me to give at some length a general description of the tree, and the various modes in which the fruit is prepared.

The bread-fruit tree, in its glorious prime, is a grand and towering object, forming the same feature in a Marquesan landscape that the patriarchal elm does in New England scenery. The latter tree it not a little resembles in height, in the wide spread of its stalwart branches, and in its venerable and imposing aspect.

The leaves of the bread-fruit tree are of great size, and their edges are cut and scolloped as fantastically as those of a lady's lace collar. As they annually tend towards decay, they almost rival in the brilliant variety of their gradually changing hues the fleeting shades of the expiring dolphin. The autumnal tints of our American forests, glorious as they are, sink into nothing in comparison with this tree.

The leaf, in one particular stage, when nearly all the prismatic colors are blended on its surface, is often converted by the natives into a superb and striking head-dress. The principal fiber traversing its length being split open a convenient distance, and the elastic sides of the aperture pressed apart, the head is inserted between them, the leaf drooping on one side, with its forward half turned jauntily up on the brows, and the remaining part spreading laterally behind the ears.

The fruit somewhat resembles in magnitude and general appearance one of our citron melons of ordinary size; but, unlike the citron, it has no sectional lines drawn along the outside. Its surface is dotted all over with little conical prominences, looking not unlike the knobs on an antiquated church door. The rind is perhaps an eighth of an inch in thickness; and denuded of this, at the time when it is in the greatest perfection, the fruit presents a beautiful globe of white pulp, the whole of which may be eaten, with the exception of a slender core, which is easily removed.

The bread-fruit, however, is never used, and is indeed altogether unfit to be eaten, until submitted in one form or other to the action of fire.

The most simple manner in which this operation is performed, and I think, the best, consists in placing any number of the freshly plucked fruit, when in a particular state of greenness, among the embers of a fire, in the same way that you would roast a potato. After the lapse of ten or fifteen minutes, the green rind embrowns and cracks, showing through the fissures in its sides the milk-white interior. As soon as it cools, the rind drops off, and you then have the soft round pulp in its purest and most delicious state. Thus eaten, it has a mild and pleasing flavor.

Sometimes after having been roasted in the fire, the natives snatch it briskly from the embers, and permitting it to slip out of the yielding rind into a vessel of cold water, stir up the mixture, which they call "bo-a-sho." I never could endure this compound, and indeed the preparation is not greatly in vogue among the more polite Typees.

There is one form, however, in which the fruit is occasionally served, that renders it a dish fit for a king. As soon as it is taken from the fire the exterior is removed, the core extracted, and the remaining part is placed in a sort of shallow stone mortar, and briskly worked with a pestle of the same substance. While one person is performing this operation, another takes a ripe cocoanut, and breaking it in half, which they also do very cleverly, proceeds to grate the juicy meat into fine particles. This is done by means of a piece of mother-of-pearl shell, lashed firmly to the extreme end of a heavy stick, with its straight side accurately notched like a saw. The stick is sometimes a grotesquely-formed limb of a tree, with three or four branches twisting from its body like so many shapeless legs, and sustaining it two or three feet from the ground.

The native, first placing a calabash beneath the nose, as it were, of his curious-looking log-steed, for the purpose of receiving the grated fragments as they fall, mounts astride of it as if it were a hobby-horse, and twirling the inside of his hemispheres of cocoanut around the sharp teeth of the mother-of-pearl shell, the pure white meat falls in snowy showers into the receptacle provided. Having obtained a quantity sufficient for his purpose, he places it in a bag made of the net-like fibrous substance attached to all cocoanut-trees, and compressing it over the bread-fruit, which being now sufficiently pounded, is put into a wooden bowl—extracts a thick creamy milk. The delicious liquid soon bubbles round the fruit, and leaves it at last just peeping above its surface.

This preparation is called "kokoo," and a most luscious preparation it is. The hobby-horse and the pestle and mortar were in great requisition during the time I remained in the house of Marheyo, and Kory-Kory had frequent occasion to show his skill in their use.

But the great staple articles of food into which the bread-fruit is converted by these natives are known respectively by the names of Amar and Poee-Poee.

At a certain season of the year, when the fruit of the hundred groves of the valley has reached its maturity, and hangs in golden spheres from every branch, the islanders assemble in harvest groups, and garner in the abundance which surrounds them. The trees are stripped of their nodding burdens, which, easily freed from the rind and core, are gathered together in capacious wooden vessels, where the pulpy fruit is soon worked by a stone pestle, vigorously applied, into a blended mass of a doughy consistency, called by the natives "Tutao." This is then divided into separate parcels, which, after being made up into stout packages, enveloped in successive folds of leaves, and bound round with thongs of bark, are stored away in large receptacles hollowed in the earth, from whence they are drawn as occasion may require.

In this condition the Tutao sometimes remains for years, and even is thought to improve by age. Before it is fit to be eaten, however, it has to undergo an additional process. A primitive oven is scooped in the ground, and its bottom being loosely covered with stones, a large fire is kindled within it. As soon as the requisite degree of heat is attained, the embers are removed, and the surface of the stones being covered with thick layers of leaves, one of the large packages of Tutao is deposited upon them, and overspread with another layer of leaves. The whole is then quickly heaped up with earth, and forms a sloping mound.

The Tutao thus baked is called "Amar"; the action of the oven having converted it into an amber-colored caky substance, a little tart, but not at all disagreeable to the taste.

By another and final process the "Amar" is changed into "Poee-Poee." This transition is rapidly effected. The amar is placed in a vessel, and mixed with water until it gains a proper pudding-like consistency, when, without further preparation, it is in readiness for use. This is the form in which the "Tutao" is generally consumed. The singular mode of eating it I have already described.

Were it not that the bread-fruit is thus capable of being preserved for a length of time, the natives might be reduced to a state of starvation; for owing to some unknown cause the trees sometimes fail to bear fruit; and on such occasions the islanders chiefly depend upon the supplies they have been enabled to store away.

This stately tree, which is rarely met with upon the Sandwich Islands, and at Tahiti does not abound to a degree that renders its fruit the principal article of food, attains its greatest excellence in the genial climate of the Marquesan group, where it grows to an enormous magnitude, and flourishes in the utmost abundance.

Chapter XVI

MELANCHOLY CONDITION—OCCURRENCE AT THE TI—ANECDOTE OF MARHEYO—SHAVING THE HEAD OF A WARRIOR

IN LOOKING BACK TO THIS PERIOD, AND CALLING TO REMEMBRANCE THE NUMBERLESS PROOFS OF kindness and respect which I received from the natives of the valley, I can scarcely understand how it was that, in the midst of so many consolatory circumstances, my mind should still have been consumed by the most dismal forebodings, and have remained a prey to the profoundest melancholy. It is true that the suspicious circumstances which had attended the disappearance of Toby were enough of themselves to excite distrust with regard to the savages, in whose power I felt myself to be entirely placed, especially when it was combined with the knowledge that these very men, kind and respectful as they were to me, were, after all, nothing better than a set of cannibals.

But my chief source of anxiety, and that which poisoned every temporary enjoyment, was the mysterious disease in my leg, which still remained unabated. All the herbal applications of Tinor, united with the severer discipline of the old leech, and the affectionate nursing of Kory-Kory, had failed to relieve me. I was almost a cripple, and the pain I endured at intervals was agonizing. The unaccountable malady showed no signs of amendment: on the contrary, its violence increased day by day, and threatened the most fatal results, unless some powerful means were employed to counteract it. It seemed as if I were destined to sink under this grievous affliction, or at least that it would hinder me from availing myself of any opportunity of escaping from the valley.

An incident which occurred as nearly as I can estimate about three weeks after the disappearance of Toby, convinced me that the natives, from some reason or other, would interpose every possible obstacle to my leaving them.

One morning there was no little excitement evinced by the people near my abode, and which I soon discovered proceeded from a vague report that boats had been seen at a great distance approaching the bay. Immediately all was bustle and animation. It so happened that day that the pain I suffered having somewhat abated, and feeling in much better spirits than usual, I had complied with Kory-Kory's invitation to visit the chief Mehevi at the place called the "Ti," which I have before described as being situated within the precincts of the Taboo Groves. These sacred recesses were at no great distance from Marheyo's habitation, and lay between it and the sea; the path that conducted to the beach passing directly in front of the Ti, and thence skirting along the border of the groves.

I was reposing upon the mats, within the sacred building, in company with Mehevi and several other chiefs, when the announcement was first made. It sent a thrill of joy through my whole frame;—perhaps Toby was about to return. I rose at once to my feet, and my instinctive impulse was to hurry down to the beach, equally regardless of the distance that separated me from it, and of my disabled condition. As soon as Mehevi noticed the effect the intelligence had produced upon me, and the impatience I betrayed to reach the sea, his countenance assumed that inflexible rigidity of expression which had so awed me on the afternoon of our arrival at the house of Marheyo. As I was proceeding to leave the Ti, he laid his hand upon my shoulder, and said gravely, "abo, abo" (wait, wait). Solely intent upon the one thought that occupied my mind, and heedless of his request, I was brushing past him, when suddenly he assumed a tone of authority, and told me to "moee" (sit down). Though struck by the alteration in his demeanor, the excitement under which I labored was too strong to permit me to obey the unexpected command, and I was still limping towards the edge of the pi-pi with Kory-Kory clinging to one arm in his efforts to restrain me, when the natives around started to their feet, ranged themselves along the open front of the building, while Mehevi looked at me scowlingly, and reiterated his commands still more sternly.

It was at this moment, when fifty savage countenances were glaring upon me, that I first truly experienced I was indeed a captive in the valley. The conviction rushed upon me with staggering force, and I was overwhelmed by this confirmation of my worst fears. I saw at once that it was useless for me to resist, and sick at heart, I reseated myself upon the mats, and for the moment abandoned myself to despair.

I now perceived the natives one after the other hurrying past the Ti and pursuing the route that conducted to the sea. These savages, thought I, will soon be holding communication with some of my own countrymen perhaps, who with ease could restore me to liberty did they know of the situation I was in. No language can describe the wretchedness which I felt; and in the bitterness of my soul I imprecated a thousand curses on the perfidious Toby, who had thus abandoned me to destruction. It was in vain that Kory-Kory tempted me with food, or lighted my pipe, or sought to attract my attention by performing the uncouth antics that had sometimes diverted me. I was fairly knocked down by this last misfortune, which, much as I had feared it, I had never before had the courage calmly to contemplate.

Regardless of everything but my own sorrow, I remained in the Ti for several hours, until shouts proceeding at intervals from the groves beyond the house proclaimed the return of the natives from the beach.

Whether any boats visited the bay that morning or not, I never could ascertain. The savages assured me that there had not—but I was inclined to believe that by deceiving me in this particular they sought to allay the violence of my grief. However that might be, this incident showed plainly that the Typees intended to hold me a prisoner. As they still treated me with the same sedulous attention as before, I was utterly at a loss how to account for their singular conduct. Had I been in a situation to instruct them in any of the rudiments of the mechanic arts, or had I manifested a disposition to render myself in any way useful among them, their conduct might have been attributed to some adequate motive, but as it was, the matter seemed to me inexplicable.

During my whole stay on the island there occurred but two or three instances where the natives applied to me with the view of availing themselves of my superior information. And these now appear so ludicrous that I cannot forbear relating them.

The few things we had brought from Nukuheva had been done up into a small bundle which we had carried with us in our descent to the valley. This bundle, the first night of our arrival, I had used as a pillow, but on the succeeding morning, opening it for the inspection of the natives, they gazed upon the miscellaneous contents as though I had just revealed to them a casket of diamonds, and they insisted that so precious a treasure should be properly secured. A line was accordingly attached to it, and the other end being passed over the ridgepole of the house, it was hoisted up to the apex of the roof, where it hung suspended directly over the mats where I usually reclined. When I desired anything from it I merely raised my finger to a bamboo beside me, and taking hold of the string which was there fastened, lowered the package. This was exceedingly handy, and I took care to let the natives understand how much I applauded the invention. Of this package the chief contents were a razor with its case, a supply of needles and thread, a pound or two of tobacco, and a few yards of bright-colored calico.

I should have mentioned that shortly after Toby's disappearance, perceiving the uncertainty of the time I might be obliged to remain in the valley—if, indeed, I ever should escape from it—and considering that my whole wardrobe consisted of a shirt and a pair of trousers, I resolved to doff these garments at once, in order to preserve them in a suitable condition for wear should I again appear among civilized beings. I was consequently obliged to assume the Typee costume, a little altered, however, to suit my own views of propriety, and in which I have no doubt I appeared to as much advantage as a senator of Rome enveloped in the folds of his toga. A few folds of yellow tappa tucked about my waist, descended to my feet in the style of a lady's petticoat, only I did not have recourse to those voluminous paddings in the rear with which our gentle dames are in the habit of augmenting the sublime rotundity of their figures. This usually comprised my in-door dress: whenever I walked out, I superadded to it an ample robe of the same material, which completely enveloped my person, and screened it from the rays of the sun.

One morning I made a rent in this mantle; and to show the islanders with what facility it could be repaired, I lowered my bundle, and taking from it a needle and thread, proceeded to stitch up the opening. They regarded this wonderful application of science with intense admiration; and whilst I was stitching away, old Marheyo, who was one of the lookers-on, suddenly clapped his hand to his forehead, and rushing to a corner of the house, drew forth a soiled and tattered strip of faded calico—which he must have procured some time or other in traffic on the beach—and besought me eagerly to exercise a little of my art upon it. I willingly complied, though certainly so stumpy a needle as mine never took such gigantic strides over calico before. The repairs completed, old Marheyo gave me a paternal hug; and divesting himself of his "maro" (girdle), swathed the calico about his loins, and slipping the beloved ornaments into his ears, grasped his spear and sallied out of the house, like a valiant Templar arrayed in a new and costly suit of armor.

I never used my razor during my stay in the island, but although a very subordinate affair, it had been vastly admired by the Typees; and Narmonee, a great hero among them, who was exceedingly precise in the arrangements of his toilet and the general adjustment of is person, being the most accurately tattooed and laboriously horrified individual in all the valley, thought it would be a great advantage to have it applied to the already shaven crown of his head.

The implement they usually employ is a shark's tooth, which is about as well adapted to the purpose as a one-pronged fork for pitching hay. No wonder, then, that the acute Narmonee perceived the advantage my razor possessed over the usual implement. Accordingly, one day he requested as a personal favor that I would just run over his head with the razor. In reply, I gave him to understand that it was too dull, and could not be used to any purpose without being previously sharpened. To assist my meaning, I went through an imaginary honing process on the palm of my hand. Narmonee took my meaning in an instant, and running out of the house, returned the next moment with a huge rough mass of rock as big as a mill-stone, and indicated to me that that was exactly the thing I wanted. Of course there was nothing left for me but to proceed to business, and I began scraping away at a great rate. He writhed and wriggled under the infliction, but, fully convinced of my skill, endured the pain like a martyr.

Though I never saw Narmonee in battle I will, from what I then observed, stake my life upon his courage and fortitude. Before commencing operations, his head had presented a surface of short bristling hairs, and by the time I had concluded my unskillful operation it resembled not a little a stubble field after being gone over with a harrow. However, as the chief expressed the liveliest satisfaction at the result, I was too wise to dissent from his opinion.

Chapter XVII

Improvement in Health and Spirits—Felicity of the Typees—Their Enjoyments Compared with Those of More Enlightened Communities—Comparative Wickedness of Civilized and Unenlightened People—A Skirmish in the Mountain with the Warriors of Happar

Day after day wore on, and still there was no perceptible change in the conduct of the islanders towards me. Gradually I lost all knowledge of the regular recurrence of the days of the week, and sunk insensibly into that kind of apathy which ensues after some violent outbreak of despair. My limb suddenly healed, the swelling went down, the pain subsided, and I had every reason to suppose I should soon completely recover from the affliction that had so long tormented me.

As soon as I was enabled to ramble about the valley in company with the natives, troops of whom followed me whenever I sallied out of the house, I began to experience an elasticity of mind which placed me beyond the reach of those dismal forebodings to which I had so lately been a prey. Received wherever I went with the most deferential kindness; regaled perpetually with the most delightful fruits; ministered to by dark-eyed nymphs, and enjoying besides all the services of the devoted Kory-Kory, I thought that for a sojourn among cannibals, no man could have well made a more agreeable one.

To be sure there were limits set to my wanderings. Toward the sea my progress was barred by an express prohibition of the savages; and after having made two or three ineffectual attempts to reach it, as much to gratify my curiosity as anything else, I gave up the idea. It was in vain to think of reaching it by stealth, since the natives escorted me in numbers wherever I went, and not for one single moment that I can recall to mind was I ever permitted to be alone.

The green and precipitous elevations that stood ranged around the head of the vale where Marheyo's habitation was situated effectually precluded all hope of escape in that quarter, even if I could have stolen away from the thousand eyes of the savages.

But these reflections now seldom obtruded upon me; I gave myself up to the passing hour, and if ever disagreeable thoughts arose in my mind, I drove them away. When I looked around the verdant recess in which I was buried, and gazed up to the summits of the lofty eminence that hemmed me in, I was well disposed to think that I was in the "Happy Valley," and that beyond those heights there was naught but a world of care and anxiety.

As I extended my wanderings in the valley and grew more familiar with the habits of its inmates, I was fain to confess that, despite the disadvantages of his condition, the Polynesian savage, surrounded by all the luxurious provisions of nature, enjoyed an infinitely happier, though certainly a less intellectual existence, than the self-complacent European.

The naked wretch who shivers beneath the bleak skies, and starves among the inhospitable wilds of Tierra-del-Fuego, might indeed be made happier by civilization, for it would alleviate his physical wants. But the voluptuous Indian, with every desire supplied, whom Providence has bountifully provided with all the sources of pure and natural enjoyment, and from whom are removed so many of the ills and pains of life—what has he to desire at the hands of Civilization? She may "cultivate his mind"—"may elevate his thoughts"—these I believe are the established phrases—but will he be the happier? Let the once smiling and populous Hawaiian islands, with their now diseased, starving, and dying natives, answer the question. The missionaries may seek to disguise the matter as they will, but the facts are incontrovertible; and the devoutest Christian who visits that group with an unbiased mind, must go away mournfully asking—"Are these, alas! the fruits of twenty-five years of enlightening?"

In a primitive state of society, the enjoyments of life, though few and simple, are spread over a great extent, and are unalloyed; but Civilization, for every advantage she imparts, holds a hundred evils in reserve;—the heart-burnings, the jealousies, the social rivalries, the family dissentions, and the thousand self-inflicted discomforts of refined life, which make up in units the swelling aggregate of human misery, are unknown among these unsophisticated people.

But it will be urged that these shocking, unprincipled wretches are cannibals. Very true; and a rather bad trait in their character it must be allowed. But they are such only when they seek to gratify the passion of revenge upon their enemies; and I ask whether the mere eating of human flesh so very far exceeds in barbarity that custom which only a few years since was practiced in enlightened England—a convicted traitor, perhaps a man found guilty of honesty, patriotism, and suchlike heinous crimes, had his head lopped off with a huge ax, his bowels dragged out and thrown into a fire; while his body, carved into four quarters, was with his head exposed upon pikes, and permitted to rot and fester among the public haunts of men!

The fiend-like skill we display in the invention of all manner of death-dealing engines, the vindictiveness with which we carry on our wars, and the misery and desolation that follow in their train, are enough of themselves to distinguish the white civilized man as the most ferocious animal on the face of the earth.

His remorseless cruelty is seen in many of the institutions of our own favored land. There is one in particular lately adopted in one of the States of the Union, which purports to have been dictated by the most merciful considerations. To destroy our malefactors piece-meal, drying up in their veins, drop by drop, the blood we are too chicken-hearted to shed by a single blow which would at once put a period to their sufferings, is deemed to be infinitely preferable to the old-fashioned punishment of gibbeting—much less annoying to the victim, and more in accordance with the refined spirit of the age; and yet how feeble is all language to describe the horrors we inflict upon these wretches, whom we mason up in the cells of our prisons, and condemn to perpetual solitude in the very heart of our population.

But it is needless to multiply the examples of civilized barbarity; they far exceed in the amount of misery they cause the crimes which we regard with such abhorrence in our less enlightened fellow-creatures.

The term "Savage" is, I conceive, often misapplied, and indeed, when I consider the vices, cruelties, and enormities of every kind that spring up in the tainted atmosphere of a feverish civilization, I am inclined to think that so far as the relative wickedness of the parties is concerned, four or five Marquesan Islanders sent to the United States as missionaries might be quite as useful as an equal number of Americans dispatched to the Islands in a similar capacity.

I once heard it given as an instance of the frightful depravity of a certain tribe in the Pacific, that they had no word in their language to express the idea of virtue. The assertion was unfounded; but were it otherwise, it might be met by stating that their language is almost entirely destitute of terms to express the delightful ideas conveyed by our endless catalogue of civilized crimes.

In the altered frame of mind to which I have referred, every object that presented itself to my notice in the valley struck me in a new light, and the opportunities I now enjoyed of observing the manners of its inmates tended to strengthen my favorable impressions. One peculiarity that fixed my admiration was the perpetual hilarity reigning through the whole extent of the vale. There seemed to be no cares, griefs, troubles, or vexations, in all Typee. The hours tripped along as gaily as the laughing couples down a country dance.

There were none of those thousand sources of irritation that the ingenuity of civilized man has created to mar his own felicity. There were no foreclosures of mortgages, no protested notes, no bills payable, no debts of honor in Typee; no unreasonable tailors and shoemakers perversely bent on being paid; no duns of any description and battery attorneys, to foment discord, backing their clients up to a quarrel, and then knocking their heads together; no poor relations, everlastingly occupying the spare bed-chamber, and diminishing the elbow room at the family table; no destitute widows with their children starving on the cold charities of the world; no beggars; no debtors' prisons; no proud and hard-hearted nabobs in Typee; or to sum up all in one word—no Money! "That root of all evil" was not to be found in the valley.

In this secluded abode of happiness there were no cross old women, no cruel step-dames, no withered spinsters, no love-sick maidens, no sour old bachelors, no inattentive husbands, no melancholy young men, no blubbering youngsters, and no squalling brats. All was mirth, fun, and high good humor. Blue devils, hypochondria, and doleful dumps went and hid themselves among the nooks and crannies of the rocks.

Here you would see a parcel of children frolicking together the livelong day, and no quarreling, no contention, among them. The same number in our own land could not have played together for the space of an hour without biting or scratching one another. There you might have seen a throng of young females, not filled with envyings of each other's charms, nor displaying the ridiculous affectations of gentility, nor yet moving in whalebone corsets, like so many automatons, but free, inartificially happy, and unconstrained.

There were some spots in that sunny vale where they would frequently resort to decorate themselves with garlands of flowers. To have seen them reclining beneath the shadows of one of the beautiful groves; the ground about them strewn with freshly gathered buds and blossoms, employed in weaving chaplets and necklaces, one would have thought that all the train of Flora had gathered together to keep a festival in honor of their mistress.

With the young men there seemed almost always some matter of diversion or business on hand that afforded a constant variety of enjoyment. But whether fishing, or carving canoes, or polishing their ornaments, never was there exhibited the least sign of strife or contention among them.

As for the warriors, they maintained a tranquil dignity of demeanor, journeying occasionally from house to house, where they were always sure to be received with the attention bestowed upon distinguished guests. The old men, of whom there were many in the vale, seldom stirred from their mats, where they would recline for hours and hours, smoking and talking to one another with all the garrulity of age.

But the continual happiness, which so far as I was able to judge appeared to prevail in the valley, sprang principally from that all-pervading sensation which Rousseau has told us he at one time experienced, the mere buoyant sense of a healthful physical existence. And indeed in this particular the Typees had ample reason to felicitate themselves, for sickness was almost unknown. During the whole period of my stay I saw but one invalid among them; and on their smooth skins you observed no blemish or mark of disease.

The general repose, however, upon which I have just been descanting, was broken in upon about this time by an event which proved that the islanders were not entirely exempt from those occurrences which disturb the quiet of more civilized communities.

Having now been a considerable time in the valley, I began to feel surprised that the violent hostility subsisting between its inhabitants and those of the adjoining bay of Happar should never have manifested itself in any war-like encounter. Although the valiant Typees would often by gesticulations declare their undying hatred against their enemies, and the disgust they felt at their cannibal propensities; although they dilated upon the manifold injuries they had received at their hands, yet with a forbearance truly commendable, they appeared to sit down under their grievances, and to refrain from making any reprisals. The Happars, entrenched behind their mountains, and never even showing themselves on their summits, did not appear to me to furnish adequate cause for that excess of animosity evinced towards them by the heroic tenants of our vale, and I was inclined to believe that the deeds of blood attributed to them had been greatly exaggerated.

On the other hand, as the clamors of war had not up to this period disturbed the serenity of the tribe, I began to distrust the truth of those reports which ascribed so fierce and belligerent a character to the Typee nation. Surely, thought I, all these terrible stories I have heard about the inveteracy with which they carried on the feud, their deadly intensity of hatred, and the diabolical malice with which they glutted their revenge upon the inanimate forms of the slain, are nothing more than fables, and I must confess that I experienced something like a sense of regret at having my hideous anticipations thus disappointed. I felt in some sort like a 'prentice-boy who, going to the play in the expectation of being delighted with a cut-and-thrust tragedy, is almost moved to tears of disappointment at the exhibition of a genteel comedy.

I could not avoid thinking that I had fallen in with a greatly traduced people, and I moralized not a little upon the disadvantage of having a bad name, which in this instance had given a tribe of savages, who were as pacific as so many lambkins, the reputation of a confederacy of giant-killers.

But subsequent events proved that I had been a little too premature in coming to this conclusion. One day about noon, happening to be at the Ti, I had lain down on the mats with several of the chiefs, and had gradually sunk into a most luxurious siesta, when I was awakened by a tremendous outcry, and starting up beheld the natives seizing their spears and hurrying out, while the most puissant of the chiefs, grasping the six muskets which were ranged against the bamboos, followed after, and soon disappeared in the groves. These movements were accompanied by wild shouts, in which "Happar, Happar," greatly predominated. The islanders were now seen running past the Ti, and striking across the valley to the Happar side. Presently I heard the sharp report of a musket from the adjoining hills, and then a burst of voices in the same direction. At this the women, who had congregated in the groves, set up the most violent clamors, as they invariably do here as elsewhere on every occasion of excitement and alarm, with a view of tranquillizing their own minds and disturbing other people. On this particular occasion they made such an outrageous noise, and continued it with such perseverance, that for awhile, had entire volleys of musketry been fired off in the neighboring mountains, I should not have been able to have heard them.

When this female commotion had a little subsided I listened eagerly for further information. At last bang went another shot, and then a second volley of yells from the hills. Again all was quiet, and continued so for such a length of time that I began to think the contending armies had agreed upon a suspension of hostilities; when pop went a third gun, followed as before with a yell. After this, for nearly two hours nothing occurred worthy of comment, save some straggling shouts from the hill-side, sounding like the halloos of a parcel of truant boys who had lost themselves in the woods.

During this interval I had remained standing on the piazza of the "Ti," which directly fronted the Happar mountain, and with no one near me but Kory-Kory and the old superannuated savages I have described. These latter never stirred from their mats, and seemed altogether unconscious that anything unusual was going on.

As for Kory-Kory, he appeared to think that we were in the midst of great events, and sought most zealously to impress me with a due sense of their importance. Every sound that reached us conveyed some momentous item of intelligence to him. At such times, as if he were gifted with second sight, he would go through a variety of pantomimic illustrations, showing me the precise manner in which the redoubtable Typees were at that very moment chastising the insolence of the enemy. "Mehevi hanna pippee nuee Happar," he exclaimed every five minutes, giving me to understand that under that distinguished captain the warriors of his nation were performing prodigies of valor.

Having heard only four reports from the muskets, I was led to believe that they were worked by the islanders in the same manner as the Sultan Solyman's ponderous artillery at the siege of Byzantium, one of them taking an hour or two to load and train. At last, no sound whatever proceeding from the mountains, I concluded that the contest had been determined one way or the other. Such appeared, indeed, to be the case, for in a little while a courier arrived at the "Ti," almost breathless with his exertions, and communicated the news of a great victory having been achieved by his countrymen: "Happar poo arva!—Happar poo arva!" (the cowards had fled). Kory-Kory was in ecstasies and commenced a vehement harangue, which, so far as I understood it, implied that the result exactly agreed with his expectations, and which, moreover, was intended to convince me that it would be a perfectly useless undertaking, even for an army of fire-eaters, to offer battle to the irresistible heroes of our valley. In all this I of course acquiesced, and looked forward with no little interest to the return of the conquerors, whose victory I feared might not have been purchased without cost to themselves.

But here I was again mistaken; for Mehevi, in conducting his war-like operations, rather inclined to the Fabian than to the Bonapartean tactics, husbanding his resources and exposing his troops to no unnecessary hazards. The total loss of the victors in this obstinately contested affair was, in killed, wounded, and missing—one forefinger and part of a thumb-nail (which the late proprietor brought along with him in his hand), a severely contused arm, and a considerable effusion of blood flowing from the thigh of a chief, who had received an ugly thrust from a Happar spear. What the enemy had suffered I could not discover, but I presume they had succeeded in taking off with them the bodies of their slain.

Such was the issue of the battle, as far as its results came under my observation; and as it appeared to be considered an event of prodigious importance, I reasonably concluded that the wars of the natives were marked by no very sanguinary traits. I afterwards learned how the skirmish had originated. A number of the Happars had been discovered prowling for no good purpose on the Typee side of the mountain; the alarm was sounded, and the invaders, after a protracted resistance, had been chased over the frontier. But why had not the intrepid Mehevi carried the war into Happar? Why had he not made a descent into the hostile vale, and brought away some trophy of his victory—some materials for the cannibal entertainment which I had heard usually terminated every engagement? After all, I was much inclined to believe that these shocking festivals must occur very rarely among the islanders, if, indeed, they ever take place.

For two or three days the late event was the theme of general comment; after which the excitement gradually wore away, and the valley resumed its accustomed tranquillity.

Chapter XVIII

Swimming in Company with the Girls of the Valley—A Canoe—Effects of the Taboo—A Pleasure Excursion on the Pond—Beautiful Freak of Fayaway—Mantua-making—A Stranger Arrives in the Valley—His Mysterious Conduct—Native Oratory—The Interview—Its Results—Departure of the Stranger

RETURNING HEALTH AND PEACE OF MIND GAVE A NEW INTEREST TO EVERYTHING AROUND ME. I sought to diversify my time by as many enjoyments as lay within my reach. Bathing in company with troops of girls formed one of my chief amusements. We sometimes enjoyed the recreation in the waters of a miniature lake, into which the central stream of the valley expanded. This lovely sheet of water was almost circular in figure, and about three hundred yards across. Its beauty was indescribable. All around its banks waved luxuriant masses of tropical foliage, soaring high above which was to be seen, here and there, the symmetrical shaft of the cocoanut-tree, surmounted by its tufts of graceful branches, drooping in the air like so many waving ostrich plumes.

The ease and grace with which the maidens of the valley propelled themselves through the water, and their familiarity with the element, were truly astonishing. Sometimes they might be seen gliding along, just under the surface, without apparently moving hand or foot—then throwing themselves on their sides, they darted through the water, revealing glimpses of their forms, as, in the course of their rapid progress, they shot for an instant partly into the air—at one moment they dived deep down into the water and the next they rose bounding to the surface.

I remember upon one occasion plunging in among a parcel of these river-nymphs, and counting vainly on my superior strength, sought to drag some of them under the water, but I quickly repented my temerity. The amphibious young creatures swarmed about me like a shoal of dolphins, and seizing hold of my devoted limbs, tumbled me about and ducked me under the surface, until from the strange noises which rang in my ears, and the supernatural visions dancing before my eyes, I thought I was in the land of spirits. I stood indeed as little chance among them as a cumbrous whale attacked on all sides by a legion of sword-fish. When at length they relinquished their hold of me, they swam away in every direction, laughing at my clumsy endeavors to reach them.

There was no boat on the lake; but at my solicitation and for my special use, some of the young men attached to Marheyo's household, under the direction of the indefatigable Kory-Kory, brought up a light and tastefully-carved canoe from the sea. It was launched upon the sheet of water, and floated there as gracefully as a swan. But, melancholy to relate, it produced an effect I had not anticipated. The sweet nymphs, who had sported with me before on the lake, now all fled its vicinity. The prohibited craft, guarded by the edicts of the "taboo," extended the prohibition to the waters in which it lay.

For a few days, Kory-Kory, with one or two other youths, accompanied me in my excursions to the lake, and while I paddled about in my light canoe, would swim after me shouting and gamboling in pursuit. But I was ever partial to what is termed in the "Young Men's Own Book"—"the society of virtuous and intelligent young ladies"; and in the absence of the mermaids, the amusement became dull and insipid. One morning I expressed to my faithful servitor my desire for the return of the nymphs. The honest fellow looked at me bewildered for a moment, and then shook his head solemnly, and murmured, *"Taboo! taboo!"* giving me to understand that unless the canoe was removed I could not expect to have the young ladies back again. But to this procedure I was averse; I not only wanted the canoe to stay where it was, but I wanted the beauteous Fayaway to get into it, and paddle with me about the lake. This latter proposition completely horrified Kory-Kory's notions of propriety. He inveighed against it, as something too monstrous to be thought of. It not only shocked their established notions of propriety, but was at variance with all their religious ordinances.

However, although the "taboo" was a ticklish thing to meddle with, I determined to test its capabilities of resisting an attack. I consulted the chief Mehevi, who endeavored to dissuade me from my object: but I was not to be repulsed; and accordingly increased the warmth of my solicitations. At last he entered into a long, and I have no doubt a very learned and eloquent exposition of the history and nature of the "taboo" as affecting this particular case; employing a variety of most extraordinary words, which, from their amazing length and sonorousness, I have every reason to believe were of a theological nature. But all that he said failed to convince me: partly, perhaps, because I could not comprehend a word that he uttered; but chiefly, that for the life of me I could not understand why a woman would not have as much right to enter a canoe as a man. At last he became a little more rational, and intimated that, out of the abundant love he bore me, he would consult with the priests and see what could be done.

How it was that the priesthood of Typee satisfied the affair with their consciences, I know not; but so it was, and Fayaway's dispensation from this portion of the taboo was at length procured. Such an event I believe never before had occurred in the valley; but it was high time the islanders should be taught a little gallantry, and I trust that the example I set them may produce beneficial effects. Ridiculous, indeed, that the lovely creatures should be obliged to paddle about in the water, like so many ducks, while a parcel of great strapping fellows skimmed over its surface in their canoes.

The first day after Fayaway's emancipation, I had a delightful little party on the lake—the damsels, Kory-Kory, and myself. My zealous body-servant brought from the house a calabash of poee-poee, half a dozen young cocoanuts—stripped of their husks—three pipes, as many yams, and me on his back a part of the way. Something of a load; but Kory-Kory was a very strong man for his size, and by no means brittle in the spine. We had a very pleasant day; my trusty valet plied the paddle and swept us gently along the margin of the water, beneath the shades of the overhanging thickets. Fayaway and I reclined in the stern of the canoe, on the very best terms possible with one another; the gentle nymph occasionally placing her pipe to her lip, and exhaling the mild fumes of the tobacco, to which her rosy breath added a fresh perfume. Strange as it may seem, there is nothing in which a young and beautiful female appears to more advantage than in the act of smoking. How captivating is a Peruvian lady swinging in her gaily-woven hammock of grass, extended between two orange-trees, and inhaling the fragrance of a choice cigarro! But Fayaway, holding in her delicately formed olive hand the long yellow reed of her pipe, with its quaintly carved bowl, and every few moments languishingly giving forth light wreaths of vapor from her mouth and nostrils, looked still more engaging.

We floated about thus for several hours, when I looked up to the warm, glowing, tropical sky, and then down into the transparent depths below; and when my eye, wandering from the bewitching scenery around, fell upon the grotesquely-tattooed form of Kory-Kory, and finally encountered the pensive gaze of Fayaway, I thought I had been transported to some fairy region, so unreal did everything appear.

This lovely piece of water was the coolest spot in all the valley, and I now made it a place of continual resort during the hottest period of the day. One side of it lay near the termination of a long gradually expanding gorge, which mounted to the heights that environed the vale. The strong trade wind, met in its course by these elevations, circled and eddied about their summits, and was sometimes driven down the steep ravine and swept across the valley, ruffling in its passage the otherwise tranquil surface of the lake.

One day, after we had been paddling about for some time, I disembarked Kory-Kory, and paddled the canoe to the windward side of the lake. As I turned the canoe, Fayaway, who was with me, seemed all at once to be struck with some happy idea. With a wild exclamation of delight, she disengaged from her person the ample robe of tappa which was knotted over her shoulder (for the purpose of shielding her from the sun), and spreading it out like a sail, stood erect with upraised arms in the head of the canoe. We American sailors pride ourselves upon our straight clean spars, but a prettier little mast than Fayaway's made was never shipped aboard of any craft.

In a moment the tappa was distended by the breeze—the long brown tresses of Fayaway streamed in the air—and the canoe glided rapidly through the water, and shot towards the shore. Seated in the stern, I directed its course with my paddle until it dashed up the soft sloping bank, and Fayaway, with a light spring, alighted on the ground; whilst Kory-Kory, who had watched our maneuvers with admiration, now clapped his hands in transport, and shouted like a madman. Many a time afterwards was this feat repeated.

If the reader has not observed ere this that I was the declared admirer of Miss Fayaway, all I can say is that he is little conversant with affairs of the heart, and I certainly shall not trouble myself to enlighten him any further. Out of the calico I had brought from the ship I made a dress for this lovely girl. In it she looked, I must confess, something like an opera dancer. The drapery of the latter damsel generally commences a little above the elbows, but my island beauty's began at the waist, and terminated sufficiently far above the ground to reveal the most bewitching ankle in the universe.

The day that Fayaway first wore this robe was rendered memorable by a new acquaintance being introduced to me. In the afternoon I was lying in the house, when I heard a great uproar outside; but being by this time pretty well accustomed to the wild halloos which were almost continually ringing through the valley, I paid little attention to it, until old Marheyo, under the influence of some strange excitement, rushed into my presence and communicated the astounding tidings, "Marnoo pemi!" which being interpreted, implied that an individual by the name of Marnoo was approaching. My worthy old friend evidently expected that this intelligence would produce a great effect upon me, and for a time he stood earnestly regarding me, as if curious to see how I should conduct myself, but as I remained perfectly unmoved, the old gentleman darted out of the house again, in as great a hurry as he had entered it.

"Marnoo, Marnoo," cogitated I, "I have never heard that name before. Some distinguished character, I presume, from the prodigious riot the natives are making"; the tumultuous noise drawing nearer and nearer every moment, while "Marnoo!—Marnoo!" was shouted by every tongue.

I made up my mind that some savage warrior of consequence, who had not yet enjoyed the honor of an audience, was desirous of paying his respects on the present occasion. So vain had I become by the lavish attention to which I had been accustomed, that I felt half inclined, as a punishment for such neglect, to give this Marnoo a cold reception, when the excited throng came within view, convoying one of the most striking specimens of humanity that I ever beheld.

The stranger could not have been more than twenty-five years of age, and was a little above the ordinary height; had he been a single hair's breadth taller, the matchless symmetry of his form would have been destroyed. His unclad limbs were beautifully formed; whilst the elegant outline of his figure, together with his beardless cheeks, might have entitled him to the distinction of standing for the statue of the Polynesian Apollo; and indeed the oval of his countenance and the regularity of every feature reminded one of an antique bust. But the marble repose of art was supplied by a warmth and liveliness of expression only to be seen in the South Sea islander under the most favorable developments of nature. The hair of Marnoo was a rich curling brown, and twined about his temples and neck in little close curling ringlets, which danced up and down continually when he was animated in conversation. His cheek was of a feminine softness, and his face was free from the least blemish of tattooing, although the rest of his body was drawn all over with fanciful figures, which—unlike the unconnected sketching usual among these natives—appeared to have been executed in conformity with some general design.

The tattooing on his back in particular attracted my attention. The artist employed must indeed have excelled in his profession. Traced along the course of the spine was accurately delineated the slender, tapering, and diamond-checkered shaft of the beautiful "artu" tree. Branching from the stem on each side, and disposed alternately, were the graceful branches drooping with leaves all correctly drawn, and elaborately finished. Indeed, this piece of tattoing was the best specimen of the Fine Arts I had yet seen in Typee. A rear view of the stranger might have suggested the idea of a spreading vine tacked against a garden wall. Upon his breast, arms, and legs, were exhibited an infinite variety of figures; every one of which, however, appeared to have reference to the general effect sought to be produced. The tattooing I have described was of the brightest blue, and when contrasted with the light olive color of the skin, produced an unique and even elegant effect. A slight girdle of white tappa, scarcely two inches in width, but hanging before and behind in spreading tassels, composed the entire costume of the stranger.

He advanced surrounded by the islanders, carrying under one arm a small roll of native cloth, and grasping in his other hand a long and richly decorated spear. His manner was that of a traveler conscious that he is approaching a comfortable stage in his journey. Every moment he turned good-humoredly on the throng around him, and gave some dashing sort of reply to their incessant queries, which appeared to convulse them with uncontrollable mirth.

Struck by his demeanor, and the peculiarity of his appearance, so unlike that of the shaven-crowned and face-tattooed natives in general, I involuntarily rose as he entered the house, and proffered him a seat on the mats beside me. But without deigning to notice the civility, or even the more incontrovertible fact of my existence, the stranger passed on, utterly regardless of me, and flung himself upon the further end of the long couch that traversed the sole apartment of Marheyo's habitation.

Had the belle of the season, in the pride of her beauty and power, been cut in a place of public resort by some supercilious exquisite, she could not have felt greater indignation than I did at this unexpected slight.

I was thrown into utter astonishment. The conduct of the savages had prepared me to anticipate from every newcomer the same extravagant expressions of curiosity and regard. The singularity of his conduct, however, only roused my desire to discover who this remarkable personage might be, who now engrossed the attention of everyone.

Tinor placed before him a calabash of poee-poee, from which the stranger regaled himself, alternating every mouthful with some rapid exclamation which was eagerly caught up and echoed by the crowd that completely filled the house. When I observed the striking devotion of the natives to him, and their temporary withdrawal of all attention from myself, I felt not a little piqued. The glory of Tommo is departed, thought I, and the sooner he removes from the valley the better. These were my feelings at the moment, and they were prompted by that glorious principle inherent in all heroic natures—the strong-rooted determination to have the biggest share of the pudding or to go without any of it.

Marnoo, that all-attractive personage, having satisfied his hunger, and inhaled a few whiffs from a pipe which was handed to him, launched out into an harangue which completely enchained the attention of his auditors.

Little as I understood of the language, yet from his animated gestures and the varying expressions of his features—reflected as from so many mirrors in the countenances around him, I could easily discover the nature of those passions which he sought to arouse. From the frequent recurrence of the words "Nukuheva" and "Frannee" (French), and some others with the meaning of which I was acquainted, he appeared to be rehearsing to his auditors events which had recently occurred in the neighboring bays. But how he had gained the knowledge of these matters I could not understand, unless it were that he had just come from Nukuheva—a supposition which his travel-stained appearance not a little supported. But, if a native of that region, I could not account for his friendly reception at the hands of the Typees.

Never, certainly, had I beheld so powerful an exhibition of natural eloquence as Marnoo displayed during the course of his oration. The grace of the attitudes into which he threw his flexible figure, the striking gestures of his naked arms, and above all, the fire which shot from his brilliant eyes, imparted an effect to the continually changing accents of his voice, of which the most accomplished orator might have been proud. At one moment reclining sideways upon the mat, and leaning calmly upon his bended arm, he related circumstantially the aggressions of the French—their hostile visits to the surrounding bays, enumerating each one in succession—Happar, Puerka, Nukuheva, Tior—and then starting to his feet and precipitating himself forward with clenched hands and a countenance distorted with passion, he poured out a tide of invectives. Falling back into an attitude of lofty command, he exhorted the Typees to resist these encroachments; reminding them, with a fierce glance of exultation, that as yet the terror of their name had preserved them from attack, and with a scornful sneer he sketched in ironical terms the wondrous intrepidity of the French, who, with five war-canoes and hundreds of men, had not dared to assail the naked warriors of their valley.

The effect he produced upon his audience was electric; one and all they stood regarding him with sparkling eyes and trembling limbs, as though they were listening to the inspired voice of a prophet.

But it soon appeared that Marnoo's powers were as versatile as they were extraordinary. As soon as he had finished his vehement harangue, he threw himself again upon the mats, and, singling out individuals in the crowd, addressed them by name, in a sort of bantering style, the humor of which, though nearly hidden from me, filled the whole assembly with uproarious delight.

He had a word for everybody; and, turning rapidly from one to another, gave utterance to some hasty witticism, which was sure to be followed by peals of laughter. To the females, as well as to the men, he addressed his discourse. Heaven only knows what he said to them, but he caused smiles and blushes to mantle their ingenuous faces. I am, indeed, very much inclined to believe that Marnoo, with his handsome person and captivating manners, was a sad deceiver among the simple maidens of the island.

During all this time he had never, for one moment, deigned to regard me. He appeared, indeed, to be altogether unconscious of my presence. I was utterly at a loss how to account for this extraordinary conduct. I easily perceived that he was a man of no little consequence among the islanders; that he possessed uncommon talents; and was gifted with a higher degree of knowledge than the inmates of the valley. For these reasons, I therefore greatly feared lest having, from some cause or other, unfriendly feelings towards me, he might exert his powerful influence to do me mischief.

It seemed evident that he was not a permanent resident of the vale, and yet, whence could he have come? On all sides the Typees were girt in by hostile tribes, and how could he possibly, if belonging to any of these, be received with so much cordiality?

The personal appearance of the enigmatical stranger suggested additional perplexities. The face, free from tattooing, and the unshaven crown, were peculiarities I had never before remarked in any part of the island, and I had always heard that the contrary were considered the indispensable distinction of a Marquesan warrior. Altogether the matter was perfectly incomprehensible to me, and I awaited its solution with no small degree of anxiety.

At length, from certain indications, I suspected that he was making me the subject of his remarks, although he appeared cautiously to avoid either pronouncing my name, or looking in the direction where I lay. All at once he rose from the mats where he had been reclining, and, still conversing, moved towards me, his eye purposely evading mine, and seated himself within less than a yard of me. I had hardly recovered from my surprise, when he suddenly turned round, and, with a most benignant countenance, extended his right hand gracefully towards me. Of course I accepted the courteous challenge, and, as soon as our palms met, he bent towards me, and murmured in musical accents—"How you do?" "How long you been in this bay?" "You like this bay?"

Had I been pierced simultaneously by three Happar spears, I could not have started more than I did at hearing these simple questions! For a moment I was overwhelmed with astonishment, and then answered something I know not what; but as soon as I regained my self-possession, the thought darted through my mind that from this individual I might obtain that information regarding Toby which I suspected the natives had purposely withheld from me. Accordingly I questioned him concerning the disappearance of my companion, but he denied all knowledge of the matter. I then inquired from whence he had come? He replied, from Nukuheva. When I expressed my surprise, he looked at me for a moment, as if enjoying my perplexity, and then with his strange vivacity, exclaimed—"Ah! me taboo—me go Nukuheva—me go Tior—me go Typee—me go everywhere—nobody harm me—me taboo."

This explanation would have been altogether unintelligible to me, had it not recalled to my mind something I had previously heard concerning a singular custom among these islanders. Though the country is possessed by various tribes, whose mutual hostilities almost wholly preclude any intercourse between them; yet there are instances where a person having ratified friendly relations with some individual belonging to the valley, whose inmates are at war with his own, may, under particular restrictions, venture with impunity into the country of his friend, where, under other circumstances, he would have been treated as an enemy. In this light are personal friendships regarded among them, and the individual so protected is said to be "taboo," and his person, to a certain extent, is held as sacred. Thus the stranger informed me he had access to all the valleys in the island.

Curious to know how he had acquired his knowledge of English, I questioned him on the subject. At first, for some reason or other, he evaded the inquiry, but afterwards told me that, when a boy, he had been carried to sea by the captain of a trading vessel, with whom he had stayed three years, living part of the time with him at Sydney, in Australia, and that, at a subsequent visit to the island, the captain had, at his own request, permitted him to remain among his countrymen. The natural quickness of the savage had been wonderfully improved by his intercourse with the white men, and his partial knowledge of a foreign language gave him a great ascendancy over his less accomplished countrymen.

When I asked the now affable Marnoo why it was that he had not previously spoken to me, he eagerly inquired what I had been led to think of him from his conduct in that respect. I replied, that I had supposed him to be some great chief or warrior, who had seen plenty of white men before, and did not think it worthwhile to notice a poor sailor. At this declaration of the exalted opinion I had formed of him, he appeared vastly gratified, and gave me to understand that he had purposely behaved in that manner, in order to increase my astonishment, as soon as he should see proper to address me.

Marnoo now sought to learn my version of the story as to how I came to be an inmate of the Typee valley. When I related to him the circumstances under which Toby and I had entered it, he listened with evident interest; but as soon as I alluded to the absence, yet unaccounted for, of my comrade, he endeavored to change the subject, as if it were something he desired not to agitate. It seemed, indeed, as if everything connected with Toby was destined to beget distrust and anxiety in my bosom. Notwithstanding Marnoo's denial of any knowledge of his fate, I could not avoid suspecting that he was deceiving me; and this suspicion revived those frightful apprehensions with regard to my own fate, which, for a short time past, had subsided in my breast.

Influenced by these feelings, I now felt a strong desire to avail myself of the stranger's protection, and under his safeguard to return to Nukuheva. But as soon as I hinted at this, he unhesitatingly pronounced it to be entirely impracticable; assuring me that the Typees would never consent to my leaving the valley. Although what he said merely confirmed the impression which I had before entertained, still it increased my anxiety to escape from a captivity which, however endurable, nay, delightful it might be in some respects, involved in its issues a fate marked by the most frightful contingencies.

I could not conceal from my mind that Toby had been treated in the same friendly manner as I had been, and yet all their kindness had terminated with his mysterious disappearance. Might not the same fate await me?—a fate too dreadful to think of. Stimulated by these considerations, I urged anew my request to Marnoo; but he only set forth in stronger colors the impossibility of my escape, and repeated his previous declaration that the Typees would never be brought to consent to my departure.

When I endeavored to learn from him the motives which prompted them to hold me a prisoner, Marnoo again assumed that mysterious tone which had tormented me with apprehensions when I had questioned him with regard to the fate of my companion.

Thus repulsed, in a manner which only served, by arousing the most dreadful forebodings, to excite me to renewed attempts, I conjured him to intercede for me with the natives, and endeavor to procure their consent to my leaving them. To this he appeared strongly averse; but, yielding at last to my importunities, he addressed several of the chiefs, who with the rest had been eyeing us intently during the whole of our conversation. His petition, however, was at once met with the most violent disapprobation, manifesting itself in angry glances and gestures, and a perfect torrent of passionate words, directed to both him and myself. Marnoo, evidently repenting the step he had taken, earnestly deprecated the resentment of the crowd, and, in a few moments succeeded in pacifying to some extent the clamors which had broken out as soon as his proposition had been understood.

With the most intense interest had I watched the reception his intercession might receive; and a bitter pang shot through my heart at the additional evidence, now furnished, of the unchangeable determination of the islanders. Marnoo told me, with evident alarm in his countenance, that although admitted into the bay on a friendly footing with its inhabitants, he could not presume to meddle with their concerns, as such a procedure, if persisted in, would at once absolve the Typees from the restraints of the "Taboo," although so long as he refrained from such conduct, it screened him effectually from the consequences of the enmity they bore his tribe.

At this moment, Mehevi, who was present, angrily interrupted him; and the words which he uttered, in a commanding tone, evidently meant that he must at once cease talking to me and withdraw to the other part of the house. Marnoo immediately started up, hurriedly enjoining me not to address him again, and, as I valued my safety, to refrain from all further allusion to the subject of my departure; and then, in compliance with the order of the determined chief, but not before it had again been angrily repeated, he withdrew to a distance.

I now perceived, with no small degree of apprehension, the same savage expression in the countenances of the natives which had startled me during the scene at the Ti. They glanced their eyes suspiciously from Marnoo to me, as if distrusting the nature of an intercourse carried on, as it was, in a language they could not understand, and they seemed to harbor the belief that already we had concerted measures calculated to elude their vigilance.

The lively countenances of these people are wonderfully indicative of the emotions of the soul, and the imperfections of their oral language are more than compensated for by the nervous eloquence of their looks and gestures. I could plainly trace, in every varying expression of their faces, all those passions which had been thus unexpectedly aroused in their bosoms.

It required no reflection to convince me, from what was going on, that the injunction of Marnoo was not to be rashly slighted; and accordingly, great as was the effort to suppress my feelings, I accosted Mehevi in a good-humored tone, with a view of dissipating any ill impression he might have received. But the ireful, angry chief was not so easily mollified. He rejected my advances with that peculiarly stern expression I have before described, and took care by the whole of his behavior towards me to show the displeasure and resentment which he felt.

Marnoo, at the other extremity of the house, apparently desirous of making a diversion in my favor, exerted himself to amuse with his pleasantries the crowd about him; but his lively attempts were not so successful as they had previously been, and, foiled in his efforts, he rose gravely to depart. No one expressed any regret at this movement, so seizing his roll of tappa, and grasping his spear, he advanced to the front of the pi-pi, and waving his hand in adieu to the now silent throng, cast upon me a glance of mingled pity and reproach, and flung himself into the path which led from the house. I watched his receding figure until it was lost in the obscurity of the grove, and then gave myself up to the most desponding reflections.

Chapter XIX

REFLECTIONS AFTER MARNOO'S DEPARTURE—BATTLE OF THE POP-GUNS—STRANGE CONCEIT OF MARHEYO—PROCESS OF MAKING TAPPA

THE KNOWLEDGE I HAD NOW OBTAINED AS TO THE INTENTION OF THE SAVAGES DEEPLY AFfected me.

Marnoo, I perceived, was a man who, by reason of his superior acquirements, and the knowledge he possessed of the events which were taking place in the different bays of the island, was held in no little estimation by the inhabitants of the valley. He had been received with the most cordial welcome and respect. The natives had hung upon the accents of his voice, and had manifested the highest gratification at being individually noticed by him. And yet despite all this, a few words urged in my behalf, with the intent of obtaining my release from captivity, had sufficed not only to banish all harmony and good-will; but, if I could believe what he told me, had gone nigh to endanger his own personal safety.

How strongly rooted, then, must be the determination of the Typees with regard to me, and how suddenly could they display the strangest passions! The mere suggestion of my departure had estranged from me, for the time at least, Mehevi, who was the most influential of all the chiefs, and who had previously exhibited so many instances of his friendly sentiments. The rest of the natives had likewise evinced their strong repugnance to my wishes, and even Kory-Kory himself seemed to share in the general disapprobation bestowed upon me.

In vain I racked my invention to find out some motive for the strange desire these people manifested to retain me among them; but I could discover none.

But however this might be, the scene which had just occurred admonished me of the danger of trifling with the wayward and passionate spirits against whom it was vain to struggle, and might even be fatal to do so. My only hope was to induce the natives to believe that I was reconciled to my detention in the valley, and by assuming a tranquil and cheerful demeanor, to allay the suspicions which I had so unfortunately aroused. Their confidence revived, they might in a short time remit in some degree their watchfulness over my movements, and I should then be the better enabled to avail myself of any opportunity which presented itself for escape. I determined, therefore, to make the best of a bad bargain, and to bear up manfully against whatever might betide. In this endeavor I succeeded beyond my own expectations. At the period of Marnoo's visit, I had been in the valley, as nearly as I could conjecture, some two months. Although not completely recovered from my strange illness, which still lingered about me, I was free from pain and able to take exercise. In short, I had every reason to anticipate a perfect recovery. Freed from apprehensions on this point, and resolved to regard the future without flinching, I flung myself anew into all the social pleasures of the valley, and sought to bury all regrets, and all remembrances of my previous existence, in the wild enjoyments it afforded.

In my various wanderings through the vale, and as I became better acquainted with the character of its inhabitants, I was more and more struck with the light-hearted joyousness that everywhere prevailed. The minds of these simple savages, unoccupied by matters of graver moment, were capable of deriving the utmost delight from circumstances which would have passed unnoticed in more intelligent communities. All their enjoyment, indeed, seemed to be made up of the little trifling incidents of the passing hour; but these diminutive items swelled altogether to an amount of happiness seldom experienced by more enlightened individuals, whose pleasures are drawn from more elevated but rarer sources.

What community, for instance, of refined and intellectual mortals would derive the least satisfaction from shooting pop-guns? The mere supposition of such a thing being possible would excite their indignation, and yet the whole population of Typee did little else for ten days but occupy themselves with that childish amusement, fairly screaming, too, with the delight it afforded them.

One day I was frolicking with a little spirited urchin, some six years old, who chased me with a piece of bamboo about three feet long, with which he occasionally belabored me. Seizing the stick from him, the idea happened to suggest itself, that I might make for the youngster, out of the slender tube, one of those nursery muskets with which I had sometimes seen children playing. Accordingly, with my knife I made two parallel slits in the cane several inches in length, and cutting loose at one end the elastic strip between them, bent it back and slipped the point into a little notch made for the purpose. Any small substance placed against this would be projected with considerable force through the tube, by merely springing the bent strip out of the notch.

Had I possessed the remotest idea of the sensation this piece of ordnance was destined to produce, I should certainly have taken out a patent for the invention. The boy scampered away with it, half delirious with ecstasy, and in twenty minutes afterwards I might have been seen surrounded by a noisy crowd—venerable old graybeards—responsible fathers of families—valiant warriors—matrons—young men—girls and children, all holding in their hands bits of bamboo, and each clamoring to be served first.

For three or four hours I was engaged in manufacturing pop-guns, but at last made over my good-will and interest in the concern to a lad of remarkably quick parts, whom I soon initiated into the art and mystery.

Pop, Pop, Pop, Pop, now resounded all over the valley. Duels, skirmishes, pitched battles, and general engagements were to be seen on every side. Here, as you walked along a path which led through a thicket, you fell into a cunningly-laid ambush, and became a target for a body of musketeers whose tattooed limbs you could just see peeping into view through the foliage. There, you were assailed by the intrepid garrison of a house, who leveled their bamboo rifles at you from between the upright canes which composed its sides. Farther on you were fired upon by a detachment of sharpshooters, mounted upon the top of a pi-pi.

Pop, Pop, Pop, Pop! green guavas, seeds, and berries were flying about in every direction, and during this dangerous state of affairs I was half afraid that, like the man and his brazen bull, I should fall a victim to my own ingenuity. Like everything else, however, the excitement gradually wore away, though ever after occasional pop-guns might be heard at all hours of the day.

It was towards the close of the pop-gun war, that I was infinitely diverted with a strange freak of Marheyo's.

I had worn, when I quitted the ship, a pair of thick pumps, which, from the rough usage they had received in scaling precipices and sliding down gorges, were so dilapidated as to be altogether unfit for use—so, at least, would have thought the generality of people, and so they most certainly were, when considered in the light of shoes. But things unservicable in one way, may with advantage be applied in another, that is, if one have genius enough for the purpose. This genius Marheyo possessed in a superlative degree, as he abundantly evinced by the use to which he put those sorely bruised and battered old shoes.

Every article, however trivial, which belonged to me, the natives appeared to regard as sacred; and I observed that for several days after becoming an inmate of the house, my pumps were suffered to remain, untouched, where I had first happened to throw them. I remembered, however, that after awhile I had missed them from their accustomed place; but the matter gave me no concern, supposing that Tinor—like any other tidy housewife, having come across them in some of her domestic occupations—had pitched the useless things out of the house. But I was soon undeceived.

One day I observed old Marheyo bustling about me with unusual activity, and to such a degree as almost to supersede Kory-Kory in the functions of his office. One moment he volunteered to trot off with me on his back to the stream; and when I refused, noways daunted by the repulse, he continued to frisk about me like a superannuated house-dog. I could not for the life of me conjecture what possessed the old gentleman, until all at once, availing himself of the temporary absence of the household, he went through a variety of of uncouth gestures, pointing eagerly down to my feet, then up to a little bundle which swung from the ridge-pole overhead. At last I caught a faint idea of his meaning, and motioned him to lower the package. He executed the order in the twinkling of an eye, and unrolling a piece of tappa displayed to my astonished gaze the identical pumps which I thought had been destroyed long before.

I immediately comprehended his desires, and very generously gave him the shoes, which had become quite moldy, wondering for what earthly purpose he could want them.

The same afternoon I descried the venerable warrior approaching the house, with a slow, stately gait, ear-rings in ears, and spear in hand, with this highly ornamental pair of shoes suspended from his neck by a strip of bark, and swinging backwards and forwards on his capacious chest. In the gala costume of the tasteful Marheyo, these calf-skin pendants ever after formed the most striking feature.

But to turn to something a little more important. Although the whole existence of the inhabitants of the valley seemed to pass away exempt from toil, yet there were some light employments which, although amusing rather than laborious as occupations, contributed to their comfort and luxury. Among these, the most important was the manufacture of the native cloth—"tappa"—so well known, under various modifications, throughout the whole Polynesian Archipelago. As is generally understood, this useful and sometimes elegant article is fabricated from the bark of different trees. But, as I believe that no description of its manufacture has ever been given, I shall state what I know regarding it.

In the manufacture of the beautiful white tappa generally worn on the Marquesan Islands, the preliminary operation consists in gathering a certain quantity of the young branches of the cloth-tree. The exterior green bark being pulled off as worthless, there remains a slender fibrous substance, which is carefully stripped from the stick, to which it closely adheres. When a sufficient quantity of it has been collected, the various strips are enveloped in a covering of large leaves, which the natives use precisely as we do wrapping-paper, and which are secured by a few turns of a line passed round them. The package is then laid in the bed of some running stream, with a heavy stone placed over it, to prevent its being swept away. After it has remained for two or three days in this state, it is drawn out, and exposed, for a short time, to the action of the air, every distinct piece being attentively inspected, with a view of ascertaining whether it has yet been sufficiently affected by the operation. This is repeated again and again, until the desired result is obtained.

When the substance is in a proper state for the next process, it betrays evidences of incipient decomposition; the fibers are relaxed and softened, and rendered perfectly malleable. The different strips are now extended, one by one, in successive layers, upon some smooth surface—generally the prostrate trunk of a cocoanut-tree—and the heap thus formed is subjected, at every new increase, to a moderate beating, with a sort of wooden mallet, leisurely applied. The mallet is made of a hard heavy wood resembling ebony, is about twelve inches in length, and perhaps two in breadth, with a rounded handle at one end, and in shape is the exact counterpart of one of our four-sided razor-strops. The flat surfaces of the implement are marked with shallow parallel indentations, varying in depth on the different sides, so as to be adapted to the several stages of the operation. These marks produce the corduroy sort of stripes discernible in the tappa in its finished state. After being beaten in the manner I have described, the material soon becomes blended in one mass, which, moistened occasionally with water, is at intervals hammered out, by a kind of gold-beating process, to any degree of thinness required. In this way the cloth is easily made to vary in strength and thickness, so as to suit the numerous purposes to which it is applied.

When the operation last described has been concluded, the new-made tappa is spread out on the grass to bleach and dry, and soon becomes of a dazzling whiteness. Sometimes, in the first stages of the manufacture, the substance is impregnated with a vegetable juice, which gives it a permanent color. A rich brown and a bright yellow are occasionally seen, but the simple taste of the Typee people inclines them to prefer the natural tint.

The notable wife of Kamehameha, the renowned conqueror and king of the Sandwich Islands, used to pride herself in the skill she displayed in dyeing her tappa with contrasting colors disposed in regular figures; and, in the midst of the innovations of the times, was regarded, towards the decline of her life, as a lady of the old school, clinging as she did to the national cloth, in preference to the frippery of the European calicoes. But the art of printing the tappa is unknown upon the Marquesan Islands.

In passing along the valley, I was often attracted by the noise of the mallet, which, when employed in the manufacture of the cloth, produces at every stroke of its hard, heavy wood, a clear ringing, and musical sound, capable of being heard at a great distance. When several of these implements happen to be in operation at the same time, and near one another, the effect upon the ear of a person, at a little distance, is really charming.

Chapter XX

History of a Day as Usually Spent in Typee Valley—Dances of the Marquesan Girls

NOTHING CAN BE MORE UNIFORM AND UNDIVERSIFIED THAN THE LIFE OF THE TYPEES; ONE TRANquil day of ease and happiness follows another in quiet succession; and with these unsophisticated savages the history of a day is the history of a life. I will, therefore, as briefly as I can, describe one of our days in the valley.

To begin with the morning. We were not very early risers—the sun would be shooting his golden spikes above the Happar mountain, ere I threw aside my tappa robe, and girding my long tunic about my waist, sallied out with Fayaway and Kory-Kory, and the rest of the household, and bent my steps towards the stream. Here we found congregated all those who dwelt in our section of the valley; and here we bathed with them. The fresh morning air and the cool flowing waters put both soul and body in a glow, and after a half-hour employed in this recreation, we sauntered back to the house—Tinor and Marheyo gathering dry sticks by the way for fire-wood; some of the young men laying the cocoanut-trees under contribution as they passed beneath them; while Kory-Kory played his outlandish pranks for my particular diversion, and Fayaway and I, not arm in arm to be sure, but sometimes hand in hand, strolled along, with feelings of perfect charity for all the world, and especial good-will towards each other.

Our morning meal was soon prepared. The islanders are somewhat abstemious at this repast; reserving the more powerful efforts of their appetite to a later period of the day. For my own part, with the assistance of my valet, who, as I have before stated, always officiated as spoon on these occasions, I ate sparingly from one of Tinor's trenchers of poee-poee; which was devoted exclusively for my own use, being mixed with the milky meat of ripe cocoanut. A section of a roasted breadfruit, a small cake of "Amar," or a mess of "Cokoo," two or three bananas, or a mammee-apple; an annuee, or some other agreeable and nutritious fruit served from day to day to diversify the meal, which was finished by tossing off the liquid contents of a young cocoanut or two.

While partaking of this simple repast, the inmates of Marheyo's house, after the style of the indolent Romans, reclined in sociable groups upon the divan of mats, and digestion was promoted by cheerful conversation.

After the morning meal was concluded, pipes were lighted; and among them my own especial pipe, a present from the noble Mehevi. The islanders, who only smoke a whiff or two at a time, and at long intervals, and who keep their pipes going from hand to hand continually, regarded my systematic smoking of four or five pipefuls of tobacco in succession, as something quite wonderful. When two or three pipes had circulated freely, the company gradually broke up. Marheyo went to the little hut he was forever building. Tinor began to inspect her rolls of tappa, or employed her busy fingers in plaiting grass-mats. The girls anointed themselves with their fragrant oils, dressed their hair, or looked over their curious finery, and compared together their ivory trinkets, fashioned out of boar's tusks or whale's teeth. The young men and warriors produced their spears, paddles, canoe-gear, battle-clubs, and war-conchs, and occupied themselves in carving all sorts of figures upon them with pointed bits of shell or flint, and adorning them, especially the war-conchs, with tassels of braided bark and tufts of human hair. Some, immediately after eating, threw themselves once more upon the inviting mats, and resumed the employment of the previous night, sleeping as soundly as if they had not closed their eyes for a week. Others sallied out into the groves, for the purpose of gathering fruit or fibers of bark and leaves; the last two being in constant requisition, and applied to a hundred uses. A few, perhaps, among the girls, would slip into the woods after flowers, or repair to the stream with small calabashes and cocoanut shells, in order to polish them by friction with a smooth stone in the water. In truth these innocent people seemed to be at no loss for something to occupy their time; and it would be no light task to enumerate all their employments, or rather pleasures.

My own mornings I spent in a variety of ways. Sometimes I rambled about from house to house, sure of receiving a cordial welcome wherever I went; or from grove to grove, and from one shady place to another, in company with Kory-Kory and Fayaway, and a rabble rout of merry young idlers. Sometimes I was too indolent for exercise, and accepting one of the many invitations I was continually receiving, stretched myself out on the mats of some hospitable dwelling, and occupied myself pleasantly either in watching the proceedings of those around me, or taking part in them myself. Whenever I choose to do the latter, the delight of the islanders was boundless; and there was always a throng of competitors for the honor of instructing me in any particular craft. I soon became quite an accomplished hand at making tappa—could braid a grass sling as well as the best of them—and once, with my knife, carved the handle of a javelin so exquisitely, that I have no doubt, to this day, Karnoonoo, its owner, preserves it as a surprising specimen of my skill. As noon approached, all those who had wandered forth from our habitation, began to return; and when midday was fairly come, scarcely a sound was to be heard in the valley: a deep sleep fell upon all. The luxurious siesta was hardly ever omitted, except by old Marheyo, who was so eccentric a character, that he seemed to be governed by no fixed principles whatever; but acting just according to the humor of the moment, slept, ate, or tinkered away at his little hut, without regard to the proprieties of time or place. Frequently he might have been seen taking a nap in the sun at noon-day, or a bath in the stream of midnight. Once I beheld him perched eighty feet from the ground, in the tuft of a cocoanut-tree, smoking; and often I saw him standing up to the waist in water, engaged in plucking out the stray hairs of his beard, using a piece of muscle-shell for tweezers.

The noon-tide slumber lasted generally an hour and a half; very often longer; and after the sleepers had arisen from their mats they again had recourse to their pipes, and then made preparations for the most important meal of the day.

I, however, like those gentlemen of leisure who breakfast at home and dine at their club, almost invariably, during my intervals of health, enjoyed the afternoon repast with the bachelor chiefs of the Ti, who were always rejoiced to see me, and lavishly spread before me all the good things which their larders afforded. Mehevi generally produced among other dainties a baked pig, an article which I have every reason to suppose was provided for my sole gratification.

The Ti was a right jovial place. It did my heart, as well as my body, good to visit it. Secure from female intrusion, there was no restraint upon the hilarity of the warriors, who, like the gentlemen of Europe after the cloth is drawn and the ladies retire, freely indulged their mirth.

After spending a considerable portion of the afternoon at the Ti, I usually found myself, as the cool of the evening came on, either sailing on the little lake with Fayaway, or bathing in the waters of the stream with a number of the savages, who, at this hour, always repaired thither. As the shadows of night approached, Marheyo's household were once more assembled under his roof: tapers were lit, long and curious chants were raised, interminable stories were told (for which one present was little the wiser), and all sorts of social festivities served to while away the time.

The young girls very often danced by moonlight in front of their dwellings. There are a great variety of these dances, in which, however, I never saw the men take part. They all consist of active, romping, mischievous evolutions, in which every limb is brought into requisition. Indeed, the Marquesan girls dance all over, as it were; not only do their feet dance, but their arms, hands, fingers, ay, their very eyes, seem to dance in their heads. In good sooth, they so sway their floating forms, arch their necks, toss aloft their naked arms, and glide, and swim, and whirl, that it was almost too much for a quiet, sober-minded, modest young man like myself.

The damsels wear nothing but flowers and their compendious gala tunics; and when they plume themselves for the dance, they look like a band of olive-colored Sylphides on the point of taking wing.

Unless some particular festivity was going forward, the inmates of Marheyo's house retired to their mats rather early in the evening; but not for the night, since, after slumbering lightly for a while, they rose again, relit their tapers, partook of the third and last meal of the day, at which poee-poee alone was eaten, and then, after inhaling a narcotic whiff from a pipe of tobacco, disposed themselves for the great business of night, sleep. With the Marquesans it might almost be styled the great business of life, for they pass a large portion of their time in the arms of Somnus. The native strength of their constitution is no way shown more emphatically than in the quantity of sleep they can endure. To many of them, indeed, life is little else than an often interrupted and luxurious nap.

Chapter XXI

The Spring of Arva Wai—Remarkable Monumental Remains—Some Ideas with Regard to the History of the Pi-pis Found in the Valley

ALMOST EVERY COUNTRY HAS ITS MEDICINAL SPRINGS FAMED FOR THEIR HEALING VIRTUES. THE Cheltenham of Typee is embosomed in the deepest solitude, and but seldom receives a visitor. It is situated remote from any dwelling, a little way up the mountain, near the head of the valley; and you approach it by a pathway shaded by the most beautiful foliage, and adorned with a thousand fragrant plants.

The mineral waters of Arva Wai[1] ooze forth from the crevices of a rock, and gliding down its mossy side, fall at last, in many clustering drops, into a natural basin of stone fringed round with

1. I presume this might be translated into "Strong Waters." Arva is the name bestowed upon a root the properties of which are both inebriating and medicinal. "Wai" is the Marquesan word for water.

grass and dewy-looking little violet-colored flowers, as fresh and beautiful as the perpetual moisture they enjoy can make them.

The water is held in high estimation by the islanders, some of whom consider it an agreeable as well as a medicinal beverage; they bring it from the mountain in their calabashes, and store it away beneath heaps of leaves in some shady nook near the house. Old Marheyo had a great love for the waters of the spring. Every now and then he lugged off to the mountain a great round demijohn of a calabash, and, panting with his exertions, brought it back filled with his darling fluid.

The water tasted like a solution of a dozen disagreeable things, and was sufficiently nauseous to have made the fortune of the proprietor, had the spa been situated in the midst of any civilized community.

As I am no chemist, I cannot give a scientific analysis of the water. All I know about the matter is, that one day Marheyo in my presence poured out the last drop from his huge calabash, and I observed at the bottom of the vessel a small quantity of gravelly sediment very much resembling our common sand. Whether this is always found in the water, and gives it its peculiar flavor and virtues, or whether its presence was merely incidental, I was not able to ascertain.

One day in returning from this spring by a circuitous path, I came upon a scene which reminded me of Stonehenge and the architectural labors of the Druids.

At the base of one of the mountains, and surrounded on all sides by dense groves, a series of vast terraces of stone rises, step by step, for a considerable distance up the hill-side. These terraces cannot be less than one hundred yards in length and twenty in width. Their magnitude, however, is less striking than the immense size of the blocks composing them. Some of the stones, of an oblong shape, are from ten to fifteen feet in length, and five or six feet thick. Their sides are quite smooth, but though square, and of pretty regular formation, they bear no mark of the chisel. They are laid together without cement, and here and there show gaps between. The topmost terrace and the lower one are somewhat peculiar in their construction. They have both a quadrangular depression in the center, leaving the rest of the terrace elevated several feet above it. In the intervals of the stones immense trees have taken root, and their broad boughs stretching far over, and interlacing together, support a canopy almost impenetrable to the sun. Overgrowing the greater part of them, and climbing from one to another, is a wilderness of vines, in whose sinewy embrace many of the stones lie half-hidden, while in some places a thick growth of bushes entirely covers them. There is a wild pathway which obliquely crosses two of these terraces; and so profound is the shade, so dense the vegetation, that a stranger to the place might pass along it without being aware of their existence.

These structures bear every indication of a very high antiquity and Kory-Kory, who was my authority in all matters of scientific research, gave me to understand that they were coeval with the creation of the world; that the great gods themselves were the builders; and that they would endure until time shall be no more. Kory-Kory's prompt explanation, and his attributing the work to a divine origin, at once convinced me that neither he nor the rest of his country-men knew anything about them.

As I gazed upon this monument, doubtless the work of an extinct and forgotten race, thus buried in the green nook of an island at the ends of the earth, the existence of which was yesterday unknown, a stronger feeling of awe came over me than if I had stood musing at the mighty base of the Pyramid of Cheops. There are no inscriptions, no sculpture, no clew, by which to conjecture its history: nothing but the dumb stones. How many generations of those majestic trees which overshadow them have grown and flourished and decayed since first they were erected!

These remains naturally suggest many interesting reflections. They establish the great age of the island, an opinion which the builders of theories concerning the creation of the various groups in the South Seas are not always inclined to admit. For my own part, I think it just as probable that human beings were living in the valleys of the Marquesas three thousand years ago as that they were inhabiting the land of Egypt. The origin of the island of Nukuheva cannot be imputed to the coral insect; for indefatigable as that wonderful creature is, it would be hardly muscular enough to pile rocks one upon the other more than three thousand feet above the level of the sea. That the land may have been thrown up by a submarine volcano is as possible as anything else. No one can make an affidavit to the contrary, and therefore I still say nothing against the supposition: indeed, were geologists to assert that the whole continent of America had in like manner been formed by the simultaneous explosion of a train of Etnas laid under the water all the way from the North Pole to the parallel of Cape Horn, I am the last man in the world to contradict them.

I have already mentioned that the dwellings of the islanders were almost invariably built upon massive stone foundations, which they call pi-pis. The dimensions of these, however, as well as of the stones composing them, are comparatively small: but there are other and larger erections of a similar description comprising the "morais," or burying grounds, and festival-places, in nearly all the valleys of the island. Some of these piles are so extensive, and so great a degree of labor and skill must have been requisite in constructing them, that I can scarcely believe they were built by the ancestors of the present inhabitants. If indeed they were, the race has sadly deteriorated in their knowledge of the mechanic arts. To say nothing of their habitual indolence, by what contrivance within the reach of so simple a people could such enormous masses have been moved or fixed in their places? and how could they with their rude implements have chiseled and hammered them into shape.

All of these larger pi-pis—like that of the Hoolah Hoolah ground in the Typee valley—bore incontestable marks of great age; and I am disposed to believe that their erection may be ascribed to the same race of men who were the builders of the still more ancient remains I have just described.

According to Kory-Kory's account, the pi-pi upon which stands the Hoolah Hoolah ground was built a great many moons ago, under the direction of Monoo, a great chief and warrior, and, as it would appear, master-mason among the Typees. It was erected for the express purpose to which it is at present devoted, in the incredibly short period of one sun; and was dedicated to the immortal wooden idols by a grand festival, which lasted ten days and nights.

Among the smaller pi-pis, upon which stand the dwelling-houses of the natives, I never observed any which intimated a recent erection. There are in every part of the valley a great many of these massive stone foundations which have no houses upon them. This is vastly convenient, for whenever an enterprising islander chooses to emigrate a few hundred yards from the place where he was born, all he has to do in order to establish himself in some new locality, is to select one of the many unappropriated pi-pis, and without further ceremony pitch his bamboo tent upon it.

Chapter XXII

PREPARATIONS FOR A GRAND FESTIVAL IN THE VALLEY—STRANGE DOINGS IN THE TABOO GROVES—MONUMENT OF CALABASHES—GALA COSTUME OF THE TYPEE DAMSELS—DEPARTURE FOR THE FESTIVAL

FROM THE TIME THAT MY LAMENESS HAD DECREASED, I HAD MADE A DAILY PRACTICE OF VISITING Mehevi at the Ti, who invariably gave me a most cordial reception. I was always accompanied in these excursions by Fayaway and the ever-present Kory-Kory. The former, as soon as we reached the vicinity of the Ti—which was rigorously tabooed to the whole female sex—withdrew to a neighboring hut, as if her feminine delicacy restrained her from approaching a habitation which might be regarded as a sort of Bachelor's Hall.

And in good truth it might well have been so considered. Although it was the permanent residence of several distinguished chiefs, and of the noble Mehevi in particular, it was still at certain seasons the favorite haunt of all the jolly, talkative, and elderly savages of the vale, who resorted thither in the same way that similar characters frequent a tavern in civilized countries. There they would remain hour after hour, chatting, smoking, eating poee-poee, or busily engaged in sleeping for the good of their constitutions.

This building appeared to be the head-quarters of the valley, where all flying rumors concentrated; and to have seen it filled with a crowd of the natives, all males, conversing in animated clusters, while multitudes were continually coming and going, one would have thought it a kind of savage Exchange, where the rise and fall of Polynesian Stock was discussed.

Mehevi acted as supreme lord over the place, spending the greater portion of his time there: and often when, at particular hours of the day, it was deserted by nearly everyone else except the verd-antique looking centenarians, who were fixtures in the building, the chief himself was sure to be found enjoying his "otium cum dignitate" upon the luxurious mats which covered the floor. Whenever I made my appearance he invariably rose, and, like a gentleman doing the honors of his mansion, invited me to repose myself wherever I pleased, and calling out "tamaree!" (boy), a little fellow would appear, and then retiring for an instant, return with some savory mess, from which the chief would press me to regale myself. To tell the truth, Mehevi was indebted to the excellence of his viands for the honor of my repeated visits—a matter which cannot appear singular, when it is borne in mind that bachelors, all the world over, are famous for serving up unexceptionable repasts.

One day, on drawing near to the Ti, I observed that extensive preparations were going forward, plainly betokening some approaching festival. Some of the symptoms reminded me of the stir produced among the scullions of a large hotel, where a grand jubilee dinner is about to be given. The natives were hurrying about hither and thither, engaged in various duties; some lugging off to the stream enormous hollow bamboos, for the purpose of filling them with water; others chasing furious-looking hogs through the bushes, in their endeavors to capture them; and numbers employed in kneading great mountains of poee-poee heaped up in huge wooden vessels.

After observing these lively indications for a while, I was attracted to a neighboring grove by a prodigious squeaking which I heard there. On reaching the spot I found it proceeded from a large hog which a number of natives were forcibly holding to the earth, while a muscular fellow, armed with a bludgeon, was ineffectually aiming murderous blows at the skull of the unfortunate porker. Again and again he missed his writhing and struggling victim, but though puffing and panting with his exertions, he still continued them; and after striking a sufficient number of blows to have demolished an entire drove of oxen, with one crashing stroke he laid him dead at his feet.

Without letting any blood from the body, it was immediately carried to a fire which had been kindled near at hand, and four savages taking hold of the carcass by its legs, passed it rapidly to and fro in the flames. In a moment the smell of burning bristles betrayed the object of this procedure. Having got thus far in the matter, the body was removed to a little distance; and, being disemboweled, the entrails were laid aside as choice parts, and the whole carcass thoroughly washed with water. An ample thick green cloth, composed of the long thick leaves of a species of palm-tree, ingeniously tacked together with little pins of bamboo, was now spread upon the ground, in which the body being carefully rolled, it was borne to an oven previously prepared to receive it. Here it was at once laid upon the heated stones at the bottom, and covered with thick layers of leaves, the whole being quickly hidden from sight by a mound of earth raised over it.

Such is the summary style in which the Typees convert perverse-minded and rebellious hogs into the most docile and amiable pork; a morsel of which placed on the tongue melts like a soft smile from the lips of Beauty.

I commend their peculiar mode of proceeding to the consideration of all butchers, cooks, and housewives. The hapless porker whose fate I have just rehearsed, was not the only one who suffered on that memorable day. Many a dismal grunt, many an imploring squeak, proclaimed what was going on throughout the whole extent of the valley; and I verily believe the first-born of every litter perished before the setting of that fatal sun.

The scene around the Ti was now most animated. Hogs and poee-poee were baking in numerous ovens, which, heaped up with fresh earth into slight elevations, looked like so many ant-hills. Scores of the savages were vigorously plying their stone pestles in preparing masses of poee-poee, and numbers were gathering green bread-fruit and young cocoanuts in the surrounding groves; while an exceeding great multitude, with a view of encouraging the rest in their labors, stood still, and kept shouting most lustily without intermission.

It is a peculiarity among these people, that when engaged in an employment, they always make a prodigious fuss about it. So seldom do they ever exert themselves, that when they do work they seem determined that so meritorious an action shall not escape the observation of those around. If, for example, they have occasion to remove a stone to a little distance, which perhaps might be carried by two able-bodied men, a whole swarm gather about it, and, after a vast deal of palavering, lift it up among them, everyone struggling to get hold of it, and bear it off yelling and panting as if accomplishing some mighty achievement. Seeing them on these occasions, one is reminded of an infinity of black ants clustering about and dragging away to some hole the leg of a deceased fly.

Having for some time attentively observed these demonstrations of good cheer, I entered the Ti, where Mehevi sat complacently looking out upon the busy scene, and occasionally issuing his orders. The chief appeared to be in an extraordinary flow of spirits, and gave me to understand that on the morrow there would be grand doings in the Groves generally, and at the Ti in particular; and urged me by no means to absent myself. In commemoration of what event, however, or in honor of what distinguished personage, the feast was to be given, altogether passed my comprehension. Mehevi sought to enlighten my ignorance, but he failed as signally as when he had endeavored to initiate me into the perplexing arcana of the taboo.

On leaving the Ti, Kory-Kory, who had as a matter of course accompanied me, observing that my curiosity remained unabated, resolved to make everything plain and satisfactory. With this intent, he escorted me through the Taboo Groves, pointing out to my notice a variety of objects, and endeavored to explain them in such an indescribable jargon of words, that it almost put me in bodily pain to listen to him. In particular, he led me to a remarkable pyramidical structure some three yards square at the base, and perhaps ten feet in height, which had lately been thrown up, and occupied a very conspicuous position. It was composed principally of large empty calabashes, with a few polished cocoanut shells, and looked not unlike a cenotaph of skulls. My cicerone perceived the astonishment with which I gazed at this monument of savage crockery, and immediately addressed himself to the task of enlightening me: but all in vain; and to this hour the nature of the monument remains a complete mystery to me. As, however, it formed so prominent a feature in the approaching revels, I bestowed upon the latter, in my own mind, the title of the "Feast of Calabashes."

The following morning, awaking rather late, I perceived the whole of Marheyo's family busily engaged in preparing for the festival. The old warrior himself was arranging in round balls the two gray locks of hair that were suffered to grow from the crown of his head; his ear-rings and spear, both well polished, lay beside him, while the highly decorative pair of shoes hung suspended from a projecting cane against the side of the house. The young men were similarly employed; and the fair damsels, including Fayaway, were anointing themselves with "aka," arranging their long tresses, and performing other matters connected with the duties of the toilet.

Having completed their preparations, the girls now exhibited themselves in gala costume; the most conspicuous feature of which was a necklace of beautiful white flowers, with the stems removed, and strung closely together upon a single fiber of tappa. Corresponding ornaments were inserted in their ears, and woven garlands upon their heads. About their waist they wore a short tunic of spotless white tappa, and some of them superadded to this a mantle of the same material, tied in an elaborate bow upon the left shoulder, and falling about the figure in picturesque folds.

Thus arrayed, I would have matched the charming Fayaway against any beauty in the world.

People may say what they will about the taste evinced by our fashionable ladies in dress. Their jewels, their feathers, their silks, and their furbelows would have sunk into utter insignificance beside the exquisite simplicity of attire adopted by the nymphs of the vale on this festive occasion. I should like to have seen a gallery of coronation beauties, at Westminster Abbey, confronted for a moment by this band of island girls; their stiffness, formality, and affectation contrasted with the artless vivacity and unconcealed natural graces of these savage maidens. It would be the Venus de' Medici placed beside a milliner's doll.

It was not long before Kory-Kory and myself were left alone in the house, the rest of its inmates having departed for the Taboo Groves. My valet was all impatience to follow them; and was as fidgety about my dilatory movements as a diner out waiting hat in hand at the bottom of the stairs for some lagging companion. At last, yielding to his importunities, I set out for the Ti. As we passed the houses peeping out from the groves through which our route lay, I noticed that they were entirely deserted by their inhabitants.

When we reached the rock that abruptly terminated the path, and concealed from us the festive scene, wild shouts and a confused blending of voices assured me that the occasion, whatever it might be, had drawn together a great multitude. Kory-Kory, previous to mounting the elevation, paused for a moment, like a dandy at a ball-room door, to put a hasty finish to his toilette. During this short interval, the thought struck me that I ought myself perhaps to be taking some little pains with my appearance. But as I had no holiday raiment, I was not a little puzzled to devise some means of decorating myself. However, as I felt desirous to create a sensation, I determined to do all that lay in my power; and knowing that I could not delight the savages more than by conforming to their style of dress, I removed from my person the large robe of tappa which I was accustomed to wear over my shoulders whenever I sallied into the open air, and remained merely girt about with a short tunic descending from my waist to my knees.

My quick-witted attendant fully appreciated the compliment I was paying to the costume of his race, and began more sedulously to arrange the folds of the one only garment which remained to me. Whilst he was doing this, I caught sight of a knot of young lasses, who were sitting near us on the grass surrounded by heaps of flowers which they were forming into garlands. I motioned to them to bring some of their handiwork to me; and in an instant a dozen wreaths were at my disposal. One of them I put round the apology for a hat which I had been forced to construct for myself out of palmetto-leaves, and some of the others I converted into a splendid girdle. These operations finished, with the slow and dignified step of a full-dressed beau I ascended the rock.

Chapter XXIII

The Feast of the Calabashes

The whole population of the valley seemed to be gathered within the precincts of the grove. In the distance could be seen the long front of the Ti, its immense piazza swarming with men, arrayed in every variety of fantastic costume, and all vociferating with animated gestures; while the whole interval between it and the place where I stood was enlivened by groups of females fancifully decorated, dancing, capering, and uttering wild exclamations. As soon as they descried me they set up a shout of welcome; and a band of them came dancing towards me chanting as they approached some wild recitative. The change in my garb seemed to transport them with delight, and clustering about me on all sides, they accompanied me towards the Ti. When, however, we drew near it these joyous nymphs paused in their career, and parting on either side, permitted me to pass on to the now densely thronged building.

So soon as I mounted to the pi-pi I saw at a glance that the revels were fairly under way.

What lavish plenty reigned around! Warwick feasting his retainers with beef and ale was a niggard to the noble Mehevi! All along the piazza of the Ti were arranged elaborately carved canoe-shaped vessels, some twenty feet in length, tied with newly made poee-poee, and sheltered from the sun by the broad leaves of the banana. At intervals were heaps of green bread-fruit, raised in pyramidical stacks, resembling the regular piles of heavy shot to be seen in the yard of an arsenal. Inserted into the interstices of the huge stones which formed the pi-pi were large boughs of trees; hanging from the branches of which, and screened from the sun by their foliage, were innumerable little packages with leafy coverings, containing the meat of the numerous hogs which had been slain, done up in this manner to make it more accessible to the crowd. Leaning against the railing on the piazza were an immense number of long, heavy bamboos, plugged at the lower end, and with their projecting muzzles stuffed with a wad of leaves. These were filled with water from the stream, and each of them might hold from four to five gallons.

The banquet being thus spread, naught remained but for everyone to help himself at his pleasure. Accordingly not a moment passed but the transplanted boughs I have mentioned were rifled by the throng of the fruit they certainly had never borne before. Calabashes of poee-poee were continually being replenished from the extensive receptacle in which that article was stored, and multitudes of little fires were kindled about the Ti for the purpose of roasting the bread-fruit.

Within the building itself was presented a most extraordinary scene. The immense lounge of mats lying between the parallel rows of the trunks of cocoanut-trees, and extending the entire length of the house, at least two hundred feet, was covered by the reclining forms of a host of chiefs and warriors, who were eating at a great rate, or soothing the cares of Polynesian life in the sedative fumes of tobacco. The smoke was inhaled from large pipes, the bowls of which, made out of small cocoanut shells, were curiously carved in strange heathenish devices. These were passed from mouth to mouth by the recumbent smokers, who, taking two or three prodigious whiffs, handed the pipe to his neighbor; sometimes for that purpose stretching indolently across the body of some dozing individual whose exertions at the dinner-table had already induced sleep.

The tobacco used among the Typees was of a very mild and pleasing flavor, and as I always saw it in leaves, and the natives appeared pretty well supplied with it, I was led to believe that it must have been the growth of the valley. Indeed Kory-Kory gave me to understand that this was the case; but I never saw a single plant growing on the island. At Nukuheva, and, I believe, in all the other valleys, the weed is very scarce, being only obtained in small quantities from foreigners, and smoking is consequently with the inhabitants of these places a very great luxury. How it was that the Typees were so well furnished with it I cannot divine. I should think them too indolent to devote any attention to its culture; and, indeed, as far as my observation extended, not a single atom of the soil was under any other cultivation than that of shower and sunshine. The tobacco plant, however, like the sugar-cane, may grow wild in some remote part of the vale.

There were many in the Ti for whom the tobacco did not furnish a sufficient stimulus, and who accordingly had recourse to "arva," as a more powerful agent in producing the desired effect.

"Arva" is a root very generally dispersed over the South Seas, and from it is extracted a juice, the effects of which upon the system are at first stimulating in a moderate degree; but it soon relaxes the muscles, and exerting a narcotic influence produces a luxurious sleep. In the valley this beverage was universally prepared in the following way: Some half-dozen young boys seated themselves in a circle around an empty wooden vessel, each one of them being supplied with a certain quantity of the roots of the "arva," broken into small bits and laid by his side. A cocoanut goblet of water was passed around the juvenile company, who rinsing their mouths with its contents, proceeded to the business before them. This merely consisted in thoroughly masticating the "arva," and throwing it mouthful after mouthful into the receptacle provided. When a sufficient quantity had been thus obtained water was poured upon the mass, and being stirred about with the forefinger of the right hand, the preparation was soon in readiness for use. The "arva" has medicinal qualities.

Upon the Sandwich Islands it has been employed with no small success in the treatment of scrofulous affections, and in combating the ravages of a disease for whose frightful inroads the ill-starred inhabitants of that group are indebted to their foreign benefactors. But the tenants of the Typee valley, as yet exempt from these inflictions, generally employ the "arva" as a minister to social enjoyment, and a calabash of the liquid circulates among them as the bottle with us.

Mehevi, who was greatly delighted with the change in my costume, gave me a cordial welcome. He had reserved for me a most delectable mess of "cokoo," well knowing my partiality for that dish; and had likewise selected three or four young cocoanuts, several roasted bread-fruit, and a magnificent bunch of bananas, for my especial comfort and gratification. These various matters were at once placed before me; but Kory-Kory deemed the banquet entirely insufficient for my wants until he had supplied me with one of the leafy packages of pork, which, notwithstanding the somewhat hasty manner in which it had been prepared, possessed a most excellent flavor, and was surprisingly sweet and tender. Pork is not a staple article of food among the people of the Marquesas; consequently they pay little attention to the *breeding* of the swine. The hogs are permitted to roam at large on the groves, where they obtain no small part of their nourishment from the cocoanuts which continually fall from the trees. But it is only after infinite labor and difficulty, that the hungry animal can pierce the husk and shell so as to get at the meat. I have frequently been amused at seeing one of them, after crunching the obstinate nut with his teeth for a long time unsuccessfully, get into a violent passion with it. He would then root furiously under the cocoanut, and, with a fling of his snout, toss it before him on the ground. Following it up, he would crunch at it again savagely for a moment, and then next knock it on one side, pausing immediately after, as if wondering how it could so suddenly have disappeared. In this way the persecuted cocoanuts were often chased half across the valley.

The second day of the Feast of Calabashes was ushered in by still more uproarious noises than the first. The skins of innumerable sheep seemed to be resounding to the blows of an army of drummers. Startled from my slumbers by the din, I leaped up, and found the whole household engaged in making preparations for immediate departure. Curious to discover of what strange events these novel sounds might be the precursors, and not a little desirous to catch a sight of the instruments which produced the terrific noise, I accompanied the natives as soon as they were in readiness to depart for the Taboo Groves.

The comparatively open space that extended from the Ti toward the rock, to which I have before alluded as forming the ascent to the place was, with the building itself, now altogether deserted by the men, the whole distance being filled by bands of females, shouting and dancing under the influence of some strange excitement.

I was amused at the appearance of four or five old women who, in a state of utter nudity, with their arms extended flatly down their sides, and holding themselves perfectly erect, were leaping stiffly into the air, like so many sticks bobbing to the surface, after being pressed perpendicularly into the water. They preserved the utmost gravity of countenance, and continued their extraordinary movements without a single moment's cessation. They did not appear to attract the observation of the crowd around them, but I must candidly confess that, for my own part, I stared at them most pertinaciously.

Desirous of being enlightened with regard to the meaning of this peculiar diversion, I turned, inquiringly to Kory-Kory; that learned Typee immediately proceeded to explain the whole matter thoroughly. But all that I could comprehend from what he said was, that the leaping figures before me were bereaved widows, whose partners had been slain in battle many moons previously; and who, at every festival, gave public evidence in this manner of their calamities. It was evident that Kory-Kory considered this an all-sufficient reason for so undecorous a custom; but I must say that it did not satisfy me as to its propriety.

Leaving these afflicted females, we passed on to the Hoolah-Hoolah ground. Within the spacious quadrangle, the whole population of the valley seemed to be assembled, and the sight presented was truly remarkable. Beneath the sheds of bamboo which opened towards the interior of the square, reclined the principal chiefs and warriors, while a miscellaneous throng lay at their ease under the enormous trees which spread a majestic canopy overhead. Upon the terraces of the gigantic altars, at each end, were deposited green bread-fruit in baskets of cocoanut leaves, large rolls of tappa, bunches of ripe bananas, clusters of mammee-apples, the golden-hued fruit of the artu-tree, and baked hogs, laid out in large wooden trenchers, fancifully decorated with freshly plucked leaves, whilst a variety of rude implements of war were piled in confused heaps before the ranks of hideous idols. Fruits of various kinds were likewise suspended in leafen baskets, from the tops of poles planted uprightly, and at regular intervals, along the lower terraces of both altars. At their base were arranged two parallel rows of cumbersome drums, standing at least fifteen feet in height, and formed from the hollow trunks of large trees. Their heads were covered with shark-skins, and their barrels were elaborately carved with various quaint figures and devices. At regular intervals they were bound round by a species of sinnate of various colors, and strips of native cloth flattened upon them here and there. Behind these instruments were built slight platforms, upon which stood a number of young men who, beating violently with the palms of their hands upon the drum-heads, produced those outrageous sounds which had awakened me in the morning. Every few minutes these musical performers hopped down from their elevation into the crowd below, and their places were immediately supplied by fresh recruits. Thus an incessant din was kept up that might have startled Pandemonium.

Precisely in the middle of the quadrangle were placed perpendicularly in the ground, a hundred or more slender, fresh-cut poles, stripped of their bark, and decorated at the end with a floating pennon of white tappa; the whole being fenced about with a little picket of canes. For what purpose these angular ornaments were intended I in vain endeavored to discover.

Another most striking feature of the performance was exhibited by a score of old men, who sat cross-legged in the little pulpits, which encircled the trunks of the immense trees growing in the middle of the enclosure. These venerable gentlemen, who I presume were the priests, kept up an uninterrupted monotonous chant, which was nearly drowned in the roar of drums. In the right hand they held a finely woven grass fan, with a heavy black wooden handle curiously chased: these fans they kept in continual motion.

But no attention whatever seemed to be paid to the drummers or to the old priests; the individuals who composed the vast crowd present being entirely taken up in chanting and laughing with one another, smoking, drinking "arva," and eating. For all the observation it attracted, or the good it achieved, the whole savage orchestra might with great advantage to its own members and the company in general, have ceased the prodigious uproar they were making.

In vain I questioned Kory-Kory and others of the natives, as to the meaning of the strange things that were going on; all their explanations were conveyed in such a mass of outlandish gibberish and gesticulation that I gave up the attempt in despair. All that day the drums resounded, the priests chanted, and the multitude feasted and roared till sunset, when the throng dispersed, and the Taboo Groves were again abandoned to quiet and repose. The next day the same scene was repeated until night, when this singular festival terminated.

Chapter XXIV

Ideas Suggested by the Feast of Calabashes—Inaccuracy of Certain Published Accounts of the Islands—A Reason—Neglected State of Heathenism in the Valley—Effigy of a Dead Warrior—A Singular Superstition—The Priest Kolory and the God Moa Atua—Amazing Religious Observance—A Dilapidated Shrine—Kory-Kory and the Idol—An Inference

Although I had been baffled in my attempts to learn the origin of the Feast of Calabashes, yet it seemed very plain to me that it was principally, if not wholly, of a religious character. As a religious solemnity, however, it had not at all corresponded with the horrible descriptions of Polynesian worship which we have received in some published narratives, and especially in those accounts of the evangelized islands with which the missionaries have favored us. Did not the sacred character of these persons render the purity of their intentions unquestionable, I should certainly be led to suppose that they had exaggerated the evils of Paganism, in order to enhance the merit of their own disinterested labors.

In a certain work incidentally treating of the "Washington, or Northern Marquesas Islands," I have seen the frequent immolation of human victims upon the altars of their gods, positively and repeatedly charged upon the inhabitants. The same work gives also a rather minute account of their religion—enumerates a great many of their superstitions—and makes known the particular designations of numerous orders of the priesthood. One would almost imagine from the long list that is given of cannibal primates, bishops, archdeacons, prebendaries, and other inferior ecclesiastics, that the sacerdotal order far outnumbered the rest of the population, and that the poor natives were more severely priest-ridden than even the inhabitants of the papal states. These accounts are likewise calculated to leave upon the reader's mind an impression that human victims are daily cooked and served up upon the altars; that heathenish cruelties of every description are continually practiced; and that these ignorant Pagans are in a state of the extremest wretchedness in consequence of the grossness of their superstitions. Be it observed, however, that all this information is given by a man who, according to his own statement, was only at one of the islands and remained there but two weeks, sleeping every night on board his ship, and taking little kid-glove excursions ashore in the daytime, attended by an armed party.

Now, all I can say is, that in all my excursions through the valley of Typee, I never saw any of these alleged enormities. If any of them are practiced upon the Marquesas Islands they must certainly have come to my knowledge, while living for months with a tribe of savages, wholly unchanged from their original primitive condition, and reputed the most ferocious in the South Seas.

The fact is, that there is a vast deal of unintentional humbuggery in some of the accounts we have from scientific men concerning the religious institutions of Polynesia. These learned tourists generally obtain the greater part of their information from retired old South Sea rovers, who have domesticated themselves among the barbarous tribes of the Pacific. Jack, who has long been accustomed to the long-bow, and to spin tough yarns on the ship's forecastle, invariably officiates as showman of the island on which he has settled, and having mastered a few dozen words of the language, is supposed to know all about the people who speak it. A natural desire to make himself of consequence in the eyes of the strangers, prompts him to lay claim to a much greater knowledge of such matters than he actually possesses. In reply to incessant queries, he communicates not only all he knows but a good deal more, and if there be any information deficient still he is at no loss to supply it. The avidity with which his anecdotes are noted down tickles his vanity, and his powers of invention increase with the credulity of his auditors. He knows just the sort of information wanted, and furnishes it to any extent.

This is not a supposed case; I have met with several individuals like the one described, and I have been present at two or three of their interviews with strangers.

Now, when the scientific voyager arrives at home with his collection of wonders, he attempts, perhaps, to give a description of some of the strange people he has been visiting. Instead of representing them as a community of lusty savages, who are leading a merry, idle, innocent life, he enters into a very circumstantial and learned narrative of certain unaccountable superstitions and practices, about which he knows as little as the islanders do themselves. Having had little time, and scarcely any opportunity, to become acquainted with the customs he pretends to describe, he writes them down one after another in an off-hand, haphazard style; and were the book thus produced to be translated into the tongue of the people of whom it purports to give the history, it would appear quite as wonderful to them as it does to the American public, and much more improbable.

For my own part, I am free to confess my almost entire inability to gratify any curiosity that may be felt with regard to the theology of the valley. I doubt whether the inhabitants themselves could do so. They are either too lazy or too sensible to worry themselves about abstract points of religious belief. While I was among them, they never held any synods or councils to settle the principles of their faith by agitating them. An unbounded liberty of conscience seemed to prevail. Those who pleased to do so were allowed to repose implicit faith in an ill-favored god with a large bottle-nose and fat shapeless arms crossed upon his breast; whilst others worshiped an image which, having no likeness either in heaven or on earth, could hardly be called an idol. As the islanders always maintained a discreet reserve with regard to my own peculiar views on religion, I thought it would be excessively ill-bred in me to pry into theirs.

But, although my knowledge of the religious faith of the Typees was unavoidably limited, one of their superstitious observances with which I became acquainted interested me greatly.

In one of the most secluded portions of the valley within a stone's cast of Fayaway's lake—for so I christened the scene of our island yachting—and hard by a growth of palms, which stood ranged in order along both banks of the stream, waving their green arms as if to do honor to its passage, was the mausoleum of a deceased warrior chief. Like all the other edifices of any note, it was raised upon a small pi-pi of stones, which, being of unusual height, was a conspicuous object from a distance. A light thatching of bleached palmetto-leaves hung over it like a self-supported canopy; for it was not until you came very near that you saw it was supported by four slender columns of bamboo rising at each corner to a little more than the height of a man. A clear area of a few yards surrounded the pi-pi, and was enclosed by four trunks of cocoanut-trees resting at the angles on massive blocks of stone. The place was sacred. The sign of the inscrutable taboo was seen in the shape of a mystic roll of white tappa, suspended by a twisted cord of the same material from the top of a slight pole planted within the enclosure.[1] The sanctity of the spot appeared never to have been violated. The stillness of the grave was there, and the calm solitude around was beautiful and touching. The soft shadows of those lofty palm-trees!—I can see them now—hanging over the little temple, as if to keep out the intrusive sun.

On all sides as you approached this silent spot you caught sight of the dead chief's effigy, seated in the stern of a canoe, which was raised on a light frame a few inches above the level of the pi-pi. The canoe was about seven feet in length; of a rich, dark colored wood, handsomely carved and adorned in many places with variegated bindings of stained sinnate, into which were ingeniously wrought a number of sparkling seashells, and a belt of the same shells ran all round it. The body of

1. White appears to be the sacred color among the Marquesans.

the figure—of whatever material it might have been made—was effectually concealed in a heavy robe of brown tappa, revealing only the hands and head; the latter skillfully carved in wood, and surmounted by a superb arch of plumes. These plumes, in the subdued and gentle gales which found access to this sequestered spot, were never for one moment at rest, but kept nodding and waving over the chief's brow. The long leaves of the palmetto drooped over the eaves, and through them you saw the warrior holding his paddle with both hands in the act of rowing, leaning forward and inclining his head, as if eager to hurry on his voyage. Glaring at him forever, and face to face, was a polished human skull, which crowned the prow of the canoe. The spectral figure-head, reversed in its position, glancing backwards, seemed to mock the impatient attitude of the warrior.

When I first visited this singular place with Kory-Kory, he told me—or at least I so understood him—that the chief was paddling his way to the realms of bliss and bread-fruit—the Polynesian heaven—where every moment the bread-fruit trees dropped their ripened spheres to the ground, and where there was no end to the cocoanuts and bananas: there they reposed through the livelong eternity upon mats much finer than those of Typee; and every day bathed their glowing limbs in rivers of cocoanut oil. In that happy land there were plenty of plumes and feathers and boars'-tusks and sperm-whale teeth, far preferable to all the shining trinkets and gay tappa of the white men; and, best of all, women far lovelier than the daughters of earth, were there in abundance. "A very pleasant place," Kory-Kory said it was; "but after all, not much pleasanter, he thought, than Typee." "Did he not then," I asked him, "wish to accompany the warrior?" "Oh no: he was very happy where he was; but supposed that some time or other he would go in his own canoe."

Thus far, I think, I clearly comprehended Kory-Kory. But there was a singular expression he made use of at the time, enforced by as singular a gesture, the meaning of which I would have given much to penetrate. I am inclined to believe it must have been a proverb he uttered; for I afterwards heard him repeat the same words several times, and in what appeared to me to be a somewhat similar sense. Indeed, Kory-Kory had a great variety of short, smart-sounding sentences, with which he frequently enlivened his discourse; and he introduced them with an air which plainly intimated, that, in his opinion, they settled the matter in question, whatever it might be.

Could it have been then, that when I asked him whether he desired to go to this heaven of bread-fruit, cocoanuts, and young ladies, which he had been describing, he answered by saying something equivalent to our old adage—"A bird in the hand is worth two in the bush"—if he did, Kory-Kory was a discreet and sensible fellow, and I cannot sufficiently admire his shrewdness.

Whenever in the course of my rambles through the valley I happened to be near the chief's mausoleum, I always turned aside to visit it. The place had a peculiar charm for me; I hardly know why; but so it was. As I leaned over the railing and gazed upon the strange effigy and watched the play of the feathery head-dress, stirred by the same breeze which in low tones breathed amidst the lofty palm-trees, I loved to yield myself up to the fanciful superstition of the islanders, and could almost believe that the grim warrior was bound heavenward. In this mood when I turned to depart, I bade him "God speed, and a pleasant voyage." Ay, paddle away, brave chieftain, to the land of spirits! To the material eye thou makest but little progress; but with the eye of faith, I see thy canoe cleaving the bright waves, which die away on those dimly looming shores of Paradise.

This strange superstition affords another evidence of the fact, that however ignorant man may be, he still feels within him his immortal spirit yearning after the unknown future.

Although the religious theories of the islands were a complete mystery to me, their practical every day operation could not be concealed. I frequently passed the little temples reposing in the shadows of the taboo groves and beheld the offerings—moldy fruits spread out upon a rude altar, or hanging in half-decayed baskets around some uncouth jolly-looking image; I was present during the continuance of the festival; I daily beheld the grinning idols marshaled rank and file in the Hoolah Hoolah ground, and was often in the habit of meeting those whom I supposed to be the priests. But the temples seemed abandoned to solitude; the festival had been nothing more than a jovial mingling of the tribe; the idols were quite harmless as any other logs of wood; and the priests were the merriest dogs in the valley.

In fact religious affairs in Typee were at a very low ebb: all such matters sat very lightly upon the thoughtless inhabitants; and, in the celebration of many of their strange rites, they appeared merely to seek a sort of childish amusement.

A curious evidence of this was given in a remarkable ceremony in which I frequently saw Mehevi and several other chiefs and warriors of note take part; but never a single female.

Among those whom I looked upon as forming the priesthood of the valley, there was one in particular who often attracted my notice, and whom I could not help regarding as the head of the order. He was a noble looking man, in the prime of his life, and of a most benignant aspect. The authority this man, whose name was Kolory, seemed to exercise over the rest, the episcopal part he took in the Feast of Calabashes, his sleek and complacent appearance, the mystic characters which were tattooed upon his breast, and above all the miter he frequently wore, in the shape of a towering head-dress, consisting of part of a cocoanut branch, the stalk planted uprightly on his brow, and the leaflets gathered together and passed round the temples and behind the ears, all these pointed him out as Lord Primate of Typee. Kolory was a sort of Knight Templar—a soldier-priest; for he often wore the dress of a Marquesan warrior, and always carried a long spear, which, instead of terminating in a paddle at the lower end, after the general fashion of these weapons, was curved into a heathenish-looking little image. This instrument, however, might perhaps have been emblematic of his double functions. With one end in carnal combat he transfixed the enemies of his tribe; and with the other as a pastoral crook he kept in order his spiritual flock. But this is not all I have to say about Kolory. His martial grace very often carried about with him what seemed to me the half of a broken war-club. It was swathed around with ragged bits of white tappa, and the upper part, which was intended to represent a human head, was embellished with a strip of scarlet cloth of European manufacture. It required little observation to discover that this strange object was revered as a god. By the side of the big and lusty images standing sentinel over the altars of the Hoolah Hoolah ground, it seemed a mere pigmy in tatters. But appearances all the world over are deceptive. Little men are sometimes very potent, and rags sometimes cover very extensive pretensions. In fact, this funny little image was the "crack" god of the island; lording it over all the wooden lubbers who looked so grim and dreadful; its name was Moa Atua.[1] And it was in honor of Moa Atua, and for the entertainment of those who believe in him, that the curious ceremony I am about to describe was observed.

Mehevi and the chieftains of the Ti have just risen from their noontide slumbers. There are no affairs of state to dispose of; and having eaten two or three breakfasts in the course of the morning, the magnates of the valley feel no appetite as yet for dinner. How are their leisure moments to be occupied? They smoke, they chat, and at last one of their number makes a proposition to the rest, who joyfully acquiescing, he darts out of the house, leaps from the pi-pi, and disappears in the grove. Soon you see him returning with Kolory, who bears the god Moa Atua in his arms, and carries in one hand a small trough, hollowed out in the likeness of a canoe. The priest comes along dandling his charge as if it were a lachrymose infant he was endeavoring to put into a good humor. Presently, entering the Ti, he seats himself on the mats as composedly as a juggler about to perform his sleight-of-hand tricks; and with the chiefs disposed in a circle around him, commences his ceremony.

In the first place he gives Moa Atua an affectionate hug, then caressingly lays him to his breast, and, finally, whispers something in his ear; the rest of the company listening eagerly for a reply. But the baby-god is deaf or dumb—perhaps both, for never a word does he utter. At last Kolory speaks a little louder, and soon growing angry, comes boldly out with what he has to say and bawls to him.

1. The word "Atua," although having some other significations, is in nearly all the Polynesian dialects used as the general designation of the gods.

He put me in mind of a choleric fellow, who, after trying in vain to communicate a secret to a deaf man, all at once flies into a passion and screams it out so that everyone may hear. Still Moa Atua remains as quiet as ever; and Kolory, seemingly losing his temper, fetches him a box over the head, strips him of his tappa and red cloth, and laying him in a state of nudity in a little trough, covers him from sight. At this proceeding all present loudly applaud and signify their approval by uttering the adjective "motarkee" with violent emphasis. Kolory, however, is so desirous his conduct should meet with unqualified approbation, that he inquires of each individual separately whether under existing circumstances, he has not done perfectly right in shutting up Moa Atua. The invariable response is "Aa, Aa" (yes, yes), repeated over again and again in a manner which ought to quiet the scruples of the most conscientious. After a few moments Kolory brings forth his doll again, and while arraying it very carefully in the tappa and red cloth, alternately fondles and chides it. The toilette being completed, he once more speaks to it aloud. The whole company hereupon show the greatest interest; while the priest holding Moa Atua to his ear interprets to them what he pretends the god is confidentially communicating to him. Some items of intelligence appear to tickle all present amazingly; for one claps his hands in rapture; another shouts with merriment; and a third leaps to his feet and capers about like a madman.

What under the sun Moa Atua on these occasions had to say to Kolory I never could find out; but I could not help thinking that the former showed a sad want of spirit in being disciplined into making those disclosures, which at first he seemed bent on withholding. Whether the priest honestly interpreted what he believed the divinity said to him, or whether he was not all the while guilty of a vile humbug, I shall not presume to decide. At any rate, whatever was coming from the god was imparted to those present seemed to be generally of a complimentary nature: a fact which illustrates the sagacity of Kolory, or else the time-serving disposition of this hardly used deity.

Moa Atua having nothing more to say, his bearer goes to nursing him again, in which occupation, however, he is soon interrupted by a question put by one of the warriors to the god. Kolory hereupon snatches it up to his ear again, and after listening attentively, once more officiates as the organ of communication. A multitude of questions and answers having passed between the parties, much to the satisfaction of those who propose them, the god is put tenderly to bed in the trough, and the whole company unite in a long chant, led off by Kolory. This ended, the ceremony is over; the chiefs rise to their feet in high good humor, and my Lord Archbishop, after chatting awhile, and regaling himself with a whiff or two from a pipe of tobacco, tucks the canoe under his arm and marches off with it.

The whole of these proceedings were like those of a parcel of children playing with dolls and baby houses.

For a youngster scarcely ten inches high, and with so few early advantages as he doubtless had had, Moa Atua was certainly a precocious little fellow if he really said all that was imputed to him; but for what reason this poor devil of a deity, thus cuffed about, cajoled and shut up in a box, was held in greater estimation than the full-grown and dignified personages of the Taboo Groves, I cannot divine. And yet Mehevi, and other chiefs of unquestionable veracity—to say nothing of the Primate himself—assured me over and over again that Moa Atua was the tutelary deity of Typee, and was more to be held in honor than a whole battalion of the clumsy idols in the Hoolah Hoolah grounds. Kory-Kory—who seemed to have devoted considerable attention to the study of theology, as he knew the names of all the graven images in the valley, and often repeated them over to me—likewise entertained some rather enlarged ideas with regard to the character and pretensions of Moa Atua. He once gave me to understand, with a gesture there was no misconceiving, that if he (Moa Atua) were so minded, he could cause a cocoanut-tree to sprout out of his (Kory-Kory's) head; and that it would be the easiest thing in life for him (Moa Atua) to take the whole island of Nukuheva in his mouth and dive down to the bottom of the sea with it.

But in sober seriousness, I hardly knew what to make of the religion of the valley. There was nothing that so much perplexed the illustrious Cook, in his intercourse with the South Sea islanders, as their sacred rites. Although this prince of navigators was in many instances assisted by interpreters in the prosecution of his researches, he still frankly acknowledges that he was at a loss to obtain anything like a clear insight into the puzzling arcana of their faith. A similar admission has been made by other eminent voyagers: by Carteret, Byron, Kotzebue, and Vancouver.

For my own part, although hardly a day passed while I remained upon the island that I did not witness some religious ceremony or other, it was very much like seeing a parcel of "Freemasons" making secret signs to each other; I saw everything, but could comprehend nothing.

On the whole, I am inclined to believe, that the islanders in the Pacific have no fixed and definite ideas whatever on the subject of religion. I am persuaded that Kolory himself would be effectually posed were he called upon to draw up the articles of his faith and pronounce the creed by which he hoped to be saved. In truth, the Typees, so far as their actions evince, submitted to no laws human or divine—always excepting the thrice mysterious taboo. The "independent electors" of the valley were not to be brow-beaten by chiefs, priests, idols, or devils. As for the luckless idols, they received more hard knocks than supplications. I do not wonder that some of them looked so grim, and stood so bolt upright as if fearful of looking to the right or the left lest they should give anyone offense. The fact is, they had to carry themselves *"pretty straight,"* or suffer the consequences. Their worshipers were such a precious set of fickle-minded and irreverent heathens, that there was no telling when they might topple one of them over, break it to pieces, and making a fire with it on the very altar itself, fall to roasting the offerings of bread-fruit, and eat them in spite of its teeth.

In how little reverence these unfortunate deities were held by the natives was on one occasion most convincingly proved to me.—Walking with Kory-Kory through the deepest recesses of the groves, I perceived a curious looking image, about six feet in height, which originally had been placed upright against a low pi-pi, surmounted by a ruinous bamboo temple, but having become fatigued and weak in the knees, was now carelessly leaning against it. The idol was partly concealed by the foliage of a tree which stood near, and whose leafy boughs drooped over the pile of stones, as if to protect the rude fane from the decay to which it was rapidly hastening. The image itself was nothing more than a grotesquely shaped log, carved in the likeness of a portly naked man with the arms clasped over the head, the jaws thrown wide apart, and its thick shapeless legs bowed into an arch. It was much decayed. The lower part was overgrown with a bright silky moss. Thin spears of grass sprouted from the distended mouth and fringed the outline of the head and arms. His godship had literally attained a green old age. All its prominent points were bruised and battered, or entirely rotted away. The nose had taken its departure, and from the general appearance of the head it might have been supposed that the wooden divinity, in despair at the neglect of its worshipers, had been trying to beat its own brains out against the surrounding trees.

I drew near to inspect more closely this strange object of idolatry, but halted reverently at the distance of two or three paces, out of regard to the religious prejudices of my valet. As soon, however, as Kory-Kory perceived that I was in one of my inquiring, scientific moods, to my astonishment, he sprang to the side of the idol, and pushing it away from the stones against which it rested, endeavored to make it stand upon its legs. But the divinity had lost the use of them altogether; and while Kory-Kory was trying to prop it up, by placing a stick between it and the pi-pi, the monster fell clumsily to the ground, and would infallibly have broken its neck had not Kory-Kory providentially broken its fall by receiving its whole weight on his own half-crushed back. I never saw the honest fellow in such a rage before. He leaped furiously to his feet, and seizing the stick, began beating the poor image: every moment or two pausing and talking to it in the most violent manner, as if upbraiding it for the accident. When his indignation had subsided a little he whirled the idol about most profanely, so as to give me an opportunity of examining it on all sides. I am quite sure I never should have presumed to have taken such liberties with the god myself, and I was not a little shocked at Kory-Kory's impiety.

This anecdote speaks for itself. When one of the inferior order of natives could show such contempt for a venerable and decrepit God of the Groves, what the state of religion must be among the people in general is easy to be imagined. In truth, I regard the Typees as a back-slidden generation. They are sunk in religious sloth, and require a spiritual revival. A long prosperity of bread-fruit and cocoanuts has rendered them remiss in the performance of their higher obligations. The wood-rot malady is spreading among the idols—the fruit upon their altars is becoming offensive—the temples themselves need rethatching—the tattooed clergy are altogether too light-hearted and lazy—and their flocks are going astray.

Chapter XXV

General Information Gathered at the Festival—Personal Beauty of the Typees—Their Superiority Over the Inhabitants of the Other Islands—Diversity of Complexion—A Vegetable Cosmetic and Ointment—Testimony of Voyagers to the Uncommon Beauty of the Marquesans—Few Evidences of Intercourse with Civilized Beings—Dilapidated Musket—Primitive Simplicity of Government—Regal Dignity of Mehevi

Although I had been unable during the late festival to obtain information on many interesting subjects which had much excited my curiosity, still that important event had not passed by without adding materially to my general knowledge of the islanders.

I was especially struck by the physical strength and beauty which they displayed, by their great superiority in these respects over the inhabitants of the neighboring bay of Nukuheva, and by the singular contrasts they presented among themselves in their various shades of complexion.

In beauty of form they surpassed anything I had ever seen. Not a single instance of natural deformity was observable in all the throng attending the revels. Occasionally I noticed among the men the scars of wounds they had received in battle; and sometimes, though very seldom, the loss of a finger, an eye, or an arm, attributable to the same cause. With these exceptions, every individual appeared free from those blemishes which sometimes mar the effect of an otherwise perfect form. But their physical excellence did not merely consist in an exemption from these evils; nearly every individual of their number might have been taken for a sculptor's model.

When I remembered that these islanders derived no advantage from dress, but appeared in all the naked simplicity of nature, I could not avoid comparing them with the fine gentlemen and dandies who promenade such unexceptionable figures in our frequented thoroughfares. Stripped of the cunning artifices of the tailor, and standing forth in the garb of Eden—what a sorry set of round-shouldered, spindle-shanked, crane-necked varlets would civilized men appear! Stuffed calves, padded breasts, and scientifically cut pantaloons would then avail them nothing, and the effect would be truly deplorable.

Nothing in the appearance of the islanders struck me more forcibly than the whiteness of their teeth. The novelist always compares the masticators of his heroine to ivory; but I boldly pronounce the teeth of the Typee to be far more beautiful than ivory itself. The jaws of the oldest graybeards among them were much better garnished than those of most of the youths of civilized countries; while the teeth of the young and middle-aged, in their purity and whiteness, were actually dazzling to the eye. This marvelous whiteness of the teeth is to be ascribed to the pure vegetable diet of these people, and the uninterrupted healthfulness of their natural mode of life.

The men, in almost every instance, are of lofty stature, scarcely ever less than six feet in height, while the other sex are uncommonly diminutive. The early period of life at which the human form arrives at maturity in this generous tropical climate, likewise deserves to be mentioned. A little creature, not more than thirteen years of age, and who in other particulars might be regarded as a mere child, is often seen nursing her own baby; whilst lads who, under less ripening skies, would be still at school, are here responsible fathers of families.

On first entering the Typee Valley, I had been struck with the marked contrast presented by its inhabitants with those of the bay I had previously left. In the latter place, I had not been favorably impressed with the personal appearance of the male portion of the population; although with the females, excepting in some truly melancholy instances, I had been wonderfully pleased. I had observed that even the little intercourse Europeans had carried on with the Nukuheva natives had not failed to leave its traces amongst them. One of the most dreadful curses under which humanity labors had commenced its havocks, and betrayed, as it ever does among the South Sea islanders, the most aggravated symptoms. From this, as from all other foreign inflictions, the yet uncontaminated tenants of the Typee Valley were wholly exempt; and long may they continue so. Better will it be for them forever to remain the happy and innocent heathens and barbarians that they now are, than, like the wretched inhabitants of the Sandwich Islands, to enjoy the mere name of Christians without experiencing any of the vital operations of true religion, whilst, at the same time, they are made the victims of the worst vices and evils of civilized life.

Apart, however, from these considerations, I am inclined to believe that there exists a radical difference between the two tribes, if indeed they are not distinct races of men. To those who have merely touched at Nukuheva Bay, without visiting other portions of the island, it would hardly appear credible the diversities presented between the various small clans inhabiting so diminutive a spot. But the hereditary hostility which has existed between them for ages fully accounts for this.

Not so easy, however, is it to assign an adequate cause for the endless variety of complexions to be seen in the Typee Valley. During the festival I had noticed several young females whose skins were almost as white as any Saxon damsels; a slight dash of the mantling brown being all that marked the difference. The comparative fairness of complexion, though in a great degree perfectly natural, is partly the result of an artificial process, and of an entire exclusion from the sun. The juice of the "papa" root found in great abundance at the head of the valley, is held in great esteem as a cosmetic, with which many of the females daily anoint their whole person. The habitual use of it whitens and beautifies the skin. Those of the young girls who resort to this method of heightening their charms, never expose themselves to the rays of the sun; an observance, however, that produces little or no inconvenience, since there are but few of the inhabited portions of the vale which are not shaded over with a spreading canopy of boughs, so that one may journey from house to house, scarcely deviating from the direct course, and yet never once see his shadow cast upon the ground.

The "papa," when used, is suffered to remain upon the skin for several hours; being of a light green color, it consequently imparts for the time a similar hue to the complexion. Nothing, therefore, can be imagined more singular than the appearance of these nearly naked damsels immediately after the application of the cosmetic. To look at one of them you would almost suppose she was some vegetable in an unripe state; and that, instead of living in the shade forever, she ought to be placed out in the sun to ripen.

All the islanders are more or less in the habit of anointing themselves; the women preferring the "aker" to "papa," and the men using the oil of the cocoanut. Mehevi was remarkably fond of mollifying his entire cuticle with this ointment. Sometimes he might be seen, with his whole body fairly reeking with the perfumed oil of the nut, looking as if he had just emerged from a soap-boiler's vat, or had undergone the process of dipping in a tallow-chandlery. To this cause perhaps, united to their frequent bathing and extreme cleanliness, is ascribable, in a great measure, the marvelous purity and smoothness of skin exhibited by the natives in general.

The prevailing tint among the women of the valley was a light olive, and of this style of complexion Fayaway afforded the most beautiful example. Others were still darker, while not a few were of a genuine golden color, and some of a swarthy hue.

As agreeing with much previously mentioned in this narrative, I may here observe that Mendaña, their discoverer, in his account of the Marquesas, described the natives as wondrously beautiful to behold, and as nearly resembling the people of southern Europe. The first of these islands seen by Mendaña was La Madelena, which is not far distant from Nukuheva; and its inhabitants in every respect resemble those dwelling on that and the other islands of the group. Figueroa, the chronicler of Mendaña's voyage, says, that on the morning the land was descried, when the Spaniards drew near the shore, there sallied forth, in rude procession, about seventy canoes, and at the same time many of the inhabitants (females, I presume) made towards the ships by swimming. He adds, that "in complexion they were nearly white; of good stature, and finely formed; and on their faces and bodies were delineated representations of fishes and other devices." The old Don then goes on to say, "There came, among others, two lads paddling their canoe, whose eyes were fixed on the ship: they had beautiful faces and the most promising animation of countenance; and were in all things so becoming, that the pilot-mayor Quiros affirmed, nothing in his life ever caused him so much regret as the leaving such fine creatures to be lost in that country."[1] More than two hundred years have gone by since the passage of which the above is a translation was written; and it appears to me now, as I read it, as fresh and true as if written but yesterday. The islanders are still the same; and I have seen boys in the Typee Valley of whose "beautiful faces" and "promising animation of countenance" no one who has not beheld them can form any adequate idea. Cook, in the account of his voyage, pronounces the Marquesans as by far the most splendid islanders in the South Seas. Stewart, the chaplain of the U.S. ship *Vincennes*, in his "Scenes in the South Seas," expresses, in more than one place, his amazement at the surpassing loveliness of the women; and says that many of the Nukuheva damsels reminded him forcibly of the most celebrated beauties in his own land. Fanning, a Yankee mariner of some reputation, likewise records his lively impressions of the physical appearance of these people; and Commodore David Porter of the U.S. frigate *Essex*, is said to have been vastly smitten by the beauty of the ladies. Their great superiority over all other Polynesians cannot fail to attract the notice of those who visit the principal groups in the Pacific. The voluptuous Tahitians are the only people who at all deserve to be compared with them; while the dark-hued Hawaiians and the woolly-headed Fijis are immeasurably inferior to them. The distinguishing characteristic of the Marquesan islanders, and that which at once strikes you, is the European cast of their features—a peculiarity seldom observable among other uncivilized people. Many of their faces present a profile classically beautiful, and in the valley of Typee, I saw several who, like the stranger Marnoo, were in every respect models of beauty.

Some of the natives present at the Feast of Calabashes had displayed a few articles of European dress; disposed, however, about their persons after their own peculiar fashion. Among these I perceived two pieces of cotton-cloth which poor Toby and myself had bestowed upon our youthful guides the afternoon we entered the valley. They were evidently reserved for gala days; and during those of the festival they rendered the young islanders who wore them very distinguished characters. The small number who were similarly adorned, and the great value they appeared to

1. This passage, which is cited as an almost literal translation from the original, I found in a small volume entitled "Circumnavigation of the Globe," in which volume are several extracts from "Dalrymple's Historical Collections." The last-mentioned work I have never seen, but it is said to contain a very correct English version of great part of the learned Doctor Christoval Suaverde da Figueroa's History of Mendaña's Voyage, published at Madrid, A.D. 1613.

place upon the most common and most trivial articles, furnished ample evidence of the very restricted intercourse they held with vessels touching at the island. A few cotton handkerchiefs, of a gay pattern, tied about the neck, and suffered to fall over the shoulders; strips of fanciful calico, swathed about the loins, were nearly all I saw.

Indeed, throughout the valley, there were few things of any kind to be seen of European origin. All I ever saw, besides the articles just alluded to, were the six muskets preserved in the Ti, and three or four similar implements of warfare hung up in other houses; some small canvas bags, partly filled with bullets and powder, and half a dozen old hatchet-heads, with the edges blunted and battered to such a degree as to render them utterly useless. These last seemed to be regarded as nearly worthless by the natives; and several times they held up one of them before me, and throwing it aside with a gesture of disgust, manifested their contempt for anything that could so soon become unserviceable.

But the muskets, the powder, and the bullets were held in most extravagant esteem. The former, from their great age and the peculiarities they exhibited, were well worthy a place in any antiquarian's armory. I remember in particular one that hung in the Ti, and which Mehevi—supposing as a matter of course that I was able to repair it—had put into my hands for that purpose. It was one of those clumsy, old-fashioned, English pieces known generally as Tower Hill muskets, and, for aught I know, might have been left on the island by Wallace, Carteret, Cook, or Vancouver. The stock was half rotten and worm-eaten; the lock was as rusty and about as well adapted to its ostensible purpose as an old door-hinge; the threading of the screws about the trigger was completely worn away; while the barrel shook in the wood. Such was the weapon the chief desired me to restore to its original condition. As I did not possess the accomplishments of a gunsmith, and was likewise destitute of the necessary tools, I was reluctantly obliged to signify my inability to perform the task. At this unexpected communication Mehevi regarded me, for a moment, as if he half suspected I was some inferior sort of white man, who after all did not know much more than a Typee. However, after a most labored explanation of the matter, I succeeded in making him understand the extreme difficulty of the task. Scarcely satisfied with my apologies, however, he marched off with the superannuated musket in something of a huff, as if he would no longer expose it to the indignity of being manipulated by such unskillful fingers.

During the festival I had not failed to remark the simplicity of manner, the freedom from all restraint, and, to certain degree, the equality of condition manifested by the natives in general. No one appeared to assume any arrogant pretensions. There was little more than a slight difference in costume to distinguish the chiefs from the other natives. All appeared to mix together freely, and without any reserve; although I noticed that the wishes of a chief, even when delivered in the mildest tone, received the same immediate obedience which elsewhere would have been only accorded to a peremptory command. What may be the extent of the authority of the chiefs over the rest of the tribe, I will not venture to assert; but from all I saw during my stay in the valley, I was induced to believe that in matters concerning the general welfare it was very limited. The required degree of deference towards them, however, was willingly and cheerfully yielded; and as all authority is transmitted from father to son, I have no doubt that one of the effects here, as elsewhere, of high birth, is to induce respect and obedience.

The civil institutions of the Marquesas Islands appear to be in this, as in other respects, directly the reverse of those of the Tahitian and Hawaiian groups, where the original power of the king and chiefs was far more despotic than that of any tyrant in civilized countries. At Tahiti it used to be death for one of the inferior orders to approach, without permission, under the shadow of the king's house; or fail in paying the customary reverence when food destined for the king was borne past them by his messengers. At the Sandwich Islands, Kaahumanu, the gigantic old dowager queen—a woman of nearly four hundred pounds' weight, and who is said to be still living at Mowee—was accustomed, in some of her terrific gusts of temper, to snatch up an ordinary sized man who had offended her, and snap his spine across her knee. Incredible as this may seem, it is a fact. While at Lahainaluna—the residence of this monstrous Jezebel—a humpbacked wretch was pointed out to me, who, some twenty-five years previously, had had the vertebrae of his backbone very seriously discomposed by his gentle mistress.

The particular grades of rank existing among the chiefs of Typee, I could not in all cases determine. Previous to the Feast of Calabashes I had been puzzled what particular station to assign to Mehevi. But the important part he took upon that occasion convinced me that he had no superior among the inhabitants of the valley. I had invariably noticed a certain degree of deference paid to him by all with whom I had ever seen him brought in contact; but when I remembered that my wanderings had been confined to a limited portion of the valley, and that towards the sea a number of distinguished chiefs resided, some of whom had separately visited me at Marheyo's house, and whom, until the Festival, I had never seen in the company of Mehevi, I felt disposed to believe that his rank after all might not be particularly elevated.

The revels, however, had brought together all the warriors whom I had seen individually and in groups at different times and places. Among them Mehevi moved with an easy air of superiority which was not to be mistaken; and he whom I had only looked at as the hospitable host of the Ti, and one of the military leaders of the tribe, now assumed in my eyes the dignity of royal station. His striking costume, no less than his naturally commanding figure, seemed indeed to give him preeminence over the rest. The towering helmet of feathers that he wore raised him in height above all who surrounded him; and though some others were similarly adorned, the length and luxuriance of their plumes were far inferior to his.

Mehevi was in fact the greatest of the chiefs—the head of his clan—the sovereign of the valley; and the simplicity of the social institutions of the people could not have been more completely proved than by the fact, that after having been several weeks in the valley, and almost in daily intercourse with Mehevi, I should have remained until the time of the festival ignorant of his regal character. But a new light had now broken in upon me. The Ti was the palace—and Mehevi the king. Both the one and the other of a most simple and patriarchal nature it must be allowed, and wholly unattended by the ceremonious pomp which usually surrounds the purple.

After having made this discovery I could not avoid congratulating myself that Mehevi had from the first taken me as it were under his royal protection, and that he still continued to entertain for me the warmest regard, as far at least as I was enabled to judge from appearances. For the future I determined to pay most assiduous court to him, hoping that eventually through his kindness I might obtain my liberty.

Chapter XXVI

KING MEHEVI—ALLUSION TO HIS HAWAIIAN MAJESTY—CONDUCT OF MARHEYO AND MEHEVI IN CERTAIN DELICATE MATTERS—PECULIAR SYSTEM OF MARRIAGE—NUMBER OF POPULATION—UNIFORMITY—EMBALMING—PLACES OF SEPULCHURE—FUNERAL OBSEQUIES AT NUKUHEVA—NUMBER OF INHABITANTS IN TYPEE—LOCATION OF THE DWELLINGS—HAPPINESS ENJOYED IN THE VALLEY—A WARNING—SOME IDEAS WITH REGARD TO THE CIVILIZATION OF THE ISLANDS—REFERENCE TO THE PRESENT STATE OF THE HAWAIIANS—FASHIONABLE EQUIPAGES AT OAHU—REFLECTIONS

KING MEHEVI!—A GOODLY SOUNDING TITLE!—AND WHY SHOULD I NOT BESTOW IT UPON THE foremost man in the valley of Typee? The republican missionaries of Oahu cause to be gazetted in the Court Journal, published at Honolulu, the most trivial movements of "his gracious majesty" King Kamehameha III, and "their highnesses the princes of the blood royal."[1] And who is his "gracious majesty," and what the quality of this "blood royal?"—His "gracious majesty" is a fat, lazy, negro-looking blockhead, with as little character as power. He has lost the noble traits of the barbarian, without acquiring the redeeming graces of a civilized being; and, although a member of the Hawaiian Temperance Society, is a most inveterate dram-drinker.

The "blood royal" is an extremely thick, depraved fluid; formed principally of raw fish, bad brandy, and European sweetmeats, and is charged with a variety of eruptive humors, which are developed in sundry blotches and pimples upon the august face of "majesty itself," and the angelic countenances of the "princes and princesses of the blood royal!"

Now, if the farcical puppet of a chief magistrate in the Sandwich Islands be allowed the title of King, why should it be withheld from the noble savage Mehevi, who is a thousand times more worthy of the appellation? All hail, therefore, Mehevi, King of the Cannibal Valley, and long life and prosperity to his Typeean majesty! May Heaven for many a year preserve him, the uncompromising foe of Nukuheva and the French, if a hostile attitude will secure his lovely domain from the remorseless inflictions of South Sea civilization.

Previously to seeing the Dancing Widows I had little idea that there were any matrimonial relations subsisting in Typee, and I should as soon have thought of a Platonic affection being cultivated between the sexes, as of the solemn connection of man and wife. To be sure, there were old

1. Accounts like these are sometimes copied into English and American journals. They lead the reader to infer that the arts and customs of civilized life are rapidly refining the natives of the Sandwich Islands. But let no one be deceived by these accounts. The chiefs swagger about in gold lace and broadcloth, while the great mass of the common people are nearly as primitive in their appearance as in the days of Cook. In the progress of events at these islands, the two classes are receding from each other; the chiefs are daily becoming more luxurious and extravagant in their style of living, and the common people more and more destitute of the necessaries and decencies of life. But the end to which both will arrive at last will be the same: the one are fast destroying themselves by sensual indulgences, and the other are fast *being* destroyed by a complication of disorders, and the want of wholesome food. The resources of the domineering chiefs are wrung from the starving serfs, and every additional bauble with which they bedeck themselves is purchased by the sufferings of their bondsmen; so that the measure of gew-gaw refinement attained by the chiefs is only an index to the actual state of degradation in which the greater portion of the population lie groveling.

Marheyo and Tinor, who seemed to have a sort of nuptial understanding with one another; but for all that, I had sometimes observed a comical-looking old gentleman dressed in a suit of shabby tattooing, who had the audacity to take various liberties with the lady, and that too in the very presence of the old warrior her husband, who looked on as good-naturedly as if nothing was happening. This behavior, until subsequent discoveries enlightened me, puzzled me more than anything else I witnessed in Typee.

As for Mehevi, I had supposed him a confirmed bachelor, as well as most of the principal chiefs. At any rate, if they had wives and families, they ought to have been ashamed of themselves; for sure I am, they never troubled themselves about any domestic affairs. In truth, Mehevi seemed to be the president of a club of hearty fellows, who kept "Bachelor's Hall" in fine style at the Ti. I had no doubt but that they regarded children as odious encumbrances; and their ideas of domestic felicity were sufficiently shown in the fact, that they allowed no meddlesome housekeepers to turn topsy-turvy those snug little arrangements they had made in their comfortable dwelling. I strongly suspected however, that some of these jolly bachelors were carrying on love intrigues with the maidens of the tribe; although they did not appear publicly to acknowledge them. I happened to pop upon Mehevi three or four times when he was romping—in a most undignified manner for a warrior king—with one of the prettiest little witches in the valley. She lived with an old woman and a young man, in a house near Marheyo's; and although in appearance a mere child herself, had a noble boy about a year old, who bore a marvelous resemblance to Mehevi, whom I should certainly have believed to have been the father, were it not that the little fellow had no triangle on his face—but on second thoughts, tattooing is not hereditary. Mehevi, however, was not the only person upon whom the damsel Moonoony smiled—the young fellow of fifteen, who permanently resided in the house with her, was decidedly in her good graces. I sometimes beheld both him and the chief making love at the same time. Is it possible, thought I, that the valiant warrior can consent to give up a corner in the thing he loves? This too was a mystery which, with others of the same kind, was afterwards satisfactorily explained.

During the second day of the Feast of Calabashes, Kory-Kory—being determined that I should have some understanding on these matters—had, in the course of his explanations, directed my attention to a peculiarity I had frequently remarked among many of the females;—principally those of a mature age and rather matronly appearance. This consisted in having the right hand and the left foot most elaborately tattooed; while the rest of the body was wholly free from the operation of the art, with the exception of the minutely dotted lips and slight marks on the shoulders, to which I have previously referred as comprising the sole tattooing exhibited by Fayaway, in common with other young girls of her age. The hand and foot thus embellished were, according to Kory-Kory, the distinguishing badge of wedlock, so far as that social and highly commendable institution is known among those people. It answers, indeed, the same purpose as the plain gold ring worn by our fairer spouses.

After Kory-Kory's explanation of the subject, I was for some time studiously respectful in the presence of all females thus distinguished, and never ventured to indulge in the slightest approach to flirtation with any of their number. Married women, to be sure!—I knew better than to offend them.

A further insight however into the peculiar domestic customs of the inmates of the valley did away in a measure with the severity of my scruples, and convinced me that I was deceived in some at least of my conclusions. A regular system of polygamy exists among the islanders; but of a most extraordinary nature—a plurality of husbands, instead of wives; and this solitary fact speaks volumes for the gentle disposition of the male population. Where else, indeed, could such a practice exist, even for a single day? Imagine a revolution brought about in a Turkish seraglio, and the harem rendered the abode of bearded men; or conceive some beautiful woman in our own country running distracted at the sight of her numerous lovers murdering one another before her eyes, out of jealousy for the unequal distribution of her favors! Heaven defend us from such a state of things! We are scarcely amiable and forbearing enough to submit to it.

I was not able to learn what particular ceremony was observed in forming the marriage contract, but am inclined to think that it must have been of a very simple nature. Perhaps the mere "popping the question," as it is termed with us, might have been followed by an immediate nuptial alliance. At any rate, I have more than one reason to believe that tedious courtships are unknown in the valley of Typee.

The males considerably outnumber the females. This holds true of many of the islands of Polynesia, although the reverse of what is the case in most civilized countries. The girls are first wooed and won, at a very tender age, by some stripling in the household in which they reside. This, however, is a mere frolic of the affections, and no formal engagement is contracted. By the time this first love has a little subsided, a second suitor presents himself, of graver years, and carries both boy and girl away to his own habitation. This disinterested and generous-hearted fellow now weds the young couple—marrying damsel and lover at the same time—and all three thenceforth live together as harmoniously as so many turtles. I have heard of some men who in civilized countries rashly marry large families with their wives, but had no idea that there was any place where people married supplementary husbands with them. Infidelity on either side is very rare. No man has more than one wife, and no wife of mature years has less than two husbands—sometimes she has three, but such instances are not frequent. The marriage tie, whatever it may be, does not appear to be indissoluble; for separations occasionally happen. These, however, when they do take place, produce no unhappiness, and are preceded by no bickerings; for the simple reason, that an ill-used wife or a henpecked husband is not obliged to file a bill in Chancery to obtain a divorce. As nothing stands in the way of a separation, the matrimonial yoke sits easily and lightly, and a Typee wife lives on very pleasant and sociable terms with her husband. On the whole, wedlock, as known among these Typees, seems to be of a more distinct and enduring nature than is usually the case with barbarous people. A baneful promiscuous intercourse of the sexes is hereby avoided, and virtue, without being clamorously invoked, is, as it were, unconsciously practiced.

The contrast exhibited between the Marquesas and other islanders of the Pacific in this respect, is worthy of being noticed. At Tahiti the marriage tie was altogether unknown; and the relation of husband and wife, father and son, could hardly be said to exist. The Areoi Society—one of the most singular institutions that ever existed in any part of the world—spread universal licentiousness over the island. It was the voluptuous character of these people which rendered the disease introduced among them by De Bougainville's ships, in 1768, doubly destructive. It visited them like a plague, sweeping them off by hundreds.

Notwithstanding the existence of wedlock among the Typees, the Scriptural injunction to increase and multiply seems to be but indifferently attended to. I never saw any of those large families in arithmetical or step-ladder progression which one often meets with at home. I never knew of more than two youngsters living together in the same home, and but seldom even that number. As for the women, it was very plain that the anxieties of the nursery but seldom disturbed the serenity of their souls; and they were never seen going about the valley with half a score of little ones tagging at their apron-strings, or rather at the bread-fruit-leaf they usually wore in the rear.

The ratio of increase among all the Polynesian nations is very small; and in some places as yet uncorrupted by intercourse with Europeans, the births would appear not very little to outnumber the deaths; the population in such instances remaining nearly the same for several successive generations, even upon those islands seldom or never desolated by wars, and among people with whom the crime of infanticide is altogether unknown. This would seem expressly ordained by Providence to prevent the overstocking of the islands with a race too indolent to cultivate the ground, and who, for that reason alone, would, by any considerable increase in their numbers, be exposed to the most deplorable misery. During the entire period of my stay in the valley of Typee, I never saw more than ten or twelve children under the age of six months, and only became aware of two births.

It is to the absence of the marriage tie that the late rapid decrease of the population of the Sandwich Islands and of Tahiti is in part to be ascribed. The vices and diseases introduced among these unhappy people annually swell the ordinary mortality of the islands, while, from the same cause, the originally small number of births is proportionally decreased. Thus the progress of the Hawaiians and Tahitians to utter extinction is accelerated in a sort of compound ratio.

I have before had occasion to remark that I never saw any of the ordinary signs of a place of sepulture in the valley, a circumstance which I attributed, at the time, to my living in a particular part of it, and being forbidden to extend my rambles to any considerable distance towards the sea. I have since thought it probable, however, that the Typees, either desirous of removing from their sight the evidences of mortality, or prompted by a taste for rural beauty, may have some charming cemetery situated in the shadowy recesses along the base of the mountains. At Nukuheva, two or three large quadrangular "pi-pis," heavily flagged, enclosed with regular stone walls, and shaded over and almost hidden from view by the interlacing branches of enormous trees, were pointed out to me as burial-places. The bodies, I understood, were deposited in rude vaults beneath the flagging, and were suffered to remain there without being disinterred. Although nothing could be more strange and gloomy than the aspect of these places, where the lofty trees threw their dark shadows over rude blocks of stone, a stranger in looking at them would have discerned none of the ordinary evidences of a place of sepulture.

During my stay in the valley, as none of its inmates were so accommodating as to die and be buried in order to gratify my curiosity with regard to their funeral rites, I was reluctantly obliged to remain in ignorance of them. As I have reason to believe, however, the observances of the Typees in these matters are the same with those of all the other tribes on the island, I will here relate a scene I chanced to witness at Nukuheva.

A young man had died, about daybreak, in a house near the beach. I had been sent ashore that morning, and saw a good deal of the preparations they were making for his obsequies. The body, neatly wrapped in a new white tappa, was laid out in an open shed of cocoanut boughs, upon a bier constructed of elastic bamboos ingeniously twisted together. This was supported, about two feet from the ground, by large canes planted uprightly in the earth. Two females, of a dejected appearance, watched by its side, plaintively chanting and beating the air with large grass fans whitened with pipe-clay. In the dwelling-house adjoining a numerous company were assembled, and various articles of food were being prepared for consumption. Two or three individuals, distinguished by head-dresses of beautiful tappa, and wearing a great number of ornaments, appeared to officiate as masters of the ceremonies. By noon the entertainment had fairly begun, and we were told that it would last during the whole of the two following days. With the exception of those who mourned by the corpse, everyone seemed disposed to drown the sense of the late bereavement in convivial indulgence. The girls, decked out in their savage finery, danced; the old men chanted; the warriors smoked and chatted; and the young and lusty, of both sexes, feasted plentifully, and seemed to enjoy themselves as pleasantly as they could have done had it been a wedding.

The islanders understand the art of embalming, and practice it with such success, that the bodies of their great chiefs are frequently preserved for many years in the very houses where they died. I saw three of these in my visit to the Bay of Tior. One was enveloped in immense folds of tappa, with only the face exposed, and hung erect against the side of the dwelling. The others were stretched out upon biers of bamboo, in open, elevated temples, which seemed consecrated to their memory. The heads of enemies killed in battle are invariably preserved and hung up as trophies in the house of the conqueror. I am not acquainted with the process which is in use, but believe that fumigation is the principal agency employed. All the remains which I saw presented the appearance of a ham after being suspended for some time in a smoky chimney.

But to return from the dead to the living. The late festival had drawn together, as I had every reason to believe, the whole population of the vale, and consequently I was enabled to make some estimate with regard to its numbers. I should imagine that there were about two thousand inhabitants in Typee; and no number could have been better adapted to the extent of the valley. The valley is some nine miles in length, and may average one in breadth; the houses being distributed at wide intervals throughout its whole extent, principally, however, towards the head of the vale. There are no villages: the houses stand here and there in the shadow of the groves, or are scattered along the banks of the winding stream; their golden-hued bamboo sides and gleaming white thatch forming a beautiful contrast to the perpetual verdure in which they are embowered. There are no roads of any kind in the valley—nothing but a labyrinth of footpaths twisting and turning among the thickets without end.

The penalty of the Fall presses very lightly upon the valley of Typee; for, with the one solitary exception of striking a light, I scarcely saw any piece of work performed there which caused the sweat to stand upon a single brow. As for digging and delving for a livelihood, the thing is altogether unknown. Nature had planted the bread-fruit and the banana, and in her own good time she brings them to maturity, when the idle savage stretches forth his hand, and satisfies his appetite.

Ill-fated people! I shudder when I think of the change a few years will produce in their paradisaical abode; and probably when the most destructive vices, and the worst attendances on civilization, shall have driven all peace and happiness from the valley, the magnanimous French will proclaim to the world that the Marquesas Islands have been converted to Christianity! and this the Catholic world will doubtless consider as a glorious event. Heaven help the "Isles of the Sea!"—The sympathy which Christendom feels for them, has, alas! in too many instances proved their bane.

How little do some of these poor islanders comprehend when they look around them, that no inconsiderable part of their disasters originate in certain tea-party excitements, under the influence of which benevolent-looking gentlemen in white cravats solicit alms, and old ladies in spectacles, and young ladies in sober russet gowns, contribute sixpences towards the creation of a fund, the object of which is to ameliorate the spiritual condition of the Polynesians, but whose end has almost invariably been to accomplish their temporal destruction!

Let the savages be civilized, but civilize them with benefits, and not with evils; and let heathenism be destroyed, but not by destroying the heathen. The Anglo-Saxon hive have extirpated Paganism from the greater part of the North American continent; but with it they have likewise extirpated the greater portion of the Red race. Civilization is gradually sweeping from the earth the lingering vestiges of Paganism, and at the same time the shrinking forms of its unhappy worshipers.

Among the islands of Polynesia, no sooner are the images overturned, the temples demolished, and the idolators converted into *nominal* Christians, than disease, vice, and premature death make their appearance. The depopulated land is then recruited from the rapacious hordes of enlightened individuals who settle themselves within its border, and clamorously announce the progress of the Truth. Neat villas, trim gardens, shaven lawns, spires, and cupolas arise, while the poor savage soon finds himself an interloper in the country of his fathers, and that too on the very site of the hut where he was born. The spontaneous fruits of the earth, which God in his wisdom had ordained for the support of the indolent natives, remorselessly seized upon and appropriated by the stranger, are devoured before the eyes of the starving inhabitants, or sent on board the numerous vessels which now touch at their shores.

When the famished wretches are cut off in this manner from their natural supplies, they are told by their benefactors to work and earn their support by the sweat of their brows! But to no fine gentleman born to hereditary opulence does manual labor come more unkindly than to the luxurious Indian when thus robbed of the bounty of Heaven. Habituated to a life of indolence, he cannot and will not exert himself; and want, disease, and vice, all evils of foreign growth, soon terminate his miserable existence.

But what matters all this? Behold the glorious result!—The abominations of Paganism have given way to the pure rites of the Christian worship—the ignorant savage has been supplanted by the refined European! Look at Honolulu, the metropolis of the Sandwich Islands!—A community of disinterested merchants, and devoted self-exiled heralds of the Cross, located on the very spot that twenty years ago was defiled by the presence of idolatry. What a subject for an eloquent Bible-meeting orator! Nor has such an opportunity for a display of missionary rhetoric been allowed to pass by unimproved!—But when these philanthropists send us such glowing accounts of one half of their labors, why does their modesty restrain them from publishing the other half of the good they have wrought?—Not until I visited Honolulu was I aware of the fact that the small remnant of the natives had been civilized into draft horses, and evangelized into beasts of burden. But so it is. They have been literally broken into the traces, and are harnessed to the vehicles of their spiritual instructors like so many dumb brutes!

Lest the slightest misconception should arise from anything thrown out in this chapter, or indeed in any other part of the volume, let me here observe, that against the cause of missions in the abstract no Christian can possibly be opposed: it is in truth a just and holy cause. But if the great end proposed by it be spiritual, the agency employed to accomplish that end is purely earthly; and, although the object in view be the achievement of much good, that agency may nevertheless be productive of evil. In short, missionary undertaking, however it may blessed of Heaven, is in itself but human; and subject, like everything else, to errors and abuses. And have not errors and abuses crept into the most sacred places, and may there not be unworthy or incapable missionaries abroad, as well as ecclesiastics of similar character at home? May not the unworthiness or incapacity of those who assume apostolic functions upon the remote islands of the sea more easily escape detection by the world at large than if it were displayed in the heart of a city? An unwarranted confidence in the sanctity of its apostles—a proneness to regard them as incapable of guile—and an impatience of the least suspicion to their rectitude as men or Christians, have ever been prevailing faults in the Church. Nor is this to be wondered at: for subject as Christianity is to the assaults of unprincipled foes, we are naturally disposed to regard everything like an exposure of ecclesiastical misconduct as the offspring of malevolence or irreligious feeling. Not even this last consideration, however, shall deter me from the honest expression of my sentiments.

There is something decidedly wrong in the practical operations of the Sandwich Islands Mission. Those who from pure religious motives contribute to the support of this enterprise, should take care to ascertain that their donations, flowing through many devious channels, at last effect their legitimate object, the conversion of the Hawaiians. I urge this not because I doubt the moral probity of those who disburse the funds, but because I know that they are not rightly applied. To read pathetic accounts of missionary hardships, and glowing descriptions of conversions, and baptisms taking place beneath palm-trees, is one thing; and to go to the Sandwich Islands and see the missionaries dwelling in picturesque and prettily-furnished coral-rock villas, whilst the miserable natives are committing all sorts of immoralities around them, is quite another.

In justice to the missionaries, however, I will willingly admit, that whatever evils may have resulted from their collective mismanagement of the business of the mission, and from the want of vital piety evinced by some of their number, still the present deplorable condition of the Sandwich Islands is by no means wholly chargeable against them. The demoralizing influence of a dissolute foreign population, and the frequent visits of all descriptions of vessels, have tended not a little to increase the evils alluded to. In a word, here, as in every case where Civilization has in any way been introduced among those whom we call savages, she has scattered her vices, and withheld her blessings.

As wise a man as Shakespeare has said, that the bearer of evil tidings hath but a losing office; and so I suppose will it prove with me, in communicating to the trusting friends of the Hawiian Mission what has been disclosed in various portions of this narrative. I am persuaded, however, that as these disclosures will by their very nature attract attention, so they will lead to something which will not be without ultimate benefit to the cause of Christianity in the Sandwich Islands.

I have but one more thing to add in connection with this subject—those things which I have stated as facts will remain facts, in spite of whatever the bigoted or incredulous may say or write against them. My reflections, however, on those facts may not be free from error. If such be the case, I claim no further indulgence than should be conceded to every man whose object is to do good.

Chapter XXVII

The Social Condition and General Character of the Typees

I have already mentioned that the influence exerted over the people of the valley by their chiefs was mild in the extreme: and as to any general rule or standard of conduct by which the commonality were governed in their intercourse with each other, so far as my observation extended, I should be almost tempted to say that none existed on the island, except, indeed, the mysterious "Taboo" be considered as such. During the time I lived among the Typees, no one was ever put upon his trial for any offense against the public. To all appearances there were no courts of law or equity. There was no municipal police for the purpose of apprehending vagrants and disorderly characters. In short, there were no legal provisions whatever for the well-being and conservation of society, the enlightened end of civilized legislation. And yet everything went on in the valley with a harmony and smoothness unparalleled, I will venture to assert, in the most select, refined, and pious associations of mortals in Christendom. How are we to explain this enigma? These islanders were heathens! savages! ay, cannibals! and how came they, without the aid of established law, to exhibit, in so eminent a degree, that social order which is the greatest blessing and highest pride of the social state?

It may reasonably be inquired, how were these people governed? how were their passions controlled in their every day transactions? It must have been by an inherent principle of honesty and charity towards each other. They seemed to be governed by that sort of tacit common-sense law, which, say what they will of the inborn lawlessness of the human race, has its precepts graven on every breast. The grand principles of virtue and honor, however they may be distorted by arbitrary codes, are the same all the world over: and where these principles are concerned, the right or wrong of any action appears the same to the uncultivated as to the enlightened mind. It is to this in-dwelling, this universally diffused perception of what is *just* and *noble*, that the integrity of the Marquesans in their intercourse with each other is to be attributed. In the darkest nights they slept securely, with all their worldly wealth around them, in houses the doors of which were never fastened. The disquieting ideas of theft or assassination never disturbed them. Each islander reposed beneath his own palmetto thatching, or sat under his own bread-fruit-tree, with none to molest or alarm him. There was not a padlock in the valley, nor anything that answered the purpose of one: still there was no community of goods. This long spear, so elegantly carved and highly polished, belongs to Wormoonoo: it is far handsomer than the one which old Marheyo so greatly prizes; it is the most valuable article belonging to its owner. And yet I have seen it leaning against a cocoanut-tree in the grove, and there it was found when sought for. Here is a sperm-whale tooth, graven all over with cunning devices: it is the property of Karluna: it is the most precious of the damsel's ornaments. In her estimation its price is far above rubies—and yet there hangs the dental jewel by its cord of braided bark, in the girl's house, which is far back in the valley; the door is left open, and all the inmates have gone off to bathe in the stream.[1]

So much for the respect in which "personal property" is held in Typee; how secure an investment of "real property" may be, I cannot take upon me to say. Whether the land of the valley was the joint property of its inhabitants, or whether it was parceled out among a certain number of landed proprietors who allowed everybody to "squat" and "poach" as much as he or she pleased, I never could ascertain. At any rate, musty parchments and title deeds there were none on the island; and I am half inclined to believe that its inhabitants hold their broad valleys in fee simple from Nature herself; to have and to hold, so long as grass grows and water runs; or until their French visitors, by a summary mode of conveyancing, shall appropriate them to their own benefit and behoof.

Yesterday I saw Kory-Kory hie him away, armed with a long pole, with which, standing on the ground, he knocked down the fruit from the topmost boughs of the trees, and brought them home in his basket of cocoanut leaves. To-day I see an islander, whom I know to reside in a distant part of the valley, doing the self-same thing. On the sloping bank of the stream are a number of banana-trees. I have often seen a score or two of young people making a merry foray on the great golden clusters, and bearing them off, one after another, to different parts of the vale, shouting and trampling as they went. No churlish old curmudgeon could have been the owner of that grove of bread-fruit-trees, or of these gloriously yellow bunches of bananas.

From what I have said it will be perceived that there is a vast difference between "personal property" and "real estate" in the valley of Typee. Some individuals, of course, are more wealthy than others. For example: the ridge-pole of Marheyo's house bends under the weight of many a huge package of tappa; his long couch is laid with mats placed one upon the other seven deep. Outside, Tinor has ranged along in her bamboo cupboard—or whatever the place may be called—a goodly array of calabashes and wooden trenchers. Now, the house just beyond the grove, and next to Marheyo's, occupied by Ruaruga, is not quite so well furnished. There are only three moderate-sized packages swinging overhead: there are only two layers of mats beneath, and the calabashes and trenchers are not so numerous, nor so tastefully stained and carved. But then, Ruaruga has a house—not so pretty a one, to be sure—but just as commodious as Marheyo's; and, I suppose, if he wished to vie with his neighbor's establishment, he could do so with very little trouble. These, in short, constituted the chief differences perceivable in the relative wealth of the people in Typee.

Civilization does not engross all the virtues of humanity: she has not even her full share of them. They flourish in greater abundance and attain greater strength among many barbarous people. The hospitality of the wild Arab, the courage of the North American Indian, and the faithful friendship of some of the Polynesian nations, far surpass anything of a similar kind among the polished communities of Europe. If truth and justice, and the better principles of our nature, cannot exist unless enforced by the statute-book, how are we to account for the social condition of the Typees? So pure and upright were they in all the relations of life, that entering their valley, as I did, under the most erroneous impressions of their character, I was soon led to exclaim in amazement: "Are these the ferocious savages, the blood-thirsty cannibals of whom I have heard such frightful

1. The strict honesty which the inhabitants of nearly all the Polynesian Islands manifest towards each other, is in striking contrast with the thieving propensities some of them evince in their intercourse with foreigners. It would almost seem that, according to their peculiar code of morals, the pilfering of a hatchet or a wrought nail from a European is looked upon as a praiseworthy action. Or rather, it may be presumed, that bearing in mind the wholesale forays made upon them by their nautical visitors, they consider the property of the latter as a fair object of reprisal. This consideration, while it serves to reconcile an apparent contradiction in the moral character of the islanders, should in some measure alter that low opinion of it which the reader of South Sea voyages is too apt to form.

tales! They deal more kindly with each other, and are more humane, than many who study essays on virtue and benevolence, and who repeat every night that beautiful prayer breathed first by the lips of the divine and gentle Jesus." I will frankly declare, that after passing a few weeks in this valley of the Marquesas, I formed a higher estimate of human nature than I had ever before entertained. But alas! since then I have been one of the crew of a man-of-war, and the pent-up wickedness of five hundred men has nearly overturned all my previous theories.

There was one admirable trait in the general character of the Typees which, more than anything else, secured my admiration: it was the unanimity of feeling they displayed on every occasion. With them there hardly appeared to be any difference of opinion upon any subject whatever. They all thought and acted alike. I do not conceive that they could support a debating society for a single night: there would be nothing to dispute about; and were they to call a convention to take into consideration the state of the tribe, its session would be a remarkably short one. They showed this spirit of unanimity in every action of life: everything was done in concert and good fellowship. I will give an instance of this fraternal feeling.

One day, in returning with Kory-Kory from my accustomed visit to the Ti, we passed by a little opening in the grove; on one side of which, my attendant informed me, was that afternoon to be built a dwelling of bamboo. At least a hundred of the natives were bringing materials to the ground, some carrying in their hands one or two of the canes which were to form the sides, others slender rods of the habiscus, strung with palmetto leaves, for the roof. Everyone contributed something to the work; and by the united, but easy, and even indolent, labors of all, the entire work was completed before sunset. The islanders, while employed in erecting this tenement, reminded me of a colony of beavers at work. To be sure, they were hardly as silent and demure as those wonderful creatures, nor were they by any means as diligent. To tell the truth, they were somewhat inclined to be lazy, but a perfect tumult of hilarity prevailed; and they worked together so unitedly, and seemed actuated by such an instinct of friendliness, that it was truly beautiful to behold.

Not a single female took part in this employment: and if the degree of consideration in which the ever-adorable sex is held by the men be—as the philosophers affirm—a just criterion of the degree of refinement among a people, then I may truly pronounce the Typees to be as polished a community as ever the sun shone upon. The religious restrictions of the taboo alone excepted, the women of the valley were allowed every possible indulgence. Nowhere are the ladies more assiduously courted; nowhere are they better appreciated as the contributors to our highest enjoyments; and nowhere are they more sensible of their power. Far different from their condition among many rude nations, where the women are made to perform all the work while their ungallant lords and masters lie buried in sloth, the gentle sex in the valley of Typee were exempt from toil, if toil it might be called that, even in the tropical climate, never distilled one drop of perspiration. Their light household occupations, together with the manufacture of tappa, the platting of mats, and the polishing of drinking-vessels, were the only employments pertaining to the women. And even these resembled those pleasant avocations which fill up the elegant morning leisure of our fashionable ladies at home. But in these occupations, slight and agreeable though they were, the giddy young girls very seldom engaged. Indeed these willfull, care-killing damsels were averse to all useful employment. Like so many spoiled beauties, they ranged through the groves—bathed in the stream—danced—flirted—played all manner of mischievous pranks, and passed their days in one merry round of thoughtless happiness.

During my whole stay on the island I never witnessed a single quarrel, nor anything that in the slightest degree approached even to a dispute. The natives appeared to form one household, whose members were bound together by the ties of strong affection. The love of kindred I did not so much perceive, for it seemed blended in the general love; and where all were treated as brothers and sisters, it was hard to tell who were actually related to each other by blood.

Let it not be supposed that I have overdrawn this picture. I have not done so. Nor let it be urged, that the hostility of this tribe to foreigners, and the hereditary feuds they carry on against their fellow-islanders beyond the mountains, are facts which contradict me. Not so: these apparent discrepancies are easily reconciled. By many a legendary tale of violence and wrong, as well as by events which have passed before their eyes, these people have been taught to look upon white men with abhorrence. The cruel invasion of their country by Porter has alone furnished them with ample provocation; and I can sympathize in the spirit which prompts the Typee warrior to guard all the passes to his valley with the point of his leveled spear, and, standing upon the beach, with his back turned upon his green home, to hold at bay the intruding European.

As to the origin of the enmity of this particular clan towards the neighboring tribes, I cannot so confidently speak. I will not say that their foes are the aggressors, nor will I endeavor to palliate their conduct. But surely, if our evil passions must find vent, it is far better to expend them on strangers and aliens, than in the bosom of the community in which we dwell. In many polished countries civil contentions, as well as domestic enmities, are prevalent, at the same time that the most atrocious foreign wars are waged. How much less guilty, then, are our islanders, who of these three sins are only chargeable with one, and that the least criminal!

The reader will ere long have reason to suspect that the Typees are not free from the guilt of cannibalism; and he will then, perhaps, charge me with admiring a people against whom so odious a crime is chargeable. But this only enormity in their character is not half so horrible as it is usually described. According to the popular fictions, the crews of vessels, shipwrecked on some barbarous coast, are eaten alive like so many dainty joints by the uncivil inhabitants; and unfortunate voyagers are lured into smiling and treacherous bays; knocked on the head with outlandish war-clubs; and served up without any prelimary dressing. In truth, so horrific and improbable are these accounts, that many sensible and well-informed people will not believe that any cannibals exist; and place every book of voyages which purports to give any account of them, on the same shelf with Blue Beard and Jack the Giant-Killer; while others, implicitly crediting the most extravagant fictions, firmly believe that there are people in the world with tastes so depraved that they would infinitely prefer a single mouthful of material humanity to a good dinner of roast beef and plum pudding. But here, Truth, who loves to be centrally located, is again found between the two extremes; for cannibalism to a certain moderate extent is practiced among several of the primitive tribes in the Pacific, but it is upon the bodies of slain enemies alone; and horrible and fearful as the custom is, immeasurably as it is to be abhorred and condemned, still I assert that those who indulge in it are in other respects humane and virtuous.

Chapter XXVIII

Fishing Parties—Mode of Distributing the Fish—Midnight Banquet—Timekeeping Tapers—Unceremonious Style of Eating the Fish

THERE WAS NO INSTANCE IN WHICH THE SOCIAL AND KINDLY DISPOSITIONS OF THE TYPEES WERE more forcibly evinced than in the manner the conducted their great fishing parties. Four times during my stay in the valley the young men assembled near the full of the moon, and went together on these excursions. As they were generally absent about forty-eight hours, I was led to believe that they went out towards the open sea, some distance from the bay. The Polynesians seldom use a hook and line, almost always employing large well-made nets, most ingeniously fabricated from the twisted fibers of a certain bark. I examined several of them which had been spread to dry upon the beach at Nukuheva. They resemble very much our own seines, and I should think they were nearly as durable.

All the South Sea islanders are passionately fond of fish; but none of them can be more so than the inhabitants of Typee. I could not comprehend, therefore, why they so seldom sought it in their waters, for it was only at stated times that the fishing parties were formed, and these occasions were always looked forward to with no small degree of interest.

During their absence the whole population of the place were in a ferment, and nothing was talked of but "pehee, pehee" (fish, fish). Towards the time when they were expected to return the vocal telegraph was put into operation—the inhabitants, who were scattered throughout the length of the valley, leaped upon rocks and into trees, shouting with delight at the thoughts of the anticipated treat. As soon as the approach of the party was announced, there was a general rush of the men towards the beach; some of them remaining, however, about the Ti, in order to get matters in readiness for the reception of the fish, which were brought to the Taboo groves in immense packages of leaves, each one of them being suspended from a pole carried on the shoulders of two men.

I was present at the Ti on one of these occasions, and the sight was most interesting. After all the packages had arrived, they were laid in a row under the verandah of the building and opened. The fish were all quite small, generally about the size of a herring, and of every variety. About one-eighth of the whole being reserved for the use of the Ti itself, the remainder was divided into numerous smaller packages, which were immediately dispatched in every direction to the remotest parts of the valley. Arrived at their destination, these were in turn portioned out, and equally distributed among the various houses of each particular district. The fish were under a strict Taboo, until the distribution was completed, which seemed to be effected in the most impartial manner. By the operation of this system every man, woman, and child in the vale, were at one and the same time partaking of this favorite article of food.

Once I remember the party arrived at midnight; but the unseasonableness of the hour did not repress the impatience of the islanders. The carriers dispatched from the Ti were to be seen hurrying in all directions through the deep groves; each individual preceded by a boy bearing a flaming torch of dried cocoanut boughs, which from time to time was replenished from the materials scattered along the path. The wild glare of these enormous *flambeaux*, lighting up with a startling brilliancy the innermost recesses of the vale, and seen moving rapidly along beneath the canopy of leaves, the savage shout of the excited messengers sounding the news of their approach, which was answered on all sides, and the strange appearance of their naked bodies, seen against the gloomy background, produced altogether an effect upon my mind that I shall long remember.

It was on this same occasion that Kory-Kory awakened me at the dead hour of night, and in a sort of transport communicated the intelligence contained in the words "pehee pemi" (fish come). As I happened to have been in a remarkably sound and refreshing slumber, I could not imagine why the information had not been deferred until morning; indeed, I felt very much inclined to fly into a passion and box my valet's ears; but on second thoughts I got quietly up, and on going outside the house was not a little interested by the moving illumination which I beheld.

When old Marheyo received his share of the spoils, immediate preparations were made for a midnight banquet; calabashes of poee-poee were filled to the brim; green bread-fruit were roasted; and a huge cake of "amar" was cut up with a sliver of bamboo and laid out on an immense banana-leaf.

At this supper we were lighted by several of the native tapers, held in the hands of young girls. These tapers are most ingeniously made. There is a nut abounding in the valley, called by the Typees "armor," closely resembling our common horse-chestnut. The shell is broken, and the contents extracted whole. Any number of these are strung at pleasure upon the long elastic fiber that traverses the branches of the cocoanut-tree. Some of these tapers are eight and ten feet in length; but being perfectly flexible, one end is held in a coil, while the other is lighted. The nut burns with a fitful bluish flame, and the oil that it contains is exhausted in about ten minutes. As one burns down, the next becomes ignited, and the ashes of the former are knocked into a cocoanut shell kept for the purpose. This primitive candle requires continual attention, and must be constantly held in the hand. The person so employed marks the lapse of time by the number of nuts consumed, which is easily learned by counting the bits of tappa distributed at regular intervals along the string.

I grieve to state so distressing a fact, but the inhabitants of Typee were in the habit of devouring fish much in the same way that a civilized being would eat a radish, and without any more previous preparation. They eat it raw; scales, bones, gills, and all the inside. The fish is held by the tail, and the head being introduced into the mouth, the animal disappears with a rapidity that would at first nearly lead one to imagine it had been launched bodily down the throat.

Raw fish! Shall I ever forget my sensations when I first saw my island beauty devour one? Oh, heavens! Fayaway, how could you ever have contracted so vile a habit? However, after the first shock had subsided, the custom grew less odious in my eyes, and I soon accustomed myself to the sight. Let no one imagine, however, that the lovely Fayaway was in the habit of swallowing great vulgar-looking fishes: oh, no; with her beautiful small hand she would clasp a delicate, little, golden-hued love of a fish, and eat it as elegantly and as innocently as though it were Naples biscuit. But alas! it was after all a raw fish, and all I can say is, that Fayaway ate it in a more lady-like manner than any other girl of the valley.

When at Rome do as the Romans do, I held to be so good a proverb, that being in Typee I made a point of doing as the Typees did. Thus I ate poee-poee as they did; I walked about in a garb striking for its simplicity; and I reposed on a community of couches; besides doing many other things in conformity with their peculiar habits; but the farthest I ever went in the way of conformity, was on several occasions to regale myself with raw fish. These being remarkably tender, and quite small, the undertaking was not so disagreeable in the main, and after a few trials I positively began to relish them: however, I subjected them to a slight operation with a knife previously to making my repast.

Chapter XXIX

NATURAL HISTORY OF THE VALLEY—GOLDEN LIZARDS—TAMENESS OF THE BIRDS—MOSQUITOES—FLIES—DOGS—A SOLITARY CAT—THE CLIMATE—THE COCOANUT-TREE—SINGULAR MODES OF CLIMBING IT—AN AGILE YOUNG CHIEF—FEARLESSNESS OF THE CHILDREN—TOO-TOO AND THE COCOANUT-TREE—THE BIRDS OF THE VALLEY

I THINK I MUST ENLIGHTEN THE READER A LITTLE ABOUT THE NATURAL HISTORY OF THE VALLEY.

Whence, in the name of Count Buffon and Baron Cuvier, came those dogs that I saw in Typee? Dogs!—Big hairless rats rather; all with smooth, shining, speckled hides—fat sides, and very disagreeable faces. Whence could they have come? That they were not the indigenous production of the region, I am firmly convinced. Indeed, they seemed aware of their being interlopers, looking fairly ashamed, and always trying to hide themselves in some dark corner. It was plain enough they did not feel at home in the vale—that they wished themselves well out of it, and back to the ugly country from which they must have come.

Scurvy curs! they were my abhorrence; I should have liked nothing better than to have been the death of every one of them. In fact, on one occasion, I intimated the propriety of a canine crusade to Mehevi; but the benevolent king would not consent to it. He heard me very patiently; but when I had finished, shook his head, and told me, in confidence, that they were "taboo."

As for the animal that made the fortune of the ex-lord-mayor Whittington; I shall never forget the day that I was lying in the house about noon, everybody else being fast asleep; and happening to raise my eyes, met those of a big black spectral cat, which sat erect in the doorway, looking at me with its frightful goggling green orbs, like one of those monstrous imps that torment some of Teniers' saints! I am one of those unfortunate persons to whom the sight of these animals are, at any time an insufferable annoyance.

Thus constitutionally averse to cats in general, the unexpected apparition of this one in particular utterly confounded me. When I had a little recovered from the fascination of its glance, I started up; the cat fled, and emboldened by this, I rushed out of the house in pursuit; but it had disappeared. It was the only time I ever saw one in the valley, and how it got there I cannot imagine. It is just possible that it might have escaped from one of the ships at Nukuheva. It was in vain to seek information on the subject from the natives; since none of them had seen the animal, the appearance of which remains a mystery to me to this day.

Among the few animals which are to be met with in Typee, there was none which I looked upon with more interest than a beautiful golden-hued species of lizard. It measured perhaps five inches from head to tail, and was most gracefully proportioned. Numbers of these creatures were to be seen basking in the sunshine upon the thatching of the houses, and multitudes at all hours of the day showed their glittering sides as they ran frolicking between the spears of grass or raced in troops up and down the tall shafts of the cocoanut-trees. But the remarkable beauty of these little animals and their lively ways were not their only claims upon my admiration. They were perfectly tame and insensible to fear. Frequently, after seating myself upon the ground in some shady place during the heat of the day, I would be completely overrun with them. If I brushed one off my arm, it would leap perhaps into my hair: when I tried to frighten it away by gently pinching its leg, it would turn for protection to the very hand that attacked it.

The birds are also remarkably tame. If you happened to see one perched upon a branch within reach of your arm, and advanced towards it, it did not fly away immediately, but waited quietly looking at you, until you could almost touch it, and then took wing slowly, less alarmed at your presence, it would seem, than desirous of removing itself from your path. Had salt been less scarce in the valley than it was, this was the very place to have gone birding with it.

I remember that once, on an uninhabited island of the Gallipagos, a bird alighted on my outstretched arm, while its mate chirped from an adjoining tree. Its tameness, far from shocking me, as a similar occurrence did Selkirk, imparted to me the most exquisite thrill of delight I ever experienced; and with somewhat of the same pleasure did I afterwards behold the birds and lizards of the valley show their confidence in the kindliness of man.

Among the numerous afflictions which the Europeans have entailed upon some of the natives of the South Seas, is the accidental introduction among them of that enemy of all repose and ruffler of even tempers—the Mosquito. At the Sandwich Islands and at two or three of the Society group there are now thriving colonies of these insects, who promise ere long to supplant altogether the aboriginal sand-flies. They sting, buzz, and torment, from one end of the year to the other, and by incessantly exasperating the natives materially obstruct the benevolent labors of the missionaries.

From this grievous visitation, however, the Typees are as yet wholly exempt; but its place is unfortunately in some degree supplied by the occasional presence of a minute species of fly, which, without stinging, is nevertheless productive of no little annoyance. The tameness of the birds and lizards is as nothing when compared to the fearless confidence of this insect. He will perch upon one of your eye-lashes, and go to roost there, if you do not disturb him, or force his way through your hair, or along the cavity of the nostril, till you almost fancy he is resolved to explore the very brain itself. On one occasion I was so inconsiderate as to yawn while a number of them were hovering around me. I never repeated the act. Some half-dozen darted into the open apartment, and began walking about its ceiling; the sensation was dreadful. I involuntarily closed my mouth, and the poor creatures being enveloped in inner darkness, must in their consternation have stumbled over my palate, and been precipitated into the gulf beneath. At any rate, though I afterwards charitably held my mouth open for at least five minutes, with a view of affording egress to the stragglers, none of them ever availed themselves of the opportunity.

There are no wild animals of any kind on the island, unless it be decided that the natives themselves are such. The mountains and the interior present to the eye nothing but silent solitudes, unbroken by the roar of beasts of prey, and enlivened by few tokens even of minute animated existence. There are no venomous reptiles, and no snakes of any description to be found in any of the valleys.

In a company of Marquesan natives the weather affords no topic of conversation. It can hardly be said to have any vicissitudes. The rainy season, it is true, brings frequent showers, but they are intermitting and refreshing. When an islander bound on some expedition rises from his couch in the morning, he is never solicitous to peep out and see how the sky looks, or ascertain from what quarter the wind blows. He is always sure of a "fine day," and the promise of a few genial showers he hails with pleasure. There is never any of that "remarkable weather" on the island which from time immemorial has been experienced in America, and still continues to call forth the wondering conversational exclamations of its elderly citizens. Nor do there even occur any of those eccentric meteorological changes which elsewhere surprise us. In the valley of Typee ice-creams would never be rendered less acceptable by sudden frosts, nor would picnic parties be deferred on account of inauspicious snow-storms: for there day follows day in one unvarying round of summer and sunshine, and the whole year is one long tropical month of June just melting into July.

It is this genial climate which causes the cocoanuts to flourish as they do. This invaluable fruit, brought to perfection by the rich soil of the Marquesas, and borne aloft on a stately column more than a hundred feet from the ground, would seem at first almost inaccessible to the simple natives. Indeed the slender, smooth, and soaring shaft, without a single limb or protuberance of any kind to assist one in mounting it, presents an obstacle only to be overcome by the surprising agility and ingenuity of the islanders. It might be supposed that their indolence would lead them patiently to await the period when the ripened nuts, slowly parting from their stems, fall one by one to the ground. This certainly would be the case, were it not that the young fruit, encased in a soft green husk, with the incipient meat adhering in a jelly-like pellicle to its sides, and containing a bumper of the most delicious nectar, is what they chiefly prize. They have at least twenty different terms to express as many progressive stages in the growth of the nut. Many of them reject the fruit altogether except at a particular period of its growth, which, incredible as it may appear, they seemed to me to be able to ascertain within an hour or two. Others are still more capricious in their tastes; and after gathering together a heap of the nuts of all ages, and ingeniously tapping them, will sip first from one and then from another, as fastidiously as some delicate wine-bibber experimenting glass in hand among his dusty demijohns of different vintages.

Some of the young men, with more flexible frames than their comrades, and perhaps with more courageous souls, had a way of walking up the trunk of the cocoanut-trees which to me seemed little less than miraculous; and when looking at them in the act, I experienced that curious perplexity a child feels when he beholds a fly moving feet uppermost along a ceiling.

I will endeavor to describe the way in which Narnee, a noble young chief, sometimes performed this feat for my peculiar gratification; but his preliminary performances must also be recorded. Upon my signifying my desire that he should pluck me the young fruit of some particular tree, the handsome savage, throwing himself into a sudden attitude of surprise, feigns astonishment at the apparent absurdity of the request. Maintaining this position for a moment, the strange emotions depicted on his countenance soften down into one of humorous resignation to my will, and then looking wistfully up to the tufted top of the tree, he stands on tip-toe, straining his neck and elevating his arm, as though endeavoring to reach the fruit from the ground where he stands. As if defeated in this childish attempt, he now sinks to the earth despondingly, beating his breast in well-acted despair; and then, starting to his feet all at once, and throwing back his head, raises both hands, like a school-boy about to catch a falling ball. After continuing this for a moment or two, as if in expectation that the fruit was going to be tossed down to him by some good spirit in the tree-top, he turns wildly round in another fit of despair, and scampers off to the distance of thirty or forty yards. Here he remains awhile, eyeing the tree, the very picture of misery; but the next moment, receiving, as it were, a flash of inspiration, he rushes again towards it, and clasping both arms about the trunk, with one elevated a little above the other, he presses the soles of his feet close together against the tree, extending his legs from it until they are nearly horizontal, and his body becomes doubled into an arch; then, hand over hand and foot over foot, he rises from the earth with steady rapidity, and almost before you are aware of it, has gained the cradled and embowered nest of nuts, and with boisterous glee flings the fruit to the ground.

This mode of walking the tree is only practicable where the trunk declines considerably from the perpendicular. This, however, is almost always the case; some of the perfectly straight shafts of the trees leaning at an angle of thirty degrees.

The less active among the men, and many of the children of the valley, have another method of climbing. They take a broad and stout piece of bark, and secure each end of it to their ankles; so that when the feet thus confined are extended apart, a space of little more than twelve inches is left between them. This contrivance greatly facilitates the act of climbing. The band pressed against the tree, and closely embracing it, yields a pretty firm support; while with the arms clasped about the trunk, and at regular intervals sustaining the body, the feet are drawn up nearly a yard at a time, and a corresponding elevation of the hands immediately succeeds. In this way I have seen little children, scarcely five years of age, fearlessly climbing the slender pole of a young cocoanut-tree, and while hanging perhaps fifty feet from the ground, receive the plaudits of their parents beneath, who clapped their hands, and encouraged them to mount still higher.

What, thought I, on first witnessing one of these exhibitions, would the nervous mothers of America and England say to a similar display of hardihood in any of their children? The Lacedemonian nation might have approved of it, but most modern dames would have gone into hysterics at the sight.

At the top of the cocoanut-tree the numerous branches radiating on all sides from a common center, form a sort of green and waving basket, between the leaflets of which you just discern the nuts thickly clustering together, and on the loftier trees looking no bigger from the ground than bunches of grapes. I remember one adventurous little fellow—Too-Too was the rascal's name—who had built himself a sort of aerial baby-house in the picturesque tuft of a tree adjoining Marheyo's habitation. He used to spend hours there—rustling among the branches, and shouting with delight every time the strong gusts of wind rushing down from the mountains side swayed to and fro the tall and flexible column on which he was perched. Whenever I heard Too-Too's musical voice, sounding strangely to the ear from so great a height, and beheld him peeping down upon me from out his leafy covert, he always recalled to my mind Dibdin's lines—

"There's a sweet little cherub that sits up aloft,
To look out for the life of poor Jack."

Birds—bright and beautiful birds—fly over the valley of Typee. You see them perched aloft among the immovable boughs of the majestic bread-fruit-trees, or gently swaying on the elastic branches of the Omoo: skimming over the palmetto thatching of the bamboo huts; passing like spirits on the wing through the shadows of the grove, and sometimes descending into the bosom of the valley in gleaming flights from the mountains. Their plumage is purple and azure, crimson and white, black and gold; with bills of every tint—bright bloody-red, jet black, and ivory white; and their eyes are bright and sparkling; they go sailing through the air in starry throngs; but, alas! the spell of dumbness is upon them all—there is not a single warbler in the valley!

I know not why it was, but the sight of these birds, generally the ministers of gladness, always oppressed me with melancholy. As in their dumb beauty they hovered by me whilst I was walking, or looked down upon me with steady curious eyes from out the foliage, I was almost inclined to fancy that they knew they were gazing upon a stranger, and that they commiserated his fate.

Chapter XXX

A Professor of the Fine Arts—His Persecutions—Something About Tattooing and Tabooing—Two Anecdotes in Illustration of the Latter—A Few Thoughts on the Typee Dialect

In one of my strolls with Kory-Kory, in passing along the border of a thick growth of bushes, my attention was arrested by a singular noise. On entering the thicket I witnessed for the first time the operation of tattooing as performed by these islanders.

I beheld a man extended flat upon his back on the ground, and, despite the forced composure of his countenance, it was evident that he was suffering agony. His tormentor bent over him, working away for all the world like a stone-cutter with mallet and chisel. In one hand he held a short slender stick, pointed with a shark's tooth, on the upright end of which he tapped with a small hammer-like piece of wood, thus puncturing the skin, and charging it with the coloring matter in which the instrument was dipped. A cocoanut shell containing this fluid was placed upon the ground. It is prepared by mixing with a vegetable juice the ashes of the "armor," or candle-nut, always preserved for the purpose. Beside the savage, and spread out upon a piece of soiled tappa, were a great number of curious black-looking little implements of bone and wood, used in the various divisions of his art. A few terminated in a single fine point, and, like very delicate pencils, were employed in giving the finishing touches, or in operating upon the more sensitive portions of the body, as was the case in the present instance. Others presented several points distributed in a line, somewhat resembling the teeth of a saw. These were employed in the coarser parts of the work, and particularly in pricking in straight marks. Some presented their points disposed in small figures, and being placed upon the body, were, by a single blow of the hammer, made to leave their indelible impression. I observed a few the handles of which were mysteriously curved, as if intended to be introduced into the orifice of the ear, with a view perhaps of beating the tattoo upon the tympanum. Altogether, the sight of these strange instruments recalled to mind that display of cruel-looking mother-of-pearl-handled things which one sees in their velvet-lined cases at the elbow of a dentist.

The artist was not at this time engaged on an original sketch, his subject being a venerable savage, whose tattooing had become somewhat faded with age and needed a few repairs, and accordingly he was merely employed in touching up the works of some of the old masters of the Typee school, as delineated upon the human canvas before him. The parts operated upon were the eyelids, where a longitudinal streak, like the one which adorned Kory-Kory, crossed the countenance of the victim.

In spite of all the efforts of the poor old man, sundry twitchings and screwings of the muscles of the face denoted the exquisite sensibility of these shutters to the windows of his soul, which he was now having repainted. But the artist, with a heart as callous as that of an army surgeon, continued his performance, enlivening his labors with a wild chant, tapping away the while as merrily as a woodpecker.

So deeply engaged was he in his work, that he had not observed our approach, until, after having enjoyed an unmolested view of the operation, I chose to attract his attention. As soon as he perceived me, supposing that I sought him in his professional capacity, he seized hold of me in a paroxysm of delight, and was all eagerness to begin the work. When, however, I gave him to understand that he had altogether mistaken my views, nothing could exceed his grief and disappointment. But recovering from this, he seemed determined not to credit my assertion, and grasping his implements, he flourished them about in fearful vicinity to my face, going through an imaginary performance of his art, and every moment bursting into some admiring exclamation at the beauty of his designs.

Horrified at the bare thought of being rendered hideous for life if the wretch were to execute his purpose upon me, I struggled to get away from him, while Kory-Kory, turning traitor, stood by, and besought me to comply with the outrageous request. On my reiterated refusals the excited artist got half beside himself, and was overwhelmed with sorrow at losing so noble an opportunity of distinguishing himself in his profession.

The idea of engrafting his tattooing upon my white skin filled him with all a painter's enthusiasm: again and again he gazed into my countenance, and every fresh glimpse seemed to add to the vehemence of his ambition. Not knowing to what extremities he might proceed, and shuddering at the ruin he might inflict upon my figure-head, I now endeavored to draw off his attention from it, and holding out my arm in a fit of desperation, signed to him to commence operations. But he rejected the compromise indignantly, and still continued his attack on my face, as though nothing short of that would satisfy him. When his forefinger swept across my features, in laying out the borders of those parallel bands which were to encircle my countenance, the flesh fairly crawled upon my bones. At last, half wild with terror and indignation, I succeeded in breaking away from the three savages, and fled towards old Marheyo's house, pursued by the indomitable artist, who ran after me, implements in hand. Kory-Kory, however, at last interfered and drew him off from the chase.

This incident opened my eyes to a new danger; and I now felt convinced that in some luckless hour I should be disfigured in such a manner as never more to have the *face* to return to my countrymen, even should an opportunity offer.

These apprehensions were greatly increased by the desire which King Mehevi and several of the inferior chiefs now manifested that I should be tattooed. The pleasure of the king was first signified to me some three days after my casual encounter with Karky the artist. Heavens! What imprecations I showered upon that Karky. Doubtless he had plotted a conspiracy against me and my countenance, and would never rest until his diabolical purpose was accomplished. Several times I met him in various parts of the valley, and, invariably, whenever he descried me, he came running after me with his mallet and chisel, flourishing them about my face as if he longed to begin. What an object he would have made of me!

When the king first expressed his wish to me, I made known to him my utter abhorrence of the measure, and worked myself into such a state of excitement, that he absolutely stared at me in amazement. It evidently surpassed his majesty's comprehension how any sober-minded and sensible individual could entertain the least possible objection to so beautifying an operation.

Soon afterwards he repeated his suggestion, and meeting with a little repulse, showed some symptoms of displeasure at my obduracy. On his third time renewing his request, I plainly perceived that something must be done, or my visage was ruined forever; I therefore screwed up my courage to the sticking point, and declared my willingness to have both arms tattooed from just above the wrist to the shoulder. His majesty was greatly pleased at the proposition, and I was congratulating myself with having thus compromised the matter, when he intimated that as a thing of course my face was first to undergo the operation. I was fairly driven to despair; nothing but the utter ruin of my "face divine," as the poets call it, would, I perceived, satisfy the inexorable Mehevi and his chiefs, or rather, that infernal Karky, for he was at the bottom of it all.

The only consolation afforded me was a choice of patterns: I was at perfect liberty to have my face spanned by three horizontal bars, after the fashion of my serving-man's; or to have as many oblique stripes slanting across it; or if, like a true courtier, I chose to model my style on that of royalty, I might wear a sort of freemason badge upon my countenance in the shape of a mystic triangle. However, I would have none of these, though the king most earnestly impressed upon my mind that my choice was wholly unrestricted. At last, seeing my unconquerable repugnance, he ceased to importune me.

But not so some other of the savages. Hardly a day passed but I was subjected to their annoying requests, until at last my existence became a burden to me; the pleasures I had previously enjoyed no longer afforded me delight, and all my former desire to escape from the valley now revived with additional force.

A fact which I soon afterwards learned augmented my apprehension. The whole system of tattooing was, I found, connected with their religion; and it was evident, therefore, that they were resolved to make a convert of me.

In the decoration of the chiefs it seems to be necessary to exercise the most elaborate pencilling; while some of the inferior natives looked as if they had been daubed over indiscriminately with a house-painter's brush. I remember one fellow who prided himself hugely upon a great oblong patch, placed high upon his back, and who always reminded me of a man with a blister of Spanish flies stuck between his shoulders. Another whom I frequently met had the hollow of his eyes tattooed in two regular squares, and his visual organs being remarkably brilliant, they gleamed forth from out this setting like a couple of diamonds inserted in ebony.

Although convinced that tattooing was a religious observance, still the nature of the connection between it and the superstitious idolatry of the people was a point upon which I could never obtain any information. Like the still more important system of the "Taboo," it always appeared inexplicable to me.

There is a marked similarity, almost an identity, between the religious institutions of most of the Polynesian islands, and in all exists the mysterious "Taboo," restricted in its uses to a greater or less extent. So strange and complex in its arrangements is this remarkable system, that I have in several cases met with individuals who, after residing for years among the islands in the Pacific, and acquiring a considerable knowledge of the language, have nevertheless been altogether unable to give any satisfactory account of its operations. Situated as I was in the Typee valley, I perceived every hour the effects of this all-controling power, without in the least comprehending it. Those effects were, indeed, wide-spread and universal, pervading the most important as well as the minutest transactions of life. The savage, in short, lives in the continual observance of its dictates, which guide and control every action of his being.

For several days after entering the valley I had been saluted at least fifty times in the twenty-four hours with the talismanic word "Taboo" shrieked in my ears, at some gross violation of its provisions, of which I had unconsciously been guilty. The day after our arrival I happened to hand some tobacco to Toby over the head of a native who sat between us. He started up, as if stung by an adder; while the whole company, manifesting an equal degree of horror, simultaneously screamed out "Taboo!" I never again perpetrated a similar piece of ill-manners, which, indeed, was forbidden by the canons of good breeding, as well as by the mandates of the taboo. But it was not always so easy to perceive wherein you had contravened the spirit of this institution. I was many times called to order, if I may use the phrase, when I could not for the life of me conjecture what particular offense I had committed.

One day I was strolling through a secluded portion of the valley, and hearing the musical sound of the cloth-mallet at a little distance, I turned down a path that conducted me in a few moments to a house where there were some half-dozen girls employed in making tappa. This was an operation I had frequently witnessed, and had handled the bark in all the various stages of its preparation. On the present occasion the females were intent upon their occupation, and after looking up and talking gaily to me for a few moments, they resumed their employment. I regarded them for a while in silence, and then carelessly picking up a handful of the material that lay around, proceeded unconsciously to pick it apart. While thus engaged, I was suddenly startled by a scream, like that of a whole boarding-school of young ladies just on the point of going into hysterics. Leaping up with the idea of seeing a score of Happar warriors about to perform anew the Sabine atrocity, I found myself confronted by the company of girls, who, having dropped their work, stood before me with starting eyes, swelling bosoms, and fingers pointed in horror towards me.

Thinking that some venomous reptile must be concealed in the bark which I held in my hand, I began cautiously to separate and examine it. Whilst I did so the horrified girls redoubled their shrieks. Their wild cries and frightened motions actually alarmed me, and throwing down the tappa, I was about to rush from the house, when in the same instant their clamors ceased, and one of them seizing me by the arm, pointed to the broken fibers that had just fallen from my grasp, and screamed in my ears the fatal word "Taboo!"

I subsequently found out that the fabric they were engaged in making was of a peculiar kind, destined to be worn on the heads of the females, and through every stage of its manufacture was guarded by a rigorous taboo, which interdicted the whole masculine gender from even so much as touching it.

Frequently in walking through the groves I observed bread-fruit and cocoanut-trees, with a wreath of leaves twined in a peculiar fashion about their trunks. This was the mark of the taboo. The trees themselves, their fruit, and even the shadows they cast upon the ground, were consecrated by its presence. In the same way a pipe, which the king had bestowed upon me, was rendered sacred in the eyes of the natives, none of whom could I ever prevail upon to smoke from it. The bowl was encircled by a woven band of grass, somewhat resembling those Turks' heads occasionally worked in the handles of our whip-stalks.

A similar badge was once braided about my wrist by the royal hand of Mehevi himself, who, as soon as he had concluded the operation, pronounced me "Taboo." This occurred shortly after Toby's disappearance; and, were it not that from the first moment I had entered the valley the natives had treated me with uniform kindness, I should have supposed that their conduct afterwards was to be ascribed to the fact that I had received this sacred investiture.

The capricious operations of the taboo is not its least remarkable feature: to enumerate them all would be impossible. Black hogs—infants to a certain age—women in an interesting situation—young men while the operation of tattooing their faces is going on—and certain parts of the valley during the continuance of a shower—are alike fenced about by the operation of the taboo.

I witnessed a striking instance of its effects in the bay of Tior, my visit to which place has been alluded to in a former part of this narrative. On that occasion our worthy captain formed one of the party. He was a most insatiable sportsman. Outward bound, and off the pitch of Cape Horn, he used to sit on the taffrail, and keep the steward loading three or four old fowling-pieces, with which he would bring down albatrosses, Cape pigeons, jays, petrels, and divers other marine fowl, who followed chattering in our wake. The sailors were struck aghast at his impiety, and one and all attributed our forty days' beating about that horrid headland to his sacrilegious slaughter of these inoffensive birds.

At Tior he evinced the same disregard for the religious prejudices of the islanders, as he had previously shown for the superstitions of the sailors. Having heard that there were a considerable number of fowls in the valley—the progeny of some cocks and hens accidentally left there by an English vessel, and which, being strictly tabooed, flew about almost in a wild state—he determined to break through all restraints, and be the death of them. Accordingly, he provided himself with a most formidable looking gun, and announced his landing on the beach by shooting down a noble cock that was crowing what proved to be his own funeral dirge, on the limb of an adjoining tree. "Taboo," shrieked the affrighted savages. "Oh, hang your taboo," says the nautical sportsman; "talk taboo to the marines"; and bang went the piece again, and down came another victim. At this the natives ran scampering through the groves, horror-struck at the enormity of the act.

All that afternoon the rocky sides of the valley rang with successive reports, and the superb plumage of many a beautiful fowl was ruffled by the fatal bullet. Had it not been that the French admiral, with a large party, was then in the glen, I have no doubt that the natives, although their tribe was small and dispirited, would have inflicted summary vengeance upon the man who thus outraged their most sacred institutions; as it was, they contrived to annoy him not a little.

Thirsting with his exertions, the skipper directed his steps to a stream; but the savages, who had followed at a little distance, perceiving his object, rushed towards him and forced him away from its bank—his lips would have polluted it. Wearied at last, he sought to enter a house, that he might rest for a while on the mats; its inmates gathered tumultuously about the door and denied him admittance. He coaxed and blustered by turns, but in vain; the natives were neither to be intimidated nor appeased, and as a final resort he was obliged to call together his boat's crew, and pull away from what he termed the most infernal place he ever stepped upon.

Lucky was it for him and for us that we were not honored on our departure by a salute of stones from the hands of the exasperated Tiors. In this way, on the neighboring island of Ropo, were killed, but a few weeks previously, and for a nearly similar offense, the master and three of the crew of the *K*——.

I cannot determine with anything approaching to certainty, what power it is that imposes the taboo. When I consider the slight disparity of condition among the islanders—the very limited and inconsiderable prerogatives of the king and chiefs—and the loose and indefinite functions of the priesthood, most of whom were hardly to be distinguished from the rest of their countrymen, I am wholly at a loss where to look for the authority which regulates this potent institution. It is imposed upon something to-day, and withdrawn to-morrow; while its operations in other cases are perpetual. Sometimes its restrictions only affect a single individual—sometimes a particular family—sometimes a whole tribe; and in a few instances they extend not merely over the various clans on a single island, but over all the inhabitants of an entire group. In illustration of this latter peculiarity, I may cite the law which forbids a female to enter a canoe—a prohibition which prevails upon all the northern Marquesas Islands.

The word itself (taboo) is used in more than one signification. It is sometimes used by a parent to his child, when in the exercise of parental authority he forbids it to perform a particular action. Anything opposed to the ordinary customs of the islanders, although not expressly prohibited, is said to be "taboo."

The Typee language is one very difficult to be acquired; it bears a close resemblance to the other Polynesian dialects, all of which show a common origin. The duplication of words, as "lumee lumee," "poee poee," "muee muee," is one of their peculiar features. But another, and a more annoying one, is the different senses in which one and the same word is employed; its various meanings all have a certain connection, which only makes the matter more puzzling. So one brisk, lively little word is obliged, like a servant in a poor family, to perform all sorts of duties; for instance, one particular combination of syllables expresses the ideas of sleep, rest, reclining, sitting, leaning, and all other things anywise analogous thereto, the particular meaning being shown chiefly by a variety of gestures and the eloquent expression of the countenance.

The intricacy of these dialects is another peculiarity. In the Missionary College at Lahainaluna, on Maui, one of the Sandwich Islands, I saw a tabular exhibition of a Hawaiian verb, conjugated through all its moods and tenses. It covered the side of a considerable apartment, and I doubt whether Sir William Jones himself would not have despaired of mastering it.

Chapter XXXI

Strange Custom of the Islanders—Their Chanting, and the Peculiarity of Their Voice—Rapture of the King at First Hearing a Song—A New Dignity Conferred on the Author—Musical Instruments in the Valley—Admiration of the Savages at Beholding a Pugilistic Performance—Swimming Infant—Beautiful Tresses of the Girls—Ointment for the Hair

SADLY DISCURSIVE AS I HAVE ALREADY BEEN, I MUST STILL FURTHER ENTREAT THE READER'S PAtience, as I am about to string together, without any attempt at order, a few odds and ends of things not hitherto mentioned, but which are either curious in themselves or peculiar to the Typees.

There was one singular custom observed in old Marheyo's domestic establishment, which often excited my surprise. Every night, before retiring, the inmates of the house gathered together on the mats, and squatting upon their haunches, after the universal practice of these islanders, would commence a low, dismal, and monotonous chant, accompanying the voice with the instrumental melody produced by two small half-rotten sticks tapped slowly together, a pair of which were held in the hands of each person present. Thus would they employ themselves for an hour or two, sometimes longer. Lying in the gloom which wrapped the further end of the house, I could not avoid looking at them, although the spectacle suggested nothing but unpleasant reflections. The flickering rays of the "armor" nut just served to reveal their savage lineaments, without dispelling the darkness that hovered about them.

Sometimes when, after falling into a kind of doze, and awaking suddenly in the midst of these doleful chantings, my eye would fall upon the wild-looking group engaged in their strange occupation, with their naked tattooed limbs, and shaven heads disposed in a circle, I was almost tempted to believe that I gazed upon a set of evil beings in the act of working at a frightful incantation.

What was the meaning or purpose of this custom, whether it was practiced merely as a diversion, or whether it was a religious exercise, a sort of family prayers, I never could discover.

The sounds produced by the natives on these occasions were of a most singular description; and had I not actually been present, I never would have believed that such curious noises could have been produced by human beings.

To savages generally is imputed a guttural articulation. This, however, is not always the case, especially among the inhabitants of the Polynesian Archipelago. The labial melody with which the Typee girls carry on an ordinary conversation, giving a musical prolongation to the final syllable of every sentence, and chirping out some of the words with a liquid, bird-like accent, was singularly pleasing.

The men, however, are not quite so harmonious in their utterance, and when excited upon any subject, would work themselves up into a sort of wordy paroxysm, during which all descriptions of rough-sided sounds were projected from their mouths, with a force and rapidity which was absolutely astonishing.

* * * * *

Although these savages are remarkably fond of chanting, still they appear to have no idea whatever of singing, at least as the art is practiced in other nations.

I shall never forget the first time I happened to roar out a stave in the presence of the noble Mehevi. It was a stanza from the "Bavarian broom-seller." His Typean majesty, with all his court, gazed upon me in amazement, as if I had displayed some preternatural faculty which Heaven had denied to them. The king was delighted with the verse; but the chorus fairly transported him. At his solicitation I sang it again and again, and nothing could be more ludicrous than his vain attempts to catch the air and the words. The royal savage seemed to think that by screwing all the features of his face into the end of his nose he might possibly succeed in the undertaking, but it failed to answer the purpose; and in the end he gave it up, and consoled himself by listening to my repetition of the sounds fifty times over.

Previous to Mehevi's making the discovery, I had never been aware that there was anything of the nightingale about me; but I was now promoted to the place of court-minstrel, in which capacity I was afterwards perpetually called upon to officiate.

* * * * *

Besides the sticks and the drums, there are no other musical instruments among the Typees, except one which might appropriately be denominated a nasal flute. It is somewhat longer than an ordinary fife; is made of a beautiful scarlet-colored reed; and has four or five stops, with a large hole near one end, which latter is held just beneath the left nostril. The other nostril being closed by a peculiar movement of the muscles about the nose, the breath is forced into the tube, and produces a soft dulcet sound, which is varied by the fingers running at random over the stops. This is a favorite recreation with the females, and one in which Fayaway greatly excelled. Awkward as such an instrument may appear, it was, in Fayaway's delicate little hands, one of the most graceful I have ever seen. A young lady, in the act of tormenting a guitar strung about her neck by a couple of yards of blue ribbon, is not half so engaging.

* * * * *

Singing was not the only means I possessed of diverting the royal Mehevi and his easy-going subjects. Nothing afforded them more pleasure than to see me go through the attitude of pugilistic encounter. As not one of the natives had soul enough in him to stand up like a man, and allow me to hammer away at him, for my own personal gratification and that of the king, I was necessitated to fight with an imaginary enemy, whom I invariably made to knock under to my superior prowess. Sometimes when this sorely battered shadow retreated precipitately towards a group of the savages, and, following him up, I rushed among them, dealing my blows right and left, they would disperse in all directions, much to the enjoyment of Mehevi, the chiefs, and themselves.

The noble art of self-defense appeared to be regarded by them as the peculiar gift of the white man; and I make little doubt but that they supposed armies of Europeans were drawn up provided with nothing else but bony fists and stout hearts, with which they set to in column, and pummelled one another at the word of command.

* * * * *

One day, in company with Kory-Kory, I had repaired to the stream for the purpose of bathing, when I observed a woman sitting upon a rock in the midst of the current, and watching with the liveliest interest the gambols of something, which at first I took to be an uncommonly large species of frog that was sporting in the water near her. Attracted by the novelty of the sight, I waded towards the spot where she sat, and could hardly credit the evidence of my senses when I beheld a little infant, the period of whose birth could not have extended back many days, paddling about as if it had just risen to the surface, after being hatched into existence at the bottom. Occasionally the delighted parent reached out her hands towards it, when the little thing, uttering a faint cry, and striking out its tiny limbs, would sidle for the rock, and the next moment be clasped to its mother's bosom. This was repeated again and again, the baby remaining in the stream about a minute at a time. Once or twice it made wry faces at swallowing a mouthful of water, and choked and spluttered as if on the point of strangling. At such times, however, the mother snatched it up, and by a process scarcely to be mentioned obliged it to eject the fluid. For several weeks afterwards I observed this woman bringing her child down to the stream regularly every day, in the cool of the morning and evening, and treating it to a bath. No wonder that the South Sea Islanders are so amphibious a race, when they are thus launched into the water as soon as they see the light. I am convinced that it is as natural for a human being to swim as it is for a duck. And yet in civilized communities how many able-bodied individuals die, like so many drowning kittens, from the occurrence of the most trivial accidents!

* * * * *

The long, luxuriant, and glossy tresses of the Typee damsels often attracted my admiration. A fine head of hair is the pride and joy of every woman's heart! Whether, against the express will of Providence, it is twisted up on the crown of the head and there coiled away like a rope on a ship's deck; whether it be stuck behind the ears and hangs down like the swag of a small window-curtain; or whether it be permitted to flow over the shoulders in natural ringlets, it is always the pride of the owner, and the glory of the toilette.

The Typee girls devote much of their time to the dressing of their fair and redundant locks. After bathing, as they sometimes do five or six times every day, the hair is carefully dried, and if they have been in the sea, invariably washed in fresh water, and anointed with a highly scented oil extracted from the meat of the cocoanut. This oil is obtained in great abundance by the following very simple process:

A large vessel of wood, with holes perforated in the bottom, is filled with the pounded meat, and exposed to the rays of the sun. As the oleaginous matter exudes, it falls in drops through the apertures into a wide-mouthed calabash placed underneath. After a sufficient quantity has thus been collected, the oil undergoes a purifying process, and is then poured into the small spherical shells of the nuts of the moo-tree, which are hollowed out to receive it. These nuts are then hermetically sealed with a resinous gum, and the vegetable fragrance of their green rind soon imparts to the oil a delightful odor. After the lapse of a few weeks the exterior shell of the nuts becomes quite dry and hard, and assumes a beautiful carnation tint; and when opened they are found to be about two-thirds full of an ointment of a light yellow color, and diffusing the sweetest perfume. This elegant little odorous globe would not be out of place even upon the toilette of a queen. Its merits as a preparation for the hair are undeniable—it imparts to it a superb gloss and a silky fineness.

Chapter XXXII

Apprehensions of Evil—Frightful Discovery—Some Remarks on Cannibalism—Second Battle with the Happars—Savage Spectacle—Mysterious Feast—Subsequent Disclosures

From the time of my casual encounter with Karky the artist, my life was one of absolute wretchedness. Not a day passed but I was persecuted by the solicitations of some of the natives to subject myself to the odious operation of tattooing. Their importunities drove me half wild, for I felt how easily they might work their will upon me regarding this or anything else which they took into their heads. Still, however, the behavior of the islanders towards me was as kind as ever. Fayaway was quite as engaging; Kory-Kory as devoted: and Mehevi the king just as gracious and condescending as before. But I had now been three months in their valley, as nearly as I could estimate; I had grown familiar with the narrow limits to which my wanderings had been confined; and I began bitterly to feel the state of captivity in which I was held. There was no one with whom I could freely converse; no one to whom I could communicate my thoughts, no one who could sympathize with my sufferings. A thousand times I thought how much more endurable would have been my lot had Toby still been with me. But I was left alone, and the thought was terrible to me. Still, despite my griefs, I did all in my power to appear composed and cheerful, well knowing that by manifesting any uneasiness, or any desire to escape, I should only frustrate my object.

It was during the period I was in this unhappy frame of mind that the painful malady under which I had been laboring—after having almost completely subsided—began again to show itself, and with symptoms as violent as ever. This added calamity nearly unmanned me; the recurrence of the complaint proved that without powerful remedial applications all hope of cure was futile; and when I reflected that just beyond the elevations which bound me in, was the medical relief I needed, and that, although so near, it was impossible for me to avail myself of it, the thought was misery.

In this wretched situation, every circumstance which evinced the savage nature of the beings at whose mercy I was, augmented the fearful apprehensions that consumed me. An occurrence which happened about this time affected me most powerfully.

I have already mentioned that from the ridge-pole of Marheyo's house were suspended a number of packages enveloped in tappa. Many of these I had often seen in the hands of the natives, and their contents had been examined in my presence. But there were three packages hanging very nearly over the place where I lay, which from their remarkable appearance had often excited my curiosity. Several times I had asked Kory-Kory to show me their contents; but my servitor, who in almost every other particular had acceded to my wishes, always refused to gratify me in this.

One day, returning unexpectedly from the "Ti," my arrival seemed to throw the inmates of the house into the greatest confusion. They were seated together on the mats, and by the lines which extended from the roof to the floor I immediately perceived that the mysterious packages were for some purpose or another under inspection. The evident alarm the savages betrayed filled me with forebodings of evil, and with an uncontrolable desire to penetrate the secret so jealously guarded. Despite the efforts of Marheyo and Kory-Kory to restrain me, I forced my way into the midst of the circle, and just caught a glimpse of three human heads, which others of the party were hurriedly enveloping in the coverings from which they had been taken.

One of the three I distinctly saw. It was in a state of perfect preservation, and, from the slight glimpse I had of it, seemed to have been subjected to some smoking operation which had reduced it to the dry, hard, and mummy-like appearance it presented. The two long scalp locks were twisted up into balls upon the crown of the head in the same way that the individual had worn them during life. The sunken cheeks were rendered yet more ghastly by the rows of glistening teeth which protruded from between the lips, while the sockets of the eyes—filled with oval bits of mother-of-pearl shell, with a black spot in the center—heightened the hideousness of its aspect.

Two of the three were heads of the islanders; but the third, to my horror, was that of a white man. Although it had been quickly removed from my sight, still the glimpse I had of it was enough to convince me that I could not be mistaken.

Gracious God! what dreadful thoughts entered my mind! In solving this mystery perhaps I had solved another, and the fate of my lost companion might be revealed in the shocking spectacle I had just witnessed. I longed to have torn off the folds of cloth and satisfied the awful doubts under which I labored. But before I had recovered from the consternation into which I had been thrown, the fatal packages were hoisted aloft and once more swung over my head. The natives now gathered round me tumultuously, and labored to convince me that what I had just seen were the heads of three Happar warriors, who had been slain in battle. This glaring falsehood added to my alarm, and it was not until I reflected that I had observed the packages swinging from their elevation before Toby's disappearance, that I could at all recover my composure.

But although this horrible apprehension had been dispelled, I had discovered enough to fill me, in my present state of mind, with the most bitter reflections. It was plain that I had seen the last relic of some unfortunate wretch, who must have been massacred on the beach by the savages, in one of those perilous trading adventures which I have before described.

It was not, however, alone the murder of the stranger that overcame me with gloom. I shuddered at the idea of the subsequent fate his inanimate body might have met with. Was the same doom reserved for me? Was I destined to perish like him—like him, perhaps, to be devoured, and my head to be preserved as a fearful memento of the event? My imagination ran riot in these horrid speculations, and I felt certain that the worst possible evils would befall me. But whatever were my misgivings, I studiously concealed them from the islanders, as well as the full extent of the discovery I had made.

Although the assurances which the Typees had often given me, that they never eat human flesh, had not convinced me that such was the case, yet, having been so long a time in the valley without witnessing anything which indicated the existence of the practice, I began to hope that it was an event of very rare occurrence, and that I should be spared the horror of witnessing it during my stay among them; but, alas! these hopes were soon destroyed.

It is a singular fact, that in all our accounts of cannibal tribes we have seldom received the testimony of an eye-witness to the revolting practice. The horrible conclusion has almost always been derived from the second-hand evidence of Europeans, or else from the admissions of the savages themselves, after they have in some degree become civilized. The Polynesians are aware of the detestation in which Europeans hold this custom, and therefore invariably deny its existence, and, with the craft peculiar to savages, endeavor to conceal every trace of it.

The excessive unwillingness betrayed by the Sandwich Islanders, even at the present day, to allude to the unhappy fate of Cook, has often been remarked. And so well have they succeeded in covering the event with mystery, that to this very hour, despite all that has been said and written on the subject, it still remains doubtful whether they wreaked upon his murdered body the vengance they sometimes inflicted upon their enemies.

At Kealakekau, the scene of that tragedy, a strip of ship's copper nailed against an upright post in the ground used to inform the traveler that beneath reposed the "remains" of the great circumnavigator. But I am strongly inclined to believe not only that the corpse was refused Christian burial, but that the heart which was brought to Vancouver some time after the event, and which the Hawaiians stoutly maintained was that of Captain Cook, was no such thing; and that the whole affair was a piece of imposture which was sought to be palmed off upon the credulous Englishman.

A few years since there was living on the island of Maui (one of the Sandwich group) an old chief, who, actuated by a morbid desire for notoriety, gave himself out among the foreign residents of the place as the living tomb of Captain Cook's big toe!—affirming, that at the cannibal entertainment which ensued after the lamented Briton's death, that particular portion of his body had fallen to his share. His indignant countrymen actually caused him to be prosecuted in the native courts, on a charge nearly equivalent to what we term defamation of character; but the old fellow persisting in his assertion, and no invalidating proof being adduced, the plaintiffs were cast in the suit, and the cannibal reputation of the defendant fully established. This result was the making of his fortune; ever afterwards he was in the habit of giving very profitable audiences to all curious travelers who were desirous of beholding the man who had eaten the great navigator's great toe.

About a week after my discovery of the contents of the mysterious packages, I happened to be at the Ti, when another war-alarm was sounded, and the natives rushing to their arms, sallied out to resist a second incursion of the Happar invaders. The same scene was again repeated, only that on this occasion I heard at least fifteen reports of muskets from the mountains during the time that the skirmish lasted. An hour or two after its termination, loud paeans chanted through the valley announced the approach of the victors. I stood with Kory-Kory leaning against the railing of the pi-pi awaiting their advance, when a tumultuous crowd of islanders emerged with wild clamors from the neighboring groves. In the midst of them marched four men, one preceding the other at regular intervals of eight or ten feet, with poles of a corresponding length, extending from shoulder to shoulder, to which were lashed with thongs of bark three long narrow bundles, carefully wrapped in ample coverings of freshly plucked palm-leaves, tacked together with slivers of bamboo. Here and there upon these green winding-sheets might be seen the stains of blood, while the warriors who carried the frightful burdens displayed upon their naked limbs similar sanguinary marks. The shaven head of the foremost had a deep gash upon it, and the clotted gore which had flowed from the wound remained in dry patches around it. The savage seemed to be sinking under the weight he bore. The bright tattooing upon his body was covered with blood and dust; his inflamed eyes rolled in their sockets, and his whole appearance denoted extraordinary suffering and exertion; yet, sustained by some powerful impulse, he continued to advance, while the throng around him with wild cheers sought to encourage him. The other three men were marked about the arms and breasts with several slight wounds, which they somewhat ostentatiously displayed.

These four individuals, having been the most active in the late encounter, claimed the honor of bearing the bodies of their slain enemies to the Ti. Such was the conclusion I drew from my own observations, and, as far as I could understand, from the explanation which Kory-Kory gave me.

The royal Mehevi walked by the side of these heroes. He carried in one hand a musket, from the barrel of which was suspended a small canvas pouch of powder, and in the other he grasped a short javelin, which he held before him and regarded with fierce exultation. This javelin he had wrested from a celebrated champion of the Happars, who had ignominiously fled, and was pursued by his foes beyond the summit of the mountain.

When within a short distance of the Ti, the warrior with the wounded head, who proved to be Narmonee, tottered forward two or three steps, and fell helplessly to the ground; but not before another had caught the end of the pole from his shoulder, and placed it upon his own.

The excited throng of islanders, who surrounded the person of the king and the dead bodies of the enemy, approached the spot where I stood, brandishing their rude implements of warfare, many of which were bruised and broken, and uttering continual shouts of triumph. When the crowd drew up opposite the Ti, I set myself to watch their proceedings most attentively; but scarcely had they halted when my servitor, who had left my side for an instant, touched my arm and proposed our returning to Marheyo's house. To this I objected; but, to my surprise, Kory-Kory reiterated his request, and with an unusual vehemence of manner. Still, however, I refused to comply, and was retreating before him, as in his importunity he pressed upon me, when I felt a heavy hand laid upon my shoulder, and turning round, encountered the bulky form of Mow-Mow, a one-eyed chief, who had just detached himself from the crowd below, and had mounted the rear of the pi-pi upon which we stood. His cheek had been pierced by the point of a spear, and the wound imparted a still more frightful expression to his hideously tattooed face, already deformed by the loss of an eye. The warrior, without uttering a syllable, pointed fiercely in the direction of Marheyo's house, while Kory-Kory, at the same time presenting his back, desired me to mount.

I declined this offer, but intimated my willingness to withdraw, and moved slowly along the piazza, wondering what could be the cause of this unusual treatment. A few minutes' consideration convinced me that the savages were about to celebrate some hideous rite in connection with their peculiar customs, and at which they were determined I should not be present. I descended from the pi-pi, and attended by Kory-Kory, who on this occasion did not show his usual commiseration for my lameness, but seemed only anxious to hurry me on, walked away from the place. As I passed through the noisy throng, which by this time completely environed the Ti, I looked with fearful curiosity at the three packages, which now were deposited upon the ground; but although I had no doubt as to their contents, still their thick coverings prevented my actually detecting the form of a human body.

The next morning, shortly after sunrise, the same thundering sounds which had awakened me from sleep on the second day of the Feast of Calabashes, assured me that the savages were on the eve of celebrating another, and, as I fully believed, a horrible solemnity.

All the inmates of the house, with the exception of Marheyo, his son, and Tinor, after assuming their gala dresses, departed in the direction of the Taboo Groves.

Although I did not anticipate a compliance with my request, still, with a view of testing the truth of my suspicions, I proposed to Kory-Kory that, according to our usual custom in the morning, we should take a stroll to the Ti: he positively refused; and when I renewed the request, he evinced his determination to prevent my going there; and, to divert my mind from the subject, he offered to accompany me to the stream. We accordingly went, and bathed. On our coming back to the house, I was surprised to find that all its inmates had returned, and were lounging upon the mats as usual, although the drums still sounded from the groves.

The rest of the day I spent with Kory-Kory and Fayaway, wandering about a part of the valley situated in an opposite direction from the Ti; and whenever I so much as looked towards that building, although it was hidden from view by intervening trees, and at the distance of more than a mile, my attendant would exclaim, "Taboo, taboo!"

At the various houses where we stopped, I found many of the inhabitants reclining at their ease, or pursuing some light occupation, as if nothing unusual were going forward; but amongst them all I did not perceive a single chief or warrior. When I asked several of the people why they were not at the "Hoolah Hoolah" (the feast), they uniformly answered the question in a manner which implied that it was not intended for them, but for Mehevi, Narmonee, Mow-Mow, Kolor, Womonoo, Kalow—running over, in their desire to make me comprehend their meaning, the names of all the principal chiefs.

Everything, in short, strengthened my suspicions with regard to the nature of the festival they were now celebrating; and which amounted almost to a certainty. While in Nukuheva I had frequently been informed that the whole tribe were never present at these cannibal banquets; but the chiefs and priests only, and everything I now observed agreed with the account.

The sound of the drums continued, without intermission, the whole day, and falling continually upon my ear, caused me a sensation of horror which I am unable to describe. On the following day, hearing none of those noisy indications of revelry, I concluded that the inhuman feast was terminated; and feeling a kind of morbid curiosity to discover whether the Ti might furnish any evidence of what had taken place there, I proposed to Kory-Kory to walk there. To this proposition he replied by pointing with his finger to the newly risen sun, and then up to the zenith, intimating that our visit must be deferred until noon. Shortly after that hour we accordingly proceeded to the Taboo Groves, and as soon as we entered their precincts, I looked fearfully round in quest of some memorial of the scene which had so lately been acted there; but everything appeared as usual. On reaching the Ti, we found Mehevi and a few chiefs reclining on the mats, who gave me as friendly a reception as ever. No allusions of any kind were made by them to the recent events; and I refrained, for obvious reasons, from referring to them myself.

After staying a short time I took my leave. In passing along the piazza, previously to descending from the pi-pi, I observed a curiously carved vessel of wood, of considerable size, with a cover placed over it, of the same material, and which resembled in shape a small canoe. It was surrounded by a low railing of bamboos, the top of which was scarcely a foot from the ground. As the vessel had been placed in its present position since my last visit, I at once concluded that it must have some connection with the recent festival; and, prompted by a curiosity I could not repress, in passing it I raised one end of the cover; at the same moment the chiefs, perceiving my design, loudly ejaculated, "Taboo! taboo!" But the slight glimpse sufficed; my eyes fell upon the disordered members of a human skeleton, the bones still fresh with moisture, and with particles of flesh clinging to them here and there!

Kory-Kory, who had been a little in advance of me, attracted by the exclamations of the chiefs, turned round in time to witness the expression of horror on my countenance. He now hurried towards me, pointing at the same time to the canoe, and exclaiming rapidly, "Puarkee! puarkee!" (Pig, pig). I pretended to yield to the deception, and repeated the words after him several times, as though acquiescing in what he said. The other savages, either deceived by my conduct or unwilling to manifest their displeasure at what could not now be remedied, took no further notice of the occurrence, and I immediately left the Ti.

All that night I lay awake, revolving in my mind the fearful situation in which I was placed. The last horrid revelation had now been made, and the full sense of my condition rushed upon my mind with a force I had never before experienced.

Where, thought I, desponding, is there the slightest prospect of escape? The only person who seemed to possess the ability to assist me was the stranger Marnoo; but would he ever return to the valley? and if he did, should I be permitted to hold any communication with him? It seemed as if I were cut off from every source of hope, and that nothing remained but passively to await whatever fate was in store for me. A thousand times I endeavored to account for the mysterious conduct of the natives. For what conceivable purpose did they thus retain me a captive? What could be their object in treating me with such apparent kindness, and did it not cover some treacherous scheme? Or, if they had no other design than to hold me a prisoner, how should I be able to pass away my days in this narrow valley, deprived of all intercourse with civilized beings, and forever separated from friends and home?

One only hope remained to me. The French could not long defer a visit to the bay; and if they should permanently locate any of their troops in the valley, the savages could not for any length of time conceal my existence from them. But what reason had I to suppose that I should be spared until such an event occurred—an event which might be postponed by a hundred different contingencies?

Chapter XXXIII

THE STRANGER AGAIN ARRIVES IN THE VALLEY—SINGULAR INTERVIEW WITH HIM—ATTEMPT TO ESCAPE—FAILURE—MELANCHOLY SITUATION—SYMPATHY OF MARHEYO

MARNOO, MARNOO PEMI!" SUCH WERE THE WELCOME SOUNDS WHICH FELL UPON MY EAR SOME ten days after the events related in the preceding chapter. Once more the approach of the stranger was heralded, and the intelligence operated upon me like magic. Again I should be able to converse with him in my own language; and I resolve at all hazards to concert with him some scheme, however desperate, to rescue me from a condition that had now become insupportable.

As he drew near, I remembered with many misgivings the inauspicious termination of our former interview; and when he entered the house, I watched with intense anxiety the reception he met with from its inmates. To my joy, his appearance was hailed with the liveliest pleasure; and accosting me kindly, he seated himself by my side, and entered into conversation with the natives around him. It soon appeared, however, that on this occasion he had not any intelligence of importance to communicate. I inquired of him from whence he had just come? He replied from Pueearka, his native valley, and that he intended to return to it the same day.

At once it struck me that, could I but reach that valley under his protection, I might easily from thence reach Nukuheva by water; and animated by the prospect which this plan held out, I disclosed it in a few brief words to the stranger, and asked him how it could be best accomplished. My heart sank within me when in his broken English he answered me that it could never be effected. "Kanaka no let you go nowhere," he said; "you taboo. Why you no like to stay? Plenty moee-moee (sleep)—plenty ki-ki (eat)—plenty wahenee (young girls)—Oh, very good place Typee! Suppose you no like this bay, why you come? You no hear about Typee? All white men afraid Typee, so no white men come."

These words distressed me beyond belief; and when I again related to him the circumstances under which I had descended into the valley, and sought to enlist his sympathies in my behalf by appealing to the bodily misery I endure, he listened to me with impatience, and cut me short by exclaiming passionately, "Me no hear you talk anymore; by by Kanaka get mad, kill you and me too. No you see he no want you to speak at all?—you see—ah! by by you no mind—you get well, he kill you, eat you, hang you head up there, like Happar Kanaka.—Now you listen—but no talk any more. By by I go;—you see way I go.—Ah! then some night Kanaka all moee-moee (sleep)—you run away, you come Pueearka. I speak Pueearka Kanaka—he no harm you—ah! then I take you my canoe Nukuheva—and you run away ship no more." With these words, enforced by a vehemence of gesture I cannot describe, Marnoo started from my side, and immediately engaged in conversation with some of the chiefs who had entered the house.

It would have been idle for me to have attempted resuming the interview so peremptorily terminated by Marnoo, who was evidently little disposed to compromise his own safety by any rash endeavors to insure mine. But the plan he had suggested struck me as one which might possibly be accomplished, and I resolved to act upon it as speedily as possible.

Accordingly, when he arose to depart, I accompanied him with the natives outside of the house, with a view of carefully noting the path he would take in leaving the valley. Just before leaping from the pi-pi he clasped my hand, and looking significantly at me, exclaimed, "Now you see—you do what I tell you—ah! then you do good;—you no do so—ah! then you die." The next moment he waved his spear in *adieu* to the islanders, and following the route that conducted to a defile in the mountains lying opposite the Happar side, was soon out of sight.

A mode of escape was now presented to me, but how was I to avail myself of it? I was continually surrounded by the savages; I could not stir from one house to another without being attended by some of them; and even during the hours devoted to slumber, the slightest movement which I made seemed to attract the notice of those who shared the mats with me. In spite of these obstacles, however, I determined forthwith to make the attempt. To do so with any prospect of success, it was necessary that I should have at least two hours start before the islanders should discover my absence; for with such facility was any alarm spread through the valley, and so familiar, of course, were the inhabitants with the intricacies of the groves, that I could not hope, lame and feeble as I was, and ignorant of the route, to secure my escape unless I had this advantage. It was also by night alone that I could hope to accomplish my object, and then only by adopting the utmost precaution.

The entrance to Marheyo's habitation was through a low narrow opening in its wicker-work front. This passage, for no conceivable reason that I could devise, was always closed after the household had retired to rest, by drawing a heavy slide across it, composed of a dozen or more bits of wood, ingeniously fastened together by seizings of sinnate. When any of the inmates chose to go outside, the noise occasioned by the removing of this rude door awakened everybody else; and on more than one occasion I had remarked that the islanders were nearly as irritable as more civilized beings under similar circumstances.

The difficulty thus placed in my way I determined to obviate in the following manner. I would get up boldly in the course of the night, and drawing the slide, issue from the house, and pretend that my object was merely to procure a drink from the calabash, which always stood without the dwelling on the corner of the pi-pi. On re-entering I would purposely omit closing the passage after me, and trusting that the indolence of the savages would prevent them from repairing my neglect, would return to my mat, and waiting patiently until all were again asleep, I would then steal forth, and at once take the route to Pueearka.

The very night which followed Marnoo's departure, I proceeded to put this project into execution. About midnight, as I imagined, I rose and drew the slide. The natives, just as I had expected, started up, while some of them asked, "Arware poo awa, Tommo?" (where are you going, Tommo?) "Wai" (water) I laconically answered, grasping the calabash. On hearing my reply they sank back again, and in a minute or two I returned to my mat, anxiously awaiting the result of the experiment.

One after another the savages turning restlessly, appeared to resume their slumbers, and rejoicing at the stillness which prevailed, I was about to rise again from my couch, when I heard a slight rustling—a dark form was intercepted between me and the doorway—the slide was drawn across it, and the individual, whoever he was, returned to his mat. This was a sad blow to me; but as it might have aroused the suspicions of the islanders to have made another attempt that night, I was reluctantly obliged to defer it until the next. Several times after I repeated the same maneuver, but with as little success as before. As my pretense for withdrawing from the house was to allay my thirst, Kory-Kory, either suspecting some design on my part, or else prompted by a desire to please me, regularly every evening placed a calabash of water by my side.

Even under these inauspicious circumstances I again and again renewed the attempt; but when I did so my valet always rose with me, as if determined I should not remove myself from his observation. For the present, therefore, I was obliged to abandon the attempt; but I endeavored to console myself with the idea that by this mode I might yet effect my escape.

Shortly after Marnoo's visit I was reduced to such a state, that it was with extreme difficulty I could walk, even with the assistance of a spear, and Kory-Kory, as formerly, was obliged to carry me daily to the stream.

For hours and hours during the warmest part of the day I lay upon my mat, and while those around me were nearly all dozing away in careless ease, I remained awake, gloomily pondering over the fate which it appeared now idle for me to resist, when I thought of the loved friends who were thousands and thousands of miles from the savage island in which I was held a captive, when I reflected that my dreadful fate would forever be concealed from them, and that with hope deferred they might continue to await my return long after my inanimate form had blended with the dust of the valley—I could not repress a shudder of anguish.

How vividly is impressed upon my mind every minute feature of the scene which met my view during those long days of suffering and sorrow! At my request my mats were always spread directly facing the door, opposite which, and at a little distance, was the hut of boughs that Marheyo was building.

Whenever my gentle Fayaway and Kory-Kory, laying themselves down beside me, would leave me awhile to uninterrupted repose, I took a strange interest in the slightest movements of the eccentric old warrior. All alone during the stillness of the tropical mid-day, he would pursue his quiet work, sitting in the shade and weaving together the leaflets of his cocoanut branches, or rolling upon his knee the twisted fibers of bark to form the cords with which he tied together the thatching of his tiny house. Frequently suspending his employment, and noticing my melancholy eye fixed upon him, he would raise his hand with a gesture expressive of deep commiseration, and then moving towards me slowly would enter on tip-toes, fearful of disturbing the slumbering natives, and, taking the fan from my hand, would sit before me, swaying it gently to and fro, and gazing earnestly into my face.

Just beyond the pi-pi, and disposed in a triangle before the entrance of the house, were three magnificent bread-fruit trees. At this moment I can recall to my mind their slender shafts, and the graceful inequalities of their bark, on which my eye was accustomed to dwell day after day in the midst of my solitary musings. It is strange how inanimate objects will twine themselves into our affections, especially in the hour of affliction. Even now, amidst all the bustle and stir of the proud and busy city in which I am dwelling, the image of those three trees seems to come as vividly before my eyes as if they were actually present, and I still feel the soothing quiet pleasure which I then had in watching hour after hour their topmost boughs waving gracefully in the breeze.

Chapter XXXIV

THE ESCAPE

NEARLY THREE WEEKS HAD ELAPSED SINCE THE SECOND VISIT OF MARNOO, AND IT MUST HAVE been more than four months since I entered the valley, when one day about noon, and whilst everything was in profound silence, Mow-Mow, the one-eyed chief, suddenly appeared at the door, and leaning towards me as I lay directly facing him, said in a low tone, "Toby pemi ena" (Toby has arrived here). Gracious heaven! What a tumult of emotions rushed upon me at this startling intelligence! Insensible to the pain that had before distracted me, I leaped to my feet, and called wildly to Kory-Kory, who was reposing by my side. The startled islanders sprang from their mats; the news was quickly communicated to them; and the next moment I was making my way to the Ti on the back of Kory-Kory, and surrounded by the excited savages.

All that I could comprehend of the particulars which Mow-Mow rehearsed to his auditors as we proceeded, was that my long-lost companion had arrived in a boat which had just entered the bay. These tidings made me most anxious to be carried at once to the sea, lest some untoward circumstance should prevent our meeting; but to this they would not consent, and continued their course towards the royal abode. As we approached it, Mehevi and several chiefs showed themselves from the piazza, and called upon us loudly to come to them.

As soon as we had approached, I endeavored to make them understand that I was going down to the sea to meet Toby. To this the king objected, and motioned Kory-Kory to bring me into the house. It was in vain to resist; and in a few moments I found myself within the Ti, surrounded by a noisy group engaged in discussing the recent intelligence. Toby's name was frequently repeated, coupled with violent exclamations of astonishment. It seemed as if they yet remained in doubt with regard to the fact of his arrival, at at every fresh report that was brought from the shore they betrayed the liveliest emotions.

Almost frenzied at being held in this state of suspense, I passionately besought Mehevi to permit me to proceed. Whether my companion had arrived or not, I felt a presentiment that my own fate was about to be decided. Again and again I renewed my petition to Mehevi. He regarded me with a fixed and serious eye, but at length yielding to my importunity, reluctantly granted my request.

Accompanied by some fifty of the natives, I now rapidly continued my journey; every few moments being transferred from the back of one to another, and urging my bearer forward all the while with earnest entreaties. As I thus hurried forward, no doubt as to the truth of the information I had received ever crossed my mind. I was alive only to the one overwhelming idea, that a chance of deliverance was now afforded me, if the jealous opposition of the savages could be overcome.

Having been prohibited from approaching the sea during the whole of my stay in the valley, I had always associated with it the idea of escape. Toby too—if indeed he had ever voluntarily deserted me—must have effected this flight by the sea; and now that I was drawing near to it myself, I indulged in hopes which I had never felt before. It was evident that a boat had entered the bay, and I saw little reason to doubt the truth of the report that it had brought my companion. Every time therefore that we gained an elevation, I looked eagerly around, hoping to behold him.

In the midst of an excited throng, who by their violent gestures and wild cries appeared to be under the influence of some excitement as strong as my own, I was now borne along at a rapid trot, frequently stooping my head to avoid the branches which crossed the path, and never ceasing to implore those who carried me to accelerate their already swift pace.

In this manner we had proceeded about four or five miles, when we were met by a party of some twenty islanders, between whom and those who accompanied me ensued an animated conference. Impatient of the delay occasioned by this interruption, I was beseeching the man who carried me to proceed without his loitering companions, when Kory-Kory, running to my side, informed me, in three fatal words, that the news had all proved, false—that Toby had not arrived—"Toby owlee pemi." Heaven only knows how, in the state of mind and body I then was, I ever sustained the agony which this intelligence caused me: not that the news was altogether unexpected; but I had trusted that the fact might not have been made known until we should have arrived upon the beach. As it was, I at once foresaw the course the savages would pursue. They had only yielded thus far to my entreaties, that I might give a joyful welcome to my long-absent comrade; but now that it was known he had not arrived, they would at once oblige me to turn back.

My anticipations were but too correct. In spite of the resistance I made, they carried me into a house which was near the spot, and left me upon the mats. Shortly afterwards several of those who had accompanied me from the Ti, detaching themselves from the others, proceeded in the direction of the sea. Those who remained—among whom were Marheyo, Mow-Mow, Kory-Kory, and Tinor—gathered about the dwelling and appeared to be awaiting their return.

This convinced me that strangers—perhaps some of my own countrymen—had for some cause or other entered the bay. Distracted at the idea of their vicinity, and reckless of the pain which I suffered, I heeded not the assurances of the islanders, that there were no boats at the beach, but starting to my feet endeavored to gain the door. Instantly the passage was blocked up by several men, who commanded me to resume my seat. The fierce looks of the irritated savages admonished me that I could gain nothing by force, and that it was by entreaty alone that I could hope to compass my object.

Guided by this consideration, I turned to Mow-Mow, the only chief present whom I had been much in the habit of seeing, and carefully concealing my real design, tried to make him comprehend that I still believed Toby to have arrived on the shore, and besought him to allow me to go forward to welcome him. To all his repeated assertions, that my companion had not been seen, I pretended to turn a deaf ear: while I urged my solicitations with an eloquence of gesture which the one-eyed chief appeared unable to resist. He seemed indeed to regard me as a forward child, to whose wishes he had not the heart to oppose force, and whom he must consequently humor. He spoke a few words to the natives, who at once retreated from the door, and I immediately passed out of the house.

Here I looked earnestly round for Kory-Kory; but that hitherto faithful servitor was nowhere to be seen. Unwilling to linger even for a single instant when every moment might be so important, I motioned to a muscular fellow near me to take me upon his back: to my surprise he angrily refused. I turned to another, but with a like result. A third attempt was as unsuccessful, and I immediately perceived what had induced Mow-Mow to grant my request and why the other natives conducted themselves in so strange a manner. It was evident that the chief had only given me liberty to continue my progress towards the sea because he supposed that I was deprived of the means of reaching it.

Convinced by this of their determination to retain me a captive, I became desperate; and almost insensible to the pain which I suffered, I seized a spear which was leaning against the projecting eaves of the house, and supporting myself with it, resumed the path that swept by the dwelling. To my surprise I was suffered to proceed alone, all the natives remaining in front of the house, and engaging in earnest conversation, which every moment became more loud and vehement; and to my unspeakable delight I perceived that some difference of opinion had arisen between them; that two parties, in short, were formed, and consequently that in their divided counsels there was some chance of my deliverance.

Before I had proceeded a hundred yards I was again surrounded by the savages, who were still in all the heat of argument, and appeared every moment as if they would come to blows. In the midst of this tumult old Marheyo came to my side, and I shall never forget the benevolent expression of his countenance. He placed his arm upon my shoulder, and emphatically pronounced the only two English words I had taught him—"Home" and "Mother." I at once understood what he meant, and eagerly expressed my thanks to him. Fayaway and Kory-Kory were by his side, both weeping violently; and it was not until the old man had twice repeated the command that his son could bring himself to obey him, and take me again upon his back. The one-eyed chief opposed his doing so, but he was overruled, and, as it seemed to me, by some of his own party.

We proceeded onwards, and never shall I forget the ecstasy I felt when I first heard the roar of the surf breaking upon the beach. Before long I saw the flashing billows themselves through the opening between the trees. Oh glorious sight and sound of ocean! with what rapture did I hail you as familiar friends! By this time the shouts of the crowd upon the beach were distinctly audible, and in the blended confusion of sounds I almost fancied I could distinguish the voices of my own countrymen.

When we reached the open space which lay between the groves and the sea, the first object that met my view was an English whale-boat, lying with her bow pointed from the shore, and only a few fathoms distant from it. It was manned by five islanders, dressed in short tunics of calico. My first impression was that they were in the very act of pulling out from the bay; and that, after all my exertions, I had come too late. My soul sunk within me: but a second glance convinced me that the boat was only hanging off to keep out of the surf; and the next moment I heard my own name shouted out by a voice from the midst of the crowd.

Looking in the direction of the sound, I perceived, to my indescribable joy, the tall figure of Karakoee, an Oahu Kanaka, who had often been aboard the *Dolly,* while she lay in Nukuheva. He wore the green shooting-jacket with gilt buttons, which had been given to him by an officer of the *Reine Blanche*—the French flag-ship—and in which I had always seen him dressed. I now remembered the Kanaka had frequently told me that his person was tabooed in all the valleys of the island, and the sight of him at such a moment as this filled my heart with a tumult of delight.

Karakoee stood near the edge of the water with a large roll of cotton-cloth thrown over one arm, and holding two or three canvas bags of powder; while with the other hand he grasped a musket, which he appeared to be proffering to several of the chiefs around him. But they turned with disgust from his offers, and seemed to be impatient at his presence, with vehement gestures waving him off to his boat, and commanding him to depart.

The Kanaka, however, still maintained his ground, and I at once perceived that he was seeking to purchase my freedom. Animated by the idea, I called upon him loudly to come to me; but he replied, in broken English, that the islanders had threatened to pierce him with their spears, if he stirred a foot towards me. At this time I was still advancing, surrounded by a dense throng of the natives, several of whom had their hands upon me, and more than one javelin was threateningly pointed at me. Still I perceived clearly that many of those least friendly towards me looked irresolute and anxious.

I was still some thirty yards from Karakoee when my farther progress was prevented by the natives, who compelled me to sit down upon the ground, while they still retained their hold upon my arms. The din and tumult now became tenfold, and I perceived that several of the priests were on the spot, all of whom were evidently urging Mow-Mow and the other chiefs to prevent my departure; and the detestable word "Roo-ne! Roo-ne!" which I had heard repeated a thousand times during the day, was now shouted out on every side of me. Still I saw that the Kanaka continued his exertions in my favor—that he was boldly debating the matter with the savages, and was striving to entice them by displaying his cloth and powder, and snapping the lock of his musket. But all he said or did appeared only to augment the clamors of those around him, who seemed bent upon driving him into the sea.

When I remembered the extravagant value placed by these people upon the articles which were offered to them in exchange for me, and which were so indignantly rejected, I saw a new proof of the same fixed determination of purpose they had all along manifested with regard to me, and in despair, and reckless of consequences, I exerted all my strength, and shaking myself free from the grasp of those who held me, I sprung upon my feet and rushed towards Karakoee.

The rash attempt nearly decided my fate; for, fearful that I might slip from them, several of the islanders now raised a simultaneous shout, and pressing upon Karakoee, they menaced him with furious gestures, and actually forced him into the sea. Appalled at their violence, the poor fellow, standing nearly to the waist in the surf, endeavored to pacify them; but at length, fearful that they would do him some fatal violence, he beckoned to his comrades to pull in at once, and take him into the boat.

It was at this agonizing moment, when I thought all hope was ended, that a new contest arose between the two parties who had accompanied me to the shore; blows were struck, wounds were given, and blood flowed. In the interest excited by the fray, everyone had left me except Marheyo, Kory-Kory, and poor dear Fayaway, who clung to me, sobbing indignantly. I saw that now or never was the moment. Clasping my hands together, I looked imploringly at Marheyo, and move towards the now almost deserted beach. The tears were in the old man's eyes, but neither he nor Kory-Kory attempted to hold me, and I soon reached the Kanaka, who had been anxiously watching my movements; the rowers pulled in as near as they dared to the edge of the surf; I gave one parting embrace to Fayaway, who seemed speechless with sorrow, and the next instant I found myself safe in the boat, and Karakoee by my side, who told the rowers at once to give way. Marheyo and Kory-Kory, and a great many of the women, followed me into the water, and I was determined, as the only mark of gratitude I could show, to give them the articles which had been brought as my ransom. I handed the musket to Kory-Kory, with a rapid gesture which was equivalent to a "Deed of Gift"; threw the roll of cotton to old Marheyo, pointing as I did so to poor Fayaway, who had retired from the edge of the water and was sitting down disconsolate on the shingles; and tumbled the powder-bags out to the nearest young ladies, all of whom were vastly willing to take them. This distribution did not occupy ten seconds, and before it was over the boat was under full way; the Kanaka all the while exclaiming loudly against what he considered a useless throwing away of valuable property.

Although it was clear that my movements had been noticed by several of the natives, still they had not suspended the conflict in which they were engaged, and it was not until the boat was above fifty yards from the shore that Mow-Mow and some six or seven other warriors rushed into the sea and hurled their javelins at us. Some of the weapons passed quite as close to us as was desirable, but no one was wounded, and the men pulled away gallantly. But although soon out of the reach of the spears, our progress was extremely slow; it blew strong upon the shore, and the tide was against us; and I saw Karakoee, who was steering the boat, give many a look towards a jutting point of the bay round which we had to pass.

For a minute or two after our departure, the savages, who had formed into different groups, remained perfectly motionless and silent. All at once the enraged chief showed by his gestures that he had resolved what course he would take. Shouting loudly to his companions, and pointing with his tomahawk towards the headland, he set off at full speed in that direction, and was followed by about thirty of the natives, among whom were several of the priests, all yelling out "Roo-ne! Roo-ne!" at the very top of their voices. Their intention was evidently to swim off from the headland and interrupt us in our course. The wind was freshening every minute, and was right in our teeth, and it was one of those chopping angry seas in which it is so difficult to row. Still the chances seemed in our favor, but when we came within a hundred yards of the point, the active savages were already dashing into the water, and we all feared that within five minutes' time we should have a score of the infuriated wretches around us. If so, our doom was sealed, for these savages, unlike the feeble swimmers of civilized countries, are, if anything, more formidable antagonists in the water than when on the land. It was all a trial of strength; our natives pulled till their oars bent again, and the crowd of swimmers shot through the water despite its roughness, with fearful rapidity.

By the time we had reached the headland, the savages were spread right across our course. Our rowers got out their knives and held them ready between their teeth, and I seized the boat-hook. We were well aware that if they succeeded in intercepting us they would practice upon us the maneuver which has proved so fatal to many a boat's crew in these seas. They would grapple the oars, and seizing hold of the gunwale, capsize the boat, and then we should be entirely at their mercy.

After a few breathless moments I discerned Mow-Mow. The athletic islander, with his tomahawk between his teeth, was dashing the water before him till it foamed again. He was the nearest to us, and in another instant he would have seized one of the oars. Even at the moment I felt horror at the act I was about to commit; but it was no time for pity or compunction, and with a true aim, and exerting all my strength, I dashed the boat-hook at him. It struck him just below the throat, and forced him downwards. I had no time to repeat my blow, but I saw him rise to the surface in the wake of the boat, and never shall I forget the ferocious expression of his countenance.

Only one other of the savages reached the boat. He seized the gunwhale, but the knives of our rowers so mauled his wrists, that he was forced to quit his hold, and the next minute we were past them all, and in safety. The strong excitement which had thus far kept me up, now left me, and I fell back fainting into the arms of Karakoee.

* * * * *

The circumstances connected with my most unexpected escape may be very briefly stated. The captain of an Australian vessel, being in distress for men in these remote seas, had put into Nukuheva in order to recruit his ship's company; but not a single man was to be obtained; and the barque was about to get under weigh, when she was boarded by Karakoee, who informed the disappointed Englishman that an American sailor was detained by the savages in the neighboring bay of Typee; and he offered, if supplied with suitable articles of traffic, to undertake his release. The Kanaka had gained his intelligence from Marnoo, to whom, after all, I was indebted for my escape. The proposition was acceded to; and Karakoee, taking with him five tabooed natives of Nukuheva, again repaired aboard the barque, which in a few hours sailed to that part of the island, and threw her main-top-sail aback right off the entrance to the Typee bay. The whale-boat, manned by the tabooed crew, pulled towards the head of the inlet, while the ship lay "off and on" awaiting its return.

The events which ensued have already been detailed, and little more remains to be related. On reaching the *Julia* I was lifted over the side, and my strange appearance and remarkable adventure occasioned the liveliest interest. Every attention was bestowed upon me that humanity could suggest. But to such a state was I reduced, that three months elapsed before I recovered my health.

The mystery which hung over the fate of my friend and companion Toby has never been cleared up. I still remain ignorant whether he succeeded in leaving the valley, or perished at the hands of the islanders.

Appendix

The author of this volume arrived at Tahiti the very day that the iniquitous designs of the French were consummated by inducing the subordinate chiefs, during the absence of their queen, to ratify an artfully drawn treaty, by which she was virtually deposed. Both menaces and caresses were employed on this occasion, and the 32-pounders which peeped out of the port-holes of the frigate were the principal arguments adduced to quiet the scruples of the more conscientious islanders.

And yet this piratical seizure of Tahiti, with all the woe and desolation which resulted from it, created not half so great a sensation, at least in America, as was caused by the proceedings of the English at the Sandwich Islands. No transaction has ever been more grossly misrepresented than the events which occurred upon the arrival of Lord George Paulet at Oahu. During a residence of four months at Honolulu, the metropolis of the group, the author was in the confidence of an Englishman who was much employed by his lordship; and great was the author's astonishment on his arrival at Boston, in the autumn of 1844, to read the distorted accounts and fabrications which had produced in the United States so violent an outbreak of indignation against the English. He deems it, therefore, a mere act of justice towards a gallant officer briefly to state the leading circumstances connected with the event in question.

It is needless to rehearse all the abuse that for some time previous to the spring of 1843 had been heaped upon the British residents, especially upon Captain Charlton, her Britannic Majesty's consul-general, by the native authorities of the Sandwich Islands. High in the favor of the imbecile king at this time was one Dr. Judd, a sanctimonious apothecary-adventurer, who, with other kindred and influential spirits, were animated by an inveterate dislike to England. The ascendancy of a junto of ignorant and designing Methodist elders in the councils of a half-civilized king, ruling with absolute sway over a nation just poised between barbarism and civilization, and exposed by the peculiarities of its relations with foreign states to unusual difficulties, was not precisely calculated to impart a healthy tone to the policy of the government.

At last matters were brought to such an extremity, through the iniquitous maladministration of affairs, that the endurance of further insults and injuries on the part of the British consul was no longer to be borne. Captain Charlton, insultingly forbidden to leave the islands, clandestinely withdrew, and arriving at Valparaiso, conferred with Rear-Admiral Thomas, the English commander-in-chief on the Pacific station. In consequence of this communication, Lord George Paulet was dispatched by the admiral in the Carysfort frigate, to inquire into and correct the alleged abuses. On arriving at his destination, he sent his first-lieutenant ashore with a letter to the king, couched in terms of the utmost courtesy, and soliciting the honor of an audience. The messenger was denied access to his Majesty, and Paulet was coolly referred to Doctor Judd, and informed that the apothecary was invested with plenary powers to treat with him. Rejecting this insolent proposition, his lordship again addressed the king by letter, and renewed his previous request; but he encountered another repulse. Justly indignant at this treatment, he penned a third epistle, enumerating the grievances to be redressed, and demanding a compliance with his requisitions, under penalty of immediate hostilities.

The government was now obliged to act, and an artful stroke of policy was decided upon by the despicable counselors of the king to entrap the sympathies and rouse the indignation of Christendom. His Majesty was made to intimate to the British captain that he could not, as the conscientious ruler of his beloved people, comply with the arbitrary demands of his lordship, and in deprecation of the horrors of war, tendered to his acceptance the "provisional cession" of the islands, subject to the result of the negotiations then pending in London. Paulet, a bluff and straightforward sailor, took the king at his word, and after some preliminary arrangements, entered upon the administration of Hawaiian affairs, in the same firm and benignant spirit which marked the discipline of his frigate, and which had rendered him the idol of his ship's company. He soon endeared himself to nearly all orders of the islanders; but the king and the chiefs, whose feudal sway over the common people is laboriously sought to be perpetuated by their missionary advisers, regarded all his proceedings with the most vigilant animosity. Jealous of his growing popularity, and unable to counteract it, they endeavored to assail his reputation abroad by ostentatiously protesting against his acts, and appealing in Oriental phrase to the *wide universe* to witness and compassionate their *unparalleled wrongs.*

Heedless of their idle clamors, Lord George Paulet addressed himself to the task of reconciling the differences among the foreign residents, remedying their grievances, promoting their merchantile interests, and ameliorating as far a lay in his power the condition of the degraded natives. The iniquities he brought to light and instantly suppressed are too numerous to be here recorded; but one instance may be mentioned that will give some idea of the lamentable misrule to which these poor islanders are subjected.

It is well known that the laws at the Sandwich Islands are subject to the most capricious alterations, which, by confounding all ideas of right and wrong in the minds of the natives, produce the most pernicious effects. In no case is this mischief more plainly discernible than in the continually shifting regulations concerning licentiousness. At one time the most innocent freedoms between the sexes are punished with fine and imprisonment; at another the revocation of the statute is followed by the most open and undisguised profligacy.

It so happened that at the period of Paulet's arrival the Connecticut blue laws had been for at least three weeks steadily enforced. In consequence of this, the fort at Honolulu was filled with a great number of young girls, who were confined there doing penance for their slips from virtue. Paulet, although at first unwilling to interfere with regulations having reference solely to the natives themselves, was eventually, by the prevalence of certain reports, induced to institute a strict inquiry into the internal administration of General Kekuanoa, governor of the island of Oahu, one of the pillars of the Hawaiian church, and captain of the fort. He soon ascertained that numbers of the young females employed during the day at work intended for the benefit of the king, were at night smuggled over the ramparts of the fort—which on one side directly overhangs the sea—and were conveyed by stealth on board such vessels as had contracted with the General to be supplied with them. Before daybreak they returned to their quarters, and their own silence with regard to these secret excursions was purchased by a small portion of those wages of iniquity which were placed in the hands of Kekuanoa.

The vigor with which the laws concerning licentiousness were at that period enforced, enabled the General to monopolize in a great measure the detestable trade in which he was engaged, and there consequently flowed into his coffers—and some say into those of the government also—considerable sums of money. It is indeed a lamentable fact, that the principal revenue of the Hawaiian government is derived from the fines levied upon, or rather the licenses taken out by Vice, the prosperity of which is linked with that of the government. Were the people to become virtuous the authorities would become poor; but from present indications there is little apprehension to be entertained on that score.

Some five months after the date of the cession, the Dublin frigate, carrying the flag of Rear-Admiral Thomas, entered the harbor of Honolulu. The excitement that her sudden appearance produced on shore was prodigious. Three days after her arrival an English sailor hauled down the red cross which had been flying from the heights of the fort, and the Hawaiian colors were again displayed upon the same staff. At the same moment the long 42-pounders upon Punchbowl Hill opened their iron throats in triumphant reply to the thunders of the five men-of-war in the harbor; and King Kammahamaha III, surrounded by a splendid group of British and American officers, unfurled the royal standard to assembled thousands of his subjects, who, attracted by the imposing military display of the foreigners, had flocked to witness the formal restoration of the islands to their ancient rulers.

The Admiral, after sanctioning the proceeding of his subaltern, had brought the authorities to terms; and so removed the necessity of acting any longer under the provisional cession.

The event was made an occasion of riotous rejoicing by the king and the principal chiefs, who easily secured a display of enthusiasm from the inferior orders, by remitting for a time the accustomed severity of the laws. Royal proclamations in English and Hawaiian were placarded in the streets of Honolulu, and posted up in the more populous villages of the group, in which his Majesty announced to his loving subjects the re-establishment of his throne, and called upon them to celebrate it by breaking through all moral, legal, and religious restraint for ten consecutive days, during which time all the laws of the land were solemnly declared to be suspended.

Who that happened to be at Honolulu during those ten memorable days will ever forget them! The spectacle of universal broad-day debauchery, which was then exhibited, beggars description. The natives of the surrounding islands flocked to Honolulu by hundreds, and the crews of two frigates, opportunely let loose like so many demons to swell the heathenish uproar, gave the crowning flourish to the scene. It was a sort of Polynesian saturnalia. Deeds too atrocious to be mentioned were done at noon-day in the open street, and some of the islanders caught in the very act of stealing from the foreigners, were, on being taken to the fort by the aggrieved party, suffered immediately to go at large and to retain the stone property—Kekuanoa informing the white men, with a sardonic grin, that the laws were "hannapa" (tied up).

The history of these ten days reveals in their true colors the character of the Sandwich islanders, and furnishes an eloquent commentary on the results which have flowed from the labors of the missionaries. Freed from the restraints of severe penal laws, the natives almost to a man had plunged voluntarily into every species of wickedness and excess, and by their utter disregard of all decency plainly showed, that although they had been schooled into a seeming submission to the new order of things, they were in reality as depraved and vicious as ever.

Such were the events which produced in America so general an out-break of indignation against the spirited and high-minded Paulet. He is not the first man who, in the fearless discharge of his duty, has awakened the senseless clamors of those whose narrow-minded suspicions blind them to a proper appreciation of measures which unusual exigencies may have rendered necessary.

It is almost needless to add that the British cabinet never had any idea of appropriating the islands; and it furnishes a sufficient vindication of the acts of Lord George Paulet, that he not only received the unqualified approbation of his own government, but that to this hour the great body of the Hawaiian people invoke blessings on his head, and look back with gratitude to the time when his liberal and paternal sway diffused peace and happiness among them.

The Story of Toby

The morning my comrade left me, as related in the narrative, he was accompanied by a large party of the natives, some of them carrying fruit and hogs for the purposes of traffic, as the report had spread that boats had touched at the bay.

As they proceeded through the settled parts of the valley, numbers joined them from every side, running with animated cries from every pathway. So excited were the whole party, that eager as Toby was to gain the beach, it was almost as much as he could do to keep up with them. Making the valley ring with their shouts, they hurried along on a swift trot, those in advance pausing now and then, and flourishing their weapons to urge the rest forward.

Presently they came to a place where the paths crossed a band of the main stream of the valley. Here a strange sound came through the grove beyond, and the islanders halted. It was Mow-Mow, the one-eyed chief, who had gone on before; he was striking his heavy lance against the hollow bough of a tree.

This was a signal of alarm—for nothing was now heard but shouts of "Happar! Happar!"—the warriors tilting with their spears and brandishing them in the air, and the women and boys shouting to each other, and picking up the stones in the bed of the stream. In a moment or two Mow-Mow and two or three other chiefs ran out from the grove, and the din increased ten-fold.

Now, thought Toby, for a fray; and being unarmed, he besought one of the young men domiciled with Marheyo for the loan of his spear. But he was refused; the youth roguishly telling him that the weapon was very good for him (the Typee), but that a white man could fight much better with his fists.

The merry humor of this young wag seemed to be shared by the rest, for in spite of their warlike cries and gestures, everybody was capering and laughing, as if it was one of the funniest things in the world to be awaiting the flight of a score or two of Happar javelins from an ambush in the thickets.

While my comrade was in vain trying to make out the meaning of all this, a good number of the natives separated themselves from the rest and ran off into the grove on one side, the others now keeping perfectly still, as if awaiting the result. After a little while, however, Mow-Mow, who stood in advance, motioned them to come on stealthily, which they did, scarcely rustling a leaf. Thus they crept along for ten or fifteen minutes, every now and then pausing to listen.

Toby by no means relished this sort of skulking; if there was going to be a fight he wanted it to begin at once. But all in good time—for just then, as they went prowling into the thickest of the wood, terrific howls burst upon them on all sides, and volleys of darts and stones flew across the path. Not an enemy was to be seen, and, what was still more surprising, not a single man dropped, though the pebbles fell among the leaves like hail.

There was a moment's pause, when the Typees, with wild shrieks, flung themselves into the covert, spear in hand; nor was Toby behindhand. Coming so near getting his skull broken by the stones, and animated by an old grudge he bore the Happars, he was among the first to dash at them. As he broke his way through the underbrush, trying, as he did so, to wrest a spear from a young chief, the shouts of battle all of a sudden ceased, and the wood was as still as death. The next moment, the party who had left them so mysteriously rushed out from behind every bush and tree, and united with the rest in long and merry peals of laughter.

It was all a sham, and Toby, who was quite out of breath with excitement, was much incensed at being made a fool of.

It afterwards turned out that the whole affair had been concerted for his particular benefit, though with what precise view it would be hard to tell. My comrade was the more enraged at this boys' play, since it had consumed so much time, every moment of which might be precious. Perhaps, however, it was partly intended for this very purpose; and he was led to think so, because, when the natives started again, he observed that they did not seem to be in so great a hurry as before. At last, after they had gone some distance, Toby, thinking all the while that they never would get to the sea, two men came running towards them, and a regular halt ensued, followed by a noisy discussion, during which Toby's name was often repeated. All this made him more and more anxious to learn what was going on at the beach; but it was in vain that he now tried to push forward; the natives held him back.

In a few moments the conference ended, and many of them ran down the path in the direction of the water, the rest surrounding Toby, and entreating him to "Moee," or sit down and rest himself. As an additional inducement, several calabashes of food, which had been brought along, were now placed on the ground, and opened, and pipes also were lighted. Toby bridled his impatience a while, but at last sprang to his feet and dashed forward again. He was soon overtaken nevertheless, and again surrounded, but without further detention was then permitted to go down to the sea.

They came out upon a bright green space between the groves and the water, and close under the shadow of the Happar mountain, where a path was seen, winding out of sight through a gorge.

No sign of a boat, however, was beheld, nothing but a tumultuous crowd of men and women, and someone in their midst, earnestly talking to them. As my comrade advanced, this person came forward and proved to be no stranger. He was an old grizzled sailor, whom Toby and myself had frequently seen in Nukuheva, where he lived an easy devil-may-care life in the household of Mowanna the king, going by the name of "Jimmy." In fact, he was the royal favorite, and had a good deal to say in his master's councils. He wore a Manilla hat and a sort of tappa morning gown, sufficiently loose and negligent to show the verse of a song tattooed upon his chest, and a variety of spirited cuts by native artists in other parts of his body. He sported a fishing rod in his hand, and carried a sooty old pipe slung about his neck.

This old rover having retired from active life, had resided in Nukuheva some time, could speak the language, and for that reason was frequently employed by the French as an interpreter. He was an arrant old gossip too; forever coming off in his canoe to the ships in the bay, and regaling their crews with choice little morsels of court scandal; such, for instance, as a shameful intrigue of his majesty with a Happar damsel, a public dancer at the feasts, and otherwise relating some incredible tales about the Marquesas generally. I remember in particular his telling the *Dolly*'s crew what proved to be literally a cock-and-bull story, about two natural prodigies which he said were then on the island. One was an old monster of a hermit, having a marvelous reputation for sanctity, and reputed a famous sorcerer, who lived away off in a den among the mountains, where he hid from the world a great pair of horns that grew out of his temples. Notwithstanding his reputation for piety, this horrid old fellow was the terror of all the island round, being reported to come out from his retreat, and go a man-hunting every dark night. Some anonymous Paul Pry, too, coming down the mountain, once got a peep at his den, and found it full of bones. In short, he was a most unheard-of monster.

The other prodigy Jimmy told us about, was the younger son of a chief, who, although but just turned of ten, had entered upon holy orders, because his superstitious countrymen thought him especially intended for the priesthood from the fact of his having a comb on his head like a rooster. But this was not all; for still more wonderful to relate, the boy prided himself upon this strange crest, being actually endowed with a cock's voice, and frequently crowing over his peculiarity.

But to return to Toby. The moment he saw the old rover on the beach, he ran up to him, the natives following after, and forming a circle round them.

After welcoming him to the shore, Jimmy went on to tell him how that he knew all about our having run away from the ship, and being among the Typees. Indeed, he had been urged by Mowanna to come over to the valley, and after visiting his friends there, to bring us back with him, his royal master being exceedingly anxious to share with him the reward which had been held out for our capture. He, however, assured Toby that he had indignantly spurned the offer.

All this astonished my comrade not a little, as neither of us had entertained the least idea that any white man ever visited the Typees sociably. But Jimmy told him that such was the case nevertheless, although he seldom came into the bay, and scarcely ever went back from the beach. One of the priests of the valley, in some way or other connected with an old tattooed divine in Nukuheva, was a friend of his, and through him he was "taboo."

He said, moreover, that he was sometimes employed to come round to the bay, and engage fruit for ships lying in Nukuheva. In fact, he was now on that very errand, according to his own account, having just come across the mountains by the way of Happar. By noon of the next day the fruit would be heaped up in stacks on the beach, in readiness for the boats which he then intended to bring into the bay.

Jimmy now asked Toby whether he wished to leave the island; if he did, there was a ship in want of men lying in the other harbor, and he would be glad to take him over, and see him on board that very day.

"No," said Toby, "I cannot leave the island unless my comrade goes with me. I left him up the valley because they would not let him come down. Let us go now and fetch him."

"But how is he to cross the mountain with us," replied Jimmy, "even if we get him down to the beach? Better let him stay till to-morrow, and I will bring him round to Nukuheva in the boats."

"That will never do," said Toby; "but come along with me now, and let us get him down here at any rate"; and yielding to the impulse of the moment, he started to hurry back into the valley. But hardly was his back turned, when a dozen hands were laid on him, and he learned that he could not go a step farther.

It was in vain that he fought with them; they would not hear of his stirring from the beach. Cut to the heart at this unexpected repulse, Toby now conjured the sailor to go after me alone. But Jimmy replied, that in the mood the Typees then were they would not permit him so to do, though at the same time he was not afraid of their offering him any harm.

Little did Toby then think, as he afterwards had good reason to suspect, that this very Jimmy was a heartless villain, who, by his arts, had just incited the natives to restrain him as he was in the act of going after me. Well must the old sailor have known, too, that the natives would never consent to our leaving together, and he therefore wanted to get Toby off alone, for a purpose which he afterwards made plain. Of all this, however, my comrade now knew nothing.

He was still struggling with the islanders when Jimmy again came up to him, and warned him against irritating them, saying that he was only making matters worse for both of us, and if they became enraged, there was no telling what might happen. At last he made Toby sit down on a broken canoe by a pile of stones, upon which was a ruinous little shrine supported by four upright paddles, and in front partly screened by a net. The fishing parties met there, when they came in from the sea, for their offerings were laid before an image, upon a smooth black stone within. This spot Jimmy said was strictly "taboo," and no one would molest or come near him while he stayed by its shadow. The old sailor then went off, and began speaking very earnestly to Mow-Mow and some other chiefs, while all the rest formed a circle round the taboo place, looking intently at Toby, and talking to each other without ceasing.

Now, notwithstanding what Jimmy had just told him, there presently came up to my comrade an old woman, who seated herself beside him on the canoe.

"Typee motarkee?" said she. "Motarkee nuee," said Toby.

She then asked him whether he was going to Nukuheva; he nodded yes; and with a plaintive wail and her eyes filling with tears she rose and left him.

This old woman, the sailor afterwards said, was the wife of an aged king of a small inland valley, communicating by a deep pass with the country of the Typees. The inmates of the two valleys were related to each other by blood, and were known by the same name. The old woman had gone down into the Typee valley the day before, and was now with three chiefs, her sons, on a visit to her kinsmen.

As the old king's wife left him, Jimmy again came up to Toby, and told him that he had just talked the whole matter over with the natives, and there was only one course for him to follow. They would not allow him to go back into the valley, and harm would certainly come to both him and me, if he remained much longer on the beach. "So," said he, "you and I had better go to Nukuheva now overland, and to-morrow I will bring Tommo, as they call him, by water; they have promised to carry him down to the sea for me early in the morning, so that there will be no delay."

"No, no," said Toby desperately, "I will not leave him that way; we must escape together."

"Then there is no hope for you," exclaimed the sailor; "for if I leave you here on the beach, as soon as I am gone you will be carried back into the valley, and then neither of you will ever look upon the sea again." And with many oaths he swore that if he would only go to Nukuheva with him that day, he would be sure to have me there the very next morning.

"But how do you know they will bring him down to the beach to-morrow, when they will not do so to-day?" said Toby. But the sailor had many reasons, all of which were so mixed up with the mysterious customs of the islanders, that he was none the wiser. Indeed, their conduct, especially in preventing him from returning into the valley, was absolutely unaccountable to him; and added to everything else, was the bitter reflection, that the old sailor, after all, might possibly be deceiving him. And then again he had to think of me, left alone with the natives, and by no means well. If he went with Jimmy, he might at least hope to procure some relief for me. But might not the savages who had acted so strangely, hurry me off somewhere before his return? Then, even if he remained, perhaps they would not let him go back into the valley where I was.

Thus perplexed was my poor comrade; he knew not what to do, and his courageous spirit was of no use to him now. There he was, all by himself, seated upon the broken canoe—the natives grouped around him at a distance, and eyeing him more and more fixedly. "It is getting late," said Jimmy, who was standing behind the rest. "Nukuheva is far off, and I cannot cross the Happar country by night. You see how it is: if you come along with me, all will be well; if you do not, depend upon it, neither of you will ever escape."

"There is no help for it," said Toby, at last, with a heavy heart, "I will have to trust you"; and he came out from the shadow of the little shrine, and cast a long look up the valley.

"Now keep close to my side," said the sailor, "and let us be moving quickly." Tinor and Fayaway here appeared; the kind-hearted old woman embracing Toby's knees, and giving way to a flood of tears; while Fayaway, hardly less moved, spoke some few words of English she had learned, and held up three fingers before him—in so many days he would return.

At last Jimmy pulled Toby out of the crowd, and after calling to a young Typee who was standing by with a young pig in his arms, all three started for the mountains.

"I have told them that you are coming back again," said the old fellow, laughing, as they began the ascent, "but they'll have to wait a long time." Toby turned, and saw the natives all in motion—the girls waving their tappas in adieu, and the men their spears. As the last figure entered the grove with one arm raised, and the three fingers spread, his heart smote him.

As the natives had at last consented to his going, it might have been that some of them, at least, really counted upon his speedy return, probably supposing, as indeed he had told them when they were coming down the valley, that his only object in leaving them was to procure the medicines I needed. This Jimmy also must have told them. And as they had done before, when my comrade, to oblige me, started on his perilous journey to Nukuheva, they looked upon me, in his absence, as one of two inseparable friends who was a sure guaranty for the other's return. This is only my own supposition, however, for as to all their strange conduct, it is still a mystery.

"You see what sort of a taboo man I am," said the sailor, after for some time silently following the path which led up the mountain. "Mow-Mow made me a present of this pig here, and the man who carries it will go right through Happar, and down into Nukuheva with us. So long as he stays by me he is safe, and just so it will be with you, and to-morrow with Tommo. Cheer up, then, and rely upon me, you will see him in the morning."

The ascent of the mountain was not very difficult, owing to its being near to the sea, where the island ridges are comparatively low; the path, too, was a fine one, so that in a short time all three were standing on the summit with the two valleys at their feet. The white cascade marking the green head of the Typee valley first caught Toby's eye; Marheyo's house could easily be traced by them.

As Jimmy led the way along the ridge, Toby observed that the valley of the Happars did not extend near so far inland as that of the Typees. This accounted for our mistake in entering the latter valley as we had.

A path leading down from the mountain was soon seen, and, following it, the party were in a short time fairly in the happy valley.

"Now," said Jimmy, as they hurried on, "we taboo men have wives in all the bays, and I am going to show you the two I have here."

So, when they came to the house where he said they lived—which was close by the base of the mountain in a shady nook among the groves—he went in, and was quite furious at finding it empty—the ladies had gone out. However, they soon made their appearance, and to tell the truth, welcomed Jimmy quite cordially, as well as Toby, about whom they were very inquisitive. Nevertheless, as the report of their arrival spread, and the Happars began to assemble, it became evident that the appearance of a white stranger among them was not by any means deemed so wonderful an event as in the neighboring valley.

The old sailor now bade his wives prepare something to eat, as he must be in Nukuheva before dark. A meal of fish, bread-fruit, and bananas was accordingly served up, the party regaling themselves on the mats, in the midst of a numerous company.

The Happars put many questions to Jimmy about Toby; and Toby himself looked sharply at them, anxious to recognize the fellow who gave him the wound from which he was still suffering. But this fiery gentleman, so handy with his spear, had the delicacy, it seemed, to keep out of view. Certainly the sight of him would not have been any added inducement to making a stay in the valley—some of the afternoon loungers in Happar having politely urged Toby to spend a few days with them—there was a feast coming on. He, however, declined.

All this while the young Typee stuck to Jimmy like his shadow, and though as lively a dog as any of his tribe, he was now as meek as a lamb, never opening his mouth except to eat. Although some of the Happars looked queerly at him, others were more civil, and seemed desirous of taking him abroad and showing him the valley. But the Typee was not to be cajoled in that way. How many yards he would have to remove from Jimmy before the taboo would be powerless, it would be hard to tell, but probably he himself knew to a fraction.

On the promise of a red cotton handkerchief, and something else which he kept secret, this poor fellow had undertaken a rather ticklish journey, though, as far as Toby could ascertain, it was something that had never happened before.

The island-punch—arva—was brought in at the conclusion of the repast, and passed round in a shallow calabash.

Now my comrade, while seated in the Happar house, began to feel more troubled than ever at leaving me: indeed, so sad did he feel that he talked about going back to the valley, and wanted

Jimmy to escort him as far as the mountains. But the sailor would not listen to him, and, by way of diverting his thoughts, pressed him to drink of the arva. Knowing its narcotic nature, he refused; but Jimmy said he would have something mixed with it, which would convert it into an innocent beverage that would inspirit them for the rest of their journey. So at last he was induced to drink of it, and its effects were just as the sailor had predicted; his spirits rose at once, and all his gloomy thoughts left him.

The old rover now began to reveal his true character, though he was hardly suspected at the time. "If I get you off to a ship," said he, "you will surely give a poor fellow something for saving you." In short, before they left the house, he made Toby promise that he would give him five Spanish dollars if he succeeded in getting any part of his wages advanced from the vessel, aboard of which they were going; Toby, moreover, engaging to reward him still further, as soon as my deliverance was accomplished.

A little while after this they started again, accompanied by many of the natives, and going up the valley, took a steep path near its head, which led to Nukuheva. Here the Happars paused, and watched them as they ascended the mountain, one group of bandit-looking fellows, shaking their spears and casting threatening glances at the poor Typee, whose heart as well as heels seemed much the lighter when he came to look down upon them.

On gaining the heights once more, their way led for a time along several ridges covered with enormous ferns. At last they entered upon a wooded tract, and here they overtook a party of Nukuheva natives, well-armed, and carrying bundles of long poles. Jimmy seemed to know them all very well, and stopped for a while, and had a talk about the "Wee-Wees," as the people of Nukuheva call the Monsieurs.

The party with the poles were King Mowanna's men, and by his orders they had been gathering them in the ravines for his allies the French.

Leaving these fellows to trudge on with their loads, Toby and his companions now pushed forward again, as the sun was already low in the west. They came upon the valleys of Nukuheva on one side of the bay, where the highlands slope off into the sea. The men-of-war were still lying in the harbor, and as Toby looked down upon them, the strange events which had happened so recently seemed all a dream.

They soon descended towards the beach, and found themselves in Jimmy's house before it was well dark. Here he received another welcome from his Nukuheva wives, and after some refreshments in the shape of cocoanut milk and poee-poee, they entered a canoe (the Typee, of course, going along) and paddled off to a whale-ship which was anchored near the shore. This was the vessel in want of men. Our own had sailed some time before. The captain professed great pleasure at seeing Toby, but thought, from his exhausted appearance, that he must be unfit for duty. However, he agreed to ship him, as well as his comrade, as soon as he should arrive.

Toby begged hard for an armed boat, in which to go round to Typee and rescue me, notwithstanding the promises of Jimmy. But this the captain would not hear of, and told him to have patience, for the sailor would be faithful to his word. When, too, he demanded the five silver dollars for Jimmy, the captain was unwilling to give them. But Toby insisted upon it, as he now began to think that Jimmy might be a mere mercenary, who would be sure to prove faithless if not well paid. Accordingly he not only gave him the money, but took care to assure him, over and over again, that as soon as he brought me aboard he would receive a still larger sum.

Before sun-rise the next day, Jimmy and the Typee started in two of the ship's boats, which were manned by tabooed natives. Toby, of course, was all eagerness to go along, but the sailor told him that if he did, it would spoil all; so, hard as it was, he was obliged to remain.

Towards evening he was on the watch, and descried the boats turning the headland and entering the bay. He strained his eyes, and thought he saw me; but I was not there. Descending from the mast almost distracted, he grappled Jimmy as he struck the deck, shouting in a voice that startled him, "Where is Tommo?" The old fellow faltered, but soon recovering, did all he could to soothe him, assuring him that it had proved to be impossible to get me down to the shore that morning; assigning many plausible reasons, and adding that early on the morrow he was going to visit the bay again in a French boat, when, if he did not find me on the beach—as this time he certainly expected to—he would march right back into the valley, and carry me away at all hazards. He, however, again refused to allow Toby to accompany him.

Now, situated as Toby was, his sole dependence for the present was upon this Jimmy, and therefore he was fain to comfort himself as well as he could with what the old sailor had told him.

The next morning, however, he had the satisfaction of seeing the French boat start with Jimmy in it. To-night, then, I will see him, thought Toby; but many a long day passed before he ever saw Tommo again. Hardly was the boat out of sight, when the captain came forward and ordered the anchor to be weighed; he was going to sea.

Vain were all Toby's ravings—they were disregarded; and when he came to himself, the sails were set, and the ship fast leaving the land.

. . . "Oh!" said he to me at our meeting, "what sleepless nights were mine. Often I started from my hammock, dreaming you were before me, and upbraiding me for leaving you on the island."

* * * * *

There is little more to be related. Toby left this vessel at New Zealand, and after some further adventures, arrived home in less than two years after leaving the Marquesas. He always thought of me as dead—and I had every reason to suppose that he too was no more; but a strange meeting was in store for us, one which made Toby's heart all the lighter.

NOTE

The author was more than two years in the South Seas, after escaping from the valley, as recounted in the last chapter. Some time after returning home the foregoing narrative was published, though it was little thought at the time that this would be the means of revealing the existence of Toby, who had long been given up for lost. But so it proved.

The story of his escape supplies a natural sequel to the adventure, and as such it is now added to the volume. It was related to the author by Toby himself, not ten days since.

NEW YORK, JULY, 1846.

OMOO

A NARRATIVE OF ADVENTURES IN THE SOUTH SEAS

To
Herman Gansevoort
Of Gansevoort, Saratoga County, New York
This Work
Is Cordially Inscribed, By His Nephew
The Author

Contents

Preface

Nowhere, perhaps, are the proverbial characteristics of sailors shown under wilder aspects than in the South Seas. For the most part, the vessels navigating those remote waters are engaged in the sperm-whale fishery; a business which is not only peculiarly fitted to attract the most reckless seamen of all nations, but in various ways is calculated to foster in them a spirit of the utmost license. These voyages, also, are unusually long and perilous; the only harbors accessible are among the barbarous or semi-civilized islands of Polynesia, or along the lawless western coast of South America. Hence, scenes the most novel, and not directly connected with the business of whaling, frequently occur among the crews of ships in the Pacific.

Without pretending to give any account of the whale-fishery (for the scope of the narrative does not embrace the subject), it is partly the object of this work to convey some idea of the kind of life to which allusion is made, by means of a circumstantial history of adventures befalling the author.

Another object proposed is, to give a *familiar* account of the present condition of the converted Polynesians, as affected by their promiscuous intercourse with foreigners, and the teachings of the missionaries, combined.

As a roving sailor, the author spent about three months in various parts of the islands of Tahiti and Imeeo, and under circumstances most favorable for correct observations on the social condition of the natives.

In every statement connected with missionary operations, a strict adherence to facts has, of course, been scrupulously observed; and in some instances, it has even been deemed advisable to quote previous voyages, in corroboration of what is offered as the fruit of the author's own observations. Nothing but an earnest desire for truth and good has led him to touch upon this subject at all. And if he refrains from offering hints as to the best mode of remedying the evils which are pointed out, it is only because he thinks, that after being made acquainted with the facts, others are better qualified to do so.

Should a little jocoseness be shown upon some curious traits of the Tahitians, it proceeds from no intention to ridicule: things are merely described as, from their entire novelty, they first struck an unbiased observer.

The present narrative necessarily begins where *Typee* concludes, but has no further connection with the latter work. All, therefore, necessary for the reader to understand, who has not read *Typee,* is given in a brief introduction.

No journal was kept by the author during his wanderings in the South Seas; so that, in preparing the ensuing chapters for the press, precision with respect to dates would have been impossible; and every occurrence has been put down from simple recollection. The frequency, however, with which these incidents have been verbally related, has tended to stamp them upon the memory.

Although it is believed that one or two imperfect Polynesian vocabularies have been published, none of the Tahitian dialect has as yet appeared. At any rate, the author has had access to none whatever. In the use of native words, therefore, he has been mostly governed by the bare recollection of sounds.

Upon several points connected with the history and ancient customs of Tahiti, collateral information has been obtained from the oldest books of South Sea voyages, and also from the *Polynesian Researches* of Ellis.

The title of the work—*Omoo*—is borrowed from the dialect of the Marquesas Islands, where, among other uses, the word signifies a rover, or rather, a person wandering from one island to another, like some of the natives known among their countrymen as "Taboo kanakes."

In no respect does the author make pretensions to philosophic research. In a familiar way, he has merely described what he has seen; and if reflections are occasionally indulged in, they are spontaneous, and such as would very probably suggest themselves to the most casual observer.

NEW YORK, January 28, 1847

Introduction

In the summer of 1842, the author of this narrative, as a sailor before the mast, visited the Marquesas Islands in an American South-Seaman. At the island of Nukuheva he left his vessel, which afterwards sailed without him. Wandering in the interior, he came upon the valley of Typee, inhabited by a primitive tribe of savages, from which valley a fellow-sailor who accompanied him soon afterward effected his escape. The author, however, was detained in an indulgent captivity for about the space of four months; at the end of which period he escaped in a boat which visited the bay.

This boat belonged to a vessel in need of men, which had recently touched at a neighboring harbor of the same island, where the captain had been informed of the author's detention in Typee. Desirous of adding to his crew, he sailed round thither, and "hove to" off the mouth of the bay. As the Typees were considered hostile, the boat, manned by *taboo* natives from the other harbor, was then sent in, with an interpreter at their head, to procure the author's release. This was finally accomplished, though not without peril to all concerned. At the time of his escape, the author was suffering severely from lameness.

The boat having gained the open sea, the ship appeared in the distance. Here the present narrative opens.

Chapter I

My Reception Aboard

It was in the middle of a bright tropical afternoon that we made good our escape from the bay. The vessel we sought lay with her main top-sail aback about a league from the land, and was the only object that broke the broad expanse of the ocean.

On approaching, she turned out to be a small, slatternly looking craft, her hull and spars a dingy black, rigging all slack and bleached nearly white, and everything denoting an ill state of affairs aboard. The four boats hanging from her sides proclaimed her a whaler. Leaning carelessly over the bulwarks were the sailors, wild, haggard-looking fellows in Scotch caps and faded blue frocks; some of them with cheeks of a mottled bronze, to which sickness soon changes the rich berry-brown of a seaman's complexion in the tropics.

On the quarter-deck was one whom I took for the chief mate. He wore a broad-brimmed Panama hat, and his spy-glass was leveled as we advanced.

When we came alongside, a low cry ran fore and aft the deck, and everybody gazed at us with inquiring eyes. And well they might. To say nothing of the savage boat's crew, panting with excitement, all gesture and vociferation, my own appearance was calculated to excite curiosity. A robe of the native cloth was thrown over my shoulders, my hair and beard were uncut, and I betrayed other evidences of my recent adventure. Immediately on gaining the deck they beset me on all sides with questions, the half of which I could not answer, so incessantly were they put.

As an instance of the curious coincidences which often befall the sailor, I must here mention, that two countenances before me were familiar. One was that of an old man-of-war's-man whose acquaintance I had made in Rio de Janeiro, at which place touched the ship in which I sailed from home. The other was a young man, whom, four years previous, I had frequently met in a sailor boarding-house in Liverpool. I remembered parting with him at Prince's Dock Gates, in the midst of a swarm of police-officers, truckmen, stevedores, beggars, and the like. And here we are again—years had rolled by, many a league of ocean had been traversed, and we were thrown together under circumstances which almost made me doubt my own existence.

But a few moments passed ere I was sent for into the cabin by the captain.

He was quite a young man, pale and slender, more like a sickly counting-house clerk than a bluff sea-captain. Bidding me be seated, he ordered the steward to hand me a glass of Pisco.[1] In the state I was, this stimulus almost made me delirious; so that of all I then went on to relate, concerning my residence on the island, I can scarcely remember a word. After this I was asked whether I desired to "ship"; of course I said yes; that is, if he would allow me to enter for one cruise, engaging to discharge me, if I so desired, at the next port. In this way men are frequently shipped on board whalemen in the South Seas. My stipulation was acceded to, and the ship's articles handed me to sign.

The mate was now called below, and charged to make a "well man" of me; not, let it be borne in mind, that the captain felt any great compassion for me, he only desired to have the benefit of my services as soon as possible.

Helping me on deck, the mate stretched me out on the windlass and commenced examining my limb; and then doctoring it after a fashion with something from the medicine-chest, rolled it up in

1. This spirituous liquor derives its name from a considerable town in Peru, where it is manufactured in large quantities. It is well known along the whole western coast of South America, whence some of it has been exported to Australia. It is very cheap.

a piece of an old sail, making so big a bundle, that with my feet resting on the windlass, I might have been taken for a sailor with the gout. While this was going on, someone removing my tappa cloak slipped on a blue frock in its place; and another, actuated by the same desire to make a civilized mortal of me, flourished about my head a great pair of sheep-shears, to the imminent jeopardy of both ears, and the certain destruction of hair and beard.

The day was now drawing to a close, and, as the land faded from my sight, I was all alive to the change in my condition. But how far short of our expectations is oftentimes the fulfillment of the most ardent hopes! Safe aboard of a ship—so long my earnest prayer—with home and friends once more in prospect, I nevertheless felt weighed down by a melancholy that could not be shaken off. It was the thought of never more seeing those, who, notwithstanding their desire to retain me a captive, had, upon the whole, treated me so kindly. I was leaving them forever.

So unforeseen and sudden had been my escape, so excited had I been through it all, and so great the contrast between the luxurious repose of the valley, and the wild noise and motion of a ship at sea, that at times my recent adventures had all the strangeness of a dream: and I could scarcely believe that the same sun now setting over a waste of waters, had that very morning risen above the mountains and peered in upon me as I lay on my mat in Typee.

Going below into the forecastle just after dark, I was inducted into a wretched "bunk" or sleeping-box built over another. The rickety bottoms of both were spread with several pieces of a blanket. A battered tin can was then handed me, containing about half a pint of "tea"—so called by courtesy, though whether the juice of such stalks as one finds floating therein deserves that title, is a matter all ship-owners must settle with their consciences. A cube of salt beef, on a hard round biscuit by way of platter, was also handed up; and without more ado I made a meal, the salt flavor of which, after the Nebuchadnezzar fare of the valley, was positively delicious.

While thus engaged, an old sailor on a chest just under me was puffing out volumes of tobacco smoke. My supper finished, he brushed the stem of his sooty pipe against the sleeve of his frock, and politely waved it toward me. The attention was sailor-like; as for the nicety of the thing, no man who has lived in forecastles is at all fastidious; and so, after a few vigorous whiffs to induce repose, I turned over and tried my best to forget myself. But in vain. My crib, instead of extending fore and aft, as it should have done, was placed athwart-ships, that is, at right angles to the keel; and the vessel going before the wind, rolled to such a degree, that every time my heels went up and my head went down, I thought I was on the point of turning a somerset. Beside this, there were still more annoying causes of inquietude; and, every once in a while, a splash of water came down the open scuttle, and flung the spray in my face.

At last, after a sleepless night, broken twice by the merciless call of the watch, a peep of daylight struggled into view from above, and someone came below. It was my old friend with the pipe.

"Here, shipmate," said I, "help me out of this place, and let me go on deck."

"Halloa, who's that croaking?" was the rejoinder, as he peered into the obscurity where I lay. "Ay, Typee, my king of the cannibals, is it you? But I say, my lad, how's that spar of your'n? the mate says it's in a devil of a way; and last night set the steward to sharpening the hand-saw: hope he won't have the carving of ye."

Long before daylight we arrived off the bay of Nukuheva, and, making short tacks until morning, we then ran in, and sent a boat ashore with the natives who had brought me to the ship. Upon its return we made sail again, and stood off from the land. There was a fine breeze; and, notwithstanding my bad night's rest, the cool fresh air of a morning at sea was so bracing, that, as soon as I breathed it, my spirits rose at once.

Seated upon the windlass the greater portion of the day, and chatting freely with the men, I learned the history of the voyage thus far, and everything respecting the ship and its present condition.

These matters I will now throw together in the next chapter.

Chapter II

Some Account of the Ship

First and foremost, I must give some account of the *Julia* herself, or *"Little Jule,"* as the sailors familiarly styled her.

She was a small barque of a beautiful model, something more than two hundred tons, Yankee-built, and very old. Fitted for a privateer out of a New England port during the war of 1812, she had been captured at sea by a British cruiser, and, after seeing all sorts of service, was at last employed as a government packet in the Australian seas. Being condemned, however, about two years previous, she was purchased at auction by a house in Sydney, who, after some slight repairs, dispatched her on the present voyage.

Notwithstanding the repairs, she was still in a miserable plight. The lower masts were said to be unsound; the standing rigging was much worn; and, in some places, even the bulwarks were quite rotten. Still, she was tolerably tight, and but little more than the ordinary pumping of a morning served to keep her free.

But all this had nothing to do with her sailing; at that, brave *Little Jule,* plump *Little Jule,* was a witch. Blow high, or blow low, she was always ready for the breeze; and when she dashed the waves from her prow, and pranced, and pawed the sea, you never thought of her patched sails and blistered hull. How the fleet creature would fly before the wind! rolling, now and then, to be sure, but in very playfulness. Sailing to windward, no gale could bow her over: with spars erect, she looked right up into the wind's eye, and so she went.

But after all, *Little Jule* was not to be confided in. Lively enough, and playful she was, but on that very account the more to be distrusted. Who knew, but that like some vivacious old mortal all at once sinking into a decline, she might, some dark night, spring a leak and carry us all to the bottom. However, she played us no such ugly trick, and therefore I wrong *Little Jule* in supposing it.

She had a free, roving commission. According to her papers she might go whither she pleased—whaling, sealing, or anything else. Sperm whaling, however, was what she relied upon; though, as yet, only two fish had been brought alongside.

The day they sailed out of Sydney Heads, the ship's company, all told, numbered some thirty-two souls; now, they mustered about twenty; the rest had deserted. Even the three junior mates who had headed the whale-boats were gone; and of the four harpooners, only one was left, a wild New Zealander, or *"Mowree,"* as his countrymen are more commonly called in the Pacific. But this was not all. More than half the seamen remaining were more or less unwell from a long sojourn in a dissipated port; some of them wholly unfit for duty, one or two dangerously ill, and the rest managing to stand their watch, though they could do but little.

The captain was a young cockney, who, a few years before, had emigrated to Australia, and, by some favoritism or other, had procured the command of the vessel, though in no wise competent. He was essentially a landsman, and though a man of education, no more meant for the sea than a hair-dresser. Hence everybody made fun of him. They called him "The Cabin Boy," "Paper Jack," and half a dozen other undignified names. In truth, the men made no secret of the derision in which they held him; and as for the slender gentleman himself, he knew it all very well, and bore himself with becoming meekness. Holding as little intercourse with them as possible, he left everything to the chief mate, who, as the story went, had been given his captain in charge. Yet, despite his unobtrusiveness, the silent captain had more to do with the men than they thought. In short, although one of your sheepish-looking fellows, he had a sort of still, timid cunning, which no one would have suspected, and which, for that very reason, was all the more active. So the bluff mate, who always thought he did what he pleased, was occasionally made a tool of; and some obnoxious measures which he carried out, in spite of all growlings, were little thought to originate with the dapper little fellow in nankeen jacket and white canvas pumps. But, to all appearance, at least, the mate had everything his own way; indeed, in most things this was actually the case; and it was quite plain that the captain stood in awe of him.

So far as courage, seamanship, and a natural aptitude for keeping riotous spirits in subjection were concerned, no man was better qualified for his vocation than John Jermin. He was the very beau-ideal of the efficient race of short, thick-set men. His hair curled in little rings of iron gray all over his round, bullet head. As for his countenance, it was strongly marked, deeply pitted with the small-pox. For the rest, there was a fierce little squint out of one eye; the nose had a rakish twist to one side; while his large mouth, and great white teeth, looked absolutely sharkish when he laughed. In a word, no one, after getting a fair look at him, would ever think of improving the shape of his nose, wanting in symmetry as it was. Notwithstanding his pugnacious looks, however, Jermin had a heart as big as a bullock's; that you saw at a glance.

Such was our mate; but he had one failing: he abhorred all weak infusions, and cleaved manfully to strong drink. At all times he was more or less under the influence of it. Taken in moderate quantities, I believe, in my soul, it did a man like him good; brightened his eyes, swept the cobwebs out of his brain, and regulated his pulse. But the worst of it was, that sometimes he drank too much, and a more obstreperous fellow than Jermin in his cups, you seldom came across. He was always for having a fight; but the very men he flogged loved him as a brother, for he had such an irresistibly good-natured way of knocking them down, that no one could find it in his heart to bear malice against him. So much for stout little Jermin.

All English whalemen are bound by law to carry a physician, who, of course, is rated a gentleman, and lives in the cabin, with nothing but his professional duties to attend to; but incidentally he drinks "flip," and plays cards with the captain. There was such a worthy aboard of the *Julia*; but, curious to tell, he lived in the forecastle with the men. And this was the way it happened.

In the early part of the voyage the doctor and the captain lived together as pleasantly as could be. To say nothing of many a can they drank over the cabin transom, both of them had read books, and one of them had traveled; so their stories never flagged. But once on a time they got into a dispute about politics, and the doctor, moreover, getting into a rage, drove home an argument with his fist, and left the captain on the floor literally silenced. This was carrying it with a high hand; so he was shut up in his state-room for ten days, and left to meditate on bread and water, and the impropriety of flying into a passion. Smarting under his disgrace, he undertook, a short time after his liberation, to leave the vessel clandestinely at one of the islands, but was brought back ignominiously, and again shut up. Being set at large for the second time, he vowed he would not live any longer with the captain, and went forward with his chests among the sailors, where he was received with open arms, as a good fellow and an injured man.

I must give some further account of him, for he figures largely in the narrative. His early history, like that of many other heroes, was enveloped in the profoundest obscurity; though he threw out hints of a patrimonial estate, a nabob uncle, and an unfortunate affair which sent him a-roving. All that was known, however, was this. He had gone out to Sydney as assistant-surgeon of an emigrant ship. On his arrival there, he went back into the country, and after a few months' wanderings, returned to Sydney penniless, and entered as doctor aboard of the *Julia*.

His personal appearance was remarkable. He was over six feet high—a tower of bones, with a complexion absolutely colorless, fair hair, and a light, unscrupulous gray eye, twinkling occasionally at the very devil of mischief. Among the crew, he went by the name of the Long Doctor, or, more frequently still, Doctor Long Ghost. And from whatever high estate Doctor Long Ghost might have fallen, he had certainly at some time or other spent money, drank Burgundy, and associated with gentlemen.

As for his learning, he quoted Virgil, and talked of Hobbies of Malmsbury, besides repeating poetry by the canto, especially Hudibras. He was, moreover, a man who had seen the world. In the easiest way imaginable he could refer to an amour he had in Palermo, his lion hunting before breakfast among the Caffres, and the quality of the coffee to be drunk in Muscat; and about these places, and a hundred others, he had more anecdotes than I can tell of. Then such mellow old songs as he sang, in a voice so round and racy, the real juice of sound. How such notes came forth from his lank body was a constant marvel.

Upon the whole, Long Ghost was as entertaining a companion as one could wish; and to me in the *Julia*, an absolute godsend.

Chapter III

FURTHER ACCOUNT OF THE JULIA

OWING TO THE ABSENCE OF ANYTHING LIKE REGULAR DISCIPLINE, THE VESSEL WAS IN A STATE of the greatest uproar. The captain, having for some time past been more or less confined to the cabin from sickness, was seldom seen. The mate, however, was as hearty as a young lion, and ran about the decks making himself heard at all hours. Bembo, the New Zealand harpooner, held little intercourse with anybody but the mate, who could talk to him freely in his own lingo. Part of his time he spent out on the bowsprit, fishing for albacores with a bone hook; and occasionally he waked all hands up of a dark night dancing some cannibal fandango all by himself on the forecastle. But, upon the whole, he was remarkably quiet, though something in his eye showed he was far from being harmless.

Doctor Long Ghost, having sent in a written resignation as the ship's doctor, gave himself out as a passenger for Sydney, and took the world quite easy. As for the crew, those who were sick seemed marvelously contented for men in their condition; and the rest, not displeased with the general license, gave themselves little thought of the morrow.

The *Julia*'s provisions were very poor. When opened, the barrels of pork looked as if preserved in iron rust, and diffused an odor like a stale ragout. The beef was worse yet; a mahogany-colored fibrous substance, so tough and tasteless, that I almost believed the cook's story of a horse's hoof with the shoe on having been fished up out of the pickle of one of the casks. Nor was the biscuit much better; nearly all of it was broken into hard little gunflints, honey-combed through and through, as if the worms usually infesting this article in long tropical voyages, had, in boring after nutriment, come out at the antipodes without finding anything.

Of what sailors call "small stores," we had but little. "Tea," however, we had in abundance; though, I daresay, the Hong merchants never had the shipping of it. Besides this, every other day we had what English seamen call "shot soup"—great round peas, polishing themselves like pebbles by rolling about in tepid water.

It was afterward told me, that all our provisions had been purchased by the owners at an auction sale of condemned navy stores in Sydney.

But notwithstanding the wateriness of the first course of soup, and the saline flavor of the beef and pork, a sailor might have made a satisfactory meal aboard of the *Julia* had there been any side dishes—a potato or two, a yam, or a plantain. But there was nothing of the kind. Still, there was something else, which, in the estimation of the men, made up for all deficiencies; and that was the regular allowance of Pisco.

It may seem strange, that in such a state of affairs the captain should be willing to keep the sea with his ship. But the truth was, that by lying in harbor, he ran the risk of losing the remainder of his men by desertion: and as it was, he still feared that, in some outlandish bay or other, he might one day find his anchor down, and no crew to weigh it.

With judicious officers the most unruly seamen can at sea be kept in some sort of subjection; but once get them within a cable's-length of the land, and it is hard restraining them. It is for this reason that many South Sea whalemen do not come to an anchor for eighteen or twenty months on a stretch. When fresh provisions are needed, they run for the nearest land—heave to eight or ten miles off, and send a boat ashore to trade. The crews manning vessels like these are for the most part villains of all nations and dyes; picked up in the lawless ports of the Spanish Main, and among the savages of the islands. Like galley-slaves, they are only to be governed by scourges and chains. Their officers go among them with dirk and pistol—concealed, but ready at a grasp.

Not a few of our own crew were men of this stamp, but, riotous at times as they were, the bluff, drunken energies of Jermin were just the thing to hold them in some sort of noisy subjection. Upon an emergency, he flew in among them, showering his kicks and cuffs right and left, and "creating a sensation" in every direction. And, as hinted before, they bore this knock-down authority with great good-humor. A sober, discreet, dignified officer could have done nothing with them; such a set would have thrown him and his dignity overboard.

Matters being thus, there was nothing for the ship but to keep the sea. Nor was the captain without hope that the invalid portion of his crew, as well as himself, would soon recover; and then there was no telling what luck in the fishery might yet be in store for us. At any rate, at the time of my coming aboard, the report was, that Captain Guy was resolved upon retrieving the past, and filling the vessel with oil in the shortest space possible.

With this intention, we were now shaping our course for Hytyhoo, a village on the island of St. Christina—one of the Marquesas, and so named by Mendaña—for the purpose of obtaining eight seamen, who, some weeks before, had stepped ashore there from the *Julia*. It was supposed that by this time they must have recreated themselves sufficiently, and would be glad to return to their duty.

So to Hytyhoo, with all our canvas spread, and coquetting with the warm, breezy Trades, we bowled along; gliding up and down the long, slow swells, the bonettas and albacores frolicking round us.

Chapter IV

A Scene in the Forecastle

I HAD SCARCELY BEEN ABOARD OF THE SHIP TWENTY-FOUR HOURS, WHEN A CIRCUMSTANCE OCcurred, which, although noways picturesque, is so significant of the state of affairs, that I cannot forbear relating it.

In the first place, however, it must be known, that among the crew was a man so excessively ugly, that he went by the ironical appellation of "Beauty." He was the ship's carpenter; and for that reason was sometimes known by his nautical cognomen of "Chips." There was no absolute deformity about the man; he was symmetrically ugly. But ill-favored as he was in person, Beauty was nonetheless ugly in temper; but no one could blame him; his countenance had soured his heart. Now Jermin and Beauty were always at swords' points. The truth was, the latter was the only man in the ship whom the mate had never decidedly got the better of; and hence the grudge he bore him. As for Beauty, he prided himself upon talking up to the mate, as we shall soon see.

Toward evening there was something to be done on deck, and the carpenter who belonged to the watch was missing. "Where's that skulk, Chips?" shouted Jermin down the forecastle scuttle.

"Taking his ease, d'ye see, down here on a chest, if you want to know," replied that worthy himself, quietly withdrawing his pipe from his mouth. This insolence flung the fiery little mate into a mighty rage; but Beauty said nothing, puffing away with all the tranquility imaginable. Here it must be remembered that, never mind what may be the provocation, no prudent officer ever dreams of entering a ship's forecastle on a hostile visit. If he wants to see anybody who happens to be there, and refuses to come up, why he must wait patiently until the sailor is willing. The reason is this. The place is very dark; and nothing is easier than to knock one descending on the head, before he knows where he is, and a very long while before he ever finds out who did it.

Nobody knew this better than Jermin, and so he contented himself with looking down the scuttle and storming. At last Beauty made some cool observation which set him half wild.

"Tumble on deck," he then bellowed—"come, up with you, or I'll jump down and make you." The carpenter begged him to go about it at once.

No sooner said than done; prudence forgotten, Jermin was there; and by a sort of instinct, had his man by the throat before he could well see him. One of the men now made a rush at him, but the rest dragged him off, protesting that they should have fair play.

"Now come on deck," shouted the mate, struggling like a good fellow to hold the carpenter fast.

"Take me there," was the dogged answer, and Beauty wriggled about in the nervous grasp of the other like a couple of yards of boa-constrictor.

His assailant now undertook to make him up into a compact bundle, the more easily to transport him. While thus occupied, Beauty got his arms loose, and threw him over backward. But Jermin quickly recovered himself, when for a time they had it every way, dragging each other about, bumping their heads against the projecting beams, and returning each other's blows the first favorable opportunity that offered. Unfortunately, Jermin at last slipped and fell; his foe seating himself on his chest, and keeping him down. Now this was one of those situations in which the voice of counsel, or reproof, comes with peculiar unction. Nor did Beauty let the opportunity slip. But the mate said nothing in reply, only foaming at the mouth and struggling to rise.

Just then a thin tremor of a voice was heard from above. It was the captain; who, happening to ascend to the quarter-deck at the commencement of the scuffle, would gladly have returned to the cabin, but was prevented by the fear of ridicule. As the din increased, and it became evident that his officer was in serious trouble, he thought it would never do to stand leaning over the bulwarks, so he made his appearance on the forecastle, resolved, as his best policy, to treat the matter lightly.

"Why, why," he begun, speaking pettishly, and very fast, "what's all this about? Mr. Jermin, Mr. Jermin—carpenter, carpenter; what are you doing down there? Come on deck; come on deck."

Whereupon Doctor Long Ghost cries out in a squeak, "Ah! Miss Guy, is that you? Now, my dear, go right home, or you'll get hurt."

"Pooh, pooh! you, sir, whoever you are, I was not speaking to you; none of your nonsense. Mr. Jermin, I was talking to *you;* have the kindness to come on deck, sir; I want to see you."

"And how, in the devil's name, am I to get there?" cried the mate, furiously. "Jump down here, Captain Guy, and show yourself a man. Let me up, you Chips! unhand me, I say! Oh! I'll pay you for this, someday! Come on, Captain Guy!"

At this appeal, the poor man was seized with a perfect spasm of fidgets. "Pooh, pooh, carpenter; have done with your nonsense! Let him up, sir; let him up! Do you hear? Let Mr. Jermin come on deck!"

"Go along with you, Paper Jack," replied Beauty; "this quarrel's between the mate and me; so go aft, where you belong!"

As the captain once more dipped his head down the scuttle to make answer, from an unseen hand he received, full in the face, the contents of a tin can of soaked biscuit and tea-leaves. The doctor was not far off just then. Without waiting for anything more, the discomfited gentleman, with both hands to his streaming face, retreated to the quarter-deck.

A few moments more, and Jermin, forced to a compromise, followed after, in his torn frock and scarred face, looking for all the world as if he had just disentangled himself from some intricate piece of machinery. For about half an hour both remained in the cabin, where the mate's rough tones were heard high above the low, smooth voice of the captain.

Of all his conflicts with the men, this was the first in which Jermin had been worsted; and he was proportionably enraged. Upon going below—as the steward afterward told us—he bluntly informed Guy that, for the future, he might look out for his ship himself; for *his* part, he had done with her, if that was the way he allowed his officers to be treated. After many high words, the captain finally assured him, that the first fitting opportunity the carpenter should be cordially flogged; though, as matters stood, the experiment would be a hazardous one. Upon this Jermin reluctantly consented to drop the matter for the present; and he soon drowned all thoughts of it in a can of flip which Guy had previously instructed the steward to prepare, as a sop to allay his wrath.

Nothing more ever came of this.

Chapter V

WHAT HAPPENED AT HYTYHOO

LESS THAN FORTY-EIGHT HOURS AFTER LEAVING NUKUHEVA, THE BLUE, LOOMING ISLAND OF ST. Christina greeted us from afar. Drawing near the shore, the grim, black spars and waspish hull of a small man-of-war craft crept into view; the masts and yards lined distinctly against the sky. She was riding to her anchor in the bay, and proved to be a French corvette.

This pleased our captain exceedingly, and, coming on deck, he examined her from the mizzen rigging with his glass. His original intention was not to let go an anchor; but, counting upon the assistance of the corvette in case of any difficulty, he now changed his mind, and anchored alongside of her. As soon as a boat could be lowered, he then went off to pay his respects to the commander, and, moreover, as we supposed, to concert measures for the apprehension of the runaways.

Returning in the course of twenty minutes, he brought along with him two officers in undress and whiskers, and three or four drunken obstreperous old chiefs; one with his legs thrust into the armholes of a scarlet vest, another with a pair of spurs on his heels, and a third in a cocked hat and feather. In addition to these articles, they merely wore the ordinary costume of their race—a slip of native cloth about the loins. Indecorous as their behavior was, these worthies turned out to be a deputation from the reverend, the clergy of the island; and the object of their visit was to put our ship under a rigorous "Taboo," to prevent the disorderly scenes and facilities for desertion which would ensue were the natives—men and women—allowed to come off to us freely.

There was little ceremony about the matter. The chiefs went aside for a moment, laid their shaven old crowns together, and went over a little mummery. Whereupon, their leader tore a long strip from his girdle of white tappa, and handed it to one of the French officers, who, after explaining what was to be done, gave it to Jermin. The mate at once went out to the end of the flying-jib-boom, and fastened there the mystic symbol of the ban. This put to flight a party of girls who had been observed swimming towards us. Tossing their arms about, and splashing the water like porpoises, with loud cries of "Taboo! taboo!" they turned about and made for the shore.

The night of our arrival, the mate and the Mowree were to stand "watch and watch," relieving each other every four hours; the crew, as is sometimes customary when lying at an anchor, being allowed to remain all night below. A distrust of the men, however, was, in the present instance, the principal reason for this proceeding. Indeed, it was all but certain that some kind of attempt would be made at desertion; and, therefore, when Jermin's first watch came on at eight bells (midnight)—by which time all was quiet—he mounted to the deck with a flask of spirits in one hand, and the other in readiness to assail the first countenance that showed itself above the forecastle scuttle.

Thus prepared, he doubtless meant to stay awake; but for all that, before long he fell asleep; and slept with such hearty good-will too, that the men who left us that night might have been waked up by his snoring. Certain it was, the mate snored most strangely; and no wonder, with that crooked bugle of his. When he came to himself it was just dawn, but quite light enough to show two boats gone from the side. In an instant he knew what had happened.

Dragging the Mowree out of an old sail where he was napping, he ordered him to clear away another boat, and then darted into the cabin to tell the captain the news. Springing on deck again, he dived down into the forecastle for a couple of oarsmen, but hardly got there before there was a cry, and a loud splash heard over the side. It was the Mowree and the boat—into which he had just leaped to get ready for lowering—rolling over and over in the water.

The boat having at nightfall been hoisted up to its place over the starboard quarter, someone had so cut the tackles which held it there, that a moderate strain would at once part them. Bembo's weight had answered the purpose, showing that the deserters must have ascertained his specific gravity to a fiber of hemp. There was another boat remaining: but it was as well to examine it before attempting to lower. And it was well they did; for there was a hole in the bottom large enough to drop a barrel through: she had been scuttled most ruthlessly.

Jermin was frantic. Dashing his hat upon deck, he was about to plunge overboard and swim to the corvette for a cutter, when Captain Guy made his appearance and begged him to stay where he was. By this time the officer of the deck aboard the Frenchman had noticed our movements, and hailed to know what had happened. Guy informed him through his trumpet, and men to go in pursuit were instantly promised. There was a whistling of a boatswain's pipe, an order or two, and then a large cutter pulled out from the man-of-war's stern, and in half a dozen strokes was alongside. The mate leaped into her, and they pulled rapidly ashore.

Another cutter, carrying an armed crew, soon followed.

In an hour's time the first returned, towing the two whale-boats, which had been found turned up like tortoises on the beach.

Noon came, and nothing more was heard from the deserters. Meanwhile Doctor Long Ghost and myself lounged about, cultivating an acquaintance, and gazing upon the shore scenery. The bay was as calm as death; the sun high and hot; and occasionally a still gliding canoe stole out from behind the headlands, and shot across the water.

And all the morning long our sick men limped about the deck, casting wistful glances inland, where the palm-trees waved and beckoned them into their reviving shades. Poor invalid rascals! How conducive to the restoration of their shattered health would have been those delicious groves! But hard-hearted Jermin assured them, with an oath, that foot of theirs should never touch the beach.

Toward sunset a crowd was seen coming down to the water. In advance of all were the fugitives—bareheaded—their frocks and trousers hanging in tatters, every face covered with blood and dust, and their arms pinioned behind them with green thongs. Following them up, was a shouting rabble of islanders, pricking them with the points of their long spears, the party from the corvette menacing them in flank with their naked cutlasses.

The bonus of a musket to the king of the Bay, and the promise of a tumbler full of powder for every man caught, had set the whole population on their track; and so successful was the hunt, that not only were that morning's deserters brought back, but five of those left behind on a former visit.

The natives, however, were the mere hounds of the chase, raising the game in their coverts, but leaving the securing of it to the Frenchmen. Here, as elsewhere, the islanders have no idea of taking part in such a scuffle as ensues upon the capture of a party of desperate seamen.

The runaways were at once brought aboard, and, though they looked rather sulky, soon came round, and treated the whole affair as a frolicsome adventure.

Chapter VI

We Touch at La Dominica

Fearful of spending the night at Hytyhoo, Captain Guy caused the ship to be got under way shortly after dark.

The next morning, when all supposed that we were fairly embarked for a long cruise, our course was suddenly altered for La Dominica, or Hivarhoo, an island just north of the one we had quitted. The object of this, as we learned, was to procure, if possible, several English sailors, who, according to the commander of the corvette, had recently gone ashore there from an American whaler, and were desirous of shipping aboard one of their own country vessels.

We made the land in the afternoon, coming abreast of a shady glen opening from a deep bay, and winding by green defiles far out of sight. "Hands by the weather-main-brace!" roared the mate, jumping up on the bulwarks; and in a moment the prancing *Julia,* suddenly arrested in her course, bridled her head like a steed reined in, while the foam flaked under her bows.

This was the place where we expected to obtain the men; so a boat was at once got in readiness to go ashore. Now it was necessary to provide a picked crew—men the least likely to abscond. After considerable deliberation on the part of the captain and mate, four of the seamen were pitched upon as the most trustworthy; or rather they were selected from a choice assortment of suspicious characters as being of an inferior order of rascality.

Armed with cutlasses all round—the natives were said to be an ugly set—they were followed over the side by the invalid captain, who, on this occasion, it seems, was determined to signalize himself. Accordingly, in addition to his cutlass, he wore an old boarding belt, in which was thrust a brace of pistols. They at once shoved off.

My friend Long Ghost had, among other things which looked somewhat strange in a ship's forecastle, a capital spy-glass, and on the present occasion we had it in use.

When the boat neared the head of the inlet, though invisible to the naked eye, it was plainly revealed by the glass; looking no bigger than an egg-shell, and the men diminished to pygmies.

At last, borne on what seemed a long flake of foam, the tiny craft shot up the beach amid a shower of sparkles. Not a soul was there. Leaving one of their number by the water, the rest of the pygmies stepped ashore, looking about them very circumspectly, pausing now and then hand to ear, and peering under a dense grove, which swept down within a few paces of the sea. No one came, and to all appearances everything was as still as the grave. Presently, he with the pistols, followed by the rest flourishing their bodkins, entered the wood and were soon lost to view. They did not stay long; probably anticipating some inhospitable ambush were they to stray any distance up the glen.

In a few moments they embarked again, and were soon riding pertly over the waves of the bay. All of a sudden the captain started to his feet—the boat spun round, and again made for the shore. Some twenty or thirty natives armed with spears, which through the glass looked like reeds, had just come out of the grove, and were apparently shouting to the strangers not to be in such a hurry, but return and be sociable. But they were somewhat distrusted, for the boat paused about its length from the beach, when the captain standing up in its head delivered an address in pantomime, the object of which seemed to be that the islanders should draw near. One of them stepped forward and made answer, seemingly again urging the strangers not to be diffident, but beach their boat. The captain declined, tossing his arms about in another pantomime. In the end he said something which made them shake their spears; whereupon he fired a pistol among them, which set the whole party running; while one poor little fellow, dropping his spear and clapping his hand behind him, limped away in a manner which almost made me itch to get a shot at his assailant.

Wanton acts of cruelty like this are not unusual on the part of sea captains landing at islands comparatively unknown. Even at the Pomotu group, but a day's sail from Tahiti, the islanders coming down to the shore have several times been fired at by trading schooners passing through their narrow channels; and this too as a mere amusement on the part of the ruffians.

Indeed, it is almost incredible, the light in which many sailors regard these naked heathens. They hardly consider them human. But it is a curious fact, that the more ignorant and degraded men are, the more contemptuously they look upon those whom they deem their inferiors.

All powers of persuasion being thus lost upon these foolish savages, and no hope left of holding further intercourse, the boat returned to the ship.

Chapter VII

What Happened at Hannamanoo

On the other side of the island was the large and populous bay of Hannamanoo, where the men sought might yet be found. But as the sun was setting by the time the boat came alongside, we got our off-shore tacks aboard and stood away for an offing. About daybreak we wore, and ran in, and by the time the sun was well up, entered the long, narrow channel dividing the islands of La Dominica and St. Christina.

On one hand was a range of steep green bluffs hundreds of feet high, the white huts of the natives here and there nestling like birds' nests in deep clefts gushing with verdure. Across the water, the land rolled away in bright hill-sides, so warm and undulating, that they seemed almost to palpitate in the sun. On we swept, past bluff and grove, wooded glen and valley, and dark ravines lighted up far inland with wild falls of water. A fresh land-breeze filled our sails, the embayed waters were gentle as a lake, and every wave broke with a tinkle against our coppered prow.

On gaining the end of the channel we rounded a point, and came full upon the bay of Hannamanoo. This is the only harbor of any note about the island, though as far as a safe anchorage is concerned it hardly deserves the title.

Before we held any communication with the shore, an incident occurred which may convey some further idea of the character of our crew.

Having approached as near the land as we could prudently, our headway was stopped, and we awaited the arrival of a canoe which was coming out of the bay. All at once we got into a strong current, which swept us rapidly toward a rocky promontory forming one side of the harbor. The wind had died away; so two boats were at once lowered for the purpose of pulling the ship's head round. Before this could be done, the eddies were whirling upon all sides, and the rock so near, that it seemed as if one might leap upon it from the mast-head. Notwithstanding the speechless fright of the captain, and the hoarse shouts of the unappalled Jennin, the men handled the ropes as deliberately as possible, some of them chuckling at the prospect of going ashore, and others so eager for the vessel to strike, that they could hardly contain themselves. Unexpectedly a countercurrent befriended us, and assisted by the boats we were soon out of danger.

What a disappointment for our crew! All their little plans for swimming ashore from the wreck, and having a fine time of it for the rest of their days, thus cruelly nipped in the bud.

Soon after, the canoe came alongside. In it were eight or ten natives, comely, vivacious-looking youths, all gesture and exclamation; the red feathers in their headbands perpetually nodding. With them also came a stranger, a renegado from Christendom and humanity—a white man in South Sea girdle, and tattooed in the face. A broad blue band stretched across his face from ear to ear, and on his forehead was the taper figure of a blue shark, nothing but fins from head to tail.

Some of us gazed upon this man with a feeling akin to horror, noways abated when informed that he had voluntarily submitted to this embellishment of his countenance. What an impress! Far worse than Cain's—*his* was, perhaps, a wrinkle, or a freckle, which some of our modern cosmetics might have effaced; but the blue shark was a mark indelible, which all the waters of Abana and Pharpar, rivers of Damascus, could never wash out. He was an Englishman, Lem Hardy he called himself, who had deserted from a trading brig touching at the island for wood and water some ten years previous. He had gone ashore as a sovereign power, armed with a musket and a bag of ammunition, and ready, if need were, to prosecute war on his own account. The country was divided by the hostile kings of several large valleys. With one of them, from whom he first received overtures, he formed an alliance, and became what he now was, the military leader of the tribe, and war-god of the entire island.

His campaigns beat Napoleon's. In one night-attack, his invincible musket, backed by the light infantry of spears and javelins, vanquished two clans, and the next morning brought all the others at the feet of his royal ally.

Nor was the rise of his domestic fortunes at all behind the Corsican's; three days after landing, the exquisitely tattooed hand of a princess was his; receiving along with the damsel, as her portion, one thousand fathoms of fine tappa, fifty double-braided mats of split grass, four hundred hogs, ten houses in different parts of her native valley, and the sacred protection of an express edict of the Taboo, declaring his person inviolable forever.

Now, this man was settled for life, perfectly satisfied with his circumstances, and feeling no desire to return to his friends. "Friends," indeed, he had none. He told me his history. Thrown upon the world a foundling, his paternal origin was as much a mystery to him as the genealogy of Odin; and, scorned by everybody, he fled the parish work-house when a boy, and launched upon the sea. He had followed it for several years, a dog before the mast, and now he had thrown it up forever.

And for the most part, it is just this sort of men—so many of whom are found among sailors—uncared for by a single soul, without ties, reckless, and impatient of the restraints of civilization, who are occasionally found quite at home upon the savage islands of the Pacific. And, glancing at their hard lot in their own country, what marvel at their choice?

According to the renegado, there was no other white man on the island; and as the captain could have no reason to suppose that Hardy intended to deceive us, he concluded that the Frenchmen were in some way or other mistaken in what they had told us. However, when our errand was made known to the rest of our visitors, one of them, a fine, stalwart fellow, his face all eyes and expression, volunteered for a cruise, all the wages he asked, was a red shirt, a pair of trousers, and a hat, which were to be put on there and then; besides a plug of tobacco and a pipe. The bargain was struck directly; but Wymontoo afterward came in with a codicil, to the effect that a friend of his, who had come along with him, should be given ten whole sea-biscuits, without crack or flaw, twenty perfectly new and symmetrically straight nails, and one jack-knife. This being agreed to, the articles were at once handed over, the native receiving them with great avidity, and in the absence of clothing, using his mouth as a pocket to put the nails in. Two of them, however, were first made to take the place of a pair of ear-ornaments, curiously fashioned out of bits of whitened wood.

It now began breezing strongly from seaward, and no time was to be lost in getting away from the land; so, after an affecting rubbing of noses between our shipmate and his countrymen, we sailed away with him.

To our surprise, the farewell-shouts from the canoe, as we dashed along under bellied royals, were heard unmoved by our islander; but it was not long thus. That very evening, when the dark blue of his native hills sunk in the horizon, the poor savage leaned over the bulwarks, dropped his head upon his chest, and gave way to irrepressible emotions. The ship was plunging hard, and Wymontoo, sad to tell, in addition to his other pangs, was terribly seasick.

Chapter VIII

The Tatooers of La Dominica

For a while leaving *Little Jule* to sail away by herself, I will here put down some curious information obtained from Hardy.

The renegado had lived so long on the island, that its customs were quite familiar; and I much lamented that, from the shortness of our stay, he could not tell us more than he did.

From the little intelligence gathered, however, I learned to my surprise that, in some things, the people of Hivarhoo, though of the same group of islands, differed considerably from my tropical friends in the valley of Typee.

As his tattooing attracted so much remark, Hardy had a good deal to say concerning the manner in which that art was practiced upon the island.

Throughout the entire cluster the tattooers of Hivarhoo enjoyed no small reputation. They had carried their art to the highest perfection, and the profession was esteemed most honorable. No wonder, then, that like genteel tailors they rated their services very high; so much so, that none but those belonging to the higher classes could afford to employ them. So true was this, that the elegance of one's tattooing was in most cases a sure indication of birth and riches.

Professors in large practice lived in spacious houses, divided by screens of tappa into numerous little apartments, where subjects were waited upon in private. The arrangement chiefly grew out of a singular ordinance of the Taboo, which enjoined the strictest privacy upon all men, high and low, while under the hands of a tattooer. For the time, the slightest intercourse with others is prohibited, and the small portion of food allowed is pushed under the curtain by an unseen hand. The restriction with regard to food is intended to reduce the blood, so as to diminish the inflammation consequent upon puncturing the skin. As it is, this comes on very soon, and takes some time to heal; so that the period of seclusion generally embraces many days, sometimes several weeks.

All traces of soreness vanished, the subject goes abroad; but only again to return; for, on account of the pain, only a small surface can be operated upon at once; and as the whole body is to be more or less embellished by a process so slow, the studios alluded to are constantly filled. Indeed, with a vanity elsewhere unheard of, many spend no small portion of their days thus sitting to an artist.

To begin the work, the period of adolescence is esteemed the most suitable. After casting about for some eminent tattooer, the friends of the youth take him to his house, to have the outlines of the general plan laid out. It behooves the professor to have a nice eye, for a suit to be worn for life should be well cut.

Some tattooers, yearning after perfection, employ, at large wages, one or two men of the commonest order—vile fellows, utterly regardless of appearances, upon whom they first try their patterns and practice generally. Their backs remorselessly scrawled over, and no more canvas remaining, they are dismissed, and ever after go about the scorn of their countrymen.

Hapless wights! thus martyred in the cause of the Fine Arts.

Besides the regular practitioners, there are a parcel of shabby, itinerant tattooers, who, by virtue of their calling, stroll unmolested from one hostile bay to another, doing their work dog-cheap for the multitude. They always repair to the various religious festivals, which gather great crowds. When these are concluded, and the places where they are held vacated even by the tattooers, scores of little tents of coarse tappa are left standing, each with a solitary inmate, who, forbidden to talk to his unseen neighbors, is obliged to stay there till completely healed. The itinerants are a reproach to their profession, mere cobblers, dealing in nothing but jagged lines and clumsy patches, and utterly incapable of soaring to those heights of fancy attained by gentlemen of the faculty.

All professors of the arts love to fraternize; and so, in Hannamanoo, the tattooers come together in the chapters of their worshipful order. In this society, duly organized, and conferring degrees, Hardy, from his influence as a white, was a sort of honorary Grand Master. The blue shark, and a sort of Urim and Thummim engraven upon his chest, were the seal of his initiation. All over Hivarhoo are established these orders of tattooers. The way in which the renegado's came to be founded is this. A year or two after his landing there happened to be a season of scarcity, owing to the partial failure of the bread-fruit harvest for several consecutive seasons. This brought about such a falling off in the number of subjects for tattooing, that the profession became quite needy. The royal ally of Hardy, however, hit upon a benevolent expedient to provide for their wants, at the same time conferring a boon upon many of his subjects.

By sound of conch-shell it was proclaimed before the palace, on the beach, and at the head of the valley, that Noomai, King of Hannamanoo, and friend of Hardee-Hardee, the white, kept open heart and table for all tattooers whatsoever; but, to entitle themselves to his hospitality, they were commanded to practice without fee upon the meanest native soliciting their services.

Numbers at once flocked to the royal abode, both artists and sitters. It was a famous time; and the buildings of the palace being "taboo" to all but the tattooers and chiefs, the sitters bivouacked on the common, and formed an extensive encampment.

The "Lora Tattoo," or the Time of Tattooing, will be long remembered. An enthusiastic sitter celebrated the event in verse. Several lines were repeated to us by Hardy, some of which, in a sort of colloquial chant, he translated nearly thus:

Where is that sound?
In Hannamanoo.
And wherefore that sound?
The sound of a hundred hammers
Tapping, tapping, tapping
The shark teeth.[1]

Where is that light?
Roundabout the king's house,
And the small laughter?
The small, merry laughter it is
Of the sons and daughters of the tattooed.

1. The coloring matter is inserted by means of a shark's tooth attached to the end of a short stick, which is struck upon the other end with a small mallet of wood.

Chapter IX

We Steer to the Westward—State of Affairs

The night we left Hannamanoo was bright and starry, and so warm, that when the watches were relieved, most of the men, instead of going below, flung themselves around the fore-mast.

Towards morning, finding the heat of the forecastle unpleasant, I ascended to the deck, where everything was noiseless. The Trades were blowing with a mild, steady strain upon the canvas, and the ship heading right out into the immense blank of the Western Pacific. The watch were asleep. With one foot resting on the rudder, even the man at the helm nodded, and the mate himself, with arms folded, was leaning against the capstan.

On such a night, and all alone, reverie was inevitable. I leaned over the side, and could not help thinking of the strange objects we might be sailing over.

But my meditations were soon interrupted by a gray, spectral shadow cast over the heaving billows. It was the dawn, soon followed by the first rays of the morning. They flashed into view at one end of the arched night, like—to compare great things with small—the gleamings of Guy Fawkes's lantern in the vaults of the Parliament House. Before long, what seemed a live ember rested for a moment on the rim of the ocean, and at last the blood-red sun stood full and round in the level east, and the long sea-day began.

Breakfast over, the first thing attended to was the formal baptism of Wymontoo, who, after thinking over his affairs during the night, looked dismal enough.

There were various opinions as to a suitable appellation. Some maintained that we ought to call him "Sunday," that being the day we caught him; others, "Eighteen Forty-two," the then year of our Lord; while Doctor Long Ghost remarked that he ought, by all means, to retain his original name—Wymontoo-Hee, meaning (as he maintained), in the figurative language of the island, something analogous to one who had got himself into a scrape. The mate put an end to the discussion by sousing the poor fellow with a bucket of salt water, and bestowing upon him the nautical appellation of "Luff."

Though a certain mirthfulness succeeded his first pangs at leaving home, Wymontoo—we will call him thus—gradually relapsed into his former mood, and became very melancholy. Often I noticed him crouching apart in the forecastle, his strange eyes gleaming restlessly, and watching the slightest movement of the men. Many a time he must have been thinking of his bamboo hut, when they were talking of Sydney and its dance-houses.

We were now fairly at sea, though to what particular cruising-ground we were going, no one knew; and, to all appearances, few cared. The men, after a fashion of their own, began to settle down into the routine of sea-life, as if everything was going on prosperously. Blown along over a smooth sea, there was nothing to do but steer the ship, and relieve the "look-outs" at the mast-heads. As for the sick, they had two or three more added to their number—the air of the island having disagreed with the constitutions of several of the runaways. To crown all, the captain again relapsed, and became quite ill.

The men fit for duty were divided into two small watches, headed respectively by the mate and the Mowree; the latter, by virtue of his being a harpooner, succeeding to the place of the second mate, who had absconded.

In this state of things, whaling was out of the question; but in the face of everything, Jermin maintained that the invalids would soon be well. However that might be, with the same pale blue sky overhead, we kept running steadily to the westward. Forever advancing, we seemed always in the same place, and every day was the former lived over again. We saw no ships, expected to see none. No sign of life was perceptible but the porpoises and other fish sporting under the bows like pups ashore. But, at intervals, the gray albatross, peculiar to these seas, came flapping his immense wings over us, and then skimmed away silently as if from a plague-ship; or flights of the tropic bird, known among seamen as the "boatswain," wheeled round and round us whistling shrilly as they flew.

The uncertainty hanging over our destination at this time, and the fact that we were abroad upon waters comparatively little traversed, lent an interest to this portion of the cruise which I shall never forget.

From obvious prudential considerations the Pacific has been principally sailed over in known tracts, and this is the reason why new islands are still occasionally discovered by exploring ships and adventurous whalers, notwithstanding the great number of vessels of all kinds of late navigating this vast ocean. Indeed, considerable portions still remain wholly unexplored; and there is no doubt as to the actual existence of certain shoals, and reefs, and small clusters of islands vaguely laid down in the charts. The mere circumstance, therefore, of a ship like ours penetrating into these regions, was sufficient to cause any reflecting mind to feel at least a little uneasy. For my own part, the many stories I had heard of ships striking at midnight upon unknown rocks, with all sail set, and a slumbering crew, often recurred to me, especially, as from the absence of discipline, and our being so short-handed, the watches at night were careless in the extreme.

But no thoughts like these were entertained by my reckless shipmates; and along we went, the sun every evening setting right ahead of our jib-boom.

For what reason the mate was so reserved with regard to our precise destination was never made known. The stories he told us, I, for one, did not believe; deeming them all a mere device to lull the crew.

He said we were bound to a fine cruising-ground, scarcely known to other whalemen, which he had himself discovered when commanding a small brig upon a former voyage. Here, the sea was alive with large whales, so tame, that all you had to do was to go up and kill them: they were too frightened to resist. A little to leeward of this was a small cluster of islands, where we were going to refit, abounding with delicious fruits, and peopled by a race almost wholly unsophisticated by intercourse with strangers.

In order, perhaps, to guard against the possibility of anyone finding out the precise latitude and longitude of the spot we were going to, Jermin never revealed to us the ship's place at noon, though such is the custom aboard of most vessels.

Meanwhile he was very assiduous in his attention to the invalids. Doctor Long Ghost having given up the keys of the medicine-chest, they were handed over to him; and, as physician, he discharged his duties to the satisfaction of all. Pills and powders, in most cases, were thrown to the fish, and in place thereof, the contents of a mysterious little quarter cask were produced, diluted with water from the "butt." His drafts were mixed on the capstan, in cocoanut shells marked with the patients' names. Like shore doctors, he did not eschew his own medicines, for his professional calls in the forecastle were sometimes made when he was comfortably tipsy: nor did he omit keeping his invalids in good-humor, spinning his yarns to them by the hour, whenever he went to see them.

Owing to my lameness, from which I soon began to recover, I did no active duty, except standing an occasional "trick" at the helm. It was in the forecastle chiefly that I spent my time, in company with the Long Doctor, who was at great pains to make himself agreeable. His books, though sadly torn and battered, were an invaluable resource. I read them through again and again, including a learned treatise on the yellow fever. In addition to these, he had an old file of Sydney papers, and I soon became intimately acquainted with the localities of all the advertising tradesmen there. In particular, the rhetorical flourishes of Stubbs, the real-estate auctioneer, diverted me exceedingly, and I set him down as no other than a pupil of Robins the Londoner.

Aside from the pleasure of his society, my intimacy with Long Ghost was of great service to me in other respects. His disgrace in the cabin only confirmed the good-will of the democracy in the forecastle; and they not only treated him in the most friendly manner, but looked up to him with the utmost deference, besides laughing heartily at all his jokes. As his chosen associate, this feeling for him extended to me; and gradually we came to be regarded in the light of distinguished guests. At meal-times we were always first served and otherwise were treated with much respect.

Among other devices to kill time, during the frequent calms, Long Ghost hit upon the game of chess. With a jack-knife, we carved the pieces quite tastefully out of bits of wood, and our board was the middle of a chest-lid, chalked into squares, which, in playing, we straddled at either end. Having no other suitable way of distinguishing the sets, I marked mine by tying round them little scarves of black silk, torn from an old neck handkerchief. Putting them in mourning this way, the doctor said, was quite appropriate, seeing that they had reason to feel sad three games out of four. Of chess, the men never could make head nor tail; indeed, their wonder rose to such a pitch, that they at last regarded the mysterious movements of the game with something more than perplexity; and, after puzzling over them through several long engagements, they came to the conclusion that we must be a couple of necromancers.

Chapter X

A Sea-Parlor Described, with Some of Its Tenants

I MAY AS WELL GIVE SOME IDEA OF THE PLACE IN WHICH THE DOCTOR AND I LIVED TOGETHER SO sociably.

Most persons know that a ship's forecastle embraces the forward part of the deck about the bowsprit: the same term, however, is generally bestowed upon the sailors' sleeping-quarters, which occupy a space immediately beneath, and are partitioned off by a bulkhead.

Planted right in the bows, or, as sailors say, in the very *eyes* of the ship, this delightful apartment is of a triangular shape, and is generally fitted with two tiers of rude bunks. Those of the *Julia* were in a most deplorable condition, mere wrecks, some having been torn down altogether to patch up others; and on one side there were but two standing. But with most of the men it made little difference whether they had a bunk or not, since, having no bedding, they had nothing to put in it but themselves.

Upon the boards of my own crib I spread all the old canvas and old clothes I could pick up. For a pillow, I wrapped an old jacket round a log. This helped a little the wear and tear of one's bones when the ship rolled.

Rude hammocks made out of old sails were in many cases used as substitutes for the demolished bunks; but the space they swung in was so confined, that they were far from being agreeable.

The general aspect of the forecastle was dungeon-like and dingy in the extreme. In the first place, it was not five feet from deck to deck, and even this space was encroached upon by two outlandish cross-timbers bracing the vessel, and by the sailors' chests, over which you must needs crawl in getting about. At meal-times, and especially when we indulged in after-dinner chat, we sat about the chests like a parcel of tailors.

In the middle of all, were two square wooden columns, denominated in marine architecture "Bowsprit Bitts." They were about a foot apart, and between them, by a rusty chain, swung the forecastle lamp, burning day and night, and forever casting two long black shadows. Lower down, between the bitts, was a locker, or sailors' pantry, kept in abominable disorder, and sometimes requiring a vigorous cleaning and fumigation.

All over, the ship was in a most dilapidated condition; but in the forecastle it looked like the hollow of an old tree going to decay. In every direction the wood was damp and discolored, and here and there soft and porous. Moreover, it was hacked and hewed without mercy, the cook frequently helping himself to splinters for kindling-wood from the bitts and beams. Overhead, every carline was sooty, and here and there deep holes were burned in them, a freak of some drunken sailors on a voyage long previous.

From above, you entered by a plank, with two cleats, slanting down from the scuttle, which was a mere hole in the deck. There being no slide to draw over in case of emergency, the tarpaulin temporarily placed there was little protection from the spray heaved over the bows; so that in anything of a breeze the place was miserably wet. In a squall, the water fairly poured down in sheets like a cascade, swashing about, and afterward spirting up between the chests like the jets of a fountain.

Such were our accommodations aboard of the *Julia*; but, bad as they were, we had not the undisputed possession of them. Myriads of cockroaches, and regiments of rats, disputed the place with us. A greater calamity than this can scarcely befall a vessel in the South Seas.

So warm is the climate that it is almost impossible to get rid of them. You may seal up every hatchway, and fumigate the hull till the smoke forces itself out at the seams, and enough will survive to repeople the ship in an incredibly short period. In some vessels, the crews of which after a hard fight have given themselves up, as it were, for lost, the vermin seem to take actual possession, the sailors being mere tenants by sufferance. With sperm whalemen, hanging about the Line, as many of them do for a couple of years on a stretch, it is infinitely worse than with other vessels.

As for the *Julia*, these creatures never had such free and easy times as they did in her crazy old hull; every chink and cranny swarmed with them; they did not live among you, but you among them. So true was this, that the business of eating and drinking was better done in the dark than in the light of day.

Concerning the cockroaches, there was an extraordinary phenomenon, for which none of us could ever account.

Every night they had a jubilee. The first symptom was an unusual clustering and humming among the swarms lining the beams overhead, and the inside of the sleeping-places. This was succeeded by a prodigious coming and going on the part of those living out of sight. Presently they all came forth; the larger sort racing over the chests and planks; winged monsters darting to and fro in the air; and the small fry buzzing in heaps almost in a state of fusion.

On the first alarm, all who were able darted on deck; while some of the sick who were too feeble, lay perfectly quiet—the distracted vermin running over them at pleasure. The performance lasted some ten minutes, during which no hive ever hummed louder. Often it was lamented by us that the time of the visitation could never be predicted; it was liable to come upon us at any hour of the night, and what a relief it was, when it happened to fall in the early part of the evening.

Nor must I forget the rats: they did not forget me. Tame as Trenck's mouse, they stood in their holes peering at you like old grandfathers in a doorway. Often they darted in upon us at meal-times, and nibbled our food. The first time they approached Wymontoo, he was actually frightened; but, becoming accustomed to it, he soon got along with them much better than the rest. With curious dexterity he seized the animals by their legs, and flung them up the scuttle to find a watery grave.

But I have a story of my own to tell about these rats. One day the cabin steward made me a present of some molasses, which I was so choice of, that I kept it hid away in a tin can in the farthest corner of my bunk. Faring as we did, this molasses dropped upon a biscuit was a positive luxury, which I shared with none but the doctor, and then only in private. And sweet as the treacle was, how could bread thus prepared and eaten in secret be otherwise than pleasant.

One night our precious can ran low, and in canting it over in the dark, something besides the molasses slipped out. How long it had been there, kind Providence never revealed; nor were we over anxious to know; for we hushed up the bare thought as quickly as possible. The creature certainly died a luscious death, quite equal to Clarence's in the butt of Malmsey.

Chapter XI

Doctor Long Ghost a Wag—One of His Capers

GRAVE THOUGH HE WAS AT TIMES, DOCTOR LONG GHOST WAS A DECIDED WAG. Everyone knows what lovers of fun sailors are ashore—afloat, they are absolutely mad after it. So his pranks were duly appreciated.

The poor old black cook! Unlashing his hammock for the night, and finding a wet log fast asleep in it; and then waking in the morning with his woolly head tarred. Opening his coppers, and finding an old boot boiling away as saucy as could be, and sometimes cakes of pitch candying in his oven.

Baltimore's[1] tribulations were indeed sore; there was no peace for him day nor night. Poor fellow! he was altogether too good-natured. Say what they will about easy-tempered people, it is far better, on some accounts, to have the temper of a wolf. Whoever thought of taking liberties with gruff Black Dan?

The most curious of the doctor's jokes, was hoisting the men aloft by the foot or shoulder, when they fell asleep on deck during the night-watches.

Ascending from the forecastle on one occasion, he found every soul napping, and forthwith went about his capers. Fastening a rope's end to each sleeper, he rove the lines through a number of blocks, and conducted them all to the windlass; then, by heaving round cheerily, in spite of cries and struggles, he soon had them dangling aloft in all directions by arms and legs. Waked by the uproar, we rushed up from below, and found the poor fellows swinging in the moonlight from the tops and lower yard-arms, like a parcel of pirates gibbeted at sea by a cruiser.

Connected with this sort of diversion, was another prank of his. During the night some of those on deck would come below to light a pipe, or take a mouthful of beef and biscuit. Sometimes they fell asleep; and being missed directly that anything was to be done, their shipmates often amused themselves by running them aloft with a pulley dropped down the scuttle from the fore-top.

One night, when all was perfectly still, I lay awake in the forecastle; the lamp was burning low and thick, and swinging from its blackened beam; and with the uniform motion of the ship, the men in the bunks rolled slowly from side to side; the hammocks swaying in unison.

Presently I heard a foot upon the ladder, and, looking up, saw a wide trousers' leg. Immediately, Navy Bob, a stout old Triton, stealthily descended, and at once went to groping in the locker after something to eat.

Supper ended, he proceeded to load his pipe. Now, for a good comfortable smoke at sea, there never was a better place than the *Julia*'s forecastle at midnight. To enjoy the luxury, one wants to fall into a kind of dreamy reverie, only known to the children of the weed. And the very atmosphere of the place, laden as it was with the snores of the sleepers, was inducive of this. No wonder, then, that after a while Bob's head sunk upon his breast; presently his hat fell off, the

1. He was so called from the place of his birth, being a runaway Maryland slave.

extinguished pipe dropped from his mouth, and the next moment he lay out on the chest as tranquil as an infant.

Suddenly an order was heard on deck, followed by the trampling of feet and the hauling of rigging. The yards were being braced, and soon after the sleeper was missed; for there was a whispered conference over the scuttle.

Directly a shadow glided across the forecastle and noiselessly approached the unsuspecting Bob. It was one of the watch with the end of a rope leading out of sight up the scuttle. Pausing an instant, the sailor pressed softly the chest of his victim, sounding his slumbers; and then hitching the cord to his ankle, returned to the deck.

Hardly was his back turned, when a long limb was thrust from a hammock opposite, and Doctor Long Ghost, leaping forth warily, whipped the rope from Bob's ankle, and fastened it like lightning to a great lumbering chest, the property of the man who had just disappeared.

Scarcely was the thing done, when lo! with a thundering bound, the clumsy box was torn from its fastenings, and banging from side to side, flew towards the scuttle. Here it jammed; and thinking that Bob, who was as strong as a windlass, was grappling a beam and trying to cut the line, the jokers on deck strained away furiously. On a sudden, the chest went aloft, and striking against the mast, flew open, raining down on the heads of the party a merciless shower of things too numerous to mention.

Of course the uproar roused all hands, and when we hurried on deck, there was the owner of the box, looking aghast at its scattered contents, and with one wandering hand taking the altitude of a bump on his head.

Chapter XII

DEATH AND BURIAL OF TWO OF THE CREW

THE MIRTHFULNESS WHICH AT TIMES REIGNED AMONG US WAS IN STRANGE AND SHOCKING CONtrast with the situation of some of the invalids. Thus, at least, did it seem to me, though not to others.

But an event occurred about this period, which, in removing by far the most pitiable cases of suffering, tended to make less grating to my feelings the subsequent conduct of the crew.

We had been at sea about twenty days, when two of the sick, who had rapidly grown worse, died one night within an hour of each other.

One occupied a bunk right next to mine, and for several days had not risen from it. During this period he was often delirious, starting up and glaring around him, and sometimes wildly tossing his arms.

On the night of his decease, I retired shortly after the middle watch began, and waking from a vague dream of horrors, felt something clammy resting on me. It was the sick man's hand. Two or three times during the evening previous, he had thrust it into my bunk, and I had quietly removed it; but now I started and flung it from me. The arm fell stark and stiff, and I knew that he was dead.

Waking the men, the corpse was immediately rolled up in the strips of blanketing upon which it lay, and carried on deck. The mate was then called, and preparations made for an instantaneous burial. Laying the body out on the fore-hatch, it was stitched up in one of the hammocks, some "kentlege" being placed at the feet instead of shot. This done, it was borne to the gangway, and placed on a plank laid across the bulwarks. Two men supported the inside end. By way of solemnity, the ship's headway was then stopped by hauling aback the main-top-sail.

The mate, who was far from being sober, then staggered up, and holding on to a shroud, gave the word. As the plank tipped, the body slid off slowly, and fell with a splash into the sea. A bubble or two, and nothing more was seen.

"Brace forward!" The main-yard swung round to its place, and the ship glided on, while the corpse, perhaps, was still sinking.

We had tossed a shipmate to the sharks, but no one would have thought it, to have gone among the crew immediately after. The dead man had been a churlish, unsocial fellow, while alive, and no favorite; and now that he was no more, little thought was bestowed upon him. All that was said, was concerning the disposal of his chest, which, having been always kept locked, was supposed to contain money. Someone volunteered to break it open, and distribute its contents, clothing and all, before the captain should demand it.

While myself and others were endeavoring to dissuade them from this, all started at a cry from the forecastle. There could be no one there but two of the sick, unable to crawl on deck. We went below, and found one of them dying on a chest. He had fallen out of his hammock in a fit, and was insensible. The eyes were open and fixed, and his breath coming and going convulsively. The men shrunk from him; but the doctor, taking his hand, held it a few moments in his, and suddenly letting it fall, exclaimed, "He's gone!" The body was instantly borne up the ladder.

Another hammock was soon prepared, and the dead sailor stitched up as before. Some additional ceremony, however, was now insisted upon, and a Bible was called for. But none was to be had, not even a Prayer-Book. When this was made known, Antone, a Portuguese, from the Cape-de-Verd Islands, stepped up, muttering something over the corpse of his countryman, and, with his finger, described upon the back of the hammock the figure of a large cross; whereupon it received the death-launch.

These two men both perished from the proverbial indiscretions of seamen, heightened by circumstances apparent; but had either of them been ashore under proper treatment, he would, in all human probability, have recovered.

Behold here the fate of a sailor! They give him the last toss, and no one asks whose child he was.

For the rest of that night there was no more sleep. Many stayed on deck until broad morning, relating to each other those marvelous tales of the sea which the occasion was calculated to call forth. Little as I believed in such things, I could not listen to some of these stories unaffected. Above all was I struck by one of the carpenter's.

On a voyage to India, they had a fever aboard, which carried off nearly half the crew in the space of a few days. After this the men never went aloft in the night-time, except in couples. When top-sails were to be reefed, phantoms were seen at the yard-arm ends; and in tacking ship, voices called aloud from the tops. The carpenter himself, going with another man to furl the main-top-gallant-sail in a squall, was nearly pushed from the rigging by an unseen hand; and his shipmate swore that a wet hammock was flirted in his face.

Stories like these were related as gospel truths, by those who declared themselves eye-witnesses.

It is a circumstance not generally known, perhaps, that, among ignorant seamen, Finlanders, or Finns, as they are more commonly called, are regarded with peculiar superstition. For some reason or other, which I never could get at, they are supposed to possess the gift of second sight, and the power to wreak supernatural vengeance upon those who offend them. On this account they have great influence among the sailors, and two or three with whom I have sailed at different times were persons well calculated to produce this sort of impression, at least upon minds disposed to believe in such things.

Now, we had one of these sea-prophets aboard; an old, yellow-haired fellow, who always wore a rude seal-skin cap of his own make, and carried his tobacco in a large pouch made of the same stuff. Van, as we called him, was a quiet, inoffensive man, to look at, and, among such a set, his occasional peculiarities had hitherto passed for nothing. At this time, however, he came out with a prediction, which was nonetheless remarkable from its absolute fulfillment, though not exactly in the spirit in which it was given out.

The night of the burial he laid his hand on the old horse-shoe nailed as a charm to the foremast, and solemnly told us that, in less than three weeks, not one-quarter of our number would remain aboard the ship—by that time they would have left her forever.

Some laughed; Flash Jack called him an old fool; but among the men generally it produced a marked effect. For several days a degree of quiet reigned among us, and allusions of such a kind were made to recent events, as could be attributed to no other cause than the Finn's omen.

For my own part, what had lately come to pass was not without its influence. It forcibly brought to mind our really critical condition. Doctor Long Ghost, too, frequently revealed his apprehensions, and once assured me that he would give much to be safely landed upon any island around us.

Where we were exactly no one but the mate seemed to know, nor whither we were going. The captain—a mere cipher—was an invalid in his cabin; to say nothing more of so many of his men languishing in the forecastle.

Our keeping the sea under these circumstances, a matter strange enough at first, now seemed wholly unwarranted; and added to all was the thought, that our fate was absolutely in the hand of the reckless Jermin. Were anything to happen to him, we would be left without a navigator, for, according to Jermin himself, he had, from the commencement of the voyage, always kept the ship's reckoning, the captain's nautical knowledge being insufficient.

But considerations like these, strange as it may seem, seldom or never occurred to the crew. They were alive only to superstitious fears; and when, in apparent contradiction to the Finn's prophecy, the sick men rallied a little, they began to recover their former spirits, and the recollection of what had occurred insensibly faded from their minds. In a week's time, the unworthiness of *Little Jule,* as a sea vessel, always a subject of jest, now became more so than ever. In the forecastle, Flash Jack, with his knife, often dug into the dank, rotten planks ribbed between us and death, and flung away the splinters with some sea joke.

As to the remaining invalids, they were hardly ill enough to occasion any serious apprehension, at least for the present, in the breasts of such thoughtless beings as themselves. And even those who suffered the most, studiously refrained from any expression of pain.

The truth is, that among sailors as a class, sickness at sea is so heartily detested, and the sick so little cared for, that the greatest invalid generally strives to mask his sufferings. He has given no sympathy to others, and he expects none in return. Their conduct, in this respect, so opposed to their generous-hearted behavior ashore, painfully affects the landsman on his first intercourse with them as a sailor.

Sometimes, but seldom, our invalids inveighed against their being kept at sea, where they could be of no service, when they ought to be ashore and in the way of recovery. But—"Oh! cheer up—cheer up, my hearties!"—the mate would say. And after this fashion he put a stop to their murmurings.

But there was one circumstance, to which heretofore I have but barely alluded, that tended more than anything else to reconcile many to their situation. This was the receiving regularly, twice every day, a certain portion of Pisco, which was served out at the capstan, by the steward, in little tin measures called "tots."

The lively affection seamen have for strong drink is well known; but in the South Seas, where it is so seldom to be had, a thoroughbred sailor deems scarcely any price too dear which will purchase his darling "tot." Nowadays, American whalemen in the Pacific never think of carrying spirits as a ration; and aboard of most of them, it is never served out even in times of the greatest hardships. All Sydney whalemen, however, still cling to the old custom, and carry it as a part of the regular supplies for the voyage.

In port, the allowance of Pisco was suspended; with a view, undoubtedly, of heightening the attractions of being out of sight of land.

Now, owing to the absence of proper discipline, our sick, in addition to what they took medicinally, often came in for their respective "tots" convivially; and, added to all this, the evening of the last day of the week was always celebrated by what is styled on board of English vessels, "The Saturday-night bottles." Two of these were sent down into the forecastle, just after dark; one for the starboard watch, and the other for the larboard.

By prescription, the oldest seaman in each claims the treat as his, and, accordingly, pours out the good cheer and passes it round like a lord doing the honors of his table. But the Saturday-night bottles were not all. The carpenter and cooper, in sea parlance, Chips and Bungs, who were the "Cods," or leaders of the forecastle, in some way or other, managed to obtain an extra supply, which perpetually kept them in fine after dinner spirits, and, moreover, disposed them to look favorably upon a state of affairs like the present.

But where were the sperm whales all this time? In good sooth, it made little matter where they were, since we were in no condition to capture them. About this time, indeed, the men came down from the mast-heads, where, until now, they had kept up the form of relieving each other every two hours. They swore they would go there no more. Upon this, the mate carelessly observed, that they would soon be where look-outs were entirely unnecessary, the whales he had in his eye (though Flash Jack said they were all in his) being so tame, that they made a practice of coming round ships, and scratching their backs against them.

Thus went the world of waters with us, some four weeks or more after leaving Hannamanoo.

Chapter XIII

Our Destination Changed

It was not long after the death of the two men, that Captain Guy was reported as fast declining, and in a day or two more, as dying. The doctor, who previously had refused to enter the cabin upon any consideration, now relented, and paid his old enemy a professional visit.

He prescribed a warm bath, which was thus prepared. The skylight being removed, a cask was lowered down into the cabin, and then filled with buckets of water from the ship's coppers. The cries of the patient, when dipped into this rude bath, were most painful to hear. They at last laid him on the transom, more dead than alive.

That evening, the mate was perfectly sober, and coming forward to the windlass, where we were lounging, summoned aft the doctor, myself, and two or three others of his favorites; when, in the presence of Bembo the Mowree, he spoke to us thus:

"I have something to say to ye, men. There's none but Bembo here as belongs aft, so I've picked ye out as the best men for'ard to take counsel with, d'ye see, consarning the ship. The captain's anchor is pretty nigh atrip; I shouldn't wonder if he croaked afore morning. So what's to be done? If we have to sew him up, some of those pirates there for'ard may take it into their heads to run off with the ship, because there's no one at the tiller. Now, I've detarmined what's best to be done; but I don't want to do it unless I've good men to back me, and make things all fair and square if ever we get home again."

We all asked what his plan was.

"I'll tell ye what it is, men. If the skipper dies, all agree to obey my orders, and in less than three weeks I'll engage to have five hundred barrels of sperm oil under hatches: enough to give every mother's son of ye a handful of dollars when we get to Sydney. If ye don't agree to this, ye won't have a farthing coming to ye.[1]"

Doctor Long Ghost at once broke in. He said that such a thing was not to be dreamt of; that if the captain died, the mate was in duty bound to navigate the ship to the nearest civilized port, and deliver her up into an English consul's hands; when, in all probability, after a run ashore, the crew would be sent home. Everything forbade the mate's plan. "Still," said he, assuming an air of indifference, "if the men say stick it out, stick it out say I; but in that case, the sooner we get to those islands of yours the better."

Something more he went on to say; and from the manner in which the rest regarded him, it was plain that our fate was in his hands. It was finally resolved upon, that if Captain Guy was no better in twenty-four hours, the ship's head should be pointed for the island of Tahiti.

This announcement produced a strong sensation—the sick rallied—and the rest speculated as to what was next to befall us; while the doctor, without alluding to Guy, congratulated me upon the prospect of soon beholding a place so famous as the island in question.

The night after the holding of the council, I happened to go on deck in the middle watch, and found the yards braced sharp up on the larboard tack, with the south-east trades strong on our bow. The captain was no better; and we were off for Tahiti.

Chapter XIV

Rope-Yarn

WHILE GLIDING ALONG ON OUR WAY, I CANNOT WELL OMIT SOME ACCOUNT OF A POOR DEVIL we had among us, who went by the name of Rope Yarn, or Ropey.

He was a nondescript who had joined the ship as a landsman. Being so excessively timid and awkward, it was thought useless to try and make a sailor of him; so he was translated into the cabin as steward; the man previously filling that post, a good seaman, going among the crew and taking his place. But poor Ropey proved quite as clumsy among the crockery as in the rigging; and one day when the ship was pitching, having stumbled into the cabin with a wooden tureen of soup, he scalded the officers so that they didn't get over it in a week. Upon which, he was dismissed, and returned to the forecastle.

Now, nobody is so heartily despised as a pusillanimous, lazy, good-for-nothing land-lubber; a sailor has no bowels of compassion for him. Yet, useless as such a character may be in many respects, a ship's company is by no means disposed to let him reap any benefit from his deficiencies. Regarded in the light of a mechanical power, whenever there is any plain, hard work to be done, he is put to it like a lever; everyone giving him a pry.

Then, again, he is set about all the vilest work. Is there a heavy job at tarring to be done, he is pitched neck and shoulders into a tar-barrel, and set to work at it. Moreover, he is made to fetch and carry like a dog. Like as not, if the mate sends him after his quadrant, on the way he is met by the captain, who orders him to pick some oakum; and while he is hunting up a bit of rope, a sailor comes along and wants to know what the deuce he's after, and bids him be off to the forecastle.

"Obey the last order," is a precept inviolable at sea. So the land-lubber, afraid to refuse to do

1. The men were shipped "by the lay"; in other words, they received no wages; but, by the articles, were entitled to a certain portion of the profits of the voyage.

anything, rushes about distracted, and does nothing: in the end receiving a shower of kicks and cuffs from all quarters.

Added to his other hardships, he is seldom permitted to open his mouth unless spoken to; and then, he might better keep silent. Alas for him! if he should happen to be anything of a droll; or in an evil hour should he perpetrate a joke, he would never know the last of it.

The witticisms of others, however, upon himself, must be received in the greatest good-humor.

Woe be unto him, if at meal-times he so much as look sideways at the beef-kid before the rest are helped.

Then he is obliged to plead guilty to every piece of mischief which the real perpetrator refuses to acknowledge; thus taking the place of that sneaking rascal, nobody, ashore. In short, there is no end to his tribulations.

The land-lubber's spirits often sink, and the first result of his being moody and miserable, is naturally enough an utter neglect of his toilette.

The sailors, perhaps, ought to make allowances; but heartless as they are, they do not. No sooner is his cleanliness questioned, than they rise upon him like a mob of the Middle Ages upon a Jew; drag him into the lee-scuppers, and strip him to the buff. In vain he bawls for mercy; in vain calls upon the captain to save him.

Alas! I say again, for the land-lubber at sea. He is the veriest wretch the watery world over. And such was Rope Yarn; of all landlubbers, the most lubberly and the most miserable. A forlorn, stunted, hook-visaged mortal he was too; one of those, whom you know at a glance to have been tried hard and long in the furnace of affliction. His face was an absolute puzzle; though sharp and sallow, it had neither the wrinkles of age nor the smoothness of youth; so that, for the soul of me, I could hardly tell whether he was twenty-five or fifty.

But to his history. In his better days, it seems he had been a journeyman baker in London, somewhere about Holborn; and on Sundays wore a blue coat and metal buttons, and spent his afternoons in a tavern, smoking his pipe and drinking his ale, like a free and easy journeyman baker that he was. But this did not last long; for an intermeddling old fool was the ruin of him. He was told that London might do very well for elderly gentlemen and invalids; but for a lad of spirit, Australia was the Land of Promise. In a dark day Ropey wound up his affairs and embarked.

Arriving in Sydney with a small capital, and after a while waxing snug and comfortable by dint of hard kneading, he took unto himself a wife; and so far as *she* was concerned, might then have gone into the country and retired; for she effectually did his business. In short, the lady worked him woe in heart and pocket; and in the end, ran off with his till and his foreman. Ropey went to the sign of the Pipe and Tankard; got fuddled; and over his fifth pot meditated suicide—an intention carried out; for the next day he shipped as landsman aboard the *Julia*, South Seaman.

The ex-baker would have fared far better, had it not been for his heart, which was soft and underdone. A kind word made a fool of him; and hence most of the scrapes he got into. Two or three wags, aware of his infirmity, used to "draw him out" in conversation, whenever the most crabbed and choleric old seamen were present.

To give an instance. The watch below, just waked from their sleep, are all at breakfast; and Ropey, in one corner, is disconsolately partaking of its delicacies. Now, sailors newly waked are no cherubs; and therefore not a word is spoken, everybody munching his biscuit, grim and unshaven. At this juncture an affable-looking scamp—Flash Jack—crosses the forecastle, tin can in hand, and seats himself beside the land-lubber.

"Hard fare this, Ropey," he begins; "hard enough, too, for them that's known better and lived in Lun'nun. I say now, Ropey, s'posing you were back to Holborn this morning, what would you have for breakfast, eh?"

"Have for breakfast!" cried Ropey, in a rapture. "Don't speak of it!"

"What ails that fellow?" here growled an old sea-bear, turning round savagely.

"Oh, nothing, nothing," said Jack; and then, leaning over to Rope Yarn, he bade him go on, but speak lower.

"Well, then," said he, in a smuggled tone, his eyes lighting up like two lanterns, "well, then, I'd go to Mother Moll's that makes the great muffins: I'd go there, you know, and cock my foot on the 'ob, and call for a noggin o' somethink to begin with."

"What then, Ropey?"

"Why then, Flashy," continued the poor victim, unconsciously warming with his theme; "why then, I'd draw my chair up and call for Betty, the gal wot tends to customers. Betty, my dear, says I, you looks charmin' this mornin'; give me a nice rasher of bacon and heggs, Betty, my love; and I wants a pint of hale, and three nice 'ot muffins and butter—and a slice of Cheshire; and Betty, I wants—"

"A shark-steak, and be hanged to you!" roared Black Dan, with an oath. Whereupon, dragged over the chests, the ill-starred fellow is pummeled on deck.

I always made a point of befriending poor Ropey when I could; and, for this reason, was a great favorite of his.

Chapter XV

Chips and Bungs

Bound into port, Chips and Bungs increased their devotion to the bottle; and, to the unspeakable envy of the rest, these jolly companions—or "the Partners," as the men called them—rolled about deck, day after day, in the merriest mood imaginable.

But jolly as they were in the main, two more discreet tipplers it would be hard to find. No one ever saw them take anything, except when the regular allowance was served out by the steward; and to make them quite sober and sensible, you had only to ask them how they contrived to keep otherwise. Sometime after, however, their secret leaked out.

The casks of Pisco were kept down the after-hatchway, which, for this reason, was secured with bar and padlock. The cooper, nevertheless, from time to time, effected a burglarious entry, by descending into the fore-hold; and then, at the risk of being jammed to death, crawling along over a thousand obstructions, to where the casks were stowed.

On the first expedition, the only one to be got at lay among others, upon its bilge, with the bung-hole well over. With a bit of iron hoop, suitably bent, and a good deal of prying and punching, the bung was forced in; and then the cooper's neck-handkerchief, attached to the end of the hoop, was drawn in and out—the absorbed liquor being deliberately squeezed into a small bucket.

Bungs was a man after a bar-keeper's own heart. Drinking steadily, until just manageably tipsy, he contrived to continue so; getting neither more nor less inebriated, but, to use his own phrase, remaining "just about right." When in this interesting state, he had a free lurch in his gait, a queer way of hitching up his waistbands, looked unnecessarily steady at you when speaking, and, for the rest, was in very tolerable spirits. At these times, moreover, he was exceedingly patriotic; and in a most amusing way, frequently showed his patriotism whenever he happened to encounter Dunk, a good-natured, square-faced Dane, aboard.

It must be known here, by the by, that the cooper had a true sailor admiration for Lord Nelson. But he entertained a very erroneous idea of the personal appearance of the hero. Not content with depriving him of an eye, and an arm, he stoutly maintained that he had also lost a leg in one of his battles. Under this impression, he sometimes hopped up to Dunk, with one leg curiously locked behind him into his right arm, at the same time closing an eye.

In this attitude he would call upon him to look up, and behold the man who gave his countrymen such a thrashing at Copenhagen. "Look you, Dunk," says he, staggering about, and winking hard with one eye, to keep the other shut, "Look you: one man—hang me, *half* a man—with one leg, one arm, one eye—hang me, with only a piece of a carcass, flogged your whole shabby nation. Do you deny it, you lubber?"

The Dane was a mule of a man, and understanding but little English, seldom made anything of a reply; so the cooper generally dropped his leg, and marched off, with the air of a man who despised saying anything further.

Chapter XVI

We Encounter a Gale

The mild blue weather we enjoyed after leaving the Marquesas, gradually changed as we ran farther south and approached Tahiti. In these generally tranquil seas, the wind sometimes blows with great violence; though, as every sailor knows, a spicy gale in the tropic latitudes of the Pacific is far different from a tempest in the howling North Atlantic. We soon found ourselves battling with the waves, while the before mild Trades, like a woman roused, blew fiercely, but still warmly, in our face.

For all this, the mate carried sail without stint; and as for brave *Little Jule*, she stood up to it well; and though once in a while floored in the trough of a sea, sprang to her keel again and showed play. Every old timber groaned—every spar buckled—every chafed cord strained; and yet, spite of all, she plunged on her way like a racer. Jermin, sea-jockey that he was, sometimes stood in the fore-chains, with the spray every now and then dashing over him, and shouting out, "Well done, Jule—drive into it, sweetheart! Hurrah!"

One afternoon there was a mighty queer noise aloft, which set the men running in every direction. It was the main-t'-gallant-mast. Crash! it broke off just above the cap, and held there by the rigging, dashed with every roll, from side to side, with all the hamper that belonged to it. The yard hung by a hair, and at every pitch thumped against the cross-trees; while the sails streamed in ribbons, and the loose ropes coiled, and thrashed the air, like whip-lashes. "Stand from under!" and down came the rattling blocks like so many shot. The yard, with a snap and a plunge, went hissing into the sea, disappeared, and shot its full length out again. The crest of a great wave then broke over it—the ship rushed by—and we saw the stick no more.

While this lively breeze continued, Baltimore, our old black cook, was in great tribulation.

Like most South Seamen, the *Julia*'s caboose, or cook-house, was planted on the larboard side of the forecastle. Under such a press of canvas, and with the heavy sea running, the barque, diving her bows under, now and then shipped green glassy waves, which, breaking over the head-rails, fairly deluged that part of the ship and washed clean aft. The caboose-house—thought to be firmly lashed down to its place—served as a sort of breakwater to the inundation.

About these times, Baltimore always wore what he called his "gale suit"; among other things, comprising a Sou'-Wester and a huge pair of well-anointed sea-boots, reaching almost to his knees. Thus equipped for a ducking or a drowning, as the case might be, our culinary high-priest drew to the slides of his temple, and performed his sooty rites in secret.

So afraid was the old man of being washed overboard, that he actually fastened one end of a small line to his waistbands, and coiling the rest about him, made use of it as occasion required. When engaged outside, he unwound the cord, and secured one end to a ring-bolt in the deck; so that if a chance sea washed him off his feet, it could do nothing more.

One evening, just as he was getting supper, the *Julia* reared upon her stern like a vicious colt, and when she settled again forward, fairly *dished* a tremendous sea. Nothing could withstand it. One side of the rotten head-bulwarks came in with a crash; it smote the caboose, tore it from its moorings, and after boxing it about, dashed it against the windlass, where it stranded. The water then poured along the deck like a flood, rolling over and over pots, pans, and kettles, and even old Baltimore himself, who went breaching along like a porpoise.

Striking the taffrail, the wave subsided, and, washing from side to side, left the drowning cook high and dry on the after-hatch: his extinguished pipe still between his teeth, and almost bitten in two.

The few men on deck having sprung into the main-rigging, sailor-like, did nothing but roar at his calamity.

The same night, our flying-jib-boom snapped off like a pipe-stem, and our spanker-gaff came down by the run.

By the following morning, the wind in a great measure had gone down; the sea with it; and by noon we had repaired our damages as well as we could, and were sailing along as pleasantly as ever.

But there was no help for the demolished bulwarks; we had nothing to replace them; and so, whenever it breezed again, our dauntless craft went along with her splintered prow dripping, but kicking up her fleet heels just as high as before.

Chapter XVII

THE CORAL ISLANDS

HOW FAR WE SAILED TO THE WESTWARD AFTER LEAVING THE MARQUESAS, OR WHAT MIGHT HAVE been our latitude and longitude at any particular time, or how many leagues we voyaged on our passage to Tahiti, are matters about which, I am sorry to say, I cannot with any accuracy enlighten the reader. Jermin, as navigator, kept our reckoning; and, as hinted before, kept it all to himself. At noon he brought out his quadrant, a rusty old thing, so odd-looking that it might have belonged to an astrologer.

Sometimes, when rather flustered from his potations, he went staggering about deck, instrument to eye, looking all over for the sun—a phenomenon which any sober observer might have seen right overhead. How upon earth he contrived, on some occasions, to settle his latitude, is more than I can tell. The longitude he must either have obtained by the rule of three, or else by special revelation. Not that the chronometer in the cabin was seldom to be relied on, or was any ways fidgety; quite the contrary; it stood stock-still; and by that means, no doubt, the true Greenwich time—at the period of stopping, at least—was preserved to a second.

The mate, however, in addition to his "dead reckoning," pretended to ascertain his meridian distance from Bow bells by an occasional lunar observation. This, I believe, consists in obtaining with the proper instruments, the angular distance between the moon and some one of the stars. The operation generally requires two observers to take sights, at one and the same time.

Now, though the mate *alone* might have been thought well calculated for this, inasmuch as he generally saw things double, the doctor was usually called upon to play a sort of second quadrant to Jermin's first; and what with the capers of both, they used to furnish a good deal of diversion. The mate's tremulous attempts to level his instrument at the star he was after, were comical enough. For my own part, when he *did* catch sight of it, I hardly knew how he managed to separate it from the astral host revolving in his own brain.

However, by hook or by crook, he piloted us along; and before many days, a fellow sent aloft to darn a rent in the fore-top-sail, threw his hat into the air, and bawled out, "Land, ho!"

Land it was; but in what part of the South Seas, Jermin alone knew, and some doubted whether even *he* did. But no sooner was the announcement made, than he came running on deck, spy-glass in hand, and clapping it to his eye, turned round with the air of a man receiving indubitable assurance of something he was quite certain of before. The land was precisely that for which he had been steering; and, with a wind, in less than twenty-four hours we would sight Tahiti. What he said was verified.

The island turned out to be one of the Pomotu or Low Group—sometimes called the Coral Islands—perhaps the most remarkable and interesting in the Pacific. Lying to the east of Tahiti, the nearest are within a day's sail of that place.

They are very numerous; mostly small, low, and level; sometimes wooded, but always covered with verdure. Many are crescent-shaped; others resemble a horse-shoe in figure. These last are nothing more than narrow circles of land, surrounding a smooth lagoon, connected by a single opening with the sea. Some of the lagoons, said to have subterranean outlets, have no visible ones; the enclosing island, in such cases, being a complete zone of emerald. Other lagoons still, are girdled by numbers of small green islets, very near to each other.

The origin of the entire group is generally ascribed to the coral insect.

According to some naturalists, this wonderful little creature, commencing its erections at the bottom of the sea, after the lapse of centuries, carries them up to the surface, where its labors cease. Here, the inequalities of the coral collect all floating bodies; forming, after a time, a soil, in which the seeds carried thither by birds germinate, and cover the whole with vegetation. Here and there, all over this archipelago, numberless naked, detached coral formations are seen, just emerging, as it were, from the ocean. These would appear to be islands in the very process of creation—at any rate, one involuntarily concludes so, on beholding them.[1]

As far as I know, there are but few bread-fruit-trees in any part of the Pomotu group. In many places the cocoanut even does not grow; though, in others, it largely flourishes. Consequently, some of the islands are altogether uninhabited; others support but a single family; and in no place is the population very large. In some respects the natives resemble the Tahitians: their language, too, is very similar. The people of the south-easterly clusters—concerning whom, however, but little is known—have a bad name as cannibals; and for that reason their hospitality is seldom taxed by the mariner.

Within a few years past, missionaries from the Society group have settled among the leeward islands, where the natives have treated them kindly. Indeed, nominally, many of these people are now Christians; and, through the political influence of their instructors, no doubt, a short time since came under the allegiance of Pomaree, the Queen of Tahiti; with which island they always carried on considerable intercourse.

The Coral Islands are principally visited by the pearl-shell fishermen, who arrive in small schooners, carrying not more than five or six men.

For a long while the business was engrossed by Merenhout, the French consul at Tahiti, but a Dutchman by birth, who, in one year, is said to have sent to France fifty thousand dollars' worth of shells. The oysters are found in the lagoons, and about the reefs; and, for half a dozen nails a day, or a compensation still less, the natives are hired to dive after them.

1. The above is the popular idea on the subject. But of late a theory directly the reverse has been started. Instead of regarding the phenomena last described as indicating anything like an active, creative power now in operation, it is maintained that, together with the entire group, they are merely the remains of a continent, long ago worn away, and broken up by the action of the sea.

A great deal of cocoanut oil is also obtained in various places. Some of the uninhabited islands are covered with dense groves; and the ungathered nuts which have fallen year after year, lie upon the ground in incredible quantities. Two or three men, provided with the necessary apparatus for trying out the oil, will, in the course of a week or two, obtain enough to load one of the large sea-canoes.

Cocoanut oil is now manufactured in different parts of the South Seas, and forms no small part of the traffic carried on with trading vessels. A considerable quantity is annually exported from the Society Islands to Sydney. It is used in lamps and for machinery, being much cheaper than the sperm, and, for both purposes, better than the right-whale oil. They bottle it up in large bamboos, six or eight feet long; and these form part of the circulating medium of Tahiti.

To return to the ship. The wind dying away, evening came on before we drew near the island. But we had it in view during the whole afternoon.

It was small and round, presenting one enameled level, free from trees, and did not seem four feet above the water. Beyond it was another and larger island, about which a tropical sunset was throwing its glories; flushing all that part of the heavens, and making it flame like a vast dyed oriel illuminated.

The Trades scarce filled our swooning sails; the air was languid with the aroma of a thousand strange, flowering shrubs. Upon inhaling it, one of the sick, who had recently shown symptoms of scurvy, cried out in pain, and was carried below. This is no unusual effect in such cases.

On we glided, within less than a cable's length of the shore, which was margined with foam that sparkled all round. Within nestled the still, blue lagoon. No living thing was seen, and, for aught we knew, we might have been the first mortals who had ever beheld the spot. The thought was quickening to the fancy; nor could I help dreaming of the endless grottoes and galleries, far below the reach of the mariner's lead.

And what strange shapes were lurking there! Think of those arch creatures, the mermaids, chasing each other in and out of the coral cells, and catching their long hair in the coral twigs.

Chapter XVIII

Tahiti

At early dawn of the following morning we saw the peaks of Tahiti. In clear weather they may be seen at the distance of ninety miles.

"Hivarhoo!" shouted Wymontoo, overjoyed, and running out upon the bowsprit when the land was first faintly descried in the distance. But, when the clouds floated away, and showed the three peaks standing like obelisks against the sky, and the bold shore undulating along the horizon, the tears gushed from his eyes. Poor fellow! It was not Hivarhoo. Green Hivarhoo was many a long league off.

Tahiti is by far the most famous island in the South Seas; indeed, a variety of causes has made it almost classic. Its natural features alone distinguish it from the surrounding groups. Two round and lofty promontories, whose mountains rise nine thousand feet above the level of the ocean, are connected by a low, narrow isthmus; the whole being some one hundred miles in circuit. From the great central peaks of the larger peninsula—Orohena, Aorai, and Pirohitee—the land radiates on all sides to the sea in sloping green ridges. Between these are broad and shadowy valleys—in aspect, each a Tempe—watered with fine streams, and thickly wooded. Unlike many of the other islands, there extends nearly all round Tahiti a belt of low, alluvial soil, teeming with the richest vegetation. Here, chiefly, the natives dwell.

Seen from the sea, the prospect is magnificent. It is one mass of shaded tints of green, from beach to mountain-top; endlessly diversified with valleys, ridges, glens, and cascades. Over the ridges, here and there, the loftier peaks fling their shadows, and far down the valleys. At the head of these, the waterfalls flash out into the sunlight as if pouring through vertical bowers of verdure. Such enchantment, too, breathes over the whole, that it seems a fairy world, all fresh and blooming from the hand of the Creator.

Upon a near approach, the picture loses not its attractions. It is no exaggeration to say, that to a European of any sensibility, who for the first time wanders back into these valleys—away from the haunts of the natives—the ineffable repose and beauty of the landscape is such, that every object strikes him like something seen in a dream; and for a time he almost refuses to believe that scenes like these should have a commonplace existence. No wonder that the French bestowed upon the island the appellation of the New Cytherea. "Often," says De Bougainville, "I thought I was walking in the Garden of Eden."

Nor, when first discovered, did the inhabitants of this charming country at all diminish the wonder and admiration of the voyager. Their physical beauty and amiable dispositions harmonized completely with the softness of their clime. In truth, everything about them was calculated to awaken the liveliest interest. Glance at their civil and religious institutions. To their king, divine rights were paid; while, for poetry, their mythology rivaled that of ancient Greece.

Of Tahiti, earlier and more full accounts were given, than of any other island in Polynesia; and this is the reason why it still retains so strong a hold on the sympathies of all readers of South Sea voyages. The journals of its first visitors, containing, as they did, such romantic descriptions of a country and people before unheard of, produced a marked sensation throughout Europe; and when the first Tahitians were carried thither, Omai in London, and Aotooroo in Paris, were caressed by nobles, scholars, and ladies.

In addition to all this, several eventful occurrences, more or less connected with Tahiti, have tended to increase its celebrity. Over two centuries ago, Quiros, the Spaniard, is supposed to have touched at the island; and, at intervals, Wallis, Byron, Cook, De Bougainville, Vancouver, Le Perouse, and other illustrious navigators, refitted their vessels in its harbors. Here the famous Transit of Venus was observed in 1769. Here the memorable mutiny of the *Bounty* afterward had its origin. It was to the pagans of Tahiti that the first regularly constituted Protestant missionaries were sent; and from their shores also have sailed successive missions to the neighboring islands.

These, with other events which might be mentioned, have united in keeping up the first interest which the place awakened; and the recent proceedings of the French have more than ever called forth the sympathies of the public.

Chapter XIX

A Surprise—More about Bembo

THE SIGHT OF THE ISLAND WAS RIGHT WELCOME. GOING INTO HARBOR AFTER A CRUISE, IS ALways joyous enough; and the sailor is apt to indulge in all sorts of pleasant anticipations. But to us, the occasion was heightened by many things peculiar to our situation.

Since steering for the land, our prospects had been much talked over. By many it was supposed, that should the captain leave the ship, the crew were no longer bound by her articles. This was the opinion of our forecastle Cokes; though, probably, it would not have been sanctioned by the Marine Courts of Law. At any rate, such was the state of both vessel and crew, that whatever might be the event, a long stay, and many holidays in Tahiti, were confidently predicted.

Everybody was in high spirits. The sick, who had been improving day by day since the change in our destination, were on deck, and leaning over the bulwarks; some all animation, and others silently admiring an object unrivaled for its stately beauty—Tahiti from the sea.

The quarter-deck, however, furnished a marked contrast to what was going on at the other end of the ship. The Mowree was there, as usual, scowling by himself; and Jermin walked to and fro in deep thought, every now and then looking to windward, or darting into the cabin and quickly returning.

With all our light sails wooingly spread, we held on our way, until, with the doctor's glass, Papeetee, the village metropolis of Tahiti, came into view. Several ships were descried lying in the harbor, and among them, one which loomed up black and large; her two rows of teeth proclaiming a frigate. This was the *Reine Blanche*, last from the Marquesas, and carrying at the fore, the flag of Rear Admiral Du Petit Thouars. Hardly had we made her out, when the booming of her guns came over the water. She was firing a salute, which afterwards turned out to be in honor of a treaty; or rather—as far as the natives were concerned—a forced cession of Tahiti to the French, that morning concluded.

The cannonading had hardly died away, when Jermin's voice was heard giving an order so unexpected that everyone started. "Stand by to haul back the main-yard!"

"What's that mean?" shouted the men, "are we not going into port?"

"Tumble aft here, and no words!" cried the mate; and in a moment the main-yard swung round, when, with her jib-boom pointing out to sea, the *Julia* lay as quiet as a duck. We all looked blank—what was to come next?

Presently the steward made his appearance, carrying a mattress, which he spread out in the stern-sheets of the captain's boat; two or three chests, and other things belonging to his master, were similarly disposed of.

This was enough. A slight hint suffices for a sailor.

Still adhering to his resolution to keep the ship at sea in spite of everything, the captain, doubtless, intended to set himself ashore, leaving the vessel under the mate, to resume her voyage at once; but after a certain period agreed upon, to touch at the island and take him off. All this, of course, could easily be done without approaching any nearer the land with the *Julia* than we now were. Invalid whaling captains often adopt a plan like this; but, in the present instance, it was wholly unwarranted; and, everything considered, at war with the commonest principles of prudence and humanity. And although, on Guy's part, this resolution showed more hardihood than he had ever been given credit for, it at the same time argued an unaccountable simplicity, in supposing that such a crew would, in any way, submit to the outrage.

It was soon made plain that we were right in our suspicions; and the men became furious. The cooper and carpenter volunteered to head a mutiny forthwith; and, while Jermin was below, four or five rushed aft to fasten down the cabin scuttle; others, throwing down the main-braces, called out to the rest to lend a hand, and fill away for the land. All this was done in an instant; and things were looking critical, when Doctor Long Ghost and myself prevailed upon them to wait a while, and do nothing hastily; there was plenty of time, and the ship was completely in our power.

While the preparations were still going on in the cabin, we mustered the men together, and went into council upon the forecastle.

It was with much difficulty that we could bring these rash spirits to a calm consideration of the case. But the doctor's influence at last began to tell; and, with a few exceptions, they agreed to be guided by him; assured that, if they did so, the ship would eventually be brought to her anchors, without anyone getting into trouble. Still they told us, up and down, that if peaceable means failed, they would seize *Little Jule*, and carry her into Papeetee, if they all swung for it; but, for the present, the captain should have his own way.

By this time everything was ready; the boat was lowered and brought to the gangway; and the captain was helped on deck by the mate and steward. It was the first time we had seen him in more than two weeks, and he was greatly altered. As if anxious to elude every eye, a broad-brimmed Payta hat was pulled down over his brow; so that his face was only visible when the brim flapped aside. By a sling, rigged from the main-yard, the cook and Bembo now assisted in lowering him into the boat. As he went moaning over the side, he must have heard the whispered maledictions of his crew.

While the steward was busy adjusting matters in the boat, the mate, after a private interview with the Mowree, turned round abruptly, and told us that he was going ashore with the captain, to return as soon as possible. In his absence, Bembo, as next in rank, would command; there being nothing to do but keep the ship at a safe distance from the land. He then sprang into the boat, and, with only the cook and steward as oarsmen, steered for the shore.

Guy's thus leaving the ship in the men's hands, contrary to the mate's advice, was another evidence of his simplicity; for, at this particular juncture, had neither the doctor nor myself been aboard, there is no telling what they might have done.

For the nonce, Bembo was captain; and, so far as mere seamanship was concerned, he was as competent to command as anyone. In truth, a better seaman never swore. This accomplishment, by the by, together with a surprising familiarity with most nautical names and phrases, comprised about all the English he knew.

Being a harpooner, and, as such, having access to the cabin, this man, though not yet civilized, was, according to sea usages, which know no exceptions, held superior to the sailors; and therefore, nothing was said against his being left in charge of the ship; nor did it occasion any surprise.

Some additional account must be given of Bembo. In the first place, he was far from being liked. A dark, moody savage, everybody but the mate more or less distrusted or feared him. Nor were these feelings unreciprocated. Unless duty called, he seldom went among the crew. Hard stories, too, were told about him; something, in particular, concerning a hereditary propensity to kill men and eat them. True, he came from a race of cannibals; but that was all that was known to a certainty.

Whatever unpleasant ideas were connected with the Mowree, his personal appearance noway lessened them. Unlike most of his countrymen, he was, if anything, below the ordinary height; but then, he was all compact, and under his swart, tattooed skin, the muscles worked like steel rods. Hair, crisp, and coal-black, curled over shaggy brows, and ambushed small, intense eyes, always on the glare. In short, he was none of your effeminate barbarians.

Previous to this, he had been two or three voyages in Sydney whalemen; always, however, as in the present instance, shipping at the Bay of Islands, and receiving his discharge there on the homeward-bound passage. In this way, his countrymen frequently entered on board the colonial whaling vessels.

There was a man among us who had sailed with the Mowree on his first voyage, and he told me that he had not changed a particle since then.

Some queer things this fellow told me. The following is one of his stories. I give it for what it is worth; premising, however, that from what I know of Bembo, and the foolhardy, dare-devil feats sometimes performed in the sperm-whale fishery, I believe in its substantial truth.

As may be believed, Bembo was a wild one after a fish; indeed, all New Zealanders engaged in this business are; it seems to harmonize sweetly with their blood-thirsty propensities. At sea, the best English they speak, is the South Seaman's slogan in lowering away, "A dead whale, or a stove boat!" Game to the marrow, these fellows are generally selected for harpooners; a post in which a nervous timid man would be rather out of his element.

In darting, the harpooner, of course, stands erect in the head of the boat, one knee braced against a support. But Bembo disdained this; and was always pulled up to his fish, balancing himself right on the gunwale.

But to my story. One morning, at daybreak, they brought him up to a large lone whale. He darted his harpoon, and missed; and the fish sounded. After a while, the monster rose again, about a mile off, and they made after him. But he was frightened, or "gallied," as they call it; and noon came, and the boat was still chasing him. In whaling, as long as the fish is in sight, and no matter what may have been previously undergone, there is no giving up, except when night comes; and nowadays, when whales are so hard to be got, frequently, not even then. At last, Bembo's whale was alongside for the second time. He darted both harpoons; but, as sometimes happens to the best men, by some unaccountable chance, once more missed. Though it is well known that such failures *will* happen at times, they nevertheless occasion the bitterest disappointment to a boat's crew, generally expressed in curses, both loud and deep. And no wonder. Let any man pull with might and main for hours and hours together, under a burning sun; and if it do not make him a little peevish, he is no sailor.

The taunts of the seamen may have maddened the Mowree; however it was, no sooner was he brought up again, than, harpoon in hand, he bounded upon the whale's back, and for one dizzy second was seen there. The next, all was foam and fury, and both were out of sight. The men sheered off, flinging overboard the line as fast as they could; while ahead, nothing was seen but a red whirlpool of blood and brine.

Presently, a dark object swam out; the line began to straighten; then smoked round the loggerhead, and, quick as thought, the boat sped like an arrow through the water. They were "fast," and the whale was running.

Where was the Mowree? His brown hand was on the boat's gunwale; and he was hauled aboard in the very midst of the mad bubbles that burst under the bows.

Such a man, or devil, if you will, was Bembo.

Chapter XX

The Round-Robin—Visitors from Shore

After the captain left, the land-breeze died away; and, as is usual about these islands, towards noon it fell a dead calm. There was nothing to do but haul up the courses, run down the jib, and lie and roll upon the swells. The repose of the elements seemed to communicate itself to the men; and, for a time, there was a lull.

Early in the afternoon, the mate, having left the captain at Papeetee, returned to the ship. According to the steward, they were to go ashore again right after dinner with the remainder of Guy's effects.

On gaining the deck, Jermin purposely avoided us, and went below without saying a word. Meanwhile, Long Ghost and I labored hard to diffuse the right spirit among the crew; impressing upon them that a little patience and management would, in the end, accomplish all that their violence could; and that, too, without making a serious matter of it.

For my own part, I felt that I was under a foreign flag; that an English consul was close at hand, and that sailors seldom obtain justice. It was best to be prudent. Still, so much did I sympathize with the men—so far, at least, as their real grievances were concerned—and so convinced was I of the cruelty and injustice of what Captain Guy seemed bent upon, that, if need were, I stood ready to raise a hand.

In spite of all we could do, some of them again became most refractory, breathing nothing but downright mutiny. When we went below to dinner, these fellows stirred up such a prodigious tumult that the old hull fairly echoed. Many, and fierce too, were the speeches delivered, and uproarious the comments of the sailors. Among others, Long Jim, or—as the doctor afterwards called him—Lacedæmonian Jim, rose in his place, and addressed the forecastle parliament in the following strain:

"Look ye, Britons! If, after what's happened, this here craft goes to sea with us, we are no men; and that's the way to say it. Speak the word, my livelies, and I'll pilot her in. I've been to Tahiti before, and I can do it." Whereupon, he sat down amid a universal pounding of chest-lids, and cymbaling of tin pans; the few invalids, who, as yet, had not been actively engaged with the rest, now taking part in the applause, creaking their bunk-boards and swinging their hammocks. Cries also were heard, of "Hand-spikes and a shindy!" "Out stun-sails!" "Hurrah!"

Several now ran on deck, and, for the moment, I thought it was all over with us; but we finally succeeded in restoring some degree of quiet.

At last, by way of diverting their thoughts, I proposed that a "round-robin" should be prepared and sent ashore to the consul, by Baltimore, the cook. The idea took mightily, and I was told to set about it at once. On turning to the doctor for the requisite materials, he told me he had none; there was not a fly-leaf, even, in any of his books. So, after great search, a damp, musty volume, entitled *A History of the Most Atrocious and Bloody Piracies,* was produced, and its two remaining blank leaves being torn out, were, by help of a little pitch, lengthened into one sheet. For ink, some of the soot over the lamp was then mixed with water, by a fellow of a literary turn; and an immense quill, plucked from a distended albatross's wing, which, nailed against the bowsprit bitts, had long formed an ornament of the forecastle, supplied a pen.

Making use of the stationery thus provided, I indited, upon a chest-lid, a concise statement of our grievances; concluding with the earnest hope, that the consul would at once come off, and see how matters stood, for himself. Right beneath the note was described the circle about which the names were to be written; the great object of a round-robin being to arrange the signatures in such a way, that, although they are all found in a ring, no man can be picked out as the leader of it.

Few among them had any regular names; many answering to some familiar title, expressive of a personal trait; or, oftener still, to the name of the place from which they hailed; and in one or two cases were known by a handy syllable or two, significant of nothing in particular but the men who bore them. Some, to be sure, had, for the sake of formality, shipped under a feigned cognomen, or "purser's name"; these, however, were almost forgotten by themselves; and so, to give the document an air of genuineness, it was decided that every man's name should be put down as it went among the crew. The annexed, therefore, as nearly as I can recall it, is something like a correct representation of the signatures. It is due to the doctor, to say, that the circumscribed device was his.

Folded, and sealed with a drop of tar, the round-robin was directed to "The English Consul, Tahiti"; and, handed to the cook, was by him delivered into that gentleman's hands as soon as the mate went ashore.

On the return of the boat, sometime after dark, we learned a good deal from old Baltimore, who, having been allowed to run about as much as he pleased, had spent his time gossiping.

Owing to the proceedings of the French, everything in Tahiti was in an uproar. Pritchard, the missionary consul, was absent in England; but his place was temporarily filled by one Wilson, an educated white man, born on the island, and the son of an old missionary of that name, still living.

With natives and foreigners alike, Wilson the younger was exceedingly unpopular, being held an unprincipled and dissipated man, a character verified by his subsequent conduct. Pritchard's selecting a man like this to attend to the duties of his office, had occasioned general dissatisfaction ashore.

Though never in Europe or America, the acting consul had been several voyages to Sydney in a schooner belonging to the mission; and therefore our surprise was lessened, when Baltimore told us, that he and Captain Guy were as sociable as could be—old acquaintances, in fact; and that the latter had taken up his quarters at Wilson's house. For us, this boded ill.

The mate was now assailed by a hundred questions as to what was going to be done with us. His only reply was, that in the morning the consul would pay us a visit, and settle everything.

After holding our ground off the harbor during the night, in the morning a shore boat, manned by natives, was seen coming off. In it were Wilson and another white man, who proved to be a Doctor Johnson, an Englishman, and a resident physician of Papeetee.

Stopping our headway as they approached, Jermin advanced to the gangway to receive them. No sooner did the consul touch the deck, than he gave us a specimen of what he was.

"Mr. Jermin," he cried loftily, and not deigning to notice the respectful salutation of the person addressed, "Mr. Jermin, tack ship, and stand off from the land."

Upon this, the men looked hard at him, anxious to see what sort of a looking "cove" he was. Upon inspection, he turned out to be an exceedingly minute "cove," with a viciously pugged nose, and a decidedly thin pair of legs. There was nothing else noticeable about him. Jermin, with ill-assumed suavity, at once obeyed the order, and the ship's head soon pointed out to sea.

Now, contempt is as frequently produced at first sight as love; and thus was it with respect to Wilson. No one could look at him without conceiving a strong dislike, or a cordial desire to entertain such a feeling the first favorable opportunity. There was such an intolerable air of conceit about this man, that it was almost as much as one could do to refrain from running up and affronting him.

"So the *counselor* is come," exclaimed Navy Bob, who, like all the rest, invariably styled him thus, much to mine and the doctor's diversion. "Ay," said another, "and for no good, I'll be bound."

Such were some of the observations made, as Wilson and the mate went below conversing.

But no one exceeded the cooper in the violence with which he inveighed against the ship and everything connected with her. Swearing like a trooper, he called the main-mast to witness, that if he (Bungs) ever again went out of sight of land in the *Julia,* he prayed Heaven that a fate might be his—altogether too remarkable to be here related.

Much had he to say also concerning the vileness of what we had to eat—not fit for a dog; besides enlarging upon the imprudence of entrusting the vessel longer to a man of the mate's intemperate habits. With so many sick, too, what could we expect to do in the fishery? It was no use talking; come what come might, the ship must let go her anchor.

Now, as Bungs, besides being an able seaman, a "Cod" in the forecastle, and about the oldest man in it, was, moreover, thus deeply imbued with feelings so warmly responded to by the rest, he was all at once selected to officiate as spokesman, as soon as the consul should see fit to address us. The selection was made contrary to mine and the doctor's advice; however, all assured us they would keep quiet, and hear everything Wilson had to say, before doing anything decisive.

We were not kept long in suspense; for very soon he was seen standing in the cabin gangway, with the tarnished tin case containing the ship's papers; and Jermin at once sung out for the ship's company to muster on the quarter-deck.

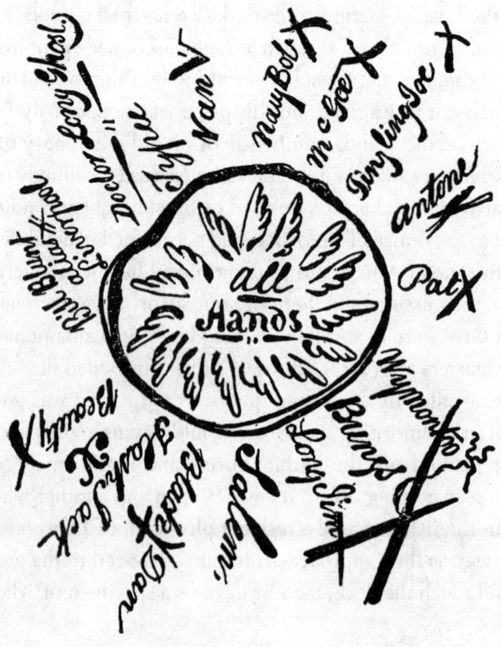

Chapter XXI

Proceedings of the Consul

The order was instantly obeyed, and the sailors ranged themselves, facing the consul. They were a wild company; men of many climes—not at all precise in their toilette arrangements, but picturesque in their very tatters. My friend, the Long Doctor, was there too; and with a view, perhaps, of enlisting the sympathies of the consul for a gentleman in distress, had taken more than ordinary pains with his appearance. But among the sailors, he looked like a land-crane blown off to sea, and consorting with petrels.

The forlorn Rope Yarn, however, was by far the most remarkable figure. Landlubber that he was, his outfit of sea-clothing had long since been confiscated; and he was now fain to go about in whatever he could pick up. His upper garment—an unsailor-like article of dress which he persisted in wearing, though torn from his back twenty times in the day—was an old "claw-hammer-jacket," or swallow-tail coat, formerly belonging to Captain Guy, and which had formed one of his perquisites when steward.

By the side of Wilson was the mate, bareheaded, his gray locks lying in rings upon his bronzed brow, and his keen eye scanning the crowd as if he knew their every thought. His frock hung loosely, exposing his round throat, mossy chest, and short and nervous arm embossed with pugilistic bruises, and quaint with many a device in India ink.

In the midst of a portentous silence, the consul unrolled his papers, evidently intending to produce an effect by the exceeding bigness of his looks.

"Mr. Jermin, call off their names"; and he handed him a list of the ship's company.

All answered but the deserters and the two mariners at the bottom of the sea.

It was now supposed that the round-robin would be produced, and something said about it. But not so. Among the consul's papers, that unique document was thought to be perceived; but, if there, it was too much despised to be made a subject of comment. Some present, very justly regarding it as an uncommon literary production, had been anticipating all sorts of miracles therefrom; and were, therefore, much touched at this neglect.

"Well, men," began Wilson again after a short pause, "although you all look hearty enough, I'm told there are some sick among you. Now then, Mr. Jermin, call off the names on that sick-list of yours, and let them go over to the other side of the deck—I should like to see who they are."

"So, then," said he, after we had all passed over, "*you* are the sick fellows, are you? Very good: I shall have you seen to. You will go down into the cabin, one by one, to Doctor Johnson, who will report your respective cases to me. Such as he pronounces in a dying state I shall have sent ashore; the rest will be provided with everything needful, and remain aboard."

At this announcement, we gazed strangely at each other, anxious to see who it was that looked like dying, and pretty nearly deciding to stay aboard and get well, rather than go ashore and be buried. There were some, nevertheless, who saw very plainly what Wilson was at, and they acted accordingly. For my own part, I resolved to assume as dying an expression as possible; hoping, that on the strength of it, I might be sent ashore, and so get rid of the ship without any further trouble.

With this intention, I determined to take no part in anything that might happen, until my case was decided upon. As for the doctor, he had all along pretended to be more or less unwell; and by a significant look now given me, it was plain that he was becoming decidedly worse.

The invalids disposed of for the present, and one of them having gone below to be examined, the consul turned round to the rest, and addressed them as follows:

"Men, I'm going to ask you two or three questions—let one of you answer yes or no, and the rest keep silent. Now then: Have you anything to say against your mate, Mr. Jermin?" And he looked sharply among the sailors, and, at last, right into the eye of the cooper, whom everybody was eyeing.

"Well, sir," faltered Bungs, "we can't say anything against Mr. Jermin's seamanship, but—"

"I want no *buts,*" cried the consul, breaking in: "answer me *yes* or *no*—have you anything to say against Mr. Jermin?"

"I was going on to say, sir, Mr. Jermin's a very good man; but then—" Here the mate looked marling-spikes at Bungs; and Bungs, after stammering out something, looked straight down to a seam in the deck, and stopped short.

A rather assuming fellow heretofore, the cooper had sported many feathers in his cap; he was now showing the white one.

"So much, then, for that part of the business," exclaimed Wilson, smartly; "you have nothing to say against him, I see."

Upon this several seemed to be on the point of saying a good deal; but disconcerted by the cooper's conduct, checked themselves, and the consul proceeded.

"Have you enough to eat, aboard? answer me, you man who spoke before."

"Well, I don't know as to that," said the cooper, looking excessively uneasy, and trying to edge back, but pushed forward again. "Some of that *salt horse* ain't as sweet as it might be."

"That's not what I asked you," shouted the consul, growing brave quite fast: "answer my questions as I put them, or I'll find a way to make you."

This was going a little too far. The ferment into which the cooper's poltroonery had thrown the sailors now brooked no restraint; and one of them—a young American who went by the name of Salem[1]—dashed out from among the rest, and fetching the cooper a blow that sent him humming over toward the consul, flourished a naked sheath-knife in the air, and burst forth with "I'm the little fellow that can answer your questions; just put them to me once, *counselor.*"

But the "counselor" had no more questions to ask just then; for at the alarming apparition of Salem's knife, and the extraordinary effect produced upon Bungs, he had popped his head down the companion-way, and was holding it there.

Upon the mate's assuring him, however, that it was all over, he looked up, quite flustered, if not frightened, but evidently determined to put as fierce a face on the matter as practicable. Speaking sharply, he warned all present to "look out"; and then repeated the question, whether there was enough to eat aboard. Everyone now turned spokesman; and he was assailed by a perfect hurricane of yells, in which the oaths fell like hail-stones.

"How's this! what d'ye mean?" he cried, upon the first lull; "who told you all to speak at once? Here, you man with the knife, you'll be putting someone's eyes out yet; d'ye hear, you sir? You seem to have a good deal to say, who are *you*, pray? where did *you* ship?"

"I'm nothing more nor a bloody *beach-comber,*"[2] retorted Salem, stepping forward piratically and eyeing him; "and if you want to know, I shipped at the Islands about four months ago."

"Only four months ago? And here you have more to say than men who have been aboard the whole voyage"; and the consul made a dash at looking furious, but failed. "Let me hear no more from *you,* sir. Where's that respectable, gray-headed man, the cooper? *he's* the one to answer my questions."

1. So called from the place he hailed from; a well-known seaport on the coast of Massachusetts.

2. This is a term much in vogue among sailors in the Pacific. It is applied to certain roving characters, who, without attaching themselves permanently to any vessel, ship now and then for a short cruise in a whaler; but upon the condition only of being honorably discharged the very next time the anchor takes hold of the bottom; no matter where. They are, mostly, a reckless, rollicking set, wedded to the Pacific, and never dreaming of ever doubling Cape Horn again on a homeward-bound passage. Hence their reputation is a bad one.

"There's no 'spectable, gray-headed men aboard," returned Salem; "we're all a parcel of mutineers and pirates!"

All this time, the mate was holding his peace; and Wilson, now completely abashed, and at a loss what to do, took him by the arm, and walked across the deck. Returning to the cabin-scuttle, after a close conversation, he abruptly addressed the sailors, without taking any further notice of what had just happened.

"For reasons you all know, men, this ship has been placed in my hands. As Captain Guy will remain ashore for the present, your mate, Mr. Jermin, will command until his recovery. According to my judgment, there is no reason why the voyage should not be at once resumed; especially as I shall see that you have two more harpooners, and enough good men to man three boats. As for the sick, neither you nor I have anything to do with them; they will be attended to by Doctor Johnson; but I've explained that matter before. As soon as things can be arranged—in a day or two, at farthest—you will go to sea for a three months' cruise, touching here, at the end of it, for your captain. Let me hear a good report of you, now, when you come back. At present, you will continue lying off and on the harbor. I will send you fresh provisions as soon as I can get them. There: I've nothing more to say; go forward to your stations."

And, without another word, he wheeled round to descend into the cabin. But hardly had he concluded before the incensed men were dancing about him on every side, and calling upon him to lend an ear. Each one for himself denied the legality of what he proposed to do; insisted upon the necessity for taking the ship in: and finally gave him to understand, roughly and roundly, that go to sea in her they would not.

In the midst of this mutinous uproar, the alarmed consul stood fast by the scuttle. His tactics had been decided upon beforehand; indeed, they must have been concerted ashore, between him and the captain; for all he said, as he now hurried below, was, "Go forward, men; I'm through with you: you should have mentioned these matters before: my arrangements are concluded: go forward, I say; I've nothing more to say to you." And, drawing over the slide of the scuttle, he disappeared.

Upon the very point of following him down, the attention of the exasperated seamen was called off to a party who had just then taken the recreant Bungs in hand. Amid a shower of kicks and cuffs, the traitor was borne along to the forecastle, where—I forbear to relate what followed.

Chapter XXII

THE CONSUL'S DEPARTURE

DURING THE SCENES JUST DESCRIBED, DOCTOR JOHNSON WAS ENGAGED IN EXAMINING THE SICK; of whom, as it turned out, all but two were to remain in the ship. He had evidently received his cue from Wilson.

One of the last called below into the cabin, just as the quarter-deck gathering dispersed, I came on deck quite incensed. My lameness, which, to tell the truth, was now much better, was put down as, in a great measure, affected; and my name was on the list of those who would be fit for any duty in a day or two. This was enough. As for Doctor Long Ghost, the shore physician, instead of extending to him any professional sympathy, had treated him very cavalierly. To a certain extent, therefore, we were now both bent on making common cause with the sailors.

I must explain myself here. All we wanted was, to have the ship snugly anchored in Papeetee Bay; entertaining no doubt that, could this be done, it would in some way or other peaceably lead to our emancipation. Without a downright mutiny, there was but one way to accomplish this: to induce the men to refuse all further duty, unless it were to work the vessel in. The only difficulty lay in restraining them within proper bounds. Nor was it without certain misgivings, that I found myself so situated, that I must necessarily link myself, however guardedly, with such a desperate company; and in an enterprise, too, of which it was hard to conjecture what might be the result. But anything like neutrality was out of the question; and unconditional submission was equally so.

On going forward, we found them ten times more tumultuous than ever. After again restoring some degree of tranquility, we once more urged our plan of quietly refusing duty, and awaiting the result. At first, few would hear of it; but in the end, a good number were convinced by our representations. Others held out. Nor were those who thought with us, in all things to be controlled.

Upon Wilson's coming on deck to enter his boat, he was beset on all sides; and, for a moment, I thought the ship would be seized before his very eyes.

"Nothing more to say to you, men; my arrangements are made. Go forward, where you belong. I'll take no insolence"; and, in a tremor, Wilson hurried over the side in the midst of a volley of execrations.

Shortly after his departure, the mate ordered the cook and steward into his boat; and saying that he was going to see how the captain did, left us, as before, under the charge of Bembo.

At this time we were lying becalmed, pretty close in with the land (having gone about again), our main-top-sail flapping against the mast with every roll.

The departure of the consul and Jermin was followed by a scene absolutely indescribable. The sailors ran about deck like madmen; Bembo, all the while, leaning against the taffrail by himself, smoking his heathenish stone pipe, and never interfering.

The cooper, who that morning had got himself into a fluid of an exceedingly high temperature, now did his best to regain the favor of the crew. "Without distinction of party," he called upon all hands to step up, and partake of the contents of his bucket.

But it was quite plain that, before offering to intoxicate others, he had taken the wise precaution of getting well tipsy himself. He was now once more happy in the affection of his shipmates, who, one and all, pronounced him sound to the kelson.

The Pisco soon told; and, with great difficulty, we restrained a party in the very act of breaking into the after-hold in pursuit of more.

All manner of pranks were now played.

"Mast-head, there! what d'ye see?" bawled Beauty, hailing the main-truck through an enormous copper tunnel. "Stand by the stays," roared Flash Jack, hauling off with the cook's ax, at the fastenings of the main-stay. "Looky out for squalls!" shrieked the Portuguese, Antone, darting a handspike through the cabin skylight. And, "Heave round cheerly, men," sung out Navy Bob, dancing a hornpipe on the forecastle.

Chapter XXIII

The Second Night Off Papeetee

Toward sunset, the mate came off, singing merrily, in the stern of his boat; and in attempting to climb up the side, succeeded in going plump into the water. He was rescued by the steward, and carried across the deck with many moving expressions of love for his bearer. Tumbled into the quarter-boat, he soon fell asleep, and waking about midnight, somewhat sobered, went forward among the men. Here, to prepare for what follows, we must leave him for a moment.

It was now plain enough that Jermin was by no means unwilling to take the *Julia* to sea; indeed, there was nothing he so much desired; though what his reasons were, seeing our situation, we could only conjecture. Nevertheless, so it was; and having counted much upon his rough popularity with the men to reconcile them to a short cruise under him, he had consequently been disappointed in their behavior. Still, thinking that they would take a different view of the matter, when they came to know what fine times he had in store for them, he resolved upon trying a little persuasion.

So on going forward, he put his head down the forecastle scuttle, and hailed us quite cordially, inviting us down into the cabin; where, he said, he had something to make merry withal. Nothing loath, we went; and throwing ourselves along the transom, waited for the steward to serve us.

As the can circulated, Jermin, leaning on the table and occupying the captain's arm-chair secured to the deck, opened his mind as bluntly and freely as ever. He was by no means yet sober.

He told us we were acting very foolishly; that if we only stuck to the ship, he would lead us all a jovial life of it; enumerating the casks still remaining untapped in the *Julia*'s wooden cellar. It was even hinted vaguely, that such a thing might happen as our not coming back for the captain; whom he spoke of but lightly; asserting, what he had often said before, that he was no sailor.

Moreover, and perhaps with special reference to Doctor Long Ghost and myself, he assured us generally, that if there were any among us studiously inclined, he would take great pleasure in teaching such the whole art and mystery of navigation, including the gratuitous use of his quadrant.

I should have mentioned, that previous to this, he had taken the doctor aside, and said something about reinstating him in the cabin with augmented dignity; besides throwing out a hint, that I myself was in some way or other to be promoted. But it was all to no purpose; bent the men were upon going ashore, and there was no moving them.

At last he flew into a rage—much increased by the frequency of his potations—and with many imprecations, concluded by driving everybody out of the cabin. We tumbled up the gangway in high good-humor.

Upon deck everything looked so quiet, that some of the most pugnacious spirits actually lamented that there was so little prospect of an exhilarating disturbance before morning. It was not five minutes, however, ere these fellows were gratified.

Sydney Ben—said to be a runaway Ticket-of-Leave-Man,[1] and for reasons of his own, one of the few who still remained on duty—had, for the sake of the fun, gone down with the rest into the cabin; where Bembo, who meanwhile was left in charge of the deck, had frequently called out for

1. Some of the most promising convicts in New South Wales are hired out to the citizens as servants; thus being, in some degree, permitted to go at large; government, however, still claiming them as wards. They are provided with tickets, which they are obliged to show to anyone who pleases to suspect their being abroad without warrant. Hence the above appellation. This was the doctor's explanation of the term.

him. At first, Ben pretended not to hear; but on being sung out for again and again, bluntly refused; at the same time casting some illiberal reflections on the Mowree's maternal origin, which the latter had been long enough among the sailors to understand as in the highest degree offensive. So just after the men came up from below, Bembo singled him out, and gave him such a cursing in his broken lingo, that it was enough to frighten one. The convict was the worse for liquor; indeed the Mowree had been tippling also, and before we knew it, a blow was struck by Ben, and the two men came together like magnets.

The Ticket-of-Leave-Man was a practiced bruiser; but the savage knew nothing of the art pugilistic: and so they were even. It was clear hugging and wrenching till both came to the deck. Here they rolled over and over in the middle of a ring which seemed to form of itself. At last the white man's head fell back, and his face grew purple. Bembo's teeth were at his throat. Rushing in all round, they hauled the savage off, but not until repeatedly struck on the head would he let go.

His rage was now absolutely demoniac; he lay glaring, and writhing on the deck, without attempting to rise. Cowed, as they supposed he was, from his attitude, the men, rejoiced at seeing him thus humbled, left him; after rating him, in sailor style, for a cannibal and a coward.

Ben was attended to, and led below.

Soon after this, the rest also, with but few exceptions, retired into the forecastle; and having been up nearly all the previous night, they quickly dropped about the chests and rolled into the hammocks. In an hour's time, not a sound could be heard in that part of the ship.

Before Bembo was dragged away, the mate had in vain endeavored to separate the combatants, repeatedly striking the Mowree; but the seamen interposing, at last kept him off.

And intoxicated as he was, when they dispersed, he knew enough to charge the steward—a steady seaman be it remembered—with the present safety of the ship; and then went below, where he fell directly into another drunken sleep.

Having remained upon deck with the doctor some time after the rest had gone below, I was just on the point of following him down, when I saw the Mowree rise, draw a bucket of water, and holding it high above his head, pour its contents right over him. This he repeated several times. There was nothing very peculiar in the act, but something else about him struck me. However, I thought no more of it, but descended the scuttle.

After a restless nap, I found the atmosphere of the forecastle so close, from nearly all the men being down at the same time, that I hunted up an old pea-jacket and went on deck; intending to sleep it out there till morning. Here I found the cook and steward, Wymontoo, Rope Yarn, and the Dane; who, being all quiet, manageable fellows, and holding aloof from the rest since the captain's departure, had been ordered by the mate not to go below until sunrise. They were lying under the lee of the bulwarks; two or three fast asleep, and the others smoking their pipes and conversing.

To my surprise, Bembo was at the helm; but there being so few to stand there now, they told me, he had offered to take his turn with the rest, at the same time heading the watch; and to this, of course, they made no objection.

It was a fine bright night; all moon and stars, and white crests of waves. The breeze was light but freshening; and close hauled, poor *Little Jule*, as if nothing had happened, was heading in for the land, which rose high and hazy in the distance.

After the day's uproar, the tranquility of the scene was soothing, and I leaned over the side to enjoy it.

More than ever did I now lament my situation—but it was useless to repine, and I could not upbraid myself. So at last, becoming drowsy, I made a bed with my jacket under the windlass, and tried to forget myself.

How long I lay there, I cannot tell; but as I rose, the first object that met my eye was Bembo at the helm; his dark figure slowly rising and falling with the ship's motion against the spangled heavens behind. He seemed all impatience and expectation; standing at arm's length from the spokes, with one foot advanced, and his bare head thrust forward. Where I was, the watch were out of sight; and no one else was stirring; the deserted decks and broad white sails were gleaming in the moonlight.

Presently, a swelling, dashing sound came upon my ear, and I had a sort of vague consciousness that I had been hearing it before. The next instant I was broad awake and on my feet. Right ahead, and so near that my heart stood still, was a long line of breakers, heaving and frothing. It was the coral reef, girdling the island. Behind it, and almost casting their shadows upon the deck, were the sleeping mountains, about whose hazy peaks the gray dawn was just breaking. The breeze had freshened, and with a steady gliding motion we were running straight for the reef.

All was taken in at a glance; the fell purpose of Bembo was obvious, and with a frenzied shout to wake the watch I rushed aft. They sprang to their feet bewildered; and after a short, but desperate scuffle, we tore him from the helm. In wrestling with him, the wheel—left for a moment unguarded—flew to leeward, thus, fortunately, bringing the ship's head to the wind, and so retarding her progress. Previous to this, she had been kept three or four points free, so as to close with the breakers. Her headway now shortened, I steadied the helm, keeping the sails just lifting, while we glided obliquely toward the land. To have run off before the wind—an easy thing—would have been almost instant destruction, owing to a curve of the reef in that direction. At this time, the Dane and the steward were still struggling with the furious Mowree, and the others were running about irresolute and shouting.

But, darting forward the instant I had the helm, the old cook thundered on the forecastle with a handspike, "Breakers! breakers close aboard!—'bout ship! 'bout ship!"

Up came the sailors, staring about them in stupid horror.

"Haul back the head-yards!" "Let go the lee fore-brace!" "Ready about! about!" were now shouted on all sides; while, distracted by a thousand orders, they ran hither and thither, fairly panic-stricken.

It seemed all over with us; and I was just upon the point of throwing the ship full into the wind (a step which, saving us for the instant, would have sealed our fate in the end), when a sharp cry shot by my ear like the flight of an arrow.

It was Salem: "All ready for'ard; hard down!"

Round and round went the spokes—the *Julia* with her short keel spinning to windward like a top. Soon the jib-sheets lashed the stays, and the men, more self-possessed, flew to the braces.

"Main-sail haul!" was now heard, as the fresh breeze streamed fore and aft the deck; and directly the after-yards were whirled round.

In a half a minute more we were sailing away from the land on the other tack, with every sail distended.

Turning on our heel within little more than a biscuit's toss of the reef, no earthly power could have saved us, were it not that, up to the very brink of the coral rampart, there are no soundings.

Chapter XXIV

OUTBREAK OF THE CREW

THE PURPOSE OF BEMBO HAD BEEN MADE KNOWN TO THE MEN GENERALLY BY THE WATCH; AND now that our salvation was certain, by an instinctive impulse they raised a cry, and rushed toward him.

Just before liberated by Dunk and the steward, he was standing doggedly by the mizzen-mast; and, as the infuriated sailors came on, his blood-shot eye rolled, and his sheath-knife glittered over his head.

"Down with him!" "Strike him down!" "Hang him at the main-yard!" such were the shouts now raised. But he stood unmoved, and, for a single instant, they absolutely faltered.

"Cowards!" cried Salem, and he flung himself upon him. The steel descended like a ray of light; but did no harm: for the sailor's heart was beating against the Mowree's before he was aware.

They both fell to the deck, when the knife was instantly seized, and Bembo secured.

"For'ard! for'ard with him!" was again the cry; "give him a sea-toss!" "overboard with him!" and he was dragged along the deck, struggling and fighting with tooth and nail.

All this uproar immediately over the mate's head at last roused him from his drunken nap, and he came staggering on deck.

"What's this?" he shouted, running right in among them.

"It's the Mowree, zur; they are going to murder him, zur," here sobbed poor Rope Yarn, crawling close up to him.

"Avast! avast!" roared Jermin, making a spring toward Bembo, and dashing two or three of the sailors aside. At this moment the wretch was partly flung over the bulwarks, which shook with his frantic struggles. In vain the doctor and others tried to save him: the men listened to nothing.

"Murder and mutiny, by the salt sea!" shouted the mate; and dashing his arms right and left, he planted his iron hand upon the Mowree's shoulder.

"There are two of us now; and as you serve him, you serve me," he cried, turning fiercely round.

"Over with them together, then," exclaimed the carpenter, springing forward; but the rest fell back before the courageous front of Jermin, and, with the speed of thought, Bembo, unharmed, stood upon deck.

"Aft with ye!" cried his deliverer, and he pushed him right among the men, taking care to follow him up close. Giving the sailors no time to recover, he pushed the Mowree before him till they came to the cabin scuttle, when he drew the slide over him, and stood still. Throughout, Bembo never spoke one word.

"Now for'ard where ye belong!" cried the mate, addressing the seamen, who, by this time, rallying again, had no idea of losing their victim.

"The Mowree! the Mowree!" they shouted.

Here the doctor, in answer to the mate's repeated questions, stepped forward, and related what Bembo had been doing; a matter which the mate but dimly understood from the violent threatenings he had been hearing.

For a moment he seemed to waver; but at last, turning the key in the padlock of the slide, he breathed through his set teeth—"Ye can't have him; I'll hand him over to the consul; so for'ard with ye, I say: when there's any drowning to be done, I'll pass the word; so away with ye, ye bloodthirsty pirates!"

It was to no purpose that they begged or threatened; Jermin, although by no means sober, stood his ground manfully, and before long they dispersed, soon to forget everything that had happened.

Though we had no opportunity to hear him confess it, Bembo's intention to destroy us was beyond all question. His only motive could have been a desire to revenge the contumely heaped upon him the night previous, operating upon a heart irreclaimably savage, and at no time fraternally disposed toward the crew.

During the whole of this scene the doctor did his best to save him. But well knowing that all I could do would have been equally useless, I maintained my place at the wheel. Indeed, no one but Jermin could have prevented this murder.

Chapter XXV

Jermin Encounters an Old Shipmate

During the morning of the day which dawned upon the events just recounted, we remained a little to leeward of the harbor, waiting the appearance of the consul, who had promised the mate to come off in a shore boat for the purpose of seeing him.

By this time the men had forced his secret from the cooper; and the consequence was, that they kept him continually coming and going from the after-hold. The mate must have known this; but he said nothing, notwithstanding all the dancing and singing, and occasional fighting which announced the flow of the Pisco.

The peaceful influence which the doctor and myself had heretofore been exerting was now very nearly at an end.

Confident, from the aspect of matters, that the ship, after all, would be obliged to go in; and learning, moreover, that the mate had said so, the sailors, for the present, seemed in no hurry about it; especially as the bucket of Bungs gave such generous cheer.

As for Bembo, we were told that, after putting him in double irons, the mate had locked him up in the captain's state-room, taking the additional precaution of keeping the cabin scuttle secured. From this time forward we never saw the Mowree again, a circumstance which will explain itself as the narrative proceeds.

Noon came, and no consul; and as the afternoon advanced without any word even from the shore, the mate was justly incensed; more especially, as he had taken great pains to keep perfectly sober against Wilson's arrival.

Two or three hours before sundown, a small schooner came out of the harbor, and headed over for the adjoining island of Imeeo, or Moreea, in plain sight, about fifteen miles distant. The wind failing, the current swept her down under our bows, where we had a fair glimpse of the natives on her decks.

There were a score of them, perhaps, lounging upon spread mats, and smoking their pipes. On floating so near, and hearing the maudlin cries of our crew, and beholding their antics, they must have taken us for a pirate; at any rate, they got out their sweeps, and pulled away as fast as they could; the sight of our two six-pounders, which, by way of a joke, were now run out of the side-ports, giving a fresh impetus to their efforts. But they had not gone far, when a white man, with a red sash about his waist, made his appearance on deck, the natives immediately desisting.

Hailing us loudly, he said he was coming aboard; and after some confusion on the schooner's decks, a small canoe was launched overboard, and in a minute or two he was with us.

He turned out to be an old shipmate of Jermin's, one Viner, long supposed dead, but now resident on the island.

The meeting of these men, under the circumstances, is one of a thousand occurrences appearing exaggerated in fiction; but, nevertheless, frequently realized in actual lives of adventure.

Some fifteen years previous, they had sailed together as officers of the barque *Jane*, of London, a South Seaman. Somewhere near the New Hebrides, they struck one night upon an unknown reef; and, in a few hours, the *Jane* went to pieces. The boats, however, were saved; some provisions also, a quadrant, and a few other articles. But several of the men were lost before they got clear of the wreck.

The three boats, commanded respectively by the captain, Jermin, and the third mate, then set sail for a small English settlement at the Bay of Islands in New Zealand. Of course they kept together as much as possible. After being at sea about a week, a Lascar in the captain's boat went crazy; and it being dangerous to keep him, they tried to throw him overboard. In the confusion that ensued, the boat capsized from the sail's "jibing"; and a considerable sea running at the time, and the other boats being separated more than usual, only one man was picked up. The very next night it blew a heavy gale; and the remaining boats taking in all sail, made bundles of their oars, flung them overboard, and rode to them with plenty of line. When morning broke, Jermin and his men were alone upon the ocean; the third mate's boat, in all probability, having gone down.

After great hardships, the survivors caught sight of a brig, which took them on board, and eventually landed them at Sydney.

Ever since then our mate had sailed from that port, never once hearing of his lost shipmates, whom, by this time, of course, he had long given up. Judge, then, his feelings, when Viner, the lost third mate, the instant he touched the deck, rushed up and wrung him by the hand.

During the gale his line had parted; so that the boat, drifting fast to leeward, was out of sight by morning. Reduced, after this, to great extremities, the boat touched, for fruit, at an island of which they knew nothing. The natives, at first, received them kindly; but one of the men getting into a quarrel on account of a woman, and the rest taking his part, they were all massacred but Viner, who, at the time, was in an adjoining village. After staying on the island more than two years, he finally escaped in the boat of an American whaler, which landed him at Valparaiso. From this period he had continued to follow the seas, as a man before the mast, until about eighteen months previous, when he went ashore at Tahiti, where he now owned the schooner we saw, in which he traded among the neighboring islands.

The breeze springing up again just after nightfall, Viner left us, promising his old shipmate to see him again, three days hence, in Papeetee harbor.

Chapter XXVI

We Enter the Harbor—Jim the Pilot

Exhausted by the day's wassail, most of the men went below at an early hour, leaving the deck to the steward and two of the men remaining on duty; the mate, with Baltimore and the Dane, engaging to relieve them at midnight. At that hour, the ship—now standing off shore, under short sail—was to be tacked.

It was not long after midnight, when we were wakened in the forecastle by the lion roar of Jermin's voice, ordering a pull at the jib-halyards; and soon afterwards, a handspike struck the scuttle, and all hands were called to take the ship into port.

This was wholly unexpected; but we learned directly, that the mate, no longer relying upon the consul, and renouncing all thought of inducing the men to change their minds, had suddenly made up his own. He was going to beat up to the entrance of the harbor, so as to show a signal for a pilot before sunrise.

Notwithstanding this, the sailors absolutely refused to assist in working the ship under any circumstances whatever: to all mine and the doctor's entreaties lending a deaf ear. Sink or strike, they swore they would have nothing more to do with her. This perverseness was to be attributed, in a great measure, to the effects of their late debauch.

With a strong breeze, all sail set, and the ship in the hands of four or five men, exhausted by two nights' watching, our situation was bad enough; especially as the mate seemed more reckless than ever, and we were now to tack ship several times closer under the land.

Well knowing that if anything untoward happened to the vessel before morning, it would be imputed to the conduct of the crew, and so lead to serious results, should they ever be brought to trial; I called together those on deck, to witness my declaration:—that now that the *Julia* was destined for the harbor (the only object for which *I*, at least, had been struggling), I was willing to do what I could, toward carrying her in safely. In this step I was followed by the doctor.

The hours passed anxiously until morning; when, being well to windward of the mouth of the harbor, we bore up for it, with the union-jack at the fore. No sign, however, of boat or pilot was seen; and after running close in several times, the ensign was set at the mizen-peak, union down in distress. But it was of no avail.

Attributing to Wilson this unaccountable remissness on the part of those ashore, Jermin, quite enraged, now determined to stand boldly in upon his own responsibility; trusting solely to what he remembered of the harbor on a visit there many years previous.

This resolution was characteristic. Even with a competent pilot, Papeetee Bay is considered a ticklish one to enter. Formed by a bold sweep of the shore, it is protected seaward by the coral reef, upon which the rollers break with great violence. After stretching across the bay, the barrier extends on toward Point Venus,[1] in the district of Matavia, eight or nine miles distant. Here there is an opening, by which ships enter, and glide down the smooth, deep canal, between the reef and the shore, to the harbor. But, by seamen generally, the leeward entrance is preferred, as the wind is extremely variable inside the reef. This latter entrance is a break in the barrier directly facing the bay and village of Papeetee. It is very narrow; and, from the baffling winds, currents, and sunken rocks, ships now and then grate their keels against the coral.

But the mate was not to be daunted; so, stationing what men he had at the braces, he sprang upon the bulwarks, and, bidding everybody keep wide awake, ordered the helm up. In a few moments, we were running in. Being toward noon, the wind was fast leaving us, and, by the time the breakers were roaring on either hand, little more than steerage-way was left. But on we glided—smoothly and deftly; avoiding the green, darkling objects here and there strewn in our path: Jermin occasionally looking down in the water, and then about him, with the utmost calmness, and not a word spoken. Just fanned along thus, it was not many minutes ere we were past all danger, and floated into the placid basin within. This was the cleverest specimen of his seamanship that he ever gave us.

As we held on toward the frigate and shipping, a canoe, coming out from among them, approached. In it were a boy and an old man—both islanders; the former nearly naked, and the latter dressed in an old naval frock-coat. Both were paddling with might and main; the old man, once in a while, tearing his paddle out of the water; and, after rapping his companion over the head, both fell to with fresh vigor. As they came within hail, the old fellow, springing to his feet and flourish-

1. The most northerly point of the island; and so called from Cook's observatory being placed there during his first visit.

ing his paddle, cut some of the queerest of capers; all the while jabbering something which at first we could not understand.

Presently we made out the following:—"Ah! you *pe mi*, ah!—you come!—What for you come?—You be fine for come no pilot—I say, you *hear?*—I say, you *ita maitai* (no good)—You *hear?*—You no pilot.—Yes, you d——me, you no pilot 't all; I d——you; you *hear?*"

This tirade, which showed plainly that, whatever the profane old rascal was at, he was in right good earnest, produced peals of laughter from the ship. Upon which, he seemed to get beside himself; and the boy, who, with suspended paddle, was staring about him, received a sound box over the head, which set him to work in a twinkling, and brought the canoe quite near. The orator now opening afresh, it turned out that his vehement rhetoric was all addressed to the mate, still standing conspicuously on the bulwarks.

But Jermin was in no humor for nonsense; so, with a sailor's blessing, he ordered him off. The old fellow then flew into a regular frenzy, cursing and swearing worse than any civilized being I ever heard.

"You *sabbee*[1] me?" he shouted. "You know me, ah? Well: me *Jim*, me *pilot*—been pilot now long time."

"Ay," cried Jermin, quite surprised, as indeed we all were, "you are the pilot, then, you old pagan. Why didn't you come off before this?"

"Ah! me *sabbee*—me know—you *piratee*" (pirate)—"see you long time, but no me come—I *sabbee* you—you *ita maitai nuee*" (superlatively bad).

"Paddle away with ye," roared Jermin in a rage; "be off; or I'll dart a harpoon at ye!"

But, instead of obeying the order, Jim, seizing his paddle, darted the canoe right up to the gangway, and, in two bounds, stood on deck.

Pulling a greasy silk handkerchief still lower over his brow, and improving the set of his frock-coat with a vigorous jerk, he then strode up to the mate; and, in a more flowery style than ever, gave him to understand that the redoubtable "Jim" himself was before him; that the ship was *his* until the anchor was down; and he should like to hear what anyone had to say to it.

As there now seemed little doubt that he was all he claimed to be, the *Julia* was at last surrendered.

Our gentleman now proceeded to bring us to an anchor, jumping up between the knight-heads, and bawling out, "Luff! luff! *keepy off! keepy off!*" and insisting upon each time being respectfully responded to by the man at the helm. At this time our steerage-way was almost gone; and yet, in giving his orders, the passionate old man made as much fuss as a white squall aboard the *Flying Dutchman.*

Jim turned out to be the regular pilot of the harbor; a post, be it known, of no small profit; and, in *his* eyes, at least, invested with immense importance.[2] Our unceremonious entrance, therefore, was regarded as highly insulting, and tending to depreciate both the dignity and lucrativeness of his office.

The old man is something of a wizard. Having an understanding with the elements, certain phenomena of theirs are exhibited for his particular benefit. Unusually clear weather, with a fine steady breeze, is a certain sign that a merchantman is at hand; whale-spouts seen from the harbor,

1. A corruption of the French word *savoir*, much in use among sailors of all nations, and hence made familiar to many of the natives of Polynesia.

2. For a few years past, more than one hundred and fifty sail have annually touched at Tahiti. They are principally whalemen, whose cruising-grounds lie in the vicinity. The harbor dues—going to the queen—are so high, that they have often been protested against. Jim, I believe, gets five silver dollars for every ship brought in.

are tokens of a whaling vessel's approach; and thunder and lightning, happening so seldom as they do, are proof positive that a man-of-war is drawing near.

In short, Jim, the pilot, is quite a character in his way; and no one visits Tahiti without hearing some curious story about him.

Chapter XXVII

A Glance at Papeetee—We are Sent Aboard the Frigate

The village of Papeetee struck us all very pleasantly. Lying in a semicircle round the bay, the tasteful mansions of the chiefs and foreign residents impart an air of tropical elegance, heightened by the palm-trees waving here and there, and the deep-green groves of the bread-fruit in the background. The squalid huts of the common people are out of sight, and there is nothing to mar the prospect.

All round the water extends a wide, smooth beach of mixed pebbles and fragments of coral. This forms the thoroughfare of the village; the handsomest houses all facing it—the fluctuations of the tides[1] being so inconsiderable, that they cause no inconvenience.

The Pritchard residence—a fine large building—occupies a site on one side of the bay: a green lawn slopes off to the sea; and in front waves the English flag. Across the water, the tri-color, also, and the stars and stripes, distinguish the residences of the other consuls.

What greatly added to the picturesqueness of the bay at this time, was the condemned hull of a large ship, which at the farther end of the harbor lay bilged upon the beach, its stern settled low in the water, and the other end high and dry. From where we lay, the trees behind seem to lock their leafy boughs over its bowsprit; which, from its position, looked nearly upright.

She was an American whaler, a very old craft. Having sprung a leak at sea, she had made all sail for the island, to heave down for repairs. Found utterly unseaworthy, however, her oil was taken out and sent home in another vessel; the hull was then stripped and sold for a trifle.

Before leaving Tahiti, I had the curiosity to go over this poor old ship, thus stranded on a strange shore. What were my emotions, when I saw upon her stern the name of a small town on the river Hudson! She was from the noble stream on whose banks I was born; in whose waters I had a hundred times bathed. In an instant, palm-trees and elms—canoes and skiffs—church spires and bamboos—all mingled in one vision of the present and the past.

But we must not leave *Little Jule*.

At last the wishes of many were gratified; and like an aeronaut's grapnel, her rusty little anchor was caught in the coral groves at the bottom of Papeetee Bay. This must have been more than forty days after leaving the Marquesas.

The sails were yet unfurled, when a boat came alongside with our esteemed friend Wilson, the consul.

"How's this, how's this, Mr. Jermin?" he began, looking very savage as he touched the deck. "What brings you in without orders?"

1. The Newtonian theory concerning the tides does not hold good at Tahiti; where, throughout the year, the waters uniformly commence ebbing at noon and midnight, and flow about sunset and daybreak. Hence the term Tooerar-Po is used alike to express high-water and midnight.

"You did not come off to us, as you promised, sir; and there was no hanging on longer with nobody to work the ship," was the blunt reply.

"So the infernal scoundrels held out—did they? Very good; I'll make them *sweat* for it," and he eyed the scowling men with unwonted intrepidity. The truth was, he felt safer *now,* than when outside the reef.

"Muster the mutineers on the quarter-deck," he continued. "Drive them aft, sir, sick and well: I have a word to say to them."

"Now, men," said he, "you think it's all well with you, I suppose. You wished the ship in, and here she is. Captain Guy's ashore, and you think you must go too: but we'll see about that—I'll miserably disappoint you." (These last were his very words.) "Mr. Jermin, call off the names of those who did not refuse duty, and let them go over to the starboard side."

This done, a list was made out of the "mutineers," as he was pleased to call the rest. Among these, the doctor and myself were included; though the former stepped forward, and boldly pleaded the office held by him when the vessel left Sydney. The mate also—who had always been friendly—stated the service rendered by himself two nights previous, as well as my conduct when he announced his intention to enter the harbor. For myself, I stoutly maintained, that according to the tenor of the agreement made with Captain Guy, my time aboard the ship had expired—the cruise being virtually at an end, however it had been brought about—and I claimed my discharge.

But Wilson would hear nothing. Marking something in my manner, nevertheless, he asked my name and country; and then observed with a sneer, "Ah, you are the lad, I see, that wrote the round-robin; I'll take good care of *you,* my fine fellow—step back, sir."

As for poor Long Ghost, he denounced him as a "Sydney Flash-Gorger"; though what under heaven he meant by that euphonious title, is more than I can tell. Upon this, the doctor gave him such a piece of his mind, that the consul furiously commanded him to hold his peace, or he would instantly have him seized into the rigging, and flogged. There was no help for either of us—we were judged by the company we kept.

All were now sent forward; not a word being said as to what he intended doing with us.

After a talk with the mate, the consul withdrew, going aboard the French frigate, which lay within a cable's-length. We now suspected his object; and, since matters had come to this pass, were rejoiced at it. In a day or two the Frenchman was to sail for Valparaiso, the usual place of rendezvous for the English squadron in the Pacific; and doubtless, Wilson meant to put us on board, and send us thither to be delivered up. Should our conjecture prove correct, all we had to expect, according to our most experienced shipmates, was the fag end of a cruise in one of her majesty's ships, and a discharge before long at Portsmouth.

We now proceeded to put on all the clothes we could—frock over frock, and trousers over trousers—so as to be in readiness for removal at a moment's warning. Armed ships allow nothing superfluous to litter up the deck; and therefore, should we go aboard the frigate, our chests and their contents would have to be left behind.

In an hour's time, the first-cutter of the *Reine Blanche* came alongside, manned by eighteen or twenty sailors, armed with cutlasses and boarding-pistols—the officers, of course, wearing their side-arms, and the consul in an official cocked hat, borrowed for the occasion. The boat was painted a "pirate black," its crew were a dark, grim-looking set, and the officers uncommonly fierce-looking little Frenchmen. On the whole they were calculated to intimidate—the consul's object, doubtless, in bringing them.

Summoned aft again, everyone's name was called separately; and being solemnly reminded that it was his last chance to escape punishment, was asked if he still refused duty. The response was instantaneous: "Ay, sir, I do." In some cases followed up by divers explanatory observations, cut short by Wilson's ordering the delinquent to the cutter. As a general thing, the order was promptly obeyed—some taking a sequence of hops, skips, and jumps, by way of showing, not only their unimpaired activity of body, but their alacrity in complying with all reasonable requests.

Having avowed their resolution not to pull another rope of the *Julia*'s—even if at once restored to perfect health—all the invalids, with the exception of the two to be set ashore, accompanied us into the cutter. They were in high spirits; so much so, that something was insinuated about their not having been quite as ill as they pretended.

The cooper's name was the last called; we did not hear what he answered, but he stayed behind. Nothing was done about the Mowree.

Shoving clear from the ship, three loud cheers were raised; Flash Jack and others receiving a sharp reprimand for it from the consul.

"Good-by, *Little Jule,*" cried Navy Bob, as we swept under the bows. "Don't fall overboard, Ropey," said another to the poor landlubber, who, with Wymontoo, the Dane, and others left behind, was looking over at us from the forecastle.

"Give her three more!" cried Salem, springing to his feet and whirling his hat round. "You *sacre* damn raskeel," shouted the lieutenant of the party, bringing the flat of his saber across his shoulders, "you now keepy steel."

The doctor and myself, more discreet, sat quietly in the bow of the cutter; and for my own part, though I did not repent what I had done, my reflections were far from being enviable.

Chapter XXVIII

Reception from the Frenchman

In a few moments we were paraded in the frigate's gangway; the first lieutenant—an elderly, yellow-faced officer, in an ill-cut coat and tarnished gold lace—coming up, and frowning upon us.

This gentleman's head was a mere bald spot; his legs, sticks; in short, his whole physical vigor seemed exhausted in the production of one enormous mustache. Old Gamboge, as he was forthwith christened, now received a paper from the consul; and, opening it, proceeded to compare the goods delivered with the invoice.

After being thoroughly counted, a meek little midshipman was called, and we were soon after given in custody to half a dozen sailor-soldiers—fellows with tarpaulins and muskets. Preceded by a pompous functionary (whom we took for one of the ship's corporals, from his ratan and the gold lace on his sleeve), we were now escorted down the ladders to the berth-deck.

Here we were politely handcuffed, all round; the man with the bamboo evincing the utmost solicitude in giving us a good fit from a large basket of the articles of assorted sizes.

Taken by surprise at such an uncivil reception, a few of the party demurred; but all coyness was, at last, overcome; and finally our feet were inserted into heavy anklets of iron, running along a great bar bolted down to the deck. After this, we considered ourselves permanently established in our new quarters.

"The deuce take their old iron!" exclaimed the doctor; "if I'd known this, I'd stayed behind."

"Ha, ha!" cried Flash Jack, "you're in for it, Doctor Long Ghost."

"My hands and feet are, any way," was the reply.

They placed a sentry over us; a great lubber of a fellow who marched up and down with a dilapidated old cutlass of most extraordinary dimensions. From its length, we had some idea that it was expressly intended to keep a crowd in order—reaching over the heads of half a dozen, say, so as to get a cut at somebody behind.

"Mercy!" ejaculated the doctor, with a shudder, "what a sensation it must be to be killed by such a tool!"

We fasted till night, when one of the boys came along with a couple of "kids" containing a thin, saffron-colored fluid, with oily particles floating on top. The young wag told us this was soup: it turned out to be nothing more than oleaginous warm water. Such as it was, nevertheless, we were fain to make a meal of it, our sentry being attentive enough to undo our bracelets. The "kids" passed from mouth to mouth, and were soon emptied.

The next morning, when the sentry's back was turned, someone, whom we took for an English sailor, tossed over a few oranges, the rinds of which we afterwards used for cups.

On the second day nothing happened worthy of record. On the third, we were amused by the following scene.

A man, whom we supposed a boatswain's mate, from the silver whistle hanging from his neck, came below, driving before him a couple of blubbering boys, and followed by a whole troop of youngsters in tears. The pair it seemed, were sent down to be punished by command of an officer: the rest had accompanied them out of sympathy.

The boatswain's mate went to work without delay, seizing the poor little culprits by their loose frocks, and using a ratan without mercy. The other boys wept, clasped their hands, and fell on their knees; but in vain: the boatswain's mate only hit out at them; once in a while making them yell ten times louder than ever.

In the midst of the tumult, down comes a midshipman, who, with a great air, orders the man on deck, and running in among the boys, sets them to scampering in all directions.

The whole of this proceeding was regarded with infinite scorn by Navy Bob, who, years before, had been captain of the fore-top, on board a line-of-battle ship. In his estimation, it was a lubberly piece of business throughout: they did things differently in the English navy.

Chapter XXIX

THE REINE BLANCHE

I CANNOT FORBEAR A BRIEF REFLECTION UPON THE SCENE ENDING THE LAST CHAPTER.

The ratanning of the young culprits, although significant of the imperfect discipline of a French man-of-war, may also be considered as in some measure characteristic of the nation.

In an American or English ship, a boy, when flogged, is either lashed to the breech of a gun, or brought right up to the gratings, the same way the men are. But as a general rule, he is never punished beyond his strength. You seldom or never draw a cry from the young rogue. He bites his tongue, and stands up to it like a hero. If practicable (which is not always the case), he makes a point of smiling under the operation. And so far from his companions taking any compassion on him, they always make merry over his misfortunes. Should he turn baby and cry, they are pretty sure to give him afterwards a sly pounding in some dark corner.

This tough training produces its legitimate results.[1] The boy becomes, in time, a thoroughbred tar, equally ready to strip and take a dozen on board his own ship, or, cutlass in hand, dash pell-mell

1. I do not wish to be understood as applauding the flogging system practiced in men-of-war. As long, however, as navies are needed, there is no substitute for it. War being the greatest of evils, all its accessories necessarily partake of the same character; and this is about all that can be said in defense of flogging.

on board the enemy's. Whereas the young Frenchman, as all the world knows, makes but an indifferent seaman; and though, for the most part, he fights well enough, somehow or other he seldom fights well enough to beat.

How few sea-battles have the French ever won! But more: how few ships have they ever carried *by the board*—that true criterion of naval courage! But not a word against French bravery—there is plenty of it; but not of the right sort. A Yankee's, or an Englishman's, is the downright Waterloo "game." The French fight better on land; and, not being essentially a maritime people, they ought to stay there. The best of shipwrights, they are no sailors.

And this carries me back to the *Reine Blanche,* as noble a specimen of what wood and iron can make as ever floated.

She was a new ship; the present her maiden cruise. The greatest pains having been taken in her construction, she was accounted the "crack" craft in the French navy. She is one of the heavy sixty-gun frigates now in vogue all over the world, and which we Yankees were the first to introduce. In action, these are the most murderous vessels ever launched.

The model of the *Reine Blanche* has all that war-like comeliness only to be seen in a fine fighting-ship. Still, there is a good deal of French flummery about her—brass-plates and other gewgaws, stuck on all over, like baubles on a handsome woman.

Among other things, she carries a stern gallery resting on the uplifted hands of two Caryatides, larger than life. You step out upon this from the commodore's cabin. To behold the rich hangings, and mirrors, and mahogany within, one is almost prepared to see a bevy of ladies trip forth on the balcony for an airing.

But come to tread the gun-deck, and all thoughts like these are put to flight. Such batteries of thunderbolt hurlers! with a sixty-eight-pounder or two thrown in as make-weights. On the spar-deck, also, are carronades of enormous caliber.

Recently built, this vessel, of course, had the benefit of the latest improvements. I was quite amazed to see on what high principles of art some exceedingly simple things were done. But your Gaul is scientific about everything; what other people accomplish by a few hard knocks, he delights in achieving by a complex arrangement of the pulley, lever, and screw.

What demi-semi-quavers in a French air! In exchanging naval courtesies, I have known a French band play "Yankee Doodle" with such a string of variations, that no one but a "pretty 'cute" Yankee could tell what they were at.

In the French navy they have no marines; their men, taking turns at carrying the musket, are sailors one moment, and soldiers the next; a fellow running aloft in his line-frock to-day, to-morrow stands sentry at the admiral's cabin-door. This is fatal to anything like proper sailor pride. To make a man a seaman, he should be put to no other duty. Indeed, a thorough tar is unfit for anything else; and what is more, this fact is the best evidence of his being a true sailor.

On board the *Reine Blanche,* they did not have enough to eat: and what they *did* have, was not of the right sort. Instead of letting the sailors file their teeth against the rim of a hard sea-biscuit, they baked their bread daily in pitiful little rolls. Then they had no "grog"; as a substitute, they drugged the poor fellows with a thin, sour wine—the juice of a few grapes, perhaps, to a pint of the juice of water-faucets. Moreover, the sailors asked for meat, and they gave them soup; a rascally substitute, as they well knew.

Ever since leaving home, they had been on "short allowance." At the present time, those belonging to the boats—and thus getting an occasional opportunity to run ashore—frequently sold their rations of bread to some less fortunate shipmate for sixfold its real value.

Another thing tending to promote dissatisfaction among the crew was, their having such a devil of a fellow for a captain. He was one of those horrid naval bores—a great disciplinarian. In port, he kept them constantly exercising yards and sails, and maneuvering with the boats; and at sea, they were forever at quarters; running in and out the enormous guns, as if their arms were made for nothing else. Then there was the admiral aboard, also; and, no doubt, *he* too had a paternal eye over them.

In the ordinary routine of duty, we could not but be struck with the listless, slovenly behavior of these men; there was nothing of the national vivacity in their movements; nothing of the quick precision perceptible on the deck of a thoroughly disciplined armed vessel.

All this, however, when we came to know the reason, was no matter of surprise; three-fourths of them were pressed men. Some old merchant sailors had been seized the very day they landed from distant voyages; while the landsmen, of whom there were many, had been driven down from the country in herds, and so sent to sea.

At the time, I was quite amazed to hear of press-gangs in a day of comparative peace: but the anomaly is accounted for by the fact, that, of late, the French have been building up a great military marine, to take the place of that which Nelson gave to the waves of the sea at Trafalgar. But it is to be hoped that they are not building their ships for the people across the Channel to take. In case of a war, what a fluttering of French ensigns there would be!

Though I say the French are no sailors, I am far from seeking to underrate them as a people. They are an ingenious and right gallant nation. And, as an American, I take pride in asserting it.

Chapter XXX

They Take Us Ashore—What Happened There

FIVE DAYS AND NIGHTS, IF I REMEMBER RIGHT, WE WERE ABOARD THE FRIGATE. ON THE AFTERnoon of the fifth, we were told that the next morning she sailed for Valparaiso. Rejoiced at this, we prayed for a speedy passage. But, as it turned out, the consul had no idea of letting us off so easily. To our no small surprise, an officer came along toward night, and ordered us out of irons. Being then mustered in the gangway, we were escorted into a cutter alongside, and pulled ashore.

Accosted by Wilson as we struck the beach, he delivered us up to a numerous guard of natives, who at once conducted us to a house nearby. Here we were made to sit down under a shade without; and the consul and two elderly European residents passed by us, and entered.

After some delay, during which we were much diverted by the hilarious good-nature of our guard—one of our number was called out for, followed by an order for him to enter the house alone.

On returning a moment after, he told us we had little to encounter. It had simply been asked, whether he still continued of the same mind; on replying yes, something was put down upon a piece of paper, and he was waved outside. All being summoned in rotation, my own turn came at last.

Within, Wilson and his two friends were seated magisterially at a table—an inkstand, a pen, and a sheet of paper, lending quite a business-like air to the apartment. These three gentlemen, being arrayed in coats and pantaloons, looked respectable, at least in a country where complete suits of garments are so seldom met with. One present essayed a solemn aspect; but having a short neck and full face only made out to look stupid.

It was this individual who condescended to take a paternal interest in myself. After declaring my resolution with respect to the ship unalterable, I was proceeding to withdraw, in compliance with a sign from the consul, when the stranger turned round to him, saying, "Wait a minute, if you please, Mr. Wilson; let me talk to that youth. Come here, my young friend: I'm extremely sorry to see you associated with these bad men; do you know what it will end in?"

"Oh, that's the lad that wrote the round-robin," interposed the consul. "He and that rascally doctor are at the bottom of the whole affair—go outside, sir."

I retired as from the presence of royalty; backing out with many bows.

The evident prejudice of Wilson against both the doctor and myself was by no means inexplicable. A man of any education before the mast is always looked upon with dislike by his captain; and, never mind how peaceable he may be, should any disturbance arise, from his intellectual superiority, he is deemed to exert an underhand influence against the officers.

Little as I had seen of Captain Guy, the few glances cast upon me after being on board a week or so, were sufficient to reveal his enmity—a feeling quickened by my undisguised companionship with Long Ghost, whom he both feared and cordially hated. Guy's relations with the consul readily explains the latter's hostility.

The examination over, Wilson and his friends advanced to the doorway; when the former, assuming a severe expression, pronounced our perverseness infatuation in the extreme. Nor was there any hope left: our last chance for pardon was gone. Even were we to become contrite, and crave permission to return to duty, it would not now be permitted.

"Oh! get along with your gammon, *counselor,*" exclaimed Black Dan, absolutely indignant that his understanding should be thus insulted.

Quite enraged, Wilson bade him hold his peace; and then, summoning a fat old native to his side, addressed him in Tahitian, giving directions for leading us away to a place of safe keeping.

Hereupon, being marshaled in order, with the old man at our head, we were put in motion, with loud shouts, along a fine pathway, running far on, through wide groves of the cocoanut and bread-fruit.

The rest of our escort trotted on beside us in high good-humor; jabbering broken English, and in a hundred ways giving us to understand that Wilson was no favorite of theirs, and that we were prime good fellows for holding out as we did. They seemed to know our whole history.

The scenery around was delightful. The tropical day was fast drawing to a close; and from where we were, the sun looked like a vast red fire burning in the woodlands—its rays falling aslant through the endless ranks of trees, and every leaf fringed with flame. Escaped from the confined decks of the frigate, the air breathed spices to us; streams were heard flowing; green boughs were rocking; and far inland, all sunset flushed, rose the still, steep peaks of the island.

As we proceeded, I was more and more struck by the picturesqueness of the wide shaded road. In several places, durable bridges of wood were thrown over large watercourses; others were spanned by a single arch of stone. In any part of the road three horsemen might have ridden abreast.

This beautiful avenue—by far the best thing which civilization has done for the island—is called by foreigners "the Broom Road," though for what reason I do not know. Originally planned for the convenience of the missionaries journeying from one station to another, it almost completely encompasses the larger peninsula; skirting for a distance of at least sixty miles along the low, fertile lands bordering the sea. But on the side next Taiarboo, or the lesser peninsula, it sweeps through a narrow, secluded valley, and thus crosses the island in that direction.

The uninhabited interior, being almost impenetrable from the densely wooded glens, frightful precipices, and sharp mountain ridges absolutely inaccessible, is but little known, even to the natives themselves; and so, instead of striking directly across from one village to another, they follow the Broom Road round and round.[1]

1. Concerning the singular ignorance of the natives respecting their own country, it may be here observed, that a considerable inland lake—Waiherea by name—is known to exist, although their accounts of it strangely vary. Some told me it had no bottom, no outlet, and no inlet; others, that it fed all the streams on the island. A sailor of my acquaintance said that he once visited this marvelous lake, as one of an exploring party from an English sloop-of-war. It was found to be a great curiosity; very small, deep, and green; a choice well of water bottled up among the mountains, and abounding with delicious fish.

It is by no means, however, altogether traveled on foot; horses being now quite plentiful. They were introduced from Chile; and possessing all the gaiety, fleetness, and docility of the Spanish breed, are admirably adapted to the tastes of the higher classes, who as equestrians have become very expert. The missionaries and chiefs never think of journeying except in the saddle; and at all hours of the day you see the latter galloping along at full speed. Like the Sandwich Islanders, they ride like Pawnee-Loups.

For miles and miles I have traveled the Broom Road, and never wearied of the continual change of scenery. But wherever it leads you—whether through level woods, across grassy glens, or over hills waving with palms—the bright blue sea on one side, and the green mountain pinnacles on the other, are always in sight.

Chapter XXXI

The Calabooza Beretanee

About a mile from the village we came to a halt.

It was a beautiful spot. A mountain stream here flowed at the foot of a verdant slope; on one hand, it murmured along until the waters, spreading themselves upon a beach of small, sparkling shells, trickled into the sea; on the other, was a long defile, where the eye pursued a gleaming, sinuous thread, lost in shade and verdure.

The ground next the road was walled in by a low, rude parapet of stones; and, upon the summit of the slope beyond, was a large native house, the thatch dazzling white, and, in shape, an oval.

"Calabooza! Calabooza Beretanee!" (the English Jail), cried our conductor, pointing to the building.

For a few months past, having been used by the consul as a house of confinement for his refractory sailors, it was thus styled to distinguish it from similar places in and about Papeetee.

Though extremely romantic in appearance, on a near approach it proved but ill adapted to domestic comfort. In short, it was a mere shell, recently built, and still unfinished. It was open all round, and tufts of grass were growing here and there under the very roof. The only piece of furniture was the "stocks," a clumsy machine for keeping people in one place, which, I believe, is pretty much out of date in most countries. It is still in use, however, among the Spaniards in South America; from whom, it seems, the Tahitians have borrowed the contrivance, as well as the name by which all places of confinement are known among them.

The stocks were nothing more than two stout timbers, about twenty feet in length, and precisely alike. One was placed edgeways on the ground, and the other resting on top, left, at regular intervals along the seam, several round holes, the object of which was evident at a glance.

By this time our guide had informed us that he went by the name of *"Capin Bob"* (Captain Bob); and a hearty old Bob he proved. It was just the name for him. From the first, so pleased were we with the old man, that we cheerfully acquiesced in his authority.

Entering the building, he set us about fetching heaps of dry leaves to spread behind the stocks for a couch. A trunk of a small cocoanut-tree was then placed for a bolster—rather a hard one, but the natives are used to it. For a pillow, they use a little billet of wood, scooped out, and standing on four short legs—a sort of head-stool.

These arrangements completed, Captain Bob proceeded to "hannapar," or secure us, for the night. The upper timber of the machine being lifted at one end, and our ankles placed in the semicircular spaces of the lower one, the other beam was then dropped; both being finally secured together by an old iron hoop at either extremity. This initiation was performed to the boisterous mirth of the natives, and diverted ourselves not a little.

Captain Bob now bustled about, like an old woman seeing the children to bed. A basket of baked "taro," or Indian turnip, was brought in, and we were given a piece all round. Then a great counterpane, of coarse, brown "tappa," was stretched over the whole party; and, after sundry injunctions to "moee-moee," and be "maitai"—in other words, to go to sleep, and be good boys—we were left to ourselves, fairly put to bed and tucked in.

Much talk was now had concerning our prospects in life; but the doctor and I, who lay side by side, thinking the occasion better adapted to meditation, kept pretty silent; and, before long, the rest ceased conversing, and, wearied with loss of rest on board the frigate, were soon sound asleep.

After sliding from one reverie into another, I started, and gave the doctor a pinch. He was dreaming, however; and, resolved to follow his example, I troubled him no more.

How the rest managed, I know not; but, for my own part, I found it very hard to get asleep. The consciousness of having one's foot *pinned*, and the impossibility of getting it anywhere else than just where it was, was most distressing.

But this was not all; there was no way of lying but straight on your back; unless, to be sure, one's limb went round and round in the ankle, like a swivel. Upon getting into a sort of doze, it was no wonder this uneasy posture gave me the nightmare. Under the delusion that I was about some gymnastics or other, I gave my unfortunate member such a twitch, that I started up with the idea that someone was dragging the stocks away.

Captain Bob and his friends lived in a little hamlet hard by; and when morning showed in the east, the old gentleman came forth from that direction likewise, emerging from a grove, and saluting us loudly as he approached.

Finding everybody awake, he set us at liberty; and, leading us down to the stream, ordered every man to strip and bathe.

"All han's, my boy, hanna-hanna, wash!" he cried. Bob was a linguist, and had been to sea in his day, as he many a time afterwards told us.

At this moment, we were all alone with him; and it would have been the easiest thing in the world to have given him the slip; but he seemed to have no idea of such a thing; treating us so frankly and cordially, indeed, that even had we thought of running, we would have been ashamed of attempting it. He very well knew, nevertheless (as we ourselves were not slow in finding out), that, for various reasons, any attempt of the kind, without some previously arranged plan for leaving the island, would be certain to fail.

As Bob was a rare one every way, I must give some account of him. There was a good deal of "personal appearance" about him; in short, he was a corpulent giant, over six feet in height, and literally as big round as a hogshead. The enormous bulk of some of the Tahitians has been frequently spoken of by voyagers.

Beside being the English consul's jailer, as it were, he carried on a little Tahitian farming; that is to say, he owned several groves of the bread-fruit and palm, and never hindered their growing. Close by was a "taro" patch of his, which he occasionally visited.

Bob seldom disposed of the produce of his lands; it was all needed for domestic consumption. Indeed, for gormandizing, I would have matched him against any three common-councilmen at a civic feast.

A friend of Bob's told me, that, owing to his voraciousness, his visits to other parts of the island were much dreaded; for, according to Tahitian customs, hospitality without charge is enjoined upon everyone; and though it is reciprocal in most cases, in Bob's it was almost out of the question. The damage done to a native larder in one of his morning calls was more than could be made good by his entertainer's spending the holidays with him.

The old man, as I have hinted, had, once upon a time, been a cruise or two in a whaling-vessel; and, therefore, he prided himself upon his English. Having acquired what he knew of it in the forecastle, he talked little else than sailor phrases, which sounded whimsically enough.

I asked him one day how old he was. "Olee!" he exclaimed, looking very profound in consequence of thoroughly understanding so subtle a question—"Oh! very olee—'tousand 'ear—more—big man when Capin Tootee (Captain Cook) heavey in sight." (in sea parlance, came into view).

This was a thing impossible; but adapting my discourse to the man, I rejoined—"Ah! you see Capin Tootee—well, how you like him?"

"Oh! he maitai (good): friend of me, and know my wife."

On my assuring him strongly, that he could not have been born at the time, he explained himself by saying, that he was speaking of his father all the while. This, indeed, might very well have been.

It is a curious fact that all these people, young and old, will tell you that they have enjoyed the honor of a personal acquaintance with the great navigator; and if you listen to them, they will go on and tell anecdotes without end. This springs from nothing but their great desire to please; well knowing that a more agreeable topic for a white man could not be selected. As for the anachronism of the thing, they seem to have no idea of it: days and years are all the same to them.

After our sunrise bath, Bob once more placed us in the stocks, almost moved to tears at subjecting us to so great a hardship; but he could not treat us otherwise, he said, on pain of the consul's displeasure. How long we were to be confined, he did not know; nor what was to be done with us in the end.

As noon advanced, and no signs of a meal were visible, someone inquired whether we were to be boarded, as well as lodged, at the Hotel de Calabooza?

"Vast heavey" (avast heaving, or wait a bit)—said Bob—"kow-kow" (food) "come ship by by."

And, sure enough, along comes Rope Yarn with a wooden bucket of the *Julia*'s villainous biscuit. With a grin, he said it was a present from Wilson; it was all we were to get that day. A great cry was now raised; and well was it for the land-lubber, that he had a pair of legs, and the men could not use theirs. One and all, we resolved not to touch the bread, come what come might; and so we told the natives.

Being extravagantly fond of ship-biscuit—the harder the better—they were quite overjoyed; and offered to give us every day a small quantity of baked bread-fruit and Indian turnip in exchange for the bread. This we agreed to; and every morning afterward, when the bucket came, its contents were at once handed over to Bob and his friends, who never ceased munching until nightfall.

Our exceedingly frugal meal of bread-fruit over, Captain Bob waddled up to us with a couple of long poles hooked at one end, and several large baskets of woven cocoanut branches.

Not far off was an extensive grove of orange-trees in full bearing; and myself and another were selected to go with him, and gather a supply for the party. When we went in among the trees, the sumptuousness of the orchard was unlike anything I had ever seen; while the fragrance shaken from the gently waving boughs regaled our senses most delightfully.

In many places the trees formed a dense shade, spreading overhead a dark, rustling vault, groined with boughs, and studded here and there with the ripened spheres, like gilded balls. In several places, the overladen branches were borne to the earth, hiding the trunk in a tent of foliage. Once fairly in the grove, we could see nothing else: it was oranges all round.

To preserve the fruit from bruising, Bob, hooking the twigs with his pole, let them fall into his basket. But this would not do for us; seizing hold of a bough, we brought such a shower to the ground, that our old friend was fain to run from under. Heedless of remonstrance, we then reclined in the shade, and feasted to our hearts' content. Heaping up the baskets afterwards, we returned to our comrades, by whom our arrival was hailed with loud plaudits; and in a marvelously short time, nothing was left of the oranges we brought but the rinds.

While inmates of the Calabooza, we had as much of the fruit as we wanted; and to this cause, and others that might be mentioned, may be ascribed the speedy restoration of our sick to comparative health.

The orange of Tahiti is delicious—small and sweet, with a thin, dry rind. Though now abounding, it was unknown before Cook's time, to whom the natives are indebted for so great a blessing. He likewise introduced several other kinds of fruit; among these were the fig, pine-apple, and lemon, now seldom met with. The lime still grows, and some of the poorer natives express the juice to sell to the shipping. It is highly valued as an anti-scorbutic. Nor was the variety of foreign fruits and vegetables which were introduced the only benefit conferred by the first visitors to the Society group. Cattle and sheep were left at various places. More of them anon.

Thus, after all that has of late years has been done for these islanders, Cook and Vancouver may, in one sense at least, be considered their greatest benefactors.

Chapter XXXII

Proceedings of the French at Tahiti

As I happened to arrive at the island at a very interesting period in its political affairs, it may be well to give some little account here of the proceedings of the French, by way of episode to the narrative. My information was obtained at the time from the general reports then rife among the natives, as well as from what I learned upon a subsequent visit, and reliable accounts which I have seen since reaching home.

It seems, that for some time back the French had been making repeated ineffectual attempts to plant a Roman Catholic mission here. But, invariably treated with contumely, they sometimes met with open violence; and, in every case, those directly concerned in the enterprise were ultimately forced to depart. In one instance, two priests, Laval and Caset, after enduring a series of persecutions, were set upon by the natives, maltreated, and finally carried aboard a small trading schooner, which eventually put them ashore at Wallis Island—a savage place—some two thousand miles to the westward.

Now, that the resident English missionaries authorized the banishment of these priests, is a fact undenied by themselves. I was also repeatedly informed, that by their inflammatory harangues they instigated the riots which preceded the sailing of the schooner. At all events, it is certain that their unbounded influence with the natives would easily have enabled them to prevent everything that took place on this occasion, had they felt so inclined.

Melancholy as such an example of intolerance on the part of Protestant missionaries must appear, it is not the only one, and by no means the most flagrant, which might be presented. But I forbear to mention any others; since they have been more than hinted at by recent voyagers, and their repetition here would, perhaps, be attended with no good effect. Besides, the conduct of the Sandwich Island missionaries, in particular, has latterly much amended in this respect.

The treatment of the two priests formed the principal ground (and the only justifiable one) upon which Du Petit Thouars demanded satisfaction; and which subsequently led to his seizure of the island. In addition to other things, he also charged, that the flag of Merenhout, the consul, had been repeatedly insulted, and the property of a certain French resident violently appropriated by the government. In the latter instance, the natives were perfectly in the right. At that time, the law against the traffic in ardent spirits (every now and then suspended and revived) happened to be in force; and finding a large quantity on the premises of Victor, a low, knavish adventurer from Marseilles, the Tahitians pronounced it forfeit.

For these, and similar alleged outrages, a large pecuniary restitution was demanded ($10,000), which there being no exchequer to supply, the island was forthwith seized, under cover of a mock treaty, dictated to the chiefs on the gun-deck of Du Petit Thouars' frigate. But, notwithstanding this formality, there seems now little doubt that the downfall of the Pomarees was decided upon at the Tuilleries.

After establishing the Protectorate, so called, the rear-admiral sailed; leaving M. Bruat governor, assisted by Reine and Carpegne, civilians, named members of the council of government, and Merenhout, the consul, now made commissioner royal. No soldiers, however, were landed, until several months afterward. As men, Reine and Carpegne were not disliked by the natives; but Bruat and Merenhout they bitterly detested. In several interviews with the poor queen, the unfeeling governor sought to terrify her into compliance with his demands; clapping his hand upon his sword, shaking his fist in her face, and swearing violently. "Oh, king of a great nation," said Pomaree, in her letter to Louis Philippe, "fetch away this man; I and my people can not endure his evil doings. He is a shameless man."

Although the excitement among the natives did not wholly subside upon the rear-admiral's departure, no overt act of violence immediately followed. The queen had fled to Imeeo; and the dissensions among the chiefs, together with the ill-advised conduct of the missionaries, prevented a union upon some common plan of resistance. But the great body of the people, as well as their queen, confidently relied upon the speedy interposition of England—a nation bound to them by many ties, and which, more than once, had solemnly guaranteed their independence.

As for the missionaries, they openly defied the French governor, childishly predicting fleets and armies from Britain. But what is the welfare of a spot like Tahiti, to the mighty interests of France and England? There was a remonstrance on one side, and a reply on the other; and there the matter rested. For once in their brawling lives, St. George and St. Denis were hand and glove; and they were not going to cross sabers about Tahiti.

During my stay upon the island, so far as I could see, there was little to denote that any change had taken place in the government. Such laws as they had were administered the same as ever; the missionaries went about unmolested, and comparative tranquility everywhere prevailed. Nevertheless, I sometimes heard the natives inveighing against the French (no favorites, by the by, throughout Polynesia), and bitterly regretting that the queen had not, at the outset, made a stand.

In the house of the chief Adea, frequent discussions took place, concerning the ability of the island to cope with the French: the number of fighting men and muskets among the natives were talked of, as well as the propriety of fortifying several heights overlooking Papeetee. Imputing these symptoms to the mere resentment of a recent outrage, and not to any determined spirit of resistance, I little anticipated the gallant, though useless warfare, so soon to follow my departure.

At a period subsequent to my first visit, the island, which before was divided into nineteen districts, with a native chief over each, in capacity of governor and judge, was, by Bruat, divided into four. Over these he set as many recreant chiefs, Kitoti, Tati, Utamai, and Paraita; to whom he paid $1,000 each, to secure their assistance in carrying out his evil designs.

The first blood shed, in any regular conflict, was at Mahanar, upon the peninsula of Taraiboo. The fight originated in the seizure of a number of women from the shore, by men belonging to one of the French vessels of war. In this affair, the islanders fought desperately, killing about fifty of the enemy, and losing ninety of their own number. The French sailors and marines, who, at the time, were reported to be infuriated with liquor, gave no quarter; and the survivors only saved themselves by fleeing to the mountains. Subsequently, the battles of Hararparpi and Fararar were fought, in which the invaders met with indifferent success.

Shortly after the engagement at Hararparpi, three Frenchmen were waylaid in a pass of the valleys, and murdered by the incensed natives. One was Lefevre, a notorious scoundrel, and a spy, whom Bruat had sent to conduct a certain Major Fergus (said to be a Pole) to the hiding-place of four chiefs, whom the governor wished to seize and execute. This circumstance violently inflamed the hostility of both parties.

About this time, Kitoti, a depraved chief, and the pliant tool of Bruat, was induced by him to give a great feast in the Vale of Paree, to which all his countrymen were invited. The governor's object was to gain over all he could to his interests; he supplied an abundance of wine and brandy, and a scene of bestial intoxication was the natural consequence. Before it came to this, however, several speeches were made by the islanders. One of these, delivered by an ancient warrior, who had formerly been at the head of the celebrated Aeorai Society, was characteristic. "This is a very good feast," said the reeling old man, "and the wine also is very good; but you evil-minded Wee-Wees (French), and you false-hearted men of Tahiti, are all very bad."

By the latest accounts, most of the islanders still refuse to submit to the French; and what turn events may hereafter take it is hard to predict. At any rate, these disorders must accelerate the final extinction of their race.

Along with the few officers left by Du Petit Thouars, were several French priests, for whose unobstructed exertions in the dissemination of their faith, the strongest guarantees were provided by an article of the treaty. But no one was bound to offer them facilities, much less a luncheon, the first day they went ashore. True, they had plenty of gold; but to the natives it was anathema—taboo—and, for several hours and some odd minutes they would not touch it. Emissaries of the Pope and the devil, as the strangers were considered—the smell of sulfur hardly yet shaken out of their canonicals—what islander would venture to jeopardize his soul, and call down a blight upon his bread-fruit, by holding any intercourse with them? That morning the priests actually picknicked in a grove of cocoanut-trees; but, before night, Christian hospitality—in exchange for a commercial equivalent of hard dollars—was given them in an adjoining house.

Wanting in civility, as the conduct of the English missionaries may be thought, in withholding a decent reception to these persons, the latter were certainly to blame in needlessly placing themselves in so unpleasant a predicament. Under far better auspices, they might have settled upon some one of the thousand unconverted isles of the Pacific, rather than have forced themselves thus upon a people already professedly Christians.

Chapter XXXIII

We Receive Calls at the Hotel de Calabooza

Our place of confinement being open all round, and so near the Broom Road, of course we were in plain sight of everybody passing; and, therefore, we had no lack of visitors among such an idle, inquisitive set as the Tahitians. For a few days, they were coming and going continually; while thus ignobly fast by the foot, we were fain to give passive audience.

During this period, we were the lions of the neighborhood; and, no doubt, strangers from the distant villages were taken to see the "Karhowrees" (white men), in the same way that countrymen, in a city, are gallanted to the Zoological Gardens.

All this gave us a fine opportunity of making observations. I was painfully struck by the considerable number of sickly or deformed persons; undoubtedly made so by a virulent complaint, which, under native treatment, almost invariably affects, in the end, the muscles and bones of the body. In particular, there is a distortion of the back, most unsightly to behold, originating in a horrible form of the malady.

Although this, and other bodily afflictions, were unknown before the discovery of the islands by the whites, there are several cases found of the Fa-Fa, or elephantiasis—a native disease, which seems to have prevailed among them from the earliest antiquity. Affecting the legs and feet alone, it swells them, in some instances, to the girth of a man's body, covering the skin with scales. It might be supposed, that one thus afflicted would be incapable of walking; but, to all appearance, they seem to be nearly as active as anybody; apparently suffering no pain, and bearing the calamity with a degree of cheerfulness truly marvelous.

The Fa-Fa is very gradual in its approaches, and years elapse before the limb is fully swollen. Its origin is ascribed by the natives to various causes: but the general impression seems to be, that it arises in most cases from the eating of unripe bread-fruit and Indian turnip. So far as I could find out, it is not hereditary. In no stage do they attempt a cure; the complaint being held incurable.

Speaking of the Fa-Fa, reminds me of a poor fellow, a sailor, whom I afterward saw at Roorootoo, a lone island, some two days' sail from Tahiti.

The island is very small, and its inhabitants nearly extinct. We sent a boat off to see whether any yams were to be had, as formerly; the yams of Roorootoo were as famous among the islands roundabout as Sicily oranges in the Mediterranean. Going ashore, to my surprise, I was accosted, near a little shanty of a church, by a white man, who limped forth from a wretched hut. His hair and beard were unshorn, his face deadly pale and haggard, and one limb swelled with the Fa-Fa to an incredible bigness. This was the first instance of a foreigner suffering from it that I had ever seen or heard of; and the spectacle shocked me accordingly.

He had been there for years. From the first symptoms, he could not believe his complaint to be what it really was, and trusted it would soon disappear. But when it became plain that his only chance for recovery was a speedy change of climate, no ship would receive him as a sailor: to think of being taken as a passenger, was idle. This speaks little for the humanity of sea captains; but the truth is, that those in the Pacific have little enough of the virtue; and, nowadays, when so many charitable appeals are made to them, they have become callous.

I pitied the poor fellow from the bottom of my heart; but nothing could I do, as our captain was inexorable. "Why," said he, "here we are—started on a six months' cruise—I can't put back; and he is better off on the island than at sea. So on Roorootoo he must die." And probably he did.

I afterwards heard of this melancholy object, from two seamen. His attempts to leave were still unavailing, and his hard fate was fast closing in.

Notwithstanding the physical degeneracy of the Tahitians as a people, among the chiefs, individuals of personable figures are still frequently met with; and, occasionally, majestic-looking men, and diminutive women as lovely as the nymphs who, nearly a century ago, swam round the ships of Wallis. In these instances, Tahitian beauty is quite as seducing as it proved to the crew of the *Bounty*; the young girls being just such creatures as a poet would picture in the tropics—soft, plump, and dreamy-eyed.

The natural complexion of both sexes is quite light; but the males appear much darker, from their exposure to the sun. A dark complexion, however, in a man, is highly esteemed, as indicating strength of both body and soul. Hence there is a saying of great antiquity among them,

If dark the cheek of the mother,
The son will sound the war-conch;
If strong her frame, he will give laws.

With this idea of manliness, no wonder the Tahitians regard all pale and tepid-looking Europeans as weak and feminine; whereas a sailor, with a cheek like the breast of a roast turkey, is held a lad of brawn: to use their own phrase, a "taata tona," or man of bones.

Speaking of bones, recalls an ugly custom of theirs, now obsolete—that of making fish-hooks and gimlets out of those of their enemies. This beats the Scandinavians turning people's skulls into cups and saucers.

But to return to the Calabooza Beretanee. Immense was the interest we excited among the throngs that called there; they would stand talking about us by the hour, growing most unnecessarily excited too, and dancing up and down with all the vivacity of their race. They invariably sided with us; flying out against the consul, and denouncing him as "Ita maitai nuee," or very bad exceedingly. They must have borne him some grudge or other.

Nor were the women, sweet souls, at all backward in visiting. Indeed, they manifested even more interest than the men; gazing at us with eyes full of a thousand meanings, and conversing with marvelous rapidity. But, alas! inquisitive though they were, and, doubtless, taking some passing compassion on us, there was little real feeling in them after all, and still less sentimental sympathy. Many of them laughed outright at us, noting only what was ridiculous in our plight.

I think it was the second day of our confinement, that a wild, beautiful girl burst into the Calabooza, and throwing herself into an arch attitude, stood afar off, and gazed at us. She was a heartless one—tickled to death with Black Dan's nursing his chafed ankle, and indulging in certain moral reflections on the consul and Captain Guy. After laughing her fill at him, she condescended to notice the rest; glancing from one to another, in the most methodical and provoking manner imaginable. Whenever anything struck her comically, you saw it like a flash—her finger leveled instantaneously, and, flinging herself back, she gave loose to strange, hollow little notes of laughter, that sounded like the bass of a music-box, playing a lively air with the lid down.

Now, I knew not that there was anything in my own appearance calculated to disarm ridicule; and, indeed, to have looked at all heroic, under the circumstances, would have been rather difficult. Still, I could not but feel exceedingly annoyed at the prospect of being screamed at in turn, by this mischievous young witch, even though she were but an islander. And, to tell a secret, her beauty had something to do with this sort of feeling; and, pinioned as I was, to a log, and clad most unbecomingly, I began to grow sentimental.

Ere her glance fell upon me, I had, unconsciously, thrown myself into the most graceful attitude I could assume, leaned my head upon my hand, and summoned up as abstracted an expression as possible. Though my face was averted, I soon felt it flush, and knew that the glance was on me: deeper and deeper grew the flush, and not a sound of laughter.

Delicious thought! she was moved at the sight of me. I could stand it no longer, but started up. Lo! there she was; her great hazel eyes rounding and rounding in her head, like two stars, her whole frame in a merry quiver, and an expression about the mouth that was sudden and violent death to anything like sentiment.

The next moment she spun round, and, bursting from peal to peal of laughter, went racing out of the Calabooza; and, in mercy to me, never returned.

Chapter XXXIV

LIFE AT THE CALABOOZA

A FEW DAYS PASSED; AND, AT LAST, OUR DOCILITY WAS REWARDED BY SOME INDULGENCE ON THE part of Captain Bob.

He allowed the whole party to be at large during the day; only enjoining upon us always to keep within hail. This, to be sure, was in positive disobedience to Wilson's orders; and so, care had to be taken that he should not hear of it. There was little fear of the natives telling him; but strangers traveling the Broom Road might. By way of precaution, boys were stationed as scouts along the road. At sight of a white man, they sounded the alarm; when we all made for our respective holes (the stocks being purposely left open): the beam then descended, and we were prisoners. As soon as the traveler was out of sight, of course we were liberated.

Notwithstanding the regular supply of food which we obtained from Captain Bob and his friends, it was so small, that we often felt most intolerably hungry. We could not blame them for not bringing us more, for we soon became aware that they had to pinch themselves, in order to give us what they did; besides, they received nothing for their kindness but the daily bucket of bread.

Among a people like the Tahitians, what we call "hard times" can only be experienced in the scarcity of edibles; yet, so destitute are many of the common people, that this most distressing consequence of civilization may be said, with them, to be ever present. To be sure, the natives about the Calabooza, had abundance of limes and oranges; but what were these good for, except to impart a still keener edge to appetites which there was so little else to gratify? During the height of the bread-fruit season, they fare better; but, at other times, the demands of the shipping exhaust the uncultivated resources of the island; and the lands being mostly owned by the chiefs, the inferior orders have to suffer for their cupidity. Deprived of their nets, many of them would starve.

As Captain Bob insensibly remitted his watchfulness, and we began to stroll farther and farther from the Calabooza, we managed by a systematic foraging upon the country roundabout, to make up for some of our deficiencies. And fortunate it was, that the houses of the wealthier natives were just as open to us as those of the most destitute: we were treated as kindly in one as the other.

Once in a while we came in at the death of a chief's pig; the noise of whose slaughtering was generally to be heard at a great distance. An occasion like this gathers the neighbors together, and they have a bit of a feast, where a stranger is always welcome. A good loud squeal, therefore, was music in our ears. It showed something going on in that direction.

Breaking in upon the party tumultuously, as we did, we always created a sensation. Sometimes, we found the animal still alive and struggling; in which case, it was generally dropped at our approach. To provide for these emergencies, Flash Jack generally repaired to the scene of operations, with a sheath knife between his teeth, and a club in his hand. Others were exceedingly officious in singeing off the bristles, and disemboweling. Doctor Long Ghost and myself, however, never meddled with these preliminaries, but came to the feast itself, with unimpaired energies.

Like all lank men, my long friend had an appetite of his own. Others occasionally went about seeking what they might devour, but *he* was always on the alert.

He had an ingenious way of obviating an inconvenience which we all experienced at times. The islanders seldom use salt with their food; so he begged Rope Yarn to bring him some from the ship; also a little pepper, if he could; which, accordingly, was done. This he placed in a small leather wallet—a "monkey bag" (so called by sailors)—usually worn as a purse about the neck.

"In my opinion," said Long Ghost, as he tucked the wallet out of sight, "it behooves a stranger in Tahiti to have his knife in readiness, and his caster slung."

Chapter XXXV

VISIT FROM AN OLD ACQUAINTANCE

WE HAD NOT BEEN MANY DAYS ASHORE, WHEN DOCTOR JOHNSON WAS ESPIED COMING ALONG the Broom Road.

We had heard that he meditated a visit, and suspected what he was after. Being upon the consul's hands, all our expenses were of course payable by him in his official capacity; and, therefore, as a friend of Wilson, and sure of good pay, the shore doctor had some idea of allowing us to run up a bill with him. True, it was rather awkward to ask us to take medicines, which, on board the ship, he told us were not needed. However, he resolved to put a bold face on the matter, and give us a call.

His approach was announced by one of the scouts, upon which someone suggested that we should let him enter, and then put him in the stocks. But Long Ghost proposed better sport. What it was, we shall presently see.

Very bland and amiable, Doctor Johnson advanced, and, resting his cane on the stocks, glanced to right and left, as we lay before him. "Well, my lads," he began, "how do you find yourselves, to-day?"

Looking very demure, the men made some rejoinder; and he went on.

"Those poor fellows I saw the other day—the sick, I mean—how are they?" and he scrutinized the company. At last, he singled out one who was assuming a most unearthly appearance, and remarked, that he looked as if he were extremely ill. "Yes," said the sailor dolefully, "I'm afeared, doctor, I'll soon be losing the number of my mess!" (a sea phrase, for departing this life), and he closed his eyes, and moaned.

"*What* does he say?" said Johnson, turning round eagerly.

"Why," exclaimed Flash Jack, who volunteered as interpreter, "he means he's going to *croak*" (die).

"*Croak!* and what does that mean, applied to a patient?"

"Oh! I understand," said he, when the word was explained; and he stepped over the stocks, and felt the man's pulse.

"What's his name?" he asked, turning this time to old Navy Bob.

"We calls him Jingling Joe," replied that worthy.

"Well, then, men, you must take good care of poor Joseph; and I will send him a powder, which must be taken according to the directions. Some of you know how to read, I presume?"

"That 'ere young cove does," replied Bob, pointing toward the place where I lay, as if he were directing attention to a sail at sea.

After examining the rest—some of whom were really invalids, but convalescent, and others only pretending to be laboring under divers maladies, Johnson turned round, and addressed the party.

"Men," said he, "if any more of you are ailing, speak up and let me know. By order of the consul, I'm to call every day; so if any of you are at all sick, it's my duty to prescribe for you. This sudden change from ship fare to shore living, plays the deuce with you sailors; so be cautious about eating fruit. Good-day! I'll send you the medicines the first thing in the morning."

Now, I am inclined to suspect, that with all his want of understanding, Johnson must have had some idea that we were quizzing him. Still, that was nothing, so long as it answered his purpose; and therefore, if he *did* see through us, he never showed it.

Sure enough, at the time appointed, along came a native lad with a small basket of cocoanut stalks, filled with powders, pill-boxes, and vials, each with names and directions written in a large, round hand. The sailors, one and all, made a snatch at the collection, under the strange impression that some of the vials were seasoned with spirits. But, asserting his privilege as physician, to the first reading of the labels, Doctor Long Ghost was at last permitted to take possession of the basket.

The first thing lighted upon was a large vial, labeled—"For William—rub well in."

This vial certainly had a spirituous smell; and upon handing it to the patient, he made a summary internal application of its contents. The doctor looked aghast.

There was now a mighty commotion. Powders and pills were voted mere drugs in the market, and the holders of vials were pronounced lucky dogs. Johnson must have known enough of sailors to make some of his medicines palatable—this, at least, Long Ghost suspected. Certain it was, everyone took to the vials; if at all spicy, directions were unheeded, their contents all going one road.

The largest one of all, quite a bottle indeed, and having a sort of burnt brandy odor, was labeled—"For Daniel; drink freely, and until relieved." This Black Dan proceeded to do; and would have made an end of it at once, had not the bottle, after a hard struggle, been snatched from his hands, and passed round, like a jovial decanter. The old tar had complained of the effects of an immoderate eating of fruit.

Upon calling the following morning, our physician found his precious row of patients reclining behind the stocks, and doing "as well as could be expected."

But the pills and powders were found to have been perfectly inactive: probably because none had been taken. To make them efficacious, it was suggested that, for the future, a bottle of Pisco should be sent along with them. According to Flash Jack's notions, unmitigated medical compounds were but dry stuff at the best, and needed something good to wash them down.

Thus far, our own M.D., Doctor Long Ghost, after starting the frolic, had taken no further part in it; but on the physician's third visit, he took him to one side, and had a private confabulation. What it was, exactly, we could not tell; but from certain illustrative signs and gestures, I fancied that he was describing the symptoms of some mysterious disorganization of the vitals, which must have come on within the hour. Assisted by his familiarity with medical terms, he seemed to produce a marked impression. At last, Johnson went his way, promising aloud that he would send Long Ghost what he desired.

When the medicine boy came along the following morning, the doctor was the first to accost him, walking off with a small purple vial. This time, there was little else in the basket but a case bottle of the burnt brandy cordial, which, after much debate, was finally disposed of by someone pouring the contents, little by little, into the half of a cocoanut shell, and so giving all who desired, a glass. No further medicinal cheer remaining, the men dispersed.

An hour or two passed, when Flash Jack directed attention to my long friend, who, since the medicine boy left, had not been noticed till now. With eyes closed, he was lying behind the stocks, and Jack was lifting his arm and letting it fall as if life were extinct. On running up with the rest, I at once connected the phenomenon with the mysterious vial. Searching his pocket, I found it, and holding it up, it proved to be laudanum. Flash Jack, snatching it from my hand in a rapture, quickly informed all present what it was; and with much glee, proposed a nap for the company. Some of them not comprehending him exactly, the apparently defunct Long Ghost—who lay so still that I a little suspected the genuineness of his sleep—was rolled about as an illustration of the virtues of the vial's contents. The idea tickled everybody mightily; and throwing themselves down, the magic draft was passed from hand to hand. Thinking that, as a matter of course, they must at once become insensible, each man, upon taking his sip, fell back, and closed his eyes.

There was little fear of the result, since the narcotic was equally distributed. But, curious to see how it would operate, I raised myself gently after a while, and looked around. It was about noon, and perfectly still; and as we all daily took the siesta, I was not much surprised to find everyone quiet. Still, in one or two instances, I thought I detected a little peeping.

Presently, I heard a footstep, and saw Doctor Johnson approaching.

And perplexed enough did he look at the sight of his prostrate file of patients, plunged apparently in such unaccountable slumbers.

"Daniel," he cried, at last, punching in the side with his cane, the individual thus designated—"Daniel, my good fellow, get up! do you hear?"

But Black Dan was immovable; and he poked the next sleeper.

"Joseph, Joseph! come, wake up! it's me, Doctor Johnson."

But Jingling Joe, with mouth open, and eyes shut, was not to be started.

"Bless my soul!" he exclaimed, with uplifted hands and cane, "what's got into 'em? I say, *men*"—he shouted, running up and down—"come to life, men! what under the sun's the matter with you?" and he struck the stocks, and bawled with increased vigor.

At last he paused, folded his hands over the head of his cane, and steadfastly gazed upon us. The notes of the nasal orchestra were rising and falling upon his ear, and a new idea suggested itself.

"Yes, yes; the rascals must have been getting boozy. Well, it's none of my business—I'll be off"; and off he went.

No sooner was he out of sight, than nearly all started to their feet, and a hearty laugh ensued.

Like myself, most of them had been watching the event from under a sly eyelid. By this time, too, Doctor Long Ghost was as wide awake as anybody. What were his reasons for taking laudanum—if, indeed, he took any whatever—is best known to himself; and, as it is neither mine nor the reader's business, we will say no more about it.

Chapter XXXVI

We are Carried Before the Consul and Captain

We had been inmates of the Calabooza Beretanee about two weeks, when, one morning, Captain Bob, coming from the bath, in a state of utter nudity, brought into the building an armful of old tappa, and began to dress to go out.

The operation was quite simple. The tappa—of the coarsest kind—was in one long, heavy piece; and, fastening one end to a column of hibiscus wood, supporting the Calabooza, he went off a few paces, and putting the other about his waist, wound himself right up to the post. This unique costume, in rotundity something like a farthingale, added immensely to his large bulk; so much so, that he fairly waddled in his gait. But he was only adhering to the fashion of his fathers; for, in the olden time, the kipee, or big girdle, was quite the mode for both sexes. Bob, despising recent innovations, still clung to it. He was a gentleman of the old school—one of the last of the Kihees.

He now told us, that he had orders to take us before the consul. Nothing loth, we formed in procession; and, with the old man at our head, sighing and laboring like an engine, and flanked by a guard of some twenty natives, we started for the village.

Arrived at the consular office, we found Wilson there, and four or five Europeans, seated in a row facing us; probably with the view of presenting as judicial an appearance as possible.

On one side was a couch, where Captain Guy reclined. He looked convalescent; and, as we found out, intended soon to go aboard his ship. He said nothing, but left everything to the consul.

The latter now rose, and drawing forth a paper from a large roll, tied with red tape, commenced reading aloud.

It purported to be, "the affidavit of John Jermin, first officer of the British Colonial barque, *Julia*; Guy, Master"; and proved to be a long statement of matters, from the time of leaving Sydney, down to our arrival in the harbor. Though artfully drawn up, so as to bear hard against every one of us, it was pretty correct in the details; excepting, that it was wholly silent as to the manifold derelictions of the mate himself—a fact which imparted unusual significance to the concluding sentence, "And furthermore, this deponent sayeth not."

No comments were made, although we all looked round for the mate, to see whether it was possible that he could have authorized this use of his name. But he was not present.

The next document produced was the deposition of the captain himself. As on all other occasions, however, he had very little to say for himself, and it was soon set aside.

The third affidavit was that of the seamen remaining aboard the vessel, including the traitor Bungs, who, it seemed, had turned ship's evidence. It was an atrocious piece of exaggeration, from beginning to end; and those who signed it could not have known what they were about. Certainly Wymontoo did not, though his mark was there. In vain the consul commanded silence during the reading of this paper; comments were shouted out upon every paragraph.

The affidavits read, Wilson, who, all the while, looked as stiff as a poker, solemnly drew forth the ship's articles from their tin case. This document was a discolored, musty, bilious-looking affair, and hard to read. When finished, the consul held it up; and, pointing to the marks of the ship's company, at the bottom, asked us, one by one, whether we acknowledged the same for our own.

"What's the use of asking that?" said Black Dan. "Captain Guy there knows as well as we they are."

"Silence, sir!" said Wilson, who, intending to produce a suitable impression by this ridiculous parade, was not a little mortified by the old sailor's bluntness.

A pause of a few moments now ensued; during which the bench of judges communed with Captain Guy, in a low tone, and the sailors canvassed the motives of the consul in having the affidavits taken.

The general idea seemed to be, that it was done with a view of "bouncing," or frightening us into submission. Such proved to be the case; for Wilson, rising to his feet again, addressed us as follows:

"You see, men, that every preparation has been made to send you to Sydney for trial. The *Rosa* (a small Australian schooner, lying in the harbor) will sail for that place in the course of ten days, at farthest. The *Julia* sails on a cruise this day week. Do you still refuse duty?"

We did.

Hereupon the consul and captain exchanged glances; and the latter looked bitterly disappointed.

Presently I noticed Guy's eye upon me; and, for the first time, he spoke, and told me to come near. I stepped forward.

"Was it not you that was taken off the island?"

"It was."

"It is *you*, then, who owe your life to my humanity. Yet this is the gratitude of a sailor, Mr. Wilson!"

"Not so, sir." And I at once gave him to understand, that I was perfectly acquainted with his motives in sending a boat into the bay; his crew was reduced, and he merely wished to procure the sailor whom he expected to find there. The *ship* was the means of my deliverance, and no thanks to the benevolence of its captain.

Doctor Long Ghost, also, had a word to say. In two masterly sentences he summed up Captain Guy's character, to the complete satisfaction of every seaman present.

Matters were now growing serious; especially as the sailors became riotous, and talked about taking the consul and the captain back to the Calabooza with them.

The other judges fidgeted, and loudly commanded silence. It was at length restored; when Wilson, for the last time addressing us, said something more about the *Rosa* and Sydney, and concluded by reminding us, that a week would elapse ere the *Julia* sailed.

Leaving these hints to operate for themselves, he dismissed the party, ordering Captain Bob and his friends to escort us back whence we came.

Chapter XXXVII

The French Priests Pay Their Respects

A day or two after the events just related, we were lounging in the Calabooza Beretanee, when we were honored by a visit from three of the French priests; and as about the only notice ever taken of us by the English missionaries was their leaving their cards for us in the shape of a package of tracts, we could not help thinking, that the Frenchmen, in making a personal call, were at least much better bred.

By this time they had settled themselves down quite near our habitation. A pleasant little stroll down the Broom Road, and a rustic cross peeped through the trees; and soon you came to as charming a place as one would wish to see: a soft knoll, planted with old bread-fruit-trees; in front, a savannah, sloping to a grove of palms, and, between these, glimpses of blue sunny waves.

On the summit of the knoll was a rude chapel of bamboos; quite small, and surmounted by the cross. Between the canes, at nightfall, the natives stole peeps at a small portable altar; a crucifix to correspond, and gilded candlesticks and censers. Their curiosity carried them no further; nothing could induce them to worship there. Such queer ideas as they entertained of the hated strangers! Masses and chants were nothing more than evil spells. As for the priests themselves, they were no better than diabolical sorcerers; like those who, in old times, terrified their fathers.

Close by the chapel, was a range of native houses, rented from a chief, and handsomely furnished. Here lived the priests, and very comfortably too. They looked sanctimonious enough abroad, but that went for nothing: since at home, in their retreat, they were a club of Friar Tucks; holding priestly wassail over many a good cup of red brandy, and rising late in the morning.

Pity it was they couldn't marry—pity for the ladies of the island, I mean, and the cause of morality; for what business had the ecclesiastical old bachelors with such a set of trim little native handmaidens? These damsels were their first converts; and devoted ones they were.

The priests, as I have said before, were accounted necromancers: the appearance of two of our three visitors might have justified the conceit.

They were little, dried-up Frenchmen, in long, straight gowns of black cloth, and unsightly three-cornered hats, so preposterously big, that, in putting them on, the reverend fathers seemed to extinguish themselves.

Their companion was dressed differently. He wore a sort of yellow flannel morning-gown, and a broad-brimmed Manilla hat. Large and portly, he was also hale and fifty; with a complexion like an autumnal leaf, handsome blue eyes, fine teeth, and a racy Milesian brogue. In short, he was an Irishman; Father Murphy by name; and, as such, pretty well known, and very thoroughly disliked, throughout all the Protestant missionary settlements in Polynesia. In early youth, he had been sent to a religious seminary in France; and, taking orders there, had but once or twice afterwards revisited his native land.

Father Murphy marched up to us briskly; and the first words he uttered were, to ask whether there were any of his countrymen among us. There were two of them; one, a lad of sixteen—a bright, curly-headed rascal—and, being a young Irishman, of course his name was Pat. The other was an ugly and rather melancholy-looking scamp; one M'Gee, whose prospects in life had been blasted by a premature transportation to Sydney. This was the report, at least, though it might have been scandal.

In most of my shipmates were some redeeming qualities; but about M'Gee there was nothing of the kind; and, forced to consort with him, I could not help regretting, a thousand times, that the gallows had been so tardy. As if impelled, against her will, to send him into the world, Nature had done all she could to insure his being taken for what he was. About the eyes there was no mistaking him; with a villainous cast in one, they seemed suspicious of each other.

Glancing away from him at once, the bluff priest rested his gaze on the good-humored face of Pat, who, with a pleasant roguishness, was "twigging" the enormous hats (or "Hytee Belteezers," as land beavers are called by sailors), from under which, like a couple of snails, peeped the two little Frenchmen.

Pat and the priest were both from the same town in Meath; and, when this was found out, there was no end to the questions of the latter. To him, Pat seemed a letter from home, and said a hundred times as much.

After a long talk between these two, and a little broken English from the Frenchmen, our visitors took leave; but Father Murphy had hardly gone a dozen rods, when back he came, inquiring whether we were in want of anything.

"Yes," cried one, "something to eat." Upon this, he promised to send us some fresh wheat bread, of his own baking; a great luxury in Tahiti.

We all felicitated Pat upon picking up such a friend, and told him his fortune was made.

The next morning, a French servant of the priest's made his appearance, with a small bundle of clothing for our young Hibernian; and the promised bread for the party. Pat, being out at the knees and elbows, and, like the rest of us, not full inside, the present was acceptable all round.

In the afternoon, Father Murphy himself came along; and, in addition to his previous gifts, gave Pat a good deal of advice: said he was sorry to see him in limbo, and that he would have a talk with the consul about having him set free.

We saw nothing more of him for two or three days; at the end of which time he paid us another call, telling Pat, that Wilson was inexorable, having refused to set him at liberty, unless to go aboard the ship. This, the priest now besought him to do forthwith; and so escape the punishment which, it seems, Wilson had been hinting at to his intercessor. Pat, however, was staunch against entreaties; and, with all the ardor of a sophomorean sailor, protested his intention to hold out to the last. With none of the meekness of a good little boy about him, the blunt youngster stormed away at such a rate, that it was hard to pacify him; and the priest said no more.

How it came to pass—whether from Murphy's speaking to the consul, or otherwise—we could not tell, but the next day Pat was sent for by Wilson, and being escorted to the village by our good old keeper, three days elapsed before he returned.

Bent upon reclaiming him, they had taken him on board the ship; feasted him in the cabin; and, finding that of no avail, down they thrust him into the hold, in double irons, and on bread and water. All would not do; and so he was sent back to the Calabooza. Boy that he was, they must have counted upon his being more susceptible to discipline than the rest.

The interest felt in Pat's welfare, by his benevolent countryman, was very serviceable to the rest of us; especially as we all turned Catholics, and went to mass every morning, much to Captain Bob's consternation. Upon finding it out, he threatened to keep us in the stocks, if we did not desist. He went no farther than this, though; and so, every few days, we strolled down to the priest's residence, and had a mouthful to eat, and something generous to drink. In particular, Dr. Long

Ghost and myself became huge favorites with Pat's friend; and many a time he regaled us from a quaint-looking traveling-case for spirits, stowed away in one corner of his dwelling. It held four square flasks, which, somehow or other, always contained just enough to need emptying. In truth, the fine old Irishman was a rosy fellow in canonicals. His countenance and his soul were always in a glow. It may be ungenerous to reveal his failings, but he often talked thick, and sometimes was perceptibly eccentric in his gait.

I never drink French brandy, but I pledge Father Murphy. His health again! And many jolly proselytes may he make in Polynesia!

Chapter XXXVIII

LITTLE JULE SAILS WITHOUT US

TO MAKE GOOD THE HINT THROWN OUT BY THE CONSUL UPON THE CONCLUSION OF THE FARCE of the Affidavits, we were again brought before him within the time specified.

It was the same thing over again: he got nothing out of us, and we were remanded; our resolute behavior annoying him prodigiously.

What we observed, led us to form the idea, that on first learning the state of affairs on board the *Julia*, Wilson must have addressed his invalid friend, the captain, something in the following style:

"Guy, my poor fellow, don't worry yourself now about those rascally sailors of yours. I'll dress them out for you—just leave it all to me, and set your mind at rest."

But handcuffs and stocks, big looks, threats, dark hints, and depositions, had all gone for naught.

Conscious that, as matters now stood, nothing serious could grow out of what had happened; and never dreaming that our being sent home for trial had ever been really thought of, we thoroughly understood Wilson, and laughed at him accordingly.

Since leaving the *Julia*, we had caught no glimpse of the mate; but we often heard of him.

It seemed that he remained on board, keeping house in the cabin for himself and Viner; who, going to see him according to promise, was induced to remain a guest. These two cronies now had fine times; tapping the captain's quarter-casks, playing cards on the transom, and giving balls of an evening to the ladies ashore. In short, they cut up so many queer capers, that the missionaries complained of them to the consul; and Jermin received a sharp reprimand.

This so affected him, that he drank still more freely than before; and one afternoon, when mellow as a grape, he took umbrage at a canoe full of natives, who, on being hailed from the deck to come aboard and show their papers, got frightened, and paddled for the shore. Lowering a boat instantly, he equipped Wymontoo and the Dane with a cutlass apiece, and seizing another himself, off they started in pursuit, the ship's ensign flying in the boat's stern. The alarmed islanders, beaching their canoe, with loud cries fled through the village, the mate after them, slashing his naked weapon to right and left. A crowd soon collected; and the "Karhowree toonee," or crazy stranger, was quickly taken before Wilson.

Now, it so chanced, that in a native house hard by, the consul and Captain Guy were having a quiet game at cribbage by themselves, a decanter on the table standing sentry. The obstreperous Jermin was brought in; and finding the two thus pleasantly occupied, it had a soothing effect upon him; and he insisted upon taking a hand at the cards, and a drink of the brandy. As the consul was nearly as tipsy as himself, and the captain dared not object for fear of giving offence, at it they went—all three of them—and made a night of it; the mate's delinquencies being summarily passed over, and his captors sent away.

An incident worth relating grew out of this freak.

There wandered about Papeetee, at this time, a shriveled little fright of an English woman, known among sailors as "Old Mother Tot." From New Zealand to the Sandwich Islands, she had been all over the South Seas; keeping a rude hut of entertainment for mariners, and supplying them with rum and dice. Upon the missionary islands, of course, such conduct was severely punishable; and at various places, Mother Tot's establishment had been shut up, and its proprietor made to quit in the first vessel that could be hired to land her elsewhere. But, with a perseverance invincible, wherever she went, she always started afresh; and so became notorious everywhere.

By some wicked spell of hers, a patient, one-eyed little cobbler followed her about, mending shoes for white men, doing the old woman's cooking, and bearing all her abuse without grumbling. Strange to relate, a battered Bible was seldom out of his sight; and whenever he had leisure, and his mistress's back was turned, he was forever poring over it. This pious propensity used to enrage the old crone past belief; and oftentimes she boxed his ears with the book, and tried to burn it. Mother Tot and her man Josy were, indeed, a curious pair.

But to my story.

A week or so after our arrival in the harbor, the old lady had once again been hunted down, and forced for the time to abandon her nefarious calling. This was brought about chiefly by Wilson, who, for some reason unknown, had contracted the most violent hatred for her; which, on her part, was more than reciprocated.

Well, passing in the evening, where the consul and his party were making merry, she peeped through the bamboos of the house; and straightway resolved to gratify her spite.

The night was very dark, and providing herself with a huge ship's lantern, which usually swung in her hut, she waited till they came forth. This happened about midnight; Wilson making his appearance, supported by two natives, holding him up by the arms. These three went first; and just as they got under a deep shade, a bright light was thrust within an inch of Wilson's nose. The old hag was kneeling before him, holding the lantern with uplifted hands.

"Ha, ha! my fine *counselor,*" she shrieked; "ye persecute a lone old body like me for selling rum—do ye? And here ye are, carried home drunk—Hoot! ye villain, I scorn ye!" And she spat upon him.

Terrified at the apparition, the poor natives—arrant believers in ghosts—dropped the trembling consul, and fled in all directions. After giving full vent to her rage, Mother Tot hobbled away, and left the three revelers to stagger home the best way they could.

The day following our last interview with Wilson, we learned that Captain Guy had gone on board his vessel, for the purpose of shipping a new crew. There was a round bounty offered; and a heavy bag of Spanish dollars, with the *Julia*'s articles ready for signing, was laid on the capstan-head.

Now there was no lack of idle sailors ashore, mostly "Beach-combers," who had formed themselves into an organized gang, headed by one Mack, a Scotchman, whom they styled the Commodore. By the laws of the fraternity, no member was allowed to ship on board a vessel, unless granted permission by the rest. In this way the gang controlled the port, all discharged seamen being forced to join them.

To Mack and his men our story was well known; indeed, they had several times called to see us; and of course, as sailors and congenial spirits, they were hard against Captain Guy.

Deeming the matter important, they came in a body to the Calabooza, and wished to know whether, all things considered, we thought it best for any of them to join the *Julia*.

Anxious to pack the ship off as soon as possible, we answered, by all means. Some went so far as to laud the *Julia* to the skies, as the best and fastest of ships. Jermin, too, as a good fellow and a sailor every inch, came in for *his* share of praise; and as for the captain—quiet man, he would never trouble anyone. In short, every inducement we could think of was presented; and Flash Jack ended by assuring the beach-combers solemnly, that now we were all well and hearty, nothing but a regard to principle prevented us from returning on board ourselves.

The result was, that a new crew was finally obtained, together with a steady New Englander for second mate, and three good whalemen for harpooners. In part, what was wanting for the ship's larder was also supplied; and as far as could be done in a place like Tahiti, the damages the vessel had sustained were repaired. As for the Mowree, the authorities refusing to let him be put ashore, he was carried to sea in irons, down in the hold. What eventually became of him, we never heard.

Ropey, poor, poor Ropey, who a few days previous had fallen sick, was left ashore at the sailor hospital at Townor, a small place upon the beach between Papeetee and Matavai. Here, some time after, he breathed his last. No one knew his complaint: he must have died of hard times. Several of us saw him interred in the sand, and I planted a rude post to mark his resting-place.

The cooper and the rest who had remained aboard from the first, of course, composed part of the *Julia*'s new crew.

To account for the conduct, all along, of the consul and captain, in trying so hard to alter our purpose with respect to the ship, the following statement is all that is requisite. Beside an advance of from fifteen to twenty-five dollars demanded by every sailor shipping at Tahiti, an additional sum for each man so shipped has to be paid into the hands of the government, as a charge of the port. Beside this, the men—with here and there an exception—will only ship for one cruise, thus becoming entitled to a discharge before the vessel reaches home; which, in time, creates the necessity of obtaining other men at a similar cost. Now, the *Julia*'s exchequer was at low-water mark, or, rather, it was quite empty: and to meet these expenses, a good part of what little oil there was aboard had to be sold for a song to a merchant of Papeetee.

It was Sunday in Tahiti, and a glorious morning, when Captain Bob, waddling into the Calabooza, startled us by announcing, "Ah—my boy—shippy you, harree—maky sail!" In other words, the *Julia* was off.

The beach was quite near, and in this quarter altogether uninhabited; so down we ran, and, at cable's-length, saw *Little Jule* gliding past—top-gallant-sails hoisting, and a boy aloft with one leg thrown over the yard, loosing the fore-royal. The decks were all life and commotion; the sailors on the forecastle singing, "Ho, cheerly men!" as they catted the anchor; and the gallant Jermin, bareheaded as his wont, standing up on the bowsprit, and issuing his orders. By the man at the helm, stood Captain Guy, very quiet and gentlemanly, and smoking a cigar. Soon the ship drew near the reef, and altering her course, glided out through the break, and went on her way.

Thus disappeared *Little Jule*, about three weeks after entering the harbor; and nothing more have I ever heard of her.

Chapter XXXIX

Jermin Serves Us a Good Turn—Friendships in Polynesia

THE SHIP OUT OF THE WAY, WE WERE QUITE ANXIOUS TO KNOW WHAT WAS GOING TO BE DONE with us. On this head, Captain Bob could tell us nothing; no further, at least, than that he still considered himself responsible for our safe-keeping. However, he never put us to bed anymore; and we had everything our own way.

The day after the *Julia* left, the old man came up to us in great tribulation, saying that the bucket of bread was no longer forthcoming, and that Wilson had refused to send anything in its place. One and all, we took this for a hint to disperse quietly, and go about our business. Nevertheless, we were not to be shaken off so easily; and taking a malicious pleasure in annoying our old enemy, we resolved, for the present, to stay where we were. For the part he had been acting, we learned that the consul was the laughing-stock of all the foreigners ashore, who frequently twitted him upon his hopeful protégés of the Calabooza Beretanee.

As we were wholly without resources, so long as we remained on the island no better place than Captain Bob's could be selected for an abiding-place. Beside, we heartily loved the old gentleman, and could not think of leaving him; so, telling him to be quite at ease on the score of our clothing and food, we resolved, by extending and systematizing our foraging operations, to provide for ourselves.

We were greatly assisted by a parting legacy of Jermin's. To him we were indebted for having all our chests sent ashore, and everything left therein. They were placed in the custody of a petty chief living nearby, who was instructed by the consul not to allow them to be taken away; but we might call and make our toilettes whenever we pleased.

We went to see Mahinee, the old chief; Captain Bob going along, and stoutly insisting upon having the chattels delivered up. At last this was done; and in solemn procession the chests were borne by the natives to the Calabooza. Here, we disposed them about quite tastefully, and made such a figure, that in the eyes of old Bob and his friends, the Calabooza Beretanee was by far the most sumptuously furnished saloon in Tahiti.

Indeed, so long as it remained thus furnished, the native courts of the district were held there; the judge, Mahinee, and his associates, sitting upon one of the chests, and the culprits and spectators thrown at full length upon the ground, both inside of the building, and under the shade of the trees without; while leaning over the stocks as from a gallery, the worshipful crew of the *Julia* looked on, and canvassed the proceedings.

I should have mentioned before, that previous to the vessel's departure the men had bartered away all the clothing they could possibly spare; but now, it was resolved to be more provident.

The contents of the chests were of the most miscellaneous description: sewing-utensils, marling-spikes, strips of calico, bits of rope, jack-knives; nearly everything, in short, that a seaman could think of. But of wearing apparel, there was little but old frocks, remnants of jackets, and legs of trousers, with now and then the foot of a stocking. These, however, were far from being valueless; for, among the poorer Tahitians, everything European is highly esteemed. They come from "Beretanee, Fenooa Pararee" (Britain, Land of Wonders), and that is enough.

The chests themselves were deemed exceedingly precious, especially those with unfractured looks, which would absolutely click, and enable the owner to walk off with the key. Scars, however, and bruises, were considered great blemishes. One old fellow, smitten with the doctor's large mahogany chest (a well filled one, by the by), and finding infinite satisfaction in merely sitting thereon, was detected in the act of applying a healing ointment to a shocking scratch which impaired the beauty of the lid.

There is no telling the love of a Tahitian for a sailor's trunk. So ornamental is it held as an article of furniture in the hut, that the women are incessantly tormenting their husbands to bestir themselves and make them a present of one. When obtained, no pier-table just placed in a drawing-room is regarded with half the delight. For these reasons, then, our coming into possession of our estate at this time, was an important event.

The islanders are much like the rest of the world; and the news of our good fortune brought us troops of "tayos" or friends, eager to form an alliance after the national custom, and do our slightest bidding.

The really curious way in which all the Polynesians are in the habit of making bosom friends at the shortest possible notice, is deserving of remark. Although, among a people like the Tahitians, vitiated as they are by sophisticating influences, this custom has in most cases degenerated into a mere mercenary relation, it nevertheless had its origin in a fine, and in some instances, heroic sentiment, formerly entertained by their fathers.

In the annals of the island are examples of extravagant friendships, unsurpassed by the story of Damon and Pythias: in truth, much more wonderful; for, notwithstanding the devotion—even of life in some cases—to which they led, they were frequently entertained at first sight for some stranger from another island.

Filled with love and admiration for the first whites that came among them, the Polynesians could not testify the warmth of their emotions more strongly, than by instantaneously making their abrupt proffer of friendship. Hence, in old voyages we read of chiefs coming off from the shore in their canoes, and going through with strange antics, expressive of this desire. In the same way, their inferiors accosted the seamen; and thus the practice has continued in some islands down to the present day.

There is a small place, not many days' sail from Tahiti, and seldom visited by shipping, where the vessel touched to which I then happened to belong.

Of course, among the simple-hearted natives, we had a friend all round. Mine was Poky, a handsome youth, who never could do enough for me. Every morning at sunrise, his canoe came alongside loaded with fruits of all kinds; upon being emptied, it was secured by a line to the bowsprit, under which it lay all day long, ready at any time to carry its owner ashore on an errand.

Seeing him so indefatigable, I told Poky one day, that I was a virtuoso in shells and curiosities of all kinds. That was enough; away he paddled for the head of the bay, and I never saw him again for twenty-four hours. The next morning, his canoe came gliding slowly along the shore, with the full-leaved bough of a tree for a sail. For the purpose of keeping the things dry, he had also built a sort of platform just behind the prow, railed in with green wicker-work; and here was a heap of yellow bananas and cowree shells; young cocoanuts and antlers of red coral; two or three pieces of carved wood; a little pocket-idol, black as jet, and rolls of printed tappa.

We were given a holiday; and upon going ashore, Poky, of course, was my companion and guide. For this, no mortal could be better qualified; his native country was not large, and he knew every inch of it. Gallanting me about, everyone was stopped and ceremoniously introduced to Poty's "tayo karhowree nuee," or his particular white friend.

He showed me all the lions, but more than all he took me to see a charming lioness—a young damsel—the daughter of a chief—the reputation of whose charms had spread to the neighboring islands, and even brought suitors therefrom. Among these was Tooboi, the heir of Tamatoy, King of Raiatea, one of the Society Isles. The girl was certainly fair to look upon. Many heavens were in her sunny eyes, and the outline of that arm of hers, peeping forth from a capricious tappa robe, was the very curve of beauty.

Though there was no end to Poky's attentions, not a syllable did he ever breathe of reward; but sometimes he looked very knowing. At last the day came for sailing, and with it, also, his canoe, loaded down to the gunwale with a sea stock of fruits. Giving him all I could spare from my chest, I went on deck to take my place at the windlass, for the anchor was weighing. Poky followed, and heaved with me at the same handspike.

The anchor was soon up, and away we went out of the bay with more than twenty shallops towing astern. At last they left us; but long as I could see him at all, there was Poky standing alone and motionless in the bow of his canoe.

Chapter XL

We Take unto Ourselves Friends

THE ARRIVAL OF THE CHESTS MADE MY FRIEND, THE DOCTOR, BY FAR THE WEALTHIEST MAN OF the party. So much the better for me, seeing that I had little or nothing myself, though from our intimacy, the natives courted my favor almost as much as his.

Among others, Kooloo was a candidate for my friendship; and being a comely youth, quite a buck in his way, I accepted his overtures. By this, I escaped the importunities of the rest; for be it known, that, though little inclined to jealousy in love matters, the Tahitian will hear of no rivals in his friendship.

Kooloo, running over his qualifications as a friend, first of all informed me that he was a "Mickonaree," thus declaring his communion with the church.

The way this "tayo" of mine expressed his regard was by assuring me over and over again that the love he bore me was "nuee, nuee, nuee," or infinitesimally extensive. All over these seas the word "nuee" is significant of quantity. Its repetition is like placing ciphers at the right hand of a numeral; the more places you carry it out to, the greater the sum. Judge, then, of Kooloo's esteem. Nor is the allusion to the ciphers at all inappropriate, seeing that, in themselves, Kooloo's professions turned out to be worthless. He was, alas! as sounding brass and a tinkling cymbal; one of those who make no music unless the clapper be silver.

In the course of a few days, the sailors, like the doctor and myself, were cajoled out of everything, and our "tayos," all round, began to cool off quite sensibly. So remiss did they become in their attentions, that we could no longer rely upon their bringing us the daily supply of food, which all of them had faithfully promised.

As for Kooloo, after sponging me well, he one morning played the part of a retrograde lover, informing me that his affections had undergone a change; he had fallen in love at first sight with a smart sailor, who had just stepped ashore quite flush from a lucky whaling-cruise.

It was a touching interview, and with it our connection dissolved. But the sadness which ensued would soon have been dissipated, had not my sensibilities been wounded by his indelicately sporting some of my gifts very soon after this transfer of his affections. Hardly a day passed, that I did not meet him on the Broom Road, airing himself in a Regatta shirt, which I had given him in happier hours.

He went by with such an easy saunter too, looking me pleasantly in the eye, and merely exchanging the cold salute of the road: "Yar onor, boyoee," a mere side-walk how d'ye do. After several experiences like this, I began to entertain a sort of respect for Kooloo, as quite a man of the world. In good sooth, he turned out to be one; in one week's time giving me the cut direct, and lounging by without even nodding. He must have taken me for part of the landscape.

Before the chests were quite empty, we had a grand washing in the stream of our best raiment, for the purpose of looking tidy, and visiting the European chapel in the village. Every Sunday morning it is open for divine service, some member of the mission officiating. This was the first time we ever entered Papeetee unattended by an escort.

In the chapel there were about forty people present, including the officers of several ships in harbor. It was an energetic discourse, and the pulpit-cushion was well pounded. Occupying a high seat in the synagogue, and stiff as a flag-staff, was our beloved guardian, Wilson. I shall never forget his look of wonder when his interesting wards filed in at the doorway, and took up a seat directly facing him.

Service over, we waited outside in hopes of seeing more of him; but, sorely annoyed at the sight of us, he reconnoitred from the window, and never came forth until we had started for home.

Chapter XLI

We Levy Contributions on the Shipping

Scarcely a week went by after the *Julia*'s sailing, when, with the proverbial restlessness of sailors, some of the men began to grow weary of the Calabooza Beretanee, and resolved to go boldly among the vessels in the bay, and offer to ship.

The thing was tried; but though strongly recommended by the commodore of the beachcombers, in the end they were invariably told by the captains to whom they applied, that they bore an equivocal character ashore, and would not answer. So often were they repulsed, that we pretty nearly gave up all thoughts of leaving the island in this way; and growing domestic again, settled down quietly at Captain Bob's.

It was about this time that the whaling ships, which have their regular seasons for cruising, began to arrive at Papeetee; and of course their crews frequently visited us. This is customary all over the Pacific. No sailor steps ashore, but he straightway goes to the "Calabooza," where he is almost sure to find some poor fellow or other in confinement for desertion, or alleged mutiny, or something of that sort. Sympathy is proffered, and, if need be, tobacco. The latter, however, is most in request; as a solace to the captive, it is invaluable.

Having fairly carried the day against both consul and captain, we were objects of even more than ordinary interest to these philanthropists; and they always cordially applauded our conduct. Besides, they invariably brought along something in the way of refreshments; occasionally smuggling in a little Pisco. Upon one occasion, when there was quite a number present, a calabash was passed round, and a pecuniary collection taken up for our benefit.

One day a newcomer proposed, that two or three of us should pay him a sly nocturnal visit aboard his ship; engaging to send us away well freighted with provisions. This was not a bad idea; nor were we at all backward in acting upon it. Night after night every vessel in the harbor was visited in rotation, the foragers borrowing Captain Bob's canoe for the purpose. As we all took turns at this, two by two, in due course it came to Long Ghost and myself, for the sailors invariably linked us together. In such an enterprise, I somewhat distrusted the doctor, for he was no sailor, and very tall; and a canoe is the most ticklish of navigable things. However, it could not be helped; and so we went.

But a word about the canoes, before we go any further. Among the Society Islands, the art of building them, like all native accomplishments, has greatly deteriorated; and they are now the most inelegant, as well as the most insecure, of any in the South Seas. In Cook's time, according to his account, there was at Tahiti a royal fleet of seventeen hundred and twenty large war-canoes, handsomely carved, and otherwise adorned. At present, those used are quite small; nothing more than logs hollowed out, sharpened at one end, and then launched into the water.

To obviate a certain rolling propensity, the Tahitians, like all Polynesians, attach to them what sailors call an "outrigger." It consists of a pole floating alongside, parallel to the canoe, and connected with it by a couple of cross sticks, a yard or more in length. Thus equipped, the canoe cannot be overturned, unless you overcome the buoyancy of the pole, or lift it entirely out of the water.

Now, Captain Bob's "gig" was exceedingly small; so small, and of such a grotesque shape, that the sailors christened it the Pill-Box; and by this appellation it always went. In fact, it was a sort of "sulky," meant for a solitary paddler, but, on an emergency, capable of floating two or three. The outrigger was a mere switch, alternately rising in air, and then depressed in the water.

Assuming the command of the expedition, upon the strength of my being a sailor, I packed the Long Doctor with a paddle in the bow, and then shoving off, leaped into the stern; thus leaving him to do all the work, and reserving to myself the dignified sinecure of steering. All would have gone on well, were it not that my paddler made such clumsy work, that the water spattered, and showered down upon us without ceasing. Continuing to ply his tool, however, quite energetically, I thought he would improve after a while, and so let him alone. But by and by, getting wet through with this little storm we were raising, and seeing no signs of its clearing off, I conjured him, in Mercy's name to stop short, and let me wring myself out. Upon this, he suddenly turned round, when the canoe gave a roll, the outrigger flew overhead, and the next moment came rap on the doctor's skull, and we were both in the water.

Fortunately, we were just over a ledge of coral, not half a fathom under the surface. Depressing one end of the filled canoe, and letting go of it quickly, it bounced up, and discharged a great part of its contents; so that we easily bailed out the remainder, and again embarked. This time, my comrade coiled himself away in a very small space; and enjoining upon him not to draw a single unnecessary breath, I proceeded to urge the canoe along by myself. I was astonished at his docility, never speaking a word, and stirring neither hand nor foot; but the secret was, he was unable to swim, and in case we met with a second mishap, there were no more ledges beneath to stand upon. "Drowning's but a shabby way of going out of the world," he exclaimed, upon my rallying him; "and I'm not going to be guilty of it."

At last, the ship was at hand, and we approached with much caution, wishing to avoid being hailed by anyone from the quarter-deck. Dropping silently under her bows, we heard a low whistle—the signal agreed upon—and presently a goodly sized bag was lowered over to us.

We cut the line, and then paddled away as fast as we could, and made the best of our way home. Here we found the rest waiting impatiently.

The bag turned out to be well filled with sweet potatoes boiled, cubes of salt beef and pork, and a famous sailors' pudding, what they call "duff," made of flour and water, and of about the consistence of an underdone brick. With these delicacies, and keen appetites, we went out into the moonlight, and had a nocturnal picnic.

Chapter XLII

MOTOO-OTOO—A TAHITIAN CASUIST

THE PILL-BOX WAS SOMETIMES EMPLOYED FOR OTHER PURPOSES THAN THAT DESCRIBED IN THE last chapter. We sometimes went a-pleasuring in it.

Right in the middle of Papeetee harbor is a bright green island, one circular grove of waving palms, and scarcely a hundred yards across. It is of coral formation; and all round, for many rods out, the bay is so shallow, that you might wade anywhere. Down in these waters, as transparent as air, you see coral plants of every hue and shape imaginable—antlers, tufts of azure, waving reeds like stalks of grain, and pale green buds and mosses. In some places, you look through prickly branches down to a snow-white floor of sand, sprouting with flinty bulbs; and crawling among these are strange shapes—some bristling with spikes, others clad in shining coats of mail, and here and there round forms all spangled with eyes.

The island is called Motoo-Otoo; and around Motoo-Otoo have I often paddled of a white moonlight night, pausing now and then to admire the marine gardens beneath.

The place is the private property of the queen, who has a residence there—a melancholy-looking range of bamboo houses—neglected and falling to decay among the trees.

Commanding the harbor as it does, her majesty has done all she could to make a fortress of the island. The margin has been raised and leveled, and built up with a low parapet of hewn blocks of coral. Behind the parapet, are ranged at wide intervals a number of rusty old cannon, of all fashions and calibers. They are mounted upon lame, decrepit-looking carriages, ready to sink under the useless burden of bearing them up. Indeed, two or three have given up the ghost altogether, and the pieces they sustained lie half-buried among their bleaching bones. Several of the cannon are spiked; probably with a view of making them more formidable; as they certainly must be to anyone undertaking to fire them off.

Presented to Pomaree at various times by captains of British armed ships, these poor old "dogs of war," thus toothless and turned out to die, formerly bayed in full pack, as the battle hounds of Old England.

There was something about Motoo-Otoo that struck my fancy; and I registered a vow to plant my foot upon its soil, notwithstanding an old bareheaded sentry menaced me in the moonlight with an unsightly musket. As my canoe drew scarcely three inches of water, I could paddle close up to the parapet without grounding; but every time I came near, the old man ran towards me, pushing his piece forward, but never clapping it to his shoulder. Thinking he only meant to frighten me, I at last dashed the canoe right up to the wall, purposing a leap. It was the rashest act of my life; for never did cocoanut come nearer getting demolished than mine did then. With the stock of his gun, the old warder fetched a tremendous blow, which I managed to dodge; and then, falling back, succeeded in paddling out of harm's reach.

He must have been dumb; for never a word did he utter; but, grinning from ear to ear, and with his white cotton robe streaming in the moonlight, he looked more like the spook of the island than anything mortal.

I tried to effect my object by attacking him in the rear—but he was all front; running about the place as I paddled, and presenting his confounded musket wherever I went. At last I was obliged to retreat; and to this day my vow remains unfulfilled.

It was a few days after my repulse from before the walls of Motoo-Otoo, that I heard a curious case of casuistry argued between one of the most clever and intelligent natives I ever saw in Tahiti, a man by the name of Arheetoo, and our learned Theban of a doctor.

It was this—whether it was right and lawful for anyone being a native to keep the European Sabbath, in preference to the day set apart as such by the missionaries, and so considered by the islanders in general.

It must be known that the missionaries of the good ship *Duff*, who more than half a century ago established the Tahitian reckoning, came hither by the way of the Cape of Good Hope; and, by thus sailing to the eastward, lost one precious day of their lives all round, getting about that much in advance of Greenwich time. For this reason, vessels coming round Cape Horn—as they most all do nowadays—find it Sunday in Tahiti, when, according to their own view of the matter, it ought to be Saturday. But as it won't do to alter the log, the sailors keep their Sabbath, and the islanders theirs.

This confusion perplexes the poor natives mightily; and it is to no purpose that you endeavor to explain so incomprehensible a phenomenon. I once saw a worthy old missionary essay to shed some light on the subject; and though I understood but few of the words employed, I could easily get at the meaning of his illustrations. They were something like the following:

"Here," says he, "you see this circle" (describing a large one on the ground with a stick): "very good; now you see this spot here" (marking a point in the perimeter): "well; this is Beretanee" (England), "and I'm going to sail round to Tahiti. Here I go, then" (following the circle round), "and there goes the sun" (snatching up another stick, and commissioning a bandy-legged native to travel round with it in a contrary direction). "Now then, we are both off, and both going away from each other; and here you see I have arrived at Tahiti" (making a sudden stop); "and look now, where Bandy Legs is!"

But the crowd strenuously maintained, that Bandy Legs ought to be somewhere above them in the atmosphere; for it was a traditionary fact, that the people from the *Duff* came ashore when the sun was high overhead. And here the old gentleman, being a very good sort of man, doubtless, but no astronomer, was obliged to give up.

Arheetoo, the casuist alluded to, though a member of the church, and extremely conscientious about what Sabbath he kept, was more liberal in other matters. Learning that I was something of a "mickonaree" (in this sense, a man able to read, and cunning in the use of the pen), he desired the slight favor of my forging for him a set of papers; for which, he said, he would be much obliged, and give me a good dinner of roast pig and Indian turnip in the bargain.

Now, Arheetoo was one of those who board the shipping for their washing; and the competition being very great (the proudest chiefs not disdaining to solicit custom in person, though the work is done by their dependants), he had decided upon a course suggested by a knowing sailor, a friend of his. He wished to have manufactured a set of certificates, purporting to come from certain man-of-war and merchant captains, known to have visited the island; recommending him as one of the best getters up of fine linen in all Polynesia.

At this time, Arheetoo had known me but two hours; and, as he made the proposition very coolly, I thought it rather presumptuous, and told him so. But as it was quite impossible to convey a hint, that there was a slight impropriety in the thing, I did not resent the insult, but simply declined.

Chapter XLIII

One Is Judged by the Company He Keeps

Although, from its novelty, life at Captain Bob's was pleasant enough for the time, there were some few annoyances connected with it, anything but agreeable to a "soul of sensibility."

Prejudiced against us by the malevolent representations of the consul and others, many worthy foreigners ashore regarded us as a set of lawless vagabonds; though, truth to speak, better behaved sailors never stepped on the island, nor any who gave less trouble to the natives. But, for all this, whenever we met a respectably dressed European, ten to one he shunned us, by going over to the other side of the road. This was very unpleasant, at least to myself; though, certes, it did not prey upon the minds of the others.

To give an instance.

Of a fine evening in Tahiti—but they are all fine evenings there—you may see a bevy of silk bonnets and parasols passing along the Broom Road: perhaps a band of pale, little white urchins—sickly exotics—and, oftener still, sedate, elderly gentlemen, with canes; at whose appearance the natives, here and there, slink into their huts. These are the missionaries, their wives, and children, taking a family airing. Sometimes, by the by, they take horse, and ride down to Point Venus and back; a distance of several miles. At this place is settled the only survivor of the first missionaries that landed—an old, white-headed, saint-like man, by the name of Wilson, the father of our friend the consul.

The little parties on foot were frequently encountered; and, recalling, as they did, so many pleasant recollections of home and the ladies, I really longed for a dress-coat and beaver, that I might step up and pay my respects. But, situated as I was, this was out of the question. On one occasion, however, I received a kind inquisitive glance from a matron in gingham. Sweet lady! I have not forgotten her: her gown was a plaid.

But a glance, like hers, was not always bestowed.

One evening, passing the verandah of a missionary's dwelling, the dame, his wife, and a pretty blonde young girl, with ringlets, were sitting there, enjoying the sea-breeze, then coming in, all cool and refreshing, from the spray of the reef. As I approached, the old lady peered hard at me; and her very cap seemed to convey a prim rebuke. The blue, English eyes, by her side, were also bent on me. But, oh Heavens! what a glance to receive from such a beautiful creature! As for the mob cap, not a fig did I care for it; but, to be taken for anything but a cavalier, by the ringleted one, was absolutely unendurable.

I resolved on a courteous salute, to show my good breeding, if nothing more. But happening to wear a sort of turban—hereafter to be particularly alluded to—there was no taking it off and putting it on again with anything like dignity. At any rate, then, here goes a bow. But, another difficulty presented itself: my loose frock was so voluminous, that I doubted whether any spinal curvature would be perceptible.

"Good-evening, ladies," exclaimed I, at last, advancing winningly; "a delightful air from the sea, ladies."

Hysterics and hartshorn! who would have thought it? The young lady screamed, and the old one came near fainting. As for myself, I retreated, in double-quick time; and scarcely drew breath, until safely housed in the Calabooza.

Chapter XLIV

Cathedral of Papoar—The Church of the Cocoanuts

On Sundays I always attended the principal native church on the outskirts of the village of Papeetee, and not far from the Calabooza Beretanee. It was esteemed the best specimen of architecture in Tahiti.

Of late, they have built their places of worship with more reference to durability than formerly. At one time there were no less than thirty-six on the island—mere barns, tied together with thongs, which went to destruction in a very few years.

One, built many years ago in this style, was a most remarkable structure. It was erected by Pomaree II, who, on this occasion, showed all the zeal of a royal proselyte. The building was over seven hundred feet in length, and of a proportionate width; the vast ridge-pole was, at intervals, supported by a row of thirty-six cylindrical trunks of the bread-fruit-tree; and, all around, the wall-plates rested on shafts of the palm. The roof—steeply inclining to within a man's height of the ground—was thatched with leaves, and the sides of the edifice were open. Thus spacious was the Royal Mission Chapel of Papoar.

At its dedication, three distinct sermons were, from different pulpits, preached to an immense concourse gathered from all parts of the island.

As the chapel was built by the king's command, nearly as great a multitude was employed in its construction as swarmed over the scaffolding of the great temple of the Jews. Much less time, however, was expended. In less than three weeks from planting the first post, the last tier of palmetto-leaves drooped from the eaves, and the work was done.

Apportioned to the several chiefs and their dependants, the labor, though immense, was greatly facilitated by everyone's bringing his post, or his rafter, or his pole strung with thatching, ready for instant use. The materials thus prepared being afterward secured together by thongs, there was literally "neither hammer, nor ax, nor any tool of iron heard in the house while it was building."

But the most singular circumstance connected with this South Sea cathedral remains to be related. As well for the beauty as the advantages of such a site, the islanders love to dwell near the mountain streams; and so, a considerable brook, after descending from the hills and watering the valley, was bridged over in three places, and swept clean through the chapel.

Flowing waters! what an accompaniment to the songs of the sanctuary; mingling with them the praises and thanksgivings of the green solitudes inland.

But the chapel of the Polynesian Solomon has long since been deserted. Its thousand rafters of habiscus have decayed, and fallen to the ground; and now the stream murmurs over them in its bed.

The present metropolitan church of Tahiti is very unlike the one just described. It is of moderate dimensions, boarded over, and painted white. It is furnished, also, with blinds, but no sashes; indeed, were it not for the rustic thatch, it would remind one of a plain chapel at home.

The wood-work was all done by foreign carpenters, of whom there are always several about Papeetee.

Within, its aspect is unique, and cannot fail to interest a stranger. The rafters overhead are bound round with fine matting of variegated dyes; and all along the ridge-pole, these strappings hang pendent, in alternate bunches of tassels and deep fringes of stained grass. The floor is composed of rude planks. Regular aisles run between ranges of native settees, bottomed with crossed braids of the cocoanut fiber, and furnished with backs.

But the pulpit, made of a dark, lustrous wood, and standing at one end, is by far the most striking object. It is preposterously lofty; indeed, a capital bird's-eye view of the congregation ought to be had from its summit.

Nor does the church lack a gallery, which runs round on three sides, and is supported by columns of the cocoanut-tree.

Its facings are here and there daubed over with a tawdry blue; and in other places (without the slightest regard to uniformity), patches of the same color may be seen. In their ardor to decorate the sanctuary, the converts must have borrowed each a brush full of paint, and zealously daubed away at the first surface that offered.

As hinted, the general impression is extremely curious. Little light being admitted, and everything being of a dark color, there is an indefinable Indian aspect of duskiness throughout. A strange, woody smell, also—more or less pervading every considerable edifice in Polynesia—is at once perceptible. It suggests the idea of worm-eaten idols packed away in some old lumber-room at hand.

For the most part, the congregation attending this church is composed of the better and wealthier orders—the chiefs and their retainers; in short, the rank and fashion of the island. This class is infinitely superior in personal beauty and general healthfulness to the "marenhoar," or common people; the latter having been more exposed to the worst and most debasing evils of foreign intercourse. On Sundays, the former are invariably arrayed in their finery; and thus appear to the best advantage. Nor are they driven to the chapel, as some of their inferiors are to other places of worship; on the contrary, capable of maintaining a handsome exterior, and possessing greater intelligence, they go voluntarily.

In respect of the woodland colonnade supporting its galleries, I called this chapel the Church of the Cocoanuts.

It was the first place for Christian worship in Polynesia that I had seen; and the impression upon entering during service was all the stronger. Majestic-looking chiefs, whose fathers had hurled the battle-club, and old men who had seen sacrifices smoking upon the altars of Oro, were there.

And hark! hanging from the bough of a bread-fruit-tree without, a bell is being struck with a bar of iron by a native lad. In the same spot, the blast of the war-conch had often resounded. But to the proceedings within.

The place is well filled. Everywhere meets the eye the gay calico draperies worn on great occasions by the higher classes, and forming a strange contrast of patterns and colors. In some instances, these are so fashioned as to resemble as much as possible European garments. This is in excessively bad taste. Coats and pantaloons, too, are here and there seen; but they look awkwardly enough, and take away from the general effect.

But it is the array of countenances that most strikes you. Each is suffused with the peculiar animation of the Polynesians, when thus collected in large numbers. Every robe is rustling, every limb in motion, and an incessant buzzing going on throughout the assembly. The tumult is so great, that the voice of the placid old missionary, who now rises, is almost inaudible. Some degree of silence is at length obtained through the exertions of half a dozen strapping fellows, in white shirts and no pantaloons. Running in among the settees, they are at great pains to inculcate the impropriety of making a noise, by creating a most unnecessary racket themselves. This part of the service was quite comical.

There is a most interesting Sabbath school connected with the church; and the scholars, a vivacious, mischievous set, were in one part of the gallery. I was amused by a party in a corner. The teacher sat at one end of the bench, with a meek little fellow by his side. When the others were disorderly, this young martyr received a rap; intended, probably, as a sample of what the rest might expect, if they didn't mend.

Standing in the body of the church, and leaning against a pillar, was an old man, in appearance very different from others of his countrymen. He wore nothing but a coarse, scant mantle, of faded tappa; and from his staring, bewildered manner, I set him down as an aged bumpkin from the interior, unaccustomed to the strange sights and sounds of the metropolis. This old worthy was sharply reprimanded for standing up, and thus intercepting the view of those behind; but not comprehending exactly what was said to him, one of the white iveried gentry made no ceremony of grasping him by the shoulders, and fairly crushing him down into a seat.

During all this, the old missionary in the pulpit—as well as his associates beneath, never ventured to interfere—leaving everything to native management. With South Sea islanders, assembled in any numbers, there is no other way of getting along.

Chapter XLV

A Missionary's Sermon; with Some Reflections

Some degree of order at length restored, the service was continued, by singing. The choir was composed of twelve or fifteen ladies of the mission, occupying a long bench to the left of the pulpit. Almost the entire congregation joined in.

The first air fairly startled me; it was the brave tune of Old Hundred, adapted to a Tahitian psalm. After the graceless scenes I had recently passed through, this circumstance, with all its accessories, moved me forcibly.

Many voices around were of great sweetness and compass. The singers, also, seemed to enjoy themselves mightily; some of them pausing, now and then, and looking round, as if to realize the scene more fully. In truth, they sang right joyously, despite the solemnity of the tune.

The Tahitians have much natural talent for singing; and, on all occasions, are exceedingly fond of it. I have often heard a stave or two of psalmody, hummed over by rakish young fellows, like a snatch from an opera.

With respect to singing, as in most other matters, the Tahitians widely differ from the people of the Sandwich Islands; where the parochial flocks may be said rather to *bleat* than *sing*.

The psalm concluded, a prayer followed. Very considerately, the good old missionary made it short; for the congregation became fidgety and inattentive as soon as it commenced.

A chapter of the Tahitian Bible was now read; a text selected, and the sermon began. It was listened to with more attention than I had anticipated.

Having been informed, from various sources, that the discourses of the missionaries, being calculated to engage the attention of their simple auditors, were, naturally enough, of a rather amusing description to strangers; in short, that they had much to say about steam-boats, lord mayors' coaches, and the way fires are put out in London, I had taken care to provide myself with a good interpreter, in the person of an intelligent Hawaiian sailor, whose acquaintance I had made.

"Now, Jack," said I, before entering, "hear every word, and tell me what you can, as the missionary goes on."

Jack's was not, perhaps, a critical version of the discourse; and, at the time, I took no notes of what he said. Nevertheless, I will here venture to give what I remember of it; and, as far as possible, in Jack's phraseology, so as to lose nothing by a double translation.

"Good friends, I glad to see you; and I very well like to have some talk with you to-day. Good friends, very bad times in Tahiti; it make me weep. Pomaree is gone—the island no more yours, but the Wee-Wee's (French). Wicked priests here, too; and wicked idols in woman's clothes, and brass chains.[1]

"Good friends, no you speak, or look at them—but I know you won't—they belong to a set of robbers—the wicked Wee-Wees. Soon these bad men be made to go very quick. Beretanee ships of thunder come, and away they go. But no more 'bout this now. I speak more by by.

"Good friends, many whale-ships here now; and many bad men come in 'em. No good sailors living—that you know very well. They come here, 'cause so bad they no keep 'em home.

"My good little girls, no run after sailors—no go where they go; they harm you. Where they come from no good people talk to 'em—just like dogs. Here, they talk to Pomaree, and drink *arva* with great Poofai.[2]

"Good friends, this very small island, but very wicked, and very poor; these two go together. Why Beretanee so great? Because that island good island, and send *mickonaree*[3] to poor *kanaka*.[4] In Beretanee, every man rich: plenty things to buy; and plenty things to sell. Houses bigger than Pomaree's, and more grand. Everybody, too, ride about in coaches, bigger than hers;[5] and wear fine tappa every day. (Several luxurious appliances of civilization were here enumerated, and described.)

"Good friends, little to eat left at my house. Schooner from Sydney no bring bag of flour; and

1. Meaning the snowy image of the Virgin in the little Catholic chapel.

2. The word "arva," as here employed, means brandy. Poofai was one of the highest chiefs on the island, and a jolly companion.

3. This word, evidently a corruption of "missionary," is used under various significations by the natives. Sometimes, it is applied to a communicant of the Church. But, above, it has its original meaning.

4. A word generally used by foreigners to designate the natives of Polynesia.

5. Pomaree, some time previous, had received a present of a chariot from Queen Victoria. It was afterwards sent to Oahu (Sandwich Islands), and there sold to pay her debts.

kanaka no bring pig and fruit enough. Mickonaree do great deal for kanaka; kanaka do little for mickonaree. So, good friends, weave plenty of cocoanut baskets, fill 'em, and bring 'em to-morrow."

Such was the substance of great part of this discourse; and, whatever may be thought of it, it was specially adapted to the minds of the islanders; who are susceptible to no impressions, except from things palpable, or novel and striking. To them, a dry sermon would be dry indeed.

The Tahitians can hardly ever be said to reflect: they are all impulse; and so, instead of expounding dogmas, the missionaries give them the large type, pleasing cuts, and short and easy lessons of the primer. Hence, anything like a permanent religious impression is seldom or never produced.

In fact, there is, perhaps, no race upon earth less disposed by nature to the monitions of Christianity than the people of the South Sea. And this assertion is made with full knowledge of what is called the "Great Revival at the Sandwich Islands," about the year 1836; when several thousands were, in the course of a few weeks, admitted into the bosom of the Church. But this result was brought about by no sober moral convictions; as an almost instantaneous relapse into every kind of licentiousness soon afterwards testified. It was the legitimate effect of a morbid feeling, engendered by the sense of severe physical wants, preying upon minds excessively prone to superstition; and by fanatical preaching, inflamed into the belief, that the gods of the missionaries were taking vengeance upon the wickedness of the land.[1]

It is a noteworthy fact, that those very traits in the Tahitians which induced the London Missionary Society to regard them as the most promising subjects for conversion, and which led, moreover, to the selection of their island as the very first field for missionary labor, eventually proved the most serious obstruction. An air of softness in their manners, great apparent ingenuousness and docility, at first misled; but these were the mere accompaniments of an indolence, bodily and mental; a constitutional voluptuousness; and an aversion to the least restraint; which, however fitted for the luxurious state of nature, in the tropics, are the greatest possible hindrances to the strict moralities of Christianity.

Added to all this, is a quality inherent in Polynesians; and more akin to hypocrisy than anything else. It leads them to assume the most passionate interest in matters for which they really feel little or none whatever, but in which those whose power they dread, or whose favor they court, they believe to be at all affected. Thus, in their heathen state, the Sandwich Islanders actually knocked out their teeth, tore their hair, and mangled their bodies with shells, to testify their inconsolable grief at the demise of a high chief, or member of the royal family. And yet, Vancouver relates, that, on such an occasion, upon which he happened to be present, those apparently the most abandoned to their feelings, immediately assumed the utmost light-heartedness, on receiving the present of a penny whistle, or a Dutch looking-glass. Similar instances, also, have come under my own observation.

The following is an illustration of the trait alluded to, as occasionally manifested among the converted Polynesians.

At one of the Society Islands—Raiatea, I believe—the natives, for special reasons, desired to commend themselves particularly to the favor of the missionaries. Accordingly, during divine service, many of them behaved in a manner otherwise unaccountable, and precisely similar to their behavior as heathens. They pretended to be wrought up to madness by the preaching which they heard. They rolled their eyes; foamed at the mouth; fell down in fits; and so were carried home. Yet, strange to relate, all this was deemed the evidence of the power of the Most High; and, as such, was heralded abroad.

But, to return to the Church of the Cocoanuts. The blessing pronounced, the congregation disperse; enlivening the Broom Road with their waving mantles. On either hand, they disappear

1. At this period, many of the population were upon the verge of starvation.

down the shaded pathways, which lead off from the main route, conducting to hamlets in the groves, or to the little marine villas upon the beach. There is considerable hilarity; and you would suppose them just from an old-fashioned "hevar," or jolly heathen dance. Those who carry Bibles, swing them carelessly from their arms, by cords of sinnate.

The Sabbath is no ordinary day with the Tahitians. So far as doing any work is concerned, it is scrupulously observed. The canoes are hauled up on the beach; the nets are spread to dry. Passing by the hen-coop huts, on the roadside, you find their occupants idle, as usual; but less disposed to gossip. After service, repose broods over the whole island; the valleys reaching inland look stiller than ever.

In short, it is Sunday—their "Taboo Day"; the very word, formerly expressing the sacredness of their pagan observances, now proclaiming the sanctity of the Christian Sabbath.

Chapter XLVI

Something about the Kannakippers

A worthy young man, formerly a friend of mine (I speak of Kooloo with all possible courtesy, since after our intimacy there would be an impropriety in doing otherwise)—this worthy youth, having some genteel notions of retirement, dwelt in a "maroo boro," or bread-fruit shade, a pretty nook in a wood, midway between the Calabooza Beretanee and the Church of Cocoanuts. Hence, at the latter place, he was one of the most regular worshipers.

Kooloo was a blade. Standing up in the congregation in all the bravery of a striped calico shirt, with the skirts rakishly adjusted over a pair of white sailor trousers, and hair well anointed with cocoanut oil, he ogled the ladies with an air of supreme satisfaction. Nor were his glances unreturned.

But such looks as the Tahitian belles cast at each other: frequently turning up their noses at the advent of a new cotton mantle recently imported in the chest of some amorous sailor. Upon one occasion, I observed a group of young girls, in tunics of coarse, soiled sheeting, disdainfully pointing at a damsel in a flaming red one. "Oee tootai owree!" said they with ineffable scorn, "itai maitai!" (you are a good-for-nothing huzzy, no better than you should be).

Now, Kooloo communed with the church; so did all these censorious young ladies. Yet after eating bread-fruit at the Eucharist, I knew several of them, the same night, to be guilty of some sad derelictions.

Puzzled by these things, I resolved to find out, if possible, what ideas, if any, they entertained of religion; but as one's spiritual concerns are rather delicate for a stranger to meddle with, I went to work as adroitly as I could.

Farnow, an old native who had recently retired from active pursuits, having thrown up the business of being a sort of running footman to the queen, had settled down in a snug little retreat, not fifty rods from Captain Bob's. His selecting our vicinity for his residence, may have been with some view to the advantages it afforded for introducing his three daughters into polite circles. At any rate, not averse to receiving the attentions of so devoted a gallant as the doctor, the sisters (communicants, be it remembered) kindly extended to him free permission to visit them sociably whenever he pleased.

We dropped in one evening, and found the ladies at home. My long friend engaged his favorites, the two younger girls, at the game of "Now," or hunting a stone under three piles of tappa. For myself, I lounged on a mat with Ideea, the eldest, dallying with her grass fan, and improving my knowledge of Tahitian.

The occasion was well adapted to my purpose, and I began.

"Ah, Ideea, mickonaree oee?" the same as drawling out—"By the by, Miss Ideea, do you belong to the church?"

"Yes, me mickonaree," was the reply.

But the assertion was at once qualified by certain reservations; so curious, that I cannot forbear their relation.

"Mickonaree *ena*" (church member *here*), exclaimed she, laying her hand upon her mouth, and a strong emphasis on the adverb. In the same way, and with similar exclamations, she touched her eyes and hands. This done, her whole air changed in an instant; and she gave me to understand, by unmistakable gestures, that in certain other respects she was not exactly a "mickonaree." In short, Ideea was

A sad good Christian at the heart—
A very heathen in the carnal part.[1]

The explanation terminated in a burst of laughter, in which all three sisters joined; and, for fear of looking silly, the doctor and myself, as soon as good breeding would permit, took leave.

The hypocrisy in matters of religion, so apparent in all Polynesian converts, is most injudiciously nourished in Tahiti, by a zealous and, in many cases, a coercive superintendence over their spiritual well-being. But it is only manifested with respect to the common people, their superiors being exempted.

On Sunday mornings, when the prospect is rather small for a full house in the minor churches, a parcel of fellows are actually sent out with rattans into the highways and by-ways as whippers-in of the congregation. This is a sober fact.[2]

These worthies constitute a religious police; and you always know them by the great white diapers they wear. On week-days, they are quite as busy as on Sundays; to the great terror of the inhabitants, going all over the island, and spying out the wickedness thereof.

Moreover, they are the collectors of fines—levied generally in grass mats—for obstinate non-attendance upon divine worship, and other offences amenable to the ecclesiastical judicature of the missionaries.

Old Bob called these fellows "kannakippers," a corruption, I fancy, of our word constable.

He bore them a bitter grudge; and one day, drawing near home, and learning that two of them were just then making a domiciliary visit at his house, he ran behind a bush; and as they came forth, two green bread-fruit from a hand unseen took them each between the shoulders. The sailors in the Calabooza were witnesses to this, as well as several natives; who, when the intruders were out of sight, applauded Captain Bob's spirit in no measured terms; the ladies present vehemently joining in. Indeed, the kannakippers have no greater enemies than the latter. And no wonder: the impertinent varlets, popping into their houses at all hours, are forever prying into their peccadilloes.

Kooloo, who at times was patriotic and pensive, and mourned the evils under which his country was groaning, frequently inveighed against the statute which thus authorized an utter stranger to interfere with domestic arrangements. He himself—quite a ladies' man—had often been annoyed thereby. He considered the kannakippers a bore.

Besides their confounded inquisitiveness, they add insult to injury, by making a point of din-

1. Pope (*Epistle to a Lady*).

2. With abhorrence and disgust the custom is alluded to by a late benevolent visitor at the island. See page 763 of the *Memoirs of the Life and Gospel Labours of the late Daniel Wheeler*. A work hereafter to be more particularly alluded to.

ing out every day at some hut within the limits of their jurisdiction. As for the gentleman of the house, his meek endurance of these things is amazing. But "good easy man," there is nothing for him but to be as hospitable as possible.

These gentry are indefatigable. At the dead of night prowling round the houses, and in the day-time hunting amorous couples in the groves. Yet in one instance the chase completely baffled them.

It was thus:

Several weeks previous to our arrival at the island, someone's husband and another person's wife, having taken a mutual fancy for each other, went out for a walk. The alarm was raised, and with hue and cry they were pursued; but nothing was seen of them again until the lapse of some ninety days, when we were called out from the Calabooza to behold a great mob enclosing the lovers, and escorting them for trial to the village.

Their appearance was most singular. The girdle excepted, they were quite naked; their hair was long, burned yellow at the ends, and entangled with burs; and their bodies scratched and scarred in all directions. It seems, that acting upon the "love-in-a-cottage" principle, they had gone right into the interior; and throwing up a hut in an uninhabited valley, had lived there, until in an unlucky stroll, they were observed and captured.

They were subsequently condemned to make one hundred fathoms of Broom Road—a six months' work, if not more.

Often, when seated in a house, conversing quietly with its inmates, I have known them betray the greatest confusion at the sudden announcement of a kannakipper's being in sight. To be reported by one of these officials as a "Tootai Owree" (in general, signifying a bad person or disbeliever in Christianity) is as much dreaded as the forefinger of Titus Oates was, leveled at an alleged papist.

But the islanders take a sly revenge upon them. Upon entering a dwelling, the kannakippers oftentimes volunteer a pharisaical prayer meeting: hence, they go in secret by the name of "Boora-Artuas," literally, "Pray-to-Gods."

Chapter XLVII

HOW THEY DRESS IN TAHITI

EXCEPT WHERE THE EMPLOYMENT OF MAKING "TAPPA" IS INFLICTED AS A PUNISHMENT, THE echoes of the cloth-mallet have long since died away in the listless valleys of Tahiti. Formerly, the girls spent their mornings like ladies at their tambour frames; *now,* they are lounged away in almost utter indolence. True, most of them make their own garments; but this comprises but a stitch or two; the ladies of the mission, by the by, being entitled to the credit of teaching them to sew.

The "kihee whihenee," or petticoat, is a mere breadth of white cotton, or calico; loosely enveloping the person from the waist to the feet. Fastened simply, by a single tuck, or by twisting the upper corners together, this garment frequently becomes disordered; thus affording an opportunity of being coquettishly adjusted. Over the "kihee," they wear a sort of gown, open in front, very loose, and as negligent as you please. The ladies here never dress for dinner.

But what shall be said of those horrid hats! Fancy a bunch of straw, plaited into the shape of a coal skuttle, and stuck, bolt upright, on the crown; with a yard or two of red ribbon, flying about like kite-strings. Milliners of Paris, what would ye say to them! Though made by the natives, they are said to have been first contrived and recommended by the missionaries' wives; a report which I really trust is nothing but scandal.

Curious to relate, these things for the head are esteemed exceedingly becoming. The braiding of the straw is one of the few employments of the higher classes; all of which but minister to the silliest vanity. The young girls, however, wholly eschew the hats; leaving those dowdy old souls, their mothers, to make frights of themselves.

As for the men, those who aspire to European garments seem to have no perception of the relation subsisting between the various parts of a gentleman's costume. To the wearer of a coat, for instance, pantaloons are by no means indispensable; and a bell-crowned hat and a girdle are full dress. The young sailor, for whom Kooloo deserted me, presented him with a shaggy old pea-jacket; and with this buttoned up to his chin, under a tropical sun, he promenaded the Broom Road, quite elated. Doctor Long Ghost, who saw him thus, ran away with the idea that he was under medical treatment at the time—in the act of taking, what the quacks call, a "sweat."

A bachelor friend of Captain Bob rejoiced in the possession of a full European suit; in which he often stormed the ladies' hearts. Having a military leaning, he ornamented the coat with a great scarlet patch on the breast; and mounted it also, here and there, with several regimental buttons, slyly cut from the uniform of a parcel of drunken marines, sent ashore on a holiday from a man-of-war. But, in spite of the ornaments, the dress was not exactly the thing. From the tightness of the cloth across the shoulders, his elbows projected from his sides, like an ungainly rider's; and his ponderous legs were jammed so hard into his slim, nether garments, that the threads of every seam showed; and at every step you looked for a catastrophe.

In general, there seems to be no settled style of dressing among the males: they wear anything they can get; in some cases, awkwardly modifying the fashions of their fathers, so as to accord with their own altered views of what is becoming.

But ridiculous as many of them now appear in foreign habiliments, the Tahitians presented a far different appearance in the original national costume; which was graceful in the extreme, modest to all but the prudish, and peculiarly adapted to the climate. But the short kilts of dyed tappa, the tasseled maroes, and other articles formerly worn, are, at the present day, prohibited by law as indecorous. For what reason necklaces and garlands of flowers, among the women were also forbidden, I never could learn; but it is said that they were associated, in some way, with a forgotten heathen observance.

Many pleasant and seemingly innocent sports and pastimes are likewise interdicted. In old times, there were several athletic games practiced, such as wrestling, foot-racing, throwing the javelin, and archery. In all these they greatly excelled; and, for some, splendid festivals were instituted. Among their everyday amusements, were dancing, tossing the foot-ball, kite-flying, flute-playing, and singing traditional ballads—*now,* all punishable offenses; though most of them have been so long in disuse that they are nearly forgotten.

In the same way, the "Opio," or festive harvest home of the bread-fruit, has been suppressed; though, as described to me by Captain Bob, it seemed wholly free from any immoral tendency. Against tattooing of any kind, there is a severe law.

That this abolition of their national amusements and customs was not willingly acquiesced in, is shown in the frequent violation of many of the statutes inhibiting them; and, especially, in the frequency with which their "hevars," or dances, are practiced in secret.

Doubtless, in thus denationalizing the Tahitians, as it were, the missionaries were prompted by a sincere desire for good; but the effect has been lamentable. Supplied with no amusements, in place of those forbidden, the Tahitians, who require more recreation than other people, have sunk into a listlessness, or indulge in sensualities, a hundred times more pernicious than all the games ever celebrated in the Temple of Tanee.

Chapter XLVIII

TAHITI AS IT IS

AS, IN THE LAST FEW CHAPTERS, SEVERAL MATTERS CONNECTED WITH THE GENERAL CONDITION of the natives have been incidentally touched upon, it may be well not to leave so important a subject in a state calculated to convey erroneous impressions. Let us bestow upon it, therefore, something more than a mere cursory glance.

But, in the first place, let it be distinctly understood, that in all I have to say upon this subject, both here and elsewhere, I mean no harm to the missionaries, nor their cause: I merely desire to set forth things as they actually exist.

Of the results which have flowed from the intercourse of foreigners with the Polynesians, including the attempts to civilize and christianize them by the missionaries, Tahiti, on many accounts, is obviously the fairest practical example. Indeed, it may now be asserted, that the experiment of christianizing the Tahitians, and improving their social condition by the introduction of foreign customs, has been fully tried. The present generation have grown up under the auspices of their religious instructors. And although it may be urged that the labors of the latter have at times been more or less obstructed by unprincipled foreigners, still this in no wise renders Tahiti any the less a fair illustration; for, with obstacles like these, the missionaries in Polynesia must always and everywhere struggle.

Nearly sixty years have elapsed since the Tahitian mission was started; and during this period it has received the unceasing prayers and contributions of its friends abroad. Nor has any enterprise of the kind called forth more devotion on the part of those directly employed in it.

It matters not, that the earlier laborers in the work, although strictly conscientious, were, as a class, ignorant, and, in many cases, deplorably bigoted: such traits have, in some degree, characterized the pioneers of all faiths. And although, in zeal and disinterestedness, the missionaries now on the island are, perhaps, inferior to their predecessors, they have, nevertheless, in their own way at least, labored hard to make a Christian people of their charge.

Let us now glance at the most obvious changes wrought in their condition.

The entire system of idolatry has been done away, together with several barbarous practices engrafted thereon. But this result is not so much to be ascribed to the missionaries as to the civilizing effects of a long and constant intercourse with whites of all nations; to whom, for many years, Tahiti has been one of the principal places of resort in the South Seas. At the Sandwich Islands, the potent institution of the Taboo, together with the entire paganism of the land, was utterly abolished by a voluntary act of the natives, some time previous to the arrival of the first missionaries among them.

The next most striking change in the Tahitians is this. From the permanent residence among them of influential and respectable foreigners, as well as from the frequent visits of ships of war, recognizing the nationality of the island, its inhabitants are no longer deemed fit subjects for the atrocities practiced upon mere savages; and hence, secure from retaliation, vessels of all kinds now enter their harbors with perfect safety.

But let us consider what results are directly ascribable to the missionaries alone.

In all cases, they have striven hard to mitigate the evils resulting from the commerce with the whites in general. Such attempts, however, have been rather injudicious, and often ineffectual: in truth, a barrier almost insurmountable is presented in the dispositions of the people themselves. Still, in this respect, the morality of the islanders is, upon the whole, improved by the presence of the missionaries.

But the greatest achievement of the latter, and one which in itself is most hopeful and gratifying, is, that they have translated the entire Bible into the language of the island; and I have myself known several who were able to read it with facility. They have also established churches, and schools for both children and adults; the latter, I regret to say, are now much neglected; which must be ascribed, in a great measure, to the disorders growing out of the proceedings of the French.

It were unnecessary here to enter diffusely into matters connected with the internal government of the Tahitian churches and schools. Nor, upon this head, is my information copious enough to warrant me in presenting details. But we do not need them. We are merely considering general *results*, as made apparent in the moral and religious condition of the island at large.

Upon a subject like this, however, it would be altogether too assuming for a single individual to decide; and so, in place of my own random observations, which may be found elsewhere, I will here present those of several known authors, made under various circumstances, at different periods, and down to a comparatively late date. A few very brief extracts will enable the reader to mark for himself what progressive improvement, if any, has taken place.

Nor must it be overlooked, that of these authorities, the two first in order are largely quoted by the Right Reverend M. Russell, in a work composed for the express purpose of imparting information on the subject of Christian missions in Polynesia. And he frankly acknowledges, moreover, that they are such as "cannot fail to have great weight with the public."[1]

After alluding to the manifold evils entailed upon the natives by foreigners, and their singularly inert condition; and after somewhat too severely denouncing the undeniable errors of the mission, Kotzebue, the Russian navigator says, "A religion like this, which forbids every innocent pleasure, and cramps or annihilates every mental power, is a libel on the divine founder of Christianity. It is true, that the religion of the missionaries has, with a great deal of evil, effected some good. It has restrained the vices of theft and incontinence; but it has given birth to ignorance, hypocrisy, and a hatred of all other modes of faith, which was once foreign to the open and benevolent character of the Tahitian."[2]

Captain Beechy says, that while at Tahiti he saw scenes "which must have convinced the greatest sceptic of the thoroughly immoral condition of the people, and which would force him to conclude, as Turnbull[3] did many years previous, that their intercourse with the Europeans had tended to debase rather than exalt their condition."[4]

About the year 1834, Daniel Wheeler, an honest-hearted Quaker, prompted by motives of the purest philanthropy, visited, in a vessel of his own, most of the missionary settlements in the South Seas. He remained some time at Tahiti; receiving the hospitalities of the missionaries there, and, from time to time, exhorting the natives.

After bewailing their social condition, he frankly says of their religious state, "Certainly, appearances are unpromising; and however unwilling to adopt such a conclusion, there is reason to apprehend, that Christian principle is a great rarity."[5]

Such, then, is the testimony of good and unbiased men who have been upon the spot; but how

1. *Polynesia; or an Historical Account of the Principal Islands of the South Sea*: By the Right Rev. M. Russell, LL.D. (Harper's Family Library Edition), pg. 96.

2. *A new Voyage round the World in the years 1823–24–25–26*: By Otto Von Kotzebue, Post Captain in the Russian Imperial Service (London, 1830; 2 vols. 8vo), vol. i. p. 168.

3. The author of a *Voyage round the World, in the years 1800–1804* (3 vols. 8vo, London, 1805).

4. *Narrative of a Voyage to the Pacific and Bhering's Straits, under the command of Captain F. W. Beechy, R. N.* (London, 1831), vol. i. pg. 287.

5. *Memoirs of the Life and Gospel Labours of the late Daniel Wheeler, a minister of the Society of Friends* (London, 1842, 8vo), p. 757.

comes it to differ so widely from impressions of others at home? Simply thus: instead of estimating the result of missionary labors by the number of heathens who have actually been made to understand and practice (in some measure at least) the precepts of Christianity, this result has been unwarrantably inferred from the number of those who, without any understanding of these things, have in any way been induced to abandon idolatry and conform to certain outward observances.

By authority of some kind or other, exerted upon the natives through their chiefs, and promoted by the hope of some worldly benefit to the latter, and not by appeals to the reason, have conversions in Polynesia been in most cases brought about.

Even in one or two instances—so often held up as wonderful examples of divine power—where the natives have impulsively burned their idols, and rushed to the waters of baptism, the very suddenness of the change has but indicated its unsoundness. Williams, the martyr of Erromanga, relates an instance where the inhabitants of an island professing Christianity voluntarily assembled, and solemnly revived all their heathen customs.

All the world over, facts are more eloquent than words; the following will show in what estimation the missionaries themselves hold the present state of Christianity and morals among the converted Polynesians.

On the island of Imeeo (attached to the Tahitian mission) is a seminary, under the charge of the Rev. Mr. Simpson and wife, for the education of the children of the missionaries exclusively. Sent home—in many cases, at a very early age—to finish their education, the pupils here are taught nothing but the rudiments of knowledge; nothing more than may be learned in the native schools. Notwithstanding this, the two races are kept as far as possible from associating; the avowed reason being, to preserve the young whites from moral contamination. The better to insure this end, every effort is made to prevent them from acquiring the native language.

They went even further at the Sandwich Islands; where, a few years ago, a play-ground for the children of the missionaries was enclosed with a fence many feet high, the more effectually to exclude the wicked little Hawaiians.

And yet, strange as it may seem, the depravity among the Polynesians, which renders precautions like these necessary, was in a measure unknown before their intercourse with the whites. The excellent Captain Wilson, who took the first missionaries out to Tahiti, affirms that the people of that island had, in many things, "more refined ideas of decency than ourselves."[1] Vancouver, also has some noteworthy ideas on this subject, respecting the Sandwich Islanders.[2]

That the immorality alluded to is continually increasing, is plainly shown in the numerous severe, and perpetually violated laws against licentiousness of all kinds, in both groups of islands.

It is hardly to be expected, that the missionaries would send home accounts of this state of things. Hence, Captain Beechy, in alluding to the *Polynesian Researches* of Ellis, says, that the author has impressed his readers with a far more elevated idea of the moral condition of the Tahitians, and the degree of civilization to which they have attained, than they deserve; or, at least, than the facts which came under his observation authorized. He then goes on to say, that in his intercourse with the islanders, "they had no fear of him, and consequently acted from the impulse of their natural feelings; so that he was the better enabled to obtain a correct knowledge of their real disposition and habits."[3]

From my own familiar intercourse with the natives, this last reflection still more forcibly applies to myself.

1. *A Missionary Voyage to the South Pacific Ocean*, Appendix, pp. 336, 342.

2. See *Vancouver's Voyages*, 4th edition, vol. i. p. 172.

3. *Beechy's Narrative*, p. 269.

Chapter XLIX

SAME SUBJECT CONTINUED

WE HAVE GLANCED AT THEIR MORAL AND RELIGIOUS CONDITION; LET US SEE HOW IT IS WITH them socially, and in other respects.

It has been said that the only way to civilize a people is to form in them habits of industry. Judged by this principle, the Tahitians are less civilized now than formerly. True, their constitutional indolence is excessive; but surely, if the spirit of Christianity is among them, so unchristian a vice ought to be, at least, partially remedied. But the reverse is the fact. Instead of acquiring new occupations, old ones have been discontinued.

As previously remarked, the manufacture of tappa is nearly obsolete in many parts of the island. So, too, with that of the native tools and domestic utensils; very few of which are now fabricated, since the superiority of European wares has been made so evident.

This, however, would be all very well, were the natives to apply themselves to such occupations as would enable them to supply the few articles they need. But they are far from doing so; and the majority being unable to obtain European substitutes for many things before made by themselves, the inevitable consequence is seen in the present wretched and destitute mode of life among the common people. To me, so recently from a primitive valley of the Marquesas, the aspect of most of the dwellings of the poorer Tahitians, and their general habits, seemed anything but tidy; nor could I avoid a comparison, immeasurably to the disadvantage of these partially civilized islanders.

In Tahiti the people have nothing to do; and idleness, everywhere, is the parent of vice. "There is scarcely anything," says the good old Quaker Wheeler, "so striking, or pitiable, as their aimless, nerveless mode of spending life."

Attempts have repeatedly been made to rouse them from their sluggishness; but in vain. Several years ago, the cultivation of cotton was introduced; and with their usual love of novelty, they went to work with great alacrity; but the interest excited quickly subsided, and now not a pound of the article is raised.

About the same time, machinery for weaving was sent out from London; and a factory was started at Afrehitoo, in Imeeo. The whiz of the wheels and spindles brought in volunteers from all quarters, who deemed it a privilege to be admitted to work: yet, in six months, not a boy could be hired; and the machinery was knocked down, and packed off to Sydney.

It was the same way with the cultivation of the sugar-cane, a plant indigenous to the island; peculiarly fitted to the soil and climate, and of so excellent a quality, that Bligh took slips of it to the West Indies. All the plantations went on famously for a while; the natives swarming in the fields, like ants, and making a prodigious stir. What few plantations now remain, are owned and worked by whites, who would rather pay a drunken sailor eighteen or twenty Spanish dollars a month than hire a sober native for his "fish and taro."

It is well worthy remark here, that every evidence of civilization among the South Sea Islands directly pertains to foreigners; though the fact of such evidence existing at all is usually urged as a proof of the elevated condition of the natives. Thus, at Honolulu, the capital of the Sandwich Islands, there are fine dwelling-houses, several hotels, and barber-shops, aye, even billiard-rooms; but all these are owned and used, be it observed, by whites. There are tailors, and blacksmiths, and carpenters also; but not one of them is a native.

The fact is, that the mechanical and agricultural employments of civilized life require a kind of exertion altogether too steady and sustained to agree with an indolent people like the Polynesians. Calculated for a state of nature, in a climate providentially adapted to it, they are unfit for any other. Nay, as a race, they cannot otherwise long exist.

The following statement speaks for itself.

About the year 1777, Captain Cook estimated the population of Tahiti at about two hundred thousand.[1] By a regular census, taken some four or five years ago, it was found to be only nine thousand.[2] This amazing decrease not only shows the malignancy of the evils necessary to produce it, but from the fact the inference unavoidably follows that all the wars, child murders, and other depopulating causes, alleged to have existed in former times, were nothing in comparison to them.

These evils, of course, are solely of foreign origin. To say nothing of the effects of drunkenness, the occasional inroads of the small-pox, and other things which might be mentioned, it is sufficient to allude to a virulent disease, which now taints the blood of at least two thirds of the common people of the island; and, in some form or other, is transmitted from father to son.

Their first horror and consternation at the earlier ravages of this scourge were pitiable in the extreme. The very name bestowed upon it, is a combination of all that is horrid and unmentionable to a civilized being.

Distracted with their sufferings, they brought forth their sick before the missionaries, when they were preaching, and cried out, "Lies, lies! you tell us of salvation; and, behold, we are dying. We want no other salvation than to live in this world. Where are there any saved through your speech? Pomaree is dead; and we are all dying with your cursed diseases. When will you give over?"

At present, the virulence of the disorder in individual cases has somewhat abated; but the poison is only the more widely diffused.

"How dreadful and appalling," breaks forth old Wheeler, "the consideration, that the intercourse of distant nations should have entailed upon these poor, untutored islanders a curse unprecedented and unheard of in the annals of history."

In view of these things, who can remain blind to the fact, that so far as mere temporal felicity is concerned, the Tahitians are far worse off now than formerly; and although their circumstances, upon the whole, are bettered by the presence of the missionaries, the benefits conferred by the latter become utterly insignificant when confronted with the vast preponderance of evil brought about by other means.

Their prospects are hopeless. Nor can the most devoted efforts now exempt them from furnishing a marked illustration of a principle which history has always exemplified. Years ago brought to a stand, where all that is corrupt in barbarism and civilization unite, to the exclusion of the virtues of either state; like other uncivilized beings, brought into contact with Europeans, they must here remain stationary until utterly extinct.

The islanders themselves are mournfully watching their doom. Several years since, Pomaree II said to Tyerman and Bennet, the deputies of the London Missionary Society, "You have come to

1. "I was convinced," he adds, "that from the vast swarms that everywhere appeared, this estimate was not at all too great."

2. For an allusion to this census, see one of the chapters on Tahiti, in the volumes of the *U.S. Exploring Expedition*. And, for the almost incredible depopulation of the Sandwich Islands, in recent years, see the same work. The progressive decrease, in certain districts, for a considerable period, is there marked.

Ruschenberger, an intelligent surgeon in the United States Navy, takes the following instance from the records kept on the islands. This district of Kohala, in Hawaii, at one time numbered 8,679 souls: four years after, the population was 6,175: decrease, in that time, 2,504. No extraordinary cause is assigned for this depopulation—*Vide A Voyage round the World in the years 1835–36–37.* By W. S. Ruschenberger, M.D. (Philadelphia, 1838. 8vo.) The chapter on the Sandwich Islands.

see me at a very bad time. Your ancestors came in the time of men, when Tahiti was inhabited: you are come to behold just the remnant of my people."

Of like import, was the prediction of Teearmoar, the high-priest of Paree, who lived over a hundred years ago. I have frequently heard it chanted, in a low, sad tone, by aged Tahitians—

A harree ta fow,
A toro ta farraro,
A now ta tararta.

The palm-tree shall grow,
The coral shall spread,
But man shall cease.

Chapter L

Something Happens to Long Ghost

We will now return to the narrative.

The day before the *Julia* sailed, Dr. Johnson paid his last call. He was not quite so bland as usual. All he wanted was the men's names to a paper, certifying to their having received from him sundry medicaments, therein mentioned. This voucher, endorsed by Captain Guy, secured his pay. But he would not have obtained for it the sailors' signs manual, had either the doctor or myself been present at the time.

Now, my long friend wasted no love upon Johnson; but, for reasons of his own, hated him heartily: all the same thing in one sense; for either passion argues an object deserving thereof. And so, to be hated cordially, is only a left-handed compliment, which shows how foolish it is to be bitter against anyone.

For my own part, I merely felt a cool—purely incidental—and passive contempt for Johnson, as a selfish, mercenary apothecary; and hence I often remonstrated with Long Ghost when he flew out against him, and heaped upon him all manner of scurrilous epithets. In his professional brother's presence, however, he never acted thus; maintaining an amiable exterior, to help along the jokes which were played.

I am now going to tell another story, in which my long friend figures with the physician: I do not wish to bring one or the other of them too often upon the stage; but, as the thing actually happened, I must relate it.

A few days after Johnson *presented his bill,* as above mentioned, the doctor expressed to me his regret, that although he (Johnson) had apparently been played off for our entertainment, yet, nevertheless, he had made money out of the transaction. And I wonder, added the doctor, if, that now he cannot expect to receive any further pay, he could be induced to call again.

By a curious coincidence, not five minutes after making this observation, Doctor Long Ghost himself fell down in an unaccountable fit; and without asking anybody's leave, Captain Bob, who was by, at once dispatched a boy, hot foot, for Johnson.

Meanwhile, we carried him into the Calabooza; and the natives, who assembled in numbers, suggested various modes of treatment. One rather energetic practitioner was for holding the patient by the shoulders, while somebody tugged at his feet. This resuscitatory operation was called the

"Potata"; but thinking our long comrade sufficiently lengthy without additional stretching, we declined *potataing* him.

Presently the physician was spied coming along the Broom Road at a great rate, and so absorbed in the business of locomotion, that he heeded not the imprudence of being in a hurry in a tropical climate. He was in a profuse perspiration, which must have been owing to the warmth of his feelings, notwithstanding we had supposed him a man of no heart. But his benevolent haste upon this occasion was subsequently accounted for: it merely arose from professional curiosity, to behold a case most unusual in his Polynesian practice. Now, under certain circumstances, sailors, generally so frolicsome, are exceedingly particular in having everything conducted with the strictest propriety. Accordingly, they deputed me, as his intimate friend, to sit at Long Ghost's head, so as to be ready to officiate as "spokesman"; and answer all questions propounded; the rest to keep silent.

"What's the matter?" exclaimed Johnson, out of breath, and bursting into the Calabooza: "how did it happen?—speak, quick!" and he looked at Long Ghost.

I told him how the fit came on.

"Singular,"—he observed—"very: good enough pulse"; and he let go of it, and placed his hand upon the heart.

"But what's all that frothing at the mouth?" he continued; "and, bless me! look at the abdomen!"

The region thus denominated exhibited the most unaccountable symptoms. A low, rumbling sound was heard; and a sort of undulation was discernible beneath the thin cotton frock.

"Colic, sir?" suggested a bystander.

"Colic be hanged!" shouted the physician; "who ever heard of anybody in a trance of the colic?"

During this, the patient lay upon his back, stark and straight, giving no signs of life except those above mentioned.

"I'll bleed him!" cried Johnson at last—"run for a calabash, one of you!"

"Life ho!" here sung out Navy Bob, as if he had just spied a sail.

"What under the sun's the matter with him!" cried the physician, starting at the appearance of the mouth, which had jerked to one side, and there remained fixed.

"P'r'aps it's St. Witus's hornpipe," suggested Bob.

"Hold the calabash!"—and the lancet was out in a moment.

But before the deed could be done, the face became natural—a sigh was heaved—the eyelids quivered, opened, closed; and Long Ghost, twitching all over, rolled on his side, and breathed audibly. By degrees, he became sufficiently recovered to speak.

After trying to get something coherent out of him, Johnson withdrew; evidently disappointed in the scientific interest of the case. Soon after his departure, the doctor sat up; and upon being asked what upon earth ailed him, shook his head mysteriously. He then deplored the hardship of being an invalid in such a place, where there was not the slightest provision for his comfort. This awakened the compassion of our good old keeper, who offered to send him to a place where he would be better cared for. Long Ghost acquiesced; and being at once mounted upon the shoulders of four of Captain Bob's men, was marched off in state, like the Grand Lama of Thibet.

Now, I do not pretend to account for his remarkable swoon; but his reason for suffering himself to be thus removed from the Calabooza was strongly suspected to be nothing more than a desire to insure more regularity in his dinner-hour; hoping that the benevolent native to whom he was going would set a good table.

The next morning we were all envying his fortune; when, of a sudden, he bolted in upon us, looking decidedly out of humor.

"Hang it!" he cried, "I'm worse off than ever; let me have some breakfast!" We lowered our slender bag of ship-stores from a rafter, and handed him a biscuit. While this was being munched, he went on and told us his story.

"After leaving here, they trotted me back into a valley, and left me in a hut, where an old woman lived by herself. This must be the nurse, thought I; and so I asked her to kill a pig, and bake it; for I felt my appetite returning. *'Ita! Ita!—oee mattee—mattee nuee'*—(no, no; you too sick.) 'The devil *mattee* ye,' said I—'give me something to eat!' But nothing could be had. Night coming on, I had to stay. Creeping into a corner, I tried to sleep; but it was to no purpose—the old crone must have had the quinsy, or something else; and she kept up such a wheezing and choking, that at last I sprang up and groped after her; but she hobbled away like a goblin; and that was the last of her. As soon as the sun rose, I made the best of my way back; and here I am."

He never left us more, nor ever had a second fit.

Chapter LI

Wilson Gives Us the Cut—Departure for Imeeo

About three weeks after the *Julia's* sailing, our condition began to be a little precarious. We were without any regular supply of food; the arrival of ships was growing less frequent; and, what was worse yet, all the natives but good old Captain Bob began to tire of us. Nor was this to be wondered at; we were obliged to live upon their benevolence, when they had little enough for themselves. Besides, we were sometimes driven to acts of marauding: such as kidnapping pigs, and cooking them in the groves; at which their proprietors were by no means pleased.

In this state of affairs, we determined to march off to the consul in a body; and, as he had brought us to these straits, demand an adequate maintenance.

On the point of starting, Captain Bob's men raised the most outrageous cries, and tried to prevent us. Though hitherto we had strolled about wherever we pleased, this grand conjunction of our whole force upon one particular expedition, seemed to alarm them. But we assured them that we were not going to assault the village; and so, after a good deal of gibberish, they permitted us to leave.

We went straight to the Pritchard residence, where the consul dwelt. This house—to which I have before referred—is quite commodious. It has a wide verandah, glazed windows, and other appurtenances of a civilized mansion. Upon the lawn in front are palm-trees standing erect here and there, like sentinels. The Consular Office, a small building by itself, is enclosed by the same picket which fences in the lawn.

We found the office closed; but in the verandah of the dwelling-house was a lady performing a tonsorial operation on the head of a prim-looking, elderly European, in a low, white cravat—the most domestic little scene I had witnessed since leaving home. Bent upon an interview with Wilson, the sailors now deputed the doctor to step forward as a polite inquirer after his health.

The pair stared very hard as he advanced; but noways disconcerted, he saluted them gravely, and inquired for the consul.

Upon being informed that he had gone down to the beach, we proceeded in that direction; and soon met a native, who told us that, apprised of our vicinity, Wilson was keeping out of the way. We resolved to meet him; and passing through the village, he suddenly came walking towards us, having apparently made up his mind that any attempt to elude us would be useless.

"What do you want of me, you rascals?" he cried—a greeting which provoked a retort in no measured terms. At this juncture, the natives began to crowd round, and several foreigners strolled along. Caught in the very act of speaking to such disreputable acquaintances, Wilson now fidgeted, and moved rapidly towards his office; the men following. Turning upon them incensed, he bade them be off—he would have nothing more to say to us; and then, hurriedly addressing Captain Bob in Tahitian, he hastened on, and never stopped till the postern of Pritchard's wicket was closed behind him.

Our good old keeper was now highly excited, bustling about in his huge petticoats, and conjuring us to return to the Calabooza. After a little debate, we acquiesced.

This interview was decisive. Sensible that none of the charges brought against us would stand, yet unwilling formally to withdraw them, the consul now wished to get rid of us altogether; but without being suspected of encouraging our escape. Thus only could we account for his conduct.

Some of the party, however, with a devotion to principle truly heroic, swore they would never leave him, happen what might. For my own part, I began to long for a change; and as there seemed to be no getting away in a ship, I resolved to hit upon some other expedient. But first, I cast about for a comrade; and of course the long doctor was chosen. We at once laid our heads together; and for the present, resolved to disclose nothing to the rest.

A few days previous, I had fallen in with a couple of Yankee lads, twins, who, originally deserting their ship at Fanning's Island (an uninhabited spot, but exceedingly prolific in fruit of all kinds), had, after a long residence there, roved about among the Society group. They were last from Imeeo—the island immediately adjoining—where they had been in the employ of two foreigners, who had recently started a plantation there. These persons, they said, had charged them to send over from Papeetee, if they could, two white men for field-laborers.

Now, all but the prospect of digging and delving, suited us exactly; but the opportunity for leaving the island was not to be slighted; and so we held ourselves in readiness to return with the planters; who, in a day or two, were expected to visit Papeetee in their boat.

At the interview which ensued, we were introduced to them as Peter and Paul; and they agreed to give Peter and Paul fifteen silver dollars a month, promising something more, should we remain with them permanently. What they wanted, was men who would stay. To elude the natives—many of whom not exactly understanding our relations with the consul, might arrest us, were they to see us departing—the coming midnight was appointed for that purpose.

When the hour drew nigh, we disclosed our intention to the rest. Some upbraided us for deserting them; others applauded, and said, that on the first opportunity they would follow our example. At last, we bade them farewell. And there would now be a serene sadness in thinking over the scene—since we never saw them again—had not all been dashed by M'Gee's picking the doctor's pocket of a jack-knife, in the very act of embracing him.

We stole down to the beach, where, under the shadow of a grove, the boat was waiting. After some delay, we shipped the oars, and pulling outside of the reef, set the sail; and with a fair wind, glided away for Imeeo.

It was a pleasant trip. The moon was up—the air, warm—the waves, musical—and all above was the tropical night, one purple vault hung round with soft, trembling stars.

The channel is some five leagues wide. On one hand, you have the three great peaks of Tahiti lording it over ranges of mountains and valleys; and on the other, the equally romantic elevations of Imeeo, high above which a lone peak, called by our companions, "the Marling-spike," shot up its verdant spire.

The planters were quite sociable. They had been sea-faring men, and this, of course, was a bond between us. To strengthen it, a flask of wine was produced, one of several which had been procured in person from the French admiral's steward; for whom the planters, when on a former visit to Papeetee, had done a good turn, by introducing the amorous Frenchman to the ladies ashore. Besides this, they had a calabash filled with wild boar's meat, baked yams, bread-fruit, and Tombez potatoes. Pipes and tobacco also were produced; and while regaling ourselves, plenty of stories were told about the neighboring islands.

At last we heard the roar of the Imeeo reef; and gliding through a break, floated over the expanse within, which was smooth as a young girl's brow, and beached the boat.

Chapter LII

THE VALLEY OF MARTAIR

WE WENT UP THROUGH GROVES TO AN OPEN SPACE, WHERE WE HEARD VOICES, AND A LIGHT was seen glimmering from out a bamboo dwelling. It was the planters' retreat; and in their absence, several girls were keeping house, assisted by an old native, who, wrapped up in tappa, lay in the corner, smoking.

A hasty meal was prepared, and after it we essayed a nap; but, alas! a plague, little anticipated, prevented. Unknown in Tahiti, the mosquitoes here fairly eddied round us. But more of them anon.

We were up betimes, and strolled out to view the country. We were in the valley of Martair; shut in, on both sides, by lofty hills. Here and there were steep cliffs, gay with flowering shrubs, or hung with pendulous vines, swinging blossoms in the air. Of considerable width at the sea, the vale contracts as it runs inland; terminating, at the distance of several miles, in a range of the most grotesque elevations, which seem embattled with turrets and towers, grown over with verdure, and waving with trees. The valley itself is a wilderness of woodland; with links of streams flashing through, and narrow pathways, fairly tunneled through masses of foliage.

All alone, in this wild place, was the abode of the planters; the only one back from the beach—their sole neighbors, the few fishermen and their families, dwelling in a small grove of cocoanut-trees, whose roots were washed by the sea.

The cleared tract which they occupied comprised some thirty acres, level as a prairie, part of which was under cultivation; the whole being fenced in by a stout palisade of trunks and boughs of trees staked firmly in the ground. This was necessary, as a defense against the wild cattle and hogs overrunning the island.

Thus far, Tombez potatoes[1] were the principal crop raised; a ready sale for them being obtained among the shipping touching at Papeetee. There was a small patch of the *taro*, or Indian turnip, also; another of yams; and, in one corner, a thrifty growth of the sugar-cane, just ripening.

On the side of the enclosure next the sea was the house; newly built of bamboos, in the native style. The furniture consisted of a couple of sea-chests, an old box, a few cooking utensils, and agricultural tools; together with three fowling-pieces, hanging from a rafter; and two enormous hammocks, swinging in opposite corners, and composed of dried bullocks' hides, stretched out with poles.

The whole plantation was shut in by a dense forest; and, close by the house, a dwarfed "Aoa," or species of banian-tree, had purposely been left twisting over the palisade, in the most grotesque manner, and thus made a pleasant shade. The branches of this curious tree afforded low perches,

1. Perhaps the finest sweet potato in the world. It derives its name from a district of Peru, near Cape Blanco, very favorable to its growth; where, also, it is extensively cultivated: the root is very large, sometimes as big as a good-sized melon.

upon which the natives frequently squatted, after the fashion of their race, and smoked and gossiped by the hour.

We had a good breakfast of fish—speared by the natives, before sunrise, on the reef—pudding of Indian turnip, fried bananas, and roasted bread-fruit.

During the repast, our new friends were quite sociable and communicative. It seems that, like nearly all uneducated foreigners residing in Polynesia, they had, some time previous, deserted from a ship; and, having heard a good deal about the money to be made by raising supplies for whaling-vessels, they determined upon embarking in the business. Strolling about, with this intention, they at last came to Martair; and, thinking the soil would suit, set themselves to work. They began, by finding out the owner of the particular spot coveted, and then making a "tayo" of him.

He turned out to be Tonoi, the chief of the fishermen, who, one day, when exhilarated with brandy, tore his meager tappa from his loins, and gave me to know that he was allied by blood with Pomaree herself; and that his mother came from the illustrious race of pontiffs who, in old times, swayed their bamboo crosier over all the pagans of Imeeo. A regal and right reverend lineage! But at the time I speak of, the dusky noble was in "decayed circumstances," and therefore by no means unwilling to alienate a few useless acres. As an equivalent, he received from the strangers two or three rheumatic old muskets, several red woolen shirts, and a promise to be provided for in his old age: he was always to find a home with the planters.

Desirous of living on the cozy footing of a father-in-law, he frankly offered his two daughters for wives; but, as such, they were politely declined; the adventurers, though not averse to courting, being unwilling to entangle themselves in a matrimonial alliance, however splendid in point of family.

Tonoi's men, the fishermen of the grove, were a sad set. Secluded, in a great measure, from the ministrations of the missionaries, they gave themselves up to all manner of lazy wickedness. Strolling among the trees of a morning, you came upon them napping on the shady side of a canoe hauled up among the bushes; lying under a tree smoking; or, more frequently still, gambling with pebbles; though, a little tobacco excepted, what they gambled for at their outlandish games, it would be hard to tell. Other idle diversions they had also, in which they seemed to take great delight. As for fishing, it employed but a small part of their time. Upon the whole, they were a merry, indigent, godless race.

Tonoi, the old sinner, leaning against the fallen trunk of a cocoanut-tree, invariably squandered his mornings at pebbles; a gray-headed rook of a native regularly plucking him of every other stick of tobacco obtained from his friends, the planters. Toward afternoon, he strolled back to their abode; where he tarried till the next morning, smoking and snoozing, and, at times, prating about the hapless fortunes of the House of Tonoi. But, like any other easy-going old dotard, he seemed for the most part perfectly content with cheerful board and lodging.

On the whole, the valley of Martair was the quietest place imaginable. Could the mosquitoes be induced to emigrate, one might spend the month of August there quite pleasantly. But this was not the case with the luckless Long Ghost and myself; as will presently be seen.

Chapter LIII

Farming in Polynesia

The planters were both whole-souled fellows; but, in other respects, as unlike as possible.

One was a tall, robust Yankee, born in the backwoods of Maine, sallow, and with a long face—the other was a short little Cockney, who had first clapped his eyes on the Monument.

The voice of Zeke, the Yankee, had a twang like a cracked viol; and Shorty (as his comrade called him) clipped the aspirate from every word beginning with one. The latter, though not the tallest man in the world, was a good-looking young fellow, of twenty-five. His cheeks were dyed with the fine Saxon red, burned deeper from his roving life; his blue eye opened well, and a profusion of fair hair curled over a well-shaped head.

But Zeke was no beauty. A strong, ugly man, he was well adapted for manual labor; and that was all. His eyes were made to see with, and not for ogling. Compared with the Cockney, he was grave, and rather taciturn; but there was a deal of good old humor bottled up in him, after all. For the rest, he was frank, good-hearted, shrewd, and resolute; and like Shorty, quite illiterate.

Though a curious conjunction, the pair got along together famously. But as no two men were ever united in any enterprise, without one getting the upper hand of the other; so, in most matters, Zeke had his own way. Shorty, too, had imbibed from him a spirit of invincible industry; and Heaven only knows what ideas of making a fortune on their plantation.

We were much concerned at this; for the prospect of their setting us in their own persons an example of downright hard labor, was anything but agreeable. But it was now too late to repent what we had done.

The first day—thank fortune—we did nothing. Having treated us as guests thus far, they no doubt thought it would be wanting in delicacy to set us to work before the compliments of the occasion were well over. The next morning, however, they both looked business-like, and we were put to.

"Wall, b'ys," (boys) said Zeke, knocking the ashes out of his pipe, after breakfast—"we must get at it. Shorty, give Peter there (the doctor), the big hoe, and Paul the other, and let's be off." Going to a corner, Shorty brought forth three of the implements; and distributing them impartially, trudged on after his partner, who took the lead with something in the shape of an ax.

For a moment left alone in the house, we looked at each other, quaking. We were each equipped with a great, clumsy piece of a tree, armed at one end with a heavy, flat mass of iron.

The cutlery part—especially adapted to a primitive soil—was an importation from Sydney; the handles must have been of domestic manufacture. "Hoes"—so called—we had heard of, and seen; but they were harmless, in comparison with the tools in our hands.

"What's to be done with them?" inquired I of Peter.

"Lift them up and down," he replied; "or put them in motion some way or other. Paul, we are in a scrape—but hark! they are calling"; and shouldering the hoes, off we marched.

Our destination was the farther side of the plantation, where the ground, cleared in part, had not yet been broken up; but they were now setting about it. Upon halting, I asked why a plow was not used: some of the young wild steers might be caught, and trained for draft.

Zeke replied, that, for such a purpose, no cattle, to his knowledge, had ever been used in any part of Polynesia. As for the soil of Martair, so obstructed was it with roots, crossing and recrossing each other at all points, that no kind of a plow could be used to advantage. The heavy Sydney hoes were the only thing for such land.

Our work was now before us; but, previous to commencing operations, I endeavored to engage the Yankee in a little further friendly chat, concerning the nature of virgin soils in general, and that of the valley of Martair in particular. So masterly a stratagem made Long Ghost brighten up; and he stood by ready to join in. But what our friend had to say about agriculture, all referred to the particular part of his plantation upon which we stood; and having communicated enough on this head, to enable us to set to work to the best advantage, he fell to himself; and Shorty, who had been looking on, followed suit.

The surface, here and there, presented closely amputated branches of what had once been a dense thicket. They seemed purposely left projecting, as if to furnish a handle, whereby to drag out the roots beneath. After loosening the hard soil, by dint of much thumping and pounding, the Yankee jerked one of the roots, this way and that, twisting it round and round, and then tugging at it horizontally.

"Come! lend us a hand!" he cried, at last; and, running up, we all four strained away in concert. The tough obstacle convulsed the surface with throes and spasms; but stuck fast, notwithstanding.

"Dumn it!" cried Zeke, "we'll have to get a rope; run to the house, Shorty, and fetch one."

The end of this being attached, we took plenty of room, and strained away once more.

"Give us a song, Shorty," said the doctor, who was rather sociable, on a short acquaintance. Where the work to be accomplished is any way difficult, this mode of enlivening toil is quite efficacious among sailors. So, willing to make everything as cheerful as possible, Shorty struck up, *Were you ever in Dumbarton?* a marvelously inspiring, but somewhat indecorous windlass chorus.

At last, the Yankee cast a damper on his enthusiasm, by exclaiming, in a pet, "Oh! dumn your singing! keep quiet, and pull away!" This we now did, in the most uninteresting silence; until, with a jerk that made every elbow hum, the root dragged out; and, most inelegantly, we all landed upon the ground. The doctor, quite exhausted, stayed there; and, deluded into believing that, after so doughty a performance, we would be allowed a cessation of toil, took off his hat, and fanned himself.

"Rayther a hard customer, that, Peter," observed the Yankee, going up to him: "but it's no use for any on 'em to hang back; for, I'm dumned if they hain't got to come out, whether or no. Hurrah! let's get at it agin!"

"Mercy!" ejaculated the doctor, rising slowly, and turning round. "He'll be the death of us!"

Falling to with our hoes again, we worked singly, or together, as occasion required, until "nooning time" came.

The period, so called by the planters, embraced about three hours in the middle of the day; during which it was so excessively hot, in this still brooding valley, shut out from the Trades, and only open toward the leeward side of the island, that labor in the sun was out of the question. To use a hyperbolical phrase of Shorty's, "It was hot enough to melt the nose h'off a brass monkey."

Returning to the house, Shorty, assisted by old Tonoi, cooked the dinner; and, after we had all partaken thereof, both the Cockney and Zeke threw themselves into one of the hammocks, inviting us to occupy the other. Thinking it no bad idea, we did so; and, after skirmishing with the mosquitoes, managed to fall into a doze. As for the planters, more accustomed to "Nooning," they, at once, presented a nuptial back to each other; and were soon snoring away at a great rate. Tonoi snoozed on a mat in one corner.

At last, we were roused by Zeke's crying out, "Up! b'ys, up! rise, and shine; time to get at it agin!"

Looking at the doctor, I perceived very plainly that he had decided upon something.

In a languid voice, he told Zeke, that he was not very well: indeed, that he had not been himself for some time past; though a little rest, no doubt, would recruit him. The Yankee, thinking from this that our valuable services might be lost to him altogether, were he too hard upon us at the outset, at once begged us both to consult our own feelings, and not exert ourselves for the present, unless we felt like it. Then—without recognizing the fact, that my comrade claimed to be actually unwell—he simply suggested, that, since he was so *tired,* he had better, perhaps, swing in his hammock for the rest of the day. If agreeable, however, I myself might accompany him upon a little bullock hunting excursion, in the neighboring hills. In this proposition, I gladly acquiesced; though Peter, who was a great sportsman, put on a long face. The muskets and ammunition were forthwith got down from overhead; and, everything being then ready, Zeke cried out, "Tonoi! come; aramai! (get up) we want you for pilot. Shorty, my lad, look arter things, you know; and, if you likes, why, there's them roots in the field yonder."

Having thus arranged his domestic affairs to please himself, though little to Shorty's satisfaction I thought, he slung his powder-horn over his shoulder, and we started. Tonoi was at once sent on in advance; and, leaving the plantation, he struck into a path which led toward the mountains.

After hurrying through the thickets for some time, we came out into the sunlight, in an open glade, just under the shadow of the hills. Here, Zeke pointed aloft to a beetling crag, far distant; where a bullock, with horns thrown back, stood like a statue.

Chapter LIV

Some Account of the Wild Cattle in Polynesia

Before we proceed further, a word or two concerning these wild cattle, and the way they came on the island.

Some fifty years ago, Vancouver left several bullocks, sheep, and goats, at various places in the Society group. He instructed the natives to look after the animals carefully; and by no means to slaughter any, until a considerable stock had accumulated.

The sheep must have died off; for I never saw a solitary fleece in any part of Polynesia. The pair left were an ill-assorted couple, perhaps; separated in disgust, and died without issue.

As for the goats, occasionally you come across a black, misanthropic ram, nibbling the scant herbage of some height inaccessible to man, in preference to the sweet grasses of the valley below. The goats are not very numerous.

The bullocks, coming of a prolific ancestry, are a hearty set, racing over the island of Imeeo in considerable numbers; though in Tahiti but few of them are seen. At the former place, the original pair must have scampered off to the interior, since it is now so thickly populated by their wild progeny. The herds are the private property of Queen Pomaree; from whom the planters had obtained permission to shoot for their own use as many as they pleased.

The natives stand in great awe of these cattle; and, for this reason, are excessively timid in crossing the island, preferring rather to sail round to an opposite village in their canoes.

Tonoi abounded in bullock stories; most of which, by the by, had a spice of the marvelous. The following is one of these.

Once upon a time, he was going over the hills with a brother—now no more—when a great bull came bellowing out of a wood, and both took to their heels. The old chief sprang into a tree; his companion, flying in an opposite direction, was pursued, and in the very act of reaching up to a bough, trampled under foot. The unhappy man was then gored—tossed in the air—and finally run away with on the bull's horns. More dead than alive, Tonoi waited till all was over, and then made the best of his way home. The neighbors, armed with two or three muskets, at once started to recover, if possible, his unfortunate brother's remains. At nightfall, they returned without discovering any trace of him; but the next morning, Tonoi himself caught a glimpse of a bullock, marching across the mountain's brow, with a long dark object borne aloft on his horns.

Having referred to Vancouver's attempts to colonize the islands with useful quadrupeds, we may as well say something concerning his success upon Hawaii, one of the largest islands in the whole Polynesian Archipelago; and which gives the native name to the well-known cluster named by Cook in honor of Lord Sandwich.

Hawaii is some one hundred leagues in circuit, and covers an area of over four thousand square miles. Until within a few years past, its interior was almost unknown, even to the inhabitants themselves, who, for ages, had been prevented from wandering thither, by certain strange superstitions. Pele, the terrific goddess of the volcanoes Mauna Roa and Mauna Kea,[1] was supposed to guard all the passes to the extensive valleys lying round their base. There are legends of her having chased with streams of fire several impious adventurers. Near Hilo, a jet-black cliff is shown, with the vitreous torrent apparently pouring over into the sea: just as it cooled after one of these supernatural eruptions.

To these inland valleys, and the adjoining hill-sides, which are clothed in the most luxuriant vegetation, Vancouver's bullocks soon wandered; and, unmolested for a long period, multiplied in vast herds.

Some twelve or fifteen years ago, the natives, losing sight of their superstitions, and learning the value of the hides in commerce, began hunting the creatures that wore them; but being very fearful and awkward in a business so novel, their success was small; and it was not until the arrival of a party of Spanish hunters, men regularly trained to their calling upon the plains of California, that the work of slaughter was fairly begun.

The Spaniards were showy fellows, tricked out in gay blankets, leggings worked with porcupine quills, and jingling spurs. Mounted upon trained Indian mares, these heroes pursued their prey up to the very base of the burning mountains; making the profoundest solitudes ring with their shouts, and flinging the lasso under the very nose of the vixen goddess Pele. Hilo, a village upon the coast, was their place of resort; and thither flocked roving whites from all the islands of the group. As pupils of the dashing Spaniards, many of these dissipated fellows, quaffing too freely of the stirrup-cup, and riding headlong after the herds, when they reeled in the saddle, were unhorsed and killed.

This was about the year 1835, when the present king, Kamehameha III, was a lad. With royal impudence, laying claim to the sole property of the cattle, he was delighted with the idea of receiving one of every two silver dollars paid down for their hides; so, with no thought for the future, the work of extermination went madly on. In three years' time eighteen thousand bullocks were slain, almost entirely upon the single island of Hawaii.

The herds being thus nearly destroyed, the sagacious young prince imposed a rigorous "taboo" upon the few surviving cattle, which was to remain in force for ten years. During this period—not yet expired—all hunting is forbidden, unless directly authorized by the king.

The massacre of the cattle extended to the hapless goats. In one year, three thousand of their skins were sold to the merchants of Honolulu, fetching a *quartilia*, or a shilling sterling, apiece.

After this digression, it is time to run on after Tonoi and the Yankee.

1. Perhaps the most remarkable volcanoes in the world. For very interesting accounts of three adventurous expeditions to their summits (fourteen thousand feet above the level of the sea), see Lord Byron's *Voyage of H. B. M. Ship* Blonde; Ellis's *Journal of a Visit to the Sandwich Islands*; and Wilkes's *Narrative of the U.S. Exploring Expedition*.

Chapter LV

A Hunting Ramble with Zeke

At the foot of the mountain, a steep path went up among rocks and clefts, mantled with verdure. Here and there were green gulfs, down which it made one giddy to peep. At last we gained an overhanging, wooded shelf of land which crowned the heights; and along this, the path, well shaded, ran like a gallery.

In every direction, the scenery was enchanting. There was a low, rustling breeze; and below, in the vale, the leaves were quivering; the sea lay, blue and serene, in the distance; and inland the surface swelled up, ridge after ridge, and peak upon peak, all bathed in the Indian haze of the tropics, and dreamy to look upon. Still valleys, leagues away, reposed in the deep shadows of the mountains; and here and there, waterfalls lifted up their voices in the solitude. High above all, and central, the "Marling-spike" lifted its finger. Upon the hill-sides, small groups of bullocks were seen; some quietly browsing; others slowly winding into the valleys.

We went on, directing our course for a slope of these hills, a mile or two further, where the nearest bullocks were seen.

We were cautious in keeping to the windward of them; their sense of smell and hearing being, like those of all wild creatures, exceedingly acute.

As there was no knowing that we might not surprise some other kind of game in the coverts through which we were passing, we crept along warily.

The wild hogs of the island are uncommonly fierce; and as they often attack the natives, I could not help following Tonoi's example of once in a while peeping in under the foliage. Frequent retrospective glances, also, served to assure me that our retreat was not cut off.

As we rounded a clump of bushes, a noise behind them, like the crackling of dry branches, broke the stillness. In an instant Tonoi's hand was on a bough, ready for a spring, and Zeke's finger touched the trigger of his piece. Again the stillness was broken; and thinking it high time to get ready, I brought my musket to my shoulder.

"Look sharp!" cried the Yankee; and dropping on one knee, he brushed the twigs aside. Presently, off went his piece; and with a wild snort, a black, bristling boar—his cherry red lip curled up by two glittering tusks—dashed, unharmed, across the path, and crashed through the opposite thicket. I saluted him with a charge as he disappeared; but not the slightest notice was taken of the civility.

By this time Tonoi, the illustrious descendant of the Bishops of Imeeo, was twenty feet from the ground. "Aramai! come down, you old fool!" cried the Yankee; "the pesky critter's on t'other side of the island afore this."

"I rayther guess," he continued, as we began reloading, "that we've spoiled sport by firing at that 'ere 'tarnal hog. Them bullocks heard the racket, and is flinging their tails about now on the keen jump. Quick, Paul, and let's climb that rock yonder, and see if so be there's any in sight."

But none were to be seen, except at such a distance that they looked like ants.

As evening was now at hand, my companion proposed our returning home forthwith; and then, after a sound night's rest, starting in the morning upon a good day's hunt with the whole force of the plantation.

Following another path, in descending into the valley, we passed through some nobly wooded land on the face of the mountain.

One variety of tree particularly attracted my attention. The dark mossy stem, over seventy feet high, was perfectly branchless for many feet above the ground, when it shot out in broad boughs laden with lustrous leaves of the deepest green. And all round the lower part of the trunk, thin, slab-like buttresses of bark, perfectly smooth, and radiating from a common center, projected along the ground for at least two yards. From below, these natural props tapered upward until gradually blended with the trunk itself. There were signs of the wild cattle having sheltered themselves behind them. Zeke called this the canoe-tree; as in old times it supplied the navies of the kings of Tahiti. For canoe-building the wood is still used. Being extremely dense, and impervious to worms, it is very durable.

Emerging from the forest, when half-way down the hill-side, we came upon an open space, covered with ferns and grass, over which a few lonely trees were casting long shadows in the setting sun. Here, a piece of ground some hundred feet square, covered with weeds and brambles, and sounding hollow to the tread, was enclosed by a ruinous wall of stones. Tonoi said it was an almost forgotten burial-place, of great antiquity, where no one had been interred since the islanders had been Christians. Sealed up in dry, deep vaults, many a dead heathen was lying here.

Curious to prove the old man's statement, I was anxious to get a peep at the catacombs; but, hermetically overgrown with vegetation as they were, no aperture was visible.

Before gaining the level of the valley, we passed by the site of a village, near a watercourse, long since deserted. There was nothing but stone walls, and rude dismantled foundations of houses, constructed of the same material. Large trees and brushwood were growing rankly among them.

I asked Tonoi how long it was since anyone had lived here. "Me, *tamaree* (boy)—plenty *kanaka* (men) Martair," he replied. "Now, only poor *pehe kanaka* (fishermen) left—me born here."

Going down the valley, vegetation of every kind presented a different aspect from that of the high land.

Chief among the trees of the plain on this island, is the *Ati*, large and lofty, with a massive trunk, and broad, laurel-shaped leaves. The wood is splendid. In Tahiti, I was shown a narrow, polished plank, fit to make a cabinet for a king. Taken from the heart of the tree, it was of a deep, rich scarlet, traced with yellow veins, and in some places clouded with hazel.

In the same grove with the regal *Ati* you may see the beautiful flowering *Hotoo;* its pyramid of shining leaves diversified with numberless small, white blossoms.

Planted with trees as the valley is, almost throughout its entire length, I was astonished to observe so very few which were useful to the natives: not one in a hundred was a cocoanut or bread-fruit-tree.

But here Tonoi again enlightened me. In the sanguinary religious hostilities which ensued upon the conversion to Christianity of the first Pomaree, a war party from Tahiti destroyed (by girdling the bark) entire groves of these invaluable trees. For some time afterward, they stood stark and leafless in the sun; sad monuments of the fate which befell the inhabitants of the valley.

Chapter LVI

MOSQUITOES

THE NIGHT FOLLOWING THE HUNTING TRIP, LONG GHOST AND MYSELF, AFTER A VALIANT DEFENSE, had to fly the house on account of the mosquitoes.

And here I cannot avoid relating a story, rife among the natives, concerning the manner in which these insects were introduced upon the island.

Some years previous, a whaling captain, touching at an adjoining bay, got into difficulty with its inhabitants, and at last carried his complaint before one of the native tribunals; but receiving no satisfaction, and deeming himself aggrieved, he resolved upon taking signal revenge. One night, he towed a rotten old water-cask ashore, and left it in a neglected *Taro* patch, where the ground was warm and moist. Hence the mosquitoes.

I tried my best to learn the name of this man: and hereby do what I can to hand it down to posterity. It was Coleman—Nathan Coleman. The ship belonged to Nantucket.

When tormented by the mosquitoes, I found much relief in coupling the word "Coleman" with another of one syllable, and pronouncing them together energetically.

The doctor suggested a walk to the beach, where there was a long, low shed tumbling to pieces, but open lengthwise to a current of air which he thought might keep off the mosquitoes. So thither we went.

The ruin partially sheltered a relic of times gone by, which, a few days after, we examined with much curiosity. It was an old war-canoe, crumbling to dust. Being supported by the same rude blocks upon which, apparently, it had years before been hollowed out, in all probability it had never been afloat.

Outside, it seemed originally stained of a green color which, here and there, was now changed into a dingy purple. The prow terminated in a high, blunt beak; both sides were covered with carving; and upon the stern was something which Long Ghost maintained to be the arms of the royal House of Pomaree. The device had an heraldic look, certainly—being two sharks with the talons of hawks clawing a knot left projecting from the wood.

The canoe was at least forty feet long, about two wide, and four deep. The upper part—consisting of narrow planks laced together with cords of sinnate—had in many places fallen off, and lay decaying upon the ground. Still, there were ample accommodations left for sleeping; and in we sprang—the doctor into the bow, and I into the stern. I soon fell asleep; but waking suddenly, cramped in every joint from my constrained posture, I thought, for an instant, that I must have been prematurely screwed down in my coffin.

Presenting my compliments to Long Ghost, I asked how it fared with *him*.

"Bad enough," he replied, as he tossed about in the outlandish rubbish lying in the bottom of our couch. "Pah! how those old mats smell!"

As he continued talking in this exciting strain for some time, I at last made no reply, having resumed certain mathematical reveries to induce repose. But finding the multiplication-table of no avail, I summoned up a grayish image of chaos in a sort of sliding fluidity, and was just falling into a nap on the strength of it, when I heard a solitary and distinct buzz. The hour of my calamity was at hand. One blended hum, the creature darted into the canoe like a small sword-fish; and I out of it.

Upon getting into the open air, to my surprise, there was Long Ghost, fanning himself wildly with an old paddle. He had just made a noiseless escape from a swarm, which had attacked his own end of the canoe.

It was now proposed to try the water; so a small fishing canoe, hauled up nearby, was quickly launched; and paddling a good distance off, we dropped overboard the native contrivance for an anchor—a heavy stone, attached to a cable of braided bark. At this part of the island, the encircling reef was close to the shore, leaving the water within smooth, and extremely shallow.

It was a blessed thought! We knew nothing till sunrise, when the motion of our aquatic cot awakened us. I looked up, and beheld Zeke wading toward the shore, and towing us after him by the bark cable. Pointing to the reef, he told us we had had a narrow escape.

It was true enough; the water-sprites had rolled our stone out of its noose, and we had floated away.

Chapter LVII

THE SECOND HUNT IN THE MOUNTAINS

FAIR DAWNED, OVER THE HILLS OF MARTAIR, THE JOCUND MORNING OF OUR HUNT.

Everything had been prepared for it overnight; and, when we arrived at the house, a good breakfast was spread by Shorty: and old Tonoi was bustling about like an innkeeper. Several of his men, also, were in attendance, to accompany us with calabashes of food; and, in case we met with any success, to officiate as bearers of burdens, on our return.

Apprised, the evening previous, of the meditated sport, the doctor had announced his willingness to take part therein.

Now, subsequent events made us regard this expedition as a shrewd device of the Yankee's. Once get us off on a pleasure trip, and with what face could we afterwards refuse to work? Besides, he enjoyed all the credit of giving us a holiday. Nor did he omit assuring us, that, work or play, our wages were all the while running on.

A dilapidated old musket of Tonoi's was borrowed for the doctor. It was exceedingly short and heavy, with a clumsy lock, which required a strong finger to pull the trigger. On trying the piece, by firing at a mark, Long Ghost was satisfied that it could not fail of doing execution: the charge went one way, and he the other.

Upon this, he endeavored to negotiate an exchange of muskets with Shorty; but the Cockney was proof against his blandishments; at last he entrusted his weapon to one of the natives to carry for him.

Marshaling our forces, we started for the head of the valley; near which, a path ascended to a range of high land, said to be a favorite resort of the cattle.

Shortly after gaining the heights, a small herd, some way off, was perceived entering a wood. We hurried on; and, dividing our party, went in after them, at four different points; each white man followed by several natives.

I soon found myself in a dense covert; and, after looking round, was just emerging into a clear space, when I heard a report, and a bullet knocked the bark from a tree nearby. The same instant, there was a trampling and crashing; and five bullocks, nearly abreast, broke into view across the opening, and plunged right towards the spot where myself and three of the islanders were standing.

They were small, black, vicious-looking creatures; with short, sharp horns, red nostrils, and eyes like coals of fire. On they came—their dark wooly heads hanging down.

By this time, my island backers were roosting among the trees. Glancing round, for an instant, to discover a retreat in case of emergency, I raised my piece, when a voice cried out, from the wood, "Right between the 'orns, Paul! right between the 'orns!" Down went my barrel, in range with a small white tuft on the forehead of the headmost one; and, letting him have it, I darted to one side. As I turned again, the five bullocks shot by like a blast, making the air eddy in their wake.

The Yankee now burst into view, and saluted them in flank. Whereupon, the fierce little bull with the tufted forehead flirted his long tail over his buttocks, kicked out with his hind feet, and shot forward a full length. It was nothing but a graze; and in an instant they were out of sight, the thicket into which they broke rocking overhead, and marking their progress.

The action over, the heavy artillery came up, in the person of the Long Doctor, with his blunderbuss.

"Where are they?" he cried, out of breath.

"A mile or two hoff, by this time," replied the Cockney. "Lord, Paul! you ought to've sent an 'ail stone into that little black 'un."

While excusing my want of skill as well as I could, Zeke, rushing forward, suddenly exclaimed, "Creation! what are you 'bout there, Peter?"

Peter, incensed at our ill luck, and ignorantly imputing it to the cowardice of our native auxiliaries, was bringing his piece to bear upon his trembling squire—the musket carrier—now descending a tree.

Pulling trigger, the bullet went high over his head; and hopping to the ground, bellowing like a calf, the fellow ran away as fast as his heels could carry him. The rest followed us, after this, with fear and trembling.

After forming our line of march anew, we went on for several hours, without catching a glimpse of the game; the reports of the muskets having been heard at a great distance. At last, we mounted a craggy height, to obtain a wide view of the country. From this place, we beheld three cattle, quietly browsing in a green opening of a wood below; the trees shutting them in all round.

A general re-examination of the muskets now took place, followed by a hasty lunch from the calabashes: we then started. As we descended the mountain-side, the cattle were in plain sight, until we entered the forest, when we lost sight of them for a moment; but only to see them again, as we crept close up to the spot where they grazed.

They were a bull, a cow, and a calf. The cow was lying down in the shade, by the edge of the wood; the calf sprawling out before her in the grass, licking her lips; while old Taurus himself stood close by, casting a paternal glance at this domestic little scene, and conjugally elevating his nose in the air.

"Now, then," said Zeke, in a whisper, "let's take the poor creeturs, while they are huddled together. Crawl along, b'ys, crawl along. Fire together, mind; and not till I say the word."

We crept up to the very edge of the open ground, and knelt behind a clump of bushes, resting our leveled barrels among the branches. The slight rustling was heard. Taurus turned round, dropped his head to the ground, and sent forth a low, sullen bellow; then snuffed the air. The cow rose on her foreknees, pitched forward alarmedly, and stood upon her legs; while the calf, with ears pricked, got right underneath her. All three were now grouped, and, in an instant, would be off.

"I take the bull," cried our leader; "fire!"

The calf fell like a clod; its dam uttered a cry, and thrust her head into the thicket; but she turned, and came moaning up to the lifeless calf, going round and round it, snuffing fiercely with her bleeding nostrils. A crashing in the wood, and a loud roar, announced the flying bull.

Soon, another shot was fired, and the cow fell. Leaving some of the natives to look after the dead cattle, the rest of us hurried on after the bull; his dreadful bellowing guiding us to the spot where he lay. Wounded in the shoulder, in his fright and agony he had bounded into the wood; but when we came up to him, he had sunk to the earth in a green hollow, thrusting his black muzzle into a pool of his own blood, and tossing it over his hide in clots.

The Yankee brought his piece to a rest; and, the next instant, the wild brute sprang into the air, and with his forelegs crouching under him, fell dead.

Our island friends were now in high spirits; all courage and alacrity. Old Tonoi thought nothing of taking poor Taurus himself by the horns, and peering into his glazed eyes.

Our ship knives were at once in request; and, skinning the cattle, we hung them high up by cords of bark from the boughs of a tree. Withdrawing into a covert, we there waited for the wild hogs; which, according to Zeke, would soon make their appearance, lured by the smell of blood. Presently, we heard them coming, in two or three different directions; and, in a moment, they were tearing the offal to pieces.

As only one shot at these creatures could be relied on, we intended firing simultaneously; but, somehow or other, the doctor's piece went off by itself, and one of the hogs dropped. The others then breaking into the thicket, the rest of us sprang after them, resolved to have another shot at all hazards.

The Cockney darted among some bushes; and, a few moments after, we heard the report of his musket, followed by a quick cry. On running up, we saw our comrade doing battle with a young devil of a boar, as black as night, whose snout had been partly torn away. Firing when the game was in full career, and coming directly toward him, Shorty had been assailed by the enraged brute; it was now crunching the breech of the musket, with which he had tried to club it; Shorty holding fast to the barrel, and fingering his waist for a knife. Being in advance of the others, I clapped my gun to the boar's head, and so put an end to the contest.

Evening now coming on, we set to work loading our carriers. The cattle were so small, that a stout native could walk off with an entire quarter; brushing through thickets, and descending rocks without an apparent effort: though, to tell the truth, no white man present could have done the thing with any ease. As for the wild hogs, none of the islanders could be induced to carry Shorty's; some invincible superstition being connected with its black color. We were, therefore, obliged to leave it. The other, a spotted one, being slung by green thongs to a pole, was marched off with by two young natives.

With our bearers of burdens ahead, we then commenced our return down the valley. Half-way home, darkness overtook us in the woods; and torches became necessary. We stopped, and made them of dry palm branches; and then, sending two lads on in advance, for the purpose of gathering fuel to feed the flambeaux, we continued our journey.

It was a wild sight. The torches, waved aloft, flashed through the forest; and, where the ground admitted, the islanders went along on a brisk trot, notwithstanding they bent forward under their loads. Their naked backs were stained with blood; and occasionally, running by each other, they raised wild cries, which startled the hill-sides.

Chapter LVIII

THE HUNTING-FEAST; AND A VISIT TO AFREHITOO

TWO BULLOCKS AND A BOAR! NO BAD TROPHIES OF OUR DAY'S SPORT. SO BY TORCHLIGHT WE marched into the plantation, the wild hog rocking from its pole, and the doctor singing an old hunting-song—Tally-ho! the chorus of which swelled high above the yells of the natives.

We resolved to make a night of it. Kindling a great fire just outside the dwelling, and hanging one of the heifer's quarters from a limb of the banian-tree, everyone was at liberty to cut and broil for himself. Baskets of roasted bread-fruit, and plenty of taro pudding; bunches of bananas and young cocoanuts had also been provided by the natives against our return.

The fire burned bravely, keeping off the mosquitoes, and making every man's face glow like a beaker of port. The meat had the true wild-game flavor, not at all impaired by our famous appetites, and a couple of flasks of white brandy, which Zeke, producing from his secret store, circulated freely.

There was no end to my long comrade's spirits. After telling his stories, and singing his songs, he sprang to his feet, clasped a young damsel of the grove round the waist, and waltzed over the grass with her. But there's no telling all the pranks he played that night. The natives, who delight in a wag, emphatically pronounced him "maitai."

It was long after midnight ere we broke up; but when the rest had retired, Zeke, with the true thrift of a Yankee, salted down what was left of the meat.

The next day was Sunday; and, at my request, Shorty accompanied me to Afrehitoo—a neighboring bay, and the seat of a mission, almost directly opposite Papeetee. In Afrehitoo is a large church and school-house, both quite dilapidated; and planted amid shrubbery on a fine knoll, stands a very tasteful cottage, commanding a view across the channel. In passing, I caught sight of a graceful calico skirt disappearing from the piazza through a doorway. The place was the residence of the missionary.

A trim little sail-boat was dancing out at her moorings, a few yards from the beach.

Straggling over the low lands in the vicinity were several native huts—untidy enough—but much better every way than most of those in Tahiti.

We attended service at the church, where we found but a small congregation; and after what I had seen in Papeetee, nothing very interesting took place. But the audience had a curious, fidgety look, which I knew not how to account for, until we ascertained that a sermon with the eighth commandment for a text was being preached.

It seemed that there lived an Englishman in the district, who, like our friends, the planters, was cultivating Tombez potatoes for the Papeetee market.

In spite of all his precautions, the natives were in the habit of making nocturnal forays into his enclosure, and carrying off the potatoes. One night he fired a fowling-piece, charged with pepper and salt, at several shadows which he discovered stealing across his premises. They fled. But it was like seasoning anything else: the knaves stole again with a greater relish than ever; and the very next night, he caught a party in the act of roasting a basketful of potatoes under his own cooking-shed. At last, he stated his grievances to the missionary; who, for the benefit of his congregation, preached the sermon we heard.

Now, there were no thieves in Martair; but then the people of the valley were bribed to be honest. It was a regular business transaction between them and the planters. In consideration of so many potatoes "to them in hand, duly paid," they were to abstain from all depredations upon the plantation. Another security against roguery was the permanent residence upon the premises of their chief, Tonoi.

On our return to Martair, in the afternoon, we found the doctor and Zeke making themselves comfortable. The latter was reclining on the ground, pipe in mouth, watching the doctor, who, sitting like a Turk, before a large iron kettle, was slicing potatoes and Indian turnip, and now and then shattering splinters from a bone; all of which, by turns, were thrown into the pot. He was making what he called "bullock broth."

In gastronomic affairs, my friend was something of an artist; and, by way of improving his knowledge, did nothing the rest of the day but practice in what might be called Experimental Cookery; broiling and grilling, and deviling slices of meat, and subjecting them to all sorts of igneous operations. It was the first fresh beef that either of us had tasted in more than a year.

"Oh, ye'll pick up arter a while, Peter," observed Zeke, toward night, as Long Ghost was turning a great rib over the coals—"what d'ye think, Paul?"

"He'll get along, I daresay," replied I; "he only wants to get those cheeks of his tanned." To tell the truth, I was not a little pleased to see the doctor's reputation as an invalid fading away so fast; especially, as on the strength of his being one, he had promised to have such easy times of it, and very likely, too, at my expense.

Chapter LIX

THE MURPHIES

DOZING IN OUR CANOE THE NEXT MORNING ABOUT DAYBREAK, WE WERE WAKENED BY ZEKE'S hailing us loudly from the beach.

Upon paddling up, he told us that a canoe had arrived overnight, from Papeetee, with an order from a ship lying there, for a supply of his potatoes; and as they must be on board the vessel by noon, he wanted us to assist in bringing them down to his sail-boat.

My long comrade was one of those, who, from always thrusting forth the wrong foot foremost when they rise, or committing some other indiscretion of the limbs, are more or less crabbed or sullen before breakfast. It was in vain, therefore, that the Yankee deplored the urgency of the case, which obliged him to call us up thus early—the doctor only looked the more glum, and said nothing in reply.

At last, by way of getting up a little enthusiasm for the occasion, the Yankee exclaimed quite spiritedly, "What d'ye say, then, b'ys, shall we git at it?"

"Yes, in the devil's name!" replied the doctor, like a snapping turtle; and we moved on to the house. Notwithstanding his ungracious answer, he probably thought that after the gastronomic performance of the day previous, it would hardly do to hang back. At the house, we found Shorty ready with the hoes; and we at once repaired to the farther side of the enclosure, where the potatoes had yet to be taken out of the ground.

The rich, tawny soil seemed specially adapted to the crop; the great yellow murphies rolling out of the hills like eggs from a nest.

My comrade really surprised me by the zeal with which he applied himself to his hoe. For my own part, exhilarated by the cool breath of the morning, I worked away like a good fellow. As for Zeke and the Cockney, they seemed mightily pleased at this evidence of our willingness to exert ourselves.

It was not long ere all the potatoes were turned out; and then came the worst of it: they were to be lugged down to the beach, a distance of at least a quarter of a mile. And there being no such thing as a barrow or cart on the island, there was nothing for it but spinal marrows and broad shoulders. Well knowing that this part of the business would be anything but agreeable, Zeke did his best to put as encouraging a face upon it as possible; and giving us no time to indulge in desponding thoughts, gleefully directed our attention to a pile of rude baskets—made of stout stalks—which had been provided for the occasion. So, without more ado, we helped ourselves from the heap; and soon we were all four staggering along under our loads.

The first trip down, we arrived at the beach together, Zeke's enthusiastic cries proving irresistible. A trip or two more, however, and my shoulders began to grate in their sockets; while the doctor's tall figure acquired an obvious stoop. Presently, we both threw down our baskets, protesting we could stand it no longer. But our employers, bent, as it were, upon getting the work out of us by a silent appeal to our moral sense, toiled away without pretending to notice us. It was as much as to say, "There, men, we've been boarding and lodging ye for the last three days; and yesterday ye did nothing earthly but eat; so stand by now, and look at us working, if ye dare." Thus driven to it, then, we resumed our employment. Yet, in spite of all we could do, we lagged behind Zeke and Shorty, who, breathing hard, and perspiring at every pore, toiled away without pause or cessation. I almost wickedly wished that they would load themselves down with one potato too many.

Gasping as I was with my own hamper, I could not, for the life of me, help laughing at Long Ghost. There he went—his long neck thrust forward, his arms twisted behind him to form a shelf for his basket to rest on; and his stilts of legs every once in a while giving way under him, as if his knee-joints slipped either way.

"There! I carry no more!" he exclaimed all at once, flinging his potatoes into the boat, where the Yankee was just then stowing them away.

"Oh, then," said Zeke, quite briskly, "I guess you and Paul had better try the *'barrel-machine'*—come along, I'll fix ye out in no time"; and, so saying, he waded ashore, and hurried back to the house, bidding us follow.

Wondering what upon earth the *"barrel-machine"* could be, and rather suspicious of it, we limped after. On arriving at the house, we found him getting ready a sort of sedan-chair. It was nothing more than an old barrel, suspended by a rope from the middle of a stout oar. Quite an ingenious contrivance of the Yankee's; and his proposed arrangement with regard to mine and the doctor's shoulders, was equally so.

"There now!" said he, when everything was ready, "there's no back-breaking about this; you can stand right up under it, you see: jist try it once"; and he politely rested the blade of the oar on my comrade's right shoulder, and the other end on mine, leaving the barrel between us.

"Jist the thing!" he added, standing off admiringly, while we remained in this interesting attitude.

There was no help for us; with broken hearts and backs we trudged back to the field; the doctor all the while saying masses.

Upon starting with the loaded barrel, for a few paces we got along pretty well, and were constrained to think the idea not a bad one. But we did not long think so. In less than five minutes we came to a dead halt, the springing and buckling of the clumsy oar being almost unendurable.

"Let's shift ends," cried the doctor, who did not quite relish the blade of the stick, which was cutting into the blade of his shoulder.

At last, by stages short and frequent, we managed to shamble down to the beach, where we again dumped our cargo, in something of a pet.

"Why not make the natives help?" asked Long Ghost, rubbing his shoulder.

"Natives be dumned!" said the Yankee, "twenty on 'em ain't worth one white man. They never was meant to work any, them chaps; and they knows it too, for dumned little work any on 'em ever does."

But notwithstanding this abuse, Zeke was at last obliged to press a few of the bipeds into service. "Aramai!" (come here) he shouted to several, who, reclining on a bank, had hitherto been critical observers of our proceedings; and, among other things, had been particularly amused by the performance with the sedan-chair.

After making these fellows load their baskets together, the Yankee filled his own, and then drove them before him, down to the beach. Probably he had seen the herds of panniered mules, driven in this way by mounted Indians, along the great road from Callao to Lima.

The boat at last loaded, the Yankee taking with him a couple of natives, at once hoisted sail, and stood across the channel for Papeetee.

The next morning at breakfast, old Tonoi ran in, and told us that the voyagers were returning. We hurried down to the beach, and saw the boat gliding toward us, with a dozing islander at the helm, and Zeke standing up in the bows, jingling a small bag of silver, the proceeds of his cargo.

Chapter LX

WHAT THEY THOUGHT OF US IN MARTAIR

SEVERAL QUIET DAYS NOW PASSED AWAY, DURING WHICH WE JUST WORKED SUFFICIENTLY TO sharpen our appetites; the planters leniently exempting us from any severe toil.

Their desire to retain us became more and more evident; which was not to be wondered at; for, beside esteeming us from the beginning a couple of civil, good-natured fellows, who would soon become quite at home with them, they were not slow in perceiving that we were far different from the common run of rovers; and that our society was both entertaining and instructive to a couple of solitary, illiterate men, like themselves.

In a literary point of view, indeed, they soon regarded us with emotions of envy and wonder; and the doctor was considered nothing short of a prodigy. The Cockney found out, that he (the doctor) could read a book upside down, without even so much as spelling the big words beforehand; and the Yankee, in the twinkling of an eye, received from him the sum total of several arithmetical items, stated aloud, with the view of testing the extent of his mathematical lore.

Then, frequently, in discoursing upon men and things, my long comrade employed such imposing phrases, that, upon one occasion, they actually remained uncovered while he talked.

In short, their favorable opinion of Long Ghost in particular, rose higher and higher every day; and they began to indulge in all manner of dreams concerning the advantages to be derived from employing so learned a laborer. Among other projects revealed, was that of building a small craft of some forty tons, for the purpose of trading among the neighboring islands. With a native crew, we would then take turns cruising over the tranquil Pacific; touching here and there, as caprice suggested, and collecting romantic articles of commerce—biche-de-mer, the pearl-oyster, arrow-root, ambergris, sandal-wood, cocoanut oil, and edible birds' nests.

This South Sea yachting was delightful to think of; and straightway the doctor announced his willingness to navigate the future schooner clear of all shoals and reefs whatsoever. His impudence was audacious. He enlarged upon the science of navigation; treated us to a dissertation on Mercator's Sailing, and the Azimuth compass; and went into an inexplicable explanation of the Lord only knows what plan of his, for infallibly settling the longitude.

Whenever my comrade thus gave the reins to his fine fancy, it was a treat to listen, and therefore I never interfered; but, with the planters, sat in mute admiration before him. This apparent self-abasement on my part must have been considered as truly indicative of our respective merits; for, to my no small concern, I quickly perceived, that in the estimate formed of us, Long Ghost began to be rated far above myself. For aught I knew, indeed, he might have privately thrown out a hint concerning the difference in our respective stations aboard the *Julia*; or else, the planters must have considered him some illustrious individual, for certain inscrutable reasons going incog. With this idea of him, his undisguised disinclination for work became venial; and entertaining such views of extending their business, they counted more upon his ultimate value to them as a man of science than as a mere ditcher.

Nor did the humorous doctor forbear to foster an opinion every way so advantageous to himself; at times for the sake of the joke, assuming airs of superiority over myself, which, though laughable enough, were sometimes annoying.

To tell the plain truth, things at last came to such a pass, that I told him, up and down, that I had no notion to put up with his pretensions; if he were going to play the gentleman, I was going to follow suit; and then there would quickly be an explosion.

At this he laughed heartily; and after some mirthful chat, we resolved upon leaving the valley, as soon as we could do so with a proper regard to politeness.

At supper, therefore, the same evening, the doctor hinted at our intention.

Though much surprised and vexed, Zeke moved not a muscle. "Peter," said he at last—very gravely—and after mature deliberation, "would you like to do the *cooking?* It's easy work; and you needn't do anything else. Paul's heartier; he can work in the field when it suits him; and before long, we'll have ye at something more agreeable—won't we, Shorty?"

Shorty assented.

Doubtless, the proposed arrangement was a snug one; especially the sinecure for the doctor; but I by no means relished the functions allotted to myself—they were too indefinite. Nothing final, however, was agreed upon—our intention to leave was revealed, and that was enough for the present. But, as we said nothing further about going, the Yankee must have concluded that we might yet be induced to remain. He redoubled his endeavors to make us contented.

It was during this state of affairs, that one morning, before breakfast, we were set to weeding in a potato-patch; and the planters being engaged at the house, we were left to ourselves.

Now, though the pulling of weeds was considered by our employers an easy occupation (for which reason, they had assigned it to us), and although, as a garden recreation, it may be pleasant enough for those who like it—still, long persisted in, the business becomes excessively irksome.

Nevertheless, we toiled away for some time, until the doctor, who, from his height, was obliged to stoop at a very acute angle, suddenly sprang upright; and, with one hand propping his spinal column, exclaimed, "Oh, that one's joints were but provided with holes to drop a little oil through!"

Vain as the aspiration was for this proposed improvement upon our species, I cordially responded thereto; for every vertebra in my spine was articulating its sympathy.

Presently, the sun rose over the mountains, inducing that deadly morning languor so fatal to early exertion in a warm climate. We could stand it no longer; but, shouldering our hoes, moved on to the house, resolved to impose no more upon the good-nature of the planters, by continuing one moment longer in an occupation so extremely uncongenial.

We freely told them so. Zeke was exceedingly hurt, and said everything he could think of to alter our determination; but, finding all unavailing, he very hospitably urged us not to be in any hurry about leaving; for we might stay with him as guests until we had time to decide upon our future movements.

We thanked him sincerely; but replied, that the following morning we must turn our backs upon the hills of Martair.

Chapter LXI

PREPARING FOR THE JOURNEY

DURING THE REMAINDER OF THE DAY WE LOITERED ABOUT, TALKING OVER OUR PLANS.

The doctor was all eagerness to visit Tamai, a solitary inland village, standing upon the banks of a considerable lake of the same name, and embosomed among groves. From Afrehitoo you went to this place by a lonely pathway, leading through the wildest scenery in the world. Much, too, we had heard concerning the lake itself, which abounded in such delicious fish, that, in former times, angling parties occasionally came over to it from Papeetee.

Upon its banks, moreover, grew the finest fruit of the islands, and in their greatest perfection. The "Ve," or Brazilian plum, here attained the size of an orange; and the gorgeous "Arheea," or red apple of Tahiti, blushed with deeper dyes than in any of the seaward valleys.

Beside all this, in Tamai dwelt the most beautiful and unsophisticated women in the entire Society group. In short, the village was so remote from the coast, and had been so much less affected by recent changes than other places, that, in most things, Tahitian life was here seen as formerly existing in the days of young Otoo, the boy-king, in Cook's time.

After obtaining from the planters all the information which was needed, we decided upon penetrating to the village; and after a temporary sojourn there, to strike the beach again, and journey round to Taloo, a harbor on the opposite side of the island.

We at once put ourselves in traveling trim. Just previous to leaving Tahiti, having found my wardrobe reduced to two suits (frock and trousers, both much the worse for wear), I had quilted them together for mutual preservation (after a fashion peculiar to sailors); engrafting a red frock upon a blue one, and producing thereby a choice variety in the way of clothing. This was the extent of my wardrobe. Nor was the doctor by any means better off. His improvidence had at last driven him to don the nautical garb; but, by this time, his frock—a light cotton one—had almost given out, and he had nothing to replace it. Shorty very generously offered him one which was a little less ragged; but the alms were proudly refused; Long Ghost preferring to assume the ancient costume of Tahiti—the *"Roora."*

This garment, once worn as a festival dress, is now seldom met with; but Captain Bob had often shown us one which he kept as an heirloom. It was a cloak, or mantle of yellow tappa, precisely similar to the *"poncho,"* worn by the South American Spaniards. The head being slipped through a slit in the middle, the robe hangs about the person in ample drapery. Tonoi obtained sufficient coarse brown tappa to make a short mantle of this description; and in five minutes the doctor was equipped. Zeke, eyeing his *toga* critically, reminded its proprietor that there were many streams to ford, and precipices to scale, between Martair and Tamai; and if he traveled in petticoats, he had better hold them up.

Besides other deficiencies, we were utterly shoeless. In the free-and-easy Pacific, sailors seldom wear shoes; mine had been tossed overboard the day we met the Trades; and except in one or two tramps ashore, I had never worn any since. In Martair, they would have been desirable; but none were to be had. For the expedition we meditated, however, they were indispensable. Zeke, being the owner of a pair of huge, dilapidated boots, hanging from a rafter-like saddle-bag, the doctor succeeded in exchanging for them a case-knife, the last valuable article in his possession. For myself, I made sandals from a bullock's hide, such as are worn by the Indians in California. They are made in a minute; the sole, rudely fashioned to the foot, being confined across the instep by three straps of leather.

Our headgear deserves a passing word. My comrade's was a brave old Panama hat, made of grass, almost as fine as threads of silk; and so elastic, that, upon rolling it up, it sprang into perfect shape again. Set off by the jaunty slouch of this Spanish sombrero, Doctor Long Ghost, in this and his Roora, looked like a mendicant grandee.

Nor was my own appearance in an Eastern turban less distinguished. The way I came to wear it was this. My hat having been knocked overboard, a few days before reaching Papeetee, I was obliged to mount an abominable wad of parti-colored worsted—what sailors call a Scotch cap. Everyone knows the elasticity of knit wool; and this Caledonian head-dress crowned my temples so effectually, that the confined atmosphere engendered was prejudicial to my curls. In vain I tried to ventilate the cap: every gash made seemed to heal whole in no time. Then such a continual chafing as it kept up in a hot sun.

Seeing my dislike to the thing, Kooloo, my worthy friend, prevailed upon me to bestow it upon him. I did so; hinting that a good boiling might restore the original brilliancy of the colors.

It was then that I mounted the turban. Taking a new Regatta frock of the doctor's, which was of a gay calico, and winding it round my head in folds, I allowed the sleeves to droop behind—thus forming a good defense against the sun, though in a shower it was best off. The pendent sleeves adding much to the effect, the doctor always called me the Bashaw with Two Tails.

Thus arrayed, we were ready for Tamai; in whose green saloons, we counted upon creating no small sensation.

Chapter LXII

TAMAI

LONG BEFORE SUNRISE THE NEXT MORNING, MY SANDALS WERE LACED ON, AND THE DOCTOR had vaulted into Zeke's boots.

Expecting to see us again before we went to Taloo, the planters wished us a pleasant journey; and on parting, very generously presented us with a pound or two of what sailors call "plug" tobacco; telling us to cut it up into small change; the Virginian weed being the principal circulating medium on the island.

Tamai, we were told, was not more than three or four leagues distant; so making allowances for a wild road, a few hours to rest at noon, and our determination to take the journey leisurely, we counted upon reaching the shores of the lake some time in the flush of the evening.

For several hours we went on slowly through wood and ravine, and over hill and precipice, seeing nothing but occasional herds of wild cattle, and often resting; until we found ourselves, about noon, in the very heart of the island.

It was a green, cool hollow among the mountains, into which we at last descended with a bound. The place was gushing with a hundred springs, and shaded over with great solemn trees, on whose mossy boles the moisture stood in beads. Strange to say, no traces of the bullocks ever having been here were revealed. Nor was there a sound to be heard, nor a bird to be seen, nor any breath of wind stirring the leaves. The utter solitude and silence were oppressive; and after peering about under the shades, and seeing nothing but ranks of dark, motionless trunks, we hurried across the hollow, and ascended a steep mountain opposite.

Midway up we rested where the earth had gathered about the roots of three palms, and thus formed a pleasant lounge, from which we looked down upon the hollow, now one dark-green tuft of woodland at our feet. Here we brought forth a small calabash of *"poee,"* a parting present from Tonoi. After eating heartily, we obtained fire by two sticks, and throwing ourselves back, puffed forth our fatigue in wreaths of smoke. At last we fell asleep; nor did we waken till the sun had sunk so low, that its rays darted in upon us under the foliage.

Starting up, we then continued our journey; and as we gained the mountain-top—there, to our surprise, lay the lake and village of Tamai. We had thought it a good league off. Where we stood, the yellow sunset was still lingering; but over the valley below, long shadows were stealing—the rippling green lake reflecting the houses and trees just as they stood along its banks. Several small canoes, moored here and there to posts in the water, were dancing upon the waves; and one solitary fisherman was paddling over to a grassy point. In front of the houses, groups of natives were seen; some thrown at full length upon the ground, and others indolently leaning against the bamboos.

With whoop and halloo, we ran down the hills, the villagers soon hurrying forth to see who were coming. As we drew near, they gathered round, all curiosity to know what brought the "karhowrees" into their quiet country. The doctor contriving to make them understand the purely social object of our visit, they gave us a true Tahitian welcome; pointing into their dwellings, and saying they were ours as long as we chose to remain.

We were struck by the appearance of these people, both men and women, so much more healthful than the inhabitants of the bays. As for the young girls, they were more retiring and modest, more tidy in their dress, and far fresher and more beautiful than the damsels of the coast. A thousand pities, thought I, that they should bury their charms in this nook of a valley.

That night we abode in the house of Rartoo, a hospitable old chief. It was right on the shore of the lake; and at supper, we looked out through a rustling screen of foliage upon the surface of the starlit water.

The next day we rambled about, and found a happy little community, comparatively free from many deplorable evils to which the rest of their countrymen are subject. Their time, too, was more occupied. To my surprise, the manufacture of tappa was going on in several buildings. European calicoes were seldom seen, and not many articles of foreign origin of any description.

The people of Tamai were nominally Christians; but being so remote from ecclesiastical jurisdiction, their religion sat lightly upon them. We had been told, even, that many heathenish games and dances still secretly lingered in their valley.

Now the prospect of seeing an old-fashioned "hevar," or Tahitian reel, was one of the inducements which brought us here; and so, finding Rartoo rather liberal in his religious ideas, we disclosed our desire. At first, he demurred; and shrugging his shoulders like a Frenchman, declared it could not be brought about—was a dangerous matter to attempt, and might bring all concerned into trouble. But we overcame all this, convinced him that the thing could be done, and a "hevar," a genuine pagan fandango, was arranged for that very night.

Chapter LXIII

A Dance in the Valley

There were some ill-natured people—tell-tales—it seemed, in Tamai; and hence there was a deal of mystery about getting up the dance.

An hour or two before midnight, Rartoo entered the house, and, throwing robes of tappa over us, bade us follow at a distance behind him; and, until out of the village, hood our faces. Keenly alive to the adventure, we obeyed. At last, after taking a wide circuit, we came out upon the farthest shore of the lake. It was a wide, dewy space; lighted up by a full moon, and carpeted with a minute species of fern, growing closely together. It swept right down to the water, showing the village opposite, glistening among the groves.

Near the trees, on one side of the clear space, was a ruinous pile of stones, many rods in extent; upon which had formerly stood a temple of Oro. At present, there was nothing but a rude hut, planted on the lowermost terrace. It seemed to have been used as a *"tappa herree"*; or house for making the native cloth.

Here we saw lights gleaming from between the bamboos, and casting long, rod-like shadows upon the ground without. Voices also were heard. We went up, and had a peep at the dancers, who were getting ready for the ballet. They were some twenty in number; waited upon by hideous old crones, who might have been duennas. Long Ghost proposed to send the latter packing; but Rartoo said it would never do, and so they were permitted to remain.

We tried to effect an entrance at the door, which was fastened; but, after a noisy discussion with one of the old witches within, our guide became fidgety, and, at last, told us to desist, or we would spoil all. He then led us off to a distance, to await the performance; as the girls, he said, did not wish to be recognized. He, furthermore, made us promise to remain where we were, until all was over and the dancers had retired.

We waited impatiently; and at last they came forth. They were arrayed in short tunics of white tappa; with garlands of flowers on their heads. Following them were the duennas, who remained clustering about the house, while the girls advanced a few paces; and, in an instant, two of them, taller than their companions, were standing side by side, in the middle of a ring, formed by the clasped hands of the rest. This movement was made in perfect silence.

Presently, the two girls join hands overhead; and, crying out, "Ahloo! ahloo!" wave them to and fro. Upon which, the ring begins to circle slowly; the dancers moving sideways, with their arms a little drooping. Soon they quicken their pace; and, at last, fly round and round; bosoms heaving, hair streaming, flowers dropping, and every sparkling eye circling in what seemed a line of light.

Meanwhile, the pair within are passing and repassing each other incessantly. Inclining sideways, so that their long hair falls far over, they glide this way and that; one foot continually in the air, and their fingers thrown forth, and twirling in the moonbeams.

"Ahloo! ahloo!" again cry the dance queens; and, coming together in the middle of the ring, they once more lift up the arch, and stand motionless.

"Ahloo! ahloo!" Every link of the circle is broken; and the girls, deeply breathing, stand perfectly still. They pant hard and fast, a moment or two; and then, just as the deep flush is dying away from their faces, slowly recede, all round; thus enlarging the ring.

Again the two leaders wave their hands, when the rest pause; and now, far apart, stand in the still moonlight, like a circle of fairies. Presently, raising a strange chant, they softly sway themselves, gradually quickening the movement, until at length, for a few passionate moments, with throbbing bosoms, and glowing cheeks, they abandon themselves to all the spirit of the dance, apparently lost to everything around. But soon subsiding again into the same languid measure as before, they become motionless; and then, reeling forward on all sides, their eyes swimming in their heads, join in one wild chorus, and sink into each other's arms.

Such is the Lory-Lory, I think they call it; the dance of the backsliding girls of Tamai.

While it was going on, we had as much as we could do to keep the doctor from rushing forward and seizing a partner.

They would give us no more "hevars" that night; and Rartoo fairly dragged us away to a canoe, hauled up on the lake shore; when we reluctantly embarked, and paddling over to the village, arrived there in time for a good nap before sunrise.

The next day, the doctor went about, trying to hunt up the overnight dancers. He thought to detect them by their late rising; but never was man more mistaken; for, on first sallying out, the whole village was asleep, waking up in concert about an hour after. But, in the course of the day, he came across several, whom he at once charged with taking part in the "hevar." There were some prim-looking fellows standing by (visiting elders from Afrehitoo, perhaps), and the girls looked embarrassed; but parried the charge most skillfully.

Though soft as doves, in general, the ladies of Tamai are, nevertheless, flavored with a slight tincture of what we very queerly enough call the *"devil"*; and they showed it on the present occasion. For when the doctor pressed one rather hard, she all at once turned round upon him, and, giving him a box on the ear, told him to "hanree perrar!" (be off with himself).

Chapter LXIV

Mysterious

THERE WAS A LITTLE OLD MAN, OF A MOST HIDEOUS ASPECT, LIVING IN TAMAI, WHO, IN A COARSE mantle of tappa, went about the village, dancing, and singing, and making faces. He followed us about, wherever we went; and, when unobserved by others, plucked at our garments, making frightful signs for us to go along with him somewhere, and see something.

It was in vain that we tried to get rid of him. Kicks and cuffs, even, were at last resorted to; but, though he howled like one possessed, he would not go away, but still haunted us. At last, we conjured the natives to rid us of him; but they only laughed; so we were forced to endure the dispensation as well as we could.

On the fourth night of our visit, returning home late from paying a few calls through the village, we turned a dark corner of trees, and came full upon our goblin friend; as usual, chattering and motioning with his hands. The doctor, venting a curse, hurried forward; but, from some impulse or other, I stood my ground, resolved to find out what this unaccountable object wanted of us. Seeing me pause, he crept close up to me, peered into my face, and then retreated, beckoning me to follow, which I did.

In a few moments the village was behind us; and with my guide in advance, I found myself in the shadow of the heights overlooking the farther side of the valley. Here my guide paused until I came up with him; when, side by side, and without speaking, we ascended the hill.

Presently we came to a wretched hut, barely distinguishable in the shade cast by the neighboring trees. Pushing aside a rude sliding door, held together with thongs, the goblin signed me to enter. Within, it looked dark as pitch; so I gave him to understand that he must strike a light, and go in before me. Without replying, he disappeared in the darkness; and, after groping about, I heard two sticks rubbing together, and directly saw a spark. A native taper was then lighted, and I stooped and entered.

It was a mere kennel. Foul old mats, and broken cocoanut shells, and calabashes were strewn about the floor of earth; and overhead, I caught glimpses of the stars through chinks in the roof. Here and there, the thatch had fallen through, and hung down in wisps.

I now told him to set about what he was going to do, or produce whatever he had to show, without delay. Looking round fearfully, as if dreading a surprise, he commenced turning over and over the rubbish in one corner. At last, he clutched a calabash, stained black, and with a neck broken off; on one side of it was a large hole. Something seemed to be stuffed away in the vessel; and after a deal of poking at the aperture, a musty old pair of sailor trousers was drawn forth; and, holding them up eagerly, he inquired how many pieces of tobacco I would give for them?

Without replying, I hurried away; the old man chasing me, and shouting as I ran, until I gained the village. Here, I dodged him, and made my way home, resolved never to disclose so inglorious an adventure.

To no purpose, the next morning, my comrade besought me to enlighten him: I preserved a mysterious silence.

The occurrence served me a good turn, however, so long as we abode in Tamai; for the old clothesman never afterward troubled me; but forever haunted the doctor, who, in vain, supplicated Heaven to be delivered from him.

Chapter LXV

THE HEGIRA, OR FLIGHT

I SAY, DOCTOR," CRIED I, A FEW DAYS AFTER MY ADVENTURE WITH THE GOBLIN, AS, IN THE ABSENCE of our host, we were one morning lounging upon the matting in his dwelling, smoking our reed pipes, "Tamai's a thriving place; why not settle down?"

"Faith!" said he, "not a bad idea, Paul. But do you fancy they'll let us stay, though?"

"Why, certainly: they would be overjoyed to have a couple of karhowrees for townsmen."

"Gad! you're right, my pleasant fellow. Ha! ha! I'll put up a banana-leaf as physician from London—deliver lectures on Polynesian antiquities—teach English in five lessons, of one hour each—establish power-looms for the manufacture of tappa—lay out a public park in the middle of the village, and found a festival in honor of Captain Cook!"

"But, surely, not without stopping to take breath," observed I.

The doctor's projects, to be sure, were of a rather visionary cast; but we seriously thought, nevertheless, of prolonging our stay in the valley for an indefinite period; and, with this understanding, we were turning over various plans for spending our time pleasantly, when several women came running into the house, and hurriedly besought us to *heree! heree!* (make our escape), crying out something about the *mickonarees.*

Thinking that we were about to be taken up under the act for the suppression of vagrancy, we flew out of the house, sprang into a canoe before the door, and paddled with might and main over to the opposite side of the lake.

Approaching Rartoo's dwelling, was a great crowd, among which we perceived several natives, who, from their partly European dress, we were certain did not reside in Tamai.

Plunging into the groves, we thanked our stars that we had thus narrowly escaped being apprehended as runaway seamen, and marched off to the beach. This, at least, was what we thought we had escaped.

Having fled the village, we could not think of prowling about its vicinity, and then returning; in doing so, we might be risking our liberty again. We therefore determined upon journeying back to Martair; and setting our faces thitherward, we reached the planters' house about nightfall. They gave us a cordial reception, and a hearty supper; and we sat up talking until a late hour.

We now prepared to go round to Taloo, a place from which we were not far off when at Tamai; but wishing to see as much of the island as we could, we preferred returning to Martair, and then going round by way of the beach. Taloo, the only frequented harbor of Imeeo, lies on the western side of the island, almost directly over against Martair. Upon one shore of the bay stands the village of Partoowye, a missionary station. In its vicinity is an extensive sugar plantation—the best in the South Seas, perhaps—worked by a person from Sydney.

The patrimonial property of the husband of Pomaree, and every way a delightful retreat, Partoowye was one of the occasional residences of the court. But at the time I write of, it was permanently fixed there, the queen having fled thither from Tahiti.

Partoowye, they told us, was by no means the place Papeetee was. Ships seldom touched, and very few foreigners were living ashore. A solitary whaler, however, was reported to be lying in the harbor, wooding and watering, and to be in want of men.

All things considered, I could not help looking upon Taloo as offering "a splendid opening" for us adventurers. To say nothing of the facilities presented for going to sea in the whaler, or hiring ourselves out as day laborers in the sugar plantation, there were hopes to be entertained of being promoted to some office of high trust and emolument, about the person of her majesty, the queen.

Nor was this expectation altogether Quixotic. In the train of many Polynesian princes, roving whites are frequently found: gentlemen pensioners of state, basking in the tropical sunshine of the court, and leading the pleasantest lives in the world. Upon islands little visited by foreigners, the first seaman that settles down is generally domesticated in the family of the head chief or king; where he frequently discharges the functions of various offices, elsewhere filled by as many different individuals. As historiographer, for instance, he gives the natives some account of distant countries; as commissioner of the arts and sciences, he instructs them in the use of the jack-knife, and the best way of shaping bits of iron hoop into spearheads; and as interpreter to his majesty, he facilitates intercourse with strangers; besides instructing the people generally in the uses of the most common English phrases, civil and profane; but oftener the latter.

These men generally marry well; often—like Hardy of Hannamanoo—into the blood royal.

Sometimes they officiate as personal attendant, or first lord in waiting, to the king. At Amboi, one of the Tonga Islands, a vagabond Welshman bends his knee as cupbearer to his cannibal majesty. He mixes his morning cup of "arva," and, with profound genuflections presents it in a cocoanut bowl, richly carved. Upon another island of the same group, where it is customary to bestow no small pains in dressing the hair—frizzing it out by a curious process, into an enormous Pope's-head—an old man-of-war's-man fills the post of barber to the king. And as his majesty is not very neat, his mop is exceedingly populous; so that, when Jack is not engaged in dressing the head entrusted to his charge, he busies himself in gently titillating it—a sort of skewer being actually worn about in the patient's hair for that special purpose.

Even upon the Sandwich Islands, a low rabble of foreigners is kept about the person of Kamehameha, for the purpose of ministering to his ease or enjoyment.

Billy Loon, a jolly little negro, tricked out in a soiled blue jacket, studded all over with rusty bell-buttons, and garnished with shabby gold lace, is the royal drummer and pounder of the tambourine. Joe, a wooden-legged Portuguese, who lost his leg by a whale, is violinist; and Mordecai, as he is called, a villainous-looking scamp, going about with his cups and balls in a side pocket, diverts the court with his jugglery. These idle rascals receive no fixed salary, being altogether dependent upon the casual bounty of their master. Now and then they run up a score at the dance houses in Honolulu, where the illustrious Kamehameha III afterwards calls and settles the bill.

A few years since, an auctioneer to his majesty came near being added to the retinue of state. It seems that he was the first man who had practiced his vocation on the Sandwich Islands; and delighted with the sport of bidding upon his wares, the king was one of his best customers. At last he besought the man to leave his profession, and he should be handsomely provided for at court. But the auctioneer refused; and so the ivory hammer lost the chance of being borne before him on a velvet cushion, when the next king went to be crowned.

But it was not as strolling players, nor as footmen out of employ, that the doctor and myself looked forward to our approaching introduction to the court of the Queen of Tahiti. On the contrary, as before hinted, we expected to swell the appropriations of bread-fruit and cocoanuts on the civil list, by filling some honorable office in her gift.

We were told, that to resist the usurpation of the French, the queen was rallying about her person all the foreigners she could. Her partiality for the English and Americans was well known; and this was an additional ground for our anticipating a favorable reception. Zeke had informed us, moreover, that by the queen's counselors at Partoowye, a war of aggression against the invaders of Papeetee had been seriously thought of. Should this prove true, a surgeon's commission for the doctor, and a lieutenancy for myself, were certainly counted upon in our sanguine expectations.

Such, then, were our views, and such our hopes in projecting a trip to Taloo. But in our most lofty aspirations, we by no means lost sight of any minor matters which might help us to promotion. The doctor had informed me, that he excelled in playing the fiddle. I now suggested, that as soon as we arrived at Partoowye, we should endeavor to borrow a violin for him; or if this could not be done, that he should manufacture some kind of a substitute, and thus equipped, apply for an audience of the queen. Her well-known passion for music would at once secure his admittance; and so, under the most favorable auspices, bring about our introduction to her notice.

"And who knows," said my waggish comrade, throwing his head back, and performing an imaginary air by briskly drawing one arm across the other, "who knows, that I may not fiddle myself into her majesty's good graces, so as to became a sort of Rizzio to the Tahitian princess?"

Chapter LXVI

How We Were to Get to Taloo

THE INGLORIOUS CIRCUMSTANCES OF OUR SOMEWHAT PREMATURE DEPARTURE FROM TAMAI, filled the sagacious doctor and myself with sundry misgivings for the future.

Under Zeke's protection, we were secure from all impertinent interference in our concerns on the part of the natives. But as friendless wanderers over the island, we ran the risk of being apprehended as runaways, and as such, sent back to Tahiti. The truth is, that the rewards constantly offered for the apprehension of deserters from ships, induce some of the natives to eye all strangers suspiciously.

A passport was therefore desirable; but such a thing had never been heard of in Imeeo. At last, Long Ghost suggested, that as the Yankee was well known, and much respected all over the island, we should endeavor to obtain from him some sort of paper, not only certifying to our having been in his employ, but also to our not being highwaymen, kidnappers, nor yet runaway seamen. Even written in English, a paper like this would answer every purpose; for the unlettered natives, standing in great awe of the document, would not dare to molest us until acquainted with its purport. Then, if it came to the worst, we might repair to the nearest missionary, and have the passport explained.

Upon informing Zeke of these matters, he seemed highly flattered with the opinion we entertained of his reputation abroad; and he agreed to oblige us. The doctor at once offered to furnish him with a draft of the paper; but he refused, saying he would write it himself. With a rooster's quill, therefore, a bit of soiled paper, and a stout heart, he set to work. Evidently, he was not accustomed to composition; for his literary throes were so violent, that the doctor suggested that some sort of a Cæsarian operation might be necessary.

The precious paper was at last finished; and a great curiosity it was. We were much diverted with his reasons for not dating it.

"In this here dumned climate," he observed, "a feller can't keep the run of the months, no how; cause there's no seasons; no summer and winter to go by. One's etarnally thinkin' it's always July, it's so pesky hot."

A passport provided, we cast about for some means of getting to Taloo.

The island of Imeeo is very nearly surrounded by a regular breakwater of coral, extending within a mile or less of the shore. The smooth canal within furnishes the best means of communication with the different settlements; all of which, with the exception of Tamai, are right upon the water. And so indolent are the Imeeose, that they think nothing of going twenty or thirty miles round the island, in a canoe, in order to reach a place not a quarter of that distance by land. But as hinted before, the fear of the bullocks has something to do with this.

The idea of journeying in a canoe struck our fancy quite pleasantly; and we at once set about chartering one, if possible. But none could we obtain. For not only did we have nothing to pay for hiring one, but we could not expect to have it loaned; inasmuch as the good-natured owner would, in all probability, have to walk along the beach as we paddled, in order to bring back his property when we had no further use for it.

At last, it was decided to commence our journey on foot; trusting that we would soon fall in with a canoe going our way, in which we might take passage.

The planters said we would find no beaten path—all we had to do was to follow the beach; and however inviting it might look inland, on no account must we stray from it. In short, the longest way round was the nearest way to Taloo. At intervals, there were little hamlets along the shore, besides lonely fishermen's huts here and there, where we could get plenty to eat without pay; so there was no necessity to lay in any store.

Intending to be off before sunrise the next morning, so as to have the benefit of the coolest part of the day, we bade our kind hosts farewell overnight; and then, repairing to the beach, we launched our floating pallet, and slept away merrily till dawn.

Chapter LXVII

The Journey Round the Beach

It was on the fourth day of the first month of the Hegira, or flight from Tamai (we now reckoned our time thus), that, rising bright and early, we were up and away out of the valley of Martair, before the fishermen even were stirring.

It was the earliest dawn. The morning only showed itself along the lower edge of a bank of purple clouds, pierced by the misty peaks of Tahiti. The tropical day seemed too languid to rise. Sometimes, starting fitfully, it decked the clouds with faint edgings of pink and gray, which, fading away, left all dim again. Anon, it threw out thin, pale rays, growing lighter and lighter, until at last, the golden morning sprang out of the east with a bound—darting its bright beams hither and thither, higher and higher, and sending them, broadcast, over the face of the heavens.

All balmy from the groves of Tahiti, came an indolent air, cooled by its transit over the waters; and grateful under foot was the damp and slightly yielding beach, from which the waves seemed just retired.

The doctor was in famous spirits; removing his Roora, he went splashing into the sea; and, after swimming a few yards, waded ashore, hopping, skipping, and jumping along the beach; but very careful to cut all his capers in the direction of our journey.

Say what they will of the glowing independence one feels in the saddle, give me the first morning flush of your cheery pedestrian!

Thus exhilarated, we went on, as light-hearted and care-free as we could wish.

And here I cannot refrain from lauding the very superior inducements which most intertropical countries afford, not only to mere rovers like ourselves, but to penniless people generally. In these genial regions, one's wants are naturally diminished; and those which remain are easily gratified: fuel, house-shelter, and, if you please, clothing, may be entirely dispensed with.

How different, our hard northern latitudes! Alas! the lot of a "poor devil," twenty degrees north of the Tropic of Cancer, is indeed pitiable.

At last, the beach contracted to hardly a yard's width, and the dense thicket almost dipped into the sea. In place of the smooth sand, too, we had sharp fragments of broken coral, which made traveling exceedingly unpleasant. "Lord! my foot!" roared the doctor, fetching it up for inspection, with a galvanic fling of the limb. A sharp splinter had thrust itself into the flesh, through a hole in his boot. My sandals were worse yet; their soles taking a sort of fossil impression of everything trod upon.

Turning round a bold sweep of the beach, we came upon a piece of fine, open ground, with a fisherman's dwelling in the distance, crowning a knoll which rolled off into the water.

The hut proved to be a low, rude erection, very recently thrown up; for the bamboos were still green as grass, and the thatching, fresh and fragrant as meadow hay. It was open upon three sides; so that, upon drawing near, the domestic arrangements within were in plain sight. No one was stirring; and nothing was to be seen but a clumsy old chest of native workmanship, a few calabashes, and bundles of tappa hanging against a post; and a heap of something, we knew not what, in a dark corner. Upon close inspection, the doctor discovered it to be a loving old couple, locked in each other's arms, and rolled together in a tappa mantle.

"Halloa! Darby!" he cried, shaking the one with a beard. But Darby heeded him not; though Joan, a wrinkled old body, started up in affright, and yelled aloud. Neither of us attempting to gag her, she presently became quiet; and after staring hard, and asking some unintelligible questions, she proceeded to rouse her still slumbering mate.

What ailed him, we could not tell; but there was no waking him. Equally in vain were all his dear spouse's cuffs, pinches, and other endearments; he lay like a log, face up, snoring away like a cavalry trumpeter.

"Here, my good woman," said Long Ghost, "just let *me* try"; and, taking the patient right by his nose, he so lifted him bodily, into a sitting position, and held him there until his eyes opened. When this event came to pass, Darby looked round like one stupefied; and then, springing to his feet, backed away into a corner, from which place we became the objects of his earnest and respectful attention.

"Permit me, my dear Darby, to introduce to you my esteemed friend and comrade, Paul," said the doctor, gallanting me up with all the grimace and flourish imaginable. Upon this, Darby began to recover his faculties, and surprised us not a little, by talking a few words of English. So far as could be understood, they were expressive of his having been aware, that there were two "karhowrees" in the neighborhood; that he was glad to see us, and would have something for us to eat in no time.

How he came by his English, was explained to us before we left. Some time previous, he had been a denizen of Papeetee, where the native language is broidered over with the most classic sailor phrases. He seemed to be quite proud of his residence there, and alluded to it in the same significant way in which a provincial informs you that in his time he has resided in the capital. The old fellow was disposed to be garrulous; but being sharp-set, we told him to get breakfast; after which we would hear his anecdotes. While employed among the calabashes, the strange, antiquated fondness between these old semi-savages was really amusing. I made no doubt that they were saying to each other, "Yes, my love"—"No, my life," just in the same way that some young couples do at home.

They gave us a hearty meal; and, while we were discussing its merits, they assured us, over and over again, that they expected nothing in return for their attentions; more: we were at liberty to stay as long as we pleased, and, as long as we *did* stay, their house and everything they had, was no longer theirs, but ours; still more: they themselves were our slaves—the old lady, to a degree that was altogether superfluous. This, now, is Tahitian hospitality! Self-immolation upon one's own hearthstone for the benefit of the guest.

The Polynesians carry their hospitality to an amazing extent. Let a native of Waiurar, the westernmost part of Tahiti, make his appearance as a traveler at Partoowye, the most easterly village of Imeeo, though a perfect stranger, the inhabitants on all sides accost him at their doorways, inviting him to enter, and make himself at home. But the traveler passes on, examining every house attentively, until, at last, he pauses before one which suits him, and then exclaiming, "Ah, ena maitai" (this one will do, I think), he steps in, and makes himself perfectly at ease, flinging himself upon the mats, and very probably calling for a nice young cocoanut, and a piece of toasted bread-fruit, sliced thin, and done brown.

Curious to relate, however, should a stranger carrying it thus bravely, be afterward discovered to be without a house of his own, why, he may thenceforth go a-begging for his lodgings. The "karhowrees," or white men, are exceptions to this rule. Thus it is precisely as in civilized countries; where those who have houses and lands are incessantly bored to death with invitations to come and live in other people's houses, while many a poor gentleman who inks the seams of his coat, and to whom the like invitation would be really acceptable, may go and sue for it. But to the credit of the ancient Tahitians, it should here be observed, that this blemish upon their hospitality is only of recent origin, and was wholly unknown in old times. So told me Captain Bob.

In Polynesia it is esteemed a great hit, if a man succeed in marrying into a family, to which the best part of the community is related (Heaven knows it is otherwise with us). The reason is, that when he goes a-traveling, the greater number of houses are the more completely at his service.

Receiving a paternal benediction from old Darby and Joan, we continued our journey; resolved to stop at the very next place of attraction which offered.

Nor did we long stroll for it. A fine walk along a beach of shells, and we came to a spot, where with trees here and there, the land was all meadow, sloping away to the water, which stirred a sedgy growth of reeds bordering its margin. Close by was a little cove, walled in with coral, where a fleet of canoes was dancing up and down. A few paces distant, on a natural terrace overlooking the sea, were several native dwellings, newly thatched, and peeping into view out of the foliage, like summer-houses.

As we drew near, forth came a burst of voices; and presently, three gay girls, overflowing with life, health, and youth, and full of spirits and mischief. One was arrayed in a flaunting robe of calico; and her long black hair was braided behind in two immense tresses, joined together at the ends, and wreathed with the green tendrils of a vine. From her self-possessed and forward air I fancied she might be some young lady from Papeetee, on a visit to her country relations. Her companions wore mere slips of cotton cloth; their hair was disheveled; and, though very pretty, they betrayed the reserve and embarrassment characteristic of the provinces.

The little gypsy first mentioned ran up to me with great cordiality; and giving the Tahitian salutation, opened upon me such a fire of questions, that there was no understanding, much less answering, them. But our hearty welcome to Loohooloo, as she called the hamlet, was made plain enough. Meanwhile, Doctor Long Ghost gallantly presented an arm to each of the other young ladies, which at first they knew not what to make of; but at last, taking it for some kind of joke, accepted the civility.

The names of these three damsels were at once made known by themselves; and being so exceedingly romantic, I cannot forbear particularizing them. Upon my comrade's arms, then, were hanging Night and Morning, in the persons of Farnowar, or the Day-born, and Farnoopoo, or the Night-born. She with the tresses was very appropriately styled Marhar-Rarrar, the Wakeful, or Bright-eyed.

By this time, the houses were emptied of the rest of their inmates—a few old men and women, and several strapping young fellows rubbing their eyes and yawning. All crowded round putting questions as to whence we came. Upon being informed of our acquaintance with Zeke, they were delighted; and one of them recognized the boots worn by the doctor. "Keekee (Zeke) maitai," they cried, "nuee nuee hanna hanna portarto"—(makes plenty of potatoes).

There was now a little friendly altercation as to who should have the honor of entertaining the strangers. At last, a tall old gentleman, by name Marharvai, with a bald head and white beard, took us each by the hand, and led us into his dwelling. Once inside, Marharvai, pointing about with his staff, was so obsequious in assuring us that his house was ours, that Long Ghost suggested he might as well hand over the deed.

It was drawing near noon; so after a light lunch of roasted bread-fruit, a few whiffs of a pipe, and some lively chatting, our host admonished the company to lie down, and take the everlasting siesta. We complied; and had a social nap all round.

Chapter LXVIII

A Dinner-Party in Imeeo

It was just in the middle of the merry, mellow afternoon, that they ushered us to dinner, underneath a green shelter of palm boughs; open all round, and so low at the eaves, that we stooped to enter.

Within, the ground was strewn over with aromatic ferns—called "nahee"—freshly gathered; which, stirred under foot, diffused the sweetest odor. On one side was a row of yellow mats, inwrought with fibers of bark, stained a bright red. Here, seated after the fashion of the Turk, we looked out, over a verdant bank, upon the mild, blue, endless Pacific. So far round had we skirted the island, that the view of Tahiti was now intercepted.

Upon the ferns before us, were laid several layers of broad thick "pooroo" leaves, lapping over, one upon the other. And upon these were placed, side by side, newly plucked banana leaves, at least two yards in length, and very wide: the stalks were withdrawn, so as to make them lie flat. This green cloth was set out and garnished, in the manner following:

First, a number of "pooroo" leaves, by way of plates, were ranged along on one side; and by each was a rustic nut-bowl, half-filled with sea-water, and a Tahitian roll, or small bread-fruit, roasted brown. An immense flat calabash, placed in the center, was heaped up with numberless small packages of moist, steaming leaves: in each was a small fish, baked in the earth, and done to a turn. This pyramid of a dish was flanked on either side by an ornamental calabash. One was brimming with the golden-hued *poee*, or pudding, made from the red plantain of the mountains; the other was stacked up with cakes of the Indian turnip, previously macerated in a mortar, kneaded with the milk of the cocoanut, and then baked. In the spaces between the three dishes, were piled young cocoanuts, stripped of their husks. Their eyes had been opened and enlarged: so that each was a ready-charged goblet.

There was a sort of side-cloth in one corner, upon which, in bright buff jackets, lay the fattest of bananas; "avees," red-ripe; guavas, with the shadows of their crimson pulp flushing through a transparent skin, and almost coming and going there like blushes; oranges, tinged here and there, berry-brown; and great jolly melons, which rolled about in very portliness. Such a heap! All ruddy, ripe, and round—bursting with the good cheer of the tropical soil, from which they sprang!

"A land of orchards!" cried the doctor, in a rapture; and he snatched a morsel from a sort of fruit of which gentlemen of the sanguine temperament are remarkably fond; namely, the ripe cherry lips of Miss Day-born, who stood looking on.

Marharvai allotted seats to his guests; and the meal began. Thinking that his hospitality needed some acknowledgment, I rose, and pledged him in the vegetable wine of the cocoanut; merely repeating the ordinary salutation, "Yar onor boyoee." Sensible that some compliment, after the fashion of white men, was paid him, with a smile, and a courteous flourish of the hand, he bade me be seated. No people, however refined, are more easy and graceful in their manners than the Imeeose.

The doctor, sitting next our host, now came under his special protection. Laying before his guest one of the packages of fish, Marharvai opened it, and commended its contents to his particular regards. But my comrade was one of those, who, on convivial occasions, can always take care of themselves. He ate an indefinite number of "pehee lee lees" (small fish), his own and his next neighbor's bread-fruit; and helped himself, to right and left, with all the ease of an accomplished diner-out.

"Paul," said he, at last, "you don't seem to be getting along; why don't you try the pepper sauce?" and, by way of example, he steeped a morsel of food into his nutful of sea-water. On following suit, I found it quite piquant, though rather bitter; but, on the whole, a capital substitute for salt. The Imeeose invariably use sea-water in this way, deeming it quite a treat; and considering that their country is surrounded by an ocean of catsup, the luxury cannot be deemed an expensive one.

The fish were delicious; the manner of cooking them in the ground, preserving all the juices, and rendering them exceedingly sweet and tender. The plantain pudding was almost cloying; the cakes of Indian turnip, quite palatable; and the roasted bread-fruit, crisp as toast.

During the meal, a native lad walked round and round the party, carrying a long staff of bamboo. This he occasionally tapped upon the cloth before each guest; when a white clotted substance dropped forth, with a savor not unlike that of a curd. This proved to be "lownee," an excellent relish, prepared from the grated meat of ripe cocoanuts, moistened with cocoanut milk and salt water, and kept perfectly tight, until a little past the saccharine stage of fermentation.

Throughout the repast there was much lively chatting among the islanders, in which their conversational powers quite exceeded ours. The young ladies, too, showed themselves very expert in the use of their tongues, and contributed much to the gaiety which prevailed.

Nor did these lively nymphs suffer the meal to languish; for upon the doctor's throwing himself back, with an air of much satisfaction, they sprang to their feet, and pelted him with oranges and guavas. This, at last, put an end to the entertainment.

By a hundred whimsical oddities, my long friend became a great favorite with these people; and they bestowed upon him a long, comical title, expressive of his lank figure and Roora combined. The latter, by the by, never failed to excite the remark of everybody we encountered.

The giving of nicknames is quite a passion with the people of Tahiti and Imeeo. No one, with any peculiarity, whether of person or temper, is exempt; not even strangers.

A pompous captain of a man-of-war, visiting Tahiti for the second time, discovered that, among the natives, he went by the dignified title of "Atee Poee"—literally, Poee Head, or Pudding Head. Nor is the highest rank among themselves any protection. The first husband of the present queen was commonly known in the court circles, as "Pot Belly." He carried the greater part of his person before him, to be sure; and so did the gentlemanly George IV—but what a title for a king consort!

Even "Pomaree" itself, the royal patronymic, was, originally, a mere nickname, and literally signifies, one talking through his nose. The first monarch of that name, being on a war party, and sleeping overnight among the mountains, awoke one morning with a cold in his head; and some wag of a courtier had no more manners than to vulgarize him thus.

How different from the volatile Polynesian in this, as in all other respects, is our grave and decorous North American Indian. While the former bestows a name, in accordance with some humorous or ignoble trait, the latter seizes upon what is deemed the most exalted or war-like: and hence among the red tribes, we have the truly patrician appellations of "White Eagles," "Young Oaks," "Fiery Eyes," and "Bended Bows."

Chapter LXIX

THE COCOA-PALM

WHILE THE DOCTOR AND THE NATIVES WERE TAKING A DIGESTIVE NAP AFTER DINNER, I STROLLED forth to have a peep at the country which could produce so generous a meal.

To my surprise, a fine strip of land in the vicinity of the hamlet, and protected seaward by a grove of cocoanut and bread-fruit-trees, was under high cultivation. Sweet potatoes, Indian turnips, and yams were growing; also melons, a few pine-apples, and other fruits. Still more pleasing was the sight of young bread-fruit and cocoanut-trees set out with great care, as if, for once, the improvident Polynesian had thought of his posterity. But this was the only instance of native thrift which ever came under my observation. For, in all my rambles over Tahiti and Imeeo, nothing so much struck me as the comparative scarcity of these trees in many places where they ought to abound. Entire valleys, like Martair, of inexhaustible fertility, are abandoned to all the rankness of untamed vegetation. Alluvial flats bordering the sea, and watered by streams from the mountains, are overgrown with a wild, scrub guava-bush, introduced by foreigners, and which spreads with such fatal rapidity that the natives, standing still while it grows, anticipate its covering the entire island. Even tracts of clear land, which, with so little pains, might be made to wave with orchards, lie wholly neglected.

When I consider their unequaled soil and climate, thus unaccountably slighted, I often turned in amazement upon the natives about Papeetee; some of whom all but starve in their gardens run to waste. Upon other islands which I have visited, of similar fertility, and wholly unreclaimed from their first discovered condition, no spectacle of this sort was presented.

The high estimation in which many of their fruit-trees are held by the Tahitians and Imeeose—their beauty in the landscape—their manifold uses, and the facility with which they are propagated, are considerations which render the remissness alluded to still more unaccountable. The cocoa-palm is as an example; a tree by far the most important production of Nature in the tropics. To the Polynesian, it is emphatically the Tree of Life; transcending even the bread-fruit in the multifarious uses to which it is applied.

Its very aspect is imposing. Asserting its supremacy by an erect and lofty bearing, it may be said to compare with other trees, as man with inferior creatures.

The blessings it confers are incalculable. Year after year, the islanders repose beneath its shade, both eating and drinking of its fruit; he thatches his hut with its boughs, and weaves them into baskets to carry his food; he cools himself with a fan platted from the young leaflets, and shields his head from the sun by a bonnet of the leaves; sometimes he clothes himself with the cloth-like substance which wraps round the base of the stalks, whose elastic rods, strung with filberts, are used as a taper; the larger nuts, thinned and polished, furnish him with a beautiful goblet; the smaller ones, with bowls for his pipes; the dry husks kindle his fires; their fibers are twisted into fishing-lines and cords for his canoes; he heals his wounds with a balsam compounded from the juice of the nut; and with the oil extracted from its meat, embalms the bodies of the dead.

The noble trunk itself is far from being valueless. Sawn into posts, it upholds the islander's dwelling; converted into charcoal, it cooks his food; and supported on blocks of stone, rails in his lands. He impels his canoe through the water with a paddle of the wood, and goes to battle with clubs and spears of the same hard material.

In pagan Tahiti, a cocoanut branch was the symbol of regal authority. Laid upon the sacrifice in the temple, it made the offering sacred; and with it the priests chastised and put to flight the evil spirits which assailed them. The supreme majesty of Oro, the great god of their mythology, was declared in the cocoanut log from which his image was rudely carved. Upon one of the Tonga Islands, there stands a living tree, revered itself as a deity. Even upon the Sandwich Islands, the cocoa-palm retains all its ancient reputation; the people there having thought of adopting it as the national emblem.

The cocoanut is planted as follows: Selecting a suitable place, you drop into the ground a fully ripe nut, and leave it. In a few days, a thin, lance-like shoot forces itself through a minute hole in the shell, pierces the husk, and soon unfolds three pale-green leaves in the air; while originating, in the same soft white sponge which now completely fills the nut, a pair of fibrous roots, pushing away the stoppers which close two holes in an opposite direction, penetrate the shell, and strike vertically into the ground. A day or two more, and the shell and husk, which in the last and germinating stage of the nut, are so hard that a knife will scarcely make any impression, spontaneously burst by some force within; and, henceforth, the hardy young plant thrives apace; and needing no culture, pruning, or attention of any sort, rapidly arrives at maturity. In four or five years it bears; in twice as many more, it begins to lift its head among the groves, where, waxing strong, it flourishes for near a century.

Thus, as some voyager has said, the man who but drops one of these nuts into the ground, may be said to confer a greater and more certain benefit upon himself and posterity, than many a life's toil in less genial climes.

The fruitfulness of the tree is remarkable. As long as it lives, it bears; and without intermission. Two hundred nuts, besides innumerable white blossoms of others, may be seen upon it at one time; and though a whole year is required to bring any one of them to the germinating point, no two, perhaps, are at one time in precisely the same stage of growth.

The tree delights in a maritime situation. In its greatest perfection, it is perhaps found right on the seashore, where its roots are actually washed. But such instances are only met with upon islands where the swell of the sea is prevented from breaking on the beach by an encircling reef. No saline flavor is perceptible in the nut produced in such a place. Although it bears in any soil, whether upland or bottom, it does not flourish vigorously inland; and I have frequently observed, that when met with far up the valleys, its tall stem inclines seaward, as if pining after a more genial region.

It is a curious fact, that, if you deprive the cocoanut-tree of the verdant tuft at its head, it dies at once; and if allowed to stand thus, the trunk, which, when alive, is encased in so hard a bark as to be almost impervious to a bullet, molders away, and, in an incredibly short period, becomes dust. This is, perhaps, partly owing to the peculiar constitution of the trunk, a mere cylinder of minute hollow reeds, closely packed, and very hard; but when exposed at top, peculiarly fitted to convey moisture and decay through the entire stem.

The finest orchard of cocoa-palms I know, and the only plantation of them I ever saw at the islands, is one that stands right upon the southern shore of Papeetee Bay. They were set out by the first Pomaree, almost half a century ago; and the soil being especially adapted to their growth, the noble trees now form a magnificent grove, nearly a mile in extent. No other plant, scarcely a bush, is to be seen within its precincts. The Broom Road passes through its entire length.

At noon-day, this grove is one of the most beautiful, serene, witching places that ever was seen. High overhead are ranges of green rustling arches; through which the sun's rays come down to you in sparkles. You seem to be wandering through illimitable halls of pillars; everywhere you catch glimpses of stately aisles, intersecting each other at all points. A strange silence, too, reigns far and near; the air flushed with the mellow stillness of a sunset.

But after the long morning calms, the sea-breeze comes in; and creeping over the tops of these thousand trees, they nod their plumes. Soon the breeze freshens; and you hear the branches brushing against each other; and the flexible trunks begin to sway. Towards evening, the whole grove is rocking to and fro; and the traveler on the Broom Road is startled by the frequent falling of the nuts, snapped from their brittle stems. They come flying through the air, ringing like jugglers' balls; and often bound along the ground for many rods.

Chapter LXX

LIFE AT LOOHOOLOO

FINDING THE SOCIETY AT LOOHOOLOO VERY PLEASANT, THE YOUNG LADIES, IN PARTICULAR, being extremely sociable; and, moreover, in love with the famous good cheer of old Marharvai, we acquiesced in an invitation of his, to tarry a few days longer. We might then, he said, join a small canoe party, which was going to a place a league or two distant. So averse to all exertion are these people, that they really thought the prospect of thus getting rid of a few miles' walking, would prevail with us, even if there were no other inducement.

The people of the hamlet, as we soon discovered, formed a snug little community of cousins; of which our host seemed the head. Marharvai, in truth, was a petty chief, who owned the neighboring lands. And as the wealthy, in most cases, rejoice in a numerous kindred, the family footing upon which everybody visited him, was, perhaps, ascribable to the fact of his being the lord of the manor. Like Captain Bob, he was, in some things, a gentleman of the old school—a stickler for the customs of a past and pagan age.

Nowhere else, except in Tamai, did we find the manners of the natives less vitiated by recent changes. The old-fashioned Tahitian dinner they gave us on the day of our arrival, was a fair sample of their general mode of living.

Our time passed delightfully. The doctor went his way, and I mine. With a pleasant companion, he was forever strolling inland, ostensibly to collect botanical specimens; while I, for the most part, kept near the sea; sometimes taking the girls on aquatic excursions in a canoe.

Often we went fishing; not dozing over stupid hooks and lines, but leaping right into the water, and chasing our prey over the coral rocks, spear in hand.

Spearing fish is glorious sport. The Imeeose, all round the island, catch them in no other way. The smooth shallows between the reef and the shore, and, at low water, the reef itself, being admirably adapted to this mode of capturing them. At almost any time of the day—save ever the sacred hour of noon—you may see the fish-hunters pursuing their sport; with loud halloes, brandishing their spears, and splashing through the water in all directions. Sometimes a solitary native is seen, far out upon a lonely shallow, wading slowly along, with eye intent and poised spear.

But the best sport of all, is going out upon the great reef itself, by torch-light. The natives follow this recreation with as much spirit as a gentleman of England does the chase; and take full as much delight in it.

The torch is nothing more than a bunch of dry reeds, bound firmly together; the spear, a long, light pole, with an iron head, on one side barbed.

I shall never forget the night, that old Marharvai and the rest of us, paddling off to the reef, leaped at midnight upon the coral ledges with waving torches and spears. We were more than a mile from the land; the sullen ocean thundering upon the outside of the rocks, dashed the spray in our faces, almost extinguishing the flambeaux; and, far as the eye could reach, the darkness of sky and water was streaked with a long, misty line of foam, marking the course of the coral barrier. The wild fishermen, flourishing their weapons, and yelling like so many demons to scare their prey, sprang from ledge to ledge, and sometimes darted their spears in the very midst of the breakers.

But fish-spearing was not the only sport we had at Loohooloo. Right on the beach was a mighty old cocoanut-tree, the roots of which had been underwashed by the waves, so that the trunk inclined far over its base. From the tuft of the tree, a stout cord of bark depended, the end of which swept the water several yards from the shore. This was a Tahitian swing. A native lad seizes hold of the cord, and, after swinging to and fro quite leisurely, all at once sends himself fifty or sixty feet from the water, rushing through the air like a rocket. I doubt whether any of our rope-dancers would attempt the feat. For my own part, I had neither head nor heart for it; so, after sending a lad aloft with an additional cord, by way of security, I constructed a large basket of green boughs, in which I and some particular friends of mine used to swing over sea and land by the hour.

Chapter LXXI

We Start for Taloo

Bright was the morning, and brighter still the smiles of the young ladies who accompanied us, when we sprang into a sort of family canoe—wide and roomy—and bade adieu to the hospitable Marharvai and his tenantry. As we paddled away, they stood upon the beach, waving their hands, and crying out, "Aroha! aroha!" (Farewell! farewell!) as long as we were within hearing.

Very sad at parting with them, we endeavored, nevertheless, to console ourselves in the society of our fellow-passengers. Among these were two old ladies; but as they said nothing to us, we will say nothing about them; nor anything about the old men who managed the canoe. But of the three mischievous, dark-eyed young witches, who lounged in the stern of that comfortable old island gondola, I have a great deal to say.

In the first place, one of them was Marhar-Rarrar, the Bright-eyed; and, in the second place, neither she nor the romps, her companions, ever dreamed of taking the voyage, until the doctor and myself announced our intention; their going along was nothing more than a madcap frolic; in short, they were a parcel of wicked hoydens, bent on mischief, who laughed in your face when you looked sentimental, and only tolerated your company when making merry at your expense.

Something or other about us was perpetually awaking their mirth. Attributing this to his own remarkable figure, the doctor increased their enjoyment, by assuming the part of a Merry Andrew. Yet his cap and bells never jingled but to some tune; and while playing the Tom-fool, I more than suspected that he was trying to play the rake. At home, it is deemed auspicious to go a-wooing in epaulets; but among the Polynesians, your best dress in courting is motley.

A fresh breeze springing up, we set our sail of matting, and glided along as tranquilly as if floating upon an inland stream; the white reef on one hand, and the green shore on the other.

Soon as we turned a headland, we encountered another canoe, paddling with might and main in an opposite direction; the strangers shouting to each other, and a tall fellow in the bow dancing up and down like a crazy man. They shot by us like an arrow, though our fellow-voyagers shouted again and again, for them to cease paddling.

According to the natives, this was a kind of royal mail-canoe, carrying a message from the queen to her friends in a distant part of the island.

Passing several shady bowers, which looked quite inviting, we proposed touching, and diversifying the monotony of a sea-voyage by a stroll ashore. So, forcing our canoe among the bushes, behind a decayed palm, lying partly in the water, we left the old folks to take a nap in the shade, and gallanted the others among the trees, which were here trellised with vines and creeping shrubs.

In the early part of the afternoon, we drew near the place to which the party were going. It was a solitary house, inhabited by four or five old women, who, when we entered, were gathered in a circle about the mats, eating *poee* from a cracked calabash. They seemed delighted at seeing our companions, but rather drew up when introduced to ourselves. Eyeing us distrustfully, they whispered to know who we were. The answers they received were not satisfactory; for they treated us with marked coolness and reserve, and seemed desirous of breaking off our acquaintance with the girls. Unwilling, therefore, to stay where our company was disagreeable, we resolved to depart, without even eating a meal.

Informed of this, Marhar-Rarrar and her companions evinced the most lively concern; and equally unmindful of their former spirits, and the remonstrances of the old ladies, broke forth into sobs and lamentations, which were not to be withstood. We agreed, therefore, to tarry until they left for home; which would be at the "Aheharar," or Falling of the Sun; in other words, at sunset.

When the hour arrived, after much leave-taking, we saw them safely embarked. As the canoe turned a bluff, they seized the paddles from the hands of the old men, and waved them silently in the air. This was meant for a touching farewell, as the paddle is only waved thus, when the parties separating never more expect to meet.

We now continued our journey; and following the beach, soon came to a level and lofty overhanging bank, which, planted here and there with trees, took a broad sweep round a considerable part of the island. A fine pathway skirted the edge of the bank; and often we paused to admire the scenery. The evening was still and fair, even for so heavenly a climate; and all round, far as the eye could reach, was the blending blue sky and ocean.

As we went on, the reef-belt still accompanied us; turning as we turned, and thundering its distant bass upon the ear, like the unbroken roar of a cataract. Dashing forever against their coral rampart, the breakers looked, in the distance, like a line of rearing white chargers, reined in, tossing their white manes, and bridling with foam.

These great natural breakwaters are admirably designed for the protection of this land. Nearly all the Society Islands are defended by them. Were the vast swells of the Pacific to break against the soft alluvial bottoms which in many places border the sea, the soil would soon be washed away, and the natives be thus deprived of their most productive lands. As it is, the banks of no rivulet are firmer.

But the coral barriers answer another purpose. They form all the harbors of this group, including the twenty-four roundabout the shores of Tahiti. Curiously enough, the openings in the reefs, by which alone vessels enter to their anchorage, are invariably opposite the mouths of running streams: an advantage fully appreciated by the mariner who touches for the purpose of watering his ship.

It is said, that the fresh water of the land, mixing with the salts held in solution by the sea, so acts upon the latter, as to resist the formation of the coral; and hence the breaks. Here and there, these openings are sentineled, as it were, by little fairy islets, green as emerald, and waving with palms. Strangely and beautifully diversifying the long line of breakers, no objects can strike the fancy more vividly. Pomaree II, with a taste in watering-places truly Tahitian, selected one of them as a royal retreat. We passed it on our journey.

Omitting several further adventures which befell us after leaving the party from Loohooloo, we must now hurry on, to relate what happened just before reaching the place of our destination.

Chapter LXXII

A DEALER IN THE CONTRABAND

IT MUST HAVE BEEN AT LEAST THE TENTH DAY, RECKONING FROM THE HEGIRA, THAT WE FOUND ourselves the guests of Varvy, an old hermit of an islander, who kept house by himself, perhaps a couple of leagues from Taloo.

A stone's cast from the beach there was a fantastic rock, moss-grown, and deep in a dell. It was insulated by a shallow brook, which, dividing its waters, flowed on both sides, until united below. Twisting its roots round the rock, a gnarled "Aoa" spread itself overhead in a wilderness of foliage; the elastic branch-roots depending from the larger boughs, insinuating themselves into every cleft, thus forming supports to the parent stem. In some places, these pendulous branches, half-grown, had not yet reached the rock; swinging their loose fibrous ends in the air like whiplashes.

Varvy's hut, a mere coop of bamboos, was perched upon a level part of the rock, the ridge-pole resting at one end in a crotch of the "Aoa," and the other propped by a forked bough planted in a fissure.

Notwithstanding our cries as we drew near, the first hint the old hermit received of our approach, was the doctor's stepping up and touching his shoulder, as he was kneeling over on a stone, cleaning fish in the brook. He leaped up, and stared at us. But with a variety of uncouth gestures, he soon made us welcome; informing us, by the same means, that he was both deaf and dumb; he then motioned us into his dwelling.

Going in, we threw ourselves upon an old mat, and peered round. The soiled bamboos and calabashes looked so uninviting, that the doctor was for pushing on to Taloo that night, notwithstanding it was near sunset. But at length we concluded to stay where we were.

After a good deal of bustling outside under a decrepit shed, the old man made his appearance with our supper. In one hand he held a flickering taper, and in the other a huge, flat calabash, scantily filled with viands. His eyes were dancing in his head, and he looked from the calabash to us, and from us to the calabash, as much as to say, "Ah, my lads, what do ye think of this, eh? Pretty good cheer, eh?" But the fish and Indian turnip being none of the best, we made but a sorry meal. While discussing it, the old man tried hard to make himself understood by signs; most of which were so excessively ludicrous, that we made no doubt he was perpetrating a series of pantomimic jokes.

The remnants of the feast removed, our host left us for a moment, returning with a calabash of portly dimensions, and furnished with a long hooked neck, the mouth of which was stopped with a wooden plug. It was covered with particles of earth, and looked as if just taken from some place underground.

With sundry winks and horrible giggles, peculiar to the dumb, the vegetable demijohn was now tapped; the old fellow looking round cautiously, and pointing at it; as much as to intimate, that it contained something which was "taboo," or forbidden.

Aware that intoxicating liquors were strictly prohibited to the natives, we now watched our entertainer with much interest. Charging a cocoanut shell he tossed it off, and then filling it up again, presented the goblet to me. Disliking the smell, I made faces at it; upon which he became highly excited; so much so, that a miracle was wrought upon the spot. Snatching the cup from my hands, he shouted out, "Ah, karhowree sabbee lee-lee, ena arva tee maitai!" in other words, What a blockhead of a white man! this is the real stuff!

We could not have been more startled, had a frog leaped from his mouth. For an instant, he looked confused enough himself; and then, placing a finger mysteriously upon his mouth, he contrived to make us understand, that at times he was subject to a suspension of the powers of speech.

Deeming the phenomenon a remarkable one, every way, the doctor desired him to open his mouth, so that he might have a look down. But he refused.

This occurrence made us rather suspicious of our host; nor could we afterwards account for his conduct, except by supposing that his feigning dumbness might in some way or other assist him in the nefarious pursuits in which it afterwards turned out that he was engaged. This conclusion, however, was not altogether satisfactory.

To oblige him, we at last took a sip of his "arva tee," and found it very crude, and strong as Lucifer. Curious to know whence it was obtained, we questioned him; when, lighting up with pleasure, he seized the taper, and led us outside the hut, bidding us follow.

After going some distance through the woods, we came to a dismantled old shed of boughs, apparently abandoned to decay. Underneath, nothing was to be seen but heaps of decaying leaves and an immense, clumsy jar, wide-mouthed, and, by some means, rudely hollowed out from a ponderous stone.

Here, for a while, we were left to ourselves; the old man placing the light in the jar, and then disappearing. He returned, carrying a long, large bamboo, and a crotched stick. Throwing these down, he poked under a pile of rubbish, and brought out a rough block of wood, pierced through and through with a hole, which was immediately clapped on top of the jar. Then planting the crotched stick upright about two yards distant, and making it sustain one end of the bamboo, he inserted the other end of the latter into the hole in the block; concluding these arrangements, by placing an old calabash under the farther end of the bamboo.

Coming up to us now with a sly, significant look, and pointing admiringly at his apparatus, he exclaimed, "Ah, karhowree, ena hannahanna arva tee!" as much as to say, "*This*, you see, is the way it's done."

His contrivance was nothing less than a native still, where he manufactured his island "poteen." The disarray in which we found it was probably intentional, as a security against detection. Before we left the shed, the old fellow toppled the whole concern over, and dragged it away piecemeal.

His disclosing his secret to us thus was characteristic of the "Tootai Owrees," or contemners of the missionaries among the natives: who, presuming that all foreigners are opposed to the ascendancy of the missionaries, take pleasure in making them confidants, whenever the enactments of their rulers are secretly set at naught.

The substance from which the liquor is produced is called "Tee," which is a large, fibrous root, something like a yam, but smaller. In its green state, it is exceedingly acrid; but boiled or baked has the sweetness of the sugar-cane. After being subjected to the fire, macerated, and reduced to a certain stage of fermentation, the "Tee" is stirred up with water, and is then ready for distillation.

On returning to the hut, pipes were introduced; and, after a while, Long Ghost, who, at first, had relished the "Arva Tee" as little as myself, to my surprise, began to wax sociable over it with Varvy; and before long absolutely got mellow, the old toper keeping him company.

It was a curious sight. Everyone knows, that, so long as the occasion lasts, there is no stronger bond of sympathy and good feeling among men than getting tipsy together. And how earnestly, nay, movingly, a brace of worthies thus employed will endeavor to shed light upon and elucidate their mystical ideas!

Fancy Varvy and the doctor, then; lovingly tippling, and brimming over with a desire to become better acquainted; the doctor politely bent upon carrying on the conversation in the language of his host, and the old hermit persisting in trying to talk English. The result was that, between the two, they made such a fricassee of vowels and consonants, that it was enough to turn one's brain.

The next morning, on waking, I heard a voice from the tombs. It was the doctor, solemnly pronouncing himself a dead man. He was sitting up, with both hands clasped over his forehead, and his pale face a thousand times paler than ever.

"That infernal stuff has murdered me!" he cried. "Heavens! my head's all wheels and springs, like the automaton chess-player! What's to be done, Paul? I'm poisoned."

But, after drinking a herbal draft, concocted by our host, and eating a light meal at noon, he felt much better; so much so, that he declared himself ready to continue our journey.

When we came to start, the Yankee's boots were missing; and after a diligent search, were not to be found. Enraged beyond measure, their proprietor said that Varvy must have stolen them; but, considering his hospitality, I thought this extremely improbable, though to whom else to impute the theft I knew not. The doctor maintained, however, that one who was capable of drugging an innocent traveler with "Arva Tee" was capable of anything.

But it was in vain that he stormed, and Varvy and I searched; the boots were gone.

Were it not for this mysterious occurrence, and Varvy's detestable liquors, I would here recommend all travelers going round by the beach to Partoowye to stop at the Rock and patronize the old gentleman—the more especially as he entertains gratis.

Chapter LXXIII

Our Reception in Partoowye

Upon starting, at last, I flung away my sandals—by this time quite worn out—with the view of keeping company with the doctor, now forced to go barefooted. Recovering his spirits in good time, he protested that boots were a bore after all, and going without them decidedly manly.

This was said, be it observed, while strolling along over a soft carpet of grass; a little moist, even at mid-day, from the shade of the wood through which we were passing.

Emerging from this, we entered upon a blank, sandy tract, upon which the sun's rays fairly flashed; making the loose gravel under foot well-nigh as hot as the floor of an oven. Such yelling and leaping as there was in getting over this ground would be hard to surpass. We could not have crossed at all—until towards sunset—had it not been for a few small, wiry bushes, growing here and there; into which we every now and then thrust our feet to cool. There was no little judgment necessary in selecting your bush; for if not chosen judiciously, the chances were, that on springing forward again, and finding the next bush so far off that an intermediate cooling was indispensable, you would have to run back to your old place again.

Safely passing the Sahara, or Fiery Desert, we soothed our half-blistered feet by a pleasant walk through a meadow of long grass, which soon brought us in sight of a few straggling houses, sheltered by a grove on the outskirts of the village of Partoowye.

My comrade was for entering the first one we came to; but, on drawing near, they had so much an air of pretension, at least for native dwellings, that I hesitated; thinking they might be the residences of the higher chiefs, from whom no very extravagant welcome was to be anticipated.

While standing irresolute, a voice from the nearest house hailed us: "Aramai! aramai, karhowree!" ("Come in! come in, strangers!")

We at once entered, and were warmly greeted. The master of the house was an aristocratic-looking islander; dressed in loose linen drawers, a fine white shirt, and a sash of red silk tied about the waist, after the fashion of the Spaniards in Chile. He came up to us with a free, frank air, and, striking his chest with his hand, introduced himself as Ereemear Po-Po; or to render the Christian name back again into English—Jeremiah Po-Po.

These curious combinations of names, among the people of the Society Islands, originate in the following way. When a native is baptized, his patronymic often gives offence to the missionaries, and they insist upon changing to something else whatever is objectionable therein. So, when Jeremiah came to the font, and gave his name as Narmo-Nana Po-Po (something equivalent to The-Darer-of-Devils-by-Night), the reverend gentleman officiating told him that such a heathenish appellation would never do, and a substitute must be had; at least for the devil part of it. Some highly respectable Christian appellations were then submitted, from which the candidate for admission into the church was at liberty to choose. There was Adamo (Adam), Nooar (Noah), Daveedar (David), Earcobar (James), Eorna (John), Patoora (Peter), Ereemear (Jeremiah), etc. And thus did he come to be named Jeremiah Po-Po; or Jeremiah-in-the-Dark—which he certainly was, I fancy, as to the ridiculousness of his new cognomen.

We gave our names in return; upon which he bade us be seated; and sitting down himself, asked us a great many questions, in mixed English and Tahitian. After giving some directions to an old man to prepare food, our host's wife, a large, benevolent-looking woman, upwards of forty, also sat down by us. In our soiled and travel-stained appearance, the good lady seemed to find abundant matter for commiseration; and all the while kept looking at us piteously, and making mournful exclamations.

But Jeremiah and his spouse were not the only inmates of the mansion.

In one corner, upon a large native couch, elevated upon posts, reclined a nymph; who, half-veiled in her own long hair, had yet to make her toilette for the day. She was the only daughter of Po-Po; and a very beautiful little daughter she was; not more than fourteen; with the most delightful shape—like a bud just blown; and large hazel eyes. They called her Loo: a name rather pretty and genteel, and, therefore, quite appropriate; for a more genteel and lady-like little damsel there was not in all Imeeo.

She was a cold and haughty young beauty though, this same little Loo, and never deigned to notice us; further than now and then to let her eyes float over our persons, with an expression of indolent indifference. With the tears of the Loohooloo girls hardly dry from their sobbing upon our shoulders, this contemptuous treatment stung us not a little.

When we first entered, Po-Po was raking smooth the carpet of dried ferns which had that morning been newly laid; and now that our meal was ready, it was spread on a banana leaf, right upon this fragrant floor. Here we lounged at our ease; eating baked pig and bread-fruit off earthen plates, and using, for the first time in many a long month, real knives and forks.

These, as well as other symptoms of refinement, somewhat abated our surprise at the reserve of the little Loo: her parents, doubtless, were magnates in Partoowye, and she herself was an heiress.

After being informed of our stay in the vale of Martair, they were very curious to know on what errand we came to Taloo. We merely hinted, that the ship lying in the harbor was the reason of our coming.

Arfretee, Po-Po's wife, was a right motherly body. The meal over, she recommended a nap; and upon our waking much refreshed, she led us to the doorway, and pointed down among the trees; through which we saw the gleam of water. Taking the hint, we repaired thither; and finding a deep shady pool, bathed, and returned to the house. Our hostess now sat down by us; and after looking with great interest at the doctor's cloak, felt of my own soiled and tattered garments for the hundredth time, and exclaimed plaintively—"Ah nuee nuee olee manee! olee manee!" (Alas! they are very, very old! very old!)

When Arfretee, good soul, thus addressed us, she thought she was talking very respectable English. The word "nuee" is so familiar to foreigners throughout Polynesia, and is so often used by them in their intercourse with the natives, that the latter suppose it to be common to all mankind. "Olee manee" is the native pronunciation of *"old man,"* which, by Society Islanders talking Saxon, is applied indiscriminately to all aged things and persons whatsoever.

Going to a chest filled with various European articles, she took out two suits of new sailor frocks and trousers; and presenting them with a gracious smile, pushed us behind a calico screen, and left us. Without any fastidious scruples, we donned the garments; and what with the meal, the nap, and the bath, we now came forth like a couple of bridegrooms.

Evening drawing on, lamps were lighted. They were very simple: the half of a green melon, about one-third full of cocoanut oil, and a wick of twisted tappa floating on the surface. As a night lamp, this contrivance cannot be excelled; a soft dreamy light being shed through the transparent rind.

As the evening advanced, other members of the household, whom as yet we had not seen, began to drop in. There was a slender young dandy in a gay striped shirt, and whole fathoms of bright figured calico tucked about his waist, and falling to the ground. He wore a new straw hat, also, with three distinct ribbons tied about the crown; one black, one green, and one pink. Shoes or stockings, however, he had none.

There were a couple of delicate, olive-cheeked little girls—twins—with mild eyes and beautiful hair, who ran about the house, half-naked, like a couple of gazelles. They had a brother, somewhat younger—a fine dark boy, with an eye like a woman's. All these were the children of Po-Po, begotten in lawful wedlock.

Then there were two or three queer-looking old ladies, who wore shabby mantles of soiled sheeting; which fitted so badly, and withal had such a second-hand look, that I at once put their wearers down as domestic paupers—poor relations, supported by the bounty of my lady Arfretee. They were sad, meek old bodies; said little and ate less; and either kept their eyes on the ground, or lifted them up deferentially. The semi-civilization of the island must have had something to do with making them what they were.

I had almost forgotten Monee, the grinning old man who prepared our meal. His head was a shining, bald globe. He had a round little paunch, and legs like a cat. He was Po-Po's factotum—cook, butler, and climber of the bread-fruit and cocoanut-trees; and, added to all else, a mighty favorite with his mistress; with whom he would sit smoking and gossiping by the hour.

Often you saw the indefatigable Monee working away at a great rate; then dropping his employment all at once—never mind what—run off to a little distance, and after rolling himself away in a corner, and taking a nap, jump up again, and fall to with fresh vigor.

From a certain something in the behavior of Po-Po and his household, I was led to believe that he was a pillar of the church; though, from what I had seen in Tahiti, I could hardly reconcile such a supposition with his frank, cordial, unembarrassed air. But I was not wrong in my conjecture: Po-Po turned out to be a sort of elder, or deacon; he was also accounted a man of wealth, and was nearly related to a high chief.

Before retiring, the entire household gathered upon the floor; and in their midst, he read aloud a chapter from a Tahitian Bible. Then, kneeling with the rest of us, he offered up a prayer. Upon its conclusion, all separated without speaking. These devotions took place regularly every night and morning. Grace, too, was invariably said by this family both before and after eating.

After becoming familiarized with the almost utter destitution of anything like practical piety upon these islands, what I observed in our host's house astonished me much. But whatever others might have been, Po-Po was, in truth, a Christian: the only one, Arfretee excepted, whom I personally knew to be such, among all the natives of Polynesia.

Chapter LXXIV

RETIRING FOR THE NIGHT—THE DOCTOR GROWS DEVOUT

THEY PUT US TO BED VERY PLEASANTLY.

Lying across the foot of Po-Po's nuptial couch was a smaller one, made of Koar-wood; a thin, strong cord, twisted from the fibers of the husk of the cocoanut, and woven into an exceedingly light sort of net-work, forming its elastic body. Spread upon this was a single, fine mat, with a roll of dried ferns for a pillow, and a strip of white tappa for a sheet. This couch was mine. The doctor was provided for in another corner.

Loo reposed alone on a little settee, with a taper burning by her side; the dandy, her brother, swinging overhead in a sailor's hammock. The two gazelles frisked upon a mat nearby; and the indigent relations borrowed a scant corner of the old butler's pallet, who snored away by the open door. After all had retired, Po-Po placed the illuminated melon in the middle of the apartment; and so, we all slumbered till morning.

Upon awaking, the sun was streaming brightly through the open bamboos, but no one was stirring. After surveying the fine attitudes, into which forgetfulness had thrown at least one of the sleepers, my attention was called off to the general aspect of the dwelling, which was quite significant of the superior circumstances of our host.

The house itself was built in the simple, but tasteful native style. It was a long, regular oval, some fifty feet in length, with low sides of cane-work, and a roof thatched with palmetto-leaves. The ridge-pole was perhaps twenty feet from the ground. There was no foundation whatever; the bare earth being merely covered with ferns: a kind of carpeting which serves very well, if frequently renewed; otherwise, it becomes dusty, and the haunt of vermin, as in the huts of the poorer natives.

Beside the couches, the furniture consisted of three or four sailor chests; in which were stored the fine wearing-apparel of the household—the ruffled linen shirts of Po-Po, the calico dresses of his wife and children, and divers odds and ends of European articles—strings of beads, ribbons, Dutch looking-glasses, knives, coarse prints, bunches of keys, bits of crockery, and metal buttons. One of these chests—used as a bandbox by Arfretee—contained several of the native hats (coal-scuttles), all of the same pattern, but trimmed with variously colored ribbons. Of nothing was our good hostess more proud than of these hats, and her dresses. On Sundays, she went abroad a dozen times; and every time, like Queen Elizabeth, in a different robe.

Po-Po, for some reason or other, always gave us our meals before the rest of the family were served; and the doctor, who was very discerning in such matters, declared that we fared much better than they. Certain it was, that had Ereemear's guests traveled with purses, portmanteaux, and letters of introduction to the queen, they could not have been better cared for.

The day after our arrival, Monee, the old butler, brought us in for dinner a small pig, baked in the ground. All savory, it lay in a wooden trencher, surrounded by roasted hemispheres of the bread-fruit. A large calabash, filled with taro pudding, or *poee,* followed; and the young dandy, overcoming his customary languor, threw down our cocoanuts from an adjoining tree.

When all was ready, and the household looking on, Long Ghost, devoutly clasping his hands over the fated pig, implored a blessing. Hereupon everybody present looked exceedingly pleased; Po-Po coming up, and addressing the doctor with much warmth; and Arfretee, regarding him with almost maternal affection, exclaimed delightedly, "Ah! mickonaree tata matai!" in other words, "What a pious young man!"

It was just after this meal, that she brought me a roll of grass sinnate (of the kind which sailors sew into the frame of their tarpaulins), and then, handing me needle and thread, bade me begin at once, and make myself the hat which I so much needed. An accomplished hand at the business, I finished it that day—merely stitching the braid together; and Arfretee, by way of rewarding my industry, with her own olive hands ornamented the crown with a band of flame-colored ribbon, the two long ends of which, streaming behind, sailor-fashion, still preserved for me the Eastern title bestowed by Long Ghost.

Chapter LXXV

A Ramble through the Settlement

The following morning, making our toilettes carefully, we donned our sombreros, and sallied out on a tour. Without meaning to reveal our designs upon the court, our principal object was, to learn what chances there were for white men to obtain employment under the queen. On this head, it is true, we had questioned Po-Po; but his answers had been very discouraging; so we determined to obtain further information elsewhere.

But first, to give some little description of the village.

The settlement of Partoowye is nothing more than some eighty houses, scattered here and there, in the midst of an immense grove, where the trees have been thinned out, and the underbrush cleared away. Through the grove flows a stream; and the principal avenue crosses it, over an elastic bridge of cocoanut trunks, laid together side by side. The avenue is broad and serpentine; well shaded, from one end to the other; and as pretty a place for a morning promenade as any lounger could wish. The houses, constructed without the slightest regard to the road, peep into view from among the trees on either side; some looking you right in the face as you pass, and others, without any manners, turning their backs. Occasionally, you observe a rural retreat, enclosed by a picket of bamboos, or with a solitary pane of glass massively framed in the broadside of the dwelling, or with a rude, strange-looking door, swinging upon dislocated wooden hinges. Otherwise, the dwellings are built in the original style of the natives; and, never mind how mean and filthy some of them may appear within, they all look picturesque enough without.

As we sauntered along, the people we met saluted us pleasantly, and invited us into their houses; and in this way we made a good many brief morning calls. But the hour could not have been the fashionable one in Partoowye; since the ladies were invariably in *dishabille*. However, they in all cases gave us a cordial reception, and were particularly polite to the doctor; caressing him, and amorously hanging about his neck; wonderfully taken up, in short, with a gay handkerchief he wore there. Arfretee had that morning bestowed it upon the pious youth.

With some exceptions, the general appearance of the natives of Partoowye was far better than that of the inhabitants of Papeetee: a circumstance only to be imputed to their restricted intercourse with foreigners.

Strolling on, we turned a sweep of the road, when the doctor gave a start; and no wonder. Right before us, in the grove, was a block of houses: regular square frames, boarded over, furnished with windows and doorways, and two stories high. We ran up, and found them fast going to decay; very dingy, and here and there covered with moss; no sashes nor doors; and on one side, the entire block had settled down nearly a foot. On going into the basement, we looked clean up through the unboarded timbers to the roof; where rays of light, glimmering through many a chink, illuminated the cobwebs which swung all round.

The whole interior was dark and close. Burrowing among some old mats in one corner, like a parcel of gypsies in a ruin, were a few vagabond natives. They had their dwelling here.

Curious to know who on earth could have been thus trying to improve the value of real estate in Partoowye, we made inquiries; and learned that some years previous, the block had been thrown up by a veritable Yankee (one might have known that), a house carpenter by trade, and a bold enterprising fellow by nature.

Put ashore from his ship, sick, he first went to work and got well; then sallied out with chisel and plane, and made himself generally useful. A sober, steady man, it seems, he at last obtained the confidence of several chiefs, and soon filled them with all sorts of ideas concerning the alarming want of public spirit in the people of Imeeo. More especially did he dwell upon the humiliating fact of their living in paltry huts of bamboo, when magnificent palaces of boards might so be easily mortised together.

In the end, these representations so far prevailed with one old chief, that the carpenter was engaged to build a batch of these wonderful palaces. Provided with plenty of men, he at once set to work; built a saw-mill among the mountains, felled trees, and sent over to Papeetee for nails.

Presto! the castle rose; but alas, the roof was hardly on, when the Yankee's patron, having speculated beyond his means, broke all to pieces, and was absolutely unable to pay one "plug" of tobacco in the pound. His failure involved the carpenter, who sailed away from his creditors in the very next ship that touched at the harbor.

The natives despised the rickety palace of boards; and often lounged by, wagging their heads, and jeering.

We were told that the queen's residence was at the extreme end of the village; so, without waiting for the doctor to procure a fiddle, we suddenly resolved upon going thither at once, and learning whether any privy counselorships were vacant.

Now, although there was a good deal of my waggish comrade's nonsense about what has been said concerning our expectations of court preferment, we, nevertheless, really thought that something to our advantage might turn up in that quarter.

On approaching the palace grounds, we found them rather peculiar. A broad pier of hewn coral rocks was built right out into the water; and upon this, and extending into a grove adjoining, were some eight or ten very large native houses, constructed in the handsomest style, and enclosed together by a low picket of bamboos, which embraced a considerable area.

Throughout the Society Islands, the residences of the chiefs are mostly found in the immediate vicinity of the sea; a site which gives them the full benefit of a cooling breeze; nor are they so liable to the annoyance of insects; besides enjoying when they please the fine shade afforded by the neighboring groves, always most luxuriant near the water.

Lounging about the grounds were some sixty or eighty handsomely dressed natives, men and women; some reclining on the shady side of the houses, others under the trees, and a small group conversing close by the railing, facing us.

We went up to the latter; and giving the usual salutation, were on the point of vaulting over the bamboos, when they turned upon us angrily, and said we could not enter. We stated our earnest desire to see the queen; hinting that we were bearers of important dispatches. But it was to no purpose; and not a little vexed, we were obliged to return to Po-Po's without effecting anything.

Chapter LXXVI

AN ISLAND JILT—WE VISIT THE SHIP

UPON ARRIVING HOME, WE FULLY LAID OPEN TO PO-PO OUR MOTIVES IN VISITING TALOO, AND begged his friendly advice. In his broken English, he cheerfully gave us all the information we needed.

It was true, he said, that the queen entertained some idea of making a stand against the French; and it was currently reported, also, that several chiefs from Borabora, Huwyenee, Raiatair, and Tahar, the leeward islands of the group, were at that very time taking counsel with her, as to the expediency of organizing a general movement throughout the entire cluster, with a view of anticipating any further encroachments on the part of the invaders. Should war-like measures be actually decided upon, it was quite certain that Pomaree would be glad to enlist all the foreigners she could; but as to her making officers of either the doctor or me, that was out of the question; because, already, a number of Europeans, well known to her, had volunteered as such. Concerning our getting immediate access to the queen, Po-Po told us it was rather doubtful; she living at that time very retired, in poor health and spirits, and averse to receiving calls. Previous to her misfortunes, however, no one, however humble, was denied admittance to her presence; sailors, even, attended her levees.

Not at all disheartened by these things, we concluded to kill time in Partoowye, until some event turned up more favorable to our projects. So that very day we sallied out on an excursion to the ship, which, lying land-locked, far up the bay, yet remained to be visited.

Passing, on our route, a long, low shed, a voice hailed us—"White men, ahoy!" Turning round, who should we see but a rosy-cheeked Englishman (you could tell his country at a glance), up to his knees in shavings, and planing away at a bench. He turned out to be a runaway ship's carpenter, recently from Tahiti, and now doing a profitable business in Imeeo, by fitting up the dwellings of opulent chiefs with cupboards and other conveniences, and once in a while trying his hand at a lady's work-box. He had been in the settlement but a few months, and already possessed houses and lands.

But though blessed with prosperity and high health, there was one thing wanting—a wife. And when he came to speak of the matter, his countenance fell, and he leaned dejectedly upon his plane.

"It's too bad!" he sighed, "to wait three long years; and all the while dear little Lullee living in the same house with that infernal chief from Tahar!"

Our curiosity was piqued; the poor carpenter, then, had been falling in love with some island coquette, who was going to jilt him.

But such was not the case. There was a law prohibiting, under a heavy penalty, the marriage of a native with a foreigner, unless the latter, after being three years a resident on the island, was willing to affirm his settled intention of remaining for life.

William was therefore in a sad way. He told us that he might have married the girl half a dozen times, had it not been for this odious law; but, latterly, she had become less loving and more giddy, particularly with the strangers from Tahar. Desperately smitten, and desirous of securing her at all hazards, he had proposed to the damsel's friends a nice little arrangement, introductory to marriage; but they would not hear of it; besides, if the pair were discovered living together upon such a footing, they would be liable to a degrading punishment—sent to work making stone walls and opening roads for the queen.

Doctor Long Ghost was all sympathy. "Bill, my good fellow," said he, tremulously, "let *me* go and talk to her." But Bill, declining the offer, would not even inform us where his charmer lived.

Leaving the disconsolate Willie planing a plank of New Zealand pine (an importation from the

Bay of Islands), and thinking the while of Lullee, we went on our way. How his suit prospered in the end, we never learned.

Going from Po-Po's house towards the anchorage of the harbor of Taloo, you catch no glimpse of the water, until coming out from deep groves, you all at once find yourself upon the beach. A bay, considered by many voyagers the most beautiful in the South Seas, then lies before you. You stand upon one side of what seems a deep, green river, flowing through mountain passes to the sea. Right opposite, a majestic promontory divides the inlet from another, called after its discoverer, Captain Cook. The face of this promontory toward Taloo is one verdant wall; and at its base the waters lie still, and fathomless. On the left hand, you just catch a peep of the widening mouth of the bay, the break in the reef by which ships enter, and beyond, the sea. To the right, the inlet, sweeping boldly round the promontory, runs far away into the land; where, save in one direction, the hills close in on every side, knee-deep in verdure, and shooting aloft in grotesque peaks. The open space lies at the head of the bay; in the distance it extends into a broad, hazy plain lying at the foot of an amphitheater of hills. Here is the large sugar plantation previously alluded to. Beyond the first range of hills, you descry the sharp pinnacles of the interior; and among these, the same silent Marling-spike which we so often admired from the other side of the island.

All alone in the harbor lay the good ship *Leviathan.* We jumped into the canoe, and paddled off to her. Though early in the afternoon, everything was quiet; but upon mounting the side, we found four or five sailors lounging about the forecastle, under an awning. They gave us no very cordial reception; and though otherwise quite hearty in appearance, seemed to assume a look of ill-humor on purpose to honor our arrival. There was much eagerness to learn whether we wanted to "ship"; and by the unpleasant accounts they gave of the vessel, they seemed desirous to prevent such a thing, if possible.

We asked where the rest of the ship's company were; a gruff old fellow made answer, "One boat's crew of 'em is gone to Davy Jones's locker:—went off after a whale, last cruise, and never came back agin. All the starboard watch ran away last night, and the skipper's ashore kitching 'em."

"And it's *shipping* yer after, my jewels, is it?" cried a curly-pated little Belfast sailor, coming up to us, "thin arrah! my livelies, jist be after sailing ashore in a jiffy:—the devil of a skipper will carry yees both to sea, whether or no. Be off wid ye, thin, darlints, and steer clear of the likes of this ballyhoo of blazes as long as ye live. They murther us here every day, and starve us into the bargain. Here, Dick, lad, harl the poor divils' canow alongside; and paddle away wid yees for dear life."

But we loitered awhile, listening to more inducements to ship; and at last concluded to stay to supper. My sheath-knife never cut into better sea-beef than that which we found lying in the kid in the forecastle. The bread, too, was hard, dry, and brittle as glass; and there was plenty of both.

While we were below, the mate of the vessel called out for someone to come on deck. I liked his voice. Hearing it was as good as a look at his face. It betokened a true sailor, and no taskmaster.

The appearance of the *Leviathan* herself was quite pleasing. Like all large, comfortable old whalemen, she had a sort of motherly look—broad in the beam, flush decks, and four chubby boats hanging at the breast. Her sails were furled loosely upon the yards, as if they had been worn long, and fitted easy; her shrouds swung negligently slack; and as for the "running rigging," it never worked hard as it does in some of your "dandy ships," jamming in the sheaves of blocks, like Chinese slippers, too small to be useful; on the contrary, the ropes ran glibly through, as if they had many a time traveled the same road, and were used to it.

When evening came, we dropped into our canoe, and paddled ashore; fully convinced that the good ship never deserved the name which they gave her.

Chapter LXXVII

A Party of Rovers—Little Loo and the Doctor

While in Partoowye, we fell in with a band of six veteran rovers, prowling about the village and harbor, who had just come overland from another part of the island.

A few weeks previous, they had been paid off, at Papeetee, from a whaling vessel, on board of which they had, six months before, shipped for a single cruise; that is to say, to be discharged at the next port. Their cruise was a famous one; and each man stepped upon the beach at Tahiti, jingling his dollars in a sock.

Weary at last of the shore, and having some money left, they clubbed, and purchased a sail-boat; proposing a visit to a certain uninhabited island, concerning which they had heard strange and golden stories. Of course, they never could think of going to sea without a medicine-chest filled with flasks of spirits, and a small cask of the same in the hold, in case the chest should give out.

Away they sailed; hoisted a flag of their own, and gave three times three, as they staggered out of the bay of Papeetee with a strong breeze, and under all the "muslin" they could carry.

Evening coming on, and feeling in high spirits, and noways disposed to sleep, they concluded to make a night of it; which they did; all hands getting tipsy, and the two masts going over the side about midnight, to the tune of

Sailing down, sailing down,
On the coast of Barbaree.

Fortunately, one worthy could stand, by holding on to the tiller; and the rest managed to crawl about, and hack away the lanyards of the rigging, so as to break clear from the fallen spars. While thus employed, two sailors got tranquilly over the side, and went plumb to the bottom; under the erroneous impression, that they were stepping upon a wharf, to get at their work better.

After this, it blew quite a gale; and the commodore, at the helm, instinctively kept the boat before the wind; and by so doing, ran over for the opposite island of Imeeo. Crossing the channel, by almost a miracle they went straight through an opening in the reef, and shot upon a ledge of coral, where the waters were tolerably smooth. Here they lay until morning, when the natives came off to them in their canoes. By the help of the islanders, the schooner was hove over on her beam-ends; when, finding the bottom knocked to pieces, the adventurers sold the boat for a trifle to the chief of the district, and went ashore, rolling before them their precious cask of spirits. Its contents soon evaporated, and they came to Partoowye.

The day after encountering these fellows, we were strolling among the groves in the neighborhood, when we came across several parties of natives, armed with clumsy muskets, rusty cutlasses, and outlandish clubs. They were beating the bushes, shouting aloud, and apparently trying to scare somebody. They were in pursuit of the strangers, who, having in a single night set at naught all the laws of the place, had thought best to decamp.

In the daytime, Po-Po's house was as pleasant a lounge as one could wish. So, after strolling about, and seeing all there was to be seen, we spent the greater part of our mornings there; breakfasting late, and dining about two hours after noon. Sometimes we lounged on the floor of ferns, smoking, and telling stories; of which the doctor had as many as a half-pay captain in the army. Sometimes we chatted, as well as we could, with the natives; and, one day—joy to us!—Po-Po brought in three volumes of Smollett's novels, which had been found in the chest of a sailor, who some time previous had died on the island.

Amelia!—Peregrine!—you hero of rogues, Count Fathom—what a debt do we owe you!

I know not whether it was the reading of these romances, or the want of some sentimental pastime which led the doctor, about this period, to lay siege to the heart of the little Loo.

Now, as I have said before, the daughter of Po-Po was most cruelly reserved, and never deigned to notice us. Frequently I addressed her with a long face and an air of the profoundest and most distant respect—but in vain; she wouldn't even turn up her pretty olive nose. Ah! it's quite plain, thought I; she knows very well what graceless dogs sailors are, and won't have anything to do with us.

But thus thought not my comrade. Bent he was upon firing the cold glitter of Loo's passionless eyes.

He opened the campaign with admirable tact: making cautious approaches, and content, for three days, with ogling the nymph for about five minutes after every meal. On the fourth day, he asked her a question; on the fifth she dropped a nut of ointment, and he picked it up and gave it to her; on the sixth, he went over and sat down within three yards of the couch where she lay; and, on the memorable morn of the seventh, he proceeded to open his batteries in form.

The damsel was reclining on the ferns; one hand supporting her cheek, and the other listlessly turning over the leaves of a Tahitian Bible. The doctor approached.

Now the chief disadvantage under which he labored, was his almost complete ignorance of the love vocabulary of the island. But French counts, they say, make love delightfully in broken English; and what hindered the doctor from doing the same in dulcet Tahitian? So at it he went.

"Ah!" said he, smiling bewitchingly, "oee mickonaree? oee ready Biblee?"

No answer; not even a look.

"Ah! matai! very goody ready Biblee mickonaree."

Loo, without stirring, began reading, in a low tone, to herself.

"Mickonaree Biblee ready goody maitai," once more observed the doctor, ingeniously transposing his words for the third time.

But all to no purpose; Loo gave no sign.

He paused despairingly; but it would never do to give up; so he threw himself at full length beside her, and audaciously commenced turning over the leaves.

Loo gave a start, just one little start, barely perceptible, and then fumbling something in her hand, lay perfectly motionless; the doctor rather frightened at his own temerity, and knowing not what to do next. At last, he placed one arm cautiously about her waist; almost in the same instant he bounded to his feet, with a cry; the little witch had pierced him with a thorn. But there she lay just as quietly as ever, turning over the leaves, and reading to herself.

My long friend raised the siege incontinently, and made a disorderly retreat to the place where I reclined, looking on.

I am pretty sure that Loo must have related this occurrence to her father, who came in shortly afterward; for he looked queerly at the doctor. But he said nothing, and in ten minutes was quite as affable as ever. As for Loo, there was not the slightest change in her; and the doctor, of course, forever afterwards held his peace.

Chapter LXXVIII

Mrs. Bell

One day, taking a pensive afternoon stroll along one of the many bridle-paths which wind among the shady groves in the neighborhood of Taloo, I was startled by a sunny apparition. It was that of a beautiful young Englishwoman, charmingly dressed, and mounted upon a spirited little white pony. Switching a green branch, she came cantering towards me.

I looked round to see whether I could possibly be in Polynesia. There were the palm-trees; but how to account for the lady?

Stepping to one side, as the apparition drew near, I made a polite obeisance. It gave me a bold, rosy look; and then, with a gay air, patted its palfrey, crying out, "Fly away, Willie!" and galloped among the trees.

I would have followed; but Willie's heels were making such a pattering among the dry leaves, that pursuit would have been useless.

So I went straight home to Po-Po's, and related my adventure to the doctor.

The next day, our inquiries resulted in finding out, that the stranger had been in the island about two years; that she came from Sydney; and was the wife of Mr. Bell (happy dog), the proprietor of the sugar plantation, to which I have previously referred.

To the sugar plantation we went the same day.

The country roundabout was very beautiful: a level basin of verdure, surrounded by sloping hill-sides. The sugar-cane—of which there was about one hundred acres, in various stages of cultivation—looked thrifty. A considerable tract of land, however, which seemed to have been formerly tilled, was now abandoned.

The place where they extracted the saccharine matter was under an immense shed of bamboos. Here we saw several clumsy pieces of machinery for breaking the cane; also great kettles for boiling the sugar. But, at present, nothing was going on. Two or three natives were lounging in one of the kettles, smoking; the other was occupied by three sailors from the *Leviathan*, playing cards.

While we were conversing with these worthies, a stranger approached. He was a sun-burned, romantic-looking European, dressed in a loose suit of nankeen; his fine throat and chest were exposed, and he sported a Guayaquil hat, with a brim like a Chinese umbrella. This was Mr. Bell. He was very civil; showed us the grounds, and, taking us into a sort of arbor, to our surprise, offered to treat us to some wine. People often do the like; but Mr. Bell did more: he produced the bottle. It was spicy sherry; and we drank out of the halves of fresh citron melons. Delectable goblets!

The wine was a purchase from the French in Tahiti.

Now all this was extremely polite in Mr. Bell; still, we came to see *Mrs.* Bell. But she proved to be a phantom, indeed, having left the same morning for Papeetee, on a visit to one of the missionaries' wives there.

I went home much chagrined.

To be frank, my curiosity had been wonderfully piqued concerning the lady. In the first place, she was the most beautiful white woman I ever saw in Polynesia. But this is saying nothing. She had such eyes, such moss-roses in her cheeks, such a divine air in the saddle, that, to my dying day, I shall never forget Mrs. Bell.

The sugar-planter himself was young, robust, and handsome. So, merrily may the little Bells increase and multiply, and make music in the land of Imeeo.

Chapter LXXIX

Taloo Chapel—Holding Court in Polynesia

In Partoowye is to be seen one of the best constructed and handsomest chapels in the South Seas. Like the buildings of the palace, it stands upon an artificial pier, presenting a semicircular sweep to the bay. The chapel is built of hewn blocks of coral; a substance which, although extremely friable, is said to harden by exposure to the atmosphere. To a stranger, these blocks look extremely curious. Their surface is covered with strange fossil-like impressions, the seal of which must have been set before the flood. Very nearly white when hewn from the reefs, the coral darkens with age; so that several churches in Polynesia now look almost as sooty and venerable as famed St. Paul's.

In shape, the chapel is an octagon, with galleries all round. It will seat, perhaps, four hundred people. Everything within is stained a tawny red; and there being but few windows, or rather embrasures, the dusky benches and galleries, and the tall specter of a pulpit, look anything but cheerful.

On Sundays, we always went to worship here. Going in the family suite of Po-Po, we, of course, maintained a most decorous exterior; and hence, by all the elderly people of the village, were doubtless regarded as pattern young men.

Po-Po's seat was in a snug corner; and it being particularly snug, in the immediate vicinity of one of the palm pillars supporting the gallery, I invariably leaned against it: Po-Po and his lady on one side, the doctor and the dandy on the other, and the children and poor relations seated behind.

As for Loo, instead of sitting (as she ought to have done) by her good father and mother, she must needs run up into the gallery, and sit with a parcel of giddy creatures of her own age; who, all through the sermon, did nothing but look down on the congregation; pointing out, and giggling at the queer-looking old ladies in dowdy bonnets and scant tunics. But Loo herself was never guilty of these improprieties.

Occasionally during the week, they have afternoon service in the chapel, when the natives themselves have something to say; although their auditors are but few. An introductory prayer being offered by the missionary, and a hymn sung, communicants rise in their places, and exhort in pure Tahitian, and with wonderful tone and gesture. And among them all, Deacon Po-Po, though he talked most, was the one whom you would have liked best to hear. Much would I have given to have understood some of his impassioned bursts; when he tossed his arms overhead, stamped, scowled, and glared, till he looked like the very Angel of Vengeance.

"Deluded man!" sighed the doctor, on one of these occasions, "I fear he takes the fanatical view of the subject." One thing was certain; when Po-Po spoke, all listened; a great deal more than could be said for the rest; for under the discipline of two or three I could mention, some of the audience napped; others fidgeted; a few yawned; and one irritable old gentleman, in a nightcap of cocoanut leaves, used to clutch his long staff in a state of excessive nervousness, and stride out of the church, making all the noise he could, to emphasize his disgust.

Right adjoining the chapel is an immense, rickety building, with windows and shutters, and a half-decayed board flooring laid upon trunks of palm-trees. They called it a school-house; but as such we never saw it occupied. It was often used as a court-room, however; and here we attended several trials; among others, that of a decayed naval officer, and a young girl of fourteen; the latter, charged with having been very naughty on a particular occasion, set forth in the pleadings; and the former, with having aided and abetted her in her naughtiness, and with other misdemeanors.

The foreigner was a tall, military-looking fellow, with a dark cheek and black whiskers. According to his own account, he had lost a colonial armed brig on the coast of New Zealand; and since then, had been leading the life of a man about town, among the islands of the Pacific.

The doctor wanted to know why he did not go home and report the loss of his brig; but Captain Crash, as they called him, had some incomprehensible reasons for not doing so, about which he could talk by the hour, and no one be any the wiser. Probably, he was a discreet man, and thought it best to waive an interview with the lords of the admiralty.

For some time past, this extremely suspicious character had been carrying on an illicit trade in French wines and brandies, smuggled over from the men-of-war lately touching at Tahiti. In a grove near the anchorage, he had a rustic shanty and arbor; where, in quiet times, when no ships were in Taloo, a stray native once in a while got boozy, and staggered home, catching at the cocoanut-trees as he went. The captain himself lounged under a tree during the warm afternoons, pipe in mouth; thinking, perhaps, over old times, and occasionally feeling his shoulders for his lost epaulets.

But, sail ho! a ship is descried coming into the bay. Soon, she drops her anchor in its waters; and the next day Captain Crash entertains the sailors in his grove. And rare times they have of it—drinking and quarreling together, as sociably as you please.

Upon one of these occasions, the crew of the *Leviathan* made so prodigious a tumult, that the natives, indignant at the insult offered their laws, plucked up a heart, and made a dash at the rioters, one hundred strong. The sailors fought like tigers; but were at last overcome, and carried before a native tribunal; which, after a mighty clamor, dismissed everybody but Captain Crash, who was asserted to be the author of the disorders.

Upon this charge, then, he had been placed in confinement against the coming on of the assizes; the judge being expected to lounge along in the course of the afternoon. While waiting his Honor's arrival, numerous additional offences were preferred against the culprit (mostly by the old women); among others was the bit of a slip in which he stood implicated along with the young lady. Thus, in Polynesia as elsewhere—charge a man with one misdemeanor, and all his peccadilloes are raked up and assorted before him.

Going to the school-house for the purpose of witnessing the trial, the din of it assailed our ears a long way off; and upon entering the building we were almost stunned. About five hundred natives were present; each, apparently, having something to say, and determined to say it. His Honor—a handsome, benevolent-looking old man—sat cross-legged on a little platform; seemingly resigned with all Christian submission to the uproar. He was an hereditary chief in this quarter of the island, and judge for life in the district of Partoowye.

There were several cases coming on; but the captain and girl were first tried together. They were mixing freely with the crowd; and as it afterward turned out that everyone, no matter who, had a right to address the court, for aught we knew they might have been arguing their own case. At what precise moment the trial began, it would he hard to say. There was no swearing of witnesses, and no regular jury.[1] Now and then somebody leaped up and shouted out something which might have been evidence; the rest, meanwhile, keeping up an incessant jabbering. Presently, the old judge himself began to get excited; and springing to his feet, ran in among the crowd, wagging his tongue as hard as anybody.

The tumult lasted about twenty minutes; and toward the end of it, Captain Crash might have been seen, tranquilly regarding, from his Honor's platform, the judicial uproar, in which his fate was about being decided.

The result of all this was, that both he and the girl were found guilty. The latter was adjudged to make six mats for the queen; and the former, in consideration of his manifold offenses, being

1. This anomaly exists, notwithstanding that, in other respects, the missionaries have endeavored to organize the native courts upon the English model.

deemed incorrigible, was sentenced to eternal banishment from the island. Both these decrees seemed to originate in the general hubbub. His Honor, however, appeared to have considerable authority, and it was quite plain that the decision received his approval.

The above penalties were by no means indiscriminately inflicted. The missionaries have prepared a sort of penal tariff to facilitate judicial proceedings. It costs so many days' labor on the Broom Road to indulge in the pleasures of the calabash; so many fathoms of stone wall to steal a musket; and so on to the end of the catalogue. The judge being provided with a book, in which all these matters are cunningly arranged, the thing is vastly convenient. For instance: a crime is proved—say, bigamy; turn to letter B—and there you have it. Bigamy—forty days on the Broom Road, and twenty mats for the queen. Read the passage aloud, and sentence is pronounced.

After taking part in the first trial, the other delinquents present were put upon their own; in which, also, the convicted culprits seemed to have quite as much to say as the rest. A rather strange proceeding; but strictly in accordance with the glorious English principle, that every man should be tried by his peers.

They were all found guilty.

Chapter LXXX

Queen Pomaree

It is well to learn something about people before being introduced to them; and so, we will here give some account of Pomaree and her family.

Every reader of Cook's *Voyages* must remember "Otoo," who, in that navigator's time, was king of the larger peninsula of Tahiti. Subsequently, assisted by the muskets of the *Bounty*'s men, he extended his rule over the entire island. This Otoo, before his death, had his name changed into Pomaree, which has ever since been the royal patronymic.

He was succeeded by his son, Pomaree II, the most famous prince in the annals of Tahiti. Though a sad debauchee and drunkard, and even charged with unnatural crimes, he was a great friend of the missionaries, and one of their very first proselytes. During the religious wars into which he was hurried by his zeal for the new faith, he was defeated, and expelled from the island. After a short exile, he returned from Imeeo, with an army of eight hundred warriors; and, in the battle of Narii, routed the rebellious pagans with great slaughter, and re-established himself upon the throne. Thus, by force of arms was Christianity finally triumphant in Tahiti.

Pomaree II, dying in 1821, was succeeded by his infant son, under the title of Pomaree III. This young prince survived his father but six years; and the government then descended to his elder sister, Aimata, the present queen, who is commonly called Pomaree Vahinee I, or the first female Pomaree. Her Majesty must be now upwards of thirty years of age. She has been twice married. Her first husband was a son of the old King of Tahar, an island about one hundred miles from Tahiti. This proving an unhappy alliance, the pair were soon after divorced. The present husband of the queen is a chief of Imeeo.

The reputation of Pomaree is not what it ought to be. She, and also her mother, were, for a long time, excommunicated members of the Church; and the former, I believe, still is. Among other things, her conjugal fidelity is far from being unquestioned. Indeed, it was upon this ground chiefly that she was excluded from the communion of the Church.

Previous to her misfortunes, she spent the greater portion of her time sailing about from one island to another, attended by a licentious court; and wherever she went, all manner of games and festivities celebrated her arrival.

She was always given to display. For several years the maintenance of a regiment of household troops drew largely upon the royal exchequer. They were trouserless fellows, in a uniform of calico shirts and pasteboard hats; armed with muskets of all shapes and calibers, and commanded by a great noisy chief, strutting it in a coat of fiery red. These heroes escorted their mistress whenever she went abroad.

Some time ago, the queen received from her English sister, Victoria, a very showy, though uneasy, head-dress—a crown; probably made to order, at some tinman's in London. Having no idea of reserving so pretty a bauble for coronation days, which come so seldom, her majesty sported it whenever she appeared in public; and, to show her familiarity with European customs, politely touched it to all foreigners of distinction—whaling captains and the like—whom she happened to meet in her evening walk on the Broom Road.

The arrival and departure of royalty were always announced at the palace by the court artilleryman—a fat old gentleman, who, in a prodigious hurry and perspiration, discharged minute fowling-pieces, as fast as he could load and fire the same.

The Tahitian princess leads her husband a hard life. Poor fellow! he not only caught a queen, but a Tartar, when he married her. The style by which he is addressed is rather significant—"Pomaree-Tanee" (Pomaree's man). All things considered, as appropriate a title for a king-consort as could be hit upon.

If ever there were a henpecked husband, that man is the prince. One day, his cara-sposa, giving audience to a deputation from the captains of the vessels lying in Papeetee, he ventured to make a suggestion which was very displeasing to her. She turned round, and, boxing his ears, told him to go over to his beggarly island of Imeeo, if he wanted to give himself airs.

Cuffed and contemned, poor Tanee flies to the bottle, or rather to the calabash, for solace. Like his wife and mistress, he drinks more than he ought.

Six or seven years ago, when an American man-of-war was lying at Papeetee, the town was thrown into the greatest commotion by a conjugal assault and battery, made upon the sacred person of Pomaree by her intoxicated Tanee.

Captain Bob once told me the story. And by way of throwing more spirit into the description, as well as to make up for his oral deficiencies, the old man went through the accompanying action: myself being proxy for the Queen of Tahiti.

It seems, that on a Sunday morning, being dismissed contemptuously from the royal presence, Tanee was accosted by certain good fellows, friends and boon companions, who condoled with him on his misfortunes—railed against the queen, and finally dragged him away to an illicit vendor of spirits, in whose house the party got gloriously mellow. In this state, Pomaree Vahinee I was the topic upon which all dilated—"A vixen of a queen," probably suggested one. "It's infamous," said another; "and I'd have satisfaction," cried a third. "And so I will!"—Tanee must have hiccoughed; for off he went; and ascertaining that his royal half was out riding, he mounted his horse, and galloped after her.

Near the outskirts of the town, a cavalcade of women came cantering towards him, in the center of which was the object of his fury. Smiting his beast right and left, he dashed in among them; completely overturning one of the party, leaving her on the field, and dispersing everybody else except Pomaree. Backing her horse dexterously, the incensed queen heaped upon him every scandalous epithet she could think of; until at last, the enraged Tanee leaped out of his saddle, caught Pomaree by her dress, and dragging her to the earth, struck her repeatedly in the face, holding on meanwhile by the hair of her head. He was proceeding to strangle her on the spot, when the cries of the frightened attendants brought a crowd of natives to the rescue, who bore the nearly insensible queen away.

But his frantic rage was not yet sated. He ran to the palace; and before it could be prevented, demolished a valuable supply of crockery, a recent present from abroad. In the act of perpetrating some other atrocity, he was seized from behind, and carried off with rolling eyes and foaming at the mouth.

This is a fair example of a Tahitian in a passion. Though the mildest of mortals in general, and hard to be roused, when once fairly up, he is possessed with a thousand devils.

The day following, Tanee was privately paddled over to Imeeo, in a canoe; where, after remaining in banishment for a couple of weeks, he was allowed to return, and once more give in his domestic adhesion.

Though Pomaree Vahinee I be something of a Jezebel in private life, in her public rule she is said to have been quite lenient and forbearing. This was her true policy; for a hereditary hostility to her family had always lurked in the hearts of many powerful chiefs, the descendants of the old Kings of Taiarboo, dethroned by her grandfather Otoo. Chief among these, and in fact the leader of his party, was Poofai; a bold, able man, who made no secret of his enmity to the missionaries, and the government which they controlled. But while events were occurring, calculated to favor the hopes of the disaffected and turbulent, the arrival of the French gave a most unexpected turn to affairs.

During my sojourn in Tahiti, a report was rife—which I knew to originate with what is generally called the "missionary party"—that Poofai and some other chiefs of note, had actually agreed, for a stipulated bribe, to acquiesce in the appropriation of their country. But subsequent events have rebutted the calumny. Several of these very men have recently died in battle against the French.

Under the sovereignty of the Pomarees, the great chiefs of Tahiti were something like the barons of King John. Holding feudal sway over their patrimonial valleys, and, on account of their descent, warmly beloved by the people, they frequently cut off the royal revenues by refusing to pay the customary tribute due from them as vassals.

The truth is, that with the ascendancy of the missionaries, the regal office in Tahiti lost much of its dignity and influence. In the days of paganism, it was supported by all the power of a numerous priesthood, and was solemnly connected with the entire superstitious idolatry of the land. The monarch claimed to be a sort of by-blow of Tararroa, the Saturn of the Polynesian mythology, and cousin-german to inferior deities. His person was thrice holy; if he entered an ordinary dwelling, never mind for how short a time, it was demolished when he left; no common mortal being thought worthy to inhabit it afterwards.

"I'm a greater man than King George," said the incorrigible young Otoo, to the first missionaries; "he rides on a horse, and I on a man!" Such was the case. He traveled post through his dominions on the shoulders of his subjects; and relays of immortal beings were provided in all the valleys.

But alas! how times have changed! how transient human greatness! Some years since, Pomaree Vahinee I, the granddaughter of the proud Otoo, went into the laundry business; publicly soliciting, by her agents, the washing of the linen belonging to the officers of ships touching in her harbors.

It is a significant fact, and one worthy of record, that while the influence of the English missionaries at Tahiti has tended to so great a diminution of the regal dignity there, that of the American missionaries at the Sandwich Islands has been purposely exerted to bring about a contrary result.

Chapter LXXXI

We Visit the Court

It was about the middle of the second month of the hegira, and therefore some five weeks after our arrival in Partoowye, that we at last obtained admittance to the residence of the queen.

It happened thus. There was a Marquesan in the train of Pomaree, who officiated as nurse to her children. According to the Tahitian custom, the royal youngsters are carried about until it requires no small degree of strength to stand up under them. But Marbonna was just the man for this—large and muscular, well made as a statue, and with an arm like a degenerate Tahitian's thigh.

Embarking at his native island, as a sailor, on board of a French whaler, he afterwards ran away from the ship at Tahiti; where, being seen and admired by Pomaree, he had been prevailed upon to enlist in her service.

Often, when visiting the grounds, we saw him walking about in the shade, carrying two handsome boys, who encircled his neck with their arms. Marbonna's face, tattooed as it was in the ornate style of his tribe, was as good as a picture-book to these young Pomarees. They delighted to trace with their fingers the outlines of the strange shapes there delineated.

The first time my eyes lighted upon the Marquesan, I knew his country in a moment; and hailing him in his own language, he turned round, surprised that a person so speaking should be a stranger. He proved to be a native of Tior, a glen of Nukuheva. I had visited the place more than once; and so, on the island of Imeeo, we met like old friends.

In my frequent conversations with him over the bamboo picket, I found this islander a philosopher of nature—a wild heathen, moralizing upon the vices and follies of the Christian court of Tahiti—a savage, scorning the degeneracy of the people among whom fortune had thrown him.

I was amazed at the national feelings of the man. No European, when abroad, could speak of his country with more pride than Marbonna. He assured me, again and again, that so soon as he had obtained sufficient money to purchase twenty muskets and as many bags of powder, he was going to return to a place, with which Imeeo was not worthy to be compared.

It was Marbonna, who after one or two unsuccessful attempts, at last brought about our admission into the queen's grounds. Through a considerable crowd, he conducted us along the pier to where an old man was sitting; to whom he introduced us as a couple of "karhowrees" of his acquaintance, anxious to see the sights of the palace. The venerable chamberlain stared at us, and shook his head: the doctor, thinking he wanted a fee, placed a plug of tobacco in his hand. This was ingratiating, and we were permitted to pass on. Upon the point of entering one of the houses, Marbonna's name was shouted in half a dozen different directions, and he was obliged to withdraw.

Thus left at the very threshold to shift for ourselves, my companion's assurance stood us in good stead. He stalked right in, and I followed. The place was full of women, who, instead of exhibiting the surprise we expected, accosted us as cordially as if we had called to take our souchong with them, by express invitation. In the first place nothing would do but we must each devour a calabash of *poee* and several roasted bananas. Pipes were then lighted, and a brisk conversation ensued.

These ladies of the court, if not very polished, were surprisingly free and easy in their manners; quite as much so as King Charles's beauties. There was one of them—an arch little miss, who could converse with us pretty fluently—to whom we strove to make ourselves particularly agreeable, with the view of engaging her services as cicerone.

As such, she turned out to be everything we could desire. No one disputing her will, every place was entered without ceremony, curtains brushed aside, mats lifted, and each nook and corner explored. Whether the little damsel carried her mistress's signet, that everything opened to her thus, I know not; but Marbonna himself, the bearer of infants, could not have been half so serviceable.

Among other houses which we visited, was one of large size and fine exterior; the special residence of a European—formerly the mate of a merchant-vessel—who had done himself the honor of marrying into the Pomaree family. The lady he wedded being a near kinswoman of the queen, he became a permanent member of her majesty's household. This adventurer rose late, dressed theatrically in calico and trinkets, assumed a dictatorial tone in conversation, and was evidently upon excellent terms with himself.

We found him reclining on a mat, smoking a reed-pipe of tobacco, in the midst of an admiring circle of chiefs and ladies. He must have noticed our approach; but instead of rising and offering civilities, he went on talking and smoking, without even condescending to look at us.

"His Highness feels his *poee,*" carelessly observed the doctor. The rest of the company gave us the ordinary salutation, our guide announcing us beforehand.

In answer to our earnest requests to see the queen, we were now conducted to an edifice, by far the most spacious, in the enclosure. It was at least one hundred and fifty feet in length, very wide, with low eaves, and an exceedingly steep roof of pandannas leaves. There were neither doors nor windows—nothing along the sides but the slight posts supporting the rafters. Between these posts, curtains of fine matting and tappa were rustling all round; some of them were festooned, or partly withdrawn, so as to admit light and air, and afford a glimpse now and then of what was going on within.

Pushing aside one of the screens, we entered. The apartment was one immense hall; the long and lofty ridge-pole fluttering with fringed matting and tassels, full forty feet from the ground. Lounges of mats, piled one upon another, extended on either side; while here and there were slight screens, forming as many recesses, where groups of natives—all females—were reclining at their evening meal.

As we advanced, these various parties ceased their buzzing, and in explanation of our appearance among them, listened to a few cabalistic words from our guide.

The whole scene was a strange one; but what most excited our surprise, was the incongruous assemblage of the most costly objects from all quarters of the globe. Cheek by jowl, they lay beside the rudest native articles, without the slightest attempt at order. Superb writing-desks of rosewood, inlaid with silver and mother-of-pearl; decanters and goblets of cut glass; embossed volumes of plates; gilded candelabras; sets of globes and mathematical instruments; the finest porcelain; richly mounted sabers and fowling-pieces; laced hats and sumptuous garments of all sorts, with numerous other matters of European manufacture, were strewn about among greasy calabashes half filled with *poee,* rolls of old tappa and matting, paddles and fish-spears, and the ordinary furniture of a Tahitian dwelling.

All the articles first mentioned were, doubtless, presents from foreign powers. They were more or less injured: the fowling-pieces and swords were rusted; the finest woods were scratched; and a folio volume of Hogarth lay open, with a cocoanut shell of some musty preparation capsized among the miscellaneous furniture of the Rake's apartment, where that inconsiderate young gentleman is being measured for a coat.

While we were amusing ourselves in this museum of curiosities, our conductor plucked us by the sleeve, and whispered, "Pomaree! Pomaree! aramai kow kow."

"She is coming to sup, then," said the doctor, staring in the direction indicated. "What say you, Paul, suppose we step up?" Just then a curtain nearby, lifted; and from a private building a few yards distant, the queen entered, unattended.

She wore a loose gown of blue silk, with two rich shawls, one red and the other yellow, tied about her neck. Her royal majesty was barefooted.

She was about the ordinary size, rather matronly; her features not very handsome; her mouth, voluptuous; but there was a careworn expression in her face, probably attributable to her late misfortunes. From her appearance, one would judge her about forty; but she is not so old.

As the queen approached one of the recesses, her attendants hurried up, escorted her in, and smoothed the mats on which she at last reclined. Two girls soon appeared, carrying their mistress's repast; and then, surrounded by cut glass and porcelain, and jars of sweetmeats and confections, Pomaree Vahinee I, the titular Queen of Tahiti, ate fish and *poee* out of her native calabashes, disdaining either knife or spoon.

"Come on," whispered Long Ghost, "let's have an audience at once"; and he was on the point of introducing himself, when our guide, quite alarmed, held him back, and implored silence. The other natives also interfered; and as he was pressing forward, raised such an outcry that Pomaree lifted her eyes, and saw us for the first.

She seemed surprised, and offended; and issuing an order in a commanding tone to several of her women, waved us out of the house. Summary as the dismissal was, court etiquette, no doubt, required our compliance. We withdrew; making a profound inclination as we disappeared behind the tappa arras.

We departed the grounds without seeing Marbonna; and previous to vaulting over the picket, feed our pretty guide, after a fashion of our own. Looking round a few moments after, we saw the damsel escorted back by two men, who seemed to have been sent after her. I trust she received nothing more than a reprimand.

The next day Po-Po informed us that strict orders had been issued to admit no strangers within the palace precincts.

Chapter LXXXII

Which Ends the Book

DISAPPOINTED IN GOING TO COURT, WE DETERMINED UPON GOING TO SEA. IT WOULD NEVER do, longer to trespass on Po-Po's hospitality; and then, weary somewhat of life in Imeeo, like all sailors ashore, I at last pined for the billows.

Now, if her crew were to be credited, the *Leviathan* was not the craft to our mind. But I had seen the captain, and liked him. He was an uncommonly tall, robust, fine-looking man, in the prime of life. There was a deep crimson spot in the middle of each sun-burned cheek, doubtless the effect of his sea-potations. He was a Vineyarder, or native of the island of Martha's Vineyard (adjoining Nantucket), and, I would have sworn it, a sailor, and no tyrant.

Previous to this, we had rather avoided the *Leviathan*'s men, when they came ashore; but now, we purposely threw ourselves in their way, in order to learn more of the vessel.

We became acquainted with the third mate, a Prussian, and an old merchant seaman—a right jolly fellow, with a face like a ruby. We took him to Po-Po's, and gave him a dinner of baked pig and bread-fruit; with pipes and tobacco for dessert. The account he gave us of the ship agreed with my own surmises. A cosier old craft never floated; and the captain was the finest man in the world. There was plenty to eat, too; and, at sea, nothing to do but sit on the windlass and sail. The only bad trait about the vessel was this: she had been launched under some baleful star; and so, was a luckless ship in the fishery. She dropped her boats into the brine often enough, and they frequently got fast to the whales; but lance and harpoon almost invariably "drew" when darted by the men of the *Leviathan*. But what of that? We should have all the sport of chasing the monsters, with none of the detestable work which follows their capture. So, hurrah for the coast of Japan! Thither the ship was bound.

A word now, about the hard stories we heard, the first time we visited the ship. They were nothing but idle fictions, got up by the sailors for the purpose of frightening us away, so as to oblige the captain, who was in want of more hands, to lie the longer in a pleasant harbor.

The next time the Vineyarder came ashore, we flung ourselves in his path. When informed of our desire to sail with him, he wanted to know our history; and, above all, what countrymen we were. We said that we had left a whaler in Tahiti, some time previous; and, since then, had been, in the most praiseworthy manner, employed upon a plantation. As for our country, sailors belong to no nation in particular; we were, on this occasion, both Yankees. Upon this he looked decidedly incredulous; and freely told us, that he verily believed we were both from Sydney.

Be it known here, that American sea-captains, in the Pacific, are mortally afraid of these Sydney gentry; who, to tell the truth, wherever known, are in excessively bad odor. Is there a mutiny on board a ship in the South Seas, ten to one a Sydney man is the ringleader. Ashore, these fellows are equally riotous.

It was on this account, that we were anxious to conceal the fact of our having belonged to the *Julia;* though it annoyed me much, thus to deny the dashing little craft. For the same reason, also, the doctor fibbed about his birth-place.

Unfortunately, one part of our raiment—Arfretee's blue frocks—was deemed a sort of collateral evidence against us. For, curiously enough, an American sailor is generally distinguished by his red frock; and an English tar, by his blue one: thus reversing the national colors. The circumstance was pointed out by the captain; and we quickly explained the anomaly. But in vain: he seemed inveterately prejudiced against us; and, in particular, eyed the doctor most distrustfully.

By way of propping the latter's pretensions, I was throwing out a hint concerning Kentucky, as a land of tall men, when our Vineyarder turned away abruptly, and desired to hear nothing more. It was evident that he took Long Ghost for an exceedingly problematical character.

Perceiving this, I resolved to see what a private interview would do. So, one afternoon, I found the captain smoking a pipe in the dwelling of a portly old native, one Mai-Mai, who, for a reasonable compensation, did the honors of Partoowye, to illustrious strangers.

His guest had just risen from a sumptuous meal of baked pig and taro pudding; and the remnants of the repast were still visible. Two reeking bottles, also, with their necks wrenched off, lay upon the mat. All this was encouraging; for, after a good dinner, one feels affluent and amiable, and peculiarly open to conviction. So, at all events, I found the noble Vineyarder.

I began by saying, that I called for the purpose of setting him right, touching certain opinions of his concerning the place of my nativity: I was an American, thank heaven! and wanted to convince him of the fact.

After looking me in the eye for some time, and, by so doing, revealing an obvious unsteadiness in his own visual organs, he begged me to reach forth my arm. I did so; wondering what upon earth that useful member had to do with the matter in hand.

He placed his fingers upon my wrist; and holding them there for a moment, sprang to his feet; and, with much enthusiasm, pronounced me a Yankee, every beat of my pulse!

"Here, Mai-Mai!" he cried, "another bottle!" And, when it came, with one stroke of a knife, he summarily beheaded it, and commanded me to drain it to the bottom. He then told me, that if I would come on board his vessel the following morning, I would find the ship's articles on the cabin transom.

This was getting along famously. But what was to become of the doctor?

I forthwith made an adroit allusion to my long friend. But it was worse than useless. The Vineyarder swore he would have nothing to do with him—he (my long friend) was a "bird" from Sydney, and nothing would make him (the man of little faith) believe otherwise.

I could not help loving the free-hearted captain; but indignant at this most unaccountable prejudice against my comrade, I abruptly took leave.

Upon informing the doctor of the result of the interview, he was greatly amused; and laughingly declared, that the Vineyarder must be a penetrating fellow. He then insisted upon my going to sea in the ship, since he well knew how anxious I was to leave. As for himself, on second thoughts, he was no sailor; and although "landsmen" very often compose part of a whaler's crew, he did not quite relish the idea of occupying a position so humble. In short, he had made up his mind to tarry awhile in Imeeo.

I turned the matter over; and at last decided upon quitting the island. The impulse urging me to sea once more, and the prospect of eventually reaching home, were too much to be resisted; especially, as the *Leviathan,* was so comfortable a craft, was now bound on her last whaling-cruise, and, in little more than a year's time, would be going round Cape Horn.

I did not, however, covenant to remain in the vessel for the residue of the voyage; which would have been needlessly binding myself. I merely stipulated for the coming cruise, leaving my subsequent movements unrestrained; for there was no knowing that I might not change my mind, and prefer journeying home by short and easy stages.

The next day I paddled off to the ship, signed and sealed, and stepped ashore with my "advance"—fifteen Spanish dollars, tasseling the ends of my neck-handkerchief.

I forced half of the silver on Long Ghost; and having little use for the remainder, would have given it to Po-Po as some small return for his kindness; but, although he well knew the value of the coin, not a dollar would he accept.

In three days' time, the Prussian came to Po-Po's, and told us that the captain, having made good the number of his crew, by shipping several islanders, had determined upon sailing with the land-breeze at dawn the following morning. These tidings were received in the afternoon. The doctor immediately disappeared, returning soon after with a couple of flasks of wine, concealed in the folds of his frock. Through the agency of the Marquesan, he had purchased them from an understrapper of the court.

I prevailed upon Po-Po to drink a parting shell; and even little Loo, actually looking conscious that one of her hopeless admirers was about leaving Partoowye forever, sipped a few drops from a folded leaf. As for the warm-hearted Arfretee, her grief was unbounded. She even besought me to spend my last night under her own palm-thatch; and then, in the morning, she would herself paddle me off to the ship.

But this I would not consent to; and so, as something to remember her by, she presented me with a roll of fine matting, and another of tappa. These gifts placed in my hammock, I afterwards found very agreeable in the warm latitudes to which we were bound; nor did they fail to awaken most grateful remembrances.

About nightfall we broke away from this generous-hearted household, and hurried down to the water.

It was a mad, merry night among the sailors: they had on tap a small cask of wine, procured in the same way as the doctor's flasks.

An hour or two after midnight, everything was noiseless; but when the first streak of the dawn showed itself over the mountains, a sharp voice hailed the forecastle, and ordered the ship unmoored. The anchors came up cheerily; the sails were soon set; and with the early breath of the tropical morning, fresh and fragrant from the hill-sides, we slowly glided down the bay, and were swept through the opening in the reef. Presently, "we hove to," and the canoes came alongside to take off the islanders who had accompanied us thus far. As he stepped over the side, I shook the doctor long and heartily by the hand. I have never seen or heard of him since.

Crowding all sail, we braced the yards square; and, the breeze freshening, bowled straight away from the land. Once more the sailor's cradle rocked under me, and I found myself rolling in my gait.

By noon, the island had gone down in the horizon; and all before us was the wide Pacific.

MARDI
AND A VOYAGE THITHER

Dedicated to My Brother,
Allan Melville

CONTENTS

Preface

Not long ago, having published two narratives of voyages in the Pacific, which, in many quarters, were received with incredulity, the thought occurred to me, of indeed writing a romance of Polynesian adventure, and publishing it as such; to see whether, the fiction might not, possibly, be received for a verity: in some degree the reverse of my previous experience.

This thought was the germ of others, which have resulted in *Mardi*.

New York, January, 1849

Chapter I

Foot in Stirrup

We are off! The courses and topsails are set: the coral-hung anchor swings from the bow: and together the three royals are given to the breeze, that follows us out to sea like the baying of a hound. Out spreads the canvas—alow, aloft—boom stretched, on both sides, with many a stun' sail; till like a hawk, with pinions poised, we shadow the sea with our sails, and reelingly cleave the brine.

But whence and whither wend ye, mariners?

We sail from Ravavai, an isle in the sea, not very far northward from the tropic of Capricorn, nor very far westward from Pitcairn's island, where the mutineers of the *Bounty* settled. At Ravavai I had stepped ashore some few months previous; and now was embarked on a cruise for the whale, whose brain enlightens the world.

And from Ravavai we sail for the Gallipagos, otherwise called the Enchanted Islands, by reason of the many wild currents and eddies there met.

Now, round about those isles, which Dampier once trod, where the Spanish buccaneers once hived their gold moidores, the Cachalot, or sperm whale, at certain seasons abounds.

But thither, from Ravavai, your craft may not fly, as flies the sea-gull, straight to her nest. For, owing to the prevalence of the trade-winds, ships bound to the north-east from the vicinity of Ravavai are fain to take something of a circuit; a few thousand miles or so. First, in pursuit of the variable winds, they make all haste to the south; and there at length picking up a stray breeze, they stand for the main; then, making their easting, up helm, and away down the coast, towards the Line.

This roundabout way did the *Arcturion* take; and in all conscience a weary one it was. Never before had the ocean appeared so monotonous; thank fate, never since.

But bravo! in two weeks' time, an event. Out of the gray of the morning and right ahead, as we sailed along, a dark object rose out of the sea; standing dimly before us, mists wreathing and curling aloft, and creamy breakers frothing round its base. We turned aside, and at length, when day dawned, passed Massafuero. With a glass we spied two or three hermit goats winding down to the sea, in a ravine; and presently a signal: a tattered flag upon a summit beyond. Well knowing, however, that there was nobody on the island but two or three noose-fulls of runaway convicts from Chile, our captain had no mind to comply with their invitation to land. Though, haply, he may have erred in not sending a boat off with his card.

A few days more and we "took the trades." Like favors snappishly conferred they came to us, as is often the case in a very sharp squall; the shock of which carried away one of our spars; also our fat old cook off his legs, depositing him plump in the scuppers to leeward.

In good time making the desired longitude upon the Equator, a few leagues west of the Gallipagos, we spent several weeks chassezing across the Line, to and fro, in unavailing search for our prey. For some of their hunters believe, that whales, like the silver ore in Peru, run in veins through the ocean. So, day after day daily, and week after week weekly, we traversed the self-same longitudinal intersection of the self-same Line, till we were almost ready to swear that we felt the ship strike every time her keel crossed that imaginary locality.

At length, dead before the equatorial breeze, we threaded our way straight along the very Line itself. Westward sailing; peering right and peering left, but seeing naught.

It was during this weary time that I experienced the first symptoms of that bitter impatience of our monotonous craft, which ultimately led to the adventures herein recounted.

But hold you! Not a word against that rare old ship, nor its crew. The sailors were good fellows all, the half-score of pagans we had shipped at the islands included. Nevertheless they were not precisely to my mind. There was no soul a magnet to mine; none with whom to mingle sympathies, save in deploring the calms with which we were now and then overtaken, or in hailing the breeze when it came. Under other and livelier auspices the tarry knaves might have developed qualities more attractive. Had we sprung a leak, been "stove" by a whale, or been blessed with some despot of a captain against whom to stir up some spirited revolt, these shipmates of mine might have proved limber lads and men of mettle. But as it was, there was naught to strike fire from their steel.

There were other things also tending to make my lot on shipboard very hard to be borne. True, the skipper himself was a trump; stood upon no quarter-deck dignity, and had a tongue for a sailor. Let me do him justice, furthermore; he took a sort of fancy for me in particular; was sociable, nay, loquacious, when I happened to stand at the helm. But what of that? Could he talk sentiment or philosophy? Not a bit. His library was eight inches by four: Bowditch and Hamilton Moore.

And what of me, thus pining for someone who could page me a quotation from Burton on Blue Devils; what to me, indeed, were flat repetitions of long-drawn yarns and the everlasting stanzas of Black-eyed Susan sung by our full forecastle choir? Staler than stale ale.

Ay, ay, *Arcturion*! I say it in no malice, but thou wast exceedingly dull. Not only at sailing; hard though it was, that I could have borne, but in every other respect. The days went slowly round and round, endless and uneventful as cycles in space. Time and time-pieces! How many centuries did my hammock tell, as pendulum-like it swung to the ship's dull roll, and ticked the hours and ages. Sacred forever be the *Arcturion*'s fore-hatch—alas! sea-moss is over it now—and rusty forever the bolts that held together that old sea hearth-stone, about which we so often lounged. Nevertheless, ye lost and leaden hours, I will rail at ye while life lasts.

Well: weeks, chronologically speaking, went by. Bill Marvel's stories were told over and over again till the beginning and end dovetailed into each other, and were united for aye. Ned Ballad's songs were sung till the echoes lurked in the very tops, and nested in the bunts of the sails. My poor patience was clean gone.

But at last after some time sailing due westward we quitted the Line in high disgust, having seen there no sign of a whale.

But whither now? To the broiling coast of Papua? That region of sun-strokes, typhoons, and bitter pulls after whales unattainable. Far worse. We were going, it seemed, to illustrate the Whistonian theory concerning the damned and the comets—hurried from equinoctial heats to arctic frosts. To be short, with the true fickleness of his tribe, our skipper had abandoned all thought of the Cachalot. In desperation he was bent upon bobbing for the Right whale on the nor'-west coast and in the Bay of Kamschatska.

To the uninitiated in the business of whaling, my feelings at this juncture may perhaps be hard to understand. But this much let me say, that Right whaling on the nor'-west coast, in chill and dismal fogs, the sullen inert monsters rafting the sea all round like Black Forest logs on the Rhine, and submitting to the harpoon like half-stunned bullocks to the knife; this horrid and indecent Right whaling, I say, compared to a spirited hunt for the gentlemanly Cachalot in southern and more genial seas, is as the butchery of white bears upon blank Greenland icebergs to zebra hunting in Caffraria, where the lively quarry bounds before you through leafy glades.

Now this most unforeseen determination on the part of my captain to measure the arctic circle was nothing more nor less than a tacit contravention of the agreement between us. That agreement needs not to be detailed. And having shipped but for a single cruise, I had embarked on board his craft as one might put foot in stirrup for a day's following the hounds. And here, Heaven help me, he was going to carry me off to the Pole! And on such a vile errand too! For there was something degrading in it. Your true whaleman glories in keeping his harpoon unspotted by blood of aught but Cachalot. By my halidome, it touched the knighthood of a tar. Sperm and spermacetti! It was unendurable.

"Captain," said I, touching my sombrero to him as I stood at the wheel one day, "it's very hard to carry me off this way to purgatory. I shipped to go elsewhere."

"Yes, and so did I," was his reply. "But it can't be helped. Sperm whales are not to be had. We've been out now three years, and something or other must be got, for the ship is hungry for oil, and her hold a gulf to look into. But cheer up, my boy; once in the Bay of Kamschatka and we'll be all afloat with what we want, though it be none of the best."

Worse and worse! The oleaginous prospect extended into an immensity of Macassar. "Sir," said I, "I did not ship for it; put me ashore somewhere, I beseech." He stared, but no answer vouchsafed; and for a moment I thought I had roused the domineering spirit of the sea-captain, to the prejudice of the more kindly nature of the man.

But not so. Taking three turns on the deck, he placed his hand on the wheel and said, "Right or wrong, my lad, go with us you must. Putting you ashore is now out of the question. I make no port till this ship is full to the combings of her hatchways. However, you may leave her if you can." And so saying he entered his cabin, like Julius Cæsar into his tent.

He may have meant little by it, but that last sentence rung in my ear like a bravado. It savored of the turnkey's compliments to the prisoner in Newgate when he shoots-to the bolt on him.

"Leave the ship if I can!" Leave the ship when neither sail nor shore was in sight! Ay, my fine captain, stranger things have been done. For on board that very craft, the old *Arcturion,* were four tall fellows whom two years previous our skipper himself had picked up in an open boat, far from the farthest shoal. To be sure, they spun a long yarn about being the only survivors of an Indiaman burnt down to the water's edge. But who credited their tale? Like many others, they were keepers of a secret; had doubtless contracted a disgust for some ugly craft still afloat and hearty, and stolen away from her, off soundings. Among seamen in the Pacific such adventures not seldom occur. Nor are they accounted great wonders. They are but incidents, not events, in the career of the brethren of the order of South Sea rovers. For what matters it, though hundreds of miles from land, if a good whale-boat be under foot, the "trades" behind, and mild, warm seas before? And herein lies the difference between the Atlantic and Pacific—that once within the tropics the bold sailor who has a mind to quit his ship round Cape Horn, waits not for port. He regards that ocean as one mighty harbor.

Nevertheless, the enterprise hinted at was no light one, and I resolved to weigh well the chances. It's worth noticing this way we all have of pondering for ourselves the enterprise which, for others, we hold a bagatelle.

My first thoughts were of the boat to be obtained, and the right or wrong of abstracting it, under the circumstances. But to split no hairs on this point, let me say that were I placed in the same situation again I would repeat the thing I did then. The captain well knew that he was going to detain me unlawfully, against our agreement; and it was he himself who threw out the very hint, which I merely adopted with many thanks to him.

In some such willful mood as this I went aloft one day to stand my allotted two hours at the mast-head. It was towards the close of a day serene and beautiful. There I stood, high upon the mast, and away, away, illimitably rolled the ocean beneath. Where we then were was, perhaps, the most unfrequented and least known portion of these seas. Westward, however, lay numerous groups of islands, loosely laid down upon the charts, and invested with all the charms of dreamland. But soon these regions would be past; the mild equatorial breeze exchanged for cold, fierce squalls, and all the horrors of northern voyaging.

I cast my eyes downward to the brown planks of the dull plodding ship, silent from stem to stern; then abroad.

In the distance what visions were spread! The entire western horizon, high piled with gold and crimson clouds; airy arches, domes and minarets, as if the yellow, Moorish sun were setting behind some vast Alhambra. Vistas seemed leading to worlds beyond. To and fro and all over the towers of this Nineveh in the sky, flew troops of birds. Watching them long, one crossed my sight, flew through a low arch, and was lost to view. My spirit must have sailed in with it; for directly, as in a trance, came upon me the cadence of mild billows laving a beach of shells, the waving of boughs, and the voices of maidens, and the lulled beatings of my own dissolved heart, all blended together.

Now, all this, to be plain, was but one of the many visions one has up aloft. But coming upon me at this time it wrought upon me so that thenceforth my desire to quit the *Arcturion* became little short of a frenzy.

Chapter II

A Calm

NEXT DAY THERE WAS A CALM, WHICH ADDED NOT A LITTLE TO MY IMPATIENCE OF THE SHIP. And, furthermore, by certain nameless associations revived in me my old impressions upon first witnessing as a landsman this phenomenon of the sea. Those impressions may merit a page.

To a landsman a calm is no joke. It not only revolutionizes his abdomen, but unsettles his mind; tempts him to recant his belief in the eternal fitness of things; in short, almost makes an infidel of him.

At first he is taken by surprise, never having dreamed of a state of existence where existence itself seems suspended. He shakes himself in his coat, to see whether it be empty or no. He closes his eyes to test the reality of the glassy expanse. He fetches a deep breath by way of experiment, and for the sake of witnessing the effect. If a reader of books, Priestley on *Necessity* occurs to him; and he believes in that old Sir Anthony Absolute to the very last chapter. His faith in Malte-Brun, however, begins to fail; for the geography which from boyhood he had implicitly confided in, always assured him that though expatiating all over the globe, the sea was at least margined by land. That over against America, for example, was Asia. But it is a calm, and he grows madly skeptical.

To his alarmed fancy, parallels and meridians become emphatically what they are merely designated as being: imaginary lines drawn round the earth's surface.

The log assures him that he is in such a place; but the log is a liar, for no place, nor anything possessed of a local angularity, is to be lighted upon in the watery waste.

At length horrible doubts overtake him as to the captain's competency to navigate his ship. The ignoramus must have lost his way, and drifted into the outer confines of creation, the region of the everlasting lull, introductory to a positive vacuity.

Thoughts of eternity thicken. He begins to feel anxious concerning his soul.

The stillness of the calm is awful. His voice begins to grow strange and portentous. He feels it in him like something swallowed too big for the esophagus. It keeps up a sort of involuntary interior humming in him, like a live beetle. His cranium is a dome full of reverberations. The hollows of his very bones are as whispering galleries. He is afraid to speak loud lest he be stunned, like the man in the bass-drum.

But more than all else is the consciousness of his utter helplessness. Succor or sympathy there is none. Penitence for embarking avails not. The final satisfaction of despairing may not be his with a relish. Vain the idea of idling out the calm. He may sleep if he can, or purposely delude himself into a crazy fancy that he is merely at leisure. All this he may compass, but he may not lounge; for to lounge is to be idle; to be idle implies an absence of any thing to do; whereas there is a calm to be endured; enough to attend to, Heaven knows.

His physical organization, obviously intended for locomotion, becomes a fixture, for where the calm leaves him, there he remains. Even his undoubted vested rights, comprised in his glorious liberty of volition, become as naught. For of what use? He wills to go; to get away from the calm, as ashore he would avoid the plague. But he cannot, and how foolish to revolve expedients. It is more hopeless than a bad marriage in a land where there is no Doctors' Commons. He has taken the ship to wife for better or for worse, for calm or for gale, and she is not to be shuffled off. With yards akimbo, she says unto him scornfully, as the old beldam said to the little dwarf: "Help yourself."

And all this, and more than this, is a calm.

Chapter III

A King for a Comrade

At the time I now write of, we must have been something more than sixty degrees to the west of the Gallipagos. And having attained a desirable longitude, we were standing northward for our arctic destination; around us one wide sea.

But due west, though distant a thousand miles, stretched north and south an almost endless Archipelago, here and there inhabited, but little known, and mostly unfrequented even by whalemen, who go almost everywhere. Beginning at the southerly termination of this great chain, it comprises the islands loosely known as Ellice's Group, then the Kingsmill isles, then the Radack and Mulgrave clusters. These islands had been represented to me as mostly of coral formation, low and fertile, and abounding in a variety of fruits. The language of the people was said to be very similar to that of the Navigator's islands, from which their ancestors are supposed to have migrated.

And thus much being said, all has been related that I then knew of the islands in question. Enough, however, that they existed at all, and that our path thereto lay over a pleasant sea and before a reliable trade-wind. The distance, though great, was merely an extension of water; so much blankness to be sailed over; and in a craft, too, that, properly managed, has been known to outlive great ships in a gale. For this much is true of a whale-boat, the cunningest thing in its way ever fabricated by man.

Upon one of the Kingsmill islands, then, I determined to plant my foot, come what come would. And I was equally determined that one of the ship's boats should float me thither. But I had no idea of being without a companion. It would be a weary watch to keep all by myself, with naught but the horizon in sight.

Now, among the crew was a fine old seaman, one Jarl; how old, no one could tell, not even himself. Forecastle chronology is ever vague and defective. "Man and boy," said honest Jarl, "I have lived ever since I can remember." And truly who may call to mind when he was not? To ourselves we all seemed coeval with creation. Whence it comes that it is so hard to die ere the world itself is departed.

Jarl hailed from the Isle of Skye, one of the constellated Hebrides. Hence, they often called him the Skyeman. And though he was far from being piratical of soul, he was yet an old Norseman to behold. His hands were brawny as the paws of a bear; his voice hoarse as a storm roaring round the old peak of Mull; and his long yellow hair waved round his head like a sunset. My life for it, Jarl, thy ancestors were Vikings, who many a time sailed over the salt German sea and the Baltic; who wedded their Brynhildas in Jutland, and are now quaffing mead in the halls of Valhalla, and beating time with their cans to the hymns of the Scalds. Ah! how the old Sagas run through me.

Yet Jarl, the descendant of heroes and kings, was a lone, friendless mariner on the main, only true to his origin in the sea-life that he led. But so it has been, and forever will be. What yeoman shall swear that he is not descended from Alfred? What dunce that he is not sprung of old Homer? King Noah, God bless him! fathered us all. Then hold up your heads, oh, ye Helots! blood potential flows through your veins. All of us have monarchs and sages for kinsmen; nay, angels and archangels for cousins; since in antediluvian days, the sons of God did verily wed with our mothers, the irresistible daughters of Eve. Thus all generations are blended, and heaven and earth of one kin; the hierarchies of seraphs in the uttermost skies; the thrones and principalities in the zodiac; the shades that roam throughout space; the nations and families, flocks and folds of the earth; one and all, brothers in essence—oh, be we then brothers indeed! All things form but one whole; the universe a Judea, and God Jehovah its head. Then no more let us start with affright. In a theocracy, what is to fear? Let us compose ourselves to death as fagged horsemen sleep in the saddle. Let us welcome even ghosts when they rise. Away with our stares and grimaces. The New Zealander's tattooing is not a prodigy; nor the Chinaman's ways an enigma. No custom is strange; no creed is absurd; no foe, but who will in the end prove a friend. In heaven, at last, our good, old white-haired father Adam will greet all alike, and sociality forever prevail. Christian shall join hands between Gentile and Jew; grim Dante forget his Infernos, and shake sides with fat Rabelais; and monk Luther, over a flagon of old nectar, talk over old times with Pope Leo. Then, shall we sit by the sages who of yore gave laws to the Medes and Persians in the sun; by the cavalry captains in Perseus who cried, "To horse!" when waked by their Last Trumpet sounding to the charge; by the hunters who, eternities ago, hunted the moose in Orion; by the minstrels who sang in the Milky Way when Jesus our Savior was born. Then shall we list to no shallow gossip of Magellan and Drake, but give ear to the voyagers who have circumnavigated the Ecliptic; who rounded the Polar Star as Cape Horn. Then shall the Stagirite and Kant be forgotten, and another folio than theirs be turned over for wisdom; even the folio now spread with horoscopes as yet undeciphered, the heaven of heavens on high.

Now, in old Jarl's lingo there was never an idiom. Your aboriginal tar is too much of a cosmopolitan for that. Long companionship with seamen of all tribes: Manilla-men, Anglo-Saxons, Cholos, Lascars and Danes, wear away in good time all mother-tongue stammerings. You sink your clan; down goes your nation; you speak a world's language, jovially jabbering in the Lingua Franca of the forecastle.

True to his calling, the Skyeman was very illiterate; witless of Salamanca, Heidelberg, or Brazen-Nose; in Delhi had never turned over the books of the Brahmins. For geography, in which sailors should be adepts, since they are forever turning over and over the great globe of globes, poor Jarl was deplorably lacking. According to his view of the matter, this terraqueous world had been formed in the manner of a tart; the land being a mere marginal crust, within which rolled the watery world proper. Such seemed my good Viking's theory of cosmography. As for other worlds, he weened not of them, yet full as much as Chrysostom.

Ah, Jarl! an honest, earnest wight; so true and simple that the secret operations of thy soul were more inscrutable than the subtle workings of Spinoza's.

Thus much be said of the Skyeman, for he was exceedingly taciturn, and but seldom will speak for himself.

Now, higher sympathies apart, for Jarl I had a wonderful liking, for he loved me; from the first had cleaved to me.

It is sometimes the case that an old mariner like him will conceive a very strong attachment for some young sailor, his shipmate; an attachment so devoted as to be wholly inexplicable, unless originating in that heart-loneliness which overtakes most seamen as they grow aged; impelling them to fasten upon some chance object of regard. But however it was, my Viking, thy unbidden affection was the noblest homage ever paid me. And frankly I am more inclined to think well of myself as in some way deserving thy devotion than from the rounded compliments of more cultivated minds.

Now, at sea, and in the fellowship of sailors, all men appear as they are. No school like a ship for studying human nature. The contact of one man with another is too near and constant to favor deceit. You wear your character as loosely as your flowing trousers. Vain all endeavors to assume qualities not yours, or to conceal those you possess. Incognitos, however desirable, are out of the question. And thus aboard of all ships in which I have sailed, I have invariably been known by a sort of drawing-room title. Not, let me hurry to say, that I put hand in tar bucket with a squeamish air, or ascended the rigging with a Chesterfieldian mince. No, no, I was never better than my vocation, and mine have been many. I showed as brown a chest and as hard a hand as the tarriest tar of them all. And never did shipmate of mine upbraid me with a genteel disinclination to duty, though it carried me to truck of main-mast, or jib-boom-end, in the most wolfish blast that ever howled.

Whence, then, this annoying appellation? for annoying it most assuredly was. It was because of something in me that could not be hidden; stealing out in an occasional polysyllable; an otherwise incomprehensible deliberation in dining; remote, unguarded allusions to *Belles-Lettres* affairs, and other trifles superfluous to mention.

But suffice it to say that it had gone abroad among the *Arcturion*'s crew that at some indefinite period of my career, I had been a "nob." But Jarl seemed to go further. He must have taken me for one of the House of Hanover in disguise, or, haply, for bonneted Charles Edward the Pretender, who, like the Wandering Jew, may yet be a vagrant. At any rate, his loyalty was extreme. Unsolicited, he was my laundress and tailor; a most expert one, too; and when at mealtime my turn came round to look out at the mast-head or stand at the wheel, he catered for me among the "kids" in the forecastle with unwearied assiduity. Many's the good lump of "duff" for which I was indebted to my good Viking's good care of me. And, like Sesostris, I was served by a monarch. Yet in some degree the obligation was mutual. For be it known that in sea-parlance, we were chummies.

Now this *chummying* among sailors is like the brotherhood subsisting between a brace of collegians (chums) rooming together. It is a Fidus-Achatesship, a league of offense and defense, a copartnership of chests and toilets, a bond of love and good feeling, and a mutual championship of the absent one. True, my nautical reminiscenses remind me of sundry lazy, ne'er-do-well, unprofitable, and abominable chummies; chummies, who at meal-times were last at the "kids," when their unfortunate partners were high upon the spars; chummies who affected awkwardness at the needle, and conscientious scruples about dabbling in the suds; so that chummy the simple was made to do all the work of the firm, while chummy the cunning played the sleeping partner in his hammock. Out upon such chummies!

But I appeal to thee, honest Jarl, if I was ever chummy the cunning. Never mind if thou didst fabricate my tarpaulins, and with Samaritan charity bind up the rents and pour needle and thread into the frightful gashes that agonized my hapless nether integuments, which thou calledst "ducks."—Didst thou not expressly declare that all these things, and more, thou wouldst do for me, despite my own quaint thimble, fashioned from the ivory tusk of a whale? Nay, could I even wrest from thy willful hands my very shirt, when once thou hadst it steaming in an unsavory pickle in thy capacious vat, a decapitated cask? Full well thou knowest, Jarl, that these things are true, and I am bound to say it, to disclaim any lurking desire to reap advantage from thy great good nature.

Now, my Viking for me, thought I, when I cast about for a comrade, and my Viking alone.

Chapter IV

A Chat in the Clouds

The skyeman seemed so earnest and upright a seaman that to tell the plain truth, in spite of his love for me, I had many misgivings as to his readiness to unite in an undertaking which apparently savored of a moral dereliction. But, all things considered, I deemed my own resolution quite venial; and as for inducing another to join me, it seemed a precaution so indispensable as to outweigh all other considerations.

Therefore I resolved freely to open my heart to him; for that special purpose paying him a visit, when, like some old albatross in the air, he happened to be perched at the fore-mast-head, all by himself, on the look-out for whales never seen.

Now this standing upon a bit of stick one hundred feet aloft for hours at a time, swiftly sailing over the sea, is very much like crossing the Channel in a balloon. Manfred-like, you talk to the clouds; you have a fellow feeling for the sun. And when Jarl and I got conversing up there, smoking our dwarfish "dudeens," any sea-gull passing by might have taken us for Messrs. Blanchard and Jeffries, socially puffing their after-dinner Bagdads, bound to Calais *via* Heaven, from Dover. Honest Jarl, I acquainted with all; my conversation with the captain, the hint implied in his last words, my firm resolve to quit the ship in one of her boats, and the facility with which I thought the thing could be done. Then I threw out many inducements in the shape of pleasant anticipations of bearing right down before the wind upon the sunny isles under our lee.

He listened attentively, but so long remained silent that I almost fancied there was something in Jarl which would prove too much for me and my eloquence.

At last he very bluntly declared that the scheme was a crazy one; he had never known of such a thing but thrice before, and in every case the runaways had never afterwards been heard of. He entreated me to renounce my determination, not be a boy, pause and reflect, stick to the ship, and go home in her like a man. Verily, my Viking talked to me like my uncle.

But to all this I turned a deaf ear, affirming that my mind was made up, and that as he refused to accompany me, and I fancied no one else for a comrade, I would go stark alone rather than not at all. Upon this, seeing my resolution immovable, he bluntly swore that he would follow me through thick and thin.

Thanks, Jarl! thou wert one of those devoted fellows who will wrestle hard to convince one loved of error, but failing, forthwith change their wrestling to a sympathetic hug.

But now his elderly prudence came into play. Casting his eye over the boundless expanse below, he inquired how far off were the islands in question.

"A thousand miles, and no less."

"With a fair trade-breeze, then, and a boatsail, that is a good twelve days' passage; but calms and currents may make it a month, perhaps more." So saying he shook his old head, and his yellow hair streamed.

But, trying my best to chase away these misgivings, he at last gave them over. He assured me I might count upon him to his uttermost keel.

My Viking secured, I felt more at ease, and thoughtfully considered how the enterprise might best be accomplished.

There was no time to be lost. Every hour was carrying us farther and farther from the parallel most desirable for us to follow in our route to the westward. So with all possible dispatch I matured my plans, and communicated them to Jarl, who gave several old hints—having ulterior probabilities in view—which were not neglected.

Strange to relate, it was not till my Viking, with a rueful face, reminded me of the fact that I bethought me of a circumstance somewhat alarming at the first blush. We must push off without chart or quadrant; though, as will shortly be seen, a compass was by no means out of the question. The chart, to be sure, I did not so much lay to heart, but a quadrant was more than desirable. Still it was by no means indispensable. For this reason. When we started our latitude would be exactly known, and whether, on our voyage westward, we drifted north or south therefrom, we could not by any possibility get so far out of our reckoning, as to fail in striking some one of a long chain of islands which, for many degrees on both sides of the Equator, stretched right across our track.

For much the same reason it mattered little whether on our passage we daily knew our longitude, for no known land lay between us and the place we desired to reach. So what could be plainer than this: that if westward we patiently held on our way, we must eventually achieve our destination?

As for intervening shoals or reefs, if any there were, they intimidated us not. In a boat that drew but a few inches of water, but an indifferent look-out would preclude all danger on that score. At all events, the thing seemed feasible enough, notwithstanding old Jarl's superstitious reverence for nautical instruments, and the philosophical objections which might have been urged by a pedantic disciple of Mercator.

Very often, as the old maxim goes, the simplest things are the most startling, and that, too, from their very simplicity. So cherish no alarms if thus we addressed the setting sun—"Be thou, old pilot, our guide!"

Chapter V

SEATS SECURED AND PORTMANTEAUS PACKED

BUT THOUGHTS OF SEXTANTS AND QUADRANTS WERE THE LEAST OF OUR CARES.

Right from under the very arches of the eyebrows of thirty men—captain, mates, and crew—a boat was to be abstracted, they knowing nothing of the event until all knowledge would prove unavailing.

Hark ye:

At sea the boats of a South-Seaman (generally four in number, spare ones omitted), are suspended by tackles, hooked above, to curved timbers called "davits," vertically fixed to the ship's sides.

Now, no fair one with golden locks is more assiduously waited upon or more delicately handled by her tire-women than the slender whale-boat by her crew. And out of its element it seems fragile enough to justify the utmost solicitude. For truly, like a fine lady, the fine whale-boat is most delicate when idle, though little coy at a pinch.

Besides the "davits," the following supports are provided. Two small *cranes* are swung under the keel, on which the latter rests, preventing the settling of the boat's middle, while hanging suspended by the bow and stern. A broad, braided, hempen band, usually worked in a tasteful pattern, is also passed round both gunwales, and secured to the ship's bulwarks, firmly lashes the craft to its place. Being elevated above the ship's rail, the boats are in plain sight from all parts of the deck.

Now, one of these boats was to be made away with. No facile matter, truly. Harder than for any dashing young Janizary to run off with a sultana from the Grand Turk's seraglio. Still the thing could be done, for, by Jove, it had been.

What say you to slyly loosing everything by day, and when night comes, cast off the band and swing in the cranes? But how lower the tackles, even in the darkest night, without a creaking more fearful than the death rattle? Easily avoided. Anoint the ropes, and they will travel deftly through the subtle windings of the blocks.

But though I had heard of this plan being pursued, there was a degree of risk in it, after all, which I was far from fancying. Another plan was hit upon, still bolder, and hence more safe. What it was, in the right place will be seen.

In selecting my craft for this good voyage I would fain have traversed the deck and eyed the boats like a cornet choosing his steed from out a goodly stud. But this was denied me. And the "bow boat" was, perforce, singled out as the most remote from the quarter-deck, that region of sharp eyes and relentless purposes.

Then our larder was to be thought of, also an abundant supply of water, concerning which last I determined to take good heed. There were but two to be taken care of, but I resolved to lay in sufficient store of both meat and drink for four, at the same time that the supplemental twain thus provided for were but imaginary. And if it came to the last dead pitch, of which we had no fear, however, I was food for no man but Jarl.

Little time was lost in catering for our mess. Biscuit and salt beef were our sole resource; and thanks to the generosity of the *Arcturion*'s owners, our ship's company had a plentiful supply. Casks of both, with heads knocked out, were at the service of all. In bags which we made for the purpose, a sufficiency of the biscuit was readily stored away and secreted in a corner of easy access. The salt beef was more difficult to obtain, but little by little we managed to smuggle out of the cask enough to answer our purpose.

As for water, most luckily a day or two previous several "breakers" of it had been hoisted from below for the present use of the ship's company.

These "breakers" are casks, long and slender, but very strong. Of various diameters, they are made on purpose to stow into spaces intervening between the immense butts in a ship's hold.

The largest we could find was selected, first carefully examining it to detect any leak. On some pretense or other, we then rolled them all over to that side of the vessel where our boat was suspended, the selected breaker being placed in their middle.

Our compendious wardrobes were snugly packed into bundles and laid aside for the present. And at last, by due caution, we had everything arranged preliminary to the final start. Let me say, though, perhaps to the credit of Jarl, that whenever the most strategy was necessary he seemed ill at ease, and for the most part left the matter to me. It was well that he did, for as it was, by his untimely straightforwardness, he once or twice came near spoiling everything. Indeed on one occasion he was so unseasonably blunt that, curiously enough, I had almost suspected him of taking that odd sort of interest in one's welfare which leads a philanthropist, all other methods failing, to frustrate a project deemed bad by pretending clumsily to favor it. But no inuendoes; Jarl was a Viking, frank as his fathers, though not so much of a buccaneer.

Chapter VI

EIGHT BELLS

THE MOON MUST BE MONSTROUS COY, OR SOME THINGS FALL OUT OPPORTUNELY, OR ELSE almanacs are consulted by nocturnal adventurers; but so it is that when Cynthia shows a round and chubby disk, few daring deeds are done. Though true it may be that of moonlight nights, jewelers' caskets and maidens' hearts have been burglariously broken into—and rifled, for aught Copernicus can tell.

The gentle planet was in her final quarter, and upon her slender horn I hung my hopes of withdrawing from the ship undetected.

Now, making a tranquil passage across the ocean, we kept at this time what are called among whalemen "boats-crew-watches." That is, instead of the sailors being divided at night into two bands, alternately on deck every four hours, there were four watches, each composed of a boat's crew, the "headsman" (always one of the mates) excepted. To the officers this plan gives uninterrupted repose—"all-night-in," as they call it, and of course greatly lightens the duties of the crew.

The harpooneers head the boats' crews, and are responsible for the ship during the continuance of their watches.

Now, my Viking being a stalwart seaman, pulled the midship oar of the boat of which I was bowsman. Hence we were in the same watch, to which also three others belonged, including Mark, the harpooner. One of these seamen, however, being an invalid, there were only two left for us to manage.

Voyaging in these seas, you may glide along for weeks without starting a tack or sheet, hardly moving the helm a spoke, so mild and constant are the "trades." At night the watch seldom trouble themselves with keeping much of a look-out, especially as a strange sail is almost a prodigy in these lonely waters. In some ships, for weeks in and weeks out, you are puzzled to tell when your nightly turn on deck really comes round, so little heed is given to the standing of watches where, in the license of presumed safety, nearly everyone nods without fear.

But remiss as you may be in the boats-crew-watch of a heedless whaleman, the man who heads it is bound to maintain his post on the quarter-deck until regularly relieved. Yet drowsiness being incidental to all natures, even to Napoleon beside his own sentry napping in the snowy bivouac, so often in snowy moonlight or ebon eclipse, dozed Mark, our harpooneer. Lethe be his portion this blessed night, thought I, as during the morning which preceded our enterprise, I eyed the man who might possibly cross my plans.

But let me come closer to this part of my story. During what are called at sea the "dog-watches" (between four o'clock and eight in the evening), sailors are quite lively and frolicsome; their spirits even flow far into the first of the long "night-watches"; but upon its expiration at "eight bells" (midnight), silence begins to reign; if you hear a voice it is no cherub's: all exclamations are oaths.

At eight bells the mariners on deck, now relieved from their cares, crawl out from their sleepy retreats in old monkey jackets or coils of rigging, and hie to their hammocks, almost without interrupting their dreams, while the sluggards below lazily drag themselves up the ladder to resume their slumbers in the open air.

For these reasons, then, the moonless sea midnight was just the time to escape. Hence we suffered a whole day to pass unemployed, waiting for the night, when the starboard-quarter-boats'-watch, to which we belonged, would be summoned on deck at the eventful eight of the bell.

But twenty-four hours soon glide away; and "Star-boleens ahoy; eight bells, there below!" at last started me from a troubled doze.

I sprang from my hammock, and would have lighted my pipe. But the forecastle lamp had gone out. An old sea-dog was talking about sharks in his sleep. Jarl and our solitary watch-mate were groping their way into their trousers. And little was heard but the humming of the still sails aloft, the dash of the waves against the bow, and the deep breathing of the dreaming sailors around.

Chapter VII

A Pause

GOOD OLD *ARCTURION!* MATERNAL CRAFT THAT ROCKED ME SO OFTEN IN THY HEART OF OAK, I grieve to tell how I deserted thee on the broad deep. So far from home, with such a motley crew, so many islanders, whose heathen babble echoing through thy Christian hull must have grated harshly on every carline.

Old ship! where sails thy lone ghost now? For of the stout *Arcturion* no word was ever heard from the dark hour we pushed from her fated planks. In what time of tempest, to what seagull's scream, the drowning eddies did their work, knows no mortal man. Sunk she silently, helplessly, into the calm depths of that summer sea, assassinated by the ruthless blade of the swordfish? Such things have been. Or was hers a better fate? Stricken down while gallantly battling with the blast, her storm-sails set, helm manned, and every sailor at his post, as sunk the *Hornet,* her men at quarters, in some distant gale.

But surmises are idle. A very old craft, she may have foundered, or laid her bones upon some treacherous reef, but as with many a far rover, her fate is a mystery.

Pray Heaven the spirit of that lost vessel roaming abroad through the troubled mists of midnight gales—as old mariners believe of missing ships—may never haunt my future path upon the waves. Peacefully may she rest at the bottom of the sea, and sweetly sleep my shipmates in the lowest watery zone, where prowling sharks come not, nor billows roll.

By quitting the *Arcturion* when we did, Jarl and I unconsciously eluded a sailor's grave. We hear of providential deliverances. Was this one? But life is sweet to all, death comes as hard. And for myself, I am almost tempted to hang my head that I escaped the fate of my shipmates, something like him who blushed to have escaped the fell carnage at Thermopylœ.

Though I cannot repress a shudder when I think of that old ship's end, it is impossible for me so much as to imagine that our deserting her could have been in any way instrumental in her loss. Nevertheless I would to Heaven the *Arcturion* still floated; that it was given me once more to tread her familiar decks.

Chapter VIII

THEY PUSH OFF, VELIS ET REMIS

AND NOW TO TELL HOW, TEMPTED BY DEVIL OR GOOD ANGEL, AND A THOUSAND MILES FROM land, we embarked upon this western voyage.

It was midnight, mark you, when our watch began, and my turn at the helm now coming on was, of course, to be avoided. On some plausible pretense, I induced our solitary watchmate to assume it, thus leaving myself untrammeled, and at the same time satisfactorily disposing of him. For being a rather fat fellow, an enormous consumer of "duff," and with good reason supposed to be the son of a farmer, I made no doubt he would pursue his old course and fall to nodding over the wheel. As for the leader of the watch—our harpooner—he fell heir to the nest of old jackets under the lee of the mizzen-mast, left nice and warm by his predecessor.

The night was even blacker than we had anticipated; there was no trace of a moon; and the dark purple haze, sometimes encountered at night near the Line, half shrouded the stars from view.

Waiting about twenty minutes after the last man of the previous watch had gone below, I motioned to Jarl, and we slipped our shoes from our feet. He then descended into the forecastle, and I sauntered aft towards the quarter-deck. All was still. Thrice did I pass my hand full before the face of the slumbering lubber at the helm, and right between him and the light of the binnacle.

Mark, the harpooneer, was not so easily sounded. I feared to approach him. He lay quietly, though; but asleep or awake, no more delay. Risks must be run when time presses. And our ears were a pointer's to catch a sound.

To work we went without hurry, but swiftly and silently. Our various stores were dragged from their lurking places and placed in the boat, which hung from the ship's lee-side, the side depressed in the water, an indispensable requisite to an attempt to escape. And though at sundown the boat was to windward, yet, as we had foreseen, the vessel having been tacked during the first watch, brought it to leeward.

Endeavoring to man-handle our clumsy breaker and lift it into the boat, we found that by reason of the intervention of the shrouds, it could not be done without risking a jar, besides straining the craft in lowering. An expedient, however, though at the eleventh hour, was hit upon. Fastening a long rope to the breaker, which was perfectly tight, we cautiously dropped it overboard, paying out enough line to ensure its towing astern of the ship, so as not to strike against the copper. The other end of the line we then secured to the boat's stern.

Fortunately this was the last thing to be done, for the breaker, acting as a clog to the vessel's way in the water, so affected her steering as to fling her perceptibly into the wind. And by causing the helm to work, this must soon rouse the lubber there stationed, if not already awake. But our dropping overboard, the breaker greatly aided us in this respect: it diminished the ship's headway; which, owing to the light breeze, had not been very great at any time during the night. Had it been so, all hope of escaping without first arresting the vessel's progress would have been little short of madness. As it was, the sole daring of the deed that night achieved consisted in our lowering away while the ship yet clove the brine, though but moderately.

All was now ready, the cranes swung in, the lashings adrift, and the boat fairly suspended, when, seizing the ends of the tackle ropes, we silently stepped into it, one at each end. The dead weight of the breaker astern now dragged the craft horizontally through the air, so that her tackle ropes strained hard. She quivered like a dolphin. Nevertheless, had we not feared her loud splash upon striking the wave, we might have quitted the ship almost as silently as the breath the body. But this was out of the question, and our plans were laid accordingly.

"All ready, Jarl?"

"Ready!"

"A man overboard!" I shouted at the top of my compass, and like lightning the cords slid through our blistering hands, and with a tremendous shock the boat bounded on the sea's back. One mad sheer and plunge, one terrible strain on the tackles as we sunk in the trough of the waves, tugged upon by the towing breaker, and our knives severed the tackle ropes—we hazarded not unhooking the blocks—our oars were out, and the good boat headed round, with prow to leeward.

"Man overboard!" was now shouted from stem to stern. And directly we heard the confused tramping and shouting of the sailors as they rushed from their dreams into the almost inscrutable darkness.

"Man overboard! Man overboard!" My heart smote me as the human cry of horror came out of the black vaulted night.

"Down helm!" was soon heard from the chief mate. "Back the main-yard! Quick to the boats! How's this? One down already? Well done! Hold on, then, those other boats!"

Meanwhile several seamen were shouting as they strained at the braces.

"Cut! cut all! Lower away, lower away!" impatiently cried the sailors, who already had leaped into the boats.

"Heave the ship to, and hold fast every thing," cried the captain, apparently just springing to the deck. "One boat's enough. Steward! show a light there from the mizzen-top. Boat ahoy! Have you got that man?"

No reply. The voice came out of a cloud, the ship dimly showing like a ghost. We had desisted from rowing, and hand over hand were now hauling in upon the rope attached to the breaker, which we soon lifted into the boat, instantly resuming our oars.

"Pull! pull, men! and save him!" again shouted the captain.

"Ay, ay, sir," answered Jarl instinctively, "pulling as hard as ever we can, sir."

And pull we did till nothing could be heard from the ship but a confused tumult, and ever and anon the hoarse shout of the captain, too distant to be understood.

We now set our sail to a light air, and right into the darkness, and dead to leeward we rowed and sailed till morning dawned.

Chapter IX

The Watery World is All Before Them

At sea in an open boat, and a thousand miles from land!

Shortly after the break of day, in the gray transparent light, a speck to windward broke the even line of the horizon. It was the ship wending her way north-eastward.

Had I not known the final indifference of sailors to such disasters as that which the *Arcturion*'s crew must have imputed to the night past (did not the skipper suspect the truth) I would have regarded that little speck with many compunctions of conscience. Nor, as it was, did I feel in any very serene humor. For the consciousness of being deemed dead is next to the presumable unpleasantness of being so in reality. One feels like his own ghost unlawfully tenanting a defunct carcass. Even Jarl's glance seemed so queer that I begged him to look another way.

Secure now from all efforts of the captain to recover those whom he most probably supposed lost, and equally cut off from all hope of returning to the ship even had we felt so inclined, the resolution that had thus far nerved me began to succumb in a measure to the awful loneliness of the scene. Ere this I had regarded the ocean as a slave—the steed that bore me whither I listed, and whose vicious propensities, mighty though they were, often proved harmless when opposed to the genius of man. But now how changed! In our frail boat I would fain have built an altar to Neptune.

What a mere toy we were to the billows that jeeringly shouldered us from crest to crest, as from hand to hand lost souls may be tossed along by the chain of shades which enfilade the route to Tartarus.

But drown or swim, here's overboard with care! Cheer up, Jarl! Ha! ha! how merrily, yet terribly, we sail! Up, up—slowly up—toiling up the long, calm wave; then balanced on its summit awhile like a plank on a rail, and down we plunge headlong into the seething abyss, till arrested we glide upward again. And thus did we go. Now buried in watery hollows—our sail idly flapping; then lifted aloft—canvas bellying; and beholding the furthest horizon.

Had not our familiarity with the business of whaling divested our craft's wild motions of its first novel horrors we had been but a rueful pair. But day-long pulls after whales, the ship left miles astern, and entire dark nights passed moored to the monsters, killed too late to be towed to the ship far to leeward—all this, and much more, accustoms one to strange things. Death, to be sure, has a mouth as black as a wolf's, and to be thrust into his jaws is a serious thing. But true it most certainly is—and I speak from no hearsay—that to sailors, as a class, the grisly king seems not half so hideous as he appears to those who have only regarded him on shore and at a deferential distance. Like many ugly mortals, his features grow less frightful upon acquaintance; and met over often and sociably, the old adage holds true, about familiarity breeding contempt. Thus too with soldiers. Of the quaking recruit, three pitched battles make a grim grenadier, and he who shrank from the muzzle of a cannon is now ready to yield his mustache for a sponge.

And truly, since death is the last enemy of all, valiant souls will taunt him while they may. Yet rather should the wise regard him as the inflexible friend, who, even against our own wills, from life's evils triumphantly relieve us.

And there is but little difference in the manner of dying. To die, is all. And death has been gallantly encountered by those who never beheld blood that was red, only its light azure seen through the veins. And to yield the ghost proudly, and march out of your fortress with all the honors of war, is not a thing of sinew and bone. Though in prison, Geoffry Hudson, the dwarf, died more bravely than Goliath, the giant, and the last end of a butterfly shames us all. Some women have lived nobler lives and died nobler deaths than men. Threatened with the stake, mitred Cranmer recanted; but through her fortitude, the lorn widow of Edessa stayed the tide of Valens' persecutions. 'Tis no great valor to perish sword in hand, and bravado on lip, cased all in panoply complete. For even the alligator dies in his mail, and the swordfish never surrenders. To expire, mild-eyed, in one's bed, transcends the death of Epaminondas.

Chapter X

They Arrange Their Canopies and Lounges, and Try to Make Things Comfortable

Our little craft was soon in good order. From the spare rigging brought along, we made shrouds to the mast, and converted the boat-hook into a handy boom for the jib. Going large before the wind, we set this sail wing-and-wing with the main-sail. The latter, in accordance with the customary rig of whale-boats, was worked with a sprit and sheet. It could be furled or set in an instant. The bags of bread we stowed away in the covered space about the loggerhead, a useless appurtenance now, and therefore removed. At night, Jarl used it for a pillow, saying that when the boat rolled it gave easy play to his head. The precious breaker we lashed firmly amidships, thereby much improving our sailing.

Now, previous to leaving the ship, we had seen to it well that our craft was supplied with all those equipments with which, by regulations of the fishery, a whale-boat is constantly provided, night and day, afloat or suspended. Hanging along our gunwales inside were six harpoons, three lances and a blubber-spade, all keen as razors and sheathed with leather. Besides these we had three waifs, a couple of two-gallon water-kegs, several bailers, the boat-hatchet for cutting the whale-line, two auxiliary knives for the like purpose, and several minor articles also employed in hunting the leviathan. The line and line-tub, however, were on ship-board.

And here it may be mentioned, that to prevent the strain upon the boat when suspended to the ship's side, the heavy whale-line, over two hundred fathoms in length, and something more than an inch in diameter, when not in use is kept on ship-board, coiled away like an endless snake in its tub. But this tub is always in readiness to be launched into the boat. Now, having no use for the line belonging to our craft, we had purposely left it behind.

But well had we marked that by far the most important item of a whale-boat's furniture was snugly secured in its place. This was the watertight keg, at both ends firmly headed, containing a small compass, tinder-box and flint, candles, and a score or two of biscuits. This keg is an invariable precaution against what so frequently occurs in pursuing the sperm whale—prolonged absence from the ship, losing sight of her, or never seeing her more, till years after you reach home again. In this same keg of ours seemed coopered up life and death, at least so seemed it to honest Jarl. No sooner had we got clear from the *Arcturion*, than dropping his oar for an instant, he clutched at it in the dark.

And when day at last came we knocked out the head of the keg with the little hammer and chisel, always attached to it for that purpose, and removed the compass that glistened to us like a human eye. Then filling up the vacancy with biscuit we again made all tight, driving down the hoops till they would budge no more.

At first we were puzzled to fix our compass. But at last the Skyeman out knife, and cutting a round hole in the aftermost thwart, or seat of the boat, there inserted the little brass case containing the needle.

Over the stern of the boat, with some old canvas which my Viking's forethought had provided, we spread a rude sort of awning, or rather counterpane. This, however, proved but little or no protection from the glare of the sun, for the management of the main-sail forbade any considerable elevation of the shelter. And when the breeze was fresh, we were fain to strike it altogether; for the wind being from aft and getting underneath the canvas, almost lifted the light boat's stern into the air, vexing the counterpane as if it were a petticoat turning a gusty corner. But when a mere breath rippled the sea, and the sun was fiery hot, it was most pleasant to lounge in this shady asylum. It was like being transferred from the roast to cool in the cupboard. And Jarl, much the toughest fowl of the two, out of an abundant kindness for his comrade, during the day voluntarily remained exposed at the helm, almost two hours to my one. No lady-like scruples had he, the old Viking, about marring his complexion, which already was more than bronzed. Over the ordinary tanning of the sailor, he seemed masked by a visor of japanning dotted all over with freckles, so intensely yellow and symmetrically circular that they seemed scorched there by a burning glass.

In the tragico-comico moods which at times overtook me, I used to look upon the brown Skyeman with humorous complacency. If we fall in with cannibals, thought I, then, ready-roasted Norseman that thou art, shall I survive to mourn thee, at least during the period I revolve upon the spit.

But of such a fate, it needs hardly be said, we had no apprehension.

Chapter XI

JARL AFFLICTED WITH THE LOCK-JAW

IF EVER AGAIN I LAUNCH WHALE-BOAT FROM SHEERPLANK OF SHIP AT SEA I SHALL TAKE GOOD HEED that my comrade be a sprightly fellow with a rattle-box head. Be he never so silly, his very silliness, so long as he be lively at it, shall be its own excuse.

Upon occasion, who likes not a lively loon, one of your giggling, gamesome oafs, whose mouth is a grin? Are not such, well-ordered dispensations of Providence? Filling up vacuums, in intervals of social stagnation relieving the tedium of existing? Besides keeping up, here and there, in very many quarters indeed, sundry people's good opinion of themselves? What if at times their speech is insipid as water after wine? What if to ungenial and irascible souls, their very "mug" is an exasperation to behold, their clack an inducement to suicide? Let us not be hard upon them for this, but let them live on for the good they may do.

But Jarl, dear, dumb Jarl, thou wert none of these. Thou didst carry a phiz like an excommunicated deacon's. And no matter what happened, it was ever the same. Quietly in thyself thou didst revolve upon thine own sober axis, like a wheel in a machine, which forever goes round whether you look at it or no. Ay, Jarl! wast thou not forever intent upon minding that which so many neglect—thine own especial business? Wast thou not forever at it, too, with no likelihood of ever winding up thy moody affairs and striking a balance sheet?

But at times how wearisome to me these everlasting reveries in my one solitary companion. I longed for something enlivening; a burst of words, human vivacity of one kind or other. After in vain essaying to get something of this sort out of Jarl I tried it all by myself; playing upon my body as upon an instrument, singing, halloing, and making empty gestures till my Viking stared hard, and I myself paused to consider whether I had run crazy or no.

But how account for the Skyeman's gravity? Surely it was based upon no philosophic taciturnity; he was nothing of an idealist, an aerial architect, a constructor of flying buttresses. It was inconceivable that his reveries were Manfred-like and exalted, reminiscent of unutterable deeds, too mysterious even to be indicated by the remotest of hints. Suppositions all out of the question.

His ruminations were a riddle. I asked him anxiously whether in any part of the world, Savannah, Surat, or Archangel, he had ever a wife to think of, or children, that he carried so lengthy a phiz. Nowhere neither. Therefore, as by his own confession he had nothing to think of but himself, and there was little but honesty in him (having which, by the way, he may be thought full to the brim), what could I fall back upon but my original theory, namely, that in repose his intellect stepped out and left his body to itself.

Chapter XII

More about Being in an Open Boat

On the third morning, at break of day, I sat at the steering oar, an hour or two previous having relieved Jarl, now fast asleep. Somehow and suddenly a sense of peril so intense came over me that it could hardly have been aggravated by the completest solitude.

On a ship's deck the mere feeling of elevation above the water, and the reach of prospect you command, impart a degree of confidence which disposes you to exult in your fancied security. But in an open boat, brought down to the very plane of the sea, this feeling almost wholly deserts you. Unless the waves in their gambols toss you and your chip upon one of their lordly crests, your sphere of vision is little larger than it would be at the bottom of a well. At best your most extended view in any one direction, at least, is in a high, slow-rolling sea, when you descend into the dark, misty spaces, between long and uniform swells. Then for the moment it is like looking up and down in a twilight glade, interminable; where two dawns, one on each hand, seem struggling through the semi-transparent tops of the fluid mountains.

But lingering not long in those silent vales from watery cliff to cliff, a sea-chamois, sprang our solitary craft—a goat among the Alps!

How undulated the horizon; like a vast serpent with ten thousand folds coiled all round the globe; yet so nigh, apparently, that it seemed as if one's hand might touch it.

What loneliness; when the sun rose and spurred up the heavens, we hailed him as a wayfarer in Sahara the sight of a distant horseman. Save ourselves, the sun and the *Chamois* seemed all that was left of life in the universe. We yearned toward its jocund disk, as in strange lands the traveler joyfully greets a face from home which there had passed unheeded. And was not the sun a fellow-voyager? Were we not both wending westward? But how soon he daily overtook and passed us, hurrying to his journey's end.

When a week had gone by, sailing steadily on by day and by night, and nothing in sight but this self-same sea, what wonder if disquieting thoughts at last entered our hearts? If unknowingly we should pass the spot where, according to our reckoning, our islands lay, upon what shoreless sea would we launch? At times these forebodings bewildered my idea of the positions of the groups beyond. All became vague and confused; so that westward of the Kingsmill isles and the Radack chain, I fancied there could be naught but an endless sea.

Chapter XIII

OF THE CHONDROPTERYGII, AND OTHER UNCOUTH HORDES INFESTING THE SOUTH SEAS

AT INTERVALS IN OUR LONELY VOYAGE THERE WERE SIGHTS WHICH DIVERSIFIED THE SCENE, especially when the constellation Pisces was in the ascendant.

It's famous botanizing, they say, in Arkansas' boundless prairies; I commend the student of Ichthyology to an open boat and the ocean moors of the Pacific. As your craft glides along, what strange monsters float by! Elsewhere was never seen their like. And nowhere are they found in the books of the naturalists.

Though America be discovered, the Cathays of the deep are unknown. And whoso crosses the Pacific might have read lessons to Buffon. The sea-serpent is not a fable; and in the sea that snake is but a garden worm. There are more wonders than the wonders rejected, and more sights unrevealed than you or I ever ever dreamed of. Moles and bats alone should be skeptics: and the only true infidelity is for a live man to vote himself dead. Be Sir Thomas Brown our ensample who, while exploding "Vulgar Errors," heartily hugged all the mysteries in the Pentateuch.

But look! fathoms down in the sea; wherever saw you a phantom like that? An enormous crescent with antlers like a reindeer, and a Delta of mouths. Slowly it sinks, and is seen no more.

Doctor Faust saw the devil; but you have seen the "Devil Fish."

Look again! Here comes another. Jarl calls it a Bone Shark. Full as large as a whale, it is spotted like a leopard, and tusk-like teeth overlap its jaws like those of the walrus. To seamen nothing strikes more terror than the near vicinity of a creature like this. Great ships steer out of its path. And well they may, since the good craft *Essex* and others have been sunk by sea-monsters, as the alligator thrusts his horny snout through a Caribbean canoe.

Ever present to us was the apprehension of some sudden disaster from the extraordinary zoological specimens we almost hourly passed.

For the sharks we saw them not by units, nor by tens, nor by hundreds, but by thousands and by myriads. Trust me, there are more sharks in the sea than mortals on land.

And of these prolific fish there are full as many species as of dogs. But by the German naturalists, Müller and Henle, who, in christening the sharks, have bestowed upon them the most heathenish names, they are classed under one family, which family, according to Müller, king-at-arms, is an undoubted branch of the ancient and famous tribe of the Chondropterygii.

To begin. There is the ordinary Brown Shark, or sea-attorney, so called by sailors; a grasping, rapacious varlet, that in spite of the hard knocks received from it, often snapped viciously at our steering oar. At times these gentry swim in herds, especially about the remains of a slaughtered whale. They are the vultures of the deep.

Then we often encountered the dandy Blue Shark, a long, taper and mighty genteel looking fellow, with a slender waist like a Bond Street beau, and the whitest tiers of teeth imaginable. This dainty spark invariably lounged by with a careless fin and an indolent tail. But he looked infernally heartless.

How his cold-blooded, gentlemanly air contrasted with the rude, savage swagger of the Tiger Shark, a round portly gourmand, with distended mouth and collapsed conscience, swimming about seeking whom he might devour. These gluttons are the scavengers of navies, following ships in the South Seas, picking up odds and ends of garbage, and sometimes a tit-bit, a stray sailor. No wonder, then, that sailors denounce them. In substance, Jarl once assured me, that under any temporary misfortune, it was one of his sweetest consolations to remember that in his day he had murdered, not killed, shoals of Tiger Sharks.

Yet this is all wrong. As well hate a seraph as a shark. Both were made by the same hand. And that sharks are lovable, witness their domestic endearments. No Fury so ferocious as not to have some amiable side. In the wild wilderness a leopard-mother caresses her cub, as Hagar did Ishmael; or a Queen of France, the dauphin. We know not what we do when we hate. And I have the word of my gentlemanly friend Stanhope for it, that he who declared he loved a good hater was but a respectable sort of Hottentot at best. No very genteel epithet this, though coming from the genteelest of men. But when the digger of dictionaries said that saying of his, he was assuredly not much of a Christian. However, it is hard for one given up to constitutional hypos like him to be filled with the milk and meekness of the gospels. Yet with deference I deny that my old uncle Johnson really believed in the sentiment ascribed to him. Love a hater indeed! Who smacks his lips over gall? Now hate is a thankless thing. So let us only hate hatred, and once give love play, we will fall in love with a unicorn. Ah! the easiest way is the best, and to hate, a man must work hard. Love is a delight, but hate a torment. And haters are thumbscrews. Scotch boots and Spanish inquisitions to themselves. In five words—would they were a Siamese diphthong—he who hates is a fool.

For several days our *Chamois* was followed by two of these aforesaid Tiger Sharks. A brace of confidential inseparables, jogging along in our wake, side by side, like a couple of highwaymen, biding their time till you come to the cross-roads. But giving it up at last for a bootless errand, they dropped farther and farther astern until completely out of sight. Much to the Skyeman's chagrin, who long stood in the stern, lance poised for a dart.

But of all sharks, save me from the ghastly White Shark. For though we should hate naught, yet some dislikes are spontaneous, and disliking is not hating. And never yet could I bring myself to be loving or even sociable with a White Shark. He is not the sort of creature to enlist your affections.

This ghost of a fish is not often encountered, and shows plainer by night than by day. Timon-like, he always swims by himself, gliding along just under the surface, revealing a long, vague shape, of a milky hue, with glimpses now and then of his bottomless white pit of teeth. No need of a dentist hath he.

Seen at night, stealing along like a spirit in the water, with horrific serenity of aspect, the White Shark sent many a thrill to us twain in the *Chamois.*

By day, and in the profoundest calms, oft were we startled by the ponderous sigh of the grampus, as lazily rising to the surface he fetched a long breath after napping below.

And time and again we watched the darting albacore, the fish with the chain-plate armor and golden scales; the Nimrod of the seas, to whom so many flying fish fall a prey. Flying from their pursuers, many of them flew into our boat. But invariably they died from the shock. No nursing could restore them. One of their wings I removed, spreading it out to dry under a weight. In two days' time the thin membrane, all over tracings like those of a leaf, was transparent as isinglass, and tinted with brilliant hues like those of a changing silk.

Almost every day, we spied Black Fish, coal-black and glossy. They seemed to swim by revolving round and round in the water, like a wheel, their dorsal fins every now and then shooting into view like spokes.

Of a somewhat similar species, but smaller and clipper-built about the nose, were the Algerines, so called, probably, from their corsair propensities; waylaying peaceful fish on the high seas and plundering them of body and soul at a gulp. Atrocious Turks! a crusade should be preached against them.

Besides all these we encountered Killers and Thrashers, by far the most spirited and "spunky" of the finny tribes. Though little larger than a porpoise, a band of them think nothing of assailing leviathan himself. They bait the monster as dogs a bull. The Killers seizing the Right whale by his immense sulky lower lip, and the Thrashers fastening on to his back, and beating him with their sinewy tails. Often they come off conquerors, worrying the enemy to death. Though, sooth to say, if leviathan gets but one sweep at them with his terrible tail, they go flying into the air as if tossed from Taurus' horn.

This sight we beheld. Had old Wouvermans, who once painted a bull-bait, been along with us, a rare chance that for his pencil. And Gudin or Isabey might have thrown the blue rolling sea into the picture. Lastly, one of Claude's setting summer suns would have glorified the whole. Oh, believe me, God's creatures fighting fin for fin a thousand miles from land, and with the round horizon for an arena, is no ignoble subject for a masterpiece.

Such are a few of the sights of the great South Sea. But there is no telling all. The Pacific is populous as China.

Chapter XIV

Jarl's Misgivings

About this time an event took place. My good Viking opened his mouth and spoke. The prodigy occurred, as, jack-knife in hand, he was bending over the midship oar, on the loom, or handle, of which he kept our almanac; making a notch for every set sun. For some forty-eight hours past the wind had been light and variable. It was more than suspected that a current was sweeping us northward.

Now, marking these things, Jarl threw out the thought that the more wind and the less current the better, and if a long calm came on, of which there was some prospect, we had better take to our oars.

Take to our oars! as if we were crossing a ferry, and no ocean leagues to traverse. The idea indirectly suggested all possible horrors. To be rid of them forthwith, I proceeded to dole out our morning meal. For to make away with such things there is nothing better than bolting something down on top of them; albeit, oft repeated, the plan is very apt to beget dyspepsia, and the dyspepsia the blues.

But what of our store of provisions? So far as enough to eat was concerned, we felt not the slightest apprehension, our supplies proving more abundant than we had anticipated. But, curious to tell, we felt but little inclination for food. It was water, bright water, cool, sparkling water alone that we craved. And of this also our store at first seemed ample. But as our voyage lengthened and breezes blew faint and calms fell fast, the idea of being deprived of the precious fluid grew into something little short of a monomania; especially with Jarl.

Every hour or two with the hammer and chisel belonging to the tinder-box keg he tinkered away at the invaluable breaker, driving down the hoops till in his over-solicitude I thought he would burst them outright.

Now the breaker lay on its bilge in the middle of the boat, where more or less sea-water always collected. And ever and anon, dipping his finger therein, my Viking was troubled with the thought that this sea-water tasted less brackish than that alongside. Of course the breaker must be leaking. So he would turn it over till its wet side came uppermost, when it would quickly become dry as a bone. But now with his knife he would gently probe the joints of the staves, shake his head, look up, look down, taste of the water in the bottom of the boat, then that of the sea, then lift one end of the breaker, going through with every test of leakage he could dream of. Nor was he ever fully satisfied that the breaker was in all respects sound. But in reality it was as tight as the drum-heads that beat at Cerro-Gordo. Oh! Jarl, Jarl! to me in the boat's quiet stern, steering and philosophizing at one time and the same, thou and thy breaker were a study.

Besides the breaker we had, full of water, the two boat-kegs previously alluded to. These were first used. We drank from them by their leaden spouts, so many swallows three times in the day, having no other means of measuring an allowance. But when we came to the breaker, which had only a bung-hole, though a very large one, dog-like, it was so many laps a-piece, jealously counted by the observer. This plan, however, was only good for a single day; the water then getting beyond the reach of the tongue. We therefore daily poured from the breaker into one of the kegs, and drank from its spout. But to obviate the absorption, inseparable from decanting, we at last hit upon something better—my comrade's shoe, which, deprived of its quarters, narrowed at the heel, and diligently rinsed out in the sea, was converted into a handy but rather limber ladle. This we kept suspended in the bung-hole of the breaker that it might never twice absorb the water.

Now pewter imparts flavor to ale; a Meerschaum bowl the same to the tobacco of Smyrna, and goggle green glasses are deemed indispensable to the bibbing of hock. What, then, shall be said of a leathern goblet for water? Try it, ye mariners who list!

One morning, taking his wonted draft, Jarl fished up in his ladle a deceased insect, something like a Daddy-long-legs, only more corpulent. Its fate? A sea-toss? Believe it not; with all those precious drops clinging to its lengthy legs. It was held over the ladle till the last globule dribbled, and even then, being moist, honest Jarl was but loath to drop it overboard.

For our larder we could not endure the salt beef; it was raw as a live Abyssinian steak and salt as Cracow. Besides, the Fiji simile would not have held good with respect to it. It was far from being "tender as a dead man." The biscuit only could we eat—not to be wondered at, for even on shipboard seamen in the tropics are but sparing feeders.

And here let not a suggestion be omitted, most valuable to any future castaway or sailaway as the case may be. Eat not your biscuit dry, but dip it in the sea, which makes it more bulky and palatable. During meal-times it was soak and sip with Jarl and me, one on each side of the *Chamois*, dipping our biscuit in the brine. This plan obviated finger-glasses at the conclusion of our repast. Upon the whole, dwelling upon the water is not so bad after all. The Chinese are no fools. In the operation of making your toilette, how handy to float in your ewer?

Chapter XV

A Stitch in Time Saves Nine

Like most silent earnest sort of people, my good viking was a pattern of industry. When in the boats after whales I have known him carry along a roll of sinnate to stitch into a hat. And the boats lying motionless for half an hour or so, waiting the rising of the chase, his fingers would be plying at their task like an old lady knitting. Like an experienced old-wife, too, his digits had become so expert and conscientious that his eyes left them alone, deeming optic supervision unnecessary. And on this trip of ours, when not otherwise engaged, he was quite as busy with his fingers as ever—unraveling old Cape Horn hose for yarn wherewith to darn our woolen frocks with great patches from the skirts of a condemned reefing jacket, paneling the seats of our "ducks"; in short, veneering our broken garments with all manner of choice old broadcloths.

With the true forethought of an old tar, he had brought along with him nearly the whole contents of his chest. His precious "Ditty Bag," containing his sewing utensils, had been carefully packed away in the bottom of one of his bundles, of which he had as many as an old maid on her travels. In truth, an old salt is very much of an old maid, though, strictly speaking, far from deserving that misdeemed appellative. Better be an old maid, a woman with herself for a husband, than the wife of a fool, and Solomon more than hints that all men are fools, and every wise man knows himself to be one.

When playing the sempstress, Jarl's favorite perch was the triangular little platform in the bow, which, being the driest and most elevated part of the boat, was best adapted to his purpose. Here for hours and hours together the honest old tailor would sit darning and sewing away, heedless of the wide ocean around, while forever his slouched Guayaquil hat kept bobbing up and down against the horizon before us.

It was a most solemn avocation with him. Silently he nodded like the still statue in the opera of *Don Juan*. Indeed he never spoke unless to give pithy utterance to the wisdom of keeping one's wardrobe in repair. But herein my Viking at times waxed oracular. And many's the hour we glided along, myself deeply pondering in the stern, hand upon helm, while cross-legged at the other end of the boat, Jarl laid down patch upon patch, and at long intervals precept upon precept, here several saws, and there innumerable stitches.

Chapter XVI

They Are Becalmed

On the eighth day there was a calm.

It came on by night, so that waking at daybreak and folding my arms over the gunwale, I looked out upon a scene very hard to describe. The sun was still beneath the horizon, perhaps not yet out of sight from the plains of Paraguay. But the dawn was too strong for the stars, which one by one had gone out, like waning lamps after a ball.

Now as the face of a mirror is a blank, only borrowing character from what it reflects; so in a calm in the Tropics, a colorless sky overhead, the ocean upon its surface hardly presents a sign of existence. The deep blue is gone, and the glassy element lies tranced, almost viewless as the air.

But that morning the two gray firmaments of sky and water seemed collapsed into a vague ellipsis. And alike, the *Chamois* seemed drifting in the atmosphere as in the sea. Everything was fused into the calm, sky, air, water, and all. Not a fish was to be seen. The silence was that of a vacuum. No vitality lurked in the air. And this inert blending and brooding of all things seemed gray chaos in conception.

This calm lasted four days and four nights, during which but a few cats-paws of wind varied the scene. They were faint as the breath of one dying.

At times the heat was intense. The heavens, at midday, glowing like an ignited coal mine. Our skin curled up like lint, our vision became dim; the brain dizzy.

To our consternation the water in the breaker became lukewarm, brackish, and slightly putrescent, notwithstanding we kept our spare clothing piled upon the breaker to shield it from the sun. At last Jarl enlarged the vent, carefully keeping it exposed. To this precaution, doubtless, we owed more than we then thought. It was now deemed wise to reduce our allowance of water to the smallest modicum consistent with the present preservation of life, strangling all desire for more.

Nor was this all. The upper planking of the boat began to warp, here and there cracking and splintering. But though we kept it moistened with brine, one of the plank-ends started from its place, and the sharp, sudden sound, breaking the scorching silence, caused us both to spring to our feet. Instantly the sea burst in, but we made shift to secure the rebellious plank with a cord, not having a nail; we then bailed out the boat, nearly half full of water.

On the second day of the calm we unshipped the mast, to prevent its being pitched out by the occasional rolling of the vast smooth swells now overtaking us. Leagues and leagues away, after its fierce raging, some tempest must have been sending to us its last dying waves. For as a pebble dropped into a pond ruffles it to its marge, so on all sides a sea-gale operates as if an asteroid had fallen into the brine, making ringed mountain billows, interminably expanding instead of ripples.

The great September waves breaking at the base of the Neversink Highlands, far in advance of the swiftest pilot boat, carry tidings. And full often they know the last secret of many a stout ship, never heard of from the day she left port. Every wave in my eyes seems a soul.

As there was no steering to be done, Jarl and I sheltered ourselves as well as we could under the awning. And for the first two days, one at a time, and every three or four hours, we dropped overboard for a bath, clinging to the gunwales, a sharp look-out being kept for prowling sharks. A foot or two below the surface the water felt cool and refreshing.

On the third day a change came over us. We relinquished bathing, the exertion taxing us too much. Sullenly we laid ourselves down, turned our backs to each other, and were impatient of the slightest casual touch of our persons. What sort of expression my own countenance wore I know not, but I hated to look at Jarl's. When I did it was a glare, not a glance. I became more taciturn than he. I cannot tell what it was that came over me, but I wished I was alone. I felt that so long as the calm lasted we were without help; that neither could assist the other; and above all, that for one, the water would hold out longer than for two. I felt no remorse, not the slightest, for these thoughts. It was instinct. Like a desperado giving up the ghost, I desired to gasp by myself.

From being cast away with a brother, good God deliver me!

The four days passed, and on the morning of the fifth, thanks be to Heaven, there came a breeze. Dancingly, mincingly it came, just rippling the sea, until it struck our sails, previously set at the very first token of its advance. At length it slightly freshened; and our poor *Chamois* seemed raised from the dead.

Beyond expression delightful! Once more we heard the low humming of the sea under our bow, as our boat, like a bird, went singing on its way.

How changed the scene! Overhead a sweet blue haze, distilling sunlight in drops. And flung abroad over the visible creation was the sun-spangled, azure, rustling robe of the ocean, ermined with wave crests, all else, infinitely blue. Such a cadence of musical sounds! Waves chasing each other and sporting and frothing in frolicsome foam, painted fish rippling past, and anon the noise of wings as sea-fowls flew by.

Oh, Ocean, when thou choosest to smile, more beautiful thou art than flowery mead or plain!

Chapter XVII

In High Spirits, They Push on for the Terra Incognita

There were now fourteen notches on the loom of the skyeman's oar: so many days since we had pushed from the fore-chains of the *Arcturion*. But as yet no floating bough, no tern, noddy, nor reef-bird, to denote our proximity to land. In that long calm, whither might not the currents have swept us?

Where we were precisely we knew not, but according to our reckoning the loose estimation of the knots run every hour, we must have sailed due west but little more than one hundred and fifty leagues, for the most part having encountered but light winds, and frequent intermitting calms, besides that prolonged one described. But spite of past calms and currents, land there must be to the westward. Sun, compass, stout hearts, and steady breezes pointed our prow thereto. So, courage! my Viking, and never say drown!

At this time our hearts were much lightened by discovering that our water was improving in taste. It seemed to have been undergoing anew that sort of fermentation, or working, occasionally incident to ship water shortly after being taken on board. Sometimes for a period it is more or less offensive to taste and smell; again, however, becoming comparatively limpid.

But as our water improved we grew more and more miserly of so priceless a treasure.

And here it may be well to make mention of another little circumstance, however unsentimental. Thoroughpaced tar that he was, my Viking was an inordinate consumer of the Indian weed. From the *Arcturion* he had brought along with him a small half-keg, at bottom impacted with a solitary layer of sable Negro-head, fossil-marked, like the primary stratum of the geologists. It was the last tier of his abundant supply for the long whaling voyage upon which he had embarked upwards of three years previous. Now during the calm, and for some days after, poor Jarl's accustomed quid was no longer agreeable company. To pun: he eschewed his chew. I asked him wherefore. He replied that it puckered up his mouth, above all provoked thirst, and had somehow grown every way distasteful. I was sorry; for the absence of his before ever-present wad impaired what little fullness there was left in his cheek; though, sooth to say, I no longer called upon him as of yore to shift over the enormous morsel to starboard or larboard, and so trim our craft.

The calm gone by, once again my sea-tailor plied needle and thread, or turning laundress, hung our raiment to dry on oars peaked obliquely in the thole-pins. All of which tattered pennons, the wind being astern, helped us gaily on our way, as jolly poor devils, with rags flying in the breeze sail blithely through life; and are merry although they are poor!

Chapter XVIII

My Lord Shark and His Pages

THERE IS A FISH IN THE SEA THAT EVER MORE, LIKE A SURLY LORD, ONLY GOES ABROAD ATTENDED by his suite. It is the Shovel-nosed Shark. A clumsy, lethargic monster, unshapely as his name, and the last species of his kind, one would think to be so bravely waited upon, as he is. His suite is composed of those dainty little creatures called Pilot fish by sailors. But by night his retinue is frequently increased by the presence of several small luminous fish, running in advance, and flourishing their flambeaux like link-boys lighting the monster's way. Pity there were no ray-fish in rear, page-like, to carry his caudal train.

Now the relation subsisting between the Pilot fish above-mentioned and their huge ungainly lord seems one of the most inscrutable things in nature. At any rate, it poses poor me to comprehend. That a monster so ferocious should suffer five or six little sparks, hardly fourteen inches long, to gambol about his grim hull with the utmost impunity is of itself something strange. But when it is considered that by a reciprocal understanding the Pilot fish seem to act as scouts to the shark, warning him of danger and apprising him of the vicinity of prey, and, moreover, in case of his being killed, evincing their anguish by certain agitations, otherwise inexplicable, the whole thing becomes a mystery unfathomable. Truly marvels abound. It needs no dead man to be raised, to convince us of some things. Even my Viking marveled full as much at those Pilot fish as he would have marveled at the Pentecost.

But perhaps a little incident, occurring about this period, will best illustrate the matter in hand.

We were gliding along hardly three knots an hour when my comrade, who had been dozing over the gunwale, suddenly started to his feet and pointed out an immense Shovel-nosed Shark less than a boat's length distant, and about half a fathom beneath the surface. A lance was at once snatched from its place, and true to his calling, Jarl was about to dart it at the fish when, interested by the sight of its radiant little scouts, I begged him to desist.

One of them was right under the shark, nibbling at his ventral fin, another above, hovering about his dorsal appurtenance, one on each flank, and a frisking fifth pranking about his nose, seemingly having something to say of a confidential nature. They were of a bright steel-blue color, alternated with jet black stripes, with glistening bellies of a silver-white. Clinging to the back of the shark were four or five Remoras, or sucking-fish, snaky parasites, impossible to remove from whatever they adhere to without destroying their lives. The Remora has little power in swimming, hence its sole locomotion is on the backs of larger fish. Leech-like it sticketh closer than a false brother in prosperity, closer than a beggar to the benevolent, closer than Webster to the Constitution. But it feeds upon what it clings to; its feelers having a direct communication with the esophagus.

The shark swam sluggishly, creating no sign of a ripple, but ever and anon shaking his Medusa locks, writhing and curling with horrible life. Now and then the nimble Pilot fish darted from his side—this way and that—mostly towards our boat, but previous to taking a fresh start ever returning to their liege lord to report progress.

A thought struck me. Baiting a rope's end with a morsel of our almost useless salt beef, I suffered it to trail in the sea. Instantly the foremost scout swam toward it, hesitated, paused; but at last advancing, briskly snuffed at the line, and taking one finical little nibble, retreated towards the shark. Another moment, and the great Tamerlane himself turned heavily about, pointing his black, cannon-like nose directly toward our broadside. Meanwhile the little Pilot fish darted hither and thither, keeping up a mighty fidgeting, like men of small minds in a state of nervous agitation.

Presently Tamerlane swam nearer and nearer, all the while lazily eyeing the *Chamois* as a wild boar a kid. Suddenly making a rush for it, in the foam he made away with the bait. But the next instant the uplifted lance sped at his skull, and thrashing his requiem with his sinewy tail he sunk slowly, through his own blood, out of sight. Down with him swam the terrified Pilot fish, but soon after three of them were observed close to the boat, gliding along at a uniform pace, one on each side and one in advance, even as they had attended their lord. Doubtless one was under our keel.

"A good omen," said Jarl; "no harm will befall us so long as they stay."

But however that might be, follow us they did, for many days after, until an event occurred which necessitated their withdrawal.

Chapter XIX

Who Goes There?

JARL'S OAR SHOWED SIXTEEN NOTCHES ON THE LOOM WHEN ONE EVENING, AS THE EXPANDED SUN touched the horizon's rim, a ship's uppermost spars were observed, traced like a spider's web against its crimson disk. It looked like a far-off craft on fire.

In bright weather at sea, a sail, invisible in the full flood of noon, becomes perceptible toward sunset. It is the reverse in the morning. In sight at gray dawn the distant vessel, though in reality approaching, recedes from view as the sun rises higher and higher. This holds true till its vicinity makes it readily fall within the ordinary scope of vision. And thus, too, here and there, with other distant things: the more light you throw on them the more you obscure. Some revelations show best in a twilight.

The sight of the stranger not a little surprised us. But brightening up as if the encounter were welcome, Jarl looked happy and expectant. He quickly changed his demeanor, however, upon perceiving that I was bent upon shunning a meeting.

Instantly our sails were struck, and calling upon Jarl, who was somewhat backward to obey, I shipped the oars, and both rowing, we stood away obliquely from our former course.

I divined that the vessel was a whaler, and hence, that by the help of the glass, with which her look-outs must be momentarily sweeping the horizon, they might possibly have descried us, especially as we were due east from the ship, a direction which at sunset is the one most favorable for perceiving a far-off object at sea.

Furthermore, our canvas was snow-white and conspicuous. To be sure, we could not be certain what kind of a vessel it was, but whatever it might be, I for one, had no mind to risk an encounter; for it was quite plain, that if the stranger came within hailing distance there would be no resource but to link our fortunes with hers, whereas I desired to pursue none but the *Chamois'*. As for the Skyeman, he kept looking wistfully over his shoulder, doubtless praying Heaven that we might not escape what I sought to avoid.

Now, upon a closer scrutiny, being pretty well convinced that the stranger after all was steering a nearly westerly course—right away from us—we reset our sail, and as night fell my Viking's entreaties, seconded by my own curiosity, induced me to resume our original course, and so follow after the vessel, with a view of obtaining a nearer glimpse without danger of detection. So boldly we steered for the sail.

But not gaining much upon her, spite of the lightness of the breeze (a circumstance in our favor, the chase being a ship and we but a boat), at my comrade's instigation we added oars to sails, readily guiding our way by the former, though the helm was left to itself.

As we came nearer it was plain that the vessel was no whaler, but a small, two-masted craft; in short, a brigantine. Her sails were in a state of unaccountable disarray, only the foresail, mainsail, and jib being set. The first was much tattered, and the jib was hoisted but half-way up the stay, where it idly flapped, the breeze coming from over the taffrail. She continually yawed in her course, now almost presenting her broadside, then showing her stern.

Striking our sails once more, we lay on our oars and watched her in the starlight. Still she swung from side to side, and still sailed on.

Not a little terrified at the sight, superstitious Jarl more than insinuated that the craft must be a gold-huntress, haunted. But I told him, that if such were the case we must board her, come gold or goblins. In reality, however, I began to think that she must have been abandoned by her crew, or else, that from sickness those on board were incapable of managing her.

After a long and anxious reconnoiter we came still nearer, using our oars, but very reluctantly on Jarl's part, who, while rowing, kept his eyes over his shoulder, as if about to beach the little *Chamois* on the back of a whale as of yore. Indeed he seemed full as impatient to quit the vicinity of the vessel as before he had been anxiously courting it.

Now, as the silent brigantine again swung round her broadside, I hailed her loudly. No return. Again. But all was silent. With a few vigorous strokes we closed with her, giving yet another unanswered hail, when, laying the *Chamois* right alongside, I clutched at the main-chains. Instantly we felt her dragging us along. Securing our craft by its painter, I sprang over the rail, followed by Jarl, who had snatched his harpoon, his favorite arms. Long used with that weapon to overcome the monsters of the deep, he doubted not it would prove equally serviceable in any other encounter.

The deck was a complete litter. Tossed about were pearl oyster shells, husks of cocoanuts, empty casks, and cases. The deserted tiller was lashed; which accounted for the vessel's yawing. But we could not conceive how, going large before the wind, the craft could for any considerable time, at least, have guided herself without the help of a hand. Still the breeze was light and steady.

Now, seeing the helm thus lashed, I could not but distrust the silence that prevailed. It conjured up the idea of miscreants concealed below, and meditating treachery; unscrupulous mutineers—Lascars or Manilla men who, having murdered the Europeans of the crew, might not be willing to let strangers depart unmolested. Or yet worse, the entire ship's company might have been swept away by a fever, its infection still lurking in the poisoned hull. And though the first conceit, as the last, was a mere surmise, it was nevertheless deemed prudent to secure the hatches, which for the present we accordingly barred down with the oars of our boat. This done, we went about the deck in search of water; and finding some in a clumsy cask, drank long and freely, and to our thirsty souls' content.

The wind now freshening, and the rent sails like to blow from the yards, we brought the brigantine to the wind and brailed up the canvas. This left us at liberty to examine the craft, though, unfortunately, the night was growing hazy.

All this while our boat was still towing alongside, and I was about to drop it astern when Jarl, ever cautious, declared it safer where it was, since if there were people on board they would most likely be down in the cabin, from the dead-lights of which mischief might be done to the *Chamois*.

It was then that my comrade observed that the brigantine had no boats, a circumstance most unusual in any sort of a vessel at sea. But marking this, I was exceedingly gratified. It seemed to indicate, as I had opined, that from some cause or other, she must have been abandoned of her crew. And in a good measure this dispelled my fears of foul play and the apprehension of contagion. Encouraged by these reflections I now resolved to descend and explore the cabin, though sorely against Jarl's counsel. To be sure, as he earnestly said, this step might have been deferred till daylight, but it seemed too wearisome to wait. So bethinking me of our tinder-box and candles, I sent him into the boat for them. Presently two candles were lit, one of which the Skyeman tied up and down the barbed end of his harpoon, so that upon going below the keen steel might not be far off, should the light be blown out by a dastard.

Unfastening the cabin scuttle we stepped downward into the smallest and murkiest den in the world. The altar-like transom, surmounted by the closed dead-lights in the stern, together with the dim little skylight overhead, and the somber aspect of everything around, gave the place the air of some subterranean oratory, say a prayer-room of Peter the Hermit. But coils of rigging, bolts of canvas, articles of clothing, and disorderly heaps of rubbish harmonized not with this impression. Two doors, one on each side, led into wee little state-rooms, the berths of which also were littered. Among other things was a large box, sheathed with iron and stoutly clamped, containing a keg partly filled with powder, the half of an old cutlass, a pouch of bullets, and a case for a sextant—a brass plate on the lid with the maker's name, London. The broken blade of the cutlass was very rusty and stained, and the iron hilt bent in. It looked so tragical that I thrust it out of sight.

Removing a small trap-door, opening into the space beneath called the "run," we lighted upon sundry cutlasses and muskets, lying together at sixes and sevens as if pitched down in a hurry.

Casting round a hasty glance and satisfying ourselves that through the bulkhead of the cabin there was no passage to the forward part of the hold, we caught up the muskets and cutlasses, the powder-keg and the pouch of bullets, and bundling them on deck, prepared to visit the other end of the vessel. Previous to so doing, however, I loaded a musket and belted a cutlass to my side. But my Viking preferred his harpoon.

In the forecastle reigned similar confusion. But there was a snug little lair, cleared away in one corner and furnished with a grass mat and bolster, like those used among the islanders of these seas. This little lair looked to us as if some leopard had crouched there. And as it turned out, we were not far from right. Forming one side of this retreat was a sailor's chest, stoutly secured by a lock, and monstrous heavy withal. Regardless of Jarl's entreaties, I managed to burst the lid, thereby revealing a motley assemblage of millinery and outlandish knick-knacks of all sorts, together with sundry rude calico contrivances which, though of unaccountable cut, nevertheless possessed a certain petticoatish air, and latitude of skirt betokening them the habiliments of some feminine creature, most probably of the human species.

In this strong box also was a canvas bag, jingling with rusty old bell-buttons, gangrened copper bolts, and sheathing nails, damp greenish Carolus dollars (true coin all), besides divers iron screws, and battered chisels and belaying pins. Sounded on the chest lid, the dollars rang clear as convent bells. These were put aside by Jarl, the sight of substantial dollars doing away, for the nonce, with his superstitious misgivings. True to his kingship, he loved true coin; though abroad on the sea, and no land but dollarless dominions around, all this silver was worthless as charcoal or diamonds. Nearly one and the same thing, say the chemists; but tell that to the marines, say the illiterate Jews and jewelers. Go, buy a house, or a ship, if you can, with your charcoal! Yea, all the woods in Canada charred down to cinders would not be worth the one famed Brazilian diamond, though no bigger than the egg of a carrier pigeon. Ah! but these chemists are liars, and Sir Humphrey Davy a cheat. Many's the poor devil they've deluded into the charcoal business who otherwise might have made his fortune with a mattock.

Groping again into the chest, we brought to light a queer little hair trunk, very bald and rickety. At every corner was a mighty clamp, the weight of which had no doubt debilitated the box. It was jealously secured with a padlock almost as big as itself, so that it was almost a question which was meant to be security to the other. Prying at it hard, we at length effected an entrance, but saw no golden moidores, no ruddy doubloons, nothing under Heaven but three pewter mugs, such as are used in a ship's cabin, several brass screws and brass plates, which must have belonged to a quadrant, together with a famous lot of glass beads and brass rings, while pasted on the inside of the cover was a little colored print representing the harlots, the shameless hussies, having a fine time with the Prodigal Son.

It should have been mentioned ere now that while we were busy in the forecastle we were several times startled by strange sounds aloft. And just after, crashing into the little hair trunk, down came a great top-block right through the scuttle, narrowly missing my Viking's crown, a much stronger article, by the way, than your goldsmiths turn out in these days. This startled us much, particularly Jarl, as one might suppose; but accustomed to the strange creakings and wheezings of the masts and yards of old vessels at sea, and having many a time dodged stray blocks accidentally falling from aloft, I thought little more of the matter, though my comrade seemed to think the noises somewhat different from any thing of the kind he had ever heard before.

After a little more turning over of the rubbish in the forecastle, and much marveling thereat, we ascended to the deck, where we found every thing so silent that as we moved toward the taffrail, the Skyeman unconsciously addressed me in a whisper.

Chapter XX

Noises and Portents

I LONGED FOR DAY. FOR HOWEVER NOW INCLINED TO BELIEVE THAT THE BRIGANTINE WAS UNtenanted, I desired the light of the sun to place that fact beyond a misgiving.

Now, having observed previous to boarding the vessel that she lay rather low in the water, I thought proper to sound the well. But there being no line-and-sinker at hand, I sent Jarl to hunt them up in the arm-chest on the quarter-deck, where doubtless they must be kept. Meanwhile I searched for the "breaks," or pump-handles, which, as it turned out, could not have been very recently used, for they were found lashed up and down to the main-mast.

Suddenly Jarl came running toward me, whispering that all doubt was dispelled—there were spirits on board to a dead certainty. He had overheard a supernatural sneeze. But by this time I was all but convinced that we were alone in the brigantine. Since, if otherwise, I could assign no earthly reason for the crew's hiding away from a couple of sailors whom, were they so minded, they might easily have mastered, and furthermore, this alleged disturbance of the atmosphere aloft by a sneeze, Jarl averred to have taken place in the main-top, directly underneath which I was all this time standing, and had heard nothing. So complimenting my good Viking upon the exceeding delicacy of his auriculars, I bade him trouble himself no more with his piratical ghosts and goblins, which existed nowhere but in his own imagination.

Not finding the line-and-sinker, with the spare end of a bowline we rigged a substitute, and sounding the well, found nothing to excite our alarm. Under certain circumstances, however, this sounding a ship's well is a nervous sort of business enough. 'Tis like feeling your own pulse in the last stage of a fever.

At the Skyeman's suggestion, we now proceeded to throw round the brigantine's head on the other tack. For until daylight we desired to alter the vessel's position as little as possible, fearful of coming unawares upon reefs.

And here be it said that for all his superstitious misgivings about the brigantine, his imputing to her something equivalent to a purely phantom-like nature, honest Jarl was nevertheless exceedingly downright and practical in all hints and proceedings concerning her. Wherein he resembled my Right Reverend friend, Bishop Berkeley—truly one of your lords spiritual—who, metaphysically speaking, holding all objects to be mere optical delusions, was, notwithstanding, extremely matter-of-fact in all matters touching matter itself. Besides being pervious to the points of pins, and possessing a palate capable of appreciating plum-puddings—which sentence reads off like a pattering of hailstones.

Now, while we were employed bracing round the yards, whispering Jarl must needs pester me again with his confounded suspicions of goblins on board. He swore by the main-mast that when the fore-yard swung round, he had heard a half-stifled groan from that quarter, as if one of his bugbears had been getting its aerial legs jammed. I laughed—hinting that goblins were incorporeal. Whereupon he besought me to ascend the fore rigging and test the matter for myself. But here my mature judgment got the better of my first crude opinion. I civilly declined. For assuredly there was still a possibility that the fore-top might be tenanted, and that too by living miscreants; and a pretty hap would be mine, if, with hands full of rigging, and legs dangling in air, while surmounting the oblique futtock-shrouds, some unseen arm should all at once tumble me overboard. Therefore I held my peace, while Jarl went on to declare that with regard to the character of the brigantine, his mind was now pretty fully made up she was an arrant impostor, a shade of a ship, full of sailors' ghosts, and before we knew where we were, would dissolve in a supernatural squall and leave us twain in the water. In short, Jarl, the descendant of the superstitious old Norsemen, was full of old Norse conceits and all manner of Valhalla marvels concerning the land of goblins and goblets. No wonder, then, that with this catastrophe in prospect he again entreated me to quit the ill-starred craft, carrying off nothing from her ghostly hull. But I refused.

One cannot relate everything at once. While in the cabin we came across a "barge" of biscuit, and finding its contents of a quality much superior to our own, we had filled our pockets and occasionally regaled ourselves in the intervals of rummaging. Now this sea-cake basket we had brought on deck. And for the first time since bidding adieu to the *Arcturion,* having fully quenched our thirst, our appetite returned with a rush; and having nothing better to do till day dawned, we planted the bread-barge in the middle of the quarter-deck, and crossing our legs before it, laid close seige thereto, like the Grand Turk and his Vizier Mustapha sitting down before Vienna.

Our castle, the bread-barge, was of the common sort; an oblong oaken box much battered and bruised, and like the Elgin Marbles, all over inscriptions and carving—foul anchors, skewered hearts, almanacs, Burton-blocks, love verses, links of cable, Kings of Clubs, and divers mystic diagrams in chalk, drawn by old Finnish mariners in casting horoscopes and prophecies. Your old tars are all Daniels. There was a round hole in one side, through which, in getting at the bread, invited guests thrust their hands.

And mighty was the thrusting of hands that night; also, many and earnest the glances of Mustapha at every sudden creaking of the spars or rigging. Like Belshazzar, my royal Viking ate with great fear and trembling, ever and anon pausing to watch the wild shadows flitting along the bulwarks.

Chapter XXI

Man Ho!

Slowly, fitfully, broke the morning in the east, showing the desolate brig forging heavily through the water, which sluggishly thumped under her bows. While leaping from sea to sea, our faithful *Chamois,* like a faithful dog, still gamboled alongside, confined to the main-chains by its painter. At times it would long lag behind; then, pushed by a wave like lightning dash forward, till bridled by its leash, it again fell in rear.

As the gray light came on, anxiously we scrutinized the features of the craft as one by one they became more plainly revealed. Everything seemed stranger now than when partially visible in the dingy night. The stanchions, or posts of the bulwarks, were of rough stakes, still incased in the bark. The unpainted sides were of a dark-colored heathenish looking wood. The tiller was a wry-necked, elbowed bough, thrusting itself through the deck as if the tree itself was fast rooted in the hold. The binnacle containing the compass was defended at the sides by yellow matting. The rigging-shrouds, halyards and all was of "Kaiar," or cocoanut fibers, and here and there the sails were patched with plaited rushes.

But this was not all. Whoso will pry must needs light upon matters for suspicion. Glancing over the side, in the wake of every scupper-hole, we beheld a faded, crimson stain, which Jarl averred to be blood. Though now he betrayed not the slightest trepidation, for what he saw pertained not to ghosts, and all his fears hitherto had been of the supernatural.

Indeed, plucking up a heart with the dawn of the day, my Viking looked bold as a lion, and soon, with the instinct of an old seaman cast his eyes up aloft.

Directly he touched my arm—"Look; what stirs in the main-top?"

Sure enough, something alive was there.

Fingering our arms, we watched it, till as the day came on, a crouching stranger was beheld.

Presenting my piece, I hailed him to descend or be shot. There was silence for a space, when the black barrel of a musket was thrust forth, leveled at my head. Instantly Jarl's harpoon was presented at a dart;—two to one;—and my hail was repeated. But no reply.

"Who are you?"

"Samoa," at length said a clear, firm voice.

"Come down from the rigging. We are friends."

Another pause; when, rising to his feet, the stranger slowly descended, holding on by one hand to the rigging, for but one did he have, his musket partly slung from his back, and partly gripped under the stump of his mutilated arm.

He alighted about six paces from where we stood, and balancing his weapon, eyed us bravely as the Cid.

He was a tall, dark islander, a very devil to behold, theatrically arrayed in kilt and turban, the kilt of a gay calico print, the turban of a red China silk. His neck was jingling with strings of beads.

"Who else is on board?" I asked, while Jarl, thus far covering the stranger with his weapon, now dropped it to the deck.

"Look there—Annatoo," was his reply in broken English, pointing aloft to the fore-top. And lo! a woman, also an islander, and barring her skirts, dressed very much like Samoa, was beheld descending.

"Any more?"

"No more."

"Who are *you,* then; and what craft is this?"

"Ah, ah—you are no ghost—but are you my friend?" he cried, advancing nearer as he spoke, while the woman, having gained the deck, also approached, eagerly glancing.

We said we were friends, that we meant no harm, but desired to know what craft this was, and what disaster had befallen her, for that something untoward had occurred we were certain.

Whereto Samoa made answer that it was true that something dreadful had happened, and that he would gladly tell us all, and tell us the truth. And about it he went.

Now, this story of his was related in the mixed phraseology of a Polynesian sailor. With a few random reflections in substance it will be found in the six following chapters.

Chapter XXII

What Befell the Brigantine at the Pearl Shell Islands

The vessel was the *Parki,* of Lahina, a village and harbor on the coast of Maui, one of the Hawaiian Isles, where she had been miserably cobbled together with planks of native wood and fragments of a wreck there drifted ashore. Her appellative had been bestowed in honor of a high chief, the tallest and goodliest-looking gentleman in all the Sandwich Islands. With a mixed European and native crew, about thirty in number (but only four whites in all, captain included), the *Parki,* some four months previous, had sailed from her port on a voyage southward in quest of pearls and pearl oyster shells, sea-slugs, and other matters of that sort.

Samoa, a native of the Navigator Islands, had long followed the sea, and was well versed in the business of oyster diving and its submarine mysteries. The native Lahineese on board were immediately subordinate to him, the captain having bargained with Samoa for their services as divers.

The woman, Annatoo, was a native of a far-off, anonymous island to the westward, whence, when quite young, she had been carried by the commander of a ship, touching there on a passage from Macao to Valparaiso. At Valparaiso her protector put her ashore; most probably, as I afterwards had reason to think, for a nuisance.

By chance it came to pass that when Annatoo's first virgin bloom had departed, leaving nothing but a lusty frame and a lustier soul, Samoa, the Navigator, had fallen desperately in love with her. And thinking the lady to his mind, being brave like himself, and doubtless well adapted to the vicissitudes of matrimony at sea, he meditated suicide—I would have said wedlock—and the twain became one. And sometime after in capacity of wife, Annatoo the dame accompanied in the brigantine Samoa her lord. Now, as Antony flew to the refuse embraces of Cæsar, so Samoa solaced himself in the arms of this discarded fair one. And the sequel was the same. For not harder the life Cleopatra led my fine frank friend, poor Mark, than Queen Annatoo did lead this captive of her bow and her spear. But all in good time.

They left their port, and crossing the Tropic and the Line, fell in with a cluster of islands, where the shells they sought were found in round numbers. And here—not at all strange to tell—besides the natives, they encountered a couple of Cholos, or half-breed Spaniards, from the Main, one half Spanish, the other half quartered between the wild Indian and the devil; a race that from Bolivia to Panama are notorious for their unscrupulous villainy.

Now, the half-breeds having long since deserted a ship at these islands, had risen to high authority among the natives. This hearing, the *Parki*'s captain was much gratified, he, poor ignorant, never before having fallen in with any of their treacherous race. And, no doubt, he imagined that their influence over the islanders would tend to his advantage. At all events, he made presents to the Cholos, who, in turn, provided him with additional divers from among the natives. Very kindly, also, they pointed out the best places for seeking the oysters. In a word, they were exceedingly friendly, often coming off to the brigantine and socially dining with the captain in his cabin, placing the salt between them and him.

All things went on very pleasantly until, one morning, the half-breeds prevailed upon the captain to go with them in his whale-boat to a shoal on the thither side of the island, some distance from the spot where lay the brigantine. They so managed it, moreover, that none but the Lahineese under Samoa, in whom the captain much confided, were left in custody of the *Parki*, the three white men going along to row, for there happened to be little or no wind for a sail.

Now, the fated brig lay anchored within a deep, smooth, circular lagoon, margined on all sides but one by the most beautiful groves. On that side was the outlet to the sea perhaps a cable's length or more from where the brigantine had been moved. An hour or two after the party were gone, and when the boat was completely out of sight, the natives in shoals were perceived coming off from the shore, some in canoes and some swimming. The former brought bread-fruit and bananas, ostentatiously piled up in their proas; the latter dragged after them long strings of cocoanuts, for all of which, on nearing the vessel, they clamorously demanded knives and hatchets in barter.

From their actions, suspecting some treachery, Samoa stood in the gangway and warned them off saying that no barter could take place until the captain's return. But presently one of the savages stealthily climbed up from the water, and nimbly springing from the bobstays to the bowsprit, darted a javelin full at the fore-mast, where it vibrated. The signal of blood! With terrible outcries, the rest, pulling forth their weapons, hitherto concealed in the canoes or under the floating cocoanuts, leaped into the low chains of the brigantine, sprang over the bulwarks, and with clubs and spears attacked the aghast crew with the utmost ferocity.

After one faint rally the Lahineese scrambled for the rigging, but to a man were overtaken and slain.

At the first alarm Annatoo, however, had escaped to the fore-top-gallant-yard, higher than which she could not climb, and whither the savages durst not venture. For though after their nuts these Polynesians will climb palm trees like squirrels; yet, at the first blush, they decline a ship's mast like Kennebec farmers.

Upon the first token of an onslaught, Samoa, having rushed towards the cabin scuttle for arms, was there fallen upon by two young savages. But after a desperate momentary fray, in which his arm was mangled, he made shift to spring below, instantly securing overhead the slide of the scuttle. In the cabin, while yet the uproar of butchery prevailed, he quietly bound up his arm; then laying on the transom the captain's three loaded muskets, undauntedly awaited an assault.

The object of the natives, it seems, was to wreck the brigantine upon the sharp coral beach of the lagoon. And with this intent, one of their number had plunged into the water and cut the cable, which was of hemp. But the tide ebbing, cast the *Parki*'s head seaward—towards the outlet, and the savages, perceiving this, clumsily boarded the fore-tack and hauled aft the sheet, thus setting after a fashion the fore-sail, previously loosed to dry.

Meanwhile a gray-headed old chief stood calmly at the tiller, endeavoring to steer the vessel shoreward. But not managing the helm aright, the brigantine, now gliding apace through the water, only made more way towards the outlet. Seeing which, the ringleaders, six or eight in number, ran to help the old graybeard at the helm. But it was a black hour for them. Of a sudden, while they were handling the tiller, three muskets were rapidly discharged upon them from the cabin skylight. Two of the savages dropped dead. The old steersman, clutching wildly at the helm, fell over it mortally wounded, and in a wild panic at seeing their leaders thus unaccountably slain, the rest of the natives leaped overboard and made for the shore.

Hearing the splashing Samoa flew on deck, and beholding the foresail set and the brigantine heading right out to sea, he cried out to Annatoo, still aloft, to descend to the topsail-yard and loose the canvas there. His command was obeyed. Annatoo deserved a gold medal for what she did that day. Hastening down the rigging after loosing the topsail, she strained away at the sheets, in which operation she was assisted by Samoa, who snatched an instant from the helm.

The foresail and fore-topsail were now tolerably well set, and as the craft drew seaward the breeze freshened. And well that it did, for, recovered from their alarm, the savages were now in hot pursuit, some in canoes and some swimming as before. But soon the main-topsail was given to the breeze, which still freshening came from over the quarter. And with this brave show of canvas, the *Parki* made gallantly for the outlet, and loud shouted Samoa as she shot by the reef and parted the long swells without. Against these the savages could not swim. And at that turn of the tide, paddling a canoe therein was almost equally difficult. But the fugitives were not yet safe. In full chase now came in sight the whale-boat manned by the Cholos, and four or five islanders. Whereat, making no doubt that all the whites who left the vessel that morning had been massacred through the treachery of the half-breeds, and that the capture of the brigantine had been premeditated, Samoa now saw no other resource than to point his craft dead away from the land.

On came the devils buckling to their oars. Meantime Annatoo was still busy aloft, loosing the smaller sails—t'gallants and royals, which she managed partially to set.

The strong breeze from astern now filling the ill-set sails, they bellied and rocked in the air like balloons, while from the novel strain upon it, every spar quivered and sprung. And thus, like a frightened gull fleeing from sea-hawks, the little *Parki* swooped along and bravely breasted the brine.

His shattered arm in a hempen sling, Samoa stood at the helm, the muskets reloaded and planted full before him on the binnacle. For a time so badly did the brigantine steer by reason of her ill-adjusted sails, made still more unmanageable by the strength of the breeze—that it was doubtful, after all, notwithstanding her start, whether the fugitives would not yet fall a prey to their hunters. The craft wildly yawed, and the boat drew nearer and nearer. Maddened by the sight, and perhaps thinking more of revenge for the past than of security for the future, Samoa, yielding the helm to Annatoo, rested his muskets on the bulwarks, and taking long, sure aim, discharged them, one by one at the advancing foe.

The three reports were answered by loud jeers from the savages, who brandished their spears and made gestures of derision, while with might and main the Cholos tugged at their oars.

The boat still gaining on the brigantine, the muskets were again reloaded. And as the next shot sped there was a pause, when like lightning the headmost Cholo bounded upwards from his seat, and oar in hand, fell into the sea. A fierce yell, and one of the natives springing into the water, caught the sinking body by its long hair, and the dead and the living were dragged into the boat. Taking heart from this fatal shot, Samoa fired yet again, but not with the like sure result, merely grazing the remaining half-breed, who, crouching behind his comrades, besought them to turn the boat round and make for the shore. Alarmed at the fate of his brother, and seemingly distrustful of the impartiality of Samoa's fire, the pusillanimous villain refused to expose a limb above the gunwale.

Fain now would the pursuers have made good their escape, but an accident forbade. In the careening of the boat, when the stricken Cholo sprung overboard, two of their oars had slid into the water, and together with that death-griped by the half-breed, were now floating off; occasionally lost to view, as they sunk in the trough of the sea. Two of the islanders swam to recover them, but frightened by the whirring of a shot over their heads, as they unavoidably struck out towards the *Parki*, they turned quickly about, just in time to see one of their comrades smite his body with his hand, as he received a bullet from Samoa.

Enough: darting past the ill-fated boat, they swam rapidly for land, followed by the rest, who plunged overboard, leaving in the boat the surviving Cholo—who could not swim—the wounded savage and the dead man.

"Load away now, and take thy revenge, my fine fellow," said Samoa to himself. But not yet. Seeing all at his mercy, and having none, he quickly laid his fore-topsail to the mast; "Hove to" the brigantine, and opened fire anew upon the boat, every swell of the sea heaving it nearer and nearer. Vain all efforts to escape. The wounded man paddled wildly with his hands; the dead one rolled from side to side; and the Cholo, seizing the solitary oar, in his frenzied heedlessness, spun the boat round and round; while all the time shot followed shot, Samoa firing as fast as Annatoo could load. At length both Cholo and savage fell dead upon their comrades, canting the boat over sideways, till well nigh awash, in which manner she drifted off.

Chapter XXIII

Sailing from the Island, They Pillage the Cabin

There was a small carronade on the forecastle, unshipped from its carriage and lashed down to ring-bolts on the deck. This Samoa now loaded, and with an ax knocking off the round knob upon the breech, rammed it home in the tube. When, running the cannon out at one of the ports, and studying well his aim, he let fly, sunk the boat, and buried his dead.

It was now late in the afternoon; and for the present bent upon avoiding land, and gaining the shoreless sea, never mind where, Samoa again forced round his craft before the wind, leaving the island astern. The decks were still cumbered with the bodies of the Lahineese, which, heel to point and crosswise, had, log-like, been piled up on the main-hatch. These, one by one, were committed to the sea; after which the decks were washed down.

At sunrise next morning, finding themselves out of sight of land, with little or no wind, they stopped their headway and lashed the tiller a-lee, the better to enable them to overhaul the brigantine, especially the recesses of the cabin. For there, were stores of goods adapted for barter among the islanders, also several bags of dollars.

Now, nothing can exceed the cupidity of the Polynesian, when, through partial commerce with the whites, his eyes are opened to his nakedness, and he perceives that in some things they are richer than himself.

The poor skipper's wardrobe was first explored; his chests of clothes being capsized, and their contents strewn about the cabin floor.

Then took place the costuming. Samoa and Annatoo trying on coats and pantaloons, shirts and drawers, and admiring themselves in the little mirror paneled in the bulk-head. Then were broken open boxes and bales; rolls of printed cotton were inspected, and vastly admired; insomuch, that the trumpery found in the captain's chests was disdainfully doffed; and donned were loose folds of calico, more congenial to their tastes.

As case after case was opened and overturned, slippery grew the cabin deck with torrents of glass beads; and heavy the necks of Samoa and Annatoo with goodly bunches thereof.

Among other things, came to light brass jewelry—Rag Fair gewgaws and baubles aplenty, more admired than all; Annatoo, bedecking herself like a tragedy queen: one blaze of brass. Much mourned the married dame, that thus arrayed there was none to admire but Samoa her husband; but he was all the while admiring himself and not her.

And here must needs be related, what has hitherto remained unsaid. Very often this husband and wife were no Darby and Joan. Their married life was one long campaign, whereof the truces were only by night. They billed and they cooed on their arms, rising fresh in the morning to battle, and often Samoa got more than a henpecking. To be short, Annatoo was a Tartar, a regular Calmuc, and Samoa—Heaven help him—her husband.

Yet awhile, joined together by a sense of common danger, and long engrossed in turning over their tinsel acquisitions without present thought of proprietorship, the pair refrained from all squabbles. But soon burst the storm. Having given every bale and every case a good shaking, Annatoo, making an estimate of the whole, very coolly proceeded to set apart for herself whatever she fancied. To this Samoa objected, to which objection Annatoo objected, and then they went at it.

The lady vowed that the things were no more Samoa's than hers; nay, not so much, and that whatever she wanted, that same would she have. And furthermore, by way of codicil, she declared that she was slave to nobody.

Now, Samoa, sad to tell, stood in no little awe of his bellicose spouse. What, though a hero in other respects; what, though he had slain his savages, and gallantly carried his craft from their clutches—Like the valiant captains Marlborough and Belisarius, he was a poltroon to his wife. And Annatoo was worse than either Sarah or Antonina.

However, like everything partaking of the nature of a scratch, most conjugal squabbles are quickly healed; for if they healed not, they would never break out anew, which is the beauty of the thing. So at length they made up, but the treaty stipulations of Annatoo told much against the interests of Samoa. Nevertheless, ostensibly, it was agreed upon that they should strictly go halves; the lady, however, laying special claim to certain valuables more particularly fancied. But as a set-off to this, she generously renounced all claims upon the spare-rigging; all claims upon the fore-mast and main-mast; and all claims upon the captain's arms and ammunition. Of the latter, by the way, Dame Antonina stood in no need. Her voice was a park of artillery; her talons a charge of bayonets.

Chapter XXIV

DEDICATED TO THE COLLEGE OF PHYSICIANS AND SURGEONS

BY THIS TIME SAMOA'S WOUNDED ARM WAS IN SUCH A STATE THAT AMPUTATION BECAME NECESsary. Among savages severe personal injuries are, for the most part, accounted but trifles. When a European would be taking to his couch in despair, the savage would disdain to recline.

More yet. In Polynesia every man is his own barber and surgeon, cutting off his beard or arm as occasion demands. No unusual thing for the warriors of Varvoo to saw off their own limbs, desperately wounded in battle. But owing to the clumsiness of the instrument employed—a flinty, serrated shell—the operation has been known to last several days. Nor will they suffer any friend to help them; maintaining that a matter so nearly concerning a warrior is far better attended to by himself. Hence it may be said that they amputate themselves at their leisure, and hang up their tools when tired. But though thus beholden to no one for aught connected with the practice of surgery, they never cut off their own heads that ever I heard; a species of amputation to which, metaphorically speaking, many would-be independent sort of people in civilized lands are addicted.

Samoa's operation was very summary. A fire was kindled in the little caboose, or cook-house, and so made as to produce much smoke. He then placed his arm upon one of the windlass bitts (a short upright timber, breast high), and seizing the blunt cook's ax would have struck the blow; but for some reason distrusting the precision of his aim, Annatoo was assigned to the task. Three strokes, and the limb, from just above the elbow, was no longer Samoa's, and he saw his own bones; which many a centenarian cannot say. The very clumsiness of the operation was safety to the subject. The weight and bluntness of the instrument both deadened the pain and lessened the hemorrhage. The wound was then scorched, and held over the smoke of the fire till all signs of blood vanished. From that day forward it healed, and troubled Samoa but little.

But shall the sequel be told? How that, superstitiously averse to burying in the sea the dead limb of a body yet living; since in that case Samoa held that he must very soon drown and follow it; and how, that equally dreading to keep the thing near him, he at last hung it aloft from the topmast-stay; where yet it was suspended, bandaged over and over in cerements. The hand that must have locked many others in friendly clasp, or smote a foe, was no food, thought Samoa, for fowls of the air nor fishes of the sea.

Now, which was Samoa? The dead arm swinging high as Haman? Or the living trunk below? Was the arm severed from the body, or the body from the arm? The residual part of Samoa was alive, and therefore we say it was he. But which of the writhing sections of a ten times severed worm is the worm proper?

For myself, I ever regarded Samoa as but a large fragment of a man, not a man complete. For was he not an entire limb out of pocket? And the action at Teneriffe over, great Nelson himself—physiologically speaking—was but three-quarters of a man. And the smoke of Waterloo blown by, what was Anglesea, but the like? After Saratoga, what Arnold? To say nothing of Mutius Scœvola minus a hand, General Knox a thumb, and Hannibal an eye; and that old Roman grenadier, Dentatus, nothing more than a bruised and battered trunk, a knotty sort of hemlock of a warrior, hard to hack and hew into chips, though much marred in symmetry by battle-ax blows. Ah! but these warriors, like anvils, will stand a deal of hard hammering. Especially in the old knight-errant times. For at the battle of Brevieux, in Flanders, my glorious old gossiping ancestor, Froissart, informs me that ten good knights, being suddenly unhorsed, fell stiff and powerless to the plain, fatally encumbered by their armor. Whereupon, the rascally burglarious peasants, their foes, fell to picking their visors; as burglars, locks; or oystermen, oysters; to get at their lives. But all to no purpose. And at last they were fain to ask aid of a blacksmith, and not till then were the inmates of the armor dispatched. Now, it was deemed very hard that the mysterious state-prisoner of France should be riveted in an iron mask, but these knight-errants did voluntarily imprison themselves in their own iron Bastiles; and thus helpless, were murdered therein. Days of chivalry these, when gallant chevaliers died chivalric deaths!

And this was the epic age over whose departure my late eloquent and prophetic friend and correspondent, Edmund Burke, so movingly mourned! Yes, they were glorious times. But no sensible man, given to quiet domestic delights, would exchange his warm fireside and muffins for a heroic bivouac, in a wild beechen wood, of a raw gusty morning in Normandy: every knight blowing his steel-gloved fingers, and vainly striving to cook his cold coffee in his helmet.

Chapter XXV

PERIL A PEACE-MAKER

A FEW DAYS PASSED; THE BRIGANTINE DRIFTING HITHER AND THITHER, AND NOTHING IN SIGHT but the sea, when forth again on its stillness rung Annatoo's domestic alarum. The truce was up. Most egregiously had the lady infringed it, appropriating to herself various objects previously disclaimed in favor of Samoa. Besides, forever on the prowl, she was perpetually going up and down; with untiring energy, exploring every nook and cranny; carrying off her spoils and diligently secreting them. Having little idea of feminine adaptations, she pilfered whatever came handy—iron hooks, dollars, bolts, hatchets, and stopping not at balls of marline and sheets of copper. All this poor Samoa would have borne with what patience he might, rather than again renew the war, were it not that the audacious dame charged him with peculations upon her own private store, though of any such thing he was innocent as the bowsprit.

This insulting impeachment got the better of the poor islander's philosophy. He keenly resented it. And the consequence was that seeing all domineering useless, Annatoo flew off at a tangent, declaring that for the future Samoa might stay by himself; she would have nothing more to do with him. Save when unavoidable in managing the brigantine, she would not even speak to him, that she wouldn't, the monster! She then boldly demanded the forecastle—in the brig's case by far the pleasantest end of the ship—for her own independent suite of apartments. As for hapless Belisarius, he might do what he pleased in his dark little den of a cabin.

Concerning the division of the spoils, the termagant succeeded in carrying the day; also, to her quarters, bale after bale of goods, together with numerous odds and ends, sundry and divers. Moreover, she laid in a fine stock of edibles, so as in all respects possible to live independent of her spouse.

Unlovely Annatoo! Unfortunate Samoa? Thus did the pair make a divorce of it; the lady going upon a separate maintenance—and Belisarius resuming his bachelor loneliness. In the captain's stateroom, all cold and comfortless, he slept; his lady whilome retiring to her forecastle boudoir, beguiling the hours in saying her pater-nosters, and tossing over and assorting her ill-gotten trinkets and finery; like Madame De Maintenon dedicating her last days and nights to continence and calicoes.

But think you this was the quiet end of their conjugal quarrels? Ah, no! No end to those feuds till one or the other gives up the ghost.

Now, exiled from the nuptial couch, Belisarius bore the hardship without a murmur. And hero that he was, who knows that he felt not like a soldier on a furlough? But as for Antonina, she could neither get along with Belisarius nor without him. She made advances. But of what sort? Why, breaking into the cabin and purloining sundry goods therefrom, in artful hopes of breeding a final reconciliation out of the temporary outburst that might follow.

Then followed a sad scene of altercation, interrupted at last by a sudden loud roaring of the sea. Rushing to the deck they beheld themselves sweeping head-foremost towards a shoal making out from a cluster of low islands, hitherto, by banks of clouds, shrouded from view.

The helm was instantly shifted, and the yards braced about. But for several hours, owing to the freshness of the breeze, the set of the currents, and the irregularity and extent of the shoal, it seemed doubtful whether they would escape a catastrophe. But Samoa's seamanship, united to Annatoo's industry, at last prevailed, and the brigantine was saved.

Of the land where they came so near being wrecked they knew nothing, and for that reason they at once steered away. For after the fatal events which had overtaken the *Parki* at the Pearl Shell Islands, so fearful were they of encountering any islanders, that from the first they had resolved to keep open sea, shunning every appearance of land; relying upon being eventually picked up by some passing sail.

Doubtless this resolution proved their salvation. For to the navigator in these seas, no risk so great as in approaching the isles, which mostly are so guarded by outpost reefs, and far out from their margins environed by perils, that the green flowery field within lies like a rose among thorns, and hard to be reached as the heart of proud maiden. Though once attained, all three—red rose, bright shore, and soft heart—are full of love, bloom, and all manner of delights. The Pearl Shell Islands excepted.

Besides, in those generally tranquil waters, Samoa's little craft, though hundreds of miles from land, was very readily managed by himself and Annatoo. So small was the *Parki* that one hand could brace the main-yard, and a very easy thing it was even to hoist the small top-sails; for after their first clumsy attempt to perform that operation by hand, they invariably led the halyards to the windlass, and so managed it with the utmost facility.

Chapter XXVI

Containing a Pennyweight of Philosophy

STILL MANY DAYS PASSED AND THE *PARKI* YET FLOATED. THE LITTLE FLYING-FISH GOT USED TO HER familiar, loitering hull; and like swallows building their nests in quiet old trees, they spawned in the great green barnacles that clung to her sides.

The calmer the sea, the more the barnacles grow. In the tropical Pacific but a few weeks suffice thus to encase your craft in shell armor. Vast bunches adhere to the very cutwater, and if not stricken off, much impede the ship's sailing. And at intervals this clearing away of barnacles was one of Annatoo's occupations. For be it known, that, like most termagants, the dame was tidy at times, though capriciously; loving cleanliness by fits and starts. Wherefore, these barnacles oftentimes troubled her; and with a long pole she would go about brushing them aside. It beguiled the weary hours, if nothing more, and then she would return to her beads and her trinkets; telling them all over again; murmuring forth her devotions, and marking whether Samoa had been pilfering from her store.

Now, the escape from the shoal did much once again to heal the differences of the good lady and her spouse. And keeping house, as they did, all alone by themselves in that lonely craft, a marvel it is that they should ever have quarreled. And then to divorce, and yet dwell in the same tenement, was only aggravating the evil. So Belisarius and Antonina again came together. But now, grown wise by experience, they neither loved over keenly nor hated, but took things as they were; found themselves joined, without hope of a sundering, and did what they could to make a match of the mate. Annatoo concluded that Samoa was not wholly to be enslaved, and Samoa thought best to wink at Annatoo's foibles, and let her purloin when she pleased.

But as in many cases, all this philosophy about wedlock is not proof against the perpetual contact of the parties concerned; and as it is far better to revive the old days of courtship, when men's mouths are honey-combs; and, to make them still sweeter, the ladies the bees which there store their sweets; when fathomless raptures glimmer far down in the lover's fond eye; and best of all, when visits are alternated by absence; so, like my dignified lord duke and his duchess, Samoa and Annatoo, man and wife, dwelling in the same house, still kept up their separate quarters. Marlborough visiting Sarah; and Sarah, Marlborough, whenever the humor suggested.

Chapter XXVII

In Which the Past History of the Parki Is Concluded

Still days, days, days sped by; and steering now this way, now that, to avoid the green treacherous shores, which frequently rose into view, the *Parki* went to and fro in the sea; till at last it seemed hard to tell in what watery world she floated. Well knowing the risks they ran, Samoa desponded. But blessed be ignorance! For in the days of his despondency, the lively old lass his wife bade him be of stout heart, cheer up, and steer away manfully for the setting sun; following which, they must inevitably arrive at her own dear native island, where all their cares would be over. So squaring their yards, away they glided; far sloping down the liquid sphere.

Upon the afternoon of the day we caught sight of them in our boat, they had sighted a cluster of low islands, which put them in no small panic, because of their resemblance to those where the massacre had taken place. Whereas, they must have been full five hundred leagues from that fearful vicinity. However, they altered their course to avoid it; and a little before sunset, dropping the islands astern, resumed their previous track. But very soon after they espied our little sea-goat bounding over the billows from afar.

This they took for a canoe giving chase to them. It renewed and augmented their alarm.

And when at last they perceived that the strange object was a boat, their fears, instead of being allayed, only so much the more increased. For their wild superstitions led them to conclude that a white man's craft coming upon them so suddenly, upon the open sea, and by night, could be naught but a phantom. Furthermore, marking two of us in the *Chamois,* they fancied us the ghosts of the Cholos. A conceit which effectually damped Samoa's courage, like my Viking's, only proof against things tangible. So seeing us bent upon boarding the brigantine; after a hurried overturning of their chattels, with a view of carrying the most valuable aloft for safe keeping, they secreted what they could; and together made for the fore-top, the man with a musket, the woman with a bag of beads. Their endeavoring to secure these treasures against ghostly appropriation originated in no real fear that otherwise they would be stolen; it was simply incidental to the vacant panic into which they were thrown. No reproach this, to Belisarius' heart of game; for the most intrepid Fiji warrior, he who has slain his hecatombs, will not go ten yards in the dark alone for fear of ghosts.

Their purpose was to remain in the top until daylight; by which time they counted upon the withdrawal of their visitants; who, sure enough, at last sprang on board, thus verifying their worst apprehensions.

They watched us long and earnestly. But curious to tell, in that very strait of theirs, perched together in that airy top, their domestic differences again broke forth; most probably from their being suddenly forced into such very close contact.

However that might be, taking advantage of our descent into the cabin, Samoa, in desperation, fled from his wife, and one-armed as he was, sailor-like, shifted himself over by the fore and aft-stays to the main-top, his musket being slung to his back. And thus divided, though but a few yards intervened, the pair were as much asunder as if at the opposite Poles.

During the live-long night they were both in great perplexity as to the extraordinary goblins on board. Such inquisitive, meddlesome spirits, had never before been encountered. So cool and systematic; sagaciously stopping the vessel's headway the better to rummage; the very plan they themselves had adopted. But what most surprised them was our striking a light, a thing of which no true ghost would be guilty. Then, our eating and drinking on the quarter-deck including the deliberate investment of Vienna; and many other actions equally strange, almost led Samoa to fancy that we were no shades after all, but a couple of men from the moon.

Yet they had dimly caught sight of the frocks and trousers we wore, similar to those which the captain of the *Parki* had bestowed upon the two Cholos, and in which those villains had been killed. This, with the presence of the whale-boat, united to chase away the conceit of our lunar origin. But these considerations renewed their first superstitious impressions of our being the ghosts of the murderous half-breeds.

Nevertheless, while during the latter part of the night we were reclining beneath him, munching our biscuit, Samoa eyeing us intently, was half a mind to open fire upon us by way of testing our corporeality. But most luckily, he concluded to defer so doing till sunlight; if by that time we should not have evaporated.

For dame Annatoo, almost from our first boarding the brigantine, something in our manner had bred in her a lurking doubt as to the genuineness of our atmospheric organization; and abandoned to her speculations when Samoa fled from her side, her incredulity waxed stronger and stronger. Whence we came she knew not; enough that we seemed bent upon pillaging her own precious purloinings. Alas! thought she, my buttons, my nails, my tappa, my dollars, my beads, and my boxes!

Wrought up to desperation by these dismal forebodings, she at length shook the ropes leading from her own perch to Samoa's, adopting this method of arousing his attention to the heinousness of what was in all probability going on in the cabin, a prelude most probably to the invasion of her own end of the vessel. Had she dared raise her voice, no doubt she would have suggested the expediency of shooting us so soon as we emerged from the cabin. But failing to shake Samoa into an understanding of her views on the subject, her malice proved futile.

When her worst fears were confirmed, however, and we actually descended into the forecastle, there ensued such a reckless shaking of the ropes that Samoa was fain to hold on hard for fear of being tossed out of the rigging. And it was this violent rocking that caused the loud creaking of the yards, so often heard by us while below in Annatoo's apartment.

And the fore-top being just over the open forecastle scuttle, the dame could look right down upon us; hence our proceedings were plainly revealed by the lights that we carried. Upon our breaking open her strong box, her indignation almost completely overmastered her fears. Unhooking a topblock, down it came into the forecastle, charitably commissioned with the demolition of Jarl's cocoanut, then more exposed to view of an aerial observer than my own. But as it turned out, no harm was done to our porcelain.

At last, morning dawned; when ensued Jarl's discovery as the occupant of the main-top; which event, with what followed, has been duly recounted.

And such, in substance, was the first, second, third, and fourth acts of the *Parki* drama. The fifth and last, including several scenes, now follows.

Chapter XXVIII

Suspicions Laid, and Something about the Calmuc

Though abounding in details full of the savor of reality, Samoa's narrative did not at first appear altogether satisfactory. Not that it was so strange, for stranger recitals I had heard. But one reason, perhaps, was that I had anticipated a narrative quite different; something agreeing with my previous surmises.

Not a little puzzling, also, was his account of having seen islands the day preceding; though, upon reflection, that might have been the case, and yet, from his immediately altering the *Parki*'s course, the *Chamois* unknowingly might have sailed by their vicinity. Still, those islands could form no part of the chain we were seeking. They must have been some region hitherto undiscovered.

But seems it likely, thought I, that one who, according to his own account, has conducted himself so heroically in rescuing the brigantine, should be the victim of such childish terror at the mere glimpse of a couple of sailors in an open boat, so well supplied, too, with arms as he was, to resist their capturing his craft, if such proved their intention? On the contrary, would it not have been more natural, in his dreary situation, to have hailed our approach with the utmost delight? But then, again, we were taken for phantoms, not flesh and blood. Upon the whole, I regarded the narrator of these things somewhat distrustfully. But he met my gaze like a man. While Annatoo, standing by, looked so expressively the Amazonian character imputed to her, that my doubts began to waver. And recalling all the little incidents of their story, so hard to be conjured up on the spur of a presumed necessity to lie; nay, so hard to be conjured up at all; my suspicions at last gave way. And I could no longer harbor any misgivings.

For, to be downright, what object could Samoa have in fabricating such a narrative of horrors—those of the massacre, I mean—unless to conceal some tragedy still more atrocious, in which he himself had been criminally concerned? A supposition which, for obvious reasons, seemed out of the question. True, instances were known to me of half-civilized beings, like Samoa, forming part of the crews of ships in these seas, rising suddenly upon their white shipmates and murdering them, for the sake of wrecking the ship on the shore of some island nearby, and plundering her hull when stranded.

But had this been purposed with regard to the *Parki*, where the rest of the mutineers? There was no end to my conjectures; the more I indulged in them, the more they multiplied. So, unwilling to torment myself when nothing could be learned but what Samoa related, and stuck to like a hero, I gave over conjecturing at all, striving hard to repose full faith in the islander.

Jarl, however, was skeptical to the last; and never could be brought completely to credit the tale. He stoutly maintained that the hobgoblins must have had something or other to do with the *Parki*.

My own curiosity satisfied with respect to the brigantine, Samoa himself turned inquisitor. He desired to know who we were, and whence we came in our marvelous boat. But on these heads I thought best to withhold from him the truth; among other things, fancying that if disclosed, it would lessen his deference for us, as men superior to himself. I therefore spoke vaguely of our adventures, and assumed the decided air of a master; which I perceived was not lost upon the rude islander. As for Jarl and what he might reveal, I embraced the first opportunity to impress upon him the importance of never divulging our flight from the *Arcturion*; nor in any way to commit himself on that head; injunctions which he faithfully promised to observe.

If not wholly displeased with the fine form of Samoa, despite his savage lineaments and mutilated member, I was much less conciliated by the person of Annatoo; who, being sinewy of limb, and neither young, comely, nor amiable, was exceedingly distasteful to my eyes. Besides, she was a tigress. Yet how avoid admiring those Penthesilian qualities which so signally had aided Samoa, in wresting the *Parki* from its treacherous captors? Nevertheless, it was indispensable that she should at once be brought under prudent subjection; and made to know, once for all, that though conjugally a rebel, she must be nautically submissive. For to keep the sea with a Calmuc on board, seemed next to impossible. In most military marines, they are prohibited by law; no officer may take his Pandora and her bandbox off soundings.

By the way, this self-same appellative, Pandora, has been bestowed upon vessels. There was a British ship by that name, dispatched in quest of the mutineers of the *Bounty*. But any old tar might have prophesied her fate. Bound home, she was wrecked on a reef off New South Wales. Pandora indeed! A pretty name for a ship; fairly smiting Fate in the face. But in this matter of christening ships of war, Christian nations are but too apt to be dare-devils. Witness the following: British names all—The *Conqueror*, the *Defiance*, the *Revenge*, the *Spitfire*, the *Dreadnaught*, the *Thunderer*, and the *Tremendous*; not omitting the *Etna*, which, in the Roads of Corfu, was struck by lightning, coming nigh being consumed by fire from above. But almost potent as Moses' rod, Franklin's proved her salvation.

With the above catalogue, compare we the Frenchman's; quite characteristic of the aspirations of Monsieur—The *Destiny*, the *Glorious*, the *Magnanimous*, the *Magnificent*, the *Triumphant*, the *Indomitable*, the *Intrepid*, the *Mont Blanc*. Lastly the Dons; who have ransacked the theology of the religion of peace for fine names for their fighting ships, stopping not at designating one of their three-deckers, *The Most Holy Trinity*. But though, at Trafalgar, the *Santissima Trinidada* thundered like Sinai, her thunders were silenced by the victorious cannonade of the *Victory*.

And without being blown into splinters by artillery, how many of these *Redoubtables* and *Invincibles* have succumbed to the waves, and like braggarts gone down before hurricanes, their bravadoes broad on their bows?

Much better the American names (barring *Scorpions*, *Hornets*, and *Wasps*); *Ohio*, *Virginia*, *Carolina*, *Vermont*. And if ever these Yankees fight great sea engagements—which Heaven forefend!—how glorious, poetically speaking, to range up the whole federated fleet, and pour forth a broadside from Florida to Maine! Ay, ay, very glorious indeed! Yet in that proud crowing of cannon, how shall the shade of peace-loving Penn be astounded, to see the mightiest murderer of them all, the great *Pennsylvania*, a very namesake of his. Truly, the *Pennsylvania*'s guns should be the wooden ones, called by men-of-war's-men, Quakers.

But all this is an episode, made up of digressions. Time to tack ship and return.

Now, in its proper place, I omitted to mention that shortly after descending from the rigging, and while Samoa was rehearsing his adventures, dame Annatoo had stolen below into the forecastle, intent upon her chattels. And finding them all in mighty disarray, she returned to the deck prodigiously excited, and glancing angrily towards Jarl and me, showered a whole torrent of objurgations into both ears of Samoa.

This contempt of my presence surprised me at first; but perhaps women are less apt to be impressed by a pretentious demeanor than men.

Now, to use a fighting phrase, there is nothing like boarding an enemy in the smoke. And, therefore, upon this first token of Annatoo's termagant qualities, I gave her to understand—craving her pardon—that neither the vessel nor aught therein was hers; but that every thing belonged to the "owners" in Lahina. I added that, at all hazards, a stop must be put to her pilferings. Rude language for feminine ears; but how to be avoided? Here was an infatuated woman, who, according to Samoa's account, had been repeatedly detected in the act of essaying to draw out the screw-bolts which held together the planks. Tell me: was she not worse than the Loadstone Rock, sailing by which a stout ship fell to pieces?

During this scene Samoa said little. Perhaps he was secretly pleased that his matrimonial authority was reinforced by myself and my Viking, whose views of the proper position of wives at sea so fully corresponded with his own; however difficult to practice, those purely theoretical ideas of his had hitherto proved.

Once more turning to Annatoo, now looking any thing but amiable, I observed that all her clamors would be useless; and that if it came to the worst, the *Parki* had a hull that would hold her.

In the end she went off in a fit of the sulks; sitting down on the windlass and glaring; her arms akimbo, and swaying from side to side; while ever and anon she gave utterance to a dismal chant. It sounded like an invocation to the Cholos to rise and dispatch us.

Chapter XXIX

What They Lighted upon in Further Searching the Craft, and the Resolution They Came To

Descending into the cabin with Samoa, I bade him hunt up the brigantine's log, the captain's writing-desk, and nautical instruments; in a word, aught that could throw light on the previous history of the craft, or aid in navigating her homeward.

But nearly everything of the kind had disappeared: log, quadrant, and ship's papers. Nothing was left but the sextant-case, which Jarl and I had lighted upon in the state-room.

Upon this, vague though they were, my suspicions returned; and I closely questioned the islander concerning the disappearance of these important articles. In reply, he gave me to understand that the nautical instruments had been clandestinely carried down into the forecastle by Annatoo; and by that indefatigable and inquisitive dame they had been summarily taken apart for scientific inspection. It was impossible to restore them, for many of the fixtures were lost, including the colored glasses, sights, and little mirrors; and many parts still recoverable were so battered and broken as to be entirely useless. For several days afterwards, we now and then came across bits of the quadrant or sextant, but it was only to mourn over their fate.

However, though sextant and quadrant were both unattainable, I did not so quickly renounce all hope of discovering a chronometer, which, if in good order, though at present not ticking, might still be made in some degree serviceable. But no such instrument was to be seen. No: nor to be heard of; Samoa himself professing utter ignorance.

Annatoo I threatened and coaxed; describing the chronometer—a live, round creature like a toad, that made a strange noise, which I imitated; but she knew nothing about it. Whether she had lighted upon it unknown to Samoa and dissected it as usual, there was now no way to determine. Indeed, upon this one point, she maintained an air of such inflexible stupidity, that if she were really fibbing, her dead-wall countenance superseded the necessity for verbal deceit.

It may be, however, that in this particular she was wronged; for, as with many small vessels, the *Parki* might never have possessed the instrument in question. All thought, therefore, of feeling our way, as we should penetrate farther and farther into the watery wilderness, was necessarily abandoned.

The log book had also formed a portion of Annatoo's pilferings. It seems she had taken it into her studio to ponder over. But after amusing herself by again and again counting over the leaves, and wondering how so many distinct surfaces could be compacted together in so small a compass, she had very suddenly conceived an aversion to literature, and dropped the book overboard as worthless. Doubtless, it met the fate of many other ponderous tomes; sinking quickly and profoundly. What Camden or Stowe hereafter will dive for it?

One evening Samoa brought me a quarto half-sheet of yellowish ribbed paper, much soiled and tarry, which he had discovered in a dark hole of the forecastle. It had plainly formed part of the lost log; but all the writing thereon, at present decipherable, conveyed no information upon the subject then nearest my heart.

But one could not but be struck by a tragical occurrence, which the page very briefly recounted, as well as by a noteworthy pictorial illustration of the event in the margin of the text. Save the cut, there was no further allusion to the matter than the following:—"This day being calm, Tooboi, one of the Lahina men, went overboard for a bath, and was eaten up by a shark. Immediately sent forward for his bag."

Now, this last sentence was susceptible of two meanings. It is truth that immediately upon the decease of a friendless sailor at sea, his shipmates oftentimes seize upon his effects and divide them, though the dead man's clothes are seldom worn till a subsequent voyage. This proceeding seems heartless. But sailors reason thus: Better we than the captain. For by law, either scribbled or unscribbled, the effects of a mariner, dying on shipboard, should be held in trust by that officer. But as sailors are mostly foundlings and castaways, and carry all their kith and kin in their arms and their legs, there hardly ever appears any heir-at-law to claim their estate; seldom worth inheriting like Esterhazy's. Wherefore, the withdrawal of a dead man's "kit" from the forecastle to the cabin is often held tantamount to its virtual appropriation by the captain. At any rate, in small ships on long voyages such things have been done.

Thus much being said, then, the sentence above quoted from the *Parki*'s log, may be deemed somewhat ambiguous. At the time it struck me as singular; for the poor diver's grass bag could not have contained much of anything valuable, unless, peradventure, he had concealed therein some Cleopatra pearls, feloniously abstracted from the shells brought up from the sea.

Aside of the paragraph, copied above, was a pen-and-ink sketch of the casualty, most cruelly executed; the poor fellow's legs being represented half-way in the process of deglutition; his arms firmly grasping the monster's teeth, as if heroically bent upon making as tough a morsel of himself as possible.

But no doubt the honest captain sketched this cenotaph to the departed in all sincerity of heart; perhaps, during the melancholy leisure which followed the catastrophe. Half obliterated were several stains upon the page, seemingly lingering traces of a salt tear or two.

From this unwonted embellishment of the text, I was led to infer that the designer, at one time or other, must have been engaged in the vocation of whaling. For in India ink the logs of certain whalemen are decorated by somewhat similar illustrations.

When whales are seen, but not captured, the fact is denoted by an outline figure representing the creature's flukes, the broad, curving lobes of his tail. But in those cases where the monster is both chased and killed, this outline is filled up jet black; one for every whale slain; presenting striking objects in turning over the log, and so facilitating reference. Hence, it is quite imposing to behold all in a row, three or four, sometime five or six of these drawings, showing that so many monsters that day jetted their last spout. And the chief mate, whose duty it is to keep the ship's record, generally prides himself upon the beauty and flushy likeness to life of his flukes; though, sooth to say, many of these artists are no Landseers.

After vainly searching the cabin for those articles we most needed, we proceeded to explore the hold, into which as yet we had not penetrated. Here, we found a considerable quantity of pearl shells, cocoanuts, an abundance of fresh water in casks, spare sails and rigging, and some fifty barrels or more of salt beef and biscuit. Unromantic as these last mentioned objects were, I lingered over them long, and in a reverie. Branded upon each barrel head was the name of a place in America, with which I was very familiar. It is from America chiefly that ships' stores are originally procured for the few vessels sailing out of the Hawaiian Islands.

Having now acquainted myself with all things respecting the *Parki,* which could in any way be learned, I repaired to the quarter-deck, and summoning round me Samoa, Annatoo, and Jarl, gravely addressed them.

I said that nothing would give me greater satisfaction than forthwith to return to the scene of the massacre, and chastise its surviving authors. But as there were only four of us in all, and the place of those islands was wholly unknown to me; and even if known, would be altogether out of our reach, since we possessed no instruments of navigation; it was quite plain that all thought of returning thither was entirely useless. The last-mentioned reason, also, prevented our voyaging to the Hawaiian group, where the vessel belonged; though that would have been the most advisable step, resulting, as it would, if successful, in restoring the ill-fated craft to her owners.

But all things considered, it seemed best, I added, cautiously to hold on our way to the westward. It was our easiest course, for we would ever have the wind from astern; and though we could not so much as hope to arrive at any one spot previously designated, there was still a positive certainty, if we floated long enough, of falling in with islands whereat to refresh ourselves; and whence, if we thought fit, we might afterwards embark for more agreeable climes. I then reminded them of the fact that so long as we kept the sea there was always some prospect of encountering a friendly sail; in which event our solicitude would be over.

All this I said in the mild, firm tone of a superior, being anxious at once to assume the unquestioned supremacy. For otherwise Jarl and I might better quit the vessel forthwith than remain on board, subject to the outlandish caprices of Annatoo, who, through Samoa, would then have the sway. But I was sure of my Viking; and if Samoa proved docile, had no fear of his dame.

And, therefore, during my address I steadfastly eyed him; thereby learning enough to persuade me that though he deferred to me at present, he was, notwithstanding, a man who, without precisely meditating mischief, could upon occasion act an ugly part. But of his courage and savage honor, such as it was, I had little doubt. Then, wild buffalo that he was, tamed down in the yoke matrimonial, I could not but fancy that, if upon no other account, our society must please him, as rendering less afflictive the tyranny of his spouse.

For a hen-pecked husband, by the way, Samoa was a most terrible fellow to behold. And though, after all, I liked him, it was as you fancy a fiery steed with mane disheveled, as young Alexander fancied Bucephalus, which wild horse, when he patted, he preferred holding by the bridle. But more of Samoa anon.

Our course determined, and the command of the vessel tacitly yielded up to myself, the next thing done was to put everything in order. The tattered sails were replaced by others, dragged up from the sail-room below; in several places, new running-rigging was rove, blocks restrapped, and the slackened stays and shrouds set taut. For all of which we were mostly indebted to my Viking's unwearied and skillful marlin-spike, which he swayed like a scepter.

The little *Parki's* toilette being thus thoroughly made for the first time since the massacre, we gave her new raiment to the breeze, and daintily squaring her yards, she gracefully glided away; honest old Jarl at the helm watchfully guiding her path, like some devoted old foster-father.

As I stood by his side like a captain, or walked up and down on the quarter-deck, I felt no little importance upon thus assuming, for the first time in my life, the command of a vessel at sea. The novel circumstances of the case only augmented this feeling; the wild and remote seas where we were; the character of my crew, and the consideration that, to all purposes, I was owner as well as commander of the craft I sailed.

Chapter XXX

HINTS FOR A FULL LENGTH OF SAMOA

MY ORIGINAL INTENTION TO TOUCH AT THE KINGSMILL CHAIN, OR THE COUNTRIES ADJACENT, was greatly strengthened by thus encountering Samoa; and the more I had to do with my Belisarius the more I was pleased with him. Nor could I avoid congratulating myself upon having fallen in with a hero, who, in various ways, could not fail of proving exceedingly useful.

Like any man of mark, Samoa best speaks for himself; but we may as well convey some idea of his person. Though manly enough, nay, an obelisk in stature, the savage was far from being sentimentally prepossessing. Be not alarmed; but he wore his knife in the lobe of his dexter ear, which, by constant elongation, almost drooped upon his shoulder. A mode of sheathing it exceedingly handy, and far less brigandish than the Highlander's dagger concealed in his leggings.

But it was the mother of Samoa, who, at a still earlier day, had punctured him through and through in still another direction. The middle cartilage of his nose was slightly pendent, peaked, and Gothic, and perforated with a hole; in which, like a Newfoundland dog carrying a cane, Samoa sported a trinket—a well polished nail.

In other respects he was equally a coxcomb. In his style of tattooing, for instance, which seemed rather incomplete; his marks embracing but a vertical half of his person, from crown to sole, the other side being free from the slightest stain. Thus clapped together, as it were, he looked like a union of the unmatched moieties of two distinct beings; and your fancy was lost in conjecturing, where roamed the absent ones. When he turned round upon you suddenly, you thought you saw someone else, not him whom you had been regarding before.

But there was one feature in Samoa beyond the reach of the innovations of art—his eye, which in civilized man or savage ever shines in the head, just as it shone at birth. Truly, our eyes are miraculous things. But alas, that in so many instances these divine organs should be mere lenses inserted into the socket, as glasses in spectacle rims.

But my islander had a soul in his eye, looking out upon you there, like somebody in him. What an eye, to be sure! At times, brilliantly changeful as opal; in anger, glowing like steel at white heat.

Belisarius, be it remembered, had but very recently lost an arm. But you would have thought he had been born without it; so Lord Nelson-like and cavalierly did he sport the honorable stump.

But no more of Samoa; only this: that his name had been given him by a sea-captain, to whom it had been suggested by the native designation of the islands to which he belonged: the Saviian or Samoan group, otherwise known as the Navigator Islands. The island of Upolua, one of that cluster, claiming the special honor of his birth, as Corsica does Napoleon's; we shall occasionally hereafter speak of Samoa as the Upoluan, by which title he most loved to be called.

It is ever ungallant to pass over a lady. But what shall be said of Annatoo? As I live, I can make no pleasing portrait of the dame; for as in most ugly subjects, flattering would but make the matter worse. Furthermore, unalleviated ugliness should ever go unpainted, as something unnecessary to duplicate. But the only ugliness is that of the heart, seen through the face. And though beauty be obvious, the only loveliness is invisible.

Chapter XXXI

ROVINGS ALOW AND ALOFT

EVERYONE KNOWS WHAT A FASCINATION THERE IS IN WANDERING UP AND DOWN IN A DESERTED old tenement in some warm, dreamy country; where the vacant halls seem echoing of silence, and the doors creak open like the footsteps of strangers; and into every window the old garden-trees thrust their dark boughs, like the arms of night burglars; and ever and anon the nails start from the wainscot; while behind it the mice rattle like dice. Up and down in such old specter houses one loves to wander, and so much the more if the place be haunted by some marvelous story.

And during the drowsy stillness of the tropical sea-day, very much such a fancy had I, for prying about our little brigantine, whose tragic hull was haunted by the memory of the massacre, of which it still bore innumerable traces.

And so far as the indulgence of quiet strolling and reverie was concerned, it was well nigh the same as if I were all by myself. For Samoa, for a time, was rather reserved, being occupied with thoughts of his own, and Annatoo seldom troubled me with her presence. She was taken up with her calicoes and jewelry, which I had permitted her to retain, to keep her in good humor if possible. As for my royal old Viking, he was one of those individuals who seldom speak unless personally addressed.

Besides, all that by day was necessary to navigating the *Parki* was, that somebody should stand at the helm; the craft being so small, and the grating whereon the steerman stood so elevated, that he commanded a view far beyond the bowsprit; thus keeping Argus eyes on the sea as he steered us along. In all other respects, we left the brigantine to the guardianship of the gentle winds.

My own turn at the helm—for though commander I felt constrained to do duty with the rest—came but once in the twenty-four hours. And not only did Jarl and Samoa officiate as helmsmen, but also Dame Annatoo, who had become quite expert at the business, though Jarl always maintained that there was a slight drawback upon her usefulness in this vocation. Too much taken up by her lovely image, partially reflected in the glass of the binnacle before her, Annatoo now and then neglected her duty, and led us some devious dances. Nor was she, I ween, the first woman that ever led men into zigzags.

For the reasons above-stated, I had many spare hours to myself. At times I mounted aloft, and lounging in the slings of the topsail yard—one of the many snug nooks in a ship's rigging—I gazed broad off upon the blue boundless sea, and wondered what they were doing in that unknown land, towards which we were fated to be borne. Or feeling less meditative, I roved about hither and thither; slipping over, by the stays, from one mast to the other; climbing up to the truck, or lounging out to the ends of the yards; exploring wherever there was a foothold. It was like climbing about in some mighty old oak and resting in the crotches.

To a sailor a ship's ropes are a study. And to me every rope-yarn of the *Parki* was invested with interest. The outlandish fashion of her shrouds, the collars of her stays, the stirrups, seizings, Flemish-horses, gaskets—all the wilderness of her riggings—bore unequivocal traces of her origin.

But perhaps my pleasantest hours were those which I spent, stretched out on a pile of old sails, in the fore-top, lazily dozing to the craft's light roll.

Frequently I descended to the cabin, for the fiftieth time exploring the lockers and state-rooms for some new object of curiosity. And often, with a glimmering light, I went into the midnight hold, as into old vaults and catacombs; and creeping between damp ranges of casks, penetrated into its farthest recesses.

Sometimes in these underground burrowings I lighted upon sundry out-of-the-way hiding places of Annatoo's, where were snugly secreted divers articles, with which she had been smitten. In truth, no small portion of the hull seemed a mine of stolen goods, stolen out of its own bowels. I found a jaunty shore-cap of the captain's hidden away in the hollow heart of a coil of rigging, covered over in a manner most touchingly natural, with a heap of old ropes; and nearby, in a breaker, discovered several entire pieces of calico, heroically tied together with cords almost strong enough to sustain the mainmast.

Near the stray light which, when the hatch was removed, gleamed down into this part of the hold, was a huge ground-tier butt, headless as Charles the First. And herein was a mat nicely spread for repose; a discovery which accounted for what had often proved an enigma. Not seldom Annatoo had been among the missing; and though, from stem to stern, loudly invoked to come forth and relieve the poignant distress of her anxious friends, the dame remained, *perdue,* silent and invisible as a spirit. But in her own good time, she would mysteriously emerge, or be suddenly espied lounging quietly in the forecastle, as if she had been there from all eternity.

Useless to inquire, "Where hast thou been, sweet Annatoo?" For no sweet rejoinder would she give.

But now the problem was solved. Here, in this silent cask in the hold, Annatoo was wont to coil herself away like a garter-snake under a stone.

Whether she thus stood sentry over her goods secreted round about; whether she here performed penance like a nun in her cell; or was moved to this unaccountable freak by the powers of the air, no one could tell. Can you?

Verily, her ways were as the ways of the inscrutable penguins in building their inscrutable nests, which baffle all science, and make a fool of a sage.

Marvelous Annatoo! who shall expound thee!

Chapter XXXII

Xiphius Platypterus

About this time the loneliness of our voyage was relieved by an event worth relating.

Ever since leaving the Pearl Shell Islands the *Parki* had been followed by shoals of small fish, pleasantly enlivening the sea, and socially swimming by her side. But in vain did Jarl and I search among their ranks for the little steel-blue Pilot fish, so long outriders of the *Chamois.* But perhaps since the *Chamois* was now high and dry on the *Parki*'s deck, our bright little avant-couriers were lurking out of sight, far down in the brine, racing along close to the keel.

But it is not with the Pilot fish that we now have to do.

One morning our attention was attracted to a mighty commotion in the water. The shoals of fish were darting hither and thither, and leaping into the air in the utmost of fright. Samoa declared that their deadly foe, the sword-fish, must be after them.

And here let me say that since of all the bullies, and braggarts, and bravoes, and freebooters, and Hectors, and fish-at-arms, and knight-errants, and moss-troopers, and assassins, and foot-pads, and gallant soldiers, and immortal heroes that swim the seas, the Indian sword-fish is by far the most remarkable. I propose to dedicate this chapter to a special description of the warrior. In doing which, I but follow the example of all chroniclers and historians, my Peloponnesian friend, Thucydides and others, who are ever mindful of devoting much space to accounts of eminent destroyers; for the purpose, no doubt, of holding them up as examples to the world.

Now, the fish here treated of is a very different creature from the sword-fish frequenting the Northern Atlantic, being much larger every way, and a more dashing varlet to boot. Furthermore, he is denominated the Indian sword-fish in contradistinction from his namesake above-mentioned. But by seamen in the Pacific he is more commonly known as the Bill fish; while for those who love science and hard names, be it known, that among the erudite naturalists he goeth by the outlandish appellation of *"Xiphius Platypterus."*

But I waive for my hero all these his cognomens, and substitute a much better one of my own: namely, the Chevalier. And a Chevalier he is, by good right and title. A true gentleman of Black Prince Edward's bright day, when all gentlemen were known by their swords; whereas, in times present, the sword-fish excepted, they are mostly known by their high polished boots and rattans.

A right valiant and jaunty Chevalier is our hero; going about with his long Toledo perpetually drawn. Rely upon it, he will fight you to the hilt, for his bony blade has never a scabbard. He himself sprang from it at birth; yea, at the very moment he leaped into the Battle of Life, as we mortals ourselves spring all naked and scabbardless into the world. Yet, rather, are we scabbards to our soul; and the drawn soul of genius is more glittering than the drawn scimitar of Saladin. But how many let their steel sleep till it eat up the scabbard itself, and both corrode to rust-chips? Saw you ever the hillocks of old Spanish anchors, and anchor-stocks of ancient galleons, at the bottom of Callao Bay? The world is full of old Tower armories, and dilapidated Venetian arsenals, and rusty old rapiers. But true warriors polish their good blades by the bright beams of the morning, and gird them on to their brave sirloins and watch for rust spots as for foes; and by many stout thrusts and stoccadoes keep their metal lustrous and keen, as the spears of the Northern Lights charging over Greenland.

Fire from the flint is our Chevalier enraged. He takes umbrage at the cut of some ship's keel crossing his road, and straightway runs a tilt at it, with one mad lunge thrusting his Andrea Ferrara clean through and through; not seldom breaking it short off at the haft, like a bravo leaving his poignard in the vitals of his foe.

In the case of the English ship *Foxhound,* the blade penetrated through the most solid part of her hull, the bow; going completely through the copper plates and timbers, and showing for several inches in the hold. On the return of the ship to London it was carefully sawn out; and, imbedded in the original wood like a fossil, is still preserved. But this was a comparatively harmless onslaught of the valiant Chevalier. With the *Rousseau,* of Nantucket, it fared worse. She was almost mortally stabbed; her assailant withdrawing his blade. And it was only by keeping the pumps clanging that she managed to swim into a Tahitian harbor, "heave down," and have her wound dressed by a ship-surgeon with tar and oakum. This ship I met with at sea shortly after the disaster.

At what armory our Chevalier equips himself after one of his spiteful tilting-matches it would not be easy to say. But very hard for him, if ever after he goes about in the lists, swordless and disarmed, at the mercy of any caitiff shark he may meet.

Now, seeing that our fellow-voyagers, the little fish alongside, were sorely tormented and thinned out by the incursions of a pertinacious Chevalier, bent upon making a hearty breakfast out of them, I determined to interfere in their behalf, and capture the enemy.

With shark-hook and line I succeeded, and brought my brave gentleman to the deck. He made an emphatic landing, lashing the planks with his sinewy tail; while a yard and a half in advance of his eyes, reached forth his terrible blade.

As victor, I was entitled to the arms of the vanquished; so, quickly dispatching him, and sawing off his Toledo, I bore it away for a trophy. It was three-sided, slightly concave on each, like a bayonet; and some three inches through at the base, it tapered from thence to a point.

And though tempered not in Tagus or Guadalquiver, it yet revealed upon its surface that wavy grain and watery fleckiness peculiar to tried blades of Spain. It was an aromatic sword, like the ancient caliph's, giving out a peculiar musky odor by friction. But far different from steel of Tagus or Damascus, it was inflexible as Crocket's rifle tube; no doubt, as deadly.

Long hung that rapier over the head of my hammock. Was it not storied as the good trenchant blade of brave Bayard, that other chevalier? The knight's may have slain its scores or fifties, but the weapon I preserved had, doubtless, run through and riddled its thousands.

Chapter XXXIII

OTARD

AND HERE IS ANOTHER LITTLE INCIDENT.

One afternoon while all by myself curiously penetrating into the hold, I most unexpectedly obtained proof that the ill-fated captain of the *Parki* had been a man of sound judgment and most excellent taste. In brief, I lighted upon an aromatic cask of prime old Otard.

Now, I mean not to speak lightly of anything immediately connected with the unfortunate captain. Nor, on the other hand, would I resemble the inconsolable mourner, who, among other tokens of affliction, bound in funereal crape his deceased friend's copy of Joe Miller. Is there not a fitness in things?

But let that pass. I found the Otard and drank thereof; finding it, moreover, most pleasant to the palate, and right cheering to the soul. My next impulse was to share my prize with my shipmates. But here a judicious reflection obtruded. From the sea monarchs, his ancestors, my Viking had inherited one of their cardinal virtues, a detestation and abhorrence of all vinous and spirituous beverages; insomuch, that he never could see any but he instantly quaffed it out of sight. To be short, like Alexander the Great and other royalties, Jarl was prone to overmuch bibbing; and though at sea more sober than a Fifth Monarchy Elder, it was only because he was then removed from temptation. But having thus divulged my Viking's weak side, I earnestly entreat that it may not disparage him in any charitable man's estimation. Only think how many more there are like him—to say nothing further of Alexander the Great—especially among his own class; and consider, I beseech, that the most capacious-souled fellows, for that very reason, are the most apt to be too liberal in their libations; since, being so large-hearted, they hold so much more good cheer than others.

For Samoa, from his utter silence hitherto as to aught inebriating on board, I concluded that, along with his other secrets, the departed captain had very wisely kept his Otard to himself.

Nor did I doubt but that the Upoluan, like all Polynesians, much loved getting high of head; and in that state would be more intractable than a Black Forest boar. And concerning Annatoo, I shuddered to think how that Otard might inflame her into a Fury more fierce than the foremost of those that pursued Orestes.

In good time, then, bethinking me of the peril of publishing my discovery—bethinking me of the quiet, lazy, ever-present perils of the voyage, of all circumstances, the very worst under which to introduce an intoxicating beverage to my companions, I resolved to withhold it from them altogether.

So impressed was I with all this that for a moment I was almost tempted to roll over the cask on its bilge, remove the stopper, and suffer its contents to mix with the foul water at the bottom of the hold.

But no, no: what; dilute the brine with the double-distilled soul of the precious grape? Hafiz himself would have haunted me!

Then, again, it might come into play medicinally; and Paracelsus himself stands sponsor for every cup drunk for the good of the abdomen. So, at last, I determined to let it remain where it was; visiting it occasionally by myself for inspection.

But, by way of advice to all ship-masters, let me say that if your Otard magazine be exposed to view—then, in the evil hour of wreck, stave in your spirit casks ere rigging the life-boat.

Chapter XXXIV

How They Steered on Their Way

When we quitted the *Chamois* for the brigantine, we must have been at least two hundred leagues to the westward of the spot where we had abandoned the *Arcturion*. Though how far we might then have been north or south of the Equator, I could not with any certainty divine.

But that we were not removed any considerable distance from the Line, seemed obvious. For in the starriest night no sign of the extreme polar constellations was visible, though often we scanned the northern and southern horizon in search of them. So far as regards the aspect of the skies near the ocean's rim, the difference of several degrees in one's latitude at sea is readily perceived by a person long accustomed to surveying the heavens.

If correct in my supposition concerning our longitude at the time here alluded to, and allowing for what little progress we had been making in the *Parki*, there now remained some one hundred leagues to sail ere the country we sought would be found. But for obvious reasons, how long precisely we might continue to float out of sight of land it was impossible to say. Calms, light breezes and currents made every thing uncertain. Nor had we any method of estimating our due westward progress, except by what is called dead reckoning—the computation of the knots run hourly, allowances being made for the supposed deviations from our course, by reason of the ocean streams, which at times in this quarter of the Pacific run with very great velocity.

Now, in many respects we could not but feel safer aboard the *Parki* than in the *Chamois*. The sense of danger is less vivid, the greater the number of lives involved. He who is ready to despair in solitary peril, plucks up a heart in the presence of another. In a plurality of comrades is much countenance and consolation.

Still, in the brigantine there were many sources of uneasiness and anxiety unknown to me in the whale-boat. True, we had now between us and the deep five hundred good planks to one lath in our buoyant little chip. But the *Parki* required more care and attention; especially by night, when a vigilant look-out was indispensable. With impunity, in our whale-boat, we might have run close to shoal or reef; whereas, similar carelessness or temerity now might prove fatal to all concerned.

Though in the joyous sunlight, sailing through the sparkling sea, I was little troubled with serious misgivings, in the hours of darkness it was quite another thing. And the apprehensions, nay, terrors, I felt, were much augmented by the remissness of both Jarl and Samoa in keeping their night-watches. Several times I was seized with a deadly panic, and earnestly scanned the murky horizon, when rising from slumber I found the steersman, in whose hands for the time being were life and death, sleeping upright against the tiller, as much of a fixture there as the open-mouthed dragon rudely carved on our prow.

Were it not that on board of other vessels I myself had many a time dozed at the helm, spite of all struggles, I would have been almost at a loss to account for this heedlessness in my comrades.

But it seemed as if the mere sense of our situation should have been sufficient to prevent the like conduct in all on board our craft.

Samoa's aspect, sleeping at the tiller, was almost appalling. His large opal eyes were half open, and turned towards the light of the binnacle, gleamed between the lids like bars of flame. And added to all, was his giant stature and savage lineaments.

It was in vain that I remonstrated, begged, or threatened; the occasional drowsiness of my fellow-voyagers proved incurable. To no purpose, I reminded my Viking that sleeping in the night-watch in a craft like ours was far different from similar heedlessness on board the *Arcturion*; for there our place upon the ocean was always known, and our distance from land; so that when by night the seamen were permitted to be drowsy, it was mostly because the captain well knew that strict watchfulness could be dispensed with.

Though in all else the Skyeman proved a most faithful ally, in this one thing he was either perversely obtuse or infatuated. Or, perhaps, finding himself once more in a double-decked craft, which rocked him as of yore, he was lulled into a deceitful security.

For Samoa, his drowsiness was the drowsiness of one bent on sleep, come dreams or death. He seemed insensible to the peril we ran. Often I sent the sleepy savage below, and steered myself till morning. At last I made a point of slumbering much by day, the better to stand watch by night, though I made Samoa and Jarl regularly go through with their allotted four hours each.

It has been mentioned that Annatoo took her turn at the helm, but it was only by day. And in justice to the lady I must affirm that upon the whole she acquitted herself well. For notwithstanding the siren face in the binnacle, which dimly allured her glances, Annatoo after all was tolerably heedful of her steering. Indeed she took much pride therein; always ready for her turn; with marvelous exactitude calculating the approaching hour, as it came on in regular rotation. Her timepiece was ours, the sun. By night it must have been her guardian star, for frequently she gazed up at a particular section of the heavens, like one regarding the dial in a tower.

By some odd reasoning or other she had cajoled herself into the notion that whoever steered the brigantine for that period was captain. Wherefore, she gave herself mighty airs at the tiller; with extravagant gestures issuing unintelligible orders about trimming the sails, or pitching overboard something to see how fast we were going. All this much diverted my Viking, who several times was delivered of a laugh; a loud and healthy one to boot: a phenomenon worthy the chronicling.

And thus much for Annatoo, preliminary to what is further to be said. Seeing the drowsiness of Jarl and Samoa, which so often kept me from my hammock at night, forcing me to repose by day, when I far preferred being broad awake, I decided to let Annatoo take her turn at the night watches, which several times she had solicited me to do; railing at the sleepiness of her spouse; though abstaining from all reflections upon Jarl, towards whom she had of late grown exceedingly friendly.

Now, the Calmuc stood her first night watch to admiration; if anything, was altogether too wakeful. The mere steering of the craft employed not sufficiently her active mind. Ever and anon she must needs rush from the tiller to take a parenthetical pull at the fore-brace, the end of which led down to the bulwarks nearby; then refreshing herself with a draft or two of water and a biscuit, she would continue to steer away, full of the importance of her office. At any unusual flapping of the sails, a violent stamping on deck announced the fact to the startled crew. Finding her thus indefatigable, I readily induced her to stand two watches to Jarl's and Samoa's one; and when she was at the helm, I permitted myself to doze on a pile of old sails spread every evening on the quarter-deck.

It was the Skyeman who often admonished me to "heave to" every night, thus stopping her headway till morning; a plan which under other circumstances, might have perhaps warranted the slumbers of all. But as it was, such a course would have been highly imprudent. For while making no onward progress through the water, the rapid currents we encountered would continually be drifting us eastward; since, contrary to our previous experience, they seemed latterly to have reversed their flow, a phenomenon by no means unusual in the vicinity of the Line in the Pacific. And this it was that so prolonged our passage to the westward. Even in a moderate breeze I sometimes fancied that the impulse of the wind little more than counteracted the glide of the currents; so that, with much show of sailing, we were in reality almost a fixture on the sea.

The equatorial currents of the South Seas may be regarded as among the most mysterious of the mysteries of the deep. Whence they come, whither go, who knows? Tell us what hidden law regulates their flow?

Regardless of the theory which ascribes to them a nearly uniform course from east to west, induced by the eastwardly winds of the Line, and the collateral action of the Polar streams, these currents are forever shifting. Nor can the period of their revolutions be at all relied upon or predicted.

But however difficult it may be to assign a specific cause for the ocean streams, in any part of the world, one of the wholesome effects thereby produced would seem obvious enough. And though the circumstance here alluded to is perhaps known to everybody, it may be questioned whether it is generally invested with the importance it deserves. Reference is here made to the constant commingling and purification of the sea-water by reason of the currents.

For that the ocean, according to the popular theory, possesses a special purifying agent in its salts is somewhat to be doubted. Nor can it be explicitly denied, that those very salts might corrupt it, were it not for the brisk circulation of its particles consequent upon the flow of the streams. It is well known to seamen that a bucket of sea-water, left standing in a tropical climate, very soon becomes highly offensive; which is not the case with rain water.

But I build no theories. And by way of obstructing the one, which might possibly be evolved from the statement above, let me add that the offensiveness of sea-water left standing may arise in no small degree from the presence of decomposed animal matter.

Chapter XXXV

Ah, Annatoo!

In order to a complete revelation, I must needs once again discourse of Annatoo and her pilferings, and to what those pilferings led. In the simplicity of my soul, I fancied that the dame, so much flattered as she needs must have been by the confidence I began to repose in her, would now mend her ways, and abstain from her larcenies. But not so. She was possessed by some scores of devils, perpetually inciting her to mischief on their own separate behoof, and not hers, for many of her pranks were of no earthly advantage to her, present or prospective.

One day the log-reel was missing. Summon Annatoo. She came, but knew nothing about it. Jarl spent a whole morning in contriving a substitute; a few days after, pop, we came upon the lost article hidden away in the main-top.

Another time, discovering the little vessel to "gripe" hard in steering, as if someone under water were jerking her backward, we instituted a diligent examination to see what was the matter. When, lo! what should we find but a rope, cunningly attached to one of the chain-plates under the starboard main-channel. It towed heavily in the water. Upon dragging it up—much as you would the cord of a ponderous bucket far down in a well—a stout wooden box was discovered at the end; which, opened, disclosed sundry knives, hatchets, and ax-heads.

Called to the stand, the Upoluan deposed that thrice he had rescued that identical box from Annatoo's all-appropriating clutches.

Now, here were four human beings shut up in this little oaken craft, and, for the time being, their interests the same. What sane mortal, then, would forever be committing thefts, without rhyme or reason? It was like stealing silver from one pocket and decanting it into the other. And what might it not lead to in the end?

Why, ere long, in good sooth, it led to the abstraction of the compass from the binnacle; so that we were fain to substitute for it, the one brought along in the *Chamois*.

It was Jarl that first published this last and alarming theft. Annatoo being at the helm at dawn, he had gone to relieve her; and looking to see how we headed, was horror-struck at the emptiness of the binnacle.

I started to my feet, sought out the woman, and ferociously demanded the compass. But her face was a blank—every word a denial.

Further lenity was madness. I summoned Samoa, told him what had happened, and affirmed that there was no safety for us except in the nightly incarceration of his spouse. To this he privily assented; and that very evening, when Annatoo descended into the forecastle, we barred over her the scuttle-slide. Long she clamored, but unavailingly. And every night this was repeated, the dame saying her vespers most energetically.

It has somewhere been hinted that Annatoo occasionally cast sheep's eyes at Jarl. So I was not a little surprised when her manner towards him decidedly changed. Pulling at the ropes with us, she would give him sly pinches, and then look another way, innocent as a lamb. Then, again, she would refuse to handle the same piece of rigging with him; with wry faces, rinsed out the wooden can at the water cask, if it so chanced that my Viking had previously been drinking therefrom. At other times, when the honest Skyeman came up from below, she would set up a shout of derision, and loll out her tongue; accompanying all this by certain indecorous and exceedingly unlady-like gestures, significant of the profound contempt in which she held him.

Yet never did Jarl heed her ill-breeding, but patiently overlooked and forgave it. Inquiring the reason of the dame's singular conduct, I learned that with eye averted she had very lately crept close to my Viking, and met with no tender reception.

Doubtless, Jarl, who was much of a philosopher, innocently imagined that ere long the lady would forgive and forget him. But what knows a philosopher about women?

Ere long so outrageous became Annatoo's detestation of him, that the honest old tar could stand it no longer, and like most good-natured men when once fairly aroused, he was swept through and through with a terrible typhoon of passion. He proposed that forthwith the woman should be sacked and committed to the deep; he could stand it no longer.

Murder is catching. At first I almost jumped at the proposition; but as quickly rejected it. Ah! Annatoo! Woman unendurable: deliver me, ye gods, from being shut up in a ship with such a hornet again.

But are we yet through with her? Not yet. Hitherto she had continued to perform the duties of the office assigned her since the commencement of the voyage; namely, those of the culinary department. From this she was now deposed. Her skewer was broken. My Viking solemnly averring that he would eat nothing more of her concocting, for fear of being poisoned. For myself, I almost believed that there was malice enough in the minx to give us our henbane broth.

But what said Samoa to all this? Passing over the matter of the cookery, will it be credited that, living right among us as he did, he was yet blind to the premeditated though unachieved peccadilloes of his spouse? Yet so it was. And thus blind was Belisarius himself concerning the intrigues of Antonina.

Witness that noble dame's affair with the youth Theodosius; when her deluded lord charged upon the scandal-mongers with the very horns she had bestowed upon him.

Upon one occasion, seized with a sudden desire to palliate Annatoo's thievings, Samoa proudly intimated that the lady was the most virtuous of her sex.

But alas, poor Annatoo, why say more? And bethinking me of the hard fate that so soon overtook thee, I almost repent what has already and too faithfully been portrayed.

Chapter XXXVI

The Parki Gives up the Ghost

A long calm in the boat, and now, God help us, another in the brigantine. It was airless and profound.

In that hot calm we lay fixed and frozen in like Parry at the Pole. The sun played upon the glassy sea like the sun upon the glaciers.

At the end of two days we lifted up our eyes and beheld a low, creeping, hungry cloud expanding like an army, wing and wing, along the eastern horizon. Instantly Jarl bode me take heed.

Here be it said, that though for weeks and weeks reign over the equatorial latitudes of the Pacific the mildest and sunniest of days, that nevertheless, when storms do come, they come in their strength, spending in a few, brief blasts their concentrated rage. They come like the Mamelukes: they charge, and away.

It wanted full an hour to sunset, but the sun was well nigh obscured. It seemed toiling among bleak Scythian steeps in the hazy background. Above the storm-cloud flitted ominous patches of scud, rapidly advancing and receding: Attila's skirmishers thrown forward in the van of his Huns. Beneath, a fitful shadow slid along the surface. As we gazed, the cloud came nearer, accelerating its approach.

With all haste we proceeded to furl the sails, which, owing to the calm, had been hanging loose in the brails; and by help of a spare boom, used on the forecastle-deck sit a sweep or great oar, we endeavored to cast the brigantine's head towards the foe.

The storm seemed about to overtake us, but we felt no breeze. The noiseless cloud stole on; its advancing shadow lowering over a distinct and prominent milk-white crest upon the surface of the ocean. But now this line of surging foam came rolling down upon us like a white charge of cavalry, mad Hotspur and plumed Murat at its head; pouring right forward in a continuous frothy cascade, which curled over and fell upon the glassy sea before it.

Still no breath of air. But of a sudden, like a blow from a man's hand, and before our canvas could be secured, the stunned craft, giving one lurch to port, was stricken down on her beam-ends; the roaring tide dashed high up against her windward side, and drops of brine fell upon the deck, heavy as drops of gore.

It was all a din and a mist; a crashing of spars and of ropes; a horrible blending of sights and of sounds; as for an instant we seemed in the hot heart of the gale; our cordage, like harp-strings, shrieking above the fury of the blast. The masts rose and swayed, and dipped their trucks in the sea. And like unto some stricken buffalo brought low to the plain, the brigantine's black hull, shaggy with sea-weed, lay panting on its flank in the foam.

Frantically we clung to the uppermost bulwarks. And now, loud above the roar of the sea, was suddenly heard a sharp, splintering sound, as of a Norway woodman felling a pine in the forest. It was brave Jarl, who foremost of all had snatched from its rack against the mainmast, the ax, always there kept.

"Cut the lanyards to windward!" he cried; and again buried his ax into the mast. He was quickly obeyed. And upon cutting the third lanyard of the five, he shouted for us to pause. Dropping his ax, he climbed up to windward. As he clutched the rail, the wounded mast snapped in twain with a report like a cannon. A slight smoke was perceptible where it broke. The remaining lanyards parted. From the violent strain upon them, the two shrouds flew madly into the air, and one of the great blocks at their ends striking Annatoo upon the forehead, she let go her hold upon a stanchion, and sliding across the aslant deck, was swallowed up in the whirlpool under our lee. Samoa shrieked. But there was no time to mourn; no hand could reach to save.

By the connecting stays, the main-mast carried over with it the fore-mast; when we instantly righted, and for the time were saved; my own royal Viking our savior.

The first fury of the gale was gone. But far to leeward was seen the even, white line of its onset, pawing the ocean into foam. All round us the sea boiled like ten thousand caldrons; and through eddy, wave, and surge, our almost waterlogged craft waded heavily; every dead dash ringing hollow against her hull, like blows upon a coffin.

We floated a wreck. With every pitch we lifted our dangling jib-boom into the air; and beating against the side were the shattered fragments of the masts. From these we made all haste to be free, by cutting the rigging that held them.

Soon the worst of the gale was blown over. But the sea ran high. Yet the rack and scud of the tempest, its mad, tearing foam, was subdued into immense, long-extended, and long-rolling billows; the white cream on their crests like snow on the Andes. Ever and anon we hung poised on their brows; when the furrowed ocean all round looked like a panorama from Chimborazo.

A few hours more and the surges went down. There was a moderate sea, a steady breeze, and a clear, starry sky.

Such was the storm that came after our calm.

Chapter XXXVII

Once More They Take to the Chamois

TRY THE PUMPS. WE DROPPED THE SINKER, AND FOUND THE *PARKI* BLEEDING AT EVERY PORE. UP from her well, the water, spring-like, came bubbling, pure and limpid as the water of Saratoga. Her time had come. But by keeping two hands at the pumps we had no doubt she would float till daylight; previous to which we liked not to abandon her.

The interval was employed in clanging at the pump-breaks, and preparing the *Chamois* for our reception. So soon as the sea permitted, we lowered it over the side; and letting it float under the stern, stowed it with water and provisions, together with various other things, including muskets and cutlasses.

Shortly after daylight a violent jostling and thumping under foot showed that the water, gaining rapidly in the hold, spite of all pumping, had floated the lighter casks upwards to the deck, against which they were striking.

Now, owing to the number of empty butts in the hold, there would have been, perhaps, but small danger of the vessel's sinking outright, all awash as her decks would soon be—were it not that many of her timbers were of a native wood, which, like the Teak of India, is specifically heavier than water. This, with the pearl shells on board, counteracted the buoyancy of the casks.

At last, the sun—long waited for—arose; the *Parki,* meantime, sinking lower and lower.

All things being in readiness, we proceeded to embark from the wreck as from a wharf.

But not without some show of love for our poor brigantine.

To a seaman a ship is no piece of mechanism merely; but a creature of thoughts and fancies, instinct with life. Standing at her vibrating helm, you feel her beating pulse. I have loved ships as I have loved men.

To abandon the poor *Parki* was like leaving to its fate something that could feel. It was meet that she should die decently and bravely.

All this thought the Skyeman. Samoa and I were in the boat, calling upon him to enter quickly lest the vessel should sink, and carry us down in the eddies, for already she had gone round twice. But cutting adrift the last fragments of her broken shrouds, and putting her decks in order, Jarl buried his ax in the splintered stump of the main-mast, and not till then did he join us.

We slowly cheered and sailed away.

Not ten minutes after, the hull rolled convulsively in the sea, went round once more, lifted its sharp prow as a man with arms pointed for a dive, gave a long seething plunge; and went down.

Many of her old planks were twice wrecked; once strewn upon ocean's beach; now dropped into its lowermost vaults, with the bones of drowned ships and drowned men.

Once more afloat in our shell! But not with the intrepid spirit that shoved off with us from the deck of the *Arcturion*. A bold deed done from impulse, for the time carries few or no misgivings along with it. But forced upon you, its terrors stare you in the face. So now. I had pushed from the *Arcturion* with a stout heart; but quitting the sinking *Parki*, my heart sunk with her.

With a fair wind, we held on our way westward, hoping to see land before many days.

Chapter XXXVIII

The Sea on Fire

The night following our abandonment of the *Parki* was made memorable by a remarkable spectacle.

Slumbering in the bottom of the boat, Jarl and I were suddenly awakened by Samoa. Starting, we beheld the ocean of a pallid white color, corruscating all over with tiny golden sparkles. But the pervading hue of the water cast a cadaverous gleam upon the boat, so that we looked to each other like ghosts. For many rods astern our wake was revealed in a line of rushing illuminated foam; while here and there beneath the surface, the tracks of sharks were denoted by vivid, greenish trails, crossing and recrossing each other in every direction. Farther away, and distributed in clusters, floated on the sea like constellations in the heavens, innumerable Medusæ, a species of small, round, refulgent fish, only to be met with in the South Seas and the Indian Ocean.

Suddenly as we gazed there shot high into the air a bushy jet of flashes, accompanied by the unmistakable deep breathing sound of a sperm whale. Soon the sea all round us spouted in fountains of fire; and vast forms, emitting a glare from their flanks, and ever and anon raising their heads above water and shaking off the sparkles, showed where an immense shoal of Cachalots had risen from below to sport in these phosphorescent billows.

The vapor jetted forth was far more radiant than any portion of the sea; ascribable perhaps to the originally luminous fluid contracting still more brilliancy from its passage through the spouting canal of the whales.

We were in great fear, lest without any vicious intention the Leviathans might destroy us by coming into close contact with our boat. We would have shunned them; but they were all round and round us. Nevertheless we were safe; for as we parted the pallid brine, the peculiar irradiation which shot from about our keel seemed to deter them. Apparently discovering us of a sudden, many of them plunged headlong down into the water, tossing their fiery tails high into the air, and leaving the sea still more sparkling from the violent surging of their descent.

Their general course seemed the same as our own; to the westward. To remove from them, we at last out oars and pulled towards the north. So doing, we were steadily pursued by a solitary whale that must have taken our *Chamois* for a kindred fish. Spite of all our efforts, he drew nearer and nearer; at length rubbing his fiery flank against the *Chamois'* gunwale, here and there leaving long strips of the glossy transparent substance which, thin as gossamer, invests the body of the Cachalot.

In terror at a sight so new, Samoa shrank. But Jarl and I, more used to the intimate companionship of the whales, pushed the boat away from it with our oars: a thing often done in the fishery.

The close vicinity of the whale revived in the so long astute Skyeman all the enthusiasm of his daring vocation. However quiet by nature, a thoroughbred whaleman betrays no little excitement in sight of his game, and it required some persuasion to prevent Jarl from darting his harpoon: insanity under present circumstances, and, of course, without object. But "Oh! for a dart," cried my Viking. And "Where's now our old ship?" he added reminiscently.

But to my great joy, the monster at last departed; rejoining the shoal, whose lofty spoutings of flame were still visible upon the distant line of the horizon, showing there like the fitful starts of the Aurora Borealis.

The sea retained its luminosity for about three hours, at the expiration of half that period beginning to fade; and excepting occasional faint illuminations consequent upon the rapid darting of fish under water, the phenomenon at last wholly disappeared.

Heretofore, I had beheld several exhibitions of marine phosphorescence, both in the Atlantic and Pacific. But nothing in comparison with what was seen that night. In the Atlantic there is very seldom any portion of the ocean luminous, except the crests of the waves, and these mostly appear so during wet, murky weather. Whereas in the Pacific all instances of the sort, previously coming under my notice, had been marked by patches of greenish light, unattended with any pallidness of sea. Save twice on the coast of Peru, where I was summoned from my hammock by the alarming midnight cry of "All hands ahoy! tack ship!" And rushing on deck, beheld the sea white as a shroud: for which reason it was feared we were on soundings.

Now, sailors love marvels, and love to repeat them. And from many an old shipmate I have heard various sage opinings concerning the phenomenon in question. Dismissing as destitute of sound philosophic probability the extravagant notion of one of my nautical friends—no less a philosopher than my Viking himself—namely, that the phosphoresence of the sea is caused by a commotion among the mermaids, whose golden locks, all torn and disheveled, do irradiate the waters at such times; I proceed to record more reliable theories.

Faraday might, perhaps, impute the phenomenon to a peculiarly electrical condition of the atmosphere; and to that solely. But herein my scientific friend would be stoutly contradicted by many intelligent seamen, who, in part, impute it to the presence of large quantities of putrescent animal matter, with which the sea is well known to abound.

And it would seem not unreasonable to suppose that it is by this means that the fluid itself becomes charged with the luminous principle. Draw a bucket of water from the phosphorescent ocean, and it still retains traces of fire; but, standing awhile, this soon subsides. Now pour it along the deck, and it is a stream of flame; caused by its renewed agitation. Empty the bucket, and for a space sparkles cling to it tenaciously; and every stave seems ignited.

But after all, this seeming ignition of the sea cannot be wholly produced by dead matter therein. There are many living fish phosphorescent; and, under certain conditions, by a rapid throwing off of luminous particles, must largely contribute to the result. Not to particularize this circumstance as true of divers species of sharks, cuttle-fish, and many others of the larger varieties of the finny tribes; the myriads of microscopic mollusca, well known to swarm off soundings, might alone be deemed almost sufficient to kindle a fire in the brine.

But these are only surmises; likely, but uncertain.

After science comes sentiment.

A French naturalist maintains that the nocturnal radiance of the fire-fly is purposely intended as an attraction to the opposite sex; that the artful insect illuminates its body for a beacon to love.

Thus, perched upon the edge of a leaf, and waiting the approach of her Leander, who comes buffeting with his wings the aroma of the flowers, some insect Hero may show a torch to her gossamer gallant.

But alas, thrice alas, for the poor little fire-fish of the sea, whose radiance but reveals them to their foes, and lights the way to their destruction.

Chapter XXXIX

They Fall in with Strangers

After quitting the *Parki* we had much calm weather, varied by light breezes. And sailing smoothly over a sea, so recently one sheet of foam, I could not avoid bethinking me how fortunate it was that the gale had overtaken us in the brigantine and not in the Chamois. For deservedly high as the whale-shallop ranks as a sea boat, still, in a severe storm, the larger your craft the greater your sense of security. Wherefore, the thousand reckless souls tenanting a line-of-battle ship scoff at the most awful hurricanes; though, in reality, they may be less safe in their wooden-walled Troy than those who contend with the gale in a clipper.

But not only did I congratulate myself upon salvation from the past, but upon the prospect for the future. For storms happening so seldom in these seas, one just blown over is almost a sure guarantee of very many weeks' calm weather to come.

Now sun followed sun; and no land. At length it almost seemed as if we must have sailed past the remotest presumable westerly limit of the chain of islands we sought; a lurking suspicion which I sedulously kept to myself. However, I could not but nourish a latent faith that all would yet be well.

On the ninth day my forebodings were over. In the gray of the dawn, perched upon the peak of our sail, a noddy was seen fast asleep. This freak was true to the nature of that curious fowl, whose name is significant of its drowsiness. Its plumage was snow-white, its bill and legs blood-red, the latter looking like little pantalettes. In a sly attempt at catching the bird, Samoa captured three tail-feathers, the alarmed creature flying away with a scream, and leaving its quills in his hand.

Sailing on, we gradually broke in upon immense low-sailing flights of other aquatic fowls, mostly of those species which are seldom found far from land; terns, frigate-birds, mollymeaux, reef-pigeons, boobies, gulls, and the like. They darkened the air; their wings making overhead an incessant rustling like the simultaneous turning over of ten thousand leaves. The smaller sort skimmed the sea like pebbles sent skipping from the shore. Over these flew myriads of birds of broader wing. While high above all soared in air the daring "Diver," or sea-kite, the power of whose vision is truly wonderful. It perceives the little flying-fish in the water, at a height which cannot be less than four hundred feet. Spirally wheeling and screaming as it goes, the sea-kite, bill foremost, darts downward, swoops into the water, and for a moment altogether disappearing, emerges at last, its prey firmly trussed in its claws. But bearing it aloft, the bold bandit is quickly assailed by other birds of prey that strive to wrest from him his booty. And snatched from his talons, you see the fish falling through the air, till again caught up in the very act of descent by the fleetest of its pursuers.

Leaving these sights astern, we presently picked up the slimy husk of a cocoanut, all over green barnacles; and shortly after passed two or three limbs of trees, and the solitary trunk of a palm; which, upon sailing nearer, seemed but very recently started on its endless voyage. As noon came on, the dark purple land-haze, which had been dimly descried resting upon the western horizon, was very nearly obscured. Nevertheless, behind that dim drapery we doubted not bright boughs were waving.

We were now in high spirits. Samoa between times humming to himself some heathenish ditty, and Jarl ten times more intent on his silence than ever, yet his eye full of expectation and gazing broad off from our bow. Of a sudden, shading his face with his hand, he gazed fixedly for an instant, and then springing to his feet, uttered the long-drawn sound—"Sail ho!"

Just tipping the furthest edge of the sky was a little speck, dancing into view every time we rose upon the swell. It looked like one of many birds; for half intercepting our view, fell showers of plumage; a flight of milk-white noddies flying downward to the sea.

But soon the birds are seen no more. Yet there remains the speck; plainly a sail, but too small for a ship. Was it a boat after a whale, the vessel to which it belonged far astern, and shrouded by the haze? So it seemed.

Quietly, however, we waited the stranger's nearer approach, confident that for some time he would not be able to perceive us, owing to our being in what mariners denominate the "sun-glade," or that part of the ocean upon which the sun's rays flash with peculiar intensity.

As the sail drew nigh, its failing to glisten white led us to doubt whether it was indeed a whale-boat. Presently it showed yellow, and Samoa declared that it must be the sail of some island craft. True. The stranger proving a large double canoe, like those used by the Polynesians in making passages between distant islands.

The Upoluan was now clamorous for a meeting, to which Jarl was averse. Deliberating a moment, I directed the muskets to be loaded; then setting the sail—the wind on our quarter—we headed away for the canoe, now sailing at right angles with our previous course.

Here it must be mentioned that from the various gay cloths and other things provided for barter by the captain of the *Parki*, I had very strikingly improved my costume, making it free, flowing, and eastern. I looked like an Emir. Nor had my Viking neglected to follow my example, though with some few modifications of his own. With his long tangled hair and harpoon, he looked like the sea-god that boards ships for the first time crossing the Equator. For tatooed Samoa, he yet sported both kilt and turban, reminding one of a tawny leopard, though his spots were all in one place. Besides this raiment of ours, against emergencies we had provided our boat with divers nankeens and silks.

But now into full view comes a yoke of huge clumsy prows, shaggy with carving, and driving through the water with considerable velocity, the immense sprawling sail holding the wind like a bag. She seemed full of men; and from the dissonant cries borne over to us, and the canoe's widely yawing, it was plain that we had occasioned no small sensation. They seemed undetermined what course to pursue; whether to court a meeting, or avoid it; whether to regard us as friends or foes.

As we came still nearer, distinctly beholding their faces, we loudly hailed them, inviting them to furl their sails, and allow us to board them. But no answer was returned, their confusion increasing. And now, within less than two ships' lengths, they swept right across our bow, gazing at us with blended curiosity and fear.

Their craft was about thirty feet long, consisting of a pair of parallel canoes, very narrow, and at the distance of a yard or so, lengthwise, united by stout cross-timbers, lashed across the four gunwales. Upon these timbers was a raised platform or dais, quite dry; and astern an arched cabin or tent, behind which were two broad-bladed paddles terminating in rude shark-tails, by which the craft was steered.

The yard, spreading a yellow sail, was a crooked bough, supported obliquely in the crotch of a mast, to which the green bark was still clinging. Here and there were little tufts of moss. The high, beaked prow of that canoe in which the mast was placed, resembled a rude altar; and all round it was suspended a great variety of fruits, including scores of cocoanuts, unhusked. This prow was railed off, forming a sort of chancel within.

The foremost beam, crossing the gunwales, extended some twelve feet beyond the side of the dais; and at regular intervals thereupon, stout cords were fastened, which, leading up to the head of the mast, answered the purpose of shrouds. The breeze was now streaming fresh; and as if to force down into the water the windward side of the craft, five men stood upon this long beam, grasping five shrouds. Yet they failed to counterbalance the pressure of the sail; and owing to the opposite inclination of the twin canoes, these living statues were elevated high above the water; their appearance rendered still more striking by their eager attitudes, and the apparent peril of their position, as the mad spray from the bow dashed over them. Suddenly the islanders threw their craft into the wind; while, for ourselves, we lay on our oars, fearful of alarming them by now coming nearer. But hailing them again, we said we were friends, and had friendly gifts for them, if they would peaceably permit us to approach. This understood, there ensued a mighty clamor; insomuch that I bade Jarl and Samoa out oars and row very gently towards the strangers. Whereupon, amid a storm of vociferations, some of them hurried to the furthest side of their dais, standing with arms arched over their heads, as if for a dive; others menacing us with clubs and spears; and one, an old man with a bamboo trellis on his head forming a sort of arbor for his hair, planted himself full before the tent, stretching behind him a wide plaited sling.

Upon this hostile display, Samoa dropped his oar, and brought his piece to bear upon the old man, who, by his attitude, seemed to menace us with the fate of the great braggart of Gath. But I quickly knocked down the muzzle of his musket, and forbade the slightest token of hostility; enjoining it upon my companions, nevertheless, to keep well on their guard.

We now ceased rowing, and after a few minutes' uproar in the canoe, they ran to the steering-paddles, and forcing round their craft before the wind, rapidly ran away from us. With all haste we set our sail, and pulling also at our oars, soon overtook them, determined upon coming into closer communion.

Chapter XL

Sire and Sons

Seeing flight was useless, the islanders again stopped their canoe, and once more we cautiously drew nearer; myself crying out to them not to be fearful; and Samoa, with the odd humor of his race, averring that he had known every soul of them from his infancy.

We approached within two or three yards, when we paused, which somewhat allayed their alarm. Fastening a red China handkerchief to the blade of our long midship oar, I waved it in the air. A lively clapping of hands, and many wild exclamations.

While yet waving the flag, I whispered to Jarl to give the boat a sheer towards the canoe, which, being adroitly done, brought the bow, where I stood, still nearer to the islanders. I then dropped the silk among them; and the islander who caught it at once handed it to the war-like old man with the sling, who, on seating himself, spread it before him; while the rest, crowding round, glanced rapidly from the wonderful gift to the more wonderful donors.

This old man was the superior of the party. And Samoa asserted that he must be a priest of the country to which the islanders belonged; that the craft could be no other than one of their sacred canoes, bound on some priestly voyage. All this he inferred from the altar-like prow, and there being no women on board.

Bent upon conciliating the old priest, I dropped into the canoe another silk handkerchief, while

Samoa loudly exclaimed that we were only three men, and were peacefully inclined. Meantime, old Aaron, fastening the two silks crosswise over his shoulders, like a brace of Highland plaids, cross-legged sat, and eyed us.

It was a curious sight. The old priest, like a scroll of old parchment, covered all over with hieroglyphical devices, harder to interpret, I'll warrant, than any old Sanscrit manuscript. And upon his broad brow, deep-graven in wrinkles, were characters still more mysterious, which no Champollion nor gypsy could have deciphered. He looked old as the elderly hills; eyes sunken, though bright, and head white as the summit of Mont Blanc.

The rest were a youthful and comely set; their complexion that of Gold Sherry, and all tattooed after this pattern; two broad cross-stripes on the chest and back; reaching down to the waist, like a foot-soldier's harness. Their faces were full of expression; and their mouths were full of fine teeth; so that the parting of their lips was as the opening of pearl oysters. Marked here and there after the style of Tahiti, with little round figures in blue, dotted in the middle with a spot of vermilion, their brawny brown thighs looked not unlike the gallant hams of Westphalia, spotted with the red dust of Cayenne.

But what a marvelous resemblance in the features of all. Were they born at one birth? This resemblance was heightened by their uniform marks. But it was subsequently ascertained that they were the children of one sire; and that sire, old Aaron, who, no doubt, reposed upon his sons as an old general upon the trophies of his youth.

They were the children of as many mothers, and he was training them up for the priesthood.

Chapter XLI

A Fray

SO BENT WERE THE STRANGERS UPON CONCEALING WHO THEY WERE, AND THE OBJECT OF THEIR voyage, that it was some time ere we could obtain the information we desired.

They pointed towards the tent, as if it contained their Eleusinian mysteries. And the old priest gave us to know that it would be profanation to enter it.

But all this only roused my curiosity to unravel the wonder.

At last I succeeded.

In that mysterious tent was concealed a beautiful maiden. And in pursuance of a barbarous custom, by Aleema, the priest, she was being borne an offering from the island of Amma to the gods of Tedaidee.

Now, hearing of the maiden, I waited for no more. Need I add how stirred was my soul towards this invisible victim, and how hotly I swore that precious blood of hers should never smoke upon an altar. If we drowned for it, I was bent upon rescuing the captive. But as yet no gentle signal of distress had been waved to us from the tent. Thence no sound could be heard, but an occasional rustle of the matting. Was it possible that one about to be immolated could proceed thus tranquilly to her fate?

But desperately as I resolved to accomplish the deliverance of the maiden, it was best to set heedfully about it. I desired no shedding of blood, though the odds were against us.

The old priest seemed determined to prevent us from boarding his craft. But being equally determined the other way, I cautiously laid the bow of the *Chamois* against the canoe's quarter, so as to present the smallest possible chance for a hostile entrance into our boat. Then Samoa, knife in ear, and myself with a cutlass, stepped upon the dais, leaving Jarl in the boat's head equipped with his harpoon, three loaded muskets lying by his side. He was strictly enjoined to resist the slightest demonstration towards our craft.

As we boarded the canoe, the islanders slowly retreated, meantime earnestly conferring in whispers; all but the old priest, who, still seated, presented an undaunted though troubled front. To our surprise he motioned us to sit down by him, which we did, taking care, however, not to cut off our communication with Jarl.

With the hope of inspiring good will, I now unfolded a roll of printed cotton, and spreading it before the priest, directed his attention to the pictorial embellishments thereon, representing some hundreds of sailor boys simultaneously ascending some hundreds of uniform sections of a ship's rigging. Glancing at them a moment, by a significant sign he gave me to know that long previous he himself had ascended the shrouds of a ship. Making this allusion, his countenance was overcast with a ferocious expression, as if something terrific was connected with the reminiscence. But it soon passed away, and somewhat abruptly he assumed an air of much merriment.

While we were thus sitting together, and my whole soul full of the thoughts of the captive, and how best to accomplish my purpose, and often gazing towards the tent, I all at once noticed a movement among the strangers. Almost in the same instant, Samoa, right across the face of Aleema, and in his ordinary tones, bade me take heed to myself, for mischief was brewing. Hardly was this warning uttered when, with carved clubs in their hands, the islanders completely surrounded us. Then up rose the old priest, and gave us to know that we were wholly in his power, and if we did not swear to depart in our boat forthwith, and molest him no more, the peril be ours.

"Depart and you live; stay and you die."

Fifteen to three. Madness to gainsay his mandate. Yet a beautiful maiden was at stake.

The knife before dangling in Samoa's ear was now in his hand. Jarl cried out for us to regain the boat, several of the islanders making a rush for it. No time to think. All passed quicker than it can be said. They closed in upon us to push us from the canoe. Rudely the old priest flung me from his side, menacing me with his dagger, the sharp spine of a fish. A thrust and a threat! Ere I knew it, my cutlass made a quick lunge. A curse from the priest's mouth; red blood from his side; he tottered, stared about him, and fell over like a brown hemlock into the sea. A yell of maledictions rose on the air. A wild cry was heard from the tent. Making a dead breach among the crowd, we now dashed side by side for the boat. Springing into it, we found Jarl battling with two islanders, while the rest were still howling upon the dais. Rage and grief had almost disabled them.

With one stroke of my cutlass I now parted the line that held us to the canoe, and with Samoa falling upon the two islanders, by Jarl's help, we quickly mastered them, forcing them down into the bottom of the boat.

The Skyeman and Samoa holding passive the captives, I quickly set our sail, and snatching the sheet at the cavil, we rapidly shot from the canoe, the strangers defying us with their spears; several couching them as if to dart, while others held back their hands as if to prevent them from jeopardizing the lives of their countrymen in the *Chamois*.

Seemingly untoward events oftentimes lead to successful results. Far from destroying all chance of rescuing the captive, our temporary flight, indispensable for the safety of Jarl, only made the success of our enterprise more probable. For having made prisoners two of the strangers, I determined to retain them as hostages, through whom to effect my plans without further bloodshed.

And here it must needs be related that some of the natives were wounded in the fray, while all three of their assailants had received several bruises.

Chapter XLII

REMORSE

DURING THE SKIRMISH NOT A SINGLE MUSKET HAD BEEN DISCHARGED. THE FIRST SNATCHED BY Jarl had missed fire, and ere he could seize another, it was close quarters with him and no gestures to spare. His harpoon was his all. And truly, there is nothing like steel in a fray. It comes and it goes with a will, and is never a-weary. Your sword is your life, and that of your foe—to keep or to take as it happens. Closer home does it go than a rammer, and fighting with steel is a play without ever an interlude. There are points more deadly than bullets, and stocks packed full of subtle tubes, whence comes an impulse more reliable than powder.

Binding our prisoners lengthwise across the boat's seats, we rowed for the canoe, making signs of amity.

Now, if there be anything fitted to make a high tide ebb in the veins it is the sight of a vanquished foe, inferior to yourself in powers of destruction, but whom some necessity has forced you to subdue. All victories are not triumphs, nor all who conquer, heroes.

As we drew near the canoe, it was plain that the loss of their sire had again for the instant overcome the survivors. Raising hands, they cursed us; and at intervals sent forth a low, piercing wail, peculiar to their race. As before, faint cries were heard from the tent; and all the while rose and fell on the sea, the ill-fated canoe.

As I gazed at this sight, what iron mace fell on my soul; what curse rang sharp in my ear! It was I, who was the author of the deed that caused the shrill wails that I heard. By this hand the dead man had died. Remorse smote me hard; and like lightning I asked myself whether the death-deed I had done was sprung of a virtuous motive, the rescuing a captive from thrall; or whether beneath that pretense I had engaged in this fatal affray for some other and selfish purpose—the companionship of a beautiful maid. But throttling the thought, I swore to be gay. Am I not rescuing the maiden? Let them go down who withstand me.

At the dismal spectacle before him, Jarl, hitherto menacing our prisoners with his weapon, in order to intimidate their countrymen, honest Jarl dropped his harpoon. But shaking his knife in the air, Samoa yet defied the strangers; nor could we prevent him. His heathenish blood was up.

Standing foremost in the boat, I now assured the strangers that all we sought at their hands was the maiden in the tent. That captive surrendered, our own, unharmed, should be restored. If not, they must die. With a cry they started to their feet, and brandished their clubs, but seeing Jarl's harpoon quivering over the hearts of our prisoners they quickly retreated, at last signifying their acquiescence in my demand. Upon this, I sprang to the dais, and across it, indicating a line near the bow, signed the islanders to retire beyond it. Then calling upon them one by one to deliver their weapons, they were passed into the boat.

The *Chamois* was now brought round to the canoe's stern; and leaving Jarl to defend it as before, the Upoluan rejoined me on the dais. By these precautions—the hostages still remaining bound hand and foot in the boat—we deemed ourselves entirely secure.

Attended by Samoa, I stood before the tent, now still as the grave.

Chapter XLIII

THE TENT ENTERED

BY MEANS OF THIN SPACES BETWEEN THE BRAIDS OF MATTING, THE PLACE WAS OPEN TO THE AIR, but not to view. There was also a round opening on one side, only large enough, however, to admit the arm; but this aperture was partially closed from within. In front, a deep-dyed rug of osiers, covering the entrance way, was intricately laced to the standing part of the tent. As I divided this lacing with my cutlass, there arose an outburst of voices from the islanders. And they covered their faces, as the interior was revealed to my gaze.

Before me crouched a beautiful girl. Her hands were drooping. And, like a saint from a shrine, she looked sadly out from her long, fair hair. A low wail issued from her lips, and she trembled like a sound. There were tears on her cheek, and a rose-colored pearl on her bosom.

Did I dream?—a snow-white skin: blue firmament eyes: Golconda locks. For an instant spell-bound I stood; while with a slow, apprehensive movement, and still gazing fixedly, the captive gathered more closely about her a gauze-like robe. Taking one step within, and partially dropping the curtain of the tent, I so stood, as to have both sight and speech of Samoa, who tarried without; while the maiden, crouching in the farther corner of the retreat, was wholly screened from all eyes but mine.

Crossing my hands before me, I now stood without speaking. For the soul of me, I could not link this mysterious creature with the tawny strangers. She seemed of another race. So powerful was this impression, that unconsciously I addressed her in my own tongue. She started, and bending over, listened intently, as if to the first faint echo of something dimly remembered. Again I spoke, when, throwing back her hair, the maiden looked up with a piercing, bewildered gaze. But her eyes soon fell, and bending over once more, she resumed her former attitude. At length she slowly chanted to herself several musical words, unlike those of the islanders; but though I knew not what they meant, they vaguely seemed familiar.

Impatient to learn her story, I now questioned her in Polynesian. But with much earnestness, she signed me to address her as before. Soon perceiving, however, that without comprehending the meaning of the words I employed, she seemed merely touched by something pleasing in their sound, I once more addressed her in Polynesian, saying that I was all eagerness to hear her history.

After much hesitation she complied, starting with alarm at every sound from without; yet all the while deeply regarding me.

Broken as these disclosures were at the time, they are here presented in the form in which they were afterwards more fully narrated.

So unearthly was the story that at first I little comprehended it, and was almost persuaded that the luckless maiden was some beautiful maniac.

She declared herself more than mortal, a maiden from Oroolia, the Island of Delights, somewhere in the paradisiacal archipelago of the Polynesians. To this isle, while yet an infant, by some mystical power, she had been spirited from Amma, the place of her nativity. Her name was Yillah. And hardly had the waters of Oroolia washed white her olive skin, and tinged her hair with gold, when one day strolling in the woodlands, she was snared in the tendrils of a vine. Drawing her into its bowers, it gently transformed her into one of its blossoms, leaving her conscious soul folded up in the transparent petals.

Here hung Yillah in a trance, the world without all tinged with the rosy hue of her prison. At length when her spirit was about to burst forth in the opening flower, the blossom was snapped from its stem, and borne by a soft wind to the sea, where it fell into the opening valve of a shell; which, in good time, was cast upon the beach of the Island of Amma.

In a dream these events were revealed to Aleema the priest, who by a spell unlocking its pearly casket, took forth the bud, which now showed signs of opening in the reviving air, and bore faint shadowy revealings, as of the dawn behind crimson clouds. Suddenly expanding, the blossom exhaled away in perfumes; floating a rosy mist in the air. Condensing at last, there emerged from this mist the same radiant young Yillah as before; her locks all moist, and a rose-colored pearl on her bosom. Enshrined as a goddess, the wonderful child now tarried in the sacred temple of Apo, buried in a dell; never beheld of mortal eyes save Aleema's.

Moon after moon passed away, and at last, only four days gone by, Aleema came to her with a dream; that the spirits of Oroolia had recalled her home by the way of Tedaidee, on whose coast gurgled up in the sea an enchanted spring; which, streaming over upon the brine, flowed on between blue watery banks; and, plunging into a vortex, went round and round, descending into depths unknown. Into this whirlpool Yillah was to descend in a canoe, at last to well up in an inland fountain of Oroolia.

Chapter XLIV

AWAY

THOUGH CLOTHED IN LANGUAGE OF MY OWN, THE MAIDEN'S STORY IS IN SUBSTANCE THE SAME AS she related. Yet were not these things narrated as past events; she merely recounted them as impressions of her childhood, and of her destiny yet unaccomplished. And mystical as the tale most assuredly was, my knowledge of the strange arts of the island priesthood, and the rapt fancies indulged in by many of their victims, deprived it in good part of the effect it otherwise would have produced.

For ulterior purposes connected with their sacerdotal supremacy, the priests of these climes oftentimes secrete mere infants in their temples; and jealously secluding them from all intercourse with the world, craftily delude them, as they grow up, into the wildest conceit.

Thus wrought upon, their pupils almost lose their humanity in the constant indulgence of seraphic imaginings, in many cases becoming inspired as oracles; and as such, they are sometimes resorted to by devotees; always screened from view, however, in the recesses of the temples. But in every instance their end is certain. Beguiled with some fairy tale about revisiting the islands of Paradise, they are led to the secret sacrifice, and perish unknown to their kindred.

But, would that all this had been hidden from me at the time. For Yillah was lovely enough to be really divine, so I might have been tranced into a belief of her mystical legends.

But with what passionate exultation did I find myself the deliverer of this beautiful maiden; who, thinking no harm, and rapt in a dream, was being borne to her fate on the coast of Tedaidee. Nor now, for a moment, did the death of Aleema her guardian seem to hang heavy upon my heart. I rejoiced that I had sent him to his gods; that in place of the sea-moss growing over sweet Yillah, drowned in the sea, the vile priest himself had sunk to the bottom.

But though he had sunk in the deep, his ghost sunk not in the deep waters of my soul. However in exultations its surface foamed up, at bottom guilt brooded. Sifted out, my motives to this enterprise justified not the mad deed, which, in a moment of rage, I had done; though those motives had been covered with a gracious pretense, concealing myself from myself. But I beat down the thought.

In relating her story, the maiden frequently interrupted it with questions concerning myself: Whence I came: being white, from Oroolia? Whither I was going: to Amma? And what had happened to Aleema? For she had been dismayed at the fray, though knowing not what it could mean, and she had heard the priest's name called upon in lamentations. These questions for the time I endeavored to evade, only inducing her to fancy me some gentle demi-god that had come over the sea from her own fabulous Oroolia. And all this she must verily have believed. For whom, like me, ere this could she have beheld? Still fixed she her eyes upon me strangely, and hung upon the accents of my voice.

While this scene was passing, the strangers began to show signs of impatience; and a voice from the *Chamois* repeatedly hailed us to accelerate our movements.

My course was quickly decided. The only obstacle to be encountered was the possibility of Yillah's alarm at being suddenly borne into my prow. For this event I now sought to prepare her. I informed the damsel that Aleema had been dispatched on a long errand to Oroolia; leaving to my care, for the present, the guardianship of the lovely Yillah; and that, therefore, it was necessary to carry her tent into my own canoe, then waiting to receive it.

This intelligence she received with the utmost concern; and not knowing to what her perplexity might lead, I thought fit to transport her into the *Chamois,* while yet overwhelmed by the announcement of my intention.

Quitting her retreat, I apprised Jarl of my design; and then, no more delay!

At bottom, the tent was attached to a light framework of bamboos; and from its upper corners, four cords, like those of a marquee, confined it to the dais. These Samoa's knife soon parted; when lifting the light tent, we speedily transferred it to the *Chamois,* a wild yell going up from the islanders, which drowned the faint cries of the maiden. But we heeded not the din. Toss in the fruit, hanging from the altar-prow! It was done; and then running up our sail, we glided away—*Chamois,* tent, hostages, and all. Rushing to the now vacant stern of their canoe, the Islanders once more lifted up their hands and their voices in curses.

A suitable distance gained, we paused to fling overboard the arms we had taken, and Jarl proceeded to liberate the hostages.

Meanwhile I entered the tent, and by many tokens sought to allay the maiden's alarm. Thus engaged, violent plunges were heard; our prisoners taking to the sea to regain their canoe. All dripping, they were received by their brethren with wild caresses.

From something now said by the captives, the rest seemed suddenly inspirited with hopes of revenge; again wildly shaking their spears, just before picked up from the sea. With great clamor and confusion they soon set their mat-sail; and instead of sailing southward for Tedaidee, or northward for Amma, their home, they steered straight after us, in our wake.

Foremost in the prow stood three, javelins poised for a dart; at intervals raising a yell.

Did they mean to pursue me? Full in my rear they came on, baying like hounds on their game. Yillah trembled at their cries. My own heart beat hard with undefinable dread. The corpse of Aleema seemed floating before—its avengers were raging behind.

But soon these phantoms departed, for very soon it appeared that in vain the pagans pursued. Their craft our fleet *Chamois* outleaped. And farther and farther astern dropped the evil-boding canoe, till at last but a speck; when a great swell of the sea surged up before it, and it was seen no more. Samoa swore that it must have swamped and gone down. But however it was, my heart lightened apace. I saw none but ourselves on the sea; I remembered that our keel left no track as it sailed.

Let the Oregon Indian through brush, bramble, and brier, hunt his enemy's trail, far over the mountains and down in the vales; comes he to the water, he snuffs idly in air.

Chapter XLV

REMINISCENCES

IN RESCUING THE GENTLE YILLAH FROM THE HANDS OF THE ISLANDERS, A DESIGN SEEMED ACCOMplished. But what was now to be done? Here, in our adventurous *Chamois*, was a damsel more lovely than the flushes of morning; and for companions, whom had she but me and my comrades? Besides, her bosom still throbbed with alarms, her fancies all roving through mazes.

How subdue these dangerous imaginings? How gently dispel them?

But one way there was: to lead her thoughts towards me as her friend and preserver, and a better and wiser than Aleema the priest. Yet could not this be effected but by still maintaining my assumption of a divine origin in the blessed isle of Oroolia, and thus fostering in her heart the mysterious interest with which from the first she had regarded me. But if punctilious reserve on the part of her deliverer should teach her to regard him as some frigid stranger from the Arctic Zone, what sympathy could she have for him? And hence, what peace of mind, having no one else to cling to?

Now re-entering the tent, she again inquired where tarried Aleema.

"Think not of him, sweet Yillah," I cried. "Look on me. Am I not white like yourself? Behold, though since quitting Oroolia the sun has dyed my cheek, am I not even as you? Am I brown like the dusky Aleema? They snatched you away from your isle in the sea too early for you to remember me there. But you have not been forgotten by me, sweetest Yillah. Ha! ha! shook we not the palm-trees together, and chased we not the rolling nuts down the glen? Did we not dive into the grotto on the sea-shore, and come up together in the cool cavern in the hill? In my home in Oroolia, dear Yillah, I have a lock of your hair, ere yet it was golden: a little dark tress like a ring. How your cheeks were then changing from olive to white. And when shall I forget the hour that I came upon you sleeping among the flowers, with roses and lilies for cheeks. Still forgetful? Know you not my voice? Those little spirits in your eyes have seen me before. They mimic me now as they sport in their lakes. All the past a dim blank? Think of the time when we ran up and down in our arbor, where the green vines grew over the great ribs of the stranded whale. Oh, Yillah, little Yillah! has it all come to this? am I forever forgotten? Yet over the wide watery world have I sought thee: from isle to isle, from sea to sea. And now we part not. Aleema is gone. My prow shall keep kissing the waves till it kisses the beach at Oroolia. Yillah, look up."

Sunk the ghost of Aleema—sweet Yillah was mine!

Chapter XLVI

THE CHAMOIS WITH A ROVING COMMISSION

THROUGH THE ASSIDUITY OF MY VIKING, ERE NIGHTFALL OUR *CHAMOIS* WAS AGAIN IN GOOD order. And with many subtle and seaman-like splices, the light tent was lashed in its place; the sail taken up by a reef.

My comrades now questioned me as to my purposes; whether they had been modified by the events of the day. I replied that our destination was still the islands of the westward.

But from these we had steadily been drifting all the morning long; so that now no loom of the land was visible. But our prow was kept pointing as before.

As evening came on my comrades fell fast asleep, leaving me at the helm.

How soft and how dreamy the light of the hour. The rays of the sun, setting behind golden-barred clouds, came to me like the gleaming of a shaded light behind a lattice. And the low breeze, pervaded with the peculiar balm of the mid-Pacific near land, was fragrant as the breath of a bride.

Such was the scene; so still and witching that the hand of Yillah in mine seemed no hand, but a touch. Visions flitted before me and in me—something hummed in my ear—all the air was a lay.

And now entered a thought into my heart. I reflected how serenely we might thus glide along, far removed from all care and anxiety. And then, what different scenes might await us upon any of the shores roundabout. But there seemed no danger in the balmy sea; the assured vicinity of land imparting a sense of security. We had ample supplies for several days more, and, thanks to the pagan canoe, an abundance of fruit.

Besides, what cared I now for the green groves and bright shore? Was not Yillah my shore and my grove, my meadow, my mead, my soft shady vine, and my arbor? Of all things desirable and delightful, the full-plumed sheaf, and my own right arm the band? Enough: no shore for me yet. One sweep of the helm, and our light prow headed round towards the vague land of song, sun, and vine: the fabled south.

As we glided along, strange Yillah gazed down in the sea, and would fain have had me plunge into it with her, to rove through its depths. But I started dismayed; in fancy I saw the stark body of the priest drifting by. Again that phantom obtruded; again guilt laid his red hand on my soul. But I laughed. Was not Yillah my own? By my arm rescued from ill? To do her a good I had periled myself. So down, down, Aleema.

When next morning, starting from slumber, my comrades beheld the sun on our beam instead of astern as before at that hour, they eagerly inquired, "Whither now?" But very briefly I gave them to know, that after devoting the night to the due consideration of a matter so important, I had determined upon voyaging for the island Tedaidee in place of the land to the westward.

At this they were not displeased. But to tell the plain truth, I harbored some shadowy purpose of merely hovering about for a while till I felt more landwardly inclined.

But had I not declared to Yillah that our destination was the fairy isle she spoke of, even Oroolia? Yet that shore was so exceedingly remote, and the folly of endeavoring to reach it in a craft built with hands, so very apparent, that what wonder I really nourished no thought of it?

So away floated the *Chamois*, like a vagrant cloud in the heavens, bound no one knew whither.

Chapter XLVII

Yillah, Jarl, and Samoa

But time to tell how Samoa and Jarl regarded this mystical Yillah, and how Yillah regarded them.

As Beauty from the Beast, so at first shrank the damsel from my one-armed companion. But seeing my confidence in the savage, a reaction soon followed. And in accordance with that curious law by which, under certain conditions, the ugliest mortals become only amiably hideous, Yillah at length came to look upon Samoa as a sort of harmless and good-natured goblin. Whence came he, she cared not; or what was his history; or in what manner his fortunes were united to mine.

May be, she held him a being of spontaneous origin.

Now, as everywhere women are the tamers of the menageries of men, so Yillah in good time tamed down Samoa to a relinquishment of that horrible thing in his ear, and persuaded him to substitute a vacancy for the bauble in his nose. On his part, however, all this was conditional. He stipulated for the privilege of restoring both trinkets upon suitable occasions.

But if thus gaily the damsel sported with Samoa, how different his emotions towards her? The fate to which she had been destined, and every nameless thing about her, appealed to all his native superstitions, which ascribed to beings of her complexion a more than terrestrial origin. When permitted to approach her, he looked timid and awkwardly strange, suggesting the likeness of some clumsy satyr, drawing in his horns, slowly wagging his tail, crouching abashed before some radiant spirit.

And this reverence of his was most pleasing to me. Bravo! thought I; be a pagan forever. No more than myself; for, after a different fashion, Yillah was an idol to both.

But what of my Viking? Why, of good Jarl, I grieve to say, that the old-fashioned interest he took in my affairs led him to look upon Yillah as a sort of intruder, an Ammonite siren, who might lead me astray. This would now and then provoke a phillipic; but he would only turn towards my resentment his devotion; and then I was silent.

Unsophisticated as a wild flower in the germ, Yillah seemed incapable of perceiving the contrasted lights in which she was regarded by our companions. And like a true beauty, seemed to cherish the presumption that it was quite impossible for such a person as hers to prove otherwise than irresistible to all.

She betrayed much surprise at my Viking's appearance. But most of all was she struck by a characteristic device upon the arm of the wonderful mariner—our Savior on the Cross, in blue; with the crown of thorns, and three drops of blood in vermilion, falling one by one from each hand and foot.

Now, honest Jarl did vastly pride himself upon this ornament. It was the only piece of vanity about him. And like a lady keeping gloveless her hand to show off a fine turquoise ring, he invariably wore that sleeve of his frock rolled up, the better to display the embellishment.

And round and round would Yillah turn Jarl's arm, till Jarl was fain to stand firm for fear of revolving all over. How such untutored homage would have thrilled the heart of the ingenious artist!

Eventually, through the Upoluan, she made overtures to the Skyeman, concerning the possession of his picture in her own proper right. In her very simplicity, little heeding, that like a landscape in fresco, it could not be removed.

Chapter XLVIII

SOMETHING UNDER THE SURFACE

NOT TO OMIT AN OCCURRENCE OF CONSIDERABLE INTEREST, WE MUST NEEDS HERE PRESENT some account of a curious retinue of fish which overtook our *Chamois* a day or two after parting with the canoe.

A violent creaming and frothing in our rear announced their approach. Soon we found ourselves the nucleus of an incredible multitude of finny creatures, mostly anonymous.

First, far in advance of our prow, swam the helmeted Silver-heads, side by side in uniform ranks, like an army. Then came the Boneetas, with their flashing blue flanks. Then, like a third distinct regiment, wormed and twisted through the water like Archimedean screws, the quivering Wriggle-tails; followed in turn by the rank and file of the Trigger-fish—so called from their quaint dorsal fins being set in their backs with a comical curve, as if at half-cock. Far astern the rear was brought up by endless battalions of Yellow-backs, right martially vested in buff.

And slow sailing overhead were flights of birds, a wing in the air for every fin in the sea.

But let the sea-fowls fly on: turn we to the fish.

Their numbers were amazing; countless as the tears shed for perfidious lovers. Far abroad on both flanks they swam in long lines, tier above tier; the water alive with their hosts—locusts of the sea, peradventure, going to fall with a blight upon some green, mossy province of Neptune. And tame and fearless they were, as the first fish that swam in Euphrates, hardly evading the hand; insomuch that Samoa caught many without lure or line.

They formed a decorous escort; paddling along by our barnacled sides, as if they had been with us from the very beginning; neither scared by our craft's surging in the water, nor in the least sympathetic at losing a comrade by the hand of Samoa. They closed in their ranks and swam on.

How innocent, yet heartless, they looked! Had a plank dropped out of our boat, we had sunk to the bottom; and belike our cheerful retinue would have paid the last rites to our remains.

But still we kept company as sociably as you please, Samoa helping himself when he listed, and Yillah clapping her hands as the radiant creatures, by a simultaneous turning round on their silvery bellies, caused the whole sea to glow like a burnished shield.

But what has befallen this poor little Boneeta astern that he swims so toilingly on with gills showing purple? What has he there towing behind? It is tangled sea-kelp clinging to its fins. But the clogged thing strains to keep up with its fellows. Yet little they heed. Away they go; every fish for itself, and any fish for Samoa.

At last the poor Boneeta is seen no more. The myriad fins swim on; a lonely waste, where the lost one drops behind.

Strange fish! All the live-long day they were there by our side; and at night still tarried and shone; more crystal and scaly in the pale moonlight than in the golden glare of the sun.

How prettily they swim; all silver life; darting hither and thither between their long ranks, and touching their noses and scraping acquaintance. No mourning they wear for the Boneeta left far astern; nor for those so cruelly killed by Samoa. No, no; all is glee, fishy glee, and frolicking fun; light hearts and light fins; gay backs and gay spirits. Swim away, swim away! my merry fins all. Let us roam the flood; let us follow this monster fish with the barnacled sides; this strange-looking fish so high out of water, that goes without fins. What fish can it be? What rippling is that? Dost hear the great monster breathe? Why, 'tis sharp at both ends; a tail either way—nor eyes has it any, nor mouth. What a curious fish! what a comical fish! But more comical far, those creatures above, on its hollow back, clinging thereto like the snaky eels, that cling and slide on the back of the sword-fish, our terrible foe. But what curious eels these are! Do they deem themselves pretty as we? No, no; for sure, they behold our limber fins, our speckled and beautiful scales. Poor, powerless things! How they must wish they were we, that roam the flood and scour the seas with a wish. Swim away; merry fins, swim away! Let him drop, that fellow that halts; make a lane—close in and fill up. Let him drown if he cannot keep pace. No laggards for us:

We fish, we fish, we merrily swim.
We care not for friend nor for foe.
Our fins are stout,
Our tails are out,
As through the seas we go.

Fish, fish, we are fish with red gills;
Naught disturbs us, our blood is at zero:
We are buoyant because of our bags,
Being many, each fish is a hero.
We care not what is it, this life
That we follow, this phantom unknown:
To swim, it's exceedingly pleasant—
So swim away, making a foam.
This strange looking thing by our side,
Not for safety, around it we flee:—
Its shadow's so shady, that's all—
We only swim under its lee.
And as for the eels there above,
And as for the fowls in the air,
We care not for them nor their ways,
As we cheerily glide afar!

We fish, we fish, we merrily swim,
We care not for friend nor for foe:
Our fins are stout,
Our tails are out,
As through the seas we go.

But how now, my fine fish! what alarms your long ranks, and tosses them all into a hubbub of scales and of foam? Never mind that long knave with the spear there astern. Pipe away, merry fish, and give us a stave or two more, keeping time with your doggerel tails. But no, no! their singing was over. Grim death, in the shape of a Chevalier, was after them.

How they changed their boastful tune! How they hugged the vilified boat! How they wished they were in it, the braggarts! And how they all tingled with fear!

For now here, now there, is heard a terrific rushing sound under water, betokening the onslaught of the dread fish of prey, that, with spear ever in rest, charges in upon the outskirts of the shoal, transfixing the fish on his weapon. Retreating and shaking them off, the Chevalier devours them: then returns to the charge.

Hugging the boat to desperation, the poor fish fairly crowded themselves up to the surface, and floundered upon each other, as men are lifted off their feet in a mob. They clung to us thus, out of a fancied security in our presence. Knowing this, we felt no little alarm for ourselves, dreading lest the Chevalier might despise our boat full as much as his prey; and in pursuing the fish, run through the poor *Chamois* with a lunge. A jacket, rolled up was kept in readiness to be thrust into the first opening made; while as the thousand fins audibly patted against our slender planks, we felt nervously enough; as if treading upon thin, cracking ice.

At length, to our no small delight, the enemy swam away; and again by our side merrily paddled our escort; ten times merrier than ever.

Chapter XLIX

YILLAH

WHILE FOR A FEW DAYS, NOW THIS WAY, NOW THAT, AS OUR CRAFT GLIDES ALONG, SURROUNDED by these locusts of the deep, let the story of Yillah flow on.

Of her beauty say I nothing. It was that of a crystal lake in a fathomless wood: all light and shade; full of fleeting revealings; now shadowed in depths; now sunny in dimples; but all sparkling and shifting and blending together.

But her wild beauty was a veil to things still more strange. As often she gazed so earnestly into my eyes, like some pure spirit looking far down into my soul, and seeing therein some upturned faces, I stared in amaze, and asked what spell was on me that thus she gazed.

Often she entreated me to repeat over and over again certain syllables of my language. These she would chant to herself, pausing now and then, as if striving to discover wherein lay their charm.

In her accent there was something very different from that of the people of the canoe. Wherein lay the difference I knew not; but it enabled her to pronounce with readiness all the words which I taught her; even as if recalling sounds long forgotten.

If all this filled me with wonder, how much was that wonder increased, and yet baffled again, by considering her complexion, and the cast of her features.

After endeavoring in various ways to account for these things, I was led to imagine that the damsel must be an Albino (Tulla) occasionally to be met with among the people of the Pacific. These persons are of an exceedingly delicate white skin, tinted with a faint rose hue like the lips of a shell. Their hair is golden. But, unlike the Albinos of other climes, their eyes are invariably blue, and no way intolerant of light.

As a race the Tullas die early. And hence the belief that they pertain to some distant sphere, and only through irregularities in the providence of the gods, come to make their appearance upon earth; whence, the oversight discovered, they are hastily snatched. And it is chiefly on this account, that in those islands where human sacrifices are offered, the Tullas are deemed the most suitable oblations for the altar, to which from their birth many are prospectively devoted. It was these considerations, united to others, which at times induced me to fancy that, by the priest, Yillah must have been regarded as one of these beings. So mystical, however, her revelations concerning her past history that often I knew not what to divine. But plainly they showed that she had not the remotest conception of her real origin.

But these conceits of a state of being anterior to an earthly existence may have originated in one of those celestial visions seen transparently stealing over the face of a slumbering child, and craftily drawn forth and re-echoed by another, and at times repeated over to her with many additions, these imaginings must at length have assumed in her mind a hue of reality, heightened into conviction by the dreamy seclusion of her life.

But now, let her subsequent and more credible history be related, as from time to time she rehearsed it.

Chapter L

YILLAH IN ARDAIR

IN THE VERDANT GLEN OF ARDAIR, FAR IN THE SILENT INTERIOR OF AMMA, SHUT IN BY HOAR CLIFFS, Yillah the maiden abode.

So small and so deep was this glen, so surrounded on all sides by steep acclivities, and so vividly green its verdure, and deceptive the shadows that played there, that from above, it seemed more like a lake of cool, balmy air than a glen; its woodlands and grasses gleaming shadowy all, like sea groves and mosses beneath the calm sea.

Here none came but Aleema the priest, who at times was absent for days together. But at certain seasons an unseen multitude with loud chants stood upon the verge of the neighboring precipices, and traversing those shaded wilds, slowly retreated; their voices lessening and lessening as they wended their way through the more distant groves.

At other times, Yillah being immured in the temple of Apo, a band of men, entering the vale, surrounded her retreat, dancing there till evening came. Meanwhile, heaps of fruit, garlands of flowers, and baskets of fish were laid upon an altar without, where stood Aleema, arrayed in white tappa, and muttering to himself as the offerings were laid at his feet.

When Aleema was gone, Yillah went forth into the glen and wandered among the trees, and reposed by the banks of the stream. And ever as she strolled, looked down upon her the grim old cliffs, bearded with trailing moss.

Towards the lower end of the vale, its lofty walls advancing and overhanging their base, almost met in mid air. And a great rock, hurled from an adjacent height, and falling into the space intercepted, there remained fixed. Aerial trees shot up from its surface; birds nested in its cleft; and strange vines roved abroad, over-running the tops of the trees, lying thereon in coils and undulations, like anacondas basking in the light. Beneath this rock was a lofty wall of ponderous stones. Between its crevices, peeps were had of a long and leafy arcade, quivering far away to where the sea rolled in the sun. Lower down these crevices gave an outlet to the waters of the brook, which, on a long cascade, poured over sloping green ledges, near the foot of the wall, into a deep shady pool; whose rocky sides, by the perpetual eddying of the water, had been worn into a grotesque resemblance to a group of giants with heads submerged, indolently reclining about the basin.

In this pool Yillah would bathe. And once, emerging, she heard the echoes of a voice, and called aloud; but the only reply was the rustling of branches, as someone, invisible, fled down the valley beyond. Soon after a stone rolled inward, and Aleema the priest stood before her, saying that the voice she had heard was his. But it was not.

At last the weary days grew longer and longer, and the maiden pined for companionship. When the breeze blew not, but slept in the caves of the mountains, and all the leaves of the trees stood motionless as tears in the eye, Yillah would sadden, and call upon the spirits in her soul to awaken. She sang low airs she thought she had heard in Oroolia; but started affrighted, as from dingles and dells came back to her strains more wild than hers. And ever, when sad, Aleema would seek to cheer her soul by calling to mind the bright scenes of Oroolia the Blessed, to which place, he averred, she was shortly to return, never more to depart.

Now at the head of the vale of Ardair rose a tall, dark peak, presenting at the top the grim profile of a human face, whose shadow, every afternoon, crept down the verdant side of the mountain: a silent phantom, stealing all over the bosom of the glen.

At times, when the phantom drew near, Aleema would take Yillah forth, and waiting its approach, lay her down by the shadow, disposing her arms in a caress, saying, "Oh, Apo! dost accept thy bride?" And at last, when it crept beyond the place where he stood, and buried the whole valley in gloom, Aleema would say, "Arise Yillah; Apo hath stretched himself to sleep in Ardair. Go slumber where thou wilt, for thou wilt slumber in his arms."

And so, every night, slept the maiden in the arms of grim Apo.

One day when Yillah had come to love the wild shadow as something that every day moved before her eyes, where all was so deathfully still, she went forth alone to watch it, as softly it slid down from the peak. Of a sudden, when its face was just edging the chasm, that made it to look as if parting its lips, she heard a loud voice, and thought it was Apo calling "Yillah—Yillah!" But now it seemed like the voice she had heard while bathing in the pool. Glancing upward, she beheld a beautiful open-armed youth gazing down upon her from an inaccessible crag. But presently there was a rustling in the groves behind, and, swift as thought, something darted through the air. The youth bounded forward. Yillah opened her arms to receive him, but he fell upon the cliff and was seen no more. As alarmed, and in tears, she fled from the scene, someone out of sight ran before her through the wood.

Upon recounting this adventure to Aleema, he said that the being she had seen must have been a bad spirit come to molest her, and that Apo had slain him.

The sight of this youth filled Yillah with wild yearnings to escape from her lonely retreat; for a glimpse of someone beside the priest and the phantom suggested vague thoughts of worlds of fair beings in regions beyond Ardair. But Aleema sought to put away these conceits, saying that ere long she would be journeying to Oroolia, there to rejoin the spirits she dimly remembered.

Soon after he came to her with a shell—one of those ever moaning of ocean—and placing it to her ear, bade her list to the being within, which in that little shell had voyaged from Oroolia to bear her company in Amma.

Now the maiden oft held it to her ear, and closing her eyes, listened and listened to its soft inner breathings, till visions were born of the sound, and her soul lay for hours in a trance of delight.

And again the priest came, and brought her a milk-white bird with a bill jet black, and eyes like stars. "In this lurks the soul of a maiden; it hath flown from Oroolia to greet you." The soft stranger willingly nestled in her bosom, turning its bright eyes upon hers and softly warbling.

Many days passed, and Yillah, the bird, and the shell were inseparable. The bird grew familiar; pecked seeds from her mouth; perched upon her shoulder, and sang in her ear; and at night, folded its wings in her bosom, and, like a sea-fowl, went softly to sleep, rising and falling upon the maiden's heart. And every morning it flew from its nest and fluttered and chirped, and sailed to and fro, and blithely sang, and brushed Yillah's cheek till she woke. Then came to her hand, and Yillah, looking earnestly in its eyes, saw strange faces there, and said to herself as she gazed—"These are two souls, not one."

But at last, going forth into the groves with the bird, it suddenly flew from her side and perched in a bough; and throwing back its white downy throat, there gushed from its bill a clear warbling jet, like a little fountain in air. Now the song ceased, when up and away towards the head of the vale flew the bird. "Lil! Lil! come back, leave me not, blessed souls of the maidens." But on flew the bird, far up a defile, winging its way, till a speck.

It was shortly after this, and upon the evening of a day which had been tumultuous with sounds of warfare beyond the lower wall of the glen, that Aleema came to Yillah in alarm, saying—"Yillah, the time has come to follow thy bird; come, return to thy home in Oroolia." And he told her the way she would voyage there: by the vortex on the coast of Tedaidee. That night, being veiled and placed in the tent, the maiden was borne to the sea-side, where the canoe was in waiting. And setting sail quickly, by next morning the island of Amma was no longer in sight.

And this was the voyage whose sequel has already been recounted.

Chapter LI

THE DREAM BEGINS TO FADE

STRIPPED OF THE STRANGE ASSOCIATIONS WITH WHICH A MIND LIKE YILLAH'S MUST HAVE INVESTED every incident of her life, the story of her abode in Ardair seemed not incredible. But so etherealized had she become from the wild conceits she nourished, that she verily believed herself a being of the lands of dreams. Her fabulous past was her present.

Yet as our intimacy grew closer and closer, these fancies seemed to be losing their hold. And often she questioned me concerning my own reminiscences of her shadowy isle. And cautiously I sought to produce the impression that whatever I had said of that clime, had been revealed to me in dreams; but that in these dreams her own lineaments had smiled upon me, and hence the impulse which had sent me roving after the substance of this spiritual image.

And true it was to say so; and right it was to swear it upon her white arms crossed. For oh, Yillah! were you not the earthly semblance of that sweet vision that haunted my earliest thoughts?

At first she had wildly believed that the nameless affinities between us were owing to our having in times gone by dwelt together in the same ethereal region. But thoughts like these were fast dying out; yet not without many strange scrutinies. More intently than ever she gazed into my eyes, rested her ear against my heart, and listened to its beatings. And love, which in the eye of its object ever seeks to invest itself with some rare superiority, love, sometimes induced me to prop my failing divinity; though it was I myself who had undermined it.

But if it was with many regrets that in the sight of Yillah I perceived myself thus dwarfing down to a mortal; it was with quite contrary emotions that I contemplated the extinguishment in her heart of the notion of her own spirituality. For as such thoughts were chased away, she clung the more closely to me, as unto one without whom she would be desolate indeed.

And now, at intervals, she was sad, and often gazed long and fixedly into the sea. Nor would she say why it was that she did so; until at length she yielded and replied that whatever false things Aleema might have instilled into her mind, of this much she was certain, that the whirlpool on the coast of Tedaidee prefigured her fate; that in the waters she saw lustrous eyes and beckoning phantoms, and strange shapes smoothing her a couch among the mosses.

Her dreams seemed mine. Many visions I had of the green corse of the priest, outstretching its arms in the water to receive pale Yillah as she sunk in the sea.

But these forebodings departed, no happiness in the universe like ours. We lived and we loved; life and love were united—in gladness glided our days.

Chapter LII

WORLD HO!

FIVE SUNS ROSE AND SET. AND YILLAH PINING FOR THE SHORE, WE TURNED OUR PROW DUE WEST, and next morning came in sight of land.

It was innumerable islands; lifting themselves bluely through the azure air, and looking upon the distant sea, like haycocks in a hazy field. Towering above all, and midmost rose a mighty peak; one fleecy cloud sloping against its summit; a column wreathed. Beyond, like purple steeps in heaven at set of sun, stretched far away what seemed lands on lands in infinite perspective.

Gliding on, the islands grew more distinct, rising up from the billows to greet us, revealing hills, vales, and peaks grouped within a milk-white zone of reef so vast that in the distance all was dim. The jeweled vapors, erewhile hovering over these violet shores, now seemed to be shedding their gems; and as the almost level rays of the sun, shooting through the air like a variegated prism, touched the verdant land, it trembled all over with dewy sparkles.

Still nearer we came, our sail faintly distended as the breeze died away from our vicinity to the isles. The billows rolled listlessly by, as if conscious that their long task was nigh done; while gleamed the white reef, like the trail of a great fish in a calm. But as yet no sign of paddle or canoe—no distant smoke—no shining thatch. Bravo! good comrades, we've discovered some new constellation in the sea.

Sweet Yillah, no more of Oroolia; see you not this flowery land? Nevermore shall we desire to roam.

Voyaging along the zone, we came to an opening; and quitting the firmament blue of the open sea, we glided in upon the still, green waters of the wide lagoon. Mapped out in the broad shadows of the isles, and tinted here and there with the reflected hues of the sun-clouds, the mild waters stretched all around us like another sky. Nearby the break in the reef was a little island, with palm-trees harping in the breeze; an aviary of alluring sounds that seemed calling upon us to land. And here Yillah, whom the sight of the verdure had made glad, threw out a merry suggestion. Nothing less than to plant our mast, sail-set, upon the highest hill, and fly away, island and all; trees rocking, birds caroling, flowers springing; away, away, across the wide waters to Oroolia! But alas! how weigh the isle's coral anchor, leagues down in the fathomless sea?

We glanced around, but all the islands seemed slumbering in the flooding light.

"A canoe! a canoe!" cried Samoa, as three proas showed themselves rounding a neighboring shore. Instantly we sailed for them; but after shooting to and fro for a time, and standing up and gazing at us, the Islanders retreated behind the headland. Hardly were they out of sight when from many a shore roundabout other proas pushed off. Soon the water all round us was enlivened by fleets of canoes, darting hither and thither like frighted water-fowls. Presently they all made for one island.

From their actions we argued that these people could have had but little or no intercourse with whites; and most probably knew not how to account for our appearance among them. Desirous, therefore, of a friendly meeting ere any hostile suspicions might arise, we pointed our craft for the island, whither all the canoes were now hastening. Whereupon those which had not yet reached their destination turned and fled, while the occupants of the proas that had landed ran into the groves, and were lost to view.

Crossing the distinct outer line of the isle's shadow on the water, we gained the shore; and gliding along its margin, passing canoe after canoe, hauled up on the silent beach, which otherwise seemed entirely innocent of men.

A dilemma. But I decided at last upon disembarking Jarl and Samoa to seek out and conciliate the natives. So, landing them upon a jutting buttress of coral, whence they waded to the shore, I pushed off with Yillah into the water beyond to await the event.

Full an hour must have elapsed, when, to our great joy, loud shouts were heard; and there burst into view a tumultuous crowd, in the midst of which my Viking was descried, mounted upon the shoulders of two brawny natives; while the Upoluan, striding on in advance, seemed resisting a similar attempt to elevate him in the world. Good omens both.

"Come ashore!" cried Jarl. "Aramai!" cried Samoa, while storms of interjections went up from the Islanders, who, with extravagant gestures danced about the beach.

Further caution seemed needless; I pointed our prow for the shore. No sooner was this perceived than, raising an applauding shout, the Islanders ran up to their waists in the sea. And skimming like a gull over the smooth lagoon, the light shallop darted in among them. Quick as thought, fifty hands were on the gunwale; and, with all its contents lifted bodily into the air, the little *Chamois* upon many a dripping shoulder, was borne deep into the groves. Yillah shrieked at the rocking motion, and when the boughs of the trees brushed against the tent.

With his staff an old man now pointed to a couple of twin-like trees, some four paces apart, and a little way from the ground conveniently crotched.

And here, eftsoons, they deposited their burden; lowering the *Chamois* gently between the forks of the trees, whose willow-like foliage fringed the tent and its inmate.

Chapter LIII

The Chamois Ashore

UNTIL NOW, ENVELOPED IN HER ROBE, AND CROUCHING LIKE A FAWN, YILLAH HAD BEEN WELL-nigh hidden from view. But presently she withdrew her hood.

What saw the islanders that they so gazed and adored in silence: some retreating, some creeping nearer, and the women all in a flutter? Long they gazed, and following Samoa's example, stretched forth their arms in reverence.

The adoration of the maiden was extended to myself. Indeed, from the singular gestures employed, I had all along suspected that we were being received with unwonted honors.

I now sought to get speech of my comrades. But so obstreperous was the crowd that it was next to impossible. Jarl was still in his perch in the air; his enthusiastic bearers not yet suffering him to alight. Samoa, however, who had managed to keep out of the saddle, by and by contrived to draw nearer to the *Chamois*.

He advised me by no means to descend for the present, since in any event we were sure of remaining unmolested therein, the islanders regarding it as sacred.

The Upoluan attracted a great deal of attention; chiefly from his style of tattooing, which, together with other peculiarities, so interested the natives that they were perpetually hanging about him, putting eager questions, and all the time keeping up a violent clamor.

But despite the large demand upon his lungs, Samoa made out to inform me that notwithstanding the multitude assembled, there was no high chief, or person of consequence present; the king of the place, also those of the islands adjacent, being absent at a festival in another quarter of the Archipelago. But upon the first distant glimpse of the *Chamois*, fleet canoes had been dispatched to announce the surprising event that had happened.

In good time, the crowd becoming less tumultuous and abandoning the siege of Samoa, I availed myself of this welcome lull, and called upon him and my Viking to enter the *Chamois*; desirous of condensing our forces against all emergencies.

Samoa now gave me to understand that from all he could learn, the islanders regarded me as a superior being. They had inquired of him whether I was not white Taji, a sort of half-and-half deity, now and then an Avatar among them, and ranking among their inferior ex-officio demi-gods. To this Samoa had said ay; adding, moreover, all he could to encourage the idea.

He now entreated me at the first opportunity to announce myself as Taji, declaring that if once received under that title, the unbounded hospitality of our final reception would be certain, and our persons fenced about from all harm.

Encouraging this. But it was best to be wary. For although among some barbarians the first strangers landing upon their shores are frequently hailed as divine, and in more than one wild land have been actually styled gods as a familiar designation, yet this has not exempted the celestial visitants from peril when too much presuming upon the reception extended to them. In sudden tumults they have been slain outright, and while full faith in their divinity had in no wise abated. The sad fate of an eminent navigator is a well-known illustration of this unaccountable waywardness.

With no small anxiety, therefore, we awaited the approach of some of the dignitaries of Mardi, for by this collective appellation, the people informed us, their islands were known.

We waited not long. Of a sudden, from the sea-side, a single shrill cry was heard. A moment more, and the blast of numerous conch shells startled the air, a confused clamor drew nearer and nearer; and flying our eyes in the direction of these sounds, we impatiently awaited what was to follow.

Chapter LIV

A Gentleman from the Sun

NEVER BEFORE HAD I SEEN THE DEEP FOLIAGE OF WOODLANDS NAVIGATED BY CANOES. BUT ON they came sailing through the leaves; two abreast—borne on men's shoulders—in each a chief, carried along to the measured march of his bearers; paddle-blades reversed under arms. As they emerged the multitude made gestures of homage. At the distance of some eight or ten paces the procession halted, when the kings alighted to the ground.

They were fine-looking men, arrayed in various garbs. Rare the show of stained feathers and jewels and other adornments. Brave the floating of dyed mantles.

The regal bearing of these personages, the deference paid them, and their entire self-possession, not a little surprised me. And it seemed preposterous to assume a divine dignity in the presence of these undoubted potentates of terra firma. Taji seemed oozing from my fingers' ends. But courage! and erecting my crest, I strove to look every inch the character I had determined to assume.

For a time it was almost impossible to tell with what emotions precisely the chiefs were regarding me. They said not a word.

But plucking up heart of grace, I crossed my cutlass on my chest, and reposing my hand on the hilt, addressed their High Mightinesses thus: "Men of Mardi, I come from the sun. When this morning it rose and touched the wave, I pushed my shallop from its golden beach, and hither sailed before its level rays. I am Taji."

More would have been added, but I paused for the effect of my exordium.

Stepping back a pace or two, the chiefs eagerly conversed.

Emboldened, I returned to the charge, and labored hard to impress them with just such impressions of me and mine as I deemed desirable. The gentle Yillah was a seraph from the sun; Samoa I had picked off a reef in my route from that orb; and as for the Skyeman, why, as his name imported, he came from above. In a word, we were all strolling divinities.

Advancing towards the *Chamois,* one of the kings, a calm old man, now addressed me as follows: "Is this, indeed, Taji? He who, according to a tradition, was to return to us after five thousand moons? But that period is yet unexpired. What bringst thou hither then, Taji, before thy time? Thou wast but a quarrelsome demi-god, say the legends, when thou dwelt among our sires. But wherefore comest thou, Taji? Truly thou wilt interfere with the worship of thy images, and we have plenty of gods besides thee. But comest thou to fight? We have plenty of spears, and desire not thine. Comest thou to dwell? Small are the houses of Mardi. Or comest thou to fish in the sea? Tell us, Taji!"

Now, all this was a series of posers hard to be answered; furnishing a curious example, moreover, of the reception given to strange demi-gods when they travel without their portmanteaus; and also of the familiar manner in which these kings address the immortals. Much I mourned that I had not previously studied better my part, and learned the precise nature of my previous existence in the land.

But nothing like carrying it bravely.

"Attend. Taji comes, old man, because it pleases him to come. And Taji will depart when it suits him. Ask the shades of your sires whether Taji thus scurvily greeted them when they came stalking into his presence in the land of spirits. No, Taji spread the banquet. He removed their mantles. He kindled a fire to drive away the damp. He said not, 'Come you to fight, you fogs and vapors? come you to dwell? or come you to fish in the sea?' Go to, then, kings of Mardi!"

Upon this the old king fell back, and his place was supplied by a noble chief, of a free, frank bearing. Advancing quickly towards the boat, he exclaimed—"I am Media, the son of Media. Thrice welcome, Taji. On my island of Odo hast thou an altar. I claim thee for my guest." He then reminded the rest that the strangers had voyaged far, and needed repose. And, furthermore, that he proposed escorting them forthwith to his own dominions; where, next day, he would be happy to welcome all visitants.

And good as his word, he commanded his followers to range themselves under the *Chamois.* Springing out of our prow, the Upoluan was followed by Jarl; leaving Yillah and Taji to be borne therein towards the sea.

Soon we were once more afloat; by our side, Media sociably seated; six of his paddlers perched upon the gunwale, swiftly urging us over the lagoon.

The transition from the grove to the sea was instantaneous. All seemed a dream.

The place to which we were hastening being some distance away, as we rounded isle after isle, the extent of the Archipelago grew upon us greatly.

Chapter LV

TIFFIN IN A TEMPLE

UPON AT LAST DRAWING NIGH TO ODO, ITS APPEARANCE SOMEWHAT DISAPPOINTED ME. A SMALL island, of moderate elevation.

But plumb not the height of the house that feasts you.

The beach was lined with expectant natives, who, lifting the *Chamois*, carried us up the beach.

Alighting as they were bearing us along, King Media, designating a canoe-house hard by, ordered our craft to be deposited therein. This being done, we stepped upon the soil. It was the first we had pressed in very many days. It sent a sympathetic thrill through our frames.

Turning his steps inland, Media signed us to follow.

Soon we came to a rude sort of enclosure, fenced in by an imposing wall. Here a halt was sounded, and in great haste the natives proceeded to throw down a portion of the stones. This accomplished, we were signed to enter the fortress thus carried by storm. Upon an artificial mound, opposite the breach, stood a small structure of bamboo, open in front. Within was a long pedestal, like a settee, supporting three images, also of wood, and about the size of men; bearing, likewise, a remote resemblance to that species of animated nature. Before these idols was an altar, and at its base many fine mats.

Entering the temple as if he felt very much at home, Media disposed these mats so as to form a very pleasant lounge, where he deferentially entreated Yillah to recline. Then deliberately removing the first idol, he motioned me to seat myself in its place. Setting aside the middle one, he quietly established himself in its stead. The displaced ciphers, meanwhile, standing upright before us, and their blank faces looking upon this occasion unusually expressive. As yet not a syllable as to the meaning of this cavalier treatment of their wooden godships.

We now tranquilly awaited what next might happen, and I earnestly prayed that if sacrilege was being committed, the vengeance of the gods might be averted from an ignoramus like me, notwithstanding the petitioner himself hailed from the other world. Perfect silence was preserved; Jarl and Samoa standing a little without the temple, the first looking quite composed, but his comrade casting wondering glances at my sociable apotheosis with Media.

Now, happening to glance upon the image last removed, I was not long in detecting a certain resemblance between it and our host. Both were decorated in the same manner, the carving on the idol exactly corresponding with the tattooing of the king.

Presently the silence was relieved by a commotion without, and a butler approached, staggering under an immense wooden trencher, which, with profound genuflexions, he deposited upon the altar before us. The tray was loaded like any harvest wain; heaped up with good things sundry and divers; bread-fruit and cocoanuts, and plantains and guavas; all pleasant to the eye, and furnishing good earnest of something equally pleasant to the palate.

Transported at the sight of these viands, after so long an estrangement from full indulgence in things green, I was forthwith proceeding to help Yillah and myself when, like lightning, a most unwelcome query obtruded. Did deities dine? Then also recurred what Media had declared about my shrine in Odo. Was this it? Self-sacrilegious demi-god that I was, was I going to gluttonize on the very offerings laid before me in my own sacred fane? Give heed to thy ways, oh Taji, lest thou stumble and be lost!

But hereupon what saw we but his cool majesty of Odo tranquilly proceeding to lunch in the temple?

How now? Was Media, too, a god? Egad, it must be so. Else, why his image here in the fane, and the original so entirely at his ease, with legs full cozily tucked away under the very altar itself. This put to flight all appalling apprehensions of the necessity of starving to keep up the assumption of my divinity. So without more ado I helped myself right and left, taking the best care of Yillah, who ever fed her flushed beauty with juicy fruits, thereby transferring to her cheek the sweet glow of the guava.

Our hunger appeased, and Media in token thereof celestially laying his hand upon the appropriate region, we proceeded to quit the enclosure. But coming to the wall where the breach had been made, lo! and behold, no breach was to be seen. But down it came tumbling again, and forth we issued.

This overthrowing of walls, be it known, is an incidental compliment paid distinguished personages in this part of Mardi. It would seem to signify that such gentry can go nowhere without creating an impression, even upon the most obdurate substances.

But to return to our ambrosial lunch.

Sublimate, as you will, the idea of our ethereality as intellectual beings, no sensible man can harbor a doubt but that there is a vast deal of satisfaction in dining. More, there is a savor of life and immortality in substantial fare. Like balloons, we are nothing till filled.

And well knowing this, nature has provided this jolly round board, our globe, which in an endless sequence of courses and crops, spreads a perpetual feast. Though, as with most public banquets, there is no small crowding, and many go away famished from plenty.

Chapter LVI

King Media a Host

STRIKING INTO A GROVE, ABOUT SUNSET WE EMERGED UPON A FINE, CLEAR SPACE, AND SPIED A city in the woods.

In the middle of all, like a generalissimo's marquee among tents, was a structure more imposing than the rest. Here abode King Media.

Disposed round a space some fifty yards square were many palm posts staked firmly in the earth. A man's height from the ground, these supported numerous horizontal trunks, upon which lay a flooring of hibiscus. High over this dais, but resting upon independent supports beyond, a gable-ended roof sloped away to within a short distance of the ground.

Such was the palace.

We entered it by an arched, arbored entrance at one of its palmetto-thatched ends. But not through this exclusive portal entered the islanders. Humbly stooping, they found ingress under the drooping eaves. A custom immemorial, and well calculated to remind all contumacious subjects of the dignity of the habitation thus entered.

Three steps led to the summit of the dais, where piles of soft mats and light pillows of woven grass, stuffed with the golden down of a wild thistle, invited all loiterers to lounge.

How pleasant the twilight that welled up from under the low eaves, above which we were seated. And how obvious now the design of the roof. No shade more grateful and complete; the garish sun lingering without like some lackey in waiting.

But who is this in the corner, gaping at us like a butler in a quandary? Media's household deity, in the guise of a plethoric monster, his enormous head lolling back, and wide, gaping mouth stuffed full of fresh fruits and green leaves. Truly had the idol possessed a soul under his knotty ribs, how tantalizing to hold so glorious a mouthful without the power of deglutition. Far worse than the inexorable lock-jaw, which will not admit of the step preliminary to a swallow.

This jolly Josh image was that of an inferior deity, the god of Good Cheer, and often after we met with his merry round mouth in many other abodes in Mardi. Daily, his jaws are replenished as a flower vase in summer.

But did the demi-divine Media thus brook the perpetual presence of a subaltern divinity? Still more: did he render it homage? But ere long the Mardian mythology will be discussed, thereby making plain what may now seem anomalous.

Politely escorting us into his palace, Media did the honors by inviting his guests to recline. He then seemed very anxious to impress us with the fact that by bringing us to his home, and thereby charging the royal larder with our maintenance, he had taken no hasty or imprudent step. His merry butlers kept piling round us viands till we were well-nigh walled in. At every fresh deposit, Media directing our attention to the same, as yet additional evidence of his ample resources as a host. The evidence was finally closed by dragging under the eaves a felled plantain tree, the spike of red ripe fruit, sprouting therefrom, blushing all over at so rude an introduction to the notice of strangers.

During this scene, Jarl was privily nudging Samoa, in wonderment, to know what upon earth it all meant. But Samoa, scarcely deigning to notice interrogatories propounded through the elbow, only let drop a vague hint or two.

It was quite amusing what airs Samoa now gave himself, at least towards my Viking. Among the Mardians he was at home. And who, when there, stretches not out his legs and says unto himself, "Who is greater than I?"

To be plain: concerning himself and the Skyeman the tables were turned. At sea Jarl had been the oracle: an old sea-sage, learned in hemp and helm. But our craft high and dry, the Upoluan lifted his crest as the erudite pagan; master of Gog and Magog, expounder of all things heathenish and obscure.

An hour or two was now laughed away in very charming conversation with Media; when I hinted that a couch and solitude would be acceptable. Whereupon seizing a taper, our host escorted us without the palace. And ushering us into a handsome unoccupied mansion, gave me to understand that the same was mine. Mounting to the dais, he then instituted a vigorous investigation to discern whether everything was in order. Not fancying something about the mats, he rolled them up into bundles, and one by one sent them flying at the heads of his servitors, who, upon that gentle hint, made off with them, soon returning with fresh ones. These, with mathematical precision, Media in person now spread on the dais, looking carefully to the fringes or ruffles with which they were bordered as if striving to impart to them a sentimental expression.

This done, he withdrew.

Chapter LVII

TAJI TAKES COUNSEL WITH HIMSELF

MY BRIEF INTERCOURSE WITH OUR HOST HAD BY THIS TIME ENABLED ME TO FORM A PRETTY good notion of the light in which I was held by him and his more intelligent subjects.

His free and easy carriage evinced, that though acknowledging my assumptions, he was no way overawed by them; treating me as familiarly, indeed, as if I were a mere mortal, one of the abject generation of mushrooms.

The scene in the temple, however, had done much towards explaining this demeanor of his. A demi-god in his own proper person, my claims to a similar dignity neither struck him with wonder, nor lessened his good opinion of himself.

As for anything foreign in my aspect, and my ignorance of Mardian customs—all this, instead of begetting a doubt unfavorable to my pretensions, but strengthened the conviction of them as verities. Thus has it been in similar instances; but to a much greater extent. The celebrated navigator referred to in a preceding chapter, was hailed by the Hawaiians as one of their demi-gods returned to earth after a wide tour of the universe. And they worshiped him as such, though incessantly he was interrogating them as to who under the sun his worshipers were; how their ancestors came on the island, and whether they would have the kindness to provide his followers with plenty of pork during his stay.

But a word or two concerning the idols in the shrine at Odo. Superadded to the homage rendered him as a temporal prince, Media was there worshiped as a spiritual being. In his corporeal absence, his effigy receiving all oblations intended for him. And in the days of his boyhood, listening to the old legends of the Mardian mythology, Media had conceived a strong liking for the fabulous Taji; a deity whom he had often declared was worthy a niche in any temple extant. Hence he had honored my image with a place in his own special shrine, placing it side by side with his worshipful likeness.

I appreciated the compliment. But of the close companionship of the other image there, I was heartily ashamed. And with reason. The nuisance in question being the image of a deified maker of plantain-pudding, lately deceased, who had been famed far and wide as the most notable fellow of his profession in the whole Archipelago. During his sublunary career, having been attached to the household of Media, his grateful master had afterward seen fit to crown his celebrity by this posthumous distinction: a circumstance sadly subtracting from the dignity of an apotheosis. Nor must it here be omitted that in this part of Mardi culinary artists are accounted worthy of high consideration. For among these people of Odo the matter of eating and drinking is held a matter of life and of death. "Drag away my queen from my arms," said old Tyty when overcome of Adommo, "but leave me my cook."

Now, among the Mardians there were plenty of incarnated deities to keep me in countenance. Most of the kings of the Archipelago, besides Media, claiming homage as demi-gods; and that, too, by virtue of hereditary descent, the divine spark being transmissable from father to son. In illustration of this was the fact that in several instances the people of the land addressed the supreme god Oro in the very same terms employed in the political adoration of their sublunary rulers.

Ay: there were deities in Mardi far greater and taller than I: right royal monarchs to boot, living in jolly round tabernacles of jolly brown clay, and feasting and roystering, and lording it in yellow tabernacles of bamboo. These demi-gods had wherewithal to sustain their lofty pretensions. If need were, could crush out of him the infidelity of a non-conformist. And by this immaculate union of church and state, god and king, in their own proper persons reigned supreme Cæsars over the soul and bodies of their subjects.

Beside these mighty magnates, I and my divinity shrank into nothing. In their woodland antechambers plebeian deities were kept lingering. For be it known that in due time we met with several decayed, broken-down demi-gods; magnificos of no mark in Mardi; having no temples wherein to feast personal admirers or spiritual devotees. They wandered about forlorn and friendless. And oftentimes in their dinnerless despair hugely gluttonized, and would fain have grown fat, by reflecting upon the magnificence of their genealogies. But, poor fellows! like shabby Scotch lords in London in King James's time, the very multitude of them confounded distinction. And since they could show no rent roll, they were permitted to fume unheeded.

Upon the whole, so numerous were living and breathing gods in Mardi, that I held my divinity but cheaply. And seeing such a host of immortals, and hearing of multitudes more purely spiritual in their nature, haunting woodlands and streams, my views of theology grew strangely confused; I began to bethink me of the Jew that rejected the Talmud, and his all-permeating principle to which Goethe and others have subscribed.

Instead, then, of being struck with the audacity of endeavoring to palm myself off as a god—the way in which the thing first impressed me—I now perceived that I might be a god as much as I pleased, and yet not whisk a lion's tail after all; at least on that special account.

As for Media's reception, its graciousness was not wholly owing to the divine character imputed to me. His, he believed to be the same. But to a whim, a freakishness in his soul, which led him to fancy me as one among many, not as one with no peer.

But the apparent unconcern of King Media with respect to my godship by no means so much surprised me as his unaffected indifference to my amazing voyage from the sun; his indifference to the sun itself; and all the wonderful circumstances that must have attended my departure. Whether he had ever been there himself, that he regarded a solar trip with so much unconcern, almost became a question in my mind. Certain it is that as a mere traveler he must have deemed me no very great prodigy.

My surprise at these things was enhanced by reflecting, that to the people of the Archipelago the map of Mardi was the map of the world. With the exception of certain islands out of sight, and at an indefinite distance, they had no certain knowledge of any isles but their own.

And no long time elapsed ere I had still additional reasons to cease wondering at the easy faith accorded to the story which I had given of myself. For these Mardians were familiar with still greater marvels than mine, verily believing in prodigies of all sorts. Any one of them put my exploits to the blush.

Look to thy ways, then, Taji, thought I, and carry not thy crest too high. Of a surety thou hast more peers than inferiors. Thou art overtopped all round. Bear thyself discreetly and not haughtily, Taji. It will not answer to give thyself airs. Abstain from all consequential allusions to the other world, and the genteel deities among whom thou hast circled. Sport not too jauntily thy raiment, because it is novel in Mardi; nor boast of the fleetness of thy *Chamois* because it is unlike a canoe. Vaunt not of thy pedigree, Taji; for Media himself will measure it with thee there by the furlong. Be not a "snob," Taji.

So then, weighing all things well, and myself severely, I resolved to follow my Mentor's wise counsel; neither arrogating aught, nor abating of just dues; but circulating freely, sociably, and frankly among the gods, heroes, high-priests, kings, and gentlemen that made up the principalities of Mardi.

Chapter LVIII

MARDI BY NIGHT AND YILLAH BY DAY

DURING THE NIGHT FOLLOWING OUR ARRIVAL, MANY DREAMS WERE, NO DOUBT, DREAMED IN Odo. But my thoughts were wakeful. And while all others slept, obeying a restless impulse, I stole without into the magical starlight. There are those who, in a strange land, ever love to view it by night.

It has been said, that the opening in the groves where was situated Media's city was elevated above the surrounding plains. Hence was commanded a broad reach of prospect.

Far and wide was deep low-sobbing repose of man and nature. The groves were motionless;

and in the meadows, like goblins, the shadows advanced and retreated. Full before me lay the Mardian fleet of isles, profoundly at anchor within their coral harbor. Nearby was one belted round by a frothy luminous reef, wherein it lay like Saturn in its ring.

From all their summits went up a milk-white smoke as from Indian wigwams in the hazy harvest moon. And floating away, these vapors blended with the faint mist as of a cataract hovering over the circumvallating reef. Far beyond all, and far into the infinite night, surged the jet-black ocean.

But how tranquil the wide lagoon, which mirrored the burning spots in heaven! Deep down into its innermost heart penetrated the slanting rays of Hesperus like a shaft of light, sunk far into mysterious Golcondas, where myriad gnomes seemed toiling. Soon a light breeze rippled the water, and the shaft was seen no more. But the moon's bright wake was still revealed: a silver track, tipping every wave-crest in its course, till each seemed a pearly, scroll-prowed nautilus, buoyant with some elfin crew.

From earth to heaven! High above me was Night's shadowy bower, traversed, vine-like, by the Milky Way, and heavy with golden clusterings. Oh, stars! Oh, eyes that see me, wheresoe'er I roam: serene, intent, inscrutable for aye, tell me Sybils, what I am? Wondrous world on worlds! Lo, round and round me, shining, awful spells: all glorious, vivid constellations, God's diadem ye are! To you, ye stars, man owes his subtlest raptures, thoughts unspeakable, yet full of faith.

But how your mild effulgence stings the boding heart. Am I a murderer, stars?

Hours pass. The starry trance is departed. Long waited for, the dawn now comes.

First, breaking along the waking face; peeping from out the languid lids; then shining forth in longer glances, till, like the sun, up comes the soul, and sheds its rays abroad.

When thus my Yillah did daily dawn, how she lit up my world; tinging more rosily the roseate clouds that in her summer cheek played to and fro, like clouds in Italian air.

Chapter LIX

THEIR MORNING MEAL

NOT WHOLLY IS OUR WORLD MADE UP OF BRIGHT STARS AND BRIGHT EYES; SO NOW TO OUR story.

A conscientious host should ever be up betimes, to look after the welfare of his guests, and see to it that their day begin auspiciously. King Media announced the advent of the sun by rustling at my bower's eaves in person.

A repast was spread in an adjoining arbor, which Media's pages had smoothed for our reception, and where his subordinate chiefs were in attendance. Here we reclined upon mats. Balmy and fresh blew the breath of the morning; golden vapors were upon the mountains, silver sheen upon the grass; and the birds were at matins in the groves, their bright plumage flashing into view here and there as if some rainbow were crouching in the foliage.

Spread before us were viands, served in quaint shaped, curiously-dyed gourds, not Sèvres, but almost as tasteful; and like true porcelain, fire had tempered them. Green and yielding, they are plucked from the tree; and emptied of their pulp, are scratched over with minute marks, like those of a line engraving. The ground prepared, the various figures are carefully etched. And the outlines filled up with delicate punctures, certain vegetable oils are poured over them for coloring. Filled with a peculiar species of earth, the gourd is now placed in an oven in the ground. And in due time exhumed, emptied of its contents and washed in the stream, it presents a deep-dyed exterior, every figure distinctly traced and opaque, but the ground semi-transparent. In some cases owing to the variety of dyes employed, each figure is of a different hue.

More glorious goblets than these for the drinking of wine went never from hand to mouth. Capacious as pitchers, they almost superseded decanters.

Now, in a tropical climate, fruit, with light wines, forms the only fit meal of a morning. And with orchards and vineyards forever in sight, who but the Hetman of the Cossacs would desire more? We had plenty of the juice of the grape. But of this hereafter; there are some fine old cellars and plenty of good cheer in store.

During the repast, Media for a time was much taken up with our raiment. He begged me to examine for a moment the texture of his right royal robe, and observe how much superior it was to my own. It put my mantle to the blush, being tastefully stained with rare devices in red and black, and bordered with dyed fringes of feathers and tassels of red birds' claws.

Next came under observation the Skyeman's Guayaquil hat; at whose preposterous shape our host laughed in derision; clapping a great conical calabash upon the head of an attendant, and saying that now he was Jarl. At this, and all similar sallies, Samoa was sure to roar louder than any; though mirth was no constitutional thing with him. But he seemed rejoiced at the opportunity of turning upon us the ridicule which, as a barbarian among whites, he himself had so often experienced.

These pleasantries over, King Media very slightly drew himself up, as if to make amends for his previous unbending. He discoursed imperially with his chiefs; nodded his sovereign will to his pages; called for another gourd of wine; in all respects carrying his royalty bravely.

The repast concluded, we journeyed to the canoe-house, where we found the little *Chamois* stabled like a steed. One solitary depredation had been committed. Its sides and bottom had been completely denuded of the minute green barnacles and short sea-grass, which, like so many leeches, had fastened to our planks during our long, lazy voyage.

By the people they had been devoured as dainties.

Chapter LX

Belshazzar on the Bench

NOW, MEDIA WAS KING OF ODO. AND FROM THE SIMPLICITY OF HIS MANNERS HITHERTO, AND HIS easy, frank demeanor, towards ourselves, had we foolishly doubted that fact, no skepticism could have survived an illustration of it which this very day we witnessed at noon.

For at high noon, Media was wont to don his dignity, with his symbols of state; and sit on his judgment divan or throne, to hear and try all causes brought before him, and fulminate his royal decrees.

This divan was elevated at one end of a spacious arbor, formed by an avenue of regal palms, which in brave state held aloft their majestical canopy.

The crown of the island prince was of the primitive old eastern style; in shape similar, perhaps, to that jauntily sported as a foraging cap by his Sacred Majesty King Nimrod, who so lustily followed the hounds. It was a plaited turban of red tappa, radiated by the pointed and polished white bones of the Ray-fish. These diverge from a bandeau or fillet of the most precious pearls; brought up from the sea by the deepest diving mermen of Mardi. From the middle of the crown rose a trifoiled spear-head. And a spear-headed scepter graced the right hand of the king.

Now, for all the rant of your democrats, a fine king on a throne is a very fine sight to behold. He looks very much like a god. No wonder that his more dutiful subjects so swore that their good lord and master King Media was demi-divine.

A king on his throne! Ah, believe me, ye Gracchi, ye Acephali, ye Levelers, it is something worth seeing, be sure; whether beheld at Babylon the Tremendous, when Nebuchadnezzar was crowned; at old Scone in the days of Macbeth; at Rheims, among Oriflammes, at the coronation of Louis le Grand; at Westminster Abbey, when the gentlemanly George doffed his beaver for a diadem; or under the soft shade of palm-trees on an isle in the sea.

Man lording it over man, man kneeling to man, is a spectacle that Gabriel might well travel hitherward to behold; for never did he behold it in heaven. But Darius giving laws to the Medes and the Persians, or the conqueror of Bactria with king-cattle yoked to his car, was not a whit more sublime than Beau Brummel magnificently ringing for his valet.

A king on his throne! It is Jupiter nodding in the councils of Olympus; Satan, seen among the coronets in Hell.

A king on his throne! It is the sun over a mountain; the sun over law-giving Sinai; the sun in our system: planets, duke-like, dancing attendance, and baronial satellites in waiting.

A king on his throne! After all, but a gentleman seated.

And thus sat the good lord, King Media.

Time passed. And after trying and dismissing several minor affairs, Media called for certain witnesses to testify concerning one Jiromo, a foolhardy wight, who had been silly enough to plot against the majesty now sitting judge and jury upon him.

His guilt was clear. And the witnesses being heard, from a bunch of palm plumes, Media, taking a leaf, placed it in the hand of a runner or pursuivant, saying, "This to Jiromo, where he is prisoned; with his king's compliments; say we here wait for his head."

It was doffed like a turban before a Dey, and brought back on the instant.

Now came certain lean-visaged, poverty-stricken, and hence suspicious-looking varlets, grumbling and growling and amiable as Bruin. They came muttering some wild jargon about "bulwarks," "bulkheads," "cofferdams," "safeguards," "noble charters," "shields," and "paladiums," "great and glorious birthrights," and other unintelligible gibberish.

Of the pursuivants, these worthies asked audience of Media.

"Go, kneel at the throne," was the answer.

"Our knee-pans are stiff with sciatics," was the rheumatic reply.

"An artifice to keep on your legs," said the pursuivants.

And advancing they salaamed, and told Media the excuse of those sour-looking varlets. Whereupon my lord commanded them to down on their marrow-bones instanter, either before him or the headsman, whichsoever they pleased.

They preferred the former. And as they there kneeled, in vain did men with sharp ears (who abound in all courts) prick their auriculars, to list to that strange crackling and firing off of bone balls and sockets, ever incident to the genuflections of rheumatic courtiers.

In a row, then, these selfsame knee-pans did kneel before the king; who eyed them as eagles in air do goslings on dunghills; or hunters, hounds crouching round their calves.

"Your prayer?" said Media.

It was a petition, that thereafter all differences between man and man in Odo, together with all alleged offenses against the state, might be tried by twelve good men and true. These twelve to be unobnoxious to the party or parties concerned; their peers; and previously unbiased touching the matter at issue. Furthermore that unanimity in these twelve should be indispensable to a verdict; and no dinner be vouchsafed till unanimity came.

Loud and long laughed King Media in scorn.

"This be your judge," he cried, swaying his scepter. "What! are twelve wise men more wise than one? or will twelve fools, put together, make one sage? Are twelve honest men more honest than one? or twelve knaves less knavish than one? And if, of twelve men, three be fools, and three wise, three knaves, and three upright, how obtain real unanimity from such?

"But if twelve judges be better than one, then are twelve hundred better than twelve. But take the whole populace for a judge, and you will long wait for a unanimous verdict.

"If upon a thing dubious, there be little unanimity in the conflicting opinions of one man's mind, how expect it in the uproar of twelve puzzled brains? though much unanimity be found in twelve hungry stomachs.

"Judges unobnoxious to the accused! Apply it to a criminal case. Ha! ha! if peradventure a Cacti be rejected, because he had seen the accused commit the crime for which he is arraigned. Then his mind would be biased: no impartiality from him! Or your testy accused might object to another, because of his tomahawk nose, or a cruel squint of the eye.

"Of all follies the most foolish! Know ye from me that true peers render not true verdicts. Jiromo was a rebel. Had I tried him by his peers, I had tried him by rebels; and the rebel had rebelled to some purpose.

"Away! As unerring justice dwells in a unity, and as one judge will at last judge the world beyond all appeal, so—though often here below justice be hard to attain—does man come nearest the mark when he imitates that model divine. Hence, one judge is better than twelve.

"And as Justice, in ideal, is ever painted high lifted above the crowd, so from the exaltation of his rank, an honest king is the best of those unical judges, which individually are better than twelve. And therefore am I, King Media, the best judge in this land."

"Subjects! so long as I live, I will rule you and judge you alone. And though you here kneeled before me till you grew into the ground and there took root, no yea to your petition will you get from this throne. I am king: ye are slaves. Mine to command: yours to obey. And this hour I decree that henceforth no gibberish of bulwarks and bulkheads be heard in this land. For a dead bulwark and a bulkhead, to dam off sedition, will I make of that man who again but breathes those bulky words. Ho! spears! see that these knee-pans here kneel till set of sun."

High noon was now passed; and removing his crown, and placing it on the dais for the kneelers to look at during their devotions, King Media departed from that place, and once more played the agreeable host.

Chapter LXI

An Incognito

For the rest of that day, and several that followed, we were continually receiving visits from the neighboring islands, whose inhabitants in fleets and flotillas flocked round Odo to behold the guests of its lord. Among them came many messengers from the neighboring kings with soft speeches and gifts.

But it was needless to detail our various interviews, or relate in what manifold ways the royal strangers gave token of their interest concerning us.

Upon the third day, however, there was noticed a mysterious figure, like the inscrutable incognitos sometimes encountered crossing the tower-shadowed Plaza of Assignations at Lima. It was enveloped in a dark robe of tappa, so drawn and plaited about the limbs, and with one hand, so wimpled about the face, as only to expose one solitary eye. But that eye was a world.

Now it was fixed upon Yillah with a sinister glance, and now upon me, but with a different expression. However great the crowd, however tumultuous, that fathomless eye gazed on; till at last it seemed no eye, but a spirit, forever prying into my soul. Often I strove to approach it, but it would evade me, soon reappearing.

Pointing out the apparition to Media, I entreated him to take means to fix it, that my suspicions might be dispelled, as to its being incorporeal. He replied that by courtesy incognitos were sacred. Insomuch that the close-plaited robe and the wimple were secure as a castle. At last, to my relief, the phantom disappeared, and was seen no more.

Numerous and fervent the invitations received to return the calls wherewith we were honored. But for the present we declined them, preferring to establish ourselves firmly in the heart of Media ere encountering the vicissitudes of roaming. In a multitude of acquaintances is less security, than in one faithful friend.

Now, while these civilities were being received, and on the fourth morning after our arrival, there landed on the beach three black-eyed damsels, deep brunettes, habited in long variegated robes, and with gay blossoms on their heads.

With many salaams the strangers were ushered into my presence by an old white-haired servitor of Media's, who, with a parting *congé,* murmured, "From Queen Hautia," then departed. Surprised I stood mute, and welcomed them.

The first, with many smiles and blandishments, waved before me a many-tinted Iris: the flag-flower streaming with pennons. Advancing, the second then presented three rose-hued purple-veined Circea flowers, the dew still clinging to them. The third placed in my hand a moss-rose bud, then a Venus-car.

"Thanks for your favors! now your message."

Starting at this reception, graciously intended, they conferred a moment; when the Iris-bearer said in winning phrase, "We come from Hautia, whose moss-rose you hold."

"All thanks to Hautia then; the bud is very fragrant."

Then she pointed to the Venus-car.

"This too is sweet; thanks to Hautia for her flowers. Pray bring me more."

"He mocks our mistress," and gliding from me they waved witch-hazels, leaving me alone and wondering.

Informing Media of this scene, he smiled; threw out queer hints of Hautia, but knew not what her message meant.

At first this affair occasioned me no little uneasiness, with much matter for marveling; but in the novel pleasure of our sojourn in Odo, it soon slipped from my mind; nor for some time did I again hear aught of Queen Hautia.

Chapter LXII

Taji Retires from the World

After a while, when the strangers came not in shoals as before, I proposed to our host a stroll over his dominions, desirous of beholding the same, and secretly induced by the hope of selecting an abode more agreeable to my fastidious taste than the one already assigned me.

The ramble over—a pleasant one it was—it resulted in a determination on my part to quit Odo. Yet not to go very far; only ten or twelve yards, to a little green tuft of an islet, one of many, which here and there, all round the island, nestled like birds' nests in the branching boughs of the coral grove, whose roots laid hold of the foundations of the deep. Between these islets and the shore, extended shelving ledges, with shallows above, just sufficient to float a canoe. One of these islets was wooded and vined; an arbor in the sea. And here, Media permitting, I decided to dwell.

Not long was Media in complying; nor long, ere my retreat was in readiness. Laced together, the twisting boughs were closely thatched. And thatched were the sides also, with deep crimson pandannus leaves; whose long forked spears, lifted by the breeze, caused the whole place to blaze as with flames. Canes, laid on palm trunks, formed the floor. How elastic! In vogue all over Odo, among the chiefs, it imparted such a buoyancy to the person that to this special cause may be imputed in good part the famous fine spirits of the nobles.

Hypochondriac! essay the elastic flooring! It shall so pleasantly and gently jolt thee as to shake up and pack off the stagnant humors mantling thy pool-like soul.

Such was my dwelling. But I make no mention of sundry little appurtenances of tropical housekeeping: calabashes, cocoanut shells and rolls of fine tappa; till with Yillah seated at last in my arbor, I looked round and wanted for naught.

But what of Jarl and Samoa? Why Jarl must needs be fanciful as well as myself. Like a bachelor in chambers, he settled down right opposite to me, on the main land, in a little wigwam in the grove.

But Samoa, following not his comrade's example, still tarried in the camp of the Hittites and Jebusites of Odo. Beguiling men of their leisure by his marvelous stories, and maidens of their hearts by his marvelous wiles.

When I chose, I was completely undisturbed in my arbor; an ukase of Media's forbidding indiscriminate intrusion. But thrice in the day came a garrulous old man with my viands.

Thus sequestered, however, I could not entirely elude the pryings of the people of the neighboring islands; who often passed by, slowly paddling, and earnestly regarding my retreat. But gliding along at a distance, and never essaying a landing, their occasional vicinity troubled me but little. But now and then of an evening, when thick and fleet the shadows were falling, dim glimpses of a canoe would be spied, hovering about the place like a ghost. And once, in the stillness of the night, hearing the near ripple of a prow, I sallied forth, but the phantom quickly departed.

That night, Yillah shuddered as she slept. "The whirlpool," she murmured, "sweet mosses." Next day she was lost in reveries, plucking pensive hyacinths, or gazing intently into the lagoon.

Chapter LXIII

Odo and Its Lord

TIME NOW TO ENTER UPON SOME FURTHER DESCRIPTION OF THE ISLAND AND ITS LORD.

And first for Media: a gallant gentleman and king. From a goodly stock he came. In his endless pedigree, reckoning deities by decimals, innumerable kings, and scores of great heroes, chiefs, and priests. Nor in person did he belie his origin. No far-descended dwarf was he, the least of a receding race. He stood like a palm tree; about whose acanthus capital droops not more gracefully the silken fringes, than Media's locks upon his noble brow. Strong was his arm to wield the club or hurl the javelin; and potent, I ween, round a maiden's waist.

Thus much here for Media. Now comes his isle.

Our pleasant rambles found it a little round world by itself: full of beauties as a garden; chequered by charming groves, watered by roving brooks, and fringed all round by a border of palm trees, whose roots drew nourishment from the water. But though abounding in other quarters of the Archipelago, not a solitary bread-fruit grew in Odo. A noteworthy circumstance, observable in these regions where islands close adjoining so differ in their soil that certain fruits growing genially in one, are foreign to another. But Odo was famed for its guavas, whose flavor was likened to the flavor of new-blown lips; and for its grapes, whose juices prompted many a laugh and many a groan.

Beside the city where Media dwelt, there were few other clusters of habitations in Odo. The higher classes living, here and there, in separate households; but not as eremites. Some buried themselves in the cool, quivering bosoms of the groves. Others, fancying a marine vicinity, dwelt hard by the beach in little cages of bamboo, whence of mornings they sallied out with jocund cries and went plunging into the refreshing bath, whose frothy margin was the threshold of their dwellings. Others still, like birds, built their nests among the sylvan nooks of the elevated interior; whence all below, and hazy green, lay steeped in languor the island's throbbing heart.

Thus dwelt the chiefs and merry men of mark. The common sort, including serfs, and Helots, war captives held in bondage, lived in secret places, hard to find. Whence it came that, to a stranger, the whole isle looked care-free and beautiful. Deep among the ravines and the rocks these beings lived in noisome caves, lairs for beasts, not human homes; or built them coops of rotten boughs—living trees were banned them—whose moldy hearts hatched vermin. Fearing infection of some plague, born of this filth, the chiefs of Odo seldom passed that way; and looking round within their green retreats, and pouring out their wine, and plucking from orchards of the best, marveled how these swine could grovel in the mire and wear such sallow cheeks. But they offered no sweet homes; from that mire they never sought to drag them out; they open threw no orchard; and intermitted not the mandates that condemned their drudges to a life of deaths. Sad sight! to see those round-shouldered Helots, stooping in their trenches: artificial, three in number, and concentric: the isle well-nigh surrounding. And herein, fed by oozy loam, and kindly dew from heaven, and bitter sweat from men, grew as in hot-beds the nutritious Taro.

Toil is man's allotment; toil of brain, or toil of hands, or a grief that's more than either, the grief and sin of idleness. But when man toils and slays himself for masters who withhold the life he gives to them—then, then, the soul screams out, and every sinew cracks. So with these poor serfs. And few of them could choose but be the brutes they seemed.

Now needs it to be said, that Odo was no land of pleasure unalloyed, and plenty without a pause? Odo, in whose lurking-places infants turned from breasts, whence flowed no nourishment. Odo, in whose inmost haunts, dark groves were brooding, passing which you heard most dismal cries, and voices cursing Media. There, men were scourged; their crime, a heresy; the heresy that Media was no demi-god. For this they shrieked. Their fathers shrieked before; their fathers, who, tormented, said, "Happy we to groan, that our children's children may be glad." But their children's children howled. Yet these, too, echoed previous generations, and loudly swore, "The pit that's dug for us may prove another's grave."

But let all pass. To look at, and to roam about of holidays, Odo seemed a happy land. The palm-trees waved—though here and there you marked one sere and palsy-smitten; the flowers bloomed—though dead ones moldered in decay; the waves ran up the strand in glee—though, receding, they sometimes left behind bones mixed with shells.

But else than these, no sign of death was seen throughout the isle. Did men in Odo live for aye? Was Ponce de Leon's fountain there? For near and far, you saw no ranks and files of graves, no generations harvested in win-rows. In Odo no hard-hearted nabob slept beneath a gentle epitaph; no *requiescat in pace* mocked a sinner damned; no *memento mori* admonished men to live while yet they might. Here Death hid his skull, and hid it in the sea, the common sepulcher of Odo. Not dust to dust, but dust to brine; not hearses, but canoes. For all who died upon that isle were carried out beyond the outer reef, and there were buried with their sires' sires. Hence came the thought that of gusty nights, when round the isles and high toward heaven, flew the white reef's rack and foam that then and there kept chattering watch and ward, the myriads that were ocean-tombed.

But why these watery obsequies?

Odo was but a little isle, and must the living make way for the dead, and Life's small colony be dislodged by Death's grim hosts; as the gaunt tribes of Tamerlane o'erspread the tented pastures of the Khan?

And now, what follows, said these islanders: "Why sow corruption in the soil which yields us life? We would not pluck our grapes from our graves. This earth's an urn for flowers, not for ashes."

They said that Oro, the supreme, had made a cemetery of the sea.

And what more glorious grave? Was Mausolus more sublimely urned? Or do the minster-lamps that burn before the tomb of Charlemagne show more of pomp than all the stars that blaze above the shipwrecked mariner?

But no more of the dead; men shrug their shoulders, and love not their company; though full soon we shall all have them for fellows.

Chapter LXIV

Yillah a Phantom

For a time we were happy in Odo: Yillah and I in our islet. Nor did the pearl on her bosom glow more rosily than the roses in her cheeks; though at intervals they waned and departed, and deadly pale was her glance, when she murmured of the whirlpool and mosses. As pale my soul, bethinking me of Aleema the priest.

But day by day did her spell weave round me its magic, and all the hidden things of her being grew more lovely and strange. Did I commune with a spirit? Often I thought that Paradise had overtaken me on earth, and that Yillah was verily an angel, and hence the mysteries that hallowed her.

But how fleeting our joys. Storms follow bright dawnings. Long memories of short-lived scenes, sad thoughts of joyous hours—how common are ye to all mankind. When happy, do we pause and say—"Lo, thy felicity, my soul?" No: happiness seldom seems happiness, except when looked back upon from woes. A flowery landscape, you must come out of to behold.

Sped the hours, the days, the one brief moment of our joys. Fairy bower in the fair lagoon, scene of sylvan ease and heart's repose—Oh, Yillah, Yillah! All the woods repeat the sound, the wild, wild woods of my wild soul. Yillah! Yillah! cry the small strange voices in me, and evermore, and far and deep, they echo on.

Days passed. When one morning I found the arbor vacant. Gone! A dream. I closed my eyes, and would have dreamed her back. In vain. Starting, I called upon her name but none replied. Fleeing from the islet, I gained the neighboring shore and searched among the woods, and my comrades meeting, besought their aid. But idle all. No glimpse of aught, save trees and flowers. Then Media was sought out; the event made known, and quickly bands were summoned to range the isle.

Noon came; but no Yillah. When Media averred she was no longer in Odo. Whither she had gone, or how, he knew not; nor could any imagine.

At this juncture, there chanced to arrive certain messengers from abroad, who, presuming that all was well with Taji, came with renewed invitations to visit various pleasant places round about. Among these came Queen Hautia's heralds, with their Iris flag, once more bringing flowers. But they came and went unheeded.

Setting out to return, these envoys were accompanied by numerous followers of Media, dispatched to the neighboring islands, to seek out the missing Yillah. But three days passed; and one by one they all returned, and stood before me silently.

For a time I raved. Then, falling into outer repose, lived for a space in moods and reveries, with eyes that knew no closing, one glance forever fixed.

They strove to rouse me. Girls danced and sang; and tales of fairy times were told; of monstrous imps and youths enchanted; of groves and gardens in the sea. Yet still I moved not, hearing all, yet noting naught. Media cried, "For shame, oh Taji! thou, a god?" and placed a spear in my nerveless hand. And Jarl loud called upon me to awake. Samoa marveled.

Still sped the days. And at length, my memory was restored. The thoughts of things broke over me like returning billows on a beach long bared. A rush, a foam of recollection!—Sweet Yillah gone, and I bereaved.

Another interval, and that mood was past. Misery became a memory. The keen pang a deep vibration. The remembrance seemed the thing remembered; though bowed with sadness. There are thoughts that lie and glitter deep; tearful pearls beneath life's sea, that surge still, and rolls sunlit, whatever it may hide. Common woes, like fluids, mix all round. Not so with that other grief. Some mourners load the air with lamentations; but the loudest notes are struck from hollows. Their tears flow fast: but the deep spring only wells.

At last I turned to Media, saying I must hie from Odo, and rove throughout all Mardi; for Yillah might yet be found.

But hereafter, in words, little more of the maiden, till perchance her fate be learned.

Chapter LXV

Taji Makes Three Acquaintances

Down to this period, I had restrained Samoa from wandering to the neighboring islands, though he had much desired it, in compliance with the invitations continually received. But now I informed both him and his comrade of the tour I purposed, desiring their company.

Upon the announcement of my intention to depart, to my no small surprise, Media also proposed to accompany me, a proposition gladly embraced. It seems that for some reason he had not as yet extended his travels to the more distant islands. Hence the voyage in prospect was particularly agreeable to him. Nor did he forbear any pains to insure its prosperity; assuring me furthermore that its object must eventually be crowned with success. "I myself am interested in this pursuit," said he, "and trust me, Yillah will be found."

For the tour of the lagoon, the docile *Chamois* was proposed; but Media dissented, saying that it befitted not the lord of Odo to voyage in the equipage of his guest. Therefore, three canoes were selected from his own royal fleet.

One for ourselves, and a trio of companions whom he purposed introducing to my notice; the rest were reserved for attendants.

Thanks to Media's taste and heedfulness, the strangers above-mentioned proved truly acceptable.

The first was Mohi, or Braid-Beard, so called from the manner in which he wore that appendage—exceedingly long and gray. He was a venerable teller of stories and legends, one of the Keepers of the Chronicles of the Kings of Mardi.

The second was Babbalanja, a man of a mystical aspect, habited in a voluminous robe. He was learned in Mardian lore; much given to quotations from ancient and obsolete authorities: the Ponderings of Old Bardianna: the Pandects of Alla-Malolla.

Third and last was Yoomy, or the Warbler. A youthful, long-haired, blue-eyed minstrel, all fits and starts; at times absent of mind and wan of cheek, but always very neat and pretty in his apparel, wearing the most becoming of turbans, a Bird of Paradise feather its plume, and sporting the gayest of sashes. Most given was Yoomy to amorous melodies, and rondos, and roundelays, very witching to hear. But at times disdaining the oaten reed, like a clarion he burst forth with lusty lays of arms and battle, or in mournful strains sounded elegies for departed bards and heroes.

Thus much for Yoomy as a minstrel. In other respects it would be hard to depict him. He was so capricious a mortal, so swayed by contrary moods, so lofty, so humble, so sad, so merry, so made up of a thousand contradictions, that we must e'en let him depict himself as our story progresses. And herein it is hoped he will succeed, since no one in Mardi comprehended him.

Now the trio, thus destined for companions on our voyage, had for some time been anxious to take the tour of the Archipelago. In particular, Babbalanja had often expressed the most ardent desire to visit every one of the isles in quest of some object, mysteriously hinted. He murmured deep concern for my loss, the sincerest sympathy; and pressing my hand more than once, said lowly: "Your pursuit is mine, noble Taji. Where'er you search I follow."

So, too, Yoomy addressed me, but with still more feeling. And something like this also Braid-Beard repeated.

But to my sorrow I marked that both Mohi and Babbalanja, especially the last, seemed not so buoyant of hope concerning lost Yillah as the youthful Yoomy and his high-spirited lord, King Media.

As our voyage would embrace no small period of time, it behoved King Media to appoint some trustworthy regent to rule during his absence. This regent was found in Almanni, a stern-eyed, resolute warrior, a kinsman of the King.

All things at last in readiness, and the ensuing morning appointed for a start, Media, on the beach at eventide when both light and water waned, drew a rude map of the lagoon to compensate for the obstructions in the way of a comprehensive glance at it from Odo.

And thus was sketched the plan of our voyage, which islands first to visit, and which to touch at when we should be homeward bound.

Chapter LXVI

WITH A FAIR WIND AT SUNRISE THEY SAIL

TRUE EACH TO HIS WORD, UP CAME THE SUN, AND ROUND TO MY ISLE CAME MEDIA.

How glorious a morning! The new-born clouds all dappled with gold and streaked with violet; the sun in high spirits, and the pleasant air cooled overnight by the blending circumambient fountains forever playing all round the reef; the lagoon within the coral-rimmed basin, into which they poured, subsiding, hereabouts into green tranquillity.

But what monsters of canoes! Would they devour an innocent voyager? their great black prows curling aloft and thrown back like trunks of elephants, a dark, snaky length behind, like the sea-serpent's train.

The prow of the foremost terminated in a large, open shark's mouth, garnished with ten rows of pearly human teeth, curiously inserted into the sculptured wood. The gunwale was ornamented with rows of rich, spotted Leopard and Tiger-shells; here and there, varied by others, flat and round, and spirally traced; gay serpents petrified in coils. These were imbedded in a grooved margin by means of a resinous compound, exhaling such spices that the canoes were odoriferous as the Indian chests of the Maldives.

The likeness of the foremost canoe to an elephant was helped by a sort of canopied howdah in its stern of heavy, russet-dyed tappa, tasseled at the corners with long bunches of cocoanut fibers stained red. These swayed to and fro like the fox-tails on a Tuscarora robe.

But what is this in the head of the canoe just under the shark's mouth? A grinning little imp of an image, a ring in its nose, cowrie shells jingling at its ears, with an abominable leer like that of Silenus reeling on his ass. It was taking its ease; cosily smoking a pipe, its bowl a duodecimo edition of the face of the smoker. This image looked sternwards, everlastingly mocking us.

Of these canoes, it may be well to state, that although during our stay in Odo so many barges and shallops had touched there, nothing similar to Media's had been seen. But inquiring whence his sea-equipage came, we were thereupon taught to reverence the same as antiquities and heirlooms—claw-keeled, dragon-prowed crafts of a bygone generation, at present superseded in general use by the more swan-like canoes, significant of the advanced stage of marine architecture in Mardi. No sooner was this known than what had seemed almost hideous in my eyes became merely grotesque. Nor could I help being greatly delighted with the good old family pride of our host.

The upper corners of our sails displayed the family crest of Media: three upright boars' tusks in an heraldic field argent. A fierce device. Whom rends he?

All things in readiness, we glided away, the multitude waving adieu, and our flotilla disposed in the following order:

First went the royal Elephant, carrying Media, myself, Jarl, and Samoa; Mohi the Teller of Legends, Babbalanja, and Yoomy, and six vivacious paddlers, their broad paddle-blades carved with the royal boars' tusks, the same tattooed on their chests for a livery.

And thus, as Media had promised, we voyaged in state. To crown all, seated sideways in the high, open shark's mouth of our prow was a little dwarf of a boy, one of Media's pages, a red conch-shell, bugle-wise suspended at his side. Among various other offices, it was the duty of little Vee-Vee to announce the advent of his master upon drawing near to the islands in our route. Two short bars, projecting from one side of the prow, furnished him the means of ascent to his perch.

As we gained the open lagoon with bellied sails and paddles playing, a sheaf of foam borne upright at our prow, Yoomy, standing where the spicy spray flew over him, stretched forth his hand and cried: "The dawn of day is passed, and Mardi lies all before us: all her isles and all her lakes, all her stores of good and evil. Storms may come, our barques may drown. But blow before us all ye winds; give us a lively blast, good clarion; rally round us all our wits; and be this voyage full gaily sailed, for Yillah will yet be found."

Chapter LXVII

Little King Peepi

Valapee, or the Isle of Yams, being within plain sight of Media's dominions, we were not very long in drawing nigh to its shores.

Two long parallel elevations, rising some three arrow-flights into the air, double-ridged the island's entire length, lapping between a widening vale, so level withal that at either extremity the green of its groves blends with the green of the lagoon, and the isle seems divided by a strait.

Within several paces of the beach our canoes keeled the bottom, and, camel-like, mutely hinted that we voyagers must dismount.

Hereupon the assembled Islanders ran into the water, and with bent shoulders obsequiously desired the honor of transporting us to land. The beach gained, all present wearing robes, instantly stripped them to the waist—a naked chest being their salute to kings. Very convenient for the common people this, their half-clad forms presenting a perpetual and profound salutation.

Presently, Peepi, the ruler of Valapee drew near: a boy hardly ten years old, striding the neck of a burly mute, bearing a long spear erect before him, to which was attached a canopy of five broad banana leaves new plucked. Thus shaded, little Peepi advanced, steadying himself by the forelock of his bearer.

Besides his bright red robe, the young prince wore nothing but the symbol of Valapeean royalty: a string of small, close-fitting, concave shells, coiled and ambushed in his profuse curly hair, one end falling over his ear, revealing a serpent's head curiously carved from a nutmeg.

Quite proverbial, the unembarrassed air of young slips of royalty. But there was something so surprisingly precocious in this young Peepi that at first one hardly knew what to conclude.

The first compliments over, the company were invited inland to a shady retreat.

As we pursued the path, walking between old Mohi the keeper of chronicles, and Samoa the Upoluan, Babbalanja besought the former to enlighten a stranger concerning the history of this curious Peepi. Whereupon the chronicler gave us the following account, for all of which he alone is responsible.

Peepi, it seems, had been proclaimed king before he was born, his sire dying some few weeks previous to that event; and vacating his divan, declared that he left a monarch behind.

Marvels were told of Peepi. Along with the royal dignity, and superadded to the soul possessed in his own proper person, the infant monarch was supposed to have inherited the valiant spirits of some twenty heroes, sages, simpletons, and demi-gods, previously lodged in his sire.

Most opulent in spiritual gifts was this lord of Valapee; the legatee, moreover, of numerous anonymous souls, bequeathed to him by their late royal proprietors. By a slavish act of his convocation of chiefs, he also possessed the reversion of all and singular the immortal spirits, whose first grantees might die intestate in Valapee. Servile, yet audacious, senators! thus prospectively to administrate away the inalienable rights of posterity. But while yet unborn, the people of Valapee had been deprived of more than they now sought to wrest from their descendants. And former Peepies, infant and adult, had received homage more profound than Peepi the Present. Witness the demeanor of the chieftains of old upon every new investiture of the royal serpent. In a fever of loyalty they were wont to present themselves before the heir to the isle to go through with the court ceremony of the Pupera; a curious proceeding, so called: inverted endeavors to assume an erect posture, the nasal organ the base.

It was to the frequent practice of this ceremony that most intelligent observers imputed the flattened noses of the elderly chiefs of the island, who, nevertheless, much gloried therein.

It was these chiefs, also, who still observed the old-fashioned custom of retiring from the presence of royalty with their heads between their thighs, so that while advancing in the contrary direction their faces might be still deferentially turned towards their lord and master. A fine view of him did they obtain. All objects look well through an arch.

But to return to Peepi, the inheritor of souls and subjects. It was an article of faith with the people of Valapee, that Peepi not only actually possessed the souls bequeathed to him, but that his own was enriched by their peculiar qualities. The headlong valor of the late Tongatona, the pusillanimous discretion of Blandoo, the cunning of Voyo, the simplicity of Raymonda, the prodigality of Zonoree, the thrift of Titonti.

But had all these, and similar opposite qualities, simultaneously acted as motives upon Peepi, certes, he would have been a most pitiable mortal, in a ceaseless eddy of resolves, incapable of a solitary act.

But, blessed be the gods, it was otherwise. Though it fared little better for his subjects as it was. His assorted souls were uppermost and active in him, one by one. To-day valiant Tongatona ruled the isle, meditating wars and invasions; to-morrow, thrice discreet Blandoo, who, disbanding the levies, turned his attention to the terraces of yams. And so on in rotation to the end.

Whence, though capable of action, Peepi, by reason of these revolving souls in him, was one of the most unreliable of beings. What the open-handed Zonoree promised freely to-day, the parsimonious Titonti withheld to-morrow; and forever Raymonda was annulling the doings of Voyo, and Voyo the doings of Raymonda.

What marvel, then, that in Valapee all was legislative uproar and confusion, advance and retreat, abrogations and revivals, foundations without superstructures; nothing permanent but the island itself.

Nor were there those in the neighboring countries who failed to reap profit from this everlasting transition state of the affairs of the kingdom. All boons from Peepi were entreated when the prodigal Zonoree was lord of the ascendant. And audacious claims were urged upon the state when the pusillanimous Blandoo shrank from the thought of resisting them.

Thus subject to contrary impulses, over which he had not the faintest control, Peepi was plainly denuded of all moral obligation to virtue. He was no more a free agent than the heart which beat in his bosom. Wherefore his complaisant parliament had passed a law recognizing that curious but alarming fact, solemnly proclaiming that King Peepi was minus a conscience. Agreeable to truth. But when they went further, and vowed by statute that Peepi could do no wrong, they assuredly did violence to the truth, besides making a sad blunder in their logic. For far from possessing an absolute aversion to evil, by his very nature it was the hardest thing in the world for Peepi to do right.

Taking all these things into consideration, then, no wonder that this wholly irresponsible young prince should be a lad of considerable assurance, and the easiest manners imaginable.

Chapter LXVIII

How Teeth Were Regarded in Valapee

Coiling through the thickets, like the track of a serpent, wound along the path we pursued. And ere long we came to a spacious grove embowering an oval arbor. Here we reclined at our ease, and refreshments were served.

Little worthy of mention occurred save this. Happening to catch a glimpse of the white, even teeth of Hohora, one of our attendants, King Peepi coolly begged of Media the favor to have those same dentals drawn on the spot and presented to him.

Now, human teeth extracted are reckoned among the most valuable ornaments in Mardi. So open wide thy strong box, Hohora, and show thy treasure. What a gallant array! standing shoulder to shoulder! without a hiatus between. A complete set of jewelry, indeed, thought Peepi. But, it seems, not destined for him; Media leaving it to the present proprietor, whether his dentals should change owners or not.

And here, to prepare the way for certain things hereafter to be narrated, something further needs be said concerning the light in which men's molars are regarded in Mardi.

Strung together, they are sported for necklaces, or hung in drops from the ear; they are wrought into dice; in lieu of silken locks, are exchanged for love tokens.

As in all lands, men smite their breasts and tear their hair, when transported with grief; so, in some countries, teeth are stricken out under the sway of similar emotions. To a very great extent this was once practiced in the Hawaiian Islands ere idol and altar went down. Still living in Oahu are many old chiefs who were present at the famous obsequies of their royal old generalissimo, Tammahammaha, when there is no telling how many pounds of ivory were cast upon his grave.

Ah! had the regal white elephants of Siam been there, doubtless they had offered up their long, hooked tusks, whereon they impale the leopards, their foes; and the unicorn had surrendered that fixed bayonet in his forehead; and the imperial Cachalot-whale, the long chain of white towers in his jaw; yea, over that grim warrior's grave the mooses, and elks, and stags, and fallow deer had stacked their antlers, as soldiers their arms on the field.

Terrific shade of tattooed Tammahammaha! If from a vile dragon's molars rose mailed men, what heroes shall spring from the cannibal canines once pertaining to warriors themselves! Am I the witch of Endor that I conjure up this ghost? Or King Saul, that I so quake at the sight? For, lo! roundabout me Tammahammaha's tattooing expands, till all the sky seems a tiger's skin. But now, the spotted phantom sweeps by, as a man-of-war's main-sail, cloud-like, blown far to leeward in a gale.

Banquo down, we return.

In Valapee prevails not the barbarous Hindoo custom of offering up widows to the shades of their lords; for, bereaved, the widows there marry again. Nor yet prevails the savage Hawaiian custom of offering up teeth to the manes of the dead; for at the decease of a friend the people rob not their own mouths to testify their woe. On the contrary, they extract the teeth from the departed, distributing them among the mourners for memorial legacies, as elsewhere silver spoons are bestowed.

From the high value ascribed to dentals throughout the archipelago of Mardi, and also from their convenient size, they are circulated as money; strings of teeth being regarded by these people very much as belts of wampum among the Winnebagoes of the North, or cowries among the Bengalese. So that in Valapee the very beggars are born with a snug investment in their mouths; too soon, however, to be appropriated by their lords, leaving them toothless for the rest of their days, and forcing them to diet on poee-pudding and banana blanc-mange.

As a currency, teeth are far less clumsy than cocoanuts, which among certain remote barbarians, circulate for coin, one nut being equivalent, perhaps, to a penny. The voyager who records the fact chuckles over it hugely, as evincing the simplicity of those heathens, not knowing that he himself was the simpleton, since that currency of theirs was purposely devised by the men to check the extravagance of their women, cocoanuts for spending-money being such a burden to carry.

It only remains to be added, that the most solemn oath of a native of Valapee is that sworn by his tooth. "By this tooth," said Bondo to Noojoomo, "by this tooth I swear to be avenged upon thee, oh, Noojoomo!"

Chapter LXIX

The Company Discourse, and Braid-Beard Rehearses a Legend

Finding in Valapee no trace of her whom we sought, and but little pleased with the cringing demeanor of the people, and the wayward follies of Peepi, their lord, we early withdrew from the isle.

As we glided away, King Media issued a sociable decree. He declared it his royal pleasure that, throughout the voyage, all stiffness and state etiquette should be suspended; nothing must occur to mar the freedom of the party. To further this charming plan, he doffed his symbols of royalty, put off his crown, laid aside his scepter, and assured us that he would not wear them again except when we landed; and not invariably, then.

"Are we not all now friends and companions?" he said. "So companions and friends let us be. I unbend my bow; do ye likewise."

"But are we not to be dignified?" asked Babbalanja.

"If dignity be free and natural, be as dignified as you please; but away with rigidities."

"Away they go," said Babbalanja; "and, my lord, now that you mind me of it, I have often thought that it is all folly and vanity for any man to attempt a dignified carriage. Why, my lord," frankly crossing his legs where he lay "the king, who receives his ambassadors with a majestic toss of his head, may have just recovered from the toothache. That thought should cant over the spine he bears so bravely."

"Have a care, sir! There is a king within hearing."

"Pardon, my lord; I was merely availing myself of the immunity bestowed upon the company. Hereafter, permit a subject to rebel against your sociable decrees. I will not be so frank anymore."

"Well put, Babbalanja; come nearer; here, cross your legs by mine; you have risen a cubit in my regard. Vee-Vee, bring us that gourd of wine; so, pass it round with the cups. Now, Yoomy, a song!"

And a song was sung.

And thus did we sail, pleasantly reclining on the mats stretched out beneath the canopied howdah.

At length we drew nigh to a rock, called Pella, or The Theft. A high, green crag, toppling over its base, and flinging a cavernous shadow upon the lagoon beneath, bubbling with the moisture that dropped.

Passing under this cliff was like finding yourself, as some sea-hunters unexpectedly have, beneath the open, upper jaw of a whale, which, descending, infallibly entombs you. But familiar with the rock, our paddlers only threw back their heads, to catch the cool, pleasant tricklings from the mosses above.

Wiping away several glittering beads from his beard, old Mohi turning round where he sat, just outside the canopy, solemnly affirmed that the drinking of that water had cured many a man of ambition.

"How so, old man?" demanded Media.

"Because of its passing through the ashes of ten kings, of yore buried in a sepulcher, hewn in the heart of the rock."

"Mighty kings and famous, doubtless," said Babbalanja, "whose bones were thought worthy of so noble and enduring an urn. Pray, Mohi, their names and terrible deeds."

"Alas! their sepulcher only remains."

"And, no doubt, like many others, they made that sepulcher for themselves. They sleep sound, my word for it, old man. But I very much question if, were the rock rent, any ashes would be found. Mohi, I deny that those kings ever had any bones to bury."

"Why, Babbalanja," said Media, "since you intimate that they never had ghosts to give up, you ignore them in toto, denying the very fact of their being even defunct."

"Ten thousand pardons, my lord, no such discourtesy would I do the anonymous memory of the illustrious dead. But whether they ever lived or not, it is all the same with them now. Yet, grant that they lived; then, if death be a deaf-and-dumb death, a triumphal procession over their graves would concern them not. If a birth into brightness, then Mardi must seem to them the most trivial of reminiscences. Or, perhaps, theirs may be an utter lapse of memory concerning sublunary things, and they themselves be not themselves, as the butterfly is not the larva."

Said Yoomy: "Then, Babbalanja, you account that a fit illustration of the miraculous change to be wrought in man after death?"

"No, for the analogy has an unsatisfactory end. From its chrysalis state the silkworm but becomes a moth that very quickly expires. Its longest existence is as a worm. All vanity, vanity, Yoomy, to seek in nature for positive warranty to these aspirations of ours. Through all her provinces nature seems to promise immortality to life, but destruction to beings. Or, as old Bardianna has it, if not against us, nature is not for us."

Said Media, rising: "Babbalanja, you have indeed put aside the courtier, talking of worms and caterpillars to me, a king and a demi-god! To renown, for your theme: a more agreeable topic."

"Pardon once again, my lord. And since you will, let us discourse of that subject. First, I lay it down for an indubitable maxim that in itself all posthumous renown, which is the only renown, is valueless. Be not offended, my lord. To the nobly ambitious, renown hereafter may be something to anticipate. But analyzed, that feverish typhoid feeling of theirs may be nothing more than a flickering fancy, that now, while living, they are recognized as those who will be as famous in their shrouds as in their girdles."

Said Yoomy: "But those great and good deeds, Babbalanja, of which the philosophers so often discourse, must it not be sweet to believe that their memory will long survive us, and we ourselves in them?"

"I speak now," said Babbalanja, "of the ravening for fame, which even appeased, like thirst slaked in the desert, yields no felicity but only relief, and which discriminates not in aught that will satisfy its cravings. But let me resume. Not an hour ago, Braid-Beard was telling us that story of Prince Ottimo, who, inodorous while living, expressed much delight at the prospect of being perfumed and embalmed when dead. But was not Ottimo the most eccentric of mortals? For few men issue orders for their shrouds to inspect their quality beforehand. Far more anxious are they about the texture of the sheets in which their living limbs lie. And, my lord, with some rare exceptions, does not all Mardi by its actions declare that it is far better to be notorious now than famous hereafter?"

"A base sentiment, my lord," said Yoomy. "Did not poor Bonja, the unappreciated poet, console himself for the neglect of his contemporaries by inspiriting thoughts of the future?"

"In plain words by bethinking him of the glorious harvest of bravos his ghost would reap for him," said Babbalanja; "but Banjo—Bonjo—Binjo, I never heard of him."

"Nor I," said Mohi.

"Nor I," said Media.

"Poor fellow!" cried Babbalanja; "I fear me his harvest is not yet ripe."

"Alas!" cried Yoomy, "he died more than a century ago."

"But now that you speak of unappreciated poets, Yoomy," said Babbalanja, "shall I give you a piece of my mind?"

"Do," said Mohi, stroking his beard.

"He who on all hands passes for a cipher to-day, if at all remembered hereafter, will be sure to pass for the same. For there is more likelihood of being over-rated while living than of being underrated when dead. And to ensure your fame you must die."

"A rather discouraging thought that, for your race. But answer: I assume that King Media is a mortal like you: now, how may I best perpetuate my name?"

Long pondered Babbalanja; then said: "Carve it, my lord, deep into a ponderous stone, and sink it, face downwards, into the sea; for the unseen foundations of the deep are more enduring than the palpable tops of the mountains."

Sailing past Pella, we gained a view of its farther side; and, seated in a lofty cleft, beheld a lonely fisherman, solitary as a seal on an iceberg, his motionless line in the water.

"What recks he of the ten kings," said Babbalanja.

"Mohi," said Media, "methinks there is another tradition concerning that rock; let us have it."

"In old times of genii and giants, there dwelt in barren lands not very remote from our outer reef, but since submerged, a band of evil-minded, envious goblins, furlongs in stature, and with immeasurable arms, who from time to time cast covetous glances upon our blooming isles. Long they lusted, till at last they waded through the sea, strode over the reef, and seizing the nearest islet, rolled it over and over towards an adjoining outlet.

"But the task was hard, and day-break surprised them in the midst of their audacious thieving, while in the very act of giving the devoted land another doughty surge and somerset. Leaving it bottom upwards and midway poised, gardens under water, its foundations in air, they precipitately fled, in their great haste deserting a comrade vainly struggling to liberate his foot caught beneath the overturned land."

"This poor fellow now raised such an outcry, as to awaken the god Upi, or the Archer, stretched out on a long cloud in the east, who forthwith resolved to make an example of the unwilling lingerer. Snatching his bow he let fly an arrow. But overshooting its mark, it pierced through and through the lofty promontory of a neighboring island, making an arch in it which remaineth even unto this day. A second arrow, however, accomplished its errand, the slain giant sinking prone to the bottom."

"And now," added Mohi, "glance over the gunwale and you will see his remains petrified into white ribs of coral."

"Ay, there they are," said Yoomy, looking down into the water where they gleamed. "A fanciful legend, Braid-Beard."

"Very entertaining," said Media.

"Even so," said Babbalanja. "But perhaps we lost time in listening to it; for though we know it we are none the wiser."

"Be not a cynic," said Media. "No pastime is lost time."

Musing a moment, Babbalanja replied: "My lord, that maxim may be good as it stands; but had you made six words of it instead of six syllables, you had uttered a better and a deeper."

Chapter LXX

The Minstrel Leads Off with a Paddle-Song, and a Message Is Received from Abroad

From seaward now came a breeze so blithesome and fresh that it made us impatient of Babbalanja's philosophy and Mohi's incredible legends. One and all we called upon the minstrel Yoomy to give us something in unison with the spirited waves wide-foaming around us.

"If my lord will permit, we will give Taji the Paddle-Chant of the warriors of King Bello."

"By all means," said Media.

So the three canoes were brought side to side; their sails rolled up, and paddles in hand, our paddlers seated themselves sideways on the gunwales, Yoomy, as leader, occupying the place of the foremast, or bow-paddler of the royal barge.

Whereupon the six rows of paddle-blades being uplifted, and every eye on the minstrel, this song was sung, with actions corresponding, the canoes at last shooting through the water with a violent roll.

(All.)

Thrice waved on high,
Our paddles fly:
Thrice round the head, thrice dropt to feet:
And then well timed,
Of one stout mind,
All fall, and back the waters heap!

(Bow-Paddler.)

Who lifts this chant?
Who sounds this vaunt?

(All.)

The wild sea song, to the billows' throng,
Rising, falling,
Hoarsely calling,
Now high, now low, as fast we go,
Fast on our flying foe!

(Bow-Paddler.)

Who lifts this chant?
Who sounds this vaunt?

(All.)

Dip, dip, in the brine our paddles dip,
Dip, dip, the fins of our swimming ship!
How the waters part,
As on we dart;
Our sharp prows fly,

And curl on high,
As the upright fin of the rushing shark,
Rushing fast and far on his flying mark!
Like him we prey;
Like him we slay;
Swim on the foe,
Our prow a blow!

(Bow-Paddler.)
Who lifts this chant?
Who sounds this vaunt?

(All.)
Heap back; heap back; the waters back!
Pile them high astern, in billows black;
Till we leave our wake,
In the slope we make;
And rush and ride,
On the torrent's tide!

Here we were overtaken by a swift-gliding canoe, which, bearing down upon us before the wind, lowered its sails when close by, its occupants signing our paddlers to desist.

I started.

The strangers were three hooded damsels, the enigmatical Queen Hautia's heralds.

Their pursuit surprised and perplexed me. Nor was there wanting a vague feeling of alarm to heighten these emotions. But perhaps I was mistaken, and this time they meant not me.

Seated in the prow, the foremost waved her Iris flag.

Cried Yoomy: "Some message! Taji, that Iris points to you."

It was then, I first divined, that some meaning must have lurked in those flowers they had twice brought me before.

The second damsel now flung over to me Circe flowers, then a faded jonquil buried in a tuft of wormwood leaves.

The third sat in the shallop's stern, and as it glided from us, thrice waved oleanders.

"What dumb show is this?" cried Media. "But it looks like poetry; minstrel, you should know."

"Interpret then," said I.

"Shall I, then, be your Flora's flute, and Hautia's dragoman? Held aloft, the Iris signified a message. These purple-woven Circe flowers mean that some spell is weaving. That golden pining jonquil, which you hold, buried in those wormwood leaves, says plainly to you—Bitter love in absence."

Said Media, "Well done, Taji, you have killed a queen."

"Yet no Queen Hautia have these eyes beheld."

Said Babbalanja: "The thrice waved oleanders, Yoomy; what meant they?"

"Beware—beware—beware."

"Then that, at least, seems kindly meant," said Babbalanja. "Taji, beware of Hautia."

Chapter LXXI

They Land upon the Island of Juam

Crossing the lagoon, our course now lay along the reef to Juam, a name bestowed upon one of the largest islands hereabouts; and also, collectively, upon several wooded isles engulfing it, which together were known as the dominions of one monarch. That monarch was Donjalolo. Just turned of twenty-five, he was accounted not only the handsomest man in his dominions, but throughout the lagoon. His comeliness, however, was so feminine that he was sometimes called "Fonoo," or the Girl.

Our first view of Juam was imposing. A dark green pile of cliffs, towering some one hundred toises; at top, presenting a range of steep, gable-pointed projections, as if some Titanic hammer and chisel had shaped the mass.

Sailing nearer, we perceived an extraordinary rolling of the sea, which bursting into the lagoon through an adjoining breach in the reef, surged towards Juam in enormous billows. At last, dashing against the wall of the cliff, they played there in unceasing fountains. But under the brow of a beetling crag, the spray came and went unequally. There the blue billows seemed swallowed up and lost.

Right regally was Juam guarded. For at this point the rock was pierced by a cave, into which the great waves chased each other like lions; after a hollow, subterraneous roaring issuing forth with manes disheveled.

Cautiously evading the dangerous currents here ruffling the lagoon, we rounded the wall of cliff, and shot upon a smooth expanse; on one side, hemmed in by the long, verdant, northern shore of Juam; and across the water, sentineled by its tributary islets.

With sonorous Vee-Vee in the shark's mouth, we swept towards the beach, tumultuous with a throng.

Our canoes were secured. And surrounded by eager glances, we passed the lower ends of several populous valleys; and crossing a wide, open meadow, gradually ascending, came to a range of light-green bluffs. Here we wended our way down a narrow defile, almost cleaving this quarter of the island to its base. Black crags frowned overhead; among them the shouts of the islanders reverberated. Yet steeper grew the defile, and more overhanging the crags; till at last the keystone of the arch seemed dropped into its place. We found ourselves in a subterranean tunnel, dimly lighted by a span of white day at the end.

Emerging, what a scene was revealed! All round, embracing a circuit of some three leagues, stood heights inaccessible, here and there, forming buttresses sheltering deep recesses between. The bosom of the place was vivid with verdure.

Shining aslant into this wild hollow, the afternoon sun lighted up its eastern side with tints of gold. But opposite brooded a somber shadow, double-shading the secret places between the salient spurs of the mountains. Thus cut in twain by masses of day and night, it seemed as if some Last Judgment had been enacted in the glen.

No sooner did we emerge from the defile than we became sensible of a dull, jarring sound; and Yoomy was almost tempted to turn and flee when informed that the sea-cavern, whose mouth we had passed, was believed to penetrate deep into the opposite hills; and that the surface of the amphitheater was depressed beneath that of the lagoon. But all over the lowermost hillsides, and sloping into the glen, stood grand old groves: still and stately, as if no insolent waves were throbbing in the mountain's heart.

Such was Willamilla, the hereditary abode of the young monarch of Juam.

Was Yillah immured in this strange retreat? But from those around us naught could we learn.

Our attention was now directed to the habitations of the glen, comprised in two handsome villages; one to the west, the other to the east; both stretching along the base of the cliffs.

Said Media, "Had we arrived at Willamilla in the morning, we had found Donjalolo and his court in the eastern village; but being afternoon, we must travel farther, and seek him in his western retreat; for that is now in the shade."

Wending our way, Media added, that aside from his elevated station as a monarch, Donjalolo was famed for many uncommon traits; but more especially for certain peculiar deprivations, under which he labored.

Whereupon Braid-Beard unrolled his old chronicles, and regaled us with the history, which will be found in the following chapter.

Chapter LXXII

A Book from the Chronicles of Mohi

MANY AGES AGO THERE REIGNED IN JUAM A KING CALLED TEEI. THIS TEEI'S SUCCESSION TO THE sovereignty was long disputed by his brother Marjora; who at last rallying round him an army, after many vicissitudes, defeated the unfortunate monarch in a stout fight of clubs on the beach.

In those days, Willamilla during a certain period of the year was a place set apart for royal games and diversions, and was furnished with suitable accommodation for king and court. From its peculiar position, moreover, it was regarded as the last stronghold of the Juam monarchy; in remote times having twice withstood the most desperate assaults from without. And when Roonoonoo, a famous upstart, sought to subdue all the isles in this part of the Archipelago, it was to Willamilla that the banded kings had repaired to take counsel together; and while there conferring, were surprised at the sudden onslaught of Roonoonoo in person. But in the end the rebel was captured, he and all his army, and impaled on the tops of the hills.

Now, defeated and fleeing for his life, Teei with his surviving followers was driven across the plain towards the mountains. But to cut him off from all escape to inland Willamilla, Marjora dispatched a fleet band of warriors to occupy the entrance of the defile. Nevertheless, Teei the pursued ran faster than his pursuers; first gained the spot, and with his chiefs, fled swiftly down the gorge, closely hunted by Marjora's men. But arriving at the further end, they in vain sought to defend it. And after much desperate fighting, the main body of the foe coming up, with great slaughter the fugitives were driven into the glen.

They ran to the opposite wall of cliff; where turning, they fought at bay, blood for blood, and life for life, till at last, overwhelmed by numbers, they were all put to the point of the spear.

With fratricidal hate, singled out by the ferocious Marjora, Teei fell by that brother's hand. When stripping from the body the regal girdle, the victor wound it round his own loins; thus proclaiming himself king over Juam.

Long torn by this intestine war, the island acquiesced in the new sovereignty. But at length a sacred oracle declared, that since the conqueror had slain his brother in deep Willamilla, so that Teei never more issued from that refuge of death; therefore, the same fate should be Marjora's; for never, thenceforth, from that glen should he go forth; neither Marjora; nor any son of his girdled loins; nor his son's sons; nor the uttermost scion of his race.

But except this denunciation, naught was denounced against the usurper; who, mindful of the tenure by which he reigned, ruled over the island for many moons; at his death bequeathing the girdle to his son.

In those days the wildest superstitions concerning the interference of the gods in things temporal prevailed to a much greater extent than at present. Hence Marjora himself, called sometimes in the traditions of the island, The-Heart-of-Black-Coral, even unscrupulous Marjora had quailed before the oracle. "He bowed his head," say the legends. Nor was it then questioned, by his most devoted adherents, that had he dared to act counter to that edict, he had dropped dead at the very instant he went under the shadow of the defile. This persuasion also guided the conduct of the son of Marjora, and that of his grandson.

But there at last came to pass a change in the popular fancies concerning this ancient anathema. The penalty denounced against the posterity of the usurper should they issue from the glen, came to be regarded as only applicable to an invested monarch, not to his relatives, or heirs.

A most favorable construction of the ban; for all those related to the king freely passed in and out of Willamilla.

From the time of the usurpation there had always been observed a certain ceremony upon investing the heir to the sovereignty with the girdle of Teei. Upon these occasions the chief priests of the island were present, acting an important part. For the space of as many days, as there had reigned kings of Marjora's dynasty, the inner mouth of the defile remained sealed, the new monarch placing the last stone in the gap. This symbolized his relinquishment forever of all purpose of passing out of the glen. And without this observance, was no king girdled in Juam.

It was likewise an invariable custom, for the heir to receive the regal investiture immediately upon the decease of his sire. No delay was permitted. And instantly upon being girdled, he proceeded to take part in the ceremony of closing the cave; his predecessor yet remaining uninterred on the purple mat where he died.

In the history of the island three instances were recorded; wherein, upon the vacation of the sovereignty, the immediate heir had voluntarily renounced all claim to the succession rather than surrender the privilege of roving, to which he had been entitled, as a prince of the blood.

Said Rani, one of these young princes, in reply to the remonstrances of his friends, "What! shall I be a king, only to be a slave? Teei's girdle would clasp my waist less tightly, than my soul would be banded by the mountains of Willamilla. A subject, I am free. No slave in Juam but its king; for all the tassels round his loins."

To guard against a similar resolution in the mind of his only son, the wise sire of Donjalolo, ardently desirous of perpetuating his dignities in a child so well beloved, had from his earliest infancy restrained the boy from passing out of the glen to contract, in the free air of the Archipelago, tastes and predilections fatal to the inheritance of the girdle.

But as he grew in years, so impatient became young Donjalolo of the king his father's watchfulness over him, though hitherto a most dutiful son, that at last he was prevailed upon by his youthful companions to appoint a day on which to go abroad and visit Mardi. Hearing this determination, the old king sought to vanquish it. But in vain. And early on the morning of the day that Donjalolo was to set out, he swallowed poison and died, in order to force his son into the instant assumption of the honors thus suddenly inherited.

The event, but not its dreadful circumstances, was communicated to the prince, as with a gay party of young chiefs he was about to enter the mouth of the defile.

"My sire dead!" cried Donjalolo. "So sudden, it seems a bolt from Heaven." And bursting into exclamations of grief, he wept upon the bosom of Talara, his friend.

But starting from his side: "My fate converges to a point. If I but cross that shadow, my kingdom is lost. One lifting of my foot, and the girdle goes to my proud uncle Darfi, who would so joy to be my master. Haughty Darfi! Oh, Oro! would that I had ere this passed thee, fatal cavern; and seen for myself what outer Mardi is. Say ye true, comrades, that Willamilla is less lovely than the valleys without? that there is bright light in the eyes of the maidens of Mina? and wisdom in the hearts of the old priests of Maramma; that it is pleasant to tread the green earth where you will; and breathe the free ocean air? Would! oh, would, that I were but the least of yonder sun-clouds that look down alike on Willamilla and all places besides, that I might determine aright! Yet why do I pause? did not Rani, and Atama, and Mardonna, my ancestors, each see for himself, free Mardi; and did they not fly the proffered girdle, choosing rather to be free to come and go, than bury themselves forever in this fatal glen? Oh, Mardi, Mardi! art thou then so fair to see? Is liberty a thing so glorious? Yet can I be no king, and behold thee! Too late, too late, to view thy charms and then return. My sire! my sire! thou hast wrung my heart with this agony of doubt. Tell me, comrades—for ye have seen it—is Mardi sweeter to behold, than it is royal to reign over Juam? Silent, are ye? Knowing what ye do, were ye me, would ye be kings? Tell me, Talara. No king: no king: that were to obey, and not command. And none hath Donjalolo ere obeyed but the king his father. A king, and my voice may be heard in farthest Mardi, though I abide in narrow Willamilla. My sire, my sire! Ye flying clouds, what look ye down upon? Tell me, what ye see abroad? Methinks sweet spices breathe from out the cave."

"Hail, Donjalolo, King of Juam," now sounded with acclamations from the groves.

Starting, the young prince beheld a multitude approaching: warriors with spears, and maidens with flowers; and Kubla, a priest, lifting on high the tasseled girdle of Teei, and waving it towards him.

The young chiefs fell back. Kubla, advancing, came close to the prince, and unclasping the badge of royalty, exclaimed, "Donjalolo, this instant it is king or subject with thee: wilt thou be girdled monarch?"

Gazing one moment up the dark defile, then staring vacantly, Donjalolo turned and met the eager gaze of Darfi. Stripping off his mantle, the next instant he was a king.

Loud shouted the multitude, and exulted; but after mutely assisting at the closing of the cavern, the new-girdled monarch retired sadly to his dwelling, and was not seen again for many days.

Chapter LXXIII

SOMETHING MORE OF THE PRINCE

PREVIOUS TO RECORDING OUR STAY IN HIS DOMINIONS, IT ONLY REMAINS TO BE RELATED OF Donjalolo that, after assuming the girdle, a change came over him.

During the lifetime of his father he had been famed for his temperance and discretion. But when Mardi was forever shut out, and he remembered the law of his isle, interdicting abdication to its king, he gradually fell into desperate courses to drown the emotions at times distracting him.

His generous spirit, thirsting after some energetic career, found itself narrowed down within the little glen of Willamilla, where ardent impulses seemed idle. But these are hard to die; and repulsed all round, recoil upon themselves.

So with Donjalolo, who, in many a riotous scene, wasted the powers which might have compassed the noblest designs.

Not many years had elapsed since the death of the king, his father. But the still youthful prince was no longer the bright-eyed and elastic boy, who at the dawn of day, had sallied out to behold the landscapes of the neighboring isles.

Not more effeminate Sardanapalus, than he. And, at intervals, he was the victim of unaccountable vagaries; haunted by specters, and beckoned to by the ghosts of his sires.

At times, loathing his vicious pursuits, which brought him no solid satisfaction, but ever filled him with final disgust, he would resolve to amend his ways; solacing himself for his bitter captivity by the society of the wise and discreet. But brief the intervals of repentance. Anew, he burst into excesses, a hundred-fold more insane than ever.

Thus vacillating between virtue and vice; to neither constant, and upbraided by both; his mind, like his person in the glen, was continually passing and repassing between opposite extremes.

Chapter LXXIV

Advancing Deeper into the Vale, They Encounter Donjalolo

From the mouth of the cavern, a broad shaded way overarched by fraternal trees embracing in midair, conducted us to a cross-path, on either hand leading to the opposite cliffs, shading the twin villages before mentioned.

Level as a meadow was the bosom of the glen. Here, nodding with green orchards of the Bread-fruit and the Palm; there, flashing with golden plantations of the Banana. Emerging from these, we came out upon a grassy mead, skirting a projection of the mountain. And soon we crossed a bridge of boughs, spanning a trench, thickly planted with roots of the Tara, like alligators, or Hollanders, reveling in the soft alluvial. Strolling on, the wild beauty of the mountains excited our attention. The topmost crags poured over with vines; which, undulating in the air, seemed leafy cascades; their sources the upland groves.

Midway up the precipice, along a shelf of rock, sprouted the multitudinous roots of an apparently trunkless tree. Shooting from under the shallow soil, they spread all over the rocks below, covering them with an intricate network. While far aloft, great boughs—each a copse—clambered to the very summit of the mountains; then bending over, struck anew into the soil; forming along the verge an interminable colonnade; all manner of antic architecture standing against the sky.

According to Mohi, this tree was truly wonderful; its seed having been dropped from the moon; where were plenty more similar forests, causing the dark spots on its surface.

Here and there the cool fluid in the veins of the mountains gushed forth in living springs; their waters received in green mossy tanks, half buried in grasses.

In one place, a considerable stream, bounding far out from a wooded height, ere reaching the ground was dispersed in a wide misty shower, falling so far from the base of the cliff, that walking close underneath, you felt little moisture. Passing this fall of vapors, we spied many islanders taking a bath.

But what is yonder swaying of the foliage? And what now issues forth like a habitation astir? Donjalolo drawing nigh to his guests.

He came in a fair sedan; a bower, resting upon three long, parallel poles, borne by thirty men, gaily attired; five at each pole-end. Decked with dyed tappas, and looped with garlands of newly-plucked flowers, from which at every step the fragrant petals were blown; with a sumptuous elastic motion the gay sedan came on, leaving behind it a long, rosy wake of fluttering leaves and odors.

Drawing near, it revealed a slender, enervate youth, of pallid beauty, reclining upon a crimson mat near the festooned arch of the bower. His anointed head was resting against the bosom of a girl; another stirred the air with a fan of Pintado plumes. The pupils of his eyes were as floating isles in the sea. In a soft low tone he murmured: "Media!"

The bearers paused; and Media advancing, the Island Kings bowed their foreheads together.

Through tubes ignited at the end, Donjalolo's reclining attendants now blew an aromatic incense around him. These were composed of the stimulating leaves of the "Aina," mixed with the long, yellow blades of a sweet-scented upland grass, forming a hollow stem. In general, the agreeable fumes of the "Aina" were created by one's own inhalations; but Donjalolo deeming the solace too dearly purchased by any exertion of the royal lungs, regaled himself through those of his attendants, whose lips were as moss-rose buds after a shower.

In silence the young prince now eyed us attentively, meanwhile gently waving his hand to obtain a better view through the wreaths of vapor. He was about to address us, when chancing to catch a glimpse of Samoa, he suddenly started, averted his glance, and wildly commanded the warrior out of sight. Upon this his attendants would have soothed him, and Media desired the Upoluan to withdraw.

While we were yet lost in wonder at this scene, Donjalolo, with eyes closed, fell back into the arms of his damsels. Recovering, he fetched a deep sigh, and gazed vacantly around.

It seems that he had fancied Samoa the noon-day specter of his ancestor Marjora, the usurper having been deprived of an arm in the battle which gained him the girdle. Poor prince, this was one of those crazy conceits so puzzling to his subjects.

Media now hastened to assure Donjalolo that Samoa, though no cherub to behold, was good flesh and blood, nevertheless. And soon the king unconcernedly gazed, his monomania having departed as a dream.

But still suffering from the effects of an overnight feast, he presently murmured forth a desire to be left to his women, adding that his people would not fail to provide for the entertainment of his guests.

The curtains of the sedan were now drawn, and soon it disappeared in the groves. Journeying on, ere long we arrived at the western side of the glen, where one of the many little arbors scattered among the trees was assigned for our abode. Here we reclined to an agreeable repast. After which we strolled forth to view the valley at large, more especially the far-famed palaces of the prince.

Chapter LXXV

Time and Temples

In the oriental pilgrimage of the pious old Purchas, and in the fine old folio voyages of Hakluyt, Thevenot, Ramusio, and De Bry, we read of many glorious old Asiatic temples, very long in erecting. And veracious Gaudentia di Lucca hath a wondrous narration of the time consumed in rearing that mighty three-hundred-and-seventy-five pillared Temple of the Year, somewhere beyond Libya; whereof the columns did signify days, and all round fronted upon concentric zones of palaces, cross-cut by twelve grand avenues symbolizing the signs of the zodiac, all radiating from the sun-dome in their midst. And in that wild eastern tale of his, Marco Polo tells us, how the Great Mogul began him a pleasure palace on so imperial a scale, that his grandson had much ado to complete it.

But no matter for marveling all this; great towers take time to construct.

And so of all else.

And that which long endures full-fledged, must have long lain in the germ. And duration is not of the future, but of the past; and eternity is eternal, because it has been; and though a strong new monument be builded to-day, it only is lasting because its blocks are old as the sun. It is not the Pyramids that are ancient, but the eternal granite whereof they are made; which had been equally ancient though yet in the quarry. For to make an eternity, we must build with eternities; whence, the vanity of the cry for anything alike durable and new; and the folly of the reproach—Your granite hath come from the old-fashioned hills. For we are not gods and creators; and the controversialists have debated, whether indeed the All-Plastic Power itself can do more than mold. In all the universe is but one original; and the very suns must to their source for their fire; and we Prometheuses must to them for ours; which, when had, only perpetual Vestal tending will keep alive.

But let us back from fire to store. No fine firm fabric ever yet grew like a gourd. Nero's House of Gold was not raised in a day; nor the Mexican House of the Sun; nor the Alhambra; nor the Escurial; nor Titus's Amphitheater; nor the Illinois Mounds; nor Diana's great columns at Ephesus; nor Pompey's proud Pillar; nor the Parthenon; nor the Altar of Belus; nor Stonehenge; nor Solomon's Temple; nor Tadmor's towers; nor Susa's bastions; nor Persepolis' pediments. Round and round, the Moorish turret at Seville was not wound heavenward in the revolution of a day; and from its first founding, five hundred years did circle, ere Strasbourg's great spire lifted its five hundred feet into the air. No: nor were the great grottos of Elephanta hewn out in an hour, nor did the Troglodytes dig Kentucky's Mammoth Cave in a sun; nor that of Trophonius, nor Antiparos; nor the Giant's Causeway. Nor were the subterranean arched sewers of Etruria channeled in a trice; nor the airy arched aqueducts of Nerva thrown over their valleys in the ides of a month. Nor was Virginia's Natural Bridge worn under in a year; nor, in geology, were the eternal Grampians upheaved in an age. And who shall count the cycles that revolved ere earth's interior sedimentary strata were crystalized into stone. Nor Peak of Piko, nor Teneriffe, were chiseled into obelisks in a decade; nor had Mount Athos been turned into Alexander's statue so soon. And the bower of Artaxerxes took a whole Persian summer to grow; and the Czar's Ice Palace a long Muscovite winter to congeal. No, no; nor was the Pyramid of Cheops masoned in a month; though, once built, the sands left by the Deluge might not have submerged such a pile. Nor were the broad boughs of Charles' Oak grown in a spring; though they outlived the royal dynasties of Tudor and Stuart. Nor were the parts of the great *Iliad* put together in haste; though old Homer's temple shall lift up its dome, when St. Peter's is a legend. Even man himself lives months ere his Maker deems him fit to be born; and ere his proud shaft gains its full stature, twenty-one long Julian years must elapse. And his whole mortal life brings not his immortal soul to maturity; nor will all eternity perfect him. Yea, with uttermost reverence, as to human understanding, increase of dominion seems increase of power; and day by day new planets are being added to elder-born Saturns, even as six thousand years ago our own Earth made one more in this system; so, in incident, not in essence, may the Infinite himself be not less than more infinite now, than when old Aldebaran rolled forth from his hand. And if time was, when this round Earth, which to innumerable mortals has seemed an empire never to be wholly explored; which, in its seas, concealed all the Indies over four thousand five hundred years; if time was, when this great quarry of Assyrias and Romes was not extant; then, time may have been, when the whole material universe lived its Dark Ages; yea, when the Ineffable Silence, proceeding from its unimaginable remoteness, espied it as an isle in the sea. And herein is no derogation. For the Immeasurable's attitude is not heightened by the arches of Mahomet's heavens; and were all space a vacuum, yet would it be a fullness, for to Himself His own universe is He.

Thus, deeper and deeper into Time's endless tunnel, does the winged soul, like a night-hawk, wend her wild way; and finds eternities before and behind; and her last limit is her everlasting beginning.

But sent over the broad flooded sphere, even Noah's dove came back, and perched on his hand. So comes back my spirit to me, and folds up her wings.

Thus, then, though Time be the mightiest of Alarics, yet is he the mightiest mason of all. And a tutor, and a counselor, and a physician, and a scribe, and a poet, and a sage, and a king.

Yea, and a gardener, as ere long will be shown.

But first must we return to the glen.

Chapter LXXVI

A Pleasant Place for a Lounge

WHETHER THE HARD CONDITION OF THEIR KINGLY STATE, VERY NATURALLY DEMANDING SOME luxurious requital, prevailed upon the monarchs of Juam to house themselves so delightfully as they did; whether buried alive in their glen, they sought to center therein a secret world of enjoyment; however it may have been, throughout the Archipelago, this saying was a proverb—"You are lodged like the king in Willamilla." Hereby was expressed the utmost sumptuousness of a palace.

A well warranted saying; for of all the bright places, where my soul loves to linger, the haunts of Donjalolo are most delicious.

In the eastern quarter of the glen was the House of the Morning. This fanciful palace was raised upon a natural mound, many rods square, almost completely filling up a deep recess between deep-green and projecting cliffs, overlooking many abodes distributed in the shadows of the groves beyond.

Now, if it indeed be, that from the time employed in its construction, any just notion may be formed of the stateliness of an edifice, it must needs be determined, that this retreat of Donjalolo could not be otherwise than imposing.

Full five hundred moons was the palace in completing; for by some architectural arborist, its quadrangular foundations had been laid in seed-cocoanuts, requiring that period to sprout up into pillars. In front, these were horizontally connected, by elaborately carved beams, of a scarlet hue, inserted into the vital wood; which, swelling out, and overlapping, firmly secured them. The beams supported the rafters, inclining from the rear; while over the aromatic grasses, covering the roof, waved the tufted tops of the Palms, green capitals to their dusky shafts.

Through and through this vibrating verdure, bright birds flitted and sang; the scented and variegated thatch seemed a hanging-garden; and between it and the Palm tops was leaf-hung an arbor in the air.

Without these columns, stood a second and third colonnade, forming the most beautiful bowers; advancing through which, you fancied that the palace beyond must be chambered in a fountain, or frozen in a crystal. Three sparkling rivulets flowing from the heights were led across its summit, through great trunks half buried in the thatch; and emptying into a sculptured channel, running along the eaves, poured over in one wide sheet, plaited and transparent. Received into a basin beneath, they were thence conducted down the vale.

The sides of the palace were hedged by Diomi bushes, bearing a flower, from its perfume, called Lenora, or Sweet Breath; and within these odorous hedges, were heavy piles of mats, richly dyed and embroidered.

Here lounging of a glowing noon, the plaited cascade playing, the verdure waving, and the birds melodious, it was hard to say, whether you were an inmate of a garden in the glen, or a grotto in the sea.

But enough for the nonce, of the House of the Morning. Cross we the hollow, to the House of the Afternoon.

Chapter LXXVII

THE HOUSE OF THE AFTERNOON

FOR THE MOST PART, THE HOUSE OF THE AFTERNOON WAS BUT A WING BUILT AGAINST A MANSION wrought by the hand of Nature herself; a grotto running into the sides of the mountain.

From high over the mouth of this grotto, sloped a long arbor, supported by great blocks of stone, rudely chiseled into the likeness of idols, each bearing a carved lizard on its chest; a sergeant's guard of the gods condescendingly doing duty as posts.

From the grotto thus vestibuled, issued hilariously forth the most considerable stream of the glen; which, seemingly overjoyed to find daylight in Willamilla, sprang into the arbor with a cheery, white bound. But its youthful enthusiasm was soon repressed; its waters being caught in a large stone basin, scooped out of the natural rock; whence, staid and decorous, they traversed sundry moats; at last meandering away, to join floods with the streams trained to do service at the other end of the vale.

Truant streams: the live-long day wending their loitering path to the subterraneous outlets, flowing into which they disappeared. But no wonder they loitered; passing such ravishing landscapes. Thus with life; man bounds out of night; runs and babbles in the sun; then returns to his darkness again; though, peradventure, once more to emerge.

But the grotto was not a mere outlet to the stream. Flowing through a dark flume in the rock, on both sides it left a dry, elevated shelf, to which you ascend from the arbor by three artificially-wrought steps, sideways disposed, to avoid the spray of the rejoicing cataract. Mounting these, and pursuing the edge of the flume, the grotto gradually expands and heightens; your way lighted by rays in the inner distance. At last you come to a lofty subterraneous dome, lit from above by a cleft in the mountain; while full before you, in the opposite wall from a low, black arch, midway up, and inaccessible, the stream, with a hollow ring and a dash, falls in a long, snowy column into a bottomless pool, whence, after many an eddy and whirl, it entered the flume, and away with a rush. Half hidden from view by an overhanging brow of the rock, the white fall looked like the sheeted ghost of the grotto.

Yet gallantly bedecked was the cave, as any old armorial hall hung round with banners and arras. Streaming from the cleft, vines swung in the air; or crawled along the rocks, wherever a tendril could be fixed. High up, their leaves were green; but lower down, they were shriveled; and dyed of many colors; and tattered and torn with much rustling; as old banners again; sore raveled with much triumphing.

In the middle of this hall in the hill was incarcerated the stone image of one Demi, the tutelar deity of Willamilla. All green and oozy like a stone under water, poor Demi looked as if sore harassed with sciatics and lumbagos.

But he was cheered from aloft, by the promise of receiving a garland all blooming on his crown; the Dryads sporting in the woodlands above, forever peeping down the cleft, and essaying to drop him a coronal.

Now, the still, panting glen of Willamilla, nested so close by the mountains, and a goodly green mark for the archer in the sun, would have been almost untenable were it not for the grotto. Hereby, it breathed the blessed breezes of Omi; a mountain promontory buttressing the island to the east, receiving the cool stream of the upland trades; much pleasanter than the currents beneath.

At all times, even in the brooding noon-day, a gush of cool air came hand-in-hand with the cool waters that burst with a shout into the palace of Donjalolo. And as, after first refreshing the king, as in loyalty bound, the stream flowed at large through the glen, and bathed its verdure; so, the blessed breezes of Omi, not only made pleasant the House of the Afternoon; but finding ample outlet in its wide, open front, blew forth upon the bosom of all Willamilla.

"Come, let us take the air of Omi," was a very common saying in the glen. And the speaker would hie with his comrade toward the grotto; and flinging himself on the turf, pass his hand through his locks, and recline; making a joy and a business of breathing; for truly the breezes of Omi were as air wine to the lungs.

Yet was not this breeze over-cool; though at times the zephyrs grew boisterous. Especially at the season of high sea, when the strong trades, drawn down the cleft in the mountain, rushed forth from the grotto with wonderful force. Crossing it then, you had much ado to keep your robe on your back.

Thus much for the House of the Afternoon. Whither—after spending the shady morning under the eastern cliffs of the glen—daily, at a certain hour, Donjalolo in his palanquin was borne; there, finding new shades; and there tarrying till evening; when again he was transported whence he came; thereby anticipating the revolution of the sun. Thus dodging day's luminary through life, the prince hied to and fro in his dominions; on his smooth, spotless brow Sol's rays never shining.

Chapter LXXVIII

BABBALANJA SOLUS

OF THE HOUSE OF THE AFTERNOON SOMETHING YET REMAINS TO BE SAID.

It was chiefly distinguished by its pavement, where, according to the strange customs of the isles, were inlaid the reputed skeletons of Donjalolo's sires; each surrounded by a mosaic of corals—red, white, and black, intermixed with vitreous stones fallen from the skies in a meteoric shower. These delineated the tattooing of the departed. Nearby, were imbedded their arms: mace, bow, and spear, in similar marquetry; and over each skull was the likeness of a scepter.

First and conspicuous lay the half-decayed remains of Marjora, the father of these Coral Kings; by his side, the storied, sickle-shaped weapon, wherewith he slew his brother Teei.

"Line of kings and row of scepters," said Babbalanja as he gazed. "Donjalolo, come forth and ponder on thy sires. Here they lie, from dread Marjora down to him who fathered thee. Here are their bones, their spears, and their javelins; their scepters, and the very fashion of their tattooing; all that can be got together of what they were. Tell me, oh king! what are thy thoughts? Dotest thou on these thy sires? Art thou more truly royal, that they were kings. Or more a man, that they were men? Is it a fable, or a verity about Marjora and the murdered Teei? But here is the mighty conqueror—ask him. Speak to him: son to sire: king to king. Prick him, beg, buffet, entreat, spurn, split the globe, he will not budge. Walk over and over thy whole ancestral line, and they will not start. They are not here. Ay, the dead are not to be found, even in their graves. Nor have they simply departed; for they willed not to go; they died not by choice; whithersoever they have gone, thither have they been dragged; and if so be, they are extinct; their nihilities went not more against their grain, than their forced quitting of Mardi. Either way, something has become of them that they sought not. Truly, had stout-hearted Marjora sworn to live here in Willamilla for aye, and kept the vow, that would have been royalty indeed; but here he lies. Marjora! rise! Juam revolteth! Lo, I stamp upon thy scepter; base menials tread upon thee where thou hest! Up, king, up! What? no reply? Are not these bones thine? Oh, how the living triumph over the dead! Marjora! answer. Art thou? or art thou not? I see thee not; I hear thee not; I feel thee not; eyes, ears, hands, are worthless to test thy being; and if thou art, thou art something beyond all human thought to compass. We must have other faculties to know thee by. Why, thou art not even a sightless sound; not the echo of an echo; here are thy bones. Donjalolo, methinks I see thee fallen upon by assassins:—which of thy fathers riseth to the rescue? I see thee dying:—which of them telleth thee what cheer beyond the grave? But they have gone to the land unknown. Meet phrase. Where is it? Not one of Oro's priests telleth a straight story concerning it; 'twill be hard finding their paradises. Touching the life of Alma, in Mohi's chronicles, 'tis related, that a man was once raised from the tomb. But rubbed he not his eyes, and stared he not most vacantly! Not one revelation did he make. Ye gods! to have been a bystander there!

"At best, 'tis but a hope. But will a longing bring the thing desired? Doth dread avert its object? An instinct is no preservative. The fire I shrink from, may consume me. But dead, and yet alive; alive, yet dead;—thus say the sages of Maramma. But die we then living? Yet if our dead fathers somewhere and somehow live, why not our unborn sons? For backward or forward, eternity is the same; already have we been the nothing we dread to be. Icy thought! But bring it home—it will not stay. What ho! hot heart of mine: to beat thus lustily awhile, to feel in the red rushing blood, and then be ashes—can this be so? But peace, peace, thou liar in me, telling me I am immortal—shall I not be as these bones? To come to this! But the balsam-dropping palms, whose boles run milk, whose plumes wave boastful in the air, they perish in their prime, and bow their blasted trunks. Nothing abideth; the river of yesterday floweth not to-day; the sun's rising is a setting; living is dying; the very mountains melt; and all revolve:—systems and asteroids; the sun wheels through the zodiac, and the zodiac is a revolution. Ah gods! in all this universal stir, am I to prove one stable thing?

"Grim chiefs in skeletons, avaunt! Ye are but dust; belike the dust of beggars; for on this bed, paupers may lie down with kings, and filch their skulls. *This*, great Marjora's arm? No, some old paralytic's. *Ye*, kings? *ye*, men? Where are your vouchers? I do reject your brotherhood, ye libelous remains. But no, no; despise them not, oh Babbalanja! Thy own skeleton, thou thyself dost carry with thee, through this mortal life; and aye would view it, but for kind nature's screen; thou art death alive; and e'en to what's before thee wilt thou come. Ay, thy children's children will walk over thee: thou, voiceless as a calm."

And over the Coral Kings, Babbalanja paced in profound meditation.

Chapter LXXIX

The Center of Many Circumferences

LIKE DONJALOLO HIMSELF, WE HIE TO AND FRO; FOR BACK NOW MUST WE PACE TO THE HOUSE OF the Morning.

In its rear, there diverged three separate arbors, leading to less public apartments.

Traversing the central arbor, and fancying it will soon lead you to open ground, you suddenly come upon the most private retreat of the prince; a square structure, plain as a pyramid; and without, as inscrutable. Down to the very ground, its walls are thatched; but on the farther side a passage-way opens, which you enter. But not yet are you within. Scarce a yard distant, stands an inner thatched wall, blank as the first. Passing along the intervening corridor, lighted by narrow apertures, you reach the opposite side, and a second opening is revealed. This entering, another corridor, lighted as the first, but more dim, and a third blank wall. And thus, three times three, you worm round and round, the twilight lessening as you proceed; until at last, you enter the citadel itself: the innermost arbor of a nest; whereof, each has its roof, distinct from the rest.

The heart of the place is but small; illuminated by a range of open skylights, downward contracting.

Innumerable as the leaves of an endless folio, multitudinous mats cover the floor; whereon reclining by night, like Pharaoh on the top of his patrimonial pile, the inmate looks heavenward, and heavenward only; gazing at the torchlight processions in the skies, when, in state, the suns march to be crowned.

And here, in this impenetrable retreat, centrally slumbered the universe-rounded, zodiac-belted, horizon-zoned, sea-girt, reef-sashed, mountain-locked, arbor-nested, royalty-girdled, arm-clasped, self-hugged, indivisible Donjalolo, absolute monarch of Juam:—the husk-inhusked meat in a nut; the innermost spark in a ruby; the juice-nested seed in a golden-rined orange; the red royal stone in an effeminate peach; the insphered sphere of spheres.

Chapter LXXX

DONJALOLO IN THE BOSOM OF HIS FAMILY

TO PRETEND TO RELATE THE MANNER IN WHICH JUAM'S RULER PASSED HIS CAPTIVE DAYS, WITHout making suitable mention of his harem, would be to paint one's full-length likeness and omit the face. For it was his harem that did much to stamp the character of Donjalolo.

And had he possessed but a single spouse, most discourteous, surely, to have overlooked the princess; much more, then, as it is; and by how much the more, a plurality exceeds a unit.

Exclusive of the female attendants, by day waiting upon the person of the king, he had wives thirty in number, corresponding in name to the nights of the moon. For, in Juam, time is not reckoned by days, but by nights; each night of the lunar month having its own designation; which, relatively only, is extended to the day.

In uniform succession, the thirty wives ruled queen of the king's heart. An arrangement most wise and judicious; precluding much of that jealousy and confusion prevalent in ill-regulated seraglios. For as thirty spouses must be either more desirable or less desirable than one; so is a harem thirty times more difficult to manage than an establishment with one solitary mistress. But Donjalolo's wives were so nicely drilled, that for the most part, things went on very smoothly. Nor were his brows much furrowed with wrinkles referable to domestic cares and tribulations. Although, as in due time will be seen, from these he was not altogether exempt.

Now, according to Braid-Beard, who, among other abstruse political researches, had accurately informed himself concerning the internal administration of Donjalolo's harem, the following was the method pursued therein.

On the Aquella, or First Night of the month, the queen of that name assumes her diadem, and reigns. So too with Azzolino the Second, and Velluvi the Third Night of the Moon; and so on, even unto the utter eclipse thereof; through Calends, Nones, and Ides.

For convenience, the king is furnished with a card, whereon are copied the various ciphers upon the arms of his queens; and parallel thereto, the hieroglyphics significant of the corresponding nights of the month. Glancing over this, Donjalolo predicts the true time of the rising and setting of all his stars.

This Moon of wives was lodged in two spacious seraglios, which few mortals beheld. For, so deeply were they buried in a grove; so overpowered with verdure; so over-run with vines; and so hazy with the incense of flowers, that they were almost invisible, unless closely approached. Certain it was, that it demanded no small enterprise, diligence, and sagacity, to explore the mysterious wood in search of them. Though a strange, sweet, humming sound, as of the clustering and swarming of warm bees among roses, at last hinted the royal honey at hand. High in air, toward the summit of the cliff, overlooking this side of the glen, a narrow ledge of rocks might have been seen, from which, rumor whispered, was to be caught an angular peep at the tip of the apex of the roof of the nearest seraglio. But this wild report had never been established. Nor, indeed, was it susceptible of a test. For was not that rock inaccessible as the eyrie of young eagles? But to guard against the possibility of any visual profanation, Donjalolo had authorized an edict, forever tabooing that rock to foot of man or pinion of fowl. Birds and bipeds both trembled and obeyed; taking a wide circuit to avoid the spot.

Access to the seraglios was had by corresponding arbors leading from the palace. The seraglio to the right was denominated "Ravi" (Before), that to the left "Zono" (After). The meaning of which was, that upon the termination of her reign, the Queen wended her way to the Zono; there tarrying with her predecessors till the Ravi was emptied; when the entire Moon of wives, swallow-like, migrated back whence they came; and the procession was gone over again.

In due order, the queens reposed upon mats inwoven with their respective ciphers. In the Ravi, the mat of the Queen-apparent, or next in succession, was spread by the portal. In the Zono, the newly-widowed queen reposed furthest from it.

But alas for all method where thirty wives are concerned. Notwithstanding these excellent arrangements, the mature result of ages of progressive improvement in the economy of the royal seraglios in Willamilla, it must needs be related, that at times the order of precedence became confused, and was very hard to restore.

At intervals, some one of the wives was weeded out, to the no small delight of the remainder; but to their equal vexation her place would soon after be supplied by some beautiful stranger; who assuming the denomination of the vacated Night of the Moon, thenceforth commenced her monthly revolutions in the king's infallible calendar.

In constant attendance, was a band of old men; woebegone, thin of leg, and puny of frame; whose grateful task it was, to tarry in the garden of Donjalolo's delights, without ever touching the roses. Along with innumerable other duties, they were perpetually kept coming and going upon ten thousand errands; for they had it in strict charge to obey the slightest behests of the damsels; and with all imaginable expedition to run, fly, swim, or dissolve into impalpable air, at the shortest possible notice.

So laborious their avocations, that none could discharge them for more than a twelvemonth, at the end of that period giving up the ghost out of pure exhaustion of the locomotive apparatus. It was this constant drain upon the stock of masculine old age in the glen, that so bethinned its small population of gray-beards and hoary-heads. And any old man hitherto exempted, who happened to receive a summons to repair to the palace, and there wait the pleasure of the king: this unfortunate, at once suspecting his doom, put his arbor in order; oiled and suppled his joints; took a long farewell of his friends; selected his burial-place; and going resigned to his fate, in due time expired like the rest.

Had any one of them cast about for some alleviating circumstance, he might possibly have derived some little consolation from the thought, that though a slave to the whims of thirty princesses, he was nevertheless one of their guardians, and as such, he might ingeniously have concluded, their superior. But small consolation this. For the damsels were as blithe as larks, more playful than kittens; never looking sad and sentimental, projecting clandestine escapes. But supplied with the thirtieth part of all that Aspasia could desire; glorying in being the spouses of a king; nor in the remotest degree anxious about eventual dowers; they were care-free, content, and rejoicing, as the rays of the morning.

Poor old men, then; it would be hard to distill out of your fate one drop of the balm of consolation. For, commissioned to watch over those who forever kept you on the trot, affording you no time to hunt up peccadilloes; was not this circumstance an aggravation of hard times? a sharpening and edge-giving to the steel in your souls?

But much yet remains unsaid.

To dwell no more upon the eternal wear-and-tear incident to these attenuated old warders, they were intensely hated by the damsels. Inasmuch, as it was archly opined, for what ulterior purposes they were retained.

Nightly couching, on guard, round the seraglio, like fangless old bronze dragons round a fountain enchanted, the old men ever and anon cried out mightily, by reason of sore pinches and scratches received in the dark: And tri-trebly-tri-triply girt about as he was, Donjalolo himself started from his slumbers, raced round and round through his ten thousand corridors; at last bursting all dizzy among his twenty-nine queens, to see what under the seventh-heavens was the matter. When, lo and behold! there lay the innocents all sound asleep; the dragons moaning over their mysterious bruises.

Ah me! his harem, like all large families, was the delight and the torment of the days and nights of Donjalolo.

And in one special matter was he either eminently miserable, or otherwise; for all his multiplicity of wives, he had never an heir. Not his, the proud paternal glance of the Grand Turk Solyman, looking round upon a hundred sons, all bone of his bone, and squinting with his squint.

Chapter LXXXI

Wherein Babbalanja Relates the Adventure of One Karkeke in the Land of Shades

At our morning repast, on the second day of our stay in the hollow our party indulged in much lively discourse.

"Samoa," said I, "those isles of yours, of whose beauty you so often make vauntful mention, can those isles, good Samoa, furnish a valley in all respects equal to Willamilla?"

Disdainful answer was made, that Willamilla might be endurable enough for a sojourn, but as a permanent abode, any glen of his own natal isle was unspeakably superior.

"In the great valley of Savaii," cried Samoa, "for every leaf grown here in Willamilla, grows a stately tree; and for every tree here waving in Savaii flourishes a goodly warrior."

Immeasurable was the disgust of the Upoluan for the enervated subjects of Donjalolo, and for Donjalolo himself; though it was shrewdly divined that his annoying reception at the hands of the royalty of Juam, had something to do with his disdain.

To Jarl, no similar question was put; for he was sadly deficient in a taste for the picturesque. But he cursorily observed, that in his blue-water opinion, Willamilla was next to uninhabitable, all view of the sea being intercepted.

And here it may be well to relate a comical blunder on the part of honest Jarl; concerning which, Samoa, the savage, often afterward twitted him; as indicating a rusticity, and want of polish in his breeding. It rather originated, however, in his not heeding the conventionalities of the strange people among whom he was thrown.

The anecdote is not an epic; but here it is.

Reclining in our arbor, we breakfasted upon a marble slab; so frost-white, and flowingly traced with blue veins, that it seemed a little lake sheeted over with ice; Diana's virgin bosom congealed.

Before each guest was a richly carved bowl and gourd, fruit and wine freighted; also the empty hemisphere of a small nut, the purpose of which was a problem. Now, King Jarl scorned to admit the slightest degree of under-breeding in the matter of polite feeding. So nothing was a problem to him. At once reminded of the morsel of Arva-root in his mouth, a substitute for another sort of sedative then unattainable, he was instantly illuminated concerning the purpose of the nut, and very complacently introduced each to the other; in the innocence of his ignorance making no doubt that he had acquitted himself with discretion; the little hemisphere plainly being intended as a place of temporary deposit for the Arva of the guests.

The company were astounded: Samoa more than all. King Jarl, meanwhile, looking at all present with the utmost serenity. At length, one of the horrified attendants, using two sticks for a forceps, disappeared with the obnoxious nut: upon which, the meal proceeded.

This attendant was not seen again for many days; which gave rise to the supposition, that journeying to the sea-side, he had embarked for some distant strand; there, to bury out of sight the abomination with which he was freighted.

Upon this, his egregious misadventure, calculated to do discredit to our party, and bring Media himself into contempt, Babbalanja had no scruples in taking Jarl roundly to task. He assured him, that it argued but little brains to evince a desire to be thought familiar with all things; that however desirable as incidental attainments, conventionalities, in themselves, were the very least of arbitrary trifles; the knowledge of them, innate with no man. "Moreover Jarl," he added, "in essence, conventionalities are but mimickings, at which monkeys succeed best. Hence, when you find yourself at a loss in these matters, wait patiently, and mark what the other monkeys do; then follow suit. And by so doing, you will gain a vast reputation as an accomplished ape. Above all things, follow not the silly example of the young spark Karkeke, of whom Mohi was telling me. Dying, and entering the other world with a mincing gait, and there finding certain customs quite strange and new; such as friendly shades passing through each other by way of a salutation;—Karkeke, nevertheless, resolved to show no sign of embarrassment. Accosted by a phantom, with wings folded pensively, plumes interlocked across its chest, he off head; and stood obsequiously before it. Staring at him for an instant, the spirit cut him dead; murmuring to itself, 'Ah! some terrestrial bumpkin, I fancy,' and passed on with its celestial nose in the highly rarified air. But silly Karkeke undertaking to replace his head, found that it would no more stay on, but forever tumbled off, even in the act of nodding a salute, which calamity kept putting him out of countenance. And thus through all eternity is he punished for his folly, in having pretended to be wise, wherein he was ignorant. Head under arm, he wanders about, the scorn and ridicule of the other world."

Our repast concluded, messengers arrived from the prince, courteously inviting our presence at the House of the Morning. Thither we went, journeying in sedans, sent across the hollow, for that purpose by Donjalolo.

Chapter LXXXII

How Donjalolo Sent Agents to the Surrounding Isles: With the Result

Ere recounting what was beheld on entering the house of the morning, some previous information is needful. Though so many of Donjalolo's days were consumed by sloth and luxury, there came to him certain intervals of thoughtfulness, when all his curiosity concerning the things of outer Mardi revived with augmented intensity. In these moods, he would send abroad deputations, inviting to Willamilla the kings of the neighboring islands; together with the most celebrated priests, bards, story-tellers, magicians, and wise men; that he might hear them converse of those things, which he could not behold for himself.

But at last he bethought him, that the various narrations he had heard, could not have been otherwise than unavoidably faulty; by reason that they had been principally obtained from the inhabitants of the countries described; who, very naturally, must have been inclined to partiality or uncandidness in their statements. Wherefore he had very lately dispatched to the isles special agents of his own; honest of heart, keen of eye, and shrewd of understanding; to seek out everything that promised to illuminate him concerning the places they visited, and also to collect various specimens of interesting objects; so that at last he might avail himself of the researches of others, and see with their eyes.

But though two observers were sent to every one of the neighboring lands; yet each was to act independently; make his own inquiries; form his own conclusions; and return with his own specimens; wholly regardless of the proceedings of the other.

It so came to pass, that on the very day of our arrival in the glen, these pilgrims returned from their travels; and Donjalolo had set apart the following morning to giving them a grand public reception. And it was to this, that our party had been invited as related in the chapter preceding.

In the great Palm-hall of the House of the Morning, we were assigned distinguished mats to the right of the prince; his chiefs, attendants, and subjects assembled in the open colonnades without.

When all was in readiness, in marched the company of savants and travelers; and humbly standing in a semi-circle before the king, their numerous hampers were deposited at their feet.

Donjalolo was now in high spirits, thinking of the rich store of reliable information about to be furnished.

"Zuma," said he, addressing the foremost of the company, "you and Varnopi were directed to explore the island of Rafona. Proceed now, and relate all you know of that place. Your narration heard, we will list to Varnopi."

With a profound inclination the traveler obeyed.

But soon Donjalolo interrupted him. "What say you, Zuma, about the secret cavern, and the treasures therein? A very different account this from all I have heard hitherto; but perhaps yours is the true version. Go on."

But very soon, poor Zuma was again interrupted by exclamations of surprise. Nay, even to the very end of his mountings.

But when he had done, Donjalolo observed, that if from any cause Zuma was in error or obscure, Varnopi would not fail to set him right.

So Varnopi was called upon.

But not long had Varnopi proceeded, when Donjalolo changed color.

"What!" he exclaimed, "will ye contradict each other before our very face? Oh Oro! how hard is truth to be come at by proxy! Fifty accounts have I had of Rafona, none of which wholly agreed; and here, these two varlets, sent expressly to behold and report, these two lying knaves, speak crookedly both. How is it? Are the lenses in their eyes diverse-hued, that objects seem different to both? for undeniable is it, that the things they thus clashingly speak of are to be known for the same; though represented with unlike colors and qualities. But dumb things cannot lie nor err. Unpack thy hampers, Zuma. Here, bring them close. Now: what is this?"

"That," tremblingly replied Zuma, "is a specimen of the famous reef-bar on the west side of the island of Rafona; your highness perceives its deep red dyes."

Said Donjalolo, "Varnopi, hast thou a piece of this coral, also?"

"I have, your highness," said Varnopi; "here it is."

Taking it from his hand, Donjalolo gazed at its bleached, white hue; then dashing it to the pavement, "Oh, mighty Oro! Truth dwells in her fountains; where everyone must drink for himself. For me, vain all hope of ever knowing Mardi! Away! Better know nothing, than be deceived. Break up!" And Donjalolo rose, and retired.

All present now broke out in a storm of vociferations; some siding with Zuma; others with Varnopi; each of whom, in turn, was declared the man to be relied upon.

Marking all this, Babbalanja, who had been silently looking on, leaning against one of the palm pillars, quietly observed to Media—"My lord, I have seen this same reef at Rafona. In various places, it is of various hues. As for Zuma and Varnopi, both are wrong, and both are right."

Chapter LXXXIII

They Visit the Tributary Islets

In Willamilla, no Yillah being found, on the third day we took leave of Donjalolo; who lavished upon us many caresses; and somewhat reluctantly on Media's part, we quitted the vale.

One by one, we now visited the outer villages of Juam; and crossing the waters, wandered several days among its tributary isles. There we saw the viceroys of him who reigned in the hollow; chieftains of whom Donjalolo was proud; so honest, humble, and faithful; so bent upon ameliorating the condition of those under their rule. For, be it said, Donjalolo was a charitable prince; in his serious intervals, ever seeking the welfare of his subjects, though after an imperial view of his own. But alas; in that sunny donjon among the mountains, where he dwelt, how could Donjalolo be sure, that the things he decreed were executed in regions forever remote from his view. Ah! very bland, very innocent, very pious, the faces his viceroys presented during their monthly visits to Willamilla. But as cruel their visage, when, returned to their islets, they abandoned themselves to all the license of tyrants; like Verres reveling down the rights of the Sicilians.

Like Carmelites, they came to Donjalolo, barefooted; but in their homes, their proud latchets were tied by their slaves. Before their king-belted prince, they stood rope-girdled like self-abased monks of St. Francis, but with those ropes, before their palaces, they hung Innocence and Truth.

As still seeking Yillah, and still disappointed, we roved through the lands which these chieftains ruled, Babbalanja exclaimed—"Let us depart; idle our search, in isles that have viceroys for kings."

At early dawn, about embarking for a distant land, there came to us certain messengers of Donjalolo, saying that their lord the king, repenting of so soon parting company with Media and

Taji, besought them to return with all haste; for that very morning, in Willamilla, a regal banquet was preparing; to which many neighboring kings had been invited, most of whom had already arrived.

Declaring that there was no alternative but compliance, Media acceded; and with the king's messengers we returned to the glen.

Chapter LXXXIV

Taji Sits Down to Dinner with Five-and-Twenty Kings, and a Royal Time They Have

It was afternoon when we emerged from the defile. And informed that our host was receiving his guests in the House of the Afternoon, thither we directed our steps.

Soft in our face, blew the blessed breezes of Omi, stirring the leaves overhead; while, here and there, through the trees, showed the idol-bearers of the royal retreat, hand in hand, linked with festoons of flowers. Still beyond, on a level, sparkled the nodding crowns of the kings, like the constellation Corona-Borealis, the horizon just gained.

Close by his noon-tide friend, the cascade at the mouth of the grotto, reposed on his crimson mat, Donjalolo—arrayed in a vestment of the finest white tappa of Mardi, figured all over with bright yellow lizards, so curiously stained in the gauze, that he seemed overrun, as with golden mice.

Marjora's girdle girdled his loins, tasseled with the congregated teeth of his sires. A jeweled turban-tiara, milk-white, surmounted his brow, over which waved a copse of Pintado plumes.

But what sways in his hand? A scepter, similar to those likenesses of scepters, imbedded among the corals at his feet. A polished thigh-bone; by Braid-Beard declared once Teei's the Murdered. For to emphasize his intention utterly to rule, Marjora himself had selected this emblem of dominion over mankind.

But even this last despite done to dead Teei had once been transcended. In the usurper's time, prevailed the belief, that the saliva of kings must never touch ground; and Mohi's Chronicles made mention that during the life time of Marjora, Teei's skull had been devoted to the basest of purposes; Marjora's, the hate no turf could bury.

Yet, traditions like these ever seem dubious. There be many who deny the hump, moral and physical, of Gloster Richard.

Still advancing unperceived, in social hilarity we descried their Highnesses, chatting together like the most plebeian of mortals; full as merry as the monks of old. But marking our approach, all changed. A pair of potentates, who had been playfully trifling, hurriedly adjusted their diadems, threw themselves into attitudes, looking stately as statues. Phidias turned not out his Jupiter so soon.

In various-dyed robes the five-and-twenty kings were arrayed; and various their features, as the rows of lips, eyes and ears in John Caspar Lavater's physiognomical charts. Nevertheless, to a king, all their noses were aquiline.

There were long foxtail beards of silver gray, and enameled chins, like those of girls; bald pates and Merovingian locks; smooth brows and wrinkles: forms erect and stooping; an eye that squinted; one king was deaf; by his side another that was halt; and not far off, a dotard. They were old and young, tall and short, handsome and ugly, fat and lean, cunning and simple.

With animated courtesy our host received us; assigning a neighboring bower for Babbalanja and the rest; and among so many right-royal, demi-divine guests, how could the demi-gods Media and Taji be otherwise than at home?

The unwonted sprightliness of Donjalolo surprised us. But he was in one of those relapses of desperate gaiety invariably following his failures in efforts to amend his life. And the bootless issue of his late mission to outer Mardi had thrown him into a mood for revelry. Nor had he lately shunned a wild wine, called Morando.

A slave now appearing with a bowl of this beverage, it circulated freely.

Not to gainsay the truth, we fancied the Morando much. A nutty, pungent flavor it had; like some kinds of arrack distilled in the Philippine Isles. And a marvelous effect did it have, in dissolving the crystalization of the brain; leaving nothing but precious drops of good humor, beading round the bowl of the cranium.

Meanwhile, garlanded boys, climbing the limbs of the idol-pillars, and stirruping their feet in their most holy mouths, suspended hangings of crimson tappa all round the hall; so that sweeping the pavement they rustled in the breeze from the grot.

Presently, stalwart slaves advanced; bearing a mighty basin of a porphyry hue, deep-hollowed out of a tree. Outside, were innumerable grotesque conceits; conspicuous among which, for a border, was an endless string of the royal lizards circumnavigating the basin in inverted chase of their tails.

Peculiar to the groves of Willamilla, the yellow lizard formed part of the arms of Juam. And when Donjalolo's messengers went abroad, they carried its effigy, as the emblem of their royal master; themselves being known, as the Gentlemen of the Golden Lizard.

The porphyry-hued basin planted full in our midst, the attendants forthwith filled the same with the living waters from the cascade; a proceeding, for which some of the company were at a loss to account, unless his highness, our host, with all the coolness of royalty, purposed cooling himself still further, by taking a bath in presence of his guests. A conjecture, most premature; for directly, the basin being filled to within a few inches of the lizards, the attendants fell to launching therein divers goodly-sized trenchers, all laden with choice viands—wild boar meat; humps of grampuses; embrowned bread-fruit, roasted in odoriferous fires of sandal wood, but suffered to cool; gold fish, dressed with the fragrant juices of berries; citron sauce; rolls of the baked paste of yams; juicy bananas, steeped in a saccharine oil; marmalade of plantains; jellies of guava; confections of the treacle of palm sap; and many other dainties; besides numerous stained calabashes of Morando, and other beverages, fixed in carved floats to make them buoyant.

The guests assigned seats, by the woven handles attached to his purple mat, the prince, our host, was now gently moved by his servitors to the head of the porphyry-hued basin. Where, flanked by lofty crowned-heads, white-tiaraed, and radiant with royalty, he sat; like snow-turbaned Mont Blanc, at sunrise presiding over the head waters of the Rhone; to right and left, looming the gilded summits of the Simplon, the Gothard, the Jungfrau, the Great St. Bernard, and the Grand Glockner.

Yet turbid from the launching of its freight, Lake Como tossed to and fro its navies of good cheer, the shadows of the king-peaks wildly flitting thereupon.

But no frigid wine and fruit cooler, Lake Como; as at first it did seem; but a tropical dining table, its surface a slab of light blue St. Pons marble in a state of fluidity.

Now, many a crown was doffed: scepters laid aside; girdles slackened; and among those verdant viands the bearded kings like goats did browse; or tusking their wild boar's meat, like mastiffs ate.

And like unto some well-fought fight, beginning calmly, but pressing forward to a fiery rush, this well-fought feast did now wax warm.

A few royal epicures, however, there were; epicures intent upon concoctions, admixtures, and masterly compoundings; who comported themselves with all due deliberation and dignity; hurrying themselves into no reckless deglutition of the dainties. Ah! admirable conceit, Lake Como: superseding attendants. For, from hand to hand the trenchers sailed: no sooner gaining one port, than dispatched over sea to another.

Well suited they were for the occasion; sailing high out of water, to resist the convivial swell at times ruffling the sociable sea; and sharp at both ends, still better adapting them to easy navigation.

But soon, the Morando, in triumphant decanters, went round, reeling like barks before a breeze. But their voyages were brief; and ere long, in certain havens, the accumulation of empty vessels, threatened to bridge the lake with pontoons. In those directions, trade-winds were setting. But full soon, cut out were all unladen and unprofitable gourds; and replaced by jolly-bellied calabashes, for a time sailing deep, yawing heavily to the push.

At last, the whole flotilla of trenchers—wrecks and all—were sent swimming to the further end of Lake Como; and thence removed, gave place to ruddy hillocks of fruit, and floating islands of flowers. Chief among the former, a quince-like, golden sphere, that filled the air with such fragrance, you thought you were tasting its flavor.

Nor did the wine cease flowing. That day the Juam grape did bleed; that day the tendril ringlets of the vines, did all uncurl; and grape by grape, in sheer dismay, the sun-ripe clusters dropped. Grape-glad were five-and-twenty kings: five-and-twenty kings were merry.

Morando's vintage had no end; nor other liquids, in the royal cellar stored, somewhere secret in the grot. Oh! where's the endless Niger's source? Search ye here, or search ye there; on, on, through ravine, vega, vale—no head waters will ye find. But why need gain the hidden spring, when its lavish stream flows by? At three-fold mouths that Delta-grot discharged; rivers golden, white, and red.

But who may sing for aye? Down I come, and light upon the old and prosy plain.

Among other decanters set afloat, was a pompous, lordly-looking demijohn, but old and reverend withal, that sailed about, consequential as an autocrat going to be crowned, or a treasure-freighted argosie bound home before the wind. It looked solemn, however, though it reeled; peradventure, far gone with its own potent contents.

Oh! russet shores of Rhine and Rhone! oh, mellow memories of ripe old vintages! oh, cobwebs in the Pyramids! oh, dust on Pharaoh's tomb!—all, all recur, as I bethink me of that glorious gourd, its contents cogent as Tokay itself, as old as Mohi's legends; more venerable to look at than his beard. Whence came it? Buried in vases, so saith the label, with the heart of old Marjora, now dead one hundred thousand moons. Exhumed at last, it looked no wine, but was shrunk into a subtile syrup.

This special calabash was distinguished by numerous trappings caparisoned like the sacred bay steed led before the Great Khan of Tartary. A most curious and betasseled network encased it, and the royal lizard was jealously twisted about its neck, like a hand on a throat containing some invaluable secret.

All Hail, Marzilla! King's Own Royal Particular! A vinous Percy! Dating back to the Conquest! Distilled of yore from purple berries growing in the purple valley of Ardair. Thrice hail.

But the imperial Marzilla was not for all; gods only could partake; the Kings and demi-gods of the isles; excluding left-handed descendants of sad rakes of immortals in old times breaking heads and hearts in Mardi, bequeathing bars-sinister to many mortals, who now in vain might urge a claim to a cup-full of right regal Marzilla.

The Royal Particular was pressed upon me, by the now jovial Donjalolo. With his own sceptered hand charging my flagon to the brim, he declared his despotic pleasure, that I should quaff it off to the last lingering globule. No hard calamity, truly; for the drinking of this wine was as the singing of a mighty ode, or frenzied lyric to the soul.

"Drink, Taji," cried Donjalolo, "drink deep. In this wine a king's heart is dissolved. Drink long; in this wine lurks the seeds of the life everlasting. Drink deep; drink long: thou drinkest wisdom and valor at every draft. Drink forever, oh, Taji! for thou drinkest that which will enable thee to stand up and speak out before mighty Oro himself."

"Borabolla," he added, turning round upon a domed old king at his left, "was it not the god Xipho, who begged of my great-great-grandsire a draft of this same wine, saying he was about to beget a hero?"

"Even so. And thy glorious Marzilla produced thrice valiant Ononna, who slew the giants of the reef."

"Ha, ha, hear'st that, oh Taji?" And Donjalolo drained another cup.

Amazing! the Flexibility of the royal elbow, and the rigidity of the royal spine! More especially as we had been impressed with a notion of their debility. But sometimes these seemingly enervated young blades approve themselves steadier of limb, than veteran revelers of very long standing.

"Discharge the basin, and refill it with wine," cried Donjalolo. "Break all empty gourds! Drink, kings, and dash your cups at every draft."

So saying, he started from his purple mat; and with one foot planted unknowingly upon the skull of Marjora; while all the skeletons grinned at him from the pavement; Donjalolo, holding on high his blood-red goblet, burst forth with the following invocation:

Ha, ha! gods and kings! fill high, one and all;
Drink, drink! shout and drink! mad respond to the call;
Fill fast, and fill full; 'gainst the goblet ne'er sin;
Quaff there, at high tide, to the uttermost rim—
Flood-tide, and soul-tide to the brim!

Who with wine in him fears? who thinks of his cares?
Who sighs to be wise, when wine in him flares?
Water sinks down below, in currents full slow;
But wine mounts on high with its genial glow—
Welling up, till the brain overflow!

As the spheres, with a roll, some fiery of soul,
Others golden, with music, revolve round the pole;
So let our cups, radiant with many-hued wines,
Round and round in groups circle, our Zodiac's Signs:
Round reeling, and ringing their chimes!

Then drink, gods and kings; wine merriment brings;
It bounds through the veins; there, jubilant sings.
Let it ebb, then, and flow; wine never grows dim;
Drain down that bright tide at the foam-beaded rim—
Fill up, every cup, to the brim!

Caught by all present, the chorus resounded again and again. The beaded wine danced on many a beard; the cataract lifted higher its voice; the grotto sent back a shout; the ghosts of the Coral Monarchs seemed starting from their insulted bones. But ha, ha, ha! roared forth the five-and-twenty kings—alive, not dead—holding both hands to their girdles, and baying out their laughter from abysses; like Nimrod's hounds over some fallen elk.

Mad and crazy revelers, how ye drank and roared! but kings no more: vestures loosed; and scepters rolling on the ground.

Glorious agrarian, thou wine! bringing all hearts on a level, and at last all legs to the earth; even those of kings, who, to do them justice, have been much maligned for imputed qualities not theirs. For whoso has touched flagons with monarchs, bear they their backbones never so stiffly on the throne, well know the rascals, to be at bottom royal good fellows; capable of a vinous frankness exceeding that of base-born men. Was not Alexander a boon companion? And daft Cambyses? and what of old Rowley, as good a judge of wine and other matters, as ever sipped claret or kisses?

If ever Taji joins a club, be it a Beef-Steak Club of Kings!

Donjalolo emptied yet another cup.

The mirth now blew a gale; like a ship's shrouds in a typhoon, every tendon vibrated; the breezes of Omi came forth with a rush; the hangings shook; the goblets danced fandangos; and Donjalolo, clapping his hands, called before him his dancing women.

Forth came from the grotto a reed-like burst of song, making all start, and look that way to behold such enchanting strains. Sounds heralding sights! Swimming in the air, emerged the nymphs, lustrous arms interlocked like Indian jugglers' glittering snakes. Round the cascade they thronged; then paused in its spray. Of a sudden, seemed to spring from its midst, a young form of foam, that danced into the soul like a thought. At last, sideways floating off, it subsided into the grotto, a wave. Evening drawing on apace, the crimson draperies were lifted, and festooned to the arms of the idol-pillars, admitting the rosy light of the even.

Yielding to the reaction of the banquet, the kings now reclined; and two mute damsels entered; one with a gourd of scented waters; the other with napkins. Bending over Donjalolo's steaming head, the first let fall a shower of aromatic drops, slowly aborbed by her companion. Thus, in turn, all were served; nothing heard but deep breathing.

In a marble vase they now kindled some incense: a handful of spices.

Shortly after, came three of the king's beautiful smokers: who, lighting their tubes at this odorous fire, blew over the company the sedative fumes of the Aina.

Steeped in languor, I strove against it long; essayed to struggle out of the enchanted mist. But a siren hand seemed ever upon me, pressing me back.

Half-revealed, as in a dream, and the last sight that I saw, was Donjalolo; eyes closed, face pale, locks moist, borne slowly to his sedan, to cross the hollow, and wake in the seclusion of his harem.

Chapter LXXXV

After Dinner

As in dreams I behold thee again, Willamila! As in dreams, once again I stroll through thy cool shady groves, oh, fairest of the valleys of Mardi! the thought of that mad, merry feasting steals over my soul till I faint.

Prostrate here and there over the bones of Donjalolo's sires, the royal bacchanals lay slumbering till noon.

"Which are the deadest?" said Babbalanja, peeping in, "the live kings, or the dead ones?"

But the former were drooping flowers sought to be revived by watering. At intervals, the sedulous attendants went to and fro, besprinkling their heads with the scented contents of their vases.

At length, one by one, the five-and-twenty kings lifted their ambrosial curls; and shaking the dew therefrom, like eagles opened their right royal eyes, and dilated their aquiline nostrils, full upon the golden rays of the sun.

But why absented himself, Donjalolo? Had he cavalierly left them to survive the banquet by themselves? But this apparent incivility was soon explained by heralds, announcing to their prone majesties, that through the over-solicitude of his slaves, their lord the king had been borne to his harem, without being a party to the act. But to make amends, in his sedan, Donjalolo was even now drawing nigh. Not, however, again to make merry; but socially to sleep in company with his guests; for, together they had all got high, and together they must all lie low.

So at it they went; each king to his bones, and slumbered like heroes till evening; when, availing themselves of the cool moonlight approaching, the royal guests bade adieu to their host; and summoning their followers, quitted the glen.

Early next day, having determined to depart for our canoes, we proceeded to the House of the Morning, to take leave of Donjalolo.

An amazing change, one night of solitude had wrought! Pale and languid, we found him reclining; one hand on his throbbing temples.

Near an overturned vessel of wine, the royal girdle lay tossed at his feet. He had waved off his frightened attendants, who crouched out of sight. We advanced.

"Do ye too leave me? Ready enough are ye to partake of my banquetings, which, to such as ye, are but mad incidents in one round of more tranquil diversions. But heed me not, Media; I am mad. Oh, ye gods! am I forever your captive?—Ay, free king of Odo, when you list, condescend to visit the poor slave in Willamilla. I account them but charity, your visits; would fain allure ye by sumptuous fare. Go, leave me; go, and be rovers again throughout blooming Mardi. For me, I am here for aye. Bring me wine, slaves! quick! that I may pledge my guests fitly. Alas, Media! at the bottom of this cup are no sparkles as at top. Oh, treacherous, treacherous friend! full of smiles and daggers. Yet for such as me, oh wine! thou art e'en a prop, though it pierce the side; for man must lean. Thou, wine, art the friend of the friendless, though a foe to all. King Media, let us drink. More cups!—And now farewell."

Falling back, he averted his face; and silently we quitted the palace.

Chapter LXXXVI

Of Those Scamps the Plujii

The beach gained, we embarked.

In good time our party recovered from the seriousness into which we had been thrown; and a rather long passage being now before us, we whiled away the hours as best we might.

Among many entertaining narrations, old Braid-Beard, crossing his calves, and peaking his beard, regaled us with some account of certain invisible spirits, ycleped the Plujii, arrant little knaves as ever gulped moonshine.

They were spoken of as inhabiting the island of Quelquo, in a remote corner of the lagoon; the innocent people of which island were sadly fretted and put out by their diabolical proceedings. Not to be wondered at; since, dwelling as they did in the air, and completely inaccessible, these spirits were peculiarly provocative of ire.

Detestable Plujii! With malice aforethought, they brought about high winds that destroyed the banana plantations, and tumbled over the heads of its occupants many a bamboo dwelling. They cracked the calabashes, soured the "poee," induced the colic, begat the spleen, and almost rent people in twain with stitches in the side. In short, from whatever evil, the cause of which the islanders could not directly impute to their gods, or in their own opinion was not referable to themselves—of that very thing must the invisible Plujii be guilty. With horrible dreams, and blood-thirsty gnats, they invaded the most innocent slumbers.

All things they bedeviled. A man with a wry neck ascribed it to the Plujii, he with a bad memory railed against the Plujii; and the boy, bruising his finger, also cursed those abominable spirits.

Nor, to some minds, at least, was there wanting strong presumptive evidence, that at times, with invisible fingers, the above-mentioned Plujii did leave direct and tangible traces of their presence; pinching and pounding the unfortunate islanders, pulling their hair, plucking their ears, and tweaking their beards and their noses. And thus, perpetually vexing, incensing, tormenting, and exasperating their helpless victims, the atrocious Plujii reveled in their malicious dominion over the souls and bodies of the people of Quelquo.

What it was that induced them to enact such a part, Oro only knew; and never but once, it seems, did old Mohi endeavor to find out.

Once upon a time, visiting Quelquo, he chanced to encounter an old woman almost doubled together, both hands upon her abdomen; in that manner running about distracted.

"My good woman," said he, "what under the firmament is the matter?"

"The Plujii! the Plujii!" affectionately caressing the field of their operations.

"But why do they torment you?" he soothingly inquired.

"How should I know? and what good would it do me if I did?"

And on she ran.

At this part of his narration, Mohi was interrupted by Media; who, much to the surprise of all present, observed, that, unbeknown to him (Braid-Beard), he happened to have been on that very island at that very time, and saw that identical old lady in the very midst of those abdominal tribulations.

"That she was really in great distress," he went on to say, "was plainly to be seen; but that in that particular instance your Plujii had any hand in tormenting her, I had some boisterous doubts. For, hearing that an hour or two previous she had been partaking of some twenty unripe bananas, I rather fancied that that circumstance might have had something to do with her sufferings. But however it was, all the herb-leeches on the island would not have altered her own opinions on the subject."

"No," said Braid-Beard; "a post-mortem examination would not have satisfied her ghost."

"Curious to relate," he continued, "the people of that island never abuse the Plujii, notwithstanding all they suffer at their hands, unless under direct provocation; and a settled matter of faith is it, that at such times all bitter words and hasty objurgations are entirely overlooked, nay, pardoned on the spot, by the unseen genii against whom they are directed."

"Magnanimous Plujii!" cried Media. "But, Babbalanja, do you, who run a tilt at all things, suffer this silly conceit to be uttered with impunity in your presence? Why so silent?"

"I have been thinking, my lord," said Babbalanja, "that though the people of that island may at times err, in imputing their calamities to the Plujii; that, nevertheless, upon the whole, they indulge in a reasonable belief. For, Plujii or no Plujii, it is undeniable, that in ten thousand ways, as if by a malicious agency, we mortals are woefully put out and tormented; and that, too, by things in themselves so exceedingly trivial, that it would seem almost impiety to ascribe them to the august gods. No; there must exist some greatly inferior spirits; so insignificant, comparatively, as to be overlooked by the supernal powers; and through them it must be, that we are thus grievously annoyed. At any rate, such a theory would supply a hiatus in my system of metaphysics."

"Well, peace to the Plujii," said Media; "they trouble not me."

Chapter LXXXVII

NORA-BAMMA

STILL ONWARD GLIDING, THE LAGOON A CALM.

Hours pass; and full before us, round and green, a Moslem turban by us floats—Nora-Bamma, Isle of Nods.

Noon-tide rolls its flood. Vibrates the air, and trembles. And by illusion optical, thin-draped in azure haze, drift here and there the brilliant lands: swans, peacock-plumaged, sailing through the sky. Down to earth hath heaven come; hard telling sun-clouds from the isles.

And high in air nods Nora-Bamma. Nid-nods its tufted summit like three ostrich plumes; its beetling crags, bent poppies, shadows, willowy shores, all nod; its streams are murmuring down the hills; its wavelets hush the shore.

Who dwells in Nora-Bamma? Dreamers, hypochondriacs, somnambulists; who, from the cark and care of outer Mardi fleeing, in the poppy's jaded odors, seek oblivion for the past, and ecstasies to come.

Open-eyed, they sleep and dream; on their roof-trees, grapes unheeded drop. In Nora-Bamma, whispers are as shouts; and at a zephyr's breath, from the woodlands shake the leaves, as of humming-birds, a flight.

All this spake Braid-Beard, of the isle. How that none ere touched its strand, without rendering instant tribute of a nap; how that those who thither voyaged, in golden quest of golden gourds, fast dropped asleep, ere one was plucked; waking not till night; how that you must needs rub hard your eyes, would you wander through the isle; and how that silent specters would be met, haunting twilight groves, and dreamy meads; hither gliding, thither fading, end or purpose none.

True or false, so much for Mohi's Nora Bamma.

But as we floated on, it looked the place described. We yawned, and yawned, as crews of vessels may; as in warm Indian seas, their winnowing sails all swoon, when by them glides some opium argosie.

Chapter LXXXVIII

IN A CALM, HAUTIA'S HERALDS APPROACH

"HOW STILL!" CRIED BABBALANJA. "THIS CALM IS LIKE UNTO ORO'S EVERLASTING SERENITY, AND like unto man's last despair!"

But now the silence was broken by a strange, distant intermitted melody in the water.

Gazing over the side, we saw naught but a far-darting ray in its depths.

Then Yoomy, before buried in a reverie, burst forth with a verse, sudden as a jet from a Geyser:

Like the fish of the bright and twittering fin,
Bright fish! diving deep, as high soars the lark,
So, far, far, far, doth the maiden swim,
Wild song, wild light, in still ocean's dark.

"What maiden, minstrel?" cried Media.

"None of these," answered Yoomy, pointing out a shallop gliding near.

"The damsels three:—Taji, they pursue you yet."

That still canoe drew nigh, the Iris in its prow.

Gliding slowly by, one damsel flung a Venus-car, the leaves yet fresh.

Said Yoomy—"Fly to love."

The second maiden flung a pallid blossom, buried in hemlock leaves.

Said Yoomy, starting—"I have wrought a death."

Then came showering Venus-cars, and glorious moss-roses numberless, and odorous handfuls of Verbena.

Said Yoomy—"Yet fly, oh, fly to me: all rosy joys and sweets are mine!"

Then the damsels floated on.

"Was ever queen more enigmatical?" cried Media. "Love, death, joy, fly to me? But what says Taji?"

"That I turn not back for Hautia; whoe'er she be, that wild witch I contemn."

"Then spread our pinions wide! a breeze! up sails! ply paddles all! Come, Flora's flute, float forth a song!"

To pieces picking the thorny roses culled from Hautia's gift, and holding up their blighted cores, thus plumed and turbaned Yoomy sang, leaning against the mast:

Oh! royal is the rose,
But barbed with many a dart;
Beware, beware the rose,
'Tis cankered at the heart.

Sweet, sweet the sunny down,
Oh! lily, lily, lily down!
Sweet, sweet, Verbena's bloom!
Oh! pleasant, gentle, musky bloom!

Dread, dread the sunny down;
Lo! lily-hooded asp;
Blooms, blooms no more Verbena;
White-withered in your clasp.

Chapter LXXXIX

Braid-Beard Rehearses the Origin of the Isle of Rogues

JUDGE NOT THINGS BY THEIR NAMES. THIS, THE MAXIM ILLUSTRATED RESPECTING THE ISLE TOWARDS which we were sailing.

Ohonoo was its designation, in other words, the Land of Rogues. So what but a nest of villains and pirates could one fancy it to be: a downright Tortuga, swarming with "Brethren of the coast"—such as Montbars, L'Ollonais, Bartolomeo, Peter of Dieppe, and desperadoes of that kidney. But not so. The men of Ohonoo were as honest as any in Mardi. They had a suspicious appellative for their island, true; but not thus seemed it to them. For, upon nothing did they so much plume themselves as upon this very name. Why? Its origin went back to old times; and being venerable they gloried therein; though they disclaimed its present applicability to any of their race; showing, that words are but algebraic signs, conveying no meaning except what you please. And to be called one thing, is oftentimes to be another.

But how came the Ohonoose by their name?

Listen, and Braid-Beard, our Herodotus, will tell.

"Long and long ago, there were banished to Ohonoo all the buccaneers, flibusters, thieves, and malefactors of the neighboring islands; who, becoming at last quite a numerous community, resolved to make a stand for their dignity, and number one among the nations of Mardi. And even as before they had been weeded out of the surrounding countries; so now, they went to weeding out themselves; banishing all objectionable persons to still another island. These events happened at a period so remote, that at present it was uncertain whether those twice banished were thrust into their second exile by reason of their superlative knavery, or because of their comparative honesty. If the latter, then must the residue have been a precious enough set of scoundrels.

"However it was, the commonwealth of knaves now mustered together their gray-beards, and wise-pates, and knowing-ones, of which last there was a plenty, chose a king to rule over them, and went to political housekeeping for themselves.

"And in the fullness of time, this people became numerous and mighty. And the more numerous and mighty they waxed, by so much the more did they take pride and glory in their origin, frequently reverting to it with manifold boastings. The proud device of their monarch was a hand with the forefinger crooked, emblematic of the peculatory propensities of his ancestors."

"And all this, at greater length," said Mohi.

"It would seem, then, my Lord," said Babbalanja, reclining, "as if these men of Ohonoo had canonized the derelictions of their progenitors, though the same traits are deemed scandalous among themselves. But it is time that makes the difference. The knave of a thousand years ago seems a fine old fellow, full of spirit and fun, little malice in his soul; whereas, the knave of to-day seems a sour-visaged wight, with nothing to redeem him. Many great scoundrels of our Chronicler's chronicles are heroes to us—witness, Marjora the usurper. Ay, time truly works wonders. It sublimates wine; it sublimates fame; nay, is the creator thereof; it enriches and darkens our spears of the Palm; enriches and enlightens the mind; it ripens cherries and young lips; festoons old ruins, and ivies old heads; imparts a relish to old yams, and a pungency to the Ponderings of old Bardianna; of fables distills truths; and finally, smoothes, levels, glosses, softens, melts, and meliorates all things. Why, my Lord, round Mardi itself is all the better for its antiquity, and the more to be revered; to the cozy-minded, more comfortable to dwell in. Ah! if ever it lay in embryo like a green seed in the pod, what a damp, shapeless thing it must have been, and how unpleasant from the traces of its recent creation. The first man, quoth old Bardianna, must have felt like one going into a new habitation, where the bamboos are green. Is there not a legend in Maramma, that his family were long troubled with influenzas and catarrhs?"

"Oh, Time, Time, Time!" cried Yoomy—"it is Time, old midsummer time, that has made the old world what it is. Time hoared the old mountains, and balded their old summits, and spread the old prairies, and built the old forests, and molded the old vales. It is Time that has worn glorious old channels for the glorious old rivers, and rounded the old lakes, and deepened the old sea! It is Time—"

"Ay, full time to cease," cried Media. "What have you to do with cogitations not in verse, minstrel? Leave prose to Babbalanja, who is prosy enough."

"Even so," said Babbalanja, "Yoomy, you have overstepped your province. My lord Media well knows, that your business is to make the metal in you jingle in tags not ring in the ingot."

Chapter XC

RARE SPORT AT OHONOO

APPROACHED FROM THE NORTHWARD, OHONOO, MIDWAY CLOVEN DOWN TO THE SEA, ONE HALF a level plain; the other, three mountain terraces—Ohonoo looks like the first steps of a gigantic way to the sun. And such, if Braid-Beard spoke truth, it had formerly been.

"Ere Mardi was made," said that true old chronicler, "Vivo, one of the genii, built a ladder of mountains whereby to go up and go down. And of this ladder, the island of Ohonoo was the base. But wandering here and there, incognito in a vapor, so much wickedness did Vivo spy out, that in high dudgeon he hurried up his ladder, knocking the mountains from under him as he went. These here and there fell into the lagoon, forming many isles, now green and luxuriant; which, with those sprouting seeds dropped by a bird from the moon, comprise all the groups in the reef."

Surely, oh, surely, if I live till Mardi be forgotten by Mardi, I shall not forget the sight that greeted us, as we drew nigh the shores of this same island of Ohonoo; for was not all Ohonoo bathing in the surf of the sea?

But let the picture be painted.

Where eastward the ocean rolls surging against the outer reef of Mardi, there, facing a floodgate in the barrier, stands cloven Ohonoo; her plains sloping outward to the sea, her mountains a bulwark behind. As at Juam, where the wild billows from seaward roll in upon its cliffs—much more at Ohonoo, in billowy battalions charge they hotly into the lagoon, and fall on the isle like an army from the deep. But charge they never so boldly, and charge they forever, old Ohonoo gallantly throws them back till all before her is one scud and rack. So charged the bright billows of cuirassiers at Waterloo: so hurled them off the long line of living walls, whose base was as the sea-beach, wreck-strewn, in a gale.

Without the break in the reef, wide banks of coral shelve off, creating the bar, where the waves muster for the onset, thundering in water-bolts, that shake the whole reef, till its very spray trembles. And then is it, that the swimmers of Ohonoo most delight to gambol in the surf.

For this sport, a surf-board is indispensable: some five feet in length; the width of a man's body; convex on both sides; highly polished; and rounded at the ends. It is held in high estimation; invariably oiled after use; and hung up conspicuously in the dwelling of the owner.

Ranged on the beach, the bathers, by hundreds dash in; and diving under the swells, make straight for the outer sea, pausing not till the comparatively smooth expanse beyond has been gained. Here, throwing themselves upon their boards, tranquilly they wait for a billow that suits. Snatching them up, it hurries them landward, volume and speed both increasing, till it races along a watery wall, like the smooth, awful verge of Niagara. Hanging over this scroll, looking down from it as from a precipice, the bathers halloo; every limb in motion to preserve their place on the very crest of the wave. Should they fall behind, the squadrons that follow would whelm them; dismounted, and thrown forward, as certainly would they be run over by the steed they ride. 'Tis like charging at the head of cavalry: you must on.

An expert swimmer shifts his position on his plank; now half striding it; and anon, like a rider in the ring, poising himself upright in the scud, coming on like a man in the air.

At last all is lost in scud and vapor, as the overgrown billow bursts like a bomb. Adroitly emerging, the swimmers thread their way out; and like seals at the Orkneys, stand dripping upon the shore.

Landing in smooth water, some distance from the scene, we strolled forward; and meeting a group resting, inquired for Uhia, their king. He was pointed out in the foam. But presently drawing nigh, he embraced Media, bidding all welcome.

The bathing over, and evening at hand, Uhia and his subjects repaired to their canoes; and we to ours.

Landing at another quarter of the island, we journeyed up a valley called Monlova, and were soon housed in a very pleasant retreat of our host.

Soon supper was spread. But though the viands were rare, and the red wine went round and round like a foaming bay horse in the ring; yet we marked, that despite the stimulus of his day's good sport, and the stimulus of his brave good cheer, Uhia our host was moody and still.

Said Babbalanja, "My lord, he fills wine cups for others to quaff." But whispered King Media, "Though Uhia be sad, be we merry, merry men."

And merry some were, and merrily went to their mats.

Chapter XCI

Of King Uhia and His Subjects

As beseemed him, Uhia was royally lodged. Ample his roof. Beneath it a hundred attendants nightly laying their heads. But long since, he had disbanded his damsels.

Springing from siren embrace—"They shall sap and mine me no more," he cried; "my destiny commands me. I will don my manhood. By Keevi! no more will I clasp a waist."

"From that time forth," said Braid-Beard, "young Uhia spread like the tufted top of the Palm; his thigh grew brawny as the limb of the Banian; his arm waxed strong as the back-bone of the shark; yea, his voice grew sonorous as a conch.

"And now he bent his whole soul to the accomplishment of the destiny believed to be his. Nothing less than bodily to remove Ohonoo to the center of the lagoon, in fulfillment of an old prophecy running thus—'When a certain island shall stir from its foundations, and stand in the middle of the still water, then shall the ruler of that island be ruler of all Mardi.' "

The task was hard, but how glorious the reward! So at it he went, and all Ohonoo helped him. Not by hands, but by calling in the magicians. Thus far, nevertheless, in vain. But Uhia had hopes.

Now, informed of all this, said Babbalanja to Media, "My lord, if the continual looking-forward to something greater be better than an acquiescence in things present, then, wild as it is, this belief of Uhia's he should hug to his heart, as erewhile his wives. But, my lord, this faith it is that robs his days of peace, his nights of sweet unconsciousness. For, holding himself fore-ordained to the dominion of the entire Archipelago, he upbraids the gods for laggards, and curses himself as deprived of his rights; nay, as having had wrested from him what he never possessed. Discontent dwarfs his horizon till he spans it with his hand. 'Most miserable of demi-gods,' he cries, 'here am I cooped up in this insignificant islet, only one hundred leagues by fifty, when scores of broad empires own me not for their lord.' Yet Uhia himself is envied. 'Ah!' cries Karrolono, one of his chieftains, master of a snug little glen, 'here am I cabined in this paltry cell among the mountains, when that great King Uhia is lord of the whole island, and every cubic mile of matter therein.' But this same Karrolono is envied. 'Hard, oh, beggarly lot is mine,' cries Donno, one of his retainers. 'Here am I fixed and screwed down to this paltry plantation, when my lord Karrolono owns the whole glen, ten long parasangs from cliff to sea.' But Donno too is envied. 'Alas, cursed fate!' cries his servitor Flavona. 'Here am I made to trudge, sweat, and labor all day, when Donno my master does nothing but command.' But others envy Flavona; and those who envy him are envied in turn; even down to poor bed-ridden Manta, who, dying of want, groans forth, 'Abandoned wretch that I am! here I miserably perish, while so many beggars gad about and live!' But surely, none envy Manta! Yes; great Uhia himself. 'Ah!' cries the king. 'Here am I vexed and tormented by ambition; no peace night nor day; my temples chafed sore by this cursed crown that I wear; while that wight Manta gives up the ghost with none to molest him.' "

In vain we wandered up and down in this isle, and peered into its innermost recesses: no Yillah was there.

Chapter XCII

The God Keevi and the Precipice of Mondo

One object of interest in Ohonoo was the original image of Keevi, the god of thieves: hence, from time immemorial, the tutelar deity of the isle.

His shrine was a natural niche in a cliff, walling in the valley of Monlova. And here stood Keevi, with his five eyes, ten hands, and three pair of legs, equipped at all points for the vocation over which he presided. Of mighty girth, his arms terminated in hands, every finger a limb, spreading in multiplied digits; palms twice five, and fifty fingers.

According to the legend, Keevi fell from a golden cloud, burying himself to the thighs in the earth, tearing up the soil all round. Three meditative mortals, strolling by at the time, had a narrow escape.

A wonderful recital; but none of us voyagers durst flout it. Did they not show us the identical spot where the idol fell? We descended into the hollow, now verdant. Questionless, Keevi himself would have vouched for the truth of the miracle, had he not been unfortunately dumb. But by far the most cogent, and pointed argument advanced in support of this story, is a spear which the priests of Keevi brought forth, for Babbalanja to view.

"Let me look at it closer," said Babbalanja.

And turning it over and over, and curiously inspecting it, "Wonderful spear," he cried. "Doubtless, my reverends, this self-same spear must have persuaded many recusants!"

"Nay, the most stubborn," they answered.

"And all afterwards quoted as additional authority for the truth of the legend?"

"Assuredly."

From the sea to the shrine of this god, the fine valley of Monlova ascends with a gentle gradation, hardly perceptible; but upon turning round towards the water, one is surprised to find himself high elevated above its surface. Pass on, and the same silent ascent deceives you; and the valley contracts; and on both sides the cliffs advance; till at last you come to a narrow space, shouldered by buttresses of rock. Beyond, through this cleft, all is blue sky. If the trades blow high, and you came unawares upon the spot, you would think Keevi himself pushing you forward with all his hands; so powerful is the current of air rushing through this elevated defile. But expostulate not with the tornado that blows you along; sail on; but soft; look down; the land breaks off in one sheer descent of a thousand feet, right down to the wide plain below. So sudden and profound this precipice, that you seem to look off from one world to another. In a dreamy, sunny day, the spangled plain beneath assumes an uncertain fleeting aspect. Had you a deep sea-lead you would almost be tempted to sound the ocean-haze at your feet.

This, mortal! is the precipice of Mondo.

From this brink, spear in hand, sprang fifty rebel warriors, driven back into the vale by a superior force. Finding no spot to stand at bay, with a fierce shout they took the fatal leap.

Said Mohi, "Their souls ascended, ere their bodies touched."

This tragical event took place many generations gone by, and now a dizzy, devious way conducts one, firm of foot, from the verge to the plain. But none ever ascended. So perilous, indeed, is the descent itself, that the islanders venture not the feat, without invoking supernatural aid. Flanking the precipice, beneath beetling rocks, stand the guardian deities of Mondo; and on altars before them, are placed the propitiatory offerings of the traveler.

To the right of the brink of the precipice, and far over it, projects a narrow ledge. The test of legitimacy in the Ohonoo monarchs is to stand hereon, arms folded, and javelins darting by.

And there in his youth Uhia stood.

"How felt you, cousin?" asked Media.

"Like the King of Ohonoo," he replied. "As I *shall* again feel, when King of all Mardi."

Chapter XCIII

Babbalanja Steps in Between Mohi and Yoomy; and Yoomy Relates a Legend

Embarking from Ohonoo, we at length found ourselves gliding by the pleasant shores of Tupia, an islet which according to Braid-Beard had for ages remained uninhabited by man. Much curiosity being expressed to know more of the isle, Mohi was about to turn over his chronicles, when, with modesty, the minstrel Yoomy interposed; saying, that if my Lord Media permitted, he himself would relate the legend. From its nature, deeming the same pertaining to his promise as poet; though, as yet, it had not been versified. But he added, that true pearl shells rang musically, though not strung upon a cord.

Upon this presumptuous interference, Mohi looked highly offended; and nervously twitching his beard, uttered something invidious about frippery young poetasters being too full of silly imaginings to tell a plain tale.

Said Yoomy, in reply, adjusting his turban, "Old Mohi, let us not clash. I honor your calling, but, with submission, your chronicles are more wild than my cantos. I deal in pure conceits of my own; which have a shapeliness, and a unity, however unsubstantial; but you, Braid-Beard, deal in mangled realities. In all your chapters, you yourself grope in the dark. Much truth is not in thee, historian. Besides, Mohi; my songs perpetuate many things which you sage scribes entirely overlook. Have you not oftentimes come to me, and my ever-dewy ballads for information, in which you and your musty old chronicles were deficient? In much that is precious, Mohi, we poets are the true historians; we embalm; you corrode."

To this Mohi, with some ire, was about to make answer, when, flinging over his shoulder a new fold of his mantle, Babbalanja spoke thus: "Peace, rivals. As Bardianna has it, like all who dispute upon pretensions of their own, you are each nearest the right, when you speak of the other; and furthest therefrom, when you speak of yourselves."

Said Mohi and Yoomy in a breath, "Who sought your opinion, philosopher? you filcher from old Bardianna, and monger of maxims!"

"You, who have so long marked the vices of Mardi, that you flatter yourself you have none of your own," added Braid-Beard.

"You, who only seem wise; because of the contrasting follies of others, and not of any great wisdom in yourself," continued the minstrel, with unwonted asperity.

"Now, here," said Babbalanja, "am I charged upon by a bearded old ram, and a lamb. One butting with his carious and brittle old frontlet; the other pushing with its silly head before its horns are sprouted. But this comes of being impartial. Had I espoused the cause of Yoomy *versus* Mohi, or that of Mohi *versus* Yoomy, I had been sure to have had at least one voice in my favor. The impartialist insulteth all sides, saith old Bardianna; but smite with but one hand, and the other shall be kissed. Oh, incomparable Bardianna!"

"Will no one lay that troubled old ghost," exclaimed Media devoutly. "Proceed with thy legend, Yoomy; and see to it, that it be brief; for I mistrust me, these legends do but test the patience of the hearers. But draw a long breath, and begin."

"A long bow," muttered Mohi.

And Yoomy began.

"It is now about ten hundred thousand moons—"

"Great Oro! How long since, say you?" cried Mohi, making Gothic arches of his brows.

Looking at him disdainfully, but vouchsafing no reply, Yoomy began over again.

"It is now above ten hundred thousand moons since there died the last of a marvelous race, once inhabiting the very shores by which we are sailing. They were a very diminutive people, only a few inches high—"

"Stop, minstrel," cried Mohi; "how many pennyweights did they weigh?"

Continued Yoomy, unheedingly, "They were covered all over with a soft, silky down, like that on the rind of the Avee; and there grew upon their heads a green, lance-leaved vine, of a most delicate texture. For convenience, the manikins reduced their tendrils, sporting, nothing but coronals. Whereas, priding themselves upon the redundancy of their tresses, the little maidens assiduously watered them with the early dew of the morning; so that all wreathed and festooned with verdure, they moved about in arbors, trailing after them trains."

"I can hear no more," exclaimed Mohi, stopping his ears.

Continued Yoomy, "The damsels lured to their bowers, certain red-plumaged insect-birds, and taught them to nestle therein and warble; which, with the pleasant vibrating of the leaves, when the little maidens moved, produced a strange blending of sweet, singing sounds. The little maidens embraced not with their arms, but with their viny locks; whose tendrils instinctively twined about their lovers, till both were lost in the bower."

"And what then?" asked Mohi, who notwithstanding the fingers in his ears, somehow contrived to listen. "What then?"

Vouchsafing no reply, Yoomy went on.

"At a certain age, but while yet the maidens were very young, their vines bore blossoms. Ah! fatal symptoms. For soon as they burst, the maidens died in their arbors; and were buried in the valleys; and their vines spread forth; and the flowers bloomed; but the maidens themselves were no more. And now disdaining the earth, the vines shot upward: climbing to the topmost boughs of the trees; and flowering in the sunshine forever and aye."

Yoomy here paused for a space, but presently continued:

"The little eyes of the people of Tupia were very strange to behold; full of stars, that shone from within; like the Pleiades, deep-bosomed in blue. And like the stars, they were intolerant of sunlight; and slumbering through the day, the people of Tupia only went abroad by night. But it was chiefly when the moon was at full, that they were mostly in spirits.

"Then the little manikins would dive down into the sea, and rove about in the coral groves, making love to the mermaids. Or, racing round, make a mad merry night of it with the sea-urchins—plucking the reverend mullets by the beard; serenading the turtles in their cells; worrying the sea-nettles; or tormenting with their antics the touchy torpedoes. Sometimes they went prying about with the star-fish, that have an eye at the end of each ray; and often with coral files in their hands stole upon slumbering sword-fish, slyly blunting their weapons. In short, these stout little manikins were passionately fond of the sea, and swore by wave and billow, that sooner or later they would embark thereon in nautilus shells, and spend the rest of their roving days thousands of inches from Tupia. Too true, they were shameless little rakes. Oft would they return to their sweethearts, sporting musky girdles of sea-kelp, tasseled with green little pouches of grass, brimful of seed-pearls; and jingling their coin in the ears of the damsels, throw out inuendoes about the beautiful and bountiful mermaids: how wealthy and amorous they were, and how they delighted in the company of the brave gallants of Tupia. Ah! at such heartless bravadoes, how mourned the poor little nymphs. Deep into their arbors they went; and their little hearts burst like rose-buds, and filled the whole air with an odorous grief. But when their lovers were gentle and true, no happier maidens haunted the lilies than they. By some mystical process they wrought minute balls of light: touchy, mercurial globules, very hard to handle; and with these, at pitch and toss, they played in the groves. Or mischievously inclined, they toiled all night long at braiding the moonbeams together, and entangling the plaited end to a bough; so that at night, the poor planet had much ado to set."

Here Yoomy once more was mute.

"Pause you to invent as you go on?" said old Mohi, elevating his chin, till his beard was horizontal.

Yoomy resumed.

"Little or nothing more, my masters, is extant of the legend; only it must be mentioned, that these little people were very tasteful in their personal adornings; the manikins wearing girdles of fragrant leaves, and necklaces of aromatic seeds; and the little damsels, not content with their vines, and their verdure, sporting pearls in their ears; bracelets of wee little porpoise teeth; and oftentimes dancing with their mates in the moonlit glades, coquettishly fanned themselves with the transparent wings of the flying fish."

"Now, I appeal to you, royal Media; to you, noble Taji; to you, Babbalanja," said the chronicler, with an impressive gesture, "whether this seems a credible history: Yoomy has invented."

"But perhaps he has entertained, old Mohi," said Babbalanja.

"He has not spoken the truth," persisted the chronicler.

"Mohi," said Babbalanja, "truth is in things, and not in words: truth is voiceless; so at least saith old Bardianna. And I, Babbalanja, assert, that what are vulgarly called fictions are as much realities as the gross mattock of Dididi, the digger of trenches; for things visible are but conceits of the eye: things imaginative, conceits of the fancy. If duped by one, we are equally duped by the other."

"Clear as this water," said Yoomy.

"Opaque as this paddle," said Mohi, "But, come now, thou oracle, if all things are deceptive, tell us what is truth?"

"The old interrogatory; did they not ask it when the world began? But ask it no more. As old Bardianna hath it, that question is more final than any answer."

Chapter XCIV

Of That Jolly Old Lord, Borabolla; and That Jolly Island of His, Mondoldo; and of the Fish-ponds, and the Hereafters of Fish

Drawing near Mondoldo, our next place of destination, we were greeted by six fine canoes, gaily tricked out with streamers, and all alive with the gestures of their occupants. King Borabolla and court were hastening to welcome our approach; Media, unbeknown to all, having notified him at the Banquet of the Five-and-Twenty Kings of our intention to visit his dominions.

Soon, side by side, these canoes floated with ours; each barge of Odo flanked by those of Mondoldo.

Not long were we in identifying Borabolla; the portly pleasant old monarch, seated cross-legged upon a dais, projecting over the bow of the largest canoe of the six, close-grappling to the side of the Sea Elephant.

Was he not a goodly round sight to behold? Round all over; round of eye and of head; and like the jolly round Earth, roundest and biggest about the Equator. A girdle of red was his Equinoctial Line, giving a compactness to his plumpness.

This old Borabolla permitted naught to come between his head and the sun; not even gray hairs. Bald as a gourd, right down on his brazen skull, the rays of the luminary converged.

He was all hilarity; full of allusions to the feast at Willamilla, where he had done royal execution. Rare old Borabolla! thou wert made for dining out; thy ample mouth an inlet for good cheer, and a sally-port for good humor.

Bustling about on his dais, he now gave orders for the occupants of our canoes to be summarily emptied into his own; saying, that in that manner only did he allow guests to touch the beach of Mondoldo.

So, with no little trouble—for the waves were grown somewhat riotous—we proceeded to comply; bethinking ourselves all the while, how annoying is sometimes an overstrained act of hospitality.

We were now but little less than a mile from the shore. But what of that? There was plenty of time, thought Borabolla, for a hasty lunch, and the getting of a subsequent appetite ere we effected a landing. So viands were produced; to which the guests were invited to pay heedful attention; or take the consequences, and famish till the long voyage in prospect was ended.

Soon the water shoaled (approaching land is like nearing truth in metaphysics), and ere we yet touched the beach, Borabolla declared, that we were already landed. Which paradoxical assertion implied, that the hospitality of Mondoldo was such, that in all directions it radiated far out upon the lagoon, embracing a great circle; so that no canoe could sail by the island, without its occupants being so long its guests.

In most hospitable vicinity to the water, was a fine large structure, enclosed by a stockade; both rather dilapidated; as if the cost of entertaining its guests, prevented outlays for repairing the place. But it was one of Borabolla's maxims, that generally your tumble-down old homesteads yield the most entertainment; their very dilapidation betokening their having seen good service in hospitality; whereas, spruce-looking, finical portals, have a phiz full of meaning; for niggards are oftentimes neat.

Now, after what has been said, who so silly as to fancy, that because Borabolla's mansion was enclosed by a stockade, that the same was intended as a defense against guests? By no means. In the palisade was a mighty breach, not an entrance-way, wide enough to admit six Daniel Lamberts abreast.

"Look," cried Borabolla, as landing, we stepped towards the place, "Look, Media! Look, all. These gates, you here see, lashed back with osiers, have been so lashed during my lifetime; and just where they stand, shall they rot; ay, they shall perish wide open."

"But why have them at all?" inquired Media.

"Ah! there you have old Borabolla," cried the other.

"No," said Babbalanja, "a fence whose gate is ever kept open, seems unnecessary, I grant; nevertheless it gives a notable hint, otherwise not so aptly conveyed; for is not the open gate the sign of the open heart?"

"Right, right," cried Borabolla; "so enter both, cousin Media"; and with one hand smiting his chest, with the other he waved us on.

But if the stockade seemed all open gate, the structure within seemed only a roof; for nothing but a slender pillar here and there, supported it.

"This is my mode of building," said Borabolla; "I will have no outside to my palaces. Walls are superfluous; and, to a high-minded guest, the entering a narrow doorway is like passing under a yoke; every time he goes in, or comes out, it reminds him that he is being entertained at the cost of another. So storm in all round."

Within, was one wide field-bed; where reclining we looked up to endless rows of brown calabashes, and trenchers suspended along the rafters; promissory of ample cheer as regiments of old hams in a baronial refectory.

They were replenished with both meat and drink; the trenchers readily accessible by means of cords; but the gourds, containing arrack, suspended neck downward, were within easy reach where they swung.

Seeing all these indications of hard roystering; like a cautious young bridegroom at his own marriage merrymaking, Taji stood on his guard. And when Borabolla urged him to empty a gourd or two, by way of making room in him for the incidental repast about to be served, Taji civilly declined; not wishing to cumber the floor before the cloth was laid.

Jarl, however, yielding to importunity, and unmindful of the unities of time and place, went freely about, from gourd to gourd, concocting in him a punch. At which Samoa expressed much surprise, that he should be so unobservant as not to know, that in Mardi, guests might be pressed to demean themselves, without its being expected that so they would do. A true toss-pot himself, he bode his time.

The second lunch over, Borabolla placed both hands to the ground, and giving the sigh of the fat man, after three vigorous efforts, succeeded in gaining his pins; which pins of his, were but small for his body; insomuch that they hugely staggered about, under the fine old load they carried.

The specific object of his thus striving after an erect posture, was to put himself in motion, and conduct us to his fish-ponds, famous throughout the Archipelago as the hobby of the King of Mondoldo. Furthermore, as the great repast of the day, yet to take place, was to be a grand piscatory one, our host was all anxiety, that we should have a glimpse of our fish while yet alive and hearty.

We were alarmed at perceiving, that certain servitors were preparing to accompany us with trenchers of edibles. It begat the notion, that our trip to the fish-ponds was to prove a long journey. But they were not three hundred yards distant; though Borabolla being a veteran traveler, never stirred from his abode without his battalion of butlers.

The ponds were four in number, close bordering the water, embracing about an acre each, and situated in a low fen, draining several valleys. The excavated soil was thrown up in dykes, made tight by being beaten all over, while in a soft state with the heavy, flat ends of palm stalks. Lying side by side, by three connecting trenches, these ponds could be made to communicate at pleasure;

while two additional canals afforded means of letting in upon them the salt waters of the lagoon on one hand, or those of an inland stream on the other. And by a third canal with four branches, together or separately, they could be partially drained. Thus, the waters could be mixed to suit any gills; and the young fish taken from the sea, passed through a stated process of freshening; so that by the time they graduated, the salt was well out of them, like the brains out of some diplomaed collegians.

Fresh-water fish are only to be obtained in Mondoldo by the artificial process abovementioned; as the streams and brooks abound not in trout or other Waltonian prey.

Taken all floundering from the sea, Borabolla's fish, passing through their regular training for the table, and daily tended by their keepers, in course of time became quite tame and communicative. To prove which, calling his Head Ranger, the king bade him administer the customary supply of edibles.

Accordingly, mouthfuls were thrown into the ponds. Whereupon, the fish darted in a shoal towards the margin; some leaping out of the water in their eagerness. Crouching on the bank, the Ranger now called several by name, patted their scales, carrying on some heathenish nursery-talk, like St. Anthony, in ancient Coptic, instilling virtuous principles into his finny flock on the seashore.

But alas, for the hair-shirted old dominie's back-sliding disciples. For, of all nature's animated kingdoms, fish are the most unchristian, inhospitable, heartless, and cold-blooded of creatures. At least, so seem they to strangers; though at bottom, somehow, they must be all right. And truly it is not to be wondered at, that the very reverend Anthony strove after the conversion of fish. For, whoso shall Christianize, and by so doing, humanize the sharks, will do a greater good, by the saving of human life in all time to come, than though he made catechumens of the head-hunting Dyaks of Borneo, or the blood-bibbing Battas of Sumatra. And are these Dyaks and Battas one whit better than tiger-sharks? Nay, are they so good? Were a Batta your intimate friend, you would often mistake an orang-outang for him; and have orang-outangs immortal souls? True, the Battas believe in a hereafter; but of what sort? Full of Blue-Beards and bloody bones. So, also the sharks; who behold that Paradise is one vast Pacific, ploughed by navies of mortals, whom an endless gale forever drops into their maws.

Not wholly a surmise. For, does it not appear a little unreasonable to imagine, that there is any creature, fish, flesh, or fowl, so little in love with life, as not to cherish hopes of a future state? Why does man believe in it? One reason, reckoned cogent, is, that he desires it. Who shall say, then, that the leviathan this day harpooned on the coast of Japan, goes not straight to his ancestor, who rolled all Jonah, as a sweet morsel, under his tongue?

Though herein, some sailors are slow believers, or at best, hold themselves in a state of philosophical suspense. Say they—"That catastrophe took place in the Mediterranean; and the only whales frequenting the Mediterranean are of a sort having not a swallow large enough to pass a man entire; for those Mediterranean whales feed upon small things, as horses upon oats." But hence, the sailors draw a rash inference. Are not the Straits of Gibraltar wide enough to admit a sperm-whale, even though none have sailed through, since Nineveh and the gourd in its suburbs dried up?

As for the possible hereafter of the whales; a creature eighty feet long without stockings, and thirty feet round the waist before dinner, is not inconsiderately to be consigned to annihilation.

Chapter XCV

That Jolly Old Lord Borabolla Laughs on Both Sides of His Face

"A very good palace, this, coz. for you and me," said waddling old Borabolla to Media, as, returned from our excursion, he slowly lowered himself down to his mat, sighing like a grampus.

By this, he again made known the vastness of his hospitality, which led him for the nonce to parcel out his kingdom with his guests.

But apart from these extravagant expressions of good feeling, Borabolla was the prince of good fellows. His great tun of a person was indispensable to the housing of his bullock-heart; under which, any lean wight would have sunk. But alas! unlike Media and Taji, Borabolla, though a crowned king, was accounted no demi-god; his obesity excluding him from that honor. Indeed, in some quarters of Mardi, certain pagans maintain, that no fat man can be even immortal. A dogma! truly, which should be thrown to the dogs. For fat men are the salt and savor of the earth; full of good humor, high spirits, fun, and all manner of jollity. Their breath clears the atmosphere; their exhalations air the world. Of men, they are the good measures; brimmed, heaped, pressed down, piled up, and running over. They are as ships from Teneriffe; swimming deep, full of old wine, and twenty steps down into their holds. Soft and susceptible all round, they are easy of entreaty. Wherefore, for all their rotundity, they are too often circumnavigated by hatchet-faced knaves. Ah! a fat uncle, with a fat paunch, and a fat purse, is a joy and a delight to all nephews; to philosophers, a subject of endless speculation, as to how many droves of oxen and Lake Eries of wine might have run through his great mill during the full term of his mortal career. Fat men not immortal! This very instant, old Lambert is rubbing his jolly abdomen in Paradise.

Now, to the fact of his not being rated a demi-god, was perhaps ascribable the circumstance, that Borabolla comported himself with less dignity, than was the wont of their Mardian majesties. And truth to say, to have seen him regaling himself with one of his favorite cuttle-fish, its long snaky arms and feelers instinctively twining round his head as he ate; few intelligent observers would have opined that the individual before them was the sovereign lord of Mondoldo.

But what of the banquet of fish? Shall we tell how the old king ungirdled himself thereto; how as the feast waxed towards its close, with one sad exception, he still remained sunny-sided all round; his disc of a face joyous as the South Side of Madeira in the hilarious season of grapes? Shall we tell how we all grew glad and frank? and how the din of the dinner was heard far into night?

We will.

When Media ate slowly, Borabolla took him to task, bidding him dispatch his viands more speedily.

Whereupon said Media, "But, Borabolla, my round fellow, that would abridge the pleasure."

"Not at all, my dear demi-god; do like me: eat fast and eat long."

In the middle of the feast, a huge skin of wine was brought in. The portly peltry of a goat; its horns embattling its effigy head; its mouth the nozzle; and its long beard flowed to its jet-black hoofs. With many ceremonial salaams, the attendants bore it along, placing it at one end of the convivial mats, full in front of Borabolla; where, seated upon its haunches it made one of the party.

Brimming a ram's horn, the mellowest of bugles, Borabolla bowed to his silent guest, and thus spoke—"In this wine, which yet smells of the grape, I pledge you, my reverend old toper, my lord Capricornus; you alone have enough; and here's full skins to the rest!"

"How jolly he is," whispered Media to Babbalanja.

"Ay, his lungs laugh loud; but is laughing, rejoicing?"

"Help! help!" cried Borabolla, "lay me down! lay me down! good gods, what a twinge!"

The goblet fell from his hand; the purple flew from his wine to his face; and Borabolla fell back into the arms of his servitors. "That gout! that gout!" he groaned. "Lord! lord! no more cursed wine will I drink!"

Then, at ten paces distant, a clumsy attendant let fall a trencher—"Take it off my foot, you knave!"

Afar off another entered gallanting a calabash—"Look out for my toe, you hound!"

During all this, the attendants tenderly nursed him. And in good time, with its thousand fangs, the gout-fiend departed for awhile.

Reprieved, the old king brightened up; by degrees becoming jolly as ever.

"Come! let us be merry again," he cried. "What shall we eat? and what shall we drink? that infernal gout is gone. Come, what will your worships have?"

So at it once more we went.

But of our feast, little more remains to be related than this—that out of it, grew a wondrous kindness between Borabolla and Jarl. Strange to tell, from the first our fat host had regarded my Viking with a most friendly eye. Still stranger to add, this feeling was returned. But though they thus fancied each other, they were very unlike; Borabolla and Jarl. Nevertheless, thus is it ever. And as the convex fits not into the convex, but into the concave; so do men fit into their opposites; and so fitted Borabolla's arched paunch into Jarl's, hollowed out to receive it.

But how now? Borabolla was jolly and loud: Jarl demure and silent; Borabolla was a king: Jarl only a Viking—how came they together? Very plain, to repeat—because they were heterogeneous; and hence the affinity. But as the affinity between those chemical opposites chlorine and hydrogen is promoted by caloric, so the affinity between Borabolla and Jarl was promoted by the warmth of the wine that they drank at this feast. For of all blessed fluids, the juice of the grape is the greatest foe to cohesion. True, it tightens the girdle; but then it loosens the tongue, and opens the heart.

In sum, Borabolla loved Jarl; and Jarl, pleased with this sociable monarch, for all his garrulity, esteemed him the most sensible old gentleman and king he had as yet seen in Mardi. For this reason, perhaps, that his talkativeness favored that silence in listeners, which was my Viking's delight in himself.

Repeatedly during the banquet, our host besought Taji to allow his henchman to remain on the island, after the rest of our party should depart; and he faithfully promised to surrender Jarl, whenever we should return to claim him.

But though I harbored no distrust of Borabolla's friendly intentions, I could not so readily consent to his request; for with Jarl for my one only companion, had I not both famished and feasted? was he not my only link to things past?

Things past! Ah, Yillah! for all its mirth, and though we hunted wide, we found thee not in Mondoldo.

Chapter XCVI

SAMOA A SURGEON

THE SECOND DAY OF OUR STAY IN MONDOLDO WAS SIGNALIZED BY A NOTEWORTHY EXHIBITION of the surgical skill of Samoa, who had often boasted, that though well versed in the science of breaking men's heads, he was equally an adept in mending their crockery.

Overnight, Borabolla had directed his corps of sea-divers to repair early on the morrow, to a noted section of the great Mardian reef, for the purpose of procuring for our regalement some of the fine Hawk's-bill turtle, whose secret retreats were among the cells and galleries of that submerged wall of coral, from whose foamy coping no plummet dropped ever yet touched bottom.

These turtles were only to be obtained by diving far down under the surface; and then swimming along horizontally, and peering into the coral honeycomb; snatching at a flipper when seen, as at a pinion in a range of billing dove-cotes.

As the king's divers were thus employed, one of them, Karhownoo by name, perceived a Devil-shark, so called, swimming wistfully towards him from out his summer grotto in the reef. No way petrified by the sight, and pursuing the usual method adopted by these divers in such emergencies, Karhownoo, splashing the water, instantly swam towards the stranger. But the shark, undaunted, advanced; a thing so unusual, and fearful, that, in an agony of fright, the diver shot up for the surface. Heedless, he looked not up as he went; and when within a few inches of the open air, dashed his head against a projection of the reef. He would have sunk into the live tomb beneath, were it not that three of his companions, standing on the brink, perceived his peril, and dragged him into safety.

Seeing the poor fellow was insensible, they endeavored, ineffectually, to revive him; and at last, placing him in their canoe, made all haste for the shore. Here a crowd soon gathered, and the diver was borne to a habitation, close adjoining Borabolla's; whence hearing of the disaster, we sallied out to render assistance.

Upon entering the hut, the benevolent old king commanded it to be cleared; and then proceeded to examine the sufferer.

The skull proved to be very badly fractured; in one place, splintered.

"Let me mend it," said Samoa, with ardor.

And being told of his experience in such matters, Borabolla surrendered the patient.

With a gourd of water, and a tappa cloth, the one-armed Upoluan carefully washed the wound; and then calling for a sharp splinter of bamboo, and a thin, semi-transparent cup of cocoanut shell, he went about the operation: nothing less than the "Tomoti" (head-mending), in other words, the trepan.

The patient still continuing insensible, the fragments were disengaged by help of a bamboo scalpel; when a piece of the drinking cup—previously dipped in the milk of a cocoanut—was nicely fitted into the vacancy, the skin as nicely adjusted over it, and the operation was complete.

And now, while all present were crying out in admiration of Samoa's artistic skill, and Samoa himself stood complacently regarding his workmanship, Babbalanja suggested that it might be well to ascertain whether the patient survived. When, upon sounding his heart, the diver was found to be dead.

The bystanders loudly lamented; but declared the surgeon a man of marvelous science.

Returning to Borabolla's, much conversation ensued, concerning the sad scene we had witnessed, which presently branched into a learned discussion upon matters of surgery at large.

At length, Samoa regaled the company with a story; for the truth of which no one but him can vouch, for no one but him was by at the time; though there is testimony to show that it involves nothing at variance with the customs of certain barbarous tribes.

Read on.

Chapter XCVII

FAITH AND KNOWLEDGE

A THING INCREDIBLE IS ABOUT TO BE RELATED; BUT A THING MAY BE INCREDIBLE AND STILL BE true; sometimes it is incredible because it is true. And many infidels but disbelieve the least incredible things; and many bigots reject the most obvious. But let us hold fast to all we have; and stop all leaks in our faith; lest an opening, but of a hand's breadth, should sink our seventy-fours. The wide Atlantic can rush in at one port-hole; and if we surrender a plank, we surrender the fleet. Panoplied in all the armor of St. Paul, morion, hauberk, and greaves, let us fight the Turks inch by inch, and yield them naught but our corpse.

But let us not turn round upon friends, confounding them with foes. For dissenters only assent to more than we. Though Milton was a heretic to the creed of Athanasius, his faith exceeded that of Athanasius himself; and the faith of Athanasius that of Thomas, the disciple, who with his own eyes beheld the mark of the nails. Whence it comes that though we be all Christians now, the best of us had perhaps been otherwise in the days of Thomas.

The higher the intelligence, the more faith, and the less credulity; Gabriel rejects more than we, but out-believes us all. The greatest marvels are first truths; and first truths the last unto which we attain. Things nearest are furthest off. Though your ear be next door to your brain, it is forever removed from your sight. Man has a more comprehensive view of the moon, than the man in the moon himself. We know the moon is round; he only infers it. It is because we ourselves are in ourselves, that we know ourselves not. And it is only of our easy faith, that we are not infidels throughout; and only of our lack of faith, that we believe what we do.

In some universe-old truths, all mankind are disbelievers. Do you believe that you lived three thousand years ago? That you were at the taking of Tyre, were overwhelmed in Gomorrah? No. But for me, I was at the subsiding of the Deluge, and helped swab the ground, and build the first house. With the Israelites, I fainted in the wilderness; was in court, when Solomon out-did all the judges before him. I it was who suppressed the lost work of Manetho, on the Egyptian theology, as containing mysteries not to be revealed to posterity, and things at war with the canonical scriptures; I, who originated the conspiracy against that purple murderer, Domitian; I, who in the senate moved, that great and good Aurelian be Emperor. I instigated the abdication of Diocletian, and Charles V; I touched Isabella's heart, that she hearkened to Columbus. I am he, that from the King's minions hid the Charter in the old oak at Hartford; I harbored Goffe and Whalley; I am the leader of the Mohawk masks, who in the Old Commonwealth's harbor, overboard threw the East India Company's Souchong; I am the Vailed Persian Prophet; I, the man in the iron mask; I, Junius.

Chapter XCVIII

THE TALE OF A TRAVELER

IT WAS SAMOA WHO TOLD THE INCREDIBLE TALE; AND HE TOLD IT AS A TRAVELER. BUT STAY-at-homes say travelers lie. Yet a voyage to Ethiopia would cure them of that; for few skeptics are travelers; fewer travelers liars, though the proverb respecting them lies. It is false, as some say, that Bruce was cousin-german to Baron Munchausen; but true, as Bruce said, that the Abysinnians cut live steaks from their cattle. It was, in good part, his villainous transcribers who made monstrosities of Mandeville's travels. And though all liars go to Gehenna; yet, assuming that Mandeville died before Dante; still, though Dante took the census of Hell, we find not Sir John under the likeness of a roasted neat's tongue, in that infernalest of infernos, The Inferno.

But let not the truth be postponed. To the stand, Samoa, and through your interpreter speak.

Once upon a time, during his endless sea-rovings, the Upoluan was called upon to cobble the head of a friend, grievously hurt in a desperate fight of slings.

Upon examination, that part of the brain proving as much injured as the cranium itself, a young pig was obtained; and preliminaries being over, part of its live brain was placed in the cavity, the trepan accomplished with cocoanut shell, and the scalp drawn over and secured.

This man died not, but lived. But from being a warrior of great sense and spirit, he became a perverse-minded and piggish fellow, showing many of the characteristics of his swinish grafting. He survived the operation more than a year; at the end of that period, however, going mad, and dying in his delirium.

Stoutly backed by the narrator, this anecdote was credited by some present. But Babbalanja held out to the last.

"Yet, if this story be true," said he, "and since it is well settled, that our brains are somehow the organs of sense; then, I see not why human reason could not be put into a pig, by letting into its cranium the contents of a man's. I have long thought, that men, pigs, and plants, are but curious physiological experiments; and that science would at last enable philosophers to produce new species of beings, by somehow mixing, and concocting the essential ingredients of various creatures; and so forming new combinations. My friend Atahalpa, the astrologer and alchemist, has long had a jar, in which he has been endeavoring to hatch a fairy, the ingredients being compounded according to a receipt of his own."

But little they heeded Babbalanja. It was the traveler's tale that most arrested attention.

Tough the thews, and tough the tales of Samoa.

Chapter XCIX

"MARNEE ORA, ORA MARNEE"

DURING THE AFTERNOON OF THE DAY OF THE DIVER'S DECEASE, PREPARATIONS WERE MAKING for paying the last rites to his remains, and carrying them by torch-light to their sepulcher, the sea; for, as in Odo, so was the custom here.

Meanwhile, all over the isle, to and fro went heralds, dismally arrayed, beating shark-skin drums; and, at intervals, crying—"A man is dead; let no fires be kindled; have mercy, oh Oro!—Let no canoe be put to sea till the burial. This night, oh Oro!—Let no food be cooked."

And ever and anon, passed and repassed these, others in brave attire; with castanets of pearl shells, making gay music, and these sang:

Be merry, oh men of Mondoldo,
A maiden this night is to wed:
Be merry, oh damsels of Mardi—
Flowers, flowers for the bridal bed.

Informed that the preliminary rites were about being rendered, we repaired to the arbor, whither the body had been removed.

Arrayed in white, it was laid out on a mat; its arms mutely crossed, between its lips an asphodel; at the feet a withered hawthorn bough.

The relatives were wailing and cutting themselves with shells, so that blood flowed, and spotted their vesture.

Upon remonstrating with the most abandoned of these mourners, the wife of the diver, she exclaimed, "Yes; great is the pain, but greater my affliction."

Another, the deaf sire of the dead, went staggering about, and groping; saying that he was now quite blind; for some months previous he had lost one eye in the death of his eldest son; and now the other was gone.

"I am childless," he cried. "Henceforth call me Roi Mori," that is, Twice-Blind.

While the relatives were thus violently lamenting, the rest of the company occasionally scratched themselves with their shells; but very slightly, and mostly on the soles of their feet; from long exposure, quite callous. This was interrupted, however, when the real mourners averted their eyes; though at no time was there any deviation in the length of their faces.

But on all sides, lamentations afresh broke forth, upon the appearance of a person who had been called in to assist in solemnizing the obsequies, and also to console the afflicted.

In rotundity, he was another Borabolla. He puffed and panted.

As he approached the corpse, a sobbing silence ensued; when holding the hand of the dead, between his, the stranger thus spoke:

"Mourn not, oh friends of Karhownoo, that this your brother lives not. His wounded head pains him no more; he would not feel it did a javelin pierce him. Yea; Karhownoo is exempt from all the ills and evils of this miserable Mardi!"

Hereupon, the Twice-Blind, who being deaf, heard not what was said, tore his gray hair, and cried, "Alas! alas! my boy; thou wert the merriest man in Mardi, and now thy pranks are over!"

But the other proceeded—"Mourn not, I say, oh friends of Karhownoo; the dead whom ye deplore is happier than the living; is not his spirit in the aerial isles?"

"True! true!" responded the raving wife, mingling her blood with her tears, "my own poor hapless Karhownoo is thrice happy in Paradise!" And anew she wailed and lacerated her cheeks.

"Rave not, I say."

But she only raved the more.

And now the good stranger departed; saying he must hie to a wedding, waiting his presence in an arbor adjoining.

Understanding that the removal of the body would not take place till midnight, we thought to behold the mode of marrying in Mondoldo.

Drawing near the place, we were greeted by merry voices, and much singing, which greatly increased when the good stranger was perceived.

Gaily arrayed in fine robes, with plumes on their heads, the bride and groom stood in the middle of a joyous throng, in readiness for the nuptial bond to be tied.

Standing before them, the stranger was given a cord, so bedecked with flowers, as to disguise its stout fibers; and taking: the bride's hands, he bound them together to a ritual chant; about her neck, in festoons, disposing the flowery ends of the cord. Then turning to the groom, he was given another, also beflowered; but attached thereto was a great stone, very much carved, and stained; indeed, so every way disguised, that a person not knowing what it was, and lifting it, would be greatly amazed at its weight. This cord being attached to the waist of the groom, he leaned over towards the bride, by reason of the burden of the drop.

All present now united in a chant, and danced about the happy pair, who meanwhile looked ill at ease; the one being so bound by the hands, and the other solely weighed down by his stone.

A pause ensuing the good stranger, turning them back to back, thus spoke:

"By thy flowery gyves, oh bride! I make thee a wife; and by thy burdensome stone, oh groom! I make thee a husband. Live and be happy, both; for the wise and good Oro hath placed us in Mardi to be glad. Doth not all nature rejoice in her green groves and her flowers? and woo and wed not the fowls of the air, trilling their bliss in their bowers? Live then, and be happy, oh bride and groom! for Oro is offended with the unhappy, since he meant them to be gay."

And the ceremony ended with a joyful feast.

But not all nuptials in Mardi were like these. Others were wedded with different rites; without the stone and flowery gyves. These were they who plighted their troth with tears not smiles, and made responses in the heart.

Returning from the house of the merry to the house of the mournful, we lingered till midnight to witness the issuing forth of the body.

By torch light, numerous canoes, with paddlers standing by, were drawn up on the beach, to accommodate those who purposed following the poor diver to his home.

The remains embarked, some confusion ensued concerning the occupancy of the rest of the shallops. At last the procession glided off, our party included. Two by two, forming a long line of torches trailing round the isle, the canoes all headed towards the opening in the reef.

For a time, a decorous silence was preserved; but presently, some whispering was heard; perhaps melancholy discoursing touching the close of the diver's career. But we were shocked to discover, that poor Karhownoo was not much in their thoughts; they were conversing about the next bread-fruit harvest; and the recent arrival of King Media and party at Mondoldo. From far in advance, however, were heard the lamentations of the true mourners, the relatives of the diver.

Passing the reef, and sailing a little distance therefrom, the canoes were disposed in a circle; the one bearing the corpse in the center. Certain ceremonies over, the body was committed to the waves: the white foam lighting up the last, long plunge of the diver, to see sights more strange, than ever he saw in the brooding cells of the Turtle Reef.

And now, while in the still midnight, all present were gazing down into the ocean, watching the white wake of the corpse, ever and anon illuminated by sparkles, an unknown voice was heard, and all started and vacantly stared, as this wild song was sung:

We drop our dead in the sea,
The bottomless, bottomless sea;
Each bubble a hollow sigh,
As it sinks forever and aye.

We drop our dead in the sea—
The dead reck not of aught;
We drop our dead in the sea—
The sea ne'er gives it a thought.

Sink, sink, oh! corpse, still sink,
Far down in the bottomless sea,
Where the unknown forms do prowl,
Down, down in the bottomless sea.

'Tis night above, and night all round,
And night will it be with thee;
As thou sinkest, and sinkest for aye,
Deeper down in the bottomless sea.

The mysterious voice died away; no sign of the corpse was now seen; and mute with amaze, the company long listed to the low moan of the billows and the sad sough of the breeze.

At last, without speaking, the obsequies were concluded by sliding into the ocean a carved tablet of Palmetto to mark the place of the burial. But a wave-crest received it, and fast it floated away.

Returning to the isle, long silence prevailed. But, at length, as if the scene in which they had just taken part, afresh reminded them of the mournful event, which had called them together, the company again recurred to it; some present, sadly and incidentally alluding to Borabolla's banquet of turtle, thereby postponed.

Chapter C

The Pursuer Himself Is Pursued

NEXT MORNING, WHEN MUCH TO THE CHAGRIN OF BORABOLLA WE WERE PREPARING TO QUIT HIS isle, came tidings to the palace, of a wonderful event, occurring in one of the "Motoos," or little islets of the great reef; which "Motoo" was included in the dominions of the king.

The men who brought these tidings were highly excited; and no sooner did they make known what they knew, than all Mondoldo was in a tumult of marveling.

Their story was this.

Going at daybreak to the Motoo to fish, they perceived a strange proa beached on its seaward shore; and presently were hailed by voices; and saw among the palm-trees, three specter-like men, who were not of Mardi.

The first amazement of the fishermen over, in reply to their eager questions, the strangers related, that they were the survivors of a company of men, natives of some unknown island to the north-east; whence they had embarked for another country, distant three days' sail to the southward of theirs. But falling in with a terrible adventure, in which their sire had been slain, they altered their course to pursue the fugitive who murdered him; one and all vowing, never more to see home, until their father's fate was avenged. The murderer's proa outsailing theirs, soon ran out of sight; yet after him they blindly steered by day and by night: steering by the blood-red star in Boötes. Soon, a violent gale overtook them; driving them to and fro; leaving them they knew not where. But still struggling against strange currents, at times counteracting their sailing, they drifted on their way; nigh to famishing for water; and no shore in sight. In long calms, in vain they held up their dry gourds to heaven, and cried, "Send us a breeze, sweet gods!" The calm still brooded; and ere it was gone, all but three gasped; and dead from thirst, were plunged into the sea. The breeze which followed the calm, soon brought them in sight of a low, uninhabited isle; where tarrying many days, they laid in good store of cocoanuts and water, and again embarked.

The next land they saw was Mardi; and they landed on the Motoo, still intent on revenge.

This recital filled Taji with horror.

Who could these avengers be, but the sons of him I had slain? I had thought them far hence, and myself forgotten; and now, like adders, they started up in my path, as I hunted for Yillah.

But I dissembled my thoughts.

Without waiting to hear more, Borabolla, all curiosity to behold the strangers, instantly dispatched to the Motoo one of his fleetest canoes, with orders to return with the voyagers.

Ere long they came in sight; and perceiving that strange proa in tow of the king's, Samoa cried out, "Lo! Taji, the canoe that was going to Tedaidee!"

Too true; the same double-keeled craft, now sorely broken, the fatal dais in wild disarray: the canoe, the canoe of Aleema! And with it came the spearmen three, who, when the *Chamois* was fleeing from their bow, had poised their javelins. But so wan their aspect now, their faces looked like skulls.

Then came over me the wild dream of Yillah; and, for a space, like a madman I raved. It seemed as if the mysterious damsel must still be there; the rescue yet to be achieved. In my delirium, I rushed upon the skeletons, as they landed—"Hide not the maiden!" But, interposing, Media led me aside; when my transports abated.

Now, instantly, the strangers knew who I was; and, brandishing their javelins, they rushed upon me, as I had on them, with a yell. But deeming us all mad, the crowd held us apart; writhing in the arms that restrained them, the pale specters foamed out their curses again and again—"Oh, murderer! white curses upon thee! Bleached be thy soul with our hate! Living, our brethren cursed thee; and dying, dry-lipped, they cursed thee again. They died not through famishing for water, but for revenge upon thee! Thy blood, their thirst would have slaked!"

I lay fainting against the hard-throbbing heart of Samoa, while they showered their yells through the air. Once more, in my thoughts, the green corpse of the priest drifted by.

Among the people of Mondoldo a violent commotion now raged. They were amazed at Taji's recognition by the strangers, and at the deadly ferocity they betrayed.

Rallying upon this, and perceiving that by divulging all they knew, these sons of Aleema might stir up the islanders against me, I resolved to anticipate their story; and, turning to Borabolla, said—"In these strangers, oh, king! you behold the survivors of a band we encountered on our voyage. From them I rescued a maiden, called Yillah, whom they were carrying captive. Little more of their history do I know."

"Their maledictions?" exclaimed Borabolla.

"Are they not delirious with suffering?" I cried. "They know not what they say."

So, moved by all this, he commanded them to be guarded, and conducted within his palisade; and having supplied them with cheer, entered into earnest discourse. Yet all the while, the pale strangers on me fixed their eyes; deep, dry, crater-like hollows, lurid with flames, reflected from the fear-frozen glacier, my soul.

But though their hatred appalled, spite of that spell, again the sweet dream of Yillah stole over me, with all the mysterious things by her narrated, but left unexplained. And now, before me were those who might reveal the lost maiden's whole history, previous to the fatal affray.

Thus impelled, I besought them to disclose what they knew.

But, "Where now is your Yillah?" they cried. "Is the murderer wedded and merry? Bring forth the maiden!"

Yet, though they tore out my heart's core, I told them not of my loss.

Then, anxious to learn the history of Yillah, all present commanded them to divulge it; and breathlessly I heard what follows.

"Of Yillah, we know only this—that many moons ago, a mighty canoe, full of beings, white, like this murderer Taji, touched at our island of Amma. Received with wonder, they were worshiped as gods; were feasted all over the land. Their chief was a tower to behold; and with him was a being, whose cheeks were of the color of the red coral; her eye, tender as the blue of the sky. Every day our people brought her offerings of fruit, and flowers; which last she would not retain for herself, but hung them round the neck of her child, Yillah, then only an infant in her mother's arms, a bud, nestling close to a flower full-blown. All went well between our people and the gods, till at last they slew three of our countrymen, charged with stealing from their great canoe. Our warriors retired to the hills, brooding over revenge. Three days went by; when by night, descending to the plain, in silence they embarked; gained the great vessel, and slaughtered every soul but Yillah. The bud was torn from the flower, and, by our father Aleema, was carried to the valley of Ardair; there set apart as a sacred offering for Apo, our deity. Many moons passed; and there arose a tumult, hostile to our sire's longer holding custody of Yillah; when foreseeing that the holy glen would ere long be burst open, he embarked the maiden in yonder canoe, to accelerate her sacrifice at the great shrine of Apo, in Tedaidee. The rest thou knowest, murderer!"

"Yillah! Yillah!" now hunted again that sound through my soul. "Oh, Yillah! too late, too late have I learned what thou art!"

Apprised of the disappearance of their former captive, the meager strangers exulted; declaring that Apo had taken her to himself. For me, ere long, my blood they would quaff from my skull.

But though I shrunk from their horrible threats, I dissembled anew; and turning, again swore that they raved.

"Ay!" they retorted, "we rave and raven for you; and your white heart will we have!"

Perceiving the violence of their rage, and persuaded from what I had said, that much suffering at sea must have maddened them, Borabolla thought fit to confine them for the present, so that they could not molest me.

Chapter CI

THE IRIS

THAT EVENING, IN THE GROVES, CAME TO ME THREE GLIDING FORMS—HAUTIA'S HERALDS: THE Iris mixed with nettles.

Said Yoomy, "A cruel message!"

With the right hand, the second siren presented glossy, green wax-myrtle berries, those that burn like tapers; the third, a lily of the valley, crushed in its own broad leaf.

This done, they earnestly eyed Yoomy; who, after much pondering, said, "I speak for Hautia; who by these berries says, I will enlighten you."

"Oh, give me then that light! say, where is Yillah?" and I rushed upon the heralds.

But eluding me, they looked reproachfully at Yoomy, and seemed offended.

"Then I am wrong," said Yoomy. "It is thus—Taji, you have been enlightened, but the lily you seek is crushed."

Then fell my heart, and the phantoms nodded; flinging upon me bilberries, like rose pearls, which bruised against my skin, left stains. Waving oleanders, they retreated.

"Harm! treachery! beware!" cried Yoomy.

Then they glided through the wood: one showering dead leaves along the path I trod, the others gaily waving bunches of spring-crocuses, yellow, white, and purple; and thus they vanished.

Said Yoomy, "Sad your path, but merry Hautia's."

"Then merry may she be, whoe'er she is; and though woe be mine, I turn not from that to Hautia; nor ever will I woo her, though she woo me till I die—though Yillah never bless my eyes."

Chapter CII

THEY DEPART FROM MONDOLDO

NIGHT PASSED; AND NEXT MORNING, WE MADE PREPARATIONS FOR LEAVING MONDOLDO THAT day.

But fearing anew, lest after our departure, the men of Amma might stir up against me the people of the isle, I determined to yield to the earnest solicitations of Borabolla, and leave Jarl behind, for a remembrance of Taji; if necessary, to vindicate his name. Apprised hereof, my follower was loth to acquiesce. His guiltless spirit feared not the stranger: less selfish considerations prevailed. He was willing to remain on the island for a time, but not without me. Yet, setting forth my reasons; and assuring him, that our tour would not be long in completing, when we would not fail to return, previous to sailing for Odo, he at last, but reluctantly, assented.

At Mondoldo, we also parted with Samoa. Whether it was, that he feared the avengers, whom he may have thought would follow on my track; or whether the islands of Mardi answered not in attractiveness to the picture his fancy had painted; or whether the restraint put upon him by the domineering presence of King Media, was too irksome withal; or whether, indeed, he relished not those disquisitions with which Babbalanja regaled us; however it may have been, certain it was, that

Samoa was impatient of the voyage. He besought permission to return to Odo, there to await my return; and a canoe of Mondoldo being about to proceed in that direction, permission was granted; and departing for the other side of the island, from thence he embarked.

Long after, dark tidings came, that at early dawn, he had been found dead in the canoe; three arrows in his side.

Yoomy was at a loss to account for the departure of Samoa; who, while ashore, had expressed much desire to roam.

Media, however, declared that he must be returning to some inamorata.

But Babbalanja averred, that the Upoluan was not the first man, who had turned back, after beginning a voyage like our own.

To this, after musing, Yoomy assented. Indeed, I had noticed, that already the Warbler had abated those sanguine assurances of success, with which he had departed from Odo. The futility of our search thus far, seemed ominous to him, of the end.

On the eve of embarking, we were accompanied to the beach by Borabolla; who, with his own hand, suspended from the shark's mouth of Media's canoe, three red-ripe bunches of plantains, as a farewell gift.

Though he spoke not a word, Jarl was long in taking leave. His eyes seemed to say, I will see you no more.

At length we pushed from the strand; Borabolla waving his adieus with a green leaf of banana; our comrade ruefully eyeing the receding canoes; and the multitude loudly invoking for us a prosperous voyage.

But to my horror, there suddenly dashed through the crowd, the three specter sons of Aleema, escaped from their prison. With clenched hands, they stood in the water, and cursed me anew. And with that curse in our sails, we swept off.

Chapter CIII

As They Sail

As the canoes now glided across the lagoon, I gave myself up to reverie; and revolving over all that the men of Amma had rehearsed of the history of Yillah, I one by one unriddled the mysteries, before so baffling. Now, all was made plain: no secret remaining, but the subsequent event of her disappearance. Yes, Hautia! enlightened I had been—but where was Yillah?

Then I recalled that last interview with Hautia's messengers, so full of enigmas; and wondered, whether Yoomy had interpreted aright. Unseen, and unsolicited; still pursuing me with omens, with taunts, and with wooings, mysterious Hautia appalled me. Vaguely I began to fear her. And the thought, that, perhaps again and again, her heralds would haunt me, filled me with a nameless dread, which I almost shrank from acknowledging. Inwardly I prayed, that never more they might appear.

While full of these thoughts, Media interrupted them by saying, that the minstrel was about to begin one of his chants, a thing of his own composing; and therefore, as he himself said, all critics must be lenient; for Yoomy, at times, not always, was a timid youth, distrustful of his own sweet genius for poesy.

The words were about a curious hereafter, believed in by some people in Mardi: a sort of nocturnal Paradise, where the sun and its heat are excluded: one long, lunar day, with twinkling stars to keep company.

THE SONG

Far off in the sea is Marlena,
A land of shades and streams,
A land of many delights.
Dark and bold, thy shores, Marlena;
But green, and timorous, thy soft knolls,
Crouching behind the woodlands.
All shady thy hills; all gleaming thy springs,
Like eyes in the earth looking at you.
How charming thy haunts Marlena!—
Oh! the waters that flow through Onimoo:
Oh! the leaves that rustle through Ponoo:
Oh! the roses that blossom in Tarma:
Come, and see the valley of Vina:
How sweet, how sweet, the Isles from Hina:
'Tis aye afternoon of the full, full moon,
And ever the season of fruit,
And ever the hour of flowers,
And never the time of rains and gales,
All in and about Marlena.
Soft sigh the boughs in the stilly air,
Soft lap the beach the billows there;
And in the woods or by the streams,
You needs must nod in the Land of Dreams.

"Yoomy," said old Mohi with a yawn, "you composed that song, then, did you?"

"I did," said Yoomy.

"Then, minstrel, you shall sing me to sleep every night, especially with that song of Marlena; it is soporific as the airs of Nora-Banna."

"Mean you, old man, that my lines, setting forth the luxurious repose to be enjoyed hereafter, are composed with such skill, that the description begets the reality; or would you ironically suggest, that the song is a sleepy thing itself?"

"An important discrimination," said Media. "Which mean you, Mohi?"

"Now, are you not a silly boy," said Babbalanja, "when from the ambiguity of his speech, you could so easily have derived something flattering, thus to seek to extract unpleasantness from it? Be wise, Yoomy; and hereafter, whenever a remark like that seems equivocal, be sure to wrest commendation from it, though you torture it to the quick."

"And most sure am I, that I would ever do so, but often I so incline to a distrust of my powers, that I am far more keenly alive to censure, than to praise; and always deem it the more sincere of the two; and no praise so much elates me, as censure depresses."

Chapter CIV

WHEREIN BABBALANJA BROACHES A DIABOLICAL THEORY, AND, IN HIS OWN PERSON, PROVES IT

"A TRUCE!" CRIED MEDIA, "HERE COMES A GALLANT BEFORE THE WIND.—LOOK, TAJI!"

Turning, we descried a sharp-prowed canoe, dashing on, under the pressure of an immense triangular sail, whose outer edges were streaming with long, crimson pennons. Flying before it, were several small craft, belonging to the poorer sort of islanders.

"Out of his way there, ye laggards," cried Media, "or that mad prince, Tribonnora, will ride over ye with a rush!"

"And who is Tribonnora," said Babbalanja, "that he thus bravely diverts himself, running down innocent paddlers?"

"A harum-scarum young chief," replied Media, "heir to three islands; he likes nothing better than the sport you now see see him at."

"He must be possessed by a devil," said Mohi.

Said Babbalanja, "Then he is only like all of us."

"What say you?" cried Media.

"I say, as old Bardianna in the Nine hundred and ninety-ninth book of his immortal Ponderings saith, that all men—"

"As I live, my lord, he has swamped three canoes," cried Mohi, pointing off the beam.

But just then a fiery fin-back whale, having broken into the paddock of the lagoon, threw up a high fountain of foam, almost under Tribonnora's nose; who, quickly turning about his canoe, cur-like slunk off; his steering-paddle between his legs.

Comments over; "Babbalanja, you were going to quote," said Media. "Proceed."

"Thank you, my lord. Says old Bardianna, 'All men are possessed by devils; but as these devils are sent into men, and kept in them, for an additional punishment; not garrisoning a fortress, but limboed in a bridewell; so, it may be more just to say, that the devils themselves are possessed by men, not men by them.' "

"Faith!" cried Media, "though sometimes a bore, your old Bardianna is a trump."

"I have long been of that mind, my lord. But let me go on. Says Bardianna, 'Devils are divers—strong devils, and weak devils; knowing devils, and silly devils, mad devils, and mild devils; devils, merely devils; devils, themselves bedeviled; devils, doubly bedeviled.' "

"And in the devil's name, what sort of a devil is yours?" cried Mohi.

"Of him, anon; interrupt me not, old man. Thus, then, my lord, as devils are divers, divers are the devils in men. Whence, the wide difference we see. But after all, the main difference is this—that one man's devil is only more of a devil than another's; and be bedeviled as much as you will, yet, may you perform the most bedeviled of actions with impunity, so long as you only bedevil yourself. For it is only when your deviltry injures another, that the other devils conspire to confine yours for a mad one. That is to say, if you be easily handled. For there are many bedeviled Bedlamites in Mardi, doing an infinity of mischief, who are too brawny in the arms to be tied."

"A very devilish doctrine that," cried Mohi. "I don't believe it."

"My lord," said Babbalanja, "here's collateral proof—the sage lawgiver Yamjamma, who flourished long before Bardianna, roundly asserts, that all men who knowingly do evil are bedeviled; for good is happiness; happiness the object of living; and evil is not good."

"If the sage Yamjamma said that," said old Mohi, "the sage Yamjamma might have bettered the saying: it's not quite so plain as it might be."

"Yamjamma disdained to be plain; he scorned to be fully comprehended by mortals. Like all oracles, he dealt in dark sayings. But old Bardianna was of another sort; he spoke right out, going straight to the point like a javelin; especially when he laid down for a universal maxim, that minus exceptions, all men are bedeviled."

"Of course, then," said Media, "you include yourself among the number."

"Most assuredly; and so did old Bardianna, who somewhere says, that being thoroughly bedeviled himself, he was so much the better qualified to discourse upon the deviltries of his neighbors. But in another place he seems to contradict himself, by asserting, that he is not so sensible of his own deviltry as of other people's."

"Hold!" cried Media, "who have we here?" and he pointed ahead of our prow to the three men in the water, urging themselves along, each with a paddle.

We made haste to overtake them.

"Who are you?" said Media, "where from, and where bound?"

"From Variora," they answered, "and bound to Mondoldo."

"And did that devil Tribonnora swamp your canoe?" asked Media, offering to help them into ours.

"We had no such useless encumbrance to lose," they replied, resting on their backs, and panting with their exertions. "If we had had a canoe, we would have had to paddle it along with us; whereas we have only our bodies to paddle."

"You are a parcel of loons," exclaimed Media. "But go your ways, if you are satisfied with your locomotion, well and good."

"Now, it is an extreme case, I grant," said Babbalanja, "but those poor devils there, help to establish old Bardianna's position. They belong to that species of our bedeviled race, called simpletons; but their devils harming none but themselves, are permitted to be at large with the fish. Whereas, Tribonnora's devil, who daily runs down canoes, drowning their occupants, belongs to the species of out and out devils; but being high in station, and strongly backed by kith and kin, Tribonnora cannot be mastered, and put in a strait-jacket. For myself, I think my devil is somewhere between these two extremes; at any rate, he belongs to that class of devils, who harm not other devils."

"I am not so sure of that," retorted Media. "Methinks this doctrine of yours, about all mankind being bedeviled, will work a deal of mischief; seeing that by implication it absolves you mortals from mortal accountability. Furthermore; as your doctrine is exceedingly evil, by Yamjamma's theory it follows, that you must be proportionably bedeviled; and since it harms others, your devil is of the number of those whom it is best to limbo; and since he is one of those that *can* be limboed, limboed he shall be in you."

And so saying, he humorously commanded his attendants to lay hands upon the bedeviled philosopher, and place a bandage upon his mouth, that he might no more disseminate his devilish doctrine.

Against this, Babbalanja demurred, protesting that he was no orang-outang, to be so rudely handled.

"Better and better," said Media, "you but illustrate Bardianna's theory; that men are not sensible of their being bedeviled."

Thus tantalized, Babbalanja displayed few signs of philosophy.

Whereupon said Media, "Assuredly his devil is foaming; behold his mouth!" And he commanded him to be bound hand and foot.

At length, seeing all resistance ineffectual, Babbalanja submitted; but not without many objurgations.

Presently, however, they released him; when Media inquired, how he relished the application of his theory; and whether he was still of old Bardianna's mind?

To which, haughtily adjusting his robe, Babbalanja replied, "The strong arm, my lord, is no argument, though it overcomes all logic."

Chapter CV

MARAMMA

WE WERE NOW VOYAGING STRAIGHT FOR MARAMMA, WHERE LIVED AND REIGNED, IN MYSTERY, the High Pontiff of the adjoining isles; prince, priest, and god, in his own proper person; great lord paramount over many kings in Mardi; his hands full of scepters and crosiers.

Soon, rounding a lofty and insulated shore, the great central peak of the island came in sight; domineering over the neighboring hills; the same aspiring pinnacle described in drawing near the Archipelago in the *Chamois.*

"Tall Peak of Ofo!" cried Babbalanja, "how comes it that thy shadow so broods over Mardi; flinging new shades upon spots already shaded by the hill-sides; shade upon shade!"

"Yet so it is," said Yoomy, sadly, "that where that shadow falls, gay flowers refuse to spring; and men long dwelling therein become shady of face and of soul. 'Hast thou come from out the shadows of Ofo?' inquires the stranger, of one with a clouded brow."

"It was by this same peak," said Mohi, "that the nimble god Roo, a great sinner above, came down from the skies, a very long time ago. Three skips and a jump, and he landed on the plain. But alas, poor Roo! though easy the descent, there was no climbing back."

"No wonder, then," said Babbalanja, "that the peak is inaccessible to man. Though, with a strange infatuation, many still make pilgrimages thereto; and wearily climb and climb, till slipping from the rocks, they fall headlong backward, and oftentimes perish at its base."

"Ay," said Mohi, "in vain, on all sides of the Peak, various paths are tried; in vain new ones are cut through the cliffs and the brambles. Ofo yet remains inaccessible."

"Nevertheless," said Babbalanja, "by some it is believed, that those, who by dint of hard struggling, climb so high as to become invisible from the plain; that these have attained the summit; though others much doubt, whether their becoming invisible is not because of their having fallen, and perished by the way."

"And wherefore," said Media, "do you mortals undertake the ascent at all? Why not be content on the plain? and even if attainable, what would you do upon that lofty, clouded summit? Or how can you hope to breathe that rarefied air, unfitted for your human lungs?"

"True, my lord," said Babbalanja; "and Bardianna asserts that the plain alone was intended for man; who should be content to dwell under the shade of its groves, though the roots thereof descend into the darkness of the earth. But, my lord, you well know, that there are those in Mardi, who secretly regard all stories connected with this peak as inventions of the people of Maramma. They deny that anything is to be gained by making a pilgrimage thereto. And for warranty, they appeal to the sayings of the great prophet Alma."

Cried Mohi, "But Alma is also quoted by others, in vindication of the pilgrimages to Ofo. They declare that the prophet himself was the first pilgrim that thitherward journeyed: that from thence he departed to the skies."

Now, excepting this same peak, Maramma is all rolling hill and dale, like the sea after a storm;

which then seems not to roll, but to stand still, poising its mountains. Yet the landscape of Maramma has not the merriness of meadows; partly because of the shadow of Ofo, and partly because of the solemn groves in which the Morais and temples are buried.

According to Mohi, not one solitary tree bearing fruit, not one esculent root, grows in all the isle; the population wholly depending upon the large tribute remitted from the neighboring shores.

"It is not that the soil is unproductive," said Mohi, "that these things are so. It is extremely fertile; but the inhabitants say that it would be wrong to make a bread-fruit orchard of the holy island."

"And hence, my lord," said Babbalanja, "while others are charged with the business of their temporal welfare, these islanders take no thought of the morrow; and broad Maramma lies one fertile waste in the lagoon."

Chapter CVI

They Land

Coming close to the island, the pennons and trappings of our canoes were removed; and Vee-Vee was commanded to descend from the shark's mouth; and for a time to lay aside his conch. In token of reverence, our paddlers also stripped to the waist; an example which even Media followed; though, as a king, the same homage he rendered, was at times rendered himself.

At every place, hitherto visited, joyous crowds stood ready to hail our arrival; but the shores of Maramma were silent and forlorn.

Said Babbalanja, "It looks not as if the lost one were here."

At length we landed in a little cove nigh a valley, which Mohi called Uma; and here in silence we beached our canoes.

But presently, there came to us an old man, with a beard white as the mane of the pale horse. He was clad in a midnight robe. He fanned himself with a fan of faded leaves. A child led him by the hand, for he was blind, wearing a green plantain leaf over his plaited brow.

Him, Media accosted, making mention who we were, and on what errand we came; to seek out Yillah, and behold the isle.

Whereupon Pani, for such was his name, gave us a courteous reception; and lavishly promised to discover sweet Yillah; declaring that in Maramma, if anywhere, the long-lost maiden must be found. He assured us, that throughout the whole land he would lead us; leaving no place, desirable to be searched, unexplored.

And so saying, he conducted us to his dwelling, for refreshment and repose.

It was large and lofty. Nearby, however, were many miserable hovels, with squalid inmates. But the old man's retreat was exceedingly comfortable; especially abounding in mats for lounging; his rafters were bowed down by calabashes of good cheer.

During the repast which ensued, blind Pani freely partaking, enlarged upon the merit of abstinence; declaring that a thatch overhead, and a cocoanut tree, comprised all that was necessary for the temporal welfare of a Mardian. More than this, he assured us, was sinful.

He now made known, that he officiated as guide in this quarter of the country; and that as he had renounced all other pursuits to devote himself to showing strangers the island; and more particularly the best way to ascend lofty Ofo; he was necessitated to seek remuneration for his toil.

"My Lord," then whispered Mohi to Media, "the great prophet Alma always declared, that, without charge, this island was free to all."

"What recompense do you require, old man?" said Media to Pani.

"What I seek is but little!—twenty rolls of fine tappa; two score mats of best upland grass; one canoe-load of bread-fruit and yams; ten gourds of wine; and forty strings of teeth—you are a large company, but my requisitions are small."

"Very small," said Mohi.

"You are extortionate, good Pani," said Media. "And what wants an aged mortal like you with all these things?"

"I thought superfluities were worthless; nay, sinful," said Babbalanja.

"Is not this your habitation already more than abundantly supplied with all desirable furnishings?" asked Yoomy.

"I am but a lowly laborer," said the old man, meekly crossing his arms, "but does not the lowliest laborer ask and receive his reward? and shall I miss mine? But I beg charity of none. What I ask, I demand; and in the dread name of great Alma, who appointed me a guide." And to and fro he strode, groping as he went.

Marking his blindness, whispered Babbalanja to Media, "My lord, methinks this Pani must be a poor guide. In his journeys inland, his little child leads him; why not, then, take the guide's guide?"

But Pani would not part with the child.

Then said Mohi in a low voice, "My lord Media, though I am no appointed guide; yet, will I undertake to lead you aright all over this island; for I am an old man, and have been here oft by myself; though I cannot undertake to conduct you up the peak of Ofo, and to the more secret temples."

Then Pani said, "and what mortal may this be, who pretends to thread the labyrinthine wilds of Maramma? Beware!"

"He is one with eyes that see," made answer Babbalanja.

"Follow him not," said Pani, "for he will lead thee astray: no Yillah will he find; and having no warrant as a guide, the curses of Alma will accompany him."

Now, this was not altogether without effect; for Pani and his fathers before him had always filled the office of guide.

Nevertheless, Media at last decided, that, this time, Mohi should conduct us; which being communicated to Pani, he desired us to remove from his roof. So withdrawing to the skirt of a neighboring grove, we lingered awhile, to refresh ourselves for the journey in prospect.

As here we reclined, there came up from the sea-side a party of pilgrims, but newly arrived.

Apprised of their coming, Pani and his child went out to meet them; and standing in the path he cried, "I am the appointed guide; in the name of Alma I conduct all pilgrims to the temples."

"This must be the worthy Pani," said one of the strangers, turning upon the rest.

"Let us take him, then, for our guide," cried they; and all drew near.

But upon accosting him; they were told, that he guided none without recompense.

And now, being informed, that the foremost of the pilgrims was one Divino, a wealthy chief of a distant island, Pani demanded of him his requital.

But the other demurred; and by many soft speeches at length abated the recompense to three promissory cocoanuts, which he covenanted to send Pani at some future day.

The next pilgrim accosted, was a sad-eyed maiden, in decent but scanty raiment: who, without seeking to diminish Pani's demands, promptly placed in his hands a small hoard of the money of Mardi.

"Take it, holy guide," she said, "it is all I have."

But the third pilgrim, one Fanna, a hale matron, in handsome apparel, needed no asking to bestow her goods. Calling upon her attendants to advance with their burdens, she quickly unrolled them; and wound round and round Pani, fold after fold, of the costliest tappas; and filled both his hands with teeth, and his mouth with some savory marmalade; and poured oil upon his head, and knelt and besought of him a blessing.

"From the bottom of my heart I bless thee," said Pani; and still holding her hands exclaimed, "Take example from this woman, oh, Divino, and do ye likewise, ye pilgrims all."

"Not to-day," said Divino.

"We are not rich, like unto Fanna," said the rest.

Now, the next pilgrim was a very old and miserable man; stone-blind, covered with rags, and supporting his steps with a staff.

"My recompense," said Pani.

"Alas! I have naught to give. Behold my poverty!"

"I cannot see," replied Pani; but feeling of his garments, he said, "Thou wouldst deceive me; hast thou not this robe and this staff?"

"Oh! merciful Pani, take not my all!" wailed the pilgrim. But his worthless gaberdine was thrust into the dwelling of the guide.

Meanwhile the matron was still enveloping Pani in her interminable tappas.

But the sad-eyed maiden, removing her upper mantle, threw it over the naked form of the beggar.

The fifth pilgrim was a youth of an open, ingenuous aspect; and with an eye, full of eyes; his step was light.

"Who art thou?" cried Pani, as the stripling touched him in passing.

"I go to ascend the Peak," said the boy.

"Then take me for guide."

"No, I am strong and lithesome. Alone must I go."

"But how knowest thou the way?"

"There are many ways; the right one I must seek for myself."

"Ah, poor deluded one," sighed Pani; "but thus is it ever with youth; and rejecting the monitions of wisdom, suffer they must. Go on, and perish!"

Turning, the boy exclaimed, "Though I act counter to thy counsels, oh Pani! I but follow the divine instinct in me."

"Poor youth!" murmured Babbalanja. "How earnestly he struggles in his bonds. But though rejecting a guide, still he clings to that legend of the Peak."

The rest of the pilgrims now tarried with the guide, preparing for their journey inland.

Chapter CVII

They Pass Through the Woods

Refreshed by our stay in the grove, we rose, and placed ourselves under the guidance of Mohi; who went on in advance.

Winding our way among jungles, we came to a deep hollow, planted with one gigantic palm-shaft, belted round by saplings, springing from its roots. But, Laocoon-like, sire and son stood locked in the serpent folds of gnarled, distorted banians; and the banian-bark, eating into their vital wood, corrupted their veins of sap, till all those palm-nuts were poisoned chalices.

Nearby stood clean-limbed, comely manchineels, with lustrous leaves and golden fruit. You would have deemed them Trees of Life; but underneath their branches grew no blade of grass, no herb, nor moss; the bare earth was scorched by heaven's own dews, filtrated through that fatal foliage.

Farther on, there frowned a grove of blended banian boughs, thick-ranked manchineels, and many a upas; their summits gilded by the sun; but below, deep shadows, darkening night-shade ferns, and mandrakes. Buried in their midst, and dimly seen among large leaves, all halberd-shaped, were piles of stone, supporting falling temples of bamboo. Thereon frogs leaped in dampness, trailing round their slime. Thick hung the rafters with lines of pendant sloths; the upas trees dropped darkness round; so dense the shade, nocturnal birds found there perpetual night; and throve on poisoned air. Owls hooted from dead boughs; or, one by one, sailed by on silent pinions; cranes stalked abroad, or brooded in the marshes; adders hissed; bats smote the darkness; ravens croaked; and vampires, fixed on slumbering lizards, fanned the sultry air.

Chapter CVIII

HIVOHITEE MDCCCXLVIII

NOW, THOSE DOLEFUL WOODLANDS PASSED, STRAIGHTWAY CONVERSE WAS RENEWED, AND MUCH discourse took place concerning Hivohitee, Pontiff of the isle.

For, during our first friendly conversation with Pani, Media had inquired for Hivohitee, and sought to know in what part of the island he abode.

Whereto Pani had replied, that the Pontiff would be invisible for several days to come; being engaged with particular company.

And upon further inquiry, as to who were the personages monopolizing his hospitalities, Media was dumb, when informed, that they were no other than certain incorporeal deities from above passing the Capricorn Solstice at Maramma.

As on we journeyed, much curiosity being expressed to know more of the Pontiff, and his guests, old Mohi, familiar with these things, was commanded to enlighten the company. He complied; and his recital was not a little significant, of the occasional credulity of chroniclers.

According to his statement, the deities entertained by Hivohitee belonged to the third class of immortals. These, however, were far elevated above the corporeal demi-gods of Mardi. Indeed, in Hivohitee's eyes, the greatest demi-gods were as gourds. Little wonder, then, that their superiors were accounted the most genteel characters on his visiting list.

These immortals were wonderfully fastidious and dainty, as to the atmosphere they breathed; inhaling no sublunary air, but that of the elevated interior; where the Pontiff had a rural lodge for the special accommodation of impalpable guests; who were entertained at small cost; dinners being unnecessary, and dormitories superfluous.

But Hivohitee permitted not the presence of these celestial grandees to interfere with his own solid comfort. Passing his mornings in highly intensified chat, he thrice reclined at his ease; partaking of a fine plantain-pudding, and pouring out from a calabash of celestial old wine; meanwhile, carrying on the flow of soul with his guests. And truly, the sight of their entertainer thus enjoying himself in the flesh, while they themselves starved on the ether, must have been exceedingly provoking to these aristocratic and aerial strangers.

It was reported, furthermore, that Hivohitee, one of the haughtiest of Pontiffs, purposely treated his angelical guests thus cavalierly, in order to convince them, that though a denizen of earth, a sublunarian, and in respect of heaven, a mere provincial; he (Hivohitee) accounted himself full as good as seraphim from the capital; and that too at the Capricorn Solstice, or any other time of the year. Strongly bent was Hivohitee upon humbling their supercilious pretensions.

Besides, was he not accounted a great god in the land? Supreme? having power of life and death? essaying the deposition of kings? and dwelling in moody state, all by himself, in the goodliest island of Mardi? Though here, be it said, that his assumptions of temporal supremacy were but seldom made good by express interference with the secular concerns of the neighboring monarchs; who, by force of arms, were too apt to argue against his claims to authority; however, in theory, they bowed to it. And now, for the genealogy of Hivohitee; for eighteen hundred and forty-seven Hivohitees were alleged to have gone before him. He came in a right line from the divine Hivohitee I; the original grantee of the empire of men's souls and the first swayer of a crosier. The present Pontiff's descent was unquestionable; his dignity having been transmitted through none but heirs male; the whole procession of High Priests being the fruit of successive marriages between uterine brother and sister. A conjunction deemed incestuous in some lands; but, here, held the only fit channel for the pure transmission of elevated rank.

Added to the hereditary appellation, Hivohitee, which simply denoted the sacerdotal station of the Pontiffs, and was but seldom employed in current discourse, they were individualized by a distinctive name, bestowed upon them at birth. And the degree of consideration in which they were held, may be inferred from the fact, that during the lifetime of a Pontiff, the leading sound in his name was banned to ordinary uses. Whence, at every new accession to the archiepiscopal throne, it came to pass, the multitudes of words and phrases were either essentially modified, or wholly dropped. Wherefore, the language of Maramma was incessantly fluctuating; and had become so full of jargonings, that the birds in the groves were greatly puzzled not knowing where lay the virtue of sounds, so incoherent.

And, in a good measure, this held true of all tongues spoken throughout the Archipelago; the birds marveling at mankind, and mankind at the birds; wondering how they could continually sing; when, for all man knew to the contrary, it was impossible they could be holding intelligent discourse. And thus, though for thousands of years, men and birds had been dwelling together in Mardi, they remained wholly ignorant of each other's secrets; the islander regarding the fowl as a senseless songster, forever in the clouds; and the fowl him, as a screeching crane, destitute of pinions and lofty aspirations.

Over and above numerous other miraculous powers imputed to the Pontiffs as spiritual potentates, there was ascribed to them one special privilege of a secular nature: that of healing with a touch the bites of the ravenous sharks, swarming throughout the lagoon. With these they were supposed to be upon the most friendly terms; according to popular accounts, sociably bathing with them in the sea; permitting them to rub their noses against their priestly thighs; playfully mouthing their hands, with all their tiers of teeth.

At the ordination of a Pontiff, the ceremony was not deemed complete, until embarking in his barge, he was saluted High Priest by three sharks drawing near; with teeth turned up, swimming beside his canoe.

These monsters were deified in Maramma; had altars there; it was deemed worse than homicide to kill one. "And what if they destroy human life?" say the islanders, "are they not sacred?"

Now, many more wonderful things were related touching Hivohitee; and though one could not but doubt the validity of many prerogatives ascribed to him, it was nevertheless hard to do otherwise, than entertain for the Pontiff that sort of profound consideration which all render to those who indisputably possess the power of quenching human life with a wish.

Chapter CIX

THEY VISIT THE GREAT MORAI

AS GARRULOUS GUIDE TO THE PARTY, BRAID-BEARD SOON BROUGHT US NIGH THE GREAT MORAI of Maramma, the burial-place of the Pontiffs, and a rural promenade, for certain idols there inhabiting.

Our way now led through the bed of a shallow water-course; Mohi observing, as we went, that our feet were being washed at every step; whereas, to tread the dusty earth would be to desecrate the holy Morai, by transferring thereto, the base soil of less sacred ground.

Here and there, thatched arbors were thrown over the stream, for the accommodation of devotees; who, in these consecrated waters, issuing from a spring in the Morai, bathed their garments, that long life might ensue. Yet, as Braid-Beard assured us, sometimes it happened, that divers feeble old men zealously donning their raiment immediately after immersion became afflicted with rheumatics; and instances were related of their falling down dead, in this their pursuit of longevity.

Coming to the Morai, we found it enclosed by a wall; and while the rest were surmounting it, Mohi was busily engaged in the apparently childish occupation of collecting pebbles. Of these, however, to our no small surprise, he presently made use, by irreverently throwing them at all objects to which he was desirous of directing attention. In this manner, was pointed out a black boar's head, suspended from a bough. Full twenty of these sentries were on post in the neighboring trees.

Proceeding, we came to a hillock of bone-dry sand, resting upon the otherwise loamy soil. Possessing a secret, preservative virtue, this sand had, ages ago, been brought from a distant land, to furnish a sepulcher for the Pontiffs; who here, side by side, and sire by son, slumbered all peacefully in the fellowship of the grave. Mohi declared, that were the sepulcher to be opened, it would be the resurrection of the whole line of High Priests. "But a resurrection of bones after all," said Babbalanja, ever osseous in his allusions to the departed.

Passing on, we came to a number of Runic-looking stones, all over hieroglyphical inscriptions, and placed round an elliptical aperture; where welled up the sacred spring of the Morai, clear as crystal, and showing through its waters, two tiers of sharp, tusk-like stones; the mouth of Oro, so called; and it was held, that if any secular hand should be immersed in the spring, straight upon it those stony jaws would close.

We next came to a large image of a dark-hued stone, representing a burly man, with an overgrown head, and abdomen hollowed out, and open for inspection; therein, were relics of bones. Before this image we paused. And whether or no it was Mohi's purpose to make us tourists quake with his recitals, his revelations were far from agreeable. At certain seasons, human beings were offered to the idols which, being an epicure in the matter of sacrifices, would accept of no ordinary fare. To ensure his digestion, all indirect routes to the interior were avoided; the sacrifices being packed in the ventricle itself.

Near to this image of Doleema, so called, a solitary forest-tree was pointed out; leafless and dead to the core. But from its boughs hung numerous baskets brimming over with melons, grapes, and guavas. And daily these baskets were replenished.

As we here stood, there passed a hungry figure, in ragged raiment: hollow cheeks, and hollow eyes. Wistfully he eyed the offerings; but retreated, knowing it was sacrilege to touch them. There, they must decay, in honor of the god Ananna; for so this dead tree was denominated by Mohi.

Now, as we were thus strolling about the Morai, the old chronicler elucidating its mysteries, we suddenly spied Pani and the pilgrims approaching the image of Doleema; his child leading the guide.

"This," began Pani, pointing to the idol of stone, "is the holy god Ananna who lives in the sap of this green and flourishing tree."

"Thou meanest not, surely, this stone image we behold?" said Divino.

"I mean the tree," said the guide. "It is no stone image."

"Strange," muttered the chief; "were it not a guide that spoke, I would deny it. As it is, I hold my peace."

"Mystery of mysteries!" cried the blind old pilgrim; "is it, then, a stone image that Pani calls a tree? Oh, Oro, that I had eyes to see, that I might verily behold it, and then believe it to be what it is not; that so I might prove the largeness of my faith; and so merit the blessing of Alma."

"Thrice sacred Ananna," murmured the sad-eyed maiden, falling upon her knees before Doleema, "receive my adoration. Of thee, I know nothing, but what the guide has spoken. I am but a poor, weak-minded maiden, judging not for myself, but leaning upon others that are wiser. These things are above me. I am afraid to think. In Alma's name receive my homage."

And she flung flowers before the god.

But Fanna, the hale matron, turning upon Pani, exclaimed, "Receive more gifts, oh guide." And again she showered them upon him.

Upon this, the willful boy who would not have Pani for a guide, entered the Morai; and perceiving the group before the image, walked rapidly to where they were. And beholding the idol, he regarded it attentively, and said, "This must be the image of Doleema; but I am not sure."

"Nay," cried the blind pilgrim, "it is the holy tree Ananna, thou wayward boy."

"A tree? whatever it may be, it is not that; thou art blind, old man."

"But though blind, I have that which thou lackest."

Then said Pani, turning upon the boy, "Depart from the holy Morai, and corrupt not the hearts of these pilgrims. Depart, I say; and, in the sacred name of Alma, perish in thy endeavors to climb the peak."

"I may perish there in truth," said the boy, with sadness; "but it shall be in the path revealed to me in my dream. And think not, oh, guide, that I perfectly rely upon gaining that lofty summit. I will climb high Ofo with hope, not faith. Oh, mighty Oro, help me!"

"Be not impious," said Pani; "pronounce not Oro's sacred name too lightly."

"Oro is but a sound," said the boy. "They call the supreme god, Ati, in my native isle; it is the soundless thought of him, oh guide, that is in me."

"Hark to his rhapsodies! Hark, how he prates of mysteries, that not even Hivohitee can fathom!"

"Nor he, nor thou, nor I, nor any; Oro, to all is Oro the unknown."

"Why claim to know Oro, then, better than others?"

"I am not so vain; and I have little to substitute for what I cannot receive. I but feel Oro in me, yet cannot declare the thought."

"Proud boy! thy humility is a pretense; at heart, thou deemest thyself wiser than Mardi."

"Not near so wise. To believe is a haughty thing; my very doubts humiliate me. I weep and doubt; all Mardi may be right; and I too simple to discern."

"He is mad," said the chief Divino; "never before heard I such words."

"They are thoughts," muttered the guide.

"Poor fool!" cried Fanna.

"Lost youth!" sighed the maiden.

"He is but a child," said the beggar. These whims will soon depart; once I was like him; but, praise be to Alma, in the hour of sickness I repented, feeble old man that I am!"

"It is because I am young and in health," said the boy, "that I more nourish the thoughts that are born of my youth and my health. I am fresh from my Maker, soul and body unwrinkled. On thy sick couch, old man, they took thee at advantage."

"Turn from the blasphemer," cried Pani. "Hence! thou evil one, to the perdition in store."

"I will go my ways," said the boy, "but Oro will shape the end."

And he quitted the Morai.

After conducting the party round the sacred enclosure, assisting his way with his staff, for his child had left him, Pani seated himself on a low mossy stone, grimly surrounded by idols; and directed the pilgrims to return to his habitation; where, ere long, he would rejoin them.

The pilgrims departed, he remained in profound meditation; while, backward and forward, an invisible ploughshare turned up the long furrows on his brow.

Long he was silent; then muttered to himself, "That boy, that wild, wise boy, has stabbed me to the heart. His thoughts are my suspicions. But he is honest. Yet I harm none. Multitudes must have unspoken meditations as well as I. Do we then mutually deceive? Off masks, mankind, that I may know what warranty of fellowship with others, my own thoughts possess. Why, upon this one theme, oh, Oro! must all dissemble? Our thoughts are not our own. Whate'er it be, an honest thought must have some germ of truth. But we must set, as flows the general stream; I blindly follow, where I seem to lead; the crowd of pilgrims is so great, they see not there is none to guide.—It hinges upon this: Have we angelic spirits? But in vain, in vain, oh, Oro! I essay to live out of this poor, blind body, fit dwelling for my sightless soul. Death, death: blind, am I dead! for blindness seems a consciousness of death. Will my grave be more dark than all is now? From dark to dark! What is this subtle something that is in me, and eludes me? Will it have no end? When, then, did it begin? All, all is chaos! What is this shining light in heaven, this sun they tell me of? Or, do they lie? Methinks it might blaze convictions; but I brood and grope in blackness; I am dumb with doubt; yet, 'tis not doubt, but worse: I doubt my doubt. Oh, ye all-wise spirits in the air, how can ye witness all this woe, and give no sign? Would, would that mine were a settled doubt, like that wild boy's, who, without faith, seems full of it. The undoubting doubter believes the most. Oh! that I were he. Methinks that daring boy hath Alma in him, struggling to be free. But those pilgrims: that trusting girl. What, if they saw me as I am? Peace, peace, my soul; on, mask, again."

And he staggered from the Morai.

Chapter CX

They Discourse of the Gods of Mardi—And Braid-Beard Tells of One Foni

Walking from the sacred enclosure, Mohi discoursed of the plurality of gods in the land, a subject suggested by the multitudinous idols we had just been beholding.

Said Mohi, "These gods of wood and of stone are nothing in number to the gods in the air. You breathe not a breath without inhaling, you touch not a leaf without ruffling a spirit. There are gods of heaven, and gods of earth; gods of sea and of land; gods of peace and of war; gods of rock and of fell; gods of ghosts and of thieves; of singers and dancers; of lean men and of house-thatchers. Gods glance in the eyes of birds, and sparkle in the crest of the waves; gods merrily swing in the boughs of the trees, and merrily sing in the brook. Gods are here and there, and everywhere; you are never alone for them."

"If this be so, Braid-Beard," said Babbalanja, "our inmost thoughts are overheard; but not by eavesdroppers. However, my lord, these gods to whom he alludes, merely belong to the semi-intelligibles, the divided unities in unity, thin side of the First Adyta."

"Indeed?" said Media.

"Semi-intelligible, say you, philosopher?" cried Mohi. "Then, prithee, make it appear so; for what you say, seems gibberish to me."

"Babbalanja," said Media, "no more of your abstrusities; what know you mortals of us gods and demi-gods? But tell me, Mohi, how many of your deities of rock and fell think you there are? Have you no statistical table?"

"My lord, at the lowest computation, there must be at least three billion trillion of quintillions."

"A mere unit!" said Babbalanja. "Old man, would you express an infinite number? Then take the sum of the follies of Mardi for your multiplicand; and for your multiplier, the totality of sublunarians, that never have been heard of since they became no more; and the product shall exceed your quintillions, even though all their units were nonillions."

"Have done, Babbalanja!" cried Media; "you are showing the sinister vein in your marble. Have done. Take a warm bath, and make tepid your cold blood. But come, Mohi, tell us of the ways of this Maramma; something of the Morai and its idols, if you please."

And straightway Braid-Beard proceeded with a narration in substance as follows:

It seems there was a particular family upon the island whose members for many generations had been set apart as sacrifices for the deity called Doleema. They were marked by a sad and melancholy aspect, and a certain involuntary shrinking when passing the Morai. And though, when it came to the last, some of these unfortunates went joyfully to their doom, declaring that they gloried to die in the service of holy Doleema; still, were there others, who audaciously endeavored to shun their fate; upon the approach of a festival, fleeing to the innermost wilderness of the island. But little availed their flight. For swift on their track sped the hereditary butler of the insulted god, one Xiki, whose duty it was to provide the sacrifices. And when crouching in some covert, the fugitive spied Xiki's approach, so fearful did he become of the vengeance of the deity he sought to evade, that renouncing all hope of escape, he would burst from his lair, exclaiming, "Come on, and kill!" baring his breast for the javelin that slew him.

The chronicles of Maramma were full of horrors.

In the wild heart of the island was said still to lurk the remnant of a band of warriors, who, in the days of the sire of the present Pontiff, had risen in arms to dethrone him, headed by Foni, an upstart prophet, a personage distinguished for the uncommon beauty of his person. With terrible carnage, these warriors had been defeated; and the survivors, fleeing into the interior, for thirty days were pursued by the victors. But though many were overtaken and speared, a number survived; who, at last, wandering forlorn and in despair, like demoniacs, ran wild in the woods. And the islanders, who at times penetrated into the wilderness, for the purpose of procuring rare herbs, often scared from their path some specter, glaring through the foliage. Thrice had these demoniacs been discovered prowling about the inhabited portions of the isle; and at daybreak, an attendant of the holy Morai once came upon a frightful figure doubled with age, helping itself to the offerings in the image of Doleema. The demoniac was slain; and from his ineffaceable tatooing, it was proved that this was no other than Foni, the false prophet; the splendid form he had carried into the rebel fight, now squalid with age and misery.

Chapter CXI

THEY VISIT THE LAKE OF YAMMO

FROM THE MORAI, WE BENT OUR STEPS TOWARDS AN UNOCCUPIED ARBOR; AND HERE, REFRESHing ourselves with the viands presented by Borabolla, we passed the night. And next morning proceeded to voyage round to the opposite quarter of the island; where, in the sacred lake of Yammo, stood the famous temple of Oro, also the great gallery of the inferior deities.

The lake was but a portion of the smooth lagoon, made separate by an arm of wooded reef, extending from the high western shore of the island, and curving round towards a promontory, leaving a narrow channel to the sea, almost invisible, however, from the land-locked interior.

In this lake were many islets, all green with groves. Its main shore was a steep acclivity, with jutting points, each crowned with mossy old altars of stone, or ruinous temples, darkly reflected in the green, glassy water; while, from its long line of stately trees, the low reef-side of the lake looked one verdant bluff.

Gliding in upon Yammo, its many islets greeted us like a little Mardi; but ever and anon we started at long lines of phantoms in the water, reflections of the long line of images on the shore.

Towards the islet of Dolzono we first directed our way; and there we beheld the great gallery of the gods; a mighty temple, resting on one hundred tall pillars of palm, each based, below the surface, on the buried body of a man; its nave one vista of idols; names carved on their foreheads; Ogro, Tripoo, Indrimarvoki, Parzillo, Vivivi, Jojijojorora, Jorkraki, and innumerable others.

Crowds of attendants were new-grouping the images.

"My lord, you behold one of their principal occupations," said Mohi.

Said Media, "I have heard much of the famed image of Mujo, the Nursing Mother; can you point it out, Braid-Beard?"

"My lord, when last here I saw Mujo at the head of this file; but they must have removed it; I see it not now."

"Do these attendants, then," said Babbalanja, "so continually new-marshal the idols, that visiting the gallery to-day, you are at a loss to-morrow?"

"Even so," said Braid-Beard. "But, behold, my lord, this image is Mujo."

We stood before an obelisk-idol, so towering that gazing at it, we were fain to throw back our heads. According to Mohi, winding stairs led up through its legs; its abdomen a cellar, thick-stored with gourds of old wine; its head, a hollow dome; in rude alto-relievo, its scores of hillock-breasts were carved over with legions of baby deities, frog-like sprawling; while within, were secreted whole litters of infant idols, there placed to imbibe divinity from the knots of the wood.

As we stood, a strange subterranean sound was heard, mingled with a gurgling as of wine being poured. Looking up, we beheld, through arrowslits and port-holes, three masks, cross-legged seated in the abdomen, and holding stout wassail. But instantly upon descrying us, they vanished deeper into the interior; and presently was heard a sepulchral chant, and many groans and grievous tribulations.

Passing on, we came to an image, with a long anaconda-like posterior development, wound round and round its own neck.

"This must be Oloo, the god of Suicides," said Babbalanja.

"Yes," said Mohi; "you perceive, my lord, how he lays violent tail upon himself."

At length, the attendants, having, in due order, new-disposed the long lines of sphinxes and griffins, and many limbed images, a band of them, in long flowing robes, began their morning chant.

Awake, Rarni! Awake, Foloona!
Awake, unnumbered deities!

With many similar invocations to which the images made not the slightest rejoinder. Not discouraged, however, the attendants now separately proceeded to offer up petitions on behalf of various tribes, retaining them for that purpose.

One prayed for abundance of rain, that the yams of Valapee might not wilt in the ground; another for dry sunshine, as most favorable for the present state of the bread-fruit crop in Mondoldo.

Hearing all this, Babbalanja thus spoke:

"Doubtless, my lord Media, besides these petitions we hear, there are ten thousand contradictory prayers ascending to these idols. But methinks the gods will not jar the eternal progression of things, by any hints from below; even were it possible to satisfy conflicting desires."

Said Yoomy, "But I would pray, nevertheless, Babbalanja; for prayer draws us near to our own souls, and purifies our thoughts. Nor will I grant that our supplications are altogether in vain."

Still wandering among the images, Mohi had much to say concerning their respective claims to the reverence of the devout.

For though, in one way or other, all Mardians bowed to the supremacy of Oro, they were not so unanimous concerning the inferior deities; those supposed to be intermediately concerned in sublunary things. Some nations sacrificed to one god; some to another; each maintaining, that their own god was the most potential.

Observing that all the images were more or less defaced, Babbalanja sought the reason.

To which, Braid-Beard made answer, that they had been thus defaced by hostile devotees; who quarreling in the great gallery of the gods, and getting beside themselves with rage, often sought to pull down and demolish each other's favorite idols.

"But behold," cried Babbalanja, "there seems not a single image unmutilated. How is this, old man?"

"It is thus. While one faction defaces the images of its adversaries, its own images are in like manner assailed; whence it comes that no idol escapes."

"No more, no more, Braid-Beard," said Media. "Let us depart, and visit the islet, where the god of all these gods is enshrined."

Chapter CXII

They Meet the Pilgrims at the Temple of Oro

DEEP, DEEP, IN DEEP GROVES, WE FOUND THE GREAT TEMPLE OF ORO, SPREADER-OF-THE-SKY, and deity supreme.

While here we silently stood eyeing this Mardi-renowned image, there entered the fane a great multitude of its attendants, holding pearl-shells on their heads, filled with a burning incense. And ranging themselves in a crowd round Oro, they began a long-rolling chant, a sea of sounds; and the thick smoke of their incense went up to the roof.

And now approached Pani and the pilgrims; followed at a distance by the willful boy.

"Behold great Oro," said the guide.

"We see naught but a cloud," said the chief Divino.

"My ears are stunned by the chanting," said the blind pilgrim.

"Receive more gifts, oh guide!" said Fanna the matron.

"Oh Oro! invisible Oro! I kneel," slow murmured the sad-eyed maid.

But now a current of air swept aside the eddying incense; and the willful boy, all eagerness to behold the image, went hither and thither; but the gathering of attendants was great; and at last he exclaimed, "Oh Oro! I cannot see thee, for the crowd that stands between thee and me."

"Who is this babbler?" cried they with the censers, one and all turning upon the pilgrim; "let him speak no more; but bow down, and grind the dust where he stands; and declare himself the vilest creature that crawls. So Oro and Alma command."

"I feel nothing in me so utterly vile," said the boy, "and I cringe to none. But I would as lief *adore* your image, as that in my heart, for both mean the same; but more, how can I? I love great Oro, though I comprehend him not. I marvel at his works, and feel as nothing in his sight; but because he is thus omnipotent, and I a mortal, it follows not that I am vile. Nor so doth he regard me. We do ourselves degrade ourselves, not Oro us. Hath not Oro made me? And therefore am I not worthy to stand erect before him? Oro is almighty but no despot. I wonder; I hope; I love; I weep; I have in me a feeling nigh to fear, that is not fear; but wholly vile I am not; nor can we love and cringe. But Oro knows my heart, which I cannot speak."

"Impious boy," cried they with the censers, "we will offer thee up, before the very image thou contemnest. In the name of Alma, seize him."

And they bore him away unresisting.

"Thus perish the ungodly," said Pani to the shuddering pilgrims.

And they quitted the temple, to journey towards the Peak of Ofo.

"My soul bursts!" cried Yoomy. "My lord, my lord, let us save the boy."

"Speak not," said Media. "His fate is fixed. Let Mardi stand."

"Then let us away from hence, my lord; and join the pilgrims; for, in these inland vales, the lost one may be found, perhaps at the very base of Ofo."

"Not there; not there," cried Babbalanja; "Yillah may have touched these shores; but long since she must have fled."

Chapter CXIII

THEY DISCOURSE OF ALMA

SAILING TO AND FRO IN THE LAKE, TO VIEW ITS SCENERY, MUCH DISCOURSE TOOK PLACE CONcerning the things we had seen; and far removed from the censer-bearers, the sad fate that awaited the boy was now the theme of all.

A good deal was then said of Alma, to whom the guide, the pilgrims, and the censer-bearers had frequently alluded, as to some paramount authority.

Called upon to reveal what his chronicles said on this theme, Braid-Beard complied; at great length narrating what now follows condensed.

Alma, it seems, was an illustrious prophet, and teacher divine; who, ages ago, at long intervals, and in various islands, had appeared to the Mardians under the different titles of Brami, Manko, and Alma. Many thousands of moons had elasped since his last and most memorable avatar, as Alma on the isle of Maramma. Each of his advents had taken place in a comparatively dark and benighted age. Hence, it was devoutly believed, that he came to redeem the Mardians from their heathenish thrall; to instruct them in the ways of truth, virtue, and happiness; to allure them to good by promises of beatitude hereafter; and to restrain them from evil by denunciations of woe. Separated from the impurities and corruptions which in a long series of centuries had become attached to everything originally uttered by the prophet, the maxims, which as Brami he had taught, seemed similar to those inculcated by Manko. But as Alma, adapting his lessons to the improved conditions of humanity, the divine prophet had more completely unfolded his scheme; as Alma, he had made his last revelation.

This narration concluded, Babbalanja mildly observed, "Mohi, without seeking to accuse you of uttering falsehoods, since what you relate rests not upon testimony of your own; permit me to question the fidelity of your account of Alma. The prophet came to dissipate errors, you say; but superadded to many that have survived the past, ten thousand others have originated in various constructions of the principles of Alma himself. The prophet came to do away all gods but one; but since the days of Alma, the idols of Maramma have more than quadrupled. The prophet came to make us Mardians more virtuous and happy; but along with all previous good, the same wars, crimes, and miseries, which existed in Alma's day, under various modifications, are yet extant. Nay: take from your chronicles, Mohi, the history of those horrors, one way or other, resulting from the doings of Alma's nominal followers, and your chronicles would not so frequently make mention of blood. The prophet came to guarantee our eternal felicity; but according to what is held in Maramma, that felicity rests on so hard a proviso, that to a thinking mind, but very few of our sinful race may secure it. For one, then, I wholly reject your Alma; not so much, because of all that is hard to be understood in his histories; as because of obvious and undeniable things all round us; which, to me, seem at war with an unreserved faith in his doctrines as promulgated here in Maramma. Besides; everything in this isle strengthens my incredulity; I never was so thorough a disbeliever as now."

"Let the winds be laid!" cried Mohi, "while your rash confession is being made in this sacred lake."

Said Media, "Philosopher, remember the boy, and they that seized him."

"Ah! I do indeed remember him. Poor youth! in his agony, how my heart yearned towards his. But that very prudence which you deny me, my lord, prevented me from saying aught in his behalf. Have you not observed that until now, when we are completely by ourselves, I have refrained from freely discoursing of what we have seen in this island? Trust me, my lord, there is no man that bears more in mind the necessity of being either a believer or a hypocrite in Maramma, and the imminent peril of being honest here, than I, Babbalanja. And have I not reason to be wary, when in my boyhood, my own sire was burned for his temerity; and in this very isle? Just Oro! it was done in the name of Alma; what wonder, then, that, at times, I almost hate that sound. And from those flames, they devoutly swore he went to others—horrible fable!"

Said Mohi: "Do you deny, then, the everlasting torments?"

" 'Tis not worth a denial. Nor by formally denying it, will I run the risk of shaking the faith of thousands, who in that pious belief find infinite consolation for all they suffer in Mardi."

"How?" said Media; "are there those who soothe themselves with the thought of everlasting flames?"

"One would think so, my lord, since they defend that dogma more resolutely than any other. Sooner will they yield you the isles of Paradise than it. And in truth, as liege followers of Alma, they would seem but right in clinging to it as they do; for, according to all one hears in Maramma, the great end of the prophet's mission seems to have been the revealing to us Mardians the existence of horrors, most hard to escape. But better we were all annihilated, than that one man should be damned."

Rejoined Media, "But think you not that possibly Alma may have been misconceived? Are you certain that doctrine is his?"

"I know nothing more than that such is the belief in this land. And in these matters, I know not where else to go for information. But, my lord, had I been living in those days when certain men are said to have been actually possessed by spirits from hell, I had not let slip the opportunity—as our forefathers did—to cross-question them concerning the place they came from."

"Well, well," said Media, "your Alma's faith concerns not me; I am a king, and a demi-god; and leave vulgar torments to the commonality."

"But it concerns me," muttered Mohi; "yet I know not what to think."

"For me," said Yoomy, "I reject it. Could I, I would not believe it. It is at variance with the dictates of my heart; instinctively my heart turns from it, as a thirsty man from gall."

"Hush; say no more," said Mohi; "again we approach the shore."

Chapter CXIV

Mohi Tells of One Ravoo, and They Land to Visit Hevaneva, a Flourishing Artisan

Having seen all worth viewing in Yammo, we departed, to complete the circumnavigation of the island, by returning to Uma, without reversing our prows. As we glided along, we passed many objects of interest, concerning which, Mohi, as usual, was very diffuse.

Among other things pointed out, were certain little altars, like mile-stones, planted here and there upon bright bluffs, running out into the lagoon. Dedicated respectively to the guardian spirits of Maramma, these altars formed a chain of spiritual defenses; and here were presumed to stand post the most vigilant of warders; dread Hivohitee, all by himself, garrisoning the impregnable interior.

But these sentries were only subalterns, subject to the beck of the Pontiff; who frequently sent word to them concerning the duties of their watch. His mandates were entrusted to one Ravoo, the hereditary pontifical messenger; a long-limbed varlet, so swift of foot that he was said to travel like a javelin. "Art thou Ravoo, that thou so pliest thy legs?" say these islanders, to one encountered in a hurry.

Hivohitee's postman held no oral communication with the sentries. Dispatched round the island with divers bits of tappa, hieroglyphically stamped, he merely deposited one upon each altar; superadding a stone, to keep the missive in its place; and so went his rounds.

Now, his route lay over hill and over dale, and over many a coral rock; and to preserve his feet from bruises, he was fain to wear a sort of buskin, or boot, fabricated of a durable tappa, made from the thickest and toughest of fibers. As he never wore his buskins except when he carried the mail, Ravoo sorely fretted with his Hessians; though it would have been highly imprudent to travel without them. To make the thing more endurable, therefore, and, at intervals, to cool his heated pedals, he established a series of stopping-places, or stages; at each of which a fresh pair of buskins, hanging from a tree, were taken down and vaulted into by the ingenious traveler. Those relays of boots were exceedingly convenient; next, indeed, to being lifted upon a fresh pair of legs.

"Now, to what purpose that anecdote?" demanded Babbalanja of Mohi, who in substance related it.

"Marry! 'tis but the simple recital of a fact; and I tell it to entertain the company."

"But has it any meaning you know of?"

"Thou art wise, find out," retorted Braid-Beard.

"But what comes of it?" persisted Babbalanja.

"Beshrew me, this senseless catechising of thine," replied Mohi; "naught else, it seems, save a grin or two."

"And pray, what may you be driving at, philosopher?" interrupted Media.

"I am intent upon the essence of things; the mystery that lieth beyond; the elements of the tear which much laughter provoketh; that which is beneath the seeming; the precious pearl within the shaggy oyster. I probe the circle's center; I seek to evolve the inscrutable."

"Seek on; and when aught is found, cry out, that we may run to see."

"My lord the king is merry upon me. To him my more subtle cogitations seem foolishness. But believe me, my lord, there is more to be thought of than to be seen. There is a world of wonders insphered within the spontaneous consciousness; or, as old Bardianna hath it, a mystery within the obvious, yet an obviousness within the mystery."

"And did I ever deny that?" said Media.

"As plain as my hand in the dark," said Mohi.

"I dreamed a dream," said Yoomy.

"They banter me; but enough; I am to blame for discoursing upon the deep world wherein I live. I am wrong in seeking to invest sublunary sounds with celestial sense. Much that is in me is incommunicable by this ether we breathe. But I blame ye not." And wrapping round him his mantle, Babbalanja retired into its most private folds.

Ere coming in sight of Uma, we put into a little bay, to pay our respects to Hevaneva, a famous character there dwelling; who, assisted by many journeymen, carried on the lucrative business of making idols for the surrounding isles.

Know ye, that all idols not made in Maramma, and consecrated by Hivohitee; and, what is more, in strings of teeth paid down for to Hevaneva, are of no more account, than logs, stocks, or stones. Yet does not the cunning artificer monopolize the profits of his vocation; for Hevaneva being but the vassal of the Pontiff, the latter lays claim to King Leo's share of the spoils, and secures it.

The place was very prettily lapped in a pleasant dell, nigh to the margin of the water; and here, were several spacious arbors; wherein, prostrate upon their sacred faces, were all manner of idols, in every imaginable stage of statuary development.

With wonderful industry the journeymen were plying their tools—some chiseling noses; some trenching for mouths; and others, with heated flints, boring for ears; a hole drilled straight through the occiput, representing the auricular organs.

"How easily they are seen through," said Babbalanja, taking a sight through one of the heads.

The last finish is given to their godships by rubbing them all over with dried slips of consecrated shark-skin, rough as sand paper, tacked over bits of wood.

In one of the farther arbors, Hevaneva pointed out a goodly array of idols, all complete and ready for the market. They were of every variety of pattern; and of every size; from that of a giant, to the little images worn in the ears of the ultra devout.

"Of late," said the artist, "there has been a lively demand for the image of Arbino, the god of fishing; the present being the principal season for that business. For Nadams (Nadam presides over love and wine), there has also been urgent call; it being the time of the grape; and the maidens growing frolicsome, withal, and devotional."

Seeing that Hevaneva handled his wares with much familiarity, not to say irreverence, Babbalanja was minded to learn from him what he thought of his trade; whether the images he made were genuine or spurious; in a word, whether he believed in his gods.

His reply was curious. But still more so the marginal gestures wherewith he helped out the text.

"When I cut down the trees for my idols," said he, "they are nothing but logs; when upon those logs, I chalk out the figures of my images, they yet remain logs; when the chisel is applied, logs they are still; and when all complete, I at last stand them up in my studio, even then they are logs. Nevertheless, when I handle the pay, they are as prime gods as ever were turned out in Maramma."

"You must make a very great variety," said Babbalanja.

"All sorts, all sorts."

"And from the same material, I presume?"

"Ay, ay, one grove supplies them all. And, on an average, each tree stands us in full fifty idols. Then, we often take second-hand images in part pay for new ones. These we work over again into new patterns; touching up their eyes and ears; resetting their noses; and more especially new-footing their legs, where they always decay first."

Under sanction of the Pontiff, Hevaneva, in addition to his large commerce in idols, also carried on the highly lucrative business of canoe-building; the profits whereof, undivided, he dropped into his private exchequer. But Mohi averred, that the Pontiff often charged him with neglecting his images for his canoes. Be that as it may, Hevaneva drove a thriving trade at both avocations. And in demonstration of the fact, he directed our attention to three long rows of canoes, upheld by wooden supports. They were in perfect order; at a moment's notice, ready for launching; being furnished with paddles, out-riggers, masts, sails, and a human skull, with a short handle thrust through one of its eyes, the ordinary bailer of Maramma; besides other appurtenances, including on the prow a duodecimo idol to match.

Owing to a superstitious preference bestowed upon the wood and work of the sacred island, Hevaneva's canoes were in as high repute as his idols; and sold equally well.

In truth, in several ways one trade helped the other. The larger images being dug out of the hollow part of the canoes; and all knotty odds and ends reserved for the idol ear-rings.

"But after all," said the artificer, "I find a readier sale for my images than for my canoes."

"And so it will ever be," said Babbalanja. "Stick to thy idols, man! A trade more reliable than the baker's."

Chapter CXV

A Nursery Tale of Babbalanja's

Having taken to our canoes once again, we were silently sailing along, when Media observed, "Babbalanja, though I seldom trouble myself with such thoughts, I have just been thinking how difficult it must be for the more ignorant sort of people to decide upon what particular image to worship as a guardian deity, when in Maramma, it seems, there exists such a multitude of idols, and a thousand more are to be heard of."

"Not at all, your highness. The more ignorant the better. The multitude of images distracts them not. But I am in no mood for serious discourse; let me tell you a story."

"A story! hear him; the solemn philosopher is desirous of regaling us with a tale! But pray, begin."

"Once upon a time, then," said Babbalanja, indifferently adjusting his girdle, "nine blind men, with uncommonly long noses, set out on their travels to see the great island on which they were born."

"A precious beginning," muttered Mohi. "Nine blind men setting out to see sights."

Continued Babbalanja, "Staff in hand, they traveled; one in advance of the other; each man with his palm upon the shoulder next him; and he with the longest nose took the lead of the file. Journeying on in this manner, they came to a valley, in which reigned a king called Tammaro. Now, in a certain enclosure towards the head of the valley, there stood an immense wild banian tree; all over moss, and many centuries old, and forming quite a wood in itself; its thousand boughs striking into the earth, and fixing there as many gigantic trunks. With Tammaro, it had long been a question which of those many trunks was the original and true one; a matter that had puzzled the wisest heads among his subjects; and in vain had a reward been offered for the solution of the perplexity. But the tree was so vast, and its fabric so complex; and its rooted branches so similar in appearance; and so numerous, from the circumstance that every year had added to them, that it was quite impossible to determine the point. Nevertheless, no sooner did the nine blind men hear that there was a reward offered for discovering the trunk of a tree, standing all by itself, than, one and all, they assured Tammaro that they would quickly settle that little difficulty of his; and loudly inveighed against the stupidity of his sages, who had been so easily posed. So being conducted into the enclosure, and assured that the tree was somewhere within, they separated their forces, so as at wide intervals to surround it at a distance; when feeling their way, with their staves and their noses, they advanced to the search, crying out, 'Pshaw; make room there; let us wise men feel of the mystery.' Presently, striking with his nose one of the rooted branches, the foremost blind man quickly knelt down; and feeling that it struck into the earth, gleefully shouted, 'Here it is! here it is!' But almost in the same breath, his companions, also, each striking a branch with his staff or his nose, cried out in like manner, 'Here it is! here it is!' Whereupon they were all confounded; but directly, the man who first cried out thus addressed the rest, 'Good friends, surely you're mistaken. There is but one tree in the place, and here it is.' 'Very true,' said the others, all together; 'there is only *one* tree; but *here* it is.' 'Nay,' said the others, 'it is *here!*' and so saying, each blind man triumphantly felt of the branch, where it penetrated into the earth. Then again said the first speaker, 'Good friends, if you will not believe what I say, come hither, and feel for yourselves.' 'Nay, nay,' replied they, why seek further? here it is; and nowhere else can it be.' 'You blind fools, you, you contradict yourselves,' continued the first speaker, waxing wroth; 'how can you each have hold of a separate trunk, when there is but one in the place?' Whereupon, they redoubled their cries, calling each other all manner of opprobrious names, and presently they fell to beating each other with their staves, and charging upon each other with their noses. But soon after, being loudly called upon by Tammaro and his people, who all this while had been looking on; being loudly called upon, I say, to clap their hands on the trunk, they again rushed for their respective branches; and it so happened that, one and all, they changed places; but still cried out, '*Here* it is; *here* it is!' 'Peace! peace! ye silly blind men,' said Tammaro. 'Will ye without eyes, presume to see more sharply than those who have them? The tree is too much for us all. Hence! depart from the valley.' "

"An admirable story," cried Media. "I had no idea that a mere mortal, least of all a philosopher, could acquit himself so well. By my scepter, but it is well done! Ha, ha! blind men round a banian! Why, Babbalanja, no demi-god could surpass it. Taji, could you?"

"But, Babbalanja, what under the sun, mean you by your blind story?" cried Mohi. "Obverse, or reverse, I can make nothing out of it."

"Others may," said Babbalanja. "It is a polysensuum, old man."

"A pollywog!" said Mohi.

Chapter CXVI

LANDING TO VISIT HIVOHITEE THE PONTIFF, THEY ENCOUNTER AN EXTRAORDINARY OLD HERMIT; WITH WHOM YOOMY HAS A CONFIDENTIAL INTERVIEW, BUT LEARNS LITTLE

GLIDING ON, SUDDENLY WE SPIED A SOLITARY ISLANDER PUTTING OUT IN HIS CANOE FROM A neighboring cove.

Drawing near, the stranger informed us that he was just from the face of the great Pontiff Hivohitee, who, having dismissed his celestial guests, had retired to his private sanctuary. Upon this, Media resolved to land forthwith, and under the guidance of Mohi, proceed inland, and pay a visit to his Holiness.

Quitting the beach, our path penetrated into the solitudes of the groves. Skirting the way were tall Casaurinas, a species of cypress, standing motionless in the shadows, as files of mutes at a funeral. But here and there, they were overrun with the adventurous vines of the convolvulus, the morning-glory of the tropics, whose tendrils, bruised by the twigs, dropped milk upon the dragon-like scales of the trees.

This vine is of many varieties. Lying perdu, and shunning the garish sun through the day, one species rises at night with the stars; bursting forth in dazzling constellations of blossoms, which close at dawn. Others, slumbering through the darkness, are up and abroad with their petals, by peep of morn; and after inhaling its breath, again drop their lids in repose. While a third species, more capricious, refuse to expand at all, unless in the most brilliant sunshine, and upon the very tops of the loftiest trees. Ambitious flowers! that will not blow, unless in high places, with the bright day looking on and admiring.

Here and there we passed open glades in the woods, delicious with the incense of violets. Balsamic ferns, stirred by the breeze, fanned all the air with aromas. These glades were delightful.

Journeying on, we at length came to a dark glen so deftly hidden by the surrounding copses, that were it not for the miasma thence wafted, an ignorant wayfarer might pass and repass it, time and again, never dreaming of its vicinity.

Down into the gloom of this glen we descended. Its sides were mantled by noxious shrubs, whose exhalations, half-way down, unpleasantly blended with the piny breeze from the uplands. Through its bed ran a brook, whose incrusted margin had a strange metallic luster, from the polluted waters here flowing; their source a sulphur spring, of vile flavor and odor, where many invalid pilgrims resorted.

The woods all round were haunted by the dismal cawings of crows; tap-tap, the black hawk whetted his bill on the boughs; each trunk stalked a ghost; and from those trunks, Hevaneva procured the wood for his idols.

Rapidly crossing this place, Yoomy's hands to his ears, old Mohi's to his nostrils, and Babbalanja vainly trying to walk with closed eyes, we toiled among steep, flinty rocks, along a wild zigzag pathway; like a mule-track in the Andes, not so much onward as upward; Yoomy above Babbalanja, my lord Media above him, and Braid-Beard, our guide, in the air above all.

Strewn over with cinders, the vitreous marl seemed tumbled together, as if belched from a volcano's throat.

Presently we came to a tall, slender structure, hidden among the scenic projections of the cliffs, like a monument in the dark, vaulted ways of an abbey. Surrounding it, were five extinct craters. The air was sultry and still, as if full of spent thunderbolts.

Like a Hindoo pagoda, this bamboo edifice rose story above story; its many angles and points decorated with pearl-shells suspended by cords. But the uppermost story, some ten toises in the air, was closely thatched from apex to floor; which summit was gained by a series of ascents.

What eremite dwelleth here, like St. Stylites at the top of his column?—a question which Mohi seemed all eagerness to have answered.

Dropping upon his knees, he gave a peculiar low call; no response. Another: all was silent. Marching up to the pagoda, and again dropping upon his knees, he shook the bamboos till the edifice rocked, and its pearl-shells, jingled, as if a troop of Andalusian mules, with bells round their necks, were galloping along the defile.

At length the thatch aloft was thrown open, and a head was thrust forth. It was that of an old, old man; with steel-gray eyes, hair and beard, and a horrible necklace of jaw-bones.

Now, issuing from the pagoda, Mohi turned about to gain a view of the ghost he had raised; and no sooner did he behold it, than with King Media and the rest, he made a marked salutation.

Presently, the eremite pointed to where Yoomy was standing, and waved his hand upwards; when Mohi informed the minstrel that it was St. Stylites' pleasure, that he should pay him a visit.

Wondering what was to come, Yoomy proceeded to mount, and at last arriving towards the top of the pagoda, was met by an opening, from which an encouraging arm assisted him to gain the ultimate landing.

Here all was murky enough, for the aperture from which the head of the apparition had been thrust, was now closed; and what little twilight there was, came up through the opening in the floor.

In this dismal seclusion, silently the hermit confronted the minstrel; his gray hair, eyes, and beard all gleaming, as if streaked with phosphorus; while his ghastly gorget grinned hideously, with all its jaws.

Mutely Yoomy waited to be addressed; but hearing no sound, and becoming alive to the strangeness of his situation, he meditated whether it would not be well to subside out of sight, even as he had come—through the floor. An intention which the eremite must have anticipated; for of a sudden, something was slid over the opening; and the apparition seating itself thereupon, the twain were in darkness complete.

Shut up thus, with an inscrutable stranger posted at the only aperture of escape, poor Yoomy fell into something like a panic; hardly knowing what step to take next. As for endeavoring to force his way out, it was alarming to think of; for aught he knew, the eremite, availing himself of the gloom, might be bristling all over with javelin points.

At last the silence was broken.

"What see you, mortal?"

"Chiefly darkness," said Yoomy, wondering at the audacity of the question.

"I dwell in it. But what else see you, mortal?"

"The dim gleaming of thy gorget."

"But that is not me. What else dost thou see?"

"Nothing."

"Then thou hast found me out, and seen all. Descend."

And with that, the passage-way opened, and groping through the twilight, Yoomy obeyed the mandate, and retreated; full of vexation at his enigmatical reception.

On his alighting, Mohi inquired whether the hermit was not a wonderful personage.

But thinking some sage waggery lurked in the question, and at present too indignant to enter into details, the minstrel made some impatient reply; and winding through a defile, the party resumed its journey.

Straggling behind, to survey the strange plants and flowers in his path, Yoomy became so absorbed, as almost to forget the scene in the Pagoda; yet every moment expected to be nearing the stately abode of the Pontiff.

But suddenly the scene around grew familiar; the path seemed that which had been followed just after leaving the canoes; and at length the place of debarkation was in sight.

Surprised that the object of our visit should have been thus abandoned, the minstrel ran forward and sought an explanation.

Whereupon, Mohi lifted his hands in amazement; exclaiming at the blindness of the eyes, which had beheld the supreme Pontiff of Maramma without knowing it.

The old hermit was no other than the dread Hivohitee; the pagoda, the inmost oracle of the isle.

Chapter CXVII

BABBALANJA ENDEAVORS TO EXPLAIN THE MYSTERY

THIS GREAT MOGUL OF A PERSONAGE, THEN, THIS WOUNDY AHASUERUS; THIS MAN OF MEN, THIS same Hivohitee, whose name rumbled among the mountains like a peal of thunder, had been seen face to face, and taken for naught but a bearded old hermit, or at best, some equivocal conjuror.

So great was his wonderment at the time, that Yoomy could not avoid expressing it in words.

Whereupon thus discoursed Babbalanja:

"Gentle Yoomy, be not astounded that Hivohitee is so far behind your previous conceptions. The shadows of things are greater than themselves; and the more exaggerated the shadow, the more unlike to the substance."

"But, knowing now what manner of person Hivohitee is," said Yoomy, "much do I long to behold him again."

But Mohi assured him it was out of the question; that the Pontiff always acted towards strangers as towards him (Yoomy), and that but one dim blink at the eremite was all that mortal could obtain.

Debarred thus from a second and more satisfactory interview with one, concerning whom his curiosity had been violently aroused, the minstrel again turned to Mohi for enlightenment; especially touching that magnate's Egyptian reception of him in his aerial den.

Whereto, the chronicler made answer, that the Pontiff affected darkness because he liked it; that he was a ruler of few words, but many deeds; and that, had Yoomy been permitted to tarry longer with him in the pagoda he would have been privy to many strange attestations of the divinity imputed to him. Voices would have been heard in the air, gossiping with Hivohitee; noises inexplicable proceeding from him; in brief, light would have flashed out of his darkness.

"But who has seen these things, Mohi?" said Babbalanja. "Have you?"

"Nay."

"Who, then?—Media?—Anyone you know?"

"Nay; but the whole Archipelago has."

"Thus," exclaimed Babbalanja, "does Mardi, blind though it be in many things, collectively behold the marvels which one pair of eyes sees not."

Chapter CXVIII

Taji Receives Tidings and Omens

Slowly sailing on, we were overtaken by a shallop, whose inmates grappling to the side of Media's, said they came from Borabolla.

Dismal tidings! My faithful follower's death.

Absent over night, that morning early he had been discovered lifeless in the woods, three arrows in his heart. And the three pale strangers were nowhere to be found. But a fleet canoe was missing from the beach.

Slain for me! my soul sobbed out. Nor yet appeared Aleema's manes; nor yet seemed sated the avengers' malice, who, doubtless, were on my track.

But I turned; and instantly the three canoes had been reversed; and full soon, Jarl's dead hand in mine, had not Media interposed.

"To death, your presence will not bring life back."

"And we must on," said Babbalanja. "We seek the living, not the dead."

Thus they overruled me; and Borabolla's messengers departed.

Soon evening came, and in its shades, three shadows—Hautia's heralds.

Their shallop glided near.

A leaf tri-foiled was first presented; then another, arrow-shaped.

Said Yoomy, "Still I swiftly follow, behind revenge."

Then were showered faded, pallid daffodils.

Said Yoomy, "Thy hopes are blighted all."

"Not dead, but living with the life of life. Sirens! I heed ye not."

They would have showered more flowers; but crowding sail, we left them.

Much converse followed. Then, beneath the canopy, all sought repose. And ere long slouched sleep drew nigh, tending dreams innumerable; silent dotting all the downs; a shepherd with his flock.

Chapter CXIX

Dreams

Dreams! dreams! golden dreams: endless, and golden, as the flowery prairies, that stretch away from the Rio Sacramento, in whose waters Danae's shower was woven; prairies like rounded eternities: jonquil leaves beaten out; and my dreams herd like buffaloes, browsing on to the horizon, and browsing on round the world; and among them, I dash with my lance, to spear one ere they all flee.

Dreams! dreams! passing and repassing, like Oriental empires in history; and scepters wave thick, as Bruce's pikes at Bannockburn; and crowns are plenty as marigolds in June. And far in the background, hazy and blue, their steeps let down from the sky, loom Andes on Andes, rooted on Alps; and all round me, long rushing oceans, roll Amazons and Orinocos; waves, mounted Parthians; and, to and fro, toss the wide woodlands: all the world an elk, and the forest its antlers.

But far to the south, past my Sicily suns and my vineyards, stretches the Antarctic barrier of ice: a China wall, built up from the sea, and nodding its frosted towers in the dun, clouded sky. Do Tartary and Siberia lie beyond? Deathful, desolate dominions those; bleak and wild the ocean, beating at that barrier's base, hovering 'twixt freezing and foaming; and freighted with navies of icebergs—warring worlds crossing orbits; their long icicles, projecting like spears to the charge. Wide away stream the floes of drift ice, frozen cemeteries of skeletons and bones. White bears howl as they drift from their cubs; and the grinding islands crush the skulls of the peering seals.

But beneath me, at the Equator, the earth pulses and beats like a warrior's heart; till I know not whether it be not myself. And my soul sinks down to the depths, and soars to the skies; and comet-like reels on through such boundless expanses, that methinks all the worlds are my kin, and I invoke them to stay in their course. Yet, like a mighty three-decker, towing argosies by scores, I tremble, gasp, and strain in my flight, and fain would cast off the cables that hamper.

And like a frigate, I am full with a thousand souls; and as on, on, on, I scud before the wind, many mariners rush up from the orlop below, like miners from caves; running shouting across my decks; opposite braces are pulled; and this way and that, the great yards swing round on their axes; and boisterous speaking-trumpets are heard; and contending orders, to save the good ship from the shoals. Shoals, like nebulous vapors, shoreing the white reef of the Milky Way, against which the wrecked worlds are dashed; strewing all the strand with their Himmaleh keels and ribs.

Ay: many, many souls are in me. In my tropical calms, when my ship lies tranced on Eternity's main, speaking one at a time, then all with one voice; an orchestra of many French bugles and horns, rising, and falling, and swaying, in golden calls and responses.

Sometimes, when these Atlantics and Pacifics thus undulate round me, I lie stretched out in their midst; a land-locked Mediterranean, knowing no ebb nor flow. Then, again, I am dashed in the spray of these sounds: an eagle at the world's end, tossed skyward on the horns of the tempest. Again, I descend, and list to the concert.

Like a grand, ground swell, Homer's old organ rolls its vast volumes under the light frothy wave-crests of Anacreon and Hafiz; and high over my ocean, sweet Shakespeare soars, like all the larks in the spring. Throned on my sea-side, like Canute, bearded Ossian smites his hoary harp, wreathed with wild flowers, in which warble my Wallers; blind Milton sings bass to my Petrarchs and Priors, and laureates crown me with bays.

In me, many worthies recline, and converse. I list to St. Paul, who argues the doubts of Montaigne; Julian the Apostate cross-questions Augustine; and Thomas-à-Kempis unrolls his old black letters for all to decipher. Zeno murmurs maxims beneath the hoarse shout of Democritus; and though Democritus laugh loud and long, and the sneer of Pyrrho be seen; yet, divine Plato, and Proclus, and Verulam are of my counsel; and Zoroaster whispered me before I was born. I walk a world that is mine; and enter many nations, as Mungo Park rested in African cots; I am served like Bajazet: Bacchus my butler, Virgil my minstrel, Philip Sidney my page. My memory is a life beyond birth; my memory, my library of the vatican, its alcoves all endless perspectives, eve-tinted by cross-lights from Middle-Age oriels.

And as the great Mississippi musters his watery nations; Ohio, with all his leagued streams; Missouri, bringing down in torrents the clans from the highlands; Arkansas, his Tartar rivers from the plain—so, with all the past and present pouring in me, I roll down my billow from afar.

Yet not I, but another; God is my Lord; and though many satellites revolve around me, I and all mine revolve round the great central Truth, sun-like, fixed and luminous forever in the foundationless firmament.

Fire flames on my tongue; and though of old the Bactrian prophets were stoned; yet the stoners in oblivion sleep. But whoso stones me, shall be as Erostratus, who put torch to the temple though Genghis Khan with Cambyses combine to obliterate him, his name shall be extant in the mouth of the last man that lives. And if so be, down unto death, whence I came, will I go, like Xenophon retreating on Greece, all Persia brandishing her spears in his rear.

My cheek blanches white while I write; I start at the scratch of my pen; my own mad brood of eagles devours me; fain would I unsay this audacity; but an iron-mailed hand clenches mine in a vice, and prints down every letter in my spite. Fain would I hurl off this Dionysius that rides me; my thoughts crush me down till I groan; in far fields I hear the song of the reaper, while I slave and faint in this cell. The fever runs through me like lava; my hot brain burns like a coal; and like many a monarch, I am less to be envied, than the veriest hind in the land.

Chapter CXX

Media and Babbalanja Discourse

Our visiting the pontiff at a time previously unforeseen, somewhat altered our plans. All search in Maramma for the lost one proving fruitless, and nothing of note remaining to be seen, we returned not to Uma; but proceeded with the tour of the lagoon.

When day came, reclining beneath the canopy, Babbalanja would fain have seriously discussed those things we had lately been seeing, which, for all the occasional levity he had recently evinced, seemed very near his heart.

But my Lord Media forbade; saying that they necessarily included a topic which all gay, sensible Mardians, who desired to live and be merry, invariably banished from social discourse.

"Meditate as much as you will, Babbalanja, but say little aloud, unless in a merry and mythical way. Lay down the great maxims of things, but let inferences take care of themselves. Never be special, never a partisan. In safety, afar off, you may batter down a fortress; but at your peril you essay to carry a single turret by escalade. And if doubts distract you, in vain will you seek sympathy from your fellow-men. For upon this one theme, not a few of you free-minded mortals, even the otherwise honest and intelligent, are the least frank and friendly. Discourse with them, and it is mostly formulas, or prevarications, or hollow assumption of philosophical indifference, or urbane hypocrisies, or a cool, civil deference to the dominant belief; or still worse, but less common, a brutality of indiscriminate skepticism. Furthermore, Babbalanja, on this head, final, last thoughts you mortals have none; nor can have; and, at bottom, your own fleeting fancies are too often secrets to yourselves; and sooner may you get another's secret than your own. Thus with the wisest of you all; you are ever unfixed. Do you show a tropical calm without? Then, be sure a thousand contrary currents whirl and eddy within. The free, airy robe of your philosophy is but a dream, which seems true while it lasts; but waking again into the orthodox world, straightway you resume the old habit. And though in your dreams you may hie to the uttermost Orient, yet all the while you abide where you are. Babbalanja, you mortals dwell in Mardi, and it is impossible to get elsewhere."

Said Babbalanja, "My lord, you school me. But though I dissent from some of your positions, I am willing to confess that this is not the first time a philosopher has been instructed by a man."

"A demi-god, sir; and therefore I the more readily discharge my mind of all seriousness, touching the subject, with which you mortals so vex and torment yourselves."

Silence ensued. And seated apart, on both sides of the barge, solemnly swaying, in fixed meditation, to the roll of the waves, Babbalanja, Mohi, and Yoomy drooped lower and lower, like funeral plumes; and our gloomy canoe seemed a hearse.

Chapter CXXI

THEY REGALE THEMSELVES WITH THEIR PIPES

HO! MORTALS! MORTALS!" CRIED MEDIA. "GO WE TO BURY OUR DEAD? AWAKE, SONS OF MEN! Cheer up, heirs of immortality! Ho! Vee-Vee! bring forth our pipes; we'll smoke off this cloud."

Nothing so beguiling as the fumes of tobacco, whether inhaled through hookah, narghil, chibouque, Dutch porcelain, pure Principe, or Regalia. And a great oversight had it been in King Media to have omitted pipes among the appliances of this voyage that we went. Tobacco in rouleaus we had none; cigar nor cigarette; which little the company esteemed. Pipes were preferred; and pipes we often smoked; testify, oh, Vee-Vee, to that! But not of the vile clay, of which mankind and Etruscan vases were made, were these jolly fine pipes of ours. But all in good time.

Now the leaf called tobacco is of divers species and sorts. Not to dwell upon vile Shag, Pigtail, Plug, Nail-rod, Negro-head, Cavendish, and misnamed Lady's-twist, there are the following varieties: Gold-leaf, Orinoco, Cimaroza, Smyrna, Bird's-eye, James-river, Sweet-scented, Honeydew, Kentucky, Cnaster, Scarfalati, and famed Shiraz, or Persian. Of all of which, perhaps the last is the best.

But smoked by itself, to a fastidious wight, even Shiraz is not gentle enough. It needs mitigation. And the cunning craft of so mitigating even the mildest tobacco was well understood in the dominions of Media. There, in plantations ever covered with a brooding blue haze they raised its fine leaf in the utmost luxuriance; almost as broad as the broad fans of the broad-bladed banana. The stalks of the leaf withdrawn, the remainder they cut up, and mixed with soft willow-bark, and the aromatic leaves of the Betel.

"Ho! Vee-Vee, bring forth the pipes," cried Media. And forth they came, followed by a quaint, carved cocoanut, agate-lidded, containing ammunition sufficient for many stout charges and primings.

Soon we were all smoking so hard that the canopied howdah, under which we reclined, sent up purple wreaths like a Michigan wigwam. There we sat in a ring, all smoking in council—every pipe a halcyon pipe of peace.

And among those calumets, my lord Media's showed like the turbaned Grand Turk among his Bashaws. It was an extraordinary pipe, be sure; of right royal dimensions. Its mouth-piece an eagle's beak; its long stem, a bright, red-barked cherry-tree branch, partly covered with a close network of purple dyed porcupine quills; and towards the upper end, streaming with pennons, like a Versailles flag-staff of a coronation day. These pennons were managed by halyards; and after lighting his prince's pipe, it was little Vee-Vee's part to run them up towards the mast-head, or mouthpiece, in token that his lord was fairly under weigh.

But Babbalanja's was of a different sort; an immense black, serpentine stem of ebony, coiling this way and that, in endless convolutions, like an anaconda round a traveler in Brazil. Smoking this hydra, Babbalanja looked as if playing upon the trombone.

Next, gentle Yoomy's. Its stem, a slender golden reed, like musical Pan's; its bowl very merry with tassels.

Lastly, old Mohi, the chronicler's. Its Death's-head bowl forming its latter end, continually reminding him of his own. Its shank was an ostrich's leg, some feathers still waving nigh the mouth-piece.

"Here, Vee-Vee! fill me up again," cried Media, through the blue vapors sweeping round his great gonfalon, like plumed Marshal Ney, waving his baton in the smoke of Waterloo; or thrice gallant Anglesea, crossing his wooden leg mid the reek and rack of the Apsley House banquet.

Vee-Vee obeyed; and quickly, like a howitzer, the pipe-bowl was reloaded to the muzzle, and King Media smoked on.

"Ah! this is pleasant indeed," he cried. "Look, it's a calm on the waters, and a calm in our hearts, as we inhale these sedative odors."

"So calm," said Babbalanja; "the very gods must be smoking now."

"And thus," said Media, "we demi-gods hereafter shall cross-legged sit, and smoke out our eternities. Ah, what a glorious puff! Mortals, methinks these pipe-bowls of ours must be petrifactions of roses, so scented they seem. But, old Mohi, you have smoked this many a long year; doubtless, you know something about their material—the Froth-of-the-Sea they call it, I think—ere my handicraft subjects obtain it, to work into bowls. Tell us the tale."

"Delighted to do so, my lord," replied Mohi, slowly disentangling his mouth-piece from the braids of his beard. "I have devoted much time and attention to the study of pipe-bowls, and groped among many learned authorities to reconcile the clashing opinions concerning the origin of the so-called Farnoo, or Froth-of-the-Sea."

"Well, then, my old centenarian, give us the result of your investigations. But smoke away; a word and a puff: go on."

"May it please you, then, my right worshipful lord, this Farnoo is an unctuous, argillaceous substance; in its natural state, soft, malleable, and easily worked as the cornelian-red clay from the famous pipe-quarries of the wild tribes to the north. But though mostly found buried in *terra-firma*, especially in the isles towards the East, this Farnoo, my lord, is sometimes thrown up by the ocean; in seasons of high sea, being plentifully found on the reefs. But, my lord, like amber, the precise nature and origin of this Farnoo are points widely mooted."

"Stop there!" cried Media; "our mouth-pieces are of amber; so, not a word more of the Froth-of-the-Sea, until something be said to clear up the mystery of amber. What is amber, old man?"

"A still more obscure thing to trace than the other, my worshipful lord. Ancient Plinnee maintained that originally it must be a juice, exuding from balsam firs and pines; Borhavo, that, like camphor, it is the crystalized oil of aromatic ferns; Berzilli, that it is the concreted scum of the lake Cephioris; and Vondendo, against scores of antagonists, stoutly held it a sort of bituminous gold, trickling from antediluvian smugglers' caves, nigh the sea."

"Why, old Braid-Beard," cried Media, placing his pipe in rest, "you are almost as erudite as our philosopher here."

"Much more so, my lord," said Babbalanja; "for Mohi has somehow picked up all my worthless forgettings, which are more than my valuable rememberings."

"What say you, wise one?" cried Mohi, shaking his braids, like an enraged elephant with many trunks.

Said Yoomy, "My lord, I have heard that amber is nothing less than the congealed tears of broken-hearted mermaids."

"Absurd, minstrel," cried Mohi. "Hark ye; I know what it is. All other authorities to the contrary, amber is nothing more than gold-fishes' brains, made waxy, then firm, by the action of the sea."

"Nonsense!" cried Yoomy.

"My lord," said Braid-Beard, waving his pipe, this thing is just as I say. Imbedded in amber, do we not find little fishes' fins, porpoise-teeth, sea-gulls' beaks and claws; nay, butterflies' wings, and sometimes a topaz? And how could that be, unless the substance was first soft? Amber is gold-fishes' brains, I say."

"For one," said Babbalanja, "I'll not believe that, till you prove to me, Braid-Beard, that ideas themselves are found imbedded therein."

"Another of your crazy conceits, philosopher," replied Mohi, disdainfully; "yet, sometimes plenty of strange black-letter characters have been discovered in amber." And throwing back his hoary old head, he jetted forth his vapors like a whale.

"Indeed?" cried Babbalanja. "Then, my lord Media, it may be earnestly inquired, whether the gentle laws of the tribes before the flood, were not sought to be embalmed and perpetuated between transparent and sweet scented tablets of amber?"

"That, now, is not so unlikely," said Mohi; "for old King Rondo the Round once set about getting him a coffin-lid of amber; much desiring a famous mass of it owned by the ancestors of Donjalolo of Juam. But no navies could buy it. So Rondo had himself urned in a crystal."

"And that immortalized Rondo, no doubt," said Babbalanja. "Ha! ha! pity he fared not like the fat porpoise frozen and tombed in an iceberg; its icy shroud drifting south, soon melted away, and down, out of sight, sunk the dead."

"Well, so much for amber," cried Media. "Now, Mohi, go on about Farnoo."

"Know, then, my lord, that Farnoo is more like ambergris than amber."

"Is it? Then pray tell us something on that head. You know all about ambergris, too, I suppose."

"Everything about all things, my lord. Ambergris is found both on land and at sea. But especially, are lumps of it picked up on the spicy coasts of Jovanna; indeed, all over the atolls and reefs in the eastern quarter of Mardi."

"But *what* is this ambergris, Braid-Beard," said Babbalanja.

"Aquovi, the chemist, pronounced it the fragments of mushrooms growing at the bottom of the sea; Voluto held that, like naphtha, it springs from fountains down there. But it is neither."

"I have heard," said Yoomy, "that it is the honey-comb of bees, fallen from flowery cliffs into the brine."

"Nothing of the kind," said Mohi. "Do I not know all about it, minstrel? Ambergris is the petrified gall-stones of crocodiles."

"What!" cried Babbalanja, "comes sweet-scented ambergris from those musky and chain-plated river cavalry? No wonder, then, their flesh is so fragrant; their upper jaws as the visors of vinaigrettes."

"Nay, you are all wrong," cried King Media.

Then, laughing to himself—"It's pleasant to sit by, a demi-god, and hear the surmisings of mortals upon things they know nothing about; theology, or amber, or ambergris, it's all the same. But, then, did I always out with everything I know, there would be no conversing with these comical creatures.

"Listen, old Mohi; ambergris is a morbid secretion of the Spermaceti whale; for, like you, mortals, the whale is at times a sort of hypochondriac and dyspeptic. You must know, subjects, that in antediluvian times, the Spermaceti whale was much hunted by sportsmen, that being accounted better pastime, than pursuing the Behemoths on shore. Besides, it was a lucrative diversion. Now, sometimes upon striking the monster, it would start off in a dastardly fright, leaving certain fragments in its wake. These fragments the hunters picked up, giving over the chase for awhile. For in those days, as now, a quarterquintal of ambergris was more valuable than a whole ton of spermaceti."

"Nor, my lord," said Babbalanja, "would it have been wise to kill the fish that dropped such treasures no more than to murder the noddy that laid the golden eggs."

"Beshrew me! a noddy it must have been," gurgled Mohi through his pipe-stem, "to lay golden eggs for others to hatch."

"Come, no more of that now," cried Media. "Mohi, how long, think you, may one of these pipe-bowls last?"

"My lord, like one's cranium, it will endure till broken. I have smoked this one of mine more than half a century."

"But unlike our craniums, stocked full of concretions," said Babbalanja, "our pipe-bowls never need clearing out."

"True," said Mohi, "they absorb the oil of the smoke instead of allowing it offensively to incrust."

"Ay, the older the better," said Media, "and the more delicious the flavor imparted to the fumes inhaled."

"Farnoos forever! my lord," cried Yoomy. "By much smoking, the bowl waxes russet and mellow, like the berry-brown cheek of a sunburned brunette."

"And as like smoked hams," cried Braid-Beard, "we veteran old smokers grow browner and browner; hugely do we admire to see our jolly noses and pipe-bowls mellowing together."

"Well said, old man," cried Babbalanja; "for, like a good wife, a pipe is a friend and companion for life. And whoso weds with a pipe, is no longer a bachelor. After many vexations, he may go home to that faithful counselor, and ever find it full of kind consolations and suggestions. But not thus with cigars or cigarettes: the acquaintances of a moment, chatted with in by-places, whenever they come handy; their existence so fugitive, uncertain, unsatisfactory. Once ignited, nothing like longevity pertains to them. They never grow old. Why, my lord, the stump of a cigarette is an abomination; and two of them crossed are more of a *memento-mori*, than a brace of thigh-bones at right angles."

"So they are, so they are," cried King Media. "Then, mortals, puff we away at our pipes. Puff, puff, I say. Ah! how we puff! But thus we demi-gods ever puff at our ease."

"Puff, puff! how we puff!" cried Babbalanja. "But life itself is a puff and a wheeze. Our lungs are two pipes which we constantly smoke."

"Puff, puff! how we puff," cried old Mohi. "All thought is a puff."

"Ay," said Babbalanja, "not more smoke in that skull-bowl of yours than in the skull on your shoulders: both ends alike."

"Puff! puff! how we puff!" cried Yoomy. "But in every puff, there hangs a wreath. In every puff, off flies a care."

"Ay, there they go!" cried Mohi, "there goes another—and there, and there—this is the way to get rid of them, my worshipful lord; puff them aside."

"Yoomy," said Media, "give us that pipe song of thine. Sing it, my sweet and pleasant poet. We'll keep time with the flageolets of ours."

So with pipes and puffs for a chorus, thus Yoomy sang:

Care is all stuff—
Puff! Puff!
To puff is enough:—
Puff! Puff!
More musky than snuff,
And warm is a puff—
Puff! Puff!
Here we sit mid our puffs,
Like old lords in their ruffs,
Snug as bears in their muffs!—
Puff! Puff!
Then puff, puff, puff,
For care is all stuff,
Puffed off in a puff—
Puff! Puff!

"Ay, puff away!" cried Babbalanja, "puff! Puff! so we are born, and so die. Puff! Puff! my volcanoes: the great sun itself will yet go out in a snuff; and all Mardi smoke out its last wick."

"Puffs enough," said King Media, "Vee-Vee! haul down my flag. There, lie down before me, oh Gonfalon! and, subjects, hear—when I die, lay this spear on my right, and this pipe on my left, its colors at half-mast; so shall I be ambidexter, and sleep between eloquent symbols."

Chapter CXXII

THEY VISIT AN EXTRAORDINARY OLD ANTIQUARY

ABOUT PROWS THERE, YE PADDLERS," CRIED MEDIA. "IN THIS FOG WE'VE BEEN RAISING, WE HAVE sailed by Padulla, our destination."

Now Padulla was but a little island, tributary to a neighboring king; its population embracing some hundreds of thousands of leaves, and flowers, and butterflies, yet only two solitary mortals; one, famous as a venerable antiquarian; a collector of objects of Mardian vertu; a cognoscenti, and dilettante in things old and marvelous; and for that reason, very choice of himself.

He went by the exclamatory cognomen of "Oh-Oh," a name bestowed upon him by reason of the delighted interjections with which he welcomed all accessions to his museum.

Now, it was to obtain a glimpse of this very museum that Media was anxious to touch at Padulla.

Landing, and passing through a grove, we were accosted by Oh-Oh himself; who, having heard the shouts of our paddlers, had sallied forth, staff in hand.

The old man was a sight to see; especially his nose; a remarkable one. And all Mardi over, a remarkable nose is a prominent feature: an ever obvious passport to distinction. For, after all, this gaining a name, is but the individualizing of a man; as well achieved by an extraordinary nose, as by an extraordinary epic. Far better, indeed; for you may pass poets without knowing them. Even a hero is no hero without his sword; nor Beelzebub himself a lion, minus that lasso-tail of his wherewith he catches his prey. Whereas, he who is famous through his nose, it is impossible to overlook. He is a celebrity without toiling for a name. Snugly ensconced behind his proboscis, he revels in its shadow, receiving tributes of attention wherever he goes.

Not to enter at large upon the topography of Oh-Oh's nasal organ, all must be content with this; that it was of a singular magnitude, and boldly aspiring at the end; an exclamation point in the face of the wearer, forever wondering at the visible universe. The eyes of Oh-Oh were like the creature's that the Jew abhors: placed slanting in his head, and converging their rays towards the mouth; which was no mouth but a gash.

I mean not to be harsh, or unpleasant upon thee, Oh-Oh; but I must paint thee as thou wert.

The rest of his person was crooked, and dwarfed, and surmounted by a hump, that sat on his back like a burden. And a weary load is a hump, Heaven knows, only to be cast off in the grave.

Thus old, and antiquated, and gable-ended, was the tabernacle of Oh-Oh's soul. But his person was housed in as curious a structure. Built of old boughs of trees blown down in the groves, and covered over with unruly thatching, it seemed, without, some ostrich nest. But within, so intricate, and grotesque, its brown alleys and cells, that the interior of no walnut was more labyrinthine.

And here, strewn about, all dusty and disordered, were the precious antiques, and *curios,* and obsoletes, which to Oh-Oh were dear as the apple of his eye, or the memory of departed days.

The old man was exceedingly importunate in directing attention to his relics; concerning each of which he had an endless story to tell. Time would fail; nay, patience, to repeat his legends. So, in order, here follow the most prominent of his rarities:

The identical Canoe, in which, ages back, the god Unja came from the bottom of the sea.
(Very ponderous; of lignum-vitae wood.)

A stone Flower-pot, containing in the original soil, Unja's last footprints, when he embarked from Mardi for parts unknown.
(One foot-print unaccountably reversed.)

The Jaw-bones of Toorooroolоо, a great orator in the days of Unja.
(Somewhat twisted.)

A quaint little Fish-hook.
(Made from the Finger-bones of Kravi the Cunning.)

The mystic Gourd; carved all over with cabalistic triangles, and hypogriffs; by study of which a reputed prophet was said to have obtained his inspiration.
(Slightly redolent of vineyards.)

The complete Skeleton of an immense Tiger-shark; the bones of a Pearl-shell-diver's leg inside.
(Picked off the reef at low tide.)

An inscrutable, shapeless block of a mottled-hued, smoke-dried wood.
(Three unaccountable holes drilled through the middle.)

A sort of ecclesiastical Fasces, being the bony blades of nine sword-fish, basket-hilted with sharks' jaws, braided round and tasseled with cords of human hair.
(Now obsolete.)

The mystic Fan with which Unja fanned himself when in trouble.
(Woven from the leaves of the Water-Lily.)

A Tripod of a Stork's Leg, supporting a nautilus shell, containing the fragments of a bird's egg; into which was said to have been magically decanted the soul of a deceased chief.
(Unfortunately crushed in by atmospheric pressure.)

Two clasped Right Hands, embalmed; being those of twin warriors, who thus died on a battle-field.
(Impossible to sunder.)

A curious Pouch or Purse, formed from the skin of an Albatross' foot, and decorated with three sharp claws, naturally pertaining to it.
(Originally the property of a notorious old Tooth-per-Tooth.)

A long tangled lock of Mermaid's Hair, much resembling the curling silky fibers of the finer sea-weed.
(Preserved between fins of the dolphin.)

A Mermaid's Comb for the toilette. The stiff serrated crest of a Cook Storm-petrel.
(Oh-Oh was particularly curious concerning Mermaids.)

Files, Rasps, and Pincers, all bone, the implements of an eminent Chiropodist, who flourished his tools before the Flood.

(Owing to the excessive unevenness of the surface in those times, the diluvians were peculiarly liable to pedal afflictions.)

The back Tooth, that Zozo the Enthusiast, in token of grief, recklessly knocked out at the decease of a friend.

(Worn to a stump, and quite useless.)

These wonders inspected, Oh-Oh conducted us to an arbor to show us the famous telescope, by help of which he said he had discovered an ant-hill in the moon. It rested in the crotch of a bread-fruit-tree; and was a prodigiously long and hollow trunk of a palm: a scale from a sea-kraken its lens.

Then returning to his cabinet, he pointed to a bamboo microscope, which had wonderfully assisted him in his entomological pursuits.

"By this instrument, my masters," said he, "I have satisfied myself that in the eye of a dragon-fly there are precisely twelve thousand five hundred and forty-one triangular lenses; and in the leg of a flea, scores on scores of distinct muscles. Now, my masters, how far think you, a flea may leap at one spring? Why, two hundred times its own length; I have often measured their leaps, with a small measure I use for scientific purposes."

"Truly, Oh-Oh," said Babbalanja, "your discoveries must ere long result in something grand; since you furnish such invaluable data for theorists. Pray, attend, my lord Media. If, at one spring, a flea leaps two hundred times its own length, then, with the like proportion of muscles in his calves, a bandit might pounce upon the unwary traveler from a quarter of a mile off. Is it not so, Oh-Oh?"

"Indeed, but it is, my masters. And one of the greatest consolations I draw from these studies, is the ever-strengthening conviction of the beneficent wisdom that framed our Mardi. For did men possess thighs in proportion to fleas, verily, the wicked would grievously leap about, and curvet in the isles."

"But, Oh-Oh," said Babbalanja, "what other discoveries have you made? Hast yet put a usurer under your lens, to find his conscience? or a libertine, to find his heart? Hast yet brought your microscope to bear upon a downy peach, or a rosy cheek?"

"I have," said Oh-Oh, mournfully; "and from the moment I so did, I have had no heart to eat a peach, or salute a cheek."

"Then dash your lens!" cried Media.

"Well said, my lord. For all the eyes we get beyond our own, but minister to infelicity. The microscope disgusts us with our Mardi; and the telescope sets us longing for some other world."

Chapter CXXIII

THEY GO DOWN INTO THE CATACOMBS

WITH A DULL FLAMBEAU, WE NOW DESCENDED SOME NARROW STONE STEPS, TO VIEW OH-OH'S collection of ancient and curious manuscripts, preserved in a vault.

"This way, this way, my masters," cried Oh-Oh, aloft, swinging his dim torch. "Keep your hands before you; it's a dark road to travel."

"So it seems," said Babbalanja, wide-groping, as he descended lower and lower. "My lords, this is like going down to posterity."

Upon gaining the vault, forth flew a score or two of bats, extinguishing the flambeau, and leaving us in darkness, like Belzoni deserted by his Arabs in the heart of a pyramid. The torch at last relumed, we entered a tomb-like excavation, at every step raising clouds of dust; and at last stood before long rows of musty, mummyish parcels, so dingy-red, and so rolled upon sticks, that they looked like stiff sausages of Bologna; but smelled like some fine old Stilton or Cheshire.

Most ancient of all, was a hieroglyphical *Elegy on the Dumps*, consisting of one thousand and one lines; the characters, herons, weeping-willows, and ravens, supposed to have been traced by a quill from the sea-noddy.

Then there were plenty of rare old ballads:

King Kroko, and the Fisher Girl.
The Fight at the Ford of Spears.
The Song of the Skulls.

And brave old chronicles, that made Mohi's mouth water:

The Rise and Setting of the Dynasty of Foofoo.
The Heroic History of the Noble Prince Dragoni; showing how he killed ten Pinioned Prisoners with his Own Hand.
The whole Pedigree of the King of Kandidee, with that of his famous horse, Znorto.

And Tarantula books:

Sour Milk for the Young, by a Dairyman.
The Devil adrift, by a Corsair.
Grunts and Groans, by a Mad Boar.
Stings, by a Scorpion.

And poetical productions:

Suffusions of a Lily in a Shower.
Sonnet on the last Breath of an Ephemera.
The Gad-fly and Other Poems.

And metaphysical treatises:

Necessitarians not Predestinarians.
Philosophical Necessity and Predestination One Thing and The Same.
Whatever is not, is.
Whatever is, is not.

And scarce old memoirs:

The One Hundred Books of the Biography of the Great and Good King Grandissimo.
The Life of old Philo, the Philanthropist, in one Chapter.

And popular literature:

A most Sweet, Pleasant, and Unctuous Account of the Manner in which Five-and-Forty Robbers were torn asunder by Swiftly-Going Canoes.

And books by chiefs and nobles:

The Art of Making a Noise in Mardi.
On the Proper Manner of Saluting a Bosom Friend.
Letters from a Father to a Son, inculcating the Virtue of Vice.
Pastorals by a Younger Son.
A Catalogue of Chieftains who have been Authors, by a Chieftain, who disdains to be deemed an Author.
A Canto on a Cough caught by my Consort.
The Philosophy of Honesty, by a late Lord, who died in disgrace.

And theological works:

Pepper for the Perverse.
Pudding for the Pious.
Pleas for Pardon.
Pickles for the Persecuted.

And long and tedious romances with short and easy titles:

The Buck.
The Belle.
The King and the Cook, or the Cook and the King.

And books of voyages:

A Sojourn among the Anthropophagi, by One whose Hand was eaten off at Tiffin among the Savages.
Franko: its King, Court, and Tadpoles.
Three Hours in Vivenza, containing a Full and Impartial Account of that Whole Country, by a Subject of King Bello.

And works of nautical poets:

Sky-Sail-Pole Lyrics.

And divers brief books, with panic-striking titles:

Are you safe?
A Voice from Below.
Hope for none.
Fire for all.

And pamphlets by retired warriors:

On the Best Gravy for Wild Boar's Meat.
Three Receipts for Bottling New Arrack.
To Brown Bread-Fruit without Burning.
Advice to the Dyspeptic.
On Starch for Tappa.

All these MSS. were highly prized by Oh-Oh. He averred that they spoke of the mighty past, which he reverenced more than the paltry present, the dross and sediment of what had been.

Peering into a dark crypt, Babbalanja drew forth a few crumbling, illegible, black-letter sheets of his favorite old essayist, brave Bardianna. They seemed to have formed parts of a work, whose title only remained—*Thoughts by a Thinker.*

Silently Babbalanja pressed them to his heart. Then at arm's length held them, and said, "And is all this wisdom lost? Cannot the divine cunning in thee, Bardianna, transmute to brightness these sullied pages? Here, perhaps, thou didst dive into the deeps of things, treating of the normal forms of matter and of mind; how the particles of solids were first molded in the interstices of fluids; how the thoughts of men are each a soul, as the lung-cells are each a lung; how that death is but a mode of life; while mid-most is the Pharzi. But all is faded. Yea, here the Thinker's thoughts lie cheek by jowl with phrasemen's words. Oh, Bardianna! these pages were offspring of thee, thought of thy thought, soul of thy soul. Instinct with mind, they once spoke out like living voices; now, they're dust, and would not prick a fool to action. Whence, then, is this? If the fogs of some few years can make soul linked to matter naught, how can the unhoused spirit hope to live when mildewed with the damps of death?"

Piously he folded the shreds of manuscript together, kissed them, and laid them down.

Then approaching Oh-Oh, he besought him for one leaf, one shred of those most precious pages, in memory of Bardianna, and for the love of him.

But learning who he was, one of that old Ponderer's commentators, Oh-Oh tottered towards the manuscripts; with trembling fingers told them over, one by one, and said—"Thank Oro! all are here. Philosopher, ask me for my limbs, my life, my heart, but ask me not for these. Steeped in wax, these shall be my cerements."

All in vain; Oh-Oh was an antiquary.

Turning in despair, Babbalanja spied a heap of worm-eaten parchment covers, and many clippings and parings. And whereas the rolls of manuscripts did smell like unto old cheese; so these relics did marvelously resemble the rinds of the same.

Turning over this pile, Babbalanja lighted upon something that restored his good humor. Long he looked it over delighted; but bethinking him, that he must have dragged to day some lost work of the collection, and much desirous of possessing, he made bold again to ply Oh-Oh; offering a tempting price for his discovery.

Glancing at the title—*A Happy Life*—the old man cried—"Oh, rubbish! rubbish! take it for nothing."

And Babbalanja placed it in his vestment.

The catacombs surveyed, and daylight gained, we inquired the way to Jiji's, also a collector, but of another sort; one miserly in the matter of teeth, the money of Mardi.

At the mention of his name, Oh-Oh flew out into scornful philippics upon the insanity of that old dotard, who hoarded up teeth, as if teeth were of any use, but to purchase rarities. Nevertheless, he pointed out our path; following which, we crossed a meadow.

Chapter CXXIV

Babbalanja Quotes from an Antique Pagan; and Earnestly Presses it upon the Company, that What He Recites is Not His, But Another's

Journeying on, we stopped by a gurgling spring, in a beautiful grove; and here, we stretched out on the grass, and our attendants unpacked their hampers, to provide us a lunch.

But as for that Babbalanja of ours, he must needs go and lunch by himself, and, like a cannibal, feed upon an author; though in other respects he was not so partial to bones.

Bringing forth the treasure he had buried in his bosom, he was soon buried in it; and motionless on his back, looked as if laid out, to keep an appointment with his undertaker.

"What, ho! Babbalanja!" cried Media from under a tree, "don't be a duck, there, with your bill in the air; drop your metaphysics, man, and fall to on the solids. Do you hear?"

"Come, philosopher," said Mohi, handling a banana, "you will weigh more after you have eaten."

"Come, list, Babbalanja," cried Yoomy, "I am going to sing."

"Up! up! I say," shouted Media again. "But go, old man, and wake him: rap on his head, and see whether he be in."

Mohi obeyed, found him at home; and Babbalanja started up.

"In Oro's name, what ails you, philosopher? See you Paradise, that you look so wildly?"

"A Happy Life! a Happy Life!" cried Babbalanja, in an ecstasy. "My lord, I am lost in the dream of it as here recorded. Marvelous book! its goodness transports me. Let me read—'I would bear the same mind, whether I be rich or poor, whether I get or lose in the world. I will reckon benefits well placed as the fairest part of my possession, not valuing them by number or weight, but by the profit and esteem of the receiver; accounting myself never the poorer for anything I give. What I do shall be done for conscience, not ostentation. I will eat and drink, not to gratify my palate, but to satisfy nature. I will be cheerful to my friends, mild and placable to my enemies. I will prevent an honest request, if I can foresee it; and I will grant it, without asking. I will look upon the whole world as my country; and upon Oro, both as the witness and the judge of my words and my deeds. I will live and die with this testimony: that I loved a good conscience; that I never invaded another man's liberty; and that I preserved my own. I will govern my life and my thoughts as if the whole world were to see the one, and to read the other; for what does it signify, to make anything a secret to my neighbor, when to Oro all our privacies are open.' "

"Very fine," said Media.

"The very spirit of the first followers of Alma, as recorded in the legends," said Mohi.

"Inimitable," said Yoomy.

Said Babbalanja, "Listen again—'Righteousness is sociable and gentle; free, steady, and fearless: full of inexhaustible delights.' And here again, and here, and here—'The true felicity of life is to understand our duty to Oro.'—'True joy is a serene and sober motion.' And here, and here, my lord; 'tis hard quoting from this book; but listen—'A peaceful conscience, honest thoughts, and righteous actions are blessings without end, satiety, or measure. The poor man wants many things; the covetous man, all. It is not enough to know Oro, unless we obey him.' "

"Alma all over," cried Mohi; "sure, you read from his sayings?"

"I read but odd sentences from one, who though he lived ages ago, never saw, scarcely heard of Alma. And mark me, my lord, this time I improvise nothing. What I have recited is here. Mohi, this book is more marvelous than the prophecies. My lord, that a mere man, and a heathen, in that most heathenish time, should give utterance to such heavenly wisdom, seems more wonderful than that an inspired prophet should reveal it. And is it not more divine in this philosopher, to love righteousness for its own sake, and in view of annihilation, than for pious sages to extol it as the means of everlasting felicity?"

"Alas," sighed Yoomy, "and does he not promise us any good things when we are dead?"

"He speaks not by authority. He but woos us to goodness and happiness here."

"Then, Babbalanja," said Media, "keep your treasure to yourself. Without authority, and a full right hand, Righteousness better be silent. Mardi's religion must seem to come direct from Oro, and the mass of you mortals endeavor it not, except for a consideration, present or to come."

"And call you that righteousness, my lord, which is but the price paid down for something else?"

"I called it not righteousness; it is religion so called. But let us prate no more of these things; with which I, a demi-god, have but little in common. It ever impairs my digestion. No more, Babbalanja."

"My lord! my lord! out of itself, Religion has nothing to bestow. Nor will she save us from aught, but from the evil in ourselves. Her one grand end is to make us wise; her only manifestations are reverence to Oro and love to man; her only, but ample reward, herself. He who has this, has all. He who has this, whether he kneel to an image of wood, calling it Oro; or to an image of air, calling it the same; whether he fasts or feasts; laughs or weeps—that man can be no richer. And this religion, faith, virtue, righteousness, good, whate'er you will, I find in this book I hold. No written page can teach me more."

"Have you that, then, of which you speak, Babbalanja? Are you content, there where you stand?"

"My lord, you drive me home. I am not content. The mystery of mysteries is still a mystery. How this author came to be so wise, perplexes me. How he led the life he did, confounds me. Oh, my lord, I am in darkness, and no broad blaze comes down to flood me. The rays that come to me are but faint cross lights, mazing the obscurity wherein I live. And after all, excellent as it is, I can be no gainer by this book. For the more we learn, the more we unlearn; we accumulate not, but substitute; and take away more than we add. We dwindle while we grow; we sally out for wisdom, and retreat beyond the point whence we started; we essay the Fondiza, and get but the Phe. Of all simpletons, the simplest! Oh! that I were another sort of fool than I am, that I might restore my good opinion of myself. Continually I stand in the pillory, am broken on the wheel, and dragged asunder by wild horses. Yes, yes, Bardianna, all is in a nut, as thou sayest; but all my back teeth cannot crack it; I but crack my own jaws. All round me, my fellow-men are new grafting their vines, and dwelling in flourishing arbors; while I am forever pruning mine, till it is becomes but a stump. Yet in this pruning will I persist; I will not add, I will diminish; I will train myself down to the standard of what is unchangeably true. Day by day I drop off my redundancies; ere long I shall have stripped my ribs; when I die, they will but bury my spine. Ah! where, where, where, my lord, is the everlasting Tekana? Tell me, Mohi, where the Ephina? I may have come to the Penultimate, but where, sweet Yoomy, is the Ultimate? Ah, companions! I faint, I am wordless—something—nothing—riddles—does Mardi hold her?"

"He swoons!" cried Yoomy.

"Water! water!" cried Media.

"Away!" said Babbalanja serenely, "I revive."

Chapter CXXV

THEY VISIT A WEALTHY OLD PAUPER

CONTINUING OUR ROUTE TO JIJI'S, WE PRESENTLY CAME TO A MISERABLE HOVEL. HALF PROJECTING from the low, open entrance was a bald overgrown head, intent upon an upright row of dark-colored bags—pelican pouches—prepared by dropping a stone within, and suspending them, when moist.

Ever and anon the great head shook with a tremulous motion, as one by one, to a clicking sound from the old man's mouth, the strings of teeth were slowly drawn forth, and let fall, again and again, with a rattle.

But perceiving our approach, the old miser suddenly swooped his pouches out of sight; and, like a turtle into its shell, retreated into his den. But soon he decrepitly emerged upon his knees, asking what brought us thither?—to steal the teeth, which lying rumor averred he possessed in abundance? And opening his mouth, he averred he had none; not even a sentry in his head.

But Babbalanja declared that long since he must have drawn his own dentals, and bagged them with the rest.

Now, this miserable old miser must have been idiotic; for soon forgetting what he had but just told us of his utter toothlessness, he was so smitten with the pearly mouth of Hohora, one of our attendants (the same for whose pearls little King Peepi had taken such a fancy), that he made the following overture to purchase its contents; namely, one tooth of the buyer's, for every three of the seller's. A proposition promptly rejected, as involving a mercantile absurdity.

"Why?" said Babbalanja. "Doubtless, because that proposed to be given, is less than that proposed to be received. Yet, says a philosopher, this is the very principle which regulates all barterings. For where the sense of a simple exchange of quantities, alike in value?"

"Where, indeed?" said Hohora, with open eyes, "though I never heard it before, that's a staggering question. I beseech you, who was the sage that asked it?"

"Vivo, the Sophist," said Babbalanja, turning aside.

In the hearing of Jiji, allusion was made to Oh-Oh, as a neighbor of his. Whereupon he vented much slavering opprobrium upon that miserable old humpback; who accumulated useless monstrosities; throwing away the precious teeth, which otherwise might have sensibly rattled in his own pelican pouches.

When we quitted the hovel, Jiji, marking little Vee-Vee, from whose shoulder hung a calabash of edibles, seized the hem of his garment and besought him for one mouthful of food; for nothing had he tasted that day.

The boy tossed him a yam.

Chapter CXXVI

YOOMY SINGS SOME ODD VERSES, AND BABBALANJA QUOTES FROM THE OLD AUTHORS RIGHT AND LEFT

SAILING FROM PADULLA, AFTER MANY PLEASANT THINGS HAD BEEN SAID CONCERNING THE SIGHTS there beheld, Babbalanja thus addressed Yoomy—"Warbler, the last song you sung was about moonlight, and paradise, and fabulous pleasures evermore; now, have you any hymns about earthly felicity?"

"If so, minstrel," said Media, "jet it forth, my fountain, forthwith."

"Just now, my lord," replied Yoomy, "I was singing to myself, as I often do; and by your leave, I will continue aloud."

"Better begin at the beginning, I should think," said the chronicler, both hands to his chin, beginning at the top to new braid his beard.

"No: like the roots of your beard, old Mohi, all beginnings are stiff," cried Babbalanja. "We are lucky in living midway in eternity. So sing away, Yoomy, where you left off," and thus saying, he unloosed his girdle for the song, as Apicius would for a banquet.

"Shall I continue aloud, then, my lord?"

My lord nodded, and Yoomy sang:

Full round, full soft, her dewy arms—
Sweet shelter from all Mardi's harms!

"Whose arms?" cried Mohi.

Sang Yoomy:

Diving deep in the sea,
She takes sunshine along:
Down flames in the sea,
As of dolphins a throng.

"What mermaid is this?" cried Mohi.

Sang Yoomy:

Her foot, a falling sound,
That all day long might bound.
Over the beach,
The soft sand beach,
And none would find
A trace behind.

"And why not?" demanded Media. "Why could no trace be found?"

Said Braid-Beard, "Perhaps owing, my lord, to the flatness of the mermaid's foot. But no, that cannot be; for mermaids are all vertebrae below the waist."

"Your fragment is pretty good, I dare-say, Yoomy," observed Media, "but, as Braid-Beard hints, rather flat."

"Flat as the foot of a man with his mind made up," cried Braid-Beard. "Yoomy, did you sup on flounders last night?"

But Yoomy vouchsafed no reply; he was ten thousand leagues off in a reverie: somewhere in the Hyades, perhaps.

Conversation proceeding, Braid-Beard happened to make allusion to one Rotato, a portly personage, who, though a sagacious philosopher, and very ambitious to be celebrated as such, was only famous in Mardi as the fattest man of his tribe.

Said Media, "Then, Mohi, Rotato could not pick a quarrel with Fame, since she did not belie him. Fat he was, and fat she published him."

"Right, my lord," said Babbalanja, "for Fame is not always so honest. Not seldom to be famous, is to be widely known for what you are not, says Alla-Malolla. Whence it comes, as old Bardianna has it, that for years a man may move unnoticed among his fellows; but all at once, by some chance attitude, foreign to his habit, become a trumpet-full for fools; though, in himself, the same as ever. Nor has he shown himself yet; for the entire merit of a man can never be made known; nor the sum of his demerits, if he have them. We are only known by our names; as letters sealed up, we but read each other's superscriptions.

"So with the commonalty of us Mardians. How then with those beings who every way are but too apt to be riddles. In many points the works of our great poet Vavona, now dead a thousand moons, still remain a mystery. Some call him a mystic; but wherein he seems obscure, it is, perhaps, we that are in fault; not by premeditation spoke he those archangel thoughts, which made many declare, that Vavona, after all, was but a crack-pated god, not a mortal of sound mind. But had he been less, my lord, he had seemed more. Saith Fulvi, 'Of the highest order of genius, it may be truly asserted, that to gain the reputation of superior power, it must partially disguise itself; it must come down, and then it will be applauded for soaring.' And furthermore, 'that there are those who falter in the common tongue, because they think in another; and these are accounted stutterers and stammerers.' "

"Ah! how true!" cried the Warbler.

"And what says the archangel Vavona, Yoomy, in that wonderful drama of his, *The Souls of the Sages*?—'Beyond most barren hills, there are landscapes ravishing, with but one eye to behold; which no pencil can portray.' What wonder then, my lord, that Mardi itself is so blind. 'Mardi is a monster,' says old Bardianna, 'whose eyes are fixed in its head, like a whale's; it can see but two ways, and those comprising but a small arc of a perfect vision. Poets, heroes, and men of might, are all around this monster Mardi. But stand before me on stilts, or I will behold you not, says the monster; brush back your hair; inhale the wind largely; lucky are all men with dome-like foreheads; luckless those with pippin-heads; loud lungs are a blessing; a lion is no lion that cannot roar.' Says Aldina, 'There are those looking on, who know themselves to be swifter of foot than the racers, but are confounded with the simpletons that stare.' "

"The mere carping of a disappointed cripple," cried Mohi. "His biographer states that Aldina had only one leg."

"Braid-Beard, you are witty," said Babbalanja, adjusting his robe. "My lord, there are heroes without armies, who hear martial music in their souls."

"Why not blow their trumpets louder, then," cried Media, "that all Mardi may hear?"

"My lord Media, too, is witty, Babbalanja," said Mohi.

Breathed Yoomy, "There are birds of divinest plumage and most glorious song, yet singing their lyrics to themselves."

Said Media, "The lark soars high, cares for no auditor, yet its sweet notes are heard here below. It sings, too, in company with myriads of mates. Your soliloquists, Yoomy, are mostly herons and owls."

Said Babbalanja, "Very clever, my lord; but think you not, there are men eloquent, who never babble in the marketplace?"

"Ay, and arrant babblers at home. In few words, Babbalanja, you espouse a bad cause. Most of you mortals are peacocks; some having tails and some not; those who have them will be sure to thrust their plumes in your face; for the rest, they will display their bald cruppers, and still screech for admiration. But when a great genius is born into Mardi, he nods, and is known."

"More wit, but, with deference, perhaps less truth, my lord. Say what you will, Fame is an accident; merit, a thing absolute. But what matter? Of what available value reputation, unless wedded to power, dentals or place? To those who render him applause, a poet's may seem a thing tangible; but to the recipient, 'tis a fantasy; the poet never so stretches his imagination, as when striving to comprehend what it is; often, he is famous without knowing it."

"At the sacred games of Lazella," said Yoomy, "slyly crowned from behind with a laurel fillet, for many hours, the minstrel Jarmi wandered about ignorant of the honors he bore. But enlightened at last, he doffed the wreath; then, holding it at arm's length, sighed forth, 'Oh, ye laurels! to be visible to me, ye must be removed from my brow!' "

"And what said Botargo," cried Babbalanja, "hearing that his poems had been translated into the language of the remote island of Bertranda? 'It stirs me little; already, in merry fancies, have I dreamed of their being trilled by the blessed houris in paradise; I can only imagine the same of the damsels of Bertranda.' Says Boldo, the Materialist, 'Substances alone are satisfactory.' "

"And so thought the mercenary poet, Zenzi," said Yoomy. "Upon receiving fourteen ripe yams for a sonnet, one for every line, he said to me, 'Yoomy, I shall make a better meal upon these than upon so many compliments.' "

"Ay," cried Babbalanja, " 'Bravos,' saith old Bardianna, but induce flatulency.' "

Said Media, "And do you famous mortals, then, take no pleasure in hearing your bravos?"

"Much, my good lord; at least such famous mortals, so enamored of a clamorous notoriety, as to bravo for themselves, when none else will huzza; whose whole existence is an unremitting consciousness of self; whose very persons stand erect and self-sufficient as their infallible index, the capital letter I; who relish and comprehend no reputation but what attaches to the carcass; who would as lief be renowned for a splendid mustache as for a splendid drama; who know not how it was that a personage, to posterity so universally celebrated as the poet Vavona, ever passed through the crowd unobserved; who deride the very thunder for making such a noise in Mardi, and yet disdain to manifest itself to the eye."

"Wax not so warm, Babbalanja; but tell us, if to his contemporaries Vavona's person was almost unknown, what satisfaction did he derive from his genius?"

"Had he not its consciousness?—an empire boundless as the west. What to him were huzzas? Why, my lord, from his privacy, the great and good Logodora sent liniment to the hoarse throats without. But what said Bardianna, when they dunned him for autographs? 'Who keeps the register of great men? Who decides upon noble actions? and how long may ink last? Alas! Fame has dropped more rolls than she displays: and there are more lost chronicles than the perished books of the historian Livella.' But what is lost forever, my lord, is nothing to what is now unseen. There are more treasures in the bowels of the earth than on its surface."

"Ah! no gold," cried Yoomy, "but that comes from dark mines."

Said Babbalanja, "Bear witness, ye gods! cries fervent old Bardianna, that besides disclosures of good and evil undreamed of now, there will be other, and more astounding revelations hereafter, of what has passed in Mardi unbeheld."

"A truce to your everlasting pratings of old Bardianna," said King Media. "Why not speak your own thoughts, Babbalanja? Then would your discourse possess more completeness; whereas its warp and woof are of all sorts—Bardianna, Alla-Malolla, Vavona, and all the writers that ever have written. Speak for yourself, mortal!"

"May you not possibly mistake, my lord? For I do not so much quote Bardianna, as Bardianna quoted me, though he flourished before me; and no vanity, honesty to say so. The catalogue of true thoughts is but small; they are ubiquitous; no man's property; and unspoken or bruited, are the same. When we hear them, why seem they so natural, receiving our spontaneous approval? Why do we think we have heard them before? Because they but reiterate ourselves; they were in us before we were born. The truest poets are but mouth-pieces, and some men are duplicates of each other; I see myself in Bardianna."

"And there, for Oro's sake, let it rest, Babbalanja; Bardianna in you, and you in Bardianna forever!"

Chapter CXXVII

WHAT MANNER OF MEN THE TAPPARIANS WERE

THE CANOES SAILED ON. BUT WE LEAVE THEM AWHILE. FOR OUR VISIT TO JIJI, THE LAST VISIT WE made, suggests some further revelations concerning the dental money of Mardi.

Ere this, it should have been mentioned, that throughout the Archipelago, there was a restriction concerning incisors and molars, as ornaments for the person; none but great chiefs, brave warriors, and men distinguished by rare intellectual endowments, orators, romancers, philosophers, and poets, being permitted to sport them as jewels. Though, as it happened among the poets there were many who had never a tooth, save those employed at their repasts; which, coming but seldom, their teeth almost corroded in their mouths. Hence, in commerce, poets' teeth were at a discount.

For these reasons, then, many mortals blent with the promiscuous mob of Mardians, who, by any means, accumulated teeth, were fain to assert their dental claims to distinction, by clumsily carrying their treasures in pelican pouches slung over their shoulders; which pouches were a huge burden to carry about, and defend. Though, in good truth, from any of these porters, it was harder to wrench his pouches, than his limbs. It was also a curious circumstance that at the slightest casual touch, these bags seemed to convey a simultaneous thrill to the owners.

Besides these porters, there were others, who exchanged their teeth for richly stained calabashes, elaborately carved canoes, and more especially, for costly robes, and turbans; in which last, many outshone the noblest-born nobles. Nevertheless, this answered not the end they had in view; some of the crowd only admiring what they wore, and not them; breaking out into laudation of the inimitable handiwork of the artisans of Mardi.

And, strange to relate, these artisans themselves often came to be men of teeth and turbans, sporting their bravery with the best. A circumstance, which accounted for the fact, that many of the class above alluded to, were considered capital judges of tappa and tailoring.

Hence, as a general designation, the whole tribe went by the name of Tapparians; otherwise, Men of Tappa.

Now, many moons ago, according to Braid-Beard, the Tapparians of a certain cluster of islands, seeing themselves hopelessly confounded with the plebeian race of mortals; such as artificers, honest men, bread-fruit bakers, and the like; seeing, in short, that nature had denied them every inborn mark of distinction; and furthermore, that their external assumptions were derided by so many in Mardi, these self-same Tapparians, poor devils, resolved to secede from the rabble; form themselves into a community of their own; and conventionally pay that homage to each other, which universal Mardi could not be prevailed upon to render to them.

Jointly, they purchased an island, called Pimminee, towards the extreme west of the lagoon;

and thither they went; and framing a code of laws—amazingly arbitrary, considering they themselves were the framers—solemnly took the oath of allegiance to the commonwealth thus established. Regarded section by section, this code of laws seemed exceedingly trivial; but taken together, made a somewhat imposing aggregation of particles.

By this code, the minutest things in life were all ordered after a specific fashion. More especially one's dress was legislated upon, to the last warp and woof. All girdles must be so many inches in length, and with such a number of tassels in front. For a violation of this ordinance, before the face of all Mardi, the most dutiful of sons would cut the most affectionate of fathers.

Now, though like all Mardi, kings and slaves included, the people of Pimminee had dead dust for grandsires, they seldom reverted to that fact; for, like all founders of families, they had no family vaults. Nor were they much encumbered by living connections; connections, some of them appeared to have none. Like poor Logan, the last of his tribe, they seemed to have monopolized the blood of their race, having never a cousin to own.

Wherefore it was, that many ignorant Mardians, who had not pushed their investigations into the science of physiology, sagely divined, that the Tapparians must have podded into life like peas, instead of being otherwise indebted for their existence. Certain it is, they had a comical way of backing up their social pretensions. When the respectability of his clan was mooted, Paivai, one of their bucks, disdained all reference to the Doomsday Book, and the ancients. More reliable evidence was had. He referred the anxious world to a witness, still alive and hearty—his contemporary tailor; the varlet who cut out his tappa doublets, and rejoiced his soul with good fits.

"Ah!" sighed Babbalanja, "how it quenches in one the thought of immortality, to think that these Tapparians, too, will hereafter claim each a niche!"

But we rove. Our visit to Pimminee itself will best make known the ways of its denizens.

Chapter CXXVIII

THEIR ADVENTURES UPON LANDING AT PIMMINEE

A LONG SAIL OVER, THE ISLAND OF PIMMINEE CAME IN SIGHT; ONE DEAD FIAT, WREATHED IN A thin, insipid vapor.

"My lord, why land?" said Babbalanja. "No Yillah is here."

" 'Tis my humor, Babbalanja."

Said Yoomy, "Taji would leave no isle unexplored."

As we neared the beach, the atmosphere became still closer and more languid. Much did we miss the refreshing balm which breathed in the fine breezy air of the open lagoon. Of a slender and sickly growth seemed the trees; in the meadows, the grass grew small and mincing.

Said Media, "Taji, from the accounts which Braid-Beard gives, there must be much to amuse in the ways of these Tapparians."

"Yes," said Babbalanja, "their lives are a continual farce, gratuitously performed for the diversion of Mardi. My lord, perhaps we had best doff our dignity, and land among them as persons of lowly condition; for then, we shall receive more diversion, though less hospitality."

"A good proposition," said Media.

And so saying he put off his robe for one less pretentious.

All followed suit; Yoomy doffing turban and sash; and, at last, completely metamorphosed, we looked like Hungarian gypsies.

Voyaging on, we entered a bay, where numbers of menials were standing in the water, engaged in washing the carved work of certain fantastic canoes, belonging to the Tapparians, their masters.

Landing at some distance, we followed a path that soon conducted us to a betwisted dwelling of bamboos, where, gently, we knocked for admittance. So doing, we were accosted by a servitor, his portliness all in his calves. Marking our appearance, he monopolized the threshold, and gruffly demanded what was wanted.

"Strangers, kind sir, fatigued with travel, and in need of refreshment and repose."

"Then hence with ye, vagabonds!" and with an emphasis, he closed the portal in our face.

Said Babbalanja, turning, "You perceive, my lord Media, that these varlets take after their masters; who feed none but the well-fed, and house none but the well-housed."

"Faith! but they furnish most rare entertainment, nevertheless," cried Media. "Ha! ha! Taji, we had missed much had we missed Pimminee."

As this was said, we observed, at a distance, three menials, running from seaward, as if conveying important intelligence.

Halting here and there, vainly seeking admittance at other habitations, and receiving nothing but taunts for our pains, we still wandered on; and at last came upon a village, towards which, those from the sea-side had been running.

And now, to our surprise, we were accosted by an eager and servile throng.

"Obsequious varlets," said Media, "where tarry your masters?"

"Right royal, and thrice worshipful Lord of Odo, do you take us for our domestics? We are Tapparians, may it please your illustrious Highness; your most humble and obedient servants. We beseech you, super-eminent Sir, condescend to visit our habitations, and partake of our cheer."

Then turning upon their attendants, "Away with ye, hounds! and set our dwellings in order."

"How know ye me to be king?" asked Media.

"Is it not in your serene Highness's regal port, and eye?"

" 'Twas their menials," muttered Mohi, "who from the paddlers in charge of our canoes must have learned who my lord was, and published the tidings."

After some further speech, Media made a social surrender of himself, to the foremost of the Tapparians, one Nimni; who, conducting us to his abode, with much deference introduced us to a portly old Begum, and three slender damsels; his wife and daughters.

Soon, refreshments appeared—green and yellow compounds, and divers enigmatical dainties; besides vegetable liqueurs of a strange and alarming flavor served in fragile little leaves, folded into cups, and very troublesome to handle.

Excessively thirsty, Babbalanja made bold to inquire for water; which called forth a burst of horror from the old Begum, and minor shrieks from her daughters; who declared that the beverage to which remote reference had been made, was far too widely diffused in Mardi, to be at all esteemed in Pimminee.

"But though we seldom imbibe it," said the old Begum, ceremoniously adjusting her necklace of cowrie-shells, "we occasionally employ it for medicinal purposes."

"Ah, indeed!" said Babbalanja.

"But, oh! believe me, even then, we imbibe not the ordinary fluid of the springs and streams; but that which in afternoon showers softly drains from our palm-trees into the little hollow or miniature reservoir beneath its compacted roots."

A goblet of this beverage was now handed to Babbalanja; but having a curious, gummy flavor, it proved anything but palatable.

Presently, in came a company of young men, relatives of Nimni. They were slender as sky-sail-poles; standing in a row, resembled a picket-fence; and were surmounted by enormous heads of hair, combed out all round, variously dyed, and evened by being singed with a lighted wisp of straw. Like milliners' parcels, they were very neatly done up; wearing redolent robes.

"How like the woodlands they smell," whispered Yoomy.

"Ay, marvelously like sap," said Mohi.

One part of their garniture consisted of numerous tasseled cords, like those of an aiguillette, depending from the neck, and attached here and there about the person. A separate one, at a distance, united their ankles. These served to measure and graduate their movements; keeping their gestures, paces, and attitudes, within the prescribed standards of Tapparian gentility. When they went abroad, they were preceded by certain footmen; who placed before them small, carved boards, whereon their masters stepped; thus avoiding contact with the earth. The simple device of a shoe, as a fixture for the foot, was unknown in Pimminee.

Being told that Taji was lately from the sun, they manifested not the slightest surprise; one of them incidentally observing, however, that the eclipses there must be a sad bore to endure.

Chapter CXXIX

A, I, and O

The old Begum went by the euphonious appellation of Ohiro-Moldona-Fivona; a name, from its length, deemed highly genteel; though scandal averred that it was nothing more than her real name transposed; the appellation by which she had been formerly known signifying a "Getter-up-of-Fine-Tappa." But as this would have let out an ancient secret, it was thought wise to disguise it.

Her daughters respectively reveled in the pretty diminutives of A, I, and O; which, from their brevity, comical to tell, were considered equally genteel with the dame's.

The inhabitants of the three Vowels must not he omitted. Each damsel garrisoned an ample, circular farthingale of canes, serving as the framework, whereon to display a gaily dyed robe. Perhaps their charms entrenched themselves in these impregnable petticoats, as feeble armies fly to fortresses, to hide their weakness, and better resist an onset.

But polite and politic it is, to propitiate your hostess. So seating himself by the Begum, Taji led off with earnest inquiries after her welfare. But the Begum was one of those who relieve the diffident from the embarrassment of talking; all by themselves carrying on conversation for two. Hence, no wonder that my Lady was esteemed invaluable at all assemblies in the groves of Pimminee; contributing so largely to that incessant din, which is held the best test of the enjoyment of the company, as making them deaf to the general nonsense, otherwise audible.

Learning that Taji had been making the tour of certain islands in Mardi, the Begum was surprised that he could have thus hazarded his life among the barbarians of the East. She desired to know whether his constitution was not impaired by inhaling the unrefined atmosphere of those remote and barbarous regions. For her part, the mere thought of it made her faint in her innermost citadel; nor went she ever abroad with the wind at East, dreading the contagion which might lurk in the air.

Upon accosting the three damsels, Taji very soon discovered that the tongue which had languished in the presence of the Begum, was now called into active requisition, to entertain the Polysyllables, her daughters. So assiduously were they occupied in silent endeavors to look sentimental and pretty, that it proved no easy task to sustain with them an ordinary chat. In this dilemma, Taji diffused not his remarks among all three; but discreetly centered them upon O. Thinking she might be curious concerning the sun, he made some remote allusion to that luminary as the place of his nativity. Upon which, O inquired where that country was, of which mention was made.

"Some distance from here; in the air above; the sun that gives light to Pimminee, and Mardi at large."

She replied, that if that were the case, she had never beheld it; for such was the construction of her farthingale that her head could not be thrown back, without impairing its set. Wherefore, she had always abstained from astronomical investigations.

Hereupon, rude Mohi laughed out. And that lucky laugh happily relieved Taji from all further necessity of entertaining the Vowels. For at so vulgar, and in Pimminee, so unwonted a sound as a genuine laugh, the three startled nymphs fainted away in a row, their round farthingales falling over upon each other, like a file of empty tierces. But they presently revived.

Meanwhile, without stirring from their mats, the polite young bucks in the aiguillettes did nothing but hold semi-transparent leaves to their eyes by the stems; which leaves they directed downwards, towards the disordered hems of the farthingales; in wait, perhaps, for the revelation of an ankle, and its accompaniments. What the precise use of these leaves could have been, it would be hard to say, especially as the observers invariably peeped over and under them.

The calamity of the Vowels was soon followed by the breaking up of the party; when, evening coming on, and feeling much wearied with the labor of seeing company in Pimminee, we retired to our mats; there finding that repose which ever awaits the fatigued.

Chapter CXXX

A Reception Day at Pimminee

NEXT MORNING, NIMNI APPRISED US, THAT THROUGHOUT THE DAY HE PROPOSED KEEPING OPEN house, for the purpose of enabling us to behold whatever of beauty, rank, and fashion, Pimminee could boast; including certain strangers of note from various quarters of the lagoon, who doubtless would honor themselves with a call.

As inmates of the mansion, we unexpectedly had a rare opportunity of witnessing the final toilettes of the Begum and her daughters, preparatory to receiving their guests.

Their four farthingales were placed standing in the middle of the dwelling; when their future inmates, arrayed in rudimental vestments, went round and round them, attaching various articles of finery, dyed scarves, ivory trinkets, and other decorations. Upon the propriety of this, or that adornment, the three Vowels now and then pondered apart, or together consulted. They talked and they laughed; they were silent and sad; now merry at their bravery; now pensive at the thought of the charms to be hidden.

It was O who presently suggested the expediency of an artful fold in their draperies, by the merest accident in Mardi, to reveal a tantalizing glimpse of their ankles, which were thought to be pretty.

But the old Begum was more active than any; by far the most disinterested in the matter of advice. Her great object seemed to be to pile on the finery at all hazards; and she pointed out many as yet vacant and unappropriated spaces, highly susceptible of adornment.

At last all was in readiness; when, taking a valedictory glance at their entrenchments, the Begum and damsels simultaneously dipped their heads, directly after emerging from the summit, all ready for execution.

And now to describe the general reception that followed. In came the Roes, the Fees, the Lol-Lols, the Hummee-Hums, the Bidi-Bidies, and the Dedidums; the Peenees, the Yamoyamees, the

Karkies, the Fanfums, the Diddledees, and the Fiddlefies; in a word, all the aristocracy of Pimminee; people with exceedingly short names; and some all name, and nothing else. It was an imposing array of sounds; a circulation of ciphers; a marshaling of tappas; a getting together of grimaces and furbelows; a masquerade of vapidities.

Among the crowd was a bustling somebody, one Gaddi, arrayed in much apparel to little purpose; who, singling out Babbalanja, for some time adhered to his side, and with excessive complaisance, enlightened him as to the people assembled.

"*That* is rich Marmonora, accounted a mighty man in Pimminee; his bags of teeth included, he is said to weigh upwards of fourteen stone; and is much sought after by tailors for his measure, being but slender in the region of the heart. His riches are great. And that old vrow is the widow Roo; very rich; plenty of teeth; but has none in her head. And *this* is Finfi, said to be not very rich, and a maid. Who would suppose she had ever beat tappa for a living?"

And so saying, Gaddi sauntered off; his place by Babbalanja's side being immediately supplied by the damsel Finfi. That vivacious and amiable nymph at once proceeded to point out the company where Gaddi had left off; beginning with Gaddi himself, who, she insinuated, was a mere parvenu, a terrible infliction upon society, and not near so rich as he was imagined to be.

Soon we were accosted by one Nonno, a sour, saturnine personage. "I know nobody here; not a soul have I seen before; I wonder who they all are?" And just then he was familiarly nodded to by nine worthies abreast. Whereupon Nonno vanished. But after going the rounds of the company, and paying court to many, he again sauntered by Babbalanja, saying, "Nobody, nobody; nobody but nobodies, I see nobody I know."

Advancing, Nimni now introduced many strangers of distinction, parading their titles after a fashion, plainly signifying that he was bent upon convincing us that there were people present at this little affair of his, who were men of vast reputation; and that we erred if we deemed him unaccustomed to the society of the illustrious.

But not a few of his magnates seemed shy of Media and their laurels. Especially a tall robustuous fellow, with a terrible javelin in his hand, much notched and splintered, as if it had dealt many a thrust. His left arm was gallanted in a sling, and there was a patch upon his sinister eye. Him Nimni made known as a famous captain, from King Piko's island (of which anon), who had been all but mortally wounded somewhere, in a late desperate though nameless encounter.

"Ah," said Media as this redoubtable withdrew, "Fofi is a cunning knave; a braggart, driven forth by King Piko for his cowardice. He has blent his tattooing into one mass of blue, and thus disguised, must have palmed himself off here in Pimminee, for the man he is not. But I see many more like him."

"Oh, ye Tapparians," said Babbalanja, "none so easily humbugged as humbugs. Taji, to behold this folly makes one wise. Look, look; it is all round us. Oh, Pimminee, Pimminee!"

Chapter CXXXI

Babbalanja Falleth upon Pimminee Tooth and Nail

The levee over, waiving further civilities, we took courteus leave of the Begum and Nimni, and proceeding to the beach, very soon were embarked.

When all were pleasantly seated beneath the canopy, pipes in full blast, calabashes revolving, and the paddlers quietly urging us along, Media proposed that, for the benefit of the company, someone present, in a pithy, whiffy sentence or two, should sum up the character of the Tapparians; and ended by nominating Babbalanja to that office.

"Come, philosopher, let us see in how few syllables you can put the brand on those Tapparians."

"Pardon me, my lord, but you must permit me to ponder awhile; nothing requires more time, than to be brief. An example: they say that in conversation, old Bardianna dealt in nothing but trisyllabic sentences. His talk was thunder peals: sounding reports, but long intervals."

"The devil take old Bardianna. And would that the grave-digger had buried his Ponderings, along with his other remains. Can none be in your company, Babbalanja, but you must perforce make them hob-a-nob with that old prater? A brand for the Tapparians; that is what we seek."

"You shall have it, my lord. Full to the brim of themselves, for that reason, the Tapparians are the emptiest of mortals."

"A good blow, and well planted, Babbalanja."

"In sooth, a most excellent saying; it should be carved upon his tombstone," said Mohi, slowly withdrawing his pipe.

"What! would you have my epitaph read thus—'Here lies the emptiest of mortals, who was full of himself?' At best, your words are exceedingly ambiguous, Mohi."

"Now have I the philosopher," cried Yoomy with glee. "What did someone say to me, not long since, Babbalanja, when in the matter of that sleepy song of mine, Braid-Beard bestowed upon me an equivocal compliment? Was I not told to wrest commendation from it, though I tortured it to the quick?"

"Take thy own pills, philosopher," said Mohi.

"Then would he be a great original," said Media.

"Tell me, Yoomy," said Babbalanja, "are you not in fault? Because I sometimes speak wisely, you must not imagine that I should always act so."

"I never imagined that," said Yoomy, "and, if I did, the truth would belie me. It is you who are in fault, Babbalanja; not I, craving your pardon."

"The minstrel's sides are all edges to-day," said Media.

"This, then, thrice gentle Yoomy, is what I would say," resumed Babbalanja, "that since we philosophers bestow so much wisdom upon others, it is not to be wondered at, if now and then we find what is left in us too small for our necessities. It is from our very abundance that we want."

"And from the fool's poverty," said Media, "that he is opulent; for his very simplicity, is sometimes of more account than the wisdom of the sage. But we were discoursing of the Tapparians. Babbalanja, sententiously you have acquitted yourself to admiration; now amplify, and tell us more of the people of Pimminee."

"My lord, I might amplify forever."

"Then, my worshipful lord, let him not begin," interposed Braid-Beard.

"I mean," said Babbalanja, "that all subjects are inexhaustible, however trivial; as the mathematical point, put in motion, is capable of being produced into an infinite line."

"But forever extending into nothing," said Media. "A very bad example to follow. Do you, Babbalanja, come to the point, and not travel off with it, which is too much your wont."

"Since my lord insists upon it, then, thus much for the Tapparians, though but a thought or two of many in reserve. They ignore the rest of Mardi, while they themselves are but a rumor in the isles of the East; where the business of living and dying goes on with the same uniformity, as if there were no Tapparians in existence. They think themselves Mardi in full; whereas by the mass, they are stared at as prodigies; exceptions to the law, ordaining that no Mardian shall undertake to live, unless he set out with at least the average quantity of brains. For these Tapparians have no brains. In lieu, they carry in one corner of their craniums, a drop or two of attar of roses; charily used, the supply being small. They are the victims of two incurable maladies; stone in the heart, and ossification of the head. They are full of fripperies, fopperies, and finesses; knowing not that nature should be the model of art. Yet, they might appear less silly than they do, were they content to be the plain idiots which at bottom they are. For there be grains of sense in a simpleton, so long as he be natural. But what can be expected from them? They are irreclaimable Tapparians; not so much fools by contrivance of their own, as by an express, though inscrutable decree of Oro's. For one, my lord, I cannot abide them."

Nor could Taji.

In Pimminee were no hilarious running and shouting; none of the royal good cheer of old Borabolla; none of the mysteries of Maramma; none of the sentiment and romance of Donjalolo; no rehearsing of old legends; no singing of old songs; no life; no jolly commotion: in short, no men and women; nothing but their integuments; stiff trains and farthingales.

Chapter CXXXII

Babbalanja Regales the Company with Some Sandwiches

It was night. But the moon was brilliant, far and near, illuminating the lagoon. Over silvery billows we glided.

"Come, Yoomy," said Media, "moonlight and music for aye—a song! a song! my bird of paradise."

And folding his arms, and watching the sparkling waters, thus Yoomy sang:

A ray of the moon on the dancing waves,
Is the step, light step of that beautiful maid:
Mardi, with music, her footfall paves,
And her voice, no voice, but a song in the glade.

"Hold!" cried Media, "yonder is a curious rock. It looks black as a whale's hump in blue water, when the sun shines."

"That must be the Isle of Fossils," said Mohi. "Ay, my lord, it is."

"Let us land, then," said Babbalanja.

And none dissenting, the canoes were put about, and presently we debarked.

It was a dome-like surface, here and there fringed with ferns, sprouting from clefts. But at every tide the thin soil seemed gradually washing into the lagoon.

Like antique tablets, the smoother parts were molded in strange devices—Luxor marks, Tadmor ciphers, Palenque inscriptions. In long lines, as on Denderah's architraves, were bas-reliefs of beetles, turtles, ant-eaters, armadilloes, guanos, serpents, tongueless crocodiles—a long procession, frosted and crystalized in stone, and silvered by the moon.

"Strange sight!" cried Media. "Speak, antiquarian Mohi."

But the chronicler was twitching his antiquarian beard, nonplussed by these wondrous records. The cowled old father, Piaggi, bending over his calcined Herculanean manuscripts, looked not more at fault than he.

Said Media, "Expound *you,* then, sage Babbalanja."

Muffling his face in his mantle, and his voice in sepulchral tones, Babbalanja thus:

"These are the leaves of the book of Oro. Here we read how worlds are made; here read the rise and fall of Nature's kingdoms. From where this old man's furthest histories start, these unbeginning records end. These are the secret memoirs of times past, whose evidence, at last divulged, gives the grim lie to Mohi's gossipings, and makes a rattling among the dry-bone relics of old Maramma."

Braid-Beard's old eyes flashed fire. With bristling beard, he cried, "Take back the lie you send!"

"Peace! everlasting foes," cried Media, interposing, with both arms outstretched. "Philosopher, probe not too deep. All you say is very fine, but very dark. I would know something more precise. But, prithee, ghost, unmuffle! Chatter no more! Wait till you're buried for that."

"Ay, death's cold ague will set us all shivering, my lord. We'll swear our teeth are icicles."

"Will you quit driving your sleet upon us? Have done. Expound these rocks."

"My lord, if you desire, I'll turn over these stone tablets till they're dog-eared."

"Heaven and Mardi! Go on, Babbalanja."

" 'Twas thus. These were tombs burst open by volcanic throes, and hither hurled from the lowermost vaults of the lagoon. All Mardi's rocks are one wide resurrection. But look. Here, now, a pretty story's told. Ah, little thought these grand old lords, that lived and roared before the flood, that they would come to this. Here, King Media, look and learn."

He looked, and saw a picture petrified, and plain as any on the pediments of Petra.

It seemed a stately banquet of the dead, where lords in skeletons were ranged around a board heaped up with fossil fruits, and flanked with vitreous vases, grinning like empty skulls. There they sat, exchanging rigid courtesies. One's hand was on his stony heart; his other pledged a lord, who held a hollow beaker: another sat, with earnest face beneath a mitred brow. He seemed to whisper in the ear of one who listened trustingly. But on the chest of him who wore the miter, an adder lay, close-coiled in flint.

At the further end was raised a throne, its canopy surmounted by a crown, in which now rested the likeness of a raven on an egg.

The throne was void. But half concealed by drapery, behind the goodliest lord, sideway leaned a figure, diademed, a lifted poniard in its hand—a monarch fossilized in very act of murdering his guest.

"Most high and sacred majesty!" cried Babbalanja, bowing to his feet.

While all stood gazing on this sight, came there two servitors of Media's, who besought of Babbalanja to settle a dispute concerning certain tracings upon the islet's other side.

Thither we followed them.

Upon a long layer of the slaty stone were marks of ripplings of some now waveless sea, mid which were tri-toed footprints of some huge heron, or wading fowl.

Pointing to one of which, the foremost disputant thus spoke, "I maintain that these are three toes."

"And I, that it is one foot," said the other.

"And now decide between us," joined the twain.

Said Babbalanja, starting, "Is not this the very question concerning which they made such dire contention in Maramma, whose tertiary rocks are chiseled all over with these marks? Yes; this it is concerning which they once shed blood. This it is concerning which they still divide."

"Which of us is right?" again demanded the impatient twain.

"Unite, and both are right; divide, and both are wrong. Every unit is made up of parts, as well as every plurality. Nine is three threes; a unit is as many thirds; or, if you please, a thousand thousandths; no special need to stop at thirds."

"Away, ye foolish disputants!" cried Media. "Full before you is the thing disputed."

Strolling on, many marvels did we mark; and Media said, "Babbalanja, you love all mysteries; here's a fitting theme. You have given us the history of the rock; can your sapience tell the origin of all the isles? how Mardi came to be?"

"Ah, that once mooted point is settled. Though hard at first, it proved a bagatelle. Start not, my lord; there are those who have measured Mardi by perch and pole, and with their wonted lead sounded its utmost depths. Listen, it is a pleasant story. The coral wall which circumscribes the isles, but continues upwards the deep-buried crater of the primal chaos. In the first times this crucible was charged with vapors nebulous, boiling over fires volcanic. Age by age, the fluid thickened, dropping, at long intervals, heavy sediment to the bottom; which layer on layer concreted, and at length, in crusts, rose towards the surface. Then, the vast volcano burst; rent the whole mass; upthrew the ancient rocks; which now in divers mountain tops tell tales of what existed ere Mardi was completely fashioned. Hence many fossils on the hills, whose kith and kin still lurk beneath the vales. Thus Nature works, at random warring, chaos a crater, and this world a shell."

Mohi stroked his beard.

Yoomy yawned.

Media cried, "Preposterous!"

"My lord, then take another theory—which you will—the celebrated sandwich system. Nature's first condition was a soup, wherein the agglomerating solids formed granitic dumplings, which, wearing down, deposited the primal stratum made up of series, sandwiching strange shapes of mollusks, and zoophytes; then snails, and periwinkles—marmalade to sip, and nuts to crack, ere the substantials came.

"And next, my lord, we have the fine old time of the Old Red Sandstone sandwich, clapped on the underlying layer, and among other dainties, imbedding the first course of fish—all quite in rule—sturgeon-forms, cephalaspis, glyptolepis, pterichthys; and other finny things of flavor rare, but hard to mouth for bones. Served up with these, were sundry greens—lichens, mosses, ferns, and fungi.

"Now comes the New Red Sandstone sandwich; marly and magnesious, spread over with old patriarchs of crocodiles and alligators—hard carving these—and prodigious lizards, spine-skewered, tails tied in bows, and swimming in saffron saucers."

"What next?" cried Media.

"The Ool, or Oily sandwich—rare gormandizing then; for oily it was called, because of fat old joints, and hams, and rounds, and barons of sea-beeves and walruses, which then crowned the stratum-board. All piled together, glorious profusion! fillets and briskets, rumps and saddles, and haunches, shoulder to shoulder, loin against sirloin, ribs rapping knuckles, and quarter to none. And all these sandwiched right over all that went before. Course after course, and course on course, my lord; no time to clear the wreck; no stop nor let; lay on and slash; cut, thrust, and come.

"Next the Chalk, or Coral sandwich; but no dry fare for that; made up of rich side-courses—eocene, miocene, and pliocene. The first was wild game for the delicate—bantam larks, curlews, quails, and flying weasels; with a slight sprinkling of pilaus—capons, pullets, plovers, and garnished with petrels' eggs. Very savory, that, my lord. The second side-course—miocene—was out of course, flesh after fowl—marine mammalia—seals, grampuses, and whales, served up with sea-weed on their flanks, hearts and kidneys deviled, and fins and flippers fricasseed. All very nice, my lord. The third side-course, the pliocene, was goodliest of all—whole-roasted elephants, rhinoceroses, and hippopotamuses, stuffed with boiled ostriches, condors, cassowaries, turkeys. Also barbacued mastodons and megatheriums, gallantly served up with fir-trees in their mouths, and tails cock-billed.

"Thus fared the old diluvians; arrant gormandizers and beef-bolters. We Mardians famish on the superficial strata of deposits; cracking our jaws on walnuts, filberts, cocoanuts, and clams. My lord, I've done."

"And bravely done it is. Mohi tells us that Mardi was made in six days; but you, Babbalanja, have built it up from the bottom in less than six minutes."

"Nothing for us geologists, my lord. At a word we turn you out whole systems, suns, satellites, and asteroids included. Why, my good lord, my friend Annonimo is laying out a new Milky Way, to intersect with the old one, and facilitate crosscuts among the comets."

And so saying, Babbalanja turned aside.

Chapter CXXXIII

They Still Remain upon the Rock

"Gogle-goggle, fugle-fi, fugle-fogle-orum," so hummed to himself Babbalanja, slowly pacing over the fossils.

"Is he crazy again?" whispered Yoomy.

"Are you crazy, Babbalanja?" asked Media.

"From my very birth have I been so, my lord; am I not possessed by a devil?"

"Then I'll e'en interrogate him," cried Media. "Hark ye, sirrah—why rave you thus in this poor mortal?"

" 'Tis he, not I. I am the mildest devil that ever entered man; in *propria persona,* no antlers do I wear; my tail has lost its barb, as at last your Mardian lions lose their caudal horns."

"A very sing-song devil this. But, prithee, who are you, sirrah?"

"The mildest devil that ever entered man; in *propria persona,* no antlers do I wear; my tail has lost its barb, as at last your Mardian lions lose their caudal horns."

"A very iterating devil this. Sirrah! mock me not. Know you aught yet unrevealed by Babbalanja?"

"Many things I know, not good to tell; whence they call me Azzageddi."

"A very confidential devil, this; that tells no secrets. Azzageddi, can I drive thee out?"

"Only with this mortal's ghost—together we came in, together we depart."

"A very terse and ready devil this. Whence come you, Azzageddi?"

"Whither my catechist must go—a torrid clime, cut by a hot Equator."

"A very keen and witty devil this. Azzageddi, whom have you there?"

"A right down merry, jolly set, that at a roaring furnace sit and toast their hoofs for aye; so used to flames, they poke the fire with their horns, and light their tails for torches."

"A very funny devil this. Azzageddi, is not Mardi a place far pleasanter than that from whence you came?"

"Ah, home! sweet, sweet home! would, would that I were home again!"

"A very sentimental devil this. Azzageddi, would you had a hand—I'd shake it."

"Not so with us; who, rear to rear, shake each other's tails, and courteously inquire, 'Pray, worthy sir, how now stands the great thermometer?' "

"The very prince of devils this."

"How mad our Babbalanja is," cried Mohi. "My lord, take heed, he'll bite."

"Alas! alas!" sighed Yoomy.

"Hark ye, Babbalanja," cried Media, "enough of this; doff your devil, and be a man."

"My lord, I cannot doff him; but I'll down him for a time; Azzageddi! down, imp; down, down, down! so: now, my lord, I'm only Babbalanja."

"Shall I test his sanity, my lord?" cried Mohi.

"Do, old man."

"Philosopher, our great reef is surrounded by an ocean; what think you lies beyond?"

"Alas!" sighed Yoomy, "the very subject to renew his madness."

"Peace, minstrel!" said Media. "Answer, Babbalanja."

"I will, my lord. Fear not, sweet Yoomy; you see how calm I am. Braid-Beard, those strangers, that came to Mondoldo prove isles afar, as a philosopher of old surmised, but was hooted at for his surmisings. Nor is it at all impossible, Braid-Beard, that beyond their land may exist other regions, of which those strangers know not; peopled with races something like us Mardians; but perhaps with more exalted faculties, and organs that we lack. They may have some better seeing sense than ours, perhaps, have fins or wings for arms."

"This seems not like sanity," muttered Mohi.

"A most crazy hypothesis, truly," said Media.

"And are all inductions vain?" cried Babbalanja. "Have we mortals naught to rest on, but what we see with eyes? Is no faith to be reposed in that inner microcosm, wherein we see the charted universe in little, as the whole horizon is mirrored in the iris of a gnat? Alas! alas! my lord, is there no blest Odonphi? no Astrazzi?"

"His devil's uppermost again, my lord," cried Braid-Beard.

"He's stark, stark mad!" sighed Yoomy.

"Ay, the moon's at full," said Media. "Ho, paddlers, we depart."

Chapter CXXXIV

Behind and Before

It was yet moonlight when we pushed from the islet. But soon the sky grew dun, the moon went into a cavern among the clouds, and by that secret sympathy between our hearts and the elements, the thoughts of all but Media became overcast.

Again discourse was had of that dark intelligence from Mondoldo—the fell murder of Taji's follower.

Said Mohi, "Those specter sons of Aleema must have been assassins."

"They harbored deadly malice," said Babbalanja.

"Which poor Jarl's death must now have sated," sighed Yoomy.

"Then all the happier for Taji," said Media.

"But away with gloom! because the sky is clouded, why cloud your brows? Babbalanja, I grieve the moon is gone. Yet start some paradox, that we may laugh. Say a woman is a man, or you yourself a stork."

At this they smiled. When hurtling came an arrow, which struck our stern, and quivered. Another! and another! Grazing the canopy, they darted by, and hissing, dived like red-hot bars beneath the waves.

Starting, we beheld a corruscating wake, tracking the course of a low canoe, far flying for a neighboring mountain. The next moment it was lost within the mountain's shadow and pursuit was useless.

"Let us fly!" cried Yoomy.

"Peace! What murderers these?" said Media, calmly; "whom can they seek?—you, Taji?"

"The three avengers fly three bolts," said Babbalanja.

"See if the arrow yet remains astern," cried Media.

They brought it to him.

"By Oro! Taji on the barb!"

"Then it missed its aim. But I will not mine. And whatever arrows follow, still will I hunt on. Nor does the ghost, that these pale specters would avenge, at all disquiet me. The priest I slew, but to gain her, now lost; and I would slay again to bring her back. Ah, Yillah! Yillah."

All started.

"Then," said Babbalanja, "Aleema's sons raved not; 'tis true, then, Taji, that an evil deed gained you your Yillah; no wonder she is lost."

Said Media unconcernedly, "Perhaps better, Taji, to have kept your secret; but tell no more; I care not to be your foe."

"Ah, Taji! I had shrank from you," cried Yoomy, "but for the mark upon your brow. That undoes the terror of your words. But look, the stars come forth, and who are these? A waving Iris, ay, again they come—Hautia's heralds!"

They brought a black thorn, buried in withered rose-balm blossoms, red and blue.

Said Yoomy, "For that which stings, there is no cure."

"Who, who is Hautia, that she stabs me thus?"

"And this wild sardony mocks your misery."

"Away! ye fiends."

"Again a Venus car; and lo! a wreath of strawberries! Yet fly to me, and be garlanded with joys."

"Let the wild witch laugh. She moves me not. Neither hurtling arrows nor Circe flowers appall."

Said Yoomy, "They wait reply."

"Tell your Hautia that I know her not; nor care to know. I defy her incantations; she lures in vain. Yillah! Yillah! still I hope!"

Slowly they departed; heeding not my cries no more to follow.

Silence, and darkness fell.

Chapter CXXXV

BABBALANJA DISCOURSES IN THE DARK

NEXT DAY CAME AND WENT; AND STILL WE ONWARD SAILED. AT LAST, BY NIGHT, THERE FELL A calm, becalming the water of the wide lagoon, and becalming all the clouds in heaven, veiling the constellations. But though our sails were useless, our paddlers plied their broad stout blades. Thus sweeping by a rent and hoar old rock, Vee-Vee, impatient of the calm, sprang to his crow's nest in the shark's mouth, and seizing his conch, sounded a blast which ran in and out among the hollows, reverberating with the echoes.

Be sure, it was startling. But more so with respect to one of our paddlers, upon whose shoulders, elevated Vee-Vee, his balance lost, all at once came down by the run. But the heedless little bugler himself was most injured by the fall; his arm nearly being broken.

Some remedies applied, and the company grown composed, Babbalanja thus—"My lord Media, was there any human necessity for that accident?"

"None that I know, or care to tell, Babbalanja."

"Vee-Vee," said Babbalanja, "did you fall on purpose?"

"Not I," sobbed little Vee-Vee, slinging his ailing arm in its mate.

"Woe! woe to us all, then," cried Babbalanja; "for what direful events may be in store for us which we cannot avoid!"

"How now, mortal?" cried Media; "what now?"

"My lord, think of it. Minus human inducement from without, and minus volition from within,

Vee-Vee has met with an accident, which has almost maimed him for life. Is it not terrifying to think of? Are not all mortals exposed to similar, nay, worse, calamities, ineffably unavoidable? Woe, woe, I say, to us Mardians! Here, take my last breath; let me give up this beggarly ghost!"

"Nay," said Media; "pause, Babbalanja. Turn it not adrift prematurely. Let it house till midnight; the proper time for you mortals to dissolve. But, philosopher, if you harp upon Vee-Vee's mishap, know that it was owing to nothing but his carelessness."

"And what was that owing to, my lord?"

"To Vee-Vee himself."

"Then, my lord, what brought such a careless being into Mardi?"

"A long course of generations. He's someone's great-great-grandson, doubtless; who was great-great-grandson to someone else; who also had grandsires."

"Many thanks then to your highness; for you establish the doctrine of Philosophical Necessity."

"No. I establish nothing; I but answer your questions."

"All one, my lord; you are a Necessitarian; in other words, you hold that everything takes place through absolute necessity."

"Do you take me, then for a fool and a Fatalist? Pardie! a bad creed for a monarch, the distributor of rewards and punishments."

"Right there, my lord. But, for all that, your highness is a Necessitarian, yet no Fatalist. Confound not the distinction. Fatalism presumes express and irrevocable edicts of heaven concerning particular events. Whereas, Necessity holds that all events are naturally linked, and inevitably follow each other, without providential interposition, though by the eternal letting of Providence."

"Well, well, Babbalanja, I grant it all. Go on. On high authority, we are told that in times past the fall of certain nations in Mardi was prophesied of seers."

"Most true, my lord," said Mohi, "it is all down in the chronicles."

"Ha! ha!" cried Media. "Go on, philosopher."

Continued Babbalanja, "Previous to the time assigned to their fulfillment, those prophecies were bruited through Mardi; hence, previous to the time assigned to their fulfillment, full knowledge of them may have come to the nations concerned. Now, my lord, was it possible for those nations thus forwarned, so to conduct their affairs, as at the prophesied time to prove false the events revealed to be in store for them?"

"However that may be," said Mohi, "certain it is, those events did assuredly come to pass. Compare the ruins of Babbelona with book ninth, chapter tenth, of the chronicles. Yea, yea, the owl inhabits where the seers predicted; the jackals yell in the tombs of the kings."

"Go on, Babbalanja," said Media. "Of course, those nations could not have resisted their doom. Go on, then; vault over your premises."

"If it be, then, my lord, that—"

"My very worshipful lord," interposed Mohi, "is not your philosopher getting off soundings; and may it not be impious to meddle with these things?"

"Were it so, old man, he should have known it. The King of Odo is something more than you mortals."

"But are we the great gods themselves," cried Yoomy, "that we discourse of these things?"

"No, minstrel," said Babbalanja; "and no need have the great gods to discourse of things perfectly comprehended by them, and by themselves ordained. But you and I, Yoomy, are men, and not gods; hence is it for us, and not for them, to take these things for our themes. Nor is there any impiety in the right use of our reason, whatever the issue. Smote with superstition, shall we let it wither and die out, a dead, limb to a live trunk, as the mad devotee's arm held up motionless for years? Or shall we employ it but for a paw, to help us to our bodily needs, as the brutes use their instinct? Is not reason subtle as quicksilver—live as lightning—a neighing charger to advance, but a snail to recede? Can we starve that noble instinct in us, and hope that it will survive? Better slay the body than the soul; and if it be the direst of sins to be the murderers of our own bodies, how much more to be a soul-suicide? Yoomy, we are men, we are angels. And in his faculties, high Oro is but what a man would be, infinitely magnified. Let us aspire to all things. Are we babes in the woods to be scared by the shadows on the trees? What shall appall us? If eagles gaze at the sun, may not men at the gods?"

"For one," said Media, "you may gaze at me freely. Gaze on. But talk not of my kinsmen so fluently, Babbalanja. Return to your argument."

"I go back, then, my lord. By implication, you have granted that in times past the future was foreknown of Oro; hence, in times past, the future must have been foreordained. But in all things Oro is immutable. Wherefore, our own future is foreknown and foreordained. Now, if things foreordained concerning nations have in times past been revealed to them previous to their taking place, then something similar may be presumable concerning individual men now living. That is to say, out of all the events destined to befall any one man, it is not impossible that previous knowledge of some one of these events might supernaturally come to him. Say, then, it is revealed to me, that ten days hence I shall, of my own choice, fall upon my javelin; when the time comes round, could I refrain from suicide? Grant the strongest presumable motives to the act; grant that, unforewarned, I would slay myself outright at the time appointed: yet, foretold of it, and resolved to test the decree to the uttermost, under such circumstances, I say, would it be possible for me not to kill myself? If possible, then predestination is not a thing absolute; and Heaven is wise to keep secret from us those decrees, whose virtue consists in secrecy. But if not possible, then that suicide would not be mine, but Oro's. And, by consequence, not only that act, but all my acts, are Oro's. In sum, my lord, he who believes that in times past, prophets have prophesied, and their prophecies have been fulfilled; when put to it, inevitably must allow that every man now living is an irresponsible being."

"In sooth, a very fine argument very finely argued," said Media. "You have done marvels, Babbalanja. But hark ye, were I so disposed, I could deny you all over, premises and conclusions alike. And furthermore, my cogent philosopher, had you published that anarchical dogma among my subjects in Oro, I had silenced you by my spear-headed scepter, instead of my uplifted finger."

"Then all thanks and all honor to your generosity, my lord, in granting us the immunities you did at the outset of this voyage. But, my lord, permit me one word more. Is not Oro omnipresent—absolutely everywhere?"

"So you mortals teach, Babbalanja."

"But so do they *mean,* my lord. Often do we Mardians stick to terms for ages, yet truly apply not their meanings."

"Well, Oro is everywhere. What now?"

"Then, if that be absolutely so, Oro is not merely a universal onlooker, but occupies and fills all space; and no vacancy is left for any being, or any thing but Oro. Hence Oro is *in* all things, and himself *is* all things—the time-old creed. But since evil abounds, and Oro is all things, then he cannot be perfectly good; wherefore, Oro's omnipresence and moral perfection seem incompatible. Furthermore, my lord, those orthodox systems which ascribe to Oro almighty and universal attributes every way, those systems, I say, destroy all intellectual individualities but Oro, and resolve the universe into him. But this is a heresy; wherefore, orthodoxy and heresy are one. And thus is it, my lord, that upon these matters we Mardians all agree and disagree together, and kill each other with weapons that burst in our hands. Ah, my lord, with what mind must blessed Oro look down upon this scene! Think you he discriminates between the deist and atheist? Nay; for the Searcher of the cores of all hearts well knoweth that atheists there are none. For in things abstract, men but differ in the sounds that come from their mouths, and not in the wordless thoughts lying at the bottom of their beings. The universe is all of one mind. Though my twin-brother swore to me, by the blazing sun in heaven at noon-day, that Oro is not; yet would he belie the thing he intended to express. And who lives that blasphemes? What jargon of human sounds so puissant as to insult the unutterable majesty divine? Is Oro's honor in the keeping of Mardi? Oro's conscience in man's hands? Where our warrant, with Oro's sign-manual, to justify the killing, burning, and destroying, or far worse, the social persecutions we institute in his behalf? Ah, how shall these self-assumed attorneys and vice-gerents be astounded when they shall see all heaven peopled with heretics and heathens, and all hell nodding over with miters! Ah, let us Mardians quit this insanity. Let us be content with the theology in the grass and the flower, in seed-time and harvest. Be it enough for us to know that Oro indubitably is. My lord! my lord! sick with the spectacle of the madness of men, and broken with spontaneous doubts, I sometimes see but two things in all Mardi to believe—that I myself exist, and that I can most happily, or least miserably exist, by the practice of righteousness. All else is in the clouds; and naught else may I learn, till the firmament be split from horizon to horizon. Yet, alas! too often do I swing from these moorings."

"Alas! his fit is coming upon him again," whispered Yoomy.

"Why, Babbalanja," said Media, "I almost pity you. You are too warm, too warm. Why fever your soul with these things? To no use you mortals wax earnest. No thanks, but curses will you get for your earnestness. You yourself you harm most. Why not take creeds as they come? It is not so hard to be persuaded; never mind about believing."

"True, my lord; not very hard; no act is required; only passiveness. Stand still and receive. Faith is to the thoughtless, doubts to the thinker."

"Then, why think at all? Is it not better for you mortals to clutch error as in a vice, than have your fingers meet in your hand? And to what end your eternal inquisitions? You have nothing to substitute. You say all is a lie; then out with the truth. Philosopher, your devil is but a foolish one, after all. I, a demi-god, never say nay to these things."

"Yea, my lord, it would hardly answer for Oro himself, were he to come down to Mardi, to deny men's theories concerning him. Did they not strike at the rash deity in Alma?"

"Then, why deny those theories yourself? Babbalanja, you almost affect my immortal serenity. Must you forever be a sieve for good grain to run through, while you retain but the chaff? Your tongue is forked. You speak two languages; flat folly for yourself, and wisdom for others. Babbalanja, if you have any belief of your own, keep it; but, in Oro's name, keep it secret."

"Ay, my lord, in these things wise men are spectators, not actors; wise men look on, and say 'ay.' "

"Why not say so yourself, then?"

"My lord, because I have often told you, that I am a fool, and not wise."

"Your highness," said Mohi, "this whole discourse seems to have grown out of the subject of Necessity and Free-Will. Now, when a boy, I recollect hearing a sage say that these things were reconcilable."

"Ay!" said Media; "what say you to that, now, Babbalanja?"

"It may be even so, my lord. Shall I tell you a story?"

"Azzageddi's stirring now," muttered Mohi.

"Proceed," said Media.

"King Normo had a fool, called Willi, whom he loved to humor. Now, although Willi ever obeyed his lord, by the very instinct of his servitude, he flattered himself that he was free; and this conceit it was that made the fool so entertaining to the king. One day said Normo to his fool, 'Go, Willi, to yonder tree, and wait there till I come,' 'Your Majesty, I will,' said Willi, bowing beneath his jingling bells; 'but I presume your Majesty has no objection to my walking on my hands—I am free, I hope?' 'Perfectly,' said Normo, 'hands or feet, it's all the same to me; only do my bidding.' 'I thought as much,' said Willi; so, swinging his limber legs into the air, Willi, thumb after thumb, essayed progression. But soon his bottled blood so rushed downwards through his neck, that he was fain to turn a somerset and regain his feet. Said he, 'Though I am free to do it, it's not so easy turning digits into toes; I'll walk, by gad! which is my other option.' So he went straight forward, and did King Normo's bidding in the natural way."

"A curious story that," said Media; "whence came it?"

"My lord, where everything but one is to be had—within."

"You are charged to the muzzle, then," said Braid-Beard.

"Yes, Mohi; and my talk is my overflowing, not my fullness."

"And what may you be so full of?"

"Of myself."

"So it seems," said Mohi, whisking away a fly with his beard.

"Babbalanja," said Media, "you did right in selecting this ebon night for discussing this theme of yours; and truly, you mortals are but too apt to talk in the dark."

"Ay, my lord, and we mortals may prate still more in the dark, when we are dead; for methinks, that if we then prate at all, 'twill be in our sleep. Ah! my lord, think not that in aught I've said this night, I would assert any wisdom of my own. I but fight against the armed and crested Lies of Mardi, that like a host, assail me. I am stuck full of darts; but tearing them from out me, gasping, I discharge them from whence they come."

So saying, Babbalanja slowly drooped, and fell reclining; then lay motionless as the marble Gladiator, that for centuries has been dying.

Chapter CXXXVI

My Lord Media Summons Mohi to the Stand

While slowly the night wore on, and the now scudding clouds flown past, revealed against the hosts in heaven, few words were uttered save by Media; who, when all others were most sad and silent, seemed but little moved, or not stirred a jot.

But that night, he filled his flagon fuller than his wont, and drank, and drank, and pledged the stars.

"Here's to thee, old Arcturus! To thee, old Aldebaran! whoever poised your wine-red fiery spheres on high. A health to *thee*, my regal friend, Alphacca, in the constellation of the Crown. Lo! crown to crown I pledge thee! I drink to *ye*, too, Alphard! Markab! Denebola! Capella!—to *ye*, too, sailing Cygnus! Aquila soaring!—All round, a health to all your diadems! May they never fade! nor mine!"

At last, in the shadowy east, the Dawn, like a gray, distant sail before the wind, was descried drawing nearer and nearer, till her gilded prow was perceived.

And as in tropic gales, the winds blow fierce, and more fierce, with the advent of the sun; so with King Media, whose mirth now breezed up afresh. But, as at sunrise, the sea-storm only blows harder, to settle down at last into a steady wind; even so, in good time, my lord Media came to be more decorous of mood. And Babbalanja abated his reveries.

For who might withstand such a morn!

As on the night-banks of the far-rolling Ganges, the royal bridegroom sets forth for his bride, preceded by nymphs, now this side, now that, lighting up all the flowery flambeaux held on high as they pass; so came the Sun, to his nuptials with Mardi; the Hours going on before touching all the peaks, till they glowed rosy-red.

By reflex, the lagoon, here and there, seemed on fire; each curling wave-crest a flame.

Noon came as we sailed.

And now, citrons and bananas, cups and calabashes, calumets and tobacco, were passed round; and we were all very merry and mellow indeed. Smacking our lips, chatting, smoking, and sipping. Now a mouthful of citron to season a repartee; now a swallow of wine to wash down a precept; now a fragrant whiff to puff away care. Many things did beguile. From side to side, we turned and grazed like Juno's white oxen in clover meads.

Soon we drew nigh to a charming cliff, overrun with woodbines, on high suspended from flowering Tamarisk and Tamarind-trees. The blossoms of the Tamarisks, in spikes of small, red bells; the Tamarinds, wide-spreading their golden petals, red-streaked as with streaks of the dawn. Down sweeping to the water, the vines trailed over to the crisp, curling waves, little pages, all eager to hold up their trains.

Within was a bower; going behind it, like standing inside the sheet of the falls of the Genesee.

In this arbor we anchored. And with their shaded prows thrust in among the flowers, our three canoes seemed baiting by the way, like wearied steeds in a hawthorn lane.

High midsummer noon is more silent than night. Most sweet a siesta then. And noon-dreams are day-dreams indeed; born under the meridian sun. Pale Cynthia begets pale specter shapes; and her frigid rays best illuminate white nuns, marble monuments, icy glaciers and cold tombs.

The sun rolled on. And starting to his feet, arms clasped, and wildly staring, Yoomy exclaimed, "Nay, nay, thou shalt not depart, thou maid! here, here, I fold thee for aye! Flown? A dream! Then siestas henceforth while I live. And at noon, every day will I meet thee, sweet maid! And, oh! Sun! set not; and poppies bend over us, when next we embrace!"

"What ails that somnambulist?" cried Media, rising. "Yoomy, I say! what ails thee?"

"He must have indulged over freely in those citrons," said Mohi, sympathetically rubbing his fruitery. "Ho, Yoomy! a swallow of brine will help thee."

"Alas," cried Babbalanja, "do the fairies then wait on repletion? Do our dreams come from below, and not from the skies? Are we angels, or dogs? Oh, Man, Man, Man! thou art harder to solve than the Integral Calculus—yet plain as a primer; harder to find than the philosopher's stone—yet ever at hand; a more cunning compound than an alchemist's—yet a hundredweight of flesh, to a pennyweight of spirit; soul and body glued together, firm as atom to atom, seamless as the vestment without joint, warp or woof—yet divided as by a river, spirit from flesh; growing both ways, like a tree, and dropping thy topmost branches to earth, like thy beard or a banian! I give thee up, oh, Man! thou art twain—yet indivisible; all things—yet a poor unit at best."

"Philosopher you seem puzzled to account for the riddles of your race," cried Media, sideways reclining at his ease. "Now, do thou, old Mohi, stand up before a demi-god, and answer for all. Draw nigh, so I can eye thee. What art thou, mortal?"

"My worshipful lord, a man."

"And what are men?"

"My lord, before thee is a specimen."

"I fear me, my lord will get nothing out of that witness," said Babbalanja. "Pray you, King Media, let another inquisitor cross-question."

"Proceed; take the divan."

"A pace or two farther off there, Mohi; so I can garner thee all in at a glance. Attention! Rememberest thou, fellow-being, when thou wast born?"

"Not I. Old Braid-Beard had no memory then."

"When, then, wast thou first conscious of being?"

"What time I was teething: my first sensation was an ache."

"What dost thou, fellow-being, here in Mardi?"

"What doth Mardi here, fellow-being, under me?"

"Philosopher, thou gainest but little by thy questions," cried Yoomy, advancing. "Let a poet endeavor."

"I abdicate in your favor, then, gentle Yoomy; let me smooth the divan for you; there: be seated."

"Now, Mohi, who art thou?" said Yoomy, nodding his bird-of-paradise plume.

"The sole witness, it seems, in this case."

"Try again, minstrel," cried Babbalanja.

"Then, what art thou, Mohi?"

"Even what thou art, Yoomy."

"He is too sharp or too blunt for us all," cried King Media. "His devil is even more subtle than yours, Babbalanja. Let him go."

"Shall I adjourn the court then, my lord?" said Babbalanja.

"Ay."

"Oyez! Oyez! Oyez! All mortals having business at this court, know ye, that it is adjourned till sundown of the day which hath no to-morrow."

Chapter CXXXVII

Wherein Babbalanja and Yoomy Embrace

How the isles grow and multiply around us!" cried Babbalanja, as turning the bold promontory of an uninhabited shore, many distant lands bluely loomed into view. "Surely, our brief voyage may not embrace all Mardi like its reef?"

"No," said Media, "much must be left unseen. Nor everywhere can Yillah be sought, noble Taji."

Said Yoomy, "We are as birds, with pinions clipped, that in unfathomable and endless woods but flit from twig to twig of one poor tree."

"More isles! more isles!" cried Babbalanja, erect, and gazing abroad. "And lo! round all is heaving that infinite ocean. Ah! gods! what regions lie beyond?"

"But whither now?" he cried, as in obedience to Media, the paddlers suddenly altered our course.

"To the bold shores of Diranda," said Media.

"Ay: the land of clubs and javelins, where the lord seigniors Hello and Piko celebrate their famous games," cried Mohi.

"Your clubs and javelins," said Media, "remind me of the great battle-chant of Narvi.—Yoomy!"—turning to the minstrel, gazing abstractedly into the water, "Awake, Yoomy, and give us the lines."

"My lord Media, 'tis but a rude, clanging thing, dissonant as if the north wind blew through it. Methinks the company will not fancy lines so inharmonious. Better sing you, perhaps, one of my sonnets."

"Better sit and sob in our ears, silly Yoomy that thou art!—no! none of your sentiment now; my soul is martially inclined; I want clarion peals, not lute warblings. So throw out your chest, Yoomy, lift high your voice, and blow me the old battle-blast. Begin, sir minstrel."

And warning all that he himself had not composed the odious chant, Yoomy thus:

Our clubs! our clubs!
The thousand clubs of Narvi!
Of the living trunk of the Palm-tree made;
Skull breakers! Brain spatterers!
Wielded right, and wielded left;
Life quenchers! Death dealers!
Causing live bodies to run headless!

Our bows! our bows!
The thousand bows of Narvi!
Ribs of Tara, god of War!
Fashioned from the light Tola their arrows;
Swift messengers! Heart piercers!
Barbed with sharp pearl shells;
Winged with white tail-plumes;
To wild death-chants, strung with the hair of wild maidens!

Our spears! our spears!
The thousand spears of Narvi!
Of the thunder-riven Moo-tree made:
Tall tree, couched on the long mountain Lana!
No staves for gray-beards! no rods for fishermen!
Tempered by fierce sea-winds,
Splintered into lances by lightnings,
Long arrows! Heart seekers!
Toughened by fire their sharp black points!

Our slings! our slings!
The thousand slings of Narvi!
All tasseled, and braided, and gaily bedecked.
In peace, our girdles; in war, our war-nets;
Wherewith catch we heads as fish from the deep!
The pebbles they hurl, have been hurled before—
Hurled up on the beach by the stormy sea!
Pebbles, buried erewhile in the head of the shark:
To be buried erelong in the heads of our foes!
Home of hard blows, our pouches!
Nest of death-eggs! How quickly they hatch!

Uplift, and couch we our spears, men!
Ring hollow on the rocks our war clubs!
Bend we our bows, feel the points of our arrows:
Aloft, whirl in eddies our sling-nets;
To the fight, men of Narvi!
Sons of battle! Hunters of men!
Raise high your war-wood!
Shout Narvi! her groves in the storm!

"By Oro!" cried Media, "but Yoomy has well nigh stirred up all Babbalanja's devils in me. Were I a mortal, I could fight now on a pretense. And did any man say me nay, I would charge upon him like a spear-point. Ah, Yoomy, thou and thy tribe have much to answer for; ye stir up all Mardi with your lays. Your war chants make men fight; your drinking songs, drunkards; your love ditties, fools. Yet there thou sittest, Yoomy, gentle as a dove. What art thou, minstrel, that thy soft, singing soul should so master all mortals? Yoomy, like me, you sway a scepter."

"Thou honorest my calling overmuch," said Yoomy; "we minstrels but sing our lays carelessly, my lord Media."

"Ay; and the more mischief they make."

"But sometimes we poets are didactic."

"Didactic and dull; many of ye are but too apt to be prosy unless mischievous."

"Yet in our verses, my lord Media, but few of us purpose harm."

"But when all harmless to yourselves, ye may be otherwise to Mardi."

"And are not foul streams often traced to pure fountains, my lord?" said Babbalanja. "The essence of all good and all evil is in us, not out of us. Neither poison nor honey lodgeth in the flowers on which, side by side, bees and wasps oft alight. My lord, nature is an immaculate virgin, forever standing unrobed before us. True poets but paint the charms which all eyes behold. The vicious would be vicious without them."

"My lord Media," impetuously resumed Yoomy, "I am sensible of a thousand sweet, merry fancies, limpid with innocence; yet my enemies account them all lewd conceits."

"There be those in Mardi," said Babbalanja, "who would never ascribe evil to others, did they not find it in their own hearts; believing none can be different from themselves."

"My lord, my lord!" cried Yoomy, "the air that breathes my music from me is a mountain air! Purer than others am I; for though not a woman, I feel in me a woman's soul."

"Ah! have done, silly Yoomy," said Media. "Thou are becoming flighty, even as Babbalanja, when Azzageddi is uppermost."

"Thus ever—ever thus!" sighed Yoomy. "They comprehend us not."

"Nor me," said Babbalanja. "Yoomy: poets both, we differ but in seeming; thy airiest conceits are as the shadows of my deepest ponderings; though Yoomy soars, and Babbalanja dives, both meet at last. Not a song you sing, but I have thought its thought; and where dull Mardi sees but your rose, I unfold its petals, and disclose a pearl. Poets are we, Yoomy, in that we dwell without us. We live in grottoes, palms, and brooks; we ride the sea, we ride the sky; poets are omnipresent."

Chapter CXXXVIII

OF THE ISLE OF DIRANDA

IN GOOD TIME THE SHORES OF DIRANDA WERE IN SIGHT. AND INTRODUCTORY TO LANDING, BRAID-Beard proceeded to give us some little account of the island and its rulers.

As previously hinted, those very magnificent and illustrious lord seigniors, the lord seigniors Hello and Piko, who between them divided Diranda, delighted in all manner of public games, especially war-like ones; which last were celebrated so frequently, and were so fatal in their results, that, notwithstanding the multiplicity of nuptials taking place in the isle, its population remained in equilibrio. But, strange to relate, this was the very object which the lord seigniors had in view; the very object they sought to compass by instituting their games. Though, for the most part, they wisely kept the secret locked up.

But to tell how the lord seigniors Hello and Piko came to join hands in this matter.

Diranda had been amicably divided between them ever since the day they were crowned; one reigning king in the east, the other in the west. But King Piko had been long harassed with the thought that the unobstructed and indefinite increase of his browsing subjects might eventually denude of herbage his portion of the island. Posterity, thought he, is marshaling her generations in squadrons, brigades, and battalions, and ere long will be down upon my devoted empire. Lo! her locust cavalry darken the skies; her light-troop pismires cover the earth. Alas! my son and successor, thou wilt inhale choke-damp for air, and have not a private corner to say thy prayers.

By a sort of arithmetical progression, the probability, nay, the certainty of these results, if not in some way averted, was proved to King Piko; and he was furthermore admonished, that war—war to the haft with King Hello—was the only cure for so menacing an evil.

But so it was that King Piko at peace with King Hello, and well content with the tranquillity of the times, little relished the idea of picking a quarrel with his neighbor, and running its risks in order to phlebotomize his redundant population.

"Patience, most illustrious seignior," said another of his sagacious Ahithophels, "and haply a pestilence may decimate the people."

But no pestilence came. And in every direction the young men and maidens were recklessly rushing into wedlock; and so salubrious the climate, that the old men stuck to the outside of the turf, and refused to go under.

At last, some Machiavel of a philosopher suggested that peradventure the object of war might be answered without going to war; that peradventure King Hello might be brought to acquiesce in an arrangement, whereby the men of Diranda might be induced to kill off one another voluntarily, in a peaceable manner, without troubling their rulers. And to this end the games before-mentioned were proposed.

"Egad! my wise ones, you have hit it," cried Piko; "but will Hello say ay?"

"Try him, most illustrious seignior," said Machiavel.

So to Hello went ambassadors ordinary and extraordinary, and ministers plenipotentiary and peculiar; and anxiously King Piko awaited their return.

The mission was crowned with success.

Said King Hello to the ministers, in confidence:

"The very thing, Dons, the very thing I have wanted. My people are increasing too fast. They keep up the succession too well. Tell your illustrious master it's a bargain. The games! the games! by all means."

So, throughout the island, by proclamation, they were forthwith established; succeeding to a charm.

And the lord seigniors, Hello and Piko, finding their interests the same, came together like bride and bridegroom; lived in the same palace; dined off the same cloth; cut from the same breadfruit; drank from the same calabash; wore each other's crowns; and often locking arms with a charming frankness, paced up and down in their dominions, discussing the prospect of the next harvest of heads.

In his old-fashioned way, having related all this, with many other particulars, Mohi was interrupted by Babbalanja, who inquired how the people of Diranda relished the games, and how they fancied being coolly thinned out in that manner.

To which in substance the chronicler replied, that of the true object of the games, they had not the faintest conception; but hammered away at each other, and fought and died together, like jolly good fellows.

"Right again, immortal old Bardianna!" cried Babbalanja.

"And what has the sage to the point this time?" asked Media.

"Why, my lord, in his chapter on 'Cracked Crowns,' Bardianna, after many profound ponderings, thus concludes: 'In this cracked sphere we live in, then, cracked skulls would seem the inevitable allotments of many. Nor will the splintering thereof cease, till this pugnacious animal we treat of be deprived of his natural maces, videlicet, his arms. And right well doth man love to bruise and batter all occiputs in his vicinity.' "

"Seems to me our old friend must have been on his stilts that time," interrupted Mohi.

"No, Braid-Beard. But by way of apologizing for the unusual rigidity of his style in that chapter, he says in a note, that it was written upon a straight-backed settle, when he was ill of a lumbago, and a crick in the neck."

"That incorrigible Azzageddi again," said Media.

"Proceed with your quotation, Babbalanja."

"Where was I, Braid-Beard?"

"Battering occiputs at the last accounts," said Mohi.

"Ah, yes. 'And right well doth man love to bruise and batter all occiputs in his vicinity; he but follows his instincts; he is but one member of a fighting world. Spiders, vixens, and tigers all war with a relish; and on every side are heard the howls of hyenas, the throttlings of mastiffs, the din of belligerant beetles, the buzzing warfare of the insect battalions, and the shrill cries of lady Tartars rending their lords. And all this existeth of necessity. To war it is, and other depopulators, that we are beholden for elbow-room in Mardi, and for all our parks an gardens, wherein we are wont to expatiate. Come on, then, plague, war, famine, and viragos! Come on, I say, for who shall stay ye? Come on, and healthfulize the census! And more especially, oh War! do thou march forth with thy bludgeon! Cracked are our crowns by nature, and henceforth forever cracked shall they be by hard raps.' "

"And hopelessly cracked the skull that hatched such a tirade of nonsense," said Mohi.

"And think you not, old Bardianna knew that?" asked Babbalanja. "He wrote an excellent chapter on that very subject."

"What, on the cracks in his own pate?"

"Precisely. And expressly asserts that to those identical cracks was he indebted for what little light he had in his brain."

"I yield, Babbalanja; your old Ponderer is older than I."

"Ay, ay, Braid-Beard; his crest was a tortoise; and this was the motto, 'I bite, but am not to be bitten.' "

Chapter CXXXIX

They Visit the Lords Piko and Hello

In good time, we landed at Diranda. And that landing was like landing at Greenwich among the Waterloo pensioners. The people were docked right and left; some without arms, some without legs; not one with a tail; but, to a man, all had heads, though rather the worse for wear; covered with lumps and contusions.

Now, those very magnificent and illustrious lord seigniors, the lord seigniors Hello and Piko, lived in a palace, round which was a fence of the cane called Malacca, each picket helmed with a skull, of which there were fifty, one to each cane. Over the door were the blended arms of the high and mighty houses of Hello and Piko; a Clavicle crossed over an Ulna.

Escorted to the sign of the Skull-and-Cross-Bones, we received the very best entertainment which that royal inn could afford. We found our hosts Hello and Piko seated together on a dais or throne, and now and then drinking some claret-red wine from an ivory bowl, too large to have been wrought from an elephant's tusk. They were in glorious good spirits, shaking ivory coins in a skull.

"What says your majesty?" said Piko; "heads or tails?"

"Oh, heads, your majesty," said Hello.

"And heads say I," said Piko.

And heads it was. But it was heads on both sides, so both were sure to win.

And thus they were used to play merrily all day long, beheading the gourds of claret by one slicing blow with their sickle-shaped scepters. Wide round them lay empty calabashes, all feathered, red dyed, and betasseled, trickling red wine from their necks, like the decapitated pullets in the old baronial barn-yard at Kenilworth, the night before Queen Bess dined with my lord Leicester.

The first compliments over, and Media and Taji having met with a reception suitable to their rank, the kings inquired whether there were any good javelin-flingers among us; for if that were the case, they could furnish them plenty of sport. Informed, however, that none of the party were professional warriors, their majesties looked rather glum, and by way of chasing away the blues, called for some good old stuff that was red.

It seems, this soliciting guests, to keep their spears from decaying, by cut and thrust play with their subjects, was a very common thing with their illustrious majesties. But if their visitors could not be prevailed upon to spear a subject or so, our hospitable hosts resolved to have a few speared, and otherwise served up for our special entertainment. In a word, our arrival furnished a fine pretext for renewing their games; though, we learned, that only ten days previous, upwards of fifty combatants had been slain at one of these festivals.

Be that as it might, their joint majesties determined upon another one; and also upon our tarrying to behold it.

We objected, saying we must depart.

But we were kindly assured that our canoes had been dragged out of the water, and buried in a wood, there to remain till the games were over.

The day fixed upon was the third subsequent to our arrival; the interval being devoted to preparations; summoning from their villages and valleys the warriors of the land, and publishing the royal proclamations, whereby the unbounded hospitality of the kings' household was freely offered to all heroes whatsoever, who for the love of arms, and the honor of broken heads, desired to cross battle clubs, hurl spears, or die game in the royal valley of Deddo.

Meantime, the whole island was in a state of uproarious commotion, and strangers were daily arriving.

The spot set apart for the festival was a spacious down, mantled with white asters; which, waving in windrows, lay upon the land like the cream-surf surging the milk of young heifers. But that whiteness, here and there, was spotted with strawberries; tracking the plain, as if wounded creatures had been dragging themselves bleeding from some deadly encounter. All round the down, waved scarlet thickets of sumach, moaning in the wind, like the gory ghosts environing Pharsalia the night after the battle; scaring away the peasants, who, with bushel-baskets came to the jewel-harvest of the rings of Pompey's knights.

Beneath the heaped turf of this down, lay thousands of glorious corpses of anonymous heroes, who here had died glorious deaths.

Whence, in the florid language of Diranda, they called this field "The Field of Glory."

Chapter CXL

THEY ATTEND THE GAMES

AT LAST THE THIRD DAY DAWNED; AND FACING US UPON ENTERING THE PLAIN WAS A THRONE OF red logwood, canopied by the foliage of a red-dyed Pandannus. Upon this throne, purple-robed, reclined those very magnificent and illustrious lords seigniors, the lord seigniors Hello and Piko. Before them were many gourds of wine; and crosswise, staked in the sod, their own royal spears.

In the middle of the down, as if by a furrow, a long, oval space was margined off, about which a crowd of spectators were seated. Opposite the throne was reserved a clear passage to the arena, defined by air-lines, indefinitely produced from the leveled points of two spears, so poised by a brace of warriors.

Drawing near, our party was courteously received, and assigned a commodious lounge.

The first encounter was a club-fight between two warriors. Nor casque of steel, nor skull of Congo could have resisted their blows, had they fallen upon the mark; for they seemed bent upon driving each other, as stakes, into the earth. Presently one of them faltered; but his adversary, rushing in to cleave him down, slipped against a guava rind; when the falterer, with one lucky blow, high into the air sent the stumbler's club, which descended upon the crown of a spectator, who was borne from the plain.

"All one," muttered Piko.

"As good dead as another," muttered Hello.

The second encounter was a hugging-match; wherein two warriors, masked in grisly-bear skins, hugged each other to death.

The third encounter was a bumping-match between a fat warrior and a dwarf. Standing erect, his paunch like a bass-drum before a drummer, the fat man was run at, head-a-tilt by the dwarf, and sent spinning round on his axis.

The fourth encounter was a tussle between two-score warriors, who all in a mass, writhed like the limbs in Sebastian's painting of Hades. After obscuring themselves in a cloud of dust, these combatants, uninjured, but hugely blowing, drew off; and separately going among the spectators, rehearsed their experience of the fray.

"Braggarts!" mumbled Piko.

"Poltroons!" growled Hello.

While the crowd were applauding, a sober-sided observer, trying to rub the dust out of his eyes, inquired of an enthusiastic neighbor, "Pray, what was all that about?"

"Fool! saw you not the dust?"

"That I did," said Sober-Sides, again rubbing his eyes, "But I can raise a dust myself."

The fifth encounter was a fight of single-sticks between one hundred warriors, fifty on a side.

In a line, the first fifty emerged from the sumachs, their weapons interlocked in a sort of wicker-work. In advance marched a priest bearing an idol with a cracked cocoanut for a head—Krako, the god of Trepans. Preceded by damsels flinging flowers, now came on the second fifty, gaily appareled, weapons poised, and their feet nimbly moving in a martial measure.

Midway meeting, both parties touched poles, then retreated. Very courteous, this; but tantamount to bowing each other out of Mardi; for, upon Piko's throwing a javelin, they rushed in, and each striking his man, all fell to the ground.

"Well done!" cried Piko.

"Brave fellows!" cried Hello.

"But up and at it again, my heroes!" joined both. "Lo! we kings look on, and there stand the bards!"

These bards were a row of lean, sallow, old men, in threadbare robes, and chaplets of dead leaves.

"Strike up!" cried Piko.

"A stave!" cried Hello.

Whereupon, the old croakers, each with a quinsy, sang thus in cracked strains:

Quack! Quack! Quack!
With a toorooloo whack;
Hack away, merry men, hack away.
Who would not die brave,
His ear smote by a stave?
Thwack away, merry men, thwack away!
'Tis glory that calls,
To each hero that falls,
Hack away, merry men, hack away!
Quack! Quack! Quack!
Quack! Quack!
Quack!

Thus it tapered away.

"Ha, ha!" cried Piko, "how they prick their ears at that!"

"Hark ye, my invincibles!" cried Hello. "That pean is for the slain. So all ye who have lives left, spring to it! Die and be glorified! Now's the time! Strike up again, my ducklings!"

Thus incited, the survivors staggered to their feet; and hammering away at each other's sconces, till they rung like a chime of bells going off with a triple-bob-major, they finally succeeded in immortalizing themselves by quenching their mortalities all round; the bards still singing.

"Never mind your music now," cried Piko.

"It's all over," said Hello.

"What valiant fellows we have for subjects," cried Piko.

"Ho! grave-diggers, clear the field," cried Hello.

"Who else is for glory?" cried Piko.

"There stand the bards!" cried Hello.

But now there rushed among the crowd a haggard figure, trickling with blood, and wearing a robe, whose edges were burned and blacked by fire. Wielding a club, it ran to and fro, with loud yells menacing all.

A noted warrior this; who, distracted at the death of five sons slain in recent games, wandered from valley to valley, wrestling and fighting.

With wild cries of "The Despairer! The Despairer!" the appalled multitude fled; leaving the two kings frozen on their throne, quaking and quailing, their teeth rattling like dice.

The Despairer strode towards them; when, recovering their senses, they ran; for a time pursued through the woods by the phantom.

Chapter CXLI

TAJI STILL HUNTED, AND BECKONED

PREVIOUS TO THE KINGS' FLIGHT, WE HAD PLUNGED INTO THE NEIGHBORING WOODS; AND FROM thence emerging, entered brakes of cane, sprouting from morasses. Soon we heard a whirring, as if three startled partridges had taken wing; it proved three feathered arrows, from three unseen hands.

Gracing us, two buried in the ground; but from Taji's arm, the third drew blood.

On all sides round we turned, but none were seen.

"Still the avengers follow," said Babbalanja.

"Lo! the damsels three!" cried Yoomy. "Look where they come!"

We joined them by the sumach wood's red skirts; and there, they waved their cherry stalks, and heavy bloated cactus leaves, their crimson blossoms armed with nettles; and before us flung shining, yellow, tiger-flowers spotted red.

"Blood!" cried Yoomy, starting, "and leopards on your track!"

And now the sirens blew through long reeds, tasseled with their pannicles, and waving verdant scarves of vines, came dancing towards us, proffering clustering grapes.

"For all now yours, Taji; and all that yet may come," cried Yoomy, "fly to me! I will dance away your gloom, and drown it in inebriation."

"Away! woe is its own wine. What may be mine, that will I endure, in its own essence to the quick. Let me feel the poniard if it stabs."

They vanished in the wood; and hurrying on, we soon gained sunlight, and the open glade.

Chapter CXLII

THEY EMBARK FROM DIRANDA

ARRIVED AT THE SIGN OF THE SKULLS, WE FOUND THE ILLUSTRIOUS LORD SEIGNIORS AT REST from their flight, and once more quaffing their claret, all thoughts of the specter departed. Instead of rattling their own ivory in the heads on their shoulders, they were rattling their dice in the skulls in their hands. And still "Heads" was the cry, and "Heads" was the throw.

That evening they made known to my lord Media that an interval of two days must elapse ere the games were renewed, in order to reward the victors, bury their dead, and provide for the execution of an islander, who, under the provocation of a blow, had killed a stranger.

As this suspension of the festivities had been wholly unforeseen, our hosts were induced to withdraw the embargo laid upon our canoes. Nevertheless, they pressed us to remain; saying that what was to come would far exceed in interest what had already taken place. The games in prospect being of a naval description, embracing certain hand-to-hand contests in the water between shoals of web-footed warriors.

However, we decided to embark on the morrow.

It was in the cool of the early morning, at that hour when a man's face can be just known, that we set sail from Diranda; and in the ghostly twilight, our thoughts reverted to the phantom that so suddenly had cleared the plain. With interest we hearkened to the recitals of Mohi; who, discoursing of the sad end of many brave chieftains in Mardi, made allusion to the youthful Adondo, one of the most famous of the chiefs of the chronicles. In a canoe fight, after performing prodigies of valor, he was wounded in the head, and sunk to the bottom of the lagoon.

"There is a noble monody upon the death of Adondo," said Yoomy. "Shall I sing it, my lord? It is very beautiful; nor could I ever repeat it without a tear."

"We will dispense with your tears, minstrel," said Media; "but sing it, if you will."

And Yoomy sang:

Departed the pride, and the glory of Mardi:
The vaunt of her isles sleeps deep in the sea,
That rolls o'er his corse with a hush.
His warriors bend over their spears,
His sisters gaze upwards and mourn.
Weep, weep, for Adondo is dead!

The sun has gone down in a shower;
Buried in clouds in the face of the moon;
Tears stand in the eyes of the starry skies,
And stand in the eyes of the flowers;
And streams of tears are the trickling brooks,
Coursing adown the mountains.—
Departed the pride, and the glory of Mardi:
The vaunt of her isles sleeps deep in the sea.
Fast falls the small rain on its bosom that sobs—
Not showers of rain, but the tears of Oro.

"A dismal time it must have been," yawned Media; "not a dry brook then in Mardi, not a lake that was not moist. Lachrymose rivulets, and inconsolable lagoons! Call you this poetry, minstrel?"

"Mohi has something like a tear in his eye," said Yoomy.

"False!" cried Mohi, brushing it aside.

"Who composed that monody?" said Babbalanja, "I have often heard it before."

"None know, Babbalanja; but the poet must be still singing to himself; his songs bursting through the turf, in the flowers over his grave."

"But gentle Yoomy, Adondo is a legendary hero, indefinitely dating back. May not his monody, then, be a spontaneous melody, that has been with us since Mardi began? What bard composed the soft verses that our palm boughs sing at even? Nay, Yoomy, that monody was not written by man."

"Ah! Would that I had been the poet, Babbalanja; for then had I been famous indeed; those lines are chanted through all the isles, by prince and peasant. Yes, Adondo's monody will pervade the ages, like the low undertone you hear, when many singers do sing."

"My lord, my lord," cried Babbalanja, "but this were to be truly immortal; to be perpetuated in our works, and not in our names. Let me, oh, Oro! be anonymously known!"

Chapter CXLIII

WHEREIN BABBALANJA DISCOURSES OF HIMSELF

AN INTERVAL OF SILENCE WAS AT LAST BROKEN BY BABBALANJA.

Pointing to the sun, just gaining the horizon, he exclaimed, "As old Bardianna says—shut your eyes, and believe."

"And what may Bardianna have to do with yonder orb?" said Media.

"This much, my lord, the astronomers maintain that Mardi moves round the sun; which I, who never formally investigated the matter for myself, can by no means credit; unless, plainly seeing one thing, I blindly believe another. Yet even thus blindly does all Mardi subscribe to an astronomical system, which not one in fifty thousand can astronomically prove. And not many centuries back, my lord, all Mardi did equally subscribe to an astronomical system, precisely the reverse of that which they now believe. But the mass of Mardians have not as much reason to believe the first system as the exploded one; for all who have eyes must assuredly see, that the sun seems to move, and that Mardi seems a fixture, eternally *here*. But doubtless there are theories which may be true, though the face of things belie them. Hence, in such cases, to the ignorant, disbelief would seem more natural than faith; though they too often reject the testimony of their own senses, for what to them is a mere hypothesis. And thus, my lord, is it that the masts of Mardians do not believe because they know, but because they know *not*. And they are as ready to receive one thing as another, if it comes from a canonical source. My lord, Mardi is as an ostrich, which will swallow aught you offer, even a bar of iron if placed end-wise. And though the iron be indigestible, yet it serves to fill: in feeding, the end proposed. For Mardi must have something to exercise its digestion, though that something be forever indigestible. And as fishermen, for sport throw two lumps of bait, united by a cord, to albatrosses floating on the sea; which are greedily attempted to be swallowed, one lump by this fowl, the other by that; but forever are kept reciprocally going up and down in them, by means of the cord; even so, my lord, do I sometimes fancy that our theorists divert themselves with the greediness of Mardians to believe."

"Ha! ha," cried Media; "methinks this must be Azzageddi who speaks."

"No, my lord; not long since, Azzageddi received a furlough to go home and warm himself for awhile. But this leaves me not alone."

"How?"

"My lord—for the present putting Azzageddi entirely aside—though I have now been upon terms of close companionship with myself for nigh five hundred moons, I have not yet been able to decide who or what I am. To you, perhaps, I seem Babbalanja; but to myself, I seem not myself. All I am sure of is a sort of prickly sensation all over me, which they call life; and, occasionally, a head-ache or a queer conceit admonishes me that there is something astir in my attic. But how know I that these sensations are identical with myself? For aught I know, I may be somebody else. At any rate, I keep an eye on myself, as I would on a stranger. There is something going on in me, that is independent of me. Many a time have I willed to do one thing, and another has been done. I will not say by myself, for I was not consulted about it; it was done instinctively. My most virtuous thoughts are not born of my musings, but spring up in me, like bright fancies to the poet; unsought, spontaneous. Whence they come I know not. I am a blind man pushed from behind; in vain, I turn about to see what propels me. As vanity, I regard the praises of my friends; for what they commend pertains not to me, Babbalanja; but to this unknown something that forces me to it. But why am I, a middle-aged Mardian, less prone to excesses than when a youth? The same inducements and allurements are around me. But no; my more ardent passions are burned out; those which are strongest when we are least able to resist them. Thus, then, my lord, it is not so much outer temptations that prevail over us mortals; but inward instincts."

"A very curious speculation," said Media. "But, Babbalanja, have you mortals no moral sense, as they call it?"

"We have. But the thing you speak of is but an afterbirth; we eat and drink many months before we are conscious of thoughts. And though some adults would seem to refer all their actions to this moral sense, yet in reality, it is not so; for, dominant in them, their moral sense bridles their instinctive passions; wherefore, they do not govern themselves, but are governed by their very natures. Thus, some men in youth are constitutionally as staid as I am now. But shall we pronounce them pious and worthy youths for this? Does he abstain who is not incited? And on the other hand, if the instinctive passions through life naturally have the supremacy over the moral sense, as in extreme cases we see it developed in irreclaimable malefactors—shall we pronounce such criminal and detestable wretches? My lord, it is easier for some men to be saints, than for others not to be sinners."

"That will do, Babbalanja; you are on the verge, take not the leap! Go back whence you set out, and tell us of that other, and still more mysterious Azzageddi; him whom you hinted to have palmed himself off on you for you yourself."

"Well, then, my lord—Azzageddi still set aside—upon that self-same inscrutable stranger, I charge all those past actions of mine, which in the retrospect appear to me such eminent folly, that I am confident it was not I, Babbalanja, now speaking, that committed them. Nevertheless, my lord, this very day I may do some act which at a future period may seem equally senseless; for in one lifetime we live a hundred lives. By the incomprehensible stranger in me, I say this body of mine has been rented out scores of times, though always one dark chamber in me is retained by the old mystery."

"Will you never come to the mark, Babbalanja? Tell me something direct of the stranger. Who—what is he? Introduce him."

"My lord, I cannot. He is locked up in me. In a mask he dodges me. He prowls about in me, hither and thither; he peers, and I stare. This is he who talks in my sleep, revealing my secrets; and takes me to unheard of realms, beyond the skies of Mardi. So present is he always, that I seem not so much to live of myself, as to be a mere apprehension of the unaccountable being that is in me. Yet all the time, this being is I, myself."

"Babbalanja," said Media, "you have fairly turned yourself inside out."

"Yes, my lord," said Mohi, "and he has so unsettled me, that I begin to think all Mardi a square circle."

"How is that, Babbalanja?" said Media. "He is a circle square?"

"No, my lord, but ever since Mardi began, we Mardians have been essaying our best to square it."

"Cleverly retorted. Now, Babbalanja, do you not imagine that you may do harm by disseminating these sophisms of yours; which, like your devil theory, would seem to relieve all Mardi from moral accountability?"

"My lord, at bottom, men wear no bonds that other men can strike off; and have no immunities, of which other men can deprive them. Tell a good man that he is free to commit murder—will he murder? Tell a murderer that at the peril of his soul he indulges in murderous thoughts—will that make him a saint?"

"Again on the verge, Babbalanja? Take not the leap, I say."

"I can leap no more, my lord. Already I am down, down, down."

"Philosopher," said Media, "what with Azzageddi, and the mysterious in-dweller you darkly hint of, I marvel not that you are puzzled to decide upon your identity. But when do you seem most yourself?"

"When I sleep and dream not, my lord."

"Indeed?"

"Why then, a fool's cap might be put on you, and you would not know it."

"The very turban he ought to wear," muttered Mohi.

"Yet, my lord, I live while consciousness is not mine, while to all appearances I am a clod. And may not this same state of being, though but alternate with me, be continually that of many dumb, passive objects we so carelessly regard? Trust me, there are more things alive than those that crawl, or fly, or swim. Think you, my lord, there is no sensation in being a tree? feeling the sap in one's boughs, the breeze in one's foliage? think you it is nothing to be a world? one of a herd, bison-like, wending its way across boundless meadows of ether? In the sight of a fowl, that sees not our souls, what are our own tokens of animation? That we move, make a noise, have organs, pulses, and are compounded of fluids and solids. And all these are in this Mardi as a unit. Daily the slow, majestic throbbings of its heart are perceptible on the surface in the tides of the lagoon. Its rivers are its veins; when agonized, earthquakes are its throes; it shouts in the thunder, and weeps in the shower; and as the body of a bison is covered with hair, so Mardi is covered with grasses and vegetation, among which, we parasitical things do but crawl, vexing and tormenting the patient creatures to which we cling. Nor yet, hath it recovered from the pain of the first foundation that was laid. Mardi is alive to its axis. When you pour water, does it not gurgle? When you strike a pearl shell, does it not ring? Think you there is no sensation in being a rock? To exist, is to be: to be, is to be something: to be something, is—"

"Go on," said Media.

"And what is it to be something?" said Yoomy artlessly.

"Bethink yourself of what went before," said Media.

"Loose not the thread," said Mohi.

"It has snapped," said Babbalanja.

"I breathe again," said Mohi.

"But what a stepping-off place you came to then, philosopher," said Media. "By the way, is it not old Bardianna who says that no Mardian should undertake to walk without keeping one foot foremost?"

"To return to the vagueness of the notion I have of myself," said Babbalanja.

"An appropriate theme," said Media; "proceed."

"My lord," murmured Mohi, "is not this philosopher like a centipede? Cut off his head, and still he crawls."

"There are times when I fancy myself a lunatic," resumed Babbalanja.

"Ah, now he's beginning to talk sense," whispered Mohi.

"Surely you forget, Babbalanja," said Media. "How many more theories have you? First, you are possessed by a devil; then rent yourself out to the in-dweller; and now turn yourself into a madhouse. You are inconsistent."

"And for that very reason, my lord, *not* inconsistent; for the sum of my inconsistencies makes up my consistency, and to be consistent to one's self, is often to be inconsistent to Mardi. Common consistency implies unchangeableness; but much of the wisdom here below lives in a state of transition."

"Ah!" murmured Mohi, "my head goes round again."

"Azzageddi aside, then, my lord, and also, for the nonce, the mysterious in-dweller, I come now to treat of myself as a lunatic. But this last conceit is not so much based upon the madness of particular actions, as upon the whole drift of my ordinary and hourly ones; those, in which I most resemble all other Mardians. It seems like going through with some nonsensical whim-whams, destitute of fixed purpose. For though many of my actions seem to have objects, and all of them somehow run into each other, yet, where is the grand result? To what final purpose do I walk about, eat, think, dream? To what great end does Mohi, there, now stroke his beard?"

"But I was doing it unconsciously," said Mohi, dropping his hand, and lifting his head.

"Just what I would be at, old man. 'What we do, we do blindly,' says old Bardianna. Many things we do, we do without knowing—as with you and your beard, Mohi. And many others we know not, in their true bearing at least, till they are past. Are not half our lives spent in reproaches for foregone actions, of the true nature and consequences of which we were wholly ignorant at the time? Says old Bardianna, 'Did I not so often feel an appetite for my yams, I should think everything a dream'—so puzzling to him seemed the things of this Mardi. But Alla-Malolla goes further. Says he, 'Let us club together, fellow-riddles—Kings, clowns, and intermediates. We are bundles of comical sensations; we bejuggle ourselves into strange phantasies; we are air, wind, breath, bubbles; our being is told in a tick.' "

"Now, then, Babbalanja," said Media, "what have you come to in all this rhapsody? You everlastingly travel in a circle."

"And so does the sun in heaven, my lord; like me, it goes round, and gives light as it goes. Old Bardianna, too, revolved. He says so himself. In his roundabout chapter on Cycles and Epicycles, with *Notes on the Ecliptic*, he thus discourseth—'all things revolve upon some center, to them, fixed; for the centripetal is ever too much for the centrifugal. Wherefore, it is a perpetual cycling with us, without progression; and we fly round, whether we will or no. To stop, were to sink into space. So, over and over we go, and round and round; double shuffle, on our axis, and round the sun.' In an another place he says, 'There is neither apogee nor perigee, north nor south, right nor left; what to-night is our zenith, to-morrow is our nadir; stand as we will, we stand on our heads; essay to spring into the air, and down we come; here we stick; our very bones make glue.' "

"Enough, enough, Babbalanja," cried Media. "You are a very wise Mardian; but the wisest Mardians make the most consummate fools."

"So they do, my lord; but I was interrupted. I was about to say that there is no place but the universe; no limit but the limitless; no bottom but the bottomless."

Chapter CXLIV

Of the Sorcerers in the Isle of Minda

TIFFIN! TIFFIN!" CRIED MEDIA; "TIME FOR TIFFIN! UP, COMRADES! AND WHILE THE MAT IS BEING spread, walk we to the bow, and inhale the breeze for an appetite. Hark ye, Vee-Vee! forget not that calabash with the sea-blue seal, and a round ring for a brand. Rare old stuff, that, Mohi; older than you: the circumnavigator, I call it. My sire had a canoe launched for the express purpose of carrying it thrice round Mardi for a flavor. It was many moons on the voyage; the mariners never sailed faster than three knots. Ten would spoil the best wine ever floated."

Tiffin over, and the blue-sealed calabash all but hid in the great cloud raised by our pipes, Media proposed to board it in the smoke. So, goblet in hand, we all gallantly charged, and came off victorious from the fray.

Then seated again, and serenely puffing in a circle, the circumnavigator meanwhile pleasantly going the rounds, Media called upon Mohi for something entertaining.

Now, of all the old gossips in Mardi, surely our delightful old Diodorus was furnished with the greatest possible variety of histories, chronicles, anecdotes, memoirs, legends, traditions, and biographies. There was no end to the library he carried. In himself, he was the whole history of Mardi, amplified, not abridged, in one volume.

In obedience, then, to King Media's command, Mohi regaled the company with a narrative, in substance as follows:

In a certain quarter of the Archipelago was an island called Minda; and in Minda were many sorcerers, employed in the social differences and animosities of the people of that unfortunate land. If a Mindarian deemed himself aggrieved or insulted by a countryman, he forthwith repaired to one of these sorcerers; who, for an adequate consideration, set to work with his spells, keeping himself in the dark, and directing them against the obnoxious individual. And full soon, by certain peculiar sensations, this individual, discovering what was going on, would straightway hie to his own professor of the sable art, who, being well-fed, in due time brought about certain countercharms, so that in the end it sometimes fell out that neither party was gainer or loser, save by the sum of his fees.

But the worst of it was that in some cases all knowledge of these spells were at the outset hidden from the victim; who, hearing too late of the mischief brewing, almost always fell a prey to his foe; which calamity was held the height of the art. But as the great body of sorcerers were about matched in point of skill, it followed that the parties employing them were so likewise. Hence arose those interminable contests, in which many moons were spent, both parties toiling after their common destruction.

Indeed, to say nothing of the obstinacy evinced by their employers, it was marvelous, the pertinacity of the sorcerers themselves. To the very last tooth in their employer's pouches, they would stick to their spells; never giving over till he was financially or physically defunct.

But much as they were vilified, no people in Minda were half so disinterested as they. Certain indispensable conditions secured, some of them were as ready to undertake the perdition of one man as another; good, bad, or indifferent, it made little matter.

What wonder, then, that such abominable mercenaries should cause a mighty deal of mischief in Minda; privately going about, inciting peaceable folks to enmities with their neighbors; and with marvelous alacrity, proposing themselves as the very sorcerers to rid them of the annoyances suggested as existing.

Indeed, it even happened that a sorcerer would be secretly retained to work spells upon a victim, who, from his bodily sensations, suspecting something wrong, but knowing not what, would repair to that self-same sorcerer engaging him to counteract any mischief that might be brewing. And this worthy would at once undertake the business; when, having both parties in his hands, he kept them forever in suspense; meanwhile seeing to it well that they failed not in handsomely remunerating him for his pains.

At one time there was a prodigious excitement about these sorcerers, growing out of some alarming revelations concerning their practices. In several villages of Minda they were sought to be put down. But fruitless the attempt; it was soon discovered that already their spells were so spread abroad, and they themselves so mixed up with the everyday affairs of the isle, that it was better to let their vocation alone, than, by endeavoring to suppress it, breed additional troubles. Ah! they were a knowing and a cunning set, those sorcerers; very hard to overcome, cajole, or circumvent.

But in the name of the Magi, what were these spells of theirs, so potent and occult? On all hands it was agreed that they derived their greatest virtue from the fumes of certain compounds, whose ingredients—horrible to tell—were mostly obtained from the human heart; and that by variously mixing these ingredients, they adapted their multifarious enchantments.

They were a vain and arrogant race. Upon the strength of their dealing in the dark, they affected even more mystery than belonged to them; when interrogated concerning their science, would confound the inquirer by answers couched in an extraordinary jargon, employing words almost as long as anacondas. But all this greatly prevailed with the common people.

Nor was it one of the least remarkable things that oftentimes two sorcerers, contrarily employed upon a Mindarian—one to attack, the other to defend—would nevertheless be upon the most friendly terms with each other; which curious circumstance never begat the slightest suspicions in the mind of the victim.

Another phenomenon: If from any cause, two sorcerers fell out, they seldom exercised their spells upon each other; ascribable to this perhaps—that both being versed in the art, neither could hope to get the advantage.

But for all the opprobrium cast upon these sorcerers, part of which they deserved, the evils imputed to them were mainly, though indirectly, ascribable to the very persons who abused them; nay, to the very persons who employed them; the latter being by far the loudest in their vilifyings; for which, indeed, they had excellent reason.

Nor was it to be denied that in certain respects the sorcerers were productive of considerable good. The nature of their pursuits leading them deep into the arcana of mind, they often lighted upon important discoveries; along with much that was cumbersome, accumulated valuable examples concerning the inner working of the hearts of the Mindarians; and often waxed eloquent in elucidating the mysteries of iniquity.

Yet was all this their lore graven upon so uncouth, outlandish, and antiquated tablets, that it was all but lost to the mass of their countrymen; and some old sachem of a wise man is quoted as having said that their treasures were locked up after such a fashion, that for old iron, the key was worth more than the chest and its contents.

Chapter CXLV

Chiefly of King Bello

Now, Taji," said Media, "with old Bello of the hump, whose island of Dominora is before us, I am at variance."

"Ah! How so?"

"A dull recital, but you shall have it."

And forthwith his Highness began.

This princely quarrel originated, it seems, in a slight jostling concerning the proprietorship of a barren islet in a very remote quarter of the lagoon. At the outset, the matter might have been easily adjusted had the parties but exchanged a few amicable words. But each disdaining to visit the other, to discuss so trivial an affair, the business of negotiating an understanding was committed to certain plenipos, men with lengthy tongues, who scorned to utter a word short of a polysyllable.

Now, the more these worthies penetrated into the difficulty, the wider became the breach; till what was at first a mere gap, became a yawning gulf.

But that which had perhaps tended more than any thing else to deepen the variance of the kings, was hump-backed Bello's dispatching to Odo, as his thirtieth plenipo, a diminutive little negotiator, who, all by himself, in a solitary canoe, sailed over to have audience of Media; into whose presence he was immediately ushered.

Darting one glance at him, the king turned to his chieftains, and said, "By much straining of your eyes, my lords, can you perceive this insignificant manikin? What! are there no tall men in Dominora, that King Bello must needs send this dwarf hither?"

And charging his attendents to feed the ambassador extraordinary with the soft pap of the cocoanut, and provide nurses during his stay, the monarch retired from the arbor of audience.

"As I am a man," shouted the despised plenipo, raising himself on his toes, "my royal master will resent this affront! A dwarf, forsooth! Thank Oro, I am no long-drawn giant! There is as much stuff in me as in others; what is spread out in their clumsy carcasses, in me is condensed. I am much in little. And that much, thou shalt know full soon, disdainful King of Odo!"

"Speak not against our lord the king," cried the attendants.

"And speak not ye to me, ye headless spear poles!"

And so saying, under sufferance of being small, the plenipo was permitted to depart unmolested; for all his bravadoes, fobbing his credentials and affronts.

Apprised of his servant's ignoble reception, the choleric Bello burst forth in a storm of passion; issuing orders for one thousand conch shells to be blown, and his warriors to assemble by land and by sea.

But bethinking him of the hostilities that might ensue, the sagacious Media hit upon an honorable expedient to ward off an event for which he was then unprepared. With all haste he dispatched to the hump-backed king a little dwarf of his own; who, voyaging over to Dominora in a canoe, sorry and solitary as that of Bello's plenipo, in like manner received the same insults. The effect whereof was to strike a balance of affronts; upon the principle that a blow given heals one received.

Nevertheless, these proceedings but amounted to a postponement of hostilities; for soon after, nothing prevented the two kings from plunging into war but the following judicious considerations: First, Media was almost afraid of being beaten. Second, Bello was almost afraid to conquer. Media, because he was inferior in men and arms; Bello, because, his aggrandizement was already a subject of war-like comment among the neighboring kings.

Indeed, did the old chronicler Braid-Beard speak truth, there were some tribes in Mardi that accounted this king of Dominora a testy, quarrelsome, rapacious old monarch; the indefatigable breeder of contentions and wars; the elder brother of this household of nations, perpetually essaying to lord it over the juveniles; and though his patrimonial dominions were situated to the north of the lagoon, not the slightest misunderstanding took place between the rulers of the most distant islands, than this doughty old cavalier on a throne, forthwith thrust his insolent spear into the matter, though it in no wise concerned him, and fell to irritating all parties by his gratuitous interference.

Especially was he officious in the concerns of Porpheero, a neighboring island, very large and famous, whose numerous broad valleys were divided among many rival kings—the king of Franko, a small-framed, poodle-haired, fine fiery gallant; finical in his tatooing; much given to the dance and glory;—the king of Ibeereea, a tall and stately cavalier, proud, generous, punctilious, temperate in wine; one hand forever on his javelin, the other, in superstitious homage, lifted to his gods; his limbs all over marks of stakes and crosses;—the king of Luzianna, a slender, dark-browed chief; at times wrapped in a moody robe, beneath which he fumbled something, as if it were a dagger; but otherwise a sprightly troubadour, given to serenades and moonlight;—the many chiefs of sunny Latianna; minstrel monarchs, full of song and sentiment; fiercer in love than war; glorious bards of freedom; but rendering tribute while they sang;—the priest-king of Vatikanna; his chest marked over with antique tatooings; his crown, a cowl; his rusted scepter swaying over falling towers, and crumbling mounds; full of the superstitious past; askance, eyeing the suspicious time to come;—the king of Hapzaboro; portly, pleasant; a lover of wild boar's meat; a frequent quaffer from the can; in his better moods, much fancying solid comfort;—the eight-and-thirty banded kings, chieftains, seigniors, and oligarchies of the broad hill and dale of Tutoni; clubbing together their domains that none might wrest his neighbor's; an earnest race; deep thinkers, deeper drinkers; long pipes, long heads; their wise ones given to mystic cogitations, and consultations with the devil;—the twin kings of Zandinavia; hardy, frugal mountaineers; upright of spine and heart; clad in skins of bears;—the king of Jutlanda; much like their Highnesses of Zandinavia; a sealskin cap his crown; a fearless sailor of his frigid seas;—the king of Muzkovi; a shaggy, icicled White-bear of a despot in the north; said to reign over millions of acres of glaciers; had vast provinces of snow-drifts, and many flourishing colonies among the floating icebergs. Absolute in his rule as Predestination in metaphysics, did he command all his people to give up the ghost, it would be held treason to die last. Very precise and foppish in his imperial tastes was this monarch. Disgusted with the want of uniformity in the stature of his subjects, he was said to nourish thoughts of killing off all those below his prescribed standard—six feet, long measure. Immortal souls were of no account in his fatal wars; since, in some of his serf-breeding estates, they were daily manufactured to order.

Now, to all the above-mentioned monarchs, old Bello would frequently dispatch heralds; announcing, for example, his unalterable resolution, to espouse the cause of this king against that; at the very time, perhaps, that their Serene Superfluities, instead of crossing spears, were touching flagons. And upon these occasions, the kings would often send back word to old Bello that instead of troubling himself with their concerns, he might far better attend to his own; which, they hinted, were in a sad way, and much needed reform.

The royal old warrior's pretext for these and all similar proceedings was the proper adjustment in Porpheero, of what he facetiously styled the "Equipoise of Calabashes"; which he stoutly swore was essential to the security of the various tribes in that country.

"But who put the balance into thy hands, King Bello?" cried the indignant nations.

"Oro!" shouted the hump-backed king, shaking his javelin.

Superadded to the paternal interest which Bello betrayed in the concerns of the kings of Porpheero, according to our chronicler, he also manifested no less interest in those of the remotest islands. Indeed, where he found a rich country, inhabited by a people deemed by him barbarous and incapable of wise legislation, he sometimes relieved them from their political anxieties, by assuming the dictatorship over them. And if incensed at his conduct, they flew to their spears, they were accounted rebels, and treated accordingly. But as old Mohi very truly observed; herein Bello was not alone; for throughout Mardi, all strong nations, as well as all strong men, loved to govern the weak. And those who most taunted King Bello for his political rapacity, were open to the very same charge. So with Vivenza, a distant island, at times very loud in denunciations of Bello, as a great national brigand. Not yet wholly extinct in Vivenza, were its aboriginal people, a race of wild Nimrods and hunters, who year by year were driven further and further into remoteness, till as one of their sad warriors said, after continual removes along the log, his race was on the point of being remorselessly pushed off the end.

Now, Bello was a great geographer, and land surveyor, and gauger of the seas. Terraqueous Mardi, he was continually exploring in quest of strange empires. Much he loved to take the altitude of lofty mountains, the depth of deep rivers, the breadth of broad isles. Upon the highest pinnacles of commanding capes and promontories, he loved to hoist his flag. He circled Mardi with his watch-towers; and the distant voyager passing wild rocks in the remotest waters, was startled by hearing the tattoo, or the reveille, beating from hump-backed Bello's omnipresent drum. Among Antarctic glaciers his shrill bugle calls mingled with the scream of the gulls; and so impressed seemed universal nature with the sense of his dominion, that the very clouds in heaven never sailed over Dominora without rendering the tribute of a shower; whence the air of Dominora was more moist than that of any other clime.

In all his grand undertakings, King Bello was marvelously assisted by his numerous fleets of war-canoes; his navy being the largest in Mardi. Hence his logicians swore that the entire Lagoon was his; and that all prowling whales, prowling keels, and prowling sharks were invaders. And with this fine conceit to inspire them, his poets-laureate composed some glorious old salt-water odes, enough to make your very soul sing to hear them.

But though the rest of Mardi much delighted to list to such noble minstrelsy, they agreed not with Bello's poets in deeming the lagoon their old monarch's hereditary domain.

Once upon a time, the paddlers of the hump-backed king, meeting upon the broad lagoon certain canoes belonging to the before-mentioned island of Vivenza, these paddlers seized upon several of their occupants; and feeling their pulses, declared them born men of Dominora; and, therefore, not free to go whithersoever they would; for, unless they could somehow get themselves born over again, they must forever remain subject to Bello. Shed your hair; nay, your skin, if you will, but shed your allegiance you cannot; while you have bones, they are Bello's. So, in spite of all expostulations and attempts to prove alibis, these luckless paddlers were dragged into the canoes of Dominora, and commanded to paddle home their captors.

Whereof hearing, the men of Vivenza were thrown into a great ferment; and after a mighty pow-wow over their council fire, fitting out several double-keeled canoes, they sallied out to sea, in quest of those whom they styled the wholesale corsairs of Dominora.

But lucky perhaps it was at this juncture, in all parts of Mardi, the fleets of the hump-backed king were fighting, gunwale and gunwale, alongside of numerous foes; else there had borne down upon the canoes of the men of Vivenza so tremendous an armada, that the very swell under its thousand prows might have flooded their scattered proas forever out of sight.

As it was, Bello dispatched a few of his smaller craft to seek out, and incidentally run down the enemy; and without returning home, straightway proceed upon more important enterprises.

But it so chanced that Bello's crafts, one by one meeting the foe, in most cases found the canoes of Vivenza much larger than their own; and manned by more men, with hearts as bold as theirs; whence, in the ship-duels that ensued, they were worsted; and the canoes of Vivenza, locking their yard-arms into those of the vanquished, very courteously gallanted them into their coral harbors.

Solely imputing these victories to their superior intrepidity and skill, the people of Vivenza were exceedingly boisterous in their triumph; raising such obstreperous peans, that they gave themselves hoarse throats; insomuch that, according to Mohi, some of the present generation are fain to speak through their noses.

Chapter CXLVI

DOMINORA AND VIVENZA

THE THREE CANOES STILL GLIDING ON, SOME FURTHER PARTICULARS WERE NARRATED CONCERNing Dominora; and, incidentally, of other isles.

It seems that his love of wide dominion sometimes led the otherwise sagacious Bello into the most extravagant actions. If the chance accumulation of soil and driftwood about any detached shelf of coral in the lagoon held forth the remotest possibility of the eventual existence of an islet there, with all haste he dispatched canoes to the spot, to take prospective possession of the as yet nearly submarine territory; and, if possible, eject the zoophytes.

During an unusually low tide, here and there baring the outer reef of the Archipelago, Bello caused his royal spear to be planted upon every place thus exposed, in token of his supreme claim thereto.

Another anecdote was this: that to Dominora there came a rumor that in a distant island there dwelt a man with an uncommonly large nose; of most portentous dimensions, indeed; by the soothsayers supposed to foreshadow some dreadful calamity. But disregarding these superstitious conceits, Bello forthwith dispatched an agent to discover whether this huge promontory of a nose was geographically available; if so, to secure the same, by bringing the proprietor back.

Now, by sapient old Mohi, it was esteemed a very happy thing for Mardi at large that the subjects whom Bello sent to populate his foreign acquisitions, were but too apt to throw off their vassalage so soon as they deemed themselves able to cope with him.

Indeed, a fine country in the western part of Mardi, in this very same manner, became a sovereign—nay, a republican state. It was the nation to which Mohi had previously alluded—Vivenza. But in the flush and pride of having recently attained their national majority, the men of Vivenza were perhaps too much inclined to carry a vauntful crest. And because entrenched in their fastnesses, after much protracted fighting, they had eventually succeeded in repelling the warriors dispatched by Bello to crush their insurrection, they were unanimous in the opinion that the hump-backed king had never before been so signally chastised. Whereas, they had not so much vanquished Bello as defended their shores; even as a young lion will protect its den against legions of unicorns, though, away from home, he might be torn to pieces. In truth, Braid-Beard declared, that at the time of this war, Dominora couched ten long spears for every short javelin Vivenza could dart; though the javelins were stoutly hurled as the spears.

But, superior in men and arms, why, at last, gave over King Bello the hope of reducing those truculent men of Vivenza? One reason was, as Mohi said, that many of his fighting men were abundantly occupied in other quarters of Mardi; nor was he long in discovering that, fight he never so valiantly, Vivenza—not yet its inhabitants—was wholly unconquerable. Thought Bello, Mountains are sturdy foes; fate hard to dam.

Yet, the men of Vivenza were no dastards; not to lie, coming from lion-like loins, they were a lion-loined race. Did not their bards pronounce them a fresh start in the Mardian species; requiring a new world for their full development? For, be it known, that the great land of Kolumbo, no inconsiderable part of which was embraced by Vivenza, was the last island discovered in the Archipelago.

In good round truth, and as if an impartialist from Arcturus spoke it, Vivenza was a noble land. Like a young tropic tree she stood, laden down with greenness, myriad blossoms, and the ripened fruit thick-hanging from one bough. She was promising as the morning.

Or Vivenza might be likened to St. John, feeding on locusts and wild honey, and with prophetic voice, crying to the nations from the wilderness. Or, childlike, standing among the old robed kings and emperors of the Archipelago. Vivenza seemed a young Messiah, to whose discourse the bearded Rabbis bowed.

So seemed Vivenza in its better aspect. Nevertheless, Vivenza was a braggadocio in Mardi; the only brave one ever known. As an army of spurred and crested roosters, her people chanticleered at the resplendent rising of their sun. For shame, Vivenza! Whence thy undoubted valor? Did ye not bring it with ye from the bold old shores of Dominora, where there is a fullness of it left? What isle but Dominora could have supplied thee with that stiff spine of thine? That heart of boldest beat? Oh, Vivenza! know that true grandeur is too big for a boast; and nations, as well as men, may be too clever to be great.

But what more of King Bello? Notwithstanding his territorial acquisitiveness, and aversion to relinquishing stolen nations, he was yet a glorious old king; rather choleric—a word and a blow—but of a right royal heart. Rail at him as they might, at bottom, all the isles were proud of him. And almost in spite of his rapacity, upon the whole, perhaps, they were the better for his deeds. For if sometimes he did evil with no very virtuous intentions, he had fifty ways of accomplishing good with the best; and a thousand ways of doing good without meaning it. According to an ancient oracle, the hump-backed monarch was but one of the most conspicuous pieces on a board, where the gods played for their own entertainment.

But here it must not be omitted, that of late King Bello had somewhat abated his efforts to extend his dominions. Various causes were assigned. Some thought it arose from the fact that already he found his territories too extensive for one scepter to rule; that his more remote colonies largely contributed to his tribulations, without correspondingly contributing to his revenues. Others affirmed that his hump was getting too mighty for him to carry; others still, that the nations were waxing too strong for him. With prophetic solemnity, head-shaking sages averred that he was growing older and older; had passed his grand climacteric; and though it was a hale old age with him, yet it was not his lusty youth; that though he was daily getting rounder and rounder in girth and more florid of face, that these, howbeit, were rather the symptoms of a morbid obesity, than of a healthful robustness. These wise ones predicted that very soon poor Bello would go off in an apoplexy.

But in Vivenza there were certain blusterers, who often thus prated: "The Hump-back's hour is come; at last the old teamster will be gored by the nations he's yoked; his game is done—let him show his hand and throw up his scepter; he cumbers Mardi—let him be cut down and burned; he stands in the way of his betters—let him sheer to one side; he has shut up many eyes, and now himself grows blind; he hath committed horrible atrocities during his long career, the old sinner!—now let him quickly say his prayers and be beheaded."

Howbeit, Bello lived on; enjoying his dinners, and taking his jorums as of yore. Ah, I have yet a jolly long lease of life, thought he, over his wine; and like unto some obstinate old uncle, he persisted in flourishing, in spite of the prognostications of the nephew nations, which, at his demise, perhaps hoped to fall heir to odd parts of his possessions; three streaks of fat valleys to one of lean mountains!

Chapter CXLVII

They Land at Dominora

As erewhile recounted, not being on the best terms in Mardi with the king of Dominora, Media saw fit to draw nigh unto his dominions in haughty state; he (Media) being upon excellent terms with himself. Our sails were set, our paddles paddling, streamers streaming, and Vee-Vee in the shark's mouth, clamorous with his conch. The din was soon heard; and sweeping into a fine broad bay, we beheld its margin seemingly pebbled in the distance with heads; so populous the land.

Winding through a noble valley, we presently came to Bello's palace, couchant and bristling in a grove. The upright canes composing its front projected above the eaves in a long row of spear-heads fluttering with scarlet pennons; while below, from the intervals of the canes, were slantingly thrust three tiers of decorated lances. A war-like aspect! The entire structure looking like the broadside of the Macedonian phalanx, advancing to the charge, helmeted with a roof.

"Ah, Bello," said Media, "thou dwellest among thy quills like the porcupine."

"I feel a prickly heat coming over me," cried Mohi; "my lord Media, let us enter."

"Ay," said Babbalanja, "safer the center of peril than the circumference."

Passing under an arch, formed by two pikes crossed, we found ourselves targets in prospective, for certain flingers of javelins, with poised weapons, occupying the angles of the palace.

Fronting us stood a portly old warrior, spear in hand, hump on back, and fire in eye.

"Is it war?" he cried, pointing his pike, "or peace?" reversing it.

"Peace," said Media.

Whereupon advancing, King Bello courteously welcomed us.

He was an arsenal to behold: Upon his head the hereditary crown of Dominora—a helmet of the sea-porcupine's hide, bristling all over with spikes, in front displaying a river-horse's horn, leveled to the charge; thrust through his ears were barbed arrows; and from his dyed sharkskin girdle, depended a kilt of strung javelins.

The broad chest of Bello was the chart of Mardi. Tattooed in sea-blue were all the groups and clusters of the Archipelago; and every time he breathed, rose and fell the isles, as by a tide: Dominora full upon his heart.

His sturdy thighs were his triumphal arch; whereon in numerous medallions, crests and shields, were blazoned all his victories by sea and land.

His strong right arm was Dominora's scroll of Fame, where all her heroes saw their names recorded. An endless roll!

Our chronicler avouched that on the sole of Bello's dexter foot was stamped the crest of Franko's king, his hereditary foe. "Thus, thus," cried Bello, stamping, "thus I hourly crush him."

In stature, Bello was a mountaineer; but, as over some tall tower impends the hill-side cliff, so Bello's Athos hump hung over him. Could it be, as many of his nobles held, that the old monarch's hump was his sensorium and source of strength; full of nerves, muscles, ganglions, and tendons? Yet, year by year it grew, ringed like the bole of his palms. The toils of war increased it. But another skirmish with the isles, said the wiseacres of Porpheero, and Bello's mount will crush him.

Against which calamity to guard, his medicos and Sangredos sought the hump's reduction. But down it would not come. Then by divers mystic rites, his magi tried. Making a deep pit, many teeth they dropped therein. But they could not fill it. Hence, they called it the Sinking Pit, for bottom it had none. Nevertheless, the magi said, when this pit is filled, Bello's hump you'll see no more. "Then hurrah for the hump!" cried the nobles, "for he will never hurl it off. Long life to the hump! By the hump we will rally and die! Cheer up, King Bello! Stand up, old king!"

But these were they, who, when their sovereign went abroad, with that Athos on his back, followed idly in its shade; while Bello leaned heavily upon his people, staggering as they went.

Ay, sorely did Bello's goodly stature lean; but though many swore he soon must fall, nevertheless, like Pisa's Leaning Tower, he may long lean over, but never nod.

Visiting Dominora in a friendly way, in good time, we found King Bello very affable; in hospitality, almost exceeding portly Borabolla: October-plenty reigned throughout his palace borders.

Our first reception over, a sumptuous repast was served, at which much lively talk was had.

Of Taji, Bello sought to know, whether his solar Majesty had yet made a province of the moon; whether the Astral hosts were of much account as territories, or mere Motoos, as the little tufts of verdure are denominated, here and there clinging to Mardi's circle reef; whether the people in the sun vilified him (Bello) as they did in Mardi; and what they thought of an event, so ominous to the liberties of the universe, as the addition to his navy of three large canoes?

Ere long, so fused in social love we grew, that Bello, filling high his can, and clasping Media's palm, drank everlasting amity with Odo.

So over their red cups, the two kings forgot their differences, and concerning the disputed islet, nothing more was ever heard; especially, as it so turned out, that while they were most hot about it, it had suddenly gone out of sight, being of volcanic origin.

Chapter CXLVIII

Through Dominora, They Wander after Yillah

At last, withdrawing from the presence of king Bello, we went forth, still intent on our search.

Many brave sights we saw. Fair fields; the whole island a garden; green hedges all round; neat lodges, thick as white mice in the landscape; old oak woods hale and hearty as ever; old temples buried in ivy; old shrines of old heroes, deep buried in broad groves of bay-trees; old rivers, laden down with heavy freighted canoes; humped hills, like droves of camels, piled up with harvests; every sign and token of a glorious abundance, every sign and token of generations of renown. Rare sight! fine sight! none rarer, none finer in Mardi.

But roving on through this ravishing region, we passed through a corn-field in full beard, where a haggard old reaper laid down his hook, beseeching charity for the sake of the gods. "Bread, bread! or I die mid these sheaves!"

"Thrash out your grain and want not."

"Alas, masters, this grain is not mine; I plough, I sow, I reap, I bind, I stack. Lord Primo garners."

Rambling on, we came to a hamlet, hidden in a hollow; and beneath weeping willows saw many mournful maidens seated on a bank; beside each, a wheel that was broken. "Lo, we starve!" they cried; "our distaffs are snapped; no more may we weave and spin!"

Then forth issued from vaults clamorous crowds of men, hands tied to their backs—"Bread! bread!" they cried. "The magician hath turned us out from our glen, where we labored of yore in the days of the merry Green Queen. He has pinioned us hip and arm, that we starve. Like sheep, we die off with the rot. Curse on the magician. A curse on his spell."

Bending our steps towards the glen, roaring down the rocks, we descried a stream from the mountains. But ere those waters gained the sea, vassal tribute they rendered. Conducted through culverts and moats, they turned great wheels, giving life to ten thousand fangs and fingers, whose gripe no power could withstand, yet whose touch was soft as the velvet paw of a kitten. With brute force, they heaved down great weights, then daintily wove and spun; like the trunk of the elephant, which lays lifeless a river-horse, and counts the pulses of a moth. On all sides, the place seemed alive with its spindles. Round and round, round and round; throwing off wondrous births at every revolving; ceaseless as the cycles that circle in heaven. Loud hummed the loom, flew the shuttle like lightning, red roared the grim forge, rung anvil and sledge, yet no mortal was seen.

"What, ho, magician! Come forth from thy cave!"

But all deaf were the spindles, as the mutes that mutely wait on the Sultan.

"Since we are born, we will live!" so we read on a crimson banner, flouting the crimson clouds, in the van of a riotous red-bonneted mob, racing by us as we came from the glen. Many more followed, black, or blood-stained—

"Mardi is man's!"

"Down with landholders!"

"Our turn now!"

"Up rights! Down wrongs!"

"Bread! Bread!"

"Take the tide ere it turns!"

Waving their banners, and flourishing aloft clubs, hammers, and sickles, with fierce yells the crowd ran on towards the palace of Bello. Foremost and inciting the rest by mad outcries and gestures, were six masks. "This way! This way!" they cried. "By the wood; by the dark wood!" Whereupon, all darted into the groves; when of a sudden, the masks leaped forward, clearing a long covered trench, into which fell many of those they led. But on raced the masks; and gaining Bello's palace, and raising the alarm, there sallied from thence a woodland of spears, which charged upon the disordered ranks in the grove. A crash as of icicles against icebergs round Zembla, and down went the hammers and sickles. The host fled, hotly pursued. Meanwhile, brave heralds from Bello advanced, and with chaplets crowned the six masks. "Welcome, heroes! worthy and valiant!" they cried. "Thus our lord Bello rewards all those, who, to do him a service, for hire betray their kith and their kin."

Still pursuing our quest, wide we wandered through all the sun and shade of Dominora; but nowhere was Yillah found.

Chapter CXLIX

They Behold King Bello's State Canoe

At last, bidding adieu to King Bello; and in the midst of the lowing of oxen, breaking away from his many hospitalities, we departed for the beach. But ere embarking, we paused to gaze at an object which long fixed our attention.

Now, as all bold cavaliers have ever delighted in special chargers, gaily caparisoned, whereon upon grand occasions to sally forth upon the plains: even so have maritime potentates ever prided themselves upon some holiday galley, splendidly equipped, wherein to sail over the sea.

When of old, glory-seeking Jason, attended by his promising young lieutenants, Castor and Pollux, embarked on that hardy adventure to Colchis, the brave planks of the good ship Argos he trod, its model a swan to behold.

And when Trojan Æneas wandered west, and discovered the pleasant land of Latium, it was in the fine craft *Bis Taurus* that he sailed, its stern gloriously emblazoned, its prow a leveled spear.

And to the sound of sackbut and psaltery, gliding down the Nile, in the pleasant shade of its pyramids to welcome mad Mark, Cleopatra was throned on the cedar quarter-deck of a glorious gondola, silk and satin hung; its silver plated oars, musical as flutes. So, too, Queen Bess was wont to disport on old Thames.

And tough Torf-Egill, the Danish Sea-king, reckoned in his stud, a slender yacht; its masts young Zetland firs; its prow a seal, dog-like holding a sword-fish blade. He called it the *Greyhound,* so swift was its keel; the Sea-hawk, so blood-stained its beak.

And groping down his palace stairs, the blind old Doge Dandolo, oft embarked in his gilded barge, like the Lord Mayor setting forth in civic state from Guildhall in his chariot. But from another sort of prow leaped Dandolo, when, at Constantinople, he foremost sprang ashore, and with a right arm ninety years old, planted the standard of St. Mark full among the long chin-pennons of the long-bearded Turks.

And Kumbo Sama, Emperor of Japan, had a dragon-beaked junk, a floating Juggernaut, wherein he burned incense to the sea-gods.

And Kannakoko, King of New Zealand; and the first Tahitian Pomaree; and the Pelew potentate, each possessed long state canoes; sea-snakes, all; carved over like Chinese card-cases, and manned with such scores of warriors that, dipping their paddles in the sea, they made a commotion like shoals of herring.

What wonder, then, that Bello of the Hump, the old sea-king of Mardi, should sport a brave ocean-chariot?

In a broad arbor by the water-side it was housed like Alp Arsian's war-horse, or the charger Caligula deified; upon its stern a wilderness of sculpture—shell-work, medallions, masques, griffins, gulls, ogres, finned-lions, winged walruses; all manner of sea-cavalry, crusading centaurs, crocodiles, and sharks; and mermen, and mermaids, and Neptune only knows all.

And in this craft, Doge-like, yearly did King Bello stand up and wed with the Lagoon. But the custom originated not in the manner of the Doge's, which was as follows; so, at least, saith Ghibelli, who tells all about it:

When, in a stout sea-fight, Ziani defeated Barbarossa's son Otho, sending his feluccas all flying, like frightened water-fowl from a lake, then did his Holiness, the Pope, present unto him a ring, saying, "Take this, oh, Ziani! and with it, the sea for thy bride; and every year wed her again."

So the Doge's tradition; thus Bello's:

Ages ago Dominora was circled by a reef, which, expanding in proportion to the extension of the isle's naval dominion, in due time embraced the entire lagoon; and this marriage ring zoned all the world.

But if the sea was King Bello's bride, an Adriatic Tartar he wedded; who, in her mad gales of passions, often boxed about his canoes, and led his navies a very boisterous life indeed.

And hostile prognosticators opined that ere long she would desert her old lord, and marry again. Already, they held, she had made advances in the direction of Vivenza.

But truly, should she abandon old Bello, he would straightway after her with all his fleets; and never rest till his queen was regained.

Now, old sea-king! look well to thy barge of state; for, peradventure, the dry-rot may be eating into its keel; and the wood-worms exploring into its spars.

Without heedful tending, any craft will decay; yet, forever may its first, fine model be preserved, though its prow be renewed every spring, like the horns of the deer, if, in repairing, plank be put for plank, rib for rib, in exactest similitude. Even so, then, oh, Bello! do thou with thy barge.

Chapter CL

Wherein Babbalanja Bows Thrice

The next morning's twilight found us once more afloat; and yielding to that almost sullen feeling, but too apt to prevail with some mortals at that hour, all but Media long remained silent.

But now, a bright mustering is seen among the myriad white Tartar tents in the Orient; like lines of spears defiling upon some upland plain, the sunbeams thwart the sky. And see! amid the blaze of banners, and the pawings of ten thousand golden hoofs, day's mounted Sultan, Xerxes-like, moves on: the Dawn his standard, East and West his cymbals.

"Oh, morning life!" cried Yoomy, with a Persian air; "would that all time were a sunrise, and all life a youth."

"Ah! but these striplings whimper of youth," said Mohi, caressing his braids, "as if they wore this beard."

"But natural, old man," said Babbalanja. "We Mardians never seem young to ourselves; childhood is to youth, what manhood is to age—something to be looked back upon, with sorrow that it is past. But childhood recks of no future, and knows no past; hence, its present passes in a vapor."

"Mohi, how's your appetite this morning?" said Media.

"Thus, thus, ye gods," sighed Yoomy, "is feeling ever scouted. Yet, what might seem feeling in me, I cannot express."

"A good commentary on old Bardianna, Yoomy," said Babbalanja, "who somewhere says, that no Mardian can out with his heart, for his unyielding ribs are in the way. And indeed, pride, or something akin thereto, often holds check on sentiment. My lord, there are those who like not to be detected in the possession of a heart."

"Very true, Babbalanja; and I suppose that pride was at the bottom of your old Ponderer's heartless, unsentimental, bald-pated style."

"Craving pardon, my lord is deceived. Bardianna was not at all proud; though he had a queer way of showing the absence of pride. In his essay, entitled—*On the Tendency to Curl in Upper Lips*, he thus discourses: 'We hear much of pride and its sinfulness in this Mardi wherein we dwell: whereas, I glory in being brimmed with it; my sort of pride. In the presence of kings, lords, palm-trees, and all those who deem themselves taller than myself, I stand stiff as a pike, and will abate not one vertebra of my stature. But accounting no Mardian my superior, I account none my inferior; hence, with the social, I am ever ready to be sociable.' "

"An agrarian!" said Media; "no doubt he would have made the headsman the minister of equality."

"At bottom we are already equal, my honored lord," said Babbalanja, profoundly bowing. "One way we all come into Mardi, and one way we withdraw. Wanting his yams a king will starve, quick as a clown; and smote on the hip, saith old Bardianna, he will roar as loud as the next one."

"Roughly worded that, Babbalanja. Vee-Vee! my crown! So, now, Babbalanja, try if you cannot polish Bardianna's style in that last saying you father upon him."

"I will, my ever honorable lord," said Babbalanja, salaaming. "Thus we'll word it, then. In their merely Mardian nature, the sublimest demi-gods are subject to infirmities; for struck by some keen shaft, even a king oft-times dons his crown, fearful of future darts."

"Ha, ha! well done, Babbalanja; but I bade you polish, not sharpen the arrow."

"All one, my thrice honored lord; to polish is not to blunt."

Chapter CLI

Babbalanja Philosophizes, and My Lord Media Passes Round the Calabashes

An interval of silence passed; when Media cried, "Out upon thee, Yoomy! curtail that long face of thine."

"How can he, my lord," said Mohi, "when he is thinking of furlongs?"

"Fathoms, you mean, Mohi; see you not he is musing over the gunwale? And now, minstrel, a banana for thy thoughts. Come, tell me how you poets spend so many hours in meditation?"

"My lord, it is because, that when we think, we think so little of ourselves."

"I thought as much," said Mohi; "for no sooner do I undertake to be sociable with myself, than I am straightway forced to beat a retreat."

"Ay, old man," said Babbalanja, "many of us Mardians are but sorry hosts to ourselves. Some hearts are hermits."

"If not of yourself, then, Yoomy, of whom else do you think?" asked Media.

"My lord, I seldom think," said Yoomy, "I but give ear to the voices in my calm."

"Did Babbalanja speak?" said Media. "But no more of your reveries"; and so saying Media gradually sunk into a reverie himself.

The rest did likewise; and soon, with eyes enchanted, all reclined: gazing at each other, witless of what we did.

It was Media who broke the spell; calling for Vee-Vee our page, his calabashes and cups, and nectarines for all.

Eyeing his goblet, Media at length threw himself back, and said: "Babbalanja, not ten minutes since, we were all absent-minded; now, how would you like to step out of your body, in reality; and, as a spirit, haunt some shadowy grove?"

"But our lungs are not wholly superfluous, my lord," said Babbalanja, speaking loud.

"No, nor our lips," said Mohi, smacking his over his wine.

"But could you really be disembodied here in Mardi, Babbalanja, how would you fancy it?" said Media.

"My lord," said Babbalanja, speaking through half of a nectarine, "defer putting that question, I beseech, till after my appetite is satisfied; for, trust me, no hungry mortal would forfeit his palate, to be resolved into the impalpable."

"Yet pure spirits we must all become at last, Babbalanja," said Yoomy, "even the most ignoble."

"Yes, so they say, Yoomy; but if all boors be the immortal sires of endless dynasties of immortals, how little do our pious patricians bear in mind their magnificent destiny, when hourly they scorn their companionship. And if here in Mardi they cannot abide an equality with plebeians, even at the altar; how shall they endure them, side by side, throughout eternity? But since the prophet Alma asserts, that Paradise is almost entirely made up of the poor and despised, no wonder that many aristocrats of our isles pursue a career, which, according to some theologies, must forever preserve the social distinctions so sedulously maintained in Mardi. And though some say, that at death everything earthly is removed from the spirit, so that clowns and lords both stand on a footing; yet, according to the popular legends, it has ever been observed of the ghosts of boors when revisiting Mardi, that invariably they rise in their smocks. And regarding our intellectual equality hereafter, how unjust, my lord, that after whole years of days and nights consecrated to the hard gaining of wisdom, the wisest Mardian of us all should in the end find the whole sum of his attainments, at one leap outstripped by the veriest dunce, suddenly inspired by light divine. And though some hold, that all Mardian lore is vain, and that at death, all mysteries will be revealed; yet, nonetheless, do they toil and ponder now. Thus, their tongues have one mind, and their understanding another."

"My lord," said Mohi, "we have come to the lees; your pardon, Babbalanja."

"Then, Vee-Vee, another calabash! Fill up, Mohi; wash down wine with wine. Your cup, Babbalanja; any lees?"

"Plenty, my lord; we philosophers come to the lees very soon."

"Flood them over then; but cease not discoursing; thanks be to the gods, your mortal palates and tongues can both wag together; fill up, I say, Babbalanja; you are no philosopher, if you stop at the tenth cup; endurance is the test of philosophy all Mardi over; drink, I say, and make us wise by precept and example. Proceed, Yoomy, you look as if you had something to say."

"Thanks, my lord. Just now, Babbalanja, you flew from the subject—you spoke of boors; but has not the lowliest peasant an eye that can take in the vast horizon at a sweep; mountains, vales, plains, and oceans? Is such a being nothing?"

"But can that eye see itself, Yoomy?" said Babbalanja, winking. "Taken out of its socket, will it see at all? Its connection with the body imparts to it its virtue."

"He questions everything," cried Mohi. "Philosopher, have you a head?"

"I have," said Babbalanja, feeling for it; "I am finished off at the helm very much as other Mardians, Mohi."

"My lord, the first yea that ever came from him."

"Ah, Mohi," said Media, "the discourse waxes heavy. I fear me we have again come to the lees. Ho, Vee-Vee, a fresh calabash; and with it we will change the subject. Now, Babbalanja, I have this cup to drink, and then a question to propound. Ah, Mohi, rare old wine this; it smacks of the cork. But attention, Philosopher. Supposing you had a wife—which, by the way, you have not—would you deem it sensible in her to imagine you no more, because you happened to stroll out of her sight?"

"However that might be," murmured Yoomy, "young Nina bewailed herself a widow, whenever Arhinoo, her lord, was absent from her side."

"My lord Media," said Babbalanja, "during my absence, my wife would have more reason to conclude that I was not living, than that I was. To the former supposition, everything tangible around her would tend; to the latter, nothing but her own fond fancies. It is this imagination of ours, my lord, that is at the bottom of these things. When I am in one place, there exists no other. Yet am I but too apt to fancy the reverse. Nevertheless, when I am in Odo, talk not to me of Ohonoo. To me it is not, except when I am there. If it be, prove it. To prove it, you carry me thither; but you only prove, that to its substantive existence, as cognizant to me, my presence is indispensable. I say that, to me, all Mardi exists by virtue of my sovereign pleasure, and when I die, the universe will perish with me."

"Come you of a long-lived race," said Mohi, "one free from apoplexies? I have many little things to accomplish yet, and would not be left in the lurch."

"Heed him not, Babbalanja," said Media. "Dip your beak again, my eagle, and soar."

"Let us be eagles, then, indeed, my lord: eagle-like, let us look at this red wine without blinking; let us grow solemn, not boisterous, with good cheer."

Then, lifting his cup, "My lord, serenely do I pity all such who are stirred one jot from their centers by ever so much drinking of this fluid. Ply him hard as you will, through the live-long polar night, a wise man cannot be made drunk. Though, towards sunrise, his body may reel, it will reel round its center; and though he make many tracks in going home, he reaches it at last; while scores of over-plied fools are foundering by the way. My lord, when wild with much thought, 'tis to wine I fly, to sober me; its magic fumes breathe over me like the Indian summer, which steeps all nature in repose. To me, wine is no vulgar fire, no fosterer of base passions; my heart, ever open, is opened still wide; and glorious visions are born in my brain; it is then that I have all Mardi under my feet, and the constellations of the firmament in my soul."

"Superb!" cried Yoomy.

"Pooh, pooh!" said Mohi; "who does not see stars at such times? I see the Great Bear now, and the little one, its cub; and Andromeda, and Perseus' chain-armor, and Cassiopea in her golden chair, and the bright, scaly Dragon, and the glittering Lyre, and all the jewels in Orion's sword-hilt."

"Ay," cried Media, "the study of astronomy is wonderfully facilitated by wine. Fill up, old Ptolemy, and tell us should you discover a new planet. Methinks this fluid needs stirring. Ho, Vee-Vee, my scepter! be we sociable. But come, Babbalanja, my gold-headed aquila, return to your theme—the imagination, if you please."

"Well, then, my lord, I was about to say, that the imagination is the Voli-Donzini; or, to speak plainer, the unical, rudimental, and all-comprehending abstracted essence of the infinite remoteness of things. Without it we were grasshoppers."

"And with it, you mortals are little else; do you not chirp all over, Mohi? By my demi-god soul, were I not what I am, this wine would almost get the better of me."

"Without it—" continued Babbalanja.

"Without what?" demanded Media, starting to his feet. "This wine? Traitor, I'll stand by this to the last gasp; you are inebriated, Babbalanja."

"Perhaps so, my lord; but I was treating of the imagination, may it please you."

"My lord," added Mohi, "of the unical, and rudimental fundament of things, you remember."

"Ah! there's none of them sober; proceed, proceed, Azzageddi!"

"My lord waves his hand like a banner," murmured Yoomy.

"Without imagination, I say, an armless man, born blind, could not be made to believe, that he had a head of hair, since he could neither see it, nor feel it, nor has hair any feeling of itself."

"Methinks though," said Mohi, "if the cripple had a Tartar for a wife, he would not remain skeptical long."

"You all fly off at tangents," cried Media, "but no wonder! your mortal brains cannot endure much quaffing. Return to your subject, Babbalanja. Assume now, Babbalanja—assume, my dear prince, assume it, assume it, I say! Why don't you?"

"I am willing to assume anything you please, my lord; what is it?"

"Ah, yes! Assume that—that upon returning home, you should find your wife had newly wedded, under the—the—the metaphysical presumption, that being no longer visible, you—*you* Azzageddi, had departed this life; in other words, out of sight, out of mind; what then, my dear prince?"

"Why then, my lord, I would demolish my rival in a trice."

"Would you?—then—then so much for your metaphysics, Bab—Babbalanja."

Babbalanja rose to his feet, muttering to himself—"Is this assumed, or real? Can a demi-god be mastered by wine? Yet, the old mythologies make bacchanals of the gods. But he was wondrous keen! He felled me, ere he fell himself."

"Yoomy, my lord Media is in a very merry mood to-day," whispered Mohi; "but his counterfeit was not well done. No, no; a bacchanal is not used to be so logical in his cups."

Chapter CLII

They Sail Round an Island Without Landing; and Talk Round a Subject Without Getting at It

PURPOSING A VISIT TO KALEEDONI, A COUNTRY INTEGRALLY UNITED TO DOMINORA, OUR COURSE now lay northward along the western white cliffs of the isle. But finding the wind ahead, and the current too strong for our paddlers, we were fain to forego our destination; Babbalanja observing, that since in Dominora, we had not found Yillah, then in Kaleedoni the maiden could not be lurking.

And now, some conversation ensued concerning the country we were prevented from visiting. Our chronicler narrated many fine things of its people; extolling their bravery in war, their amiability in peace, their devotion in religion, their penetration in philosophy, their simplicity and sweetness in song, their loving-kindness and frugality in all things domestic—running over a long catalogue of heroes, metaphysicians, bards, and good men.

But as all virtues are convertible into vices, so in some cases did the best traits of these people degenerate. Their frugality too often became parsimony; their devotion grim bigotry; and all this in a greater degree perhaps than could be predicated of the more immediate subjects of King Bello.

In Kaleedoni was much to awaken the fervor of its bards. Upland and lowland were full of the picturesque; and many unsung lyrics yet lurked in her glens. Among her blue, heathy hills, lingered many tribes, who in their wild and tattooed attire, still preserved the garb of the mightiest nation of old times. They bared the knee, in token that it was honorable as the face, since it had never been bent.

While Braid-Beard was recounting these things, the currents were sweeping us over a strait, toward a deep green island, bewitching to behold.

Not greener that midmost terrace of the Andes, which under a torrid meridian steeps fair Quito in the dews of a perpetual spring—not greener the nine thousand feet of Pirohitee's tall peak, which, rising from out the warm bosom of Tahiti, carries all summer with it into the clouds; nay, not greener the famed gardens of Cyrus—than the vernal lawn, the knoll, the dale of beautiful Verdanna.

"Alas, sweet isle! Thy desolation is overrun with vines," sighed Yoomy, gazing.

"Land of caitiff curs!" cried Media.

"Isle, whose future is in its past. Hearth-stone, from which its children run," said Babbalanja.

"I cannot read thy chronicles for blood, Verdanna," murmured Mohi.

Gliding near, we would have landed, but the rolling surf forbade. Then thrice we circumnavigated the isle for a smooth, clear beach; but it was not found.

Meanwhile all still conversed.

"My lord," said Yoomy, "while we tarried with King Bello, I heard much of the feud between Dominora and this unhappy shore. Yet is not Verdanna as a child of King Bello's?"

"Yes, minstrel, a step-child," said Mohi.

"By way of enlarging his family circle," said Babbalanja, "an old lion once introduced a deserted young stag to his den; but the stag never became domesticated, and would still charge upon his foster-brothers. Verdanna is not of the flesh and blood of Dominora, whence, in good part, these dissensions."

"But Babbalanja, is there no way of reconciling these foes?"

"But one way, Yoomy. By filling up this strait with dry land; for, divided by water, we Mardians must ever remain more or less divided at heart. Though Kaleedoni was united to Dominora long previous to the union of Verdanna, yet Kaleedoni occasions Bello no disquiet; for, geographically one, the two populations insensibly blend at the point of junction. No hostile strait flows between the arms, that to embrace must touch."

"But, Babbalanja," said Yoomy, "what asks Verdanna of Dominora, that Verdanna so clamors at the denial?"

"They are arrant cannibals, Yoomy," said Media, "and desire the privilege of eating each other up."

"King Bello's idea," said Babbalanja; "but, in these things, my lord, you demi-gods are ever unanimous. But, whatever be Verdanna's demands, Bello persists in rejecting them."

"Why not grant everything she asks, even to renouncing all claim upon the isle?" said Mohi; "for thus, Bello would rid himself of many perplexities."

"And think you, old man," said Media, "that, bane or blessing, Bello will yield his birthright? Will a tri-crowned king resign his triple diadem? And even did Bello what you propose, he would only breed still greater perplexities. For if granted, full soon would Verdanna be glad to surrender many things she demands. And all she now asks, she has had in times past; but without turning it to advantage—and is she wiser now?"

"Does she not demand her harvests, my lord?" said Yoomy, "and has not the reaper a right to his sheaf?"

"Cant! cant! Yoomy. If you reap for me, the sheaf is mine."

"But if the reaper reaps on his own harvest-field, whose then the sheaf, my lord?" said Babbalanja.

"His for whom he reaps—his lord's!"

"Then let the reaper go with sickle and with sword," said Yoomy, "with one hand, cut down the bearded grain; and with the other, smite his bearded lord's."

"Thou growest fierce, in thy lyric moods, my war-like dove," said Media blandly. "But for thee, philosopher, know thou, that Verdanna's men are of blood and brain inferior to Bello's native race; and the better Mardian must ever rule."

"Verdanna inferior to Dominora, my lord! Has she produced no bards, no orators, no wits, no patriots? Mohi, unroll thy chronicles! Tell me, if Verdanna may not claim full many a star along King Bello's tattooed arm of Fame?

"Even so," said Mohi. "Many chapters bear you out."

"But, my lord," said Babbalanja, "as truth, omnipresent, lurks in all things, even in lies: so does some germ of it lurk in the calumnies heaped on the people of this land. For though they justly boast of many lustrous names, these jewels gem no splendid robe. And though, like a bower of grapes, Verdanna is full of gushing juices, spouting out in bright sallies of wit, yet not all her grapes make wine; and here and there hang goodly clusters mildewed; or half-devoured by worms, bred in their own tendrils."

"Drop, drop your grapes and metaphors!" cried Media. "Bring forth your thoughts like men; let them come naked into Mardi. What do you mean, Babbalanja?"

"This, my lord: Verdanna's worst evils are her own, not of another's giving. Her own hand is her own undoer. She stabs herself with bigotry, superstition, divided councils, domestic feuds, ignorance, temerity; she wills, but does not; her east is one black storm-cloud, that never bursts; her utmost fight is a defiance; she showers reproaches, where she should rain down blows. She stands a mastiff baying at the moon."

"Tropes on tropes!" said. Media. "Let me tell the tale—straightforward like a line. Verdanna is a lunatic—"

"A trope! my lord," cried Babbalanja.

"My tropes are not tropes," said Media, "but yours are. Verdanna is a lunatic, that after vainly striving to cut another's throat, grimaces before a standing pool and threatens to cut his own. And is such a madman to be entrusted with himself? No: let another govern him who is ungovernable to himself. Ay, and tight hold the rein; and curb, and rasp the bit. Do I exaggerate? Mohi, tell me, if, save one lucid interval, Verdanna, while independent of Dominora, ever discreetly conducted her affairs? Was she not always full of fights and factions? And what first brought her under the sway of Bello's scepter? Did not her own Chief Dermoddi fly to Bello's ancestor for protection against his own seditious subjects? And thereby did not her own king unking himself? What wonder, then, and where the wrong, if Henro, Bello's conquering sire, seized the diadem?"

"What my lord cites is true," said Mohi, "but cite no more, I pray; lest you harm your cause."

"Yet, for all this, Babbalanja," said Media; "Bello but holds lunatic Verdanna's lands in trust."

"And may the guardian of an estate also hold custody of the ward, my lord?"

"Ay, if he can. What *can* be done, may be; that's the creed of demi-gods."

"Alas, alas!" cried Yoomy, "why war with words over this poor, suffering land. See! for all her bloom, her people starve; perish her yams, ere taken from the soil; the blight of heaven seems upon them."

"Not so," said Media. "Heaven sends no blights. Verdanna will not learn. And if from one season's rotteness, rottenness they sow again, rottenness must they reap. But, Yoomy, you seem earnest in this matter—come; on all hands it is granted that evils exist in Verdanna; now, sweet sympathizer, what must the royal Bello do to mend them?"

"I am no sage," said Yoomy. "What would my lord Media do?"

"What would *you* do, Babbalanja," said Media.

"Mohi, what you?" asked the philosopher.

"And what would the company do?" added Mohi.

"Now, though these evils pose us all," said Babbalanja, "there lately died in Verdanna, one, who set about curing them in a humane and peaceable way, waving war and bloodshed. That man was Konno. Under a huge caldron, he kept a roaring fire."

"Well, Azzageddi, how could that answer his purpose?" asked Media.

"Nothing better, my lord. His fire boiled his bread-fruit: and so convinced were his countrymen, that he was well employed that they almost stripped their scanty orchards to fill his caldron."

"Konno was a knave," said Mohi.

"Your pardon, old man; but that is only known to his ghost, not to us. At any rate he was a great man; for even assuming he cajoled his country, no common man could have done it."

"Babbalanja," said Mohi, "my lord has been pleased to pronounce Verdanna crazy; now, may not her craziness arise from the irritating, tantalizing practices of Dominora?"

"Doubtless, Braid-Beard, many of the extravagances of Verdanna are in good part to be ascribed to the cause you mention; but, to be impartial, none the less does Verdanna essay to taunt and provoke Dominora; yet not with the like result. Perceive you, Braid-Beard, that the trade-wind blows dead across this strait from Dominora, and not from Verdanna? Hence, when King Bello's men fling gibes and insults, every missile hits; but those of Verdanna are blown back in its teeth; her enemies jeering her again and again."

"King Bello's men are dastards for that," cried Yoomy.

"It shows neither sense, nor spirit, nor humanity," said Babbalanja.

"All wide of the mark," cried Media. "What is to be done for Verdanna?"

"What will she do for herself?" said Babbalanja.

"Philosopher, you are an extraordinary sage; and since sages should be seers, reveal Verdanna's future."

"My lord, you will ever find true prophets, prudent; nor will any prophet risk his reputation upon predicting aught concerning this land. The isles are Oro's. Nevertheless, he who doctors Verdanna aright, will first medicine King Bello; who in some things is himself a patient, though he would fain be a physician. However, my lord, there is a demon of a doctor in Mardi, who at last deals with these desperate cases. He employs only pills, picked off the Conroupta Quiancensis tree."

"And what sort of a vegetable is that?" asked Mohi.

"Consult the botanists," said Babbalanja.

Chapter CLIII

THEY DRAW NIGH TO PORPHEERO; WHERE THEY BEHOLD A TERRIFIC ERUPTION

GLIDING AWAY FROM VERDANNA AT THE TURN OF THE TIDE, WE CLEARED THE STRAIT, AND GAINing the more open lagoon, pointed our prows for Porpheero, from whose magnificent monarchs my lord Media promised himself a glorious reception.

"They are one and all demi-gods," he cried, "and have the old demi-god feeling. We have seen no great valleys like theirs—their scepters are long as our spears; to their sumptuous palaces, Donjalolo's are but inns; their banqueting halls are as vistas; no generations run parallel to theirs; their pedigrees reach back into chaos.

"Babbalanja! here you will find food for philosophy. The whole land checkered with nations, side by side contrasting in costume, manners, and mind. Here you will find science and sages; manuscripts in miles; bards singing in choirs.

"Mohi! here you will flag over your page; in Porpheero the ages have hived all their treasures: like a pyramid, the past shadows over the land.

"Yoomy! here you will find stuff for your songs—blue rivers flowing through forest arches; and vineyards; velvet meads, soft as ottomans; bright maidens braiding the golden locks of the harvest; and a background of mountains, that seem the end of the world. Or if nature will not content you, then turn to the landscapes of art. See! mosaic walls, tattooed like our faces; paintings, vast as horizons; and into which, you feel you could rush. See! statues to which you could off turban; cities of columns standing thick as mankind; and firmanent domes forever shedding their sunsets of gilding. See! spire behind spire, as if the land were the ocean, and all Bello's great navy were riding at anchor.

"Noble Taji! you seek for your Yillah; give over despair! Porpheero's such a scene of enchantment that there, the lost maiden must lurk."

"A glorious picture!" cried Babbalanja, "but turn the medal, my lord; what says the reverse?"

"Cynic! have done. But bravo! we'll ere long be in Franko, the goodliest vale of them all; how I long to take her old king by the hand!"

The sun was now setting behind us, lighting up the white cliff of Dominora, and the green capes of Verdanna; while in deep shade lay before us the long winding shores of Porpheero.

It was a sunset serene.

"How the winds lowly warble in the dying day's ear," murmured Yoomy.

"A mild, bright night, we'll have," said Media.

"See you not those clouds over Franko, my lord," said Mohi, shaking his head.

"Ah! aged and weather-wise as ever, sir chronicler; I predict a fair night, and many to follow."

"Patience needs no prophet," said Babbalanja. "The night is at hand."

Hitherto the lagoon had been smooth; but anon, it grew black, and stirred; and out of the thick darkness came clamorous sounds. Soon, there shot into the air a vivid meteor, which bursting at the zenith, radiated down the firmament in fiery showers, leaving treble darkness behind.

Then, as all held their breath, from Franko there spouted an eruption, which seemed to plant all Mardi in the foreground.

As when Vesuvius lights her torch, and in the blaze, the storm-swept surges in Naples' bay rear and plunge towards it; so now, showed Franko's multitudes, as they stormed the summit where their monarch's palace blazed, fast by the burning mountain.

"By my eternal throne!" cried Media starting, "the old volcano has burst forth again!"

"But a new vent, my lord," said Babbalanja.

"More fierce this, than the eruption which happened in my youth," said Mohi; "methinks that Franko's end has come."

"You look pale, my lord," said Babbalanja, "while all other faces glow. Yoomy, doff that halo in the presence of a king."

Over the waters came a rumbling sound, mixed with the din of warfare, and thwarted by showers of embers that fell not, for the whirling blasts.

"Off shore! off shore!" cried Media; and with all haste we gained a place of safety.

Down the valley now poured Rhines and Rhones of lava, a fire-freshet, flooding the forests from their fastnesses, and leaping with them into the seething sea.

The shore was lined with multitudes pushing off wildly in canoes.

Meantime, the fiery storm from Franko, kindled new flames in the distant valleys of Porpheero; while driven over from Verdanna came frantic shouts, and direful jubilee. Upon Dominora a baleful glare was resting.

"Thrice cursed flames!" cried Media. "Is Mardi to be one conflagration? How it crackles, forks, and roars! Is this our funeral pyre?"

"Recline, recline, my lord," said Babbalanja. "Fierce flames are ever brief—a song, sweet Yoomy! Your pipe, old Mohi! Greater fires than this have ere now blazed in Mardi. Let us be calm; the isles were made to burn; Braid-Beard! hereafter in some quiet cell, of this whole scene you will but make one chapter; come, digest it now."

"My face is scorched!" cried Media.

"The last, last day!" cried Mohi.

"Not so, old man," said Babbalanja, "when that day dawns, 'twill dawn serene. Be calm, be calm, my potent lord."

"Talk not of calm brows in storm-time!" cried Media fiercely. "See! how the flames blow over upon Dominora!"

"Yet the fires they kindle there are soon extinguished," said Babbalanja. "No, no; Dominora ne'er can burn with Franko's fires; only those of her own kindling may consume her."

"Away! away!" cried Media. "We may not touch Porpheero now. Up sails! and westward be our course."

So dead before the blast, we scudded.

Morning broke, showing no signs of land.

"Hard must it go with Franko's king," said Media, "when his people rise against him with the red volcanoes. Oh, for a foot to crush them! Hard, too, with all who rule in broad Porpheero. And may she we seek survive this conflagration!"

"My lord," said Babbalanja, "where'ere she hide, ne'er yet did Yillah lurk in this Porpheero; nor have we missed the maiden, noble Taji! in not touching at its shores."

"This fire must make a desert of the land," said Mohi; "burn up and bury all her tilth."

"Yet, Mohi, vineyards flourish over buried villages," murmured Yoomy.

"True, minstrel," said Babbalanja, "and prairies are purified by fire. Ashes breed loam. Nor can any skill make the same surface forever fruitful. In all times past, things have been overlaid; and though the first fruits of the marl are wild and poisonous, the palms at last spring forth; and once again the tribes repose in shade. My lord, if calms breed storms, so storms calms; and all this dire commotion must eventuate in peace. It may be, that Perpheero's future has been cheaply won."

Chapter CLIV

Wherein King Media Celebrates the Glories of Autumn; the Minstrel, the Promise of Spring

"Ho, now!" cried Media, "across the wide waters, for that new Mardi, Vivenza! Let us, indeed, see whether she who eludes us elsewhere, be at last found in Vivenza's vales."

"There or nowhere, noble Taji," said Yoomy.

"Be not too sanguine, gentle Yoomy," said Babbalanja.

"Does Yillah choose rather to bower in the wild wilderness of Vivenza, than in the old vineyards of Porpheero?" said Braid-Beard.

Sang Yoomy:

Her bower is not of the vine,
But the wild, wild eglantine!
Not climbing a moldering arch,
But upheld by the fir-green larch.
Old ruins she flies:
To new valleys she hies;—
Not the hoar, moss-wood,
Ivied trees each a rood—
Not in Maramma she dwells,
Hollow with hermit cells.

'Tis a new, new isle!
An infant's its smile,
Soft-rocked by the sea.
Its bloom all in bud;
No tide at its flood,
In that fresh-born sea!

Spring! Spring! where she dwells,
In her sycamore dells,
Where Mardi is young and new;
Its verdure all eyes with dew.
There, there! in the bright, balmy morns,
The young deer sprout their horns,
Deep-tangled in new-branching groves,
Where the Red-Rover Robin roves—

Stooping his crest,
To his molting breast—
Rekindling the flambeau there!
Spring! Spring! where she dwells,
In her sycamore dells,
Where, fulfilling their fates,
All creatures seek mates—
The thrush, the doe, and the hare!

"Thou art most musical, sweet Yoomy," said Media, "concerning this spring-land Vivenza. But are not the old autumnal valleys of Porpheero more glorious than those of vernal Vivenza? Vivenza shows no trophies of the summer time, but Dominora's full-blown rose hangs blushing on her garden walls; her autumn groves are glory-dyed."

"My lord, autumn soon merges in winter, but the spring has all the seasons before. The full-blown rose is nearer withering than the bud. The faint morn is a blossom; the crimson sunset the flower."

Chapter CLV

IN WHICH AZZAGEDDI SEEMS TO USE BABBALANJA FOR A MOUTH-PIECE

PORPHEERO FAR ASTERN, THE SPIRITS OF THE COMPANY ROSE. ONCE AGAIN, OLD MOHI SERENELY unbraided, and rebraided his beard; and sitting Turk-wise on his mat, my lord Media smoking his gonfalon, diverted himself with the wild songs of Yoomy, the wild chronicles of Mohi, or the still wilder speculations of Babbalanja; now and then, as from pitcher to pitcher, pouring royal old wine down his soul.

Among other things, Media, who at times turned over Babbalanja for an encyclopaedia, however unreliable, demanded information upon the subject of neap tides and their alleged slavish vassalage to the moon.

When true to his cyclopediatic nature, Babbalanja quoted from a still older and better authority than himself; in brief, from no other than eternal Bardianna. It seems that that worthy essayist had discussed the whole matter in a chapter thus headed: "On seeing into Mysteries through Mill-Stones"; and throughout his disquisitions he evinced such a profundity of research, though delivered in a style somewhat equivocal, that the company were much struck by the erudition displayed.

"Babbalanja, that Bardianna of yours must have been a wonderful student," said Media after a pause, "no doubt he consumed whole thickets of rushlights."

"Not so, my lord. 'Patience, patience, philosopher,' said Bardianna; 'blow out your tapers, bolt not your dinners, take time, wisdom will be plenty soon.' "

"A notable hint! Why not follow it, Babbalanja?"

"Because, my lord, I have overtaken it, and passed on."

"True to your nature, Babbalanja; you stay nowhere."

"Ay, keep moving is my motto; but speaking of hard students, did my lord ever hear of Midni, the ontologist and entomologist?"

"No."

"Then, my lord, you shall hear of him now. Midni was of opinion that daylight was vulgar; good enough for taro-planting and traveling; but wholly unadapted to the sublime ends of study. He toiled by night; from sunset to sunrise poring over the works of the old logicians. Like most philosophers, Midni was an amiable man; but one thing invariably put him out. He read in the woods by glow-worm light; insect in hand, tracing over his pages, line by line. But glow-worm burns not long; and in the midst of some calm intricate thought, at some imminent comma, the insect often expired, and Midni groped for a meaning. Upon such an occasion, 'Ho, Ho,' he cried, 'but for one instant of sunlight to see my way to a period!' But sunlight there was none; so Midni sprang to his feet, and parchment under arm, raced about among the sloughs and bogs for another glow-worm. Often, making a rapid descent with his turban, he thought he had caged a prize; but nay. Again he tried; yet with no better succcess. Nevertheless, at last he secured one; but hardly had he read three lines by its light, when out it went. Again and again this occurred. And thus he forever went halting and stumbling through his studies, and plunging through his quagmires after a glim."

At this ridiculous tale, one of our silliest paddlers burst into uncontrollable mirth. Offended at which breach of decorum, Media sharply rebuked him.

But he protested he could not help laughing.

Again Media was about to reprimand him, when Babbalanja begged leave to interfere.

"My lord, he is not to blame. Mark how earnestly he struggles to suppress his mirth; but he cannot. It has often been the same with myself. And many a time have I not only vainly sought to check my laughter, but at some recitals I have both laughed and cried. But can opposite emotions be simultaneous in one being? No, I wanted to weep; but my body wanted to smile; and between us we almost choked. My lord Media, this man's body laughs; not the man himself."

"But his body is his own, Babbalanja; and he should have it under better control."

"The common error, my lord. Our souls belong to our bodies, not our bodies to our souls. For which has the care of the other? which keeps house? which looks after the replenishing of the aorta and auricles, and stores away the secretions? Which toils and ticks while the other sleeps? Which is ever giving timely hints, and elderly warnings? Which is the most authoritative? Our bodies, surely. At a hint you must move; at a notice to quit, you depart. Simpletons show us, that a body can get along almost without a soul; but of a soul getting along without a body, we have no tangible and indisputable proof. My lord, the wisest of us breathe involuntarily. And how many millions there are who live from day to day by the incessant operation of subtle processes in them, of which they know nothing, and care less? Little ween they, of vessels lacteal and lymphatic, of arteries femoral and temporal; of pericranium or pericardium; lymph, chyle, fibrin, albumen, iron in the blood, and pudding in the head; they live by the charity of their bodies, to which they are but butlers. I say, my lord, our bodies are our betters. A soul so simple, that it prefers evil to good, is lodged in a frame whose minutest action is full of unsearchable wisdom. Knowing this superiority of theirs, our bodies are inclined to be willful: our beards grow in spite of us; and as everyone knows, they sometimes grow on dead men."

"You mortals are alive, then, when you are dead, Babbalanja?"

"No, my lord; but our beards survive us."

"An ingenious distinction; go on, philosopher."

"Without bodies, my lord, we Mardians would be minus our strongest motive-passions, those which, in some way or other, root under our every action. Hence, without bodies, we must be something else than we essentially are. Wherefore, that saying imputed to Alma, and which, by his very followers, is deemed the most hard to believe of all his instructions, and the most at variance with all preconceived notions of immortality, I, Babbalanja, account the most reasonable of his doctrinal teachings. It is this—that at the last day, every man shall rise in the flesh."

"Pray, Babbalanja, talk not of resurrections to a demi-god."

"Then let me rehearse a story, my lord. You will find it in the *Very Merry Marvelings* of the Improvisitor Quiddi; and a quaint book it is. Fugle-fi is its finis: fugle-fi, fugle-fo, fugle-fogle-orum!"

"That wild look in his eye again," murmured Yoomy.

"Proceed, Azzageddi," said Media.

"The philosopher Grando had a sovereign contempt for his carcass. Often he picked a quarrel with it; and always was flying out in its disparagement. 'Out upon you, you beggarly body! you clog, drug, drag! You keep me from flying; I could get along better without you. Out upon you, I say, you vile pantry, cellar, sink, sewer; abominable body! what vile thing are you not? And think you, beggar! to have the upper hand of me? Make a leg to that man, if you dare, without my permission. This smell is intolerable; but turn from it, if you can, unless I give the word. Bolt this yam! it is done. Carry me across yon field! off we go. Stop! it's a dead halt. There, I've trained you enough for to-day, now, sirrah, crouch down in the shade, and be quiet. I'm rested. So, here's for a stroll, and a reverie homeward. Up, carcass, and march.' So the carcass demurely rose and paced, and the philosopher meditated. He was intent upon squaring the circle; but bump he came against a bough. 'How now, clodhopping bumpkin! you would take advantage of my reveries, would you? But I'll be even with you'; and seizing a cudgel, he laid across his shoulders with right good-will. But one of his back-handed thwacks injured his spinal cord; the philosopher dropped; but presently came to. 'Adzooks! I'll bend or break you! Up, up, and I'll run you home for this.' But wonderful to tell, his legs refused to budge; all sensation had left them. But a huge wasp happening to sting his foot, not him, for he felt it not, the leg incontinently sprang into the air, and of itself, cut all manner of capers. 'Be still! Down with you!' But the leg refused. 'My arms are still loyal,' thought Grando; and with them he at last managed to confine his refractory member. But all commands, volitions, and persuasions, were as naught to induce his limbs to carry him home. It was a solitary place, and five days after, Grando the philosopher was found dead under a tree."

"Ha! ha!" laughed Media, "Azzageddi is full as merry as ever."

"But, my lord," continued Babbalanja, "some creatures have still more perverse bodies than Grando's. In the fables of Ridendiabola, this is to be found. 'A fresh-water Polyp, despising its marine existence, longed to live upon air. But all it could do, its tentacles or arms still continued to cram its stomach. By a sudden preternatural impulse, however, the Polyp at last turned itself inside out; supposing that after such a proceeding it would have no gastronomic interior. But its body proved ventricle outside as well as in. Again its arms went to work; food was tossed in, and digestion continued!' "

"Is the literal part of that a fact?" asked Mohi.

"True as truth," said Babbalanja, "the Polyp will live turned inside out."

"Somewhat curious, certainly," said Media. "But methinks, Babbalanja, that somewhere I have heard something about organic functions, so called; which may account for the phenomena you mention; and I have heard too, methinks, of what are called reflex actions of the nerves, which, duly considered, might deprive of its strangeness that story of yours concerning Grando and his body."

"Mere substitutions of sounds for inexplicable meanings, my lord. In some things science cajoles us. Now, what is undeniable of the Polyp, some physiologists analogically maintain with regard to us Mardians; that, forasmuch, as the lining of our interiors is nothing more than a continuation of the epidermis, or scarf-skin, therefore, that in a remote age, we too must have been turned wrong side out, an hypothesis, which, indirectly might account for our moral perversities; and also, for that otherwise nonsensical term—'the coat of the stomach'; for originally it must have been a surtout, instead of an inner garment."

"Pray, Azzageddi," said Media, "are you not a fool?"

"One of a jolly company, my lord; but some creatures besides wearing their surtouts within, sport their skeletons without; witness the lobster and turtle, who, alive, study their own anatomies."

"Azzageddi, you are a zany."

"Pardon, my lord," said Mohi, "I think him more of a lobster; it's hard telling his jaws from his claws."

"Yes, Braid-Beard, I am a lobster, a mackerel, anything you please; but my ancestors were kangaroos, not monkeys, as old Boddo erroneously opined. My idea is more susceptible of demonstration than his. Among the deepest discovered land fossils, the relics of kangaroos are discernible, but no relics of men. Hence, there were no giants in those days; but on the contrary, kangaroos; and those kangaroos formed the first edition of mankind; since revised and corrected."

"What has become of our finises, or tails, then?" asked Mohi, wriggling in his seat.

"The old question, Mohi. But where are the tails of the tadpoles, after their gradual metamorphosis into frogs? Have frogs any tails, old man? Our tails, Mohi, were worn off by the process of civilization; especially at the period when our fathers began to adopt the sitting posture; the fundamental evidence of all civilization, for neither apes, nor savages, can be said to sit; invariably, they squat on their hams. Among barbarous tribes benches and settles are unknown. But, my lord Media, as your liege and loving subject, I cannot sufficiently deplore the deprivation of your royal tail. That stiff and vertebrated member, as we find it in those rustic kinsmen we have disowned, would have been useful as a supplement to your royal legs; and whereas my good lord is now fain to totter on two stanchions, were he only a kangaroo, like the monarchs of old, the majesty of Odo would be dignified, by standing firm on a tripod."

"A very witty conceit! But have a care, Azzageddi; your theory applies not to me."

"Babbalanja," said Mohi, "you must be the last of the kangaroos."

"I am, Mohi."

"But the old-fashioned pouch or purse of your grandams?" hinted Media.

"My lord, I take it, that must have been transferred; nowadays our sex carries the purse."

"Ha, ha!"

"My lord, why this mirth? Let us be serious. Although man is no longer a kangaroo, he may be said to be an inferior species of plant. Plants proper are perhaps insensible of the circulation of their sap; we mortals are physically unconscious of the circulation of the blood; and for many ages were not even aware of the fact. Plants know nothing of their interiors; three score years and ten we trundle about ours, and never get a peep at them; plants stand on their stalks; we stalk on our legs; no plant flourishes over its dead root; dead in the grave, man lives no longer above ground; plants die without food: so we. And now for the difference. Plants elegantly inhale nourishment, without looking it up: like lords, they stand still and are served; and though green, never suffer from the colic; whereas, we mortals must forage all round for our food; we cram our insides; and are loaded down with odious sack and intestines. Plants make love and multiply; but excel us in all amorous enticements, wooing and winning by soft pollens and essences. Plants abide in one place, and live; we must travel or die. Plants flourish without us: we must perish without them."

"Enough, Azzageddi!" cried Media. "Open not thy lips till to-morrow."

Chapter CLVI

THE CHARMING YOOMY SINGS

THE MORROW CAME; AND THREE ABREAST, WITH SNORTING PROWS, WE RACED ALONG; OUR MATsails panting to the breeze. All present partook of the life of the air; and unanimously Yoomy was called upon for a song. The canoes were passing a long, white reef, sparkling with shells, like a jeweler's case; and thus Yoomy sang in the same old strain as of yore; beginning aloud,

Her sweet, sweet mouth!
The peach-pearl shell:—
Red edged its lips,
That softly swell,
Just oped to speak,
With blushing cheek,
That fisherman
With lonely spear
On the reef ken,
And lift to ear
Its voice to hear—
Soft sighing South!
Like this, like this—
The rosy kiss!—
That maiden's mouth.

A shell! a shell!
A vocal shell!
Song-dreaming,
In its inmost dell!

Her bosom! Two buds half blown, they tell;
A little valley between perfuming;
That roves away,
Deserting the day—
The day of her eyes illuming;—
That roves away, o'er slope and fell,
Till a soft, soft meadow becomes the dell.

Thus far, old Mohi had been wriggling about in his seat, twitching his beard, and at every couplet looking up expectantly, as if he desired the company to think, that he was counting upon that line as the last. But now, starting to his feet, he exclaimed, "Hold, minstrel! thy muse's drapery is becoming disordered: no more!"

"Then no more it shall be," said Yoomy. "But you have lost a glorious sequel."

Chapter CLVII

THEY DRAW NIGH UNTO LAND

IN GOOD TIME, AFTER MANY DAYS' SAILING, WE SNUFFED THE LAND FROM AFAR, AND CAME TO A great country, full of inland mountains, north and south stretching far out of sight.

"All hail, Kolumbo!" cried Yoomy.

Coasting by a portion of it, which Mohi called Kanneeda, a province of King Bello's, we perceived the groves rocking in the wind; their flexible boughs bending like bows; and the leaves flying forth, and darkening the landscape, like flocks of pigeons.

"Those groves must soon fall," said Mohi.

"Not so," said Babbalanja. "My lord, as these violent gusts are formed by the hostile meeting of two currents, one from over the lagoon, the other from land; they may be taken as significant of the occasional variances between Kanneeda and Dominora."

"Ay," said Media, "and as Mohi hints, the breeze from Dominora must soon overthrow the groves of Kanneeda."

"Not if the land-breeze holds, my lord; one breeze oft blows another home. Stand up, and gaze! From cape to cape, this whole main we see, is young and froward. And far southward, past this Kanneeda and Vivenza, are haughty, overbearing streams, which at their mouths dam back the ocean, and long refuse to mix their freshness with the foreign brine: so bold, so strong, so bent on hurling off aggression is this brave main, Kolumbo; last sought, last found, Mardi's estate, so long kept back; pray Oro, it be not squandered foolishly. Here lie plantations, held in fee by stout hearts and arms; and boundless fields, that may be had for seeing. Here, your foes are forests, struck down with bloodless maces. Ho! Mardi's Poor, and Mardi's Strong! ye, who starve or beg; seventh sons who slave for earth's first-born—here is your home; predestinated yours. Come over, Empire-founders! fathers of the wedded tribes to come! abject now, illustrious evermore. Ho: Sinew, Brawn, and Thigh!"

"A very fine invocation," said Media; "now Babbalanja, be seated; and tell us whether Dominora and the kings of Porpheero do not own some small portion of this great continent, which just now you poetically pronounced as the spoil of any vagabonds who may choose to settle therein? Is not Kanneeda, Dominora's?"

"And was not Vivenza once Dominora's also? And what Vivenza now is, Kanneeda soon must be. I speak not, my lord, as wishful of what I say, but simply as foreknowing it. The thing must come. Vain for Dominora to claim allegiance from all the progeny she spawns. As well might the old patriarch of the flood reappear, and claim the right of rule over all mankind, as descended from the loins of his three roving sons.

" 'Tis the old law—the east peoples the west, the west the east; flux and reflux. And time may come, after the rise and fall of nations yet unborn, that, risen from its future ashes, Porpheero shall be the promised land, and from her surplus hordes, Kolumbo people it."

Still coasting on, next day, we came to Vivenza; and as Media desired to land first at a point midway between its extremities, in order to behold the convocation of chiefs supposed to be assembled at this season, we held on our way, till we gained a lofty ridge, jutting out into the lagoon, a bastion to the neighboring land. It terminated in a lofty natural arch of solid trap. Billows beat against its base. But above, waved an inviting copse, wherein was revealed an open temple of canes, containing one only image, that of a helmeted female, the tutelar deity of Vivenza.

The canoes drew near.

"Lo! what inscription is that?" cried Media; "there chiseled over the arch?"

Studying those immense hieroglyphics awhile, antiquarian Mohi still eyeing them, said slowly:

"In-this-re-publi-can-land-all-men-are-born-free-and-equal."

"False!" said Media.

"And how long stay they so?" said Babbalanja.

"But look lower, old man," cried Media, "methinks there's a small hieroglyphic or two hidden away in yonder angle. Interpret them, old man."

After much screwing of his eyes, for those characters were very minute, Champollion Mohi thus spoke: "Except-the-tribe-of-Hamo."

"That nullifies the other," cried Media. "Ah, ye republicans!"

"It seems to have been added for a postscript," rejoined Braid-Beard, screwing his eyes again.

"Perhaps so," said Babbalanja, "but some wag must have done it."

Shooting through the arch, we rapidly gained the beach.

Chapter CLVIII

They Visit the Great Central Temple of Vivenza

The throng that greeted us upon landing were exceedingly boisterous.

"Whence came ye?" they cried. "Whither bound? Saw ye ever such a land as this? Is it not a great and extensive republic? Pray, observe how tall we are; just feel of our thighs; are we not a glorious people? Here, feel of our beards. Look round; look round; be not afraid. Behold those palms; swear now, that this land surpasses all others. Old Bello's mountains are mole-hills to ours; his rivers, rills; his empires, villages; his palm-trees, shrubs."

"True," said Babbalanja. "But great Oro must have had some hand in making your mountains and streams. Would ye have been as great in a desert?"

"Where is your king?" asked Media drawing himself up in his robe, and cocking his crown.

"Ha, ha, my fine fellow! We are all kings here; royalty breathes in the common air. But come on, come on. Let us show you our great Temple of Freedom."

And so saying, irreverently grasping his sacred arm, they conducted us toward a lofty structure, planted upon a bold hill, and supported by thirty pillars of palm; four quite green; as if recently added; and beyond these, an almost interminable vacancy, as if all the palms in Mardi were, at some future time, to aid in upholding that fabric.

Upon the summit of the temple was a staff; and as we drew nigh, a man with a collar round his neck, and the red marks of stripes upon his back, was just in the act of hoisting a tappa standard—correspondingly striped. Other collared menials were going in and out of the temple.

Near the porch, stood an image like that on the top of the arch we had seen. Upon its pedestal, were pasted certain hieroglyphical notices; according to Mohi, offering rewards for missing men, so many hands high.

Entering the temple, we beheld an amphitheatrical space, in the middle of which, a great fire was burning. Around it, were many chiefs, robed in long togas, and presenting strange contrasts in their style of tattooing.

Some were sociably laughing, and chatting; others diligently making excavations between their teeth with slivers of bamboo; or turning their heads into mills, were grinding up leaves and ejecting their juices. Some were busily inserting the down of a thistle into their ears. Several stood erect, intent upon maintaining striking attitudes; their javelins tragically crossed upon their chests. They would have looked very imposing were it not, that in rear their vesture was sadly disordered. Others, with swelling fronts, seemed chiefly indebted to their dinners for their dignity. Many were nodding and napping. And, here and there, were sundry indefatigable worthies, making a great show of imperious and indispensable business; sedulously folding banana leaves into scrolls, and recklessly placing them into the hands of little boys, in gay turbans and trim little girdles, who thereupon fled as if with salvation for the dying.

It was a crowded scene; the dusky chiefs here and there, grouped together, and their fantastic tattooings showing like the carved work on quaint old chimney-stacks seen from afar. But one of their number overtopped all the rest. As when, drawing nigh unto old Rome, amid the crowd of sculptured columns and gables, St. Peter's grand dome soars far aloft, serene in the upper air; so, showed one calm grand forehead among those of this mob of chieftains. That head was Saturnina's. Gall and Spurzheim! saw you ever such a brow?—poised like an avalanche, under the shadow of a forest! woe betide the devoted valleys below! Lavatar! behold those lips, like mystic scrolls! Those eyes, like panthers' caves at the base of Popocatepetl!

"By my right hand, Saturnina," cried Babbalanja, "but thou wert made in the image of thy Maker! Yet, have I beheld men, to the eye as commanding as thou; and surmounted by heads globe-like as thine, who never had thy caliber. We must measure brains, not heads, my lord; else, the sperm whale, with his tun of an occiput, would transcend us all."

Nearby, were arched ways, leading to subterranean places, whence issued a savory steam, and an extraordinary clattering of calabashes, and smacking of lips, as if something were being eaten down there by the fattest of fat fellows, with the heartiest of appetites, and the most irresistible of relishes. It was a quaffing, guzzling, gobbling noise. Peeping down, we beheld a company, breasted up against a board, groaning under numerous viands. In the middle of all, was a mighty great gourd, yellow as gold, and jolly round like a pumpkin in October, and so big it must have grown in the sun. Thence flowed a tide of red wine. And before it, stood plenty of paunches being filled therewith like portly stone jars at a fountain. Melancholy to tell, before that fine flood of old wine, and among those portly old topers, was a lean man; who occasionally ducked in his bill. He looked like an ibis standing in the Nile at flood tide; among a tongue-lapping herd of hippopotami.

They were jolly as the jolliest; and laughed as uproariously, that their hemispheres all quivered and shook, like vast provinces in an earthquake. Ha! ha! ha! how they laughed, and they roared. A deaf man might have heard them; and no milk could have soured within a forty-two-pounder ball shot of that place.

Now, the smell of good things is no very bad thing in itself. It is the savor of good things beyond; proof positive of a glorious good meal. So snuffing up those zephyrs from Araby the blessed, those boisterous gales, blowing from out the mouths of baked boars, stuffed with bread-fruit, bananas, and sage, we would fain have gone down and partaken.

But this could not be; for we were told that those worthies below were a club in secret conclave; very busy in settling certain weighty state affairs upon a solid basis. They were all chiefs of immense capacity—how many gallons, there was no finding out.

Be sure, now, a most riotous noise came up from those catacombs, which seemed full of the ghosts of fat Lamberts; and this uproar it was, that heightened the din above-ground.

But, heedless of all, in the midst of the amphitheater, stood a tall, gaunt warrior, ferociously tattooed, with a beak like a buzzard; long dusty locks, and his hands full of headless arrows. He was laboring under violent paroxysms; three benevolent individuals essaying to hold him. But repeatedly breaking loose, he burst anew into his delirium; while with an absence of sympathy, distressing to behold, the rest of the assembly seemed wholly engrossed with themselves; nor did they appear to care how soon the unfortunate lunatic might demolish himself by his frantic proceedings.

Toward one side of the amphitheatrical space, perched high upon an elevated dais, sat a white-headed old man with a tomahawk in his hand, earnestly engaged in overseeing the tumult, though not a word did he say. Occasionally, however, he was regarded by those present with a mysterious sort of deference; and when they chanced to pass between him and the crazy man, they invariably did so in a stooping position; probably to elude the atmospheric grape and canister continually flying from the mouth of the lunatic.

"What mob is this?" cried Media.

" 'Tis the grand council of Vivenza," cried a bystander. "Hear ye not Alanno?" and he pointed to the lunatic.

Now coming close to Alanno, we found, that with incredible volubility, he was addressing the assembly upon some all-absorbing subject connected with King Bello, and his presumed encroachments towards the north-west of Vivenza.

One hand smiting his hip, and the other his head, the lunatic thus proceeded; roaring like a wild beast, and beating the air like a windmill:

"I have said it! the thunder is flashing, the lightning is crashing! already there's an earthquake in Dominora! Full soon will old Bello discover that his diabolical machinations against this ineffable land must soon come to naught. Who dare not declare, that we are not invincible? I repeat it, we are. Ha! ha! Audacious Bello must bite the dust! Hair by hair, we will trail his gory gray beard at the end of our spears! Ha! ha! I grow hoarse, but would mine were a voice like the wild bulls of Bullorom, that I might be heard from one end of this great and gorgeous land to its farthest zenith; ay, to the uttermost diameter of its circumference. Awake! oh, Vivenza. The signs of the times are portentous; nay, extraordinary; I hesitate not to add, peculiar! Up! up! Let us not descend to the bathos, when we should soar to the climax! Does not all Mardi wink and look on? Is the great sun itself a frigid spectator? Then let us double up our mandibles to the deadly encounter. Methinks I see it now. Old Bello is crafty, and his oath is recorded to obliterate us! Across this wide lagoon he casts his serpent eyes; whets his insatiate bill; mumbles his barbarous tusks; licks his forked tongues; and who knows when we shall have the shark in our midst? Yet be not deceived; for though as yet Bello has forborne molesting us openly, his emissaries are at work; his infernal sappers, and miners, and wet-nurses, and midwives, and grave-diggers, are busy! His canoe-yards are all in commotion! In navies his forests are being launched upon the wave; and ere long typhoons, zephyrs, white squalls, balmy breezes, hurricanes, and besoms will be raging round us?"

His philippic concluded, Alanno was conducted from the place; and being now quite exhausted, cold cobblestones were applied to his temples, and he was treated to a bath in a stream.

This chieftain, it seems, was from a distant western valley, called Hio-Hio, one of the largest and most fertile in Vivenza, though but recently settled. Its inhabitants and those of the vales adjoining—a right sturdy set of fellows—were accounted the most dogmatically democratic and ultra of all the tribes in Vivenza; ever seeking to push on their brethren to the uttermost; and especially were they bitter against Bello. But they were a fine young tribe, nevertheless. Like strong new wine they worked violently in becoming clear. Time, perhaps, would make them all right.

An interval of greater uproar than ever now ensued; during which, with his tomahawk, the white-headed old man repeatedly thumped and pounded the seat where he sat, apparently to augment the din, though he looked anxious to suppress it.

At last, tiring of his posture, he whispered in the ear of a chief, his friend; who, approaching a portly warrior present, prevailed upon him to rise and address the assembly. And no sooner did this one do so, than the whole convocation dispersed, as if to their yams; and with a grin, the little old man leaped from his seat, and stretched his legs on a mat.

The fire was now extinguished, and the temple deserted.

Chapter CLIX

Wherein Babbalanja Comments upon the Speech of Alanno

As we lingered in the precincts of the temple after all others had departed, sundry comments were made upon what we had seen; and having remarked the hostility of the lunatic orator towards Dominora, Babbalanja thus addressed Media:

"My lord, I am constrained to believe, that all Vivenza cannot be of the same mind with the grandiloquent chief from Hio-Hio. Nevertheless, I imagine, that between Dominora and this land, there exists at bottom a feeling akin to animosity, which is not yet wholly extinguished; though but the smoldering embers of a once raging fire. My lord, you may call it poetry if you will, but there are nations in Mardi, that to others stand in the relation of sons to sires. Thus with Dominora and Vivenza. And though, its majority attained, Vivenza is now its own master, yet should it not fail in a reverential respect for its parent. In man or nation, old age is honorable; and a boy, however tall, should never take his sire by the beard. And though Dominora did indeed ill merit Vivenza's esteem, yet by abstaining from criminations, Vivenza should ever merit its own. And if in time to come, which Oro forbid, Vivenza must needs go to battle with King Bello, let Vivenza first cross the old veteran's spear with all possible courtesy. On the other hand, my lord, King Bello should never forget that whatever be glorious in Vivenza, redounds to himself. And as some gallant old lord proudly measures the brawn and stature of his son, and joys to view in his noble young lineaments the likeness of his own; bethinking him, that when at last laid in his tomb, he will yet survive in the long, strong life of his child, the worthy inheritor of his valor and renown; even so, should King Bello regard the generous promise of this young Vivenza of his own lusty begetting. My lord, behold these two states! Of all nations in the Archipelago, they alone are one in blood. Dominora is the last and greatest Anak of Old Times; Vivenza, the foremost and goodliest stripling of the Present. One is full of the past; the other brims with the future. Ah! did this sire's old heart but beat to free thoughts, and back his bold son, all Mardi would go down before them. And high Oro may have ordained for them a career, little divined by the mass. Methinks, that as Vivenza will never cause old Bello to weep for his son, so, Vivenza will not, this many a long year, be called to weep over the grave of his sire. And though King Bello may yet lay aside his old-fashioned cocked hat of a crown, and comply with the plain costume of the times, yet will his frame remain sturdy as of yore, and equally grace any habiliments he may don. And those who say, Dominora is old and worn out, may very possibly err. For if, as a nation, Dominora be old—her present generation is full as young as the youths in any land under the sun. Then, ho! worthy twain! Each worthy the other, join hands on the instant, and weld them together. Lo! the past is a prophet. Be the future, its prophecy fulfilled."

Chapter CLX

A Scene in the Land of Warwicks, or King-makers

WENDING OUR WAY FROM THE TEMPLE, WE WERE ACCOMPANIED BY A FLUENT, OBSTREPEROUS wight, one Znobbi, a runaway native of Porpheero, but now an inhabitant of Vivenza.

"Here comes our great chief!" he cried. "Behold him! It was I that had a hand in making him what he is!"

And so saying, he pointed out a personage, no way distinguished, except by the tattooing on his forehead—stars, thirty in number; and an uncommonly long spear in his hand. Freely, he mingled with the crowd.

"Behold, how familiar I am with him!" cried Znobbi, approaching, and pitcher-wise taking him by the handle of his face.

"Friend," said the dignitary, "thy salute is peculiar, but welcome. I reverence the enlightened people of this land."

"Mean-spirited hound!" muttered Media; "were I him, I had impaled that audacious plebeian."

"There's a Head-Chief for you, now, my fine fellow!" cried Znobbi. "Hurrah! Three cheers! Ay, ay! All kings here—all equal. Everything's in common."

Here, a bystander, feeling something grazing his side, looked down; and perceived Znobbi's hand in clandestine vicinity to the pouch at his girdle-end.

Whereupon the crowd shouted, "A thief! a thief!" And with a loud voice the starred chief cried, "Seize him, people, and tie him to yonder tree."

And they seized and tied him on the spot.

"Ah," said Media, "this chief has something to say, after all; he pinions a king at a word, though a plebeian takes him by the nose. Beshrew me, I doubt not, that spear of his, though without a tassel, is longer and sharper than mine."

"There's not so much freedom here as these freemen think," said Babbalanja, turning; "I laugh and admire."

Chapter CLXI

They Hearken unto a Voice from the Gods

Next day we retraced our voyage northward, to visit that section of Vivenza. In due time we landed.

To look round was refreshing. Of all the lands we had seen, none looked more promising. The groves stood tall and green; the fields spread flush and broad; the dew of the first morning seemed hardly vanished from the grass. On all sides was heard the fall of waters, the swarming of bees, and the rejoicing hum of a thriving population.

"Ha, ha!" laughed Yoomy. "Labor laughs in this land; and claps his hands in the jubilee groves! methinks that Yillah will yet be found."

Generously entertained, we tarried in this land; till at length, from over the lagoon, came full tidings of the eruption we had witnessed in Franko, with many details. The conflagration had spread through Porpheero; and the kings were to and fro hunted like malefactors by blood-hounds; all that part of Mardi was heaving with throes.

With the utmost delight, these tidings were welcomed by many; yet others heard them with boding concern.

Those, too, there were, who rejoiced that the kings were cast down; but mourned that the people themselves stood not firmer. A victory, turned to no wise and enduring account, said they, is no victory at all. Some victories revert to the vanquished.

But day by day great crowds ran down to the beach, in wait for canoes periodically bringing further intelligence. Every hour new cries startled the air. "Hurrah! another kingdom is burned down to the earth's edge; another demi-god is unhelmed; another republic is dawning. Shake hands, freemen, shake hands! Soon will we hear of Dominora down in the dust; of hapless Verdanna free as ourselves; all Porpheero's volcanoes are bursting! Who may withstand the people? The times tell terrible tales to tyrants! Ere we die, freemen, all Mardi will be free!"

Overhearing these shouts, Babbalanja thus addressed Media—"My lord, I cannot but believe, that these men are far more excited than those with whom they so ardently sympathize. But no wonder. The single discharges which are heard in Porpheero, here come condensed in one tremendous report. Every arrival is a firing off of events by platoons."

Now, during this tumultuous interval, King Media very prudently kept himself exceedingly quiet. He doffed his regalia; and in all things carried himself with a dignified discretion. And many hours he absented himself; none knowing whither he went, or what his employment.

So also with Babbalanja. But still pursuing our search, at last we all journeyed into a great valley, whose inhabitants were more than commonly inflated with the ardor of the times.

Rambling on, we espied a clamorous crowd gathered about a conspicuous palm, against which a scroll was fixed.

The people were violently agitated; storming out maledictions against the insolent knave, who, overnight must have fixed there that scandalous document. But whoever he may have been, certain it was, he had contrived to hood himself effectually.

After much vehement discussion, during which sundry inflammatory harangues were made from the stumps of trees nearby, it was proposed, that the scroll should be read aloud, so that all might give ear.

Seizing it, a fiery youth mounted upon the bowed shoulders of an old man, his sire; and with a shrill voice, ever and anon interrupted by outcries, read as follows:

"Sovereign Kings of Vivenza! it is fit you should hearken to wisdom. But well aware, that you give ear to little wisdom except of your own; and that as freemen, you are free to hunt down him who dissents from your majesties; I deem it proper to address you anonymously.

"And if it please you, you may ascribe this voice to the gods, for never will you trace it to man.

"It is not unknown, sovereign kings! that in these boisterous days, the lessons of history are almost discarded, as superseded by present experiences. And that while all Mardi's Present has grown out of its Past, it is becoming obsolete to refer to what has been. Yet, peradventure, the Past is an apostle.

"The grand error of this age, sovereign kings! is the general supposition, that the very special Diabolus is abroad; whereas, the very special Diabolus has been abroad ever since Mardi began.

"And the grand error of your nation, sovereign kings! seems this—The conceit that Mardi is now in the last scene of the last act of her drama; and that all preceding events were ordained to bring about the catastrophe you believe to be at hand—a universal and permanent Republic.

"May it please you, those who hold to these things, are fools, and not wise.

"Time is made up of various ages; and each thinks its own a novelty. But imbedded in the walls of the pyramids, which outrun all chronologies, sculptured stones are found, belonging to yet older fabrics. And as in the mound-building period of yore, so every age thinks its erections will forever endure. But as your forests grow apace, sovereign kings! overrunning the tumuli in your western vales; so, while deriving their substance from the past, succeeding generations overgrow it; but in time, themselves decay.

"Oro decrees these vicissitudes.

"In chronicles of old, you read, sovereign kings! that an eagle from the clouds presaged royalty to the fugitive Taquinoo; and a king, Taquinoo reigned. No end to my dynasty, thought he.

"But another omen descended, foreshadowing the fall of Zooperbi, his son; and Zooperbi, returning from his camp, found his country a fortress against him. No more kings would she have. And for five hundred twelve-moons, the Regifugium, or King's-flight, was annually celebrated like your own jubilee-day. And rampant young orators stormed out detestation of kings; and augurs swore that their birds presaged immortality to freedom.

"Then, Romara's free eagles flew over all Mardi, and perched on the topmost diadems of the east.

"Ever thus must it be.

"For, mostly, monarchs are as gemmed bridles upon the world, checking the plungings of a steed from the Pampas. And republics are as vast reservoirs, draining down all streams to one level; and so, breeding a fullness which cannot remain full, without overflowing. And thus, Romara flooded all Mardi, till scarce an Ararat was left of the lofty kingdoms which had been.

"Thus, also, did Franko, fifty twelve-moons ago. Thus may she do again. And though not yet, have you, sovereign kings! in any large degree done likewise, it is because you overflow your redundancies within your own mighty borders; having a wild western waste, which many shepherds with their flocks could not overrun in a day. Yet overrun at last it will be; and then, the recoil must come.

"And, may it please you, that thus far your chronicles had narrated a very different story, had your population been pressed and packed, like that of your old sire-land Dominora. Then, your great experiment might have proved an explosion; like the chemist's who, stirring his mixture, was blown by it into the air.

"For though crossed, and recrossed by many brave quarterings, and boasting the great Bull in your pedigree; yet, sovereign kings! you are not meditative philosophers like the people of a small republic of old; nor enduring stoics, like their neighbors. Pent up, like them, may it please you, your thirteen original tribes had proved more turbulent, than so many mutinous legions. Free horses need wide prairies; and fortunate for you, sovereign kings! that you have room enough, wherein to be free.

"And, may it please you, you are free, partly, because you are young. Your nation is like a fine, florid youth, full of fiery impulses, and hard to restrain; his strong hand nobly championing his heart. On all sides, freely, he gives, and still seeks to acquire. The breath of his nostrils is like smoke in spring air; every tendon is electric with generous resolves. The oppressor he defies to his beard; the high walls of old opinions he scales with a bound. In the future he sees all the domes of the east.

"But years elapse, and this bold boy is transformed. His eyes open not as of yore; his heart is shut up as a vice. He yields not a groat; and seeking no more acquisitions, is only bent on preserving his hoard. The maxims once trampled under foot, are now printed on his front; and he who hated oppressors, is become an oppressor himself.

"Thus, often, with men; thus, often, with nations. Then marvel not, sovereign kings! that old states are different from yours; and think not, your own must forever remain liberal as now.

"Each age thinks its own is eternal. But though for five hundred twelve-moons, all Romara, by courtesy of history, was republican; yet, at last, her terrible king-tigers came, and spotted themselves with gore.

"And time was, when Dominora was republican, down to her sturdy back-bone. The son of an absolute monarch became the man Karolus; and his crown and head both rolled in the dust. And Dominora had her patriots by thousands; and lusty Defenses, and glorious Areopagiticas were written, not since surpassed; and no turban was doffed save in homage of Oro.

"Yet, may it please you, to the sound of pipe and tabor, the second King Karolus returned in good time; and was hailed gracious majesty by high and low.

"Throughout all eternity, the parts of the past are but parts of the future reversed. In the old foot-prints, up and down, you mortals go, eternally traveling your Sierras. And not more infallible the ponderings of the Calculating Machine than the deductions from the decimals of history.

"In nations, sovereign kings! there is a transmigration of souls; in you, is a marvelous destiny. The eagle of Romara revives in your own mountain bird, and once more is plumed for her flight. Her screams are answered by the vauntful cries of a hawk; his red comb yet reeking with slaughter. And one east, one west, those bold birds may fly, till they lock pinions in the mid-most beyond.

"But, soaring in the sky over the nations that shall gather their broods under their wings, that bloody hawk may hereafter be taken for the eagle.

"And though crimson republics may rise in constellations like fiery Aldebarans, speeding to their culminations; yet, down must they sink at last, and leave the old sultan-sun in the sky; in time, again to be deposed.

"For little longer, may it please you, can republics subsist now, than in days gone by. For, assuming that Mardi is wiser than of old; nevertheless, though all men approached sages in intelligence, some would yet be more wise than others; and so, the old degrees be preserved. And no exemption would an equality of knowledge furnish, from the inbred servility of mortal to mortal; from all the organic causes, which inevitably divide mankind into brigades and battalions, with captains at their head.

"Civilization has not ever been the brother of equality. Freedom was born among the wild eyries in the mountains; and barbarous tribes have sheltered under her wings, when the enlightened people of the plain have nestled under different pinions.

"Though, thus far, for you, sovereign kings! your republic has been fruitful of blessings; yet, in themselves, monarchies are not utterly evil. For many nations, they are better than republics; for many, they will ever so remain. And better, on all hands, that peace should rule with a scepter, than that the tribunes of the people should brandish their broadswords. Better be the subject of a king, upright and just, than a freeman in Franko, with the executioner's ax at every corner.

"It is not the prime end, and chief blessing, to be politically free. And freedom is only good as a means; is no end in itself. Nor, did man fight it out against his masters to the haft, not then, would he uncollar his neck from the yoke. A born thrall to the last, yelping out his liberty, he still remains a slave unto Oro; and well is it for the universe, that Oro's scepter is absolute.

"World-old the saying, that it is easier to govern others, than oneself. And that all men should govern themselves as nations, needs that all men be better, and wiser, than the wisest of one-man rulers. But in no stable democracy do all men govern themselves. Though an army be all volunteers, martial law must prevail. Delegate your power, you leagued mortals must. The hazard you must stand. And though unlike King Bello of Dominora, your great chieftain, sovereign kings! may not declare war of himself; nevertheless, has he done a still more imperial thing—gone to war without declaring intentions. You yourselves were precipitated upon a neighboring nation, ere you knew your spears were in your hands.

"But, as in stars you have written it on the welkin, sovereign kings! you are a great and glorious people. And verily, yours is the best and happiest land under the sun. But not wholly, because you, in your wisdom, decreed it; your origin and geography necessitated it. Nor, in their germ, are all your blessings, to be ascribed to the noble sires, who of yore fought in your behalf, sovereign kings! Your nation enjoyed no little independence before your Declaration declared it. Your ancient pilgrims fathered your liberty; and your wild woods harbored the nursling. For the state that to-day is made up of slaves, cannot to-morrow transmute her bond into free; though lawlessness may transform them into brutes. Freedom is the name for a thing that is *not* freedom; this, a lesson never learned in an hour or an age. By some tribes it will never be learned.

"Yet, if it please you, there may be such a thing as being free under Cæsar. Ages ago, there were as many vital freemen, as breathe vital air to-day.

"Names make not distinctions; some despots rule without swaying scepters. Though King Bello's palace was not put together by yoked men, your federal temple of freedom, sovereign kings! was the handiwork of slaves.

"It is not gildings, and gold maces, and crown jewels alone, that make a people servile. There is much bowing and cringing among you yourselves, sovereign kings! Poverty is abased before riches, all Mardi over; anywhere, it is hard to be a debtor; anywhere, the wise will lord it over fools; everywhere, suffering is found.

"Thus freedom is more social than political. And its real felicity is not to be shared. *That* is of a man's own individual getting and holding. It is not, who rules the state, but who rules me. Better be secure under one king, than exposed to violence from twenty millions of monarchs, though oneself be of the number.

"But superstitious notions you harbor, sovereign kings! Did you visit Dominora, you would not be marched straight into a dungeon. And though you would behold sundry sights displeasing, you would start to inhale such liberal breezes; and hear crowds boasting of their privileges; as you, of yours. Nor has the wine of Dominora, a monarchical flavor.

"Now, though far and wide, to keep equal pace with the times, great reforms, of a verity, be needed; nowhere are bloody revolutions required. Though it be the most certain of remedies, no prudent invalid opens his veins, to let out his disease with his life. And though all evils may be assuaged; all evils cannot be done away. For evil is the chronic malady of the universe; and checked in one place, breaks forth in another.

"Of late, on this head, some wild dreams have departed.

"There are many, who erewhile believed that the age of pikes and javelins was passed; that after a heady and blustering youth, old Mardi was at last settling down into a serene old age; and that the Indian summer first discovered in your land, sovereign kings! was the hazy vapor emitted from its tranquil pipe. But it has not so proved. Mardi's peaces are but truces. Long absent, at last the red comets have returned. And return they must, though their periods be ages. And should Mardi endure till mountain melt into mountain, and all the isles form one table-land, yet, would it but expand the old battle plain.

"Students of history are horror-struck at the massacres of old; but in the shambles, men are being murdered to-day. Could time be reversed, and the future change places with the past, the past would cry out against us, and our future, full as loudly, as we against the ages foregone. All the Ages are his children, calling each other names.

"Hark ye, sovereign kings! cheer not on the yelping pack too furiously. Hunters have been torn by their hounds. Be advised: wash your hands. Hold aloof. Oro has poured out an ocean for an everlasting barrier between you and the worst folly which other republics have perpetrated. That barrier hold sacred. And swear never to cross over to Porpheero, by manifesto or army, unless you traverse dry land.

"And be not too grasping, nearer home. It is not freedom to filch. Expand not your area too widely now. Seek you proselytes? Neighboring nations may be free, without coming under your banner. And if you cannot lay your ambition, know this; that it is best served by waiting events.

"Time, but Time only, may enable you to cross the Equator; and give you the Arctic Circles for your boundaries."

So read the anonymous scroll; which straightway, was torn into shreds.

"Old tory and monarchist!" they shouted. "Preaching over his benighted sermons in these enlightened times! Fool! does he not know that all the Past and its graves are being dug over?"

They were furious; so wildly rolling their eyes after victims, that well was it for King Media, he wore not his crown; and in silence, we moved unnoted from out the crowd.

"My lord, I am amazed at the indiscretion of a demi-god," said Babbalanja, as we passed on our way; "I recognized your sultanic style the very first sentence. This, then, is the result of your hours of seclusion."

"Philosopher! I am astounded at your effrontery; I detected your philosophy the very first maxim. Who posted that parchment for you?"

So, each charged the other with its authorship: and there was no finding out, whether, indeed, either knew aught of its origin.

Now, could it have been Babbalanja? Hardly. For, philosophic as the document was, it seemed too dogmatic and conservative for him. King Media? But though imperially absolute in his political sentiments, Media delivered not himself so boldly, when actually beholding the eruption in Franko.

Indeed, the settlement of this question must be left to the commentators on Mardi, some four or five hundred centuries hence.

Chapter CLXII

They Visit the Extreme South of Vivenza

We penetrated further and further into the valleys around; but though, as elsewhere, at times we heard whisperings that promised an end to our wanderings; we still wandered on; and once again, even Yoomy abated his sanguine hopes.

And now we prepared to embark for the extreme south of the land.

But we were warned by the people, that in that portion of Vivenza, whither we were going, much would be seen repulsive to strangers. Such things, however, indulgent visitors overlooked. For themselves, they were well aware of those evils. Northern Vivenza, had done all it could to assuage them; but in vain, the inhabitants of those southern valleys were a fiery, and intractable race; heeding neither expostulations, nor entreaties. They were wedded to their ways. Nay, they swore, that if the northern tribes persisted in intermeddling they would dissolve the common alliance, and establish a distinct confederacy among themselves.

Our coasting voyage was at an end, our keels grated the beach among many prostrate palms, decaying, and washed by the billows. Though part and parcel of the shore we had left, this region seemed another land. Fewer thriving things were seen; fewer cheerful sounds were heard.

"Here labor has lost his laugh!" cried Yoomy. It was a great plain where we landed; and there, under a burning sun, hundreds of collared men, were toiling in trenches, filled with the taro plant, a root most flourishing in that soil. Standing grimly over these, were men unlike them; armed with long thongs, which descended upon the toilers and made wounds. Blood and sweat mixed; and in great drops fell.

"Who eat these plants thus nourished?" cried Yoomy.

"Are these men?" asked Babbalanja.

"Which mean you?" said Mohi.

Heeding him not, Babbalanja advanced toward the foremost of those with the thongs—one Nulli, a cadaverous, ghost-like man: with a low ridge of forehead; hair, steel-gray, and wondrous eyes;—bright, nimble as the twin Corposant balls, playing about the ends of ships' royal-yards in gales.

The sun passed under a cloud; and Nulli, darting at Babbalanja those wondrous eyes, there fell upon him a baleful glare.

"Have they souls?" he asked, pointing to the serfs.

"No," said Nulli, "their ancestors may have had; but their souls have been bred out of their descendants; as the instinct of scent is killed in pointers."

Approaching one of the serfs, Media took him by the hand, and felt of it long; and looked into his eyes; and placed his ear to his side; and exclaimed, "Surely this being has flesh that is warm; he has Oro in his eye; and a heart in him that beats. I swear he is a man."

"Is this our lord the king?" cried Mohi, starting.

"What art thou?" said Babbalanja to the serf. "Dost ever feel in thee a sense of right and wrong? Art ever glad or sad? They tell us thou art not a man: speak, then, for thyself; say, whether thou believest thy Maker."

"Speak not of my Maker to me. Under the lash, I believe my masters, and account myself a brute; but in my dreams, bethink myself an angel. But I am bond; and my little ones;—their mother's milk is gall."

"Just Oro!" cried Yoomy, "do no thunders roll—no lightnings flash in this accursed land?"

"Asylum for all Mardi's thralls!" cried Media.

"Incendiaries!" cried he with the wondrous eyes. "Come ye, firebrands, to light the flame of revolt? Know ye not, that here are many serfs, who, incited to obtain their liberty, might wreak some dreadful vengeance? Avaunt, *thou* king! thou horrified at this? Go back to Odo, and right her wrongs! These serfs are happier than thine; though thine, no collars wear; more happy as they are, than if free. Are they not fed, clothed, and cared for? Thy serfs pine for food; never yet did these; who have no thoughts, no cares."

"Thoughts and cares are life, and liberty, and immortality," cried Babbalanja; "and are their souls, then, blown out as candles?"

"Ranter! they are content," cried Nulli. "They shed no tears."

"Frost never weeps," said Babbalanja; "and tears are frozen in those frigid eyes."

"Oh, fettered sons of fettered mothers, conceived and born in manacles," cried Yoomy; "dragging them through life; and falling with them, clanking in the grave!—oh! beings as ourselves, how my stiff arm shivers to avenge you! 'Twere absolution for the matricide, to strike one rivet from your chains. My heart outswells its home!"

"Oro! Art thou?" cried Babbalanja; "and doth this thing exist? It shakes my little faith." Then, turning upon Nulli, "How can ye abide to sway this cursed dominion?"

"Peace, fanatic! Who else may till unwholesome fields, but these? And as these beings are, so shall they remain; 'tis right and righteous! Maramma champions it! *I* swear it! The first blow struck for them, dissolves the union of Vivenza's vales. The northern tribes well know it; and know me."

Said Media, "Yet if—"

"No more! another word, and, king as thou art, thou shalt be dungeoned—here, there is such a law; thou art not among the northern tribes."

"And this is freedom!" murmured Media; "when heaven's own voice is throttled. And were these serfs to rise, and fight for it, like dogs, they would be hunted down by her pretended sons!"

"Pray heaven!" cried Yoomy, "they may yet find a way to loose their bonds without one drop of blood. But hear me, Oro! were there no other way, and should their masters not relent, all honest hearts must cheer this tribe of Hamo on; though they cut their chains with blades thrice edged, and gory to the haft! 'Tis right to fight for freedom, whoever be the thrall."

"These South savannahs may yet prove battle-fields," said Mohi, gloomily, as we retraced our steps.

"Be it," said Yoomy. "Oro will van the right."

"Not always has it proved so," said Babbalanja. "Ofttimes, the right fights single-handed against the world; and Oro champions none. In all things, man's own battles man himself must fight. Yoomy: so far as feeling goes, your sympathies are not more hot than mine; but for these serfs you would cross spears; yet, I would not. Better present woes for some, than future woes for all."

"No need to fight," cried Yoomy, "to liberate that tribe of Hamo instantly; a way may be found, and no irretrievable evil ensue."

"Point it out, and be blessed, Yoomy."

"That is for Vivenza; but the head is dull, where the heart is cold."

"My lord," said Babbalanja, "you have startled us by your kingly sympathy for suffering; say thou, then, in what wise manner it shall be relieved?"

"That is for Vivenza," said Media.

"Mohi, you are old: speak thou."

"Let Vivenza speak," said Mohi.

"Thus, then, we all agree; and weeping, all but echo hard-hearted Nulli. Tears are not swords; and wrongs seem almost natural as rights. For the righteous to suppress an evil, is sometimes harder than for others to uphold it. Humanity cries out against this vast enormity—not one man knows a prudent remedy. Blame not, then, the North, and wisely judge the South. Ere, as a nation, they became responsible, this thing was planted in their midst. Such roots strike deep. Place to-day those serfs in Dominora; and with them, all Vivenza's Past; and serfs, for many years, in Dominora, they would be. Easy is it to stand afar and rail. All men are censors who have lungs. We can say, the stars are wrongly marshaled. Blind men say the sun is blind. A thousand muscles wag our tongues; though our tongues were housed, that they might have a home. Whoso is free from crime, let him cross himself—but hold his cross upon his lips. That he is not bad, is not of him. Potters' clay and wax are all molded by hands invisible. The soil decides the man. And, ere birth, man wills not to be born here or there. These southern tribes have grown up with this thing; bond-women were their nurses, and bond-men serve them still. Nor are all their serfs such wretches as those we saw. Some seem happy; yet not as men. Unmanned, they know not what they are. And though, of all the south, Nulli must stand almost alone in his insensate creed; yet, to all wrongdoers, custom backs the sense of wrong. And if to every Mardian, conscience be the awarder of its own doom; then, of these tribes, many shall be found exempted from the least penalty of this sin. But sin it is, no less—a blot, foul as the crater-pool of hell; it puts out the sun at noon; it parches all fertility; and conscience or no conscience—ere he die—let every master who wrenches bond-babe from mother, that the nipple tear, unwreathes the arms of sisters; or cuts the holy unity in twain; till apart fall man and wife; like one bleeding body cleft; let that master thrice shrive his soul; take every sacrament; on his bended knees give up the ghost; yet shall he die despairing; and live again, to die forever damned. The future is all hieroglyphics. Who may read? But, methinks the great laggard Time must now march up apace, and somehow befriend these thralls. It cannot be, that misery is perpetually entailed; though, in a land proscribing primogeniture, the first-born and last of Hamo's tribe must still succeed to all their sires' wrongs. Yes: Time—all-healing Time—Time, great Philanthropist!—Time must befriend these thralls!"

"Oro grant it!" cried Yoomy "and let Mardi say, Amen!"

"Amen! amen! amen!" cried echoes echoing echoes.

We traversed many of these southern vales; but as in Dominora—so, throughout Vivenza, North and South—Yillah harbored not.

Chapter CLXIII

THEY CONVERSE OF THE MOLLUSCA, KINGS, TOAD-STOOLS, AND OTHER MATTERS

ONCE MORE EMBARKING, WE GAINED VIVENZA'S SOUTH-WESTERN SIDE; AND THERE, BEHELD VAST swarms of laborers, discharging from canoes, great loads of earth; which they tossed upon the beach.

"It is true, then," said Media, "that these freemen are engaged in digging down other lands, and adding them to their own, piece-meal. And this, they call extending their dominions agriculturally, and peaceably."

"My lord, they pay a price for every canoe-load," said Mohi.

"Ay, old man, holding the spear in one hand, and striking the bargain with the other."

"Yet charge it not upon all Vivenza," said Babbalanja. "Some of her tribes are hostile to these things; and when their countryman fight for land, are only war-like in opposing war."

"And therein, Babbalanja, is involved one of those anomalies in the condition of Vivenza," said Media, "which I can hardly comprehend. How comes it, that with so many things to divide them, the valley-tribes still keep their mystic league intact?"

"All plain, it is because the model, whence they derive their union, is one of nature's planning. My lord, have you ever observed the mysterious federation subsisting among the mollusca of the Tunicata order—in other words, a species of cuttle-fish, abounding at the bottom of the lagoon?"

"Yes: in clear weather about the reefs, I have beheld them time and again: but never with an eye to their political condition."

"Ah! my lord king, we should not cut off the nervous communication between our eyes, and our cerebellums."

"What were you about to say concerning the Tunicata order of Mollusca, sir philosopher?"

"My very honorable lord, I hurry to conclude. They live in a compound structure; but though connected by membranous canals, freely communicating throughout the league—each member has a heart and stomach of its own; provides and digests its own dinners; and grins and bears its own gripes, without imparting the same to its neighbors. But if a prowling shark touches one member, it ruffles all. Precisely thus now with Vivenza. In that confederacy, there are as many consciences as tribes; hence, if one member on its own behalf, assumes aught afterwards repudiated, the sin rests on itself alone; is not participated."

"A very subtle explanation, Babbalanja. You must allude, then, to those recreant tribes; which, while in their own eyes presenting a sublime moral spectacle to Mardi—in King Bello's do but present a hopeless example of bad debts. And these, the tribes that boast of boundless wealth."

"Most true, my lord. But Bello errs, when for this thing, he stigmatizes all Vivenza, as a unity."

"Babbalanja, you yourself are made up of members; then, if you be sick of a lumbago, 'tis not *you* that are unwell; but your spine!"

"As you will, my lord. I have said. But to speak no more on that head—what sort of a sensation, think you, life is to such creatures as those mollusca?"

"Answer your own question, Babbalanja."

"I will, but first tell me what sort of a sensation life is to you, yourself, my lord?"

"Pray, answer that along with the other, Azzageddi."

"Directly; but tell me, if you will, my lord, what sort of a sensation life is to a toad-stool."

"Pray, Babbalanja, put all three questions together; and then, do what you have often done before—pronounce yourself a lunatic."

"My lord, I beseech you, remind me not of that fact so often. It is true, but annoying. Nor will any wise man call another a fool."

"Do you take me for a mere man, then, Babbalanja, that you talk to me thus?"

"My demi-divine lord, and master, I was deeply concerned at your indisposition last night—may a loving subject inquire, whether his prince is completely recovered from the effect of those guavas?"

"Have a care, Azzageddi; you are far too courteous to be civil. But proceed."

"I obey. In kings, mollusca, and toad-stools, life is one thing and the same. The Philosopher Dumdi pronounces it a certain febral vibration of organic parts, operating upon the vis inertia of unorganized matter. But Bardianna says nay. Hear him. 'Who put together this marvelous mechanism of mine; and wound it up to go for three score years and ten; when it runs out, and strikes Time's hours no more? And what is it, that daily and hourly renews, and by a miracle, creates in me my flesh and my blood? What keeps up the perpetual telegraphic communication between my out-post toes and digits, and that domed grandee up aloft, my brain? It is not I; nor you; nor he; nor it. No; when I place my hand to that king muscle my heart, I am appalled. I feel the great God himself at work in me. Oro is life.' "

"And what is death?" demanded Media.

"Death, my lord? it is the deadest of all things."

Chapter CLXIV

Wherein, That Gallant Gentleman and Demi-God, King Media, Scepter in Hand, Throws Himself into the Breach

Sailing south from Vivenza, not far from its coast, we passed a cluster of islets, green as new-fledged grass; and like the mouths of floating cornucopias, their margins brimmed over upon the brine with flowers. On some, grew stately roses; on others stood twin-pillars; across others, tri-hued rainbows rested.

Cried Babbalanja, pointing to the last, "Franko's pledge of peace!—with that, she loudly vaunts she'll span the reef! Strike out all hues but red, and the token's nearer truth."

All these isles were prolific gardens; where King Bello and the Princes of Porpheero grew their most delicious fruits, nectarines and grapes.

But, though hard by, Vivenza owned no garden here; yet longed and lusted; and her hottest tribes oft roundly swore, to root up all roses the half-reef over; pull down all pillars; and dissolve all rainbows. "Mardi's half is ours," said they. Stand back, invaders! Full of Vanity; and mirroring themselves in the future; they deemed all reflected there, their own. 'Twas now high noon.

"Methinks the sun grows hot," said Media, retreating deeper under the canopy. "Ho! Vee-Vee; have you no cooling beverage? none of that golden wine distilled from torrid grapes, and then sent northward to be cellared in an iceberg? That wine was placed among our stores. Search, search the crypt, little Vee-Vee! Ha! I see it!—that yellow gourd! Come: drag it forth, my boy. Let's have the amber cups; so, pass them round; fill all! Taji! my demi-god, up heart! Old Mohi, my babe, may you live ten thousand centuries! Ah! this way you mortals have of dying out at three score years and ten, is but a craven habit. So, Babbalanja! may you never die. Yoomy! my sweet poet, may you live to sing to me in Paradise. Ha! ha! would that we floated in this glorious stuff, instead of this pestilent brine. Hark ye! were I to make a Mardi now, I'd have every continent a huge haunch of venison; every ocean a wine-vat! I'd stock every cavern with choice old spirits, and make three surplus suns to ripen the grapes all the year round. Let's drink to that! Brimmers! So: may the next Mardi that's made, be one entire grape; and mine the squeezing!"

"Look, look, my lord!" cried Yoomy; "what a glorious shore we pass."

Sallying out into the high golden noon, with golden-beaming goblets suspended, we gazed.

"This must be Kolumbo of the south," said Mohi.

It was a long, hazy reach of land; piled up in terraces, traced here and there with rushing streams, that worked up gold dust alluvian, and seemed to flash over pebbled diamonds. Heliotropes, sun-flowers, marigolds gemmed, or starred the violet meads, and vassal-like, still sunward bowed their heads. The rocks were pierced with grottoes, blazing with crystals, many-tinted.

It was a land of mints and mines; its east a ruby; west a topaz. Inland, the woodlands stretched an ocean, bottomless with foliage; its green surges bursting through cable-vines, like Xerxes' brittle chains which vainly sought to bind the Hellespont. Hence flowed a tide of forest sounds; of parrots, paroquets, macaws; blent with the howl of jaguars, hissing of anacondas, chattering of apes, and herons screaming.

Out from those depths up rose a stream.

The land lay basking in the world's round torrid brisket, hot with solar fire.

"No need here to land," cried Yoomy, "Yillah lurks not here."

"Heat breeds life, and sloth, and rage," said Babbalanja. "Here live bastard tribes and mongrel nations, wrangling and murdering to prove their freedom. Refill, my lord."

"Methinks, Babbalanja, you savor of the mysterious parchment, in Vivenza read:—Ha? Yes, philosopher, these are the men, who toppled castles to make way for hovels; these, they who fought for freedom, but find it despotism to rule themselves. These, Babbalanja, are, of the race, to whom a tyrant would prove a blessing." So saying he drained his cup.

"My lord, that last sentiment decides the authorship of the scroll. But, with deference, tyrants seldom can prove blessings; inasmuch as evil seldom eventuates in good. Yet will these people soon have a tyrant over them, if long they cleave to war. Of many javelins, one must prove a scepter; of many helmets, one a crown. It is but in the wearing. Refill, my lord."

"Fools, fools!" cried Media, "these tribes hate us kings; yet know not, that Peace is War against all kings. We seldom are undone by spears, which are our ministers. This wine is strong."

"Ha, now's the time. In his cups learn kingcraft from a king. Ay, ay, my lord, your royal order will endure, so long as men will fight. Break the spears, and free the nations. Kings reap the harvests that wave on battle-fields. And oft you kings do snatch the aloe-flower, whose slow blossoming mankind watches for a hundred years. Say on, my lord."

"All this I know; and, therefore, rest content. My children's children will be kings; though, haply, called by other titles. Mardi grows fastidious in names: we royalties will humor it. The steers would burst their yokes, but have not hands. The whole herd rears and plunges, but soon will bow again; the old, old way!"

"Yet, in Porpheero, strong scepters have been wrested from anointed hands. Mankind seems in arms."

"Let them arm on. They hate us: good; they always have; yet still we've reigned, son after sire. Sometimes they slay us, Babbalanja; pour out our marrow, as I this wine; but they spill no kinless blood. 'Twas justly held of old, that but to touch a monarch, was to strike at Oro. Truth. The palest vengeance is a royal ghost; and regicides but father slaves. Thrones, not scepters, have been broken. Mohi, what of the past? Has it not ever proved so?"

"Pardon, my lord; the times seem changed. 'Tis held, that demi-gods no more rule by right divine. In Vivenza's land, they swear the last kings now reign in Mardi!"

"Is the last day at hand, old man? Mohi, your beard is gray; but, Yoomy, listen. When you die, look around; mark then if any mighty change be seen. Old kingdoms may be on the wane: but new dynasties advance. Though revolutions rise to high spring-tide, monarchs will still drown hard; monarchs survived the flood!"

"Are all our dreams, then, vain?" sighed Yoomy. "Is this no dawn of day that streaks the crimson East. Naught but the false and flickering lights which sometimes mock Aurora in the north! Ah, man, my brother! have all martyrs for thee bled in vain; in vain we poets sang and prophets spoken? Nay, nay, great Mardi, helmed and mailed, strikes at Oppression's shield, and challenges to battle! Oro will defend the right, and royal crests must roll!"

"Thus, Yoomy, ages since, you mortal poets sang; but the world may not be moved from out the orbit in which first it rolled. On the map that charts the spheres, Mardi is marked 'the world of kings.' Round centuries on centuries have wheeled by—has all this been its nonage? Now, when the rocks grow gray, does man first sprout his beard? Or, is your golden time, your equinoctial year, at hand, that your race fast presses toward perfection; and every hand grasps at a scepter, that kings may be no more?"

"But free Vivenza! Is she not the star, that must ere long, lead up the constellations, though now unrisen? No kings are in Vivenza; yet, spite her thralls, in that land seems more of good than elsewhere. Our hopes are not wild dreams: Vivenza cheers our hearts. She is a rainbow to the isles!"

"Ay, truth it is, that in Vivenza they have prospered. But thence it comes not, that all men may be as they. Are all men of one heart and brain; one bone and sinew? Are all nations sprung of Dominora's loins? Or, has Vivenza yet proved her creed? Yoomy! the years that prove a man, prove not a nation. But two kings' reigns have passed since Vivenza was a monarch's. Her climacteric is not come; hers is not yet a nation's manhood even; though now in childhood, she anticipates her youth, and lusts for empire like any czar. Yoomy! judge not yet. Time hath tales to tell. Many books and many long, long chapters, are wanting to Vivenza's history; and what history but is full of blood?"

"There stop, my lord," said Babbalanja, "nor aught predict. Fate laughs at prophets; and of all birds, the raven is a liar!"

Chapter CLXV

THEY ROUND THE STORMY CAPE OF CAPES

LONG LEAGUES, FOR WEARY DAYS, WE VOYAGED ALONG THAT COAST TILL WE CAME TO REGIONS where we multiplied our mantles.

The sky grew overcast. Each a night, black storm-clouds swept the wintry sea; and like Sahara caravans, which leave their sandy wakes, so, thick and fleet, slanted the scud behind. Through all this rack and mist, ten thousand foam-flaked dromedary-humps uprose.

Deep among those panting, moaning fugitives, the three canoes raced on.

And now, the air grew nipping cold. The clouds shed off their fleeces; a snow-hillock, each canoe; our beards, white-frosted.

And so, as seated in our shrouds, we sailed in among great mountain passes of ice-isles; from icy ledges scaring shivering seals, and white bears, musical with icicles, jingling from their shaggy ermine.

Far and near, in towering ridges, stretched the glassy Andes; with their own frost, shuddering through all their domes and pinnacles. Ice splinters rattled down the cliffs, and seethed into the sea.

Broad away, in amphitheaters undermined by currents, whole cities of ice-towers, in crashes, toward one center, fell. In their earthquakes, Lisbon and Lima never saw the like. Churned and broken in the boiling tide, they swept off amain—over and over rolling; like porpoises to vessels tranced in calms, bringing down the gale.

At last, rounding an antlered headland, that seemed a moose at bay—ere long, we launched upon blue lake-like waters, serene as Windermere, or Horicon. Thus, from the boisterous storms of youth, we glide upon senility. But as we northward voyaged, another aspect wore the sea.

In far-off, endless vistas, colonnades of water-spouts were seen: all heaven's dome upholding on their shafts; and bright forms gliding up and down within. So at Luz, in his strange vision, Jacob saw the angels.

A boundless cave of stalactites, it seemed; the cloud-born vapors downward spiraling, till they met the whirlpool-column from the sea; then, uniting, over the waters stalked, like ghosts of gods. Or midway sundered—down, sullen, sunk the watery half; and far up into heaven, was drawn the vapory. As, at death, we mortals part in twain; our earthly half still here abiding; but our spirits flying whence they came.

In good time, we gained the thither side of great Kolumbo of the South; and sailing on, long waited for the day; and wondered at the darkness.

"What steadfast clouds!" cried Yoomy, "yonder far aloft: that ridge, with many points; it fades below, but shows a faint white crest."

"Not clouds, but mountains," said Babbalanja, "the vast spine that traverses Kolumbo; spurring off in ribs, that nestle loamy valleys, veined with silver streams and silver ores."

It was a long, embattled line of pinnacles. And high posted in the East, those thousand bucklered peaks stood forth, and breasted back the dawn. Before their purple bastions bold, Aurora long arrayed her spears, and clashed her golden shells. The summons dies away. But now her lancers charge the steep, and gain its crest aglow; their glittering spears and blazoned shields triumphant in the morn.

But ere that sight, we glided on for hours in twilight, when, on those mountains' farther side, the hunters must have been abroad, morning-glories all astir.

Chapter CLXVI

THEY ENCOUNTER GOLD-HUNTERS

NOW, NORTHWARD COASTING ALONG KOLUMBO'S WESTERN SHORE, WHENCE CAME THE SAME wild forest-sounds, as from the Eastern; and where we landed not, to seek among those wrangling tribes;—after many, many days, we spied prow after prow, before the wind all northward bound; sails wide-spread, and paddles plying; scaring the fish from before them.

Their inmates answered not our earnest hailing.

But as they sped, with frantic glee, in one long chorus thus they sang:—

We rovers bold,
To the land of Gold,
Over bowling billows are gliding:
Eager to toil,
For the golden spoil,
And every hardship biding.
See! See!
Before our prows' resistless dashes,
The gold-fish fly in golden flashes,
'Neath a sun of gold,
We rovers bold,
On the golden land are gaining;
And every night,
We steer aright,
By golden stars unwaning!
All fires burn a golden glare:
No locks so bright as golden hair!
All orange groves have golden gushings!
All mornings dawn with golden flushings!
In a shower of gold, say fables old,
A maiden was won by the god of gold!
In golden goblets wine is beaming:
On golden couches kings are dreaming!
The Golden Rule dries many tears!
The Golden Number rules the spheres!
Gold, gold it is, that sways the nations:
Gold! gold! the center of all rotations!
On golden axles worlds are turning:
With phosphorescence seas are burning!
All fire-flies flame with golden gleamings:
Gold-hunters' hearts with golden dreamings!
With golden arrows kings are slain:
With gold we'll buy a freeman's name!
In toilsome trades, for scanty earnings,
At home we've slaved, with stifled yearnings,

No light! no hope! Oh, heavy woe!
When nights fled fast, and days dragged slow.
But joyful now, with eager eye,
Fast to the Promised Land we fly:
Where in deep mines,
The treasure shines;
Or down in beds of golden streams,
The gold-flakes glance in golden gleams!
How we long to sift,
That yellow drift!
Rivers! Rivers! cease your going!
Sand-bars! rise, and stay the tide
'Till we've gained the golden flowing;
And in the golden haven ride!

"Quick, quick, my lord," cried Yoomy, "let us follow them; and from the golden waters where she lies, our Yillah may emerge."

"No, no!" said Babbalanja, "no Yillah there! from yonder promised land, fewer seekers will return, than go. Under a gilded guise, happiness is still their instinctive aim. But vain, Yoomy, to snatch at Happiness. Of that we may not pluck and eat. It is the fruit of our own toilsome planting; slow it grows, nourished by many tears, and all our earnest tendings. Yet ere it ripens, frosts may nip; and then, we plant again; and yet again. Deep, Yoomy, deep, true treasure lies; deeper than all Mardi's gold, rooted to Mardi's axis. But unlike gold, it lurks in every soil, all Mardi over. With golden pills and potions is sickness warded off? the shrunken veins of age dilated with new wine of youth? Will gold the heart-ache cure? turn towards us hearts estranged? will gold, on solid centers empires fix? 'Tis toil world-wasted to toil in mines. Were all the isles gold globes, set in a quicksilver sea, all Mardi were then a desert. Gold is the only poverty: of all glittering ills the first. And that man might not impoverish himself thereby, Oro hath hidden it, with all other banes—saltpeter and explosives, deep in mountain bowels, and river beds. But man still will mine for it; and mining, dig his doom. Yoomy! Yoomy! she we seek, lurks not in the Golden Hills!"

"Lo! a vision!" cried Yoomy, his hands wildly passed across his eyes. "A vast and silent bay, belted by silent villages; gaunt dogs howling over grassy thresholds, at stark corpses of old age and infancy; gray hairs mingling with sweet flaxen curls; fields, with turned furrows, choked with briars; arbor-floors strewn over with hatchet-helves, rotting in the iron; a thousand paths, marked with footprints, all inland leading, none villageward, and strewn with traces, as of a flying host. On: over forest, hill, and dale, and lo! the golden region! After the glittering spoil, by strange river-margins, and beneath impending cliffs, thousands delve in quicksands; and, sudden, sink in graves of their own making: with gold dust mingling their own ashes. Still deeper, in some solid ground, other thousands slave, and pile their earth so high, they gasp for air, and die; their comrades mounting on them, and delving still, and dying—grave pile on grave! Here, one haggard hunter murders another in his pit; and murdering, himself is murdered by a third. Shrieks and groans! cries and curses! It seems a golden Hell! With many camels, a sleek stranger comes—pauses before the shining heaps, and shows *his* treasures: yams and bread-fruit. 'Give, give,' the famished hunters cry—'a thousand shekels for a yam! a prince's ransom for a meal! Oh, stranger! on our knees we worship thee: take, take our gold; but let us live!' Yams are thrown them; and they fight. Then he who toiled not, dug not, slaved not, straight loads his caravans with gold; regains the beach, and swift embarks for home. 'Home! home!' the hunters cry, with bursting eyes. 'With this bright gold, could we but join our waiting wives, who wring their hands on distant shores, all then were well. But we cannot fly; our prows lie rotting on the beach. Ah! home! thou only happiness! better thy silver earnings than all these golden findings. Oh, bitter end to all our hopes, we die in golden graves."

Chapter CLXVII

They Seek Through the Isles of Palms; and Pass the Isles of Myrrh

Now, our prows we turned due west, across the blue lagoon. Soon, no land appeared. Far as the eye could sweep, one azure plain; all over flaked with foamy fleeces—a boundless flock upon a boundless mead!

Again all changed. Like stars in multitude, bright islets multiplied around. Emerald-green, they dotted shapes fantastic: circles, arcs, and crescents—atolls all, or coral carcanets, begemmed and flashing in the sun.

By these we glided, group after group; and through the foliage, spied sweet forms of maidens, like Eves in Edens ere the Fall, or Proserpines in Ennas. Artless airs came from the shore; and from the censer-swinging roses, a bloom, as if from Hebe's cheek.

"Here, at last, we find sweet Yillah!" murmured Yoomy. "Here must she lurk in innocence! Quick! Let us land and search."

"If here," said Babbalanja, "Yillah will not stay our coming, but fly before us through the groves. Wherever a canoe is beached, see you not the palm-trees pine? Not so, where never keel yet smote the strand. In mercy, let us fly from hence. I know not why, but our breath here must prove a blight."

These regions passed, we came to savage islands, where the glittering coral seemed bones imbedded, bleaching in the sun. Savage men stood naked on the strand, and brandished uncouth clubs, and gnashed their teeth like boars.

The full red moon was rising; and, in long review there passed before it, phantom shapes of victims, led bound to altars through the groves. Death-rattles filled the air. But a cloud descended, and all was gloom.

Again blank water spread before us; and after many days, there came a gentle breeze, fraught with all spicy breathings; cinnamon aromas; and in the rose-flushed evening air, like glow worms, glowed the islets, where this incense burned.

"Sweet isles of myrrh! oh crimson groves," cried Yoomy. "Woe, woe's your fate! your brightness and your bloom, like musky fire-flies, double-lure to death! On ye, the nations prey like bears that gorge themselves with honey."

Swan-like, our prows sailed in among these isles; and oft we landed; but in vain; and leaving them, we still pursued the setting sun.

Chapter CLXVIII

Concentric, Inward, with Mardi's Reef, They Leave Their Wake Around the World

WEST, WEST! WEST, WEST! WHITHERWARD POINT HOPE AND PROPHET-FINGERS; WHITHERWARD, at sunset, kneel all worshipers of fire: whitherward in mid-ocean, the great whales turn to die; whitherward face all the Moslem dead in Persia; whitherward lie Heaven and Hell! West, west! Whitherward mankind and empires—flocks, caravans, armies, navies, worlds, suns, and stars all wend! West, west! Oh boundless boundary! Eternal goal! Whitherward rush, in thousand worlds, ten thousand thousand keels! Beacon, by which the universe is steered!—Like the north-star, attracting all needles! Unattainable forever; but forever leading to great things this side thyself! Hive of all sunsets! Gabriel's pinions may not overtake thee!

Over balmy waves, still westward sailing! From dawn till eve, the bright, bright days sped on, chased by the gloomy nights; and, in glory dying, lent their luster to the starry skies. So, long the radiant dolphins fly before the sable sharks; but seized, and torn in flames—die, burning:—their last splendor left, in sparkling scales that float along the sea.

Cymbals, drums, and psalteries! the air beats like a pulse with music! High land! high land; and moving lights, and painted lanterns! What grand shore is this?

"Reverence we render thee, Old Orienda!" cried Media with bared brow. "Original of all empires and emperors! a crowned king salutes thee!"

"Mardi's fatherland!" cried Mohi; "grandsire of the nations—hail!"

"All hail!" cried Yoomy. "Kings and sages hither coming, should come like palmers—scrip and staff! Oh, Orienda! thou wert our East, where first dawned song and science, with Mardi's primal mornings! But now, how changed! the dawn of light become a darkness, which we kindle with the gleam of spears! On the world's ancestral hearth, we spill our brothers' blood!"

"Herein," said Babbalanja, "have many distant tribes proved parricidal. In times gone by, Luzianna hither sent her proas; Franko, her scores of captains; and the Dykemen, their peddler hosts, with yard-stick spears! But thou, oh Bello! lord of the empire lineage! Noah of the moderns; sire of the long line of nations yet in germ; thou, Bello, and thy locust armies, are the present curse of Orienda. Down ancient streams, from holy plains, in rafts thy murdered float! The pestilence that thins thy armies here, is bred of corpses, made by thee. Maramma's priests, thy pious heralds, loud proclaim that of all pagans, Orienda's most resist the truth! ay! vain all pious voices, that speak from clouds of war! The march of conquest through wild provinces, may be the march of Mind; but not the march of Love."

"Thou, Bello!" cried Yoomy, "wouldst wrest the crook from Alma's hand, and place in it a spear. But vain to make a conqueror of him, who put off the purple when he came to Mardi: and declining gilded miters, entered the nations meekly on an ass."

"Oh, curse of commerce!" cried Babbalanja, "that it barters souls for gold. Bello! with opium, thou wouldst drug this land, and murder it in sleep! And what boot thy conquests here? Seed sown by spears but seldom springs; and harvests reaped thereby, are poisoned by the sickle's edge."

Yet on, and on we coasted, counting not the days.

"Oh, folds and flocks of nations! dusky tribes innumerable!" cried Yoomy, "camped on plains and steppes: on thousand mountains, worshiping the stars; in thousand valleys, offering up first-fruits, till all the forests seem in flames; where, in fire, the widow's spirit mounts to meet her lord! Oh, Orienda, in thee 'tis vain to seek our Yillah!"

"How dark as death the night!" said Mohi, shaking the dew from his braids, "the Heavens blaze not here with stars as over Dominora's land, and broad Vivenza."

One only constellation was beheld; but every star was brilliant as the one, that promises the morning. That constellation was the Crux-Australis, the badge and type of Alma.

And now, south-west we steered, till another island vast, was reached—Hamora! far trending toward the Antarctic Pole.

Coasting on by barbarous beaches, where painted men with spears, charged on all attempts to land, at length we rounded a mighty bluff, lit by a beacon; and heard a bugle call: Bello's! hurrying to their quarters, the World-End's garrison.

Here, the sea rolled high, in mountain surges: mid which, we toiled and strained, as if ascending cliffs of Caucasus.

But not long thus. As when from howling Rh'tian heights, the traveler spies green Lombardy below, and downward rushes toward that pleasant plain; so, sloping from long rolling swells, at last we launched upon the calm lagoon.

But as we northward sailed, once more the storm-trump blew, and charger-like, the seas ran mustering to the call; and in battalions crouched before a towering rock, far distant from the main. No moon, eclipsed in Egypt's skies, looked half so lone. But from out that darkness, on the loftiest peak, Bello's standard waved.

"Oh, rifled tomb!" cried Babbalanja. "Wherein lay the Mars and Moloch of our times, whose constellated crown was gemmed with diadems. Thou god of war! who didst seem the devouring Beast of the Apocalypse; casting so vast a shadow over Mardi, that yet it lingers in old Franko's vale; where still they start at thy tremendous ghost; and, late, have hailed a phantom King! Almighty hero-spell! that after the lapse of half a century, can so bewitch all hearts! But one drop of hero-blood will deify a fool.

"Franko! thou wouldst be free; yet thy free homage is to the buried ashes of a King; thy first choice, the exaltation of his race. In furious fires, thou burn'st Ludwig's throne; and over thy new-made chieftain's portal in golden letters print'st, 'The Palace of our Lord!' In thy New Dispensation, thou cleavest to the exploded Law. And on Freedom's altar—ah, I fear—still, may slay thy hecatombs. But Freedom turns away; she is sick with burned blood of offerings. Other rituals she loves; and like Oro, unseen herself, would be worshiped only by invisibles. Of long drawn cavalcades, pompous processions, frenzied banners, mystic music, marching nations, she will none. Oh, may thy peaceful Future, Franko, sanctify thy bloody Past. Let not history say, 'To her old gods, she turned again.' "

This rocky islet passed, the sea went down; once more we neared Hamora's western shore. In the deep darkness here and there, its margin was lit up by foam-white, breaking billows rolled over from Vivenza's strand, and down from northward Dominora; marking places where light was breaking in, upon the interior's jungle-gloom.

In heavy sighs, the night-winds from shore came over us.

"Ah, vain to seek sweet Yillah here," cried Yoomy. "Poor land! cursed of man, not Oro! how thou faintest for thy children, torn from thy soil to till a stranger's, Vivenza! did these winds not spend their plaints, ere reaching thee, thy every vale would echo them. Oh, tribe of Hamo! thy cup of woe so brims, that soon it must overflow upon the land which holds ye thralls. No misery born of crime, but spreads and poisons wide. Suffering hunteth sin, as the gaunt hound the hare, and tears it in the greenest brakes."

Still on we sailed; and after many tranquil days and nights, a storm came down, and burst its thousand bombs. The lightnings forked and flashed; the waters boiled; our three prows lifted themselves in supplication; but the billows smote them as they reared.

Said Babbalanja, bowing to the blast, "Thus, oh, Vivenza! retribution works! Though long delayed, it comes at last—Judgment, with all her bolts."

Now, a current seized us, and like three darts, our keels sped eastward, through a narrow strait, far in, upon a smooth expanse, an inland ocean, without a throb.

On our left, Porpheero's south-west point, a mighty rock, long tiers of galleries within, deck on deck; and flag-staffs, like an admiral's masts: a line-of-battle-ship, all purple stone, and anchored in the sea. Here Bello's lion crouched; and, through a thousand port-holes, eyed the world.

On our right, Hamora's northern shore gleamed thick with crescents; numerous as the crosses along the opposing strand.

"How vain to say, that progress is the test of truth, my lord," said Babbalanja, "when, after many centuries, those crescents yet unwaning shine, and count a devotee for every worshiper of yonder crosses. Truth and Merit have other symbols than success; and in this mortal race all competitors may enter; and the field is clear to all. Side by side, Lies run with Truths, and fools with wise; but, like geometric lines, though they pierce infinity, never may they join."

Over that tideless sea we sailed; and landed right, and landed left; but the maiden never found; till, at last, we gained the water's limit; and inland saw great pointed masses, crowned with halos.

"Granite continents," cried Babbalanja, "that seem created like the planets, not built with human hands. Lo, Landmarks! upon whose flanks Time leaves its traces, like old tide-rips of diluvian seas."

As, after wandering round and round some purple dell, deep in a boundless prairie's heart, the baffled hunter plunges in; then, despairing, turns once more to gain the open plain; even so we seekers now curved round our keels, and from that inland sea emerged. The universe again before us; our quest, as wide.

Chapter CLXIX

SAILING ON

MORNING DAWNED UPON THE SAME MILD, BLUE LAGOON AS ERST; AND ALL THE LANDS THAT WE had passed, since leaving Piko's shore of spears, were faded from the sight.

Part and parcel of the Mardian isles, they formed a cluster by themselves; like the Pleiades, that shine in Taurus, and are eclipsed by the red splendor of his fiery eyes, and the thick clusterings of the constellations round.

And as in Orion, to some old king-astronomer—say, King of Rigel, or Betelgeuse—this Earth's four quarters show but four points afar; so, seem they to terrestrial eyes, that broadly sweep the spheres.

And, as the sun, by influence divine, wheels through the Ecliptic; threading Cancer, Leo, Pisces, and Aquarius; so, by some mystic impulse am I moved, to this fleet progress, through the groups in white-reefed Mardi's zone.

Oh, reader, list! I've chartless voyaged. With compass and the lead, we had not found these Mardian Isles. Those who boldly launch, cast off all cables; and turning from the common breeze, that's fair for all, with their own breath, fill their own sails. Hug the shore, naught new is seen; and "Land Ho!" at last was sung, when a new world was sought.

That voyager steered his barque through seas, untracked before; plowed his own path mid jeers; though with a heart that oft was heavy with the thought, that he might only be too bold, and grope where land was none. So I.

And though essaying but a sportive sail, I was driven from my course, by a blast resistless; and ill-provided, young, and bowed to the brunt of things before my prime, still fly before the gale—hard have I striven to keep stout heart.

And if it harder be, than e'er before, to find new climes, when now our seas have oft been circled by ten thousand prows—much more the glory!

But this new world here sought, is stranger far than his, who stretched his vans from Palos. It is the world of mind; wherein the wanderer may gaze round, with more of wonder than Balboa's band roving through the golden Aztec glades.

But fiery yearnings their own phantom-future make, and deem it present. So, if after all these fearful, fainting trances, the verdict be, the golden haven was not gained; yet, in bold quest thereof, better to sink in boundless deeps, than float on vulgar shoals; and give me, ye gods, an utter wreck, if wreck I do.

Chapter CLXX

A Flight of Nightingales from Yoomy's Mouth

By noon down came a calm.

"Oh, Neeva! good Neeva! kind Neeva! thy sweet breath, dear Neeva!" So from his shark's mouth prayed little Vee-Vee to the god of Fair Breezes. And along they swept; till the three prows neighed to the blast; and pranced on their path, like steeds of Crusaders.

Now, that this fine wind had sprung up; the sun riding joyously in the heavens; and the lagoon all tossed with white, flying manes; Media called upon Yoomy to ransack his whole assortment of songs: war-like, amorous, and sentimental—and regale us with something inspiring; for too long the company had been gloomy.

"Thy best," he cried.

"Then will I e'en sing you a song, my lord, which is a song-full of songs. I composed it long, long since, when Yillah yet bowered in Odo. Ere now, some fragments have been heard. Ah, Taji! in this my lay, live over again your happy hours. Some joys have thousand lives; can never die; for when they droop, sweet memories bind them up. My lord, I deem these verses good; they came bubbling out of me, like live waters from a spring in a silver mine. And by your good leave, my lord, I have much faith in inspiration. Whoso sings is a seer."

"Tingling is the test," said Babbalanja; "Yoomy, did you tingle when that song was composing?"

"All over, Babbalanja."

"From sole to crown?"

"From finger to finger."

"My life for it! true poetry, then, my lord! For this self-same tingling, I say, is the test."

"And infused into a song," cried Yoomy, "it evermore causes it so to sparkle, vivify, and irradiate, that no son of man can repeat it, without tingling himself. This very song of mine may prove what I say."

"Modest youth!" sighed Media.

"Not more so, than sincere," said Babbalanja. "He who is frank, will often appear vain, my lord. Having no guile, he speaks as freely of himself, as of another; and is just as ready to honor his own merits, even if imaginary, as to lament over undeniable deficiencies. Besides, such men are prone to moods, which to shallow-minded, unsympathizing mortals, make their occasional distrust of themselves, appear but as a phase of self-conceit. Whereas, the man who, in the presence of his very friends, parades a barred and bolted front, that man so highly prizes his sweet self, that he cares not to profane the shrine he worships, by throwing open its portals. He is locked up; and Ego is the key. Reserve alone is vanity. But all mankind are egotists. The world revolves upon an I; and we upon ourselves; for we are our own worlds: all other men as strangers, from outlandish, distant climes, going clad in furs. Then, whate'er they be, let us show our worlds; and not seek to hide from men what Oro knows."

"Truth, my lord," said Yoomy, "but all this applies to men in mass; not specially to my poor craft. Of all mortals, we poets are most subject to contrary moods. Now, heaven over heaven in the skies; now layer under layer in the dust. This, the penalty we pay for being what we are. But Mardi only sees, or thinks it sees, the tokens of our self-complacency; whereas, all our agonies operate unseen. Poets are only seen when they soar."

"The song! the song!" cried Media. "Never mind the metaphysics of genius."

And Yoomy, thus clamorously invoked, hemmed thrice, tuning his voice for the air.

But here, be it said, that the minstrel was miraculously gifted with three voices; and, upon occasions, like a mocking-bird, was a concert of sweet sounds in himself. Had kind friends died, and bequeathed him their voices? But hark! in a low, mild tenor, he begins:

Half-veiled above the hills, yet rosy bright,
Stands fresh, and fair, the meek and blushing morn!
So Yillah looks! her pensive eyes the stars,
That mildly beam from out her cheek's young dawn!

But the still meek Dawn,
Is not aye the form
Of Yillah nor Morn!
Soon rises the sun,
Day's race to run
His rays abroad,
Flash each a sword—
And merrily forth they flare!
Sun-music in the air!
So Yillah now rises and flashes!
Rays shooting from ont her long lashes—
Sun-music in the air!

Her laugh! How it bounds!
Bright cascade of sounds!
Peal after peal, and ringing afar—
Ringing of waters, that silvery jar,
From basin to basin fast falling!
Fast falling, and shining, and streaming:
Yillah's bosom, the soft, heaving lake,
Where her laughs at last dimple, and flake!

Oh, beautiful Yillah! Thy step so free!
Fast fly the sea-ripples,
Revealing their dimples,
When forth, thou hi'st to the frolicsome sea!

All the stars laugh,
When upward she looks:
All the trees chat
In their woody nooks:
All the brooks sing:
All the caves ring;
All the buds blossom;
All the boughs bound;
All the birds carol;
And leaves turn round,
Where Yillah looks!

Light wells from her soul's deep sun
Causing many toward her to run!
Vines to climb, and flowers to spring;
And youths their love by hundreds bring!

"Proceed, gentle Yoomy," said Babbalanja.

"The meaning?" said Mohi.

"The sequel?" said Media.

"My lord, I have ceased in the middle; the end is not yet."

"Mysticism!" cried Babbalanja. "What, minstrel, must nothing ultimate come of all that melody? no final and inexhaustible meaning? nothing that strikes down into the soul's depths; till, intent upon itself, it pierces in upon its own essence, and is resolved into its pervading original, becoming a thing constituent of the all embracing deific; whereby we mortals become part and parcel of the gods; our souls to them as thought; and we privy to all things occult, ineffable, and sublime? Then, Yoomy, is thy song nothing worth. Alla Mollolla saith: 'That is no true, vital breath, which leaves no moisture behind.' I must trust thee, minstrel; that thou hast not yet been impregnated by the arcane mysteries; that thou dost not sufficiently ponder on the Adyta, the Monads, and the Hyparxes; the Dianoias, the Unical Hypostases, the Gnostic powers of the Psychical Essence, and the Supermundane and Pleromatic Triads; to say nothing of the Abstract Noumenons."

"Oro forbid!" cried Yoomy; "the very sound of thy words affrights me." Then, whispering to Mohi, "Is he daft again?"

"My brain is battered," said Media. "Azzageddi! you must diet, and be bled."

"Ah!" sighed Babbalanja, turning; "how little they ween of the Rudimental Quincunxes, and the Hecatic Spherula!"

Chapter CLXXI

THEY VISIT ONE DOXODOX

NEXT MORNING, WE CAME TO A DEEP, GREEN WOOD, SLOWLY NODDING OVER THE WAVES; ITS margin frothy-white with foam. A charming sight!

While delighted, all our paddlers gazed, Media, observing Babbalanja plunged in reveries, called upon him to awake; asking what might so absorb him.

"Ah, my lord! what seraphic sounds have ye driven from me!"

"Sounds! Sure, there's naught heard but yonder murmuring surf; what other sound heard you?"

"The thrilling of my soul's monochord, my lord. But prick not your ears to hear it; that divine harmony is overheard by the rapt spirit alone; it comes not by the auditory nerves."

"No more, Azzageddi! No more of that. Look yonder!"

"A most lovely wood, in truth. And methinks it is here, the sage Doxodox, surnamed the Wise One, dwells."

"Hark, I hear the hootings of his owls," said Mohi.

"My lord, you must have read of him. He is said to have penetrated from the zoned, to the unzoned principles. Shall we seek him out, that we may hearken to his wisdom? Doubtless he knows many things, after which we pant."

The lagoon was calm, as we landed, not a breath stirred the plumes of the trees; and as we entered the voiceless shades, lifting his hand, Babbalanja whispered: "This silence is a fit introduction to the portals of Telestic lore. Somewhere, beneath this moss, lurks the mystic stone Mnizuris; whereby Doxodox hath attained unto a knowledge of the ungenerated essences. Nightly, he bathes his soul in archangelical circumlucencies. Oh, Doxodox! whip me the Strophalunian top! Tell o'er thy Jynges!"

"Down, Azzageddi! down!" cried Media. "Behold: there sits the Wise One; now, for true wisdom!"

From the voices of the party, the sage must have been aware of our approach: but seated on a green bank, beneath the shade of a red mulberry, upon the boughs of which, many an owl was perched, he seemed intent upon describing divers figures in the air, with a jet-black wand.

Advancing with much deference and humility, Babbalanja saluted him.

"Oh wise Doxodox! Drawn hither by thy illustrious name, we seek admittance to thy innermost wisdom. Of all Mardian, thou alone comprehendest those arcane combinations, whereby to drag to day the most deftly hidden things, present and to come. Thou knowest what we are, and what we shall be. We beseech thee, evoke thy Tselmns!"

"Tetrads; Pentads; Hexads; Heptads; Ogdoads: meanest thou those?"

"New terms all!"

"Foiled at thy own weapons," said Media.

"Then, if thou comprehendest not my nomenclature: how my science? But let me test thee in the portico.—Why is it, that as some things extend more remotely than others; so, Quadammodotatives are larger than Qualitatives; forasmuch, as Quadammodotatives extend to those things which include the Quadammodotatives themselves."

"Azzageddi has found his match," said Media.

"Still posed, Babbalanja?" asked Mohi.

"At a loss, most truly! But I beseech thee, wise Doxodox! instruct me in thy dialectics, that I may embrace thy more recondite lore."

"To begin then, my child: all Dicibles reside in the mind."

"But what are Dicibles?" said Media.

"Meanest thou, Perfect or Imperfect Dicibles?"

"Any kind you please—but what are they?"

"Perfect Dicibles are of various sorts: Interrogative; Percontative; Adjurative; Optative; Imprecative; Execrative; Substitutive; Compellative; Hypothetical; and lastly, Dubious."

"Dubious enough! Azzageddi! forever, hereafter, hold thy peace."

"Ah, my children! I must go back to my Axioms."

"And what are they?" said old Mohi.

"Of various sorts; which, again, are diverse. Thus: my contrary axioms are Disjunctive, and Subdisjunctive; and so, with the rest. So, too, with my Syllogisms."

"And what of them?"

"Did I not just hint what they were, my child? I repeat, they are of various sorts: Connex, and Conjunct, for example."

"And what of them?" persisted Mohi; while Babbalanja, arms folded, stood serious and mute; a sneer on his lip.

"As with other branches of my dialectics; so, too, in their way, with my Syllogisms. Thus: when I say—If it be warm, it is not cold: that's a simple Sumption. If I add, But it *is* warm: that's an *As*sumption."

"So called from the syllogist himself, doubtless," said Mohi, stroking his beard.

"Poor ignorant babe! no. Listen: if finally, I say, Therefore it is not cold: that's the final inference."

"And a most triumphant one it is!" cried Babbalanja. "Thrice profound, and sapient Doxodox! Light of Mardi! and Beacon of the universe! didst ever hear of the Shark-Syllogism?"

"Though thy epithets be true, my child, I distrust thy sincerity. I have not yet heard of the syllogism to which thou referrest!"

"It was thus. A shark seized a swimmer by the leg, addressing him: 'Friend, I will liberate you, if you truly answer whether you think I purpose harm.' Well knowing that sharks seldom were magnanimous, he replied, 'Kind sir, you mean me harm; now go your ways.' 'No, no; my conscience forbids. Nor will I falsify the words of so voracious a mortal. You were to answer truly; but you say I mean you harm; so harm it is: here goes your leg.' "

"Profane jester! Would'st thou insult me with thy tom-foolery? Begone, all of ye! tramp! pack! I say; away with ye!" and into the woods Doxodox himself disappeared.

"Bravely done, Babbalanja!" cried Media. "You turned the corner to admiration."

"I have hopes of our Philosopher yet," said Mohi.

"Outrageous impostor! fool, dotard, oaf! Did he think to bejuggle me with his preposterous gibberish? And is this shallow phraseman the renowned Doxodox whom I have been taught so highly to reverence! Alas, alas—Odonphi there is none!"

"His fit again," sighed Yoomy.

Chapter CLXXII

KING MEDIA DREAMS

THAT AFTERNOON WAS MELTING DOWN TO EVE; ALL BUT MEDIA BROAD AWAKE; YET ALL MOtionless, as the slumberer upon the purple mat. Sailing on, with open eyes, we slept the wakeful sleep of those, who to the body only give repose; while the spirit still toils on, threading her mountain passes.

King Media's slumbers were like the helmed sentry's in the saddle. From them, he started like an antlered deer, bursting from out a copse. Some said he never slept; that deep within himself he but intensified the hour; or, leaving his crowned brow in marble quiet, unseen, departed to far-off councils of the gods. Howbeit, his lids never closed; in the noon-day sun, those crystal eyes, like diamonds, sparkled with a fixed light.

As motionless we thus reclined, Media turned and muttered, "Brother gods, and demi-gods, it is not well. These mortals should have less or more. Among my subjects is a man, whose genius scorns the common theories of things; but whose still mortal mind cannot fathom the ocean at his feet. His soul's a hollow, wherein he raves."

"List, list," whispered Yoomy, "our lord is dreaming; and what a royal dream."

"A very royal and imperial dream," said Babbalanja; "he is arraigning me before high heaven; ay, ay; in dreams, at least, he deems himself a demi-god."

"Hist," said Mohi; "he speaks again."

"Gods and demi-gods! With one gesture all abysses we may disclose; and before this Mardi's eyes, evoke the shrouded time to come. Were this well? Like lost children groping in the woods they falter through their tangled paths; and at a thousand angles, baffled, start upon each other. And even when they make an onward move, 'tis but an endless vestibule, that leads to naught. In my own isle of Odo—Odo! Odo! How rules my viceroy there? Down, down, ye madding mobs! Ho, spearmen, charge! By the firmament, but my halberdiers fly!"

"His dream has changed," said Babbalanja. "He is in Odo, whither his anxieties impel him."

"Hist, hist," said Yoomy.

"I leap upon the soil! Render thy account, Almanni! Where's my throne? Mohi, am I not a king? Do not thy chronicles record me? Yoomy, am I not the soul of some one glorious song? Babbalanja, speak—Mohi! Yoomy!"

"What is it, my lord? thou dost but dream."

Staring wildly; then calmly gazing round, Media smiled.

"Ha! how we royalties ramble in our dreams! I've told no secrets?"

"While he seemed to sleep, my lord spoke much," said Mohi.

"I knew it not, old man; nor would now; but that ye tell me."

"We dream not ourselves," said Babbalanja, "but the thing within us."

"Ay? good-morrow Azzageddi! But come; no more dreams. Vee-Vee! wine."

And straight through that live-long night, immortal Media plied the can.

Chapter CLXXIII

After a Long Interval, by Night They are Becalmed

Now, suns rose, and set; moons grew, and waned; till, at last, the star that erewhile heralded the dawn, presaged the eve; to us, sad token!—while deep within the deepest heart of Mardi's circle, we sailed from sea to sea; and isle to isle; and group to group;—vast empires explored, and inland valleys, to their utmost heads; and for every ray in heaven, beheld a king.

Needless to recount all that then befell; what tribes and caravans we saw; what vast horizons; boundless plains; and sierras, in their every intervale, a nation nestling.

Enough that still we roamed.

It was evening; and as the red sun, magnified, launched into the wave, once more, from a wild strand, we launched our three canoes.

Soon, from her clouds, hooded Night, like a nun from a convent, drew nigh. Rustled her train, yet no spangles were there. But high on her brow, still shone her pale crescent; haloed by bandelets—violet, red, and yellow. So looked the lone watcher through her rainbow-iris; so sad, the night without stars.

The winds were laid; the lagoon, still, as a prairie of an August noon.

"Let us dream out the calm," said Media. "One of ye paddlers watch. Ho, companions! who's for Cathay?"

Sleep reigned throughout the canoes, sleeping upon the waters. But nearer and nearer, low-creeping along, came mists and vapors, a thousand; spotted with twinklings of Will-o-Wisps from neighboring shores. Dusky leopards, stealing on by crouches, those vapors seemed.

Hours silently passed. When startled by a cry, Taji sprang to his feet; against which something rattled; then, a quick splash; and a dark form bounded into the lagoon.

The dozing watcher had called aloud; and, about to stab, the assassin, dropping his stiletto, plunged.

Peering hard through those treacherous mists, two figures in a shallop, were espied; dragging another, dripping from the brine.

"Foiled again, and foiled forever. No foe's corpse was I."

As we gazed, in the gloom quickly vanished the shallop; ere ours could be reversed to pursue.

Then, from the opposite mists, glided a second canoe; and beneath the Iris round the moon, shone now another:—Hautia's flowery flag!

Vain to wave the sirens off; so still they came.

One waved a plant of sickly silver-green.

"The Midnight Tremmella!" cried Yoomy; "the falling-star of flowers!—Still I come, when least foreseen; then, flee."

The second waved a hemlock top, the spike just tapering its final point. The third a convolvulus, half closed.

"The end draws nigh, and all thy hopes are waning."

Then they proffered grapes.

But once more waved off, silently they vanished.

Again the buried barb tore at my soul; again Yillah was invoked, but Hautia made reply.

Slowly wore out the night. But when uprose the sun, fled clouds, and fled sadness.

Chapter CLXXIV

THEY LAND AT HOOLOOMOOLOO

KEEP ALL THREE PROWS, FOR YONDER ROCK." CRIED MEDIA. "NO SADNESS ON THIS MERRY MORN! And now for the Isle of Cripples—even Hooloomooloo."

"The Isle of Cripples?"

"Ay; why not? Mohi, tell how they came to club."

In substance, this was the narration.

Averse to the barbarous custom of destroying at birth all infants not symmetrically formed; but equally desirous of removing from their sight those unfortunate beings; the islanders of a neighboring group had long ago established an asylum for cripples; where they lived, subject to their own regulations; ruled by a king of their own election; in short, forming a distinct class of beings by themselves.

One only restriction was placed upon them; on no account must they quit the isle assigned them. And to the surrounding islanders, so unpleasant the sight of a distorted mortal, that a stranger landing at Hooloomooloo, was deemed a prodigy. Wherefore, respecting any knowledge of aught beyond them, the cripples were well nigh as isolated, as if Hooloomooloo was the only terra-firma extant.

Dwelling in a community of their own, these unfortunates, who otherwise had remained few in number, increased and multiplied greatly. Nor did successive generations improve in symmetry upon those preceding them.

Soon, we drew nigh to the isle.

Heaped up, and jagged with rocks; and, here and there, covered with dwarfed, twisted thickets, it seemed a fit place for its denizens.

Landing, we were surrounded by a heterogeneous mob; and thus escorted, took our way inland, toward the abode of their lord, King Yoky.

What a scene.

Here, helping himself along with two crotched roots, hobbled a dwarf without legs; another stalked before, one arm fixed in the air, like a lightning rod; a third, more active than any, seal-like, flirted a pair of flippers, and went skipping along; a fourth hopped on a solitary pin, at every bound, spinning round like a top, to gaze; while still another, furnished with feelers or fins, rolled himself up in a ball, bowling over the ground in advance.

With curious instinct, the blind stuck close to our side; with chattering fingers, the deaf and the dumb described angles, obtuse and acute in the air; and like stones rolling down rocky ravines, scores of stammerers stuttered. Discord wedded deformity. All asses' brays were now harmonious memories; all Calibans, as angels. Yet for every stare we gave them, three stares they gave us.

At last, we halted before a tenement of rude stones; crooked Banian boughs its rafters, thatched with fantastic leaves. So rambling and irregular its plan, it seemed thrown up by the eruption, according to sage Mohi, the origin of the isle itself. Entering we saw King Yoky.

Ah! sadly lacking was he, in all the requisites of an efficient ruler. Deaf and dumb he was; and save arms, minus every thing but an indispensable trunk and head. So huge his all-comprehensive mouth, it seemed to swallow up itself.

But shapeless, helpless as was Yoky—as king of Hooloomooloo, he was competent; the state being a limited monarchy, of which his Highness was but the passive and ornamental head.

As his visitors advanced, he fell to gossiping with his fingers; a servitor interpreting. Very curious to note the rapidity with which motion was translated into sound; and the simultaneousness with which meaning made its way through four successive channels to the mind—hand, sight, voice, and tympanum.

Much amazement His Highness now expressed; horrified his glances.

"Why club such frights as ye? Herd ye, to keep in countenance; or are afraid of your own hideousness, that ye dread to go alone? Monsters! speak."

"Great Oro!" cried Mohi, "are we then taken for cripples, by the very King of the Cripples? My lord, are not our legs and arms all right?"

"Comelier ones were never turned by turners, Mohi. But royal Yoky! in sooth we feel abashed before thee."

Some further stares were then exchanged; when His Highness sought to know, whether there were any Comparative Anatomists among his visitors.

"Comparative Anatomists! not one."

"And why may King Yoky ask that question?" inquired Babbalanja.

Then was made the following statement.

During the latter part of his reign, when he seemed fallen into his dotage, the venerable predecessor of King Yoky had been much attached to an old gray-headed Chimpanzee, one day found meditating in the woods. Rozoko was his name. He was very grave, and reverend of aspect; much of a philosopher. To him, all gnarled and knotty subjects were familiar; in his day he had cracked many a crabbed nut. And so in love with his Timonean solitude was Rozoko, that it needed many bribes and bland persuasions, to induce him to desert his mossy, hill-side, misanthropic cave, for the distracting tumult of a court.

But ere long, promoted to high offices, and made the royal favorite, the woodland sage forgot his forests; and, love for love, returned the aged king's caresses. Ardent friends, they straight became; dined and drank together with quivering lips, quaffed long-drawn, sober bumpers; comparing all their past experiences and canvassing those hidden themes, on which octogenarians dilate.

For when the fires and broils of youth are passed, and Mardi wears its truer aspect—then we love to think, not act; the present seems more unsubstantial than the past; then, we seek out graybeards like ourselves; and hold discourse of palsies, hearses, shrouds, and tombs; appoint our undertakers; our mantles gather round us like to winding-sheets; and every night lie down to die. Then, the world's great bubble bursts; then, Life's clouds seem sweeping by, revealing heaven to our straining eyes; then, we tell our beads, and murmur pater-nosters; and in trembling accents cry—"Oro! be merciful!" So, the monarch and Rozoko.

But not always were they thus. Of bright, cheerful mornings, they took slow, tottering rambles in the woods; nodding over grotesque walking sticks, of Chimpanzee's handiwork. For sedate Rozoko was a dilettante-arborist; an amateur in canes. Indeed, canes at last became his hobby. For half daft with age, sometimes he straddled his good staff and gently rode abroad, to take the salubrious evening air; deeming it more befitting exercise, at times, than walking. Into this menage, he soon initiated his friend, the king; and side by side they often pranced; or, wearying of the saddle, dismounted; and paused to ponder over prostrate palms, decaying across the path. Their mystic rings they counted, and for every ring, a year in their own calendars.

Now, so closely did the monarch cleave to the Chimpanzee, that, in good time, summoning his subjects, earnestly he charged it on them, that at death, he and his faithful friend should be buried in one tomb.

It came to pass, the monarch died; and poor Rozoko, now reduced to second childhood, wailed most dismally; no one slept that night in Hooloomooloo. Never did he leave the body; and at last, slowly going round it thrice, he laid him down; close nestled; and noiselessly expired. The King's injunctions were remembered; and one vault received them both.

Moon followed moon; and wrought upon by jeers and taunts, the people of the isle became greatly scandalized, that a base-born baboon should share the shroud of their departed lord; though they themselves had tucked in the aged Æneas fast by the side of his Achates.

They straight resolved, to build another vault; and over it, a lofty cairn; and thither carry the remains they reverenced.

But at the disinterring, a sad perplexity arose. For lo! surpassing Saul and Jonathan, not even in decay were these fast friends divided. So mingled every relic—ilium and ulna, carpus and metacarpus—and so similar the corresponding parts, that like the literary remains of Beaumont and of Fletcher, which was which, no spectacles could tell. Therefore, they desisted; lest the towering monument they had reared, might commemorate an ape, and not a king.

Such the narration; hearing which, my lord Media kept stately silence. But in courtly phrase, as beseemed him, Babbalanja, turban in hand, thus spoke:

"My concern is extreme, King Yoky, at the embarrassment into which your island is thrown. Nor less my grief, that I myself am not the man to put an end to it. I could weep that Comparative Anatomists are not so numerous now, as hereafter they assuredly must become; when their services shall be in greater request; when, at the last, last day of all, millions of noble and ignoble spirits will loudly clamor for lost skeletons; when contending claimants shall start up for one poor, carious spine; and, dog-like, we shall quarrel over our own bones."

Then entered dwarf-stewards, and major-domos; aloft bearing twisted antlers; all hollowed out in goblets, grouped; announcing dinner.

Loving not, however, to dine with misshapen Mardians, King Media was loath to move. But Babbalanja, quoting the old proverb—"Strike me in the face, but refuse not my yams," induced him to sacrifice his fastidiousness.

So, under a flourish of ram-horn bugles court and company proceeded to the banquet.

Central was a long, dislocated trunk of a wild Banian; like a huge centipede crawling on its hundred branches, sawn of even lengths for legs. This table was set out with wry-necked gourds; deformities of calabashes and shapeless trenchers, dug out of knotty woods.

The first course was shrimp-soup, served in great clam-shells; the second, lobsters, cuttle-fish, crabs, cockles, cray-fish; the third, hunch-backed roots of the Taro-plant-plantains, perversely curling at the end, like the inveterate tails of pertinacious pigs; and for dessert, ill-shaped melons, huge as idiots' heads, plainly suffering from water in the brain.

Now these viands were commended to the favorable notice of all guests; not only for their delicacy of flavor, but for their symmetry.

And in the intervals of the courses, we were bored with hints to admire numerous objects of vertu: bow-legged stools of mangrove wood; zig-zag rapiers of bone; armlets of grampus-vertebrae; outlandish tureens of the callipees of terrapin; and cannakins of the skulls of baboons.

The banquet over, with many congees, we withdrew.

Returning to the water-side, we passed a field, where dwarfs were laboring in beds of yams, heaping the soil around the roots, by scratching it backwards as a dog.

All things in readiness, Yoky's valet, a tri-armed dwarf, treated us to a glorious start, by giving each canoe a vigorous triple push, crying, "Away with ye, monsters!"

Nor must it be omitted that just previous to embarking, Vee-Vee, spying a curious looking stone, turned it over, and found a snake.

Chapter CLXXV

A Book from the "Ponderings of Old Bardianna"

NOW," SAID BABBALANJA, LIGHTING HIS TROMBONE AS WE SAILED FROM THE ISLE, "WHO ARE THE monsters, we or the cripples?"

"You yourself are a monster, for asking the question," said Mohi.

"And so, to the cripples I am; though not, old man, for the reason you mention. But I am, as I am; whether hideous, or handsome, depends upon who is made judge. There is no supreme standard yet revealed, whereby to judge of ourselves; 'Our very instincts are prejudice,' saith Alla Mallolla; 'Our very axioms, and postulates are far from infallible.' 'In respect of the universe, mankind is but a sect,' saith Diloro: 'and first principles but dogmas.' What ethics prevail in the Pleiades? What things have the synods in Sagittarius decreed?"

"Never mind your old authors," said Media. "Stick to the cripples; enlarge upon them."

"But I have done with them now, my lord; the sermon is not the text. Give ear to old Bardianna. I know him by heart. Thus saith the sage in Book X of the *Ponderings of 'Zermalmende,'* the title: *'Je pense,'* the motto: 'My supremacy over creation, boasteth man, is declared in my natural attitude: I stand erect! But so do the palm-trees; and the giraffes that graze off their tops. And the fowls of the air fly high over our heads; and from the place where we fancy our heaven to be, defile the tops of our temples. Belike, the eagles, from their eyries look down upon us Mardians, in our hives, even as upon the beavers in their dams, marveling at our incomprehensible ways. And cunning though we be, some things, hidden from us, may not be mysteries to them. Having five keys, hold we all that open to knowledge? Deaf, blind, and deprived of the power of scent, the bat will steer its way unerringly: could we? Yet man is lord of the bat and the brute, lord over the crows; with whom, he must needs share the grain he garners. We sweat for the fowls, as well as ourselves. The curse of labor rests only on us. Like slaves, we toil; at their good leisure they glean.

" 'Mardi is not wholly ours. We are the least populous part of creation. To say nothing of other tribes, a census of the herring would find us far in the minority. And what life is to us; sour or sweet, so is it to them. Like us, they die, fighting death to the last; like us they spawn and depart. We inhabit but a crust, rough surfaces, odds and ends of the isles; the abounding lagoon being its two-thirds, its grand feature from afar, and forever unfathomable. What shaft has yet been sunk to the antipodes? What underlieth the gold mines?

" 'But even here, above-ground, we grope with the sun at meridian. Vainly, we seek our North-west Passages—old alleys, and thoroughfares of the whales.

" 'Oh, men! Fellow-men! we are only what we are; not what we would be; nor everything we hope for. We are but a step in a scale, that reaches further above us than below. We breathe but oxygen. Who in Arcturus hath heard of us? They know us not in the Milky Way. We prate of faculties divine; and know not how sprouteth a spear of grass; we go about shrugging our shoulders; when the firmament-arch is over us; we rant of etherealities; and long tarry over our banquet; we demand Eternity for a life-time; when our mortal half-hours too often prove tedious. We know not of what we talk. The Bird of Paradise outflies our flutterings. What it is to be immortal, has not yet entered into our thoughts. At will, we build our futurities; tier above tier, all galleries full of laureates; resounding with everlasting oratorios! Pater-nosters forever, or eternal Misereres! forgetting that in Mardi, our breviaries oft fall from our hands. But divans there are, some say, whereon we shall recline, basking in effulgent suns, knowing neither Orient nor Occident. Is it so? Fellow-men! our mortal lives have an end; but that end is no goal: no place of repose. Whatever it may be, it will prove but as the beginning of another race. We will hope, joy, weep, as before; though our tears may be such as the spice-trees shed. Supine, we can only be annihilated.

" 'The thick film is breaking; the ages have long been circling. Fellow-men; if we live hereafter, it will not be in lyrics; nor shall we yawn, and our shadows lengthen, while the eternal cycles are revolving. To live at all, is a high vocation; to live forever, and run parallel with Oro, may truly appall us. Toil we not here? and shall we be forever slothful elsewhere? Other worlds differ not much from this, but in degree. Doubtless, a pebble is a fair specimen of the universe.

" 'We point at random. Peradventure at this instant there are beings gazing up to this very world as their future heaven. But the universe is all over a heaven: nothing but stars on stars, throughout infinities of expansion. All we see are but a cluster. Could we get to Boötes, we would be no nearer Oro, than now; he hath no place; but is here. Already, in its unimaginable roamings, our system may have dragged us through and through the spaces, where we plant cities of beryl and jasper. Even now, we may be inhaling the ether, which we fancy seraphic wings are fanning. But look round. There is much to be seen here, and now. Do the archangels survey aught more glorious than the constellations we nightly behold? Continually we slight the wonders, we deem in reserve. We await the present. With marvels we are glutted, till we hold them no marvels at all. But had these eyes first opened upon all the prodigies in the Revelation of the Dreamer, long familiarity would have made them appear, even as these things we see. Now, *now,* the page is outspread; to the simple, easy as a primer; to the wise, more puzzling than hieroglyphics. The eternity to come is but a prolongation of time present: and the beginning may be more wonderful than the end.

" 'Then let us be wise. But much of the knowledge we seek, already we have in our cores. Yet so simple it is, we despise it; so bold, we fear it.

" 'In solitude, let us exhume our ingots. Let us hear our own thoughts. The soul needs no mentor, but Oro; and Oro, without proxy. Wanting Him, it is both the teacher and the taught. Undeniably, reason was the first revelation; and so far as it tests all others, it has precedence over them. It comes direct to us, without suppression or interpolation; and with Oro's indisputable imprimatur. But inspiration though it be, it is not so arrogant as some think. Nay, far too humble at times, it submits to the grossest indignities. Though in its best estate, not infallible; so far as it goes, for us, it is reliable. When at fault, it stands still. We speak not of visionaries. But if this our first revelation stops short of the uttermost, so with all others. If, often, it only perplexes; much more the rest. They leave much unexpounded; and disclosing new mysteries, add to the enigma. Fellow-men; the ocean we would sound is unfathomable; and however much we add to our line, when it is out, we feel not the bottom. Let us be truly lowly, when not lifted up with a Pharisaic humility. We crawl not like worms; nor wear we the liveries of angels.

" 'The firmament arch has no key-stone; least of all, is man its prop. He stands alone. We are everything to ourselves, but how little to others. What are others to us? Assure life everlasting to this generation, and their immediate forefathers; and what tears would flow, were there no resurrection for the countless generations from the first man to five cycles since? And soon we ourselves shall have fallen in with the rank and file of our sires. At a blow, annihilate some distant tribe, now alive and jocund—and what would we reck? Curiosity apart, do we really care whether the people in Bellatrix are immortal or no?

" 'Though they smite us, let us not turn away from these things, if they be really thus.

" 'There was a time, when near Cassiopeia, a star of the first magnitude, most lustrous in the north, grew lurid as a fire, then dim as ashes, and went out. Now, its place is a blank. A vast world, with all its continents, say the astronomers, blazing over the heads of our fathers; while in Mardi were merry-makings, and maidens given in marriage. Who now thinks of that burning sphere? How few are aware that ever it was?

" 'These things are so.

" 'Fellow-men! we must go, and obtain a glimpse of what we are from the Belts of Jupiter and the Moons of Saturn, ere we see ourselves aright. The universe can wax old without us; though by Oro's grace we may live to behold a wrinkle in the sky. Eternity is not ours by right; and, alone, unrequited sufferings here, form no title thereto, unless resurrections are reserved for maltreated brutes. Suffering is suffering; be the sufferer man, brute or thing.

" 'How small—how nothing, our deserts! Let us stifle all vain speculations; we need not to be told what righteousness is; we were born with the whole Law in our hearts. Let us do; let us act; let us down on our knees. And if, after all, we should be no more forever, far better to perish meriting immortality, than to enjoy it unmeritorious. While we fight over creeds, ten thousand fingers point to where vital good may be done. All round us, Want crawls to her lairs; and, shivering, dies unrelieved. Here, *here*, fellow-men, we can better minister as angels, than in heaven, where want and misery come not.

" 'We Mardians talk as though the future was all in all; but act as though the present was everything. Yet so far as, in our theories, we dwarf our Mardi; we go not beyond an archangel's apprehension of it, who takes in all suns and systems at a glance. Like pebbles, were the isles to sink in space, Sirius, the Dog-star, would still flame in the sky. But as the atom to the animalculae, so Mardi to us. And lived aright, these mortal lives are long; looked into, these souls, fathomless as the nethermost depths.

" 'Fellow-men! we split upon hairs; but stripped, mere words and phrases cast aside, the great bulk of us are orthodox. None who think, dissent from the grand belief. The first man's thoughts were as ours. The paramount revelation prevails with us; and all that clashes therewith, we do not so much believe, as believe that we cannot disbelieve. Common sense is a sturdy despot; that, for the most part, has its own way. It inspects and ratifies much independent of it. But those who think they do wholly reject it, are but held in a sly sort of bondage; under a semblance of something else, wearing the old yoke.' "

"Cease, cease, Babbalanja," said Media, "and permit me to insinuate a word in your ear. You have long been in the habit, philosopher, of regaling us with chapters from your old Bardianna; and with infinite gusto, you have just recited the longest of all. But I do not observe, oh, Sage! that for all these things, you yourself are practically the better or wiser. You live not up to Bardianna's main thought. Where he stands, he stands immovable; but you are a Dog-vane. How is this?"

"Gogle-goggle, fugle-fi, fugle-fogle-orum!"

"Mad, mad again," cried Yoomy.

Chapter CLXXVI

BABBALANJA STARTS TO HIS FEET

FOR TWENTY-FOUR HOURS, SEATED STIFF AND MOTIONLESS, BABBALANJA SPOKE NOT A WORD; then, almost without moving a muscle, muttered thus, "At banquets, surfeit not, but fill; partake, and retire; and eat not again till you crave. Thereby you give nature time to work her magic transformings; turning all solids to meat, and wine into blood. After a banquet you incline to repose: do so; digestion commands. All this follow those, who feast at the tables of Wisdom; and all such are they, who partake of the fare of old Bardianna."

"Art resuscitated, then, Babbalanja?" said Media.

"Ay, my lord, I am just risen from the dead."

"And did Azzageddi conduct you to their realms?"

"Fangs off! fangs off! depart, thou fiend! unhand me! or by Oro, I will die and spite thee!"

"Quick, quick, Mohi! let us change places," cried Yoomy.

"How now, Babbalanja?" said Media.

"Oh my lord man—not *you,* my lord Media! high and mighty Puissance! great King of Creation! thou art but the biggest of braggarts! In every age, thou boastest of thy valorous advances: flat fools, old dotards, and numskulls, our sires! All the Past, wasted time! the Present knows all! right lucky, fellow-beings, we live now! every man an author! books plenty as men! strike a light in a minute! teeth sold by the pound! all the elements fetching and carrying! lightning running on errands! rivers made to order! the ocean a puddle! But ages back they boasted like us; and ages to come, forever and ever, they'll boast. Ages back they black-balled the past, thought the last day was come; so wise they were grown. Mardi could not stand long; have to annex one of the planets; invade the great sun; colonize the moon; conquerors sighed for new Mardis; and sages for heaven—having by heart all the primers here below. Like us, ages back they groaned under their books; made bonfires of libraries, leaving ashes behind, mid which we reverentially grope for charred pages, forgetting we are so much wiser than they. But amazing times! astounding revelations; preternatural divulgings! How now? more wonderful than all our discoveries is this: that they never were discovered before. So simple, no doubt our ancestors overlooked them; intent on deeper things—the deep things of the soul. All we discover has been with us since the sun began to roll; and much we discover, is not worth the discovering. We are children, climbing trees after birds' nests, and making a great shout, whether we find eggs in them or no. But where are our wings, which our forefathers surely had not? Tell us, ye sages! something worth an archangel's learning; discover, ye discoverers, something new. Fools, fools: Mardi's not changed: the sun yet rises in its old place in the east; all things go on in the same old way; we cut our eye-teeth just as late as they did, three thousand years ago."

"Your pardon," said Mohi, "for beshrew me, they are not yet all cut. At three-score and ten, here have I a new tooth coming now."

"Old man! it but clears the way for another. The teeth sown by the alphabet-founder were eye-teeth, not yet all sprung from the soil. Like spring wheat, blade by blade, they break ground late; like spring wheat, many seeds have perished in the hard winter glebe. Oh, my lord, though we galvanize corpses into St. Vitus' dances, we raise not the dead from their graves! Though we have discovered the circulation of the blood, men die as of yore; oxen graze, sheep bleat, babies bawl, asses bray—loud and lusty as the day before the flood. Men fight and make up; repent and go at it; feast and starve; laugh and weep; pray and curse; cheat, chaffer, trick, truckle, cozen, defraud, fib, lie, beg, borrow, steal, hang, drown—as in the laughing and weeping, tricking and truckling, hanging and drowning times that have been. Nothing changes, though much be new-fashioned; new fashions but revivals of things previous. In the books of the past we learn naught but of the present; in those of the present, the past. All Mardi's history—beginning, middle, and finis—was written out in capitals in the first page penned. The whole story is told in a title-page. An exclamation point is entire Mardi's autobiography."

"Who speaks now?" said Media, "Bardianna, Azzageddi, or Babbalanja?"

"All three; is it not a pleasant concert?"

"Very fine. Go on; and tell us something of the future."

"I have never departed this life yet, my lord."

"But just now you said you were risen from the dead."

"From the buried dead within me; not from myself, my lord."

"If you, then, know nothing of the future—did Bardianna?"

"If he did, naught did he reveal. I have ever observed, my lord, that even in their deepest lucubrations, the profoundest, frankest, ponderers always reserve a vast deal of precious thought for their own private behoof. They think, perhaps, that 'tis too good, or too bad; too wise, or too foolish, for the multitude. And this unpleasant vibration is ever consequent upon striking a new vein of ideas in the soul. As with buried treasures, the ground over them sounds strange and hollow. At any rate, the profoundest ponderer seldom tells us all he thinks; seldom reveals to us the ultimate, and the innermost; seldom makes us open our eyes under water; seldom throws open the totus-in-toto; and never carries us with him, to the unconsubsistent, the idea-immanens, the super-essential, and the One."

"Confusion! Remember the Quadammodotatives!"

"Ah!" said Braid-Beard, "that's the crack in his calabash which all the Dicibles of Doxdox will not mend."

"And from that crazy calabash he gives us to drink, old Mohi."

"But never heed his leaky gourd nor its contents, my lord. Let these philosophers muddle themselves as they will, we wise ones refuse to partake."

"And fools like me drink till they reel," said Babbalanja. "But in these matters one's calabash must needs go round to keep afloat. Fogle-orum!"

Chapter CLXXVII

At Last, the Last Mention is Made of Old Bardianna; and His Last Will and Testament is Recited at Length

The day was waning. And, as after many a tale of ghosts, around their forest fires, Hungarian gypsies silent sit; watching the ruddy glow kindling each other's faces; so, now we solemn sat; the crimson west our fire; all our faces flushed.

"Testators!" then cried Media, "when your last wills are all round settled, speak, and make it known!"

"Mine, my lord, has long been fixed," said Babbalanja.

"And how runs it?"

"Fugle-fogle—"

"Hark ye, intruding Azzageddi! rejoin thy merry mates below; go there, and wag thy saucy tail; or I will nail it to our bow, till ye roar for liberation. Begone, I say."

"Down, devil! deeper down!" rumbled Babbalanja. "My lord, I think he's gone. And now, by your good leave, I'll repeat old Bardianna's Will. It's worth all Mardi's hearing; and I have so studied it, by rote I know it."

"Proceed then; but I mistrust that Azzageddi is not yet many thousand fathoms down."

"Attend, my lord. 'Anno Mardis 50,000,000, o.s. I, Bardianna, of the island of Vamba, and village of the same name, having just risen from my yams, in high health, high spirits, and sound mind, do hereby cheerfully make and ordain this my last will and testament.

" 'Imprimis:

" 'All my kith and kin being well to do in Mardi, I wholly leave them out of this my will.

" 'Item. Since, in divers ways, verbally, and otherwise, my good friend Pondo has evinced a strong love for me, Bardianna, as the owner and proprietor of all that capital messuage with the appurtenances, in Vamba aforesaid, called 'The Lair,' wherein I now dwell; also for all my bread-fruit orchards, palm-groves, banana-plantations, taro-patches, gardens, lawns, lanes, and hereditaments whatsoever, adjoining the aforesaid messuage; I do hereby give and bequeath the same to Bomblum of the island of Adda; the aforesaid Bomblum having never expressed any regard for me, as a holder of real estate.

" 'Item. My esteemed neighbor Lakreemo having since the last lunar eclipse called daily to inquire after the state of my health: and having nightly made tearful inquiries of my herb-doctor, concerning the state of my viscera;—I do hereby give and bequeath to the aforesaid Lakreemo all and sundry those vegetable pills, potions, powders, aperients, purgatives, expellatives, evacuatives, tonics, emetics, cathartics, clysters, injections, scarifiers, cataplasms, lenitives, lotions, decoctions, washes, gargles, and phlegmagogues; together with all the jars, calabashes, gourds, and galipots, thereunto pertaining; situate, lying, and being, in the west-by-north corner of my east-south-east crypt, in my aforesaid tenement known as 'The Lair.'

" 'Item. The woman Pesti; a native of Vamba, having oftentimes hinted that I, Bardianna, sorely needed a spouse, and having also intimated that she bore me a conjugal affection; I do hereby give and bequeath to the aforesaid Pesti—my blessing; forasmuch, as by the time of the opening of this my last will and testament, I shall have been forever delivered from the aforesaid Pesti's persecutions.

" 'Item. Having a high opinion of the probity of my worthy and excellent friend Bidiri, I do hereby entirely, and wholly, give, will, grant, bestow, devise, and utterly hand over unto the said Bidiri, all that tenement where my servant Oram now dwelleth; with all the lawns, meadows, uplands and lowlands, fields, groves, and gardens, thereunto belonging: IN TRUST NEVERTHELESS to have and to hold the same for the sole use and benefit of Lanbranke Hohinna, spinster, now resident of the aforesaid island of Vamba.

" 'Item. I give and bequeath my large carved drinking gourd to my good comrade Topo.

" 'Item. My fast friend Doldrum having at sundry times, and in sundry places, uttered the prophecy, that upon my decease his sorrow would be great; I do hereby give and bequeath to the aforesaid Doldrum, ten yards of my best soft tappa, to be divided into handkerchiefs, for his sole benefit and behoof.

" 'Item. My sensible friend Solo having informed me, that he intended to remain a bachelor for life; I give and devise to the aforesaid Solo, the mat for one person, whereon I nightly repose.

" 'Item. Concerning my private Arbor and Palm-groves, adjoining, lying, and being in the isle of Vamba, I give and devise the same, with all appurtenances whatsoever, to my friend Minta the Cynic, to have and to hold, in trust for the first through-and-through honest man, issue, of my neighbor Mondi; and in default of such issue, for the first through-and-through honest man, issue, of my neighbor Pendidda; and in default of such issue, for the first through-and-through honest man, issue of my neighbor Wynodo; and in default of such issue, to any through-and-through honest man, issue of any body, to be found through the length and breadth of Mardi.

" 'Item. My friend Minta the Cynic to be sole judge of all claims to the above-mentioned devise; and to hold the said premises for his own use, until the aforesaid person be found.

" 'Item. Knowing my devoted scribe Marko to be very sensitive touching the receipt of a favor; I willingly spare him that pain; and hereby bequeath unto the aforesaid scribe, three milk-teeth, not as a pecuniary legacy, but as a very slight token of my profound regard.

" 'Item. I give to the poor of Vamba the total contents of my red-labeled bags of bicuspids and canines (which I account three-fourths of my whole estate); to my body servant Fidi, my staff, all my robes and togas, and three hundred molars in cash; to that discerning and sagacious philosopher, my disciple Krako, one complete set of denticles, to buy him a vertebral bone ring; and to that pious and promising youth Cangi, two fathoms of my best kaiar rope, with the privilege of any bough in my groves.

" 'All the rest of my goods, chattels, and household stuff whatever; and all my loose denticles, remaining after my debts and legacies are paid, and my body is out of sight, I hereby direct to be distributed among the poor of Vamba.

" 'Ultimo. I give and bequeath to all Mardi this my last advice and counsel: videlicet: live as long as you can; close your own eyes when you die.

" 'I have no previous wills to revoke; and publish this to be my first and last.

" 'In witness whereof, I have hereunto set my right hand; and hereunto have caused a true copy of the tattooing on my right temple to be affixed during the year first above-written.

" 'By me, BARDIANNA.' "

"Babbalanja, that's an extraordinary document," said Media.

"Bardianna was an extraordinary man, my lord."

"Were there no codicils?"

"The will is all codicils; all after-thoughts; ten thoughts for one act, was Bardianna's motto."

"Left he nothing whatever to his kindred?"

"Not a stump."

"From his will, he seems to have lived single."

"Yes; Bardianna never sought to improve upon nature; a bachelor he was born, and a bachelor he died."

"According to the best accounts, how did he depart, Babbalanja?" asked Mohi.

"With a firm lip, and his hand on his heart, old man."

"His last words?"

"Calmer and better."

"Where think you, he is now?"

"In his Ponderings. And those, my lord, we all inherit; for like the great chief of Romara, who made a whole empire his legatee; so, great authors have all Mardi for an heir."

Chapter CLXXVIII

A Death-Cloud Sweeps by Them, as They Sail

NEXT DAY, A FEARFUL SIGHT.

As in Sooloo's seas, one vast water-spout will, sudden, form; and whirling, chase the flying Malay keels; so, before a swift-winged cloud, a thousand prows sped by, leaving braided, foaming wakes; their crowded inmates' arms, in frenzied supplications wreathed; like tangled forest-boughs.

"See, see," cried Yoomy, "how the Death-cloud flies! Let us dive down in the sea."

"Nay," said Babbalanja. "All things come of Oro; if we must drown, let Oro drown us."

"Down sails; drop paddles," said Media; "here we float."

Like a rushing bison, sweeping by, the Death-cloud grazed us with its foam; and whirling in upon the thousand prows beyond, sudden burst in deluges; and scooping out a maelstrom, dragged down every plank and soul.

Long we rocked upon the circling billows, which expanding from that center, dashed every isle, till, moons afterward, faint, they laved all Mardi's reef.

"Thanks unto Oro," murmured Mohi, "this heart still beats."

That sun-flushed eve, we sailed by many tranquil harbors, whence fled those thousand prows. Serene, the waves chimed around the stakes of palm, to which the thousand prows that morning had been fastened.

"Flying death they ran to meet it," said Babbalanja. "But 'tis not that they fled, they died; for maelstroms, of these harbors, the Death-cloud might have made. But they died, because they might not longer live. Could we gain one glimpse of the great calendar of eternity, all our names would there be found, glued against their dates of death. We die by land, and die by sea, we die by earthquakes, famines, plagues, and wars; by fevers, agues, woe, or mirth excessive. This mortal air is one wide pestilence, that kills us all at last. Whom the Death-cloud spares, sleeping, dies in silent watches of the night. He whom the spears of many battles could not slay, dies of a grape-stone beneath the vine-clad bower he built, to shade declining years. We die, because we live. But nonetheless does Babbalanja quake. And if he flies not, 'tis because he stands the center of a circle; its every point a leveled dart; and every bow bent back—a twang, and Babbalanja dies."

Chapter CLXXIX

They Visit the Palmy King Abrazza

NIGHT AND MORN DEPARTED; AND IN THE AFTERNOON, WE DREW NIGH TO AN ISLAND, OVERCAST with shadows; a shower was falling; and pining, plaintive notes forth issued from the groves: half-suppressed, and sobbing whisperings of leaves. The shore sloped to the water; thither our prows were pointed.

"Sheer off! no landing here," cried Media, "let us gain the sunny side; and like the care-free bachelor Abrazza, who here is king, turn our back on the isle's shadowy side, and revel in its morning-meads."

"And lord Abrazza—who is he?" asked Yoomy.

"The one hundred and twentieth in lineal descent from Phipora," said Mohi; "and connected on the maternal side to the lord seigniors of Klivonia. His uttermost uncle was nephew to the niece of Queen Zmiglandi; who flourished so long since, she wedded at the first Transit of Venus. His pedigree is endless."

"But who is lord Abrazza?"

"Has he not said?" answered Babbalanja. "Why so dull? Uttermost nephew to him, who was nephew to the niece of the peerless Queen Zmiglandi; and the one hundred and twentieth in descent from the illustrious Phipora."

"Will none tell who Abrazza is?"

"Cannot a man then be described by running off the catalogue of his ancestors?" said Babbalanja. "Or must we e'en descend to himself? Then, listen, dull Yoomy! and know that lord Abrazza is six feet two; plump thighs, blue eyes, and brown hair; likes his bread-fruit baked, not roasted; sometimes carries filberts in his crown; and has a way of winking when he speaks. His teeth are good."

"Are you publishing some decamped burglar," said Media, "that you speak thus of my royal friend, the Lord Abrazza? Go on, sir; and say he reigns sole king of Bonovona!"

"My lord, I had not ended. Abrazza, Yoomy, is a fine and florid king; high-fed, and affluent of heart; of speech, mellifluent. And for a royalty extremely amiable. He is a sceptered gentleman, who does much good. Kind king! in person, he gives orders for relieving those, who daily dive for pearls to grace his royal robe; and gasping hard, with blood-shot eyes, come up from shark-infested depths, and fainting, lay their treasure at his feet. Sweet Lord Abrazza! how he pities those, who in his furthest woodlands day-long toil to do his bidding. Yet king-philosopher, he never weeps; but pities with a placid smile: and that but seldom."

"There seems much iron in your blood," said Media. "But say your say."

"Say I not truth, my lord? Abrazza, I admire. Save his royal pity, all else is jocund round him. He loves to live for life's own sake. He vows he'll have no cares; and often says, in pleasant reveries, 'Sure, my lord Abrazza, if anyone should be care-free, 'tis thou; who strike down none, but pity all the fallen!' Yet none he lifteth up."

At length we gained the sunny side, and shoreward tended. Vee-Vee's horn was sonorous; and issuing from his golden groves, my lord Abrazza, like a host that greets you on the threshold, met us, as we keeled the beach.

"Welcome! fellow demi-god, and king! Media, my pleasant guest!"

His servitors salaamed; his chieftains bowed; his yeoman-guard, in meadow-green, presented palm-stalks—royal tokens; and hand in hand, the nodding, jovial, regal friends, went up a lane of salutations; dragging behind, a train of envyings.

Much we marked Abrazza's jeweled crown; that shot no honest blaze of ruddy rubies; nor looked stern-white like Media's pearls; but cast a green and yellow glare; rays from emeralds, crossing rays from many a topaz. In those beams, so sinister, all present looked cadaverous; Abrazza's cheek alone beamed bright, but hectic.

Upon its fragrant mats a spacious hall received the kings; and gathering courtiers blandly bowed; and gushing with soft flatteries, breathed idol-incense round them.

The hall was terraced thrice; its elevated end was curtained; and thence, at every chime of words, there burst a girl, gay scarfed, with naked bosom, and poured forth wild and hollow laughter, as she raced down all the terraces, and passed their merry kingships.

Wide round the hall, in avenues, waved almond-woods; their whiteness frosted into bloom. But every vine-clad trunk was hollow-hearted; hollow sounds came from the grottos: hollow broke the billows on the shore; and hollow pauses filled the air, following the hollow laughter. Guards, with spears, paced the groves, and in the inner shadows, oft were seen to lift their weapons, and backward press some ugly phantom, saying, "Subjects; haunt him not; Abrazza would be merry; Abrazza feasts his guests."

So, banished from our sight seemed all things uncongenial; and pleasant times were ours, in these dominions. Not a face passed by, but smiled; mocking-birds perched on the boughs, and singing, made us vow the woods were warbling forth thanksgiving, with a thousand throats! The stalwart yeomen grinned beneath their trenchers, heaped with citrons, pomegrantes, grapes; the pages tittered, pouring out the wine; and all the lords loud laughed, smote their gilded spears, and swore the isle was glad.

Such the isle, in which we tarried; but in our rambles, found no Yillah.

Chapter CLXXX

Same Pleasant, Shady Talk in the Groves, Between My Lords Abrazza and Media, Babbalanja, Mohi, and Yoomy

Abrazza had a cool retreat—a grove of dates; where we were used to lounge of noons, and mix our converse with the babble of the rills; and mix our punches in goblets chased with grapes. And as ever, King Abrazza was the prince of hosts.

"Your crown," he said to Media; and with his own, he hung it on a bough.

"Be not ceremonious," and stretched his royal legs upon the turf.

"Wine!" and his pages poured it out.

So on the grass we lounged: and King Abrazza, who loved his antique ancestors; and loved old times; and would not talk of moderns; bade Yoomy sing old songs; bade Mohi rehearse old histories; bade Babbalanja tell of old ontologies; and commanded all, meanwhile, to drink his old, old wine.

So, all round we quaffed and quoted.

At last, we talked of old Homeric bards: those who, ages back, harped, and begged, and groped their blinded way through all this charitable Mardi; receiving coppers then, and immortal glory now.

Abrazza—How came it, that they all were blind?

Babbalanja—It was endemical, your highness. Few grand poets have good eyes; for they needs blind must be, whoever gaze upon the sun. Vavona himself was blind: when, in the silence of his secret bower, he said, "I will build another world. Therein, let there be kings and slaves, philosophers and wits; whose checkered actions—strange, grotesque, and merry-sad, will entertain my idle moods." So, my lord, Vavona played at kings and crowns, and men and manners; and loved that lonely game to play.

Abrazza—Vavona seemed a solitary Mardian; who seldom went abroad; had few friends; and shunning others, was shunned by them.

Babbalanja—But shunned not himself, my lord; like gods, great poets dwell alone; while round them, roll the worlds they build.

Media—You seem to know all authors, you must have heard of Lombardo, Babbalanja; he who flourished many ages since.

Babbalanja—I have; and his grand *Koztanza*, know by heart.

Media (to Abrazza)—A very curious work, that, my lord.

Abrazza—Yes, my dearest king. But, Babbalanja, if Lombardo had aught to tell to Mardi—why choose a vehicle so crazy?

Babbalanja—It was his nature, I suppose.

Abrazza—But so it would not have been, to me.

Babbalanja—Nor would it have been natural for my noble lord Abrazza, to have worn Lombardo's head; every man has his own, thank Oro!

Abrazza—A curious work: a very curious work. Babbalanja, are you acquainted with the history of Lombardo?

Babbalanja—None better. All his biographies have I read.

Abrazza—Then, tell us how he came to write that work. For one, I cannot imagine how those poor devils contrive to roll such thunders through all Mardi.

Media—Their thunder and lightning seem spontaneous combustibles, my lord.

Abrazza—With which, they but consume themselves, my prince beloved.

Babbalanja—In a measure, true, your highness. But pray you, listen; and I will try to tell the way in which Lombardo produced his great *Koztanza.*

Media—But hark you, philosopher! this time no incoherencies; gag that devil, Azzageddi. And now, what was it that originally impelled Lombardo to the undertaking?

Babbalanja—Primus and forever, a full heart—brimful, bubbling, sparkling, and running over like the flagon in your hand, my lord. Secundo, the necessity of bestirring himself to procure his yams.

Abrazza—Wanting the second motive, would the first have sufficed, philosopher?

Babbalanja—Doubtful. More conduits than one to drain off the soul's overflowings. Besides, the greatest fullnesses overflow not spontaneously; and, even when decanted, like rich syrups, slowly ooze; whereas, poor fluids glibly flow, wide-spreading. Hence, when great fullness weds great indolence—that man, to others, too often proves a cipher; though, to himself, his thoughts form an Infinite Series, indefinite, from its vastness; and incommunicable; not for lack of power, but for lack of an omnipotent volition, to move his strength. His own world is full before him; the fulcrum set; but lever there is none. To such a man, the giving of any boor's resoluteness, with tendons braided, would be as hanging a claymore to Valor's side, before unarmed. Our minds are cunning, compound mechanisms; and one spring, or wheel, or axle wanting, the movement lags or halts. Cerebrum must not overbalance cerebellum; our brains should be round as globes; and planted on capacious chests, inhaling mighty morning-inspirations. We have had vast developments of parts of men; but none of manly wholes. Before a full-developed man, Mardi would fall down and worship. We are idiot, younger-sons of gods, begotten in dotages divine; and our mothers all miscarry. Giants are in our germs; but we are dwarfs, staggering under heads overgrown. Heaped, our measures burst. We die of too much life.

Media (to Abrazza)—Be not impatient, my lord; he'll recover presently. You were talking of Lombardo, Babbalanja?

Babbalanja—I was, your highness. Of all Mardians, by nature, he was the most inert. Hast ever seen a yellow lion, all day basking in the yellow sun: in reveries, rending droves of elephants; but his vast loins supine, and eyelids winking? Such, Lombardo; but fierce Want, the hunter, came and roused his roar. In hairy billows his great mane tossed like the sea; his eyeballs flamed two hells; his paw had stopped a rolling world.

Abrazza—In other words, yams were indispensable, and, poor devil, he roared to get them.

Babbalanja (bowing)—Partly so, my literal lord. And as with your own golden scepter, at times upon your royal teeth, indolent tattoos you beat; then, potent, sway it o'er your isle; so, Lombardo. And ere Necessity plunged spur and rowel into him, he knew not his own paces. *That* churned him into consciousness; and brought ambition, ere then dormant, seething to the top, till he trembled at himself. No mailed hand lifted up against a traveler in woods, can so appall, as we ourselves. We are full of ghosts and spirits: we are as graveyards full of buried dead, that start to life before us. And all our dead sires, verily are in us; *that* is their immortality. From sire to son, we go on multiplying corpses in ourselves; for all of which, are resurrections. Every thought's a soul of some past poet, hero, sage. We are fuller than a city. Woe it is, that reveals these things. He knows himself, and all that's in him, who knows adversity. To scale great heights, we must come out of lowermost depths. The way to heaven is through hell. We need fiery baptisms in the fiercest flames of our own bosoms. We must feel our hearts hot-hissing in us. And ere their fire is revealed, it must burn its way out of us; though it consume us and itself. Oh, sleek-cheeked Plenty! smiling at thine own dimples; vain for thee to reach out after greatness. Turn! turn! from all your tiers of cushions of eider-down!—turn, and be broken on the wheels of many woes. At white-heat, brand thyself; and count the scars, like old war-worn veterans, over camp fires. Soft poet! brushing tears from lilies—this way! and howl in sackcloth and in ashes! Know, thou, that the lines that live are turned out of a furrowed brow. Oh! there is a fierce, a cannibal delight, in the grief that shrieks to multiply itself. That grief is miserly of its own; it pities all the happy. Some damned spirits would not be otherwise, could they?

Abrazza (to Media)—Pray, my lord, is this good gentleman a devil?

Media—No, my lord; but he's possessed by one. His name is Azzageddi. You may hear more of him. But come, Babbalanja, hast forgotten all about Lombardo? How set he about that great undertaking, his *Koztanza?*

Abrazza (to Media)—Oh, for all the ravings of your Babbalanja, Lombardo took no special pains; hence, deserves small commendation. For genius must be somewhat like us kings—calm, content, in consciousness of power. And to Lombardo, the scheme of his *Koztanza* must have come full-fledged, like an eagle from the sun.

Babbalanja—No, your highness; but like eagles, his thoughts were first callow; yet, born plumeless, they came to soar.

Abrazza—Very fine. I presume, Babbalanja, the first thing he did, was to fast, and invoke the muses?

Babbalanja—Pardon, my lord; on the contrary he first procured a ream of vellum, and some sturdy quills; indispensable preliminaries, my worshipful lords, to the writing of the sublimest epics.

Abrazza—Ah! then the muses were afterwards invoked.

Babbalanja—Pardon again. Lombardo next sat down to a fine plantain pudding.

Yoomy—When the song-spell steals over me, I live upon olives.

Babbalanja—Yoomy, Lombardo eschewed olives. Said he, "What fasting soldier can fight? and the fight of all fights is to write." In ten days Lombardo had written—

Abrazza—Dashed off, you mean.

Babbalanja—He never dashed off aught.

Abrazza—As you will.

Babbalanja—In ten days, Lombardo had written full fifty folios; he loved huge acres of vellum whereon to expatiate.

Media—What then?

Babbalanja—He read them over attentively; made a neat package of the whole: and put it into the fire.

All—How?

Media—What! these great geniuses writing trash?

Abrazza—I thought as much.

Babbalanja—My lords, they abound in it! more than any other men in Mardi. Genius is full of trash. But genius essays its best to keep it to itself; and giving away its ore, retains the earth; whence, the too frequent wisdom of its works, and folly of its life.

Abrazza—Then genius is not inspired, after all. How they must slave in their mines! I weep to think of it.

Babbalanja—My lord, all men are inspired; fools are inspired; your highness is inspired; for the essence of all ideas is infused. Of ourselves, and in ourselves, we originate nothing. When Lombardo set about his work, he knew not what it would become. He did not build himself in with plans; he wrote right on; and so doing, got deeper and deeper into himself; and like a resolute traveler, plunging through baffling woods, at last was rewarded for his toils. "In good time," saith he, in his autobiography, "I came out into a serene, sunny, ravishing region; full of sweet scents, singing birds, wild plaints, roguish laughs, prophetic voices. "Here we are at last, then," he cried; "I have created the creative." And now the whole boundless landscape stretched away. Lombardo panted; the sweat was on his brow; he off mantle; braced himself; sat within view of the ocean; his face to a cool, rushing breeze; placed flowers before him; and gave himself plenty of room. On one side was his ream of vellum—

Abrazza—And on the other, a brimmed beaker.

Babbalanja—No, your highness; though he loved it, no wine for Lombardo while actually at work.

Mohi—Indeed? Why, I ever thought that it was to the superior quality of Lombardo's punches, that Mardi was indebted for that abounding humor of his.

Babbalanja—Not so; he had another way of keeping himself well braced.

Yoomy—Quick! tell us the secret.

Babbalanja—He never wrote by rush-light. His lamp swung in heaven. He rose from his East, with the sun; he wrote when all nature was alive.

Mohi—Doubtless, then, he always wrote with a grin; and none laughed louder at his quips, than Lombardo himself.

Babbalanja—Hear you laughter at the birth of a man child, old man? The babe may have many dimples; not so, the parent. Lombardo was a hermit to behold.

Media—What! did Lombardo laugh with a long face?

Babbalanja—His merriment was not always merriment to him, your highness. For the most part, his meaning kept him serious. Then he was so intensely riveted to his work, he could not pause to laugh.

Mohi—My word for it, but he had a sly one, now and then.

Babbalanja—For the nonce, he was not his own master; a mere amanuensis writing by dictation.

Yoomy—Inspiration, that!

Babbalanja—Call it as you will, Yoomy, it was a sort of sleep-walking of the mind. Lombardo never threw down his pen; it dropped from him; and then, he sat disenchanted; rubbing his eyes; staring; and feeling faint—sometimes, almost unto death.

Media—But pray, Babbalanja, tell us how he made acquaintance with some of those rare worthies, he introduces us to in his *Koztanza*.

Babbalanja—He first met them in his reveries; they were walking about in him, sour and moody: and for a long time, were shy of his advances; but still importuned, they at last grew ashamed of their reserve; they stepped forward; and gave him their hands. After that, they were frank and friendly. Lombardo set places for them at his board; when he died, he left them something in his will.

Media—What! those imaginary beings?

Abrazza—Wondrous witty! infernal fine!

Media—But, Babbalanja; after all, the *Koztanza* found no favor in the eyes of some Mardians.

Abrazza—Ay: the arch-critics Verbi and Batho denounced it.

Babbalanja—Yes: on good authority, Verbi is said to have detected a superfluous comma; and Batho declared that, with the materials he could have constructed a far better world than Lombardo's. But, did'st ever hear of his laying his axis?

Abrazza—But the unities; Babbalanja, the unities! they are wholly wanting in the *Koztanza*.

Babbalanja—Your highness; upon that point, Lombardo was frank. Saith he, in his autobiography: "For some time, I endeavored to keep in the good graces of those nymphs; but I found them so captious, and exacting; they threw me into such a violent passion with their fault-findings, that, at last, I renounced them."

Abrazza—Very rash!

Babbalanja—No, your highness; for though Lombardo abandoned all monitors from without; he retained one autocrat within; his crowned and sceptered instinct. And what, if he pulled down one gross world, and ransacked thee the real spheres to build up something of his own—a composite—what, then? matter and mind, though matching not, are mates; and sundered oft, in his *Koztanza* they unite: the airy waist, embraced by stalwart arms.

Media—Incoherent again! I thought we were to have no more of this?

Babbalanja—My lord Media, there are things infinite in the finite, and dualities in unities. Our eyes are pleased with the redness of the rose, but another sense lives upon its fragrance. Its redness you must approach, to view; its invisible fragrance pervades the field. So with the *Koztanza*. Its mere beauty is restricted to its form; its expanding soul, past Mardi does embalm. Modak is Modako, but fogle-foggle is not fugle-fi.

Media (to Abrazza)—My lord, you start again; but 'tis only another phase of Azzageeddi; sometimes he's quite mad. But all this you must needs overlook.

Abrazza—I will, my dear prince; what one cannot see through, one must needs look over, as you say.

Yoomy—But trust me, your highness, some of those strange things fall far too melodiously upon the ear, to be wholly deficient in meaning.

Abrazza—Your gentle minstrel, *this* must be, my lord. But, Babbalanja, the *Koztanza* lacks cohesion; it is wild, unconnected, all episode.

Babbalanja—And so is Mardi itself; nothing but episodes; valleys and hills; rivers, digressing from plains; vines, roving all over; boulders and diamonds; flowers and thistles; forests and thickets; and, here and there, fens and moors. And so, the world in the *Koztanza*.

Abrazza—Ay, plenty of dead-desert chapters there; horrible sands to wade through.

Media—Now, Babbalanja, away with your tropes, and tell us of the work, directly it was done. What did Lombardo then? Did he show it to anyone for an opinion?

Babbalanja—Yes, to Zenzori, who asked him where he picked up so much trash; to Hanto, who bade him not be cast down, it was pretty good; to Lucree, who desired to know how much he was going to get for it; to Roddi, who offered a suggestion.

Media—And what was that?

Babbalanja—That he had best make a faggot of the whole, and try again.

Abrazza—Very encouraging.

Media—Anyone else?

Babbalanja—To Pollo, who, conscious his opinion was sought, was thereby puffed up; and marking the faltering of Lombardo's voice, when the manuscript was handed him, straightway concluded, that the man who stood thus trembling at the bar, must needs be inferior to the judge. But his verdict was mild. After sitting up all night over the work, and diligently taking notes: "Lombardo, my friend! here, take your sheets. I have run through them loosely. You might have done better, but then you might have done worse. Take them, my friend; I have put in some good things for you:"

Media—And who was Pollo?

Babbalanja—Probably someone who lived in Lombardo's time, and went by that name. He is incidentally mentioned, and cursorily immortalized in one of the posthumous notes to the *Koztanza*.

Media—What is said of him there?

Babbalanja—Not much. In a very old transcript of the work—that of Aldina—the note alludes to a brave line in the text, and runs thus: "Diverting to tell, it was this passage that an old prosodist, one Pollo, claimed for his own. He maintained he made a free-will offering of it to Lombardo. Several things are yet extant of this Pollo, who died some weeks ago. He seems to have been one of those who would do great things if they could, but are content to compass the small. He imagined that the precedence of authors he had established in his library was their Mardi order of merit. He condemned the sublime poems of Vavona to his lowermost shelf. 'Ah,' thought he, 'how we library princes lord it over these beggarly authors!' Well read in the history of their woes, Pollo pitied them all, particularly the famous; and wrote little essays of his own, which he read to himself."

Media—Well; and what said Lombardo to those good friends of his—Zenzori, Hanto, and Roddi?

Babbalanja—Nothing. Taking home his manuscript, he glanced it over, making three corrections.

Abrazza—And what then?

Babbalanja—Then, your highness, he thought to try a conclave of professional critics, saying to himself: "Let them privately point out to me, now, all my blemishes, so that, what time they come to review me in public, all will be well." But, curious to relate, those professional critics, for the most part, held their peace concerning a work yet unpublished. And, with some generous exceptions, in their vague, learned way, betrayed such base, beggarly notions of authorship, that Lombardo could have wept, had tears been his. But in his very grief, he ground his teeth. Muttered he, "They are fools. In their eyes, bindings not brains make books. They criticize my tattered cloak, not my soul, caparisoned like a charger. He is the great author, think they, who drives the best bargain with his wares; and no bargainer am I. Because he is old, they worship some mediocrity of an ancient, and mock at the living prophet with the live coal on his lips. They are men who would not be men, had they no books. Their sires begat them not, but the authors they have read. Feelings they have none, and their very opinions they borrow. They cannot say yea, nor nay, without first consulting all Mardi as an Encyclopedia. And all the learning in them, is as a dead corpse in a coffin. Were they worthy the dignity of being damned, I would damn them; but they are not. Critics? asses! rather mules! so emasculated from vanity, they cannot father a true thought. Like mules, too, from dunghills, they trample down gardens of roses, and deem that crushed fragrance their own. Oh! that all round the domains of genius should lie thus unhedged, for such cattle to uproot! Oh! that an eagle should be stabbed by a goose-quill! But at best the greatest reviewers but prey on my leavings. For I am critic and creator; and as critic, in cruelty surpass all critics merely, as a tiger, jackals. For ere Mardi sees aught of mine, I scrutinize it myself, remorseless as a surgeon. I cut right and left; I probe, tear, and wrench; kill, burn, and destroy; and what's left after that, the jackals are welcome to. It is *I* that stab false thoughts, ere hatched; *I* that pull down wall and tower, rejecting materials which would make palaces for others. Oh! could Mardi but see how we work, it would marvel more at our primal chaos, than at the round world thence emerging. It would marvel at our scaffoldings, scaling heaven; marvel at the hills of earth, banked all round our fabrics ere completed. How plain the pyramid! In this grand silence, so intense, pierced by that pointed mass—could ten thousand slaves have ever toiled? ten thousand hammers rung? There it stands, part of Mardi; claiming kin with mountains; was this thing piecemeal built? It was. Piecemeal? atom by atom it was laid. The world is made of mites."

Yoomy (musing)—It is even so.

Abrazza—Lombardo was severe upon the critics; and they as much so upon him; of that, be sure.

Babbalanja—Your highness, Lombardo never presumed to criticize true critics; who are more rare than true poets. A great critic is a sultan among satraps; but pretenders are thick as ants, striving to scale a palm, after its aerial sweetness. And they fight among themselves. Essaying to pluck eagles, they themselves are geese, stuck full of quills, of which they rob each other.

Abrazza (to Media)—Oro help the victim that falls in Babbalanja's hands!

Media—Ay, my lord; at times, his every finger is a dagger; every thought a falling tower that whelms! But resume, philosopher—what of Lombardo now?

Babbalanja—"For this thing," said he, "I have agonized over it enough. I can wait no more. It has faults—all mine; its merits all its own; but I can toil no longer. The beings knit to me implore; my heart is full; my brain is sick. Let it go—let it go, and Oro with it. Somewhere Mardi has a mighty heart—*that* struck, all the isles shall resound!"

Abrazza—Poor devil! he took the world too hard.

Media—As most of these mortals do, my lord. That's the load, self-imposed, under which Babbalanja reels. But now, philosopher, ere Mardi saw it, what thought Lombardo of his work, looking at it objectively, as a thing out of him, I mean?

Abrazza—No doubt, he hugged it.

Babbalanja—Hard to answer. Sometimes, when by himself, he thought hugely of it, as my lord Abrazza says; but when abroad, among men, he almost despised it; but when he bethought him of those parts, written with full eyes, half blinded; temples throbbing; and pain at the heart—

Abrazza—Pooh! pooh!

Babbalanja—He would say to himself, "Sure, it cannot be in vain!" Yet again, when he bethought him of the hurry and bustle of Mardi, dejection stole over him. "Who will heed it?" thought he; "what care these fops and brawlers for me? But am I not myself an egregious coxcomb? Who will read me? Say one thousand pages—twenty-five lines each—every line ten words—every word ten letters. That's two million five hundred thousand *a*'s and *i*'s and *o*'s to read! How many are superfluous? Am I not mad to saddle Mardi with such a task? Of all men, am I the wisest, to stand upon a pedestal, and teach the mob? Ah, my own *Koztanza*! child of many prayers! in whose earnest eyes, so fathomless, I see my own; and recall all past delights and silent agonies—thou may'st prove, as the child of some fond dotard—beauteous to me; hideous to Mardi! And methinks, that while so much slaving merits that thou should'st not die; it has not been intense, prolonged enough, for the high meed of immortality. Yet, things immortal have been written; and by men as me;—men, who slept and waked; and ate and talked with tongues like mine. Ah, Oro! how may we know or not, we are what we would be? Hath genius any stamp and imprint, obvious to possessors? Has it eyes to see itself; or is it blind? Or do we delude ourselves with being gods, and end in grubs? Genius, genius? a thousand years hence, to be a household word? I? Lombardo? but yesterday cut in the market-place by a spangled fool! Lombardo immortal?—Ha, ha, Lombardo! but thou art an ass, with vast ears brushing the tops of palms! Ha, ha, ha! Methinks I see thee immortal! 'Thus great Lombardo saith; and thus; and thus; and thus; thus saith he—illustrious Lombardo!—Lombardo, our great countryman—Lombardo, prince of poets—Lombardo! great Lombardo!' Ha, ha, ha! go, go! dig thy grave, and bury thyself!"

Abrazza—He was very funny, then, at times.

Babbalanja—Very funny, your highness: amazing jolly! And from my nethermost soul, would to Oro, thou could'st but feel one touch of that jolly woe! It would appall thee, my Right Worshipful Lord Abrazza!

Abrazza (to Media)—My dear lord, his teeth are marvelously white and sharp; some she-shark must have been his dam: does he often grin thus? It was infernal!

Media—Ah! that's Azzageddi. But, prithee, Babbalanja, proceed.

Babbalanja—Your highness, even in his calmer critic moods, Lombardo was far from fancying his work. He confesses, that it ever seemed to him but a poor, scrawled copy of something within, which, do what he would, he could not completely transfer. "My canvas was small," said he; "crowded out were hosts of things that came last. But fate is in it." And fate it was, too, your highness, which forced Lombardo, ere his work was well done, to take it off his easel, and send it to be multiplied. "Oh, that I was not thus spurred," he cried, "but like many another, in its very childhood, this poor child of mine must go out into Mardi, and get bread for its sire."

Abrazza (with a sigh)—Alas! the poor devil! But methinks 'twas wondrous arrogant in him to talk to all Mardi at that lofty rate. Did he think himself a god?

Babbalanja—He himself best knew what he thought; but like all others, he was created by Oro to some special end; doubtless, partly answered in his *Koztanza*.

Media—And now that Lombardo is long dead and gone—and his work, hooted during life, lives after him—what think the present company of it? Speak, my lord Abrazza! Babbalanja! Mohi! Yoomy!

Abrazza (tapping his sandal with his scepter)—I never read it.
Babbalanja (looking upward)—It was written with a divine intent.
Mohi (stroking his beard)—I never hugged it in a corner, and ignored it before Mardi.
Yoomy (musing)—It has bettered my heart.
Media (rising)—And I have read it through nine times.
Babbalanja (starting up)—Ah, Lombardo! this must make thy ghost glad!

Chapter CLXXXI

They Sup

There seemed something sinister, hollow, heartless, about Abrazza, and that green-and-yellow, evil-starred crown that he wore.

But why think of that? Though we like not something in the curve of one's brow, or distrust the tone of his voice; yet, let us away with suspicions if we may, and make a jolly comrade of him, in the name of the gods. Miserable! thrice miserable he, who is forever turning over and over one's character in his mind, and weighing by nice avoirdupois, the pros and the cons of his goodness and badness. For we are all good and bad. Give me the heart that's huge as all Asia; and unless a man be a villain outright, account him one of the best tempered blades in the world.

That night, in his right regal hall, King Abrazza received us. And in merry good time a fine supper was spread.

Now, in thus nocturnally regaling us, our host was warranted by many ancient and illustrious examples.

For old Jove gave suppers; the god Woden gave suppers; the Hindoo deity Brahma gave suppers; the Red Man's Great Spirit gave suppers: chiefly venison and game.

And many distinguished mortals besides.

Ahasuerus gave suppers; Xerxes gave suppers; Montezuma gave suppers; Powhattan gave suppers; the Jews' Passovers were suppers; the Pharaohs gave suppers; Julius Cæsar gave suppers:—and rare ones they were; Great Pompey gave suppers; Nabob Crassus gave suppers; and Heliogabalus, surnamed the Gobbler, gave suppers.

It was a common saying of old, that King Pluto gave suppers; some say he is giving them still. If so, he is keeping tip-top company, old Pluto; Emperors and Czars; Great Moguls and Great Khans; Grand Lamas and Grand Dukes; Prince Regents and Queen Dowagers; Tamerlane hob-a-nobbing with Bonaparte; Antiochus with Solyman the Magnificent; Pisistratus pledging Pilate; Semiramis eating bon-bons with Bloody Mary, and her namesake of Medicis; the Thirty Tyrants quaffing three to one with the Council of Ten; and Sultans, Satraps, Viziers, Hetmans, Soldans, Landgraves, Bashaws, Doges, Dauphins, Infantas, Incas, and Caçiques looking on.

Again: at Arbela, the conqueror of conquerors, conquering son of Olympia by Jupiter himself, sent out cards to his captains—Hephestion, Antigonus, Antipater, and the rest—to join him at ten P.M., in the Temple of Belus; there, to sit down to a victorious supper, off the gold plate of the Assyrian High Priests. How majestically he poured out his old Madeira that night!—feeling grand and lofty as the Himmalehs; yea, all Babylon nodded her towers in his soul!

Spread, heaped up, stacked with good things; and redolent of citrons and grapes, hilling round tall vases of wine; and here and there, waving with fresh orange-boughs, among whose leaves, myriads of small tapers gleamed like fire-flies, in groves—Abrazza's glorious board showed like some banquet in Paradise; Ceres and Pomona presiding; and jolly Bacchus, like a recruit with a mettlesome rifle, staggering back as he fires off the bottles of vivacious champagne.

In ranges, roundabout stood living candelabras:—lackeys, gaily bedecked, with tall torches in their hands; and at one end, stood trumpeters, bugles at their lips.

"This way, my dear Media! this seat at my left. Noble Taji! my right. Babbalanja!—Mohi—where you are. But where's pretty Yoomy?—Gone to meditate in the moonlight? Ah! very good. Let the banquet begin. A blast there!" And charge all did.

The venison, wild boar's meat, and buffalo-humps, were extraordinary; the wine, of rare vintages, like bottled lightning; and the first course, a brilliant affair, went off like a rocket.

But as yet, Babbalanja joined not in the revels. His mood was on him; and apart he sat; silently eyeing the banquet; and ever and anon muttering, "Fogle-foggle, fugle-fi—"

The first fury of the feast over, said King Media, pouring out from a heavy flagon into his goblet, "Abrazza, these suppers are wondrous fine things."

"Ay, my dear lord, much better than dinners."

"So they are, so they are. The dinner-hour is the summer of the day: full of sunshine, I grant; but not like the mellow autumn of supper. A dinner, you know, may go off rather stiffly; but invariably suppers are jovial. At dinners, 'tis not till you take in sail, furl the cloth, bow the lady-passengers out, and make all snug; 'tis not till then that one begins to ride out the gale with complacency. But at these suppers—Good Oro! your cup is empty, my dear demi-god!—But at these suppers, I say, all is snug and ship-shape before you begin; and when you begin, you waive the beginning, and begin in the middle. And as for the cloth—but tell us, Braid-Beard, what that old king of Franko, Ludwig the Fat, said of that matter. The cloth for suppers, you know. It's down in your chronicles."

"My lord," wiping his beard, "Old Ludwig was of opinion, that at suppers the cloth was superfluous, unless on the back of some jolly good friar. Said he, 'For one, I prefer sitting right down to the unrobed table!' "

"High and royal authority, that of Ludwig the Fat," said Babbalanja; "far higher than the authority of Ludwig the Great: the one, only great by courtesy; the other, fat beyond a peradventure. But they are equally famous; and in their graves, both on a par. For after devouring many a fair province, and grinding the poor of his realm, Ludwig the Great has long since, himself, been devoured by very small worms, and ground into very fine dust. And after stripping many a venison rib, Ludwig the Fat has had his own polished and bleached in the Valley of Death; yea, and his cranium chased with corrodings, like the carved flagon once held to its jaws."

"My lord! my lord!" cried Abrazza to Media, "this ghastly devil of yours grins worse than a skull. I feel the worms crawling over me! By Oro, we must eject him!"

"No, no, my lord. Let him sit there, as of old the Death's-head graced the feasts of the Pharaohs—let him sit—let him sit—for Death but imparts a flavor to life. Go on; wag your tongue without fear, Azzageddi! But come, Braid-Beard, let's hear more of the Ludwigs."

"Well, then, your highness, of all the eighteen royal Ludwigs of Franko—"

"Who like so many ten-pins, all in a row," interposed Babbalanja, "have been bowled off the course by grim Death!"

"Heed him not," said Media; "go on."

"The Debonnaire, the Pious, the Stammerer, the Do-Nothing, the Juvenile, the Quarreler: of all these, I say, Ludwig the Fat was the best table-man of them all. Such a full orbed paunch was his, that no way could he devise of getting to his suppers but by getting right into them. Like the Zodiac his table was circular, and full in the middle he sat, like a sun; all his jolly stews and ragouts revolving around him."

"Yea," said Babbalanja, "a very round sun was Ludwig the Fat. No wonder he's down in the chronicles; several ells about the waist, and King of cups and Tokay. Truly, a famous king: three hundred-weight of lard, with a diadem on top; lean brains and a fat doublet—a demijohn of a demi-god!"

"Is this to be longer borne?" cried Abrazza, starting up. "Quaff that sneer down, devil! on the instant! down with it to the dregs! This comes, my lord Media, of having a slow drinker at one's board. Like an iceberg, such a fellow frosts the whole atmosphere of a banquet, and is felt a league off. We must thrust him out. Guards!"

"Back! touch him not, hounds!" cried Media. "Your pardon, my lord, but we'll keep him to it; and melt him down in this good wine. Drink! I command it; drink, Babbalanja!"

"And am I not drinking, my lord? Surely you would not that I should imbibe more than I can hold. The measure being full, all poured in after that is but wasted. I am for being temperate in these things, my good lord. And my one cup outlasts three of yours. Better to sip a pint, than pour down a quart. All things in moderation are good; whence, wine in moderation is good. But all things in excess are bad; whence wine in excess is bad."

"Away with your logic and conic sections! Drink!—But no, no, I am too severe. For of all meals a supper should be the most social and free. And going thereto we kings, my lord, should lay aside our scepters. Do as you please Babbalanja."

"You are right, you are right, after all, my dear demi-god," said Abrazza. "And to say truth, I seldom worry myself with the ways of these mortals; for no thanks do we demi-gods get. We kings should be ever indifferent. Nothing like a cold heart; warm ones are ever chafing, and getting into trouble. I let my mortals here in this isle take heed to themselves; only barring them out when they would thrust in their petitions. This very instant, my lord, my yeoman-guard is on duty without to drive off intruders. Hark! what noise is that? Ho, who comes?"

At that instant there burst into the hall, a crowd of spearmen, driven before a pale, ragged rout, that loudly invoked King Abrazza.

"Pardon, my lord king, for thus forcing an entrance! But long in vain have we knocked at thy gates! Our grievances are more than we can bear! Give ear to our spokesman, we beseech!"

And from their tumultuous midst, they pushed forward, a tall, grim, pine-tree of a fellow, who loomed up out of the throng, like the Peak of Teneriffe among the Canaries in a storm.

"Drive the knaves out! Ho, cowards, guards, turn about! charge upon them! Away with your grievances! Drive them out, I say; drive them out! High time, truly, my lord Media, when demi-gods are thus annoyed at their wine. Oh! who would reign over mortals!"

So at last, with much difficulty, the ragged rout were ejected; the Peak of Teneriffe going last, a pent storm on his brow; and muttering about some black time that was corning.

While the hoarse murmurs without still echoed through the hall, King Abrazza refilling his cup, thus spoke, "You were saying, my dear lord, that of all meals a supper is the most social and free. Very true. And of all suppers those given by us bachelor demi-gods are the best. Are they not?"

"They are. For Benedict mortals must be home betimes; bachelor demi-gods are never away."

"Ay, your highnesses, bachelors are all the year round at home," said Mohi, "sitting out life in the chimney corner, cozy and warm as the dog, whilome turning the old-fashioned roasting-jack."

"And to us bachelor demi-gods," cried Media "our to-morrows are as long rows of fine punches ranged on a board, and waiting the hand."

"But my good lords," said Babbalanja, now brightening with wine, "if, of all suppers those given by bachelors be the best: of all bachelors, are not your priests and monks the jolliest? I mean, behind the scenes? Their prayers all said, and their futurities securely invested, who so care-free and cozy as they? Yea, a supper for two in a friar's cell in Maramma, is merrier far, than a dinner for five-and-twenty, in the broad right wing of Donjalolo's great Palace of the Morn."

"Bravo, Babbalanja!" cried Media; "your iceberg is thawing. More of that, more of that. Did I not say we would melt him down at last, my lord?"

"Ay," continued Babbalanja, "bachelors are a noble fraternity: I'm a bachelor myself. One of ye, in that matter, my lord demi-gods. And if unlike the patriarchs of the world, we father not our brigades and battalions; and send not out into the battles of our country whole regiments of our own individual raising: yet do we oftentimes leave behind us goodly houses and lands; rare old brandies and mountain Malagas; and more especially warm doublets and togas, and spatterdashes, wherewithal to keep comfortable those who survive us; casing the legs and arms, which others beget. Then compare not invidiously Benedicts with Bachelors, since thus we make an equal division of the duties, which both owe to posterity."

"Suppers forever!" cried Media. "See, my lord, what yours has done for Babbalanja. He came to it a skeleton; but will go away every bone padded!"

"Ay, my lord demi-gods," said Babbalanja, drop by drop refilling his goblet. "These suppers are all very fine, very pleasant, and merry. But we pay for them roundly. Everything, my good lords, has its price, from a marble to a world. And easier of digestion, and better for both body and soul, are a half-haunch of venison and a gallon of mead, taken under the sun at meridian than the soft bridal breast of a partridge, with some gentle negus, at the noon of night!"

"No lie that!" said Mohi. "Beshrew me, in no well-appointed mansion doth the pantry lie adjoining the sleeping chamber. A good thought; I'll fill up, and ponder on it."

"Let not Azzageddi get uppermost again, Babbalanja," cried Media. "Your goblet is only half-full."

"Permit it to remain so, my lord. For whoso takes much wine to bed with him, has a bed-fellow, more restless than a somnambulist. And though Wine be a jolly blade at the board, a sulky knave is he under a blanket. I know him of old. Yet, your highness, for all this, to many a Mardian, suppers are still better than dinners, at whatever cost purchased; forasmuch, as many have more leisure to sup, than dine. And though you demi-gods, may dine at your ease, and dine it out into night; and sit and chirp over your Burgundy, till the morning larks join your crickets, and wed matins to vespers; far otherwise, with us plebeian mortals. From our dinners, we must hie to our anvils; and the last jolly jorum evaporates in a cark and a care."

"Methinks he relapses," said Abrazza.

"It waxes late," said Mohi; "your highnesses, is it not time to break up?"

"No, no!" cried Abrazza; "let the day break when it will; but no breakings for us. It's only midnight. This way with the wine; pass it along, my dear Media. We are young yet, my sweet lord; light hearts and heavy purses; short prayers and long rent-rolls. Pass round the Tokay! We demi-gods have all our old age for a dormitory. Come! Round and round with the flagons! Let them disappear like mile-stones on a race-course!"

"Ah!" murmured Babbalanja, holding his full goblet at arm's length on the board, "not thus with the hapless wight, born with a hamper on his back, and blisters in his palms. Toil and sleep—sleep and toil, are his days and his nights. He goes to bed with a lumbago, and wakes with the rheumatics; I know what it is; he snatches lunches, not dinners, and makes of all life a cold snack! Yet praise be to Oro, though to such men dinners are scarce worth the eating; nevertheless, praise Oro again, a good supper is something. Off jackboots: nay, off shirt, if you will, and go at it. Hurrah! the fagged day is done: the last blow is an echo. Twelve long hours to sunrise! And would it were an Antarctic night, and six months to to-morrow. But, hurrah! the very bees have their hives, and after a day's weary wandering, hie home to their honey. So they stretch out their stiff legs, rub their lame elbows, and putting their tired right arms in a sling, set the others to fetching and carrying from dishes to dentals, from foaming flagons to the demijohn, which never pours out at the end you pour in. Ah! after all, the poorest devil in Mardi lives not in vain. There's a soft side to the hardest oak plank in the world!"

"Methinks! I have heard some such sentimental gabble as this before from my slaves, my lord," said Abrazza to Media. "It has the old gibberish flavor."

"Gibberish, your highness? Gibberish? I'm full of it—I'm a gibbering ghost, my right worshipful lord! Here, pass your hand through me—here, *here,* and scorch it where I most burn. By Oro! King! but I will gibe and gibber at thee, till thy crown feels like another skull clapped on thy own. Gibberish? Ay, in hell we'll gibber in concert, king! we'll howl, and roast, and hiss together!"

"Devil, that thou art, begone! Ho, guards! seize him!"

"Back, curs!" cried Media. "Harm not a hair of his head. I crave pardon, King Abrazza, but no violence must be done Babbalanja."

"Trumpets there!" said Abrazza; "so: the banquet is done, lights for King Media! Good-night, my lord!"

Now, thus, for the nonce, with good cheer, we close. And after many fine dinners and banquets—through light and through shade; through mirth, sorrow, and all—drawing nigh to the evening end of these wanderings wild—meet is it that all should be regaled with a supper.

Chapter CLXXXII

THEY EMBARK

NEXT MORNING, KING ABRAZZA SENT FRIGID WORD TO MEDIA THAT THE DAY WAS VERY FINE FOR yachting; but he much regretted that indisposition would prevent his making one of the party, who that morning doubtless would depart his isle.

"My compliments to your king," said Media to the chamberlains, "and say the royal notice to quit was duly received."

"Take Azzageddi's also," said Babbalanja; "and say, I hope his Highness will not fail in his appointment with me: the first midnight after he dies; at the graveyard corner; there I'll be, and grin again!"

Sailing on, the next land we saw was thickly wooded: hedged round about by mangrove trees; which growing in the water, yet lifted high their boughs. Here and there were shady nooks, half verdure and half water. Fishes rippled, and canaries sung.

"Let us break through, my lord," said Yoomy, "and seek the shore. Its solitudes must prove reviving."

"Solitudes they are," cried Mohi.

"Peopled, but not enlivened," said Babbalanja. "Hard landing here, minstrel! see you not the isle is hedged?"

"Why, break through, then," said Media. "Yillah is not here."

"I mistrusted it," sighed Yoomy; "an imprisoned island! full of uncomplaining woes: like many others we must have glided by, unheedingly. Yet of them have I heard. This isle may pass, marking its outward brightness, but dreaming not of the sad secrets here embowered. Haunt of the hopeless! In those inland woods brood Mardians who have tasted Mardi, and found it bitter—the draft so sweet to others! maidens whose unimparted bloom has cankered in the bud; and children with eyes averted from life's dawn—like those new-oped morning blossoms which, foreseeing storms, turn and close."

"Yoomy's rendering of the truth," said Mohi.

"Why land, then?" said Media. "No merry man of sense, no demi-god like me, will do it. Let's away; let's see all that's pleasant, or that seems so, in our circuit, and, if possible, shun the sad."

"Then we have circled not the round reef wholly," said Babbalanja, "but made of it a segment. For this is far from being the first sad land, my lord, that we have slighted at your instance."

"No more. I will have no gloom. A chorus! there, ye paddlers! spread all your sails; ply paddles; breeze up, merry winds!"

And so, in the saffron sunset, we neared another shore.

A gloomy-looking land! black, beetling crags, rent by volcanic clefts; ploughed up with watercourses, and dusky with charred woods. The beach was strewn with scoria and cinders; in dolorous soughs, a chill wind blew; wails issued from the caves; and yellow, spooming surges, lashed the moaning strand.

"Shall we land?" said Babbalanja.

"Not here," cried Yoomy; "no Yillah here."

"No," said Media. "This is another of those lands far better to avoid."

"Know ye not," said Mohi, "that here are the mines of King Klanko, whose scourged slaves, toiling in their pits, so nigh approach the volcano's bowels, they hear its rumblings? 'Yet they must work on,' cries Klanko, 'the mines still yield!' And daily his slaves' bones are brought above ground, mixed with the metal masses."

"Set all sail there, men! away!"

"My lord," said Babbalanja; "still must we shun the unmitigated evil; and only view the good; or evil so mixed therewith, the mixture's both!"

Half veiled in misty clouds, the harvest moon now rose; and in that pale and haggard light, all sat silent; each man in his own secret mood: best knowing his own thoughts.

Chapter CLXXXIII

BABBALANJA AT THE FULL OF THE MOON

HO, MORTALS! GO WE TO A FUNERAL, THAT OUR PADDLES SEEM THUS MUFFLED? UP HEART, TAJI! or does that witch Hautia, haunt thee? Be a demi-god once more, and laugh. Her flowers are not barbs; and the avengers' arrows are too blunt to slay. Babbalanja! Mohi! Yoomy! up heart! up heart! By Oro! I will debark the whole company on the next land we meet. No tears for me. Ha, ha! let us laugh. Ho, Vee-Vee! awake; quick, boy; some wine! and let us make glad, beneath the glad moon. Look! it is stealing forth from its clouds. Perdition to Hautia! Long lives, and merry ones to ourselves! Taji, my charming fellow, here's to you! May your heart be a stone! Ha, ha! will nobody join me? My laugh is lonely as his who laughed in his tomb. Come, laugh; will no one quaff wine, I say? See! the round moon is abroad."

"Say you so, my lord? then for one, I am with you," cried Babbalanja. "Fill me a brimmer. Ah! but this wine leaps through me like a panther. Ay, let us laugh; let us roar; let us yell! What, if I was sad but just now? Life is an April day, that both laughs and weeps in a breath. But whoso is wise, laughs when he can. Men fly from a groan, but run to a laugh. Vee-Vee, your gourd. My lord, let me help you. Ah, how it sparkles! Cups, cups, Vee-Vee, more cups! Here, Taji, take that; Mohi, take that: Yoomy, take that. And now let us drown away grief. Ha! ha! the house of mourning is deserted, though of old good cheer kept the funeral guests; and so keep I mine; here I sit by my dead, and replenish your wine cups. Old Mohi, your cup; Yoomy, yours. Ha! ha! let us laugh, let us scream! Weeds are put off at a fair; no heart bursts but in secret; it is good to laugh, though the laugh be hollow; and wise to make merry, now and for aye. Laugh, and make friends; weep, and they go. Women sob, and are rid of their grief; men laugh, and retain it. There is laughter in heaven, and laughter in hell. And a deep thought whose language is laughter. Though wisdom be wedded to woe, though the way thereto is by tears, yet all ends in a shout. But wisdom wears no weeds; woe is more merry than mirth; 'tis a shallow grief that is sad. Ha! ha! how demoniacs shout; how all skeletons grin; we all die with a rattle. Laugh! laugh! Are the cherubim grave? Humor, thy laugh is divine; whence, mirth-making idiots have been revered; and therefore may I. Ho! let us be gay, if it be only for an hour, and Death hand us the goblet. Vee-Vee! bring on your gourds! Let us pledge each other in bumpers! let us laugh, laugh, laugh it out to the last. All sages have laughed—let us; Bardianna laughed, let us; Demorkriti laughed—let us; Amoree laughed—let us; Rabeelee roared—let us; the hyenas grin, the jackals yell—let us.—But you don't laugh, my lord? laugh away!"

"No, thank you, Azzageddi, not after that infernal fashion; better weep."

"He makes me crawl all over, as if I were an ant-hill," said Mohi.

"He's mad, mad, mad!" cried Yoomy.

"Ay, mad, mad, mad!—mad as the mad fiend that rides me! But come, sweet minstrel, will list to a song? We madmen are all poets, you know. Ha! ha!

Stars laugh in the sky:
Oh fugle-fi!
The waves dimple below:
Oh fugle-fo!

The wind strikes her dulcimers; the groves give a shout; the hurricane is only an hysterical laugh; and the lightning that blasts, blasts only in play. We must laugh or we die; to laugh is to live. Not to laugh is to have the tetanus. Will you weep? then laugh while you weep. For mirth and sorrow are kin; are published by identical nerves. Go, Yoomy; go study anatomy; there is much to be learned from the dead, more than you may learn from the living, and I am dead, though I live; and as soon dissect myself as another; I curiously look into my secrets; and grope under my ribs. I have found that the heart is not whole, but divided; that it seeks a soft cushion whereon to repose; that it vitalizes the blood; which else were weaker than water; I have found that we cannot live without hearts; though the heartless live longest. Yet hug your hearts, ye handful that have them; 'tis a blessed inheritance! Thus, thus, my lord, I run on; from one pole to the other; from this thing to that. But so the great world goes round, and in one somerset, shows the sun twenty-five thousand miles of a landscape."

At that instant, down went the fiery full moon, and the Dog-Star; and far down into Media, a Tivoli of wine.

Chapter CLXXXIV

MORNING

LIFE OR DEATH, WEAL OR WOE, THE SUN STAYS NOT HIS COURSE. ON: OVER BATTLE-FIELD AND bower; over tower, and town, he speeds; peers in at births, and death-beds; lights up cathedral, mosque, and pagan shrine; laughing over all; a very Democritus in the sky; and in one brief day sees more than any pilgrim in a century's round.

So, the sun; nearer heaven than we—with what mind, then, may blessed Oro downward look.

It was a purple, red, and yellow east—streaked, and crossed. And down from breezy mountains, robust and ruddy Morning came; a plaided Highlander, waving his plumed bonnet to the isles.

Over the neighboring groves the larks soared high; and soaring, sang in jubilees; while across our bows, between two isles, a mighty moose swam stately as a seventy-four; and backward tossed his antlered wilderness in air.

Just bounding from fresh morning groves, with the brine he mixed the dew of leaves; his antlers dripping on the swell, that rippled before his brown and bow-like chest.

"Five hundred thousand centuries since," said Babbalanja, "this same sight was seen. With Oro, the sun is co-eternal; and the same life that moves that moose animates alike the sun and Oro. All are parts of One. In me, in *me,* flit thoughts participated by the beings peopling all the stars. Saturn, and Mercury, and Mardi, are brothers, one and all; and across their orbits, to each other talk, like souls. Of these things what chapters might be writ! Oh! that flesh cannot keep pace with spirit. Oh! that these myriad germ-dramas in me, should so perish hourly, for lack of power mechanic. Worlds pass worlds in space, as men, men—in thoroughfares; and after periods of thousand years, cry!—'Well met, my friend, again!' To me, to *me,* they talk in mystic music; I hear them think through all their zones. Hail, furthest worlds! and all the beauteous beings in ye! Fan me, sweet Zenora! with thy twilight wings! Ho! let's voyage to Aldebaran. Ha! indeed, a ruddy world. What a buoyant air! Not like to Mardi, this. Ruby columns: minarets of amethyst; diamond domes! Who is this?—a god? What a lake-like brow! transparent as the morning air. I see his thoughts like worlds revolving—and in his eyes—like unto heavens—soft falling stars are shooting. How these thousand passing wings winnow away my breath! I faint: back, back to some small asteroid.—Sweet being! if, by Mardian word I may address thee, speak! 'I bear a soul in germ within me; I feel the first faint trembling, like to a harp-string, vibrate in my inmost being. Kill me, and generations die.' So, of old, the unbegotten lived within the virgin; who then loved her God, as new-made mothers their babes ere born. Oh, Alma, Alma, Alma!—Fangs off, fiend! will that name ever lash thee into foam? Smite not my face so, forked flames!"

"Babbalanja! Babbalanja! rouse, man! rouse! Art in hell and damned, that thy sinews so snake-like coil and twist all over thee? Thy brow is black as Ops! Turn, turn! see yonder moose!"

"Hail, mighty brute!—thou feelest not these things; never canst *thou* be damned. Moose! would thy soul were mine; for if that scorched thing, mine, be immortal, so thine; and thy life hath not the consciousness of death. I read profound placidity—deep—million—violet fathoms down in that soft, pathetic, woman eye! What is man's shrunk form to thine, thou woodland majesty? Moose, moose! my soul is shot again. Oh, Oro! Oro!"

"He falls!" cried Media.

"Mark the agony in his waning eye!" said Yoomy; "alas, poor Babbalanja! Is this thing of madness conscious to thyself? If ever thou art sane again, wilt thou have reminiscences? Take my robe: here, I strip me to cover thee and all thy woes. Oro! by this, thy being's side, I kneel! grant death or happiness to Babbalanja."

Chapter CLXXXV

L'Ultima Sera

THUS FAR, THROUGH MYRIAD ISLANDS, HAD WE SEARCHED; OF ALL, NO ONE PEN MAY WRITE; least, mine: and still no trace of Yillah.

But though my hopes revived not from their ashes, yet, so much of Mardi had we searched, it seemed as if the long pursuit must, ere many moons, be ended; whether for weal or woe, my frenzy sometimes recked not.

After its first fair morning flushings, all that day was overcast. We sailed upon an angry sea, beneath an angry sky. Deep scowled on deep; and in dun vapors, the blinded sun went down, unseen; though full toward the West our three prows were pointed; steadfast as three printed points upon the compass-card.

"When we set sail from Odo, 'twas a glorious morn in spring," said Yoomy; "towards the rising sun we steered. But now, beneath autumnal night-clouds, we hasten to its setting."

"How now?" cried Media. "Why is the minstrel mournful? He whose place it is to chase away despondency: not be its minister."

"Ah, my lord, so *thou* thinkest. But better can my verses soothe the sad, than make them light of heart. Nor are we minstrels so gay of soul as Mardi deems us. The brook that sings the sweetest, murmurs through the loneliest woods:

The isles hold thee not, thou departed!
From thy bower, now issues no lay:
In vain we recall perished warblings:
Spring birds, to far climes, wing their way!"

As Yoomy thus sang; unmindful of the lay, with paddle plying, in low, pleasant tones, thus hummed to himself our bowsman, a gamesome wight:—

Ho! merrily ho! we paddlers sail!
Ho! over sea-dingle, and dale!—
Our pulses fly,
Our hearts beat high,
Ho! merrily, merrily, ho!

But a sudden splash, and a shrill, gurgling sound, like that of a fountain subsiding, now broke upon the air. Then all was still, save the rush of the waves by our keels.

"Save him! Put back!"

From his elevated seat, the merry bowsman, too gleefully reaching forward, had fallen into the lagoon.

With all haste, our speeding canoes were reversed; but not till we had darted in upon another darkness than that in which the bowsman fell.

As, blindly, we groped back, deep Night dived deeper down in the sea.

"Drop paddles all, and list."

Holding their breath, over the six gunwales all now leaned; but the only moans were the wind's.

Long time we lay thus; then slowly crossed and recrossed our track, almost hopeless; but yet loth to leave him who, with a song in his mouth, died and was buried in a breath.

"Let us away," said Media; "why seek more? He is gone."

"Ay, gone," said Babbalanja, "and whither? But a moment since, he was among us; now, the fixed stars are not more remote than he. So far off, can he live? Oh, Oro! this death thou ordainest, unmans the manliest. Say not nay, my lord. Let us not speak behind Death's back. Hard and horrible is it to die; blindfold to leap from life's verge! But thus, in clouds of dust, and with a trampling as of hoofs, the generations disappear; death driving them all into his treacherous fold, as wild Indians the bison herds. Nay, nay, Death is Life's last despair. Hard and horrible is it to die. Oro himself, in Alma, died not without a groan. Yet why, why live? Life is wearisome to all; the same dull round. Day and night, summer and winter, round about us revolving for aye. One moment lived, is a life. No new stars appear in the sky; no new lights in the soul. Yet, of changes there are many.

For though, with rapt sight in childhood, we behold many strange things beneath the moon, and all Mardi looks a tented fair—how soon everything fades. All of us, in our very bodies, outlive our own selves. I think of green youth as of a merry playmate departed; and to shake hands, and be pleasant with my old age, seems in prospect even harder, than to draw a cold stranger to my bosom. But old age is not for me. I am not of the stuff that grows old. This Mardi is not our home. Up and down we wander, like exiles transported to a planet afar: 'tis not the world *we* were born in; not the world once so lightsome and gay; not the world where we once merrily danced, dined, and supped; and wooed, and wedded our long-buried wives. Then let us depart. But whither! We push ourselves forward—then, start back in affright. Essay it again, and flee. Hard to live; hard to die; intolerable suspense! But the grim despot at last interposes; and with a viper in our winding-sheets, we are dropped in the sea."

"To me," said Mohi, his gray locks damp with night dews, "death's dark defile at times seems at hand, with no voice to cheer. That all have died, makes it not easier for me to depart. And that many have been quenched in infancy seems a mercy to the slow perishing of my old age, limb by limb, and sense by sense. I have long been the tomb of my youth. And more has died out of me, already, than remains for the last death to finish. Babbalanja says truth. In childhood, death stirred me not; in middle age, it pursued me like a prowling bandit on the road; now, grown an old man, it boldly leads the way; and ushers me on; and turns round upon me its skeleton gaze; poisoning the last solaces of life. Maramma but adds to my gloom."

"Death! death!" cried Yoomy, "must I be not, and millions be? Must I go, and the flowers still bloom? Oh, I have marked what it is to be dead; how shouting boys, of holidays, hide-and-seek among the tombs, which must hide all seekers at last."

"Clouds on clouds," cried Media, "but away with them all. Why not leap your graves, while ye may? Time to die, when death comes, without dying by inches. 'Tis no death, to die; the only death is the fear of it. I, a demi-god, fear death not."

"But when the jackals howl round you?" said Babbalanja.

"Drive them off! Die the demi-god's death! On his last couch of crossed spears, my brave old sire cried, 'Wine, wine; strike up, conch and cymbal; let the king die with martial melodies!' "

"More valiant dying, than dead," said Babbalanja. "Our end of the winding procession resounds with music, and flaunts banners with brave devices: 'Cheer up!' 'Fear not!' 'Millions have died before!' but in the endless van, not a pennon streams; all there, is silent and solemn. The last wisdom is dumb."

Silence ensued; during which, each dip of the paddles in the now calm water, fell full and long upon the ear.

Anon, lifting his head, Babbalanja thus—"Yillah still eludes us. And in all this tour of Mardi, how little have we found to fill the heart with peace; how much to slaughter all our yearnings?"

"Croak no more, raven!" cried Media. "Mardi is full of spring-time sights, and jubilee sounds. I never was sad in my life."

"But for thy one laugh, my lord, how many groans! Were all happy? or all miserable, more tolerable then, than as it is. But happiness and misery are so broadly marked, that this Mardi may be the retributive future of some forgotten past. Yet vain our surmises. Still vainer to say, that all Mardi is but a means to an end; that this life is a state of probation; that evil is but permitted for a term; that for specified ages a rebel angel is viceroy. Nay, nay. Oro delegates his scepter to none; in his everlasting reign there are no interregnums; and Time is Eternity; and we live in Eternity now. Yet, some tell of a hereafter, where all the mysteries of life will be over; and the sufferings of the virtuous recompensed. Oro is just, they say. Then, always, now, and evermore. But to make restitution implies a wrong; and Oro can do no wrong. Yet what seems evil to us, may be good to him. If he fears not, nor hopes, he has no other passion; no ends, no purposes. He lives content; all ends are compassed in Him; He has no past, no future; He is the everlasting now; which is an everlasting calm; and things that are, have been, will be. This gloom's enough. But hoot! hoot! the night-owl ranges through the woodlands of Maramma; its dismal notes pervade our lives; and when we would fain depart in peace, that bird flies on before: cloud-like, eclipsing our setting suns, and filling the air with dolor."

"Too true!" cried Yoomy. "Our calms must come by storms. Like helmless vessels, tempest-tossed, our only anchorage is when we founder."

"Our beginnings," murmured Mohi, "are lost in clouds; we live in darkness all our days, and perish without an end."

"Croak on, cowards!" cried Media, "and fly before the hideous phantoms that pursue ye."

"No coward he, who hunted, turns and finds no foe to fight," said Babbalanja. "Like the stag, whose brow is beat with wings of hawks, perched in his heavenward antlers; so I, blinded, goaded, headlong rush! this way and that; nor knowing whither; one forest wide around!"

Chapter CLXXXVI

THEY SAIL FROM NIGHT TO DAY

ERE LONG THE THREE CANOES LURCHED HEAVILY IN A VIOLENT SWELL. LIKE PALLS, THE CLOUDS swept to and fro, hooding the gibbering winds. At every headbeat wave, our arching prows reared up, and shuddered; the night ran out in rain.

Whither to turn we knew not; nor what haven to gain; so dense the darkness.

But at last, the storm was over. Our shattered prows seemed gilded. Day dawned; and from his golden vases poured red wine upon the waters.

That flushed tide rippled towards us; floating from the east, a lone canoe; in which, there sat a mild old man; a palm-bough in his hand; a bird's beak holding amaranth and myrtles, his slender prow.

"Alma's blessing upon ye, voyagers! ye look storm-worn."

"The storm we have survived, old man; and many more, we yet must ride," said Babbalanja.

"The sun is risen; and all is well again. We but need to repair our prows," said Media.

"Then, turn aside to Serenia, a pleasant isle, where all are welcome; where many storm-worn rovers land at last to dwell."

"Serenia!" said Babbalanja; "methinks Serenia is that land of enthusiasts, of which we hear, my lord; where Mardians pretend to the unnatural conjunction of reason with things revealed; where Alma, they say, is restored to his divine original; where, deriving their principles from the same sources, whence flow the persecutions of Maramma—men strive to live together in gentle bonds of peace and charity;—folly! folly!"

"Ay," said Media; "much is said of those people of Serenia; but their social fabric must soon fall to pieces; it is based upon the idlest of theories. Thanks for thy courtesy, old man, but we care not to visit thy isle. Our voyage has an object, which, something tells me, will not be gained by touching at thy shores. Elsewhere we may refit. Farewell! 'Tis breezing; set the sails! Farewell, old man."

"Nay, nay! think again; the distance is but small; the wind fair; but 'tis ever so, thither;—come: we people of Serenia, are most anxious to be seen of Mardi, so that if our manner of life seem good, all Mardi may live as we. In blessed Alma's name, I pray ye, come!"

"Shall we then, my lord?"

"Lead on, old man! We will e'en see this wondrous isle."

So, guided by the venerable stranger, by noon we descried an island blooming with bright savannas, and pensive with peaceful groves.

Wafted from this shore, came balm of flowers, and melody of birds: a thousand summer sounds and odors. The dimpled tide sang round our splintered prows; the sun was high in heaven, and the waters were deep below.

"The land of Love," the old man murmured, as we neared the beach, where innumerable shells were gently rolling in the playful surf, and murmuring from their tuneful valves. Behind, another, and a verdant surf played against lofty banks of leaves; where the breeze, likewise, found its shore.

And now, emerging from beneath the trees, there came a goodly multitude in flowing robes; palm-branches in their hands; and as they came, they sang:

Hail! voyagers, hail!
Whence e'er ye come, where'er ye rove,
No calmer strand,
No sweeter land,
Will e'er ye view, than the Land of Love!

Hail! voyagers, hail!
To these, our shores, soft gales invite:
The palm plumes wave,
The billows lave,
And hither point fix'd stars of light!

Hail! voyagers, hail!
Think not our groves wide brood with gloom;
In this, our isle,
Bright flowers smile:
Full urns, rose-heaped, these valleys bloom.

Hail! voyagers, hail!
Be not deceived: renounce vain things:
Ye may not find
A tranquil mind,
Though hence ye sail with swiftest wings.

Hail! voyagers, hail!
Time flies full fast: life soon is o'er;
And ye may mourn,
That hither borne,
Ye left behind our pleasant shore.

Chapter CLXXXVII

THEY LAND

THE SONG WAS ENDED; AND AS WE GAINED THE STRAND, THE CROWD EMBRACED US; AND CALLED us brothers; ourselves and our humblest attendants.

"Call ye us brothers, whom ere now ye never saw?"

"Even so," said the old man, "is not Oro the father of all? Then, are we not brothers? Thus Alma, the master, hath commanded."

"This was not our reception in Maramma," said Media, "the appointed place of Alma, where his precepts are preserved."

"No, no," said Babbalanja; "old man! your lesson of brotherhood was learned elsewhere than from Alma; for in Maramma and in all its tributary isles true brotherhood there is none. Even in the Holy Island many are oppressed; for heresies, many murdered; and thousands perish beneath the altars, groaning with offerings that might relieve them."

"Alas! too true. But, I beseech ye, judge not Alma by all those who profess his faith. Hast thou thyself his records searched?"

"Fully, I have not. So long, even from my infancy, have I witnessed the wrongs committed in his name; the sins and inconsistencies of his followers; that thinking all evil must flow from a congenial fountain, I have scorned to study the whole record of your Master's life. By parts I only know it."

"Ah! baneful error! But thus is it, brothers! that the wisest are set against the Truth, because of those who wrest it from itself."

"Do ye then claim to live what your Master hath spoken? Are your precepts practices?"

"Nothing do we claim; we but earnestly endeavor."

"Tell me not of your endeavors, but of your life. What hope for the fatherless among ye?"

"Adopted as a son."

"Of one poor, and naked?"

"Clothed, and he wants for naught."

"If ungrateful, he smite you?"

"Still we feed and clothe him."

"If yet an ingrate?"

"Long, he cannot be; for Love is a fervent fire."

"But what, if widely he dissent from your belief in Alma; then, surely, ye must cast him forth?"

"No, no; we will remember, that if he dissent from us, we then equally dissent from him; and men's faculties are Oro-given. Nor will we say that he is wrong, and we are right, for this we know not, absolutely. But we care not for men's words; we look for creeds in actions; which are the truthful symbols of the things within. He who hourly prays to Alma, but lives not up to world-wide love and charity—that man is more an unbeliever than he who verbally rejects the Master, but does his bidding. Our lives are our Amens."

"But some say that what your Alma teaches is wholly new—a revelation of things before unimagined, even by the poets. To do his bidding, then, some new faculty must be vouchsafed, whereby to apprehend aright."

"So have I always thought," said Mohi.

"If Alma teaches love, I want no gift to learn," said Yoomy.

"All that is vital in the Master's faith, lived here in Mardi, and in humble dells was practiced, long previous to the Master's coming. But never before was virtue so lifted up among us, that all might see; never before did rays from heaven descend to glorify it. But are Truth, Justice, and Love, the revelations of Alma alone? Were they never heard of till he came? Oh! Alma but opens unto us our own hearts. Were his precepts strange we would recoil—not one feeling would respond; whereas, once hearkened to, our souls embrace them as with the instinctive tendrils of a vine."

"But," said Babbalanja, "since Alma, they say, was solely intent upon the things of the Mardi to come—which to all must seem uncertain—of what benefit his precepts for the daily lives led here?"

"Would! would that Alma might once more descend! Brother! were the turf our everlasting pillow, still would the Master's faith answer a blessed end; making us more truly happy *here. That* is the first and chief result; for holy here, we must be holy elsewhere. 'Tis Mardi, to which loved Alma gives his laws, not Paradise."

"Full soon will I be testing all these things," murmured Mohi.

"Old man," said Media, "thy years and Mohi's lead ye both to dwell upon the unknown future. But speak to me of other themes. Tell me of this island and its people. From all I have heard, and now behold, I gather that here, there dwells no king; that ye are left to yourselves; and that this mystic Love ye speak of, is your ruler. Is it so? Then, are ye full as visionary, as Mardi rumors. And though for a time, ye may have prospered—long, ye cannot be without some sharp lesson to convince ye, that your faith in Mardian virtue is entirely vain."

"Truth. We have no king; for Alma's precepts rebuke the arrogance of place and power. He is the tribune of mankind, nor will his true faith be universal Mardi's, till our whole race is kingless. But think not we believe in man's perfection. Yet, against all good, he is not absolutely set. In his heart, there is a germ. *That* we seek to foster. To *that* we cling; else, all were hopeless!"

"Your social state?"

"It is imperfect, and long must so remain. But we make not the miserable many support the happy few. Nor, by annulling reason's laws, seek to breed equality, by breeding anarchy. In all things, equality is not for all. Each has his own. Some have wider groves of palms than others, fare better, dwell in more tasteful arbors, oftener renew their fragrant thatch. Such differences must be. But none starve outright, while others feast. By the abounding, the needy are supplied. Yet not by statute, but from dictates born half dormant in us, and warmed into life by Alma. Those dictates we but follow in all we do; we are not dragged to righteousness, but go running. Nor do we live in common. For vice and virtue, blindly mingled, form a union where vice too often proves the alkali. The vicious we make dwell apart, until reclaimed. And reclaimed they soon must be, since everything invites. The sin of others rests not upon our heads; none we drive to crime. Our laws are not of vengeance bred, but Love and Alma."

"Fine poetry all this," said Babbalanja, "but not so new. Oft do they warble thus in bland Maramma."

"It sounds famously, old man!" said Media; "but men are men. Some must starve; some be scourged. Your doctrines are impracticable."

"And are not these things enjoined by Alma? And would Alma inculcate the impossible? of what merit his precepts, unless they may be practiced? But I beseech ye, speak no more of Maramma. Alas! did Alma revisit Mardi, think you, it would be among those Morals he would lay his head?"

"No, no," said Babbalanja, "as an intruder he came, and an intruder would he be this day. On all sides, would he jar our social systems."

"Not here, not here! Rather would we welcome Alma hungry and athirst, than though he came floating hither on the wings of seraphs; the blazing zodiac his diadem. In all his aspects we adore him; needing no pomp and power to kindle worship. Though he came from Oro, though he did miracles, though through him is life; not for these things alone, do we thus love him. We love him from an instinct in us; a fond, filial, reverential feeling. And this would yet stir in our souls, were death our end, and Alma incapable of befriending us. We love him because we do."

"Is this man divine?" murmured Babbalanja. "But thou speakest most earnestly of adoring Alma: I see no temples in your groves."

"Because this isle is all one temple to his praise; every leaf is consecrated his. We fix not Alma here and there; and say, 'those groves for him, and these broad fields for us.' It is all his own; and we ourselves; our every hour of life; and all we are, and have."

"Then, ye forever fast and pray; and stand and sing; as at long intervals the censer-bearers in Maramma supplicate their gods?"

"Alma forbid! We never fast; our aspirations are our prayers; our lives are worship. And when we laugh, with human joy at human things, *then* do we most sound great Oro's praise, and prove the merits of sweet Alma's love! Our love in Alma makes us glad, not sad. Ye speak of temples;—behold! 'tis by not building *them* that we widen charity among us. The treasures which, in the islands round about, are lavished on a thousand fanes; with these we every day relieve the Master's suffering disciples. In Mardi, Alma preached in open fields, and must his worshipers have palaces?"

"No temples, then, no priests?" said Babbalanja; "for few priests will enter where lordly arches form not the portal."

"We have no priests, but one; and he is Alma's self. We have his precepts; we seek no comments but our hearts."

"But without priests and temples, how long will flourish this your faith?" said Media.

"For many ages has not this faith lived, in spite of priests and temples? and shall it not survive them? What we believe, we hold divine; and things divine endure forever."

"But how enlarge your bounds? how convert the vicious, without persuasion of some special seers? Must your religion go hand in hand with all things secular?"

"We hold not, that one man's words should be a gospel to the rest; but that Alma's words should be a gospel to us all. And not by precepts would we have some few endeavor to persuade; but all, by practice fix convictions, that the life we lead is the life for all. We are apostles, every one. Where'er we go, our faith we carry in our hands, and hearts. It is our chiefest joy. We do not put it wide away six days out of seven; and then, assume it. In it we all exult, and joy; as that which makes us happy here; as that, without which, we could be happy nowhere; as something meant for this time present, and henceforth for aye. It is our vital mode of being; not an incident. And when we die, this faith shall be our pillow; and when we rise, our staff; and at the end, our crown. For we are all immortal. Here, Alma joins with our own hearts, confirming nature's promptings."

"How eloquent he is!" murmured Babbalanja. "Some black cloud seems floating from me. I begin to see. I come out in light. The sharp fang tears me less. The forked flames wane. My soul sets back like ocean streams, that sudden change their flow. Have I been sane? Quickened in me is a hope. But pray you, old man—say on—methinks, that in your faith must be much that jars with reason."

"No, brother! Right-reason, and Alma are the same; else Alma, not reason, would we reject. The Master's great command is Love; and here do all things wise and all things good, unite. Love is all in all. The more we love, the more we know; and so reversed. Oro we love; this isle; and our wide arms embrace all Mardi like its reef. How can we err, thus feeling? We hear loved Alma's pleading, prompting voice, in every breeze, in every leaf; we see his earnest eye in every star and flower."

"Poetry!" cried Yoomy, "and poetry is truth! He stirs me."

"When Alma dwelt in Mardi, 'twas with the poor and friendless. He fed the famishing; he healed the sick; he bound up wounds. For every precept that he spoke, he did ten thousand mercies. And Alma is our loved example."

"Sure, all this is in the histories!" said Mohi, starting.

"But not alone to poor and friendless, did Alma wend his charitable way. From lowly places, he looked up, and long invoked great chieftains in their state; and told them all their pride was vanity; and bade them ask their souls. 'In *me*,' he cried, 'is that heart of mild content, which in vain ye seek in rank and title. I am Love; love ye then me.' "

"Cease, cease, old man!" cried Media; "thou movest me beyond my seeming. What thoughts are these? Have done! Wouldst thou unking me?"

"Alma is for all; for high and low. Like heaven's own breeze, he lifts the lily from its lowly stem, and sweeps, reviving, through the palmy groves. High thoughts he gives the sage, and humble trust the simple. Be the measure what it may, his grace doth fill it to the brim. He lays the lashings of the soul's wild aspirations after things unseen: oil he poureth on the waters; and stars come out of night's black concave at his great command. In him is hope for all; for all, unbounded joys. Fast locked in his loved clasp, no doubts dismay. He opes the eye of faith, and shuts the eye of fear. He is all we pray for, and beyond; all, that in the wildest hour of ecstasy, rapt fancy paints in bright Auroras upon the soul's wide, boundless Orient!"

"Oh, Alma, Alma! prince divine!" cried Babbalanja, sinking on his knees, "in *thee,* at last, I find repose. Hope perches in my heart a dove; a thousand rays illume; all Heaven's a sun. Gone, gone! are all distracting doubts. Love and Alma now prevail. I see with other eyes. Are these my hands? What wild, wild dreams were mine? I have been mad. Some things there are, we must not think of. Beyond one obvious mark, all human lore is vain. Where have I lived till now? Had dark Maramma's zealot tribe but murmured to me as this old man, long since had I been wise! Reason no longer domineers; but still doth speak. All I have said ere this, that wars with Alma's precepts, I here recant. Here I kneel, and own great Oro and his sovereign son."

"And here another kneels and prays," cried Yoomy. "In Alma all my dreams are found, my inner longings for the Love supreme, that prompts my every verse. Summer is in my soul."

"Nor now, too late for these gray hairs," cried Mohi, with devotion. "Alma, thy breath is on my soul. I see bright light."

"No more a demi-god," cried Media, "but a subject to our common chief. No more shall dismal cries be heard from Odo's groves. Alma, I am thine!"

With swimming eyes the old man kneeled; and round him grouped king, sage, gray hairs, and youth.

There, as they kneeled, and as the old man blessed them, the setting sun burst forth from mists, gilded the island round about, shed rays upon their heads, and went down in a glory—all the East radiant with red burnings, like an altar-fire.

Chapter CLXXXVIII

BABBALANJA RELATES TO THEM A VISION

LEAVING BABBALANJA IN THE OLD MAN'S BOWER, DEEP IN MEDITATION, THOUGHTFULLY WE strolled along the beach, inspiring the musky, midnight air; the tropical stars glistening in heaven, like drops of dew among violets.

Returning, we espied Babbalanja advancing in his snow-white mantel. The fiery tide was ebbing; and in the soft, moist sand, at every step, he left a lustrous footprint.

"Sweet friends! this isle is full of mysteries!" he said; "I have dreamed of wondrous things. After I had laid me down, thought pressed hard upon me. By my eyes passed pageant visions. I started at a low strange melody, deep in my inmost soul. At last, methought my eyes were fixed on heaven; and there, I saw a shining spot, unlike a star. Thwarting the sky, it grew, and grew, descending; till bright wings were visible: between them, a pensive face, angelic, downward beaming; and for one golden moment, gauze-veiled in spangled Berenice's locks.

"Then, as white flame from yellow, out from that starry cluster it emerged; and brushed the astral crosses, crowns and cups. And as in violet, tropic seas, ships leave a radiant white, and firefly wake; so in long extension tapering, behind the vision, gleamed another Milky Way.

"Strange throbbings seized me; my soul tossed on its own tides. But soon the inward harmony bounded in exulting choral strains. I heard a feathery rush; and straight beheld a form, traced all over with veins of vivid light. The vision undulated round me.

" 'Oh! Spirit!! angel! god! whate'er thou art,' I cried, 'leave me; I am but man.'

"Then, I heard a low, sad sound—no voice. It said, or breathed upon me, 'Thou hast proved the grace of Alma: tell me what thou'st learned?'

"Silent replied my soul, for voice was gone. 'This have I learned, oh! spirit! In things mysterious, to seek no more; but rest content, with knowing naught but Love.'

" 'Blessed art thou for that, thrice blessed.' Then I heard, 'And since humility is thine, thou art one apt to learn. That which thy own wisdom could not find, thy ignorance confessed shall gain. Come and see new things.'

"Once more it undulated round me; its lightning wings grew dim; nearer, nearer; till I felt a shock electric, and nested 'neath its wing.

"We clove the air; passed systems, suns, and moons; what seem from Mardi's isles the glowworm stars.

"By distant fleets of worlds we sped, as voyagers pass far sails at sea, and hail them not. Foam played before them as they darted on; wild music was their wake; and many tracks of sound we crossed, where worlds had sailed before.

"Soon we gained a point, where a new heaven was seen; whence all our firmament seemed one nebula. Its glories burned like thousand steadfast-flaming lights.

"Here hived the worlds in swarms; and gave forth sweets ineffable.

"We lighted on a ring, circling a space, where mornings seemed forever dawning over worlds unlike.

" 'Here,' I heard, 'thou viewest thy Mardi's Heaven. Herein each world is portioned.'

"As he who climbs to mountain tops pants hard for breath; so panted I for Mardi's grosser air. But that which caused my flesh to faint, was new vitality to my soul. My eyes swept over all before me. The spheres were plain as villages that dot a landscape. I saw most beauteous forms, yet like our own. Strange sounds I heard of gladness that seemed mixed with sadness; a low, sweet harmony of both. Else, I know not how to phrase what never man but me e'er heard.

" 'In these blessed souls are blent,' my guide discoursed, 'far higher thoughts, and sweeter plaints than thine. Rude joys were discord here. And as a sudden shout in thy hushed mountain-passes brings down the awful avalanche; so one note of laughter here, might start some white and silent world.'

"Then low I murmured, 'Is theirs, oh, guide! no happiness supreme? Their state still mixed? Sigh these yet to know? Can these sin?'

"Then I heard, 'No mind but Oro's can know all; no mind that knows not all can be content; content alone approximates to happiness. Holiness comes by wisdom; and it is because great Oro is supremely wise, that He's supremely holy. But as perfect wisdom can be only Oro's; so, perfect holiness is his alone. And whoso is otherwise than perfect in his holiness, is liable to sin.

" 'And though death gave these beings knowledge, it also opened other mysteries, which they pant to know, and yet may learn. And still they fear the thing of evil; though for them 'tis hard to fall. Thus hoping and thus fearing, then, their's is no state complete. And since Oro is past finding out, and mysteries ever open into mysteries beyond; so, though these beings will for aye progress in wisdom and in good; yet, will they never gain a fixed beatitude. Know, then, oh, mortal Mardian! that when translated hither, thou wilt but put off lowly temporal pinings, for angel and eternal aspirations. Start not! thy human joy hath here no place: no name.'

"Still, I mournful mused; then said:—'Many Mardians live, who have no aptitude for Mardian lives of thought: how then endure more earnest, everlasting meditations?'

" 'Such have their place,' I heard.

" 'Then low I moaned, 'And what, oh! guide! of those who, living thoughtless lives of sin, die unregenerate; no service done to Oro or to Mardi?'

" 'They, too, have their place,' I heard; 'but 'tis not here. And Mardian! know, that as your Mardian lives are long preserved through strict obedience to the organic law, so are your spiritual lives prolonged by fast keeping of the law of mind. Sin is death.'

" 'Ah, then,' yet lower moan made I, 'and why create the germs that sin and suffer, but to perish?'

" 'That,' breathed my guide, 'is the last mystery which underlieth all the rest. Archangel may not fathom it; that makes of Oro the everlasting mystery he is; that to divulge, were to make equal to himself in knowledge all the souls that are; that mystery Oro guards; and none but him may know.'

"Alas! were it recalled, no words have I to tell of all that now my guide discoursed, concerning things unsearchable to us. My sixth sense which he opened, sleeps again, with all the wisdom that it gained.

"Time passed; it seemed a moment, might have been an age; when from high in the golden haze that canopied this heaven, another angel came; its vans like East and West; a sunrise one, sunset the other. As silver-fish in vases, so, in his azure eyes swam tears unshed.

"Quick my guide close nested me; through its veins the waning light throbbed hard.

" 'Oh! spirit! archangel! god! whate'er thou art,' it breathed; 'leave me: I am but blessed, not glorified.'

"So saying, as down from doves, from its wings dropped sounds. Still nesting me, it crouched its plumes.

"Then, in a snow of softest syllables, thus breathed the greater and more beautiful, 'From far away, in fields beyond thy ken, I heard thy fond discourse with this lone Mardian. It pleased me well; for thy humility was manifest; no arrogance of knowing. Come *thou*, and learn new things.'

"And straight it over-arched us with its plumes; which, then, down-sweeping, bore us up to regions where my first guide had sunk, but for the power that buoyed us, trembling, both.

"My eyes did wane, like moons eclipsed in overwhelming dawns; such radiance was around; such vermeil light, born of no sun, but pervading all the scene. Transparent, fleckless, calm, all glowed one flame.

"Then said the greater guide, 'This is the night of all ye here behold—its day ye could not bide. Your utmost heaven is far below.'

"Abashed, smote down, I quaking, upward gazed; where, to and fro, the spirits sailed, like broad-winged, crimson-dyed flamingos, spiraling in sunset-clouds. But a sadness glorified, deep-fringed their mystic temples, crowned with weeping halos, bird-like, floating o'er them, whereso'er they roamed.

"Sights and odors blended. As when new morning winds, in summer's prime, blow down from hanging gardens, wafting sweets that never pall; so, from those flowery pinions, at every motion, came a flood of fragrance.

"And now the spirits twain discoursed of things, whose very terms, to me, were dark. But my first guide grew wise. For me, I could but blankly list; yet comprehended naught; and, like the fish that's mocked with wings, and vainly seeks to fly; again I sought my lower element.

"As poised, we hung in this rapt ether, a sudden trembling seized the four wings now folding me. And afar of, in zones still upward reaching, suns' orbits off, I, tranced, beheld an awful glory.

Sphere in sphere, it burned: the one Shekinah! The air was flaked with fire; deep in which, fell showers of silvery globes, tears magnified—braiding the flame with rainbows. I heard a sound; but not for me, nor my first guide, was that unutterable utterance. Then, my second guide was swept aloft, as rises a cloud of red-dyed leaves in autumn whirlwinds.

"Fast clasping me, the other drooped, and instant sank, as in a vacuum; myriad suns' diameters in a breath—my five senses merged in one, of falling; till we gained the nether sky, descending still.

"Then strange things—soft, sad, and faint, I saw or heard; as, when, in sunny summer seas, down, down you dive, starting at pensive phantoms that you cannot fix.

" 'These,' breathed my guide, 'are spirits in their essences; sad, even in undevelopment. With these all space is peopled; all the air is vital with intelligence, which seeks embodiment.

" 'This it is, that unbeknown to Mardians, causes them to strangely start in solitudes of night, and in the fixed flood of their enchanted noons. From hence, are formed your mortal souls; and all those sad and shadowy dreams and boundless thoughts man hath, are vague remembrances of the time when the soul's sad germ, wide wandered through these realms. And hence it is, that when ye Mardians feel most sad, then ye feel most immortal.

"Like a spark new-struck from flint, soon Mardi showed afar. It glowed within a sphere, which seemed, in space, a bubble, rising from vast depths to the sea's surface. Piercing it, my Mardian strength returned; but the angel's veins once more grew dim.

"Nearing the isles, thus breathed my guide, 'Loved one, love on! But know, that heaven hath no roof. To know all, is to be all. Beatitude there is none. And your only Mardian happiness is but exemption from great woes—no more. Great Love is sad; and heaven is Love. Sadness makes the silence throughout the realms of space; sadness is universal and eternal; but sadness is tranquility; tranquility the uttermost that souls may hope for.'

"Then, with its wings it fanned adieu; and disappeared where the sun flames highest."

We heard the dream, and, silent, sought repose, to dream away our wonder.

Chapter CLXXXIX

THEY DEPART FROM SERENIA

AT SUNRISE, WE STOOD UPON THE BEACH.

Babbalanja thus—"My voyage is ended. Not because what we sought is found; but that I now possess all which may be had of what I sought in Mardi. Here, tarry to grow wiser still: then I am Alma's and the world's. Taji! for Yillah thou wilt hunt in vain; she is a phantom that but mocks thee; and while for her thou madly huntest, the sin thou didst cries out, and its avengers still will follow. But here they may not come: nor those, who, tempting, track thy path. Wise counsel take. Within our hearts is all we seek; though in that search many need a prompter. Him I have found in blessed Alma. Then rove no more. Gain now, in flush of youth, that last wise thought, too often purchased, by a life of woe. Be wise: be wise.

"Media! thy station calls thee home. Yet from this isle, thou carriest that, wherewith to bless thy own. These flowers, that round us spring, may be transplanted; and Odo made to bloom with amaranths and myrtles, like this Serenia. Before thy people act the things thou here hast heard. Let no man weep, that thou mayst laugh; no man toil too hard, that thou mayst idle be. Abdicate thy throne: but still retain the scepter. None need a king; but many need a ruler.

"Mohi, Yoomy! do we part? then bury in forgetfulness much that hitherto I've spoken. But let not one syllable of this old man's words be lost.

"Mohi! Age leads thee by the hand. Live out thy life, and die calm-browed.

"But, Yoomy! many days are thine. And in one life's span, great circles may be traversed, eternal good be done. Take all Mardi for thy home. Nations are but names; and continents but shifting sands.

"Once more; Taji! be sure thy Yillah never will be found; or found, will not avail thee. Yet search, if so thou wilt; more isles, thou say'st are still unvisited; and when all is seen, return, and find thy Yillah here.

"Companions all! adieu."

And from the beach, he wended through the woods.

Our shallops now refitted, we silently embarked; and as we sailed away the old man blessed us.

For a time, each prow's ripplings were distinctly heard: ripple after ripple.

With silent, steadfast eyes, Media still preserved his noble mien; Mohi his reverend repose; Yoomy his musing mood.

But as a summer hurricane leaves all nature still, and smiling to the eye; yet, in deep woods, there lie concealed some anguished roots torn up:—so, with these. Much they longed, to point our prows for Odo's isle; saying our search was over. But I was fixed as fate.

On we sailed, as when we first embarked; the air was bracing as before. More isles we visited; thrice encountered the avengers; but unharmed; thrice Hautia's heralds; but turned not aside—saw many checkered scenes—wandered through groves, and open fields—traversed many vales—climbed hill-tops whence broad views were gained—tarried in towns—broke into solitudes—sought far, sought near:—Still Yillah there was none.

Then again they all would fain dissuade me.

"Closed is the deep blue eye," said Yoomy.

"Fate's last leaves are turning, let me home and die," said Mohi.

"So nigh the circuit's done," said Media, "our morrow's sun must rise o'er Odo; Taji! renounce the hunt."

"I am the hunter that never rests! the hunter without a home! She I seek, still flies before; and I will follow, though she lead me beyond the reef; through sunless seas; and into night and death. Her, will I seek, through all the isles and stars; and find her, whate'er betide!"

Again they yielded; and again we glided on—our storm-worn prows, now pointed here, now there—beckoned, repulsed—their half-rent sails, still courting every breeze.

But that same night, once more, they wrestled with me. Now, at last, the hopeless search must be renounced; Yillah there was none; back must I hie to blue Serenia. Then sweet Yillah called me from the sea; still must I on! but gazing whence that music seemed to come, I thought I saw the green corse drifting by: and striking 'gainst our prow, as if to hinder. Then, then, my heart grew hard, like flint; and black, like night; and sounded hollow to the hand I clenched. Hyenas fill me with their laughs; death-damps chilled my brow; I prayed not, but blasphemed.

Chapter CXC

THEY MEET THE PHANTOMS

THAT STARLESS MIDNIGHT, THERE STOLE FROM OUT THE DARKNESS, THE IRIS FLAG OF HAUTIA.

Again the sirens came. They bore a large and stately urn-like flower, white as alabaster, and glowing, as if lit up within. From its calyx, flame-like trembled forked and crimson stamens, burning with intensest odors.

The phantoms nearer came; their flower, as an urn of burning niter. Then it changed, and glowed like Persian dawns; or passive, was shot over by palest lightnings; so variable its tints.

"The night-blowing Cereus!" said Yoomy, shuddering, "that never blows in sun-light; that blows but once; and blows but for an hour. For the last time I come: now, in your midnight of despair, and promise you this glory. Take heed! short time hast thou to pause; through me, perhaps, thy Yillah may be found."

"Away! away! tempt me not by that, enchantress! Hautia! I know thee not; I fear thee not; but instinct makes me hate thee. Away! my eyes are frozen shut; I will not be tempted more."

"How glorious it burns!" cried Media. "I reel with incense: can such sweets be evil?"

"Look! look!" cried Yoomy, "its petals wane, and creep; one moment more, and the night-flower shuts up forever the last, last hope of Yillah!"

"Yillah! Yillah! Yillah!" bayed three vengeful voices far behind.

"Yillah! Yillah! dash the urn! I follow, Hautia! though thy lure be death!"

The Cereus closed; and in a mist the siren prow went on before; we, following.

When day dawned, three radiant pilot-fish swam in advance: three ravenous sharks astern.

And, full before us, rose the isle of Hautia.

Chapter CXCI

THEY DRAW NIGH TO FLOZELLA

AS IF MARDI WERE A POEM, AND EVERY ISLAND A CANTO, THE SHORE NOW IN SIGHT WAS CALLED Flozella-a-Nina, or The-Last-Verse-of-the-Song.

According to Mohi, the origin of this term was traceable to the remotest antiquity.

In the beginning there were other beings in Mardi besides Mardians; winged beings, of purer minds, and cast in gentler molds, who would fain have dwelt forever with mankind. But the hearts of the Mardians were bitter against them, because of their superior goodness. Yet those beings returned love for malice, and long entreated to virtue and charity. But in the end, all Mardi rose up against them, and hunted them from isle to isle; till, at last, they rose from the woodlands like a flight of birds, and disappeared in the skies. Thereafter, abandoned of such sweet influences, the Mardians fell into all manner of sins and sufferings, becoming the erring things their descendants were now. Yet they knew not, that their calamities were of their own bringing down. For deemed a victory, the expulsion of the winged beings was celebrated in choruses, throughout Mardi. And among other jubilations, so ran the legend, a paean was composed, corresponding in the number of its stanzas to the number of islands. And a band of youths, gaily appareled, voyaged in gala canoes all round the lagoon, singing upon each isle one verse of their song. And Flozella being the last isle in their circuit, its queen commemorated the circumstance by new naming her realm.

That queen had first incited Mardi to wage war against the beings with wings. She it was, who had been foremost in every assault. And that queen was ancestor of Hautia, now ruling the isle.

Approaching the dominions of one who so long had haunted me, conflicting emotions tore up my soul in tornadoes. Yet Hautia had held out some prospect of crowning my yearnings. But how connected were Hautia and Yillah? Something I hoped; yet more I feared. Dire presentiments, like poisoned arrows, shot through me. Had they pierced me before, straight to Flozella would I have voyaged; not waiting for Hautia to woo me by that last victorious temptation. But unchanged remained my feelings of hatred for Hautia; yet vague those feelings, as the language of her flowers. Nevertheless, in some mysterious way seemed Hautia and Yillah connected. But Yillah was all beauty and innocence; my crown of felicity; my heaven below; and Hautia, my whole heart abhorred. Yillah I sought; Hautia sought me. One, openly, beckoned me here; the other dimly allured me there. Yet now was I wildly dreaming to find them together. But so distracted my soul, I knew not what it was, that I thought.

Slowly we neared the land. Flozella-a-Nina! An omen? Was this isle, then, to prove the last place of my search, even as it was the Last-Verse-of-the-Song?

Chapter CXCII

THEY LAND

A JEWELED TIARA, NODDING IN SPRAY, LOOKS FLOWERY FLOZELLA, APPROACHED FROM THE SEA. For, lo you! the glittering foam all round its white marge; where, forcing themselves underneath the coral hedge, and up through its crevices, in fountains, the blue billows gush. While, within, zone above zone, thrice zoned in belts of bloom, all the isle, as a hanging-garden soars; its tapering cone blending aloft, with heaven's own blue.

"What flies through the spray! what incense is this?" cried Media.

"Ha! you wild breeze! you have been plundering the gardens of Hautia," cried Yoomy.

"No sweets can be sweeter," said Braid-Beard, "but no Upas more deadly."

Anon we came nearer; sails idly flapping, and paddles suspended; sleek currents our coursers. And round about the isle, like winged rainbows, shoals of dolphins were leaping over floating fragments of wrecks; dark-green, long-haired ribs, and keels of canoes. For many shallops, inveigled by the eddies, were oft dashed to pieces against that flowery strand. But what cared the dolphins? Mardian wrecks were their homes. Over and over they sprang: from east to west: rising and setting: many suns in a moment; while all the sea, like a harvest plain, was stacked with their glittering sheaves of spray.

And far down, fathoms on fathoms, flitted rainbow hues:—as seines-full of mermaids; half-screening the bones of the drowned.

Swifter and swifter the currents now ran; till with a shock, our prows were beached.

There, beneath an arch of spray, three dark-eyed maidens stood; garlanded with columbines, their nectaries nodding like jesters' bells; and robed in vestments blue.

"The pilot-fish transformed!" cried Yoomy.

"The night-eyed heralds three!" cried Mohi.

Following the maidens, we now took our way along a winding vale; where, by sweet-scented hedges, flowed blue-braided brooks; their tributaries, rivulets of violets, meandering through the meads.

On one hand, forever glowed the rosy mountains with a tropic dawn; and on the other, lay an Arctic eve;—the white daisies drifted in long banks of snow, and snowed the blossoms from the orange boughs. There, summer breathed her bridal bloom; her hill-top temples crowned with bridal wreaths.

We wandered on, through orchards arched in long arcades, that seemed baronial halls, hung o'er with trophies; so spread the boughs in antlers. This orchard was the frontlet of the isle.

The fruit hung high in air, that only beaks, not hands, might pluck.

Here, the peach tree showed her thousand cheeks of down, kissed often by the wooing winds; here, in swarms; the yellow apples hived, like golden bees upon the boughs; here, from the kneeling, fainting trees, thick fell the cherries, in great drops of blood; and here, the pomegranate, with cold rind and sere, deep pierced by bills of birds, revealed the mellow of its ruddy core. So, oft the heart, that cold and withered seems, within yet hides its juices.

This orchard passed, the vale became a lengthening plain, that seemed the Straits of Ormus bared; so thick it lay with flowery gems; turquoise-hyacinths, ruby-roses, lily-pearls. Here roved the vagrant vines; their flaxen ringlets curling over arbors, which laughed and shook their golden locks. From bower to bower, flew the wee bird, that ever hovering, seldom lights; and flights of gay canaries passed, like jonquils, winged.

But now, from out half-hidden bowers of clematis, there issued swarms of wasps, which flying wide, settled on all the buds.

And, fifty nymphs preceding, who now follows from those bowers, with gliding, artful steps: the very snares of love! Hautia. A gorgeous amaryllis in her hand; Circe-flowers in her ears; her girdle tied with vervain.

She came by privet hedges, drooping; downcast honeysuckles; she trod on pinks and pansies, bluebells, heath, and lilies. She glided on; her crescent brow calm as the moon, when most it works its evil influences.

Her eye was fathomless.

But the same mysterious, evil-boding gaze was there, which long before had haunted me in Odo, ere Yillah fled. Queen Hautia the incognito! Then two wild currents met, and dashed me into foam.

"Yillah! Yillah! tell me, queen!" But she stood motionless; radiant, and scentless: a dahlia on its stalk.

"Where? Where?"

"Is not thy voyage now ended? Take flowers! Damsels, give him wine to drink. After his weary hunt, be the wanderer happy."

I dashed aside their cups and flowers; still rang the vale with Yillah!

"Taji! did I know her fate, naught would I now disclose; my heralds pledged their queen to naught. Thou but comest here to supplant thy mourner's night-shade, with marriage roses. Damsels! give him wreaths; crowd round him; press him with your cups!"

Once more I spilled their wine, and tore their garlands.

"Is not that, the evil eye that long ago did haunt me? and thou, the Hautia who hast followed me, and wooed, and mocked, and tempted me, through all this long, long voyage? I swear! thou knowest all."

"I am Hautia. Thou hast come at last. Crown him with your flowers! Drown him in your wine! To all questions, Taji! I am mute. Away! damsels, dance; reel round him; round and round!"

Then, their feet made music on the rippling grass, like thousand leaves of lilies on a lake. And gliding nearer, Hautia welcomed Media; and said, "Your comrade here is sad; be ye gay. Ho, wine! I pledge ye, guests!"

Then, marking all, I thought to seem what I was not, that I might learn at last the thing I sought.

So, three cups in hand I held; drank wine, and laughed; and half-way met Queen Hautia's blandishments.

Chapter CXCIII

They Enter the Bower of Hautia

Conducted to the arbor, from which the queen had emerged, we came to a sweet-briar bower within; and reclined upon odorous mats.

Then, in citron cups, sherbet of tamarinds was offered to Media, Mohi, Yoomy; to me, a nautilus shell, brimmed with a light-like fluid, that welled, and welled like a fount.

"Quaff, Taji, quaff! every drop drowns a thought!"

Like a blood-freshet, it ran through my veins.

A philter? How Hautia burned before me! Glorious queen! with all the radiance, lighting up the equatorial night.

"Thou art most magical, oh, queen! about thee a thousand constellations cluster."

"They blaze to burn," whispered Mohi.

"I see ten million Hautias! all space reflects her as a mirror."

Then, in reels, the damsels once more mazed, the blossoms shaking from their brows, till Hautia glided, near; arms lustrous as rainbows: chanting some wild invocation.

My soul ebbed out; Yillah there was none! but as I turned round open-armed, Hautia vanished.

"She is deeper than the sea," said Media.

"Her bow is bent," said Yoomy.

"I could tell wonders of Hautia and her damsels," said Mohi.

"What wonders?"

"Listen; and in his own words will I recount the adventure of the youth Ozonna. It will show thee, Taji, that the maidens of Hautia are all Yillahs, held captive, unknown to themselves; and that Hautia, their enchantress, is the most treacherous of queens.

" 'Camel-like, laden with woe,' said Ozonna, 'after many wild rovings in quest of a maiden long lost—beautiful Ady! and after being repelled in Maramma; and in vain hailed to land at Serenia, represented as naught but another Maramma: with vague promises of discovering Ady, three sirens, who long had pursued, at last inveigled me to Flozella; where Hautia made me her thrall. But ere long, in Rea, one of her maidens, I thought I discovered my Ady transformed. My arms opened wide to embrace; but the damsel knew not Ozonna. And even, when after hard wooing I won her again, she seemed not lost Ady, but Rea. Yet all the while, from deep in her strange, black orbs, Ady's blue eyes seemed pensively looking; blue eyes within black; sad, silent soul within merry. Long I strove, by fixed ardent gazing to break the spell, and restore in Rea my lost one's Past. But in vain. It was only Rea, not Ady, who at stolen intervals looked on me now. One morning Hautia started as she greeted me; her quick eye rested on my bosom; and glancing there, affrighted, I beheld a distinct, fresh mark, the impress of Rea's necklace drop. Fleeing, I revealed what had passed to the maiden, who broke from my side, as I from Hautia's. The queen summoned her damsels, but for many hours the call was unheeded; and when at last they came, upon each bosom lay a necklace-drop like Rea's. On the morrow, lo! my arbor was strewn over with bruised Linden-leaves, exuding a vernal juice.

Full of forebodings, again I sought Rea; who, casting down her eyes, beheld her feet stained green. Again she fled; and again Hautia summoned her damsels; malicious triumph in her eye; but dismay succeeded; each maid had spotted feet. That night Rea was torn from my side by three masks; who, stifling her cries, rapidly bore her away; and as I pursued, disappeared in a cave. Next morning, Hautia was surrounded by her nymphs, but Rea was absent. Then, gliding near, she snatched from my hair a jet-black tress, loose-hanging. 'Ozonna is the murderer! See! Rea's torn hair entangled with his!' Aghast, I swore that I knew not her fate. 'Then let the witch Larfee be called!' The maidens darted from the bower; and soon after, there rolled into it a green cocoanut, followed by the witch, and all the damsels, flinging anemones upon it. Bowling this way and that, the nut at last rolled to my feet. 'It is he!' cried all. Then they bound me with osiers; and at midnight, unseen and irresistible hands placed me in a shallop; which sped far out into the lagoon, where they tossed me to the waves; but so violent the shock, the osiers burst, and as the shallop fled one way, swimming another, ere long, I gained land.

" 'Thus in Flozella, I found but the phantom of Ady, and slew the last hope of Ady the true.' "

This recital sank deep into my soul. In some wild way, Hautia had made a captive of Yillah; in someone of her black-eyed maids, the blue-eyed One was transformed. From side to side, in frenzy, I turned; but in all those cold, mystical eyes, saw not the warm ray that I sought.

"Hast taken root within this treacherous soil?" cried Media. "Away! thy Yillah is behind thee, not before. Deep she dwells in blue Serenia's groves; which thou wouldst not search. Hautia mocks thee; away! The reef is rounded; but a strait flows between this isle and Odo, and thither its ruler must return. Every hour, I tarry here, some wretched serf is dying there, for whom, from blest Serenia, I carry life and joy. Away!"

"Art still bent on finding evil for thy good?" cried Mohi. "How can Yillah harbor here? Beware! Let not Hautia so enthrall thee."

"Come away, come away!" cried Yoomy. "Far hence is Yillah! and he who tarries among these flowers, must needs burn juniper."

"Look on me, Media, Mohi, Yoomy. Here I stand, my own monument, till Hautia breaks the spell."

In grief they left me.

Vee-Vee's conch I heard no more.

Chapter CXCIV

TAJI WITH HAUTIA

AS THEIR LAST ECHOES DIED AWAY DOWN THE VALLEY, HAUTIA GLIDED NEAR;—ZONE UNBOUND, the amaryllis in her hand. Her bosom ebbed and flowed; the motes danced in the beams that darted from her eyes.

"Come! let us sin, and be merry. Ho! wine, wine, wine! and lapfuls of flowers! let all the cane-brakes pipe their flutes. Damsels! dance; reel, swim, around me. I, the vortex that draws all in, Taji! Taji!—as a berry, that name is juicy in my mouth! Taji, Taji!" and in choruses she warbled forth the sound, till it seemed issuing from her siren eyes.

My heart flew forth from out its bars, and soared in air; but as my hand touched Hautia's, down dropped a dead bird from the clouds.

"Ha! how he sinks! but did'st ever dive in deep waters, Taji? Did'st ever see where pearls grow? To the cave! damsels! lead on!"

Then wending through constellations of flowers, we entered deep groves. And thus, thrice from sunlight to shade, it seemed three brief nights and days, ere we paused before the mouth of the cavern.

A bow-shot from the sea, it pierced the hill-side like a vaulted way; and glancing in, we saw far gleams of water; crossed, here and there, by long-flung distant shadows of domes and columns. All Venice seemed within.

From a stack of golden palm-stalks, the damsels now made torches; then stood grouped; a sheaf of sirens in a sheaf of frame.

Illuminated, the cavern shone like a Queen of Kandy's casket; full of dawns and sunsets.

From rocky roof to bubbling floor, it was columned with stalactites; and galleried all round, in spiral tiers, with sparkling, coral ledges.

And now, their torches held aloft, into the water the maidens softly glided; and each a lotus floated; while, from far above, into the air Hautia flung her flambeau; then bounding after, in the lake, two meteors were quenched.

Where she dived, the flambeaux clustered; and up among them, Hautia rose; hands full of pearls.

"Lo! Taji; all these may be had for the diving; and Beauty, Health, Wealth, Long Life, and the Last Lost Hope of man. But through me alone, may these be had. Dive thou, and bring up one pearl if thou canst."

Down, down, down, down, in the clear, sparkling water, till I seemed crystalized in the flashing heart of a diamond; but from those bottomless depths, I uprose empty handed.

"Pearls, pearls! thy pearls! thou art fresh from the mines. Ah, Taji! for thee, bootless deep diving. Yet to Hautia, one shallow plunge reveals many Golcondas. But come; dive with me: join hands—let me show thee strange things."

"Show me that which I seek, and I will dive with thee straight through the world, till we come up in oceans unknown."

"Nay, nay; but join hands, and I will take thee, where thy past shall be forgotten; where thou wilt soon learn to love the living, not the dead."

"Better to me, oh Hautia; all the bitterness of my buried dead, than all the sweets of the life thou canst bestow; even, were it eternal."

Chapter CXCV

Mardi Behind! An Ocean Before!

Returned from the cave, Hautia reclined in her clematis bower, invisible hands flinging fennel around her. And nearer, and nearer stole dulcet sounds dissolving my woes, as warm beams, snow. Strange languors made me droop; once more within my inmost vault, side by side, the Past and Yillah lay: two bodies tranced: while like a rounding sun, before me Hautia magnified magnificence; and through her fixed eyes, slowly drank up my soul.

Thus we stood—snake and victim: life ebbing out from me, to her.

But from that spell, I burst again, as all the Past smote all the Present in me.

"Oh, Hautia! thou knowest the mystery I die to fathom. I see it crouching in thine eye. Reveal!"

"Weal or woe?"

"Life or death!"

"See, see!" and Yillah's rose-pearl danced before me.

I snatched it from her hand: Yillah! Yillah!

"Rave on; she lies too deep to answer; stranger voices than thine she hears: bubbles are bursting round her."

"Drowned! Drowned, then, even as she dreamed; I come, I come! Ha, what form is this? hast mosses? sea-thyme? pearls? Help, help! I sink! Back, shining monster! What, Hautia, is it thou? Oh, vipress, I could slay thee!"

"Go, go, and slay thyself; I may not make thee mine; go—dead to dead! There is another cavern in the hill."

Swift I fled along the valley side; passed Hautia's cave of pearls; and gained a twilight arch; within, a lake transparent shone. Conflicting currents met, and wrestled; and one dark arch led to channels, seaward tending.

Round and round, a gleaming form slow circled in the deepest eddies; white and vaguely Yillah.

Straight I plunged; but the currents were as fierce head-winds off capes, that beat back ships.

Then, as I frenzied gazed; gaining the one dark arch, the revolving shade darted out of sight, and the eddies whirled as before.

"Stay, stay! let me go with thee, though thou glidest to gulfs of blackness; naught can exceed the hell of this despair! Why beat longer in this corpse, oh, my heart!"

As somnambulists fast frozen in some horrid dream, ghost-like glide abroad, and fright the wakeful world, so that night, with death-glazed eyes, to and fro I flitted on the damp and weedy beach.

"Is this specter, Taji?" and Mohi and the minstrel stood before me.

"Taji lives no more. So dead, he has no ghost. I am his spirit's phantom's phantom."

"Nay, then, phantom; the time has come to flee."

They dragged me to the water's brink, where a prow was beached. Soon—Mohi at the helm—we shot beneath the far-flung shadow of a cliff; when, as in a dream, I hearkened to a voice.

Arrived at Odo, Media had been met with yells. Sedition was in arms, and to his beard defied him. Vain all concessions then. Foremost stood the three pale sons of him whom I had slain, to gain the maiden lost. Avengers, from the first hour we had parted on the sea, they had drifted on my track; survived starvation; and lived to hunt me round all Mardi's reef; and now at Odo, that last threshold, waited to destroy; or there, missing the revenge they sought, still swore to hunt me round Eternity.

Behind the avengers raged a stormy mob, invoking Media to renounce his rule. But one hand waving like a pennant above the smoke of some sea-fight, straight through that tumult Media sailed serene: the rioters parting from before him, as wild waves before a prow inflexible.

A haven gained, he turned to Mohi and the minstrel: "Oh, friends! after our long companionship, hard to part! But henceforth, for many moons, Odo will prove no home for old age, or youth. In Serenia only, will ye find the peace ye seek; and thither ye must carry Taji, who else must soon be slain or lost. Go: release him from the thrall of Hautia. Outfly the avengers, and gain Serenia. Reck not of me. The state is tossed in storms; and where I stand, the combing billows must break over. But among all noble souls, in tempest-time, the headmost man last flies the wreck. So, here in Odo, will I abide, though every plank breaks up beneath me. And then, great Oro! let the king die clinging to the keel! Farewell!" Such Mohi's tale.

In trumpet-blasts the hoarse night-winds now blew; the Lagoon, black with the still shadows of the mountains, and the driving shadows of the clouds. Of all the stars, only red Arcturus shone. But through the gloom, and on the circumvallating reef, the breakers dashed ghost-white. An outlet in that outer barrier was nigh.

"Ah! Yillah! Yillah! the currents sweep thee oceanward; nor will I tarry behind. Mardi, farewell! Give me the helm, old man!"

"Nay, madman! Serenia is our haven. Through yonder strait, for thee, perdition lies. And from the deep beyond, no voyager e'er puts back."

"And why put back? is a life of dying worth living o'er again? Let *me,* then, be the unreturning wanderer. The helm! By Oro! I will steer my own fate, old man. Mardi, farewell!"

"Nay, Taji! commit not the last, last crime!" cried Yoomy.

"He's seized the helm! eternity is in his eye! Yoomy, for our lives we must now swim."

And plunging, they struck out for land: Yoomy buoying Mohi up, and the salt waves dashing the tears from his pallid face, as through the scud, he turned it on me mournfully.

"Now, I am my own soul's emperor; and my first act is abdication! Hail! realm of shades!" and turning my prow into the racing tide, which seized me like a hand omnipotent, I darted through.

Churned in foam, that outer ocean lashed the clouds; and straight in my white wake, headlong dashed a shallop, three fixed specters leaning o'er its prow: three arrows poising.

And thus, pursuers and pursued flew on, over an endless sea.

REDBURN

HIS FIRST VOYAGE

Being the Sailor Boy Confessions and Reminiscences of the Son-of-a-Gentleman in the Merchant Service

TO MY YOUNGER BROTHER,

THOMAS MELVILLE

NOW A SAILOR ON A VOYAGE TO CHINA,

THIS VOLUME IS INSCRIBED.

CONTENTS

Chapter I

How Wellingborough Redburn's Taste for the Sea was Born and Bred in Him

"Wellingborough, as you are going to sea, suppose you take this shooting-jacket of mine along; it's just the thing—take it, it will save the expense of another. You see, it's quite warm; fine long skirts, stout horn buttons, and plenty of pockets."

Out of the goodness and simplicity of his heart, thus spoke my elder brother to me, upon the eve of my departure for the seaport.

"And, Wellingborough," he added, "since we are both short of money, and you want an outfit, and I have none to give, you may as well take my fowling-piece along, and sell it in New York for what you can get.—Nay, take it; it's of no use to me now; I can't find it in powder anymore."

I was then but a boy. Some time previous my mother had removed from New York to a pleasant village on the Hudson River, where we lived in a small house, in a quiet way. Sad disappointments in several plans which I had sketched for my future life; the necessity of doing something for myself, united to a naturally roving disposition, had now conspired within me, to send me to sea as a sailor.

For months previous I had been poring over old New York papers, delightedly perusing the long columns of ship advertisements, all of which possessed a strange, romantic charm to me. Over and over again I devoured such announcements as the following:

FOR BREMEN.

The coppered and copper-fastened brig Leda, *having nearly completed her cargo, will sail for the above port on Tuesday the twentieth of May.*

For freight or passage apply on board at Coenties Slip.

To my young inland imagination every word in an advertisement like this, suggested volumes of thought.

A *brig!* The very word summoned up the idea of a black, sea-worn craft, with high, cozy bulwarks, and rakish masts and yards.

Coppered and copper-fastened! That fairly smelled of the salt water! How different such vessels must be from the wooden, one-masted, green-and-white-painted sloops, that glided up and down the river before our house on the bank.

Nearly completed her cargo! How momentous the announcement; suggesting ideas, too, of musty bales, and cases of silks and satins, and filling me with contempt for the vile deck-loads of hay and lumber, with which my river experience was familiar.

Will sail on Tuesday the 20th of May—and the newspaper bore date the fifth of the month! Fifteen whole days beforehand; think of that; what an important voyage it must be, that the time of sailing was fixed upon so long beforehand; the river sloops were not used to make such prospective announcements.

For freight or passage apply on board! Think of going on board a coppered and copper-fastened brig, and taking passage for Bremen! And who could be going to Bremen? No one but foreigners, doubtless; men of dark complexions and jet-black whiskers, who talked French.

Coenties Slip. Plenty more brigs and any quantity of ships must be lying there. Coenties Slip must be somewhere near ranges of grim-looking warehouses, with rusty iron doors and shutters, and tiled roofs; and old anchors and chain-cable piled on the walk. Old-fashioned coffeehouses, also, much abound in that neighborhood, with sunburned sea-captains going in and out, smoking cigars, and talking about Havanna, London, and Calcutta.

All these my imaginations were wonderfully assisted by certain shadowy reminiscences of wharves, and warehouses, and shipping, with which a residence in a seaport during early childhood had supplied me.

Particularly, I remembered standing with my father on the wharf when a large ship was getting under way, and rounding the head of the pier. I remembered the *yo heave ho!* of the sailors, as they just showed their woolen caps above the high bulwarks. I remembered how I thought of their crossing the great ocean; and that that very ship, and those very sailors, so near to me then, would after a time be actually in Europe.

Added to these reminiscences my father, now dead, had several times crossed the Atlantic on business affairs, for he had been an importer in Broad-street. And of winter evenings in New York, by the well-remembered sea-coal fire in old Greenwich-street, he used to tell my brother and me of the monstrous waves at sea, mountain high; of the masts bending like twigs; and all about Havre, and Liverpool, and about going up into the ball of St. Paul's in London. Indeed, during my early life, most of my thoughts of the sea were connected with the land; but with fine old lands, full of mossy cathedrals and churches, and long, narrow, crooked streets without side-walks, and lined with strange houses. And especially I tried hard to think how such places must look of rainy days and Saturday afternoons; and whether indeed they did have rainy days and Saturdays there, just as we did here; and whether the boys went to school there, and studied geography, and wore their shirt collars turned over, and tied with a black ribbon; and whether their papas allowed them to wear boots, instead of shoes, which I so much disliked, for boots looked so manly.

As I grew older my thoughts took a larger flight, and I frequently fell into long reveries about distant voyages and travels, and thought how fine it would be, to be able to talk about remote and barbarous countries; with what reverence and wonder people would regard me, if I had just returned from the coast of Africa or New Zealand; how dark and romantic my sunburned cheeks would look; how I would bring home with me foreign clothes of a rich fabric and princely make, and wear them up and down the streets, and how grocers' boys would turn back their heads to look at me, as I went by. For I very well remembered staring at a man myself, who was pointed out to me by my aunt one Sunday in Church, as the person who had been in Stony Arabia, and passed through strange adventures there, all of which with my own eyes I had read in the book which he wrote, an arid-looking book in a pale yellow cover.

"See what big eyes he has," whispered my aunt, "they got so big, because when he was almost dead with famishing in the desert, he all at once caught sight of a date tree, with the ripe fruit hanging on it."

Upon this, I stared at him till I thought his eyes were really of an uncommon size, and stuck out from his head like those of a lobster. I am sure my own eyes must have magnified as I stared. When church was out, I wanted my aunt to take me along and follow the traveler home. But she said the constables would take us up, if we did; and so I never saw this wonderful Arabian traveler again. But he long haunted me; and several times I dreamed of him, and thought his great eyes were grown still larger and rounder; and once I had a vision of the date tree.

In course of time, my thoughts became more and more prone to dwell upon foreign things; and in a thousand ways I sought to gratify my tastes. We had several pieces of furniture in the house, which had been brought from Europe. These I examined again and again, wondering where the wood grew; whether the workmen who made them still survived, and what they could be doing with themselves now.

Then we had several oil-paintings and rare old engravings of my father's, which he himself had bought in Paris, hanging up in the dining-room.

Two of these were sea-pieces. One represented a fat-looking, smoky fishing-boat, with three whiskerandoes in red caps, and their trousers legs rolled up, hauling in a seine. There was high French-like land in one corner, and a tumble-down gray lighthouse surmounting it. The waves were toasted brown, and the whole picture looked mellow and old. I used to think a piece of it might taste good.

The other represented three old-fashioned French men-of-war with high castles, like pagodas, on the bow and stern, such as you see in Froissart; and snug little turrets on top of the mast, full of little men, with something undefinable in their hands. All three were sailing through a bright-blue sea, blue as Sicily skies; and they were leaning over on their sides at a fearful angle; and they must have been going very fast, for the white spray was about the bows like a snow-storm.

Then, we had two large green French portfolios of colored prints, more than I could lift at that age. Every Saturday my brothers and sisters used to get them out of the corner where they were kept, and spreading them on the floor, gaze at them with never-failing delight.

They were of all sorts. Some were pictures of Versailles, its masquerades, its drawing-rooms, its fountains, and courts, and gardens, with long lines of thick foliage cut into fantastic doors and windows, and towers and pinnacles. Others were rural scenes, full of fine skies, pensive cows standing up to the knees in water, and shepherd-boys and cottages in the distance, half concealed in vineyards and vines.

And others were pictures of natural history, representing rhinoceroses and elephants and spotted tigers; and above all there was a picture of a great whale, as big as a ship, stuck full of harpoons, and three boats sailing after it as fast as they could fly.

Then, too, we had a large library-case, that stood in the hall; an old brown library-case, tall as a small house; it had a sort of basement, with large doors, and a lock and key; and higher up, there were glass doors, through which might be seen long rows of old books, that had been printed in Paris, and London, and Leipsic. There was a fine library edition of the *Spectator*, in six large volumes with gilded backs; and many a time I gazed at the word *"London"* on the title-page. And there was a copy of *D'Alembert* in French, and I wondered what a great man I would be, if by foreign travel I should ever be able to read straight along without stopping, out of that book, which now was a riddle to everyone in the house but my father, whom I so much liked to hear talk French, as he sometimes did to a servant we had.

That servant, too, I used to gaze at with wonder; for in answer to my incredulous cross-questions, he had over and over again assured me, that he had really been born in Paris. But this I never entirely believed; for it seemed so hard to comprehend, how a man who had been born in a foreign country, could be dwelling with me in our house in America.

As years passed on, this continual dwelling upon foreign associations, bred in me a vague prophetic thought, that I was fated, one day or other, to be a great voyager; and that just as my father used to entertain strange gentlemen over their wine after dinner, I would hereafter be telling my own adventures to an eager auditory. And I have no doubt that this presentiment had something to do with bringing about my subsequent rovings.

But that which perhaps more than anything else, converted my vague dreamings and longings into a definite purpose of seeking my fortune on the sea, was an old-fashioned glass ship, about eighteen inches long, and of French manufacture, which my father, some thirty years before, had brought home from Hamburgh as a present to a great-uncle of mine: Senator Wellingborough, who had died a member of Congress in the days of the old Constitution, and after whom I had the honor of being named. Upon the decease of the Senator, the ship was returned to the donor.

It was kept in a square glass case, which was regularly dusted by one of my sisters every morning, and stood on a little claw-footed Dutch tea-table in one corner of the sitting-room. This ship, after being the admiration of my father's visitors in the capital, became the wonder and delight of all the people of the village where we now resided, many of whom used to call upon my mother, for no other purpose than to see the ship. And well did it repay the long and curious examinations which they were accustomed to give it.

In the first place, every bit of it was glass, and that was a great wonder of itself; because the masts, yards, and ropes were made to resemble exactly the corresponding parts of a real vessel that could go to sea. She carried two tiers of black guns all along her two decks; and often I used to try to peep in at the portholes, to see what else was inside; but the holes were so small, and it looked so very dark indoors, that I could discover little or nothing; though, when I was very little, I made no doubt, that if I could but once pry open the hull, and break the glass all to pieces, I would infallibly light upon something wonderful, perhaps some gold guineas, of which I have always been in want, ever since I could remember. And often I used to feel a sort of insane desire to be the death of the glass ship, case, and all, in order to come at the plunder; and one day, throwing out some hint of the kind to my sisters, they ran to my mother in a great clamor; and after that, the ship was placed on the mantel-piece for a time, beyond my reach, and until I should recover my reason.

I do not know how to account for this temporary madness of mine, unless it was, that I had been reading in a story-book about Captain Kidd's ship, that lay somewhere at the bottom of the Hudson near the Highlands, full of gold as it could be; and that a company of men were trying to dive down and get the treasure out of the hold, which no one had ever thought of doing before, though there she had lain for almost a hundred years.

Not to speak of the tall masts, and yards, and rigging of this famous ship, among whose mazes of spun-glass I used to rove in imagination, till I grew dizzy at the main-truck, I will only make mention of the people on board of her. They, too, were all of glass, as beautiful little glass sailors as anybody ever saw, with hats and shoes on, just like living men, and curious blue jackets with a sort of ruffle round the bottom. Four or five of these sailors were very nimble little chaps, and were mounting up the rigging with very long strides; but for all that, they never gained a single inch in the year, as I can take my oath.

Another sailor was sitting astride of the spanker-boom, with his arms over his head, but I never could find out what that was for; a second was in the fore-top, with a coil of glass rigging over his shoulder; the cook, with a glass ax, was splitting wood near the fore-hatch; the steward, in a glass apron, was hurrying toward the cabin with a plate of glass pudding; and a glass dog, with a red mouth, was barking at him; while the captain in a glass cap was smoking a glass cigar on the quarter-deck. He was leaning against the bulwark, with one hand to his head; perhaps he was unwell, for he looked very glassy out of the eyes.

The name of this curious ship was *La Reine,* or *The Queen,* which was painted on her stern where anyone might read it, among a crowd of glass dolphins and sea-horses carved there in a sort of semicircle.

And this *Queen* rode undisputed mistress of a green glassy sea, some of whose waves were breaking over her bow in a wild way, I can tell you, and I used to be giving her up for lost and foundered every moment, till I grew older, and perceived that she was not in the slightest danger in the world.

A good deal of dust, and fuzzy stuff like down, had in the course of many years worked through the joints of the case, in which the ship was kept, so as to cover all the sea with a light dash of white, which if anything improved the general effect, for it looked like the foam and froth raised by the terrible gale the good *Queen* was battling against.

So much for *La Reine.* We have her yet in the house, but many of her glass spars and ropes are now sadly shattered and broken—but I will not have her mended; and her figure-head, a gallant warrior in a cocked-hat, lies pitching head-foremost down into the trough of a calamitous sea under the bows—but I will not have him put on his legs again, till I get on my own; for between him and me there is a secret sympathy; and my sisters tell me, even yet, that he fell from his perch the very day I left home to go to sea on this *my first voyage.*

Chapter II

REDBURN'S DEPARTURE FROM HOME

IT WAS WITH A HEAVY HEART AND FULL EYES, THAT MY POOR MOTHER PARTED WITH ME; PERHAPS she thought me an erring and a willful boy, and perhaps I was; but if I was, it had been a hard-hearted world, and hard times that had made me so. I had learned to think much and bitterly before my time; all my young mounting dreams of glory had left me; and at that early age, I was as unambitious as a man of sixty.

Yes, I will go to sea; cut my kind uncles and aunts, and sympathizing patrons, and leave no heavy hearts but those in my own home, and take none along but the one which aches in my bosom. Cold, bitter cold as December, and bleak as its blasts, seemed the world then to me; there is no misanthrope like a boy disappointed; and such was I, with the warm soul of me flogged out by adversity. But these thoughts are bitter enough even now, for they have not yet gone quite away; and they must be uncongenial enough to the reader; so no more of that, and let me go on with my story.

"Yes, I will write you, dear mother, as soon as I can," murmured I, as she charged me for the hundredth time, not fail to inform her of my safe arrival in New York.

"And now Mary, Martha, and Jane, kiss me all round, dear sisters, and then I am off. I'll be back in four months—it will be autumn then, and we'll go into the woods after nuts, and I'll tell you all about Europe. Good-bye! good-bye!"

So I broke loose from their arms, and not daring to look behind, ran away as fast as I could, till I got to the corner where my brother was waiting. He accompanied me part of the way to the place, where the steam-boat was to leave for New York; instilling into me much sage advice above his age, for he was but eight years my senior, and warning me again and again to take care of myself; and I solemnly promised I would; for what castaway will not promise to take of care himself, when he sees that unless he himself does, no one else will.

We walked on in silence till I saw that his strength was giving out—he was in ill health then—and with a mute grasp of the hand, and a loud thump at the heart, we parted.

It was early on a raw, cold, damp morning toward the end of spring, and the world was before me; stretching away a long muddy road, lined with comfortable houses, whose inmates were taking their sunrise naps, heedless of the wayfarer passing. The cold drops of drizzle trickled down my leather cap, and mingled with a few hot tears on my cheeks.

I had the whole road to myself, for no one was yet stirring, and I walked on, with a slouching, dogged gait. The gray shooting-jacket was on my back, and from the end of my brother's rifle hung a small bundle of my clothes. My fingers worked moodily at the stock and trigger, and I thought that this indeed was the way to begin life, with a gun in your hand!

Talk not of the bitterness of middle-age and after life; a boy can feel all that, and much more, when upon his young soul the mildew has fallen; and the fruit, which with others is only blasted after ripeness, with him is nipped in the first blossom and bud. And never again can such blights be made good; they strike in too deep, and leave such a scar that the air of Paradise might not erase it. And it is a hard and cruel thing thus in early youth to taste beforehand the pangs which should be reserved for the stout time of manhood, when the gristle has become bone, and we stand up and fight out our lives, as a thing tried before and foreseen; for then we are veterans used to sieges and battles, and not green recruits, recoiling at the first shock of the encounter.

At last gaining the boat we pushed off, and away we steamed down the Hudson. There were few passengers on board, the day was so unpleasant; and they were mostly congregated in the after cabin round the stoves. After breakfast, some of them went to reading: others took a nap on the settees; and others sat in silent circles, speculating, no doubt, as to who each other might be.

They were certainly a cheerless set, and to me they all looked stony-eyed and heartless. I could not help it, I almost hated them; and to avoid them, went on deck, but a storm of sleet drove me below. At last I bethought me, that I had not procured a ticket, and going to the captain's office to pay my passage and get one, was horror-struck to find, that the price of passage had been suddenly raised that day, owing to the other boats not running; so that I had not enough money to pay for my fare. I had supposed it would be but a dollar, and only a dollar did I have, whereas it was two. What was to be done? The boat was off, and there was no backing out; so I determined to say nothing to anybody, and grimly wait until called upon for my fare.

The long weary day wore on till afternoon; one incessant storm raged on deck; but after dinner the few passengers, waked up with their roast-beef and mutton, became a little more sociable. Not with me, for the scent and savor of poverty was upon me, and they all cast toward me their evil eyes and cold suspicious glances, as I sat apart, though among them. I felt that desperation and recklessness of poverty which only a pauper knows. There was a mighty patch upon one leg of my trousers, neatly sewed on, for it had been executed by my mother, but still very obvious and incontrovertible to the eye. This patch I had hitherto studiously endeavored to hide with the ample skirts of my shooting-jacket; but now I stretched out my leg boldly, and thrust the patch under their noses, and looked at them so, that they soon looked away, boy though I was. Perhaps the gun that I clenched frightened them into respect; or there might have been something ugly in my eye; or my teeth were white, and my jaws were set. For several hours, I sat gazing at a jovial party seated round a mahogany table, with some crackers and cheese, and wine and cigars. Their faces were flushed with the good dinner they had eaten; and mine felt pale and wan with a long fast. If I had presumed to offer to make one of their party; if I had told them of my circumstances, and solicited something to refresh me, I very well knew from the peculiar hollow ring of their laughter, they would have had the waiters put me out of the cabin, for a beggar, who had no business to be warming himself at their stove. And for that insult, though only a conceit, I sat and gazed at them, putting up no petitions for their prosperity. My whole soul was soured within me, and when at last the captain's clerk, a slender young man, dressed in the height of fashion, with a gold watch chain and broach, came round collecting the tickets, I buttoned up my coat to the throat, clutched my gun, put on my leather cap, and pulling it well down, stood up like a sentry before him. He held out his hand, deeming any remark superfluous, as his object in pausing before me must be obvious. But I stood motionless and silent, and in a moment he saw how it was with me. I ought to have spoken and told him the case, in plain, civil terms, and offered my dollar, and then waited the event. But I felt too wicked for that. He did not wait a great while, but spoke first himself; and in a gruff voice, very unlike his urbane accents when accosting the wine and cigar party, demanded my ticket. I replied that I had none. He then demanded the money; and upon my answering that I had not enough, in a loud angry voice that attracted all eyes, he ordered me out of the cabin into the storm. The devil in me then mounted up from my soul, and spread over my frame, till it tingled at my finger ends; and I muttered out my resolution to stay where I was, in such a manner, that the ticket man faltered back.

"There's a dollar for you," I added, offering it.

"I want two," said he.

"Take that or nothing," I answered; "it is all I have."

I thought he would strike me. But, accepting the money, he contented himself with saying something about sportsmen going on shooting expeditions, without having money to pay their expenses; and hinted that such chaps might better lay aside their fowling-pieces, and assume the buck and saw. He then passed on, and left every eye fastened upon me.

I stood their gazing some time, but at last could stand it no more. I pushed my seat right up before the most insolent gazer, a short fat man, with a plethora of cravat round his neck, and fixing my gaze on his, gave him more gazes than he sent. This somewhat embarrassed him, and he looked round for someone to take hold of me; but no one coming, he pretended to be very busy counting the gilded wooden beams overhead. I then turned to the next gazer, and clicking my gun-lock, deliberately presented the piece at him.

Upon this, he overset his seat in his eagerness to get beyond my range, for I had him point blank, full in the left eye; and several persons starting to their feet, exclaimed that I must be crazy. So I was at that time; for otherwise I know not how to account for my demoniac feelings, of which I was afterward heartily ashamed, as I ought to have been, indeed; and much more than that.

I then turned on my heel, and shouldering my fowling-piece and bundle, marched on deck, and walked there through the dreary storm, till I was wet through, and the boat touched the wharf at New York.

Such is boyhood.

Chapter III

He Arrives in Town

From the boat's bow, I jumped ashore, before she was secured, and following my brother's directions, proceeded across the town toward St. John's Park, to the house of a college friend of his, for whom I had a letter.

It was a long walk; and I stepped in at a sort of grocery to get a drink of water, where some six or eight rough looking fellows were playing dominoes upon the counter, seated upon cheese boxes. They winked, and asked what sort of sport I had had gunning on such a rainy day, but I only gulped down my water and stalked off.

Dripping like a seal, I at last grounded arms at the doorway of my brother's friend, rang the bell and inquired for him.

"What do you want?" said the servant, eyeing me as if I were a housebreaker.

"I want to see your lord and master; show me into the parlor."

Upon this my host himself happened to make his appearance, and seeing who I was, opened his hand and heart to me at once, and drew me to his fireside; he had received a letter from my brother, and had expected me that day.

The family were at tea; the fragrant herb filled the room with its aroma; the brown toast was odoriferous; and everything pleasant and charming. After a temporary warming, I was shown to a room, where I changed my wet dress, and returning to the table, found that the interval had been we improved by my hostess; a meal for a traveler was spread, and I laid into it sturdily. Every mouthful pushed the devil that had been tormenting me all day farther and farther out of me, till at last I entirely ejected him with three successive bowls of Bohea.

Magic of kind words, and kind deeds, and good tea! That night I went to bed thinking the world pretty tolerable, after all; and I could hardly believe that I had really acted that morning as I had, for I was naturally of an easy and forbearing disposition; though when such a disposition is temporarily roused, it is perhaps worse than a cannibal's.

Next day, my brother's friend, whom I choose to call Mr. Jones, accompanied me down to the docks among the shipping, in order to get me a place. After a good deal of searching, we lighted upon a ship for Liverpool, and found the captain in the cabin; which was a very handsome one, lined with mahogany and maple; and the steward, an elegant looking mulatto in a gorgeous turban, was setting out on a sort of sideboard some dinner service which looked like silver, but it was only Britannia ware highly polished.

As soon as I clapped my eye on the captain, I thought to myself he was just the captain to suit me. He was a fine looking man, about forty, splendidly dressed, with very black whiskers, and very white teeth, and what I took to be a free, frank look-out of a large hazel eye. I liked him amazingly. He was promenading up and down the cabin, humming some brisk air to himself when we entered.

"Good-morning, sir," said my friend.

"Good-morning, good-morning, sir," said the captain. "Steward, chairs for the gentlemen."

"Oh! never mind, sir," said Mr. Jones, rather taken aback by his extreme civility. "I merely called to see whether you want a fine young lad to go to sea with you. Here he is; he has long wanted to be a sailor; and his friends have at last concluded to let him go for one voyage, and see how he likes it."

"Ah! indeed!" said the captain, blandly, and looking where I stood. "He's a fine fellow; I like him. So you want to be a sailor, my boy, do you?" added he, affectionately patting my head. "It's a hard life, though; a hard life."

But when I looked round at his comfortable, and almost luxurious cabin, and then at his handsome care-free face, I thought he was only trying to frighten me, and I answered, "Well, sir, I am ready to try it."

"I hope he's a country lad, sir," said the captain to my friend, "these city boys are sometimes hard cases."

"Oh! yes, he's from the country," was the reply, "and of a highly respectable family; his great-uncle died a Senator."

"But his great-uncle don't want to go to sea too?" said the captain, looking funny.

"Oh! no, oh, no!—Ha! ha!"

"Ha! ha!" echoed the captain.

A fine funny gentleman, thought I, not much fancying, however, his levity concerning my great-uncle, he'll be cracking his jokes the whole voyage; and so I afterward said to one of the riggers on board; but he bade me look out, that he did not crack my head.

"Well, my lad," said the captain, "I suppose you know we haven't any pastures and cows on board; you can't get any milk at sea, you know."

"Oh! I know all about that, sir; my father has crossed the ocean, if I haven't."

"Yes," cried my friend, "his father, a gentleman of one of the first families in America, crossed the Atlantic several times on important business."

"Embassador extraordinary?" said the captain, looking funny again.

"Oh! no, he was a wealthy merchant."

"Ah! indeed"; said the captain, looking grave and bland again, "then this fine lad is the son of a gentleman?"

"Certainly," said my friend, "and he's only going to sea for the humor of it; they want to send him on his travels with a tutor, but he *will* go to sea as a sailor."

The fact was, that my young friend (for he was only about twenty-five) was not a very wise man; and this was a huge fib, which out of the kindness of his heart, he told in my behalf, for the purpose of creating a profound respect for me in the eyes of my future lord.

Upon being apprised, that I had willfully forborne taking the grand tour with a tutor, in order to put my hand in a tar-bucket, the handsome captain looked ten times more funny than ever; and said that *he* himself would be my tutor, and take me on my travels, and pay for the privilege.

"Ah!" said my friend, "that reminds me of business. Pray, captain, how much do you generally pay a handsome young fellow like this?"

"Well," said the captain, looking grave and profound, "we are not so particular about beauty, and we never give more than three dollars to a green lad like Wellingborough here, that's your name, my boy? Wellingborough Redburn!—Upon my soul, a fine sounding name."

"Why, captain," said Mr. Jones, quickly interrupting him, "that won't pay for his clothing."

"But you know his highly respectable and wealthy relations will doubtless see to all that," replied the captain, with his funny look again.

"Oh! yes, I forgot that," said Mr. Jones, looking rather foolish. "His friends will of course see to that."

"Of course," said the captain smiling.

"Of course," repeated Mr. Jones, looking ruefully at the patch on my pantaloons, which just then I endeavored to hide with the skirt of my shooting-jacket.

"You are quite a sportsman I see," said the captain, eyeing the great buttons on my coat, upon each of which was a carved fox.

Upon this my benevolent friend thought that here was a grand opportunity to befriend me.

"Yes, he's quite a sportsman," said he, "he's got a very valuable fowling-piece at home, perhaps you would like to purchase it, captain, to shoot gulls with at sea? It's cheap."

"Oh! no, he had better leave it with his relations," said the captain, "so that he can go hunting again when he returns from England."

"Yes, perhaps that *would* be better, after all," said my friend, pretending to fall into a profound musing, involving all sides of the matter in hand. "Well, then, captain, you can only give the boy three dollars a month, you say?"

"Only three dollars a month," said the captain.

"And I believe," said my friend, "that you generally give something in advance, do you not?"

"Yes, that is sometimes the custom at the shipping offices," said the captain, with a bow, "but in this case, as the boy has rich relations, there will be no need of that, you know."

And thus, by his ill-advised, but well-meaning hints concerning the respectability of my paternity, and the immense wealth of my relations, did this really honest-hearted but foolish friend of mine, prevent me from getting three dollars in advance, which I greatly needed. However, I said nothing, though I thought the more; and particularly, how that it would have been much better for me, to have gone on board alone, accosted the captain on my own account, and told him the plain truth. Poor people make a very poor business of it when they try to seem rich.

The arrangement being concluded, we bade the captain good-morning; and as we were about leaving the cabin, he smiled again, and said, "Well, Redburn, my boy, you won't get home-sick before you sail, because that will make you very sea-sick when you get to sea."

And with that he smiled very pleasantly, and bowed two or three times, and told the steward to open the cabin-door, which the steward did with a peculiar sort of grin on his face, and a slanting glance at my shooting-jacket.

And so we left.

Chapter IV

How He Disposed of His Fowling-Piece

NEXT DAY I WENT ALONE TO THE SHIPPING OFFICE TO SIGN THE ARTICLES, AND THERE I MET A great crowd of sailors, who as soon as they found what I was after, began to tip the wink all round, and I overheard a fellow in a great flapping sou'wester cap say to another old tar in a shaggy monkey-jacket, "Twig his coat, d'ye see the buttons, that chap ain't going to sea in a merchantman, he's going to shoot whales. I say, maty—look here—how d'ye sell them big buttons by the pound?"

"Give us one for a saucer, will ye?" said another.

"Let the youngster alone," said a third. "Come here, my little boy, has your ma put up some sweetmeats for ye to take to sea?"

They are all witty dogs, thought I to myself, trying to make the best of the matter, for I saw it would not do to resent what they said; they can't mean any harm, though they are certainly very impudent; so I tried to laugh off their banter, but as soon as ever I could, I put down my name and beat a retreat.

On the morrow, the ship was advertised to sail. So the rest of that day I spent in preparations. After in vain trying to sell my fowling-piece for a fair price to chance customers, I was walking up Chatham-street with it, when a curly-headed little man with a dark oily face, and a hooked nose, like the pictures of Judas Iscariot, called to me from a strange-looking shop, with three gilded balls hanging over it.

With a peculiar accent, as if he had been over-eating himself with Indian-pudding or some other plushy compound, this curly-headed little man very civilly invited me into his shop; and making a polite bow, and bidding me many unnecessary good-mornings, and remarking upon the fine weather, begged me to let him look at my fowling-piece. I handed it to him in an instant, glad of the chance of disposing of it, and told him that was just what I wanted.

"Ah!" said he, with his Indian-pudding accent again, which I will not try to mimic, and abating his look of eagerness, "I thought it was a better article, it's very old."

"Not," said I, starting in surprise, "it's not been used more than three times; what will you give for it?"

"We don't *buy* anything here," said he, suddenly looking very indifferent, "this is a place where people *pawn* things."

Pawn being a word I had never heard before, I asked him what it meant; when he replied, that when people wanted any money, they came to him with their fowling-pieces, and got one third its value, and then left the fowling-piece there, until they were able to pay back the money.

What a benevolent little old man, this must be, thought I, and how very obliging.

"And pray," said I, "how much will you let me have for my gun, by way of a pawn?"

"Well, I suppose it's worth six dollars, and seeing you're a boy, I'll let you have three dollars upon it"

"No," exclaimed I, seizing the fowling-piece, "it's worth five times that, I'll go somewhere else."

"Good-morning, then," said he, "I hope you'll do better," and he bowed me out as if he expected to see me again pretty soon.

I had not gone very far when I came across three more balls hanging over a shop. In I went, and saw a long counter, with a sort of picket-fence, running all along from end to end, and three little holes, with three little old men standing inside of them, like prisoners looking out of a jail. Back of the counter were all sorts of things, piled up and labeled. Hats, and caps, and coats, and guns, and swords, and canes, and chests, and planes, and books, and writing-desks, and every thing else. And in a glass case were lots of watches, and seals, chains, and rings, and breastpins, and all kinds of trinkets. At one of the little holes, earnestly talking with one of the hook-nosed men, was a thin woman in a faded silk gown and shawl, holding a pale little girl by the hand. As I drew near, she spoke lower in a whisper; and the man shook his head, and looked cross and rude; and then some more words were exchanged over a miniature, and some money was passed through the hole, and the woman and child shrank out of the door.

I won't sell my gun to that man, thought I; and I passed on to the next hole; and while waiting there to be served, an elderly man in a high-waisted surtout, thrust a silver snuff-box through; and a young man in a calico shirt and a shiny coat with a velvet collar presented a silver watch; and a sheepish boy in a cloak took out a frying-pan; and another little boy had a Bible; and all these things were thrust through to the hook-nosed man, who seemed ready to hook anything that came along; so I had no doubt he would gladly hook my gun, for the long picketed counter seemed like a great seine, that caught every variety of fish.

At last I saw a chance, and crowded in for the hole; and in order to be beforehand with a big man who just then came in, I pushed my gun violently through the hole; upon which the hook-nosed man cried out, thinking I was going to shoot him. But at last he took the gun, turned it end for end, clicked the trigger three times, and then said, "one dollar."

"What about one dollar?" said I.

"That's all I'll give," he replied.

"Well, what do you want?" and he turned to the next person. This was a young man in a seedy red cravat and a pimply face, that looked as if it was going to seed likewise, who, with a mysterious tapping of his vest-pocket and other hints, made a great show of having something confidential to communicate.

But the hook-nosed man spoke out very loud, and said, "None of that; take it out. Got a stolen watch? We don't deal in them things here."

Upon this the young man flushed all over, and looked round to see who had heard the pawnbroker; then he took something very small out of his pocket, and keeping it hidden under his palm, pushed it into the hole.

"Where did you get this ring?" said the pawnbroker.

"I want to pawn it," whispered the other, blushing all over again.

"What's your name?" said the pawnbroker, speaking very loud.

"How much will you give?" whispered the other in reply, leaning over, and looking as if he wanted to hush up the pawnbroker.

At last the sum was agreed upon, when the man behind the counter took a little ticket, and tying the ring to it began to write on the ticket; all at once he asked the young man where he lived, a question which embarrassed him very much; but at last he stammered out a certain number in Broadway.

"That's the City Hotel: you don't live there," said the man, cruelly glancing at the shabby coat before him.

"Oh! well," stammered the other blushing scarlet, "I thought this was only a sort of form to go through; I don't like to tell where I do live, for I ain't in the habit of going to pawnbrokers."

"You stole that ring, you know you did," roared out the hook-nosed man, incensed at this slur upon his calling, and now seemingly bent on damaging the young man's character for life. "I'm a good mind to call a constable; we don't take stolen goods here, I tell you."

All eyes were now fixed suspiciously upon this martyrized young man; who looked ready to drop into the earth; and a poor woman in a nightcap, with some baby-clothes in her hand, looked fearfully at the pawnbroker, as if dreading to encounter such a terrible pattern of integrity. At last the young man sunk off with his money, and looking out of the window, I saw him go round the corner so sharply that he knocked his elbow against the wall.

I waited a little longer, and saw several more served; and having remarked that the hook-nosed men invariably fixed their own price upon every thing, and if that was refused told the person to be off with himself; I concluded that it would be of no use to try and get more from them than they had offered; especially when I saw that they had a great many fowling-pieces hanging up, and did not have particular occasion for mine; and more than that, they must be very well off and rich, to treat people so cavalierly.

My best plan then seemed to be, to go right back to the curly-headed pawnbroker, and take up with my first offer. But when I went back, the curly-headed man was very busy about something else, and kept me waiting a long time; at last I got a chance and told him I would take the three dollars he had offered.

"Ought to have taken it when you could get it," he replied. "I won't give but two dollars and a half for it now."

In vain I expostulated; he was not to be moved, so I pocketed the money and departed.

Chapter V

He Purchases His Sea-Wardrobe, and on a Dismal Rainy Day Picks Up His Board and Lodging along the Wharves

The first thing I now did was to buy a little stationery, and keep my promise to my mother, by writing her; and I also wrote to my brother informing him of the voyage I purposed making, and indulging in some romantic and misanthropic views of life, such as many boys in my circumstances, are accustomed to do.

The rest of the two dollars and a half I laid out that very morning in buying a red woolen shirt near Catharine Market, a tarpaulin hat, which I got at an out-door stand near Peck Slip, a belt and jack-knife, and two or three trifles. After these purchases, I had only one penny left, so I walked out to the end of the pier, and threw the penny into the water. The reason why I did this, was because I somehow felt almost desperate again, and didn't care what became of me. But if the penny had been a dollar, I would have kept it.

I went home to dinner at Mr. Jones', and they welcomed me very kindly, and Mrs. Jones kept my plate full all the time during dinner, so that I had no chance to empty it. She seemed to see that I felt bad, and thought plenty of pudding might help me. At any rate, I never felt so bad yet but I could eat a good dinner. And once, years afterward, when I expected to be killed everyday, I remember my appetite was very keen, and I said to myself, "Eat away, Wellingborough, while you can, for this may be the last supper you will have."

After dinner I went into my room, locked the door carefully, and hung a towel over the knob, so that no one could peep through the keyhole, and then went to trying on my red woolen shirt before the glass, to see what sort of a looking sailor I was going to make. As soon as I got into the shirt I began to feel sort of warm and red about the face, which I found was owing to the reflection of the dyed wool upon my skin. After that, I took a pair of scissors and went to cutting my hair, which was very long. I thought every little would help, in making me a light hand to run aloft.

Next morning I bade my kind host and hostess good-bye, and left the house with my bundle, feeling somewhat misanthropical and desperate again.

Before I reached the ship, it began to rain hard; and as soon as I arrived at the wharf, it was plain that there would be no getting to sea that day.

This was a great disappointment to me, for I did not want to return to Mr. Jones' again after bidding them good-bye; it would be so awkward. So I concluded to go on board ship for the present.

When I reached the deck, I saw no one but a large man in a large dripping pea-jacket, who was calking down the main-hatches.

"What do you want, Pillgarlic?" said he.

"I've shipped to sail in this ship," I replied, assuming a little dignity, to chastise his familiarity.

"What for? a tailor?" said he, looking at my shooting jacket.

I answered that I was going as a "boy"; for so I was technically put down on the articles.

"Well," said he, "have you got your traps aboard?"

I told him I didn't know there were any rats in the ship, and hadn't brought any "trap."

At this he laughed out with a great guffaw, and said there must be hay-seed in my hair.

This made me mad; but thinking he must be one of the sailors who was going in the ship, I thought it wouldn't be wise to make an enemy of him, so only asked him where the men slept in the vessel, for I wanted to put my clothes away.

"*Where's* your clothes?" said he.

"Here in my bundle," said I, holding it up.

"Well if that's all you've got," he cried, "you'd better chuck it overboard. But go forward, go forward to the forecastle; that's the place you'll live in aboard here."

And with that he directed me to a sort of hole in the deck in the bow of the ship; but looking down, and seeing how dark it was, I asked him for a light.

"Strike your eyes together and make one," said he, "we don't have any lights here." So I groped my way down into the forecastle, which smelled so bad of old ropes and tar, that it almost made me sick. After waiting patiently, I began to see a little; and looking round, at last perceived I was in a smoky looking place, with twelve wooden boxes stuck round the sides. In some of these boxes were large chests, which I at once supposed to belong to the sailors, who must have taken that method of appropriating their "bunks," as I afterward found these boxes were called. And so it turned out.

After examining them for a while, I selected an empty one, and put my bundle right in the middle of it, so that there might be no mistake about my claim to the place, particularly as the bundle was so small.

This done, I was glad to get on deck; and learning to a certainty that the ship would not sail till the next day, I resolved to go ashore, and walk about till dark, and then return and sleep out the night in the forecastle. So I walked about all over, till I was weary, and went into a mean liquor shop to rest; for having my tarpaulin on, and not looking very gentlemanly, I was afraid to go into any better place, for fear of being driven out. Here I sat till I began to feel very hungry; and seeing some doughnuts on the counter, I began to think what a fool I had been, to throw away my last penny; for the doughnuts were but a penny apiece, and they looked very plump, and fat, and round. I never saw doughnuts look so enticing before; especially when a negro came in, and ate one before my eyes. At last I thought I would fill up a little by drinking a glass of water; having read somewhere that this was a good plan to follow in a case like the present. I did not feel thirsty, but only hungry; so had much ado to get down the water; for it tasted warm; and the tumbler had an ugly flavor; the negro had been drinking some spirits out of it just before.

I marched off again, every once in a while stopping to take in some more water, and being very careful not to step into the same shop twice, till night came on, and I found myself soaked through, for it had been raining more or less all day. As I went to the ship, I could not help thinking how lonesome it would be, to spend the whole night in that damp and dark forecastle, without light or fire, and nothing to lie on but the bare boards of my bunk. However, to drown all such thoughts, I gulped down another glass of water, though I was wet enough outside and in by this time; and trying to put on a bold look, as if I had just been eating a hearty meal, I stepped aboard the ship.

The man in the big pea-jacket was not to be seen; but on going forward I unexpectedly found a young lad there, about my own age; and as soon as he opened his mouth I knew he was not an American. He talked such a curious language though, half English and half gibberish, that I knew not what to make of him; and was a little astonished, when he told me he was an English boy, from Lancashire.

It seemed, he had come over from Liverpool in this very ship on her last voyage, as a steerage passenger; but finding that he would have to work very hard to get along in America, and getting home-sick into the bargain, he had arranged with the captain to work his passage back.

I was glad to have some company, and tried to get him conversing; but found he was the most stupid and ignorant boy I had ever met with. I asked him something about the river Thames; when he said that he hadn't traveled any in America and didn't know anything about the rivers here. And when I told him the river Thames was in England, he showed no surprise or shame at his ignorance, but only looked ten times more stupid than before.

At last we went below into the forecastle, and both getting into the same bunk, stretched ourselves out on the planks, and I tried my best to get asleep. But though my companion soon began to snore very loud, for me, I could not forget myself, owing to the horrid smell of the place, my being so wet, cold, and hungry, and besides all that, I felt damp and clammy about the heart. I lay turning over and over, listening to the Lancashire boy's snoring, till at last I felt so, that I had to go on deck; and there I walked till morning, which I thought would never come.

As soon as I thought the groceries on the wharf would be open I left the ship and went to make my breakfast of another glass of water. But this made me very qualmish; and soon I felt sick as death; my head was dizzy; and I went staggering along the walk, almost blind. At last I dropped on a heap of chain-cable, and shutting my eyes hard, did my best to rally myself, in which I succeeded, at last, enough to get up and walk off. Then I thought that I had done wrong in not returning to my friend's house the day before; and would have walked there now, as it was, only it was at least three miles up town; too far for me to walk in such a state, and I had no sixpence to ride in an omnibus.

Chapter VI

He Is Initiated in the Business of Cleaning out the Pig-Pen, and Slushing Down the Top-Mast

By the time I got back to the ship, everything was in an uproar. The pea-jacket man was there, ordering about a good many men in the rigging, and people were bringing off chickens, and pigs, and beef, and vegetables from the shore. Soon after, another man, in a striped calico shirt, a short blue jacket and beaver hat, made his appearance, and went to ordering about the man in the big pea-jacket; and at last the captain came up the side, and began to order about both of them.

These two men turned out to be the first and second mates of the ship.

Thinking to make friends with the second mate, I took out an old tortoise-shell snuff-box of my father's, in which I had put a piece of Cavendish tobacco, to look sailor-like, and offered the box to him very politely. He stared at me a moment, and then exclaimed, "Do you think we take snuff aboard here, youngster? no, no, no time for snuff-taking at sea; don't let the 'old man' see that snuff-box; take my advice and pitch it overboard as quick as you can."

I told him it was not snuff, but tobacco; when he said, he had plenty of tobacco of his own, and never carried any such nonsense about him as a tobacco-box. With that, he went off about his business, and left me feeling foolish enough. But I had reason to be glad he had acted thus, for if he had not, I think I should have offered my box to the chief mate, who in that case, from what I afterward learned of him, would have knocked me down, or done something else equally uncivil.

As I was standing looking round me, the chief mate approached in a great hurry about something, and seeing me in his way, cried out, "Ashore with you, you young loafer! There's no stealings here; sail away, I tell you, with that shooting-jacket!"

Upon this I retreated, saying that I was going out in the ship as a sailor.

"A sailor!" he cried, "a barber's clerk, you mean; *you* going out in the ship? what, in that jacket? Hang me, I hope the old man hasn't been shipping anymore greenhorns like you—he'll make a shipwreck of it if he has. But this is the way nowadays; to save a few dollars in seamen's wages, they think nothing of shipping a parcel of farmers and clodhoppers and baby-boys. What's your name, Pillgarlic?"

"Redburn," said I.

"A pretty handle to a man, that; scorch you to take hold of it; haven't you got any other?"

"Wellingborough," said I.

"Worse yet. Who had the baptizing of ye? Why didn't they call you Jack, or Jill, or something short and handy. But I'll baptize you over again. D'ye hear, sir, henceforth your name is *Buttons*. And now do you go, Buttons, and clean out that pig-pen in the long-boat; it has not been cleaned out since last voyage. And bear a hand about it, d'ye hear; there's them pigs there waiting to be put in; come, be off about it, now."

Was this then the beginning of my sea-career? set to cleaning out a pig-pen, the very first thing?

But I thought it best to say nothing; I had bound myself to obey orders, and it was too late to retreat. So I only asked for a shovel, or spade, or something else to work with.

"We don't dig gardens here," was the reply; "dig it out with your teeth!"

After looking round, I found a stick and went to scraping out the pen, which was awkward work enough, for another boat called the "jolly-boat," was capsized right over the long-boat, which brought them almost close together. These two boats were in the middle of the deck. I managed to crawl inside of the long-boat; and after barking my shins against the seats, and bumping my head a good many times, I got along to the stern, where the pig-pen was.

While I was hard at work a drunken sailor peeped in, and cried out to his comrades, "Look here, my lads, what sort of a pig do you call this? Hallo! inside there! what are you 'bout there? trying to stow yourself away to steal a passage to Liverpool? Out of that! out of that, I say." But just then the mate came along and ordered this drunken rascal ashore.

The pig-pen being cleaned out, I was set to work picking up some shavings, which lay about the deck; for there had been carpenters at work on board. The mate ordered me to throw these shavings into the long-boat at a particular place between two of the seats. But as I found it hard work to push the shavings through in that place, and as it looked wet there, I thought it would be better for the shavings as well as myself, to thrust them where there was a larger opening and a dry spot. While I was thus employed, the mate observing me, exclaimed with an oath, "Didn't I tell you to put those shavings somewhere else? Do what I tell you, now, Buttons, or mind your eye!"

Stifling my indignation at his rudeness, which by this time I found was my only plan, I replied that that was not so good a place for the shavings as that which I myself had selected, and asked him to tell me *why* he wanted me to put them in the place he designated. Upon this, he flew into a terrible rage, and without explanation reiterated his order like a clap of thunder.

This was my first lesson in the discipline of the sea, and I never forgot it. From that time I learned that sea-officers never gave reasons for anything they order to be done. It is enough that they command it, so that the motto is, *"Obey orders, though you break owners."*

I now began to feel very faint and sick again, and longed for the ship to be leaving the dock; for then I made no doubt we would soon be having something to eat. But as yet, I saw none of the sailors on board, and as for the men at work in the rigging, I found out that they were *"riggers,"* that is, men living ashore, who worked by the day in getting ships ready for sea; and this I found out to my cost, for yielding to the kind blandishment of one of these *riggers*, I had swapped away my jack-knife with him for a much poorer one of his own, thinking to secure a sailor friend for the voyage.

At last I watched my chance, and while people's backs were turned, I seized a carrot from several bunches lying on deck, and clapping it under the skirts of my shooting-jacket, went forward to eat it; for I had often eaten raw carrots, which taste something like chestnuts. This carrot refreshed me a good deal, though at the expense of a little pain in my stomach. Hardly had I disposed of it, when I heard the chief mate's voice crying out for "Buttons." I ran after him, and received an order to go aloft and "slush down the main-top mast."

This was all Greek to me, and after receiving the order, I stood staring about me, wondering what it was that was to be done. But the mate had turned on his heel, and made no explanations. At length I followed after him, and asked what I must do.

"Didn't I tell you to slush down the main-top mast?" he shouted.

"You did," said I, "but I don't know what that means."

"Green as grass! a regular cabbage-head!" he exclaimed to himself. "A fine time I'll have with such a greenhorn aboard. Look you, youngster. Look up to that long pole there—d'ye see it? that piece of a tree there, you timber-head—well—take this bucket here, and go up the rigging—that rope-ladder there—do you understand?—and dab this slush all over the mast, and look out for your head if one drop falls on deck. Be off now, Buttons."

The eventful hour had arrived; for the first time in my life I was to ascend a ship's mast. Had I been well and hearty, perhaps I should have felt a little shaky at the thought; but as I was then, weak and faint, the bare thought appalled me.

But there was no hanging back; it would look like cowardice, and I could not bring myself to confess that I was suffering for want of food; so rallying again, I took up the bucket.

It was a heavy bucket, with strong iron hoops, and might have held perhaps two gallons. But it was only half full now of a sort of thick lobbered gravy, which I afterward learned was boiled out of the salt beef used by the sailors. Upon getting into the rigging, I found it was no easy job to carry this heavy bucket up with me. The rope handle of it was so slippery with grease, that although I twisted it several times about my wrist, it would be still twirling round and round, and slipping off. Spite of this, however, I managed to mount as far as the "top," the clumsy bucket half the time straddling and swinging about between my legs, and in momentary danger of capsizing. Arrived at the "top," I came to a dead halt, and looked up. How to surmount that overhanging impediment completely posed me for the time. But at last, with much straining, I contrived to place my bucket in the "top"; and then, trusting to Providence, swung myself up after it. The rest of the road was comparatively easy; though whenever I incautiously looked down toward the deck, my head spun round so from weakness, that I was obliged to shut my eyes to recover myself. I do not remember much more. I only recollect my safe return to the deck.

In a short time the bustle of the ship increased; the trunks of cabin passengers arrived, and the chests and boxes of the steerage passengers, besides baskets of wine and fruit for the captain.

At last we cast loose, and swinging out into the stream, came to anchor, and hoisted the signal for sailing. Everything, it seemed, was on board but the crew; who in a few hours after, came off, one by one, in Whitehall boats, their chests in the bow, and themselves lying back in the stern like lords; and showing very plainly the complacency they felt in keeping the whole ship waiting for their lordships.

"Ay, ay," muttered the chief mate, as they rolled out of their boats and swaggered on deck, "it's your turn now, but it will be mine before long. Yaw about while you may, my hearties, I'll do the yawing after the anchor's up."

Several of the sailors were very drunk, and one of them was lifted on board insensible by his landlord, who carried him down below and dumped him into a bunk. And two other sailors, as soon as they made their appearance, immediately went below to sleep off the fumes of their drink.

At last, all the crew being on board, word was passed to go to dinner fore and aft, an order that made my heart jump with delight, for now my long fast would be broken. But though the sailors, surfeited with eating and drinking ashore, did not then touch the salt beef and potatoes which the black cook handed down into the forecastle; and though this left the whole allowance to me; to my surprise, I found that I could eat little or nothing; for now I only felt deadly faint, but not hungry.

Chapter VII

He Gets to Sea, and Feels Very Bad

EVERYTHING AT LAST BEING IN READINESS, THE PILOT CAME ON BOARD, AND ALL HANDS WERE called to up anchor. While I worked at my bar, I could not help observing how haggard the men looked, and how much they suffered from this violent exercise, after the terrific dissipation in which they had been indulging ashore. But I soon learnt that sailors breathe nothing about such things, but strive their best to appear all alive and hearty, though it comes very hard for many of them.

The anchor being secured, a steam tug-boat with a strong name, the *Hercules,* took hold of us; and away we went past the long line of shipping, and wharves, and warehouses; and rounded the green south point of the island where the Battery is, and passed Governor's Island, and pointed right out for the Narrows.

My heart was like lead, and I felt bad enough, Heaven knows; but then, there was plenty of work to be done, which kept my thoughts from becoming too much for me.

And I tried to think all the time, that I was going to England, and that, before many months, I should have actually been there and home again, telling my adventures to my brothers and sisters; and with what delight they would listen, and how they would look up to me then, and reverence my sayings; and how that even my elder brother would be forced to treat me with great consideration, as having crossed the Atlantic Ocean, which he had never done, and there was no probability he ever would.

With such thoughts as these I endeavored to shake off my heavy-heartedness; but it would not do at all; for this was only the first day of the voyage, and many weeks, nay, several whole months must elapse before the voyage was ended; and who could tell what might happen to me; for when I looked up at the high, giddy masts, and thought how often I must be going up and down them, I thought sure enough that some luckless day or other, I would certainly fall overboard and be drowned. And then, I thought of lying down at the bottom of the sea, stark alone, with the great waves rolling over me, and no one in the wide world knowing that I was there. And I thought how much better and sweeter it must be, to be buried under the pleasant hedge that bounded the sunny south side of our village grave-yard, where every Sunday I had used to walk after church in the afternoon; and I almost wished I was there now; yes, dead and buried in that church-yard. All the time my eyes were filled with tears, and I kept holding my breath, to choke down the sobs, for indeed I could not help feeling as I did, and no doubt any boy in the world would have felt just as I did then.

As the steamer carried us further and further down the bay, and we passed ships lying at anchor, with men gazing at us and waving their hats; and small boats with ladies in them waving their handkerchiefs; and passed the green shore of Staten Island, and caught sight of so many beautiful cottages all overrun with vines, and planted on the beautiful fresh mossy hill-sides; oh! then I would have given anything if instead of sailing *out* of the bay, we were only coming *into* it; if we had crossed the ocean and returned, gone over and come back; and my heart leaped up in me like something alive when I thought of really entering that bay at the end of the voyage. But that was so far distant, that it seemed it could never be. No, never, never more would I see New York again.

And what shocked me more than anything else, was to hear some of the sailors, while they were at work coiling away the hawsers, talking about the boarding-houses they were going to, when they came back; and how that some friends of theirs had promised to be on the wharf when the ship returned, to take them and their chests right up to Franklin-square where they lived; and how that they would have a good dinner ready, and plenty of cigars and spirits out on the balcony. I say this kind of talking shocked me, for they did not seem to consider, as I did, that before anything like that could happen, we must cross the great Atlantic Ocean, cross over from America to Europe and back again, many thousand miles of foaming ocean.

At that time I did not know what to make of these sailors; but this much I thought, that when they were boys, they could never have gone to the Sunday School; for they swore so, it made my ears tingle, and used words that I never could hear without a dreadful loathing.

And are these the men, I thought to myself, that I must live with so long? these the men I am to eat with, and sleep with all the time? And besides, I now began to see, that they were not going to be very kind to me; but I will tell all about that when the proper time comes.

Now you must not think, that because all these things were passing through my mind, that I had nothing to do but sit still and think; no, no, I was hard at work: for as long as the steamer had hold of us, we were very busy coiling away ropes and cables, and putting the decks in order; which were littered all over with odds and ends of things that had to be put away.

At last we got as far as the Narrows, which everybody knows is the entrance to New York Harbor from sea; and it may well be called the Narrows, for when you go in or out, it seems like going in or out of a doorway; and when you go out of these Narrows on a long voyage like this of mine, it seems like going out into the broad highway, where not a soul is to be seen. For far away and away, stretches the great Atlantic Ocean; and all you can see beyond it where the sky comes down to the water. It looks lonely and desolate enough, and I could hardly believe, as I gazed around me, that there could be any land beyond, or any place like Europe or England or Liverpool in the great wide world. It seemed too strange, and wonderful, and altogether incredible, that there could really be cities and towns and villages and green fields and hedges and farm-yards and orchards, away over that wide blank of sea, and away beyond the place where the sky came down to the water. And to think of steering right out among those waves, and leaving the bright land behind, and the dark night coming on, too, seemed wild and foolhardy; and I looked with a sort of fear at the sailors standing by me, who could be so thoughtless at such a time. But then I remembered, how many times my own father had said he had crossed the ocean; and I had never dreamed of such a thing as doubting him; for I always thought him a marvelous being, infinitely purer and greater than I was, who could not by any possibility do wrong, or say an untruth. Yet now, how could I credit it, that he, my own father, whom I so well remembered, had ever sailed out of these Narrows, and sailed right through the sky and water line, and gone to England, and France, Liverpool, and Marseilles. It was too wonderful to believe.

Now, on the right hand side of the Narrows as you go out, the land is quite high; and on the top of a fine cliff is a great castle or fort, all in ruins, and with the trees growing round it. It was built by Governor Tompkins in the time of the last war with England, but was never used, I believe, and so they left it to decay. I had visited the place once when we lived in New York, as long ago almost as I could remember, with my father, and an uncle of mine, an old sea-captain, with white hair, who used to sail to a place called Archangel in Russia, and who used to tell me that he was with Captain Langsdorff, when Captain Langsdorff crossed over by land from the sea of Okotsk in Asia to St. Petersburgh, drawn by large dogs in a sled. I mention this of my uncle, because he was the very first sea-captain I had ever seen, and his white hair and fine handsome florid face made so strong an impression upon me, that I have never forgotten him, though I only saw him during this one visit of his to New York, for he was lost in the White Sea some years after.

But I meant to speak about the fort. It was a beautiful place, as I remembered it, and very wonderful and romantic, too, as it appeared to me, when I went there with my uncle. On the side away from the water was a green grove of trees, very thick and shady; and through this grove, in a sort of twilight you came to an arch in the wall of the fort, dark as night; and going in, you groped about in long vaults, twisting and turning on every side, till at last you caught a peep of green grass and sunlight, and all at once came out in an open space in the middle of the castle. And there you would see cows quietly grazing, or ruminating under the shade of young trees, and perhaps a calf frisking about, and trying to catch its own tail; and sheep clambering among the mossy ruins, and cropping the little tufts of grass sprouting out of the sides of the embrasures for cannon. And once I saw a black goat with a long beard, and crumpled horns, standing with his forefeet lifted high up on the topmost parapet, and looking to sea, as if he were watching for a ship that was bringing over his cousin. I can see him even now, and though I have changed since then, the black goat looks just the same as ever; and so I suppose he would, if I live to be as old as Methusaleh, and have as great a memory as he must have had. Yes, the fort was a beautiful, quiet, charming spot. I should like to build a little cottage in the middle of it, and live there all my life. It was noon-day when I was there, in the month of June, and there was little wind to stir the trees, and everything looked as if it was waiting for something, and the sky overhead was blue as my mother's eye, and I was so glad and happy then. But I must not think of those delightful days, before my father became a bankrupt, and died, and we removed from the city; for when I think of those days, something rises up in my throat and almost strangles me.

Now, as we sailed through the Narrows, I caught sight of that beautiful fort on the cliff, and could not help contrasting my situation now, with what it was when with my father and uncle I went there so long ago. Then I never thought of working for my living, and never knew that there were hard hearts in the world; and knew so little of money, that when I bought a stick of candy, and laid down a sixpence, I thought the confectioner returned five cents, only that I might have money to buy something else, and not because the pennies were my change, and therefore mine by good rights. How different my idea of money now!

Then I was a schoolboy, and thought of going to college in time; and had vague thoughts of becoming a great orator like Patrick Henry, whose speeches I used to speak on the stage; but now, I was a poor friendless boy, far away from my home, and voluntarily in the way of becoming a miserable sailor for life. And what made it more bitter to me, was to think of how well off were my cousins, who were happy and rich, and lived at home with my uncles and aunts, with no thought of going to sea for a living. I tried to think that it was all a dream, that I was not where I was, not on board of a ship, but that I was at home again in the city, with my father alive, and my mother bright and happy as she used to be. But it would not do. I was indeed where I was, and here was the ship, and there was the fort. So, after casting a last look at some boys who were standing on the parapet, gazing off to sea, I turned away heavily, and resolved not to look at the land anymore.

About sunset we got fairly "outside," and well may it so be called; for I felt thrust out of the world. Then the breeze began to blow, and the sails were loosed, and hoisted; and after a while, the steam-boat left us, and for the first time I felt the ship roll, a strange feeling enough, as if it were a great barrel in the water. Shortly after, I observed a swift little schooner running across our bows, and re-crossing again and again; and while I was wondering what she could be, she suddenly lowered her sails, and two men took hold of a little boat on her deck, and launched it overboard as if it had been a chip. Then I noticed that our pilot, a red-faced man in a rough blue coat, who to my astonishment had all this time been giving orders instead of the captain; I noticed that he began to button up his coat to the throat, like a prudent person about leaving a house at night in a lonely square, to go home; and he left the giving orders to the chief mate, and stood apart talking with the captain, and put his hand into his pocket, and gave him some newspapers.

And in a few minutes, when we had stopped our headway, and allowed the little boat to come alongside, he shook hands with the captain and officers and bade them good-bye, without saying a syllable of farewell to me and the sailors; and so he went laughing over the side, and got into the boat, and they pulled him off to the schooner, and then the schooner made sail and glided under our stern, her men standing up and waving their hats, and cheering; and that was the last we saw of America.

Chapter VIII

He Is Put into the Larboard Watch; Gets Sea-Sick; and Relates Some Other of His Experiences

It was now getting dark, when all at once the sailors were ordered on the quarter-deck, and of course I went along with them.

What is to come now, thought I; but I soon found out. It seemed we were going to be divided into watches. The chief mate began by selecting a stout good-looking sailor for his watch; and then the second mate's turn came to choose, and he also chose a stout good-looking sailor. But it was not me;—no; and I noticed, as they went on choosing, one after the other in regular rotation, that both of the mates never so much as looked at me, but kept going round among the rest, peering into their faces, for it was dusk, and telling them not to hide themselves away so in their jackets. But the sailors, especially the stout good-looking ones, seemed to make a point of lounging as much out of the way as possible, and slouching their hats over their eyes; and although it may only be a fancy of mine, I certainly thought that they affected a sort of lordly indifference as to whose watch they were going to be in; and did not think it worthwhile to look any way anxious about the matter. And the very men who, a few minutes before, had showed the most alacrity and promptitude in jumping into the rigging and running aloft at the word of command, now lounged against the bulwarks and most lazily; as if they were quite sure, that by this time the officers must know who the best men were, and they valued themselves well enough to be willing to put the officers to the trouble of searching them out; for if they were worth having, they were worth seeking.

At last they were all chosen but me; and it was the chief mate's next turn to choose; though there could be little choosing in my case, since I was a thirteener, and must, whether or no, go over to the next column, like the odd figure you carry along when you do a sum in addition.

"Well, Buttons," said the chief mate, "I thought I'd got rid of you. And as it is, Mr. Rigs," he added, speaking to the second mate, "I guess you had better take him into your watch;—there, I'll let you have him, and then you'll be one stronger than me."

"No, I thank you," said Mr. Rigs.

"You had better," said the chief mate—"see, he's not a bad looking chap—he's a little green, to be sure, but you were so once yourself, you know, Rigs."

"No, I thank you," said the second mate again. "Take him yourself—he's yours by good rights—I don't want him." And so they put me in the chief mate's division, that is the larboard watch.

While this scene was going on, I felt shabby enough; there I stood, just like a silly sheep, over whom two butchers are bargaining. Nothing that had yet happened so forcibly reminded me of where I was, and what I had come to. I was very glad when they sent us forward again.

As we were going forward, the second mate called one of the sailors by name:—"You, Bill?" and Bill answered, "Sir?" just as if the second mate was a born gentleman. It surprised me not a little, to see a man in such a shabby, shaggy old jacket addressed so respectfully; but I had been quite as much surprised when I heard the chief mate call him *Mr.* Rigs during the scene on the quarter-deck; as if this *Mr. Rigs* was a great merchant living in a marble house in Lafayette Place. But I was not very long in finding out, that at sea all officers are *Misters,* and would take it for an insult if any seaman presumed to omit calling them so. And it is also one of their rights and privileges to be called *sir* when addressed—*Yes, sir; No, sir; Ay, ay, sir*; and they are as particular about being sirred as so many knights and baronets; though their titles are not hereditary, as is the case with the Sir Johns and Sir Joshuas in England. But so far as the second mate is concerned, his titles are the only dignities he enjoys; for, upon the whole, he leads a puppyish life indeed. He is not deemed company at anytime for the captain, though the chief mate occasionally is, at least deck-company, though not in the cabin; and besides this, the second mate has to breakfast, lunch, dine, and sup off the leavings of the cabin table, and even the steward, who is accountable to nobody but the captain, sometimes treats him cavalierly; and he has to run aloft when top-sails are reefed; and put his hand a good way down into the tar-bucket; and keep the key of the boatswain's locker, and fetch and carry balls of marline and seizing-stuff for the sailors when at work in the rigging; besides doing many other things, which a true-born baronet of any spirit would rather die and give up his title than stand.

Having been divided into watches we were sent to supper; but I could not eat anything except a little biscuit, though I should have liked to have some good tea; but as I had no pot to get it in, and was rather nervous about asking the rough sailors to let me drink out of theirs; I was obliged to go without a sip. I thought of going to the black cook and begging a tin cup; but he looked so cross and ugly then, that the sight of him almost frightened the idea out of me.

When supper was over, for they never talk about going to *tea* aboard of a ship, the watch to which I belonged was called on deck; and we were told it was for us to stand the first night-watch, that is, from eight o'clock till midnight.

I now began to feel unsettled and ill at ease about the stomach, as if matters were all topsy-turvy there; and felt strange and giddy about the head; and so I made no doubt that this was the beginning of that dreadful thing, the sea-sickness. Feeling worse and worse, I told one of the sailors how it was with me, and begged him to make my excuses very civilly to the chief mate, for I thought I would go below and spend the night in my bunk. But he only laughed at me, and said something about my mother not being aware of my being out; which enraged me not a little, that a man whom I had heard swear so terribly, should dare to take such a holy name into his mouth. It seemed a sort of blasphemy, and it seemed like dragging out the best and most cherished secrets of my soul, for at that time the name of mother was the center of all my heart's finest feelings, which ere that, I had learned to keep secret, deep down in my being.

But I did not outwardly resent the sailor's words, for that would have only made the matter worse.

Now this man was a Greenlander by birth, with a very white skin where the sun had not burned it, and handsome blue eyes placed wide apart in his head, and a broad good-humored face, and plenty of curly flaxen hair. He was not very tall, but exceedingly stout-built, though active; and his back was as broad as a shield, and it was a great way between his shoulders. He seemed to be a sort of lady's sailor, for in his broken English he was always talking about the nice ladies of his acquaintance in Stockholm and Copenhagen and a place he called the Hook, which at first I fancied must be the place where lived the hook-nosed men that caught fowling-pieces and every other article that came along. He was dressed very tastefully, too, as if he knew he was a good-looking fellow. He had on a new blue woolen Havre frock, with a new silk handkerchief round his neck, passed through one of the vertebral bones of a shark, highly polished and carved. His trousers were of clear white duck, and he sported a handsome pair of pumps, and a tarpaulin hat bright as a looking-glass, with a long black ribbon streaming behind, and getting entangled every now and then in the rigging; and he had gold anchors in his ears, and a silver ring on one of his fingers, which was very much worn and bent from pulling ropes and other work on board ship. I thought he might better have left his jewelry at home.

It was a long time before I could believe that this man was really from Greenland, though he looked strange enough to me, then, to have come from the moon; and he was full of stories about that distant country; how they passed the winters there; and how bitter cold it was; and how he used to go to bed and sleep twelve hours, and get up again and run about, and go to bed again, and get up again—there was no telling how many times, and all in one night; for in the winter time in his country, he said, the nights were so many weeks long, that a Greenland baby was sometimes three months old, before it could properly be said to be a day old.

I had seen mention made of such things before, in books of voyages; but that was only reading about them, just as you read the *Arabian Nights*, which no one ever believes; for somehow, when I read about these wonderful countries, I never used really to believe what I read, but only thought it very strange, and a good deal too strange to be altogether true; though I never thought the men who wrote the book meant to tell lies. But I don't know exactly how to explain what I mean; but this much I will say, that I never believed in Greenland till I saw this Greenlander. And at first, hearing him talk about Greenland, only made me still more incredulous. For what business had a man from Greenland to be in my company? Why was he not at home among the icebergs, and how could he stand a warm summer's sun, and not be melted away? Besides, instead of icicles, there were earrings hanging from his ears; and he did not wear bear-skins, and keep his hands in a huge muff; things, which I could not help connecting with Greenland and all Greenlanders.

But I was telling about my being sea-sick and wanting to retire for the night. This Greenlander seeing I was ill, volunteered to turn doctor and cure me; so going down into the forecastle, he came back with a brown jug, like a molasses jug, and a little tin cannikin, and as soon as the brown jug got near my nose, I needed no telling what was in it, for it smelled like a still-house, and sure enough proved to be full of Jamaica spirits.

"Now, Buttons," said he, "one little dose of this will be better for you than a whole night's sleep; there, take that now, and then eat seven or eight biscuits, and you'll feel as strong as the main-mast."

But I felt very little like doing as I was bid, for I had some scruples about drinking spirits; and to tell the plain truth, for I am not ashamed of it, I was a member of a society in the village where my mother lived, called the Juvenile Total Abstinence Association, of which my friend, Tom Legare, was president, secretary, and treasurer, and kept the funds in a little purse that his cousin knit for him. There was three and sixpence on hand, I believe, the last time he brought in his accounts, on a May day, when we had a meeting in a grove on the river-bank. Tom was a very honest treasurer, and never spent the Society's money for peanuts; and besides all, was a fine, generous boy, whom I much loved. But I must not talk about Tom now.

When the Greenlander came to me with his jug of medicine, I thanked him as well as I could; for just then I was leaning with my mouth over the side, feeling ready to die; but I managed to tell him I was under a solemn obligation never to drink spirits upon any consideration whatever; though, as I had a sort of presentiment that the spirits would now, for once in my life, do me good, I began to feel sorry, that when I signed the pledge of abstinence, I had not taken care to insert a little clause, allowing me to drink spirits in case of sea-sickness. And I would advise temperance people to attend to this matter in future; and then if they come to go to sea, there will be no need of breaking their pledges, which I am truly sorry to say was the case with me. And a hard thing it was, too, thus to break a vow before unbroken; especially as the Jamaica tasted anything but agreeable, and indeed burned my mouth so, that I did not relish my meals for some time after. Even when I had become quite well and strong again, I wondered how the sailors could really like such stuff; but many of them had a jug of it, besides the Greenlander, which they brought along to sea with them, *to taper off with*, as they called it. But this tapering off did not last very long, for the Jamaica was all gone on the second day, and the jugs were tossed overboard. I wonder where they are now?

But to tell the truth, I found, in spite of its sharp taste, the spirits I drank was just the thing I needed; but I suppose, if I could have had a cup of nice hot coffee, it would have done quite as well, and perhaps much better. But that was not to be had at that time of night, or, indeed, at any other time; for the thing they called *coffee*, which was given to us every morning at breakfast, was the most curious tasting drink I ever drank, and tasted as little like coffee, as it did like lemonade;

though, to be sure, it was generally as cold as lemonade, and I used to think the cook had an ice-house, and dropped ice into his coffee. But what was more curious still, was the different quality and taste of it on different mornings. Sometimes it tasted fishy, as if it was a decoction of Dutch herrings; and then it would taste very salt, as if some *old horse,* or sea-beef, had been boiled in it; and then again it would taste a sort of cheesy, as if the captain had sent his cheese-parings forward to make our coffee of; and yet another time it would have such a very bad flavor, that I was almost ready to think some old stocking-heels had been boiled in it. What under heaven it was made of, that it had so many different bad flavors, always remained a mystery; for when at work at his vocation, our old cook used to keep himself close shut-up in his caboose, a little cook-house, and never told any of his secrets.

Though a very serious character, as I shall hereafter show, he was for all that, and perhaps for that identical reason, a very suspicious looking sort of a cook, that I don't believe would ever succeed in getting the cooking at Delmonico's in New York. It was well for him that he was a black cook, for I have no doubt his color kept us from seeing his dirty face! I never saw him wash but once, and that was at one of his own soup pots one dark night when he thought no one saw him. What induced him to be washing his face then, I never could find out; but I suppose he must have suddenly waked up, after dreaming about some real estate on his cheeks. As for his coffee, notwithstanding the disagreeableness of its flavor, I always used to have a strange curiosity every morning, to see what new taste it was going to have; and though, sure enough, I never missed making a new discovery, and adding another taste to my palate, I never found that there was any change in the badness of the beverage, which always seemed the same in that respect as before.

It may well be believed, then, that now when I was sea-sick, a cup of such coffee as our old cook made would have done me no good, if indeed it would not have come near making an end of me. And bad as it was, and since it was not to be had at that time of night, as I said before, I think I was excusable in taking something else in place of it, as I did; and under the circumstances, it would be unhandsome of them, if my fellow-members of the Temperance Society should reproach me for breaking my bond, which I would not have done except in case of necessity. But the evil effect of breaking one's bond upon any occasion whatever, was witnessed in the present case; for it insidiously opened the way to subsequent breaches of it, which though very slight, yet carried no apology with them.

Chapter IX

The Sailors Becoming a Little Social, Redburn Converses with Them

The latter part of this first long watch that we stood was very pleasant, so far as the weather was concerned. From being rather cloudy, it became a soft moonlight; and the stars peeped out, plain enough to count one by one; and there was a fine steady breeze; and it was not very cold; and we were going through the water almost as smooth as a sled sliding down hill. And what was still better, the wind held so steady, that there was little running aloft, little pulling ropes, and scarcely anything disagreeable of that kind.

The chief mate kept walking up and down the quarter-deck, with a lighted long-nine cigar in his mouth by way of a torch; and spoke but few words to us the whole watch. He must have had a good deal of thinking to attend to, which in truth is the case with most seamen the first night out of port, especially when they have thrown away their money in foolish dissipation, and got very sick into the bargain. For when ashore, many of these sea-officers are as wild and reckless in their way, as the sailors they command.

While I stood watching the red cigar-end promenading up and down, the mate suddenly stopped and gave an order, and the men sprang to obey it. It was not much, only something about hoisting one of the sails a little higher up on the mast. The men took hold of the rope, and began pulling upon it; the foremost man of all setting up a song with no words to it, only a strange musical rise and fall of notes. In the dark night, and far out upon the lonely sea, it sounded wild enough, and made me feel as I had sometimes felt, when in a twilight room a cousin of mine, with black eyes, used to play some old German airs on the piano. I almost looked round for goblins, and felt just a little bit afraid. But I soon got used to this singing; for the sailors never touched a rope without it. Sometimes, when no one happened to strike up, and the pulling, whatever it might be, did not seem to be getting forward very well, the mate would always say, *"Come, men, can't any of you sing? Sing now, and raise the dead."* And then someone of them would begin, and if every man's arms were as much relieved as mine by the song, and he could pull as much better as I did, with such a cheering accompaniment, I am sure the song was well worth the breath expended on it. It is a great thing in a sailor to know how to sing well, for he gets a great name by it from the officers, and a good deal of popularity among his shipmates. Some sea-captains, before shipping a man, always ask him whether he can sing out at a rope.

During the greater part of the watch, the sailors sat on the windlass and told long stories of their adventures by sea and land, and talked about Gibraltar, and Canton, and Valparaiso, and Bombay, just as you and I would about Peck Slip and the Bowery. Every man of them almost was a volume of *Voyages and Travels round the World.* And what most struck me was that like books of voyages they often contradicted each other, and would fall into long and violent disputes about who was keeping the Foul Anchor tavern in Portsmouth at such a time; or whether the King of Canton lived or did not live in Persia; or whether the bar-maid of a particular house in Hamburg had black eyes or blue eyes; with many other mooted points of that sort.

At last one of them went below and brought up a box of cigars from his chest, for some sailors always provide little delicacies of that kind, to break off the first shock of the salt water after laying idle ashore; and also by way of *tapering off,* as I mentioned a little while ago. But I wondered that they never carried any pies and tarts to sea with them, instead of spirits and cigars.

Ned, for that was the man's name, split open the box with a blow of his fist, and then handed it round along the windlass, just like a waiter at a party, everyone helping himself. But I was a member of an Anti-Smoking Society that had been organized in our village by the Principal of the Sunday School there, in conjunction with the Temperance Association. So I did not smoke any then, though I did afterward upon the voyage, I am sorry to say. Notwithstanding I declined; with a good deal of unnecessary swearing, Ned assured me that the cigars were real genuine Havannas; for he had been in Havanna, he said, and had them made there under his own eye. According to his account, he was very particular about his cigars and other things, and never made any importations, for they were unsafe; but always made a voyage himself direct to the place where any foreign thing was to be had that he wanted. He went to Havre for his woolen shirts, to Panama for his hats, to China for his silk handkerchiefs, and direct to Calcutta for his cheroots; and as a great joker in the watch used to say, no doubt he would at last have occasion to go to Russia for his halter; the wit of which saying was presumed to be in the fact, that the Russian hemp is the best; though that is not wit which needs explaining.

By dint of the spirits which, besides stimulating my fainting strength, united with the cool air of the sea to give me an appetite for our hard biscuit; and also by dint of walking briskly up and down the deck before the windlass, I had now recovered in good part from my sickness, and finding the sailors all very pleasant and sociable, at least among themselves, and seated smoking together like old cronies, and nothing on earth to do but sit the watch out, I began to think that they were a pretty good set of fellows after all, barring their swearing and another ugly way of talking they had; and I thought I had misconceived their true characters; for at the outset I had deemed them such a parcel of wicked hard-hearted rascals that it would be a severe affliction to associate with them.

Yes, I now began to look on them with a sort of incipient love; but more with an eye of pity and compassion, as men of naturally gentle and kind dispositions, whom only hardships, and neglect, and ill-usage had made outcasts from good society; and not as villains who loved wickedness for the sake of it, and would persist in wickedness, even in Paradise, if they ever got there. And I called to mind a sermon I had once heard in a church in behalf of sailors, when the preacher called them strayed lambs from the fold, and compared them to poor lost children, babes in the wood, orphans without fathers or mothers.

And I remembered reading in a magazine, called the *Sailors' Magazine,* with a sea-blue cover, and a ship painted on the back, about pious seamen who never swore, and paid over all their wages to the poor heathen in India; and how that when they were too old to go to sea, these pious old sailors found a delightful home for life in the Hospital, where they had nothing to do, but prepare themselves for their latter end. And I wondered whether there were any such good sailors among my shipmates; and observing that one of them laid on deck apart from the rest, I thought to be sure he must be one of them: so I did not disturb his devotions: but I was afterward shocked at discovering that he was only fast asleep, with one of the brown jugs by his side.

I forgot to mention by the way, that every once in a while, the men went into one corner, where the chief mate could not see them, to take a "swig at the halyards," as they called it; and this swigging at the halyards it was, that enabled them "to taper off" handsomely, and no doubt it was this, too, that had something to do with making them so pleasant and sociable that night, for they were seldom so pleasant and sociable afterward, and never treated me so kindly as they did then. Yet this might have been owing to my being something of a stranger to them, then; and our being just out of port. But that very night they turned about, and taught me a bitter lesson; but all in good time.

I have said, that seeing how agreeable they were getting, and how friendly their manner was, I began to feel a sort of compassion for them, grounded on their sad conditions as amiable outcasts; and feeling so warm an interest in them, and being full of pity, and being truly desirous of benefiting them to the best of my poor powers, for I knew they were but poor indeed, I made bold to ask one of them, whether he was ever in the habit of going to church, when he was ashore, or dropping in at the Floating Chapel I had seen lying off the dock in the East River at New York; and whether he would think it too much of a liberty, if I asked him, if he had any good books in his chest. He stared a little at first, but marking what good language I used, seeing my civil bearing toward him, he seemed for a moment to be filled with a certain involuntary respect for me, and answered, that he had been to church once, some ten or twelve years before, in London, and on a week-day had helped to move the Floating Chapel round the Battery, from the North River; and that was the only time he had seen it. For his books, he said he did not know what I meant by good books; but if I wanted the *Newgate Calendar,* and *Pirate's Own,* he could lend them to me.

When I heard this poor sailor talk in this manner, showing so plainly his ignorance and absence of proper views of religion, I pitied him more and more, and contrasting my own situation with his, I was grateful that I was different from him; and I thought how pleasant it was, to feel wiser and better than he could feel; though I was willing to confess to myself, that it was not altogether my own good endeavors, so much as my education, which I had received from others, that had made me the upright and sensible boy I at that time thought myself to be. And it was now, that I began to feel a good degree of complacency and satisfaction in surveying my own character; for, before this, I had previously associated with persons of a very discreet life, so that there was little opportunity to magnify myself, by comparing myself with my neighbors.

Thinking that my superiority to him in a moral way might sit uneasily upon this sailor, I thought it would soften the matter down by giving him a chance to show his own superiority to me, in a minor thing; for I was far from being vain and conceited.

Having observed that at certain intervals a little bell was rung on the quarter-deck by the man at the wheel; and that as soon as it was heard, someone of the sailors forward struck a large bell which hung on the forecastle; and having observed that how many times soever the man astern rang his bell, the man forward struck his—tit for tat—I inquired of this Floating Chapel sailor, what all this ringing meant; and whether, as the big bell hung right over the scuttle that went down to the place where the watch below were sleeping, such a ringing every little while would not tend to disturb them and beget unpleasant dreams; and in asking these questions I was particular to address him in a civil and condescending way, so as to show him very plainly that I did not deem myself one whit better than he was, that is, taking all things together, and not going into particulars. But to my great surprise and mortification, he in the rudest kind of manner laughed aloud in my face, and called me a "Jimmy Dux," though that was not my real name, and he must have known it; and also the "son of a farmer," though as I have previously related, my father was a great merchant and French importer in Broad-street in New York. And then he began to laugh and joke about me, with the other sailors, till they all got round me, and if I had not felt so terribly angry, I should certainly have felt very much like a fool. But my being so angry prevented me from feeling foolish, which is very lucky for people in a passion.

Chapter X

He Is Very Much Frightened; The Sailors Abuse Him; and He Becomes Miserable and Forlorn

While the scene last described was going on, we were all startled by a horrid groaning noise down in the forecastle; and all at once someone came rushing up the scuttle in his shirt, clutching something in his hand, and trembling and shrieking in the most frightful manner, so that I thought one of the sailors must be murdered below.

But it all passed in a moment; and while we stood aghast at the sight, and almost before we knew what it was, the shrieking man jumped over the bows into the sea, and we saw him no more. Then there was a great uproar; the sailors came running up on deck; and the chief mate ran forward, and learning what had happened, began to yell out his orders about the sails and yards; and we all went to pulling and hauling the ropes, till at last the ship lay almost still on the water. Then they loosed a boat, which kept pulling round the ship for more than an hour, but they never caught sight of the man. It seemed that he was one of the sailors who had been brought aboard dead drunk, and tumbled into his bunk by his landlord; and there he had lain till now. He must have suddenly waked up, I suppose, raging mad with the delirium tremens, as the chief mate called it, and finding himself in a strange silent place, and knowing not how he had got there, he rushed on deck, and so, in a fit of frenzy, put an end to himself.

This event, happening at the dead of night, had a wonderfully solemn and almost awful effect upon me. I would have given the whole world, and the sun and moon, and all the stars in heaven, if they had been mine, had I been safe back at Mr. Jones', or still better, in my home on the Hudson River. I thought it an ill-omened voyage, and railed at the folly which had sent me to sea, sore against the advice of my best friends, that is to say, my mother and sisters.

Alas! poor Wellingborough, thought I, you will never see your home anymore. And in this melancholy mood I went below, when the watch had expired, which happened soon after. But to my terror, I found that the suicide had been occupying the very bunk which I had appropriated to myself, and there was no other place for me to sleep in. The thought of lying down there now, seemed too horrible to me, and what made it worse, was the way in which the sailors spoke of my being frightened. And they took this opportunity to tell me what a hard and wicked life I had entered upon, and how that such things happened frequently at sea, and they were used to it. But I did not believe this; for when the suicide came rushing and shrieking up the scuttle, they looked as frightened as I did; and besides that, and what makes their being frightened still plainer, is the fact, that if they had had any presence of mind, they could have prevented his plunging overboard, since he brushed right by them. However, they lay in their bunks smoking, and kept talking on some time in this strain, and advising me as soon as ever I got home to pin my ears back, so as not to hold the wind, and sail straight away into the interior of the country, and never stop until deep in the bush, far off from the least running brook, never mind how shallow, and out of sight of even the smallest puddle of rainwater.

This kind of talking brought the tears into my eyes, for it was so true and real, and the sailors who spoke it seemed so false-hearted and insincere; but for all that, in spite of the sickness at my heart, it made me mad, and stung me to the quick, that they should speak of me as a poor trembling coward, who could never be brought to endure the hardships of a sailor's life; for I felt myself trembling, and knew that I was but a coward then, well enough, without their telling me of it. And they did not say I was cowardly, because they perceived it in me, but because they merely supposed I must be, judging, no doubt, from their own secret thoughts about themselves; for I felt sure that the suicide frightened them very badly. And at last, being provoked to desperation by their taunts, I told them so to their faces; but I might better have kept silent; for they now all united to abuse me. They asked me what business I, a boy like me, had to go to sea, and take the bread out of the mouth of honest sailors, and fill a good seaman's place; and asked me whether I ever dreamed of becoming a captain, since I was a gentleman with white hands; and if I ever *should* be, they would like nothing better than to ship aboard my vessel and stir up a mutiny. And one of them, whose name was Jackson, of whom I shall have a good deal more to say by and by, said, I had better steer clear of him ever after, for if ever I crossed his path, or got into his way, he would be the death of me, and if ever I stumbled about in the rigging near *him*, he would make nothing of pitching me overboard; and that he swore too, with an oath. At first, all this nearly stunned me, it was so unforeseen; and then I could not believe that they meant what they said, or that they could be so cruel and black-hearted. But how could I help seeing, that the men who could thus talk to a poor, friendless boy, on the very first night of his voyage to sea, must be capable of almost any enormity. I loathed, detested, and hated them with all that was left of my bursting heart and soul, and I thought myself the most forlorn and miserable wretch that ever breathed. May I never be a man, thought I, if to be a boy is to be such a wretch. And I wailed and wept, and my heart cracked within me, but all the time I defied them through my teeth, and dared them to do their worst.

At last they ceased talking and fell fast asleep, leaving me awake, seated on a chest with my face bent over my knees between my hands. And there I sat, till at length the dull beating against the ship's bows, and the silence around soothed me down, and I fell asleep as I sat.

Chapter XI

He Helps Wash the Decks, and Then Goes to Breakfast

The next thing I knew, was the loud thumping of a handspike on deck as the watch was called again. It was now four o'clock in the morning, and when we got on deck the first signs of day were shining in the east. The men were very sleepy, and sat down on the windlass without speaking, and some of them nodded and nodded, till at last they fell off like little boys in church during a drowsy sermon. At last it was broad day, and an order was given to wash down the decks. A great tub was dragged into the waist, and then one of the men went over into the chains, and slipped in behind a band fastened to the shrouds, and leaning over, began to swing a bucket into the sea by a long rope; and in that way with much expertness and sleight of hand, he managed to fill the tub in a very short time. Then the water began to splash about all over the decks, and I began to think I should surely get my feet wet, and catch my death of cold. So I went to the chief mate, and told him I thought I would just step below, till this miserable wetting was over; for I did not have any water-proof boots, and an aunt of mine had died of consumption. But he only roared out for me to get a broom and go to scrubbing, or he would prove a worse consumption to me than ever got hold of my poor aunt. So I scrubbed away fore and aft, till my back was almost broke, for the brooms had uncommon short handles, and we were told to scrub hard.

At length the scrubbing being over, the mate began heaving buckets of water about, to wash everything clean, by way of finishing off. He must have thought this fine sport, just as captains of fire engines love to point the tube of their hose; for he kept me running after him with full buckets of water, and sometimes chased a little chip all over the deck, with a continued flood, till at last he sent it flying out of a scupper-hole into the sea; when if he had only given me permission, I could have picked it up in a trice, and dropped it overboard without saying one word, and without wasting so much water. But he said there was plenty of water in the ocean, and to spare; which was true enough, but then I who had to trot after him with the buckets, had no more legs and arms than I wanted for my own use.

I thought this washing down the decks was the most foolish thing in the world, and besides that it was the most uncomfortable. It was worse than my mother's house-cleanings at home, which I used to abominate so.

At eight o'clock the bell was struck, and we went to breakfast. And now some of the worst of my troubles began. For not having had any friend to tell me what I would want at sea, I had not provided myself, as I should have done, with a good many things that a sailor needs; and for my own part, it had never entered my mind, that sailors had no table to sit down to, no cloth, or napkins, or tumblers, and had to provide every thing themselves. But so it was.

The first thing they did was this. Every sailor went to the cook-house with his tin pot, and got it filled with coffee; but of course, having no pot, there was no coffee for me. And after that, a sort of little tub called a "kid," was passed down into the forecastle, filled with something they called "burgoo." This was like mush, made of Indian corn, meal, and water. With the "kid," a little tin cannikin was passed down with molasses. Then the Jackson that I spoke of before, put the kid between his knees, and began to pour in the molasses, just like an old landlord mixing punch for a party. He scooped out a little hole in the middle of the mush, to hold the molasses; so it looked for all the world like a little black pool in the Dismal Swamp of Virginia.

Then they all formed a circle round the kid; and one after the other, with great regularity, dipped their spoons into the mush, and after stirring them round a little in the molasses-pool, they swallowed down their mouthfuls, and smacked their lips over it, as if it tasted very good; which I have no doubt it did; but not having any spoon, I wasn't sure.

I sat some time watching these proceedings, and wondering how polite they were to each other; for, though there were a great many spoons to only one dish, they never got entangled. At last, seeing that the mush was getting thinner and thinner, and that it was getting low water, or rather low molasses in the little pool, I ran on deck, and after searching about, returned with a bit of stick; and thinking I had as good a right as anyone else to the mush and molasses, I worked my way into the circle, intending to make one of the party. So I shoved in my stick, and after twirling it about, was just managing to carry a little *burgoo* toward my mouth, which had been for some time standing ready open to receive it, when one of the sailors perceiving what I was about, knocked the stick out of my hands, and asked me where I learned my manners; Was that the way gentlemen eat in my country? Did they eat their victuals with splinters of wood, and couldn't that wealthy gentleman my father afford to buy his gentlemanly son a spoon?

All the rest joined in, and pronounced me an ill-bred, coarse, and unmannerly youngster, who, if permitted to go on with such behavior as that, would corrupt the whole crew, and make them no better than swine.

As I felt conscious that a stick was indeed a thing very unsuitable to eat with, I did not say much to this, though it vexed me enough; but remembering that I had seen one of the steerage passengers with a pan and spoon in his hand eating his breakfast on the fore hatch, I now ran on deck again, and to my great joy succeeded in borrowing his spoon, for he had got through his meal, and down I came again, though at the eleventh hour, and offered myself once more as a candidate.

But alas! there was little more of the Dismal Swamp left, and when I reached over to the opposite end of the kid, I received a rap on the knuckles from a spoon, and was told that I must help myself from my own side, for that was the rule. But *my* side was scraped clean, so I got no *burgoo* that morning.

But I made it up by eating some salt beef and biscuit, which I found to be the invariable accompaniment of every meal; the sailors sitting cross-legged on their chests in a circle, and breaking the hard biscuit, very sociably, over each other's heads, which was very convenient indeed, but gave me the headache, at least for the first four or five days till I got used to it; and then I did not care much about it, only it kept my hair full of crumbs; and I had forgot to bring a fine comb and brush, so I used to shake my hair out to windward over the bulwarks every evening.

Chapter XII

He Gives Some Account of One of His Shipmates Called Jackson

While we sat eating our beef and biscuit, two of the men got into a dispute, about who had been sea-faring the longest; when Jackson, who had mixed the *burgoo*, called upon them in a loud voice to cease their clamor, for he would decide the matter for them. Of this sailor, I shall have something more to say, as I get on with my narrative; so, I will here try to describe him a little.

Did you ever see a man, with his hair shaved off, and just recovered from the yellow fever? Well, just such a looking man was this sailor. He was as yellow as gamboge, had no more whisker on his cheek, than I have on my elbows. His hair had fallen out, and left him very bald, except in the nape of his neck, and just behind the ears, where it was stuck over with short little tufts, and looked like a worn-out shoe-brush. His nose had broken down in the middle, and he squinted with one eye, and did not look very straight out of the other. He dressed a good deal like a Bowery boy; for he despised the ordinary sailor-rig; wearing a pair of great over-all blue trousers, fastened with suspenders, and three red woolen shirts, one over the other; for he was subject to the rheumatism, and was not in good health, he said; and he had a large white wool hat, with a broad rolling brim. He was a native of New York city, and had a good deal to say about *highbinders,* and *rowdies,* whom he denounced as only good for the gallows; but I thought he looked a good deal like a *highbinder* himself.

His name, as I have said, was Jackson; and he told us, he was a near relation of General Jackson of New Orleans, and swore terribly, if anyone ventured to question what he asserted on that head. In fact he was a great bully, and being the best seaman on board, and very overbearing every way, all the men were afraid of him, and durst not contradict him, or cross his path in anything. And what made this more wonderful was, that he was the weakest man, bodily, of the whole crew; and I have no doubt that young and small as I was then, compared to what I am now, I could have thrown him down. But he had such an overawing way with him; such a deal of brass and impudence, such an unflinching face, and withal was such a hideous looking mortal, that Satan himself would have run from him. And besides all this, it was quite plain, that he was by nature a marvelously clever, cunning man, though without education; and understood human nature to a kink, and well knew whom he had to deal with; and then, one glance of his squinting eye, was as good as a knock-down, for it was the most deep, subtle, infernal looking eye, that I ever saw lodged in a human head. I believe, that by good rights it must have belonged to a wolf, or starved tiger; at any rate, I would defy any oculist, to turn out a glass eye, half so cold, and snaky, and deadly. It was a horrible thing; and I would give much to forget that I have ever seen it; for it haunts me to this day.

It was impossible to tell how old this Jackson was; for he had no beard, and no wrinkles, except small crowsfeet about the eyes. He might have seen thirty, or perhaps fifty years. But according to his own account, he had been to sea ever since he was eight years old, when he first went as a cabin-boy in an Indiaman, and ran away at Calcutta. And according to his own account, too, he had passed through every kind of dissipation and abandonment in the worst parts of the world. He had served in Portuguese slavers on the coast of Africa; and with a diabolical relish used to tell of the *middle-passage,* where the slaves were stowed, heel and point, like logs, and the suffocated and dead were unmanacled, and weeded out from the living every morning, before washing down the decks; how he had been in a slaving schooner, which being chased by an English cruiser off Cape Verde, received three shots in her hull, which raked through and through a whole file of slaves, that were chained.

He would tell of lying in Batavia during a fever, when his ship lost a man every few days, and how they went reeling ashore with the body, and got still more intoxicated by way of precaution against the plague. He would talk of finding a cobra-di-capello, or hooded snake, under his pillow in India, when he slept ashore there. He would talk of sailors being poisoned at Canton with drugged *"shampoo,"* for the sake of their money; and of the Malay ruffians, who stopped ships in the straits of Gaspar, and always saved the captain for the last, so as to make him point out where the most valuable goods were stored.

His whole talk was of this kind; full of piracies, plagues and poisonings. And often he narrated many passages in his own individual career, which were almost incredible, from the consideration that few men could have plunged into such infamous vices, and clung to them so long, without paying the death-penalty.

But in truth, he carried about with him the traces of these things, and the mark of a fearful end nigh at hand; like that of King Antiochus of Syria, who died a worse death, history says, than if he had been stung out of the world by wasps and hornets.

Nothing was left of this Jackson but the foul lees and dregs of a man; he was thin as a shadow; nothing but skin and bones; and sometimes used to complain, that it hurt him to sit on the hard chests. And I sometimes fancied, it was the consciousness of his miserable, broken-down condition, and the prospect of soon dying like a dog, in consequence of his sins, that made this poor wretch always eye me with such malevolence as he did. For I was young and handsome, at least my mother so thought me, and as soon as I became a little used to the sea, and shook off my low spirits somewhat, I began to have my old color in my cheeks, and, spite of misfortune, to appear well and hearty; whereas *he* was being consumed by an incurable malady, that was eating up his vitals, and was more fit for a hospital than a ship.

As I am sometimes by nature inclined to indulge in unauthorized surmisings about the thoughts going on with regard to me, in the people I meet; especially if I have reason to think they dislike me; I will not put it down for a certainty that what I suspected concerning this Jackson relative to his thoughts of me, was really the truth. But only state my honest opinion, and how it struck me at the time; and even now, I think I was not wrong. And indeed, unless it was so, how could I account to myself, for the shudder that would run through me, when I caught this man gazing at me, as I often did; for he was apt to be dumb at times, and would sit with his eyes fixed, and his teeth set, like a man in the moody madness.

I well remember the first time I saw him, and how I was startled at his eye, which was even then fixed upon me. He was standing at the ship's helm, being the first man that got there, when a steersman was called for by the pilot; for this Jackson was always on the alert for easy duties, and used to plead his delicate health as the reason for assuming them, as he did; though I used to think, that for a man in poor health, he was very swift on the legs; at least when a good place was to be jumped to; though that might only have been a sort of spasmodic exertion under strong inducements, which everyone knows the greatest invalids will sometimes show.

And though the sailors were always very bitter against anything like *sogering*, as they called it; that is, anything that savored of a desire to get rid of downright hard work; yet, I observed that, though this Jackson was a notorious old *soger* the whole voyage (I mean, in all things not perilous to do, from which he was far from hanging back), and in truth was a great veteran that way, and one who must have passed unhurt through many campaigns; yet, they never presumed to call him to account in any way; or to let him so much as think, what they thought of his conduct. But I often heard them call him many hard names behind his back; and sometimes, too, when, perhaps, they had just been tenderly inquiring after his health before his face. They all stood in mortal fear of him; and cringed and fawned about him like so many spaniels; and used to rub his back, after he was undressed and lying in his bunk; and used to run up on deck to the cook-house, to warm some cold coffee for him; and used to fill his pipe, and give him chews of tobacco, and mend his jackets and trousers; and used to watch, and tend, and nurse him every way. And all the time, he would sit scowling on them, and found fault with what they did; and I noticed, that those who did the most for him, and cringed the most before him, were the very ones he most abused; while two or three who held more aloof, he treated with a little consideration.

It is not for me to say, what it was that made a whole ship's company submit so to the whims of one poor miserable man like Jackson. I only know that so it was; but I have no doubt, that if he had had a blue eye in his head, or had had a different face from what he did have, they would not have stood in such awe of him. And it astonished me, to see that one of the seamen, a remarkably robust and good-humored young man from Belfast in Ireland, was a person of no mark or influence among the crew; but on the contrary was hooted at, and trampled upon, and made a butt and laughing-stock; and more than all, was continually being abused and snubbed by Jackson, who seemed to hate him cordially, because of his great strength and fine person, and particularly because of his red cheeks.

But then, this Belfast man, although he had shipped for an *able-seaman,* was not much of a sailor; and that always lowers a man in the eyes of a ship's company; I mean, when he ships for an *able-seaman*, but is not able to do the duty of one. For sailors are of three classes—*able-seaman, ordinary-seaman*, and *boys*; and they receive different wages according to their rank. Generally, a ship's company of twelve men will only have five or six able seamen, who if they prove to understand their duty every way (and that is no small matter either, as I shall hereafter show, perhaps), are looked up to, and thought much of by the ordinary-seamen and boys, who reverence their very pea-jackets, and lay up their sayings in their hearts.

But you must not think from this, that persons called *boys* aboard merchant-ships are all youngsters, though to be sure, I myself was called a *boy*, and a boy I was. No. In merchant-ships, a boy means a green-hand, a landsman on his first voyage. And never mind if he is old enough to be a grandfather, he is still called a *boy*; and boys' work is put upon him.

But I am straying off from what I was going to say about Jackson's putting an end to the dispute between the two sailors in the forecastle after breakfast. After they had been disputing some time about who had been to sea the longest, Jackson told them to stop talking; and then bade one of them open his mouth; for, said he, I can tell a sailor's age just like a horse's—by his teeth. So the man laughed, and opened his mouth; and Jackson made him step out under the scuttle, where the light came down from deck; and then made him throw his head back, while he looked into it, and probed a little with his jack-knife, like a baboon peering into a junk-bottle. I trembled for the poor fellow, just as if I had seen him under the hands of a crazy barber, making signs to cut his throat, and he all the while sitting stock still, with the lather on, to be shaved. For I watched Jackson's eye and saw it snapping, and a sort of going in and out, very quick, as if it were something like a forked tongue; and somehow, I felt as if he were longing to kill the man; but at last he grew more composed, and after concluding his examination, said, that the first man was the oldest sailor, for the ends of his teeth were the evenest and most worn down; which, he said, arose from eating so much hard sea-biscuit; and this was the reason he could tell a sailor's age like a horse's.

At this, everybody made merry, and looked at each other, as much as to say—*come, boys, let's laugh*; and they did laugh; and declared it was a rare joke.

This was always the way with them. They made a point of shouting out, whenever Jackson said anything with a grin; that being the sign to them that he himself thought it funny; though I heard many good jokes from others pass off without a smile; and once Jackson himself (for, to tell the truth, he sometimes had a comical way with him, that is, when his back did not ache) told a truly funny story, but with a grave face; when, not knowing how he meant it, whether for a laugh or otherwise, they all sat still, waiting what to do, and looking perplexed enough; till at last Jackson roared out upon them for a parcel of fools and idiots; and told them to their beards, how it was; that he had purposely put on his grave face, to see whether they would not look grave, too; even when he was telling something that ought to split their sides. And with that, he flouted, and jeered at them, and laughed them all to scorn; and broke out in such a rage, that his lips began to glue together at the corners with a fine white foam.

He seemed to be full of hatred and gall against everything and everybody in the world; as if all the world was one person, and had done him some dreadful harm, that was rankling and festering in his heart. Sometimes I thought he was really crazy; and often felt so frightened at him, that I thought of going to the captain about it, and telling him Jackson ought to be confined, lest he should do some terrible thing at last. But upon second thoughts, I always gave it up; for the captain would only have called me a fool, and sent me forward again.

But you must not think that all the sailors were alike in abasing themselves before this man. No: there were three or four who used to stand up sometimes against him; and when he was absent at the wheel, would plot against him among the other sailors, and tell them what a shame and ignominy it was, that such a poor miserable wretch should be such a tyrant over much better men than himself. And they begged and conjured them as men, to put up with it no longer, but the very next time, that Jackson presumed to play the dictator, that they should all withstand him, and let him know his place. Two or three times nearly all hands agreed to it, with the exception of those who used to slink off during such discussions; and swore that they would not anymore submit to being ruled by Jackson. But when the time came to make good their oaths, they were mum again, and let everything go on the old way; so that those who had put them up to it, had to bear all the brunt of Jackson's wrath by themselves. And though these last would stick up a little at first, and even mutter something about a fight to Jackson; yet in the end, finding themselves unbefriended by the rest, they would gradually become silent, and leave the field to the tyrant, who would then fly out worse than ever, and dare them to do their worst, and jeer at them for white-livered poltroons, who did not have a mouthful of heart in them. At such times, there were no bounds to his contempt; and indeed, all the time he seemed to have even more contempt than hatred, for everybody and everything.

As for me, I was but a boy; and at anytime aboard ship, a boy is expected to keep quiet, do what he is bid, never presume to interfere, and seldom to talk, unless spoken to. For merchant sailors have a great idea of their dignity, and superiority to *greenhorns* and *landsmen*, who know nothing about a ship; and they seem to think, that an *able-seaman* is a great man; at least a much greater man than a little boy. And the *able-seamen* in the *Highlander* had such grand notions about their seamanship, that I almost thought that able seamen received diplomas, like those given at colleges; and were made a sort *A.M.'s, or Masters of Arts.*

But though I kept thus quiet, and had very little to say, and well knew that my best plan was to get along peaceably with everybody, and indeed endure a good deal before showing fight, yet I could not avoid Jackson's evil eye, nor escape his bitter enmity. And his being my foe, set many of the rest against me; or at least they were afraid to speak out for me before Jackson; so that at last I found myself a sort of Ishmael in the ship, without a single friend or companion; and I began to feel a hatred growing up in me against the whole crew—so much so, that I prayed against it, that it might not master my heart completely, and so make a fiend of me, something like Jackson.

Chapter XIII

He Has a Fine Day at Sea, Begins to Like It; But Changes His Mind

The second day out of port, the decks being washed down and breakfast over, the watch was called, and the mate set us to work.

It was a very bright day. The sky and water were both of the same deep hue; and the air felt warm and sunny; so that we threw off our jackets. I could hardly believe that I was sailing in the same ship I had been in during the night, when everything had been so lonely and dim; and I could hardly imagine that this was the same ocean, now so beautiful and blue, that during part of the night-watch had rolled along so black and forbidding.

There were little traces of sunny clouds all over the heavens; and little fleeces of foam all over the sea; and the ship made a strange, musical noise under her bows, as she glided along, with her sails all still. It seemed a pity to go to work at such a time; and if we could only have sat in the windlass again; or if they would have let me go out on the bowsprit, and lay down between the *manropes* there, and look over at the fish in the water, and think of home, I should have been almost happy for a time.

I had now completely got over my sea-sickness, and felt very well; at least in my body, though my heart was far from feeling right; so that I could now look around me, and make observations.

And truly, though we were at sea, there was much to behold and wonder at; to me, who was on my first voyage. What most amazed me was the sight of the great ocean itself, for we were out of sight of land. All round us, on both sides of the ship, ahead and astern, nothing was to be seen but water—water—water; not a single glimpse of green shore, not the smallest island, or speck of moss anywhere. Never did I realize till now what the ocean was: how grand and majestic, how solitary, and boundless, and beautiful and blue; for that day it gave no tokens of squalls or hurricanes, such as I had heard my father tell of; nor could I imagine, how anything that seemed so playful and placid, could be lashed into rage, and troubled into rolling avalanches of foam, and great cascades of waves, such as I saw in the end.

As I looked at it so mild and sunny, I could not help calling to mind my little brother's face, when he was sleeping an infant in the cradle. It had just such a happy, careless, innocent look; and every happy little wave seemed gamboling about like a thoughtless little kid in a pasture; and seemed to look up in your face as it passed, as if it wanted to be patted and caressed. They seemed all live things with hearts in them, that could feel; and I almost felt grieved, as we sailed in among them, scattering them under our broad bows in sun-flakes, and riding over them like a great elephant among lambs.

But what seemed perhaps the most strange to me of all, was a certain wonderful rising and falling of the sea; I do not mean the waves themselves, but a sort of wide heaving and swelling and sinking all over the ocean. It was something I can not very well describe; but I know very well what it was, and how it affected me. It made me almost dizzy to look at it; and yet I could not keep my eyes off it, it seemed so passing strange and wonderful.

I felt as if in a dream all the time; and when I could shut the ship out, almost thought I was in some new, fairy world, and expected to hear myself called to, out of the clear blue air, or from the depths of the deep blue sea. But I did not have much leisure to indulge in such thoughts; for the men were now getting some *stun'-sails* ready to hoist aloft, as the wind was getting fairer and fairer for us; and these stun'-sails are light canvas which are spread at such times, away out beyond the ends of the yards, where they overhang the wide water, like the wings of a great bird.

For my own part, I could do but little to help the rest, not knowing the name of anything, or the proper way to go about aught. Besides, I felt very dreamy, as I said before; and did not exactly know where, or what I was; everything was so strange and new.

While the stun'-sails were lying all tumbled upon the deck, and the sailors were fastening them to the booms, getting them ready to hoist, the mate ordered me to do a great many simple things, none of which could I comprehend, owing to the queer words he used; and then, seeing me stand quite perplexed and confounded, he would roar out at me, and call me all manner of names, and the sailors would laugh and wink to each other, but durst not go farther than that, for fear of the mate, who in his own presence would not let anybody laugh at me but himself.

However, I tried to wake up as much as I could, and keep from dreaming with my eyes open; and being, at bottom, a smart, apt lad, at last I managed to learn a thing or two, so that I did not appear so much like a fool as at first.

People who have never gone to sea for the first time as sailors, can not imagine how puzzling and confounding it is. It must be like going into a barbarous country, where they speak a strange dialect, and dress in strange clothes, and live in strange houses. For sailors have their own names, even for things that are familiar ashore; and if you call a thing by its shore name, you are laughed at for an ignoramus and a land-lubber. This first day I speak of, the mate having ordered me to draw some water, I asked him where I was to get the pail; when I thought I had committed some dreadful crime; for he flew into a great passion, and said they never had any *pails* at sea, and then I learned that they were always called *buckets.* And once I was talking about sticking a little wooden peg into a bucket to stop a leak, when he flew out again, and said there were no *pegs* at sea, only *plugs*. And just so it was with everything else.

But besides all this, there is such an infinite number of totally new names of new things to learn, that at first it seemed impossible for me to master them all. If you have ever seen a ship, you must have remarked what a thicket of ropes there are; and how they all seemed mixed and entangled together like a great skein of yarn. Now the very smallest of these ropes has its own proper name, and many of them are very lengthy, like the names of young royal princes, such as the *starboard-main-top-gallant-bowline*, or the *larboard-fore-top-sail-clew-line*.

I think it would not be a bad plan to have a grand new naming of a ship's ropes, as I have read, they once had a simplifying of the classes of plants in Botany. It is really wonderful how many names there are in the world. There is no counting the names, that surgeons and anatomists give to the various parts of the human body; which, indeed, is something like a ship; its bones being the stiff standing-rigging, and the sinews the small running ropes, that manage all the motions.

I wonder whether mankind could not get along without all these names, which keep increasing everyday, and hour, and moment; till at last the very air will be full of them; and even in a great plain, men will be breathing each other's breath, owing to the vast multitude of words they use, that consume all the air, just as lamp-burners do gas. But people seem to have a great love for names; for to know a great many names, seems to look like knowing a good many things; though I should not be surprised, if there were a great many more names than things in the world. But I must quit this rambling, and return to my story.

At last we hoisted the stun'-sails up to the top-sail yards, and as soon as the vessel felt them, she gave a sort of bound like a horse, and the breeze blowing more and more, she went plunging along, shaking off the foam from her bows, like foam from a bridle-bit. Every mast and timber seemed to have a pulse in it that was beating with life and joy; and I felt a wild exulting in my own heart, and felt as if I would be glad to bound along so round the world.

Then was I first conscious of a wonderful thing in me, that responded to all the wild commotion of the outer world; and went reeling on and on with the planets in their orbits, and was lost in one delirious throb at the center of the All. A wild bubbling and bursting was at my heart, as if a hidden spring had just gushed out there; and my blood ran tingling along my frame, like mountain brooks in spring freshets.

Yes! yes! give me this glorious ocean life, this salt-sea life, this briny, foamy life, when the sea neighs and snorts, and you breathe the very breath that the great whales respire! Let me roll around the globe, let me rock upon the sea; let me race and pant out my life, with an eternal breeze astern, and an endless sea before!

But how soon these raptures abated, when after a brief idle interval, we were again set to work, and I had a vile commission to clean out the chicken-coops, and make up the beds of the pigs in the long-boat.

Miserable dog's life is this of the sea! commanded like a slave, and set to work like an ass! vulgar and brutal men lording it over me, as if I were an African in Alabama. Yes, yes, blow on, ye breezes, and make a speedy end to this abominable voyage!

Chapter XIV

He Contemplates Making a Social Call on the Captain in His Cabin

What reminded me most forcibly of my ignominious condition, was the widely altered manner of the captain toward me. I had thought him a fine, funny gentleman, full of mirth and good humor, and good-will to seamen, and one who could not fail to appreciate the difference between me and the rude sailors among whom I was thrown. Indeed, I had made no doubt that he would in some special manner take me under his protection, and prove a kind friend and benefactor to me; as I had heard that some sea-captains are fathers to their crew; and so they are; but such fathers as Solomon's precepts tend to make—severe and chastising fathers, fathers whose sense of duty overcomes the sense of love, and who everyday, in some sort, play the part of Brutus, who ordered his son away to execution, as I have read in our old family Plutarch.

Yes, I thought that Captain Riga, for Riga was his name, would be attentive and considerate to me, and strive to cheer me up, and comfort me in my lonesomeness. I did not even deem it at all impossible that he would invite me down into the cabin of a pleasant night, to ask me questions concerning my parents, and prospects in life; besides obtaining from me some anecdotes touching my great-uncle, the illustrious senator; or give me a slate and pencil, and teach me problems in navigation; or perhaps engage me at a game of chess. I even thought he might invite me to dinner on a sunny Sunday, and help me plentifully to the nice cabin fare, as knowing how distasteful the salt beef and pork, and hard biscuit of the forecastle must at first be to a boy like me, who had always lived ashore, and at home.

And I could not help regarding him with peculiar emotions, almost of tenderness and love, as the last visible link in the chain of associations which bound me to my home. For, while yet in port, I had seen him and Mr. Jones, my brother's friend, standing together and conversing; so that from the captain to my brother there was but one intermediate step; and my brother and mother and sisters were one.

And this reminds me how often I used to pass by the places on deck, where I remembered Mr. Jones had stood when we first visited the ship lying at the wharf; and how I tried to convince myself that it was indeed true, that he had stood there, though now the ship was so far away on the wide Atlantic Ocean, and he perhaps was walking down Wall-street, or sitting reading the newspaper in his counting room, while poor I was so differently employed.

When two or three days had passed without the captain's speaking to me in any way, or sending word into the forecastle that he wished me to drop into the cabin to pay my respects. I began to think whether I should not make the first advances, and whether indeed he did not expect it of me, since I was but a boy, and he a man; and perhaps that might have been the reason why he had not spoken to me yet, deeming it more proper and respectful for me to address him first. I thought he might be offended, too, especially if he were a proud man, with tender feelings. So one evening, a little before sundown, in the second dog-watch, when there was no more work to be done, I concluded to call and see him.

After drawing a bucket of water, and having a good washing, to get off some of the chicken-coop stains, I went down into the forecastle to dress myself as neatly as I could. I put on a white shirt in place of my red one, and got into a pair of cloth trousers instead of my duck ones, and put on my new pumps, and then carefully brushing my shooting-jacket, I put that on over all, so that upon the whole, I made quite a genteel figure, at least for a forecastle, though I would not have looked so well in a drawing-room.

When the sailors saw me thus employed, they did not know what to make of it, and wanted to know whether I was dressing to go ashore; I told them no, for we were then out of sight of land; but that I was going to pay my respects to the captain. Upon which they all laughed and shouted, as if I were a simpleton; though there seemed nothing so very simple in going to make an evening call upon a friend. When some of them tried to dissuade me, saying I was green and raw; but Jackson, who sat looking on, cried out, with a hideous grin, "Let him go, let him go, men—he's a nice boy. Let him go; the captain has some nuts and raisins for him." And so he was going on, when one of his violent fits of coughing seized him, and he almost choked.

As I was about leaving the forecastle, I happened to look at my hands, and seeing them stained all over of a deep yellow, for that morning the mate had set me to tarring some strips of canvas for the rigging I thought it would never do to present myself before a gentleman that way; so for want of kids, I slipped on a pair of woolen mittens, which my mother had knit for me to carry to sea. As I was putting them on, Jackson asked me whether he shouldn't call a carriage; and another bade me not forget to present his best respects to the skipper. I left them all tittering, and coming on deck was passing the cook-house, when the old cook called after me, saying I had forgot my cane.

But I did not heed their impudence, and was walking straight toward the cabin-door on the quarter-deck, when the chief mate met me. I touched my hat, and was passing him, when, after staring at me till I thought his eyes would burst out, he all at once caught me by the collar, and with a voice of thunder, wanted to know what I meant by playing such tricks aboard a ship that he was mate of? I told him to let go of me, or I would complain to my friend the captain, whom I intended to visit that evening. Upon this he gave me such a whirl round, that I thought the Gulf Stream was in my head; and then shoved me forward, roaring out I know not what. Meanwhile the sailors were all standing round the windlass looking aft, mightily tickled.

Seeing I could not effect my object that night, I thought it best to defer it for the present; and returning among the sailors, Jackson asked me how I had found the captain, and whether the next time I went, I would not take a friend along and introduce him.

The upshot of this business was, that before I went to sleep that night, I felt well satisfied that it was not customary for sailors to call on the captain in the cabin; and I began to have an inkling of the fact, that I had acted like a fool; but it all arose from my ignorance of sea usages.

And here I may as well state, that I never saw the inside of the cabin during the whole interval that elapsed from our sailing till our return to New York; though I often used to get a peep at it through a little pane of glass, set in the house on deck, just before the helm, where a watch was kept hanging for the helmsman to strike the half hours by, with his little bell in the binnacle, where the compass was. And it used to be the great amusement of the sailors to look in through the pane of glass, when they stood at the wheel, and watch the proceedings in the cabin; especially when the steward was setting the table for dinner, or the captain was lounging over a decanter of wine on a little mahogany stand, or playing the game called *solitaire*, at cards, of an evening; for at times he was all alone with his dignity; though, as will ere long be shown, he generally had one pleasant companion, whose society he did not dislike.

The day following my attempt to drop in at the cabin, I happened to be making fast a rope on the quarter-deck, when the captain suddenly made his appearance, promenading up and down, and smoking a cigar. He looked very good-humored and amiable, and it being just after his dinner, I thought that this, to be sure, was just the chance I wanted.

I waited a little while, thinking he would speak to me himself; but as he did not, I went up to him, and began by saying it was a very pleasant day, and hoped he was very well. I never saw a man fly into such a rage; I thought he was going to knock me down; but after standing speechless awhile, he all at once plucked his cap from his head and threw it at me. I don't know what impelled me, but I ran to the lee-scuppers where it fell, picked it up, and gave it to him with a bow; when the mate came running up, and thrust me forward again; and after he had got me as far as the windlass, he wanted to know whether I was crazy or not; for if I was, he would put me in irons right off, and have done with it.

But I assured him I was in my right mind, and knew perfectly well that I had been treated in the most rude and ungentlemanly manner both by him and Captain Riga. Upon this, he rapped out a great oath, and told me if I ever repeated what I had done that evening, or ever again presumed so much as to lift my hat to the captain, he would tie me into the rigging, and keep me there until I learned better manners. "You are very green," said he, "but I'll ripen you." Indeed this chief mate seemed to have the keeping of the dignity of the captain; who, in some sort, seemed too dignified personally to protect his own dignity.

I thought this strange enough, to be reprimanded, and charged with rudeness for an act of common civility. However, seeing how matters stood, I resolved to let the captain alone for the future, particularly as he had shown himself so deficient in the ordinary breeding of a gentleman. And I could hardly credit it, that this was the same man who had been so very civil, and polite, and witty, when Mr. Jones and I called upon him in port.

But this astonishment of mine was much increased, when some days after, a storm came upon us, and the captain rushed out of the cabin in his nightcap, and nothing else but his shirt on; and leaping up on the poop, began to jump up and down, and curse and swear, and call the men aloft all manner of hard names, just like a common loafer in the street.

Besides all this, too, I noticed that while we were at sea, he wore nothing but old shabby clothes, very different from the glossy suit I had seen him in at our first interview, and after that on the steps of the City Hotel, where he always boarded when in New York. Now, he wore nothing but old-fashioned snuff-colored coats, with high collars and short waists; and faded, short-legged pantaloons, very tight about the knees; and vests, that did not conceal his waistbands, owing to their being so short, just like a little boy's. And his hats were all caved in, and battered, as if they had been knocked about in a cellar; and his boots were sadly patched. Indeed, I began to think that he was but a shabby fellow after all; particularly as his whiskers lost their gloss, and he went days together without shaving; and his hair, by a sort of miracle, began to grow of a pepper and salt color, which might have been owing, though, to his discontinuing the use of some kind of dye while at sea. I put him down as a sort of impostor; and while ashore, a gentleman on false pretenses; for no gentleman would have treated another gentleman as he did me.

Yes, Captain Riga, thought I, you are no gentleman, and you know it!

Chapter XV

The Melancholy State of His Wardrobe

And now that I have been speaking of the captain's old clothes, I may as well speak of mine.

It was very early in the month of June that we sailed; and I had greatly rejoiced that it was that time of the year; for it would be warm and pleasant upon the ocean, I thought; and my voyage would be like a summer excursion to the sea shore, for the benefit of the salt water, and a change of scene and society.

So I had not given myself much concern about what I should wear; and deemed it wholly unnecessary to provide myself with a great outfit of pilot-cloth jackets, and trousers, and Guernsey frocks, and oil-skin suits, and sea-boots, and many other things, which old seamen carry in their chests. But one reason was, that I did not have the money to buy them with, even if I had wanted to. So in addition to the clothes I had brought from home, I had only bought a red shirt, a tarpaulin hat, and a belt and knife, as I have previously related, which gave me a sea outfit, something like the Texian rangers', whose uniform, they say, consists of a shirt collar and a pair of spurs.

But I was not many days at sea, when I found that my shore clothing, or *"long togs,"* as the sailors call them, were but ill adapted to the life I now led. When I went aloft, at my yard-arm gymnastics, my pantaloons were all the time ripping and splitting in every direction, particularly about the seat, owing to their not being cut sailor-fashion, with low waistbands, and to wear without suspenders. So that I was often placed in most unpleasant predicaments, straddling the rigging, sometimes in plain sight of the cabin, with my table linen exposed in the most inelegant and ungentlemanly manner possible.

And worse than all, my best pair of pantaloons, and the pair I most prided myself upon, was a very conspicuous and remarkable looking pair.

I had had them made to order by our village tailor, a little fat man, very thin in the legs, and who used to say he imported the latest fashions direct from Paris; though all the fashion plates in his shop were very dirty with fly-marks.

Well, this tailor made the pantaloons I speak of, and while he had them in hand, I used to call and see him two or three times a day to try them on, and hurry him forward; for he was an old man with large round spectacles, and could not see very well, and had no one to help him but a sick wife, with five grandchildren to take care of; and besides that, he was such a great snuff-taker, that it interfered with his business; for he took several pinches for every stitch, and would sit snuffing and blowing his nose over my pantaloons, till I used to get disgusted with him. Now, this old tailor had shown me the pattern, after which he intended to make my pantaloons; but I improved upon it, and bade him have a slit on the outside of each leg, at the foot, to button up with a row of six brass bell buttons; for a grown-up cousin of mine, who was a great sportsman, used to wear a beautiful pair of pantaloons, made precisely in that way.

And these were the very pair I now had at sea; the sailors made a great deal of fun of them, and were all the time calling on each other to *"twig"* them; and they would ask me to lend them a button or two, by way of a joke; and then they would ask me if I was not a soldier. Showing very plainly that they had no idea that my pantaloons were a very genteel pair, made in the height of the sporting fashion, and copied from my cousin's, who was a young man of fortune and drove a tilbury.

When my pantaloons ripped and tore, as I have said, I did my best to mend and patch them; but not being much of a sempstress, the more I patched the more they parted; because I put my patches on, without heeding the joints of the legs, which only irritated my poor pants the more, and put them out of temper.

Nor must I forget my boots, which were almost new when I left home. They had been my Sunday boots, and fitted me to a charm. I never had had a pair of boots that I liked better; I used to turn my toes out when I walked in them, unless it was night time, when no one could see me, and I had something else to think of; and I used to keep looking at them during church; so that I lost a good deal of the sermon. In a word, they were a beautiful pair of boots. But all this only unfitted them the more for sea-service; as I soon discovered. They had very high heels, which were all the time tripping me in the rigging, and several times came near pitching me overboard; and the salt water made them shrink in such a manner, that they pinched me terribly about the instep; and I was obliged to gash them cruelly, which went to my very heart. The legs were quite long, coming a good way up toward my knees, and the edges were mounted with red morocco. The sailors used to call them my *"gaff-top-sail-boots."* And sometimes they used to call me "Boots," and sometimes "Buttons," on account of the ornaments on my pantaloons and shooting-jacket.

At last, I took their advice, and *"razeed"* them, as they phrased it. That is, I amputated the legs, and shaved off the heels to the bare soles; which, however, did not much improve them, for it made my feet feel flat as flounders, and besides, brought me down in the world, and made me slip and slide about the decks, as I used to at home, when I wore straps on the ice.

As for my tarpaulin hat, it was a very cheap one; and therefore proved a real sham and shave; it leaked like an old shingle roof; and in a rain-storm, kept my hair wet and disagreeable. Besides, from lying down on deck in it, during the night-watches, it got bruised and battered, and lost all its beauty; so that it was unprofitable every way.

But I had almost forgotten my shooting-jacket, which was made of moleskin. Everyday, it grew smaller and smaller, particularly after a rain, until at last I thought it would completely exhale, and leave nothing but the bare seams, by way of a skeleton, on my back. It became unspeakably unpleasant, when we got into rather cold weather, crossing the Banks of Newfoundland, when the only way I had to keep warm during the night, was to pull on my waistcoat and my roundabout, and then clap the shooting-jacket over all. This made it pinch me under the arms, and it vexed, irritated, and tormented me every way; and used to incommode my arms seriously when I was pulling the ropes; so much so, that the mate asked me once if I had the cramp.

I may as well here glance at some trials and tribulations of a similar kind. I had no mattress, or bed-clothes, of any sort; for the thought of them had never entered my mind before going to sea; so that I was obliged to sleep on the bare boards of my bunk; and when the ship pitched violently, and almost stood upon end, I must have looked like an Indian baby tied to a plank, and hung up against a tree like a crucifix.

I have already mentioned my total want of table-tools; never dreaming, that, in this respect, going to sea as a sailor was something like going to a boarding-school, where you must furnish your own spoon and knife, fork, and napkin. But at length, I was so happy as to barter with a steerage passenger a silk handkerchief of mine for a half-gallon iron pot, with hooks to it, to hang on a grate; and this pot I used to present at the cook-house for my allowance of coffee and tea. It gave me a good deal of trouble, though, to keep it clean, being much disposed to rust; and the hooks sometimes scratched my face when I was drinking; and it was unusually large and heavy; so that my breakfasts were deprived of all ease and satisfaction, and became a toil and a labor to me. And I was forced to use the same pot for my bean-soup, three times a week, which imparted to it a bad flavor for coffee.

I can not tell how I really suffered in many ways for my improvidence and heedlessness, in going to sea so ill provided with everything calculated to make my situation at all comfortable, or even tolerable. In time, my wretched "long togs" began to drop off my back, and I looked like a Sam Patch, shambling round the deck in my rags and the wreck of my gaff-top-sail-boots. I often thought what my friends at home would have said, if they could but get one peep at me. But I hugged myself in my miserable shooting-jacket, when I considered that that degradation and shame never could overtake me; yet, I thought it a galling mockery, when I remembered that my sisters had promised to tell all inquiring friends, that Wellingborough had gone *"abroad"*; just as if I was visiting Europe on a tour with my tutor, as poor simple Mr. Jones had hinted to the captain.

Still, in spite of the melancholy which sometimes overtook me, there were several little incidents that made me forget myself in the contemplation of the strange and to me most wonderful sights of the sea.

And perhaps nothing struck into me such a feeling of wild romance, as a view of the first vessel we spoke. It was of a clear sunny afternoon, and she came bearing down upon us, a most beautiful sight, with all her sails spread wide. She came very near, and passed under our stern; and as she leaned over to the breeze, showed her decks fore and aft; and I saw the strange sailors grouped upon the forecastle, and the cook looking out of his cook-house with a ladle in his hand, and the captain in a green jacket sitting on the taffrail with a speaking-trumpet.

And here, had this vessel come out of the infinite blue ocean, with all these human beings on board, and the smoke tranquilly mounting up into the sea-air from the cook's funnel as if it were a chimney in a city; and everything looking so cool, and calm, and of course, in the midst of what to me, at least, seemed a superlative marvel.

Hoisted at her mizzen-peak was a red flag, with a turreted white castle in the middle, which looked foreign enough, and made me stare all the harder.

Our captain, who had put on another hat and coat, and was lounging in an elegant attitude on the poop, now put his high polished brass trumpet to his mouth, and said in a very rude voice for conversation, *"Where from?"*

To which the other captain rejoined with some outlandish Dutch gibberish, of which we could only make out, that the ship belonged to Hamburg, as her flag denoted.

Hamburg! Bless my soul! and here I am on the great Atlantic Ocean, actually beholding a ship from Holland! It was passing strange. In my intervals of leisure from other duties, I followed the strange ship till she was quite a little speck in the distance.

I could not but be struck with the manner of the two sea-captains during their brief interview. Seated at their ease on their respective "poops" toward the stern of their ships, while the sailors were obeying their behests; they touched hats to each other, exchanged compliments, and drove on, with all the indifference of two Arab horsemen accosting each other on an airing in the Desert. To them, I suppose, the great Atlantic Ocean was a puddle.

Chapter XVI

At Dead of Night He Is Sent Up to Loose the Main-Skysail

I must now run back a little, and tell of my first going aloft at sea.

It happened on the second night out of port, during the middle watch, when the sea was quite calm, and the breeze was mild.

The order was given to loose the *main-skysail,* which is the fifth and highest sail from deck. It was a very small sail, and from the forecastle looked no bigger than a cambric pocket-handkerchief. But I have heard that some ships carry still smaller sails, above the skysail; called *moon-sails,* and *skys-crapers,* and *cloud-rakers.* But I shall not believe in them till I see them; a *skysail* seems high enough in all conscience; and the idea of anything higher than that, seems preposterous. Besides, it looks almost like tempting heaven, to brush the very firmament so, and almost put the eyes of the stars out; when a flaw of wind, too, might very soon take the conceit out of these cloud-defying *cloud-rakers.*

Now, when the order was passed to loose the skysail, an old Dutch sailor came up to me, and said, "Buttons, my boy, it's high time you be doing something; and it's boy's business, Buttons, to loose de royals, and not old men's business, like me. Now, d'ye see dat leelle fellow way up dare? *dare,* just behind dem stars dare: well, tumble up, now, Buttons, I zay, and looze him; way you go, Buttons."

All the rest joining in, and seeming unanimous in the opinion, that it was high time for me to be stirring myself, and doing *boy's business,* as they called it, I made no more ado, but jumped into the rigging. Up I went, not daring to look down, but keeping my eyes glued, as it were, to the shrouds, as I ascended.

It was a long road up those stairs, and I began to pant and breathe hard, before I was half-way.

But I kept at it till I got to the *Jacob's Ladder*; and they may well call it so, for it took me almost into the clouds; and at last, to my own amazement, I found myself hanging on the skysail-yard, holding on might and main to the mast; and curling my feet round the rigging, as if they were another pair of hands.

For a few moments I stood awe-stricken and mute. I could not see far out upon the ocean, owing to the darkness of the night; and from my lofty perch, the sea looked like a great, black gulf, hemmed in, all round, by beetling black cliffs. I seemed all alone; treading the midnight clouds; and every second, expected to find myself falling—falling—falling, as I have felt when the nightmare has been on me.

I could but just perceive the ship below me, like a long narrow plank in the water; and it did not seem to belong at all to the yard, over which I was hanging. A gull, or some sort of sea-fowl, was flying round the truck over my head, within a few yards of my face; and it almost frightened me to hear it; it seemed so much like a spirit, at such a lofty and solitary height.

Though there was a pretty smooth sea, and little wind; yet, at this extreme elevation, the ship's motion was very great; so that when the ship rolled one way, I felt something as a fly must feel, walking the ceiling; and when it rolled the other way, I felt as if I was hanging along a slanting pine-tree.

But presently I heard a distant, hoarse noise from below; and though I could not make out anything intelligible, I knew it was the mate hurrying me. So in a nervous, trembling desperation, I went to casting off the *gaskets,* or lines tying up the sail; and when all was ready, sung out as I had been told, to *"hoist away!"* And hoist they did, and me too along with the yard and sail; for I had no time to get off, they were so unexpectedly quick about it. It seemed like magic; there I was, going up higher and higher; the yard rising under me, as if it were alive, and no soul in sight. Without knowing it at the time, I was in a good deal of danger, but it was so dark that I could not see well enough to feel afraid—at least on that account; though I felt frightened enough in a promiscuous way. I only held on hard, and made good the saying of old sailors, that the last person to fall overboard from the rigging is a landsman, because he grips the ropes so fiercely; whereas old tars are less careful, and sometimes pay the penalty.

After this feat, I got down rapidly on deck, and received something like a compliment from Max the Dutchman.

This man was perhaps the best natured man among the crew; at any rate, he treated me better than the rest did; and for that reason he deserves some mention.

Max was an old bachelor of a sailor, very precise about his wardrobe, and prided himself greatly upon his seamanship, and entertained some straight-laced, old-fashioned notions about the duties of boys at sea. His hair, whiskers, and cheeks were of a fiery red; and as he wore a red shirt, he was altogether the most combustible looking man I ever saw.

Nor did his appearance belie him; for his temper was very inflammable; and at a word, he would explode in a shower of hard words and imprecations. It was Max that several times set on foot those conspiracies against Jackson, which I have spoken of before; but he ended by paying him a grumbling homage, full of resentful reservations.

Max sometimes manifested some little interest in my welfare; and often discoursed concerning the sorry figure I would cut in my tatters when we got to Liverpool, and the discredit it would bring on the American Merchant Service; for like all European seamen in American ships, Max prided himself not a little upon his naturalization as a Yankee, and if he could, would have been very glad to have passed himself off for a born native.

But notwithstanding his grief at the prospect of my reflecting discredit upon his adopted country, he never offered to better my wardrobe, by loaning me anything from his own well-stored chest. Like many other well-wishers, he contented him with sympathy. Max also betrayed some anxiety to know whether I knew how to dance; lest, when the ship's company went ashore, I should disgrace them by exposing my awkwardness in some of the sailor saloons. But I relieved his anxiety on that head.

He was a great scold, and fault-finder, and often took me to task about my short-comings; but herein, he was not alone; for everyone had a finger, or a thumb, and sometimes both hands, in my unfortunate pie.

Chapter XVII

The Cook and Steward

It was on a Sunday we made the banks of Newfoundland; a drizzling, foggy, clammy Sunday. You could hardly see the water, owing to the mist and vapor upon it; and everything was so flat and calm, I almost thought we must have somehow got back to New York, and were lying at the foot of Wall-street again in a rainy twilight. The decks were dripping with wet, so that in the dense fog, it seemed as if we were standing on the roof of a house in a shower.

It was a most miserable Sunday; and several of the sailors had twinges of the rheumatism, and pulled on their monkey-jackets. As for Jackson, he was all the time rubbing his back and snarling like a dog.

I tried to recall all my pleasant, sunny Sundays ashore; and tried to imagine what they were doing at home; and whether our old family friend, Mr. Bridenstoke, would drop in, with his silver-mounted tasseled cane, between churches, as he used to; and whether he would inquire about myself.

But it would not do. I could hardly realize that it was Sunday at all. Everything went on pretty much the same as before. There was no church to go to; no place to take a walk in; no friend to call upon. I began to think it must be a sort of second Saturday; a foggy Saturday, when school-boys stay at home reading *Robinson Crusoe*.

The only man who seemed to be taking his ease that day, was our black cook; who according to the invariable custom at sea, always went by the name of *the doctor.*

And *doctors,* cooks certainly are, the very best medicos in the world; for what pestilent pills and potions of the Faculty are half so serviceable to man, and health-and-strength-giving, as roasted lamb and green peas, say, in spring; and roast beef and cranberry sauce in winter? Will a dose of calomel and jalap do you as much good? Will a bolus build up a fainting man? Is there any satisfaction in dining off a powder? But these doctors of the frying-pan sometimes kill men off by a surfeit; or give them the headache, at least. Well, what then? No matter. For if with their most goodly and ten times jolly medicines, they now and then fill our nights with tribulations, and abridge our days, what of the social homicides perpetrated by the Faculty? And when you die by a pill-doctor's hands, it is never with a sweet relish in your mouth, as though you died by a frying-pan-doctor; but your last breath villainously savors of ipecac and rhubarb. Then, what charges they make for the abominable lunches they serve out so stingily! One of their bills for boluses would keep you in good dinners a twelvemonth.

Now, our doctor was a serious old fellow, much given to metaphysics, and used to talk about original sin. All that Sunday morning, he sat over his boiling pots, reading out of a book which was very much soiled and covered with grease spots: for he kept it stuck into a little leather strap, nailed to the keg where he kept the fat skimmed off the water in which the salt beef was cooked. I could hardly believe my eyes when I found this book was the Bible.

I loved to peep in upon him, when he was thus absorbed; for his smoky studio or study was a strange-looking place enough; not more than five feet square, and about as many high; a mere box to hold the stove, the pipe of which stuck out of the roof.

Within, it was hung round with pots and pans; and on one side was a little looking-glass, where he used to shave; and on a small shelf were his shaving tools, and a comb and brush. Fronting the stove, and very close to it, was a sort of narrow shelf, where he used to sit with his legs spread out very wide, to keep them from scorching; and there, with his book in one hand, and a pewter spoon in the other, he sat all that Sunday morning, stirring up his pots, and studying away at the same time; seldom taking his eye off the page. Reading must have been very hard work for him; for he muttered to himself quite loud as he read; and big drops of sweat would stand upon his brow, and roll off, till they hissed on the hot stove before him.

But on the day I speak of, it was no wonder that he got perplexed, for he was reading a mysterious passage in the *Book of Chronicles*. Being aware that I knew how to read, he called me as I was passing his premises, and read the passage over, demanding an explanation. I told him it was a mystery that no one could explain; not even a parson. But this did not satisfy him, and I left him poring over it still.

He must have been a member of one of those negro churches, which are to be found in New York. For when we lay at the wharf, I remembered that a committee of three reverend looking old darkies, who, besides their natural canonicals, wore quaker-cut black coats, and broad-brimmed black hats, and white neck-cloths; these colored gentlemen called upon him, and remained conversing with him at his cook-house door for more than an hour; and before they went away they stepped inside, and the sliding doors were closed; and then we heard someone reading aloud and preaching; and after that a psalm was sung and a benediction given; when the door opened again, and the congregation came out in a great perspiration; owing, I suppose, to the chapel being so small, and there being only one seat besides the stove.

But notwithstanding his religious studies and meditations, this old fellow used to use some bad language occasionally; particularly of cold, wet stormy mornings, when he had to get up before daylight and make his fire; with the sea breaking over the bows, and now and then dashing into his stove.

So, under the circumstances, you could not blame him much, if he did rip a little, for it would have tried old Job's temper, to be set to work making a fire in the water.

Without being at all neat about his premises, this old cook was very particular about them; he had a warm love and affection for his cook-house. In fair weather, he spread the skirt of an old jacket before the door, by way of a mat; and screwed a small ring-bolt into the door for a knocker; and wrote his name, "Mr. Thompson," over it, with a bit of red chalk.

The men said he lived round the corner of *Forecastle-square*, opposite the *Liberty Pole*; because his cook-house was right behind the fore-mast, and very near the quarters occupied by themselves.

Sailors have a great fancy for naming things that way on shipboard. When a man is hung at sea, which is always done from one of the lower yard-arms, they say he *"takes a walk up Ladder-lane, and down Hemp-street."*

Mr. Thompson was a great crony of the steward's, who, being a handsome, dandy mulatto, that had once been a barber in West-Broadway, went by the name of Lavender. I have mentioned the gorgeous turban he wore when Mr. Jones and I visited the captain in the cabin. He never wore that turban at sea, though; but sported an uncommon head of frizzled hair, just like the large, round brush, used for washing windows, called a *Pope's Head*.

He kept it well perfumed with Cologne water, of which he had a large supply, the relics of his West-Broadway stock in trade. His clothes, being mostly cast-off suits of the captain of a London liner, whom he had sailed with upon many previous voyages, were all in the height of the exploded fashions, and of every kind of color and cut. He had claret-colored suits, and snuff-colored suits, and red velvet vests, and buff and brimstone pantaloons, and several full suits of black, which, with his dark-colored face, made him look quite clerical; like a serious young colored gentleman of Barbadoes, about to take orders.

He wore an uncommon large pursy ring on his forefinger, with something he called a real diamond in it; though it was very dim, and looked more like a glass eye than anything else. He was very proud of his ring, and was always calling your attention to something, and pointing at it with his ornamented finger.

He was a sentimental sort of a darky, and read the *Three Spaniards*, and *Charlotte Temple*, and carried a lock of frizzled hair in his vest pocket, which he frequently volunteered to show to people, with his handkerchief to his eyes.

Every fine evening, about sunset, these two, the cook and steward, used to sit on the little shelf in the cook-house, leaning up against each other like the Siamese twins, to keep from falling off, for the shelf was very short; and there they would stay till after dark, smoking their pipes, and gossiping about the events that had happened during the day in the cabin.

And sometimes Mr. Thompson would take down his Bible, and read a chapter for the edification of Lavender, whom he knew to be a sad profligate and gay deceiver ashore; addicted to every youthful indiscretion. He would read over to him the story of Joseph and Potiphar's wife; and hold Joseph up to him as a young man of excellent principles, whom he ought to imitate, and not be guilty of his indiscretion anymore. And Lavender would look serious, and say that he knew it was all true—he was a wicked youth, he knew it—he had broken a good many hearts, and many eyes were weeping for him even then, both in New York, and Liverpool, and London, and Havre. But how could he help it? He hadn't made his handsome face, and fine head of hair, and graceful figure. It was not *he*, but the others, that were to blame; for his bewitching person turned all heads and subdued all hearts, wherever he went. And then he would look very serious and penitent, and go up to the little glass, and pass his hands through his hair, and see how his whiskers were coming on.

Chapter XVIII

He Endeavors to Improve His Mind; and Tells of One Blunt and His Dream-Book

On the Sunday afternoon I spoke of, it was my watch below, and I thought I would spend it profitably, in improving my mind.

My bunk was an upper one; and right over the head of it was a *bull's-eye*, or circular piece of thick ground glass, inserted into the deck to give light. It was a dull, dubious light, though; and I often found myself looking up anxiously to see whether the bull's-eye had not suddenly been put out; for whenever anyone trod on it, in walking the deck, it was momentarily quenched; and what was still worse, sometimes a coil of rope would be thrown down on it, and stay there till I dressed myself and went up to remove it—a kind of interruption to my studies which annoyed me very much, when diligently occupied in reading.

However, I was glad of any light at all, down in that gloomy hole, where we burrowed like rabbits in a warren; and it was the happiest time I had, when all my messmates were asleep, and I could lie on my back, during a forenoon watch below, and read in comparative quiet and seclusion.

I had already read two books loaned to me by Max, to whose share they had fallen, in dividing the effects of the sailor who had jumped overboard. One was an account of *Shipwrecks and Disasters at Sea,* and the other was a large black volume, with *Delirium Tremens* in great gilt letters on the back. This proved to be a popular treatise on the subject of that disease; and I remembered seeing several copies in the sailor book-stalls about Fulton Market, and along South-street, in New York.

But this Sunday I got out a book, from which I expected to reap great profit and sound instruction. It had been presented to me by Mr. Jones, who had quite a library, and took down this book from a top shelf, where it lay very dusty. When he gave it to me, he said, that although I was going to sea, I must not forget the importance of a good education; and that there was hardly any situation in life, however humble and depressed, or dark and gloomy, but one might find leisure in it to store his mind, and build himself up in the exact sciences. And he added, that though it *did* look rather unfavorable for my future prospects, to be going to sea as a common sailor so early in life; yet, it would no doubt turn out for my benefit in the end; and, at any rate, if I would only take good care of myself, would give me a sound constitution, if nothing more; and *that* was not to be undervalued, for how many very rich men would give all their bonds and mortgages for my boyish robustness.

He added, that I need not expect any light, trivial work, that was merely entertaining, and nothing more; but here I would find entertainment and edification beautifully and harmoniously combined; and though, at first, I might possibly find it dull, yet, if I perused the book thoroughly, it would soon discover hidden charms and unforeseen attractions; besides teaching me, perhaps, the true way to retrieve the poverty of my family, and again make them all well-to-do in the world.

Saying this, he handed it to me, and I blew the dust off, and looked at the back: Smith's *Wealth of Nations.* This not satisfying me, I glanced at the title page, and found it was an *"Enquiry into the Nature and Causes"* of the alleged wealth of nations. But happening to look further down, I caught sight of *"Aberdeen,"* where the book was printed; and thinking that anything from Scotland, a foreign country, must prove some way or other pleasing to me, I thanked Mr. Jones very kindly, and promised to peruse the volume carefully.

So, now, lying in my bunk, I began the book methodically, at page number one, resolved not to permit a few flying glimpses into it, taken previously, to prevent me from making regular approaches to the gist and body of the book, where I fancied lay something like the philosopher's stone, a secret talisman, which would transmute even pitch and tar to silver and gold.

Pleasant, though vague visions of future opulence floated before me, as I commenced the first chapter, entitled *"Of the causes of improvement in the productive power of labor."* Dry as crackers and cheese, to be sure; and the chapter itself was not much better. But this was only getting initiated; and if I read on, the grand secret would be opened to me. So I read on and on, about *"wages and profits of labor,"* without getting any profits myself for my pains in perusing it.

Dryer and dryer; the very leaves smelled of saw-dust; till at last I drank some water, and went at it again. But soon I had to give it up for lost work; and thought that the old backgammon board, we had at home, lettered on the back, *"The History of Rome"* was quite as full of matter, and a great deal more entertaining. I wondered whether Mr. Jones had ever read the volume himself; and could not help remembering, that he had to get on a chair when he reached it down from its dusty shelf; *that* certainly looked suspicious.

The best reading was on the fly leaves; and, on turning them over, I lighted upon some half effaced pencil-marks to the following effect: *"Jonathan Jones, from his particular friend Daniel Dods,* 1798." So it must have originally belonged to Mr. Jones' father; and I wondered whether *he* had ever read it; or, indeed, whether anybody had ever read it, even the author himself; but then authors, they say, never read their own books; writing them, being enough in all conscience.

At length I fell asleep, with the volume in my hand; and never slept so sound before; after that, I used to wrap my jacket round it, and use it for a pillow; for which purpose it answered very well; only I sometimes waked up feeling dull and stupid; but of course the book could not have been the cause of that.

And now I am talking of books, I must tell of Jack Blunt the sailor, and his Dream Book.

Jackson, who seemed to know everything about all parts of the world, used to tell Jack in reproach, that he was an *Irish Cockney*. By which I understood, that he was an Irishman born, but had graduated in London, somewhere about Radcliffe Highway; but he had no sort of brogue that I could hear.

He was a curious looking fellow, about twenty-five years old, as I should judge; but to look at his back, you would have taken him for a little old man. His arms and legs were very large, round, short, and stumpy; so that when he had on his great monkey-jacket, and sou'west cap flapping in his face, and his sea boots drawn up to his knees, he looked like a fat porpoise, standing on end. He had a round face, too, like a walrus; and with about the same expression, half human and half indescribable. He was, upon the whole, a good-natured fellow, and a little given to looking at sea-life romantically; singing songs about susceptible mermaids who fell in love with handsome young oyster boys and gallant fishermen. And he had a sad story about a man-of-war's-man who broke his heart at Portsmouth during the late war, and threw away his life recklessly at one of the quarter-deck caronades, in the battle between the *Guerriere* and *Constitution*; and another incomprehensible story about a sort of fairy sea-queen, who used to be dunning a sea-captain all the time for his autograph to boil in some eel soup, for a spell against the scurvy.

He believed in all kinds of witch-work and magic; and had some wild Irish words he used to mutter over during a calm for a fair wind.

And he frequently related his interviews in Liverpool with a fortune-teller, an old negro woman by the name of De Squak, whose house was much frequented by sailors; and how she had two black cats, with remarkably green eyes, and nightcaps on their heads, solemnly seated on a claw-footed table near the old goblin; when she felt his pulse, to tell what was going to befall him.

This Blunt had a large head of hair, very thick and bushy; but from some cause or other, it was rapidly turning gray; and in its transition state made him look as if he wore a shako of badger skin.

The phenomenon of gray hairs on a young head, had perplexed and confounded this Blunt to such a degree that he at last came to the conclusion it must be the result of the black art, wrought upon him by an enemy; and that enemy, he opined, was an old sailor landlord in Marseilles, whom he had once seriously offended, by knocking him down in a fray.

So while in New York, finding his hair growing grayer and grayer, and all his friends, the ladies and others, laughing at him, and calling him an old man with one foot in the grave, he slipped out one night to an apothecary's, stated his case, and wanted to know what could be done for him.

The apothecary immediately gave him a pint bottle of something he called "*Trafalgar Oil* for restoring the hair," *price one dollar*; and told him that after he had used that bottle, and it did not have the desired effect, he must try bottle No. 2, called *"Balm of Paradise, or the Elixir of the Battle of Copenhagen."* These high-sounding naval names delighted Blunt, and he had no doubt there must be virtue in them.

I saw both bottles; and on one of them was an engraving, representing a young man, presumed to be gray-headed, standing in his night-dress in the middle of his chamber, and with closed eyes applying the Elixir to his head, with both hands; while on the bed adjacent stood a large bottle, conspicuously labeled, *"Balm of Paradise."* It seemed from the text, that this gray-headed young man was so smitten with his hair-oil, and was so thoroughly persuaded of its virtues, that he had got out of bed, even in his sleep; groped into his closet, seized the precious bottle, applied its contents, and then to bed again, getting up in the morning without knowing anything about it. Which, indeed, was a most mysterious occurrence; and it was still more mysterious, how the engraver came to know an event, of which the actor himself was ignorant, and where there were no bystanders.

Three times in the twenty-four hours, Blunt, while at sea, regularly rubbed in his liniments; but though the first bottle was soon exhausted by his copious applications, and the second half gone, he still stuck to it, that by the time we got to Liverpool, his exertions would be crowned with success. And he was not a little delighted, that this gradual change would be operating while we were at sea; so as not to expose him to the invidious observations of people ashore; on the same principle that dandies go into the country when they purpose raising whiskers. He would often ask his shipmates, whether they noticed any change yet; and if so, how much of a change? And to tell the truth, there was a very great change indeed; for the constant soaking of his hair with oil, operating in conjunction with the neglect of his toilette, and want of a brush and comb, had matted his locks together like a wild horse's mane, and imparted to it a blackish and extremely glossy hue.

Besides his collection of hair-oils, Blunt had also provided himself with several boxes of pills, which he had purchased from a sailor doctor in New York, who by placards stuck on the posts along the wharves, advertised to remain standing at the north-east corner of Catharine Market, every Monday and Friday, between the hours of ten and twelve in the morning, to receive calls from patients, distribute medicines, and give advice gratis.

Whether Blunt thought he had the dyspepsia or not, I can not say; but at breakfast, he always took three pills with his coffee; something as they do in Iowa, when the bilious fever prevails; where, at the boarding-houses, they put a vial of blue pills into the castor, along with the pepper and mustard, and next door to another vial of toothpicks. But they are very ill-bred and unpolished in the western country.

Several times, too, Blunt treated himself to a flowing bumper of *horse salts* (Glauber salts); for like many other seamen, he never went to sea without a good supply of that luxury. He would frequently, also, take this medicine in a wet jacket, and then go on deck into a rain-storm. But this is nothing to other sailors, who at sea will doctor themselves with calomel off Cape Horn, and still remain on duty. And in this connection, some really frightful stories might be told; but I forbear.

For a landsman to take salts as this Blunt did, it would perhaps be the death of him; but at sea the salt air and the salt water prevent you from catching cold so readily as on land; and for my own part, on board this very ship, being so illy-provided with clothes, I frequently turned into my bunk soaking wet, and turned out again piping hot, and smoking like a roasted sirloin; and yet was never the worse for it; for then, I bore a charmed life of youth and health, and was dagger-proof to bodily ill.

But it is time to tell of the Dream Book. Snugly hidden in one corner of his chest, Blunt had an extraordinary looking pamphlet, with a red cover, marked all over with astrological signs and ciphers, and purporting to be a full and complete treatise on the art of Divination; so that the most simple sailor could teach it to himself.

It also purported to be the selfsame system, by aid of which Napoleon Bonaparte had risen in the world from being a corporal to an emperor. Hence it was entitled the *Bonaparte Dream Book*; for the magic of it lay in the interpretation of dreams, and their application to the foreseeing of future events; so that all preparatory measures might be taken beforehand; which would be exceedingly convenient, and satisfactory every way, if true. The problems were to be cast by means of figures, in some perplexed and difficult way, which, however, was facilitated by a set of tables in the end of the pamphlet, something like the Logarithm Tables at the end of Bowditch's *Navigator*.

Now, Blunt revered, adored, and worshiped this *Bonaparte Dream Book* of his; and was fully persuaded that between those red covers, and in his own dreams, lay all the secrets of futurity. Every morning before taking his pills, and applying his hair-oils, he would steal out of his bunk before the rest of the watch were awake; take out his pamphlet, and a bit of chalk; and then straddling his chest, begin scratching his oily head to remember his fugitive dreams; marking down strokes on his chest-lid, as if he were casting up his daily accounts.

Though often perplexed and lost in mazes concerning the cabalistic figures in the book, and the chapter of directions to beginners; for he could with difficulty read at all; yet, in the end, if not interrupted, he somehow managed to arrive at a conclusion satisfactory to him. So that, as he generally wore a good-humored expression, no doubt he must have thought, that all his future affairs were working together for the best.

But one night he started us all up in a fright, by springing from his bunk, his eyes ready to start out of his head, and crying, in a husky voice—"Boys! boys! get the benches ready! Quick, quick!"

"What benches?" growled Max—"What's the matter?"

"Benches! benches!" screamed Blunt, without heeding him, "cut down the forests, bear a hand, boys; the Day of Judgment's coming!"

But the next moment, he got quietly into his bunk, and laid still, muttering to himself, he had only been rambling in his sleep.

I did not know exactly what he had meant by his *benches*; till, shortly after, I overheard two of the sailors debating, whether mankind would stand or sit at the Last Day.

Chapter XIX

A Narrow Escape

THIS DREAM BOOK OF BLUNT'S REMINDS ME OF A NARROW ESCAPE WE HAD, EARLY ONE MORNING. It was the larboard watch's turn to remain below from midnight till four o'clock; and having turned in and slept, Blunt suddenly turned out again about three o'clock, with a wonderful dream in his head; which he was desirous of at once having interpreted.

So he goes to his chest, gets out his tools, and falls to ciphering on the lid. When, all at once, a terrible cry was heard, that routed him and all the rest of us up, and sent the whole ship's company flying on deck in the dark. We did not know what it was; but somehow, among sailors at sea, they seem to know when real danger of any kind is at hand, even in their sleep.

When we got on deck, we saw the mate standing on the bowsprit, and crying out *Luff! Luff!* to someone in the dark water before the ship. In that direction, we could just see a light, and then, the great black hull of a strange vessel, that was coming down on us obliquely; and so near, that we heard the flap of her top-sails as they shook in the wind, the trampling of feet on the deck, and the same cry of *Luff! Luff!* that our own mate was raising.

In a minute more, I caught my breath, as I heard a snap and a crash, like the fall of a tree, and suddenly, one of our flying-jib guys jerked out the bolt near the cat-head; and presently, we heard our jib-boom thumping against our bows.

Meantime, the strange ship, scraping by us thus, shot off into the darkness, and we saw her no more. But she, also, must have been injured; for when it grew light, we found pieces of strange rigging mixed with ours. We repaired the damage, and replaced the broken spar with another jib-boom we had; for all ships carry spare spars against emergencies.

The cause of this accident, which came near being the death of all on board, was nothing but the drowsiness of the look-out men on the forecastles of both ships. The sailor who had the look-out on our vessel was terribly reprimanded by the mate.

No doubt, many ships that are never heard of after leaving port, meet their fate in this way; and it may be, that sometimes two vessels coming together, jib-boom-and-jib-boom, with a sudden shock in the middle watch of the night, mutually destroy each other; and like fighting elks, sink down into the ocean, with their antlers locked in death.

While I was at Liverpool, a fine ship that lay near us in the docks, having got her cargo on board, went to sea, bound for India, with a good breeze; and all her crew felt sure of a prosperous voyage. But in about seven days after, she came back, a most distressing object to behold. All her starboard side was torn and splintered; her starboard anchor was gone; and a great part of the starboard bulwarks; while every one of the lower yard-arms had been broken, in the same direction; so that she now carried small and unsightly *jury-yards.*

When I looked at this vessel, with the whole of one side thus shattered, but the other still in fine trim; and when I remembered her gay and gallant appearance, when she left the same harbor into which she now entered so forlorn; I could not help thinking of a young man I had known at home, who had left his cottage one morning in high spirits, and was brought back at noon with his right side paralyzed from head to foot.

It seems that this vessel had been run against by a strange ship, crowding all sail before a fresh breeze; and the stranger had rushed past her starboard side, reducing her to the sad state in which she now was.

Sailors can not be too wakeful and cautious, when keeping their night look-outs; though, as I well know, they too often suffer themselves to become negligent, and nod. And this is not so wonderful, after all; for though every seaman has heard of those accidents at sea; and many of them, perhaps, have been in ships that have suffered from them; yet, when you find yourself sailing along on the ocean at night, without having seen a sail for weeks and weeks, it is hard for you to realize that any are near. Then, if they *are* near, it seems almost incredible that on the broad, boundless sea, which washes Greenland at one end of the world, and the Falkland Islands at the other, that any one vessel upon such a vast highway, should come into close contact with another. But the likelihood of great calamities occurring, seldom obtrudes upon the minds of ignorant men, such as sailors generally are; for the things which wise people know, anticipate, and guard against, the ignorant can only become acquainted with, by meeting them face to face. And even when experience has taught them, the lesson only serves for that day; inasmuch as the foolish in prosperity are infidels to the possibility of adversity; they see the sun in heaven, and believe it to be far too bright ever to set.

And even, as suddenly as the bravest and fleetest ships, while careering in pride of canvas over the sea, have been struck, as by lightning, and quenched out of sight; even so, do some lordly men, with all their plans and prospects gallantly trimmed to the fair, rushing breeze of life, and with no thought of death and disaster, suddenly encounter a shock unforeseen, and go down, foundering, into death.

Chapter XX

In a Fog He Is Set to Work as a Bell-Toller, and Beholds a Herd of Ocean-Elephants

What is this that we sail through? What palpable obscure? What smoke and reek, as if the whole steaming world were revolving on its axis, as a spit?

It is a Newfoundland Fog; and we are yet crossing the Grand Banks, wrapped in a mist, that no London in the Novemberest November ever equaled. The chronometer pronounced it noon; but do you call this midnight or mid-day? So dense is the fog, that though we have a fair wind, we shorten sail for fear of accidents; and not only that, but here am I, poor Wellingborough, mounted aloft on a sort of belfry, the top of the *"Sampson-Post,"* a lofty tower of timber, so called; and tolling the ship's bell, as if for a funeral.

This is intended to proclaim our approach, and warn all strangers from our track.

Dreary sound! toll, toll, toll, through the dismal mist and fog.

The bell is green with verdigris, and damp with dew; and the little cord attached to the clapper, by which I toll it, now and then slides through my fingers, slippery with wet. Here I am, in my slouched black hat, like the *"bull that could pull,"* announcing the decease of the lamented Cock-Robin.

A better device than the bell, however, was once pitched upon by an ingenious sea-captain, of whom I have heard. He had a litter of young porkers on board; and while sailing through the fog, he stationed men at both ends of the pen with long poles, wherewith they incessantly stirred up and irritated the porkers, who split the air with their squeals; and no doubt saved the ship, as the geese saved the *Capitol.*

The most strange and unheard-of noises came out of the fog at times: a vast sound of sighing and sobbing. What could it be? This would be followed by a spout, and a gush, and a cascading commotion, as if some fountain had suddenly jetted out of the ocean.

Seated on my Sampson-Post, I stared more and more, and suspended my duty as a sexton. But presently someone cried out—*"There she blows! whales! whales close alongside!"*

A whale! Think of it! whales close to *me,* Wellingborough;—would my own brother believe it? I dropped the clapper as if it were red-hot, and rushed to the side; and there, dimly floating, lay four or five long, black snaky-looking shapes, only a few inches out of the water.

Can these be whales? Monstrous whales, such as I had heard of? I thought they would look like mountains on the sea; hills and valleys of flesh! regular krakens, that made it high tide, and inundated continents, when they descended to feed!

It was a bitter disappointment, from which I was long in recovering. I lost all respect for whales; and began to be a little dubious about the story of Jonah; for how could Jonah reside in such an insignificant tenement; how could he have had elbow-room there? But perhaps, thought I, the whale which according to Rabbinical traditions was a female one, might have expanded to receive him like an anaconda, when it swallows an elk and leaves the antlers sticking out of its mouth.

Nevertheless, from that day, whales greatly fell in my estimation.

But it is always thus. If you read of St. Peter's, they say, and then go and visit it, ten to one, you account it a dwarf compared to your high-raised ideal. And, doubtless, Jonah himself must have been disappointed when he looked up to the domed midriff surmounting the whale's belly, and surveyed the ribbed pillars around him. A pretty large belly, to be sure, thought he, but not so big as it might have been.

On the next day, the fog lifted; and by noon, we found ourselves sailing through fleets of fishermen at anchor. They were very small craft; and when I beheld them, I perceived the force of that sailor saying, intended to illustrate restricted quarters, or being *on the limits. It is like a fisherman's walk,* say they, *three steps and overboard.*

Lying right in the track of the multitudinous ships crossing the ocean between England and America, these little vessels are sometimes run down, and obliterated from the face of the waters; the cry of the sailors ceasing with the last whirl of the whirlpool that closes over their craft. Their sad fate is frequently the result of their own remissness in keeping a good look-out by day, and not having their lamps trimmed, like the wise virgins, by night.

As I shall not make mention of the Grand Banks on our homeward-bound passage, I may as well here relate, that on our return, we approached them in the night; and by way of making sure of our whereabouts, the deep-sea-lead was heaved. The line attached is generally upward of three hundred fathoms in length; and the lead itself, weighing some forty or fifty pounds, has a hole in the lower end, in which, previous to sounding, some tallow is thrust, that it may bring up the soil at the bottom, for the captain to inspect. This is called *"arming"* the lead.

We "hove" our deep-sea-line by night, and the operation was very interesting, at least to me. In the first place, the vessel's heading was stopped; then, coiled away in a tub, like a whale-rope, the line was placed toward the after part of the quarter-deck; and one of the sailors carried the lead outside of the ship, away along to the end of the jib-boom, and at the word of command, far ahead and overboard it went, with a plunge; scraping by the side, till it came to the stern, when the line ran out of the tub like light.

When we came to haul it up, I was astonished at the force necessary to perform the work. The whole watch pulled at the line, which was rove through a block in the mizzen-rigging, as if we were hauling up a fat porpoise. When the lead came in sight, I was all eagerness to examine the tallow, and get a peep at a specimen of the bottom of the sea; but the sailors did not seem to be much interested by it, calling me a fool for wanting to preserve a few grains of the sand.

I had almost forgotten to make mention of the Gulf Stream, in which we found ourselves previous to crossing the Banks. The fact, of our being in it was proved by the captain in person, who superintended the drawing of a bucket of salt water, in which he dipped his thermometer. In the absence of the Gulf-weed, this is the general test; for the temperature of this current is eight degrees higher than that of the ocean, and the temperature of the ocean is twenty degrees higher than that of the Grand Banks. And it is to this remarkable difference of temperature, for which there can be no equilibrium, that many seamen impute the fogs on the coast of Nova Scotia and Newfoundland; but why there should always be such ugly weather in the Gulf, is something that I do not know has ever been accounted for.

It is curious to dip one's finger in a bucket full of the Gulf Stream, and find it so warm; as if the Gulf of Mexico, from whence this current comes, were a great caldron or boiler, on purpose to keep warm the North Atlantic, which is traversed by it for a distance of two thousand miles, as some large halls in winter are by hot air tubes. Its mean breadth being about two hundred leagues, it comprises an area larger than that of the whole Mediterranean, and may be deemed a sort of Mississippi of hot water flowing through the ocean; off the coast of Florida, running at the rate of one mile and a half an hour.

Chapter XXI

A Whaleman and a Man-of-War's-Man

THE SIGHT OF THE WHALES MENTIONED IN THE PRECEDING CHAPTER WAS THE BRINGING OUT OF Larry, one of our crew, who hitherto had been quite silent and reserved, as if from some conscious inferiority, though he had shipped as an *ordinary seaman,* and, for aught I could see, performed his duty very well.

When the men fell into a dispute concerning what kind of whales they were which we saw, Larry stood by attentively, and after garnering in their ignorance, all at once broke out, and astonished everybody by his intimate acquaintance with the monsters.

"They ar'n't sperm whales," said Larry, "their spouts ar'n't bushy enough; they ar'n't Sulphur-bottoms, or they wouldn't stay up so long; they ar'n't Hump-backs, for they ar'n't got any humps; they ar'n't Fin-backs, for you won't catch a Fin-back so near a ship; they ar'n't Greenland whales, for we ar'n't off the coast of Greenland; and they ar'n't right whales, for it wouldn't be right to say so. I tell ye, men, them's Crinkum-crankum whales."

"And what are them?" said a sailor.

"Why, them is whales that can't be cotched."

Now, as it turned out that this Larry had been bred to the sea in a whaler, and had sailed out of Nantucket many times; no one but Jackson ventured to dispute his opinion; and even Jackson did not press him very hard. And ever after, Larry's judgment was relied upon concerning all strange fish that happened to float by us during the voyage; for whalemen are far more familiar with the wonders of the deep than any other class of seaman.

This was Larry's first voyage in the merchant service, and that was the reason why, hitherto, he had been so reserved; since he well knew that merchant seamen generally affect a certain superiority to *"blubber-boilers,"* as they contemptuously style those who hunt the leviathan. But Larry turned out to be such an inoffensive fellow, and so well understood his business aboard ship, and was so ready to jump to an order, that he was exempted from the taunts which he might otherwise have encountered.

He was a somewhat singular man, who wore his hat slanting forward over the bridge of his nose, with his eyes cast down, and seemed always examining your boots, when speaking to you. I loved to hear him talk about the wild places in the Indian Ocean, and on the coast of Madagascar, where he had frequently touched during his whaling voyages. And this familiarity with the life of nature led by the people in that remote part of the world, had furnished Larry with a sentimental distaste for civilized society. When opportunity offered, he never omitted extolling the delights of the free and easy Indian Ocean.

"Why," said Larry, talking through his nose, as usual, "in *Madagasky* there, they don't wear any togs at all, nothing but a bowline round the midships; they don't have no dinners, but keeps a dinin' all day off fat pigs and dogs; they don't go to bed any where, but keeps a noddin' all the time; and they gets drunk, too, from some first rate arrack they make from cocoanuts; and smokes plenty of 'baccy, too, I tell ye. Fine country, that! Blast Ameriky, I say!"

To tell the truth, this Larry dealt in some illiberal insinuations against civilization.

"And what's the use of bein' *snivelized?*" said he to me one night during our watch on deck; "snivelized chaps only learns the way to take on 'bout life, and snivel. You don't see any Methodist chaps feelin' dreadful about their souls; you don't see any darned beggars and pesky constables in *Madagasky,* I tell ye; and none o' them kings there gets their big toes pinched by the gout. Blast Ameriky, I say."

Indeed, this Larry was rather cutting in his innuendoes.

"Are *you* now, Buttons, any better off for bein' snivelized?" coming close up to me and eyeing the wreck of my gaff-top-sail-boots very steadfastly. "No; you ar'n't a bit—but you're a good deal *worse* for it, Buttons. I tell ye, ye wouldn't have been to sea here, leadin' this dog's life, if you hadn't been snivelized—that's the cause why, now. Snivelization has been the ruin on ye; and it's spiled me complete; I might have been a great man in Madagasky; it's too darned bad! Blast Ameriky, I say." And in bitter grief at the social blight upon his whole past, present, and future, Larry turned away, pulling his hat still lower down over the bridge of his nose.

In strong contrast to Larry, was a young man-of-war's man we had, who went by the name of *"Gun-Deck,"* from his always talking of sailor life in the navy. He was a little fellow with a small face and a prodigious mop of brown hair; who always dressed in man-of-war style, with a wide, braided collar to his frock, and Turkish trousers. But he particularly prided himself upon his feet, which were quite small; and when we washed down decks of a morning, never mind how chilly it might be, he always took off his boots, and went paddling about like a duck, turning out his pretty toes to show his charming feet.

He had served in the armed steamers during the Seminole War in Florida, and had a good deal to say about sailing up the rivers there, through the everglades, and popping off Indians on the banks. I remember his telling a story about a party being discovered at quite a distance from them; but one of the savages was made very conspicuous by a pewter plate, which he wore round his neck, and which glittered in the sun. This plate proved his death; for, according to *Gun-Deck,* he himself shot it through the middle, and the ball entered the wearer's heart. It was a rat-killing war, he said.

Gun-Deck had touched at Cadiz: had been to Gibraltar; and ashore at Marseilles. He had sunned himself in the Bay of Naples: eaten figs and oranges in Messina; and cheerfully lost one of his hearts at Malta, among the ladies there. And about all these things, he talked like a romantic man-of-war's man, who had seen the civilized world, and loved it; found it good, and a comfortable place to live in. So he and Larry never could agree in their respective views of civilization, and of savagery, of the Mediterranean and *Madagasky*.

Chapter XXII

The Highlander Passes a Wreck

We were still on the banks, when a terrific storm came down upon us, the like of which I had never before beheld, or imagined. The rain poured down in sheets and cascades; the scupper holes could hardly carry it off the decks; and in bracing the yards we waded about almost up to our knees; everything floating about, like chips in a dock.

This violent rain was the precursor of a hard squall, for which we duly prepared, taking in our canvas to double-reefed-top-sails.

The tornado came rushing along at last, like a troop of wild horses before the flaming rush of a burning prairie. But after bowing and cringing to it awhile, the good *Highlander* was put off before it; and with her nose in the water, went wallowing on, plowing milk-white waves, and leaving a streak of illuminated foam in her wake.

It was an awful scene. It made me catch my breath as I gazed. I could hardly stand on my feet, so violent was the motion of the ship. But while I reeled to and fro, the sailors only laughed at me; and bade me look-out that the ship did not fall overboard; and advised me to get a handspike, and hold it down hard in the weather-scuppers, to steady her wild motions. But I was now getting a little too wise for this foolish kind of talk; though all through the voyage, they never gave it over.

This storm past, we had fair weather until we got into the Irish Sea.

The morning following the storm, when the sea and sky had become blue again, the man aloft sung out that there was a wreck on the lee-beam. We bore away for it, all hands looking eagerly toward it, and the captain in the mizzen-top with his spy-glass. Presently, we slowly passed alongside of it.

It was a dismantled, water-logged schooner, a most dismal sight, that must have been drifting about for several long weeks. The bulwarks were pretty much gone; and here and there the bare *stanchions*, or posts, were left standing, splitting in two the waves which broke clear over the deck, lying almost even with the sea. The fore-mast was snapped off less than four feet from its base; and the shattered and splintered remnant looked like the stump of a pine tree thrown over in the woods. Everytime she rolled in the trough of the sea, her open main-hatchway yawned into view; but was as quickly filled, and submerged again, with a rushing, gurgling sound, as the water ran into it with the lee-roll.

At the head of the stump of the main-mast, about ten feet above the deck, something like a sleeve seemed nailed; it was supposed to be the relic of a jacket, which must have been fastened there by the crew for a signal, and been frayed out and blown away by the wind.

Lashed, and leaning over sideways against the taffrail, were three dark, green, grassy objects, that slowly swayed with every roll, but otherwise were motionless. I saw the captain's glass directed toward them, and heard him say at last, "They must have been dead a long time." These were sailors, who long ago had lashed themselves to the taffrail for safety; but must have famished.

Full of the awful interest of the scene, I surely thought the captain would lower a boat to bury the bodies, and find out something about the schooner. But we did not stop at all; passing on our course, without so much as learning the schooner's name, though everyone supposed her to be a New Brunswick lumberman.

On the part of the sailors, no surprise was shown that our captain did not send off a boat to the wreck; but the steerage passengers were indignant at what they called his barbarity. For me, I could not but feel amazed and shocked at his indifference; but my subsequent sea experiences have shown me, that such conduct as this is very common, though not, of course, when human life can be saved.

So away we sailed, and left her; drifting, drifting on; a garden spot for barnacles, and a playhouse for the sharks.

"Look there," said Jackson, hanging over the rail and coughing—"look there; that's a sailor's coffin. Ha! ha! Buttons," turning round to me—"how do you like that, Buttons? Wouldn't you like to take a sail with them 'ere dead men? Wouldn't it be nice?" And then he tried to laugh, but only coughed again.

"Don't laugh at dem poor fellows," said Max, looking grave; "do' you see dar bodies, dar souls are farder off dan de Cape of Dood Hope."

"Dood Hope, Dood Hope," shrieked Jackson, with a horrid grin, mimicking the Dutchman, "dare is no dood hope for dem, old boy; dey are drowned and d. . . . d, as you and I will be, Red Max, one of dese dark nights."

"No, no," said Blunt, "all sailors are saved; they have plenty of squalls here below, but fair weather aloft."

"And did you get that out of your silly Dream Book, you Greek?" howled Jackson through a cough. "Don't talk of heaven to me—it's a lie—I know it—and they are all fools that believe in it. Do you think, you Greek, that there's any heaven for *you?* Will they let *you* in there, with that tarry hand, and that oily head of hair? Avast! when some shark gulps you down his hatchway one of these days, you'll find, that by dying, you'll only go from one gale of wind to another; mind that, you Irish cockney! Yes, you'll be bolted down like one of your own pills: and I should like to see the whole ship swallowed down in the Norway maelstrom, like a box on 'em. That would be a dose of salts for ye!" And so saying, he went off, holding his hands to his chest, and coughing, as if his last hour was come.

Everyday this Jackson seemed to grow worse and worse, both in body and mind. He seldom spoke, but to contradict, deride, or curse; and all the time, though his face grew thinner and thinner, his eyes seemed to kindle more and more, as if he were going to die out at last, and leave them burning like tapers before a corpse.

Though he had never attended churches, and knew nothing about Christianity; no more than a Malay pirate; and though he could not read a word, yet he was spontaneously an atheist and an infidel; and during the long night-watches, would enter into arguments, to prove that there was nothing to be believed; nothing to be loved, and nothing worth living for; but everything to be hated, in the wide world. He was a horrid desperado; and like a wild Indian, whom he resembled in his tawny skin and high cheek bones, he seemed to run amuck at heaven and earth. He was a Cain afloat; branded on his yellow brow with some inscrutable curse; and going about corrupting and searing every heart that beat near him.

But there seemed even more woe than wickedness about the man; and his wickedness seemed to spring from his woe; and for all his hideousness, there was that in his eye at times, that was ineffably pitiable and touching; and though there were moments when I almost hated this Jackson, yet I have pitied no man as I have pitied him.

Chapter XXIII

AN UNACCOUNTABLE CABIN-PASSENGER, AND A MYSTERIOUS YOUNG LADY

As yet, I have said nothing special about the passengers we carried out. But before making what little mention I shall of them, you must know that the *Highlander* was not a Liverpool liner, or packet-ship, plying in connection with a sisterhood of packets, at stated intervals, between the two ports. No: she was only what is called a *regular trader* to Liverpool; sailing upon no fixed days, and acting very much as she pleased, being bound by no obligations of any kind: though in all her voyages, ever having New York or Liverpool for her destination. Merchant vessels which are neither liners nor regular traders, among sailors come under the general head of *transient ships*; which implies that they are here to-day, and somewhere else to-morrow, like Mullins's dog.

But I had no reason to regret that the *Highlander* was not a liner; for aboard of those liners, from all I could gather from those who had sailed in them, the crew have terrible hard work, owing to their carrying such a press of sail, in order to make as rapid passages as possible, and sustain the ship's reputation for speed. Hence it is, that although they are the very best of sea-going craft, and built in the best possible manner, and with the very best materials, yet, a few years of scudding before the wind, as they do, seriously impairs their constitutions—like robust young men, who live too fast in their teens—and they are soon sold out for a song; generally to the people of Nantucket, New Bedford, and Sag Harbor, who repair and fit them out for the whaling business.

Thus, the ship that once carried over gay parties of ladies and gentlemen, as tourists, to Liverpool or London, now carries a crew of harpooners round Cape Horn into the Pacific. And the mahogany and bird's-eye maple cabin, which once held rosewood card-tables and brilliant coffee-urns, and in which many a bottle of champagne, and many a bright eye sparkled, *now* accommodates a bluff Quaker captain from Martha's Vineyard; who, perhaps, while lying with his ship in the Bay of Islands, in New Zealand, entertains a party of naked chiefs and savages at dinner, in place of the packet-captain doing the honors to the literati, theatrical stars, foreign princes, and gentlemen of leisure and fortune, who generally talked gossip, politics, and nonsense across the table, in transatlantic trips. The broad quarter-deck, too, where these gentry promenaded, is now often choked up by the enormous head of the sperm-whale, and vast masses of unctuous blubber; and every where reeks with oil during the prosecution of the fishery. *Sic transit gloria mundi!* Thus departs the pride and glory of packet-ships! It is like a broken down importer of French silks embarking in the soap-boiling business.

So, not being a liner, the *Highlander* of course did not have very ample accommodations for cabin passengers. I believe there were not more than five or six state-rooms, with two or three berths in each. At any rate, on this particular voyage she only carried out one regular cabin-passenger; that is, a person previously unacquainted with the captain, who paid his fare down, and came on board soberly, and in a business-like manner with his baggage.

He was an extremely little man, that solitary cabin-passenger—the passenger who came on board in a business-like manner with his baggage; never spoke to anyone, and the captain seldom spoke to him.

Perhaps he was a deputy from the Deaf and Dumb Institution in New York, going over to London to address the public in pantomime at Exeter Hall concerning the signs of the times.

He was always in a brown study; sometimes sitting on the quarter-deck with arms folded, and head hanging upon his chest. Then he would rise, and gaze out to windward, as if he had suddenly discovered a friend. But looking disappointed, would retire slowly into his state-room, where you could see him through the little window, in an irregular sitting position, with the back part of him inserted into his berth, and his head, arms, and legs hanging out, buried in profound meditation, with his forefinger aside of his nose. He never was seen reading; never took a hand at cards; never smoked; never drank wine; never conversed; and never staid to the dessert at dinner-time.

He seemed the true microcosm, or little world to himself: standing in no need of levying contributions upon the surrounding universe. Conjecture was lost in speculating as to who he was, and what was his business. The sailors, who are always curious with regard to such matters, and criticize cabin-passengers more than cabin-passengers are perhaps aware at the time, completely exhausted themselves in suppositions, some of which are characteristically curious.

One of the crew said he was a mysterious bearer of secret dispatches to the English court; others opined that he was a traveling surgeon and bonesetter, but for what reason they thought so, I never could learn; and others declared that he must either be an unprincipled bigamist, flying from his last wife and several small children; or a scoundrelly forger, bank-robber, or general burglar, who was returning to his beloved country with his ill-gotten booty. One observing sailor was of opinion that he was an English murderer, overwhelmed with speechless remorse, and returning home to make a full confession and be hanged.

But it was a little singular, that among all their sage and sometimes confident opinings, not one charitable one was made; no! they were all sadly to the prejudice of his moral and religious character. But this is the way all the world over. Miserable man! could you have had an inkling of what they thought of you, I know not what you would have done.

However, not knowing anything about these surmisings and suspicions, this mysterious cabin-passenger went on his way, calm, cool, and collected; never troubled anybody, and nobody troubled him. Sometimes, of a moonlight night he glided about the deck, like the ghost of a hospital attendant; flitting from mast to mast; now hovering round the skylight, now vibrating in the vicinity of the binnacle. Blunt, the Dream Book tar, swore he was a magician; and took an extra dose of salts, by way of precaution against his spells.

When we were but a few days from port, a comical adventure befell this cabin-passenger. There is an old custom, still in vogue among some merchant sailors, of tying fast in the rigging any lubberly landsman of a passenger who may be detected taking excursions aloft, however moderate the flight of the awkward fowl. This is called *"making a spread eagle"* of the man; and before he is liberated, a promise is exacted, that before arriving in port, he shall furnish the ship's company with money enough for a treat all round.

Now this being one of the perquisites of sailors, they are always on the keen look-out for an opportunity of levying such contributions upon incautious strangers; though they never attempt it in presence of the captain; as for the mates, they purposely avert their eyes, and are earnestly engaged about something else, whenever they get an inkling of this proceeding going on. But, with only one poor fellow of a cabin-passenger on board of the *Highlander,* and *he* such a quiet, unobtrusive, unadventurous wight, there seemed little chance for levying contributions.

One remarkably pleasant morning, however, what should be seen, half-way up the mizzen rigging, but the figure of our cabin-passenger, holding on with might and main by all four limbs, and with his head fearfully turned round, gazing off to the horizon. He looked as if he had the nightmare; and in some sudden and unaccountable fit of insanity, he must have been impelled to the taking up of that perilous position.

"Good heavens!" said the mate, who was a bit of a wag, "you will surely fall, sir! Steward, spread a mattress on deck, under the gentleman!"

But no sooner was our Greenland sailor's attention called to the sight, than snatching up some rope-yarn, he ran softly up behind the passenger, and without speaking a word, began binding him hand and foot. The stranger was more dumb than ever with amazement; at last violently remonstrated; but in vain; for as his fearfulness of falling made him keep his hands glued to the ropes, and so prevented him from any effectual resistance, he was soon made a handsome *spread-eagle* of, to the great satisfaction of the crew.

It was now discovered for the first, that this singular passenger stammered and stuttered very badly, which, perhaps, was the cause of his reservedness.

"Wha-wha-what i-i-is this f-f-for?"

"Spread-eagle, sir," said the Greenlander, thinking that those few words would at once make the matter plain.

"Wha-wha-what that me-me-mean?"

"Treats all round, sir," said the Greenlander, wondering at the other's obtusity, who, however, had never so much as heard of the thing before.

At last, upon his reluctant acquiescence in the demands of the sailor, and handing him two half-crown-pieces, the unfortunate passenger was suffered to descend.

The last I ever saw of this man was his getting into a cab at Prince's Dock Gates in Liverpool, and driving off alone to parts unknown. He had nothing but a valise with him, and an umbrella; but his pockets looked stuffed out; perhaps he used them for carpet-bags.

I must now give some account of another and still more mysterious, though very different, sort of an occupant of the cabin, of whom I have previously hinted. What say you to a charming young girl?—just the girl to sing the *Dashing White Sergeant*; a martial, military-looking girl; her father must have been a general. Her hair was auburn; her eyes were blue; her cheeks were white and red; and Captain Riga was her most devoted.

To the curious questions of the sailors concerning who she was, the steward used to answer, that she was the daughter of one of the Liverpool dock-masters, who, for the benefit of her health and the improvement of her mind, had sent her out to America in the *Highlander,* under the captain's charge, who was his particular friend; and that now the young lady was returning home from her tour.

And truly the captain proved an attentive father to her, and often promenaded with her hanging on his arm, past the forlorn bearer of secret dispatches, who would look up now and then out of his reveries, and cast a furtive glance of wonder, as if he thought the captain was audacious.

Considering his beautiful ward, I thought the captain behaved ungallantly, to say the least, in availing himself of the opportunity of her charming society, to wear out his remaining old clothes; for no gentleman ever pretends to save his best coat when a lady is in the case; indeed, he generally thirsts for a chance to abase it, by converting it into a pontoon over a puddle, like Sir Walter Raleigh, that the ladies may not soil the soles of their dainty slippers. But this Captain Riga was no Raleigh, and hardly any sort of a true gentleman whatever, as I have formerly declared. Yet, perhaps, he might have worn his old clothes in this instance, for the express purpose of proving, by his disdain for the toilette, that he was nothing but the young lady's guardian; for many guardians do not care one fig how shabby they look.

But for all this, the passage out was one long paternal sort of a shabby flirtation between this hoydenish nymph and the ill-dressed captain. And surely, if her good mother, were she living, could have seen this young lady, she would have given her an endless lecture for her conduct, and a copy of Mrs. Ellis's *Daughters of England* to read and digest.

I shall say no more of this anonymous nymph; only, that when we arrived at Liverpool, she issued from her cabin in a richly embroidered silk dress, and lace hat and veil, and a sort of Chinese umbrella or parasol, which one of the sailors declared "spandangalous"; and the captain followed after in his best broadcloth and beaver, with a gold-headed cane; and away they went in a carriage, and that was the last of her; I hope she is well and happy now; but I have some misgivings.

It now remains to speak of the steerage passengers. There were not more than twenty or thirty of them, mostly mechanics, returning home, after a prosperous stay in America, to escort their wives and families back. These were the only occupants of the steerage that I ever knew of; till early one morning, in the gray dawn, when we made Cape Clear, the south point of Ireland, the apparition of a tall Irishman, in a shabby shirt of bed-ticking, emerged from the fore hatchway, and stood leaning on the rail, looking landward with a fixed, reminiscent expression, and diligently scratching its back with both hands. We all started at the sight, for no one had ever seen the apparition before; and when we remembered that it must have been burrowing all the passage down in its bunk, the only probable reason of its so manipulating its back became shockingly obvious.

I had almost forgotten another passenger of ours, a little boy not four feet high, an English lad, who, when we were about forty-eight hours from New York, suddenly appeared on deck, asking for something to eat.

It seems he was the son of a carpenter, a widower, with this only child, who had gone out to America in the *Highlander* some six months previous, where he fell to drinking, and soon died, leaving the boy a friendless orphan in a foreign land.

For several weeks the boy wandered about the wharves, picking up a precarious livelihood by sucking molasses out of the casks discharged from West India ships, and occasionally regaling himself upon stray oranges and lemons found floating in the docks. He passed his nights sometimes in a stall in the markets, sometimes in an empty hogshead on the piers, sometimes in a doorway, and once in the watchhouse, from which he escaped the next morning, running as he told me, right between the doorkeeper's legs, when he was taking another vagrant to task for repeatedly throwing himself upon the public charities.

At last, while straying along the docks, he chanced to catch sight of the *Highlander,* and immediately recognized her as the very ship which brought him and his father out from England. He at once resolved to return in her; and, accosting the captain, stated his case, and begged a passage. The captain refused to give it; but, nothing daunted, the heroic little fellow resolved to conceal himself on board previous to the ship's sailing; which he did, stowing himself away in the *between-decks*; and moreover, as he told us, in a narrow space between two large casks of water, from which he now and then thrust out his head for air. And once a steerage passenger rose in the night and poked in and rattled about a stick where he was, thinking him an uncommon large rat, who was after stealing a passage across the Atlantic. There are plenty of passengers of that kind continually plying between Liverpool and New York.

As soon as he divulged the fact of his being on board, which he took care should not happen till he thought the ship must be out of sight of land; the captain had him called aft, and after giving him a thorough shaking, and threatening to toss her overboard as a tit-bit for *John Shark,* he told the mate to send him forward among the sailors, and let him live there. The sailors received him with open arms; but before caressing him much, they gave him a thorough washing in the lee-scuppers, when he turned out to be quite a handsome lad, though thin and pale with the hardships he had suffered. However, by good nursing and plenty to eat, he soon improved and grew fat; and before many days was as fine a looking little fellow, as you might pick out of Queen Victoria's nursery.

The sailors took the warmest interest in him. One made him a little hat with a long ribbon; another a little jacket; a third a comical little pair of man-of-war's-man's trousers; so that in the end, he looked like a juvenile boatswain's mate. Then the cook furnished him with a little tin pot and pan; and the steward made him a present of a pewter tea-spoon; and a steerage passenger gave him a jack-knife. And thus provided, he used to sit at meal-times half-way up on the forecastle ladder, making a great racket with his pot and pan, and merry as a cricket. He was an uncommonly fine, cheerful, clever, arch little fellow, only six years old, and it was a thousand pities that he should be abandoned, as he was. Who can say, whether he is fated to be a convict in New South Wales, or a member of Parliament for Liverpool? When we got to that port, by the way, a purse was made up for him; the captain, officers, and the mysterious cabin passenger contributing their best wishes, and the sailors and poor steerage passengers something like fifteen dollars in cash and tobacco. But I had almost forgot to add that the daughter of the dock-master gave him a fine lace pocket-handkerchief and a card-case to remember her by; very valuable, but somewhat inappropriate presents. Thus supplied, the little hero went ashore by himself; and I lost sight of him in the vast crowds thronging the docks of Liverpool.

I must here mention, as some relief to the impression which Jackson's character must have made upon the reader, that in several ways he at first befriended this boy; but the boy always shrunk from him; till, at last, stung by his conduct, Jackson spoke to him no more; and seemed to hate him, harmless as he was, along with all the rest of the world.

As for the Lancashire lad, he was a stupid sort of fellow, as I have before hinted. So, little interest was taken in him, that he was permitted to go ashore at last, without a good-bye from any person but one.

Chapter XXIV

He Begins to Hop About in the Rigging Like a Saint Jago's Monkey

But we have not got to Liverpool yet; though, as there is little more to be said concerning the passage out, the *Highlander* may as well make sail and get there as soon as possible. The brief interval will perhaps be profitably employed in relating what progress I made in learning the duties of a sailor.

After my heroic feat in loosing the main-skysail, the mate entertained good hopes of my becoming a rare mariner. In the fullness of his heart, he ordered me to turn over the superintendence of the chicken-coop to the Lancashire boy; which I did, very willingly. After that, I took care to show the utmost alacrity in running aloft, which by this time became mere fun for me; and nothing delighted me more than to sit on one of the top-sail-yards, for hours together, helping Max or the Greenlander as they worked at the rigging.

At sea, the sailors are continually engaged in *"parceling,"* *"serving,"* and in a thousand ways ornamenting and repairing the numberless shrouds and stays; mending sails, or turning one side of the deck into a rope-walk, where they manufacture a clumsy sort of twine, called *spun-yarn*. This is spun with a winch; and many an hour the Lancashire boy had to play the part of an engine, and contribute the motive power. For material, they use odds and ends of old rigging called *"junk,"* the yarns of which are picked to pieces, and then twisted into new combinations, something as most books are manufactured.

This "junk" is bought at the junk shops along the wharves; outlandish looking dens, generally subterranean, full of old iron, old shrouds, spars, rusty blocks, and superannuated tackles; and kept by villainous looking old men, in tarred trousers, and with yellow beards like oakum. They look like wreckers; and the scattered goods they expose for sale, involuntarily remind one of the sea-beach, covered with keels and cordage, swept ashore in a gale.

Yes, I was now as nimble as a monkey in the rigging, and at the cry of *"tumble up there, my hearties, and take in sail,"* I was among the first ground-and-lofty tumblers, that sprang aloft at the word.

But the first time we reefed top-sails of a dark night, and I found myself hanging over the yard with eleven others, the ship plunging and rearing like a mad horse, till I felt like being jerked off the spar; then, indeed, I thought of a feather-bed at home, and hung on with tooth and nail; with no chance for snoring. But a few repetitions, soon made me used to it; and before long, I tied my reef-point as quickly and expertly as the best of them; never making what they call a *"granny-knot,"* and slipped down on deck by the bare stays, instead of the shrouds. It is surprising, how soon a boy overcomes his timidity about going aloft. For my own part, my nerves became as steady as the earth's diameter, and I felt as fearless on the royal yard, as Sam Patch on the cliff of Niagara. To my amazement, also, I found, that running up the rigging at sea, especially during a squall, was much easier than while lying in port. For as you always go up on the windward side, and the ship leans over, it makes more of a *stairs* of the rigging; whereas, in harbor, it is almost straight up and down.

Besides, the pitching and rolling only imparts a pleasant sort of vitality to the vessel; so that the difference in being aloft in a ship at sea, and a ship in harbor, is pretty much the same, as riding a real live horse and a wooden one. And even if the live charger should pitch you over his head, *that* would be much more satisfactory, than an inglorious fall from the other.

I took great delight in furling the top-gallant sails and royals in a hard blow; which duty required two hands on the yard.

There was a wild delirium about it; a fine rushing of the blood about the heart; and a glad, thrilling, and throbbing of the whole system, to find yourself tossed up at every pitch into the clouds of a stormy sky, and hovering like a judgment angel between heaven and earth; both hands free, with one foot in the rigging, and one somewhere behind you in the air. The sail would fill out like a balloon, with a report like a small cannon, and then collapse and sink away into a handful. And the feeling of mastering the rebellious canvas, and tying it down like a slave to the spar, and binding it over and over with the *gasket,* had a touch of pride and power in it, such as young King Richard must have felt, when he trampled down the insurgents of Wat Tyler.

As for steering, they never would let me go to the helm, except during a calm, when I and the figure-head on the bow were about equally employed.

By the way, that figure-head was a passenger I forgot to make mention of before.

He was a gallant six-footer of a *Highlander "in full fig,"* with bright tartans, bare knees, barred leggings, and blue bonnet and the most vermilion of cheeks. He was game to his wooden marrow, and stood up to it through thick and thin; one foot a little advanced, and his right arm stretched forward, daring on the waves. In a gale of wind it was glorious to watch him standing at his post like a hero, and plunging up and down the watery Highlands and Lowlands, as the ship went foaming on her way. He was a veteran with many wounds of many sea-fights; and when he got to Liverpool a figure-head-builder there, amputated his left leg, and gave him another wooden one, which I am sorry to say, did not fit him very well, forever after he looked as if he limped. Then this figure-head-surgeon gave him another nose, and touched up one eye, and repaired a rent in his tartans. After that the painter came and made his toilette all over again; giving him a new suit throughout, with a plaid of a beautiful pattern.

I do not know what has become of Donald now, but I hope he is safe and snug with a handsome pension in the "Sailors'-Snug-Harbor" on Staten Island.

The reason why they gave me such a slender chance of learning to steer was this. I was quite young and raw, and steering a ship is a great art, upon which much depends; especially the making a short passage; for if the helmsman be a clumsy, careless fellow, or ignorant of his duty, he keeps the ship going about in a melancholy state of indecision as to its precise destination; so that on a voyage to Liverpool, it may be pointing one while for Gibraltar, then for Rotterdam, and now for John o' Groat's; all of which is worse than wasted time. Whereas, a true steersman keeps her to her work night and day; and tries to make a bee-line from port to port.

Then, in a sudden squall, inattention, or want of quickness at the helm, might make the ship *"lurch to"*—or *"bring her by the lee."* And what those things are, the cabin passengers would never find out, when they found themselves going down, down, down, and bidding good-bye forever to the moon and stars.

And they little think, many of them, fine gentlemen and ladies that they are, what an important personage, and how much to be had in reverence, is the rough fellow in the pea-jacket, whom they see standing at the wheel, now cocking his eye aloft, and then peeping at the compass, or looking out to windward.

Why, that fellow has all your lives and eternities in his hand; and with one small and almost imperceptible motion of a spoke, in a gale of wind, might give a vast deal of work to surrogates and lawyers, in proving last wills and testaments.

Ay, you may well stare at him now. He does not look much like a man who might play into the hands of an heir-at-law, does he? Yet such is the case. Watch him close, therefore; take him down into your state-room occasionally after a stormy watch, and make a friend of him. A glass of cordial will do it.

And if you or your heirs are interested with the underwriters, then also have an eye on him. And if you remark, that of the crew, all the men who come to the helm are careless, or inefficient; and if you observe the captain scolding them often, and crying out: *"Luff, you rascal; she's falling off!"* or, *"Keep her steady, you scoundrel, you're boxing the compass!"* then hurry down to your state-room, and if you have not yet made a will, get out your stationery and go at it; and when it is done, seal it up in a bottle, like Columbus' log, and it may possibly drift ashore, when you are drowned in the next gale of wind.

Chapter XXV

QUARTER-DECK FURNITURE

THOUGH, FOR REASONS HINTED AT ABOVE, THEY WOULD NOT LET ME STEER, I CONTENTED MYself with learning the compass, a graphic fac-simile of which I drew on a blank leaf of the *Wealth of Nations,* and studied it every morning, like the multiplication table.

I liked to peep in at the binnacle, and watch the needle; and I wondered how it was that it pointed north, rather than south or west; for I do not know that any reason can be given why it points in the precise direction it does. One would think, too, that, as since the beginning of the world almost, the tide of emigration has been setting west, the needle would point that way; whereas, it is forever pointing its fixed forefinger toward the Pole, where there are few inducements to attract a sailor, unless it be plenty of ice for mint-juleps.

Our binnacle, by the way, the place that holds a ship's compasses, deserves a word of mention. It was a little house, about the bigness of a common bird-cage, with sliding panel doors, and two drawing-rooms within, and constantly perched upon a stand, right in front of the helm. It had two chimney-stacks to carry off the smoke of the lamp that burned in it by night. It was painted green, and on two sides had Venetian blinds; and on one side two glazed sashes; so that it looked like a cool little summer retreat, a snug bit of an arbor at the end of a shady garden lane. Had I been the captain, I would have planted vines in boxes, and placed them so as to overrun this binnacle; or I would have put canary-birds within; and so made an aviary of it. It is surprising what a different air may be imparted to the meanest thing by the dainty hand of taste.

Nor must I omit the helm itself, which was one of a new construction, and a particular favorite of the captain. It was a complex system of cogs and wheels and spindles, all of polished brass, and looked something like a printing-press, or power-loom. The sailors, however, did not like it much, owing to the casualties that happened to their imprudent fingers, by catching in among the cogs and other intricate contrivances. Then, sometimes in a calm, when the sudden swells would lift the ship, the helm would fetch a lurch, and send the helmsman revolving round like Ixion, often seriously hurting him; a sort of breaking on the wheel.

The *harness-cask*, also, a sort of sea side-board, or rather meat-safe, in which a week's allowance of salt pork and beef is kept, deserves being chronicled. It formed part of the standing furniture of the quarter-deck. Of an oval shape, it was banded round with hoops all silver-gilt, with gilded bands secured with gilded screws, and a gilded padlock, richly chased. This formed the captain's smoking-seat, where he would perch himself of an afternoon, a tasseled Chinese cap upon his head, and a fragrant Havanna between his white and canine-looking teeth. He took much solid comfort, Captain Riga.

Then the magnificent *capstan!* The pride and glory of the whole ship's company, the constant care and dandled darling of the cook, whose duty it was to keep it polished like a tea-pot; and it was an object of distant admiration to the steerage passengers. Like a parlor center-table, it stood full in the middle of the quarter-deck, radiant with brazen stars, and variegated with diamond-shaped veneerings of mahogany and satin wood. This was the captain's lounge, and the chief mate's secretary, in the bar-holes keeping paper and pencil for memorandums.

I might proceed and speak of the *booby-hatch*, used as a sort of settee by the officers, and the *fife-rail* round the main-mast, enclosing a little ark of canvas, painted green, where a small white dog with a blue ribbon round his neck, belonging to the dock-master's daughter, used to take his morning walks, and air himself in this small edition of the New York Bowling-Green.

Chapter XXVI

A Sailor a Jack of All Trades

As I began to learn my sailor duties, and show activity in running aloft, the men, I observed, treated me with a little more consideration, though not at all relaxing in a certain air of professional superiority. For the mere knowing of the names of the ropes, and familiarizing yourself with their places, so that you can lay hold of them in the darkest night; and the loosing and furling of the canvas, and reefing top-sails, and hauling braces; all this, though of course forming an indispensable part of a seaman's vocation, and the business in which he is principally engaged; yet these are things which a beginner of ordinary capacity soon masters, and which are far inferior to many other matters familiar to an *"able-seaman."*

What did I know, for instance, about *striking a top-gallant-mast*, and sending it down on deck in a gale of wind? Could I have *turned in a dead-eye*, or in the approved nautical style have *clapped a seizing on the main-stay?* What did I know of *"passing a gammoning," "reiving a Burton," "strapping a shoe-block," "clearing a foul hawse,"* and innumerable other intricacies?

The business of a thoroughbred sailor is a special calling, as much of a regular trade as a carpenter's or locksmith's. Indeed, it requires considerably more adroitness, and far more versatility of talent.

In the English merchant service boys serve a long apprenticeship to the sea, of seven years. Most of them first enter the Newcastle colliers, where they see a great deal of severe coasting service. In an old copy of the *Letters of Junius*, belonging to my father, I remember reading, that coal to supply the city of London could be dug at Blackheath, and sold for one half the price that the people of London then paid for it; but the Government would not suffer the mines to be opened, as it would destroy the great nursery for British seamen.

A thorough sailor must understand much of other avocations. He must be a bit of an embroiderer, to work fanciful collars of hempen lace about the shrouds; he must be something of a weaver, to weave mats of rope-yarns for lashings to the boats; he must have a touch of millinery, so as to tie graceful bows and knots, such as *Matthew Walker's roses,* and *Turk's heads*; he must be a bit of a musician, in order to sing out at the halyards; he must be a sort of jeweler, to set dead-eyes in the standing rigging; he must be a carpenter, to enable him to make a jurymast out of a yard in case of emergency; he must be a sempstress, to darn and mend the sails; a ropemaker, to twist *marline* and *Spanish foxes*; a blacksmith, to make hooks and thimbles for the blocks: in short, he must be a sort of Jack of all trades, in order to master his own. And this, perhaps, in a greater or less degree, is pretty much the case with all things else; for you know nothing till you know all; which is the reason we never know anything.

A sailor, also, in working at the rigging, uses special tools peculiar to his calling—*fids, serving-mallets, toggles, prickers, marling-spikes, palms, heavers,* and many more. The smaller sort he generally carries with him from ship to ship in a sort of canvas reticule.

The estimation in which a ship's crew hold the knowledge of such accomplishments as these, is expressed in the phrase they apply to one who is a clever practitioner. To distinguish such a mariner from those who merely *"hand, reef, and steer,"* that is, run aloft, furl sails, haul ropes, and stand at the wheel, they say he is *"a sailor-man"*; which means that he not only knows how to reef a top-sail, but is an artist in the rigging.

Now, alas! I had no chance given me to become initiated in this art and mystery; no further, at least, than by looking on, and watching how that these things might be done as well as others, the reason was, that I had only shipped for this one voyage in the *Highlander,* a short voyage too; and it was not worthwhile to teach *me* anything, the fruit of which instructions could be only reaped by the next ship I might belong to. All they wanted of me was the good-will of my muscles, and the use of my backbone—comparatively small though it was at that time—by way of a lever, for the above-mentioned artists to employ when wanted. Accordingly, when any embroidery was going on in the rigging, I was set to the most inglorious avocations; as in the merchant service it is a religious maxim to keep the hands always employed at something or other, never mind what, during their watch on deck.

Often furnished with a club-hammer, they swung me over the bows in a bowline, to pound the rust off the anchor: a most monotonous, and to me a most uncongenial and irksome business. There was a remarkable fatality attending the various hammers I carried over with me. Somehow they *would* drop out of my hands into the sea. But the supply of reserved hammers seemed unlimited: also the blessings and benedictions I received from the chief mate for my clumsiness.

At other times, they set me to picking oakum, like a convict, which hempen business disagreeably obtruded thoughts of halters and the gallows; or whittling belaying-pins, like a Down-Easter.

However, I endeavored to bear it all like a young philosopher, and whiled away the tedious hours by gazing through a port-hole while my hands were plying, and repeating Lord Byron's *Address to the Ocean,* which I had often spouted on the stage at the High School at home.

Yes, I got used to all these matters, and took most things coolly, in the spirit of Seneca and the stoics.

All but the *"turning out,"* or rising from your berth when the watch was called at night—*that* I never fancied. It was a sort of acquaintance, which the more I cultivated, the more I shrunk from; a thankless, miserable business, truly.

Consider that after walking the deck for four full hours, you go below to sleep: and while thus innocently employed in reposing your wearied limbs, you are started up—it seems but the next instant after closing your lids—and hurried on deck again, into the same disagreeably dark and, perhaps, stormy night, from which you descended into the forecastle.

The previous interval of slumber was almost wholly lost to me; at least the golden opportunity could not be appreciated: for though it is usually deemed a comfortable thing to be asleep, yet at the time no one is conscious that he is so enjoying himself. Therefore I made a little private arrangement with the Lancashire lad, who was in the other watch, just to step below occasionally, and shake me, and whisper in my ear—*"Watch below, Buttons; watch below"*—which pleasantly reminded me of the delightful fact. Then I would turn over on my side, and take another nap; and in this manner I enjoyed several complete watches in my bunk to the other sailor's one. I recommend the plan to all landsmen contemplating a voyage to sea.

But notwithstanding all these contrivances, the dreadful sequel could not be avoided. Eight bells would at last be struck, and the men on deck, exhilarated by the prospect of changing places with us, would call the watch in a most provoking but mirthful and facetious style.

As thus:

"Starboard watch, ahoy! eight bells there, below! Tumble up, my lively hearties; steam-boat alongside waiting for your trunks: bear a hand, bear a hand with your knee-buckles, my sweet and pleasant fellows! fine shower-bath here on deck. Hurrah, hurrah! your ice-cream is getting cold!"

Whereupon some of the old croakers who were getting into their trousers would reply with—"Oh, stop your gabble, will you? don't be in such a hurry, now. You feel sweet, don't you?" with other exclamations, some of which were full of fury.

And it was not a little curious to remark, that at the expiration of the ensuing watch, the tables would be turned; and we on deck became the wits and jokers, and those below the grizzly bears and growlers.

Chapter XXVII

He Gets a Peep at Ireland, and at Last Arrives at Liverpool

THE *HIGHLANDER* WAS NOT A GREYHOUND, NOT A VERY FAST SAILER; AND SO, THE PASSAGE, which some of the packet ships make in fifteen or sixteen days, employed us about thirty.

At last, one morning I came on deck, and they told me that Ireland was in sight.

Ireland in sight! A foreign country actually visible! I peered hard, but could see nothing but a bluish, cloud-like spot to the north-east. Was that Ireland? Why, there was nothing remarkable about that; nothing startling. If *that's* the way a foreign country looks, I might as well have staid at home.

Now what, exactly, I had fancied the shore would look like, I can not say; but I had a vague idea that it would be something strange and wonderful. However, there it was; and as the light increased and the ship sailed nearer and nearer, the land began to magnify, and I gazed at it with increasing interest.

Ireland! I thought of Robert Emmet, and that last speech of his before Lord Norbury; I thought of Tommy Moore, and his amatory verses: I thought of Curran, Grattan, Plunket, and O'Connell; I thought of my uncle's ostler, Patrick Flinnigan; and I thought of the shipwreck of the gallant *Albion*, tossed to pieces on the very shore now in sight; and I thought I should very much like to leave the ship and visit Dublin and the Giant's Causeway.

Presently a fishing-boat drew near, and I rushed to get a view of it; but it was a very ordinary looking boat, bobbing up and down, as any other boat would have done; yet, when I considered that the solitary man in it was actually a born native of the land in sight; that in all probability he had never been in America, and knew nothing about my friends at home, I began to think that he looked somewhat strange.

He was a very fluent fellow, and as soon as we were within hailing distance, cried out—"Ah, my fine sailors, from Ameriky, ain't ye, my beautiful sailors?" And concluded by calling upon us to stop and heave a rope. Thinking he might have something important to communicate, the mate accordingly backed the main yard, and a rope being thrown, the stranger kept hauling in upon it, and coiling it down, crying, "pay out! pay out, my honeys; ah! but you're noble fellows!" Till at last the mate asked him why he did not come alongside, adding, "Haven't you enough rope yet?"

"Sure and I have," replied the fisherman, "and it's time for Pat to cut and run!" and so saying, his knife severed the rope, and with a Kilkenny grin, he sprang to his tiller, put his little craft before the wind, and bowled away from us, with some fifteen fathoms of our tow-line.

"And may the Old Boy hurry after you, and hang you in your stolen hemp, you Irish blackguard!" cried the mate, shaking his fist at the receding boat, after recovering from his first fit of amazement.

Here, then, was a beautiful introduction to the eastern hemisphere; fairly robbed before striking soundings. This trick upon experienced travelers certainly beat all I had ever heard about the wooden nutmegs and bass-wood pumpkin seeds of Connecticut. And I thought if there were anymore Hibernians like our friend Pat, the Yankee peddlers might as well give it up.

The next land we saw was Wales. It was high noon, and a long line of purple mountains lay like banks of clouds against the east.

Could this be really Wales?—Wales?—and I thought of the Prince of Wales.

And did a real queen with a diadem reign over that very land I was looking at, with the identical eyes in my own head?—And then I thought of a grandfather of mine, who had fought against the ancestor of this queen at Bunker's Hill.

But, after all, the general effect of these mountains was mortifyingly like the general effect of the Catskill Mountains on the Hudson River.

With a light breeze, we sailed on till next day, when we made Holyhead and Anglesea. Then it fell almost calm, and what little wind we had, was ahead; so we kept tacking to and fro, just gliding through the water, and always hovering in sight of a snow-white tower in the distance, which might have been a fort, or a light-house. I lost myself in conjectures as to what sort of people might be tenanting that lonely edifice, and whether they knew anything about us.

The third day, with a good wind over the taffrail, we arrived so near our destination, that we took a pilot at dusk.

He, and everything connected with him were very different from our New York pilot. In the first place, the pilot boat that brought him was a plethoric looking sloop-rigged boat, with flat bows, that went wheezing through the water; quite in contrast to the little gull of a schooner, that bade us adieu off Sandy Hook.

Aboard of her were ten or twelve other pilots, fellows with shaggy brows, and muffled in shaggy coats, who sat grouped together on deck like a fire-side of bears, wintering in Aroostook. They must have had fine sociable times, though, together; cruising about the Irish Sea in quest of Liverpool-bound vessels; smoking cigars, drinking brandy-and-water, and spinning yarns; till at last, one by one, they are all scattered on board of different ships, and meet again by the side of a blazing sea-coal fire in some Liverpool taproom, and prepare for another yachting.

Now, when this English pilot boarded us, I stared at him as if he had been some wild animal just escaped from the Zoological Gardens; for here was a real live Englishman, just from England. Nevertheless, as he soon fell to ordering us here and there, and swearing vociferously in a language quite familiar to me; I began to think him very common-place, and considerable of a bore after all.

After running till about midnight, we *"hove-to"* near the mouth of the Mersey; and next morning, before day-break, took the first of the flood; and with a fair wind, stood into the river; which, at its mouth, is quite an arm of the sea. Presently, in the misty twilight, we passed immense buoys, and caught sight of distant objects on shore, vague and shadowy shapes, like Ossian's ghosts.

As I stood leaning over the side, and trying to summon up some image of Liverpool, to see how the reality would answer to my conceit; and while the fog, and mist, and gray dawn were investing everything with a mysterious interest, I was startled by the doleful, dismal sound of a great bell, whose slow intermitting tolling seemed in unison with the solemn roll of the billows. I thought I had never heard so boding a sound; a sound that seemed to speak of judgment and the resurrection, like belfry-mouthed Paul of Tarsus.

It was not in the direction of the shore; but seemed to come out of the vaults of the sea, and out of the mist and fog.

Who was dead, and what could it be?

I soon learned from my shipmates, that this was the famous *Bell-Buoy,* which is precisely what its name implies; and tolls fast or slow, according to the agitation of the waves. In a calm, it is dumb; in a moderate breeze, it tolls gently; but in a gale, it is an alarum like the tocsin, warning all mariners to flee. But it seemed fuller of dirges for the past, than of monitions for the future; and no one can give ear to it, without thinking of the sailors who sleep far beneath it at the bottom of the deep.

As we sailed ahead the river contracted. The day came, and soon, passing two lofty landmarks on the Lancashire shore, we rapidly drew near the town, and at last, came to anchor in the stream.

Looking shoreward, I beheld lofty ranges of dingy warehouses, which seemed very deficient in the elements of the marvelous; and bore a most unexpected resemblance to the warehouses along South-street in New York. There was nothing strange; nothing extraordinary about them. There they stood; a row of calm and collected warehouses; very good and substantial edifices, doubtless, and admirably adapted to the ends had in view by the builders; but plain, matter-of-fact warehouses, nevertheless, and that was all that could be said of them.

To be sure, I did not expect that every house in Liverpool must be a Leaning Tower of Pisa, or a Strasbourg Cathedral; but yet, these edifices I must confess, were a sad and bitter disappointment to me.

But it was different with Larry the whaleman; who to my surprise, looking about him delighted, exclaimed, "Why, this 'ere is a considerable place—I'm *dummed* if it ain't quite a place.—Why, them 'ere houses is considerable houses. It beats the coast of Afriky, all hollow; nothing like this in *Madagasky,* I tell you;—I'm *dummed,* boys if Liverpool ain't a city!"

Upon this occasion, indeed, Larry altogether forgot his hostility to civilization. Having been so long accustomed to associate foreign lands with the savage places of the Indian Ocean, he had been under the impression, that Liverpool must be a town of bamboos, situated in some swamp, and whose inhabitants turned their attention principally to the cultivation of log-wood and curing of flying-fish. For that any great commercial city existed three thousand miles from home, was a thing, of which Larry had never before had a *"realizing sense."* He was accordingly astonished and delighted; and began to feel a sort of consideration for the country which could boast so extensive a town. Instead of holding Queen Victoria on a par with the Queen of Madagascar, as he had been accustomed to do; he ever after alluded to that lady with feeling and respect.

As for the other seamen, the sight of a foreign country seemed to kindle no enthusiasm in them at all: no emotion in the least. They looked around them with great presence of mind, and acted precisely as you or I would, if, after a morning's absence round the corner, we found ourselves returning home. Nearly all of them had made frequent voyages to Liverpool.

Not long after anchoring, several boats came off; and from one of them stepped a neatly-dressed and very respectable-looking woman, some thirty years of age, I should think, carrying a bundle. Coming forward among the sailors, she inquired for Max the Dutchman, who immediately was forthcoming, and saluted her by the mellifluous appellation of *Sally.*

Now during the passage, Max in discoursing to me of Liverpool, had often assured me, that

that city had the honor of containing a spouse of his; and that in all probability, I would have the pleasure of seeing her. But having heard a good many stories about the bigamies of seamen, and their having wives and sweethearts in every port, the round world over; and having been an eye-witness to a nuptial parting between this very Max and a lady in New York; I put down this relation of his, for what I thought it might reasonably be worth. What was my astonishment, therefore, to see this really decent, civil woman coming with a neat parcel of Max's shore clothes, all washed, plaited, and ironed, and ready to put on at a moment's warning.

They stood apart a few moments giving loose to those transports of pleasure, which always take place, I suppose, between man and wife after long separations.

At last, after many earnest inquiries as to how he had behaved himself in New York; and concerning the state of his wardrobe; and going down into the forecastle, and inspecting it in person, Sally departed; having exchanged her bundle of clean clothes for a bundle of soiled ones, and this was precisely what the New York wife had done for Max, not thirty days previous.

So long as we laid in port, Sally visited the *Highlander* daily; and approved herself a neat and expeditious getter-up of duck frocks and trousers, a capital tailoress, and as far as I could see, a very well-behaved, discreet, and reputable woman.

But from all I had seen of her, I should suppose Meg, the New York wife, to have been equally well-behaved, discreet, and reputable; and equally devoted to the keeping in good order Max's wardrobe.

And when we left England at last, Sally bade Max good-bye, just as Meg had done; and when we arrived at New York, Meg greeted Max precisely as Sally had greeted him in Liverpool. Indeed, a pair of more amiable wives never belonged to one man; they never quarreled, or had so much as a difference of any kind; the whole broad Atlantic being between them; and Max was equally polite and civil to both. For many years, he had been going Liverpool and New York voyages, plying between wife and wife with great regularity, and sure of receiving a hearty domestic welcome on either side of the ocean.

Thinking this conduct of his, however, altogether wrong and every way immoral, I once ventured to express to him my opinion on the subject. But I never did so again. He turned round on me, very savagely; and after rating me soundly for meddling in concerns not my own, concluded by asking me triumphantly, whether *old King Sol,* as he called the son of David, did not have a whole frigate-full of wives; and that being the case, whether he, a poor sailor, did not have just as good a right to have two? "What was not wrong then, is right now," said Max; "so, mind your eye, Buttons, or I'll crack your pepper-box for you!"

Chapter XXVIII

HE GOES TO SUPPER AT THE SIGN OF THE BALTIMORE CLIPPER

In the afternoon our pilot was all alive with his orders; we hove up the anchor, and after a deal of pulling, and hauling, and jamming against other ships, we wedged our way through a lock at high tide; and about dark, succeeded in working up to a berth in *Prince's Dock*. The hawsers and tow-lines being then coiled away, the crew were told to go ashore, select their boarding-house, and sit down to supper.

Here it must be mentioned, that owing to the strict but necessary regulations of the Liverpool docks, no fires of any kind are allowed on board the vessels within them; and hence, though the sailors are supposed to sleep in the forecastle, yet they must get their meals ashore, or live upon cold potatoes. To a ship, the American merchantmen adopt the former plan; the owners, of course, paying the landlord's bill; which, in a large crew remaining at Liverpool more than six weeks, as we of the *Highlander* did, forms no inconsiderable item in the expenses of the voyage. Other ships, however—the economical Dutch and Danish, for instance, and sometimes the prudent Scotch—feed their luckless tars in dock, with precisely the same fare which they give them at sea; taking their salt junk ashore to be cooked, which, indeed, is but scurvy sort of treatment, since it is very apt to induce the scurvy. A parsimonious proceeding like this is regarded with immeasurable disdain by the crews of the New York vessels, who, if their captains treated them after that fashion, would soon bolt and run.

It was quite dark, when we all sprang ashore; and, for the first time, I felt dusty particles of the renowned British soil penetrating into my eyes and lungs. As for *stepping* on it, that was out of the question, in the well-paved and flagged condition of the streets; and I did not have an opportunity to do so till some time afterward, when I got out into the country; and then, indeed, I saw England, and snuffed its immortal loam—but not till then.

Jackson led the van; and after stopping at a tavern, took us up this street, and down that, till at last he brought us to a narrow lane, filled with boarding-houses, spirit-vaults, and sailors. Here we stopped before the sign of a Baltimore Clipper, flanked on one side by a gilded bunch of grapes and a bottle, and on the other by the British Unicorn and American Eagle, lying down by each other, like the lion and lamb in the millennium.—A very judicious and tasty device, showing a delicate apprehension of the propriety of conciliating American sailors in an English boarding-house; and yet in no way derogating from the honor and dignity of England, but placing the two nations, indeed, upon a footing of perfect equality.

Near the unicorn was a very small animal, which at first I took for a young unicorn; but it looked more like a yearling lion. It was holding up one paw, as if it had a splinter in it; and on its head was a sort of basket-hilted, low-crowned hat, without a rim. I asked a sailor standing by, what this animal meant, when, looking at me with a grin, he answered, "Why, youngster, don't you know what that means? It's a young jackass, limping off with a kedgeree pot of rice out of the cuddy."

Though it was an English boarding-house, it was kept by a broken-down American mariner, one Danby, a dissolute, idle fellow, who had married a buxom English wife, and now lived upon her industry; for the lady, and not the sailor, proved to be the head of the establishment.

She was a hale, good-looking woman, about forty years old, and among the seamen went by the name of *"Handsome Mary."* But though, from the dissipated character of her spouse, Mary had become the business personage of the house, bought the marketing, overlooked the tables, and conducted all the more important arrangements, yet she was by no means an Amazon to her husband, if she *did* play a masculine part in other matters. No; and the more is the pity, poor Mary seemed too much attached to Danby, to seek to rule him as a termagant. Often she went about her household concerns with the tears in her eyes, when, after a fit of intoxication, this brutal husband of hers had been beating her. The sailors took her part, and many a time volunteered to give him a thorough thrashing before her eyes; but Mary would beg them not to do so, as Danby would, no doubt, be a better boy next time.

But there seemed no likelihood of this, so long as that abominable bar of his stood upon the premises. As you entered the passage, it stared upon you on one side, ready to entrap all guests.

It was a grotesque, old-fashioned, castellated sort of a sentry-box, made of a smoky-colored wood, and with a grating in front, that lifted up like a portcullis. And here would this Danby sit all the day long; and when customers grew thin, would patronize his own ale himself, pouring down mug after mug, as if he took himself for one of his own quarter-casks.

Sometimes an old crony of his, one Bob Still, would come in; and then they would occupy the sentry-box together, and swill their beer in concert. This pot-friend of Danby was portly as a drayhorse, and had a round, sleek, oily head, twinkling eyes, and moist red cheeks. He was a lusty troller of ale-songs; and, with his mug in his hand, would lean his waddling bulk partly out of the sentry-box, singing:

No frost, no snow, no wind, I trow,
Can hurt me if I wold,
I am so wrapt, and thoroughly lapt
In jolly good ale and old—
I stuff my skin so full within,
Of jolly good ale and old.

Or this—

Your wines and brandies I detest,
Here's richer juice from barley press'd.
It is the quintessence of malt,
And they that drink it want no salt.
Come, then, quick come, and take this beer,
And water henceforth you'll forswear.

Alas! Handsome Mary. What avail all thy private tears and remonstrances with the incorrigible Danby, so long as that brewery of a toper, Bob Still, daily eclipses thy threshold with the vast diameter of his paunch, and enthrones himself in the sentry-box, holding divided rule with thy spouse?

The more he drinks, the fatter and rounder waxes Bob; and the songs pour out as the ale pours in, on the well-known principle, that the air in a vessel is displaced and expelled, as the liquid rises higher and higher in it.

But as for Danby, the miserable Yankee grows sour on good cheer, and dries up the thinner for every drop of fat ale he imbibes. It is plain and demonstrable, that much ale is not good for Yankees, and operates differently upon them from what it does upon a Briton: ale must be drank in a fog and a drizzle.

Entering the sign of the Clipper, Jackson ushered us into a small room on one side, and shortly after, Handsome Mary waited upon us with a courtesy, and received the compliments of several old guests among our crew. She then disappeared to provide our supper. While my shipmates were now engaged in tippling, and talking with numerous old acquaintances of theirs in the neighborhood, who thronged about the door, I remained alone in the little room, meditating profoundly upon the fact, that I was now seated upon an English bench, under an English roof, in an English tavern, forming an integral part of the English empire. It was a staggering fact, but none the less true.

I examined the place attentively; it was a long, narrow, little room, with one small arched window with red curtains, looking out upon a smoky, untidy yard, bounded by a dingy brick-wall, the top of which was horrible with pieces of broken old bottles, stuck into mortar.

A dull lamp swung overhead, placed in a wooden ship suspended from the ceiling. The walls were covered with a paper, representing an endless succession of vessels of all nations continually circumnavigating the apartment. By way of a pictorial main-sail to one of these ships, a map was hung against it, representing in faded colors the flags of all nations. From the street came a confused uproar of ballad-singers, bawling women, babies, and drunken sailors.

And this is England?

But where are the old abbeys, and the York Minsters, and the lord mayors, and coronations, and the May-poles, and fox-hunters, and Derby races, and the dukes and duchesses, and the Count d'Orsays, which, from all my reading, I had been in the habit of associating with England? Not the most distant glimpse of them was to be seen.

Alas! Wellingborough, thought I, I fear you stand but a poor chance to see the sights. You are nothing but a poor sailor boy; and the Queen is not going to send a deputation of noblemen to invite you to St. James's.

It was then, I began to see, that my prospects of seeing the world as a sailor were, after all, but very doubtful; for sailors only go *round* the world, without going *into* it; and their reminiscences of travel are only a dim recollection of a chain of tap-rooms surrounding the globe, parallel with the Equator. They but touch the perimeter of the circle; hover about the edges of terra-firma; and only land upon wharves and pier-heads. They would dream as little of traveling inland to see Kenilworth, or Blenheim Castle, as they would of sending a car overland to the Pope, when they touched at Naples.

From these reveries I was soon roused, by a servant girl hurrying from room to room, in shrill tones exclaiming, "Supper, supper ready."

Mounting a rickety staircase, we entered a room on the second floor. Three tall brass candlesticks shed a smoky light upon smoky walls, of what had once been sea-blue, covered with sailor-scrawls of foul anchors, lovers' sonnets, and ocean ditties. On one side, nailed against the wainscot in a row, were the four knaves of cards, each Jack putting his best foot foremost as usual. What these signified I never heard.

But such ample cheer! Such a groaning table! Such a superabundance of solids and substantials! Was it possible that sailors fared thus?—the sailors, who at sea live upon salt beef and biscuit?

First and foremost, was a mighty pewter dish, big as Achilles' shield, sustaining a pyramid of smoking sausages. This stood at one end; midway was a similar dish, heavily laden with farmers' slices of head-cheese; and at the opposite end, a congregation of beef-steaks, piled tier over tier. Scattered at intervals between, were side dishes of boiled potatoes, eggs by the score, bread, and pickles; and on a stand adjoining, was an ample reserve of everything on the supper table.

We fell to with all our hearts; wrapped ourselves in hot jackets of beef-steaks; curtailed the sausages with great celerity; and sitting down before the head-cheese, soon razed it to its foundations.

Toward the close of the entertainment, I suggested to Peggy, one of the girls who had waited upon us, that a cup of tea would be a nice thing to take; and I would thank her for one. She replied that it was too late for tea; but she would get me a cup of *"swipes"* if I wanted it.

Not knowing what *"swipes"* might be, I thought I would run the risk and try it; but it proved a miserable beverage, with a musty, sour flavor, as if it had been a decoction of spoiled pickles. I never patronized *swipes* again; but gave it a wide berth; though, at dinner afterward, it was furnished to an unlimited extent, and drunk by most of my shipmates, who pronounced it good.

But Bob Still would not have pronounced it so; for this *swripes,* as I learned, was a sort of cheap substitute for beer; or a bastard kind of beer; or the washings and rinsings of old beer-barrels. But I do not remember now what they said it was, precisely. I only know, that *swipes* was my abomination. As for the taste of it, I can only describe it as answering to the name itself; which is certainly significant of something vile. But it is drunk in large quantities by the poor people about Liverpool, which, perhaps, in some degree, accounts for their poverty.

Chapter XXIX

Redburn Deferentially Discourses Concerning the Prospects of Sailors

THE SHIP REMAINED IN PRINCE'S DOCK OVER SIX WEEKS; BUT AS I DO NOT MEAN TO PRESENT A diary of my stay there, I shall here simply record the general tenor of the life led by our crew during that interval; and will then proceed to note down, at random, my own wanderings about town, and impressions of things as they are recalled to me now, after the lapse of so many years.

But first, I must mention that we saw little of the captain during our stay in the dock. Sometimes, cane in hand, he sauntered down of a pleasant morning from the *Arms Hotel*, I believe it was, where he boarded; and after lounging about the ship, giving orders to his Prime Minister and Grand Vizier, the chief mate, he would saunter back to his drawing-rooms.

From the glimpse of a play-bill, which I detected peeping out of his pocket, I inferred that he patronized the theaters; and from the flush of his cheeks, that he patronized the fine old Port wine, for which Liverpool is famous.

Occasionally, however, he spent his nights on board; and mad, roystering nights they were, such as rare Ben Jonson would have delighted in. For company over the cabin-table, he would have four or five whiskered sea-captains, who kept the steward drawing corks and filling glasses all the time. And once, the whole company were found under the table at four o'clock in the morning, and were put to bed and tucked in by the two mates. Upon this occasion, I agreed with our woolly Doctor of Divinity, the black cook, that they should have been ashamed of themselves; but there is no shame in some sea-captains, who only blush after the third bottle.

During the many visits of Captain Riga to the ship, he always said something courteous to a gentlemanly, friendless custom-house officer, who staid on board of us nearly all the time we lay in the dock.

And weary days they must have been to this friendless custom-house officer; trying to kill time in the cabin with a newspaper; and rapping on the transom with his knuckles. He was kept on board to prevent smuggling; but he used to smuggle himself ashore very often, when, according to law, he should have been at his post on board ship. But no wonder; he seemed to be a man of fine feelings, altogether above his situation; a most inglorious one, indeed; worse than driving geese to water.

And now, to proceed with the crew.

At daylight, all hands were called, and the decks were washed down; then we had an hour to go ashore to breakfast; after which we worked at the rigging, or picked oakum, or were set to some employment or other, never mind how trivial, till twelve o'clock, when we went to dinner. At half-past one we resumed work; and finally *knocked off* at four o'clock in the afternoon, unless something particular was in hand. And after four o'clock, we could go where we pleased, and were not required to be on board again till next morning at daylight.

As we had nothing to do with the cargo, of course, our duties were light enough; and the chief mate was often put to it to devise some employment for us.

We had no watches to stand, a ship-keeper, hired from shore, relieving us from that; and all the while the men's wages ran on, as at sea. Sundays we had to ourselves.

Thus, it will be seen, that the life led by sailors of American ships in Liverpool, is an exceedingly easy one, and abounding in leisure. They live ashore on the fat of the land; and after a little wholesome exercise in the morning, have the rest of the day to themselves.

Nevertheless, these Liverpool voyages, likewise those to London and Havre, are the least profitable that an improvident seaman can take. Because, in New York he receives his month's advance; in Liverpool, another; both of which, in most cases, quickly disappear; so that by the time his voyage terminates, he generally has but little coming to him; sometimes not a cent. Whereas, upon a long voyage, say to India or China, his wages accumulate; he has more inducements to economize, and far fewer motives to extravagance; and when he is paid off at last, he goes away jingling a quart measure of dollars.

Besides, of all sea-ports in the world, Liverpool, perhaps, most abounds in all the variety of land-sharks, land-rats, and other vermin, which make the hapless mariner their prey. In the shape of landlords, bar-keepers, clothiers, crimps, and boarding-house loungers, the land-sharks devour him, limb by limb; while the land-rats and mice constantly nibble at his purse.

Other perils he runs, also, far worse; from the denizens of notorious Corinthian haunts in the vicinity of the docks, which in depravity are not to be matched by anything this side of the pit that is bottomless.

And yet, sailors love this Liverpool; and upon long voyages to distant parts of the globe, will be continually dilating upon its charms and attractions, and extolling it above all other sea-ports in the world. For in Liverpool they find their Paradise—not the well known street of that name—and one of them told me he would be content to lie in Prince's Dock till *he hove up anchor* for the world to come.

Much is said of ameliorating the condition of sailors; but it must ever prove a most difficult endeavor, so long as the antidote is given before the bane is removed.

Consider, that, with the majority of them, the very fact of their being sailors, argues a certain recklessness and sensualism of character, ignorance, and depravity; consider that they are generally friendless and alone in the world; or if they have friends and relatives, they are almost constantly beyond the reach of their good influences; consider that after the rigorous discipline, hardships, dangers, and privations of a voyage, they are set adrift in a foreign port, and exposed to a thousand enticements, which, under the circumstances, would be hard even for virtue itself to withstand, unless virtue went about on crutches; consider that by their very vocation they are shunned by the better classes of people, and cut off from all access to respectable and improving society; consider all this, and the reflecting mind must very soon perceive that the case of sailors, as a class, is not a very promising one.

Indeed, the bad things of their condition come under the head of those chronic evils which can only be ameliorated, it would seem, by ameliorating the moral organization of all civilization.

Though old seventy-fours and old frigates are converted into chapels, and launched into the docks; though the "Boatswain's Mate" and other clever religious tracts in the nautical dialect are distributed among them; though clergymen harangue them from the pier-heads: and chaplains in the navy read sermons to them on the gun-deck; though evangelical boarding-houses are provided for them; though the parsimony of ship-owners has seconded the really sincere and pious efforts of Temperance Societies, to take away from seamen their old rations of grog while at sea:—notwithstanding all these things, and many more, the relative condition of the great bulk of sailors to the rest of mankind, seems to remain pretty much where it was, a century ago.

It is too much the custom, perhaps, to regard as a special advance, that unavoidable, and merely participative progress, which any one class makes in sharing the general movement of the race. Thus, because the sailor, who to-day steers the *Hibernia* or *Unicorn* steam-ship across the Atlantic, is a somewhat different man from the exaggerated sailors of Smollett, and the men who fought with Nelson at Copenhagen, and survived to riot themselves away at North Corner in Plymouth;—because the modern tar is not quite so gross as heretofore, and has shaken off some of his shaggy jackets, and docked his Lord Rodney queue—therefore, in the estimation of some observers, he has begun to see the evils of his condition, and has voluntarily improved. But upon a closer scrutiny, it will be seen that he has but drifted along with that great tide, which, perhaps, has two flows for one ebb; he has made no individual advance of his own.

There are classes of men in the world, who bear the same relation to society at large, that the wheels do to a coach: and are just as indispensable. But however easy and delectable the springs upon which the insiders pleasantly vibrate: however sumptuous the hammer-cloth, and glossy the door-panels; yet, for all this, the wheels must still revolve in dusty, or muddy revolutions. No contrivance, no sagacity can lift *them* out of the mire; for upon something the coach must be bottomed; on something the insiders must roll.

Now, sailors form one of these wheels: they go and come round the globe; they are the true importers, and exporters of spices and silks; of fruits and wines and marbles; they carry missionaries, embassadors, opera-singers, armies, merchants, tourists, and scholars to their destination: they are a bridge of boats across the Atlantic; they are the *primum mobile* of all commerce; and, in short, were they to emigrate in a body to man the navies of the moon, almost everything would stop here on earth except its revolution on its axis, and the orators in the American Congress.

And yet, what are sailors? What in your heart do you think of that fellow staggering along the dock? Do you not give him a wide berth, shun him, and account him but little above the brutes that perish? Will you throw open your parlors to him; invite him to dinner? or give him a season ticket to your pew in church?—No. You will do no such thing; but at a distance, you will perhaps subscribe a dollar or two for the building of a hospital, to accommodate sailors already broken down; or for the distribution of excellent books among tars who can not read. And the very mode and manner in which such charities are made, bespeak, more than words, the low estimation in which sailors are held. It is useless to gainsay it; they are deemed almost the refuse and offscourings of the earth; and the romantic view of them is principally had through romances.

But can sailors, one of the wheels of this world, be wholly lifted up from the mire? There seems not much chance for it, in the old systems and programs of the future, however well-intentioned and sincere; for with such systems, the thought of lifting them up seems almost as hopeless as that of growing the grape in Nova Zembla.

But we must not altogether despair for the sailor; nor need those who toil for his good be at bottom disheartened, or Time must prove his friend in the end; and though sometimes he would almost seem as a neglected step-son of heaven, permitted to run on and riot out his days with no hand to restrain him, while others are watched over and tenderly cared for; yet we feel and we know that God is the true Father of all, and that none of his children are without the pale of his care.

Chapter XXX

REDBURN GROWS INTOLERABLY FLAT AND STUPID OVER SOME OUTLANDISH OLD GUIDE-BOOKS

AMONG THE ODD VOLUMES IN MY FATHER'S LIBRARY, WAS A COLLECTION OF OLD EUROPEAN AND English guide-books, which he had bought on his travels, a great many years ago. In my childhood, I went through many courses of studying them, and never tired of gazing at the numerous quaint embellishments and plates, and staring at the strange title-pages, some of which I thought resembled the mustached faces of foreigners.

Among others was a Parisian-looking, faded, pink-covered pamphlet, the rouge here and there effaced upon its now thin and attenuated cheeks, entitled, *Voyage Descriptif et Philosophique de L'Ancien et du Nouveau Paris: Miroir Fidèle* also a time-darkened, mossy old book, in marbleized binding, much resembling verd-antique, entitled, *Itinéraire Instructif de Rome, ou Description Générale des*

Monumens Antiques et Modernes et des Ouvrages les plus Remarquables de Peinteur, de Sculpture, et de Architecture de cette Célébre Ville; on the russet title-page is a vignette representing a barren rock, partly shaded by a scrub-oak (a forlorn bit of landscape), and under the lee of the rock and the shade of the tree, maternally reclines the houseless foster-mother of Romulus and Remus, giving suck to the illustrious twins; a pair of naked little cherubs sprawling on the ground, with locked arms, eagerly engaged at their absorbing occupation; a large cactus-leaf or diaper hangs from a bough, and the wolf looks a good deal like one of the no-horn breed of barn-yard cows; the work is published *Avec privilege du Souverain Pontife*. There was also a velvet-bound old volume, in brass clasps, entitled, *The Conductor through Holland*, with a plate of the Stadt House; also a venerable *Picture of London*, abounding in representations of St. Paul's, the Monument, Temple-Bar, Hyde-Park-Corner, the Horse Guards, the Admiralty, Charing-Cross, and Vauxhall Bridge. Also, a bulky book, in a dusty-looking yellow cover, reminding one of the paneled doors of a mail-coach, and bearing an elaborate title-page, full of printer's flourishes, in emulation of the cracks of a four-in-hand whip, entitled, in part, *The Great Roads, both direct and cross, throughout England and Wales, from an actual Admeasurement by order of His Majesty's Postmaster-General: This work describes the Cities, Market and Borough and Corporate Towns, and those at which the Assizes are held, and gives the time of the Mails' arrival and departure from each: Describes the Inns in the Metropolis from which the stages go, and the Inns in the country which supply post-horses and carriages: Describes the Noblemen and Gentlemen's Seats situated near the Road, with Maps of the Environs of London, Bath, Brighton, and Margate*. It is dedicated "*To the Right Honorable the Earls of Chesterfield and Leicester, by their Lordships' Most Obliged, Obedient, and Obsequious Servant, John Gary*, 1798." Also a green pamphlet, with a motto from Virgil, and an intricate coat of arms on the cover, looking like a diagram of the Labyrinth of Crete, entitled, *A Description of York, its Antiquities and Public Buildings, particularly the Cathedral; compiled with great pains from the most authentic records*. Also a small scholastic-looking volume, in a classic vellum binding, and with a frontispiece bringing together at one view the towers and turrets of King's College and the magnificent Cathedral of Ely, though geographically sixteen miles apart, entitled, *The Cambridge Guide: its Colleges, Halls, Libraries, and Museums, with the Ceremonies of the Town and University, and some account of Ely Cathedral*. Also a pamphlet, with a japanned sort of cover, stamped with a disorderly higgledy-piggledy group of pagoda-looking structures, claiming to be an accurate representation of the "*North or Grand Front of Blenheim*," and entitled, *A Description of Blenheim, the Seat of His Grace the Duke of Marlborough; containing a full account of the Paintings, Tapestry, and Furniture: a Picturesque Tour of the Gardens and Parks, and a General Description of the famous China Gallery, &c.; with an Essay on Landscape Gardening: and embellished with a View of the Palace, and a New and Elegant Plan of the Great Park*. And lastly, and to the purpose, there was a volume called *The Picture of Liverpool*.

It was a curious and remarkable book; and from the many fond associations connected with it, I should like to immortalize it, if I could.

But let me get it down from its shrine, and paint it, if I may, from the life.

As I now linger over the volume, to and fro turning the pages so dear to my boyhood—the very pages which, years and years ago, my father turned over amid the very scenes that are here described; what a soft, pleasing sadness steals over me, and how I melt into the past and forgotten!

Dear book! I will sell my Shakespeare, and even sacrifice my old quarto Hogarth, before I will part with you. Yes, I will go to the hammer myself, ere I send you to be knocked down in the auctioneer's shambles. I will, my beloved—old family relic that you are;—till you drop leaf from leaf, and letter from letter, you shall have a snug shelf somewhere, though I have no bench for myself.

In size, it is what the booksellers call an 18*mo*; it is bound in green morocco, which from my earliest recollection has been spotted and tarnished with time; the corners are marked with triangular patches of red, like little cocked hats; and some unknown Goth has inflicted an incurable wound upon the back. There is no lettering outside; so that he who lounges past my humble shelves, seldom dreams of opening the anonymous little book in green. There it stands; day after day, week after week, year after year; and no one but myself regards it. But I make up for all neglects, with my own abounding love for it.

But let us open the volume.

What are these scrawls in the fly-leaves? what incorrigible pupil of a writing-master has been here? what crayon sketcher of wild animals and falling air-castles? Ah, no!—these are all part and parcel of the precious book, which go to make up the sum of its treasure to me.

Some of the scrawls are my own; and as poets do with their juvenile sonnets, I might write under this horse, *"Drawn at the age of three years,"* and under this autograph, *"Executed at the age of eight."*

Others are the handiwork of my brothers, and sisters, and cousins; and the hands that sketched some of them are now moldered away.

But what does this anchor here? this ship? and this sea-ditty of Dibdin's? The book must have fallen into the hands of some tarry captain of a forecastle. No: that anchor, ship, and Dibdin's ditty are mine; this hand drew them; and on this very voyage to Liverpool. But not so fast; I did not mean to tell that yet.

Full in the midst of these pencil scrawlings, completely surrounded indeed, stands in indelible, though faded ink, and in my father's hand-writing, the following:

WALTER REDBURN.
Riddough's Royal Hotel,
Liverpool, March 20th, 1808.

Turning over that leaf, I come upon some half-effaced miscellaneous memoranda in pencil, characteristic of a methodical mind, and therefore indubitably my father's, which he must have made at various times during his stay in Liverpool. These are full of a strange, subdued, old, mid-summer interest to me: and though, from the numerous effacements, it is much like cross-reading to make them out; yet, I must here copy a few at random:

	£	*s.*	*d*
Guide-Book		3	6
Dinner at the Star and Garter		10	
Trip to Preston (distance 31 m.)	2	6	3
Gratuities		4	
Hack		4	6
Thompson's Seasons		5	
Library		1	
Boat on the river		6	
Port wine and cigars		4	

And on the opposite page, I can just decipher the following:

Dine with Mr. Roscoe on Monday.
Call upon Mr. Morille same day.
Leave card at Colonel Digby's on Tuesday.
Theatre Friday night—Richard III *and new farce.*
Present letter at Miss L——'s on Tuesday.
Call on Sampson & Wilt, Friday.
Get my draft on London cashed.
Write home by the Princess.
Letter-bag at Sampson and Wilt's.

Turning over the next leaf, I unfold a map, which in the midst of the British Arms, in one corner displays in sturdy text, that this is *"A Plan of the Town of Liverpool."* But there seems little plan in the confined and crooked looking marks for the streets, and the docks irregularly scattered along the bank of the Mersey, which flows along, a peaceful stream of shaded line engraving.

On the north-east corner of the map, lies a level Sahara of yellowish white: a desert, which still bears marks of my zeal in endeavoring to populate it with all manner of uncouth monsters in crayons. The space designated by that spot is now, doubtless, completely built up in Liverpool.

Traced with a pen, I discover a number of dotted lines, radiating in all directions from the foot of Lord-street, where stands marked *"Riddough's Hotel,"* the house my father stopped at.

These marks delineate his various excursions in the town; and I follow the lines on, through street and lane; and across broad squares; and penetrate with them into the narrowest courts.

By these marks, I perceive that my father forgot not his religion in a foreign land; but attended St. John's Church near the Hay-market, and other places of public worship: I see that he visited the News Room in Duke-street, the Lyceum in Bold-street, and the Theater Royal; and that he called to pay his respects to the eminent Mr. Roscoe, the historian, poet, and banker.

Reverentially folding this map, I pass a plate of the Town Hall, and come upon the Title Page, which, in the middle, is ornamented with a piece of landscape, representing a loosely clad lady in sandals, pensively seated upon a bleak rock on the sea shore, supporting her head with one hand, and with the other, exhibiting to the stranger an oval sort of salver, bearing the figure of a strange bird, with this motto elastically stretched for a border—*"Deus nobis hæc otia fecit."*

The bird forms part of the city arms, and is an imaginary representation of a now extinct fowl, called the *"Liver,"* said to have inhabited a *"pool,"* which antiquarians assert once covered a good part of the ground where Liverpool now stands; and from that bird, and this pool, Liverpool derives its name.

At a distance from the pensive lady in sandals, is a ship under full sail; and on the beach is the figure of a small man, vainly essaying to roll over a huge bale of goods.

Equally divided at the top and bottom of this design, is the following title complete; but I fear the printer will not be able to give a fac-simile:

The
Picture
of
Liverpool:
or,
Stranger's Guide
and
Gentleman's Pocket Companion
FOR THE TOWN.

Embellished
With Engravings
By the Most Accomplished and Eminent Artists.

Liverpool:
Printed in Swift's Court,
And sold by Woodward and Alderson, 56 Castle St.
1803.

A brief and reverential preface, as if the writer were all the time bowing, informs the reader of the flattering reception accorded to previous editions of the work; and quotes *"testimonies of respect which had lately appeared in various quarters—the British Critic, Review, and the seventh volume of the Beauties of England and Wales"*—and concludes by expressing the hope, that this new, revised, and illustrated edition might *"render it less unworthy of the public notice, and less unworthy also of the subject it is intended to illustrate."*

A very nice, dapper, and respectful little preface, the time and place of writing which is solemnly recorded at the end—*Hope Place, 1st Sept.* 1803.

But how much fuller my satisfaction, as I fondly linger over this circumstantial paragraph, if the writer had recorded the precise hour of the day, and by what timepiece; and if he had but mentioned his age, occupation, and name.

But all is now lost; I know not who he was; and this estimable author must needs share the oblivious fate of all literary incognitos.

He must have possessed the grandest and most elevated ideas of true fame, since he scorned to be perpetuated by a solitary initial. Could I find him out now, sleeping neglected in some churchyard, I would buy him a head-stone, and record upon it naught but his title-page, deeming that his noblest epitaph.

After the preface, the book opens with an extract from a prologue written by the excellent Dr. Aiken, the brother of Mrs. Barbauld, upon the opening of the Theater Royal, Liverpool, in 1772:

Where Mersey's stream, long winding o'er the plain,
Pours his full tribute to the circling main,
A band of fishers chose their humble seat;
Contented labor blessed the fair retreat,
Inured to hardship, patient, bold, and rude,
They braved the billows for precarious food:
Their straggling huts were ranged along the shore,
Their nets and little boats their only store.

Indeed, throughout, the work abounds with quaint poetical quotations, and old-fashioned classical allusions to the *Æneid* and Falconer's *Shipwreck*.

And the anonymous author must have been not only a scholar and a gentleman, but a man of gentle disinterestedness, combined with true city patriotism; for in his *"Survey of the Town"* are nine thickly printed pages of a neglected poem by a neglected Liverpool poet.

By way of apologizing for what might seem an obtrusion upon the public of so long an episode, he courteously and feelingly introduces it by saying, that *"the poem has now for several years been scarce, and is at present but little known; and hence a very small portion of it will no doubt be highly acceptable to the cultivated reader; especially as this noble epic is written with great felicity of expression and the sweetest delicacy of feeling."*

Once, but once only, an uncharitable thought crossed my mind, that the author of the *Guide-Book* might have been the author of the epic. But that was years ago; and I have never since permitted so uncharitable a reflection to insinuate itself into my mind.

This epic, from the specimen before me, is composed in the old stately style, and rolls along commanding as a coach and four. It sings of Liverpool and the Mersey; its docks, and ships, and warehouses, and bales, and anchors; and after descanting upon the abject times, when *"his noble waves, inglorious, Mersey rolled,"* the poet breaks forth like all Parnassus with:

Now o'er the wondering world her name resounds,
From northern climes to India's distant bounds—

Where'er his shores the broad Atlantic waves;
Where'er the Baltic rolls his wintry waves;
Where'er the honored flood extends his tide,
That clasps Sicilia like a favored bride.
Greenland for her its bulky whale resigns,
And temperate Gallia rears her generous vines:
'Midst warm Iberia citron orchards blow,
And the ripe fruitage bends the laboring bough;
In every clime her prosperous fleets are known,
She makes the wealth of every clime her own.

It also contains a delicately-curtained allusion to Mr. Roscoe:—

*And here R*s*o*, with genius all his own,*
New tracks explores, and all before unknown.

Indeed, both the anonymous author of the *Guide-Book,* and the gifted bard of the Mersey, seem to have nourished the warmest appreciation of the fact, that to their beloved town Roscoe imparted a reputation which gracefully embellished its notoriety as a mere place of commerce. He is called the modern Guicciardini of the modern Florence, and his histories, translations, and Italian Lives, are spoken of with classical admiration.

The first chapter begins in a methodical, business-like way, by informing the impatient reader of the precise latitude and longitude of Liverpool; so that, at the outset, there may be no misunderstanding on that head. It then goes on to give an account of the history and antiquities of the town, beginning with a record in the *Doomsday-Book* of William the Conqueror.

Here, it must be sincerely confessed, however, that notwithstanding his numerous other merits, my favorite author betrays a want of the uttermost antiquarian and penetrating spirit, which would have scorned to stop in its researches at the reign of the Norman monarch, but would have pushed on resolutely through the dark ages, up to Moses, the man of Uz, and Adam; and finally established the fact beyond a doubt, that the soil of Liverpool was created with the creation.

But, perhaps, one of the most curious passages in the chapter of antiquarian research, is the pious author's moralizing reflections upon an interesting fact he records: to wit, that in A.D. 1571, the inhabitants sent a memorial to Queen Elizabeth, praying relief under a subsidy, wherein they style themselves *"her majesty's poor decayed town of Liverpool."*

As I now fix my gaze upon this faded and dilapidated old guide-book, bearing every token of the ravages of near half a century, and read how this piece of antiquity enlarges like a modern upon previous antiquities, I am forcibly reminded that the world is indeed growing old. And when I turn to the second chapter, *"On the increase of the town, and number of inhabitants,"* and then skim over page after page throughout the volume, all filled with allusions to the immense grandeur of a place, which, since then, has more than quadrupled in population, opulence, and splendor, and whose present inhabitants must look back upon the period here spoken of with a swelling feeling of immeasurable superiority and pride, I am filled with a comical sadness at the vanity of all human exaltation. For the cope-stone of to-day is the corner-stone of to-morrow; and as St. Peter's church was built in great part of the ruins of old Rome, so in all our erections, however imposing, we but form quarries and supply ignoble materials for the grander domes of posterity.

And even as this old guide-book boasts of the, to us, insignificant Liverpool of fifty years ago, the New York guide-books are now vaunting of the magnitude of a town, whose future inhabitants, multitudinous as the pebbles on the beach, and girdled in with high walls and towers, flanking endless avenues of opulence and taste, will regard all our Broadways and Bowerys as but the paltry nucleus to their Nineveh. From far up the Hudson, beyond Harlem River, where the young saplings are now growing, that will overarch their lordly mansions with broad boughs, centuries old; they may send forth explorers to penetrate into the then obscure and smoky alleys of the Fifth Avenue and Fourteenth-street; and going still farther south, may exhume the present Doric Custom-house, and quote it as a proof that their high and mighty metropolis enjoyed a Hellenic antiquity.

As I am extremely loth to omit giving a specimen of the dignified style of this *Picture of Liverpool,* so different from the brief, pert, and unclerkly hand-books to Niagara and Buffalo of the present day, I shall now insert the chapter of antiquarian researches; especially as it is entertaining in itself, and affords much valuable, and perhaps rare information, which the reader may need, concerning the famous town, to which I made *my first voyage.* And I think that with regard to a matter, concerning which I myself am wholly ignorant, it is far better to quote my old friend verbatim, than to mince his substantial baron-of-beef of information into a flimsy ragout of my own; and so, pass it off as original. Yes, I will render unto my honored guide-book its due.

But how can the printer's art so dim and mellow down the pages into a soft sunset yellow; and to the reader's eye, shed over the type all the pleasant associations which the original carries to me!

No! by my father's sacred memory, and all sacred privacies of fond family reminiscences, I will not! I will *not* quote thee, old Morocco, before the cold face of the marble-hearted world; for your antiquities would only be skipped and dishonored by shallow-minded readers; and for me, I should be charged with swelling out my volume by plagiarizing from a guide-book—the most vulgar and ignominious of thefts!

Chapter XXXI

WITH HIS PROSY OLD GUIDE-BOOK, HE TAKES A PROSY STROLL THROUGH THE TOWN

WHEN I LEFT HOME, I TOOK THE GREEN MOROCCO GUIDE-BOOK ALONG, SUPPOSING THAT FROM the great number of ships going to Liverpool, I would most probably ship on board of one of them, as the event itself proved.

Great was my boyish delight at the prospect of visiting a place, the infallible clue to all whose intricacies I held in my hand.

On the passage out I studied its pages a good deal. In the first place, I grounded myself thoroughly in the history and antiquities of the town, as set forth in the chapter I intended to quote. Then I mastered the columns of statistics, touching the advance of population; and pored over them, as I used to do over my multiplication-table. For I was determined to make the whole subject my own; and not be content with a mere smattering of the thing, as is too much the custom with most students of guide-books. Then I perused one by one the elaborate descriptions of public edifices, and scrupulously compared the text with the corresponding engraving, to see whether they corroborated each other. For be it known that, including the map, there were no less than seventeen plates in the work. And by often examining them, I had so impressed every column and cornice in my mind, that I had no doubt of recognizing the originals in a moment.

In short, when I considered that my own father had used this very guide-book, and that thereby it had been thoroughly tested, and its fidelity proved beyond a peradventure; I could not but think that I was building myself up in an unerring knowledge of Liverpool; especially as I had familiarized myself with the map, and could turn sharp corners on it, with marvelous confidence and celerity.

In imagination, as I lay in my berth on ship-board, I used to take pleasant afternoon rambles through the town; down St. James-street and up Great George's, stopping at various places of interest and attraction. I began to think I had been born in Liverpool, so familiar seemed all the features of the map. And though some of the streets there depicted were thickly involved, endlessly angular and crooked, like the map of Boston, in Massachusetts, yet, I made no doubt, that I could march through them in the darkest night, and even run for the most distant dock upon a pressing emergency.

Dear delusion!

It never occurred to my boyish thoughts, that though a guide-book, fifty years old, might have done good service in its day, yet it would prove but a miserable cicerone to a modern. I little imagined that the Liverpool my father saw, was another Liverpool from that to which I, his son Wellingborough was sailing. No; these things never obtruded; so accustomed had I been to associate my old morocco guide-book with the town it described, that the bare thought of there being any discrepancy, never entered my mind.

While we lay in the Mersey, before entering the dock, I got out my guide-book to see how the map would compare with the identical place itself. But they bore not the slightest resemblance. However, thinks I, this is owing to my taking a horizontal view, instead of a bird's-eye survey. So, never mind old guide-book, *you*, at least, are all right.

But my faith received a severe shock that same evening, when the crew went ashore to supper, as I have previously related.

The men stopped at a curious old tavern, near the Prince's Dock's walls; and having my guide-book in my pocket, I drew it forth to compare notes, when I found, that precisely upon the spot where I and my shipmates were standing, and a cherry-cheeked bar-maid was filling their glasses, my infallible old Morocco, in that very place, located a fort; adding, that it was well worth the intelligent stranger's while to visit it for the purpose of beholding the guard relieved in the evening.

This was a staggerer; for how could a tavern be mistaken for a castle? and this was about the hour mentioned for the guard to turn out; yet not a red coat was to be seen. But for all this, I could not, for one small discrepancy, condemn the old family servant who had so faithfully served my own father before me; and when I learned that this tavern went by the name of *"The Old Fort Tavern"*; and when I was told that many of the old stones were yet in the walls, I almost completely exonerated my guide-book from the half-insinuated charge of misleading me.

The next day was Sunday, and I had it all to myself; and now, thought I, my guide-book and I shall have a famous ramble up street and down lane, even unto the furthest limits of this Liverpool.

I rose bright and early; from head to foot performed my ablutions "with Eastern scrupulosity," and I arrayed myself in my red shirt and shooting-jacket, and the sportsman's pantaloons; and crowned my entire man with the tarpaulin; so that from this curious combination of clothing, and particularly from my red shirt, I must have looked like a very strange compound indeed: three parts sportsman, and two soldier, to one of the sailor.

My shipmates, of course, made merry at my appearance; but I heeded them not; and after breakfast, jumped ashore, full of brilliant anticipations.

My gait was erect, and I was rather tall for my age; and that may have been the reason why, as I was rapidly walking along the dock, a drunken sailor passing, exclaimed, *"Eyes right! quick step there!"*

Another fellow stopped me to know whether I was going fox-hunting; and one of the dock-police, stationed at the gates, after peeping out upon me from his sentry box, a snug little den, furnished with benches and newspapers, and hung round with storm jackets and oiled capes, issued forth in a great hurry, crossed my path as I was emerging into the street, and commanded me to *halt!* I obeyed; when scanning my appearance pertinaciously, he desired to know where I got that tarpaulin hat, not being able to account for the phenomenon of its roofing the head of a broken-down fox-hunter. But I pointed to my ship, which lay at no great distance; when remarking from my voice that I was a Yankee, this faithful functionary permitted me to pass.

It must be known that the police stationed at the gates of the docks are extremely observant of strangers going out; as many thefts are perpetrated on board the ships; and if they chance to see anything suspicious, they probe into it without mercy. Thus, the old men who buy *"shakings,"* and rubbish from vessels, must turn their bags wrong side out before the police, ere they are allowed to go outside the walls. And often they will search a suspicious looking fellow's clothes, even if he be a very thin man, with attenuated and almost imperceptible pockets.

But where was I going?

I will tell. My intention was in the first place, to visit Riddough's Hotel, where my father had stopped, more than thirty years before: and then, with the map in my hand, follow him through all the town, according to the dotted lines in the diagram. For thus would I be performing a filial pilgrimage to spots which would be hallowed in my eyes.

At last, when I found myself going down Old Hall-street toward Lord-street, where the hotel was situated, according to my authority; and when, taking out my map, I found that Old Hall-street was marked there, through its whole extent with my father's pen; a thousand fond, affectionate emotions rushed around my heart.

Yes, in this very street, thought I, nay, on this very flagging my father walked. Then I almost wept, when I looked down on my sorry apparel, and marked how the people regarded me; the men staring at so grotesque a young stranger, and the old ladies, in beaver hats and ruffles, crossing the walk a little to shun me.

How differently my father must have appeared; perhaps in a blue coat, buff vest, and Hessian boots. And little did he think, that a son of his would ever visit Liverpool as a poor friendless sailor-boy. But I was not born then: no, when he walked this flagging, I was not so much as thought of; I was not included in the census of the universe. My own father did not know me then; and had never seen, or heard, or so much as dreamed of me. And that thought had a touch of sadness to me; for if it had certainly been, that my own parent, at one time, never cast a thought upon me, how might it be with me hereafter? Poor, poor Wellingborough! thought I, miserable boy! you are indeed friendless and forlorn. Here you wander a stranger in a strange town, and the very thought of your father's having been here before you, but carries with it the reflection that, he then knew you not, nor cared for you one whit.

But dispelling these dismal reflections as well as I could, I pushed on my way, till I got to Chapel-street, which I crossed; and then, going under a cloister-like arch of stone, whose gloom and narrowness delighted me, and filled my Yankee soul with romantic thoughts of old Abbeys and Minsters, I emerged into the fine quadrangle of the Merchants' Exchange.

There, leaning against the colonnade, I took out my map, and traced my father right across Chapel-street, and actually through the very arch at my back, into the paved square where I stood.

So vivid was now the impression of his having been here, and so narrow the passage from which he had emerged, that I felt like running on, and overtaking him around the Town Hall adjoining, at the head of Castle-street. But I soon checked myself, when remembering that he had gone whither no son's search could find him in this world. And then I thought of all that must have happened to him since he paced through that arch. What trials and troubles he had encountered; how he had been shaken by many storms of adversity, and at last died a bankrupt. I looked at my own sorry garb, and had much ado to keep from tears.

But I rallied, and gazed round at the sculptured stonework, and turned to my guide-book, and looked at the print of the spot. It was correct to a pillar; but wanted the central ornament of the quadrangle. This, however, was but a slight subsequent erection, which ought not to militate against the general character of my friend for comprehensiveness.

The ornament in question is a group of statuary in bronze, elevated upon a marble pedestal and basement, representing Lord Nelson expiring in the arms of Victory. One foot rests on a rolling foe, and the other on a cannon. Victory is dropping a wreath on the dying admiral's brow; while Death, under the similitude of a hideous skeleton, is insinuating his bony hand under the hero's robe, and groping after his heart. A very striking design, and true to the imagination; I never could look at Death without a shudder.

At uniform intervals round the base of the pedestal, four naked figures in chains, somewhat larger than life, are seated in various attitudes of humiliation and despair. One has his leg recklessly thrown over his knee, and his head bowed over, as if he had given up all hope of ever feeling better. Another has his head buried in despondency, and no doubt looks mournfully out of his eyes, but as his face was averted at the time, I could not catch the expression. These woe-begone figures of captives are emblematic of Nelson's principal victories; but I never could look at their swarthy limbs and manacles, without being involuntarily reminded of four African slaves in the market-place.

And my thoughts would revert to Virginia and Carolina; and also to the historical fact, that the African slave-trade once constituted the principal commerce of Liverpool; and that the prosperity of the town was once supposed to have been indissolubly linked to its prosecution. And I remembered that my father had often spoken to gentlemen visiting our house in New York, of the unhappiness that the discussion of the abolition of this trade had occasioned in Liverpool; that the struggle between sordid interest and humanity had made sad havoc at the fire-sides of the merchants; estranged sons from sires; and even separated husband from wife. And my thoughts reverted to my father's friend, the good and great Roscoe, the intrepid enemy of the trade; who in every way exerted his fine talents toward its suppression; writing a poem (*"the Wrongs of Africa"*), several pamphlets; and in his place in Parliament, he delivered a speech against it, which, as coming from a member for Liverpool, was supposed to have turned many votes, and had no small share in the triumph of sound policy and humanity that ensued.

How this group of statuary affected me, may be inferred from the fact, that I never went through Chapel-street without going through the little arch to look at it again. And there, night or day, I was sure to find Lord Nelson still falling back; Victory's wreath still hovering over his sword-point; and Death grim and grasping as ever; while the four bronze captives still lamented their captivity.

Now, as I lingered about the railing of the statuary, on the Sunday I have mentioned, I noticed several persons going in and out of an apartment, opening from the basement under the colonnade; and, advancing, I perceived that this was a news-room, full of files of papers. My love of literature prompted me to open the door and step in; but a glance at my soiled shooting-jacket prompted a dignified looking personage to step up and shut the door in my face. I deliberated a minute what I should do to him; and at last resolutely determined to let him alone, and pass on; which I did; going down Castle-street (so called from a castle which once stood there, said my guide-book), and turning down into Lord.

Arrived at the foot of the latter street, I in vain looked round for the hotel. How serious a disappointment was this may well be imagined, when it is considered that I was all eagerness to behold the very house at which my father stopped; where he slept and dined, smoked his cigar, opened his letters, and read the papers. I inquired of some gentlemen and ladies where the missing hotel was; but they only stared and passed on; until I met a mechanic, apparently, who very civilly stopped to hear my questions and give me an answer.

"Riddough's Hotel?" said he, "upon my word, I think I have heard of such a place; let me see—yes, yes—that was the hotel where my father broke his arm, helping to pull down the walls. My lad, you surely can't be inquiring for Riddough's Hotel! What do you want to find there?"

"Oh! nothing," I replied, "I am much obliged for your information"—and away I walked.

Then, indeed, a new light broke in upon me concerning my guide-book; and all my previous dim suspicions were almost confirmed. It was nearly half a century behind the age! and no more fit to guide me about the town, than the map of Pompeii.

It was a sad, a solemn, and a most melancholy thought. The book on which I had so much relied; the book in the old morocco cover; the book with the cocked-hat corners; the book full of fine old family associations; the book with seventeen plates, executed in the highest style of art; this precious book was next to useless. Yes, the thing that had guided the father, could not guide the son. And I sat down on a shop step, and gave loose to meditation.

Here, now, oh, Wellingborough, thought I, learn a lesson, and never forget it. This world, my boy, is a moving world; its Riddough's Hotels are forever being pulled down; it never stands still; and its sands are forever shifting. This very harbor of Liverpool is gradually filling up, they say; and who knows what your son (if you ever have one) may behold, when he comes to visit Liverpool, as long after you as you come after his grandfather. And, Wellingborough, as your father's guide-book is no guide for you, neither would yours (could you afford to buy a modern one to-day) be a true guide to those who come after you. Guide-books, Wellingborough, are the least reliable books in all literature; and nearly all literature, in one sense, is made up of guide-books. Old ones tell us the ways our fathers went, through the thoroughfares and courts of old; but how few of those former places can their posterity trace, amid avenues of modern erections; to how few is the old guide-book now a clue! Every age makes its own guide-books, and the old ones are used for waste paper. But there is one Holy Guide-Book, Wellingborough, that will never lead you astray, if you but follow it aright; and some noble monuments that remain, though the pyramids crumble.

But though I rose from the door-step a sadder and a wiser boy, and though my guide-book had been stripped of its reputation for infallibility, I did not treat with contumely or disdain, those sacred pages which had once been a beacon to my sire.

No.—Poor old guide-book, thought I, tenderly stroking its back, and smoothing the dog-ears with reverence; I will not use you with despite, old Morocco! and you will yet prove a trusty conductor through many old streets in the old parts of this town; even if you are at fault, now and then, concerning a Riddough's Hotel, or some other forgotten thing of the past.

As I fondly glanced over the leaves, like one who loves more than he chides, my eye lighted upon a passage concerning *"The Old Dock,"* which much aroused my curiosity. I determined to see the place without delay: and walking on, in what I presumed to be the right direction, at last found myself before a spacious and splendid pile of sculptured brown stone; and entering the porch, perceived from incontrovertible tokens that it must be the Custom-house. After admiring it awhile, I took out my guide-book again; and what was my amazement at discovering that, according to its authority, I was entirely mistaken with regard to this Custom-house; for precisely where I stood, *"The Old Dock"* must be standing, and reading on concerning it, I met with this very apposite passage: *"The first idea that strikes the stranger in coming to this dock, is the singularity of so great a number of ships afloat in the very heart of the town, without discovering any connection with the sea."*

Here, now, was a poser! Old Morocco confessed that there was a good deal of "singularity" about the thing; nor did he pretend to deny that it was, without question, amazing, that this fabulous dock should seem to have no *connection with the sea!* However, the same author went on to say, that the *"astonished stranger must suspend his wonder for awhile, and turn to the left."* But, right or left, no place answering to the description was to be seen.

This was too confounding altogether, and not to be easily accounted for, even by making ordinary allowances for the growth and general improvement of the town in the course of years. So, guide-book in hand, I accosted a policeman standing by, and begged him to tell me whether he was acquainted with any place in that neighborhood called the *"Old Dock."* The man looked at me wonderingly at first, and then seeing I was apparently sane, and quite civil into the bargain, he whipped his well-polished boot with his rattan, pulled up his silver-laced coat-collar, and initiated me into a knowledge of the following facts.

It seems that in this place originally stood the *"pool,"* from which the town borrows a part of its name, and which originally wound round the greater part of the old settlements; that this pool was made into the "Old Dock," for the benefit of the shipping; but that, years ago, it had been filled up, and furnished the site for the Custom-house before me.

I now eyed the spot with a feeling somewhat akin to the Eastern traveler standing on the brink of the Dead Sea. For here the doom of Gomorrah seemed reversed, and a lake had been converted into substantial stone and mortar.

Well, well, Wellingborough, thought I, you had better put the book into your pocket, and carry it home to the Society of Antiquaries; it is several thousand leagues and odd furlongs behind the march of improvement. Smell its old morocco binding, Wellingborough; does it not smell somewhat mummyish? Does it not remind you of Cheops and the Catacombs? I tell you it was written before the lost books of Livy, and is cousin-german to that irrecoverably departed volume, entitled, *The Wars of the Lord,* quoted by Moses in the Pentateuch. Put it up, Wellingborough, put it up, my dear friend; and hereafter follow your nose throughout Liverpool; it will stick to you through thick and thin: and be your ship's main-mast and St. George's spire your landmarks.

No!—And again I rubbed its back softly, and gently adjusted a loose leaf: No, no, I'll not give you up yet. Forth, old Morocco! and lead me in sight of the venerable Abbey of Birkenhead; and let these eager eyes behold the mansion once occupied by the old earls of Derby!

For the book discoursed of both places, and told how the Abbey was on the Cheshire shore, full in view from a point on the Lancashire side, covered over with ivy, and brilliant with moss! And how the house of the noble Derby's was now a common jail of the town; and how that circumstance was full of suggestions, and pregnant with wisdom!

But, alas! I never saw the Abbey; at least none was in sight from the water: and as for the house of the earls, I never saw that.

Ah me, and ten times alas! am I to visit old England in vain? in the land of Thomas-à-Becket and stout John of Gaunt, not to catch the least glimpse of priory or castle? Is there nothing in all the British empire but these smoky ranges of old shops and warehouses? is Liverpool but a brick-kiln? Why, no buildings here look so ancient as the old gable-pointed mansion of my maternal grandfather at home, whose bricks were brought from Holland long before the revolutionary war! 'Tis a deceit—a gull—a sham—a hoax! This boasted England is no older than the State of New York: if it is, show me the proofs—point out the vouchers. Where's the tower of Julius Caesar? Where's the Roman wall? Show me Stonehenge!

But, Wellingborough, I remonstrated with myself, you are only in Liverpool; the old monuments lie to the north, south, east, and west of you; you are but a sailor-boy, and you can not expect to be a great tourist, and visit the antiquities, in that preposterous shooting-jacket of yours. Indeed, you can not, my boy.

True, true—that's it. I am not the traveler my father was. I am only a common-carrier across the Atlantic.

After a weary day's walk, I at last arrived at the sign of the Baltimore Clipper to supper; and Handsome Mary poured me out a brimmer of tea, in which, for the time, I drowned all my melancholy.

Chapter XXXII

THE DOCKS

FOR MORE THAN SIX WEEKS, THE SHIP *HIGHLANDER* LAY IN PRINCE'S DOCK; AND DURING THAT time, besides making observations upon things immediately around me, I made sundry excursions to the neighboring docks, for I never tired of admiring them.

Previous to this, having only seen the miserable wooden wharves, and slip-shod, shambling piers of New York, the sight of these mighty docks filled my young mind with wonder and delight. In New York, to be sure, I could not but be struck with the long line of shipping, and tangled thicket of masts along the East River; yet, my admiration had been much abated by those irregular, unsightly wharves, which, I am sure, are a reproach and disgrace to the city that tolerates them.

Whereas, in Liverpool, I beheld long China walls of masonry; vast piers of stone; and a succession of granite-rimmed docks, completely enclosed, and many of them communicating, which almost recalled to mind the great American chain of lakes: Ontario, Erie, St. Clair, Huron, Michigan, and Superior. The extent and solidity of these structures seemed equal to what I had read of the old Pyramids of Egypt.

Liverpool may justly claim to have originated the model of the Wet Dock,[1] so called, of the present day; and everything that is connected with its design, construction, regulation, and improvement. Even London was induced to copy after Liverpool, and Havre followed her example. In magnitude, cost, and durability, the docks of Liverpool, even at the present day surpass all others in the world.

The first dock built by the town was the *"Old Dock,"* alluded to in my Sunday stroll with my guide-book. This was erected in 1710, since which period has gradually arisen that long line of dock-masonry, now flanking the Liverpool side of the Mersey.

For miles you may walk along that river-side, passing dock after dock, like a chain of immense fortresses—Prince's, George's, Salt-House, Clarence, Brunswick, Trafalgar, King's, Queen's, and many more.

In a spirit of patriotic gratitude to those naval heroes, who by their valor did so much to protect the commerce of Britain, in which Liverpool held so large a stake; the town, long since, bestowed upon its more modern streets, certain illustrious names, that Broadway might be proud of—Duncan, Nelson, Rodney, St. Vincent, Nile.

But it is a pity, I think, that they had not bestowed these noble names upon their noble docks; so that they might have been as a rank and file of most fit monuments to perpetuate the names of the heroes, in connection with the commerce they defended.

And how much better would such stirring monuments be; full of life and commotion; than hermit obelisks of Luxor, and idle towers of stone; which, useless to the world in themselves, vainly hope to eternize a name, by having it carved, solitary and alone, in their granite. Such monuments are cenotaphs indeed; founded far away from the true body of the fame of the hero; who, if he be truly a hero, must still be linked with the living interests of his race; for the true fame is something free, easy, social, and companionable. They are but tomb-stones, that commemorate his death, but celebrate not his life. It is well enough that over the inglorious and thrice miserable grave of a Dives, some vast

1. This term—*Wet Dock*—did not originate (as has been erroneously opined by the otherwise learned Bardoldi); from the fact, that persons falling into one, never escaped without a soaking; but it is simply used, in order to distinguish these docks from the *Dry-dock*, where the bottoms of ships are repaired.

marble column should be reared, recording the fact of his having lived and died; for such records are indispensable to preserve his shrunken memory among men; though that memory must soon crumble away with the marble, and mix with the stagnant oblivion of the mob. But to build such a pompous vanity over the remains of a hero, is a slur upon his fame, and an insult to his ghost. And more enduring monuments are built in the closet with the letters of the alphabet, than even Cheops himself could have founded, with all Egypt and Nubia for his quarry.

Among the few docks mentioned above, occur the names of the *King's* and *Queen's.* At the time, they often reminded me of the two principal streets in the village I came from in America, which streets once rejoiced in the same royal appellations. But they had been christened previous to the Declaration of Independence; and some years after, in a fever of freedom, they were abolished, at an enthusiastic town-meeting, where King George and his lady were solemnly declared unworthy of being immortalized by the village of L——. A country antiquary once told me, that a committee of two barbers were deputed to write and inform the distracted old gentleman of the fact.

As the description of anyone of these Liverpool docks will pretty much answer for all, I will here endeavor to give some account of Prince's Dock, where the *Highlander* rested after her passage across the Atlantic.

This dock, of comparatively recent construction, is perhaps the largest of all, and is well known to American sailors, from the fact, that it is mostly frequented by the American shipping. Here lie the noble New York packets, which at home are found at the foot of Wall-street; and here lie the Mobile and Savannah cotton ships and traders.

This dock was built like the others, mostly upon the bed of the river, the earth and rock having been laboriously scooped out, and solidified again as materials for the quays and piers. From the river, Prince's Dock is protected by a long pier of masonry, surmounted by a massive wall; and on the side next the town, it is bounded by similar walls, one of which runs along a thoroughfare. The whole space thus enclosed forms an oblong, and may, at a guess, be presumed to comprise about fifteen or twenty acres; but as I had not the rod of a surveyor when I took it in, I will not be certain.

The area of the dock itself, exclusive of the enclosed quays surrounding it, may be estimated at, say, ten acres. Access to the interior from the streets is had through several gateways; so that, upon their being closed, the whole dock is shut up like a house. From the river, the entrance is through a water-gate, and ingress to ships is only to be had, when the level of the dock coincides with that of the river; that is, about the time of high tide, as the level of the dock is always at that mark. So that when it is low tide in the river, the keels of the ships enclosed by the quays are elevated more than twenty feet above those of the vessels in the stream. This, of course, produces a striking effect to a stranger, to see hundreds of immense ships floating high aloft in the heart of a mass of masonry.

Prince's Dock is generally so filled with shipping, that the entrance of a new-comer is apt to occasion a universal stir among all the older occupants. The dock-masters, whose authority is declared by tin signs worn conspicuously over their hats, mount the poops and forecastles of the various vessels, and hail the surrounding strangers in all directions:—*"Highlander ahoy! Cast off your bowline, and sheer alongside the Neptune!"*—*"Neptune ahoy! get out a stern-line, and sheer alongside the Trident!"*—*"Trident ahoy! get out a bowline, and drop astern of the Undaunted!"* And so it runs round like a shock of electricity; touch one, and you touch all. This kind of work irritates and exasperates the sailors to the last degree; but it is only one of the unavoidable inconveniences of enclosed docks, which are outweighed by innumerable advantages.

Just without the water-gate, is a basin, always connecting with the open river, through a narrow entrance between pier-heads. This basin forms a sort of ante-chamber to the dock itself, where vessels lie waiting their turn to enter. During a storm, the necessity of this basin is obvious; for it would be impossible to *"dock"* a ship under full headway from a voyage across the ocean. From the turbulent waves, she first glides into the ante-chamber between the pier-heads and from thence into the docks.

Concerning the cost of the docks, I can only state, that the *King's Dock*, comprehending but a comparatively small area, was completed at an expense of some £20,000.

Our old ship-keeper, a Liverpool man by birth, who had long followed the seas, related a curious story concerning this dock. One of the ships which carried over troops from England to Ireland in King William's war, in 1688, entered the King's Dock on the first day of its being opened in 1788, after an interval of just one century. She was a dark little brig, called the *Port-a-Ferry*. And probably, as her timbers must have been frequently renewed in the course of a hundred years, the name alone could have been all that was left of her at the time.

A paved area, very wide, is included within the walls; and along the edge of the quays are ranges of iron sheds, intended as a temporary shelter for the goods unladed from the shipping. Nothing can exceed the bustle and activity displayed along these quays during the day; bales, crates, boxes, and cases are being tumbled about by thousands of laborers; trucks are coming and going; dock-masters are shouting; sailors of all nations are singing out at their ropes; and all this commotion is greatly increased by the resoundings from the lofty walls that hem in the din.

Chapter XXXIII

The Salt-Droghers, and German Emigrant Ships

Surrounded by its broad belt of masonry, each Liverpool dock is a walled town, full of life and commotion; or rather, it is a small archipelago, an epitome of the world, where all the nations of Christendom, and even those of Heathendom, are represented. For, in itself, each ship is an island, a floating colony of the tribe to which it belongs.

Here are brought together the remotest limits of the earth; and in the collective spars and timbers of these ships, all the forests of the globe are represented, as in a grand parliament of masts. Canada and New Zealand send their pines; America her live oak; India her teak; Norway her spruce; and the Right Honorable Mahogany, member for Honduras and Campeachy, is seen at his post by the wheel. Here, under the beneficent sway of the Genius of Commerce, all climes and countries embrace; and yard-arm touches yard-arm in brotherly love.

A Liverpool dock is a grand caravansary inn, and hotel, on the spacious and liberal plan of the *Astor House*. Here ships are lodged at a moderate charge, and payment is not demanded till the time of departure. Here they are comfortably housed and provided for; sheltered from all weathers and secured from all calamities. For I can hardly credit a story I have heard, that sometimes, in heavy gales, ships lying in the very middle of the docks have lost their top-gallant-masts. Whatever the toils and hardships encountered on the voyage, whether they come from Iceland or the coast of New Guinea, here their sufferings are ended, and they take their ease in their watery inn.

I know not how many hours I spent in gazing at the shipping in Prince's Dock, and speculating concerning their past voyages and future prospects in life. Some had just arrived from the most distant ports, worn, battered, and disabled; others were all a-taunt-o—spruce, gay, and brilliant, in readiness for sea.

Everyday the *Highlander* had some new neighbor. A black brig from Glasgow, with its crew of sober Scotch caps, and its staid, thrifty-looking skipper, would be replaced by a jovial French hermaphrodite, its forecastle echoing with songs, and its quarter-deck elastic from much dancing.

On the other side, perhaps, a magnificent New York Liner, huge as a seventy-four, and suggesting the idea of a Mivart's or Delmonico's afloat, would give way to a Sydney emigrant ship, receiving on board its live freight of shepherds from the Grampians, ere long to be tending their flocks on the hills and downs of New Holland.

I was particularly pleased and tickled, with a multitude of little salt-droghers, rigged like sloops, and not much bigger than a pilot-boat, but with broad bows painted black, and carrying red sails, which looked as if they had been pickled and stained in a tan-yard. These little fellows were continually coming in with their cargoes for ships bound to America; and lying, five or six together, alongside of those lofty Yankee hulls, resembled a parcel of red ants about the carcass of a black buffalo.

When loaded, these comical little craft are about level with the water; and frequently, when blowing fresh in the river, I have seen them flying through the foam with nothing visible but the mast and sail, and a man at the tiller; their entire cargo being snugly secured under hatches.

It was diverting to observe the self-importance of the skipper of any of these diminutive vessels. He would give himself all the airs of an admiral on a three-decker's poop; and no doubt, thought quite as much of himself. And why not? What could Cæsar want more? Though his craft was none of the largest, it was subject to *him*; and though his crew might only consist of himself; yet if he governed it well, he achieved a triumph, which the moralists of all ages have set above the victories of Alexander.

These craft have each a little cabin, the prettiest, charmingest, most delightful little dog-hole in the world; not much bigger than an old-fashioned alcove for a bed. It is lighted by little round glasses placed in the deck; so that to the insider, the ceiling is like a small firmament twinkling with astral radiations. For tall men, nevertheless, the place is but ill-adapted; a sitting, or recumbent position being indispensable to an occupancy of the premises. Yet small, low, and narrow as the cabin is, somehow, it affords accommodations to the skipper and his family. Often, I used to watch the tidy good-wife, seated at the open little scuttle, like a woman at a cottage door, engaged in knitting socks for her husband; or perhaps, cutting his hair, as he kneeled before her. And once, while marveling how a couple like this found room to turn in, below, I was amazed by a noisy irruption of cherry-cheeked young tars from the scuttle, whence they came rolling forth, like so many curly spaniels from a kennel.

Upon one occasion, I had the curiosity to go on board a salt-drogher, and fall into conversation with its skipper, a bachelor, who kept house all alone. I found him a very sociable, comfortable old fellow, who had an eye to having things cozy around him. It was in the evening; and he invited me down into his sanctum to supper; and there we sat together like a couple in a box at an oyster-cellar.

"He, he," he chuckled, kneeling down before a fat, moist, little cask of beer, and holding a cocked-hat pitcher to the faucet—"You see, Jack, I keep everything down here; and nice times I have by myself. Just before going to bed, it ain't bad to take a nightcap, you know; eh! Jack?—here now, smack your lips over that, my boy—have a pipe?—but stop, let's to supper first."

So he went to a little locker, a fixture against the side, and groping in it awhile, and addressing it with—*"What cheer here, what cheer?"* at last produced a loaf, a small cheese, a bit of ham, and a jar of butter. And then placing a board on his lap, spread the table, the pitcher of beer in the center. "Why that's but a two legged table," said I, "let's make it four."

So we divided the burthen, and supped merrily together on our knees.

He was an old ruby of a fellow, his cheeks toasted brown; and it did my soul good, to see the froth of the beer bubbling at his mouth, and sparkling on his nut-brown beard. He looked so like a great mug of ale, that I almost felt like taking him by the neck and pouring him out.

"Now Jack," said he, when supper was over, "now Jack, my boy, do you smoke?—Well then, load away." And he handed me a seal-skin pouch of tobacco and a pipe. We sat smoking together in this little sea-cabinet of his, till it began to look much like a state-room in Tophet; and notwithstanding my host's rubicund nose, I could hardly see him for the fog.

"He, he, my boy," then said he—"I don't never have any bugs here, I tell ye: I smokes 'em all out every night before going to bed."

"And where may you sleep?" said I, looking round, and seeing no sign of a bed.

"Sleep?" says he, "why I sleep in my jacket, that's the best counterpane; and I use my head for a pillow. He-he, funny, ain't it?"

"Very funny," says I.

"Have some more ale?" says he; "plenty more."

"No more, thank you," says I; "I guess I'll go"; for what with the tobacco-smoke and the ale, I began to feel like breathing fresh air. Besides, my conscience smote me for thus freely indulging in the pleasures of the table.

"Now, don't go," said he; "don't go, my boy; don't go out into the damp; take an old Christian's advice," laying his hand on my shoulder; "it won't do. You see, by going out now, you'll shake off the ale, and get broad awake again; but if you stay here, you'll soon be dropping off for a nice little nap."

But notwithstanding these inducements, I shook my host's hand and departed.

There was hardly anything I witnessed in the docks that interested me more than the German emigrants who come on board the large New York ships several days before their sailing, to make everything comfortable ere starting. Old men, tottering with age, and little infants in arms; laughing girls in bright-buttoned bodices, and astute, middle-aged men with pictured pipes in their mouths, would be seen mingling together in crowds of five, six, and seven or eight hundred in one ship.

Every evening these countrymen of Luther and Melancthon gathered on the forecastle to sing and pray. And it was exalting to listen to their fine ringing anthems, reverberating among the crowded shipping, and rebounding from the lofty walls of the docks. Shut your eyes, and you would think you were in a cathedral.

They keep up this custom at sea; and every night, in the dog-watch, sing the songs of Zion to the roll of the great ocean-organ: a pious custom of a devout race, who thus send over their hallelujahs before them, as they hie to the land of the stranger.

And among these sober Germans, my country counts the most orderly and valuable of her foreign population. It is they who have swelled the census of her Northwestern States; and transferring their plows from the hills of Transylvania to the prairies of Wisconsin; and sowing the wheat of the Rhine on the banks of the Ohio, raise the grain, that, a hundred fold increased, may return to their kinsmen in Europe.

There is something in the contemplation of the mode in which America has been settled, that, in a noble breast, should forever extinguish the prejudices of national dislikes.

Settled by the people of all nations, all nations may claim her for their own. You can not spill a drop of American blood without spilling the blood of the whole world. Be he Englishman, Frenchman, German, Dane, or Scot; the European who scoffs at an American, calls his own brother *Raca,* and stands in danger of the judgment. We are not a narrow tribe of men, with a bigoted Hebrew nationality—whose blood has been debased in the attempt to ennoble it, by maintaining an exclusive succession among ourselves. No: our blood is as the flood of the Amazon, made up of a thousand noble currents all pouring into one. We are not a nation, so much as a world; for unless we may claim all the world for our sire, like Melchisedec, we are without father or mother.

For who was our father and our mother? Or can we point to any Romulus and Remus for our founders? Our ancestry is lost in the universal paternity; and Cæsar and Alfred, St. Paul and Luther, and Homer and Shakespeare are as much ours as Washington, who is as much the world's as our own. We are the heirs of all time, and with all nations we divide our inheritance. On this Western Hemisphere all tribes and people are forming into one federated whole; and there is a future which shall see the estranged children of Adam restored as to the old hearth-stone in Eden.

The other world beyond this, which was longed for by the devout before Columbus' time, was found in the New; and the deep-sea-lead, that first struck these soundings, brought up the soil of Earth's Paradise. Not a Paradise then, or now; but to be made so, at God's good pleasure, and in the fullness and mellowness of time. The seed is sown, and the harvest must come; and our children's children, on the world's jubilee morning, shall all go with their sickles to the reaping. Then shall the curse of Babel be revoked, a new Pentecost come, and the language they shall speak shall be the language of Britain. Frenchmen, and Danes, and Scots; and the dwellers on the shores of the Mediterranean, and in the regions round about; Italians, and Indians, and Moors; there shall appear unto them cloven tongues as of fire.

Chapter XXXIV

THE IRRAWADDY

AMONG THE VARIOUS SHIPS LYING IN PRINCE'S DOCK, NONE INTERESTED ME MORE THAN THE *Irrawaddy*, of Bombay, a *"country ship,"* which is the name bestowed by Europeans upon the large native vessels of India. Forty years ago, these merchantmen were nearly the largest in the world; and they still exceed the generality. They are built of the celebrated teak wood, the oak of the East, or in Eastern phrase, *"the King of the Oaks."*

The *Irrawaddy* had just arrived from Hindostan, with a cargo of cotton. She was manned by forty or fifty Lascars, the native seamen of India, who seemed to be immediately governed by a countryman of theirs of a higher caste. While his inferiors went about in strips of white linen, this dignitary was arrayed in a red army-coat, brilliant with gold lace, a cocked hat, and drawn sword. But the general effect was quite spoiled by his bare feet.

In discharging the cargo, his business seemed to consist in flagellating the crew with the flat of his saber, an exercise in which long practice had made him exceedingly expert. The poor fellows jumped away with the tackle-rope, elastic as cats.

One Sunday, I went aboard of the *Irrawaddy*, when this oriental usher accosted me at the gangway, with his sword at my throat. I gently pushed it aside, making a sign expressive of the pacific character of my motives in paying a visit to the ship. Whereupon he very considerately let me pass.

I thought I was in Pegu, so strangely woody was the smell of the dark-colored timbers, whose odor was heightened by the rigging of *kayar*, or cocoanut fiber.

The Lascars were on the forecastle-deck. Among them were Malays, Mahrattas, Burmese, Siamese, and Cingalese. They were seated round "kids" full of rice, from which, according to their invariable custom, they helped themselves with one hand, the other being reserved for quite another purpose. They were chattering like magpies in Hindostanee, but I found that several of them could also speak very good English. They were a small-limbed, wiry, tawny set; and I was informed made excellent seamen, though ill adapted to stand the hardships of northern voyaging.

They told me that seven of their number had died on the passage from Bombay; two or three after crossing the Tropic of Cancer, and the rest met their fate in the Channel, where the ship had been tossed about in violent seas, attended with cold rains, peculiar to that vicinity. Two more had been lost overboard from the flying-jib-boom.

I was condoling with a young English cabin-boy on board, upon the loss of these poor fellows, when he said it was their own fault; they would never wear monkey-jackets, but clung to their thin

India robes, even in the bitterest weather. He talked about them much as a farmer would about the loss of so many sheep by the murrain.

The captain of the vessel was an Englishman, as were also the three mates, master and boatswain. These officers lived astern in the cabin, where every Sunday they read the Church of England's prayers, while the heathen at the other end of the ship were left to their false gods and idols. And thus, with Christianity on the quarter-deck, and paganism on the forecastle, the *Irrawaddy* plowed the sea.

As if to symbolize this state of things, the *"fancy piece"* astern comprised, among numerous other carved decorations, a cross and a miter; while forward, on the bows, was a sort of devil for a figure-head—a dragon-shaped creature, with a fiery red mouth, and a switchy-looking tail.

After her cargo was discharged, which was done "to the sound of flutes and soft recorders"—something as work is done in the navy to the music of the boatswain's pipe—the Lascars were set to *"stripping the ship"*; that is, to sending down all her spars and ropes.

At this time, she lay alongside of us, and the Babel on board almost drowned our own voices. In nothing but their girdles, the Lascars hopped about aloft, chattering like so many monkeys; but, nevertheless, showing much dexterity and seamanship in their manner of doing their work.

Every Sunday, crowds of well-dressed people came down to the dock to see this singular ship; many of them perched themselves in the shrouds of the neighboring craft, much to the wrath of Captain Riga, who left strict orders with our old ship-keeper, to drive all strangers out of the *Highlander*'s rigging. It was amusing at these times, to watch the old women with umbrellas, who stood on the quay staring at the Lascars, even when they desired to be private. These inquisitive old ladies seemed to regard the strange sailors as a species of wild animal, whom they might gaze at with as much impunity, as at leopards in the Zoological Gardens.

One night I was returning to the ship, when just as I was passing through the Dock Gate, I noticed a white figure squatting against the wall outside. It proved to be one of the Lascars who was smoking, as the regulations of the docks prohibit his indulging this luxury on board his vessel. Struck with the curious fashion of his pipe, and the odor from it, I inquired what he was smoking; he replied *"Joggerry,"* which is a species of weed, used in place of tobacco.

Finding that he spoke good English, and was quite communicative, like most smokers, I sat down by *Dattabdoolmans,* as he called himself, and we fell into conversation. So instructive was his discourse, that when we parted, I had considerably added to my stock of knowledge. Indeed, it is a God-send to fall in with a fellow like this. He knows things you never dreamed of; his experiences are like a man from the moon—wholly strange, a new revelation. If you want to learn romance, or gain an insight into things quaint, curious, and marvelous, drop your books of travel, and take a stroll along the docks of a great commercial port. Ten to one, you will encounter Crusoe himself among the crowds of mariners from all parts of the globe.

But this is no place for making mention of all the subjects upon which I and my Lascar friend mostly discoursed; I will only try to give his account of the *teakwood* and *kayar rope,* concerning which things I was curious, and sought information.

The *"sagoon,"* as he called the tree which produces the teak, grows in its greatest excellence among the mountains of Malabar, whence large quantities are sent to Bombay for ship-building. He also spoke of another kind of wood, the *"sissor,"* which supplies most of the *"shin-logs,"* or "knees," and crooked timbers in the *country ships*. The sagoon grows to an immense size; sometimes there is fifty feet of trunk, three feet through, before a single bough is put forth. Its leaves are very large; and to convey some idea of them, my Lascar likened them to elephants' ears. He said a purple dye was extracted from them, for the purpose of staining cottons and silks. The wood is specifically heavier than water; it is easily worked, and extremely strong and durable. But its chief merit lies in resisting the action of the salt water, and the attacks of insects; which resistance is caused by its containing a resinous oil called *"poonja."*

To my surprise, he informed me that the *Irrawaddy* was wholly built by the native shipwrights of India, who, he modestly asserted, surpassed the European artisans.

The rigging, also, was of native manufacture. As the *kayar*, of which it is composed, is now getting into use both in England and America, as well for ropes and rigging as for mats and rugs, my Lascar friend's account of it, joined to my own observations, may not be uninteresting.

In India, it is prepared very much in the same way as in Polynesia. The cocoa-nut is gathered while the husk is still green, and but partially ripe; and this husk is removed by striking the nut forcibly, with both hands, upon a sharp-pointed stake, planted uprightly in the ground. In this way a boy will strip nearly fifteen hundred in a day. But the *kayar* is not made from the husk, as might be supposed, but from the rind of the nut; which, after being long soaked in water, is beaten with mallets, and rubbed together into fibers. After this being dried in the sun, you may spin it, just like hemp, or any similar substance. The fiber thus produced makes very strong and durable ropes, extremely well adapted, from their lightness and durability, for the running rigging of a ship; while the same causes, united with its great strength and buoyancy, render it very suitable for large cables and hawsers.

But the elasticity of the *kayar* ill fits it for the shrouds and standing-rigging of a ship, which require to be comparatively firm. Hence, as the *Irrawaddy*'s shrouds were all of this substance, the Lascar told me, they were continually setting up or slacking off her standing-rigging, according as the weather was cold or warm. And the loss of a fore-top-mast, between the tropics, in a squall, he attributed to this circumstance.

After a stay of about two weeks, the *Irrawaddy* had her heavy Indian spars replaced with Canadian pine, and her *kayar* shrouds with hempen ones. She then mustered her pagans, and hoisted sail for London.

Chapter XXXV

Galliots, Coast-of-Guinea-Man, and Floating Chapel

Another very curious craft often seen in the Liverpool docks, is the Dutch galliot, an old-fashioned looking gentleman, with hollow waist, high prow and stern, and which, seen lying among crowds of tight Yankee traders, and pert French brigantines, always reminded me of a cocked hat among modish beavers.

The construction of the galliot has not altered for centuries; and the northern European nations, Danes and Dutch, still sail the salt seas in this flat-bottomed salt-cellar of a ship; although, in addition to these, they have vessels of a more modern kind.

They seldom paint the galliot; but scrape and varnish all its planks and spars, so that all over it resembles the *"bright side"* or polished *streak*, usually banding round an American ship.

Some of them are kept scrupulously neat and clean, and remind one of a well-scrubbed wooden platter, or an old oak table, upon which much wax and elbow vigor has been expended. Before the wind, they sail well; but on a bowline, owing to their broad hulls and flat bottoms, they make leeway at a sad rate.

Everyday, some strange vessel entered Prince's Dock; and hardly would I gaze my fill at some outlandish craft from Surat or the Levant, ere a still more outlandish one would absorb my attention.

Among others, I remember, was a little brig from the Coast of Guinea. In appearance, she was the ideal of a slaver; low, black, clipper-built about the bows, and her decks in a state of most piratical disorder.

She carried a long, rusty gun, on a swivel, amid-ships; and that gun was a curiosity in itself. It must have been some old veteran, condemned by the government, and sold for anything it would fetch. It was an antique, covered with half-effaced inscriptions, crowns, anchors, eagles; and it had two handles near the trunnions, like those of a tureen. The knob on the breach was fashioned into a dolphin's head; and by a comical conceit, the touch-hole formed the orifice of a human ear; and a stout tympanum it must have had, to have withstood the concussions it had heard.

The brig, heavily loaded, lay between two large ships in ballast; so that its deck was at least twenty feet below those of its neighbors. Thus shut in, its hatchways looked like the entrance to deep vaults or mines; especially as her men were wheeling out of her hold some kind of ore, which might have been gold ore, so scrupulous were they in evening the bushel measures, in which they transferred it to the quay; and so particular was the captain, a dark-skinned whiskerando, in a Maltese cap and tassel, in standing over the sailors, with his pencil and memorandum-book in hand.

The crew were a buccaneering looking set; with hairy chests, purple shirts, and arms wildly tattooed. The mate had a wooden leg, and hobbled about with a crooked cane like a spiral staircase. There was a deal of swearing on board of this craft, which was rendered the more reprehensible when she came to moor alongside the Floating Chapel.

This was the hull of an old sloop-of-war, which had been converted into a mariner's church. A house had been built upon it, and a steeple took the place of a mast. There was a little balcony near the base of the steeple, some twenty feet from the water; where, on week-days, I used to see an old pensioner of a tar, sitting on a camp-stood, reading his Bible. On Sundays he hoisted the Bethel flag, and like the *muezzin* or cryer of prayers on the top of a Turkish mosque, would call the strolling sailors to their devotions; not officially, but on his own account; conjuring them not to make fools of themselves, but muster round the pulpit, as they did about the capstan on a man-of-war. This old worthy was the sexton. I attended the chapel several times, and found there a very orderly but small congregation. The first time I went, the chaplain was discoursing of future punishments, and making allusions to the Tartarean Lake; which, coupled with the pitchy smell of the old hull, summoned up the most forcible image of the thing which I ever experienced.

The floating chapels which are to be found in some of the docks, form one of the means which have been tried to induce the seamen visiting Liverpool to turn their thoughts toward serious things. But as very few of them ever think of entering these chapels, though they might pass them twenty times in the day, some of the clergy, of a Sunday, address them in the open air, from the corners of the quays, or wherever they can procure an audience.

Whenever, in my Sunday strolls, I caught sight of one of these congregations, I always made a point of joining it; and would find myself surrounded by a motley crowd of seamen from all quarters of the globe, and women, and lumpers, and dock laborers of all sorts. Frequently the clergyman would be standing upon an old cask, arrayed in full canonicals, as a divine of the Church of England. Never have I heard religious discourses better adapted to an audience of men, who, like sailors, are chiefly, if not only, to be moved by the plainest of precepts, and demonstrations of the misery of sin, as conclusive and undeniable as those of Euclid. No mere rhetoric avails with such men; fine periods are vanity. You can not touch them with tropes. They need to be pressed home by plain facts.

And such was generally the mode in which they were addressed by the clergy in question: who, taking familiar themes for their discourses, which were leveled right at the wants of their auditors, always succeeded in fastening their attention. In particular, the two great vices to which sailors are most addicted, and which they practice to the ruin of both body and soul; these things, were the most enlarged upon. And several times on the docks, I have seen a robed clergyman addressing a large audience of women collected from the notorious lanes and alleys in the neighborhood.

Is not this as it ought to be? since the true calling of the reverend clergy is like their divine Master's;—not to bring the righteous, but sinners to repentance. Did some of them leave the converted and comfortable congregations, before whom they have ministered year after year; and plunge at once, like St. Paul, into the infected centers and hearts of vice: *then* indeed, would they find a strong enemy to cope with; and a victory gained over *him*, would entitle them to a conqueror's wreath. Better to save one sinner from an obvious vice that is destroying him, than to indoctrinate ten thousand saints. And as from every corner, in Catholic towns, the shrines of Holy Mary and the Child Jesus perpetually remind the commonest wayfarer of his heaven; even so should Protestant pulpits be founded in the market-places, and at street corners, where the men of God might be heard by all of His children.

Chapter XXXVI

The Old Church of St. Nicholas, and the Dead-House

The floating chapel recalls to mind the "*old church*," well known to the seamen of many generations, who have visited Liverpool. It stands very near the docks, a venerable mass of brown stone, and by the town's people is called the Church of St. Nicholas. I believe it is the best preserved piece of antiquity in all Liverpool.

Before the town rose to any importance, it was the only place of worship on that side of the Mersey; and under the adjoining Parish of Walton was a *chapel-of-ease*; though from the straight backed pews, there could have been but little comfort taken in it.

In old times, there stood in front of the church a statue of St. Nicholas, the patron of mariners; to which all pious sailors made offerings, to induce his saintship to grant them short and prosperous voyages. In the tower is a fine chime of bells; and I well remember my delight at first hearing them on the first Sunday morning after our arrival in the dock. It seemed to carry an admonition with it; something like the premonition conveyed to young Whittington by Bow Bells. "*Wellingborough! Wellingborough! you must not forget to go to church, Wellingborough! Don't forget, Wellingborough! Wellingborough! don't forget.*"

Thirty or forty years ago, these bells were rung upon the arrival of every Liverpool ship from a foreign voyage. How forcibly does this illustrate the increase of the commerce of the town! Were the same custom now observed, the bells would seldom have a chance to cease.

What seemed the most remarkable about this venerable old church, and what seemed the most barbarous, and grated upon the veneration with which I regarded this time-hallowed structure, was the condition of the grave-yard surrounding it. From its close vicinity to the haunts of the swarms of laborers about the docks, it is crossed and re-crossed by thoroughfares in all directions; and the tomb-stones, not being erect, but horizontal (indeed, they form a complete flagging to the spot), multitudes are constantly walking over the dead; their heels erasing the death's-heads and crossbones, the last mementos of the departed. At noon, when the lumpers employed in loading and unloading the shipping, retire for an hour to snatch a dinner, many of them resort to the grave-yard; and seating themselves upon a tomb-stone use the adjoining one for a table. Often, I saw men stretched out in a drunken sleep upon these slabs; and once, removing a fellow's arm, read the following inscription, which, in a manner, was true to the life, if not to the death:

HERE LYETH YE BODY OF

TOBIAS DRINKER

For two memorable circumstances connected with this church, I am indebted to my excellent friend, Morocco, who tells me that in 1588 the Earl of Derby, coming to his residence, and waiting for a passage to the Isle of Man, the corporation erected and adorned a sumptuous stall in the church for his reception. And moreover, that in the time of Cromwell's wars, when the place was taken by that mad nephew of King Charles, Prince Rupert, he converted the old church into a military prison and stable; when, no doubt, another "sumptuous stall" was erected for the benefit of the steed of some noble cavalry officer.

In the basement of the church is a Dead-House, like the Morgue in Paris, where the bodies of the drowned are exposed until claimed by their friends, or till buried at the public charge.

From the multitudes employed about the shipping, this dead-house has always more or less occupants. Whenever I passed up Chapel-street, I used to see a crowd gazing through the grim iron grating of the door, upon the faces of the drowned within. And once, when the door was opened, I saw a sailor stretched out, stark and stiff, with the sleeve of his frock rolled up, and showing his name and date of birth tattooed upon his arm. It was a sight full of suggestions; he seemed his own head-stone.

I was told that standing rewards are offered for the recovery of persons falling into the docks; so much, if restored to life, and a less amount if irrecoverably drowned. Lured by this, several horrid old men and women are constantly prying about the docks, searching after bodies. I observed them principally early in the morning, when they issued from their dens, on the same principle that the rag-rakers, and rubbish-pickers in the streets, sally out bright and early; for then, the night-harvest has ripened.

There seems to be no calamity overtaking man, that can not be rendered merchantable. Undertakers, sextons, tomb-makers, and hearse-drivers, get their living from the dead; and in times of plague most thrive. And these miserable old men and women hunted after corpses to keep from going to the church-yard themselves; for they were the most wretched of starvelings.

Chapter XXXVII

What Redburn Saw in Launcelott's-Hey

The dead-house reminds me of other sad things; for in the vicinity of the docks are many very painful sights.

In going to our boarding-house, the sign of the Baltimore Clipper, I generally passed through a narrow street called "Launcelott's-Hey," lined with dingy, prison-like cotton warehouses. In this street, or rather alley, you seldom see anyone but a truck-man, or some solitary old warehouse-keeper, haunting his smoky den like a ghost.

Once, passing through this place, I heard a feeble wail, which seemed to come out of the earth. It was but a strip of crooked side-walk where I stood; the dingy wall was on every side, converting the mid-day into twilight; and not a soul was in sight. I started, and could almost have run, when I heard that dismal sound. It seemed the low, hopeless, endless wail of someone forever lost. At last I advanced to an opening which communicated downward with deep tiers of cellars beneath a crumbling old warehouse; and there, some fifteen feet below the walk, crouching in nameless squalor, with her head bowed over, was the figure of what had been a woman. Her blue arms folded to her livid bosom two shrunken things like children, that leaned toward her, one on each side. At first, I knew not whether they were alive or dead. They made no sign; they did not move or stir; but from the vault came that soul-sickening wail.

I made a noise with my foot, which, in the silence, echoed far and near; but there was no response. Louder still; when one of the children lifted its head, and cast upward a faint glance; then closed its eyes, and lay motionless. The woman also, now gazed up, and perceived me; but let fall her eye again. They were dumb and next to dead with want. How they had crawled into that den, I could not tell; but there they had crawled to die. At that moment I never thought of relieving them; for death was so stamped in their glazed and unimploring eyes, that I almost regarded them as already no more. I stood looking down on them, while my whole soul swelled within me; and I asked myself, What right had anybody in the wide world to smile and be glad, when sights like this were to be seen? It was enough to turn the heart to gall; and make a man-hater of a Howard. For who were these ghosts that I saw? Were they not human beings? A woman and two girls? With eyes, and lips, and ears like any queen? with hearts which, though they did not bound with blood, yet beat with a dull, dead ache that was their life.

At last, I walked on toward an open lot in the alley, hoping to meet there some ragged old women, whom I had daily noticed groping amid foul rubbish for little particles of dirty cotton, which they washed out and sold for a trifle.

I found them; and accosting one, I asked if she knew of the persons I had just left. She replied, that she did not; nor did she want to. I then asked another, a miserable, toothless old woman, with a tattered strip of coarse baling stuff round her body. Looking at me for an instant, she resumed her raking in the rubbish, and said that she knew who it was that I spoke of; but that she had no time to attend to beggars and their brats. Accosting still another, who seemed to know my errand, I asked if there was no place to which the woman could be taken. "Yes," she replied, "to the church-yard." I said she was alive, and not dead.

"Then she'll never die," was the rejoinder. "She's been down there these three days, with nothing to eat;—that I know myself."

"She desarves it," said an old hag, who was just placing on her crooked shoulders her bag of pickings, and who was turning to totter off, "that Betsy Jennings desarves it—was she ever married? tell me that."

Leaving Launcelott's-Hey, I turned into a more frequented street; and soon meeting a policeman, told him of the condition of the woman and the girls.

"It's none of my business, Jack," said he. "I don't belong to that street."

"Who does then?"

"I don't know. But what business is it of yours? Are you not a Yankee?"

"Yes," said I, "but come, I will help you remove that woman, if you say so."

"There, now, Jack, go on board your ship and stick to it; and leave these matters to the town."

I accosted two more policemen, but with no better success; they would not even go with me to the place. The truth was, it was out of the way, in a silent, secluded spot; and the misery of the three outcasts, hiding away in the ground, did not obtrude upon anyone.

Returning to them, I again stamped to attract their attention; but this time, none of the three looked up, or even stirred. While I yet stood irresolute, a voice called to me from a high, iron-shuttered window in a loft over the way; and asked what I was about. I beckoned to the man, a sort of porter, to come down, which he did; when I pointed down into the vault.

"Well," said he, "what of it?"

"Can't we get them out?" said I, "haven't you some place in your warehouse where you can put them? have you nothing for them to eat?"

"You're crazy, boy," said he; "do you suppose, that Parkins and Wood want their warehouse turned into a hospital?"

I then went to my boarding-house, and told Handsome Mary of what I had seen; asking her if she could not do something to get the woman and girls removed; or if she could not do that, let me have some food for them. But though a kind person in the main, Mary replied that she gave away enough to beggars in her own street (which was true enough) without looking after the whole neighborhood.

Going into the kitchen, I accosted the cook, a little shriveled-up old Welshwoman, with a saucy tongue, whom the sailors called *Brandy-Nan*; and begged her to give me some cold victuals, if she had nothing better, to take to the vault. But she broke out in a storm of swearing at the miserable occupants of the vault, and refused. I then stepped into the room where our dinner was being spread; and waiting till the girl had gone out, I snatched some bread and cheese from a stand, and thrusting it into the bosom of my frock, left the house. Hurrying to the lane, I dropped the food down into the vault. One of the girls caught at it convulsively, but fell back, apparently fainting; the sister pushed the other's arm aside, and took the bread in her hand; but with a weak uncertain grasp like an infant's. She placed it to her mouth; but letting it fall again, murmuring faintly something like "water." The woman did not stir; her head was bowed over, just as I had first seen her.

Seeing how it was, I ran down toward the docks to a mean little sailor tavern, and begged for a pitcher; but the cross old man who kept it refused, unless I would pay for it. But I had no money. So as my boarding-house was some way off, and it would be lost time to run to the ship for my big iron pot; under the impulse of the moment, I hurried to one of the Boodle Hydrants, which I remembered having seen running near the scene of a still smoldering fire in an old rag house; and taking off a new tarpaulin hat, which had been loaned me that day, filled it with water.

With this, I returned to Launcelott's-Hey; and with considerable difficulty, like getting down into a well, I contrived to descend with it into the vault; where there was hardly space enough left to let me stand. The two girls drank out of the hat together; looking up at me with an unalterable, idiotic expression, that almost made me faint. The woman spoke not a word, and did not stir. While the girls were breaking and eating the bread, I tried to lift the woman's head; but, feeble as she was, she seemed bent upon holding it down. Observing her arms still clasped upon her bosom, and that something seemed hidden under the rags there, a thought crossed my mind, which impelled me forcibly to withdraw her hands for a moment; when I caught a glimpse of a meager little babe, the lower part of its body thrust into an old bonnet. Its face was dazzlingly white, even in its squalor; but the closed eyes looked like balls of indigo. It must have been dead some hours.

The woman refusing to speak, eat, or drink, I asked one of the girls who they were, and where they lived; but she only stared vacantly, muttering something that could not be understood.

The air of the place was now getting too much for me; but I stood deliberating a moment, whether it was possible for me to drag them out of the vault. But if I did, what then? They would only perish in the street, and here they were at least protected from the rain; and more than that, might die in seclusion.

I crawled up into the street, and looking down upon them again, almost repented that I had brought them any food; for it would only tend to prolong their misery, without hope of any permanent relief: for die they must very soon; they were too far gone for any medicine to help them. I hardly know whether I ought to confess another thing that occurred to me as I stood there; but it was this—I felt an almost irresistible impulse to do them the last mercy, of in some way putting an end to their horrible lives; and I should almost have done so, I think, had I not been deterred by thoughts of the law. For I well knew that the law, which would let them perish of themselves without giving them one cup of water, would spend a thousand pounds, if necessary, in convicting him who should so much as offer to relieve them from their miserable existence.

The next day, and the next, I passed the vault three times, and still met the same sight. The girls leaning up against the woman on each side, and the woman with her arms still folding the babe, and her head bowed. The first evening I did not see the bread that I had dropped down in the morning; but the second evening, the bread I had dropped that morning remained untouched. On the third morning the smell that came from the vault was such, that I accosted the same policeman I had accosted before, who was patrolling the same street, and told him that the persons I had spoken to him about were dead, and he had better have them removed. He looked as if he did not believe me, and added, that it was not his street.

When I arrived at the docks on my way to the ship, I entered the guard-house within the walls, and asked for one of the captains, to whom I told the story; but, from what he said, was led to infer that the Dock Police was distinct from that of the town, and this was not the right place to lodge my information.

I could do no more that morning, being obliged to repair to the ship; but at twelve o'clock, when I went to dinner, I hurried into Launcelott's-Hey, when I found that the vault was empty. In place of the woman and children, a heap of quick-lime was glistening.

I could not learn who had taken them away, or whither they had gone; but my prayer was answered—they were dead, departed, and at peace.

But again I looked down into the vault, and in fancy beheld the pale, shrunken forms still crouching there. Ah! what are our creeds, and how do we hope to be saved? Tell me, oh Bible, that story of Lazarus again, that I may find comfort in my heart for the poor and forlorn. Surrounded as we are by the wants and woes of our fellow-men, and yet given to follow our own pleasures, regardless of their pains, are we not like people sitting up with a corpse, and making merry in the house of the dead?

Chapter XXXVIII

The Dock-Wall Beggars

I might relate other things which befell me during the six weeks and more that I remained in Liverpool, often visiting the cellars, sinks, and hovels of the wretched lanes and courts near the river. But to tell of them, would only be to tell over again the story just told; so I return to the docks.

The old women described as picking dirty fragments of cotton in the empty lot, belong to the same class of beings who at all hours of the day are to be seen within the dock walls, raking over and over the heaps of rubbish carried ashore from the holds of the shipping.

As it is against the law to throw the least thing overboard, even a rope yarn; and as this law is very different from similar laws in New York, inasmuch as it is rigidly enforced by the dock-masters; and, moreover, as after discharging a ship's cargo, a great deal of dirt and worthless dunnage remains in the hold, the amount of rubbish accumulated in the appointed receptacles for depositing it within the walls is extremely large, and is constantly receiving new accessions from every vessel that unlades at the quays.

Standing over these noisome heaps, you will see scores of tattered wretches, armed with old rakes and picking-irons, turning over the dirt, and making as much of a rope-yarn as if it were a skein of silk. Their findings, nevertheless, are but small; for as it is one of the immemorial perquisites of the second mate of a merchant-ship to collect, and sell on his own account, all the condemned "old junk" of the vessel to which he belongs, he generally takes good heed that in the buckets of rubbish carried ashore, there shall be as few rope-yarns as possible.

In the same way, the cook preserves all the odds and ends of pork-rinds and beef-fat, which he sells at considerable profit; upon a six months' voyage frequently realizing thirty or forty dollars from the sale, and in large ships, even more than that. It may easily be imagined, then, how desperately driven to it must these rubbish-pickers be, to ransack heaps of refuse which have been previously gleaned.

Nor must I omit to make mention of the singular beggary practiced in the streets frequented by sailors; and particularly to record the remarkable army of paupers that beset the docks at particular hours of the day.

At twelve o'clock the crews of hundreds and hundreds of ships issue in crowds from the dock gates to go to their dinner in the town. This hour is seized upon by multitudes of beggars to plant themselves against the outside of the walls, while others stand upon the curbstone to excite the charity of the seamen. The first time that I passed through this long lane of pauperism, it seemed hard to believe that such an array of misery could be furnished by any town in the world.

Every variety of want and suffering here met the eye, and every vice showed here its victims. Nor were the marvelous and almost incredible shifts and stratagems of the professional beggars, wanting to finish this picture of all that is dishonorable to civilization and humanity.

Old women, rather mummies, drying up with slow starving and age; young girls, incurably sick, who ought to have been in the hospital; sturdy men, with the gallows in their eyes, and a whining lie in their mouths; young boys, hollow-eyed and decrepit; and puny mothers, holding up puny babes in the glare of the sun, formed the main features of the scene.

But these were diversified by instances of peculiar suffering, vice, or art in attracting charity, which, to me at least, who had never seen such things before, seemed to the last degree uncommon and monstrous.

I remember one cripple, a young man rather decently clad, who sat huddled up against the wall, holding a painted board on his knees. It was a picture intending to represent the man himself caught in the machinery of some factory, and whirled about among spindles and cogs, with his limbs mangled and bloody. This person said nothing, but sat silently exhibiting his board. Next him, leaning upright against the wall, was a tall, pallid man, with a white bandage round his brow, and his face cadaverous as a corpse. He, too, said nothing; but with one finger silently pointed down to the square of flagging at his feet, which was nicely swept, and stained blue, and bore this inscription in chalk:

I have had no food for three days;
My wife and children are dying.

Further on lay a man with one sleeve of his ragged coat removed, showing an unsightly sore; and above it a label with some writing.

In some places, for the distance of many rods, the whole line of flagging immediately at the base of the wall, would be completely covered with inscriptions, the beggars standing over them in silence.

But as you passed along these horrible records, in an hour's time destined to be obliterated by the feet of thousands and thousands of wayfarers, you were not left unassailed by the clamorous petitions of the more urgent applicants for charity. They beset you on every hand; catching you by the coat; hanging on, and following you along; and, *for Heaven's sake,* and *for God's sake,* and *for Christ's sake,* beseeching of you but one *ha'penny.* If you so much as glanced your eye on one of them, even for an instant, it was perceived like lightning, and the person never left your side until you turned into another street, or satisfied his demands. Thus, at least, it was with the sailors; though I observed that the beggars treated the town's people differently.

I can not say that the seamen did much to relieve the destitution which three times everyday was presented to their view. Perhaps habit had made them callous; but the truth might have been that very few of them had much money to give. Yet the beggars must have had some inducement to infest the dock walls as they did.

As an example of the caprice of sailors, and their sympathy with suffering among members of their own calling, I must mention the case of an old man, who everyday, and all day long, through sunshine and rain, occupied a particular corner, where crowds of tars were always passing. He was an uncommonly large, plethoric man, with a wooden leg, and dressed in the nautical garb; his face was red and round; he was continually merry; and with his wooden stump thrust forth, so as almost to trip up the careless wayfarer, he sat upon a great pile of monkey jackets, with a little depression in them between his knees, to receive the coppers thrown him. And plenty of pennies were tossed into his poor-box by the sailors, who always exchanged a pleasant word with the old man, and passed on, generally regardless of the neighboring beggars.

The first morning I went ashore with my shipmates, some of them greeted him as an old acquaintance; for that corner he had occupied for many long years. He was an old man-of-war's man, who had lost his leg at the battle of Trafalgar; and singular to tell, he now exhibited his wooden one as a genuine specimen of the oak timbers of Nelson's ship, the *Victory*.

Among the paupers were several who wore old sailor hats and jackets, and claimed to be destitute tars; and on the strength of these pretensions demanded help from their brethren; but Jack would see through their disguise in a moment, and turn away, with no benediction.

As I daily passed through this lane of beggars, who thronged the docks as the Hebrew cripples did the Pool of Bethesda, and as I thought of my utter inability in any way to help them, I could not but offer up a prayer, that some angel might descend, and turn the waters of the docks into an elixir, that would heal all their woes, and make them, man and woman, healthy and whole as their ancestors, Adam and Eve, in the garden.

Adam and Eve! If indeed ye are yet alive and in heaven, may it be no part of your immortality to look down upon the world ye have left. For as all these sufferers and cripples are as much your family as young Abel, so, to you, the sight of the world's woes would be a parental torment indeed.

Chapter XXXIX

The Booble-Alleys of the Town

THE SAME SIGHTS THAT ARE TO BE MET WITH ALONG THE DOCK WALLS AT NOON, IN A LESS DEgree, though diversified with other scenes, are continually encountered in the narrow streets where the sailor boarding-houses are kept.

In the evening, especially when the sailors are gathered in great numbers, these streets present a most singular spectacle, the entire population of the vicinity being seemingly turned into them. Hand-organs, fiddles, and cymbals, plied by strolling musicians, mix with the songs of the seamen, the babble of women and children, and the groaning and whining of beggars. From the various boarding-houses, each distinguished by gilded emblems outside—an anchor, a crown, a ship, a windlass, or a dolphin—proceeds the noise of revelry and dancing; and from the open casements lean young girls and old women, chattering and laughing with the crowds in the middle of the street. Every moment strange greetings are exchanged between old sailors who chance to stumble upon a shipmate, last seen in Calcutta or Savannah; and the invariable courtesy that takes place upon these occasions, is to go to the next spirit-vault, and drink each other's health.

There are particular paupers who frequent particular sections of these streets, and who, I was told, resented the intrusion of mendicants from other parts of the town.

Chief among them was a white-haired old man, stone-blind; who was led up and down through the long tumult by a woman holding a little saucer to receive contributions. This old man sang, or rather chanted, certain words in a peculiarly long-drawn, guttural manner, throwing back his head, and turning up his sightless eyeballs to the sky. His chant was a lamentation upon his infirmity; and at the time it produced the same effect upon me, that my first reading of Milton's *Invocation to the Sun* did, years afterward. I can not recall it all; but it was something like this, drawn out in an endless groan—

"Here goes the blind old man; blind, blind, blind; no more will he see sun nor moon—no more see sun nor moon!" And thus would he pass through the middle of the street; the woman going on in advance, holding his hand, and dragging him through all obstructions; now and then leaving him standing, while she went among the crowd soliciting coppers.

But one of the most curious features of the scene is the number of sailor ballad-singers, who, after singing their verses, hand you a printed copy, and beg you to buy. One of these persons, dressed like a man-of-war's-man, I observed everyday standing at a corner in the middle of the street. He had a full, noble voice, like a church-organ; and his notes rose high above the surrounding din. But the remarkable thing about this ballad-singer was one of his arms, which, while singing, he somehow swung vertically round and round in the air, as if it revolved on a pivot. The feat was unnaturally unaccountable; and he performed it with the view of attracting sympathy; since he said that in falling from a frigate's mast-head to the deck, he had met with an injury, which had resulted in making his wonderful arm what it was.

I made the acquaintance of this man, and found him no common character. He was full of marvelous adventures, and abounded in terrific stories of pirates and sea murders, and all sorts of nautical enormities. He was a monomaniac upon these subjects; he was a Newgate Calendar of the robberies and assassinations of the day, happening in the sailor quarters of the town; and most of his ballads were upon kindred subjects. He composed many of his own verses, and had them printed for sale on his own account. To show how expeditious he was at this business, it may be mentioned, that one evening on leaving the dock to go to supper, I perceived a crowd gathered about the *Old Fort Tavern*; and mingling with the rest, I learned that a woman of the town had just been killed at the bar by a drunken Spanish sailor from Cadiz. The murderer was carried off by the police before my eyes, and the very next morning the ballad-singer with the miraculous arm, was singing the tragedy in front of the boarding-houses, and handing round printed copies of the song, which, of course, were eagerly bought up by the seamen.

This passing allusion to the murder will convey some idea of the events which take place in the lowest and most abandoned neighborhoods frequented by sailors in Liverpool. The pestilent lanes and alleys which, in their vocabulary, go by the names of Rotten-row, Gibraltar-place, and Booble-alley, are putrid with vice and crime; to which, perhaps, the round globe does not furnish a parallel. The sooty and begrimed bricks of the very houses have a reeking, Sodom-like, and murderous look; and well may the shroud of coal-smoke, which hangs over this part of the town, more than any other, attempt to hide the enormities here practiced. These are the haunts from which sailors sometimes disappear forever; or issue in the morning, robbed naked, from the broken doorways. These are the haunts in which cursing, gambling, pickpocketing, and common iniquities, are virtues too lofty for the infected gorgons and hydras to practice. Propriety forbids that I should enter into details; but kidnappers, burkers, and resurrectionists are almost saints and angels to them. They seem leagued together, a company of miscreant misanthropes, bent upon doing all the malice to mankind in their power. With sulphur and brimstone they ought to be burned out of their arches like vermin.

Chapter XL

PLACARDS, BRASS-JEWELERS, TRUCK-HORSES, AND STEAMERS

AS I WISH TO GROUP TOGETHER WHAT FELL UNDER MY OBSERVATION CONCERNING THE LIVERpool docks, and the scenes roundabout, I will try to throw into this chapter various minor things that I recall.

The advertisements of pauperism chalked upon the flagging round the dock walls, are singularly accompanied by a multitude of quite different announcements, placarded upon the walls themselves. They are principally notices of the approaching departure of *"superior, fast-sailing, coppered and copper-fastened ships,"* for the United States, Canada, New South Wales, and other places. Interspersed with these, are the advertisements of Jewish clothesmen, informing the judicious seamen where he can procure of the best and the cheapest; together with ambiguous medical announcements of the tribe of quacks and empirics who prey upon all sea-faring men. Not content with thus publicly giving notice of their whereabouts, these indefatigable Sangrados and pretended Samaritans hire a parcel of shabby workhouse-looking knaves, whose business consists in haunting the dock walls about meal times, and silently thrusting mysterious little billets—duodecimo editions of the larger advertisements—into the astonished hands of the tars.

They do this, with such a mysterious hang-dog wink; such a sidelong air; such a villainous assumption of your necessities; that, at first, you are almost tempted to knock them down for their pains.

Conspicuous among the notices on the walls, are huge Italic inducements to all seamen disgusted with the merchant service, to accept a round bounty, and embark in her Majesty's navy.

In the British armed marine, in time of peace, they do not ship men for the general service, as in the American navy; but for particular ships, going upon particular cruises. Thus, the frigate *Thetis* may be announced as about to sail under the command of that fine old sailor, and noble father to his crew, *Lord George Flagstaff.*

Similar announcements may be seen upon the walls concerning enlistments in the army. And never did auctioneer dilate with more rapture upon the charms of some country-seat put up for sale, than the authors of these placards do, upon the beauty and salubrity of the distant climes, for which the regiments wanting recruits are about to sail. Bright lawns, vine-clad hills, endless meadows of verdure, here make up the landscape; and adventurous young gentlemen, fond of travel, are informed, that here is a chance for them to see the world at their leisure, and be paid for enjoying themselves into the bargain. The regiments for India are promised plantations among valleys of palms; while to those destined for New Holland, a novel sphere of life and activity is opened; and the companies bound to Canada and Nova Scotia are lured by tales of summer suns, that ripen grapes in December. No word of war is breathed; hushed is the clang of arms in these announcements; and the sanguine recruit is almost tempted to expect that pruning-hooks, instead of swords, will be the weapons he will wield.

Alas! is not this the cruel stratagem of Brace at Bannockburn, who decoyed to his war-pits by covering them over with green boughs? For instead of a farm at the blue base of the Himalayas, the Indian recruit encounters the keen saber of the Sikh; and instead of basking in sunny bowers, the Canadian soldier stands a shivering sentry upon the bleak ramparts of Quebec, a lofty mark for the bitter blasts from Baffin's Bay and Labrador. There, as his eye sweeps down the St. Lawrence, whose every billow is bound for the main that laves the shore of Old England; as he thinks of his long term of enlistment, which sells him to the army as Doctor Faust sold himself to the devil; how the poor fellow must groan in his grief, and call to mind the church-yard stile, and his Mary.

These army announcements are well fitted to draw recruits in Liverpool. Among the vast number of emigrants, who daily arrive from all parts of Britain to embark for the United States or the colonies, there are many young men, who, upon arriving at Liverpool, find themselves next to penniless; or, at least, with only enough money to carry them over the sea, without providing for future contingencies. How easily and naturally, then, may such youths be induced to enter upon the military life, which promises them a free passage to the most distant and flourishing colonies, and certain pay for doing nothing; besides holding out hopes of vineyards and farms, to be verified in the fullness of time. For in a moneyless youth, the decision to leave home at all, and embark upon a long voyage to reside in a remote clime, is a piece of adventurousness only one remove from the spirit that prompts the army recruit to enlist.

I never passed these advertisements, surrounded by crowds of gaping emigrants, without thinking of rattraps.

Besides the mysterious agents of the quacks, who privily thrust their little notes into your hands, folded up like a powder; there are another set of rascals prowling about the docks, chiefly at dusk; who make strange motions to you, and beckon you to one side, as if they had some state secret to disclose, intimately connected with the weal of the commonwealth. They nudge you with an elbow full of indefinite hints and intimations; they glitter upon you an eye like a Jew's or a pawnbroker's; they dog you like Italian assassins. But if the blue coat of a policeman chances to approach, how quickly they strive to look completely indifferent, as to the surrounding universe; how they saunter off, as if lazily wending their way to an affectionate wife and family.

The first time one of these mysterious personages accosted me, I fancied him crazy, and hurried forward to avoid him. But arm in arm with my shadow, he followed after; till amazed at his conduct, I turned round and paused.

He was a little, shabby, old man, with a forlorn looking coat and hat; and his hand was fumbling in his vest pocket, as if to take out a card with his address. Seeing me stand still he made a sign toward a dark angle of the wall, near which we were; when taking him for a cunning foot-pad, I again wheeled about, and swiftly passed on. But though I did not look round, I *felt* him following me still; so once more I stopped. The fellow now assumed so mystic and admonitory an air, that I began to fancy he came to me on some warning errand; that perhaps a plot had been laid to blow up the Liverpool docks, and he was some Monteagle bent upon accomplishing my flight. I was determined to see what he was. With all my eyes about me, I followed him into the arch of a warehouse; when he gazed round furtively, and silently showing me a ring, whispered, "You may have it for a shilling; it's pure gold—I found it in the gutter—hush! don't speak! give me the money, and it's yours."

"My friend," said I, "I don't trade in these articles; I don't want your ring."

"Don't you? Then take that," he whispered, in an intense hushed passion; and I fell flat from a blow on the chest, while this infamous jeweler made away with himself out of sight. This business transaction was conducted with a counting-house promptitude that astonished me.

After that, I shunned these scoundrels like the leprosy: and the next time I was pertinaciously followed, I stopped, and in a loud voice, pointed out the man to the passers-by; upon which he absconded; rapidly turning up into sight a pair of obliquely worn and battered boot-heels. I could not help thinking that these sort of fellows, so given to running away upon emergencies, must furnish a good deal of work to the shoemakers; as they might, also, to the growers of hemp and gallows-joiners.

Belonging to a somewhat similar fraternity with these irritable merchants of brass jewelry just mentioned, are the peddlers of Sheffield razors, mostly boys, who are hourly driven out of the dock gates by the police; nevertheless, they contrive to saunter back, and board the vessels, going among the sailors and privately exhibiting their wares. Incited by the extreme cheapness of one of the razors, and the gilding on the case containing it, a shipmate of mine purchased it on the spot for a commercial equivalent of the price, in tobacco. On the following Sunday, he used that razor; and the result was a pair of tormented and tomahawked cheeks, that almost required a surgeon to dress them. In old times, by the way, it was not a bad thought, that suggested the propriety of a barber's practicing surgery in connection with the chin-harrowing vocation.

Another class of knaves, who practice upon the sailors in Liverpool, are the pawnbrokers, inhabiting little rookeries among the narrow lanes adjoining the dock. I was astonished at the multitude of gilded balls in these streets, emblematic of their calling. They were generally next neighbors to the gilded grapes over the spirit-vaults; and no doubt, mutually to facilitate business operations, some of these establishments have connecting doors inside, so as to play their customers into each other's hands. I often saw sailors in a state of intoxication rushing from a spirit-vault into a pawnbroker's; stripping off their boots, hats, jackets, and neckerchiefs, and sometimes even their pantaloons on the spot, and offering to pawn them for a song. Of course such applications were never refused.

But though on shore, at Liverpool, poor Jack finds more sharks than at sea, he himself is by no means exempt from practices, that do not savor of a rigid morality; at least according to law. In tobacco smuggling he is an adept: and when cool and collected, often manages to evade the Customs completely, and land goodly packages of the weed, which owing to the immense duties upon it in England, commands a very high price.

As soon as we came to anchor in the river, before reaching the dock, three Custom-house underlings boarded us, and coming down into the forecastle, ordered the men to produce all the tobacco they had. Accordingly several pounds were brought forth.

"Is that all?" asked the officers.

"All," said the men.

"We will see," returned the others.

And without more ado, they emptied the chests right and left; tossed over the bunks and made a thorough search of the premises; but discovered nothing. The sailors were then given to understand, that while the ship lay in dock, the tobacco must remain in the cabin, under custody of the chief mate, who every morning would dole out to them one plug per head, as a security against their carrying it ashore.

"Very good," said the men.

But several of them had secret places in the ship, from whence they daily drew pound after pound of tobacco, which they smuggled ashore in the manner following.

When the crew went to meals, each man carried at least one plug in his pocket; *that* he had a right to; and as many more were hidden about his person as he dared. Among the great crowds pouring out of the dock-gates at such hours, of course these smugglers stood little chance of detection; although vigilant looking policemen were always standing by. And though these *"Charlies"* might suppose there were tobacco smugglers passing; yet to hit the right man among such a throng, would be as hard, as to harpoon a speckled porpoise, one of ten thousand darting under a ship's bows.

Our forecastle was often visited by foreign sailors, who knowing we came from America, were anxious to purchase tobacco at a cheap rate; for in Liverpool it is about an American penny per pipe-full. Along the docks they sell an English pennyworth, put up in a little roll like confectioners' mottoes, with poetical lines, or instructive little moral precepts printed in red on the back.

Among all the sights of the docks, the noble truck-horses are not the least striking to a stranger. They are large and powerful brutes, with such sleek and glossy coats, that they look as if brushed and put on by a valet every morning. They march with a slow and stately step, lifting their ponderous hoofs like royal Siam elephants. Thou shalt not lay stripes upon these Roman citizens; for their docility is such, they are guided without rein or lash; they go or come, halt or march on, at a whisper. So grave, dignified, gentlemanly, and courteous did these fine truck-horses look—so full of calm intelligence and sagacity, that often I endeavored to get into conversation with them, as they stood in contemplative attitudes while their loads were preparing. But all I could get from them was the mere recognition of a friendly neigh; though I would stake much upon it that, could I have spoken in their language, I would have derived from them a good deal of valuable information touching the docks, where they passed the whole of their dignified lives.

There are unknown worlds of knowledge in brutes; and whenever you mark a horse, or a dog, with a peculiarly mild, calm, deep-seated eye, be sure he is an Aristotle or a Kant, tranquilly speculating upon the mysteries in man. No philosophers so thoroughly comprehend us as dogs and horses. They see through us at a glance. And after all, what is a horse but a species of four-footed dumb man, in a leathern overall, who happens to live upon oats, and toils for his masters, half-requited or abused, like the biped hewers of wood and drawers of water? But there is a touch of divinity even in brutes, and a special halo about a horse, that should forever exempt him from indignities. As for those majestic, magisterial truck-horses of the docks, I would as soon think of striking a judge on the bench, as to lay violent hand upon their holy hides.

It is wonderful what loads their majesties will condescend to draw. The truck is a large square platform, on four low wheels; and upon this the lumpers pile bale after bale of cotton, as if they were filling a large warehouse, and yet a procession of three of these horses will tranquilly walk away with the whole.

The truckmen themselves are almost as singular a race as their animals. Like the Judiciary in England, they wear gowns—not of the same cut and color though—which reach below their knees; and from the racket they make on the pavements with their hob-nailed brogans, you would think they patronized the same shoemaker with their horses. I never could get anything out of these truckmen. They are a reserved, sober-sided set, who, with all possible solemnity, march at the head of their animals; now and then gently advising them to sheer to the right or the left, in order to avoid some passing vehicle. Then spending so much of their lives in the high-bred company of their horses, seems to have mended their manners and improved their taste, besides imparting to them something of the dignity of their animals; but it has also given to them a sort of refined and uncomplaining aversion to human society.

There are many strange stories told of the truck-horse. Among others is the following: There was a parrot, that from having long been suspended in its cage from a low window fronting a dock, had learned to converse pretty fluently in the language of the stevedores and truckmen. One day a truckman left his vehicle standing on the quay, with its back to the water. It was noon, when an interval of silence falls upon the docks; and Poll, seeing herself face to face with the horse, and having a mind for a chat, cried out to him, *"Back! back! back!"*

Backward went the horse, precipitating himself and truck into the water.

Brunswick Dock, to the west of Prince's, is one of the most interesting to be seen. Here lie the various black steamers (so unlike the American boats, since they have to navigate the boisterous Narrow Seas) plying to all parts of the three kingdoms. Here you see vast quantities of produce, imported from starving Ireland; here you see the decks turned into pens for oxen and sheep; and often, side by side with these enclosures, Irish deck-passengers, thick as they can stand, seemingly penned in just like the cattle. It was the beginning of July when the *Highlander* arrived in port; and the Irish laborers were daily coming over by thousands, to help harvest the English crops.

One morning, going into the town, I heard a tramp, as of a drove of buffaloes, behind me; and turning round, beheld the entire middle of the street filled by a great crowd of these men, who had just emerged from Brunswick Dock gates, arrayed in long-tailed coats of hoddin-gray, corduroy knee-breeches, and shod with shoes that raised a mighty dust. Flourishing their Donnybrook shillelahs, they looked like an irruption of barbarians. They were marching straight out of town into the country; and perhaps out of consideration for the finances of the corporation, took the middle of the street, to save the side-walks.

"Sing Langolee, and the Lakes of Killarney," cried one fellow, tossing his stick into the air, as he danced in his brogans at the head of the rabble. And so they went! capering on, merry as pipers.

When I thought of the multitudes of Irish that annually land on the shores of the United States and Canada, and, to my surprise, witnessed the additional multitudes embarking from Liverpool to New Holland; and when, added to all this, I daily saw these hordes of laborers, descending, thick as locusts, upon the English corn-fields; I could not help marveling at the fertility of an island, which, though her crop of potatoes may fail, never yet failed in bringing her annual crop of men into the world.

Chapter XLI

Redburn Roves about Hither and Thither

I do not know that any other traveler would think it worthwhile to mention such a thing; but the fact is, that during the summer months in Liverpool, the days are exceedingly lengthy; and the first evening I found myself walking in the twilight after nine o'clock, I tried to recall my astronomical knowledge, in order to account satisfactorily for so curious a phenomenon. But the days in summer, and the nights in winter, are just as long in Liverpool as at Cape Horn; for the latitude of the two places very nearly corresponds.

These Liverpool days, however, were a famous thing for me; who, thereby, was enabled after my day's work aboard the *Highlander*, to ramble about the town for several hours. After I had visited all the noted places I could discover, of those marked down upon my father's map, I began to extend my rovings indefinitely; forming myself into a committee of one, to investigate all accessible parts of the town; though so many years have elapsed, ere I have thought of bringing in my report.

This was a great delight to me: for wherever I have been in the world, I have always taken a vast deal of lonely satisfaction in wandering about, up and down, among out-of-the-way streets and alleys, and speculating upon the strangers I have met. Thus, in Liverpool I used to pace along endless streets of dwelling-houses, looking at the names on the doors, admiring the pretty faces in the windows, and invoking a passing blessing upon the chubby children on the door-steps. I was stared at myself, to be sure: but what of that? We must give and take on such occasions. In truth, I and my shooting-jacket produced quite a sensation in Liverpool: and I have no doubt, that many a father of a family went home to his children with a curious story, about a wandering phenomenon they had encountered, traversing the side-walks that day. In the words of the old song, *"I cared for nobody, no not I, and nobody cared for me."* I stared my fill with impunity, and took all stares myself in good part.

Once I was standing in a large square, gaping at a splendid chariot drawn up at a portico. The glossy horses quivered with good-living, and so did the sumptuous calves of the gold-laced coachman and footmen in attendance. I was particularly struck with the red cheeks of these men: and the many evidences they furnished of their enjoying this life with a wonderful relish.

While thus standing, I all at once perceived, that the objects of my curiosity, were making me an object of their own; and that they were gazing at me, as if I were some unauthorized intruder upon the British soil. Truly, they had reason: for when I now think of the figure I must have cut in those days, I only marvel that, in my many strolls, my passport was not a thousand times demanded.

Nevertheless, I was only a forlorn looking mortal among tens of thousands of rags and tatters. For in some parts of the town, inhabited by laborers, and poor people generally; I used to crowd my way through masses of squalid men, women, and children, who at this evening hour, in those quarters of Liverpool, seem to empty themselves into the street, and live there for the time. I had never seen anything like it in New York.

Often, I witnessed some curious, and many very sad scenes; and especially I remembered encountering a pale, ragged man, rushing along frantically, and striving to throw off his wife and children, who clung to his arms and legs; and, in God's name, conjured him not to desert them. He seemed bent upon rushing down to the water, and drowning himself, in some despair, and craziness of wretchedness. In these haunts, beggary went on before me wherever I walked, and dogged me unceasingly at the heels. Poverty, poverty, poverty, in almost endless vistas: and want and woe staggered arm in arm along these miserable streets.

And here, I must not omit one thing, that struck me at the time. It was the absence of negroes; who in the large towns in the "free states" of America, almost always form a considerable portion of the destitute. But in these streets, not a negro was to be seen. All were whites; and with the exception of the Irish, were natives of the soil: even Englishmen; as much Englishmen, as the dukes in the House of Lords. This conveyed a strange feeling: and more than anything else, reminded me that I was not in my own land. For *there,* such a being as a native beggar is almost unknown; and to be a born American citizen seems a guarantee against pauperism; and this, perhaps, springs from the virtue of a vote.

Speaking of negroes, recalls the looks of interest with which negro-sailors are regarded when they walk the Liverpool streets. In Liverpool indeed the negro steps with a prouder pace, and lifts his head like a man; for here, no such exaggerated feeling exists in respect to him, as in America. Three or four times, I encountered our black steward, dressed very handsomely, and walking arm in arm with a good-looking English woman. In New York, such a couple would have been mobbed in three minutes; and the steward would have been lucky to escape with whole limbs. Owing to the friendly reception extended to them, and the unwonted immunities they enjoy in Liverpool, the black cooks and stewards of American ships are very much attached to the place and like to make voyages to it.

Being so young and inexperienced then, and unconsciously swayed in some degree by those local and social prejudices, that are the marring of most men, and from which, for the mass, there seems no possible escape; at first I was surprised that a colored man should be treated as he is in this town; but a little reflection showed that, after all, it was but recognizing his claims to humanity and normal equality; so that, in some things, we Americans leave to other countries the carrying out of the principle that stands at the head of our Declaration of Independence.

During my evening strolls in the wealthier quarters, I was subject to a continual mortification. It was the humiliating fact, wholly unforeseen by me, that upon the whole, and barring the poverty and beggary, Liverpool, away from the docks, was very much such a place as New York. There were the same sort of streets pretty much; the same rows of houses with stone steps; the same kind of side-walks and curbs; and the same elbowing, heartless-looking crowd as ever.

I came across the Leeds Canal, one afternoon; but, upon my word, no one could have told it from the Erie Canal at Albany. I went into St. John's Market on a Saturday night; and though it was strange enough to see that great roof supported by so many pillars, yet the most discriminating observer would not have been able to detect any difference between the articles exposed for sale, and the articles exhibited in Fulton Market, New York.

I walked down Lord-street, peering into the jewelers' shops; but I thought I was walking down a block in Broadway. I began to think that all this talk about travel was a humbug; and that he who lives in a nut-shell, lives in an epitome of the universe, and has but little to see beyond him.

It is true, that I often thought of London's being only seven or eight hours' travel by railroad from where I was; and that *there,* surely, must be a world of wonders waiting my eyes: but more of London anon.

Sundays were the days upon which I made my longest explorations. I rose bright and early, with my whole plan of operations in my head. First walking into some dock hitherto unexamined, and then to breakfast. Then a walk through the more fashionable streets, to see the people going to church; and then I myself went to church, selecting the goodliest edifice, and the tallest Kentuckian of a spire I could find.

For I am an admirer of church architecture; and though, perhaps, the sums spent in erecting magnificent cathedrals might better go to the founding of charities, yet since these structures are built, those who disapprove of them in one sense, may as well have the benefit of them in another.

It is a most Christian thing, and a matter most sweet to dwell upon and simmer over in solitude, that any poor sinner may go to church wherever he pleases; and that even St. Peter's in Rome is open to him, as to a cardinal; that St. Paul's in London is not shut against him; and that the Broadway Tabernacle, in New York, opens all her broad aisles to him, and will not even have doors and thresholds to her pews, the better to allure him by an unbounded invitation. I say, this consideration of the hospitality and democracy in churches, is a most Christian and charming thought. It speaks whole volumes of folios, and Vatican libraries, for Christianity; it is more eloquent, and goes farther home than all the sermons of Massillon, Jeremy Taylor, Wesley, and Archbishop Tillotson.

Nothing daunted, therefore, by thinking of my being a stranger in the land; nothing daunted by the architectural superiority and costliness of any Liverpool church; or by the streams of silk dresses and fine broadcloth coats flowing into the aisles, I used humbly to present myself before the sexton, as a candidate for admission. He would stare a little, perhaps (one of them once hesitated), but in the end, what could he do but show me into a pew; not the most commodious of pews, to be sure; nor commandingly located; nor within very plain sight or hearing of the pulpit. No; it was remarkable, that there was always some confounded pillar or obstinate angle of the wall in the way; and I used to think, that the sextons of Liverpool must have held a secret meeting on my account, and resolved to apportion me the most inconvenient pew in the churches under their charge. However, they always gave me a seat of some sort or other; sometimes even on an oaken bench in the open air of the aisle, where I would sit, dividing the attention of the congregation between myself and the clergyman. The whole congregation seemed to know that I was a foreigner of distinction.

It was sweet to hear the service read, the organ roll, the sermon preached—just as the same things were going on three thousand five hundred miles off, at home! But then, the prayer in behalf of her majesty the Queen, somewhat threw me back. Nevertheless, I joined in that prayer, and invoked for the lady the best wishes of a poor Yankee.

How I loved to sit in the holy hush of those brown old monastic aisles, thinking of Harry the Eighth, and the Reformation! How I loved to go a roving with my eye, all along the sculptured walls and buttresses; winding in among the intricacies of the pendent ceiling, and wriggling my fancied way like a wood-worm. I could have sat there all the morning long, through noon, unto night. But at last the benediction would come; and appropriating my share of it, I would slowly move away, thinking how I should like to go home with some of the portly old gentlemen, with high-polished boots and Malacca canes, and take a seat at their cozy and comfortable dinner-tables. But, alas! there was no dinner for me except at the sign of the Baltimore Clipper.

Yet the Sunday dinners that Handsome Mary served up were not to be scorned. The roast beef of Old England abounded; and so did the immortal plum-puddings, and the unspeakably capital gooseberry pies. But to finish off with that abominable "*swipes*" almost spoiled all the rest: not that I myself patronized "*swipes*," but my shipmates did; and every cup I saw them drink, I could not choose but taste in imagination, and even then the flavor was bad.

On Sundays, at dinner-time, as, indeed, on every other day, it was curious to watch the proceedings at the sign of the Clipper. The servant girls were running about, mustering the various crews, whose dinners were spread, each in a separate apartment; and who were collectively known by the names of their ships.

"Where are the *Arethusas?*—Here's their beef been smoking this half-hour."—"Fly, Betty, my dear, here come the *Splendids*."—"Run, Molly, my love; get the salt-cellars for the *Highlanders*."—"You Peggy, where's the *Siddons*' pickle-pot?"—"I say, Judy, are you never coming with that pudding for the *Lord Nelsons*?"

On week-days, we did not fare quite so well as on Sundays; and once we came to dinner, and found two enormous bullock hearts smoking at each end of the *Highlanders*' table. Jackson was indignant at the outrage.

He always sat at the head of the table; and this time he squared himself on his bench, and erecting his knife and fork like flag-staffs, so as to include the two hearts between them, he called out for Danby, the boarding-house keeper; for although his wife Mary was in fact at the head of the establishment, yet Danby himself always came in for the fault-findings.

Danby obsequiously appeared, and stood in the doorway, well knowing the philippics that were coming. But he was not prepared for the peroration of Jackson's address to him; which consisted of the two bullock hearts, snatched bodily off the dish, and flung at his head, by way of a recapitulation of the preceding arguments. The company then broke up in disgust, and dined elsewhere.

Though I almost invariably attended church on Sunday mornings, yet the rest of the day I spent on my travels; and it was on one of these afternoon strolls, that on passing through St. George's-square, I found myself among a large crowd, gathered near the base of George the Fourth's equestrian statue.

The people were mostly mechanics and artisans in their holiday clothes; but mixed with them were a good many soldiers, in lean, lank, and dinnerless undresses, and sporting attenuated rattans. These troops belonged to the various regiments then in town. Police-officers, also, were conspicuous in their uniforms. At first perfect silence and decorum prevailed.

Addressing this orderly throng was a pale, hollow-eyed young man, in a snuff-colored surtout, who looked worn with much watching, or much toil, or too little food. His features were good, his whole air was respectable, and there was no mistaking the fact, that he was strongly in earnest in what he was saying.

In his hand was a soiled, inflammatory-looking pamphlet, from which he frequently read; following up the quotations with nervous appeals to his hearers, a rolling of his eyes, and sometimes the most frantic gestures. I was not long within hearing of him, before I became aware that this youth was a Chartist.

Presently the crowd increased, and some commotion was raised, when I noticed the police-officers augmenting in number; and by and by, they began to glide through the crowd, politely hinting at the propriety of dispersing. The first persons thus accosted were the soldiers, who accordingly sauntered off, switching their rattans, and admiring their high-polished shoes. It was plain that the Charter did not hang very heavy round their hearts. For the rest, they also gradually broke up; and at last I saw the speaker himself depart.

I do not know why, but I thought he must be some despairing elder son, supporting by hard toil his mother and sisters; for of such many political desperadoes are made.

That same Sunday afternoon, I strolled toward the outskirts of the town, and attracted by the sight of two great Pompey's pillars, in the shape of black steeples, apparently rising directly from the soil, I approached them with much curiosity. But looking over a low parapet connecting them, what was my surprise to behold at my feet a smoky hollow in the ground, with rocky walls, and dark holes at one end, carrying out of view several lines of iron railways; while far beyond, straight out toward the open country, ran an endless railroad. Over the place, a handsome Moorish arch of stone was flung; and gradually, as I gazed upon it, and at the little side arches at the bottom of the hollow, there came over me an undefinable feeling, that I had previously seen the whole thing before. Yet how could that be? Certainly, I had never been in Liverpool before: but then, that Moorish arch!

surely I remembered that very well. It was not till several months after reaching home in America, that my perplexity upon this matter was cleared away. In glancing over an old number of the Penny Magazine, there I saw a picture of the place to the life; and remembered having seen the same print years previous. It was a representation of the spot where the Manchester railroad enters the outskirts of the town.

Chapter XLII

His Adventure with the Cross Old Gentleman

My adventure in the news-room in the exchange, which I have related in a previous chapter, reminds me of another, at the Lyceum, some days after, which may as well be put down here, before I forget it.

I was strolling down Bold-street, I think it was, when I was struck by the sight of a brown stone building, very large and handsome. The windows were open, and there, nicely seated, with their comfortable legs crossed over their comfortable knees, I beheld several sedate, happy-looking old gentlemen reading the magazines and papers, and one had a fine gilded volume in his hand.

Yes, this must be the Lyceum, thought I; let me see. So I whipped out my guide-book, and opened it at the proper plate; and sure enough, the building before me corresponded stone for stone. I stood awhile on the opposite side of the street, gazing at my picture, and then at its original; and often dwelling upon the pleasant gentlemen sitting at the open windows; till at last I felt an uncontrollable impulse to step in for a moment, and run over the news.

I'm a poor, friendless sailor-boy, thought I, and they can not object; especially as I am from a foreign land, and strangers ought to be treated with courtesy. I turned the matter over again, as I walked across the way; and with just a small tapping of a misgiving at my heart, I at last scraped my feet clean against the curb-stone, and taking off my hat while I was yet in the open air, slowly sauntered in.

But I had not got far into that large and lofty room, filled with many agreeable sights, when a crabbed old gentleman lifted up his eye from the *London Times,* which words I saw boldly printed on the back of the large sheet in his hand, and looking at me as if I were a strange dog with a muddy hide, that had stolen out of the gutter into this fine apartment, he shook his silver-headed cane at me fiercely, till the spectacles fell off his nose. Almost at the same moment, up stepped a terribly cross man, who looked as if he had a mustard plaster on his back, that was continually exasperating him; who throwing down some papers which he had been filing, took me by my innocent shoulders, and then, putting his foot against the broad part of my pantaloons, wheeled me right out into the street, and dropped me on the walk, without so much as offering an apology for the affront. I sprang after him, but in vain; the door was closed upon me.

These Englishmen have no manners, that's plain, thought I; and I trudged on down the street in a reverie.

Chapter XLIII

He Takes a Delightful Ramble into the Country; and Makes the Acquaintance of Three Adorable Charmers

WHO THAT DWELLS IN AMERICA HAS NOT HEARD OF THE BRIGHT FIELDS AND GREEN HEDGES OF England, and longed to behold them? Even so had it been with me; and now that I was actually in England, I resolved not to go away without having a good, long look at the open fields.

On a Sunday morning I started, with a lunch in my pocket. It was a beautiful day in July; the air was sweet with the breath of buds and flowers, and there was a green splendor in the landscape that ravished me. Soon I gained an elevation commanding a wide sweep of view; and meadow and mead, and woodland and hedge, were all around me.

Ay, ay! this was old England, indeed! I had found it at last—there it was in the country! Hovering over the scene was a soft, dewy air, that seemed faintly tinged with the green of the grass; and I thought, as I breathed my breath, that perhaps I might be inhaling the very particles once respired by Rosamond the Fair.

On I trudged along the London road—smooth as an entry floor—and every white cottage I passed, embosomed in honeysuckles, seemed alive in the landscape.

But the day wore on; and at length the sun grew hot; and the long road became dusty. I thought that some shady place, in some shady field, would be very pleasant to repose in. So, coming to a charming little dale, undulating down to a hollow, arched over with foliage, I crossed over toward it; but paused by the road-side at a frightful announcement, nailed against an old tree, used as a gate-post—

☞ "MAN-TRAPS AND SPRING-GUNS!"

In America I had never heard of the like. What could it mean? They were not surely *cannibals*, that dwelled down in that beautiful little dale, and lived by catching men, like weasels and beavers in Canada! "*A man-trap!*" It must be so. The announcement could bear but one meaning—that there was something nearby, intended to catch human beings; some species of mechanism, that would suddenly fasten upon the unwary rover, and hold him by the leg like a dog; or, perhaps, devour him on the spot.

Incredible! In a Christian land, too! Did that sweet lady, Queen Victoria, permit such diabolical practices? Had her gracious majesty ever passed by this way, and seen the announcement?

And who put it there?

The proprietor, probably.

And what right had he to do so?

Why, he owned the soil.

And where are his title-deeds?

In his strong-box, I suppose.

Thus I stood wrapped in cogitations.

You are a pretty fellow, Wellingborough, thought I to myself; you are a mighty traveler, indeed:—stopped on your travels by a *man-trap!* Do you think Mungo Park was so served in Africa? Do you think Ledyard was so entreated in Siberia? Upon my word, you will go home not very much wiser than when you set out; and the only excuse you can give, for not having seen more sights, will be man-traps—*man-traps, my masters!* that frightened you!

And then, in my indignation, I fell back upon first principles. What right has this man to the soil he thus guards with dragons? What excessive effrontery, to lay sole claim to a solid piece of this planet, right down to the earth's axis, and, perhaps, straight through to the antipodes! For a moment I thought I would test his traps, and enter the forbidden Eden. But the grass grew so thickly, and seemed so full of sly things, that at last I thought best to pace off.

Next, I came to a hawthorn lane, leading down very prettily to a nice little church; a mossy little church; a beautiful little church; just such a church as I had always dreamed to be in England. The porch was viny as an arbor; the ivy was climbing about the tower; and the bees were humming about the hoary old head-stones along the walls.

Any man-traps here? thought I—any spring-guns?

No.

So I walked on, and entered the church, where I soon found a seat. No Indian, red as a deer, could have startled the simple people more. They gazed and they gazed; but as I was all attention to the sermon, and conducted myself with perfect propriety, they did not expel me, as at first I almost imagined they might.

Service over, I made my way through crowds of children, who stood staring at the marvelous stranger, and resumed my stroll along the London Road.

My next stop was at an inn, where under a tree sat a party of rustics, drinking ale at a table.

"Good-day," said I.

"Good-day; from Liverpool?"

"I guess so."

"For London?"

"No; not this time. I merely come to see the country."

At this, they gazed at each other; and I, at myself; having doubts whether I might not look something like a horse-thief.

"Take a seat," said the landlord, a fat fellow, with his wife's apron on, I thought.

"Thank you."

And then, little by little, we got into a long talk: in the course of which, I told who I was, and where I was from. I found these rustics a good-natured, jolly set; and I have no doubt they found me quite a sociable youth. They treated me to ale; and I treated them to stories about America, concerning which, they manifested the utmost curiosity. One of them, however, was somewhat astonished that I had not made the acquaintance of a brother of his, who had resided somewhere on the banks of the Mississippi for several years past; but among twenty millions of people, I had never happened to meet him, at least to my knowledge.

At last, leaving this party, I pursued my way, exhilarated by the lively conversation in which I had shared, and the pleasant sympathies exchanged: and perhaps, also, by the ale I had drunk:—fine old ale; yes, English ale, ale brewed in England! And I trod English soil; and breathed English air; and every blade of grass was an Englishman born. Smoky old Liverpool, with all its pitch and tar was now far behind; nothing in sight but open meadows and fields.

Come, Wellingborough, why not push on for London?—Hurra! what say you? let's have a peep at St. Paul's! Don't you want to see the queen? Have you no longing to behold the duke? Think of Westminster Abbey, and the Tunnel under the Thames! Think of Hyde Park, and the ladies!

But then, thought I again, with my hands wildly groping in my two vacuums of pockets—who's to pay the bill?—You can't beg your way, Wellingborough; that would never do; for you are your father's son, Wellingborough; and you must not disgrace your family in a foreign land; you must not turn pauper.

Ah! Ah! it was indeed too true; there was no St. Paul's or Westminster Abbey for me; that was flat.

Well, well, up heart, you'll see it one of these days.

But think of it! here I am on the very road that leads to the Thames—think of *that!*—here I am—ay, treading in the wheel-tracks of coaches that are bound for the metropolis!—It was too bad; too bitterly bad. But I shoved my old hat over my brows, and walked on; till at last I came to a green bank, deliriously shaded by a fine old tree with broad branching arms, that stretched themselves over the road, like a hen gathering her brood under her wings. Down on the green grass I threw myself and there lay my head, like a last year's nut. People passed by, on foot and in carriages, and little thought that the sad youth under the tree was the great-nephew of a late senator in the American Congress.

Presently, I started to my feet, as I heard a gruff voice behind me from the field, crying out—"What are you doing there, you young rascal?—run away from the work'us, have ye? Tramp, or I'll set Blucher on ye!"

And who was Blucher? A cut-throat looking dog, with his black bull-muzzle thrust through a gap in the hedge. And his master? A sturdy farmer, with an alarming cudgel in his hand.

"Come, are you going to start?" he cried.

"Presently," said I, making off with great dispatch. When I had got a few yards into the middle of the highroad (which belonged as much to me as it did to the queen herself), I turned round, like a man on his own premises, and said—"Stranger! if you ever visit America, just call at our house, and you'll always find there a dinner and a bed. Don't fail."

I then walked on toward Liverpool, full of sad thoughts concerning the cold charities of the world, and the infamous reception given to hapless young travelers, in broken-down shooting-jackets.

On, on I went, along the skirts of forbidden green fields; until reaching a cottage, before which I stood rooted.

So sweet a place I had never seen: no palace in Persia could be pleasanter; there were flowers in the garden; and six red cheeks, like six moss-roses, hanging from the casement. At the embowered doorway, sat an old man, confidentially communing with his pipe: while a little child, sprawling on the ground, was playing with his shoestrings. A hale matron, but with rather a prim expression, was reading a journal by his side: and three charmers, three Peris, three Houris! were leaning out of the window close by.

Ah! Wellingborough, don't you wish you could step in?

With a heavy heart at his cheerful sigh, I was turning to go, when—is it possible? the old man called me back, and invited me in.

"Come, come," said he, "you look as if you had walked far; come, take a bowl of milk. Matilda, my dear" (how my heart jumped), "go fetch some from the dairy." And the white-handed angel did meekly obey, and handed me—*me*, the vagabond, a bowl of bubbling milk, which I could hardly drink down, for gazing at the dew on her lips.

As I live, I could have married that charmer on the spot!

She was by far the most beautiful rosebud I had yet seen in England. But I endeavored to dissemble my ardent admiration; and in order to do away at once with any unfavorable impressions arising from the close scrutiny of my miserable shooting-jacket, which was now taking place, I declared myself a Yankee sailor from Liverpool, who was spending a Sunday in the country.

"And have you been to church to-day, young man?" said the old lady, looking daggers.

"Good madam, I have; the little church down yonder, you know—a most excellent sermon—I am much the better for it."

I wanted to mollify this severe looking old lady; for even my short experience of old ladies had convinced me that they are the hereditary enemies of all strange young men.

I soon turned the conversation toward America, a theme which I knew would be interesting, and upon which I could be fluent and agreeable. I strove to talk in Addisonian English, and ere long could see very plainly that my polished phrases were making a surprising impression, though that miserable shooting-jacket of mine was a perpetual drawback to my claims to gentility.

Spite of all my blandishments, however, the old lady stood her post like a sentry; and to my inexpressible chagrin, kept the three charmers in the background, though the old man frequently called upon them to advance. This fine specimen of an old Englishman seemed to be quite as free from ungenerous suspicions as his vinegary spouse was full of them. But I still lingered, snatching furtive glances at the young ladies, and vehemently talking to the old man about Illinois, and the river Ohio, and the fine farms in the Genesee country, where, in harvest time, the laborers went into the wheat fields a thousand strong.

Stick to it, Wellingborough, thought I; don't give the old lady time to think; stick to it, my boy, and an invitation to tea will reward you. At last it came, and the old lady abated her frowns.

It was the most delightful of meals; the three charmers sat all on one side, and I opposite, between the old man and his wife. The middle charmer poured out the souchong, and handed me the buttered muffins; and such buttered muffins never were spread on the other side of the Atlantic. The butter had an aromatic flavor; by Jove, it was perfectly delicious.

And there they sat—the charmers, I mean—eating these buttered muffins in plain sight. I wished I was a buttered muffin myself. Every minute they grew handsomer and handsomer; and I could not help thinking what a fine thing it would be to carry home a beautiful English wife! how my friends would stare! a lady from England!

I might have been mistaken; but certainly I thought that Matilda, the one who had handed me the milk, sometimes looked rather benevolently in the direction where I sat. She certainly *did* look at my jacket; and I am constrained to think at my face. Could it be possible she had fallen in love at first sight? Oh, rapture! But oh, misery! that was out of the question; for what a looking suitor was Wellingborough?

At length, the old lady glanced toward the door, and made some observations about its being yet a long walk to town. She handed me the buttered muffins, too, as if performing a final act of hospitality; and in other fidgety ways vaguely hinted her desire that I should decamp.

Slowly I rose, and murmured my thanks, and bowed, and tried to be off; but as quickly I turned, and bowed, and thanked, and lingered again and again. Oh, charmers! oh, Peris! thought I, must I go? Yes, Wellingborough, you must; so I made one desperate congée, and darted through the door.

I have never seen them since: no, nor heard of them; but to this day I live a bachelor on account of those ravishing charmers.

As the long twilight was waning deeper and deeper into the night, I entered the town; and, plodding my solitary way to the same old docks, I passed through the gates, and scrambled my way among tarry smells, across the tiers of ships between the quay and the *Highlander.* My only resource was my bunk; in I turned, and, wearied with my long stroll, was soon fast asleep, dreaming of red cheeks and roses.

Chapter XLIV

Redburn Introduces Master Harry Bolton to the Favorable Consideration of the Reader

It was the day following my Sunday stroll into the country, and when I had been in England four weeks or more, that I made the acquaintance of a handsome, accomplished, but unfortunate youth, young Harry Bolton. He was one of those small, but perfectly formed beings, with curling hair, and silken muscles, who seem to have been born in cocoons. His complexion was a mantling brunette, feminine as a girl's; his feet were small; his hands were white; and his eyes were large, black, and womanly; and, poetry aside, his voice was as the sound of a harp.

But where, among the tarry docks, and smoky sailor-lanes and by-ways of a seaport, did I, a battered Yankee boy, encounter this courtly youth?

Several evenings I had noticed him in our street of boarding-houses, standing in the doorways, and silently regarding the animated scenes without. His beauty, dress, and manner struck me as so out of place in such a street, that I could not possibly divine what had transplanted this delicate exotic from the conservatories of some Regent-street to the untidy potato-patches of Liverpool.

At last I suddenly encountered him at the sign of the Baltimore Clipper. He was speaking to one of my shipmates concerning America; and from something that dropped, I was led to imagine that he contemplated a voyage to my country. Charmed with his appearance, and all eagerness to enjoy the society of this incontrovertible son of a gentleman—a kind of pleasure so long debarred me—I smoothed down the skirts of my jacket, and at once accosted him; declaring who I was, and that nothing would afford me greater delight than to be of the least service, in imparting any information concerning America that he needed.

He glanced from my face to my jacket, and from my jacket to my face, and at length, with a pleased but somewhat puzzled expression, begged me to accompany him on a walk.

We rambled about St. George's Pier until nearly midnight; but before we parted, with uncommon frankness, he told me many strange things respecting his history.

According to his own account, Harry Bolton was a native of Bury St. Edmunds, a borough of Suffolk, not very far from London, where he was early left an orphan, under the charge of an only aunt. Between his aunt and himself, his mother had divided her fortune; and young Harry thus fell heir to a portion of about five thousand pounds.

Being of a roving mind, as he approached his majority he grew restless of the retirement of a country place; especially as he had no profession or business of any kind to engage his attention.

In vain did Bury, with all its fine old monastic attractions, lure him to abide on the beautiful banks of her Larke, and under the shadow of her stately and storied old Saxon tower.

By all my rare old historic associations, breathed Bury; by my Abbey-gate, that bears to this day the arms of Edward the Confessor; by my carved roof of the old church of St. Mary's, which escaped the low rage of the bigoted Puritans; by the royal ashes of Mary Tudor, that sleep in my midst; by my Norman ruins, and by all the old abbots of Bury, do not, oh Harry! abandon me. Where will you find shadier walks than under my lime-trees? where lovelier gardens than those within the old walls of my monastery, approached through my lordly Gate? Or if, oh Harry! indifferent to my historic mosses, and caring not for my annual verdure, thou must needs be lured by other tassels, and wouldst fain, like the Prodigal, squander thy patrimony, then, go not away from old Bury to do it. For here, on Angel-Hill, are my coffee and card-rooms, and billiard saloons, where you may lounge away your mornings, and empty your glass and your purse as you list.

In vain. Bury was no place for the adventurous Harry, who must needs hie to London, where in one winter, in the company of gambling sportsmen and dandies, he lost his last sovereign.

What now was to be done? His friends made interest for him in the requisite quarters, and Harry was soon embarked for Bombay, as a midshipman in the East India service; in which office he was known as a *"guinea-pig,"* a humorous appellation then bestowed upon the middies of the Company. And considering the perversity of his behavior, his delicate form, and soft complexion, and that gold guineas had been his bane, this appellation was not altogether, in poor Harry's case, inapplicable.

He made one voyage, and returned; another, and returned; and then threw up his warrant in disgust. A few weeks' dissipation in London, and again his purse was almost drained; when, like many prodigals, scorning to return home to his aunt, and amend—though she had often written him the kindest of letters to that effect—Harry resolved to precipitate himself upon the New World, and there carve out a fresh fortune.

With this object in view, he packed his trunks, and took the first train for Liverpool. Arrived in that town, he at once betook himself to the docks, to examine the American shipping, when a new crotchet entered his brain, born of his old sea reminiscences. It was to assume duck trousers and tarpaulin, and gallantly cross the Atlantic as a sailor. There was a dash of romance in it; a taking abandonment; and scorn of fine coats, which exactly harmonized with his reckless contempt, at the time, for all past conventionalities.

Thus determined, he exchanged his trunk for a mahogany chest; sold some of his superfluities; and moved his quarters to the sign of the Gold Anchor in Union-street.

After making his acquaintance, and learning his intentions, I was all anxiety that Harry should accompany me home in the *Highlander,* a desire to which he warmly responded.

Nor was I without strong hopes that he would succeed in an application to the captain; inasmuch as during our stay in the docks, three of our crew had left us, and their places would remain unsupplied till just upon the eve of our departure.

And here, it may as well be related, that owing to the heavy charges to which the American ships long staying in Liverpool are subjected, from the obligation to continue the wages of their seamen, when they have little or no work to employ them, and from the necessity of boarding them ashore, like lords, at their leisure, captains interested in the ownership of their vessels, are not at all indisposed to let their sailors abscond, if they please, and thus forfeit their money; for they well know that, when wanted, a new crew is easily to be procured, through the crimps of the port.

Though he spake English with fluency, and from his long service in the vessels of New York, was almost an American to behold, yet Captain Riga was in fact a Russian by birth, though this was a fact that he strove to conceal. And though extravagant in his personal expenses, and even indulging in luxurious habits, costly as Oriental dissipation, yet Captain Riga was a niggard to others; as, indeed, was evinced in the magnificent stipend of three dollars, with which he requited my own valuable services. Therefore, as it was agreed between Harry and me, that he should offer to ship as a *"boy,"* at the same rate of compensation with myself, I made no doubt that, incited by the cheapness of the bargain, Captain Riga would gladly close with him; and thus, instead of paying sixteen dollars a month to a thorough-going tar, who would consume all his rations, buy up my young blade of Bury, at the rate of half a dollar a week; with the cheering prospect, that by the end of the voyage, his fastidious palate would be the means of leaving a handsome balance of salt beef and pork in the *harness-cask.*

With part of the money obtained by the sale of a few of his velvet vests, Harry, by my advice, now rigged himself in a Guernsey frock and man-of-war trousers; and thus equipped, he made his appearance, one fine morning, on the quarter-deck of the *Highlander,* gallantly doffing his virgin tarpaulin before the redoubtable Riga.

No sooner were his wishes made known, than I perceived in the captain's face that same bland, benevolent, and bewitchingly merry expression, that had so charmed, but deceived me, when, with Mr. Jones, I had first accosted him in the cabin.

Alas, Harry! thought I—as I stood upon the forecastle looking astern where they stood—that *"gallant, gay deceiver"* shall not altogether cajole you, if Wellingborough can help it. Rather than that should be the case, indeed, I would forfeit the pleasure of your society across the Atlantic.

At this interesting interview the captain expressed a sympathetic concern touching the sad necessities, which he took upon himself to presume must have driven Harry to sea; he confessed to a warm interest in his future welfare; and did not hesitate to declare that, in going to America, under such circumstances, to seek his fortune, he was acting a manly and spirited part; and that the voyage thither, as a sailor, would be an invigorating preparative to the landing upon a shore, where he must battle out his fortune with Fate.

He engaged him at once; but was sorry to say, that he could not provide him a home on board till the day previous to the sailing of the ship; and during the interval, he could not honor any drafts upon the strength of his wages.

However, glad enough to conclude the agreement upon any terms at all, my young blade of Bury expressed his satisfaction; and full of admiration at so urbane and gentlemanly a sea-captain, he came forward to receive my congratulations.

"Harry," said I, "be not deceived by the fascinating Riga—that gay Lothario of all inexperienced, sea-going youths, from the capital or the country; he has a Janus-face, Harry; and you will not know him when he gets you out of sight of land, and mouths his cast-off coats and trousers. For *then* he is another personage altogether, and adjusts his character to the shabbiness of his integuments. No more condolings and sympathy then; no more blarney; he will hold you a little better than his boots, and would no more think of addressing you than of invoking wooden Donald, the figure-head on our bows."

And I further admonished my friend concerning our crew, particularly of the diabolical Jackson, and warned him to be cautious and wary. I told him, that unless he was somewhat accustomed to the rigging, and could furl a royal in a squall, he would be sure to subject himself to a sort of treatment from the sailors, in the last degree ignominious to any mortal who had ever crossed his legs under mahogany.

And I played the inquisitor, in cross-questioning Harry respecting the precise degree in which he was a practical sailor;—whether he had a giddy head; whether his arms could bear the weight of his body; whether, with but one hand on a shroud, a hundred feet aloft in a tempest, he felt he could look right to windward and beard it.

To all this, and much more, Harry rejoined with the most off-hand and confident air; saying that in his *"guinea-pig"* days, he had often climbed the masts and handled the sails in a gentlemanly and amateur way; so he made no doubt that he would very soon prove an expert tumbler in the *Highlander*'s rigging.

His levity of manner, and sanguine assurance, coupled with the constant sight of his most unseaman-like person—more suited to the Queen's drawing-room than a ship's forecastle—bred many misgivings in my mind. But after all, everyone in this world has his own fate entrusted to himself; and though we may warn, and forewarn, and give sage advice, and indulge in many apprehensions touching our friends; yet our friends, for the most part, will *"gang their ain gate"*; and the most we can do is, to hope for the best. Still, I suggested to Harry, whether he had not best cross the sea as a steerage passenger, since he could procure enough money for that; but no, he was bent upon going as a sailor.

I now had a comrade in my afternoon strolls, and Sunday excursions; and as Harry was a generous fellow, he shared with me his purse and his heart. He sold off several more of his fine vests and trousers, his silver-keyed flute and enameled guitar; and a portion of the money thus furnished was pleasantly spent in refreshing ourselves at the road-side inns in the vicinity of the town.

Reclining side by side in some agreeable nook, we exchanged our experiences of the past. Harry enlarged upon the fascinations of a London life; described the curricle he used to drive in Hyde Park; gave me the measurement of Madame Vestris' ankle; alluded to his first introduction at a club to the madcap Marquis of Waterford; told over the sums he had lost upon the turf on a Derby day; and made various but enigmatical allusions to a certain Lady Georgiana Theresa, the noble daughter of an anonymous earl.

Even in conversation, Harry was a prodigal; squandering his aristocratic narrations with a careless hand; and, perhaps, sometimes spending funds of reminiscences not his own.

As for me, I had only my poor old uncle the senator to fall back upon; and I used him upon all emergencies, like the knight in the game of chess; making him hop about, and stand stiffly up to the encounter, against all my fine comrade's array of dukes, lords, curricles, and countesses.

In these long talks of ours, I frequently expressed the earnest desire I cherished, to make a visit to London; and related how strongly tempted I had been one Sunday, to walk the whole way, without a penny in my pocket. To this, Harry rejoined, that nothing would delight him more, than to show me the capital; and he even meaningly but mysteriously hinted at the possibility of his doing so, before many days had passed. But this seemed so idle a thought, that I only imputed it to my friend's good-natured, rattling disposition, which sometimes prompted him to out with anything, that he thought would be agreeable. Besides, would this fine blade of Bury be seen, by his aristocratic acquaintances, walking down Oxford-street, say, arm in arm with the sleeve of my shooting-jacket? The thing was preposterous; and I began to think, that Harry, after all, was a little bit disposed to impose upon my Yankee credulity.

Luckily, my Bury blade had no acquaintance in Liverpool, where, indeed, he was as much in a foreign land, as if he were already on the shores of Lake Erie; so that he strolled about with me in perfect abandonment; reckless of the cut of my shooting-jacket; and not caring one whit who might stare at so singular a couple.

But once, crossing a square, faced on one side by a fashionable hotel, he made a rapid turn with me round a corner; and never stopped, till the square was a good block in our rear. The cause of this sudden retreat, was a remarkably elegant coat and pantaloons, standing upright on the hotel steps, and containing a young buck, tapping his teeth with an ivory-headed riding-whip.

"Who was he, Harry?" said I.

"My old chum, Lord Lovely," said Harry, with a careless air, "and Heaven only knows what brings Lovely from London."

"A lord?" said I starting; "then I must look at him again"; for lords are very scarce in Liverpool.

Unmindful of my companion's remonstrances, I ran back to the corner; and slowly promenaded past the upright coat and pantaloons on the steps.

It was not much of a lord to behold; very thin and limber about the legs, with small feet like a doll's, and a small, glossy head like a seal's. I had seen just such looking lords standing in sentimental attitudes in front of Palmo's in Broadway.

However, he and I being mutual friends of Harry's, I thought something of accosting him, and taking counsel concerning what was best to be done for the young prodigal's welfare; but upon second thoughts I thought best not to intrude; especially, as just then my lord Lovely stepped to the open window of a flashing carriage which drew up; and throwing himself into an interesting posture, with the sole of one boot vertically exposed, so as to show the stamp on it—a coronet—fell into a sparkling conversation with a magnificent white satin hat, surmounted by a regal marabou feather, inside.

I doubted not, this lady was nothing short of a peeress; and thought it would be one of the pleasantest and most charming things in the world, just to seat myself beside her, and order the coachman to take us a drive into the country.

But, as upon further consideration, I imagined that the peeress might decline the honor of my company, since I had no formal card of introduction; I marched on, and rejoined my companion, whom I at once endeavored to draw out, touching Lord Lovely; but he only made mysterious answers; and turned off the conversation, by allusions to his visits to Ickworth in Suffolk, the magnificent seat of the Most Noble Marquis of Bristol, who had repeatedly assured Harry that he might consider Ickworth his home.

Now, all these accounts of marquises and Ickworths, and Harry's having been hand in glove with so many lords and ladies, began to breed some suspicions concerning the rigid morality of my friend, as a teller of the truth. But, after all, thought I to myself, who can prove that Harry has fibbed? Certainly, his manners are polished, he has a mighty easy address; and there is nothing altogether impossible about his having consorted with the master of Ickworth, and the daughter of the anonymous earl. And what right has a poor Yankee, like me, to insinuate the slightest suspicion against what he says? What little money he has, he spends freely; he can not be a polite blackleg, for I am no pigeon to pluck; so *that* is out of the question;—perish such a thought, concerning my own bosom friend!

But though I drowned all my suspicions as well as I could, and ever cherished toward Harry a heart, loving and true; yet, spite of all this, I never could entirely digest some of his imperial reminiscences of high life. I was very sorry for this; as at times it made me feel ill at ease in his company; and made me hold back my whole soul from him; when, in its loneliness, it was yearning to throw itself into the unbounded bosom of some immaculate friend.

Chapter XLV

Harry Bolton Kidnaps Redburn, and Carries Him off to London

It might have been a week after our glimpse of Lord Lovely, that Harry, who had been expecting a letter, which, he told me, might possibly alter his plans, one afternoon came bounding on board the ship, and sprang down the hatchway into the *between-decks,* where, in perfect solitude, I was engaged picking oakum; at which business the mate had set me, for want of anything better.

"Hey for London, Wellingborough!" he cried. "Off to-morrow! first train—be there the same night—come! I have money to rig you all out—drop that hangman's stuff there, and away! Pah! how it smells here! Come; up you jump!"

I trembled with amazement and delight.

London? it could not be!—and Harry—how kind of him! he was then indeed what he seemed. But instantly I thought of all the circumstances of the case, and was eager to know what it was that had induced this sudden departure.

In reply my friend told me, that he had received a remittance, and had hopes of recovering a considerable sum, lost in some way that he chose to conceal.

"But how am I to leave the ship, Harry?" said I; "they will not let me go, will they? You had better leave me behind, after all; I don't care very much about going; and besides, I have no money to share the expenses."

This I said, only pretending indifference, for my heart was jumping all the time.

"Tut! my Yankee bantam," said Harry; "look here!" and he showed me a handful of gold.

"But they are *yours*, and not *mine*, Harry," said I.

"Yours *and* mine, my sweet fellow," exclaimed Harry. "Come, sink the ship, and let's go!"

"But you don't consider, if I quit the ship, they'll be sending a constable after me, won't they?"

"What! and do you think, then, they value your services so highly? Ha! ha!—Up, up, Wellingborough: I can't wait."

True enough. I well knew that Captain Riga would not trouble himself much, if I *did* take French leave of him. So, without further thought of the matter, I told Harry to wait a few moments, till the ship's bell struck four; at which time I used to go to supper, and be free for the rest of the day.

The bell struck; and off we went. As we hurried across the quay, and along the dock walls, I asked Harry all about his intentions. He said, that go to London he must, and to Bury St. Edmunds; but that whether he should for any time remain at either place, he could not now tell; and it was by no means impossible, that in less than a week's time we would be back again in Liverpool, and ready for sea. But all he said was enveloped in a mystery that I did not much like; and I hardly know whether I have repeated correctly what he said at the time.

Arrived at the *Golden Anchor*, where Harry put up, he at once led me to his room, and began turning over the contents of his chest, to see what clothing he might have, that would fit me.

Though he was some years my senior, we were about the same size—if anything, I was larger than he; so, with a little stretching, a shirt, vest, and pantaloons were soon found to suit. As for a coat and hat, those Harry ran out and bought without delay; returning with a loose, stylish sack-coat, and a sort of foraging cap, very neat, genteel, and unpretending.

My friend himself soon doffed his Guernsey frock, and stood before me, arrayed in a perfectly plain suit, which he had bought on purpose that very morning. I asked him why he had gone to that unnecessary expense, when he had plenty of other clothes in his chest. But he only winked, and looked knowing. This, again, I did not like. But I strove to drown ugly thoughts.

Till quite dark, we sat talking together; when, locking his chest, and charging his landlady to look after it well, till he called, or sent for it; Harry seized my arm, and we sallied into the street.

Pursuing our way through crowds of frolicking sailors and fiddlers, we turned into a street leading to the Exchange. There, under the shadow of the colonnade, Harry told me to stop, while he left me, and went to finish his toilette. Wondering what he meant, I stood to one side; and presently was joined by a stranger in whiskers and mustache.

"It's *me*," said the stranger; and who was *me* but Harry, who had thus metamorphosed himself? I asked him the reason; and in a faltering voice, which I tried to make humorous, expressed a hope that he was not going to turn gentleman forger.

He laughed, and assured me that it was only a precaution against being recognized by his own particular friends in London, that he had adopted this mode of disguising himself.

"And why afraid of your friends?" asked I, in astonishment, "and we are not in London yet."

"Pshaw! what a Yankee you are, Wellingborough. Can't you see very plainly that I have a plan in my head? And this disguise is only for a short time, you know. But I'll tell you all by and by."

I acquiesced, though not feeling at ease; and we walked on, till we came to a public house, in the vicinity of the place at which the cars are taken.

We stopped there that night, and next day were off, whirled along through boundless landscapes of villages, and meadows, and parks: and over arching viaducts, and through wonderful tunnels; till, half delirious with excitement, I found myself dropped down in the evening among gas-lights, under a great roof in Euston Square.

London at last, and in the West-End!

Chapter XLVI

A Mysterious Night in London

No time to lose, said Harry, come along.

He called a cab: in an undertone mentioned the number of a house in some street to the driver; we jumped in, and were off.

As we rattled over the boisterous pavements, past splendid squares, churches, and shops, our cabman turning corners like a skater on the ice, and all the roar of London in my ears, and no end to the walls of brick and mortar; I thought New York a hamlet, and Liverpool a coal-hole, and myself somebody else: so unreal seemed everything about me. My head was spinning round like a top, and my eyes ached with much gazing; particularly about the comers, owing to my darting them so rapidly, first this side, and then that, so as not to miss anything; though, in truth, I missed much.

"Stop," cried Harry, after a long while, putting his head out of the window, all at once—"stop! do you hear, you deaf man? you have passed the house—No. 40 I told you—that's it—the high steps there, with the purple light!"

The cabman being paid, Harry adjusting his whiskers and mustache, and bidding me assume a lounging look, pushed his hat a little to one side, and then locking arms, we sauntered into the house; myself feeling not a little abashed; it was so long since I had been in any courtly society.

It was some semi-public place of opulent entertainment; and far surpassed anything of the kind I had ever seen before.

The floor was tesselated with snow-white, and russet-hued marbles; and echoed to the tread, as if all the Paris catacombs were underneath. I started with misgivings at that hollow, boding sound, which seemed sighing with a subterraneous despair, through all the magnificent spectacle around me; mocking it, where most it glared.

The walls were painted so as to deceive the eye with interminable colonnades; and groups of columns of the finest Scagliola work of variegated marbles—emerald-green and gold, St. Pons veined with silver, Sienna with porphyry—supported a resplendent fresco ceiling, arched like a bower, and thickly clustering with mimic grapes. Through all the east of this foliage, you spied in a crimson dawn, Guido's ever youthful Apollo, driving forth the horses of the sun. From sculptured stalactites of vine-boughs, here and there pendent hung galaxies of gas lights, whose vivid glare was softened by pale, cream-colored, porcelain spheres, shedding over the place a serene, silver flood; as if every porcelain sphere were a moon; and this superb apartment was the moon-lit garden of Portia at Belmont; and the gentle lovers, Lorenzo and Jessica, lurked somewhere among the vines.

At numerous Moorish looking tables, supported by Caryatides of turbaned slaves, sat knots of gentlemanly men, with cut decanters and taper-waisted glasses, journals and cigars, before them.

To and fro ran obsequious waiters, with spotless napkins thrown over their arms, and making a profound salaam, and hemming deferentially, whenever they uttered a word.

At the further end of this brilliant apartment, was a rich mahogany turret-like structure, partly built into the wall, and communicating with rooms in the rear. Behind, was a very handsome florid old man, with snow-white hair and whiskers, and in a snow-white jacket—he looked like an almond tree in blossom—who seemed to be standing, a polite sentry over the scene before him; and it was he, who mostly ordered about the waiters; and with a silent salute, received the silver of the guests.

Our entrance excited little or no notice; for everybody present seemed exceedingly animated about concerns of their own; and a large group was gathered around one tall, military looking gentleman, who was reading some India war-news from the *Times,* and commenting on it, in a very loud voice, condemning, in toto, the entire campaign.

We seated ourselves apart from this group, and Harry, rapping on the table, called for wine; mentioning some curious foreign name.

The decanter, filled with a pale yellow wine, being placed before us, and my comrade having drunk a few glasses; he whispered me to remain where I was, while he withdrew for a moment.

I saw him advance to the turret-like place, and exchange a confidential word with the almond tree there, who immediately looked very much surprised—I thought, a little disconcerted—and then disappeared with him.

While my friend was gone, I occupied myself with looking around me, and striving to appear as indifferent as possible, and as much used to all this splendor as if I had been born in it. But, to tell the truth, my head was almost dizzy with the strangeness of the sight, and the thought that I was really in London. What would my brother have said? What would Tom Legare, the treasurer of the Juvenile Temperance Society, have thought?

But I almost began to fancy I had no friends and relatives living in a little village three thousand five hundred miles off, in America; for it was hard to unite such a humble reminiscence with the splendid animation of the London-like scene around me.

And in the delirium of the moment, I began to indulge in foolish golden visions of the counts and countesses to whom Harry might introduce me; and every instant I expected to hear the waiters addressing some gentleman as *"My Lord,"* or *"Your Grace."* But if there were really any lords present, the waiters omitted their titles, at least in my hearing.

Mixed with these thoughts were confused visions of St. Paul's and the Strand, which I determined to visit the very next morning, before breakfast, or perish in the attempt. And I even longed for Harry's return, that we might immediately sally out into the street, and see some of the sights, before the shops were all closed for the night.

While I thus sat alone, I observed one of the waiters eyeing me a little impertinently, as I thought, and as if he saw something queer about me. So I tried to assume a careless and lordly air, and by way of helping the thing, threw one leg over the other, like a young Prince Esterhazy; but all the time I felt my face burning with embarrassment, and for the time, I must have looked very guilty of something. But spite of this, I kept looking boldly out of my eyes, and straight through my blushes, and observed that every now and then little parties were made up among the gentlemen, and they retired into the rear of the house, as if going to a private apartment. And I overheard one of them drop the word *Rouge*; but he could not have used rouge, for his face was exceedingly pale. Another said something about *Loo.*

At last Harry came back, his face rather flushed.

"Come along, Redburn," said he.

So making no doubt we were off for a ramble, perhaps to Apsley House, in the Park, to get a sly peep at the old Duke before he retired for the night, for Harry had told me the Duke always went to bed early, I sprang up to follow him; but what was my disappointment and surprise, when he only led me into the passage, toward a staircase lighted by three marble Graces, unitedly holding a broad candelabra, like an elk's antlers, over the landing.

We rambled up the long, winding slope of those aristocratic stairs, every step of which, covered with Turkey rugs, looked gorgeous as the hammer-cloth of the Lord Mayor's coach; and Harry hied straight to a rosewood door, which, on magical hinges, sprang softly open to his touch.

As we entered the room, methought I was slowly sinking in some reluctant, sedgy sea; so thick and elastic the Persian carpeting, mimicking parterres of tulips, and roses, and jonquils, like a bower in Babylon.

Long lounges lay carelessly disposed, whose fine damask was interwoven, like the Gobelin tapestry, with pictorial tales of tilt and tourney. And oriental ottomans, whose cunning warp and woof were wrought into plaited serpents, undulating beneath beds of leaves, from which, here and there, they flashed out sudden splendors of green scales and gold.

In the broad bay windows, as the hollows of King Charles' oaks, were Laocoon-like chairs, in the antique taste, draped with heavy fringers of bullion and silk.

The walls, covered with a sort of tartan-French paper, variegated with bars of velvet, were hung round with mythological oil-paintings, suspended by tasseled cords of twisted silver and blue.

They were such pictures as the high-priests, for a bribe, showed to Alexander in the innermost shrine of the white temple in the Libyan oasis: such pictures as the pontiff of the sun strove to hide from Cortez, when, sword in hand, he burst open the sanctorum of the pyramid-fane at Cholula: such pictures as you may still see, perhaps, in the central alcove of the excavated mansion of Pansa, in Pompeii—in that part of it called by Varro *the hollow of the house:* such pictures as Martial and Seutonius mention as being found in the private cabinet of the Emperor Tiberius: such pictures as are delineated on the bronze medals, to this day dug up on the ancient island of Capræs: such pictures as you might have beheld in an arched recess, leading from the left hand of the secret side-gallery of the temple of Aphrodite in Corinth.

In the principal pier was a marble bracket, sculptured in the semblance of a dragon's crest, and supporting a bust, most wonderful to behold. It was that of a bald-headed old man, with a mysteriously-wicked expression, and imposing silence by one thin finger over his lips. His marble mouth seemed tremulous with secrets.

"Sit down, Wellingborough," said Harry; "don't be frightened, we are at home.—Ring the bell, will you? But stop";—and advancing to the mysterious bust, he whispered something in its ear.

"He's a knowing mute, Wellingborough," said he; "who stays in this one place all the time, while he is yet running of errands. But mind you don't breathe any secrets in his ear."

In obedience to a summons so singularly conveyed, to my amazement a servant almost instantly appeared, standing transfixed in the attitude of a bow.

"Cigars," said Harry. When they came, he drew up a small table into the middle of the room, and lighting his cigar, bade me follow his example, and make myself happy.

Almost transported with such princely quarters, so undreamed of before, while leading my dog's life in the filthy forecastle of the *Highlander,* I twirled round a chair, and seated myself opposite my friend.

But all the time, I felt ill at heart; and was filled with an under current of dismal forebodings. But I strove to dispel them; and turning to my companion, exclaimed, "And pray, do you live here, Harry, in this Palace of Aladdin?"

"Upon my soul," he cried, "you have hit it—you must have been here before! Aladdin's Palace! Why, Wellingborough, it goes by that very name."

Then he laughed strangely: and for the first time, I thought he had been quaffing too freely: yet, though he looked wildly from his eyes, his general carriage was firm.

"Who are you looking at so hard, Wellingborough?" said he.

"I am afraid, Harry," said I, "that when you left me just now, you must have been drinking something stronger than wine."

"Hear him now," said Harry, turning round, as if addressing the bald-headed bust on the bracket—"a parson 'pon honor!—But remark you, Wellingborough, my boy, I must leave you again, and for a considerably longer time than before:—I may not be back again to-night."

"What?" said I.

"Be still," he cried, "hear me, I know the old duke here, and—"

"Who? not the Duke of Wellington," said I, wondering whether Harry was really going to include *him* too, in his long list of confidential friends and acquaintances.

"Pooh!" cried Harry, "I mean the white-whiskered old man you saw below; they call him *the Duke—he* keeps the house. I say, I know him well, and he knows *me*; and he knows what brings me here, also. Well; we have arranged everything about you; you are to stay in this room, and sleep here to-night, and—and—" continued he, speaking low—"you must guard this letter—" slipping a sealed one into my hand—"and, if I am not back by morning, you must post right on to Bury, and leave the letter there;—here, take this paper—it's all set down here in black and white—where you are to go, and what you are to do. And after that's done—mind, this is all in case I don't return—then you may do what you please: stay here in London awhile, or go back to Liverpool. And here's enough to pay all your expenses."

All this was a thunder stroke. I thought Harry was crazy. I held the purse in my motionless hand, and stared at him, till the tears almost started from my eyes.

"What's the matter, Redburn?" he cried, with a wild sort of laugh—"you are not afraid of me, are you?—No, no! I believe in you, my boy, or you would not hold that purse in your hand; no, nor that letter."

"What in heaven's name do you mean?" at last I exclaimed, "you don't really intend to desert me in this strange place, do you, Harry?" and I snatched him by the hand.

"Pooh, pooh," he cried, "let me go. I tell you, it's all right: do as I say: that's all. Promise me now, will you? Swear it!—no, no," he added, vehemently, as I conjured him to tell me more—"no, I won't: I have nothing more to tell you—not a word. Will you swear?"

"But one sentence more for your own sake, Harry: hear me!"

"Not a syllable! Will you swear?—you will not? then here, give me that purse:—there—there—take that—and that—and that;—that will pay your fare back to Liverpool; good-bye to you: you are not my friend," and he wheeled round his back.

I know not what flashed through my mind, but something suddenly impelled me; and grasping his hand, I swore to him what he demanded.

Immediately he ran to the bust, whispered a word, and the white-whiskered old man appeared: whom he clapped on the shoulder, and then introduced me as his friend—young Lord Stormont; and bade the almond tree look well to the comforts of his lordship, while he—Harry—was gone.

The almond tree blandly bowed, and grimaced, with a peculiar expression, that I hated on the spot. After a few words more, he withdrew. Harry then shook my hand heartily, and without giving me a chance to say one word, seized his cap, and darted out of the room, saying, "Leave not this room to-night; and remember the letter, and Bury!"

I fell into a chair, and gazed round at the strange-looking walls and mysterious pictures, and up to the chandelier at the ceiling; then rose, and opened the door, and looked down the lighted passage; but only heard the hum from the roomful below, scattered voices, and a hushed ivory rattling from the closed apartments adjoining. I stepped back into the room, and a terrible revulsion came over me: I would have given the world had I been safe back in Liverpool, fast asleep in my old bunk in Prince's Dock.

I shuddered at every footfall, and almost thought it must be some assassin pursuing me. The whole place seemed infected; and a strange thought came over me, that in the very damasks around, some eastern plague had been imported. And was that pale yellow wine, that I drank below, drugged? thought I. This must be some house whose foundations take hold on the pit. But these fearful reveries only enchanted me fast to my chair; so that, though I then wished to rush forth from the house, my limbs seemed manacled.

While thus chained to my seat, something seemed suddenly flung open; a confused sound of imprecations, mixed with the ivory rattling, louder than before, burst upon my ear, and through the partly open door of the room where I was, I caught sight of a tall, frantic man, with clenched hands, wildly darting through the passage, toward the stairs.

And all the while, Harry ran through my soul—in and out, at every door, that burst open to his vehement rush.

At that moment my whole acquaintance with him passed like lightning through my mind, till

I asked myself why he had come here, to London, to do this thing?—why would not Liverpool have answered? and what did he want of me? But, every way, his conduct was unaccountable. From the hour he had accosted me on board the ship, his manner seemed gradually changed; and from the moment we had sprung into the cab, he had seemed almost another person from what he had seemed before.

But what could I do? He was gone, that was certain;—would he ever come back? But he might still be somewhere in the house; and with a shudder, I thought of that ivory rattling, and was almost ready to dart forth, search every room, and save him. But that would be madness, and I had sworn not to do so. There seemed nothing left, but to await his return. Yet, if he did not return, what then? I took out the purse, and counted over the money, and looked at the letter and paper of memoranda.

Though I vividly remember it all, I will not give the superscription of the letter, nor the contents of the paper. But after I had looked at them attentively, and considered that Harry could have no conceivable object in deceiving me, I thought to myself, Yes, he's in earnest; and here I am—yes, even in London! And here in this room will I stay, come what will. I will implicitly follow his directions, and so see out the last of this thing.

But spite of these thoughts, and spite of the metropolitan magnificence around me, I was mysteriously alive to a dreadful feeling, which I had never before felt, except when penetrating into the lowest and most squalid haunts of sailor iniquity in Liverpool. All the mirrors and marbles around me seemed crawling over with lizards; and I thought to myself, that though gilded and golden, the serpent of vice is a serpent still.

It was now grown very late; and faint with excitement, I threw myself upon a lounge; but for some time tossed about restless, in a sort of night-mare. Every few moments, spite of my oath, I was upon the point of starting up, and rushing into the street, to inquire where I was; but remembering Harry's injunctions, and my own ignorance of the town, and that it was now so late, I again tried to be composed.

At last, I fell asleep, dreaming about Harry fighting a duel of dice-boxes with the military-looking man below; and the next thing I knew, was the glare of a light before my eyes, and Harry himself, very pale, stood before me.

"The letter and paper," he cried.

I fumbled in my pockets, and handed them to him.

"There! there! there! thus I tear you," he cried, wrenching the letter to pieces with both hands like a madman, and stamping upon the fragments. "I am off for America; the game is up."

"For God's sake explain," said I, now utterly bewildered, and frightened. "Tell me, Harry, what is it? You have not been gambling?"

"Ha, ha," he deliriously laughed. "Gambling? red and white, you mean?—cards?—dice?—the bones?—Ha, ha!—Gambling? gambling?" he ground out between his teeth—"what two devilish, stiletto-sounding syllables they are!"

"Wellingborough," he added, marching up to me slowly, but with his eyes blazing into mine—"Wellingborough"—and fumbling in his breast-pocket, he drew forth a dirk—"Here, Wellingborough, take it—take it, I say—are you stupid?—there, there"—and he pushed it into my hands. "Keep it away from me—keep it out of my sight—I don't want it near me, while I feel as I do. They serve suicides scurvily here, Wellingborough; they don't bury them decently. See that bell-rope! By Heaven, it's an invitation to hang myself"—and seizing it by the gilded handle at the end, he twitched it down from the wall.

"In God's name, what ails you?" I cried.

"Nothing, oh nothing," said Harry, now assuming a treacherous, tropical calmness—"nothing, Redburn; nothing in the world. I'm the serenest of men."

"But give me that dirk," he suddenly cried—"let me have it, I say. Oh! I don't mean to murder myself—I'm past that now—give it me"—and snatching it from my hand, he flung down an empty purse, and with a terrific stab, nailed it fast with the dirk to the table.

"There now," he cried, "there's something for the old duke to see to-morrow morning; that's about all that's left of me—that's my skeleton, Wellingborough. But come, don't be down-hearted; there's a little more gold yet in Golconda; I have a guinea or two left. Don't stare so, my boy; we shall be in Liverpool to-morrow night; we start in the morning"—and turning his back, he began to whistle very fiercely.

"And this, then," said I, "is your showing me London, is it, Harry? I did not think this; but tell me your secret, whatever it is, and I will not regret not seeing the town."

He turned round upon me like lightning, and cried, "Redburn! you must swear another oath, and instantly."

"And why?" said I, in alarm, "what more would you have me swear?"

"Never to question me again about this infernal trip to London!" he shouted, with the foam at his lips—"never to breathe it! swear!"

"I certainly shall not trouble you, Harry, with questions, if you do not desire it," said I, "but there's no need of swearing."

"Swear it, I say, as you love me, Redburn," he added, imploringly.

"Well, then, I solemnly do. Now lie down, and let us forget ourselves as soon as we can; for me, you have made me the most miserable dog alive."

"And what am I?" cried Harry; "but pardon me, Redburn, I did not mean to offend; if you knew all—but no, no!—never mind, never mind!" And he ran to the bust, and whispered in its ear. A waiter came.

"Brandy," whispered Harry, with clenched teeth.

"Are you not going to sleep, then?" said I, more and more alarmed at his wildness, and fearful of the effects of his drinking still more, in such a mood.

"No sleep for me! sleep if *you* can—*I* mean to sit up with a decanter!—let me see"—looking at the ormolu clock on the mantel—"it's only two hours to morning."

The waiter, looking very sleepy, and with a green shade on his brow, appeared with the decanter and glasses on a salver, and was told to leave it and depart.

Seeing that Harry was not to be moved, I once more threw myself on the lounge. I did not sleep; but, like a somnambulist, only dozed now and then; starting from my dreams; while Harry sat, with his hat on, at the table; the brandy before him; from which he occasionally poured into his glass. Instead of exciting him, however, to my amazement, the spirits seemed to soothe him down; and, ere long, he was comparatively calm.

At last, just as I had fallen into a deep sleep, I was wakened by his shaking me, and saying our cab was at the door.

"Look! it is broad day," said he, brushing aside the heavy hangings of the window.

We left the room; and passing through the now silent and deserted hall of pillars, which, at this hour, reeked as with blended roses and cigar-stumps decayed; a dumb waiter; rubbing his eyes, flung open the street door; we sprang into the cab; and soon found ourselves whirled along northward by railroad, toward Prince's Dock and the *Highlander.*

Chapter XLVII

HOMEWARD BOUND

ONCE MORE IN LIVERPOOL; AND WENDING MY WAY THROUGH THE SAME OLD STREETS TO THE sign of the Golden Anchor; I could scarcely credit the events of the last thirty-six hours.

So unforeseen had been our departure in the first place; so rapid our journey; so unaccountable the conduct of Harry; and so sudden our return; that all united to overwhelm me. That I had been at all in London seemed impossible; and that I had been there, and come away little the wiser, was almost distracting to one who, like me, had so longed to behold that metropolis of marvels.

I looked hard at Harry as he walked in silence at my side; I stared at the houses we passed; I thought of the cab, the gas lighted hall in the Palace of Aladdin, the pictures, the letter, the oath, the dirk; the mysterious place where all these mysteries had occurred; and then, was almost ready to conclude, that the pale yellow wine had been drugged.

As for Harry, stuffing his false whiskers and mustache into his pocket, he now led the way to the boarding-house; and saluting the landlady, was shown to his room; where we immediately shifted our clothes, appearing once more in our sailor habiliments.

"Well, what do you propose to do now, Harry?" said I, with a heavy heart.

"Why, visit your Yankee land in the *Highlander*, of course—what else?' he replied.

"And is it to be a visit, or a long stay?" asked I.

"That's as it may turn out," said Harry; "but I have now more than ever resolved upon the sea. There is nothing like the sea for a fellow like me, Redburn; a desperate man can not get any further than the wharf, you know; and the next step must be a long jump. But come, let's see what they have to eat here, and then for a cigar and a stroll. I feel better already. Never say die, is my motto."

We went to supper; after that, sallied out; and walking along the quay of Prince's Dock, heard that the ship *Highlander* had that morning been advertised to sail in two days' time.

"Good!" exclaimed Harry; and I was glad enough myself.

Although I had now been absent from the ship a full forty-eight hours, and intended to return to her, yet I did not anticipate being called to any severe account for it from the officers; for several of our men had absented themselves longer than I had, and upon their return, little or nothing was said to them. Indeed, in some cases, the mate seemed to know nothing about it. During the whole time we lay in Liverpool, the discipline of the ship was altogether relaxed; and I could hardly believe they were the same officers who were so dictatorial at sea. The reason of this was, that we had nothing important to do; and although the captain might now legally refuse to receive me on board, yet I was not afraid of that, as I was as stout a lad for my years, and worked as cheap, as anyone he could engage to take my place on the homeward passage.

Next morning we made our appearance on board before the rest of the crew; and the mate perceiving me, said with an oath, "Well, sir, you have thought best to return then, have you? Captain Riga and I were flattering ourselves that you had made a run of it for good."

Then, thought I, the captain, who seems to affect to know nothing of the proceedings of the sailors, has been aware of my absence.

"But turn to, sir, turn to," added the mate; "here! aloft there, and free that pennant; it's foul of the back-stay—jump!"

The captain coming on board soon after, looked very benevolently at Harry; but, as usual, pretended not to take the slightest notice of myself.

We were all now very busy in getting things ready for sea. The cargo had been already stowed in the hold by the stevedores and lumpers from shore; but it became the crew's business to clear away the *between-decks*, extending from the cabin bulkhead to the forecastle, for the reception of about five hundred emigrants, some of whose boxes were already littering the decks.

To provide for their wants, a far larger supply of water was needed than upon the outward-bound passage. Accordingly, besides the usual number of casks on deck, rows of immense tierces were lashed amid-ships, all along the *between-decks*, forming a sort of aisle on each side, furnishing access to four rows of bunks—three tiers, one above another—against the ship's sides; two tiers being placed over the tierces of water in the middle. These bunks were rapidly knocked together with coarse planks. They looked more like dog-kennels than anything else; especially as the place was so gloomy and dark; no light coming down except through the fore and after-hatchways, both of which were covered with little houses called *"booby-hatches."* Upon the main-hatches, which were well calked and covered over with heavy tarpaulins, the *"passengers'-galley"* was solidly lashed down.

This *galley* was a large open stove, or iron range—made expressly for emigrant ships, wholly unprotected from the weather, and where alone the emigrants are permitted to cook their food while at sea.

After two days' work, everything was in readiness; most of the emigrants on board; and in the evening we worked the ship close into the outlet of Prince's Dock, with the bow against the water-gate, to go out with the tide in the morning.

In the morning, the bustle and confusion about us was indescribable. Added to the ordinary clamor of the docks, was the hurrying to and fro of our five hundred emigrants, the last of whom, with their baggage, were now coming on board; the appearance of the cabin passengers, following porters with their trunks; the loud orders of the dock-masters, ordering the various ships behind us to preserve their order of going out; the leave-takings, and good-bye's, and God-bless-you's, between the emigrants and their friends; and the cheers of the surrounding ships.

At this time we lay in such a way, that no one could board us except by the bowsprit, which overhung the quay. Staggering along that bowsprit, now came a one-eyed *crimp* leading a drunken tar by the collar, who had been shipped to sail with us the day previous. It has been stated before, that two or three of our men had left us for good, while in port. When the crimp had got this man and another safely lodged in a bunk below, he returned on shore; and going to a miserable cab, pulled out still another apparently drunken fellow, who proved completely helpless. However, the ship now swinging her broadside more toward the quay, this stupefied sailor, with a Scotch cap pulled down over his closed eyes, only revealing a sallow Portuguese complexion, was lowered on board by a rope under his arms, and passed forward by the crew, who put him likewise into a bunk in the forecastle, the crimp himself carefully tucking him in, and bidding the bystanders not to disturb him till the ship was away from the land.

This done, the confusion increased, as we now glided out of the dock. Hats and handkerchiefs were waved; hurrahs were exchanged; and tears were shed; and the last thing I saw, as we shot into the stream, was a policeman collaring a boy, and walking him off to the guard-house.

A steam-tug, the *Goliath,* now took us by the arm, and gallanted us down the river past the fort.

The scene was most striking.

Owing to a strong breeze, which had been blowing up the river for four days past, holding wind-bound in the various docks a multitude of ships for all parts of the world; there was now under weigh, a vast fleet of merchantmen, all steering broad out to sea. The white sails glistened in the clear morning air like a great Eastern encampment of sultans; and from many a forecastle, came the deep mellow old song *Ho-o-he-yo, cheerily men!* as the crews catted their anchors.

The wind was fair; the weather mild; the sea most smooth; and the poor emigrants were in high spirits at so auspicious a beginning of their voyage. They were reclining all over the decks, talking of soon seeing America, and relating how the agent had told them, that twenty days would be an uncommonly long voyage.

Here it must be mentioned, that owing to the great number of ships sailing to the Yankee ports from Liverpool, the competition among them in obtaining emigrant passengers, who as a cargo are much more remunerative than crates and bales, is exceedingly great; so much so, that some of the agents they employ, do not scruple to deceive the poor applicants for passage, with all manner of fables concerning the short space of time, in which their ships make the run across the ocean.

This often induces the emigrants to provide a much smaller stock of provisions than they otherwise would; the effect of which sometimes proves to be in the last degree lamentable; as will be seen further on. And though benevolent societies have been long organized in Liverpool, for the purpose of keeping offices, where the emigrants can obtain reliable information and advice, concerning their best mode of embarkation, and other matters interesting to them; and though the English authorities have imposed a law, providing that every captain of an emigrant ship bound for any port of America shall see to it, that each passenger is provided with rations of food for sixty days; yet, all this has not deterred mercenary ship-masters and unprincipled agents from practicing the grossest deception; nor exempted the emigrants themselves, from the very sufferings intended to be averted.

No sooner had we fairly gained the expanse of the Irish Sea, and, one by one, lost sight of our thousand consorts, than the weather changed into the most miserable cold, wet, and cheerless days and nights imaginable. The wind was tempestuous, and dead in our teeth; and the hearts of the emigrants fell. Nearly all of them had now hied below, to escape the uncomfortable and perilous decks: and from the two *"booby-hatches"* came the steady hum of a subterranean wailing and weeping. That irresistible wrestler, sea-sickness, had overthrown the stoutest of their number, and the women and children were embracing and sobbing in all the agonies of the poor emigrant's first storm at sea.

Bad enough is it at such times with ladies and gentlemen in the cabin, who have nice little staterooms; and plenty of privacy; and stewards to run for them at a word, and put pillows under their heads, and tenderly inquire how they are getting along, and mix them a posset: and even then, in the abandonment of this soul and body subduing malady, such ladies and gentlemen will often give up life itself as unendurable, and put up the most pressing petitions for a speedy annihilation; all of which, however, only arises from their intense anxiety to preserve their valuable lives.

How, then, with the friendless emigrants, stowed away like bales of cotton, and packed like slaves in a slave-ship; confined in a place that, during storm time, must be closed against both light and air; who can do no cooking, nor warm so much as a cup of water; for the drenching seas would instantly flood their fire in their exposed galley on deck? How, then, with these men, and women, and children, to whom a first voyage, under the most advantageous circumstances, must come just as hard as to the Honorable De Lancey Fitz Clarence, lady, daughter, and seventeen servants.

Nor is this all: for in some of these ships, as in the case of the *Highlander,* the emigrant passengers are cut off from the most indispensable conveniences of a civilized dwelling. This forces them in storm time to such extremities, that no wonder fevers and plagues are the result. We had not been at sea one week, when to hold your head down the fore hatchway was like holding it down a suddenly opened cesspool.

But still more than this. Such is the aristocracy maintained on board some of these ships, that the most arbitrary measures are enforced, to prevent the emigrants from intruding upon the most holy precincts of the quarter-deck, the only completely open space on ship-board. Consequently—even in fine weather—when they come up from below, they are crowded in the waist of the ship, and jammed among the boats, casks, and spars; abused by the seamen, and sometimes cuffed by the officers, for unavoidably standing in the way of working the vessel.

The cabin-passengers of the *Highlander* numbered some fifteen in all; and to protect this detachment of gentility from the barbarian incursions of the *"wild Irish"* emigrants, ropes were passed athwart-ships, by the main-mast, from side to side: which defined the boundary line between those who had paid three pounds passage-money, from those who had paid twenty guineas. And the cabin-passengers themselves were the most urgent in having this regulation maintained.

Lucky would it be for the pretensions of some parvenus, whose souls are deposited at their banker's, and whose bodies but serve to carry about purses, knit of poor men's heartstrings, if thus easily they could precisely define, ashore, the difference between them and the rest of humanity.

But, I, Redburn, am a poor fellow, who have hardly ever known what it is to have five silver dollars in my pocket at one time; so, no doubt, this circumstance has something to do with my slight and harmless indignation at these things.

Chapter XLVIII

A Living Corpse

IT WAS DESTINED THAT OUR DEPARTURE FROM THE ENGLISH STRAND, SHOULD BE MARKED BY A tragical event, akin to the sudden end of the suicide, which had so strongly impressed me on quitting the American shore.

Of the three newly shipped men, who in a state of intoxication had been brought on board at the dock gates, two were able to be engaged at their duties, in four or five hours after quitting the pier. But the third man yet lay in his bunk, in the self-same posture in which his limbs had been adjusted by the crimp, who had deposited him there.

His name was down on the ship's papers as Miguel Saveda, and for Miguel Saveda the chief mate at last came forward, shouting down the forecastle-scuttle, and commanding his instant presence on deck. But the sailors answered for their new comrade; giving the mate to understand that Miguel was still fast locked in his trance, and could not obey him; when, muttering his usual imprecation, the mate retired to the quarter-deck.

This was in the first dog-watch, from four to six in the evening. At about three bells, in the next watch, Max the Dutchman, who, like most old seamen, was something of a physician in cases of drunkenness, recommended that Miguel's clothing should be removed, in order that he should lie more comfortably. But Jackson, who would seldom let anything be done in the forecastle that was not proposed by himself, capriciously forbade this proceeding.

So the sailor still lay out of sight in his bunk, which was in the extreme angle of the forecastle, behind the *bowsprit-bitts*—two stout timbers rooted in the ship's keel. An hour or two afterward, some of the men observed a strange odor in the forecastle, which was attributed to the presence of some dead rat among the hollow spaces in the side planks; for some days before, the forecastle had been smoked out, to extirpate the vermin overrunning her. At midnight, the larboard watch, to which I belonged, turned out; and instantly as every man waked, he exclaimed at the now intolerable smell, supposed to be heightened by the shaking up the bilge-water, from the ship's rolling.

"Blast that rat!" cried the Greenlander.

"He's blasted already," said Jackson, who in his drawers had crossed over to the bunk of Miguel. "It's a water-rat, shipmates, that's dead; and here he is"—and with that, he dragged forth the sailor's arm, exclaiming, "Dead as a timber-head!"

Upon this the men rushed toward the bunk, Max with the light, which he held to the man's face.

"No, he's not dead," he cried, as the yellow flame wavered for a moment at the seaman's motionless mouth. But hardly had the words escaped, when, to the silent horror of all, two threads of greenish fire, like a forked tongue, darted out between the lips; and in a moment, the cadaverous face was crawled over by a swarm of worm-like flames.

The lamp dropped from the hand of Max, and went out; while covered all over with spires and sparkles of flame, that faintly crackled in the silence, the uncovered parts of the body burned before us, precisely like phosphorescent shark in a midnight sea.

The eyes were open and fixed; the mouth was curled like a scroll, and every lean feature firm as in life; while the whole face, now wound in curls of soft blue flame, wore an aspect of grim defiance, and eternal death. Prometheus, blasted by fire on the rock.

One arm, its red shirt-sleeve rolled up, exposed the man's name, tattooed in vermilion, near the hollow of the middle joint; and as if there was something peculiar in the painted flesh, every vibrating letter burned so white, that you might read the flaming name in the flickering ground of blue.

"Where's that d—d Miguel?" was now shouted down among us from the scuttle by the mate, who had just come on deck, and was determined to have every man up that belonged to his watch.

"He's gone to the harbor where they never weigh anchor," coughed Jackson. "Come you down, sir, and look."

Thinking that Jackson intended to beard him, the mate sprang down in a rage; but recoiled at the burning body as if he had been shot by a bullet. "My God!" he cried, and stood holding fast to the ladder.

"Take hold of it," said Jackson, at last, to the Greenlander; "it must go overboard. Don't stand shaking there, like a dog; take hold of it, I say! But stop"—and smothering it all in the blankets, he pulled it partly out of the bunk.

A few minutes more, and it fell with a bubble among the phosphorescent sparkles of the damp night sea, leaving a coruscating wake as it sank.

This event thrilled me through and through with unspeakable horror; nor did the conversation of the watch during the next four hours on deck at all serve to soothe me.

But what most astonished me, and seemed most incredible, was the infernal opinion of Jackson, that the man had been actually dead when brought on board the ship; and that knowingly, and merely for the sake of the month's advance, paid into his hand upon the strength of the bill he presented, the body-snatching crimp had knowingly shipped a corpse on board of the *Highlander*, under the pretense of its being a live body in a drunken trance. And I heard Jackson say, that he had known of such things having been done before. But that a really dead body ever burned in that manner, I can not even yet believe. But the sailors seemed familiar with such things; or at least with the stories of such things having happened to others.

For me, who at that age had never so much as happened to hear of a case like this, of animal combustion, in the horrid mood that came over me, I almost thought the burning body was a premonition of the hell of the Calvinists, and that Miguel's earthly end was a foretaste of his eternal condemnation.

Immediately after the burial, an iron pot of red coals was placed in the bunk, and in it two handfuls of coffee were roasted. This done, the bunk was nailed up, and was never opened again during the voyage; and strict orders were given to the crew not to divulge what had taken place to the emigrants; but to this, they needed no commands.

After the event, no one sailor but Jackson would stay alone in the forecastle, by night or by noon; and no more would they laugh or sing, or in any way make merry there, but kept all their pleasantries for the watches on deck. All but Jackson: who, while the rest would be sitting silently smoking on their chests, or in their bunks, would look toward the fatal spot, and cough, and laugh, and invoke the dead man with incredible scoffs and jeers. He froze my blood, and made my soul stand still.

Chapter XLIX

CARLO

THERE WAS ON BOARD OUR SHIP, AMONG THE EMIGRANT PASSENGERS, A RICH-CHEEKED, chestnut-haired Italian boy, arrayed in a faded, olive-hued velvet jacket, and tattered trousers rolled up to his knee. He was not above fifteen years of age; but in the twilight pensiveness of his full morning eyes, there seemed to sleep experiences so sad and various, that his days must have seemed to him years. It was not an eye like Harry's tho' Harry's was large and womanly. It shone with a soft and spiritual radiance, like a moist star in a tropic sky; and spoke of humility, deep-seated thoughtfulness, yet a careless endurance of all the ills of life.

The head was if anything small; and heaped with thick clusters of tendril curls, half over-hanging the brows and delicate ears, it somehow reminded you of a classic vase, piled up with Falernian foliage.

From the knee downward, the naked leg was beautiful to behold as any lady's arm; so soft and rounded, with infantile ease and grace. His whole figure was free, fine, and indolent; he was such a boy as might have ripened into life in a Neapolitan vineyard; such a boy as gypsies steal in infancy; such a boy as Murillo often painted, when he went among the poor and outcast, for subjects where-with to captivate the eyes of rank and wealth; such a boy, as only Andalusian beggars are, full of poetry, gushing from every rent.

Carlo was his name; a poor and friendless son of earth, who had no sire; and on life's ocean was swept along, as spoon-drift in a gale.

Some months previous, he had landed in Prince's Dock, with his hand-organ, from a Messina vessel; and had walked the streets of Liverpool, playing the sunny airs of southern climes, among the northern fog and drizzle. And now, having laid by enough to pay his passage over the Atlantic, he had again embarked, to seek his fortunes in America.

From the first, Henry took to the boy.

"Carlo," said Henry, "how did you succeed in England?"

He was reclining upon an old sail spread on the long-boat; and throwing back his soiled but tasseled cap, and caressing one leg like a child, he looked up, and said in his broken English—that seemed like mixing the potent wine of Oporto with some delicious syrup:—said he, "Ah! I succeed very well!—for I have tunes for the young and the old, the gay and the sad. I have marches for military young men, and love-airs for the ladies, and solemn sounds for the aged. I never draw a crowd, but I know from their faces what airs will best please them; I never stop before a house, but I judge from its portico for what tune they will soonest toss me some silver. And I ever play sad airs to the merry, and merry airs to the sad; and most always the rich best fancy the sad, and the poor the merry."

"But do you not sometimes meet with cross and crabbed old men," said Harry, "who would much rather have your room than your music?"

"Yes, sometimes," said Carlo, playing with his foot, "sometimes I do."

"And then, knowing the value of quiet to unquiet men, I suppose you never leave them under a shilling?"

"No," continued the boy, "I love my organ as I do myself, for it is my only friend, poor organ! it sings to me when I am sad, and cheers me; and I never play before a house, on purpose to be paid for leaving off, not I; would I, poor organ?"—looking down the hatchway where it was. "No, that I never have done, and never will do, though I starve; for when people drive me away, I do not think my organ is to blame, but they themselves are to blame; for such people's musical pipes are cracked, and grown rusted, that no more music can be breathed into their souls."

"No, Carlo; no music like yours, perhaps," said Harry, with a laugh.

"Ah! there's the mistake. Though my organ is as full of melody, as a hive is of bees; yet no organ can make music in unmusical breasts; no more than my native winds can, when they breathe upon a harp without chords."

Next day was a serene and delightful one; and in the evening when the vessel was just rippling along impelled by a gentle yet steady breeze, and the poor emigrants, relieved from their late sufferings, were gathered on deck; Carlo suddenly started up from his lazy reclinings; went below, and, assisted by the emigrants, returned with his organ.

Now, music is a holy thing, and its instruments, however humble, are to be loved and revered. Whatever has made, or does make, or may make music, should be held sacred as the golden bridle-bit of the Shah of Persia's horse, and the golden hammer, with which his hoofs are shod. Musical instruments should be like the silver tongs, with which the high-priests tended the Jewish altars—never to be touched by a hand profane. Who would bruise the poorest reed of Pan, though plucked from a beggar's hedge, would insult the melodious god himself.

And there is no humble thing with music in it, not a fife, not a negro-fiddle, that is not to be reverenced as much as the grandest architectural organ that ever rolled its flood-tide of harmony down a cathedral nave. For even a Jew's-harp may be so played, as to awaken all the fairies that are in us, and make them dance in our souls, as on a moon-lit sward of violets.

But what subtle power is this, residing in but a bit of steel, which might have made a tenpenny nail, that so enters, without knocking, into our inmost beings, and shows us all hidden things?

Not in a spirit of foolish speculation altogether, in no merely transcendental mood, did the glorious Greek of old fancy the human soul to be essentially a harmony. And if we grant that theory of Paracelsus and Campanella, that every man has four souls within him; then can we account for those banded sounds with silver links, those quartettes of melody, that sometimes sit and sing within us, as if our souls were baronial halls, and our music were made by the hoarest old harpers of Wales.

But look! here is poor Carlo's organ; and while the silent crowd surrounds him, there he stands, looking mildly but inquiringly about him; his right hand pulling and twitching the ivory knobs at one end of his instrument.

Behold the organ!

Surely, if much virtue lurk in the old fiddles of Cremona, and if their melody be in proportion to their antiquity, what divine ravishments may we not anticipate from this venerable, embrowned old organ, which might almost have played the *Dead March* in Saul, when King Saul himself was buried.

A fine old organ! carved into fantastic old towers, and turrets, and belfries; its architecture seems somewhat of the Gothic, monastic order; in front, it looks like the West-Front of York Minster.

What sculptured arches, leading into mysterious intricacies!—what mullioned windows, that seem as if they must look into chapels flooded with devotional sunsets!—what flying buttresses, and gable-ends, and niches with saints!—But stop! 'tis a Moorish iniquity; for here, as I live, is a Saracenic arch; which, for aught I know, may lead into some interior Alhambra.

Ay, it does; for as Carlo now turns his hand, I hear the gush of the Fountain of Lions, as he plays some thronged Italian air—a mixed and liquid sea of sound, that dashes its spray in my face.

Play on, play on, Italian boy! what though the notes be broken, here's that within that mends them. Turn hither your pensive, morning eyes; and while I list to the organs twain—one yours, one mine—let me gaze fathoms down into thy fathomless eye;—'tis good as gazing down into the great South Sea, and seeing the dazzling rays of the dolphins there.

Play on, play on! for to every note come trooping, now, triumphant standards, armies marching—all the pomp of sound. Methinks I am Xerxes, the nucleus of the martial neigh of all the Persian studs. Like gilded damask-flies, thick clustering on some lofty bough, my satraps swarm around me.

But now the pageant passes, and I droop; while Carlo taps his ivory knobs; and plays some flute-like saraband—soft, dulcet, dropping sounds, like silver oars in bubbling brooks. And now a clanging, martial air, as if ten thousand brazen trumpets, forged from spurs and sword-hilts, called North, and South, and East, to rush to West!

Again—what blasted heath is this?—what goblin sounds of Macbeth's witches?—Beethoven's *Spirit Waltz!* the muster-call of sprites and specters. Now come, hands joined, Medusa, Hecate, she of Endor, and all the Blocksberg's, demons dire.

Once more the ivory knobs are tapped; and long-drawn, golden sounds are heard—some ode to Cleopatra; slowly loom, and solemnly expand, vast, rounding orbs of beauty; and before me float innumerable queens, deep dipped in silver gauzes.

All this could Carlo do—make, unmake me; build me up; to pieces take me; and join me limb to limb. He is the architect of domes of sound, and bowers of song.

And all is done with that old organ! Reverenced, then, be all street organs; more melody is at the beck of my Italian boy, than lurks in squadrons of Parisian orchestras.

But look! Carlo has that to feast the eye as well as ear; and the same wondrous magic in me, magnifies them into grandeur; though every figure greatly needs the artist's repairing hand, and sadly needs a dusting.

His York Minster's West-Front opens; and like the gates of Milton's heaven, it turns on golden hinges.

What have we here? The inner palace of the Great Mogul? Group and gilded columns, in confidential clusters; fixed fountains; canopies and lounges; and lords and dames in silk and spangles.

The organ plays a stately march; and presto! wide open arches; and out come, two and two, with nodding plumes, in crimson turbans, a troop of martial men; with jingling scimiters, they pace the hall; salute, pass on, and disappear.

Now, ground and lofty tumblers; jet black Nubian slaves. They fling themselves on poles; stand on their heads; and downward vanish.

And now a dance and masquerade of figures, reeling from the side-doors, among the knights and dames. Some sultan leads a sultaness; some emperor, a queen; and jeweled sword-hilts of carpet knights fling back the glances tossed by coquettes of countesses.

On this, the curtain drops; and there the poor old organ stands, begrimed, and black, and rickety.

Now, tell me, Carlo, if at street corners, for a single penny, I may thus transport myself in dreams Elysian, who so rich as I? Not he who owns a million.

And Carlo! ill betide the voice that ever greets thee, my Italian boy, with aught but kindness; cursed the slave who ever drives thy wondrous box of sights and sounds forth from a lordling's door!

Chapter L

Harry Bolton at Sea

As yet I have said nothing about how my friend, Harry, got along as a sailor.

Poor Harry! a feeling of sadness, never to be comforted, comes over me, even now when I think of you. For this voyage that you went, but carried you part of the way to that ocean grave, which has buried you up with your secrets, and whither no mourning pilgrimage can be made.

But why this gloom at the thought of the dead? And why should we not be glad? Is it, that we ever think of them as departed from all joy? Is it, that we believe that indeed they are dead? They revisit us not, the departed; their voices no more ring in the air; summer may come, but it is winter with them; and even in our own limbs we feel not the sap that every spring renews the green life of the trees.

But Harry! you live over again, as I recall your image before me. I see you, plain and palpable as in life; and can make your existence obvious to others. Is he, then, dead, of whom this may be said?

But Harry! you are mixed with a thousand strange forms, the centaurs of fancy; half real and human, half wild and grotesque. Divine imaginings, like gods, come down to the groves of our Thessalies, and there, in the embrace of wild, dryad reminiscences, beget the beings that astonish the world.

But Harry! though your image now roams in my Thessaly groves, it is the same as of old; and among the droves of mixed beings and centaurs, you show like a zebra, banding with elks.

And indeed, in his striped Guernsey frock, dark glossy skin and hair, Harry Bolton, mingling with the *Highlander*'s crew, looked not unlike the soft, silken quadruped-creole, that, pursued by wild Bushmen, bounds through Caffrarian woods.

How they hunted you, Harry, my zebra! those ocean barbarians, those unimpressible, uncivilized sailors of ours! How they pursued you from bowsprit to main-mast, and started you out of your every retreat!

Before the day of our sailing, it was known to the seamen that the girlish youth, whom they daily saw near the sign of the Clipper in Union-street, would form one of their homeward-bound crew. Accordingly, they cast upon him many a critical glance; but were not long in concluding that Harry would prove no very great accession to their strength; that the hoist of so tender an arm would not tell many hundred-weight on the main-top-sail halyards. Therefore they disliked him before they became acquainted with him; and such dislikes, as everyone knows, are the most inveterate, and liable to increase. But even sailors are not blind to the sacredness that hallows a stranger; and for a time, abstaining from rudeness, they only maintained toward my friend a cold and unsympathizing civility.

As for Harry, at first the novelty of the scene filled up his mind; and the thought of being bound for a distant land, carried with it, as with everyone, a buoyant feeling of undefinable expectation. And though his money was now gone again, all but a sovereign or two, yet that troubled him but little, in the first flush of being at sea.

But I was surprised, that one who had certainly seen much of life, should evince such an incredible ignorance of what was wholly inadmissible in a person situated as he was. But perhaps his familiarity with lofty life, only the less qualified him for understanding the other extreme. Will you believe me, this Bury blade once came on deck in a brocaded dressing-gown, embroidered slippers, and tasseled smoking-cap, to stand his morning watch.

As soon as I beheld him thus arrayed, a suspicion, which had previously crossed my mind, again recurred, and I almost vowed to myself that, spite his protestations, Harry Bolton never could have been at sea before, even as a *Guinea-pig* in an Indiaman; for the slightest acquaintance with the sea-life and sailors, should have prevented him, it would seem, from enacting this folly.

"Who's that Chinese mandarin?" cried the mate, who had made voyages to Canton. "Look you, my fine fellow, douse that main-sail now, and furl it in a trice."

"Sir?" said Harry, starting back. "Is not this the morning watch, and is not mine a morning gown?"

But though, in my refined friend's estimation, nothing could be more appropriate; in the mate's, it was the most monstrous of incongruities; and the offensive gown and cap were removed.

"It is too bad!" exclaimed Harry to me; "I meant to lounge away the watch in that gown until coffee time;—and I suppose your Hottentot of a mate won't permit a gentleman to smoke his Turkish pipe of a morning; but by gad, I'll wear straps to my pantaloons to spite him!"

Oh! that was the rock on which you split, poor Harry! Incensed at the want of polite refinement in the mates and crew, Harry, in a pet and pique, only determined to provoke them the more; and the storm of indignation he raised very soon overwhelmed him.

The sailors took a special spite to his chest, a large mahogany one, which he had had made to order at a furniture warehouse. It was ornamented with brass screw-heads, and other devices; and was well filled with those articles of the wardrobe in which Harry had sported through a London season; for the various vests and pantaloons he had sold in Liverpool, when in want of money, had not materially lessened his extensive stock.

It was curious to listen to the various hints and opinings thrown out by the sailors at the occasional glimpses they had of this collection of silks, velvets, broadcloths, and satins. I do not know exactly what they thought Harry had been; but they seemed unanimous in believing that, by abandoning his country, Harry had left more room for the gamblers. Jackson even asked him to lift up the lower hem of his trousers, to test the color of his calves.

It is a noteworthy circumstance, that whenever a slender made youth, of easy manners and polite address happens to form one of a ship's company, the sailors almost invariably impute his seagoing to an irresistible necessity of decamping from terra-firma in order to evade the constables.

These white-fingered gentry must be light-fingered too, they say to themselves, or they would not be after putting their hands into our tar. What else can bring them to sea?

Cogent and conclusive this; and thus Harry, from the very beginning, was put down for a very equivocal character.

Sometimes, however, they only made sport of his appearance; especially one evening, when his monkey jacket being wet through, he was obliged to mount one of his swallow-tailed coats. They said he carried two mizen-peaks at his stern; declared he was a broken-down quill-driver, or a footman to a Portuguese running barber, or some old maid's tobacco-boy. As for the captain, it had become all the same to Harry as if there were no gentlemanly and complaisant Captain Riga on board. For to his no small astonishment—but just as I had predicted—Captain Riga never noticed him now, but left the business of indoctrinating him into the little experiences of a greenhorn's career solely in the hands of his officers and crew.

But the worst was to come. For the first few days, whenever there was any running aloft to be done, I noticed that Harry was indefatigable in coiling away the slack of the rigging about decks; ignoring the fact that his shipmates were springing into the shrouds. And when all hands of the watch would be engaged *clewing up a t'-gallant-sail,* that is, pulling the proper ropes on deck that wrapped the sail up on the yard aloft, Harry would always manage to get near the *belaying-pin,* so that when the time came for two of us to spring into the rigging, he would be inordinately fidgety in making fast the *clew-lines,* and would be so absorbed in that occupation, and would so elaborate the hitchings round the pin, that it was quite impossible for him, after doing so much, to mount over the bulwarks before his comrades had got there. However, after securing the clew-lines beyond a possibility of their getting loose, Harry would always make a feint of starting in a prodigious hurry for the shrouds; but suddenly looking up, and seeing others in advance, would retreat, apparently quite chagrined that he had been cut off from the opportunity of signalizing his activity.

At this I was surprised, and spoke to my friend; when the alarming fact was confessed, that he had made a private trial of it, and it never would do: *he could not go aloft*; his nerves would not hear of it.

"Then, Harry," said I, "better you had never been born. Do you know what it is that you are coming to? Did you not tell me that you made no doubt you would acquit yourself well in the rigging? Did you not say that you had been two voyages to Bombay? Harry, you were mad to ship. But you only imagine it: try again; and my word for it, you will very soon find yourself as much at home among the spars as a bird in a tree."

But he could not be induced to try it over again; the fact was, *his nerves could not stand it*; in the course of his courtly career, he had drunk too much strong Mocha coffee and gunpowder tea, and had smoked altogether too many Havannas.

At last, as I had repeatedly warned him, the mate singled him out one morning, and commanded him to mount to the main-truck, and unreeve the short signal halyards.

"Sir?" said Harry, aghast.

"Away you go!" said the mate, snatching a whip's end.

"Don't strike me!" screamed Harry, drawing himself up.

"Take that, and along with you," cried the mate, laying the rope once across his back, but lightly.

"By heaven!" cried Harry, wincing—not with the blow, but the insult: and then making a dash at the mate, who, holding out his long arm, kept him lazily at bay, and laughed at him, till, had I not feared a broken head, I should infallibly have pitched my boy's bulk into the officer.

"Captain Riga!" cried Harry.

"Don't call upon *him*" said the mate; "he's asleep, and won't wake up till we strike Yankee soundings again. Up you go!" he added, flourishing the rope's end.

Harry looked round among the grinning tars with a glance of terrible indignation and agony; and then settling his eye on me, and seeing there no hope, but even an admonition of obedience, as his only resource, he made one bound into the rigging, and was up at the main-top in a trice. I thought a few more springs would take him to the truck, and was a little fearful that in his desperation he might then jump overboard; for I had heard of delirious greenhorns doing such things at sea, and being lost forever. But no; he stopped short, and looked down from the top. Fatal glance! it unstrung his every fiber; and I saw him reel, and clutch the shrouds, till the mate shouted out for him not to squeeze the tar out of the ropes.

"Up you go, sir."

But Harry said nothing.

"You Max," cried the mate to the Dutch sailor, "spring after him, and help him; you understand?"

Max went up the rigging hand over hand, and brought his red head with a bump against the base of Harry's back. Needs must when the devil drives; and higher and higher, with Max bumping him at every step, went my unfortunate friend. At last he gained the royal yard, and the thin signal halyards—hardly bigger than common twine—were flying in the wind.

"Unreeve!" cried the mate.

I saw Harry's arm stretched out—his legs seemed shaking in the rigging, even to us, down on deck; and at last, thank heaven! the deed was done.

He came down pale as death, with blood-shot eyes, and every limb quivering. From that moment he never put foot in rattlin; never mounted above the bulwarks; and for the residue of the voyage, at least, became an altered person.

At the time, he went to the mate—since he could not get speech of the captain—and conjured him to intercede with Riga, that his name might be stricken off from the list of the ship's company, so that he might make the voyage as a steerage passenger; for which privilege, he bound himself to pay, as soon as he could dispose of some things of his in New York, over and above the ordinary passage-money. But the mate gave him a blunt denial; and a look of wonder at his effrontery. Once a sailor on board a ship, and *always* a sailor for that voyage, at least; for within so brief a period, no officer can bear to associate on terms of anything like equality with a person whom he has ordered about at his pleasure.

Harry then told the mate solemnly, that he might do what he pleased, but go aloft again he *could* not, and *would* not. He would do anything else but that.

This affair sealed Harry's fate on board of the *Highlander*; the crew now reckoned him fair play for their worst jibes and jeers, and he led a miserable life indeed.

Few landsmen can imagine the depressing and self-humiliating effects of finding one's self, for the first time, at the beck of illiterate sea-tyrants, with no opportunity of exhibiting any trait about you, but your ignorance of everything connected with the sea-life that you lead, and the duties you are constantly called upon to perform. In such a sphere, and under such circumstances, Isaac Newton and Lord Bacon would be sea-clowns and bumpkins; and Napoleon Bonaparte be cuffed and kicked without remorse. In more than one instance I have seen the truth of this; and Harry, poor Harry, proved no exception. And from the circumstances which exempted me from experiencing the bitterest of these evils, I only the more felt for one who, from a strange constitutional nervousness, before unknown even to himself, was become as a hunted hare to the merciless crew.

But how was it that Harry Bolton, who spite of his effeminacy of appearance, had evinced, in our London trip, such unmistakable flashes of a spirit not easily tamed—how was it, that he could now yield himself up to the almost passive reception of contumely and contempt? Perhaps his spirit, for the time, had been broken. But I will not undertake to explain; we are curious creatures, as everyone knows; and there are passages in the lives of all men, so out of keeping with the common tenor of their ways, and so seemingly contradictory of themselves, that only He who made us can expound them.

Chapter LI

The Emigrants

After the first miserable weather we experienced at sea, we had intervals of foul and fair, mostly the former, however, attended with head-winds; till at last, after a three days' fog and rain, the sun rose cheerily one morning, and showed us Cape Clear. Thank heaven, we were out of the weather emphatically called "Channel weather," and the last we should see of the eastern hemisphere was now in plain sight, and all the rest was broad ocean.

Land ho! was cried, as the dark purple headland grew out of the north. At the cry, the Irish emigrants came rushing up the hatchway, thinking America itself was at hand.

"Where is it?" cried one of them, running out a little way on the bowsprit. "Is that it?"

"Ay, it doesn't look much like *ould* Ireland, does it?" said Jackson.

"Not a bit, honey—and how long before we get there? to-night?"

Nothing could exceed the disappointment and grief of the emigrants, when they were at last informed, that the land to the north was their own native island, which, after leaving three or four weeks previous in a steam-boat for Liverpool, was now close to them again; and that, after newly voyaging so many days from the Mersey, the *Highlander* was only bringing them in view of the original home whence they started.

They were the most simple people I had ever seen. They seemed to have no adequate idea of distances; and to them, America must have seemed as a place just over a river. Every morning some of them came on deck, to see how much nearer we were: and one old man would stand for hours together, looking straight off from the bows, as if he expected to see New York city every minute, when, perhaps, we were yet two thousand miles distant, and steering, moreover, against a head-wind.

The only thing that ever diverted this poor old man from his earnest search for land, was the occasional appearance of porpoises under the bows; when he would cry out at the top of his voice—"Look, look, ye divils! look at the great pigs of the s'a!"

At last, the emigrants began to think, that the ship had played them false; and that she was bound for the East Indies, or some other remote place; and one night, Jackson set a report going among them, that Riga purposed taking them to Barbary, and selling them all for slaves; but though some of the old women almost believed it, and a great weeping ensued among the children, yet the men knew better than to believe such a ridiculous tale.

Of all the emigrants, my Italian boy Carlo, seemed most at his ease. He would lie all day in a dreamy mood, sunning himself in the long boat, and gazing out on the sea. At night, he would bring up his organ, and play for several hours; much to the delight of his fellow voyagers, who blessed him and his organ again and again; and paid him for his music by furnishing him his meals. Sometimes, the steward would come forward, when it happened to be very much of a moonlight, with a message from the cabin, for Carlo to repair to the quarter-deck, and entertain the gentlemen and ladies.

There was a fiddler on board, as will presently be seen; and sometimes, by urgent entreaties, he was induced to unite his music with Carlo's, for the benefit of the cabin occupants; but this was only twice or thrice: for this fiddler deemed himself considerably elevated above the other steerage-passengers; and did not much fancy the idea of fiddling to strangers; and thus wear out his elbow, while persons, entirely unknown to him, and in whose welfare he felt not the slightest interest, were curveting about in famous high spirits. So for the most part, the gentlemen and ladies were fain to dance as well as they could to my little Italian's organ.

It was the most accommodating organ in the world; for it could play any tune that was called for; Carlo pulling in and out the ivory knobs at one side, and so manufacturing melody at pleasure.

True, some censorious gentlemen cabin-passengers protested, that such or such an air, was not precisely according to Handel or Mozart; and some ladies, whom I overheard talking about throwing their nosegays to Malibran at Covent Garden, assured the attentive Captain Riga, that Carlo's organ was a most wretched affair, and made a horrible din.

"Yes, ladies," said the captain, bowing, "by your leave, I think Carlo's organ must have lost its mother, for it squeals like a pig running after its dam."

Harry was incensed at these criticisms; and yet these cabin-people were all ready enough to dance to poor Carlo's music.

"Carlo"—said I, one night, as he was marching forward from the quarter-deck, after one of these sea-quadrilles, which took place during my watch on deck—"Carlo"—said I, "what do the gentlemen and ladies give you for playing?"

"Look!"—and he showed me three copper medals of Britannia and her shield—three English pennies.

Now, whenever we discover a dislike in us, toward anyone, we should ever be a little suspicious of ourselves. It may be, therefore, that the natural antipathy with which almost all seamen and steerage-passengers, regard the inmates of the cabin, was one cause at least, of my not feeling very charitably disposed toward them, myself.

Yes: that might have been; but nevertheless, I will let nature have her own way for once; and here declare roundly, that, however it was, I cherished a feeling toward these cabin-passengers, akin to contempt. Not because they happened to be cabin-passengers: not at all: but only because they seemed the most finical, miserly, mean men and women, that ever stepped over the Atlantic.

One of them was an old fellow in a robust looking coat, with broad skirts; he had a nose like a bottle of port-wine; and would stand for a whole hour, with his legs straddling apart, and his hands deep down in his breeches pockets, as if he had two mints at work there, coining guineas. He was an abominable looking old fellow, with cold, fat, jelly-like eyes; and avarice, heartlessness, and sensuality stamped all over him. He seemed all the time going through some process of mental arithmetic; doing sums with dollars and cents: his very mouth, wrinkled and drawn up at the corners, looked like a purse. When he dies, his skull ought to be turned into a savings box, with the till-hole between his teeth.

Another of the cabin inmates, was a middle-aged Londoner, in a comical Cockney-cut coat, with a pair of semicircular tails: so that he looked as if he were sitting in a swing. He wore a spotted neckerchief; a short, little, fiery-red vest; and striped pants, very thin in the calf, but very full about the waist. There was nothing describable about him but his dress; for he had such a meaningless face, I can not remember it; though I have a vague impression, that it looked at the time, as if its owner was laboring under the mumps.

Then there were two or three buckish looking young fellows, among the rest; who were all the time playing at cards on the poop, under the lee of the *spanker*; or smoking cigars on the taffrail; or sat quizzing the emigrant women with opera-glasses, leveled through the windows of the upper cabin. These sparks frequently called for the steward to help them to brandy and water, and talked about going on to Washington, to see Niagara Falls.

There was also an old gentleman, who had brought with him three or four heavy files of the *London Times*, and other papers; and he spent all his hours in reading them, on the shady side of the deck, with one leg crossed over the other; and without crossed legs, he never read at all. That was indispensable to the proper understanding of what he studied. He growled terribly, when disturbed by the sailors, who now and then were obliged to move him to get at the ropes.

As for the ladies, I have nothing to say concerning them; for ladies are like creeds; if you can not speak well of them, say nothing.

Chapter LII

THE EMIGRANTS' KITCHEN

I HAVE MADE SOME MENTION OF THE "GALLEY," OR GREAT STOVE FOR THE STEERAGE PASSENGERS, which was planted over the main hatches.

During the outward-bound passage, there were so few occupants of the steerage, that they had abundant room to do their cooking at this galley. But it was otherwise now; for we had four or five hundred in the steerage; and all their cooking was to be done by one fire; a pretty large one, to be sure, but, nevertheless, small enough, considering the number to be accommodated, and the fact that the fire was only to be kindled at certain hours.

For the emigrants in these ships are under a sort of martial-law; and in all their affairs are regulated by the despotic ordinances of the captain. And though it is evident, that to a certain extent this is necessary, and even indispensable; yet, as at sea no appeal lies beyond the captain, he too often makes unscrupulous use of his power. And as for going to law with him at the end of the voyage, you might as well go to law with the Czar of Russia.

At making the fire, the emigrants take turns; as it is often very disagreeable work, owing to the pitching of the ship, and the heaving of the spray over the uncovered "galley." Whenever I had the morning watch, from four to eight, I was sure to see some poor fellow crawling up from below about day-break, and go to groping over the deck after bits of rope-yarn, or tarred canvas, for kindling-stuff. And no sooner would the fire be fairly made, than up came the old women, and men, and children; each armed with an iron pot or saucepan; and invariably a great tumult ensued, as to whose turn to cook came next; sometimes the more quarrelsome would fight, and upset each other's pots and pans.

Once, an English lad came up with a little coffee-pot, which he managed to crowd in between two pans. This done, he went below. Soon after a great strapping Irishman, in knee-breeches and bare calves, made his appearance; and eyeing the row of things on the fire, asked whose coffee-pot that was; upon being told, he removed it, and put his own in its place; saying something about that individual place belonging to him; and with that, he turned aside.

Not long after, the boy came along again; and seeing his pot removed, made a violent exclamation, and replaced it; which the Irishman no sooner perceived, than he rushed at him, with his fists doubled. The boy snatched up the boiling coffee, and spirted its contents all about the fellow's bare legs; which incontinently began to dance involuntary hornpipes and fandangoes, as a preliminary to giving chase to the boy, who by this time, however, had decamped.

Many similar scenes occurred everyday; nor did a single day pass, but scores of the poor people got no chance whatever to do their cooking.

This was bad enough; but it was a still more miserable thing, to see these poor emigrants wrangling and fighting together for the want of the most ordinary accommodations. But thus it is, that the very hardships to which such beings are subjected, instead of uniting them, only tends, by imbittering their tempers, to set them against each other; and thus they themselves drive the strongest rivet into the chain, by which their social superiors hold them subject.

It was with a most reluctant hand, that every evening in the second dog-watch, at the mate's command, I would march up to the fire, and giving notice to the assembled crowd, that the time was come to extinguish it, would dash it out with my bucket of salt water; though many, who had long waited for a chance to cook, had now to go away disappointed.

The staple food of the Irish emigrants was oatmeal and water, boiled into what is sometimes called *mush*; by the Dutch is known as *supaan*; by sailors *burgoo*; by the New Englanders *hasty-pudding*; in which hasty-pudding, by the way, the poet Barlow found the materials for a sort of epic.

Some of the steerage passengers, however, were provided with sea-biscuit, and other perennial food, that was eatable all the year round, fire or no fire.

There were several, moreover, who seemed better to do in the world than the rest; who were well furnished with hams, cheese, Bologna sausages, Dutch herrings, alewives, and other delicacies adapted to the contingencies of a voyager in the steerage.

There was a little old Englishman on board, who had been a grocer ashore, whose greasy trunks seemed all pantries; and he was constantly using himself for a cupboard, by transferring their contents into his own interior. He was a little light of head, I always thought. He particularly doated on his long strings of sausages; and would sometimes take them out, and play with them, wreathing them round him, like an Indian juggler with charmed snakes. What with this diversion, and eating his cheese, and helping himself from an inexhaustible junk bottle, and smoking his pipe, and meditating, this crack-pated grocer made time jog along with him at a tolerably easy pace.

But by far the most considerable man in the steerage, in point of pecuniary circumstances at least, was a slender little pale-faced English tailor, who it seemed had engaged a passage for himself and wife in some imaginary section of the ship, called the *second cabin*, which was feigned to combine the comforts of the first cabin with the cheapness of the steerage. But it turned out that this second cabin was comprised in the after part of the steerage itself, with nothing intervening but a name. So to his no small disgust, he found himself herding with the rabble; and his complaints to the captain were unheeded.

This luckless tailor was tormented the whole voyage by his wife, who was young and handsome; just such a beauty as farmers'-boys fall in love with; she had bright eyes, and red cheeks, and looked plump and happy.

She was a sad coquette; and did not turn away, as she was bound to do, from the dandy glances of the cabin bucks, who ogled her through their double-barreled opera glasses. This enraged the tailor past telling; he would remonstrate with his wife, and scold her; and lay his matrimonial commands upon her, to go below instantly, out of sight. But the lady was not to be tyrannized over; and so she told him. Meantime, the bucks would be still framing her in their lenses, mightily enjoying the fun. The last resources of the poor tailor would be, to start up, and make a dash at the rogues, with clenched fists; but upon getting as far as the main-mast, the mate would accost him from over the rope that divided them, and beg leave to communicate the fact, that he could come no further. This unfortunate tailor was also a fiddler; and when fairly baited into desperation, would rush for his instrument, and try to get rid of his wrath by playing the most savage, remorseless airs he could think of.

While thus employed, perhaps his wife would accost him—

"Billy, my dear"; and lay her soft hand on his shoulder.

But Billy, he only fiddled harder.

"Billy, my love!"

The bow went faster and faster.

"Come, now, Billy, my dear little fellow, let's make it all up"; and she bent over his knees, looking bewitchingly up at him, with her irresistible eyes.

Down went fiddle and bow; and the couple would sit together for an hour or two, as pleasant and affectionate as possible.

But the next day, the chances were, that the old feud would be renewed, which was certain to be the case at the first glimpse of an opera-glass from the cabin.

Chapter LIII

THE HORATII AND CURIATII

WITH A SLIGHT ALTERATION, I MIGHT BEGIN THIS CHAPTER AFTER THE MANNER OF LIVY, IN THE 24th section of his first book: *"It happened, that in each family were three twin brothers, between whom there was little disparity in point of age or of strength."*

Among the steerage passengers of the *Highlander*, were two women from Armagh, in Ireland, widows and sisters, who had each three twin sons, born, as they said, on the same day.

They were ten years old. Each three of these six cousins were as like as the mutually reflected figures in a kaleidoscope; and like the forms seen in a kaleidoscope, together, as well as separately, they seemed to form a complete figure. But, though besides this fraternal likeness, all six boys bore a strong cousin-german resemblance to each other; yet, the O'Briens were in disposition quite the reverse of the O'Regans. The former were a timid, silent trio, who used to revolve around their mother's waist, and seldom quit the maternal orbit; whereas, the O'Regans were "broths of boys," full of mischief and fun, and given to all manner of devilment, like the tails of the comets.

Early every morning, Mrs. O'Regan emerged from the steerage, driving her spirited twins before her, like a riotous herd of young steers; and made her way to the capacious deck-tub, full of salt water, pumped up from the sea, for the purpose of washing down the ship. Three splashes, and the three boys were ducking and diving together in the brine; their mother engaged in *shampooing* them, though it was haphazard sort of work enough; a rub here, and a scrub there, as she could manage to fasten on a stray limb.

"Pat, ye divil, hould still while I wash ye. Ah! but it's you, Teddy, you rogue. Arrah, now, Mike, ye spalpeen, don't be mixing your legs up with Pat's."

The little rascals, leaping and scrambling with delight, enjoyed the sport mightily; while this indefatigable, but merry matron, manipulated them all over, as if it were a matter of conscience.

Meanwhile, Mrs. O'Brien would be standing on the boatswain's locker—or rope and tar-pot pantry in the vessel's bows—with a large old quarto Bible, black with age, laid before her between the knight-heads, and reading aloud to her three meek little lambs.

The sailors took much pleasure in the deck-tub performances of the O'Regans, and greatly admired them always for their archness and activity; but the tranquil O'Briens they did not fancy so much. More especially they disliked the grave matron herself; hooded in rusty black; and they had a bitter grudge against her book. To that, and the incantations muttered over it, they ascribed the head-winds that haunted us; and Blunt, our Irish cockney, really believed that Mrs. O'Brien purposely came on deck every morning, in order to secure a foul wind for the next ensuing twenty-four hours.

At last, upon her coming forward one morning, Max the Dutchman accosted her, saying he was sorry for it, but if she went between the knight-heads again with her book, the crew would throw it overboard for her.

Now, although contrasted in character, there existed a great warmth of affection between the two families of twins, which upon this occasion was curiously manifested.

Notwithstanding the rebuke and threat of the sailor, the widow silently occupied her old place; and with her children clustering round her, began her low, muttered reading, standing right in the extreme bows of the ship, and slightly leaning over them, as if addressing the multitudinous waves from a floating pulpit. Presently Max came behind her, snatched the book from her hands, and threw it overboard. The widow gave a wail, and her boys set up a cry. Their cousins, then ducking in the water close by, at once saw the cause of the cry; and springing from the tub, like so many dogs, seized Max by the legs, biting and striking at him: which, the before timid little O'Briens no sooner perceived, than they, too, threw themselves on the enemy, and the amazed seaman found himself baited like a bull by all six boys.

And here it gives me joy to record one good thing on the part of the mate. He saw the fray, and its beginning; and rushing forward, told Max that he would harm the boys at his peril; while he cheered them on, as if rejoiced at their giving the fellow such a tussle. At last Max, sorely scratched, bit, pinched, and every way aggravated, though of course without a serious bruise, cried out "enough!" and the assailants were ordered to quit him; but though the three O'Briens obeyed, the three O'Regans hung on to him like leeches, and had to be dragged off.

"There now, you rascal," cried the mate, "throw overboard another Bible, and I'll send you after it without a bowline."

This event gave additional celebrity to the twins throughout the vessel. That morning all six were invited to the quarter-deck, and reviewed by the cabin-passengers, the ladies manifesting particular interest in them, as they always do concerning twins, which some of them show in public parks and gardens, by stopping to look at them, and questioning their nurses.

"And were you all born at one time?" asked an old lady, letting her eye run in wonder along the even file of white heads.

"Indeed, an' we were," said Teddy; "wasn't we, mother?"

Many more questions were asked and answered, when a collection was taken up for their benefit among these magnanimous cabin-passengers, which resulted in starting all six boys in the world with a penny apiece.

I never could look at these little fellows without an inexplicable feeling coming over me; and though there was nothing so very remarkable or unprecedented about them, except the singular coincidence of two sisters simultaneously making the world such a generous present; yet, the mere fact of there being twins always seemed curious; in fact, to me at least, all twins are prodigies; and still I hardly know why this should be; for all of us in our own persons furnish numerous examples of the same phenomenon. Are not our thumbs twins? A regular Castor and Pollux? And all of our fingers? Are not our arms, hands, legs, feet, eyes, ears, all twins; born at one birth, and as much alike as they possibly can be?

Can it be, that the Greek grammarians invented their dual number for the particular benefit of twins?

Chapter LIV

Some Superior Old Nail-Rod and Pig-Tail

IT HAS BEEN MENTIONED HOW ADVANTAGEOUSLY MY SHIPMATES DISPOSED OF THEIR TOBACCO IN Liverpool; but it is to be related how those nefarious commercial speculations of theirs reduced them to sad extremities in the end.

True to their improvident character, and seduced by the high prices paid for the weed in England, they had there sold off by far the greater portion of what tobacco they had; even inducing the mate to surrender the portion he had secured under lock and key by command of the Custom-house officers. So that when the crew were about two weeks out, on the homeward-bound passage, it became sorrowfully evident that tobacco was at a premium.

Now, one of the favorite pursuits of sailors during a dog-watch below at sea is cards; and though they do not understand whist, cribbage, and games of that kidney, yet they are adepts at what is called *"High-low-Jack-and-the-game,"* which name, indeed, has a Jackish and nautical flavor. Their stakes are generally so many plugs of tobacco, which, like rouleaux of guineas, are piled on their chests when they play. Judge, then, the wicked zest with which the *Highlander*'s crew now shuffled and dealt the pack; and how the interest curiously and invertedly increased, as the stakes necessarily became less and less; and finally resolved themselves into *"chaws."*

So absorbed, at last, did they become at this business, that some of them, after being hard at work during a night-watch on deck, would rob themselves of rest below, in order to have a brush at the cards. And as it is very difficult sleeping in the presence of gamblers; especially if they chance to be sailors, whose conversation at all times is apt to be boisterous; these fellows would often be driven out of the forecastle by those who desired to rest. They were obliged to repair on deck, and make a card-table of it; and invariably, in such cases, there was a great deal of contention, a great many ungentlemanly charges of nigging and cheating; and, now and then, a few parenthetical blows were exchanged.

But this was not so much to be wondered at, seeing they could see but very little, being provided with no light but that of a midnight sky; and the cards, from long wear and rough usage, having become exceedingly torn and tarry, so much so, that several members of the four suits might have seceded from their respective clans, and formed into a fifth tribe, under the name of *"Tar-spots."*

Everyday the tobacco grew scarcer and scarcer; till at last it became necessary to adopt the greatest possible economy in its use. The modicum constituting an ordinary *"chaw,"* was made to last a whole day; and at night, permission being had from the cook, this self-same "chaw" was placed in the oven of the stove, and there dried; so as to do duty in a pipe.

In the end not a plug was to be had; and deprived of a solace and a stimulus, on which sailors so much rely while at sea, the crew became absent, moody, and sadly tormented with the hypos. They were something like opium-smokers, suddenly cut off from their drug. They would sit on their chests, forlorn and moping; with a steadfast sadness, eyeing the forecastle lamp, at which they had lighted so many a pleasant pipe. With touching eloquence they recalled those happier evenings—the time of smoke and vapor; when, after a whole day's delectable *"chawing,"* they beguiled themselves with their genial, and most companionable puffs.

One night, when they seemed more than usually cast down and disconsolate, Blunt, the Irish cockney, started up suddenly with an idea in his head—"Boys, let's search under the bunks!"

Bless you, Blunt! what a happy conceit!

Forthwith, the chests were dragged out; the dark places explored; and two sticks of *nail-rod* tobacco, and several old *"chaws,"* thrown aside by sailors on some previous voyage, were their cheering reward. They were impartially divided by Jackson, who, upon this occasion, acquitted himself to the satisfaction of all.

Their mode of dividing this tobacco was the rather curious one generally adopted by sailors, when the highest possible degree of impartiality is desirable. I will describe it, recommending its earnest consideration to all heirs, who may hereafter divide an inheritance; for if they adopted this nautical method, that universally slanderous aphorism of Lavater would be forever rendered nugatory—*"Expert not to understand any man till you have divided with him an inheritance."*

The *nail-rods* they cut as evenly as possible into as many parts as there were men to be supplied; and this operation having been performed in the presence of all, Jackson, placing the tobacco before him, his face to the wall, and back to the company, struck one of the bits of weed with his knife, crying out, "Whose is this?" Whereupon a respondent, previously pitched upon, replied, at a venture, from the opposite corner of the forecastle, "Blunt's"; and to Blunt it went; and so on, in like manner, till all were served.

I put it to you, lawyers—shade of Blackstone, I invoke you—if a more impartial procedure could be imagined than this?

But the nail-rods and last-voyage *"chaws"* were soon gone, and then, after a short interval of comparative gaiety, the men again drooped, and relapsed into gloom.

They soon hit upon an ingenious device, however—but not altogether new among seamen—to allay the severity of the depression under which they languished. Ropes were unstranded, and the yarns picked apart; and, cut up into small bits, were used as a substitute for the weed. Old ropes were preferred; especially those which had long lain in the hold, and had contracted an epicurean dampness, making still richer their ancient, cheese-like flavor.

In the middle of most large ropes, there is a straight, central part, round which the exterior strands are twisted. When in picking oakum, upon various occasions, I have chanced, among the old junk used at such times, to light upon a fragment of this species of rope, I have ever taken, I know not what kind of strange, nutty delight in untwisting it slowly, and gradually coming upon its deftly hidden and aromatic *"heart"*; for so this central piece is denominated.

It is generally of a rich, tawny, Indian hue, somewhat inclined to luster; is exceedingly agreeable to the touch; diffuses a pungent odor, as of an old dusty bottle of Port, newly opened above ground; and, altogether, is an object which no man, who enjoys his dinners, could refrain from hanging over, and caressing.

Nor is this delectable morsel of *old junk* wanting in many interesting, mournful, and tragic suggestions. Who can say in what gales it may have been; in what remote seas it may have sailed?

How many stout masts of seventy-fours and frigates it may have staid in the tempest? How deep it may have lain, as a hawser, at the bottom of strange harbors? What outlandish fish may have nibbled at it in the water, and what uncatalogued sea-fowl may have pecked at it, when forming part of a lofty stay or a shroud?

Now, this particular part of the rope, this nice little "cut" it was, that among the sailors was the most eagerly sought after. And getting hold of a foot or two of old cable, they would cut into it lovingly, to see whether it had any *"tenderloin."*

For my own part, nevertheless, I can not say that this tit-bit was at all an agreeable one in the mouth; however pleasant to the sight of an antiquary, or to the nose of an epicure in nautical fragrancies. Indeed, though possibly I might have been mistaken, I thought it had rather an astringent, acrid taste; probably induced by the tar, with which the flavor of all ropes is more or less vitiated. But the sailors seemed to like it, and at any rate nibbled at it with great gusto. They converted one pocket of their trousers into a junk-shop, and when solicited by a shipmate for a "chaw," would produce a small coil of rope.

Another device adopted to alleviate their hardships, was the substitution of dried tea-leaves, in place of tobacco, for their pipes. No one has ever supped in a forecastle at sea, without having been struck by the prodigious residuum of tea-leaves, or cabbage stalks, in his tin-pot of bohea. There was no lack of material to supply every pipe-bowl among us.

I had almost forgotten to relate the most noteworthy thing in this matter; namely, that notwithstanding the general scarcity of the genuine weed, Jackson was provided with a supply; nor did it give out, until very shortly previous to our arrival in port.

In the lowest depths of despair at the loss of their precious solace, when the sailors would be seated inconsolable as the Babylonish captives, Jackson would sit cross-legged in his bunk, which was an upper one, and enveloped in a cloud of tobacco smoke, would look down upon the mourners below, with a sardonic grin at their forlornness.

He recalled to mind their folly in selling for filthy lucre, their supplies of the weed; he painted their stupidity; he enlarged upon the sufferings they had brought upon themselves; he exaggerated those sufferings, and every way derided, reproached, twitted, and hooted at them. No one dared to return his scurrilous animadversions, nor did any presume to ask him to relieve their necessities out of his fullness. On the contrary, as has been just related, they divided with him the *nail-rods* they found.

The extraordinary dominion of this one miserable Jackson, over twelve or fourteen strong, healthy tars, is a riddle, whose solution must be left to the philosophers.

Chapter LV

Drawing Nigh to the Last Scene in Jackson's Career

The closing allusion to Jackson in the chapter preceding, reminds me of a circumstance—which, perhaps, should have been mentioned before—that after we had been at sea about ten days, he pronounced himself too unwell to do duty, and accordingly went below to his bunk. And here, with the exception of a few brief intervals of sunning himself in fine weather, he remained on his back, or seated cross-legged, during the remainder of the homeward-bound passage.

Brooding there, in his infernal gloom, though nothing but a castaway sailor in canvas trousers, this man was still a picture, worthy to be painted by the dark, moody hand of Salvator. In any of that master's lowering sea-pieces, representing the desolate crags of Calabria, with a midnight shipwreck in the distance, this Jackson's would have been the face to paint for the doomed vessel's figure-head, seamed and blasted by lightning.

Though the more sneaking and cowardly of my shipmates whispered among themselves, that Jackson, sure of his wages, whether on duty or off, was only feigning indisposition, nevertheless it was plain that, from his excesses in Liverpool, the malady which had long fastened its fangs in his flesh, was now gnawing into his vitals.

His cheek became thinner and yellower, and the bones projected like those of a skull. His snaky eyes rolled in red sockets; nor could he lift his hand without a violent tremor; while his racking cough many a time startled us from sleep. Yet still in his tremulous grasp he swayed his scepter, and ruled us all like a tyrant to the last.

The weaker and weaker he grew, the more outrageous became his treatment of the crew. The prospect of the speedy and unshunable death now before him, seemed to exasperate his misanthropic soul into madness; and as if he had indeed sold it to Satan, he seemed determined to die with a curse between his teeth.

I can never think of him, even now, reclining in his bunk, and with short breaths panting out his maledictions, but I am reminded of that misanthrope upon the throne of the world—the diabolical Tiberius at Capreæ; who even in his self-exile, imbittered by bodily pangs, and unspeakable mental terrors only known to the damned on earth, yet did not give over his blasphemies but endeavored to drag down with him to his own perdition, all who came within the evil spell of his power. And though Tiberius came in the succession of the Cæsars, and though unmatchable Tacitus has embalmed his carrion, yet do I account this Yankee Jackson full as dignified a personage as he, and as well meriting his lofty gallows in history; even though he was a nameless vagabond without an epitaph, and none, but I, narrate what he was. For there is no dignity in wickedness, whether in purple or rags; and hell is a democracy of devils, where all are equals. There, Nero howls side by side with his own malefactors. If Napoleon were truly but a martial murderer, I pay him no more homage than I would a felon. Though Milton's Satan dilutes our abhorrence with admiration, it is only because he is not a genuine being, but something altered from a genuine original. We gather not from the four gospels alone, any high-raised fancies concerning this Satan; we only know him from thence as the personification of the essence of evil, which, who but pickpockets and burglars will admire? But this takes not from the merit of our high-priest of poetry; it only enhances it, that with such unmitigated evil for his material, he should build up his most goodly structure.

But in historically canonizing on earth the condemned below, and lifting up and lauding the illustrious damned, we do but make examples of wickedness; and call upon ambition to do some great iniquity, and be sure of fame.

Chapter LVI

Under the Lee of the Long-Boat, Redburn and Harry Hold Confidential Communion

A SWEET THING IS A SONG; AND THOUGH THE HEBREW CAPTIVES HUNG THEIR HARPS ON THE WILlows, that they could not sing the melodies of Palestine before the haughty beards of the Babylonians; yet, to themselves, those melodies of other times and a distant land were as sweet as the June dew on Hermon.

And poor Harry was as the Hebrews. He, too, had been carried away captive, though his chief captor and foe was himself; and he, too, many a night, was called upon to sing for those who through the day had insulted and derided him.

His voice was just the voice to proceed from a small, silken person like his; it was gentle and liquid, and meandered and tinkled through the words of a song, like a musical brook that winds and wantons by pied and pansied margins.

"I can't sing to-night"—sadly said Harry to the Dutchman, who with his watchmates requested him to while away the middle watch with his melody—"I can't sing to-night. But, Wellingborough," he whispered—and I stooped my ear—"come *you* with me under the lee of the long-boat, and there I'll hum you an air."

It was *The Banks of the Blue Moselle.*

Poor, poor Harry! and a thousand times friendless and forlorn! To be singing that thing, which was only meant to be warbled by falling fountains in gardens, or in elegant alcoves in drawing-rooms—to be singing it *here*—here, as I live, under the tarry lee of our long-boat.

But he sang, and sang, as I watched the waves, and peopled them all with sprites, and cried *"chassez!" "hands across!"* to the multitudinous quadrilles, all danced on the moonlit, musical floor.

But though it went so hard with my friend to sing his songs to this ruffian crew, whom he hated, even in his dreams, till the foam flew from his mouth while he slept; yet at last I prevailed upon him to master his feelings, and make them subservient to his interests. For so delighted, even with the rudest minstrelsy, are sailors, that I well knew Harry possessed a spell over them, which, for the time at least, they could not resist; and it might induce them to treat with more deference the being who was capable of yielding them such delight. Carlo's organ they did not so much care for; but the voice of my Bury blade was an accordeon in their ears.

So one night, on the windlass, he sat and sang; and from the ribald jests so common to sailors, the men slid into silence at every verse. Hushed, and more hushed they grew, till at last Harry sat among them like Orpheus among the charmed leopards and tigers. Harmless now the fangs with which they were wont to tear my zebra, and backward curled in velvet paws; and fixed their once glaring eyes in fascinated and fascinating brilliancy. Ay, still and hissingly all, for a time, they relinquished their prey.

Now, during the voyage, the treatment of the crew threw Harry more and more upon myself for companionship; and few can keep constant company with another, without revealing some, at least, of their secrets; for all of us yearn for sympathy, even if we do not for love; and to be intellectually alone is a thing only tolerable to genius, whose cherisher and inspirer is solitude.

But though my friend became more communicative concerning his past career than ever he had been before, yet he did not make plain many things in his hitherto but partly divulged history, which I was very curious to know; and especially he never made the remotest allusion to aught connected with our trip to London; while the oath of secrecy by which he had bound me held my curiosity on that point a captive. However, as it was, Harry made many very interesting disclosures; and if he did not gratify me more in that respect, he atoned for it in a measure, by dwelling upon the future, and the prospects, such as they were, which the future held out to him.

He confessed that he had no money but a few shillings left from the expenses of our return from London; that only by selling some more of his clothing, could he pay for his first week's board in New York; and that he was altogether without any regular profession or business, upon which, by his own exertions, he could securely rely for support. And yet, he told me that he was determined never again to return to England; and that somewhere in America he must work out his temporal felicity.

"I have forgotten England," he said, "and never more mean to think of it; so tell me, Wellingborough, what am I to do in America?"

It was a puzzling question, and full of grief to me, who, young though I was, had been well rubbed, curried, and ground down to fine powder in the hopper of an evil fortune, and who therefore could sympathize with one in similar circumstances. For though we may look grave and behave kindly and considerately to a friend in calamity; yet, if we have never actually experienced something like the woe that weighs him down, we can not with the best grace proffer our sympathy. And perhaps there is no true sympathy but between equals; and it may be, that we should distrust that man's sincerity, who stoops to condole with us.

So Harry and I, two friendless wanderers, beguiled many a long watch by talking over our common affairs. But inefficient, as a benefactor, as I certainly was; still, being an American, and returning to my home; even as he was a stranger, and hurrying from his; therefore, I stood toward him in the attitude of the prospective doer of the honors of my country; I accounted him the nation's guest. Hence, I esteemed it more befitting, that I should rather talk with him, than he with me: that *his* prospects and plans should engage our attention, in preference to my own.

Now, seeing that Harry was so brave a songster, and could sing such bewitching airs: I suggested whether his musical talents could not be turned to account. The thought struck him most favorably—"Gad, my boy, you have hit it, you have," and then he went on to mention, that in some places in England, it was customary for two or three young men of highly respectable families, of undoubted antiquity, but unfortunately in lamentably decayed circumstances, and thread-bare coats;—it was customary for two or three young gentlemen, so situated, to obtain their livelihood by their voices: coining their silvery songs into silvery shillings.

They wandered from door to door, and rang the bell—*Are the ladies and gentlemen in?* Seeing them at least gentlemanly looking, if not sumptuously appareled, the servant generally admitted them at once; and when the people entered to greet them, their spokesman would rise with a gentle bow, and a smile, and say, *We come, ladies and gentlemen, to sing you a song: we are singers, at your service.* And so, without waiting reply, forth they burst into song; and having most mellifluous voices, enchanted and transported all auditors; so much so, that at the conclusion of the entertainment, they very seldom failed to be well recompensed, and departed with an invitation to return again, and make the occupants of that dwelling once more delighted and happy.

"Could not something of this kind now, be done in New York?" said Harry, "or are there no parlors with ladies in them, there?" he anxiously added.

Again I assured him, as I had often done before, that New York was a civilized and enlightened town; with a large population, fine streets, fine houses, nay, plenty of omnibuses; and that for the most part, he would almost think himself in England; so similar to England, in essentials, was this outlandish America that haunted him.

I could not but be struck—and had I not been, from my birth, as it were, a cosmopolite—I had been amazed at his skepticism with regard to the civilization of my native land. A greater patriot than myself might have resented his insinuations. He seemed to think that we Yankees lived in wigwams, and wore bear-skins. After all, Harry was a spice of a Cockney, and had shut up his Christendom in London.

Having then assured him, that I could see no reason, why he should not play the troubadour in New York, as well as elsewhere; he suddenly popped upon me the question, whether I would not join him in the enterprise; as it would be quite out of the question to go alone on such a business.

Said I, "My dear Bury, I have no more voice for a ditty, than a dumb man has for an oration. Sing? Such Macadamized lungs have I, that I think myself well off, that I can talk; let alone nightingaling."

So that plan was quashed; and by and by Harry began to give up the idea of singing himself into a livelihood.

"No, I won't sing for my mutton," said he—"what would Lady Georgiana say?"

"If I could see her ladyship once, I might tell you, Harry," returned I, who did not exactly doubt him, but felt ill at ease for my bosom friend's conscience, when he alluded to his various noble and right honorable friends and relations.

"But surely, Bury, my friend, you must write a clerkly hand, among your other accomplishments; and *that* at least, will be sure to help you."

"I *do* write a hand," he gladly rejoined—"there, look at the implement!—do you not think, that such a hand as *that* might dot an *i*, or cross a *t*, with a touching grace and tenderness?"

Indeed, but it did betoken a most excellent penmanship. It was small; and the fingers were long and thin; the knuckles softly rounded; the nails hemispherical at the base; and the smooth palm furnishing few characters for an Egyptian fortune-teller to read. It was not as the sturdy farmer's hand of Cincinnatus, who followed the plow and guided the state; but it was as the perfumed hand of Petronius Arbiter, that elegant young buck of a Roman, who once cut great Seneca dead in the forum.

His hand alone, would have entitled my Bury blade to the suffrages of that Eastern potentate, who complimented Lord Byron upon his feline fingers, declaring that they furnished indubitable evidence of his noble birth. And so it did: for Lord Byron was as all the rest of us—the son of a *man*. And so are the dainty-handed, and wee-footed half-cast paupers in Lima; who, if their hands and feet were entitled to consideration, would constitute the oligarchy of all Peru.

Folly and foolishness! to think that a gentleman is known by his finger-nails, like Nebuchadnezzar, when his grew long in the pasture: or that the badge of nobility is to be found in the smallness of the foot, when even a fish has no foot at all!

Dandies! amputate yourselves, if you will; but know, and be assured, oh, democrats, that, like a pyramid, a great man stands on a broad base. It is only the brittle porcelain pagoda, that tottles on a toe.

But though Harry's hand was lady-like looking, and had once been white as the queen's cambric handkerchief, and free from a stain as the reputation of Diana; yet, his late pulling and hauling of halyards and clew-lines, and his occasional dabbling in tar-pots and slush-shoes, had somewhat subtracted from its original daintiness.

Often he ruefully eyed it.

Oh! hand! thought Harry, ah, hand! what have you come to? Is it seemly, that you should be polluted with pitch, when you once handed countesses to their coaches? Is *this* the hand I kissed to the divine Georgiana? with which I pledged Lady Blessington, and ratified my bond to Lord Lovely? *This* the hand that Georgiana clasped to her bosom, when she vowed she was mine?—Out of sight, recreant and apostate!—deep down—disappear in this foul monkey-jacket pocket where I thrust you!

After many long conversations, it was at last pretty well decided, that upon our arrival at New York, some means should be taken among my few friends there, to get Harry a place in a mercantile house, where he might flourish his pen, and gently exercise his delicate digits, by traversing some soft foolscap; in the same way that slim, pallid ladies are gently drawn through a park for an airing.

Chapter LVII

ALMOST A FAMINE

"MAMMY! MAMMY! COME AND SEE THE SAILORS EATING OUT OF LITTLE TROUGHS, JUST LIKE OUR pigs at home." Thus exclaimed one of the steerage children, who at dinner-time was peeping down into the forecastle, where the crew were assembled, helping themselves from the "kids," which, indeed, resemble hog-troughs not a little.

"Pigs, is it?" coughed Jackson, from his bunk, where he sat presiding over the banquet, but not partaking, like a devil who had lost his appetite by chewing sulphur.—"Pigs, is it?—and the day is close by, ye spalpeens, when you'll want to be after taking a sup at our troughs!"

This malicious prophecy proved true.

As day followed day without glimpse of shore or reef, and head-winds drove the ship back, as hounds a deer; the improvidence and shortsightedness of the passengers in the steerage, with regard to their outfits for the voyage, began to be followed by the inevitable results.

Many of them at last went aft to the mate, saying that they had nothing to eat, their provisions were expended, and they must be supplied from the ship's stores, or starve.

This was told to the captain, who was obliged to issue a ukase from the cabin, that every steerage passenger, whose destitution was demonstrable, should be given one sea-biscuit and two potatoes a day; a sort of substitute for a muffin and a brace of poached eggs.

But this scanty ration was quite insufficient to satisfy their hunger: hardly enough to satisfy the necessities of a healthy adult. The consequence was, that all day long, and all through the night, scores of the emigrants went about the decks, seeking what they might devour. They plundered the chicken-coop; and disguising the fowls, cooked them at the public galley. They made inroads upon the pig-pen in the boat, and carried off a promising young shoat: *him* they devoured raw, not venturing to make an incognito of his carcass; they prowled about the cook's caboose, till he threatened them with a ladle of scalding water; they waylaid the steward on his regular excursions from the cook to the cabin; they hung round the forecastle, to rob the bread-barge; they beset the sailors, like beggars in the streets, craving a mouthful in the name of the Church.

At length, to such excesses were they driven, that the Grand Russian, Captain Riga, issued another ukase, and to this effect: Whatsoever emigrant is found guilty of stealing, the same shall be tied into the rigging and flogged.

Upon this, there were secret movements in the steerage, which almost alarmed me for the safety of the ship; but nothing serious took place, after all; and they even acquiesced in, or did not resent, a singular punishment which the captain caused to be inflicted upon a culprit of their clan, as a substitute for a flogging. For no doubt he thought that such rigorous discipline as *that* might exasperate five hundred emigrants into an insurrection.

A head was fitted to one of the large deck-tubs—the half of a cask; and into this head a hole was cut; also, two smaller holes in the bottom of the tub. The head—divided in the middle, across the diameter of the orifice—was now fitted round the culprit's neck; and he was forthwith coopered up into the tub, which rested on his shoulders, while his legs protruded through the holes in the bottom.

It was a burden to carry; but the man could walk with it; and so ridiculous was his appearance, that spite of the indignity, he himself laughed with the rest at the figure he cut.

"Now, Pat, my boy," said the mate, "fill that big wooden belly of yours, if you can."

Compassionating his situation, our old "doctor" used to give him alms of food, placing it upon the cask-head before him; till at last, when the time for deliverance came, Pat protested against mercy, and would fain have continued playing Diogenes in the tub for the rest of this starving voyage.

Chapter LVIII

Though the Highlander Puts into No Harbor As Yet; She Here and There Leaves Many of Her Passengers Behind

ALTHOUGH FAST-SAILING SHIPS, BLEST WITH PROSPEROUS BREEZES, HAVE FREQUENTLY MADE THE run across the Atlantic in eighteen days; yet, it is not uncommon for other vessels to be forty, or fifty, and even sixty, seventy, eighty, and ninety days, in making the same passage. Though in the latter cases, some signal calamity or incapacity must occasion so great a detention. It is also true, that generally the passage out from America is shorter than the return; which is to be ascribed to the prevalence of westerly winds.

We had been outside of Cape Clear upward of twenty days, still harassed by head-winds, though with pleasant weather upon the whole, when we were visited by a succession of rain-storms, which lasted the greater part of a week.

During the interval, the emigrants were obliged to remain below; but this was nothing strange to some of them; who, not recovering, while at sea, from their first attack of sea-sickness, seldom or never made their appearance on deck, during the entire passage.

During the week, now in question, fire was only once made in the public galley. This occasioned a good deal of domestic work to be done in the steerage, which otherwise would have been done in the open air. When the lulls of the rain-storms would intervene, some unusually cleanly emigrant would climb to the deck, with a bucket of slops, to toss into the sea. No experience seemed sufficient to instruct some of these ignorant people in the simplest, and most elemental principles of ocean-life. Spite of all lectures on the subject, several would continue to shun the leeward side of the vessel, with their slops. One morning, when it was blowing very fresh, a simple fellow pitched over a gallon or two of something to windward. Instantly it flew back in his face; and also, in the face of the chief mate, who happened to be standing by at the time. The offender was collared, and shaken on the spot; and ironically commanded, never, for the future, to throw anything to windward at sea, but fine ashes and scalding hot water.

During the frequent *hard blows* we experienced, the hatchways on the steerage were, at intervals, hermetically closed; sealing down in their noisome den, those scores of human beings. It was something to be marveled at, that the shocking fate, which, but a short time ago, overtook the poor passengers in a Liverpool steamer in the Channel, during similar stormy weather, and under similar treatment, did not overtake some of the emigrants of the *Highlander.*

Nevertheless, it was, beyond question, this noisome confinement in so close, unventilated, and crowded a den: joined to the deprivation of sufficient food, from which many were suffering; which, helped by their personal uncleanliness, brought on a malignant fever.

The first report was, that two persons were affected. No sooner was it known, than the mate promptly repaired to the medicine-chest in the cabin: and with the remedies deemed suitable, descended into the steerage. But the medicines proved of no avail; the invalids rapidly grew worse; and two more of the emigrants became infected.

Upon this, the captain himself went to see them; and returning, sought out a certain alleged physician among the cabin-passengers; begging him to wait upon the sufferers; hinting that, thereby, he might prevent the disease from extending into the cabin itself. But this person denied being a physician; and from fear of contagion—though he did not confess that to be the motive—refused even to enter the steerage.

The cases increased: the utmost alarm spread through the ship: and scenes ensued, over which, for the most part, a veil must be drawn; for such is the fastidiousness of some readers, that, many times, they must lose the most striking incidents in a narrative like mine.

Many of the panic-stricken emigrants would fain now have domiciled on deck; but being so scantily clothed, the wretched weather—wet, cold, and tempestuous—drove the best part of them again below. Yet any other human beings, perhaps, would rather have faced the most outrageous storm, than continued to breathe the pestilent air of the steerage. But some of these poor people must have been so used to the most abasing calamities, that the atmosphere of a lazar-house almost seemed their natural air.

The first four cases happened to be in adjoining bunks; and the emigrants who slept in the farther part of the steerage, threw up a barricade in front of those bunks; so as to cut off communication. But this was no sooner reported to the captain, than he ordered it to be thrown down; since it could be of no possible benefit; but would only make still worse, what was already direful enough.

It was not till after a good deal of mingled threatening and coaxing, that the mate succeeded in getting the sailors below, to accomplish the captain's order.

The sight that greeted us, upon entering, was wretched indeed. It was like entering a crowded jail. From the rows of rude bunks, hundreds of meager, begrimed faces were turned upon us; while seated upon the chests, were scores of unshaven men, smoking tea-leaves, and creating a suffocating vapor. But this vapor was better than the native air of the place, which from almost unbelievable causes, was fetid in the extreme. In every corner, the females were huddled together, weeping and lamenting; children were asking bread from their mothers, who had none to give; and old men, seated upon the floor, were leaning back against the heads of the water-casks, with closed eyes and fetching their breath with a gasp.

At one end of the place was seen the barricade, hiding the invalids; while—notwithstanding the crowd—in front of it was a clear area, which the fear of contagion had left open.

"That bulkhead must come down," cried the mate, in a voice that rose above the din. "Take hold of it, boys."

But hardly had we touched the chests composing it, when a crowd of pale-faced, infuriated men rushed up; and with terrific howls, swore they would slay us, if we did not desist.

"Haul it down!" roared the mate.

But the sailors fell back, murmuring something about merchant seamen having no pensions in case of being maimed, and they had not shipped to fight fifty to one. Further efforts were made by the mate, who at last had recourse to entreaty; but it would not do; and we were obliged to depart, without achieving our object.

About four o'clock that morning, the first four died. They were all men; and the scenes which ensued were frantic in the extreme. Certainly, the bottomless profound of the sea, over which we were sailing, concealed nothing more frightful.

Orders were at once passed to bury the dead. But this was unnecessary. By their own countrymen, they were torn from the clasp of their wives, rolled in their own bedding, with ballast-stones, and with hurried rites, were dropped into the ocean.

At this time, ten more men had caught the disease; and with a degree of devotion worthy all praise, the mate attended them with his medicines; but the captain did not again go down to them.

It was all-important now that the steerage should be purified; and had it not been for the rains and squalls, which would have made it madness to turn such a number of women and children upon the wet and unsheltered decks, the steerage passengers would have been ordered above, and their den have been given a thorough cleansing. But, for the present, this was out of the question. The sailors peremptorily refused to go among the defilements to remove them; and so besotted were the greater part of the emigrants themselves, that though the necessity of the case was forcibly painted to them, they would not lift a hand to assist in what seemed their own salvation.

The panic in the cabin was now very great; and for fear of contagion to themselves, the cabin passengers would fain have made a prisoner of the captain, to prevent him from going forward beyond the main-mast. Their clamors at last induced him to tell the two mates, that for the present they must sleep and take their meals elsewhere than in their old quarters, which communicated with the cabin.

On land, a pestilence is fearful enough; but there, many can flee from an infected city; whereas, in a ship, you are locked and bolted in the very hospital itself. Nor is there any possibility of escape from it; and in so small and crowded a place, no precaution can effectually guard against contagion.

Horrible as the sights of the steerage now were, the cabin, perhaps, presented a scene equally despairing. Many, who had seldom prayed before, now implored the merciful heavens, night and day, for fair winds and fine weather. Trunks were opened for Bibles; and at last, even prayer-meetings were held over the very table across which the loud jest had been so often heard.

Strange, though almost universal, that the seemingly nearer prospect of that death which any-body at anytime may die, should produce these spasmodic devotions, when an everlasting Asiatic Cholera is forever thinning our ranks; and die by death we all must at last.

On the second day, seven died, one of whom was the little tailor; on the third, four; on the fourth, six, of whom one was the Greenland sailor, and another, a woman in the cabin, whose death, however, was afterward supposed to have been purely induced by her fears. These last deaths brought the panic to its height; and sailors, officers, cabin-passengers, and emigrants—all looked upon each other like lepers. All but the only true leper among us—the mariner Jackson, who seemed elated with the thought, that for *him*—already in the deadly clutches of another disease—no danger was to be apprehended from a fever which only swept off the comparatively healthy. Thus, in the midst of the despair of the healthful, this incurable invalid was not cast down; not, at least, by the same considerations that appalled the rest.

And still, beneath a gray, gloomy sky, the doomed craft beat on; now on this tack, now on that; battling against hostile blasts, and drenched in rain and spray; scarcely making an inch of progress toward her port.

On the sixth morning, the weather merged into a gale, to which we stripped our ship to a storm-stay-sail. In ten hours' time, the waves ran in mountains; and the *Highlander* rose and fell like some vast buoy on the water. Shrieks and lamentations were driven to leeward, and drowned in the roar of the wind among the cordage; while we gave to the gale the blackened bodies of five more of the dead.

But as the dying departed, the places of two of them were filled in the rolls of humanity, by the birth of two infants, whom the plague, panic, and gale had hurried into the world before their time. The first cry of one of these infants, was almost simultaneous with the splash of its father's body in the sea. Thus we come and we go. But, surrounded by death, both mothers and babes survived.

At midnight, the wind went down; leaving a long, rolling sea; and, for the first time in a week, a clear, starry sky.

In the first morning-watch, I sat with Harry on the windlass, watching the billows; which, seen in the night, seemed real hills, upon which fortresses might have been built; and real valleys, in which villages, and groves, and gardens, might have nestled. It was like a landscape in Switzerland; for down into those dark, purple glens, often tumbled the white foam of the wave-crests, like avalanches; while the seething and boiling that ensued, seemed the swallowing up of human beings.

By the afternoon of the next day this heavy sea subsided; and we bore down on the waves, with all our canvas set; stun'-sails alow and aloft; and our best steersman at the helm; the captain himself at his elbow;—bowling along, with a fair, cheering breeze over the taffrail.

The decks were cleared, and swabbed bone-dry; and then, all the emigrants who were not invalids, poured themselves out on deck, snuffing the delightful air, spreading their damp bedding in the sun, and regaling themselves with the generous charity of the captain, who of late had seen fit to increase their allowance of food. A detachment of them now joined a band of the crew, who proceeding into the steerage, with buckets and brooms, gave it a thorough cleansing, sending on deck, I know not how many bucketsful of defilements. It was more like cleaning out a stable, than a retreat for men and women. This day we buried three; the next day one, and then the pestilence left us, with seven convalescent; who, placed near the opening of the hatchway, soon rallied under the skillful treatment, and even tender care of the mate.

But even under this favorable turn of affairs, much apprehension was still entertained, lest in crossing the Grand Banks of Newfoundland, the fogs, so generally encountered there, might bring on a return of the fever. But, to the joy of all hands, our fair wind still held on; and we made a rapid run across these dreaded shoals, and southward steered for New York.

Our days were now fair and mild, and though the wind abated, yet we still ran our course over a pleasant sea. The steerage-passengers—at least by far the greater number—wore a still, subdued aspect, though a little cheered by the genial air, and the hopeful thought of soon reaching their port. But those who had lost fathers, husbands, wives, or children, needed no crape, to reveal to others, who they were. Hard and bitter indeed was their lot; for with the poor and desolate, grief is no indulgence of mere sentiment, however sincere, but a gnawing reality, that eats into their vital beings; they have no kind condolers, and bland physicians, and troops of sympathizing friends; and they must toil, though to-morrow be the burial, and their pallbearers throw down the hammer to lift up the coffin.

How, then, with these emigrants, who, three thousand miles from home, suddenly found themselves deprived of brothers and husbands, with but a few pounds, or perhaps but a few shillings, to buy food in a strange land?

As for the passengers in the cabin, who now so jocund as they? drawing nigh, with their long purses and goodly portmanteaus to the promised land, without fear of fate. One and all were generous and gay, the jelly-eyed old gentleman, before spoken of, gave a shilling to the steward.

The lady who had died, was an elderly person, an American, returning from a visit to an only brother in London. She had no friend or relative on board, hence, as there is little mourning for a stranger dying among strangers, her memory had been buried with her body.

But the thing most worthy of note among these now light-hearted people in feathers, was the gay way in which some of them bantered others, upon the panic into which nearly all had been thrown.

And since, if the extremest fear of a crowd in a panic of peril, proves grounded on causes sufficient, they must then indeed come to perish;—therefore it is, that at such times they must make up their minds either to die, or else survive to be taunted by their fellow-men with their fear. For except in extraordinary instances of exposure, there are few living men, who, at bottom, are not very slow to admit that any other living men have ever been very much nearer death than themselves. Accordingly, *craven* is the phrase too often applied to anyone who, with however good reason, has been appalled at the prospect of sudden death, and yet lived to escape it. Though, should he have perished in conformity with his fears, not a syllable of *craven* would you hear. This is the language of one, who more than once has beheld the scenes, whence these principles have been deduced. The subject invites much subtle speculation; for in every being's ideas of death, and his behavior when it suddenly menaces him, lies the best index to his life and his faith. Though the Christian era had not then begun, Socrates died the death of the Christian; and though Hume was not a Christian in theory, yet he, too, died the death of the Christian—humble, composed, without bravado; and though the most skeptical of philosophical skeptics, yet full of that firm, creedless faith, that embraces the spheres. Seneca died dictating to posterity; Petronius lightly discoursing of essences and love-songs; and Addison, calling upon Christendom to behold how calmly a Christian could die; but not even the last of these three, perhaps, died the best death of the Christian.

The cabin passenger who had used to read prayers while the rest kneeled against the transoms and settees, was one of the merry young sparks, who had occasioned such agonies of jealousy to the poor tailor, now no more. In his rakish vest, and dangling watch-chain, this same youth, with all the awfulness of fear, had led the earnest petitions of his companions; supplicating mercy, where before he had never solicited the slightest favor. More than once had he been seen thus engaged by the observant steersman at the helm: who looked through the little glass in the cabin bulkhead.

But this youth was an April man; the storm had departed; and now he shone in the sun, none braver than he.

One of his jovial companions ironically advised him to enter into holy orders upon his arrival in New York.

"Why so?" said the other, "have I such an orotund voice?"

"No"; profanely returned his friend—"but you are a coward—just the man to be a parson, and pray."

However this narrative of the circumstances attending the fever among the emigrants on the *Highlander* may appear; and though these things happened so long ago; yet just such events, nevertheless, are perhaps taking place to-day. But the only account you obtain of such events, is generally contained in a newspaper paragraph, under the shipping-head. *There* is the obituary of the destitute dead, who die on the sea. They die, like the billows that break on the shore, and no more are heard or seen. But in the events, thus merely initialized in the catalogue of passing occurrences, and but glanced at by the readers of news, who are more taken up with paragraphs of fuller flavor; what a world of life and death, what a world of humanity and its woes, lies shrunk into a three-worded sentence!

You see no plague-ship driving through a stormy sea; you hear no groans of despair; you see no corpses thrown over the bulwarks; you mark not the wringing hands and torn hair of widows and orphans—all is a blank. And one of these blanks I have but filled up, in recounting the details of the *Highlander*'s calamity.

Besides that natural tendency, which hurries into oblivion the last woes of the poor; other causes combine to suppress the detailed circumstances of disasters like these. Such things, if widely known, operate unfavorably to the ship, and make her a bad name; and to avoid detention at quarantine, a captain will state the case in the most palliating light, and strive to hush it up, as much as he can.

In no better place than this, perhaps, can a few words be said, concerning emigrant ships in general.

Let us waive that agitated national topic, as to whether such multitudes of foreign poor should be landed on our American shores; let us waive it, with the one only thought, that if they can get here, they have God's right to come; though they bring all Ireland and her miseries with them. For the whole world is the patrimony of the whole world; there is no telling who does not own a stone in the Great Wall of China. But we waive all this; and will only consider, how best the emigrants can come hither, since come they do, and come they must and will.

Of late, a law has been passed in Congress, restricting ships to a certain number of emigrants, according to a certain rate. If this law were enforced, much good might be done; and so also might much good be done, were the English law likewise enforced, concerning the fixed supply of food for every emigrant embarking from Liverpool. But it is hardly to be believed, that either of these laws is observed.

But in all respects, no legislation, even nominally, reaches the hard lot of the emigrant. What ordinance makes it obligatory upon the captain of a ship, to supply the steerage-passengers with decent lodgings, and give them light and air in that foul den, where they are immured, during a long voyage across the Atlantic? What ordinance necessitates him to place the *galley*, or steerage-passengers' stove, in a dry place of shelter, where the emigrants can do their cooking during a storm, or wet weather? What ordinance obliges him to give them more room on deck, and let them have an occasional run fore and aft?—There is no law concerning these things. And if there was, who but some Howard in office would see it enforced? and how seldom is there a Howard in office!

We talk of the Turks, and abhor the cannibals; but may not some of *them,* go to heaven, before some of *us?* We may have civilized bodies and yet barbarous souls. We are blind to the real sights of this world; deaf to its voice; and dead to its death. And not till we know, that one grief outweighs ten thousand joys, will we become what Christianity is striving to make us.

Chapter LIX

THE LAST END OF JACKSON

"OFF CAPE COD!" SAID THE STEWARD, COMING FORWARD FROM THE QUARTER-DECK, WHERE THE captain had just been taking his noon observation; sweeping the vast horizon with his quadrant, like a dandy circumnavigating the dress-circle of an amphitheater with his glass.

"Off Cape Cod!" and in the shore-bloom that came to us—even from that desert of sand-hillocks—methought I could almost distinguish the fragrance of the rose-bush my sisters and I had planted, in our far inland garden at home. Delicious odors are those of our mother Earth; which like a flower-pot set with a thousand shrubs, greets the eager voyager from afar.

The breeze was stiff, and so drove us along that we turned over two broad, blue furrows from our bows, as we plowed the watery prairie. By night it was a reef-top-sail-breeze; but so impatient was the captain to make his port before a shift of wind overtook us, that even yet we carried a main-top-gallant-sail, though the light mast sprung like a switch.

In the second dog-watch, however, the breeze became such, that at last the order was given to douse the top-gallant-sail, and clap a reef into all three top-sails.

While the men were settling away the halyards on deck, and before they had begun to haul out the reef-tackles, to the surprise of several, Jackson came up from the forecastle, and, for the first time in four weeks or more, took hold of a rope.

Like most seamen, who during the greater part of a voyage, have been off duty from sickness, he was, perhaps, desirous, just previous to entering port, of reminding the captain of his existence, and also that he expected his wages; but, alas! his wages proved the wages of sin.

At no time could he better signalize his disposition to work, than upon an occasion like the present; which generally attracts every soul on deck, from the captain to the child in the steerage.

His aspect was damp and death-like; the blue hollows of his eyes were like vaults full of snakes; and issuing so unexpectedly from his dark tomb in the forecastle, he looked like a man raised from the dead.

Before the sailors had made fast the reef-tackle, Jackson was tottering up the rigging; thus getting the start of them, and securing his place at the extreme weather-end of the top-sail-yard—which in reefing is accounted the post of honor. For it was one of the characteristics of this man, that though when on duty he would shy away from mere dull work in a calm, yet in tempest-time he always claimed the van, and would yield it to none; and this, perhaps, was one cause of his unbounded dominion over the men.

Soon, we were all strung along the main-top-sail-yard; the ship rearing and plunging under us, like a runaway steed; each man gripping his reef-point, and sideways leaning, dragging the sail over toward Jackson, whose business it was to confine the reef corner to the yard.

His hat and shoes were off; and he rode the yard-arm end, leaning backward to the gale, and pulling at the earing-rope, like a bridle. At all times, this is a moment of frantic exertion with sailors, whose spirits seem then to partake of the commotion of the elements, as they hang in the gale, between heaven and earth; and *then* it is, too, that they are the most profane.

"Haul out to windward!" coughed Jackson, with a blasphemous cry, and he threw himself back with a violent strain upon the bridle in his hand. But the wild words were hardly out of his mouth, when his hands dropped to his side, and the bellying sail was spattered with a torrent of blood from his lungs.

As the man next him stretched out his arm to save, Jackson fell headlong from the yard, and with a long seethe, plunged like a diver into the sea.

It was when the ship had rolled to windward, which, with the long projection of the yard-arm over the side, made him strike far out upon the water. His fall was seen by the whole upward-gazing crowd on deck, some of whom were spotted with the blood that trickled from the sail, while they raised a spontaneous cry, so shrill and wild, that a blind man might have known something deadly had happened.

Clutching our reef-points, we hung over the stick, and gazed down to the one white, bubbling spot, which had closed over the head of our shipmate; but the next minute it was brewed into the common yeast of the waves, and Jackson never arose. We waited a few minutes, expecting an order to descend, haul back the fore-yard, and man the boat; but instead of that, the next sound that greeted us was, "Bear a hand, and reef away, men!" from the mate.

Indeed, upon reflection, it would have been idle to attempt to save Jackson; for besides that he must have been dead, ere he struck the sea—and if he had not been dead then, the first immersion must have driven his soul from his lacerated lungs—our jolly-boat would have taken full fifteen minutes to launch into the waves.

And here it should be said, that the thoughtless security in which too many sea-captains indulge, would, in case of some sudden disaster befalling the *Highlander*, have let us all drop into our graves.

Like most merchant-ships, we had but two boats: the long-boat and the jolly-boat. The long-boat, by far the largest and stoutest of the two, was permanently bolted down to the deck, by iron bars attached to its sides. It was almost as much of a fixture as the vessel's keel. It was filled with pigs, fowls, firewood, and coals. Over this the jolly-boat was capsized without a *thole-pin* in the gunwales; its bottom bleaching and cracking in the sun.

Judge, then, what promise of salvation for us, had we shipwrecked; yet in this state, one merchant-ship out of three, keeps its boats. To be sure, no vessel full of emigrants, by any possible precautions, could in case of a fatal disaster at sea, hope to save the tenth part of the souls on board; yet provision should certainly be made for a handful of survivors, to carry home the tidings of her loss; for even in the worst of the calamities that befell patient Job, some*one* at least of his servants escaped to report it.

In a way that I never could fully account for, the sailors, in my hearing at least, and Harry's, never made the slightest allusion to the departed Jackson. One and all they seemed tacitly to unite in hushing up his memory among them. Whether it was, that the severity of the bondage under which this man held every one of them, did really corrode in their secret hearts, that they thought to repress the recollection of a thing so degrading, I can not determine; but certain it was, that *his* death was *their* deliverance; which they celebrated by an elevation of spirits, unknown before. Doubtless, this was to be in part imputed, however, to their now drawing near to their port.

Chapter LX

HOME AT LAST

NEXT DAY WAS SUNDAY; AND THE MID-DAY SUN SHONE UPON A GLASSY SEA.

After the uproar of the breeze and the gale, this profound, pervading calm seemed suited to the tranquil spirit of a day, which, in godly towns, makes quiet vistas of the most tumultuous thoroughfares.

The ship lay gently rolling in the soft, subdued ocean swell; while all around were faint white spots; and nearer to, broad, milky patches, betokening the vicinity of scores of ships, all bound to one common port, and tranced in one common calm. Here the long, devious wakes from Europe, Africa, India, and Peru converged to a line, which braided them all in one.

Full before us quivered and danced, in the noon-day heat and mid-air, the green heights of New Jersey; and by an optical delusion, the blue sea seemed to flow under them.

The sailors whistled and whistled for a wind; the impatient cabin-passengers were arrayed in their best; and the emigrants clustered around the bows, with eyes intent upon the long-sought land.

But leaning over, in a reverie, against the side, my Carlo gazed down into the calm, violet sea, as if it were an eye that answered his own; and turning to Harry, said, "This America's skies must be down in the sea; for, looking down in this water, I behold what, in Italy, we also behold overhead. Ah! after all, I find my Italy somewhere, wherever I go. I even found it in rainy Liverpool."

Presently, up came a dainty breeze, wafting to us a white wing from the shore—the pilot-boat! Soon a monkey-jacket mounted the side, and was beset by the captain and cabin people for news. And out of bottomless pockets came bundles of newspapers, which were eagerly caught by the throng.

The captain now abdicated in the pilot's favor, who proved to be a tiger of a fellow, keeping us hard at work, pulling and hauling the braces, and trimming the ship, to catch the least *cat's-paw* of wind.

When, among sea-worn people, a strange man from shore suddenly stands among them, with the smell of the land in his beard, it conveys a realization of the vicinity of the green grass, that not even the distant sight of the shore itself can transcend.

The steerage was now as a bedlam; trunks and chests were locked and tied round with ropes; and a general washing and rinsing of faces and hands was beheld. While this was going on, forth came an order from the quarter-deck, for every bed, blanket, bolster, and bundle of straw in the steerage to be committed to the deep.—A command that was received by the emigrants with dismay, and then with wrath. But they were assured, that this was indispensable to the getting rid of an otherwise long detention of some weeks at the quarantine. They therefore reluctantly complied; and overboard went pallet and pillow. Following them, went old pots and pans, bottles and baskets. So, all around, the sea was strewn with stuffed bed-ticks, that limberly floated on the waves—couches for all mermaids who were not fastidious. Numberless things of this sort, tossed overboard from emigrant ships nearing the harbor of New York, drift in through the Narrows, and are deposited on the shores of Staten Island; along whose eastern beach I have often walked, and speculated upon the broken jugs, torn pillows, and dilapidated baskets at my feet.

A second order was now passed for the emigrants to muster their forces, and give the steerage a final, thorough cleaning with sand and water. And to this they were incited by the same warning which had induced them to make an offering to Neptune of their bedding. The place was then fumigated, and dried with pans of coals from the galley; so that by evening, no stranger would have imagined, from her appearance, that the *Highlander* had made otherwise than a tidy and prosperous voyage. Thus, some sea-captains take good heed that benevolent citizens shall not get a glimpse of the true condition of the steerage while at sea.

That night it again fell calm; but next morning, though the wind was somewhat against us, we set sail for the Narrows; and making short tacks, at last ran through, almost bringing our jib-boom over one of the forts.

An early shower had refreshed the woods and fields, that glowed with a glorious green; and to our salted lungs, the land breeze was spiced with aromas. The steerage passengers almost neighed with delight, like horses brought back to spring pastures; and every eye and ear in the *Highlander* was full of the glad sights and sounds of the shore.

No more did we think of the gale and the plague; nor turn our eyes upward to the stains of blood, still visible on the top-sail, whence Jackson had fallen; but we fixed our gaze on the orchards and meads, and like thirsty men, drank in all their dew.

On the Staten Island side, a white staff displayed a pale yellow flag, denoting the habitation of the quarantine officer; for as if to symbolize the yellow fever itself, and strike a panic and premonition of the black vomit into every beholder, all quarantines all over the world, taint the air with the streamings of their fever-flag.

But though the long rows of white-washed hospitals on the hill-side were now in plain sight, and though scores of ships were here lying at anchor, yet no boat came off to us; and to our surprise and delight, on we sailed, past a spot which everyone had dreaded. How it was that they thus let us pass without boarding us, we never could learn.

Now rose the city from out the bay, and one by one, her spires pierced the blue; while thick and more thick, ships, brigs, schooners, and sail-boats, thronged around. We saw the Hartz Forest of masts and black rigging stretching along the East River; and northward, up the stately old Hudson, covered with white sloop-sails like fleets of swans, we caught a far glimpse of the purple Palisades.

Oh! he who has never been afar, let him once go from home, to know what home is. For as you draw nigh again to your old native river, he seems to pour through you with all his tides, and in your enthusiasm, you swear to build altars like mile-stones, along both his sacred banks.

Like the Czar of all the Russias, and Siberia to boot, Captain Riga, telescope in hand, stood on the poop, pointing out to the passengers, Governor's Island, Castle Garden, and the Battery.

"And *that,*" said he, pointing out a vast black hull which, like a shark, showed tiers of teeth, "*that*, ladies, is a line-of-battle-ship, the *North Carolina.*"

"Oh, dear!"—and "Oh my!"—ejaculated the ladies, and—"Lord, save us," responded an old gentleman, who was a member of the Peace Society.

Hurra! hurra! and ten thousand times hurra! down goes our old anchor, fathoms down into the free and independent Yankee mud, one handful of which was now worth a broad manor in England.

The Whitehall boats were around us, and soon, our cabin passengers were all off, gay as crickets, and bound for a late dinner at the Astor House; where, no doubt, they fired off a salute of champagne corks in honor of their own arrival. Only a very few of the steerage passengers, however, could afford to pay the high price the watermen demanded for carrying them ashore; so most of them remained with us till morning. But nothing could restrain our Italian boy, Carlo, who, promising the watermen to pay them with his music, was triumphantly rowed ashore, seated in the stern of the boat, his organ before him, and something like *Hail Columbia!* his tune. We gave him three rapturous cheers, and we never saw Carlo again.

Harry and I passed the greater part of the night walking the deck, and gazing at the thousand lights of the city.

At sunrise, we *warped* into a berth at the foot of Wall-street, and knotted our old ship, stem and stern, to the pier. But that knotting of *her,* was the unknotting of the bonds of the sailors, among whom, it is a maxim, that the ship once fast to the wharf, they are free. So with a rush and a shout, they bounded ashore, followed by the tumultuous crowd of emigrants, whose friends, day-laborers and housemaids, stood ready to embrace them.

But in silent gratitude at the end of a voyage, almost equally uncongenial to both of us, and so bitter to one, Harry and I sat on a chest in the forecastle. And now, the ship that we had loathed, grew lovely in our eyes, which lingered over every familiar old timber; for the scene of suffering is a scene of joy when the suffering is past; and the silent reminiscence of hardships departed, is sweeter than the presence of delight.

Chapter LXI

REDBURN AND HARRY, ARM IN ARM, IN HARBOR

THERE WE SAT IN THAT TARRY OLD DEN, THE ONLY INHABITANTS OF THE DESERTED OLD SHIP, but the mate and the rats.

At last, Harry went to his chest, and drawing out a few shillings, proposed that we should go ashore, and return with a supper, to eat in the forecastle. Little else that was eatable being for sale in the paltry shops along the wharves, we bought several pies, some doughnuts, and a bottle of ginger-pop, and thus supplied we made merry. For to us, whose very mouths were become pickled and puckered, with the continual flavor of briny beef, those pies and doughnuts were most delicious. And as for the ginger-pop, why, that ginger-pop was divine! I have reverenced ginger-pop ever since.

We kept late hours that night; for, delightful certainty! placed beyond all doubt—like royal landsmen, we were masters of the watches of the night, and no *starb-o-leens ahoy!* would annoy us again.

"All night in! think of *that*, Harry, my friend!"

"Ay, Wellingborough, it's enough to keep me awake forever, to think I may now sleep as long as I please."

We turned out bright and early, and then prepared for the shore, first stripping to the waist, for a toilette.

"I shall never get these confounded tar-stains out of my fingers," cried Harry, rubbing them hard with a bit of oakum, steeped in strong suds. "No! they will *not* come out, and I'm ruined for life. Look at my hand once, Wellingborough!"

It was indeed a sad sight. Every finger-nail, like mine, was dyed of a rich, russet hue; looking something like bits of fine tortoise shell.

"Never mind, Harry," said I—"You know the ladies of the east steep the tips of their fingers in some golden dye."

"And by Plutus," cried Harry—"I'd steep mine up to the arm-pits in gold; since you talk about *that*. But never mind, I'll swear I'm just from Persia, my boy."

We now arrayed ourselves in our best, and sallied ashore; and, at once, I piloted Harry to the sign of a Turkey Cock in Fulton-street, kept by one Sweeny, a place famous for cheap Souchong, and capital buckwheat cakes.

"Well, gentlemen, what will you have?"—said a waiter, as we seated ourselves at a table.

"Gentlemen!" whispered Harry to me—*"gentlemen!*—hear him!—I say now, Redburn, they didn't talk to us that way on board the old *Highlander*. By heaven, I begin to feel my straps again—

Coffee and hot rolls," he added aloud, crossing his legs like a lord, "and fellow—come back—bring us a venison-steak."

"Haven't got it, gentlemen."

"Ham and eggs," suggested I, whose mouth was watering at the recollection of that particular dish, which I had tasted at the sign of the Turkey Cock before. So ham and eggs it was; and royal coffee, and imperial toast.

But the butter!

"Harry, did you ever taste such butter as this before?"

"Don't say a word"—said Harry, spreading his tenth slice of toast. "I'm going to turn dairyman, and keep within the blessed savor of butter, so long as I live."

We made a breakfast, never to be forgotten; paid our bill with a flourish, and sallied into the street, like two goodly galleons of gold, bound from Acapulco to Old Spain.

"Now," said Harry, "lead on; and let's see something of these United States of yours. I'm ready to pace from Maine to Florida; ford the Great Lakes; and jump the River Ohio, if it comes in the way. Here, take my arm;—lead on."

Such was the miraculous change, that had now come over him. It reminded me of his manner, when we had started for London, from the sign of the Golden Anchor, in Liverpool.

He was, indeed, in most wonderful spirits; at which I could not help marveling; considering the cavity in his pockets; and that he was a stranger in the land.

By noon he had selected his boarding-house, a private establishment, where they did not charge much for their board, and where the landlady's butcher's bill was not very large.

Here, at last, I left him to get his chest from the ship; while I turned up town to see my old friend Mr. Jones, and learn what had happened during my absence.

With one hand, Mr. Jones shook mine most cordially; and with the other, gave me some letters, which I eagerly devoured. Their purport compelled my departure homeward; and I at once sought out Harry to inform him.

Strange, but even the few hours' absence which had intervened; during which, Harry had been left to himself, to stare at strange streets, and strange faces, had wrought a marked change in his countenance. He was a creature of the suddenest impulses. Left to himself, the strange streets seemed now to have reminded him of his friendless condition; and I found him with a very sad eye; and his right hand groping in his pocket.

"Where am I going to dine, this day week?"—he slowly said. "What's to be done, Wellingborough?"

And when I told him that the next afternoon I must leave him; he looked downhearted enough. But I cheered him as well as I could; though needing a little cheering myself; even though I *had* got home again. But no more about that.

Now, there was a young man of my acquaintance in the city, much my senior, by the name of Goodwell; and a good natured fellow he was; who had of late been engaged as a clerk in a large forwarding house in South-street; and it occurred to me, that he was just the man to befriend Harry, and procure him a place. So I mentioned the thing to my comrade; and we called upon Goodwell.

I saw that he was impressed by the handsome exterior of my friend; and in private, making known the case, he faithfully promised to do his best for him; though the times, he said, were quite dull.

That evening, Goodwell, Harry, and I, perambulated the streets, three abreast: Goodwell spending his money freely at the oyster-saloons; Harry full of allusions to the London Club-houses: and myself contributing a small quota to the general entertainment.

Next morning, we proceeded to business.

Now, I did not expect to draw much of a salary from the ship; so as to retire for life on the profits of *my first voyage*; but nevertheless, I thought that a dollar or two might be coming. For dollars are valuable things; and should not be overlooked, when they are owing. Therefore, as the second morning after our arrival, had been set apart for paying off the crew, Harry and I made our appearance on ship-board, with the rest. We were told to enter the cabin; and once again I found myself, after an interval of four months, and more, surrounded by its mahogany and maple.

Seated in a sumptuous arm-chair, behind a lustrous, inlaid desk, sat Captain Riga, arrayed in his City Hotel suit, looking magisterial as the Lord High Admiral of England. Hat in hand, the sailors stood deferentially in a semicircle before him, while the captain held the ship-papers in his hand, and one by one called their names; and in mellow bank notes—beautiful sight!—paid them their wages.

Most of them had less than ten, a few twenty, and two, thirty dollars coming to them; while the old cook, whose piety proved profitable in restraining him from the expensive excesses of most seafaring men, and who had taken no pay in advance, had the goodly round sum of seventy dollars as his due.

Seven ten dollar bills! each of which, as I calculated at the time, was worth precisely one hundred dimes, which were equal to one thousand cents, which were again subdivisible into fractions. So that he now stepped into a fortune of seventy thousand American "mills." Only seventy dollars, after all; but then, it has always seemed to me, that stating amounts in sounding fractional sums, conveys a much fuller notion of their magnitude, than by disguising their immensity in such aggregations of value, as doubloons, sovereigns, and dollars. Who would not rather be worth 125,000 francs in Paris, than only £5000 in London, though the intrinsic value of the two sums, in round numbers, is pretty much the same.

With a scrape of the foot, and such a bow as only a negro can make, the old cook marched off with his fortune; and I have no doubt at once invested it in a grand, underground oyster-cellar.

The other sailors, after counting their cash very carefully, and seeing all was right, and not a bank-note was dog-eared, in which case they would have demanded another: for they are not to be taken in and cheated, your sailors, and they know their rights, too; at least, when they are at liberty, after the voyage is concluded: the sailors also salaamed, and withdrew, leaving Harry and me face to face with the Paymaster-general of the Forces.

We stood awhile, looking as polite as possible, and expecting every moment to hear our names called, but not a word did we hear; while the captain, throwing aside his accounts, lighted a very fragrant cigar, took up the morning paper—I think it was the *Herald*—threw his leg over one arm of the chair, and plunged into the latest intelligence from all parts of the world.

I looked at Harry, and he looked at me; and then we both looked at this incomprehensible captain.

At last Harry hemmed, and I scraped my foot to increase the disturbance.

The Paymaster-general looked up.

"Well, where do you come from? Who are *you*, pray? and what do you want? Steward, show these young gentlemen out."

"I want my money," said Harry.

"My wages are due," said I.

The captain laughed. Oh! he was exceedingly merry; and taking a long inspiration of smoke, removed his cigar, and sat sideways looking at us, letting the vapor slowly wriggle and spiralize out of his mouth.

"Upon my soul, young gentlemen, you astonish me. Are your names down in the City Directory? have you any letters of introduction, young gentlemen?"

"Captain Riga!" cried Harry, enraged at his impudence—"I tell you what it is, Captain Riga; this won't do—where's the rhino?"

"Captain Riga," added I, "do you not remember, that about four months ago, my friend Mr. Jones and myself had an interview with you in this very cabin; when it was agreed that I was to go out in your ship, and receive three dollars per month for my services? Well, Captain Riga, I have gone out with you, and returned; and now, sir, I'll thank you for my pay."

"Ah, yes, I remember," said the captain. "*Mr. Jones!* Ha! ha! I remember Mr. Jones: a very gentlemanly gentleman; and stop—*you*, too, are the son of a wealthy French importer; and—let me think—was not your great-uncle a barber?"

"No!" thundered I.

"Well, well, young gentleman, really I beg your pardon. Steward, chairs for the young gentlemen—be seated, young gentlemen. And now, let me see," turning over his accounts—"Hum, hum!—yes, here it is: Wellingborough Redburn, at three dollars a month. Say four months, that's twelve dollars; less three dollars advanced in Liverpool—that makes it nine dollars; less three hammers and two scrapers lost overboard—that brings it to four dollars and a quarter. I owe you four dollars and a quarter, I believe, young gentleman?"

"So it seems, sir," said I, with staring eyes.

"And now let me see what you owe me, and then well be able to square the yards, Monsieur Redburn."

Owe *him!* thought I—what do I owe him but a grudge, but I concealed my resentment; and presently he said, "By running away from the ship in Liverpool, you forfeited your wages, which amount to twelve dollars; and as there has been advanced to you, in money, hammers, and scrapers, seven dollars and seventy-five cents, you are therefore indebted to me in precisely that sum. Now, young gentleman, I'll thank you for the money"; and he extended his open palm across the desk.

"Shall I pitch into him?" whispered Harry.

I was thunderstruck at this most unforeseen announcement of the state of my account with Captain Riga; and I began to understand why it was that he had till now ignored my absence from the ship, when Harry and I were in London. But a single minute's consideration showed that I could not help myself; so, telling him that he was at liberty to begin his suit, for I was a bankrupt, and could not pay him, I turned to go.

Now, here was this man actually turning a poor lad adrift without a copper, after he had been slaving aboard his ship for more than four mortal months. But Captain Riga was a bachelor of expensive habits, and had run up large wine bills at the City Hotel. He could not afford to be munificent. Peace to his dinners.

"Mr. Bolton, I believe," said the captain, now blandly bowing toward Harry. "Mr. Bolton, *you* also shipped for three dollars per month: and you had one month's advance in Liverpool; and from dock to dock we have been about a month and a half; so I owe you just one dollar and a half, Mr. Bolton; and here it is"; handing him six two-shilling pieces.

"And this," said Harry, throwing himself into a tragical attitude, "*this* is the reward of my long and faithful services!"

Then, disdainfully flinging the silver on the desk, he exclaimed, "There, Captain Riga, you may keep your tin! It has been in *your* purse, and it would give me the itch to retain it. Good-morning, sir."

"Good-morning, young gentlemen; pray, call again," said the captain, coolly bagging the coins. His politeness, while in port, was invincible.

Quitting the cabin, I remonstrated with Harry upon his recklessness in disdaining his wages, small though they were; I begged to remind him of his situation; and hinted that every penny he could get might prove precious to him. But he only cried *Pshaw!* and that was the last of it.

Going forward, we found the sailors congregated on the forecastle-deck, engaged in some earnest discussion; while several carts on the wharf, loaded with their chests, were just in the act of driving off, destined for the boarding-houses up-town. By the looks of our shipmates, I saw very plainly that they must have some mischief under weigh; and so it turned out.

Now, though Captain Riga had not been guilty of any particular outrage against the sailors;

yet, by a thousand small meannesses—such as indirectly causing their allowance of bread and beef to be diminished, without betraying any appearance of having any inclination that way, and without speaking to the sailors on the subject—by this, and kindred actions, I say, he had contracted the cordial dislike of the whole ship's company; and long since they had bestowed upon him a name unmentionably expressive of their contempt.

The voyage was now concluded; and it appeared that the subject being debated by the assembly on the forecastle was, how best they might give a united and valedictory expression of the sentiments they entertained toward their late lord and master. Some emphatic symbol of those sentiments was desired; some unmistakable token, which should forcibly impress Captain Riga with the justest possible notion of their feelings.

It was like a meeting of the members of some mercantile company, upon the eve of a prosperous dissolution of the concern; when the subordinates, actuated by the purest gratitude toward their president, or chief, proceed to vote him a silver pitcher, in token of their respect. It was something like this, I repeat—but with a material difference, as will be seen.

At last, the precise manner in which the thing should be done being agreed upon, Blunt, the "Irish cockney," was deputed to summon the captain. He knocked at the cabin-door, and politely requested the steward to inform Captain Riga, that some gentlemen were on the pier-head, earnestly seeking him; whereupon he joined his comrades.

In a few moments the captain sallied from the cabin, and found the *gentlemen* alluded to, strung along the top of the bulwarks, on the side next to the wharf. Upon his appearance, the row suddenly wheeled about, presenting their backs; and making a motion, which was a polite salute to everything before them, but an abominable insult to all who happened to be in their rear, they gave three cheers, and at one bound, cleared the ship.

True to his imperturbable politeness while in port, Captain Riga only lifted his hat, smiled very blandly, and slowly returned into his cabin.

Wishing to see the last movements of this remarkable crew, who were so clever ashore and so craven afloat, Harry and I followed them along the wharf, till they stopped at a sailor retreat, poetically denominated "The Flashes." And here they all came to anchor before the bar; and the landlord, a lantern-jawed landlord, bestirred himself behind it, among his villainous old bottles and decanters. He well knew, from their looks, that his customers were "flush," and would spend their money freely, as, indeed, is the case with most seamen, recently paid off.

It was a touching scene.

"Well, maties," said one of them, at last—"I spose we shan't see each other again:—come, let's splice the main-brace all round, and drink to *the last voyage!*"

Upon this, the landlord danced down his glasses, on the bar, uncorked his decanters, and deferentially pushed them over toward the sailors, as much as to say—*"Honorable gentlemen, it is not for me to allowance your liquor;—help yourselves, your honors."*

And so they did; each glass a bumper; and standing in a row, tossed them all off; shook hands all round, three times three; and then disappeared in couples, through the several doorways; for *"The Flashes"* was on a corner.

If to everyone, life be made up of farewells and greetings, and a *"Good-bye, God bless you,"* is heard for every *"How d'ye do, welcome, my boy"*—then, of all men, sailors shake the most hands, and wave the most hats. They are here and then they are there; ever shifting themselves, they shift among the shifting: and like rootless sea-weed, are tossed to and fro.

As, after shaking our hands, our shipmates departed, Harry and I stood on the corner awhile, till we saw the last man disappear.

"They are gone," said I.

"Thank heaven!" said Harry.

Chapter LXII

THE LAST THAT WAS EVER HEARD OF HARRY BOLTON

THAT SAME AFTERNOON, I TOOK MY COMRADE DOWN TO THE BATTERY; AND WE SAT ON ONE OF the benches, under the summer shade of the trees.

It was a quiet, beautiful scene; full of promenading ladies and gentlemen; and through the foliage, so fresh and bright, we looked out over the bay, varied with glancing ships; and then, we looked down to our boots; and thought what a fine world it would be, if we only had a little money to enjoy it. But that's the everlasting rub—oh, who can cure an empty pocket?

"I have no doubt, Goodwell will take care of you, Harry," said I, "he's a fine, good-hearted fellow; and will do his best for you, I know."

"No doubt of it," said Harry, looking hopeless.

"And I need not tell you, Harry, how sorry I am to leave you so soon."

"And I am sorry enough myself," said Harry, looking very sincere.

"But I will be soon back again, I doubt not," said I.

"Perhaps so," said Harry, shaking his head. "How far is it off?"

"Only a hundred and eighty miles," said I.

"A hundred and eighty miles!" said Harry, drawing the words out like an endless ribbon. "Why, I couldn't walk that in a month."

"Now, my dear friend," said I, "Take my advice, and while I am gone, keep up a stout heart; never despair, and all will be well."

But notwithstanding all I could say to encourage him, Harry felt so bad, that nothing would do, but a rush to a neighboring bar, where we both gulped down a glass of ginger-pop; after which we felt better.

He accompanied me to the steam-boat, that was to carry me homeward; he stuck close to my side, till she was about to put off; then, standing on the wharf, he shook me by the hand, till we almost counteracted the play of the paddles; and at last, with a mutual jerk at the arm-pits, we parted. I never saw Harry again.

I pass over the reception I met with at home; how I plunged into embraces, long and loving—I pass over this; and will conclude *my first voyage* by relating all I know of what overtook Harry Bolton.

Circumstances beyond my control, detained me at home for several weeks; during which, I wrote to my friend, without receiving an answer.

I then wrote to young Goodwell, who returned me the following letter, now spread before me.

> DEAR REDBURN—Your poor friend, Harry, I can not find anywhere. After you left, he called upon me several times, and we walked out together; and my interest in him increased everyday. But you don't know how dull are the times here, and what multitudes of young men, well qualified, are seeking employment in counting-houses. I did my best; but could not get Harry a place. However, I cheered him. But he grew more and more melancholy, and at last told me, that he had sold all his clothes but those on his back to pay his board. I offered to loan him a few dollars, but he would not receive them. I called upon him two or three times after this, but he was not in; at last, his landlady told me that he had permanently left her house the very day before. Upon my questioning her closely, as to where he had gone, she answered, that she did not know, but from certain hints that had dropped from our poor

friend, she feared he had gone on a whaling voyage. I at once went to the offices in South-street, where men are shipped for the Nantucket whalers, and made inquiries among them; but without success. And this, I am heartily grieved to say, is all I know of our friend. I can not believe that his melancholy could bring him to the insanity of throwing himself away in a whaler; and I still think, that he must be somewhere in the city. You must come down yourself, and help me seek him out.

This letter gave me a dreadful shock. Remembering our adventure in London, and his conduct there; remembering how liable he was to yield to the most sudden, crazy, and contrary impulses; and that, as a friendless, penniless foreigner in New York, he must have had the most terrible incitements to committing violence upon himself; I shuddered to think, that even now, while I thought of him, he might no more be living. So strong was this impression at the time, that I quickly glanced over the papers to see if there were any accounts of suicides, or drowned persons floating in the harbor of New York.

I now made all the haste I could to the seaport, but though I sought him all over, no tidings whatever could be heard.

To relieve my anxiety, Goodwell endeavored to assure me, that Harry must indeed have departed on a whaling voyage. But remembering his bitter experience on board of the *Highlander*, and more than all, his nervousness about going aloft, it seemed next to impossible.

At last I was forced to give him up.

* * * * * *

Years after this, I found myself a sailor in the Pacific, on board of a whaler. One day at sea, we spoke another whaler, and the boat's crew that boarded our vessel, came forward among us to have a little sea-chat, as is always customary upon such occasions.

Among the strangers was an Englishman, who had shipped in his vessel at Callao, for the cruise. In the course of conversation, he made allusion to the fact, that he had now been in the Pacific several years, and that the good craft *Huntress* of Nantucket had had the honor of originally bringing him round upon that side of the globe. I asked him why he had abandoned her; he answered that she was the most unlucky of ships.

"We had hardly been out three months," said he, "when on the Brazil banks we lost a boat's crew, chasing a whale after sundown; and next day lost a poor little fellow, a countryman of mine, who had never entered the boats; he fell over the side, and was jammed between the ship, and a whale, while we were cutting the fish in. Poor fellow, he had a hard time of it, from the beginning; he was a gentleman's son, and when you could coax him to it, he sang like a bird."

"What was his name?" said I, trembling with expectation; "what kind of eyes did he have? what was the color of his hair?"

"Harry Bolton was not your brother?" cried the stranger, starting.

Harry Bolton! It was even he!

But yet, I, Wellingborough Redburn, chance to survive, after having passed through far more perilous scenes than any narrated in this, *My First Voyage*—which here I end.

WHITE-JACKET

OR THE WORLD IN A MAN-OF-WAR

"Conceive him now in a man-of-war; with his letters of mart, well armed, victualed, and appointed, and see how he acquits himself."

—FULLER'S *Good Sea-Captain*

Contents

Preface

IN THE YEAR 1843 THE AUTHOR SHIPPED AS A COMMON SAILOR ON BOARD OF A UNITED STATES frigate then lying in a harbor of the Pacific Ocean. His man-of-war experiences have have been incorporated in the present volume; but as the object is not to portray the particular ship in which he sailed and its officers and men, but by illustrative scenes to paint general life in the Navy, the name of the frigate is not given, nor is it asserted that any of the personages here introduced are real individuals. Wherever statements are made concerning the established laws and usages of the Navy, facts have been strictly adhered to.

The book opens at the frigate's last harbor in the Pacific just previous to weighing her anchor for the homeward bound passage by way of Cape Horn.

NEW YORK, March, 1850

Chapter I

The Jacket

It was not a *very* white jacket, but white enough, in all conscience, as the sequel will show.

The way I came by it was this.

When our frigate lay in Callao, on the coast of Peru—her last harbor in the Pacific—I found myself without a *grego*, or sailor's surtout; and as, toward the end of a three years' cruise, no pea-jackets could be had from the purser's steward: and being bound for Cape Horn, some sort of a substitute was indispensable; I employed myself, for several days, in manufacturing an outlandish garment of my own devising, to shelter me from the boisterous weather we were so soon to encounter.

It was nothing more than a white duck frock, or rather shirt: which, laying on deck, I folded double at the bosom, and by then making a continuation of the slit there, opened it lengthwise—much as you would cut a leaf in the last new novel. The gash being made, a metamorphosis took place, transcending any related by Ovid. For, presto! the shirt was a coat!—a strange-looking coat, to be sure; of a Quakerish amplitude about the skirts; with an infirm, tumble-down collar; and a clumsy fullness about the wristbands; and white, yea, white as a shroud. And my shroud it afterward came very near proving, as he who reads further will find.

But, bless me, my friend, what sort of a summer jacket is this, in which to weather Cape Horn? A very tasty, and beautiful white linen garment it may have seemed; but then, people almost universally sport their linen next to their skin.

Very true; and that thought very early occurred to me; for no idea had I of scudding round Cape Horn in my shirt; for *that* would have been almost scudding under bare poles, indeed.

So, with many odds and ends of patches—old socks, old trouser-legs, and the like—I bedarned and bequilted the inside of my jacket, till it became, all over, stiff and padded, as King James's cotton-stuffed and dagger-proof doublet; and no buckram or steel hauberk stood up more stoutly.

So far, very good; but pray, tell me, White-Jacket, how do you propose keeping out the rain and the wet in this quilted *grego* of yours? You don't call this wad of old patches a Mackintosh, do you?—you don't pretend to say that worsted is water-proof?

No, my dear friend; and that was the deuce of it. Water-proof it was not, no more than a sponge. Indeed, with such recklessness had I bequilted my jacket, that in a rain-storm I became a universal absorber; swabbing bone-dry the very bulwarks I leaned against. Of a damp day, my heartless shipmates even used to stand up against me, so powerful was the capillary attraction between this luckless jacket of mine and all drops of moisture. I dripped like a turkey a roasting; and long after the rain-storms were over, and the sun showed his face, I still stalked a Scotch mist; and when it was fair weather with others, alas! it was foul weather with me.

Me? Ah me! Soaked and heavy, what a burden was that jacket to carry about, especially when I was sent up aloft; dragging myself up step by step, as if I were weighing the anchor. Small time then, to strip, and wring it out in a rain, when no hanging back or delay was permitted. No, no; up you go: fat or lean: Lambert or Edson: never mind how much avoirdupois you might weigh. And thus, in my own proper person, did many showers of rain reascend toward the skies, in accordance with the natural laws.

But here be it known, that I had been terribly disappointed in carrying out my original plan concerning this jacket. It had been my intention to make it thoroughly impervious, by giving it a coating of paint. But bitter fate ever overtakes us unfortunates. So much paint had been stolen by the sailors, in daubing their overhaul trousers and tarpaulins, that by the time I—an honest man—had completed my quiltings, the paint-pots were banned, and put under strict lock and key.

Said old Brush, the captain of the *paint-room*—"Look ye, White-Jacket," said he, "ye can't have any paint."

Such, then, was my jacket: a well-patched, padded, and porous one; and in a dark night, gleaming white as the White Lady of Avenel!

Chapter II

HOMEWARD BOUND

"ALL HANDS UP ANCHOR! MAN THE CAPSTAN!"

"High die! my lads, we're homeward bound!"

Homeward bound!—harmonious sound! Were you ever homeward bound?—No?—Quick! take the wings of the morning, or the sails of a ship, and fly to the uttermost parts of the earth. There, tarry a year or two; and then let the gruffest of boatswains, his lungs all goose-skin, shout forth those magical words, and you'll swear "the harp of Orpheus were not more enchanting."

All was ready; boats hoisted in, stun' sail gear rove, messenger passed, capstan-bars in their places, accommodation-ladder below; and in glorious spirits, we sat down to dinner. In the ward-room, the lieutenants were passing round their oldest port, and pledging their friends; in the steerage, the *middies* were busy raising loans to liquidate the demands of their laundress, or else—in the navy phrase—preparing to pay their creditors *with a flying fore-topsail.* On the poop, the captain was looking to windward; and in his grand, inaccessible cabin, the high and mighty commodore sat silent and stately, as the statue of Jupiter in Dodona.

We were all arrayed in our best, and our bravest; like strips of blue sky, lay the pure blue collars of our frocks upon our shoulders; and our pumps were so springy and playful, that we danced up and down as we dined.

It was on the gun-deck that our dinners were spread; all along between the guns; and there, as we cross-legged sat, you would have thought a hundred farm-yards and meadows were nigh. Such a cackling of ducks, chickens, and ganders; such a lowing of oxen, and bleating of lambkins, penned up here and there along the deck, to provide sea repasts for the officers. More rural than naval were the sounds; continually reminding each mother's son of the old paternal homestead in the green old clime; the old arching elms; the hill where we gamboled; and down by the barley banks of the stream where we bathed.

"All hands up anchor!"

When that order was given, how we sprang to the bars, and heaved round that capstan; every man a Goliath, every tendon a hawser!—round and round—round, round it spun like a sphere, keeping time with our feet to the time of the fifer, till the cable was straight up and down, and the ship with her nose in the water.

"Heave and pall! unship your bars, and make sail!"

It was done; barmen, nipper-men, tierers, veerers, idlers and all, scrambled up the ladder to the braces and halyards; while like monkeys in palm-trees, the sail-loosers ran out on those broad boughs, our yards; and down fell the sails like white clouds from the ether—top-sails, top-gallants, and royals; and away we ran with the halyards, till every sheet was distended.

"Once more to the bars!"

"Heave, my hearties, heave hard!"

With a jerk and a yerk, we broke ground; and up to our bows came several thousand pounds of old iron, in the shape of our ponderous anchor.

Where was White-Jacket then?

White-Jacket was where he belonged. It was White-Jacket that loosed that main-royal, so far up aloft there, it looks like a white albatross's wing. It was White-Jacket that was taken for an albatross himself, as he flew out on the giddy yard-arm!

Chapter III

A Glance at the Principal Divisions into Which a Man-of-War's Crew is Divided

Having just designated the place where White-Jacket belonged, it must needs be related how White-Jacket came to belong there.

Everyone knows that in merchantmen the seamen are divided into watches—starboard and larboard—taking their turn at the ship's duty by night. This plan is followed in all men-of-war. But in all men-of war, besides this division, there are others, rendered indispensable from the great number of men, and the necessity of precision and discipline. Not only are particular bands assigned to the three *tops,* but in getting under weigh, or any other proceeding requiring all hands, particular men of these bands are assigned to each yard of the tops. Thus, when the order is given to loose the main-royal, White-Jacket flies to obey it; and no one but him.

And not only are particular bands stationed on the three decks of the ship at such times, but particular men of those bands are also assigned to particular duties. Also, in tacking ship, reefing top-sails, or "coming to," every man of a frigate's five-hundred-strong, knows his own special place, and is infallibly found there. He sees nothing else, attends to nothing else, and will stay there till grim death or an epaulette orders him away. Yet there are times when, through the negligence of the officers, some exceptions are found to this rule. A rather serious circumstance growing out of such a case will be related in some future chapter.

Were it not for these regulations a man-of-war's crew would be nothing but a mob, more ungovernable stripping the canvas in a gale than Lord George Gordon's tearing down the lofty house of Lord Mansfield.

But this is not all. Besides White-Jacket's office as looser of the main-royal, when all hands were called to make sail; and besides his special offices, in tacking ship, coming to anchor, etc.; he permanently belonged to the Starboard Watch, one of the two primary, grand divisions of the ship's company. And in this watch he was a maintop-man; that is, was stationed in the main-top, with a number of other seamen, always in readiness to execute any orders pertaining to the main-mast, from above the main-yard. For, including the main-yard, and below it to the deck, the main-mast belongs to another detachment.

Now the fore, main, and mizen-top-men of each watch—Starboard and Larboard—are at sea respectively subdivided into Quarter Watches; which regularly relieve each other in the tops to which they may belong; while, collectively, they relieve the whole Larboard Watch of top-men.

Besides these topmen, who are always made up of active sailors, there are Sheet-Anchor-men—old veterans all—whose place is on the forecastle; the fore-yard, anchors, and all the sails on the bowsprit being under their care.

They are an old weather-beaten set, culled from the most experienced seamen on board. These are the fellows that sing you *"The Bay of Biscay Oh!"* and *"Here a Sheer Hulk Lies Poor Tom Bowling!" "Cease, Rude Boreas, Blustering Railer!"* who, when ashore, at an eating-house, call for a bowl of tar and a biscuit. These are the fellows who spin interminable yarns about Decatur, Hull, and Bainbridge; and carry about their persons bits of *Old Ironsides,* as Catholics do the wood of the true cross. These are the fellows that some officers never pretend to damn, however much they may anathematize others. These are the fellows that it does your soul good to look at—hearty old members of the Old Guard; grim sea-grenadiers, who, in tempest time, have lost many a tarpaulin overboard. These are the fellows whose society some of the youngster midshipmen much affect; from whom they learn their best seamanship; and to whom they look up as veterans; if so be, that they have any reverence in their souls, which is not the case with all midshipmen.

Then, there is the *After-guard,* stationed on the Quarter-deck; who, under the Quarter-Masters and Quarter-Gunners, attend to the main-sail and spanker, and help haul the main-brace, and other ropes in the stern of the vessel.

The duties assigned to the After-Guard's-Men being comparatively light and easy, and but little seamanship being expected from them, they are composed chiefly of landsmen; the least robust, least hardy, and least sailor-like of the crew; and being stationed on the Quarter-deck, they are generally selected with some eye to their personal appearance. Hence, they are mostly slender young fellows, of a genteel figure and gentlemanly address; not weighing much on a rope, but weighing considerably in the estimation of all foreign ladies who may chance to visit the ship. They lounge away the most part of their time, in reading novels and romances; talking over their lover affairs ashore; and comparing notes concerning the melancholy and sentimental career which drove them—poor young gentlemen—into the hard-hearted navy. Indeed, many of them show tokens of having moved in very respectable society. They always maintain a tidy exterior; and express an abhorrence of the tar-bucket, into which they are seldom or never called to dip their digits. And pluming themselves upon the cut of their trousers, and the glossiness of their tarpaulins, from the rest of the ship's company, they acquire the name of *"sea-dandies"* and *"silk-sock-gentry."*

Then, there are the *Waisters,* always stationed on the gun-deck. These haul aft the fore-and main-sheets, besides being subject to ignoble duties; attending to the drainage and sewerage below hatches. These fellows are all Jimmy Duxes—sorry chaps, who never put foot in ratlin, or venture above the bulwarks. Inveterate *"sons of farmers,"* with the hayseed yet in their hair, they are consigned to the congenial superintendence of the chicken-coops, pig-pens, and potato-lockers. These are generally placed amidships, on the gun-deck of a frigate, between the fore and main hatches; and comprise so extensive an area, that it much resembles the market-place of a small town. The melodious sounds thence issuing, continually draw tears from the eyes of the Waisters; reminding them of their old paternal pig-pens and potato-patches. They are the tag-rag and bob-tail of the crew; and he who is good for nothing else is good enough for a *Waister.*

Three decks down—spar-deck, gun-deck, and berth-deck—and we come to a parcel of Troglodytes or *"holders,"* who burrow, like rabbits in warrens, among the water-tanks, casks, and cables. Like Cornwall miners, wash off the soot from their skins, and they are all pale as ghosts. Unless upon rare occasions, they seldom come on deck to sun themselves. They may circumnavigate the world fifty times, and they see about as much of it as Jonah did in the whale's belly. They are a lazy, lumpish, torpid set; and when going ashore after a long cruise, come out into the day like terrapins from their caves, or bears in the spring, from tree-trunks. No one ever knows the names of these fellows; after a three years' voyage, they still remain strangers to you. In time of tempests, when all hands are called to save ship, they issue forth into the gale, like the mysterious old men of Paris, during the massacre of the Three Days of September: everyone marvels who they are, and whence they come; they disappear as mysteriously; and are seen no more, until another general commotion.

Such are the principal divisions into which a man-of-war's crew is divided; but the inferior allotments of duties are endless, and would require a German commentator to chronicle.

We say nothing here of Boatswain's mates, Gunner's mates, Carpenter's mates, Sail-maker's mates, Armorer's mates, Master-at-Arms, Ship's corporals, Cockswains, Quarter-masters, Quarter-gunners, Captains of the Forecastle, Captains of the Fore-top, Captains of the Main-top, Captains of the Mizen-top, Captains of the After-Guard, Captains of the Main-Hold, Captains of the Fore-Hold, Captains of the Head, Coopers, Painters, Tinkers, Commodore's Steward, Captain's Steward, Ward-Room Steward, Steerage Steward, Commodore's cook, Captain's cook, Officers' cook, Cooks of the range, Mess-cooks, hammock-boys, messenger boys, cot-boys, loblolly-boys and numberless others, whose functions are fixed and peculiar.

It is from this endless subdivision of duties in a man-of-war, that, upon first entering one, a sailor has need of a good memory, and the more of an arithmetician he is, the better.

White-Jacket, for one, was a long time rapt in calculations, concerning the various "numbers" allotted him by the *First Luff*, otherwise known as the First Lieutenant. In the first place, White-Jacket was given the *number of his mess*; then, his *ship's number*, or the number to which he must answer when the watch-roll is called; then, the number of his hammock; then, the number of the gun to which he was assigned; besides a variety of other numbers; all of which would have taken Jedediah Buxton himself some time to arrange in battalions, previous to adding up. All these numbers, moreover, must be well remembered, or woe betide you.

Consider, now, a sailor altogether unused to the tumult of a man-of-war, for the first time stepping on board, and given all these numbers to recollect. Already, before hearing them, his head is half stunned with the unaccustomed sounds ringing in his ears; which ears seem to him like belfries full of tocsins. On the gun-deck, a thousand scythed chariots seem passing; he hears the tread of armed marines; the clash of cutlasses and curses. The Boatswain's mates whistle round him, like hawks screaming in a gale, and the strange noises under decks are like volcanic rumblings in a mountain. He dodges sudden sounds, as a raw recruit falling bombs.

Well-nigh useless to him, now, all previous circumnavigations of this terraqueous globe; of no account his arctic, antarctic, or equinoctial experiences; his gales off Beachy Head, or his dismastings off Hatteras. He must begin anew; he knows nothing; Greek and Hebrew could not help him, for the language he must learn has neither grammar nor lexicon.

Mark him, as he advances along the files of old ocean-warriors; mark his debased attitude, his deprecating gestures, his Sawney stare, like a Scotchman in London; his—*"cry your merry, noble seignors!"* He is wholly nonplussed, and confounded. And when, to crown all, the First Lieutenant, whose business it is to welcome all new-comers, and assign them their quarters: when this officer—none of the most bland or amiable either—gives him number after number to recollect—246—139—478—351—the poor fellow feels like decamping.

Study, then, your mathematics, and cultivate all your memories, oh ye! who think of cruising in men-of-war.

Chapter IV

JACK CHASE

THE FIRST NIGHT OUT OF PORT WAS A CLEAR, MOONLIGHT ONE; THE FRIGATE GLIDING THROUGH the water, with all her batteries.

It was my Quarter Watch in the top; and there I reclined on the best possible terms with my top-mates. Whatever the other seamen might have been, these were a noble set of tars, and well worthy an introduction to the reader.

First and foremost was Jack Chase, our noble First Captain of the Top. He was a Briton, and a true-blue; tall and well-knit, with a clear open eye, a fine broad brow, and an abounding nut-brown beard. No man ever had a better heart or a bolder. He was loved by the seamen and admired by the officers; and even when the Captain spoke to him, it was with a slight air of respect. Jack was a frank and charming man.

No one could be better company in forecastle or saloon; no man told such stories, sang such songs, or with greater alacrity sprang to his duty. Indeed, there was only one thing wanting about him; and that was a finger of his left hand, which finger he had lost at the great battle of Navarino.

He had a high conceit of his profession as a seaman; and being deeply versed in all things pertaining to a man-of-war, was universally regarded as an oracle. The main-top, over which he presided, was a sort of oracle of Delphi; to which many pilgrims ascended, to have their perplexities or differences settled.

There was such an abounding air of good sense and good feeling about the man, that he who could not love him, would thereby pronounce himself a knave. I thanked my sweet stars, that kind fortune had placed me near him, though under him, in the frigate; and from the outset Jack and I were fast friends.

Wherever you may be now rolling over the blue billows, dear Jack! take my best love along with you; and God bless you, wherever you go!

Jack was a gentleman. What though his hand was hard, so was not his heart, too often the case with soft palms. His manners were easy and free; none of the boisterousness, so common to tars; and he had a polite, courteous way of saluting you, if it were only to borrow your knife. Jack had read all the verses of Byron, and all the romances of Scott. He talked of Rob Roy, Don Juan, and Pelham; Macbeth and Ulysses; but, above all things, was an ardent admirer of Camoens. Parts of the *Lusiad*, he could recite in the original. Where he had obtained his wonderful accomplishments, it is not for me, his humble subordinate, to say. Enough, that those accomplishments were so various; the languages he could converse in, so numerous; that he more than furnished an example of that saying of Charles the Fifth—*he who speaks five languages is as good as five men.* But Jack, he was better than a hundred common mortals; Jack was a whole phalanx, an entire army; Jack was a thousand strong; Jack would have done honor to the Queen of England's drawing-room; Jack must have been a by-blow of some British Admiral of the Blue. A finer specimen of the island race of Englishmen could not have been picked out of Westminster Abbey of a coronation day.

His whole demeanor was in strong contrast to that of one of the Captains of the fore-top. This man, though a good seaman, furnished an example of those insufferable Britons, who, while preferring other countries to their own as places of residence; still, overflow with all the pompousness of national and individual vanity combined. "When I was on board the *Audacious*"— for a long time, was almost the invariable exordium to the fore-top Captain's most cursory remarks. It is often the custom of men-of-war's-men, when they deem anything to be going on wrong aboard ship to refer to *last cruise* when of course everything was done *ship-shape and Bristol fashion.* And by referring to the *Audacious*—an expressive name by the way—the fore-top Captain meant a ship in the English navy, in which he had had the honor of serving. So continual were his allusions to this craft with the amiable name, that at last, the *Audacious* was voted a bore by his shipmates. And one hot afternoon, during a calm, when the fore-top Captain like many others, was standing still and yawning on the spar-deck; Jack Chase, his own countryman, came up to him, and pointing at his open mouth, politely inquired, whether that was the way they caught *flies* in Her Britannic Majesty's ship, the *Audacious?* After that, we heard no more of the craft.

Now, the tops of a frigate are quite spacious and cozy. They are railed in behind so as to form a kind of balcony, very pleasant of a tropical night. From twenty to thirty loungers may agreeably recline there, cushioning themselves on old sails and jackets. We had rare times in that top. We accounted ourselves the best seamen in the ship; and from our airy perch, literally looked down upon the landlopers below, sneaking about the deck, among the guns. In a large degree, we nourished that feeling of *"esprit de corps,"* always pervading, more or less, the various sections of a man-of-war's crew. We main-top-men were brothers, one and all, and we loaned ourselves to each other with all the freedom in the world.

Nevertheless, I had not long been a member of this fraternity of fine fellows, ere I discovered that Jack Chase, our captain was—like all prime favorites and oracles among men—a little bit of a dictator; not peremptorily, or annoyingly so, but amusingly intent on egotistically mending our manners and improving our taste, so that we might reflect credit upon our tutor.

He made us all wear our hats at a particular angle—instructed us in the tie of our neck-handkerchiefs; and protested against our wearing vulgar *dungaree* trousers; besides giving us lessons in seamanship; and solemnly conjuring us, forever to eschew the company of any sailor we suspected of having served in a whaler. Against all whalers, indeed, he cherished the unmitigated detestation of a true man-of-war's man. Poor Tubbs can testify to that.

Tubbs was in the After-Guard; a long, lank Vineyarder, eternally talking of line-tubs, Nantucket, sperm oil, stove boats, and Japan. Nothing could silence him; and his comparisons were ever invidious.

Now, with all his soul, Jack abominated this Tubbs. He said he was vulgar, an upstart—Devil take him, he's been in a whaler. But like many men, who have been where *you* haven't been; or seen what *you* haven't seen; Tubbs, on account of his whaling experiences, absolutely affected to look down upon Jack, even as Jack did upon him; and this it was that so enraged our noble captain.

One night, with a peculiar meaning in his eye, he sent me down on deck to invite Tubbs up aloft for a chat. Flattered by so marked an honor—for we were somewhat fastidious, and did not extend such invitations to everybody—Tubb's quickly mounted the rigging, looking rather abashed at finding himself in the august presence of the assembled Quarter-Watch of main-top-men. Jack's courteous manner, however, very soon relieved his embarrassment; but it is no use to be courteous to *some* men in this world. Tubbs belonged to that category. No sooner did the bumpkin feel himself at ease, than he launched out, as usual, into tremendous laudations of whalemen; declaring that whalemen alone deserved the name of sailors. Jack stood it some time; but when Tubbs came down upon men-of-war, and particularly upon main-top-men, his sense of propriety was so outraged, that he launched into Tubbs like a forty-two pounder.

"Why, you limb of Nantucket! you train-oil man! you sea-tallow strainer! you bobber after carrion! do *you* pretend to vilify a man-of-war? Why, you lean rogue, you, a man-of-war is to whalemen, as a metropolis to shire-towns, and sequestered hamlets. *Here's* the place for life and commotion; *here's* the place to be gentlemanly and jolly. And what did you know, you bumpkin! before you came on board this *Andrew Miller?* What knew you of gun-deck, or orlop, mustering round the capstan, beating to quarters, and piping to dinner? Did you ever roll to *grog* on board your greasy ballyhoo of blazes? Did you ever winter at Mahon? Did you ever *'lash and carry?'* Why, what are even a merchant-seaman's sorry yarns of voyages to China after tea-caddies, and voyages to the West Indies after sugar puncheons, and voyages to the Shetlands after seal-skins—what are even these yarns, you Tubbs you! to high life in a man-of-war? Why, you dead-eye! I have sailed with lords and marquises for captains; and the King of the Two Sicilies has passed me, as I here stood up at my gun. Bah! you are full of the fore-peak and the forecastle; you are only familiar with Burtons and Billy-tackles; your ambition never mounted above pig-killing! which, in my poor opinion, is the proper phrase for whaling! Topmates! has not this Tubbs here been but a misuser of good oak planks, and a vile desecrator of the thrice holy sea? turning his ship, my hearties! into a fat-kettle, and the ocean into a whale-pen? Begone! you graceless, godless knave! pitch him over the top there, White-Jacket!"

But there was no necessity for my exertions. Poor Tubbs, astounded at these fulminations, was already rapidly descending by the rigging.

This outburst on the part of my noble friend Jack made me shake all over, spite of my padded surtout; and caused me to offer up devout thanksgivings, that in no evil hour had I divulged the fact of having myself served in a whaler; for having previously marked the prevailing prejudice of men-of-war's men to that much-maligned class of mariners, I had wisely held my peace concerning stove boats on the coast of Japan.

Chapter V

JACK CHASE ON A SPANISH QUARTER-DECK

HERE, I MUST FRANKLY TELL A STORY ABOUT JACK, WHICH AS TOUCHING HIS HONOR AND INtegrity, I am sure, will not work against him, in any charitable man's estimation. On this present cruise of the frigate *Neversink*, Jack had deserted; and after a certain interval, had been captured.

But with what purpose had he deserted? To avoid naval discipline? to riot in some abandoned sea-port? for love of some worthless signorita? Not at all. He abandoned the frigate from far higher and nobler, nay, glorious motives. Though bowing to naval discipline afloat; yet ashore, he was a stickler for the Rights of Man, and the liberties of the world. He went to draw a partisan blade in the civil commotions of Peru; and befriend, heart and soul, what he deemed the cause of the Right.

At the time, his disappearance excited the utmost astonishment among the officers, who had little suspected him of any such conduct of deserting.

"What? Jack, my great man of the main-top, gone!" cried the Captain; "I'll not believe it."

"Jack Chase cut and run!" cried a sentimental middy. "It must have been all for love, then; the signoritas have turned his head."

"Jack Chase not to be found?" cried a growling old sheet-anchor-man, one of your malicious prophets of past events: "I thought so; I know'd it; I could have sworn it—just the chap to make sail on the sly. I always s'pected him."

Months passed away, and nothing was heard of Jack; till at last, the frigate came to anchor on the coast, alongside of a Peruvian sloop of war.

Bravely clad in the Peruvian uniform, and with a fine, mixed martial and naval step, a tall, striking figure of a long-bearded officer was descried, promenading the Quarter-deck of the stranger; and superintending the salutes, which are exchanged between national vessels on these occasions.

This fine officer touched his laced hat most courteously to our Captain, who, after returning the compliment, stared at him, rather impolitely, through his spy-glass.

"By Heaven!" he cried at last—"it is he—he can't disguise his walk—that's his beard; I'd know him in Cochin China.—Man the first cutter there! Lieutenant Blink, go on board that sloop of war, and fetch me yon officer."

All hands were aghast—What? when a piping-hot peace was between the United States and Peru, to send an armed body on board a Peruvian sloop of war, and seize one of its officers, in broad daylight?—Monstrous infraction of the Law of Nations! What would Vattel say?

But Captain Claret must be obeyed. So off went the cutter, every man armed to the teeth, the lieutenant-commanding having secret instructions, and the midshipmen attending looking ominously wise, though, in truth, they could not tell what was coming.

Gaining the sloop of war, the lieutenant was received with the customary honors; but by this time the tall, bearded officer had disappeared from the Quarter-deck. The Lieutenant now inquired for the Peruvian Captain; and being shown into the cabin, made known to him, that on board his vessel was a person belonging to the United States Ship *Neversink*; and his orders were, to have that person delivered up instanter.

The foreign captain curled his mustache in astonishment and indignation; he hinted something about beating to quarters, and chastizing this piece of Yankee insolence.

But resting one gloved hand upon the table, and playing with his sword-knot, the Lieutenant, with a bland firmness, repeated his demand. At last, the whole case being so plainly made out, and the person in question being so accurately described, even to a mole on his cheek, there remained nothing but immediate compliance.

So the fine-looking, bearded officer, who had so courteously doffed his chapeau to our Captain, but disappeared upon the arrival of the Lieutenant, was summoned into the cabin, before his superior, who addressed him thus:

"Don John, this gentleman declares, that of right you belong to the frigate *Neversink*. Is it so?"

"It is even so, Don Sereno," said Jack Chase, proudly folding his gold-laced coat-sleeves across his chest—"and as there is no resisting the frigate, I comply.—Lieutenant Blink, I am ready. Adieu! Don Sereno, and Madre de Dios protect you. You have been a most gentlemanly friend and captain to me. I hope you will yet thrash your beggarly foes."

With that he turned; and entering the cutter, was pulled back to the frigate, and stepped up to Captain Claret, where that gentleman stood on the quarter-deck.

"Your servant, my fine Don," said the Captain, ironically lifting his chapeau, but regarding Jack at the same time with a look of intense displeasure.

"Your most devoted and penitent Captain of the Main-top, sir; and one who, in his very humility of contrition is yet proud to call Captain Claret his commander," said Jack, making a glorious bow, and then tragically flinging overboard his Peruvian sword.

"Reinstate him at once," shouted Captain Claret—"and now, sir, to your duty; and discharge that well to the end of the cruise, and you will hear no more of your having run away."

So Jack went forward among crowds of admiring tars, who swore by his nut-brown beard, which had amazingly lengthened and spread during his absence. They divided his laced hat and coat among them; and on their shoulders, carried him in triumph along the gun-deck.

Chapter VI

THE QUARTER-DECK OFFICERS, WARRANT OFFICERS, AND BERTH-DECK UNDERLINGS OF A MAN-OF-WAR; WHERE THEY LIVE IN THE SHIP; HOW THEY LIVE; THEIR SOCIAL STANDING ON SHIP-BOARD; AND WHAT SORT OF GENTLEMEN THEY ARE

SOME ACCOUNT HAS BEEN GIVEN OF THE VARIOUS DIVISIONS INTO WHICH OUR CREW WAS DIVIDED; so it may be well to say something of the officers; who they are, and what are their functions.

Our ship, be it know, was the flag-ship; that is, we sported a *broad-pennant*, or *bougee*, at the main, in token that we carried a Commodore—the highest rank of officers recognized in the American navy. The bougee is not to be confounded with the *long pennant* or *coach-whip*, a tapering serpentine streamer worn by all men-of-war.

Owing to certain vague, republican scruples, about creating great officers of the navy, America has thus far had no admirals; though, as her ships of war increase, they may become indispensable. This will assuredly be the case, should she ever have occasion to employ large fleets; when she must adopt something like the English plan, and introduce three or four grades of flag-officers, above a Commodore—Admirals, Vice-Admirals, and Rear-Admirals of Squadrons; distinguished by the color of their flags—red, white, and blue, corresponding to the center, van, and rear. These rank respectively with Generals, Lieutenant-Generals, and Major-Generals in the army; just as a Commodore takes rank with a Brigadier-General. So that the same prejudice which prevents the American Government from creating Admirals should have precluded the creation of all army officers above a Brigadier.

An American Commodore, like an English Commodore, or the French *Chef d'Escadre*, is but a senior Captain, temporarily commanding a small number of ships, detached for any special purpose. He has no permanent rank, recognized by Government, above his captaincy; though once employed as a Commodore, usage and courtesy unite in continuing the title.

Our Commodore was a gallant old man, who had seen service in his time. When a lieutenant, he served in the late war with England; and in the gun-boat actions on the Lakes near New Orleans, just previous to the grand land engagements, received a musket-ball in his shoulder; which, with the two balls in his eyes, he carries about with him to this day.

Often, when I looked at the venerable old warrior, doubled up from the effect of his wound, I thought what a curious, as well as painful sensation, it must be, to have one's shoulder a lead-mine; though, sooth to say, so many of us civilized mortals convert our mouths into Golcondas.

On account of this wound in his shoulder, our Commodore had a body-servant's pay allowed him, in addition to his regular salary. I cannot say a great deal, personally, of the Commodore; he never sought my company at all, never extended any gentlemanly courtesies.

But though I cannot say much of him personally, I can mention something of him in his general character, as a flag-officer. In the first place, then, I have serious doubts, whether, for the most part, he was not dumb; for, in my hearing, he seldom or never uttered a word. And not only did he seem dumb himself, but his presence possessed the strange power of making other people dumb for the time. His appearance on the Quarter-deck seemed to give every officer the lock-jaw.

Another phenomenon about him was the strange manner in which everyone shunned him. At the first sign of those epaulets of his on the weather side of the poop, the officers there congregated invariably shrunk over to leeward, and left him alone. Perhaps he had an evil eye; may be he was the Wandering Jew afloat. The real reason probably was, that like all high functionaries, he deemed it indispensable religiously to sustain his dignity; one of the most troublesome things in the world, and one calling for the greatest self-denial. And the constant watch, and many-sided guardedness, which this sustaining of a Commodore's dignity requires, plainly enough shows that, apart from the common dignity of manhood, Commodores, in general, possess no real dignity at all. True, it is expedient for crowned heads, generalissimos, Lord-high-admirals, and Commodores, to carry themselves straight, and beware of the spinal complaint; but it is not the less veritable, that it is a piece of assumption, exceedingly uncomfortable to themselves, and ridiculous to an enlightened generation.

Now, how many rare good fellows there were among us main-top-men, who, invited into his cabin over a social bottle or two, would have rejoiced our old Commodore's heart, and caused that ancient wound of his to heal up at once.

Come, come, Commodore don't look so sour, old boy; step up aloft here into the *top*, and we'll spin you a sociable yarn.

Truly, I thought myself much happier in that white jacket of mine, than our old Commodore in his dignified epaulets.

One thing, perhaps, that more than anything else helped to make our Commodore so melancholy and forlorn, was the fact of his having so little to do. For as the frigate had a captain; of course, so far as *she* was concerned, our Commodore was a supernumerary. What abundance of leisure he must have had, during a three years' cruise; how indefinitely he might have been improving his mind!

But as everyone knows that idleness is the hardest work in the world, so our Commodore was specially provided with a gentleman to assist him. This gentleman was called the *Commodore's secretary*. He was a remarkably urbane and polished man; with a very graceful exterior, and looked much like an Ambassador Extraordinary from Versailles. He messed with the Lieutenants in the Ward-room, where he had a state-room, elegantly furnished as the private cabinet of Pelham. His cot-boy used to entertain the sailors with all manner of stories about the silver-keyed flutes and flageolets, fine oil paintings, morocco-bound volumes, Chinese chess-men, gold shirt-buttons, enameled pencil cases, extraordinary fine French boots with soles no thicker than a sheet of scented note-paper, embroidered vests, incense-burning sealing-wax, alabaster statuettes of Venus and Adonis, tortoise-shell snuff-boxes, inlaid toilet-cases, ivory-handled hair-brushes and mother-of-pearl combs, and a hundred other luxurious appendages scattered about this magnificent secretary's state-room.

I was a long time in finding out what this secretary's duties comprised. But it seemed, he wrote the Commodore's dispatches for Washington, and also was his general amanuensis. Nor was this a very light duty, at times; for some commodores, though they do not *say* a great deal on board ship, yet they have a vast deal to write. Very often, the regimental orderly, stationed at our Commodore's cabin-door, would touch his hat to the First Lieutenant, and with a mysterious air hand him a note. I always thought these notes must contain most important matters of state; until one day, seeing a slip of wet, torn paper in a scupper-hole, I read the following:

SIR, you will give the people pickles to-day with their fresh meat.
To Lieutenant Bridewell.

By command of the Commodore;
ADOLPHUS DASHMAN, Priv. Sec.

This was a new revelation; for, from his almost immutable reserve, I had supposed that the Commodore never meddled immediately with the concerns of the ship, but left all that to the captain. But the longer we live, the more we learn of commodores.

Turn we now to the second officer in rank, almost supreme, however, in the internal affairs of his ship. Captain Claret was a large, portly man, a Harry the Eighth afloat, bluff and hearty; and as kingly in his cabin as Harry on his throne. For a ship is a bit of terra firma cut off from the main; it is a state in itself; and the captain is its king.

It is no limited monarchy, where the sturdy Commons have a right to petition, and snarl if they please; but almost a despotism, like the Grand Turk's. The captain's word is law; he never speaks but in the imperative mood. When he stands on his Quarter-deck at sea, he absolutely commands as far as eye can reach. Only the moon and stars are beyond his jurisdiction. He is lord and master of the sun.

It is not twelve o'clock till he says so. For when the sailing-master, whose duty it is to take the regular observation at noon, touches his hat, and reports twelve o'clock to the officer of the deck; that functionary orders a midshipman to repair to the captain's cabin, and humbly inform him of the respectful suggestion of the sailing-master.

"Twelve o'clock reported, sir," says the middy.

"*Make* it so," replies the captain.

And the bell is struck eight by the messenger-boy, and twelve o'clock it is.

As in the case of the Commodore, when the captain visits the deck, his subordinate officers generally beat a retreat to the other side; and, as a general rule, would no more think of addressing him, except concerning the ship, than a lackey would think of hailing the Czar of Russia on his throne, and inviting him to tea. Perhaps no mortal man has more reason to feel such an intense sense of his own personal consequence, as the captain of a man-of-war at sea.

Next in rank comes the First or Senior Lieutenant, the chief executive officer. I have no reason to love the particular gentleman who filled that post aboard our frigate, for it was he who refused my petition for as much black paint as would render water-proof that white-jacket of mine. All my soakings and drenchings lie at his state-room door. I hardly think I shall ever forgive him; every twinge of the rheumatism, which I still occasionally feel, is directly referable to him. The Immortals have a reputation for clemency; and *they* may pardon him; but he must not dun me to be merciful. But my personal feelings toward the man shall not prevent me from here doing him justice. In most things he was an excellent seaman; prompt, loud, and to the point; and as such was well fitted for his station. The First Lieutenancy of a frigate demands a good disciplinarian, and, every way, an energetic man. By the captain he is held responsible for everything; by that magnate, indeed, he is supposed to be omnipresent; down in the hold, and up aloft, at one and the same time.

He presides at the head of the Ward-room officers' table, who are so called from their messing together in a part of the ship thus designated. In a frigate it comprises the after part of the berth-deck. Sometimes it goes by the name of the Gun-room, but oftener is called the Ward-room. Within, this Ward-room much resembles a long, wide corridor in a large hotel; numerous doors opening on both hands to the private apartments of the officers. I never had a good interior look at it but once; and then the Chaplain was seated at the table in the center, playing chess with the Lieutenant of Marines. It was mid-day, but the place was lighted by lamps.

Besides the First Lieutenant, the Ward-room officers include the junior lieutenants, in a frigate six or seven in number, the Sailing-master, Purser, Chaplain, Surgeon, Marine officers, and Midshipmen's Schoolmaster, or "the Professor." They generally form a very agreeable club of good fellows; from their diversity of character, admirably calculated to form an agreeable social whole. The Lieutenants discuss sea-fights, and tell anecdotes of Lord Nelson and Lady Hamilton; the Marine officers talk of storming fortresses, and the siege of Gibraltar; the Purser steadies this wild conversation by occasional allusions to the rule of three; the Professor is always charged with a scholarly reflection, or an apt line from the classics, generally Ovid; the Surgeon's stories of the amputation-table judiciously serve to suggest the mortality of the whole party as men; while the good chaplain stands ready at all times to give them pious counsel and consolation.

Of course these gentlemen all associate on a footing of perfect social equality.

Next in order come the Warrant or Forward officers, consisting of the Boatswain, Gunner, Carpenter, and Sailmaker. Though these worthies sport long coats and wear the anchor-button; yet, in the estimation of the Ward-room officers, they are not, technically speaking, rated gentlemen. The First Lieutenant, Chaplain, or Surgeon, for example, would never dream of inviting them to dinner. In sea parlance, "they come in at the hawse holes"; they have hard hands; and the carpenter and sail-maker practically understand the duties which they are called upon to superintend. They mess by themselves. Invariably four in number, they never have need to play whist with a dummy.

In this part of the category now come the "reefers," otherwise "middies" or midshipmen. These boys are sent to sea, for the purpose of making commodores; and in order to become commodores, many of them deem it indispensable forthwith to commence chewing tobacco, drinking brandy and water, and swearing at the sailors. As they are only placed on board a sea-going ship to go to school and learn the duty of a Lieutenant; and until qualified to act as such, have few or no special functions to attend to; they are little more, while midshipmen, than supernumeraries on board. Hence, in a crowded frigate, they are so everlastingly crossing the path of both men and officers, that in the navy it has become a proverb, that a useless fellow is *"as much in the way as a reefer."*

In a gale of wind, when all hands are called and the deck swarms with men, the little "middies" running about distracted and having nothing particular to do, make it up in vociferous swearing; exploding all about under foot like torpedoes. Some of them are terrible little boys, cocking their cups at alarming angles, and looking fierce as young roosters. They are generally great consumers of Macassar oil and the Balm of Columbia; they thirst and rage after whiskers; and sometimes, applying their ointments, lay themselves out in the sun, to promote the fertility of their chins.

As the only way to learn to command, is to learn to obey, the usage of a ship of war is such that the midshipmen are constantly being ordered about by the Lieutenants; though, without having assigned them their particular destinations, they are always going somewhere, and never arriving. In some things, they almost have a harder time of it than the seamen themselves. They are messengers and errand-boys to their superiors.

"Mr. Pert," cries an officer of the deck, hailing a young gentleman forward. Mr. Pert advances, touches his hat, and remains in an attitude of deferential suspense. "Go and tell the boatswain I want him." And with this perilous errand, the middy hurries away, looking proud as a king.

The middies live by themselves in the steerage, where, nowadays, they dine off a table, spread with a cloth. They have a castor at dinner; they have some other little boys (selected from the ship's company) to wait upon them; they sometimes drink coffee out of china. But for all these, their modern refinements, in some instances the affairs of their club go sadly to rack and ruin. The china is broken; the japanned coffee-pot dented like a pewter mug in an ale-house; the pronged forks resemble tooth-picks (for which they are sometimes used); the table-knives are hacked into hand-saws; and the cloth goes to the sail-maker to be patched. Indeed, they are something like collegiate freshmen and sophomores, living in the college buildings, especially so far as the noise they make in their quarters is concerned. The steerage buzzes, hums, and swarms like a hive; or like an infant-school of a hot day, when the school-mistress falls asleep with a fly on her nose.

In frigates, the ward-room—the retreat of the Lieutenants—immediately adjoining the steerage, is on the same deck with it. Frequently, when the middies, waking early of a morning, as most youngsters do, would be kicking up their heels in their hammocks, or running about with double-reefed night-gowns, playing *tag* among the "clews"; the Senior Lieutenant would burst among them with a—"Young gentlemen, I am astonished. You must stop this skylarking. Mr. Pert, what are you doing at the table there, without your pantaloons? To your hammock, sir. Let me see no more of this. If you disturb the ward-room again, young gentleman, you shall hear of it." And so saying, this hoary-headed Senior Lieutenant would retire to his cot in his state-room, like the father of a numerous family after getting up in his dressing-gown and slippers, to quiet a daybreak tumult in his populous nursery.

Having now descended from Commodore to Middy, we come lastly to a set of nondescripts, forming also a "mess" by themselves, apart from the seamen. Into this mess, the usage of a man-of-war thrusts various subordinates—including the master-at-arms, purser's steward, ship's corporals, marine sergeants, and ship's yeomen, forming the first aristocracy above the sailors.

The master-at-arms is a sort of high constable and school-master, wearing citizen's clothes, and known by his official rattan. He it is whom all sailors hate. His is the universal duty of a universal informer and hunter-up of delinquents. On the berth-deck he reigns supreme; spying out all grease-spots made by the various cooks of the seamen's messes, and driving the laggards up the hatches, when all hands are called. It is indispensable that he should be a very Vidocq in vigilance. But as it is a heartless, so is it a thankless office. Of dark nights, most masters-of-arms keep themselves in readiness to dodge forty-two pound balls, dropped down the hatchways near them.

The ship's corporals are this worthy's deputies and ushers.

The marine sergeants are generally tall fellows with unyielding spines and stiff upper lips, and very exclusive in their tastes and predilections.

The ship's yeoman is a gentleman who has a sort of counting-room in a tar-cellar down in the fore-hold. More will be said of him anon.

Except the officers above enumerated, there are none who mess apart from the seamen. The *"petty officers,"* so called; that is, the Boatswain's, Gunner's, Carpenter's, and Sail-maker's mates, the Captains of the Tops, of the Forecastle, and of the After-Guard, and of the Fore and Main holds, and the Quarter-Masters, all mess in common with the crew, and in the American navy are only distinguished from the common seamen by their slightly additional pay. But in the English navy they wear crowns and anchors worked on the sleeves of their jackets, by way of badges of office. In the French navy they are known by strips of worsted worn in the same place, like those designating the Sergeants and Corporals in the army.

Thus it will be seen, that the dinner-table is the criterion of rank in our man-of-war world. The Commodore dines alone, because he is the only man of his rank in the ship. So too with the Captain; and the Ward-room officers, warrant officers, midshipmen, the master-at-arms' mess, and the common seamen—all of them, respectively, dine together, because they are, respectively, on a footing of equality.

Chapter VII

BREAKFAST, DINNER, AND SUPPER

NOT ONLY IS THE DINNER-TABLE A CRITERION OF RANK ON BOARD A MAN-OF-WAR, BUT ALSO THE dinner hour. He who dines latest is the greatest man; and he who dines earliest is accounted the least. In a flag-ship, the Commodore generally dines about four or five o'clock; the Captain about three; the Lieutenants about two; while *the people* (by which phrase the common seamen are specially designated in the nomenclature of the quarter-deck) sit down to their salt beef exactly at noon.

Thus it will be seen, that while the two estates of sea-kings and sea-lords dine at rather patrician hours—and thereby, in the long run, impair their digestive functions—the sea-commoners, or *the people,* keep up their constitutions, by keeping up the good old-fashioned, Elizabethan, Franklin-warranted dinner hour of twelve.

Twelve o'clock! It is the natural center, key-stone, and very heart of the day. At that hour, the sun has arrived at the top of his hill; and as he seems to hang poised there a while, before coming down on the other side, it is but reasonable to suppose that he is then stopping to dine; setting an eminent example to all mankind. The rest of the day is called *afternoon*; the very sound of which fine old Saxon word conveys a feeling of the lee bulwarks and a nap; a summer sea—soft breezes creeping over it; dreamy dolphins gliding in the distance. *Afternoon!* the word implies, that it is an after-piece, coming after the grand drama of the day; something to be taken leisurely and lazily. But how can this be, if you dine at five? For, after all, though *Paradise Lost* be a noble poem, and we men-of-war's men, no doubt, largely partake in the immortality of the immortals yet, let us candidly confess it, shipmates, that, upon the whole, our dinners are the most momentous affairs of these lives we lead beneath the moon. What were a day without a dinner? a dinnerless day! such a day had better be a night.

Again: twelve o'clock is the natural hour for us men-of-war's men to dine, because at that hour the very time-pieces we have invented arrive at their terminus; they can get no further than twelve; when straightway they continue their old rounds again. Doubtless, Adam and Eve dined at twelve; and the Patriarch Abraham in the midst of his cattle; and old Job with his noon mowers and reapers, in that grand plantation of Uz; and old Noah himself, in the Ark, must have gone to dinner at precisely *eight bells* (noon), with all his floating families and farm-yards.

But though this antediluvian dinner hour is rejected by modern Commodores and Captains, it still lingers among "*the people*" under their command. Many sensible things banished from high life find an asylum among the mob.

Some Commodores are very particular in seeing to it, that no man on board the ship dare to dine after his (the Commodore's) own dessert is cleared away.—not even the Captain. It is said, on good authority, that a Captain once ventured to dine at five, when the Commodore's hour was four. Next day, as the story goes, that Captain received a private note, and in consequence of that note, dined for the future at half-past three.

Though in respect of the dinner hour on board a man-of-war, *the people* have no reason to complain; yet they have just cause, almost for mutiny, in the outrageous hours assigned for their breakfast and supper.

Eight o'clock for breakfast; twelve for dinner; four for supper; and no meals but these; no lunches and no cold snacks. Owing to this arrangement (and partly to one watch going to their meals before the other, at sea), all the meals of the twenty-four hours are crowded into a space of less than eight! Sixteen mortal hours elapse between supper and breakfast; including, to one watch, eight hours on deck! This is barbarous; any physician will tell you so. Think of it! Before the Commodore has dined, you have supped. And in high latitudes, in summer-time, you have taken your last meal for the day, and five hours, or more, daylight to spare!

Mr. Secretary of the Navy, in the name of *the people*, you should interpose in this matter. Many a time have I, a maintop-man, found myself actually faint of a tempestuous morning watch, when all my energies were demanded—owing to this miserable, unphilosophical mode of allotting the government meals at sea. We beg you, Mr. Secretary, not to be swayed in this matter by the Honorable Board of Commodores, who will no doubt tell you that eight, twelve, and four are the proper hours for *the people* to take their meals; inasmuch, as at these hours the watches are relieved. For, though this arrangement makes a neater and cleaner thing of it for the officers, and looks very nice and superfine on paper; yet it is plainly detrimental to health; and in time of war is attended with still more serious consequences to the whole nation at large. If the necessary researches were made, it would perhaps be found that in those instances where men-of-war adopting the above-mentioned hours for meals have encountered an enemy at night, they have pretty generally been beaten; that is, in those cases where the enemies' meal times were reasonable; which is only to be accounted for by the fact that *the people* of the beaten vessels were fighting on an empty stomach instead of a full one.

Chapter VIII

SELVAGEE CONTRASTED WITH MAD JACK

HAVING GLANCED AT THE GRAND DIVISIONS OF A MAN-OF-WAR, LET US NOW DESCEND TO SPECIALITIES: and, particularly, to two of the junior lieutenants; lords and noblemen; members of that House of Peers, the gun-room. There were several young lieutenants on board; but from these two—representing the extremes of character to be found in their department—the nature of the other officers of their grade in the *Neversink* must be derived.

One of these two quarter-deck lords went among the sailors by a name of their own devising—Selvagee. Of course, it was intended to be characteristic; and even so it was.

In frigates, and all large ships of war, when getting under weigh, a large rope, called a *messenger,* is used to carry the strain of the cable to the capstan; so that the anchor may be weighed, without the muddy, ponderous cable, itself going round the capstan. As the cable enters the hawse-hole, therefore, something must be constantly used, to keep this traveling chain attached to this traveling *messenger*; something that may be rapidly wound round both, so as to bind them together. The article used is called a *selvagee.* And what could be better adapted to the purpose? It is a slender, tapering, unstranded piece of rope; prepared with much solicitude; peculiarly flexible; and wreathes and serpentines round the cable and messenger like an elegantly-modeled garter-snake round the twisted stalks of a vine. Indeed, *Selvagee* is the exact type and symbol of a tall, genteel, limber, spiralizing exquisite. So much for the derivation of the name which the sailors applied to the Lieutenant.

From what sea-alcove, from what mermaid's milliner's shop, hast thou emerged, Selvagee! with that dainty waist and languid cheek? What heartless step-dame drove thee forth, to waste thy fragrance on the salt sea-air?

Was it *you,* Selvagee! that, outward-bound, off Cape Horn, looked at Hermit Island through an opera-glass? Was it *you,* who thought of proposing to the Captain that, when the sails were furled in a gale, a few drops of lavender should be dropped in their "bunts," so that when the canvas was set again, your nostrils might not be offended by its musty smell? I do not *say* it was you, Selvagee; I but deferentially inquire.

In plain prose, Selvagee was one of those officers whom the sight of a trim-fitting naval coat had captivated in the days of his youth. He fancied, that if a sea-officer dressed well, and conversed genteelly, he would abundantly uphold the honor of his flag, and immortalize the tailor that made him. On that rock many young gentlemen split. For upon a frigate's quarter-deck, it is not enough to sport a coat fashioned by a Stultz; it is not enough to be well braced with straps and suspenders; it is not enough to have sweet reminiscences of Lauras and Matildas. It is a right down life of hard wear and tear, and the man who is not, in a good degree, fitted to become a common sailor will never make an officer. Take that to heart, all ye naval aspirants. Thrust your arms up to the elbow in pitch and see how you like it, ere you solicit a warrant. Prepare for white squalls, living gales and typhoons; read accounts of shipwrecks and horrible disasters; peruse the Narratives of Byron and Bligh; familiarize yourselves with the story of the English frigate *Alceste* and the French frigate *Medusa.* Though you may go ashore, now and then, at Cadiz and Palermo; for every day so spent among oranges and ladies, you will have whole months of rains and gales.

And even thus did Selvagee prove it. But with all the intrepid effeminacy of your true dandy, he still continued his Cologne-water baths, and sported his lace-bordered handkerchiefs in the very teeth of a tempest. Alas, Selvagee! there was no getting the lavender out of you.

But Selvagee was no fool. Theoretically he understood his profession; but the mere theory of seamanship forms but the thousandth part of what makes a seaman. You cannot save a ship by working out a problem in the cabin; the deck is the field of action.

Well aware of his deficiency in some things, Selvagee never took the trumpet—which is the badge of the deck officer for the time—without a tremulous movement of the lip, and an earnest inquiring eye to the windward. He encouraged those old Tritons, the Quarter-masters, to discourse with him concerning the likelihood of a squall; and often followed their advice as to taking in, or making sail. The smallest favors in that way were thankfully received. Sometimes, when all the North looked unusually lowering, by many conversational blandishments, he would endeavor to prolong his predecessor's stay on deck, after that officer's watch had expired. But in fine, steady weather, when the Captain would emerge from his cabin, Selvagee might be seen, pacing the poop with long, bold, indefatigable strides, and casting his eye up aloft with the most ostentatious fidelity.

But vain these pretenses; he could not deceive. Selvagee! you know very well, that if it comes on to blow pretty hard, the First Lieutenant will be sure to interfere with his paternal authority. Every man and every boy in the frigate knows, Selvagee, that you are no Neptune.

How unenviable his situation! His brother officers do not insult him, to be sure; but sometimes their looks are as daggers. The sailors do not laugh at him outright; but of dark nights they jeer, when they hearken to that mantuamaker's voice ordering *a strong pull at the main brace*, or *hands by the halyards!* Sometimes, by way of being terrific, and making the men jump, Selvagee raps out an oath; but the soft bomb stuffed with confectioner's kisses seems to burst like a crushed rose-bud diffusing its odors. Selvagee! Selvagee! take a main-top-man's advice; and this cruise over, never more tempt the sea.

With this gentleman of cravats and curling irons, how strongly contrasts the man who was born in a gale! For in some time of tempest—off Cape Horn or Hatteras—*Mad Jack* must have entered the world—such things have been—not with a silver spoon, but with a speaking-trumpet in his mouth; wrapped up in a caul, as in a main-sail—for a charmed life against shipwrecks he bears—and crying, *Luff! luff, you may!—steady!—port! World ho!—here I am!*

Mad Jack is in his saddle on the sea. *That* is his home; he would not care much, if another Flood came and overflowed the dry land; for what would it do but float his good ship higher and higher and carry his proud nation's flag round the globe, over the very capitals of all hostile states! Then would masts surmount spires; and all mankind, like the Chinese boatmen in Canton River, live in flotillas and fleets, and find their food in the sea.

Mad Jack was expressly created and labeled for a tar. Five feet nine is his mark, in his socks; and not weighing over eleven stone before dinner. Like so many ship's shrouds, his muscles and tendons are all set true, trim, and taut; he is braced up fore and aft, like a ship on the wind. His broad chest is a bulkhead, that dams off the gale; and his nose is an aquiline, that divides it in two, like a keel. His loud, lusty lungs are two belfries, full of all manner of chimes; but you only hear his deepest bray, in the height of some tempest—like the great bell of St. Paul's, which only sounds when the King or the Devil is dead.

Look at him there, where he stands on the poop—one foot on the rail, and one hand on a shroud—his head thrown back, and his trumpet like an elephant's trunk thrown up in the air. Is he going to shoot dead with sounds, those fellows on the main-topsail-yard?

Mad Jack was a bit of a tyrant—they *say* all good officers are—but the sailors loved him all round; and would much rather stand fifty watches with him, than one with a rose-water sailor.

But Mad Jack, alas! has one fearful failing. He drinks. And so do we all. But Mad Jack, *he* only drinks brandy. The vice was inveterate; surely, like Ferdinand, Count Fathom, he must have been suckled at a puncheon. Very often, this bad habit got him into very serious scrapes. Twice was he put off duty by the Commodore; and once he came near being broken for his frolics. So far as his efficiency as a sea-officer was concerned, on shore at least, Jack might *bouse away* as much as he pleased; but afloat it will not do at all.

Now, if he only followed the wise example set by those ships of the desert, the camels; and while in port, drank for the thirst past, the thirst present, and the thirst to come—so that he might cross the ocean sober; Mad Jack would get along pretty well. Still better, if he would but eschew brandy altogether; and only drink of the limpid white-wine of the rills and the brooks.

Chapter IX

OF THE POCKETS THAT WERE IN THE JACKET

I MUST MAKE SOME FURTHER MENTION OF THAT WHITE JACKET OF MINE.

And here be it known—by way of introduction to what is to follow—that to a common sailor, the living on board a man-of-war is like living in a market; where you dress on the door-steps, and sleep in the cellar. No privacy can you have; hardly one moment's seclusion. It is almost a physical impossibility, that you can ever be alone. You dine at a vast *table d'hote*; sleep in commons, and make your toilette where and when you can. There is no calling for a mutton chop and a pint of claret by yourself; no selecting of chambers for the night; no hanging of pantaloons over the back of a chair; no ringing your bell of a rainy morning, to take your coffee in bed. It is something like life in a large manufactory. The bell strikes to dinner, and hungry or not, you must dine.

Your clothes are stowed in a large canvas bag, generally painted black, which you can get out of the "rack" only once in the twenty-four hours; and then, during a time of the utmost confusion; among five hundred other bags, with five hundred other sailors diving into each, in the midst of the twilight of the berth-deck. In some measure to obviate this inconvenience, many sailors divide their wardrobes between their hammocks and their bags; stowing a few frocks and trousers in the former; so that they can shift at night, if they wish, when the hammocks are piped down. But they gain very little by this.

You have no place whatever but your bag or hammock, in which to put anything in a man-of-war. If you lay anything down, and turn your back for a moment, ten to one it is gone.

Now, in sketching the preliminary plan, and laying out the foundation of that memorable white jacket of mine, I had had an earnest eye to all these inconveniences, and resolved to avoid them. I proposed, that not only should my jacket keep me warm, but that it should also be so constructed as to contain a shirt or two, a pair of trousers, and divers knick-knacks—sewing utensils, books, biscuits, and the like. With this object, I had accordingly provided it with a great variety of pockets, pantries, clothes-presses, and cupboards.

The principal apartments, two in number, were placed in the skirts, with a wide, hospitable entrance from the inside; two more, of smaller capacity, were planted in each breast, with folding-doors communicating, so that in case of emergency, to accommodate any bulky articles, the two pockets in each breast could be thrown into one. There were, also, several unseen recesses behind the arras; insomuch, that my jacket, like an old castle, was full of winding stairs, and mysterious closets, crypts, and cabinets; and like a confidential writing-desk, abounded in snug little out-of-the-way lairs and hiding-places, for the storage of valuables.

Superadded to these, were four capacious pockets on the outside; one pair to slip books into when suddenly startled from my studies to the main-royal-yard; and the other pair, for permanent mittens, to thrust my hands into of a cold night-watch. This last contrivance was regarded as needless by one of my top-mates, who showed me a pattern for sea-mittens, which he said was much better than mine.

It must be known, that sailors, even in the bleakest weather, only cover their hands when unemployed; they never wear mittens aloft, since aloft they literally carry their lives in their hands, and want nothing between their grasp of the hemp, and the hemp itself.—Therefore, it is desirable, that whatever things they cover their hands with, should be capable of being slipped on and off in a moment. Nay, it is desirable, that they should be of such a nature, that in a dark night, when you are in a great hurry—say, going to the helm—they may be jumped into, indiscriminately; and not be like a pair of right-and-left kids; neither of which will admit any hand, but the particular one meant for it.

My top-mate's contrivance was this—he ought to have got out a patent for it—each of his mittens was provided with two thumbs, one on each side; the convenience of which needs no comment. But though for clumsy seamen, whose fingers are all thumbs, this description of mitten might do very well, White-Jacket did not so much fancy it. For when your hand was once in the bag of the mitten, the empty thumb-hole sometimes dangled at your palm, confounding your ideas of where your real thumb might be; or else, being carefully grasped in the hand, was continually suggesting the insane notion, that you were all the while having hold of someone else's thumb.

No; I told my good top-mate to go away with his four thumbs, I would have nothing to do with them; two thumbs were enough for any man.

For some time after completing my jacket, and getting the furniture and household stores in it; I thought that nothing could exceed it for convenience. Seldom now did I have occasion to go to my bag, and be jostled by the crowd who were making their wardrobe in a heap. If I wanted anything in the way of clothing, thread, needles, or literature, the chances were that my invaluable jacket contained it. Yes: I fairly hugged myself, and reveled in my jacket; till, alas! a long rain put me out of conceit of it. I, and all my pockets and their contents, were soaked through and through, and my pocket-edition of Shakespeare was reduced to an omelet.

However, availing myself of a fine sunny day that followed, I emptied myself out in the main-top, and spread all my goods and chattels to dry. But spite of the bright sun, that day proved a black one. The scoundrels on deck detected me in the act of discharging my saturated cargo; they now knew that the white jacket was used for a storehouse. The consequence was that, my goods being well dried and again stored away in my pockets, the very next night, when it was my quarter-watch on deck, and not in the top (where they were all honest men), I noticed a parcel of fellows skulking about after me, wherever I went. To a man, they were pickpockets, and bent upon pillaging me. In vain I kept clapping my pocket like a nervous old gentlemen in a crowd; that same night I found myself minus several valuable articles. So, in the end, I masoned up my lockers and pantries; and save the two used for mittens, the white jacket ever after was pocketless.

Chapter X

FROM POCKETS TO PICKPOCKETS

AS THE LATTER PART OF THE PRECEDING CHAPTER MAY SEEM STRANGE TO THOSE LANDSMEN, who have been habituated to indulge in high-raised, romantic notions of the man-of-war's man's character; it may not be amiss, to set down here certain facts on this head, which may serve to place the thing in its true light.

From the wild life they lead, and various other causes (needless to mention), sailors, as a class, entertain the most liberal notions concerning morality and the Decalogue; or rather, they take their own views of such matters, caring little for the theological or ethical definitions of others concerning what may be criminal, or wrong.

Their ideas are much swayed by circumstances. They will covertly abstract a thing from one, whom they dislike; and insist upon it, that, in such a case, stealing is not robbing. Or, where the theft involves something funny, as in the case of the white jacket, they only steal for the sake of the joke; but this much is to be observed nevertheless, *i.e.*, that they never spoil the joke by returning the stolen article.

It is a good joke; for instance, and one often perpetrated on board ship, to stand talking to a man in a dark night watch, and all the while be cutting the buttons from his coat. But once off, those buttons never grow on again. There is no spontaneous vegetation in buttons.

Perhaps it is a thing unavoidable, but the truth is that, among the crew of a man-of-war, scores of desperadoes are too often found, who stop not at the largest enormities. A species of highway robbery is not unknown to them. A *gang* will be informed that such a fellow has three or four gold pieces in the money-bag, so-called, or purse, which many tars wear round their necks, tucked out of sight. Upon this, they deliberately lay their plans; and in due time, proceed to carry them into execution. The man they have marked is perhaps strolling along the benighted berth-deck to his mess-chest; when of a sudden, the foot-pads dash out from their hiding-place, throw him down, and while two or three gag him, and hold him fast, another cuts the bag from his neck, and makes away with it, followed by his comrades. This was more than once done in the *Neversink*.

At other times, hearing that a sailor has something valuable secreted in his hammock, they will rip it open from underneath while he sleeps, and reduce the conjecture to a certainty.

To enumerate all the minor pilferings on board a man-of-war would be endless. With some highly commendable exceptions, they rob from one another, and rob back again, till, in the matter of small things, a community of goods seems almost established; and at last, as a whole, they become relatively honest, by nearly every man becoming the reverse. It is in vain that the officers, by threats of condign punishment, endeavor to instill more virtuous principles into their crew; so thick is the mob, that not one thief in a thousand is detected.

Chapter XI

THE PURSUIT OF POETRY UNDER DIFFICULTIES

THE FEELING OF INSECURITY CONCERNING ONE'S POSSESSIONS IN THE *NEVERSINK*, WHICH THE things just narrated begat in the minds of honest men, was curiously exemplified in the case of my poor friend Lemsford, a gentlemanly young member of the After-Guard. I had very early made the acquaintance of Lemsford. It is curious, how unerringly a man pitches upon a spirit, any way akin to his own, even in the most miscellaneous mob.

Lemsford was a poet; so thoroughly inspired with the divine afflatus, that not even all the tar and tumult of a man-of-war could drive it out of him.

As may readily be imagined, the business of writing verse is a very different thing on the gun-deck of a frigate, from what the gentle and sequestered Wordsworth found it at placid Rydal Mount in Westmoreland. In a frigate, you cannot sit down and meander off your sonnets, when the full heart prompts; but only, when more important duties permit: such as bracing round the yards, or reefing top-sails fore and aft. Nevertheless, every fragment of time at his command was religiously devoted by Lemsford to the Nine. At the most unseasonable hours, you would behold him, seated apart, in some corner among the guns—a shot-box before him, pen in hand, and eyes *"in a fine frenzy rolling."*

"What's that 'ere born nat'ral about?"—"He's got a fit, hain't he?" were exclamations often made by the less learned of his shipmates. Some deemed him a conjurer; others a lunatic; and the knowing ones said, that he must be a crazy Methodist. But well knowing by experience the truth of the saying, that *poetry is its own exceeding great reward,* Lemsford wrote on; dashing off whole epics, sonnets, ballads, and acrostics, with a facility which, under the circumstances, amazed me. Often he read over his effusions to me; and well worth the hearing they were. He had wit, imagination, feeling, and humor in abundance; and out of the very ridicule with which some persons regarded him, he made rare metrical sport, which we two together enjoyed by ourselves; or shared with certain select friends.

Still, the taunts and jeers so often leveled at my friend the poet, would now and then rouse him into rage; and at such times the haughty scorn he would hurl on his foes, was proof positive of his possession of that one attribute, irritability, almost universally ascribed to the votaries of Parnassus and the Nine.

My noble captain, Jack Chase, rather patronized Lemsford, and he would stoutly take his part against scores of adversaries. Frequently, inviting him up aloft into his top, he would beg him to recite some of his verses; to which he would pay the most heedful attention, like Mæcenas listening to Virgil, with a book of *Æneid* in his hand. Taking the liberty of a well-wisher, he would sometimes gently criticize the piece, suggesting a few immaterial alterations. And upon my word, noble Jack, with his native-born good sense, taste, and humanity, was not ill qualified to play the true part of a *Quarterly Review*;—which is, to give quarter at last, however severe the critique.

Now Lemsford's great care, anxiety, and endless source of tribulation was the preservation of his manuscripts. He had a little box, about the size of a small dressing-case, and secured with a lock, in which he kept his papers and stationery. This box, of course, he could not keep in his bag or hammock, for, in either case, he would only be able to get at it once in the twenty-four hours. It was necessary to have it accessible at all times. So when not using it, he was obliged to hide it out of sight, where he could. And of all places in the world, a ship of war, above her *hold,* least abounds in secret nooks. Almost every inch is occupied; almost every inch is in plain sight; and almost every inch is continually being visited and explored. Added to all this, was the deadly hostility of the whole tribe of ship-underlings—master-at-arms, ship's corporals, and boatswain's mates—both to the poet and his casket. They hated his box, as if it had been Pandora's, crammed to the very lid with hurricanes and gales. They hunted out his hiding-places like pointers, and gave him no peace night or day.

Still, the long twenty-four-pounders on the main-deck offered some promise of a hiding-place to the box; and, accordingly, it was often tucked away behind the carriages, among the side tackles; its black color blending with the ebon hue of the guns.

But Quoin, one of the quarter-gunners, had eyes like a ferret. Quoin was a little old man-of-war's man, hardly five feet high, with a complexion like a gun-shot wound after it is healed. He was indefatigable in attending to his duties; which consisted in taking care of one division of the guns, embracing ten of the aforesaid twenty-four-pounders. Ranged up against the ship's side at regular intervals, they resembled not a little a stud of sable chargers in their stall. Among this iron stud little Quoin was continually running in and out, currying them down, now and then, with an old rag, or keeping the flies off with a brush. To Quoin, the honor and dignity of the United States of America seemed indissolubly linked with the keeping his guns unspotted and glossy. He himself was black as a chimney-sweep with continually tending them, and rubbing them down with black paint. He would sometimes get outside of the port-holes and peer into their muzzles, as a monkey into a bottle. Or, like a dentist, he seemed intent upon examining their teeth. Quite as often, he would be brushing out their touch-holes with a little wisp of oakum, like a Chinese barber in Canton, cleaning a patient's ear.

Such was his solicitude, that it was a thousand pities he was not able to dwarf himself still more, so as to creep in at the touch-hole, and examining the whole interior of the tube, emerge at last from the muzzle. Quoin swore by his guns, and slept by their side. Woe betide the man whom he found leaning against them, or in any way soiling them. He seemed seized with the crazy fancy, that his darling twenty-four-pounders were fragile, and might break, like glass retorts.

Now, from this Quoin's vigilance, how could my poor friend the poet hope to escape with his box? Twenty times a week it was pounced upon, with a "here's that d—d pillbox again!" and a loud threat, to pitch it overboard the next time, without a moment's warning, or benefit of clergy. Like many poets, Lemsford was nervous, and upon these occasions he trembled like a leaf. Once, with an inconsolable countenance, he came to me, saying that his casket was nowhere to be found; he had sought for it in his hiding-place, and it was not there.

I asked him where he had hidden it?

"Among the guns," he replied.

"Then depend upon it, Lemsford, that Quoin has been the death of it."

Straight to Quoin went the poet. But Quoin knew nothing about it. For ten mortal days the poet was not to be comforted; dividing his leisure time between cursing Quoin and lamenting his loss. The world is undone, he must have thought: no such calamity has befallen it since the Deluge—my verses are perished.

But though Quoin, as it afterward turned out, had indeed found the box, it so happened that he had not destroyed it; which no doubt led Lemsford to infer that a superintending Providence had interposed to preserve to posterity his invaluable casket. It was found at last, lying exposed near the galley.

Lemsford was not the only literary man on board the *Neversink*. There were three or four persons who kept journals of the cruise. One of these journalists embellished his work—which was written in a large blank account-book—with various colored illustrations of the harbors and bays at which the frigate had touched; and also, with small crayon sketches of comical incidents on board the frigate itself. He would frequently read passages of his book to an admiring circle of the more refined sailors, between the guns. They pronounced the whole performance a miracle of art. As the author declared to them that it was all to be printed and published so soon as the vessel reached home, they vied with each other in procuring interesting items, to be incorporated into additional chapters. But it having been rumored abroad that this journal was to be ominously entitled "*The Cruise of the Neversink, or a Paixhan Shot into Naval Abuses*"; and it having also reached the ears of the Ward-room that the work contained reflections somewhat derogatory to the dignity of the officers, the volume was seized by the master-at-arms, armed with a warrant from the Captain. A few days after, a large nail was driven straight through the two covers, and clinched on the other side, and, thus everlastingly sealed, the book was committed to the deep. The ground taken by the authorities on this occasion was, perhaps, that the book was obnoxious to a certain clause in the Articles of War, forbidding any person in the Navy to bring any other person in the Navy into contempt, which the suppressed volume undoubtedly did.

Chapter XII

The Good or Bad Temper of Men-of-War's Men, in a Great Degree, Attributable to Their Particular Stations and Duties Aboard Ship

QUOIN, THE QUARTER-GUNNER, WAS THE REPRESENTATIVE OF A CLASS ON BOARD THE *NEVersink*, altogether too remarkable to be left astern, without further notice, in the rapid wake of these chapters.

As has been seen, Quoin was full of unaccountable whimsies; he was, withal, a very cross, bitter, ill-natured, inflammable old man. So, too, were all the members of the gunner's gang; including the two gunner's mates, and all the quarter-gunners. Every one of them had the same dark brown complexion; all their faces looked like smoked hams. They were continually grumbling and growling about the batteries; running in and out among the guns; driving the sailors away from them; and cursing and swearing as if all their conscience had been powder-singed, and made callous, by their calling. Indeed they were a most unpleasant set of men; especially Priming, the nasal-voiced gunner's mate, with the hare-lip; and Cylinder, his stuttering coadjutor, with the clubbed foot. But you will always observe, that the gunner's gang of every man-of-war are invariably ill-tempered, ugly featured, and quarrelsome. Once when I visited an English line-of-battle ship, the gunner's gang were fore and aft, polishing up the batteries, which, according to the Admiral's fancy, had been painted white as snow. Fidgeting round the great thirty-two-pounders, and making stinging remarks at the sailors and each other, they reminded one of a swarm of black wasps, buzzing about rows of white head-stones in a church-yard.

Now, there can be little doubt, that their being so much among the guns is the very thing that makes a gunner's gang so cross and quarrelsome. Indeed, this was once proved to the satisfaction of our whole company of main-top-men. A fine top-mate of ours, a most merry and companionable fellow, chanced to be promoted to a quarter-gunner's berth. A few days afterward, some of us main-top-men, his old comrades, went to pay him a visit, while he was going his regular rounds through the division of guns allotted to his care. But instead of greeting us with his usual heartiness, and cracking his pleasant jokes, to our amazement, he did little else but scowl; and at last, when we rallied him upon his ill-temper, he seized a long black rammer from overhead, and drove us on deck; threatening to report us, if we ever dared to be familiar with him again.

My top-mates thought that this remarkable metamorphose was the effect produced upon a weak, vain character suddenly elevated from the level of a mere seaman to the dignified position of a *petty officer*. But though, in similar cases, I had seen such effects produced upon some of the crew; yet, in the present instance, I knew better than that—it was solely brought about by his consorting with with those villainous, irritable, ill-tempered cannon; more especially from his being subject to the orders of those deformed blunderbusses, Priming and Cylinder.

The truth seems to be, indeed, that all people should be very careful in selecting their callings and vocations; very careful in seeing to it, that they surround themselves by good-humored, pleasant-looking objects; and agreeable, temper-soothing sounds. Many an angelic disposition has had its even edge turned, and hacked like a saw; and many a sweet draft of piety has soured on the heart from people's choosing ill-natured employments, and omitting to gather round them good-natured landscapes. Gardeners are almost always pleasant, affable people to converse with; but beware of quarter-gunners, keepers of arsenals, and lonely light-house men.

It would be advisable for any man, who from an unlucky choice of a profession, which it is too late to change for another, should find his temper souring, to endeavor to counteract that misfortune, by filling his private chamber with amiable, pleasurable sights and sounds. In summer time, an Æolian harp can be placed in your window at a very trifling expense; a conch-shell might stand on your mantel, to be taken up and held to the ear, that you may be soothed by its continual lulling sound, when you feel the blue fit stealing over you. For sights, a gay-painted punch-bowl, or Dutch tankard—never mind about filling it—might be recommended. It should be placed on a bracket in the pier. Nor is an old-fashioned silver ladle, nor a chased dinner-castor, nor a fine portly demijohn, nor anything, indeed, that savors of eating and drinking, bad to drive off the spleen. But perhaps the best of all is a shelf of merrily-bound books, containing comedies, farces, songs, and humorous novels. You need never open them; only have the titles in plain sight. For this purpose, *Peregrine Pickle* is a good book; so is *Gil Blas*; so is Goldsmith.

But of all chamber furniture in the world, best calculated to cure a had temper, and breed a pleasant one, is the sight of a lovely wife. If you have children, however, that are teething, the nursery should be a good way up stairs; at sea, it ought to be in the mizzen-top. Indeed, teething children play the very deuce with a husband's temper. I have known three promising young husbands completely spoil on their wives' hands, by reason of a teething child, whose worrisomeness happened to be aggravated at the time by the summer-complaint. With a breaking heart, and my handkerchief to my eyes, I followed those three hapless young husbands, one after the other, to their premature graves.

Gossiping scenes breed gossips. Who so chatty as hotel-clerks, market women, auctioneers, bar-keepers, apothecaries, newspaper-reporters, monthly-nurses, and all those who live in bustling crowds, or are present at scenes of chatty interest.

Solitude breeds taciturnity; *that* everybody knows; who so taciturn as authors, taken as a race?

A forced, interior quietude, in the midst of great outward commotion, breeds moody people. Who so moody as railroad-brakemen, steam-boat-engineers, helmsmen, and tenders of power-looms in cotton factories? For all these must hold their peace while employed, and let the machinery do the chatting; they cannot even edge in a single syllable.

Now, this theory about the wondrous influence of habitual sights and sounds upon the human temper, was suggested by my experiences on board our frigate. And although I regard the example furnished by our quarter-gunners—especially him who had once been our top-mate—as by far the strongest argument in favor of the general theory; yet, the entire ship abounded with illustrations of its truth. Who were more liberal-hearted, lofty-minded, gayer, more jocund, elastic, adventurous, given to fun and frolic, than the top-men of the fore, main, and mizzen masts? The reason of their liberal-heartedness was, that they were daily called upon to expatiate themselves all over the rigging. The reason of their lofty-mindedness was, that they were high lifted above the petty tumults, carping cares, and paltrinesses of the decks below.

And I feel persuaded in my inmost soul, that it is to the fact of my having been a main-top-man; and especially my particular post being on the loftiest yard of the frigate, the main-royal-yard; that I am now enabled to give such a free, broad, off-hand, bird's-eye, and, more than all, impartial account of our man-of-war world; withholding nothing; inventing nothing; nor flattering, nor scandalizing any; but meting out to all—commodore and messenger-boy alike—their precise descriptions and deserts.

The reason of the mirthfulness of these top-men was, that they always looked out upon the blue, boundless, dimpled, laughing, sunny sea. Nor do I hold, that it militates against this theory, that of a stormy day, when the face of the ocean was black, and overcast, that some of them would grow moody, and chose to sit apart. On the contrary, it only proves the thing which I maintain. For even on shore, there are many people naturally gay and light-hearted, who, whenever the autumnal wind begins to bluster round the corners, and roar along the chimney-stacks, straight becomes cross, petulant, and irritable. What is more mellow than fine old ale? Yet thunder will sour the best nut-brown ever brewed.

The *Holders* of our frigate, the Troglodytes, who lived down in the tarry cellars and caves below the berth-deck, were, nearly all of them, men of gloomy dispositions, taking sour views of things; one of them was a blue-light Calvinist. Whereas, the old-sheet-anchor-men, who spent their time in the bracing sea-air and broad-cast sunshine of the forecastle, were free, generous-hearted, charitable, and full of good-will to all hands; though some of them, to tell the truth, proved sad exceptions; but exceptions only prove the rule.

The "steady-cooks" on the berth-deck, the "steady-sweepers," and "steady-spit-box-musterers," in all divisions of the frigate, fore and aft, were a narrow-minded set; with contracted souls; imputable, no doubt, to their groveling duties. More especially was this evinced in the case of those odious ditchers and night scavengers, the ignoble "Waisters."

The members of the band, some ten or twelve in number, who had nothing to do but keep their instruments polished, and play a lively air now and then, to stir the stagnant current in our poor old Commodore's torpid veins, were the most gleeful set of fellows you ever saw. They were Portuguese, who had been shipped at the Cape De Verd islands, on the passage out. They messed by themselves; forming a dinner-party, not to be exceeded in mirthfulness, by a club of young bridegrooms, three months after marriage, completely satisfied with their bargains, after testing them.

But what made them, now, so full of fun? What indeed but their merry, martial, mellow calling. Who could he a churl, and play a flageolet? who mean and spiritless, braying forth the souls of thousand heroes from his brazen trump? But still more efficacious, perhaps, in ministering to the light spirits of the band, was the consoling thought, that should the ship ever go into action, they would be exempted from the perils of battle. In ships of war, the members of the "music," as the band is called, are generally non-combatants; and mostly ship, with the express understanding, that as soon as the vessel comes within long gun-shot of an enemy, they shall have the privilege of burrowing down in the cable-tiers, or sea coal-hole. Which shows that they are inglorious, but uncommonly sensible fellows.

Look at the barons of the gun-room—Lieutenants, Purser, Marine officers, Sailing-master—all of them gentlemen with stiff upper lips, and aristocratic cut noses. Why was this? Will anyone deny, that from their living so long in high military life, served by a crowd of menial stewards and cot-boys, and always accustomed to command right and left; will anyone deny, I say, that by reason of this, their very noses had become thin, peaked, aquiline, and aristocratically cartilaginous? Even old Cuticle, the Surgeon, had a Roman nose.

But I never could account how it came to be, that our gray-headed First Lieutenant was a little lop-sided; that is, one of his shoulders disproportionately dropped. And when I observed, that nearly all the First Lieutenants I saw in other men-of-war, besides many Second and Third Lieutenants, were similarly lop-sided, I knew that there must be some general law which induced the phenomenon; and I put myself to studying it out, as an interesting problem. At last, I came to the conclusion—to which I still adhere—that their so long wearing only one epaulet (for to only one does their rank entitle them) was the infallible clue to this mystery. And when anyone reflects upon so well-known a fact, that many sea Lieutenants grow decrepit from age, without attaining a Captaincy and wearing *two* epaulets, which would strike the balance between their shoulders, the above reason assigned will not appear unwarrantable.

Chapter XIII

A Man-of-War Hermit in a Mob

The allusion to the poet Lemsford in a previous chapter, leads me to speak of our mutual friends, Nord and Williams, who, with Lemsford himself, Jack Chase, and my comrades of the main-top, comprised almost the only persons with whom I unreservedly consorted while on board the frigate. For I had not been long on board ere I found that it would not do to be intimate with everybody. An indiscriminate intimacy with all hands leads to sundry annoyances and scrapes, too often ending with a dozen at the gang-way. Though I was above a year in the frigate, there were scores of men who to the last remained perfect strangers to me, whose very names I did not know, and whom I would hardly be able to recognize now should I happen to meet them in the streets.

In the dog-watches at sea, during the early part of the evening, the main-deck is generally filled with crowds of pedestrians, promenading up and down past the guns, like people taking the air in Broadway. At such times, it is curious to see the men nodding to each other's recognitions (they might not have seen each other for a week); exchanging a pleasant word with a friend; making a hurried appointment to meet him somewhere aloft on the morrow, or passing group after group without deigning the slightest salutation. Indeed, I was not at all singular in having but comparatively few acquaintances on board, though certainly carrying my fastidiousness to an unusual extent.

My friend Nord was a somewhat remarkable character; and if mystery includes romance, he certainly was a very romantic one. Before seeking an introduction to him through Lemsford, I had often marked his tall, spare, upright figure stalking like Don Quixote among the pigmies of the Afterguard, to which he belonged. At first I found him exceedingly reserved and taciturn; his saturnine brow wore a scowl; he was almost repelling in his demeanor. In a word, he seemed desirous of hinting, that his list of man-of-war friends was already made up, complete, and full; and there was no room for more. But observing that the only man he ever consorted with was Lemsford, I had too much magnanimity, by going off in a pique at his coldness, to let him lose forever the chance of making so capital an acquaintance as myself. Besides, I saw it in his eye, that the man had been a reader of good books; I would have staked my life on it, that he seized the right meaning of Montaigne. I saw that he was an earnest thinker; I more than suspected that he had been bolted in the mill of adversity. For all these things, my heart yearned toward him; I determined to know him.

At last I succeeded; it was during a profoundly quiet midnight watch, when I perceived him walking alone in the waist, while most of the men were dozing on the carronade-slides.

That night we scoured all the prairies of reading; dived into the bosoms of authors, and tore out their hearts; and that night White-Jacket learned more than he has ever done in any single night since.

The man was a marvel. He amazed me, as much as Coleridge did the troopers among whom he enlisted. What could have induced such a man to enter a man-of-war, all my sapience cannot fathom. And how he managed to preserve his dignity, as he did, among such a rabble rout was equally a mystery. For he was no sailor; as ignorant of a ship, indeed, as a man from the sources of the Niger. Yet the officers respected him; and the men were afraid of him. This much was observable, however, that he faithfully discharged whatever special duties devolved upon him; and was so fortunate as never to render himself liable to a reprimand. Doubtless, he took the same view of the thing that another of the crew did; and had early resolved, so to conduct himself as never to run the risk of the scourge. And this it must have been—added to whatever incommunicable grief which might have been his—that made this Nord such a wandering recluse, even among our man-of-war mob. Nor could he have long swung his hammock on board, ere he must have found that, to insure his exemption from that thing which alone affrighted him, he must be content for the most part to turn a man-hater, and socially expatriate himself from many things, which might have rendered his situation more tolerable. Still more, several events that took place must have horrified him, at times, with the thought that, however he might isolate and entomb himself, yet for all this, the improbability of his being overtaken by what he most dreaded never advanced to the infallibility of the impossible.

In my intercourse with Nord, he never made allusion to his past career—a subject upon which most high-bred castaways in a man-of-war are very diffuse; relating their adventures at the gaming-table; the recklessness with which they have run through the amplest fortunes in a single season; their alms-givings, and gratuities to porters and poor relations; and above all, their youthful indiscretions, and the broken-hearted ladies they have left behind. No such tales had Nord to tell. Concerning the past, he was barred and locked up like the specie vaults of the Bank of England. For anything that dropped from him, none of us could be sure that he had ever existed till now. Altogether, he was a remarkable man.

My other friend, Williams, was a thorough-going Yankee from Maine, who had been both a peddler and a pedagogue in his day. He had all manner of stories to tell about nice little country frolics, and would run over an endless list of his sweethearts. He was honest, acute, witty, full of mirth and good humor—a laughing philosopher. He was invaluable as a pill against the spleen; and, with the view of extending the advantages of his society to the saturnine Nord, I introduced them to each other; but Nord cut him dead the very same evening, when we sallied out from between the guns for a walk on the main-deck.

Chapter XIV

A Drought in a Man-of-War

We were not many days out of port, when a rumor was set afloat that dreadfully alarmed many tars. It was this: that, owing to some unprecedented oversight in the Purser, or some equally unprecedented remissness in the Naval-storekeeper at Callao, the frigate's supply of that delectable beverage, called "grog," was well-nigh expended.

In the American Navy, the law allows one gill of spirits per day to every seaman. In two portions, it is served out just previous to breakfast and dinner. At the roll of the drum, the sailors assemble round a large tub, or cask, filled with liquid; and, as their names are called off by a midshipman, they step up and regale themselves from a little tin measure called a "tot." No high-liver helping himself to Tokay off a well-polished sideboard, smacks his lips with more mighty satisfaction than the sailor does over this *tot*. To many of them, indeed, the thought of their daily *tots* forms a perpetual perspective of ravishing landscapes, indefinitely receding in the distance. It is their great "prospect in life." Take away their grog, and life possesses no further charms for them. It is hardly to be doubted, that the controlling inducement which keeps many men in the Navy, is the unbounded confidence they have in the ability of the United States government to supply them, regularly and unfailingly, with their daily allowance of this beverage. I have known several forlorn individuals, shipping as landsmen, who have confessed to me, that having contracted a love for ardent spirits, which they could not renounce, and having by their foolish courses been brought into the most abject poverty—insomuch that they could no longer gratify their thirst ashore—they incontinently entered the Navy; regarding it as the asylum for all drunkards, who might there prolong their lives by regular hours and exercise, and twice every day quench their thirst by moderate and undeviating doses.

When I once remonstrated with an old toper of a top-man about this daily dram-drinking; when I told him it was ruining him, and advised him to *stop his grog* and receive the money for it, in addition to his wages as provided by law, he turned about on me, with an irresistibly waggish look, and said, "Give up my grog? And why? Because it is ruining me? No, no; I am a good Christian, White-Jacket, and love my enemy too much to drop his acquaintance."

It may be readily imagined, therefore, what consternation and dismay pervaded the gun-deck at the first announcement of the tidings that the grog was expended.

"The grog gone!" roared an old Sheet-anchor-man.

"Oh! Lord! what a pain in my stomach!" cried a Main-top-man.

"It's worse than the cholera!" cried a man of the After-guard.

"I'd sooner the water-casks would give out!" said a Captain of the Hold.

"Are we ganders and geese, that we can live without grog?" asked a Corporal of Marines.

"Ay, we must now drink with the ducks!" cried a Quarter-master.

"Not a tot left?" groaned a Waister.

"Not a toothful!" sighed a Holder, from the bottom of his boots.

Yes, the fatal intelligence proved true. The drum was no longer heard rolling the men to the tub, and deep gloom and dejection fell like a cloud. The ship was like a great city, when some terrible calamity has overtaken it. The men stood apart, in groups, discussing their woes, and mutually condoling. No longer, of still moonlight nights, was the song heard from the giddy tops; and few and far between were the stories that were told.

It was during this interval, so dismal to many, that to the amazement of all hands, ten men were reported by the master-at-arms to be intoxicated. They were brought up to the mast, and at their appearance the doubts of the most skeptical were dissipated; but whence they had obtained their liquor no one could tell. It was observed, however at the time, that the tarry knaves all smelled of lavender, like so many dandies.

After their examination they were ordered into the "brig," a jail-house between two guns on the main-deck, where prisoners are kept. Here they laid for some time, stretched out stark and stiff, with their arms folded over their breasts, like so many effigies of the Black Prince on his monument in Canterbury Cathedral.

Their first slumbers over, the marine sentry who stood guard over them had as much as he could do to keep off the crowd, who were all eagerness to find out how, in such a time of want, the prisoners had managed to drink themselves into oblivion. In due time they were liberated, and the secret simultaneously leaked out.

It seemed that an enterprising man of their number, who had suffered severely from the common deprivation, had all at once been struck by a brilliant idea. It had come to his knowledge that the purser's steward was supplied with a large quantity of *Eau-de-Cologne,* clandestinely brought out in the ship, for the purpose of selling it on his own account, to the people of the coast; but the supply proving larger than the demand, and having no customers on board the frigate but Lieutenant Selvagee, he was now carrying home more than a third of his original stock. To make a short story of it, this functionary, being called upon in secret, was readily prevailed upon to part with a dozen bottles, with whose contents the intoxicated party had regaled themselves.

The news spread far and wide among the men, being only kept secret from the officers and underlings, and that night the long, crane-necked Cologne bottles jingled in out-of-the-way corners and by-places, and, being emptied, were sent flying out of the ports. With brown sugar, taken from the mess-chests, and hot water begged from the galley-cooks, the men made all manner of punches, toddies, and cocktails, letting fall therein a small drop of tar, like a bit of brown toast, by way of imparting a flavor. Of course, the thing was managed with the utmost secrecy; and as a whole dark night elapsed after their orgies, the revelers were, in a good measure, secure from detection; and those who indulged too freely had twelve long hours to get sober before daylight obtruded.

Next day, fore and aft, the whole frigate smelled like a lady's toilet; the very tar-buckets were fragrant; and from the mouth of many a grim, grizzled old quarter-gunner came the most fragrant of breaths. The amazed Lieutenants went about snuffing up the gale; and, for once. Selvagee had no further need to flourish his perfumed handkerchief. It was as if we were sailing by some odoriferous shore, in the vernal season of violets. Sabæan odors!

For many a league,
Cheered with grateful smell, old Ocean smiled.

But, alas! all this perfume could not be wasted for nothing; and the masters-at-arms and ship's corporals, putting this and that together, very soon burrowed into the secret. The purser's steward was called to account, and no more lavender punches and Cologne toddies were drank on board the *Neversink*.

Chapter XV

A Salt-Junk Club in a Man-of-War, with a Notice to Quit

IT WAS ABOUT THE PERIOD OF THE COLOGNE-WATER EXCITEMENT THAT MY SELF-CONCEIT WAS NOT a little wounded, and my sense of delicacy altogether shocked, by a polite hint received from the cook of the mess to which I happened to belong. To understand the matter, it is needful to enter into preliminaries.

The common seamen in a large frigate are divided into some thirty or forty messes, put down on the purser's books as *Mess* No. 1, *Mess* No. 2, *Mess* No. 3, etc. The members of each mess-club, their rations of provisions, and breakfast, dine, and sup together in allotted intervals between the guns on the main-deck. In undeviating rotation, the members of each mess (excepting the petty-officers) take their turn in performing the functions of cook and steward. And for the time being, all the affairs of the club are subject to their inspection and control.

It is the cook's business, also, to have an eye to the general interests of his mess; to see that, when the aggregated allowances of beef, bread, etc., are served out by one of the master's mates, the mess over which he presides receives its full share, without stint or subtraction. Upon the berth-deck he has a chest, in which to keep his pots, pans, spoons, and small stores of sugar, molasses, tea, and flour.

But though entitled a cook, strictly speaking, the head of the mess is no cook at all; for the cooking for the crew is all done by a high and mighty functionary, officially called the *"ship's cook,"* assisted by several deputies. In our frigate, this personage was a dignified colored gentleman, whom the men dubbed *"Old Coffee"*; and his assistants, negroes also, went by the poetical appellations of *"Sunshine," "Rose-water,"* and *"May-day."*

Now the *ship's cooking* required very little science, though Old Coffee often assured us that he had graduated at the New York Astor House, under the immediate eye of the celebrated Coleman and Stetson. All he had to do was, in the first place, to keep bright and clean the three huge coppers, or caldrons, in which many hundred pounds of beef were daily boiled. To this end, Rose-water, Sunshine, and May-day every morning sprang into their respective apartments, stripped to the waist, and well provided with bits of soap-stone and sand. By exercising these in a very vigorous manner, they threw themselves into a violent perspiration, and put a fine polish upon the interior of the coppers.

Sunshine was the bard of the trio; and while all three would be busily employed clattering their soap-stones against the metal, he would exhilarate them with some remarkable St. Domingo melodies; one of which was the following:

Oh! I los' my shoe in an old canoe,
Johnio! come Winum so!
Oh! I los' my boot in a pilot-boat,
Johnio! come Winum so!
Den rub-a-dub de copper, oh!
Oh! copper rub-a-dub-a-oh!

When I listened to these jolly Africans, thus making gleeful their toil by their cheering songs, I could not help murmuring against that immemorial rule of men-of-war, which forbids the sailors to sing out, as in merchant-vessels, when pulling ropes, or occupied at any other ship's duty. Your only music, at such times, is the shrill pipe of the boatswain's mate, which is almost worse than no music at all. And if the boatswain's mate is not by, you must pull the ropes, like convicts, in profound silence; or else endeavor to impart unity to the exertions of all hands, by singing out mechanically, *one, two, three,* and then pulling all together.

Now, when Sunshine, Rose-water, and May-day have so polished the ship's coppers, that a white kid glove might be drawn along the inside and show no stain, they leap out of their holes, and the water is poured in for the coffee. And the coffee being boiled, and decanted off in bucketfuls, the cooks of the messes march up with their salt beef for dinner, strung upon strings and tallied with labels; all of which are plunged together into the self-same coppers, and there boiled. When, upon the beef being fished out with a huge pitch-fork, the water for the evening's tea is poured in; which, consequently possesses a flavor not unlike that of shank-soup.

From this it will be seen, that, so far as cooking is concerned, a "*cook of the mess*" has very little to do; merely carrying his provisions to and from the grand democratic cookery. Still, in some things, his office involves many annoyances. Twice a week butter and cheese are served out—so much to each man—and the mess-cook has the sole charge of these delicacies. The great difficulty consists in so catering for the mess, touching these luxuries, as to satisfy all. Some guzzlers are for devouring the butter at a meal, and finishing off with the cheese the same day; others contend for saving it up against *Banyan Day,* when there is nothing but beef and bread; and others, again, are for taking a very small bit of butter and cheese, by way of dessert, to each and every meal through the week. All this gives rise to endless disputes, debates, and altercations.

Sometimes, with his mess-cloth—a square of painted canvas—set out on deck between the guns, garnished with pots, and pans, and *kids,* you see the mess-cook seated on a matchtub at its head, his trouser legs rolled up and arms bared, presiding over the convivial party.

"Now, men, you can't have any butter to-day. I'm saving it up for to-morrow. You don't know the value of butter, men. You, Jim, take your hoof off the cloth! Devil take me, if some of you chaps haven't no more manners than so many swines! Quick, men, quick; bear a hand, and *'scoff'* (eat) away.—I've got my to-morrow's *duff* to make yet, and some of you fellows keep *scoffing* as if I had nothing to do but sit still here on this here tub here, and look on. There, there, men, you've all had enough: so sail away out of this, and let me clear up the wreck."

In this strain would one of the periodical cooks of mess No. 15 talk to us. He was a tall, resolute fellow, who had once been a brakeman on a railroad, and he kept us all pretty straight; from his fiat there was no appeal.

But it was not thus when the turn came to others among us. Then it was *look out for squalls.* The business of dining became a bore, and digestion was seriously impaired by the unamiable discourse we had over our *salt horse.*

I sometimes thought that the junks of lean pork—which were boiled in their own bristles, and looked gaunt and grim, like pickled chins of half-famished, unwashed Cossacks—had something to do with creating the bristling bitterness at times prevailing in our mess. The men tore off the tough hide from their pork, as if they were Indians scalping Christians.

Some cursed the cook for a rogue, who kept from us our butter and cheese, in order to make away with it himself in an underhand manner; selling it at a premium to other messes, and thus accumulating a princely fortune at our expense. Others anthematized him for his slovenliness, casting hypercritical glances into their pots and pans, and scraping them with their knives. Then he would be railed at for his miserable "duffs," and other shortcoming preparations.

Marking all this from the beginning, I, White-Jacket, was sorely troubled with the idea, that, in the course of time, my own turn would come round to undergo the same objurgations. How to escape, I knew not. However, when the dreaded period arrived, I received the keys of office (the keys of the mess-chest) with a resigned temper, and offered up a devout ejaculation for fortitude under the trial. I resolved, please Heaven, to approve myself an unexceptionable caterer, and the most impartial of stewards.

The first day there was "*duff*" to make—a business which devolved upon the mess-cooks, though the boiling of it pertained to Old Coffee and his deputies. I made up my mind to lay myself out on that *duff*; to center all my energies upon it; to put the very soul of art into it, and achieve an unrivalled *duff*—a *duff* that should put out of conceit all other *duffs*, and forever make my administration memorable.

From the proper functionary the flour was obtained, and the raisins; the beef-fat, or "*slush*," from Old Coffee; and the requisite supply of water from the scuttle-butt. I then went among the various cooks, to compare their receipts for making "duffs:" and having well weighed them all, and gathered from each a choice item to make an original receipt of my own, with due deliberation and solemnity I proceeded to business. Placing the component parts in a tin pan, I kneaded them together for an hour, entirely reckless as to pulmonary considerations, touching the ruinous expenditure of breath; and having decanted the semi-liquid dough into a canvas bag, secured the muzzle, tied on the tally, and delivered it to Rose-water, who dropped the precious bag into the coppers, along with a score or two of others.

Eight bells had struck. The boatswain and his mates had piped the hands to dinner; my mess-cloth was set out, and my messmates were assembled, knife in hand, all ready to precipitate themselves upon the devoted *duff*: Waiting at the grand cookery till my turn came, I received the bag of pudding, and gallanting it into the mess, proceeded to loosen the string.

It was an anxious, I may say, a fearful moment. My hands trembled; every eye was upon me; my reputation and credit were at stake. Slowly I undressed the *duff*, dandling it upon my knee, much as a nurse does a baby about bed-time. The excitement increased, as I curled down the bag from the pudding; it became intense, when at last I plumped it into the pan, held up to receive it by an eager hand. Bim! it fell like a man shot down in a riot. Distraction! It was harder than a sinner's heart; yea, tough as the cock that crowed on the morn that Peter told a lie.

"Gentlemen of the mess, for heaven's sake! permit me one word. I have done my duty by that duff—I have—"

But they beat down my excuses with a storm of criminations. One present proposed that the fatal pudding should be tied round my neck, like a mill-stone, and myself pushed overboard. No use, no use; I had failed; ever after, that duff lay heavy at my stomach and my heart.

After this, I grew desperate; despised popularity; returned scorn for scorn; till at length my week expired, and in the duff-bag I transferred the keys of office to the next man on the roll.

Somehow, there had never been a very cordial feeling between this mess and me; all along they had nourished a prejudice against my white jacket. They must have harbored the silly fancy that in it I gave myself airs, and wore it in order to look consequential; perhaps, as a cloak to cover pilferings of tit-bits from the mess. But to out with the plain truth, they themselves were not a very irreproachable set. Considering the sequel I am coming to, this avowal may be deemed sheer malice; but for all that, I cannot avoid speaking my mind.

After my week of office, the mess gradually changed their behavior to me; they cut me to the heart; they became cold and reserved; seldom or never addressed me at meal-times without invidious allusions to my *duff*, and also to my jacket, and its dripping in wet weather upon the mess-cloth. However, I had no idea that anything serious, on their part, was brewing; but alas! so it turned out.

We were assembled at supper one evening when I noticed certain winks and silent hints tipped to the cook, who presided. He was a little, oily fellow, who had once kept an oyster-cellar ashore; he bore me a grudge. Looking down on the mess-cloth, he observed that some fellows never knew when their room was better than their company. This being a maxim of indiscriminate application, of course I silently assented to it, as any other reasonable man would have done. But this remark was followed up by another, to the effect that, not only did some fellows never know when their room was better than their company, but they persisted in staying when their company wasn't wanted; and by so doing disturbed the serenity of society at large. But this, also, was a general observation that could not be gainsaid. A long and ominous pause ensued; during which I perceived every eye upon me, and my white jacket; while the cook went on to enlarge upon the disagreeableness of a perpetually damp garment in the mess, especially when that garment was white. This was coming nearer home.

Yes, they were going to black-ball me; but I resolved to sit it out a little longer; never dreaming that my moralist would proceed to extremities, while all hands were present. But bethinking him that by going this roundabout way he would never get at his object, he went off on another tack; apprising me, in substance, that he was instructed by the whole mess, then and there assembled, to give me warning to seek out another club, as they did not longer fancy the society either of myself or my jacket.

I was shocked. Such a want of tact and delicacy! Common propriety suggested that a point-blank intimation of that nature should be conveyed in a private interview; or, still better, by note. I immediately rose, tucked my jacket about me, bowed, and departed.

And now, to do myself justice, I must add that, the next day, I was received with open arms by a glorious set of fellows—Mess No. 1!—numbering, among the rest, my noble Captain Jack Chase.

This mess was principally composed of the headmost men of the gun-deck; and, out of a pardonable self-conceit, they called themselves the *"Forty-two-pounder Club"*; meaning that they were, one and all, fellows of large intellectual and corporeal caliber. Their mess-cloth was well located. On their starboard hand was Mess No. 2, embracing sundry rare jokers and high livers, who waxed gay and epicurean over their salt fare, and were known as the *"Society for the Destruction of Beef and Pork."* On the larboard hand was Mess No. 31, made up entirely of fore-top-men, a dashing, blaze-away set of men-of-war's-men, who called themselves the *"Cape Horn Snorters and Neversink Invincibles."* Opposite, was one of the marine messes, mustering the aristocracy of the marine corps—the two corporals, the drummer and fifer, and some six or eight rather gentlemanly privates, native-born Americans, who had served in the Seminole campaigns of Florida; and they now enlivened their salt fare with stories of wild ambushes in the Everglades; and one of them related a surprising tale of his hand-to-hand encounter with Osceola, the Indian chief, whom he fought one morning from daybreak till breakfast time. This slashing private also boasted that he could take a chip from between your teeth at twenty paces; he offered to bet any amount on it; and as he could get no one to hold the chip, his boast remained forever good.

Besides many other attractions which the *Forty-two-pounder Club* furnished, it had this one special advantage, that, owing to there being so many *petty officers* in it, all the members of the mess were exempt from doing duty as cooks and stewards. A fellow called *a steady-cook,* attended to that business during the entire cruise. He was a long, lank, pallid varlet, going by the name of Shanks. In very warm weather this Shanks would sit at the foot of the mess-cloth, fanning himself with the front flap of his frock or shirt, which he inelegantly wore over his trousers. Jack Chase, the President of the Club, frequently remonstrated against this breach of good manners; but the *steady-cook* had somehow contracted the habit, and it proved incurable. For a time, Jack Chase, out of a polite nervousness touching myself, as a newly-elected member of the club, would frequently endeavor to excuse to me the vulgarity of Shanks. One day he wound up his remarks by the philosophic reflection—"But White-Jacket, my dear fellow, what can you expect of him? Our real misfortune is, that our noble club should be obliged to dine with its cook."

There were several of these *steady-cooks* on board; men of no mark or consideration whatever in the ship; lost to all noble promptings; sighing for no worlds to conquer, and perfectly contented with mixing their *duffs*, and spreading their mess-cloths, and mustering their pots and pans together three times every day for a three years' cruise. They were very seldom to be seen on the spar-deck, but kept below out of sight.

Chapter XVI

General Training in a Man-of-War

To a quiet, contemplative character, averse to uproar, undue exercise of his bodily members, and all kind of useless confusion, nothing can be more distressing than a proceeding in all men-of-war called *"general quarters."* And well may it be so called, since it amounts to a general drawing and quartering of all the parties concerned.

As the specific object for which a man-of-war is built and put into commission is to fight and fire off cannon, it is, of course, deemed indispensable that the crew should be duly instructed in the art and mystery involved. Hence these "general quarters," which is a mustering of all hands to their stations at the guns on the several decks, and a sort of sham-fight with an imaginary foe.

The summons is given by the ship's drummer, who strikes a peculiar beat—short, broken, rolling, shuffling—like the sound made by the march into battle of iron-heeled grenadiers. It is a regular tune, with a fine song composed to it; the words of the chorus, being most artistically arranged, may give some idea of the air:

Hearts of oak are our ships, jolly tars are our men,
We always are ready, steady, boys, steady,
To fight and to conquer, again and again.

In warm weather this pastime at the guns is exceedingly unpleasant, to say the least, and throws a quiet man into a violent passion and perspiration. For one, I ever abominated it.

I have a heart like Julius Cæsar, and upon occasions would fight like Caius Marcius Coriolanus. If my beloved and forever glorious country should be ever in jeopardy from invaders, let Congress put me on a war-horse, in the van-guard, and *then* see how I will acquit myself. But to toil and sweat in a fictitious encounter; to squander the precious breath of my precious body in a ridiculous fight of shams and pretensions; to hurry about the decks, pretending to carry the killed and wounded below; to be told that I must consider the ship blowing up, in order to exercise myself in presence of mind, and prepare for a real explosion; all this I despise, as beneath a true tar and man of valor.

These were my sentiments at the time, and these remain my sentiments still; but as, while on board the frigate, my liberty of thought did not extend to liberty of expression, I was obliged to keep these sentiments to myself; though, indeed, I had some thoughts of addressing a letter, marked *Private and Confidential,* to his Honor the Commodore, on the subject.

My station at the batteries was at one of the thirty-two-pound carronades, on the starboard side of the quarter-deck.[1]

I did not fancy this station at all; for it is well known on shipboard that, in time of action, the quarter-deck is one of the most dangerous posts of a man-of-war. The reason is, that the officers of the highest rank are there stationed; and the enemy have an ungentlemanly way of target-shooting at their buttons. If we should chance to engage a ship, then, who could tell but some bungling small-arm marks-man in the enemy's tops might put a bullet through *me* instead of the Commodore? If they hit *him,* no doubt he would not feel it much, for he was used to that sort of thing, and, indeed, had a bullet in him already. Whereas, *I* was altogether unaccustomed to having blue pills playing round my head in such an indiscriminate way. Besides, ours was a flag-ship; and everyone knows what a peculiarly dangerous predicament the quarter-deck of Nelson's flag-ship was in at the battle of Trafalgar; how the lofty tops of the enemy were full of soldiers, peppering away at the English Admiral and his officers. Many a poor sailor, at the guns of that quarter-deck, must have received a bullet intended for some wearer of an epaulet.

By candidly confessing my feelings on this subject, I do by no means invalidate my claims to being held a man of prodigious valor. I merely state my invincible repugnance to being shot for somebody else. If I am shot, be it with the express understanding in the shooter that I am the identical person intended so to be served. That Thracian who, with his compliments, sent an arrow into the King of Macedon, superscribed "*for Philip's right eye,*" set a fine example to all warriors. The hurried, hasty, indiscriminate, reckless, abandoned manner in which both sailors and soldiers nowadays fight is really painful to any serious-minded, methodical old gentleman, especially if he chance to have systematized his mind as an accountant. There is little or no skill and bravery about it. Two parties, armed with lead and old iron, envelop themselves in a cloud of smoke, and pitch their lead and old iron about in all directions. If you happen to be in the way, you are hit; possibly, killed; if not, you escape. In sea-actions, if by good or bad luck, as the case may be, a round shot, fired at random through the smoke, happens to send overboard your fore-mast, another to unship your rudder, there you lie crippled, pretty much at the mercy of your foe: who, accordingly, pronounces himself victor, though that honor properly belongs to the Law of Gravitation operating on the enemy's balls in the smoke. Instead of tossing this old lead and iron into the air, therefore, it would be much better amicably to toss up a copper and let heads win.

The carronade at which I was stationed was known as "Gun No. 5," on the First Lieutenant's

1. For the benefit of a Quaker reader here and there, a word or two in explanation of a carronade may not be amiss. The carronade is a gun comparatively short and light for its caliber. A carronade throwing a thirty-two-pound shot weighs considerably less than a long-gun only throwing a twenty-four-pound shot. It further differs from a long-gun, in working with a joint and bolt underneath, instead of the short arms or *trunnions* at the sides. Its *carriage,* likewise, is quite different from that of a long-gun, having a sort of sliding apparatus, something like an extension dining-table; the goose on it, however, is a tough one, and villaniously stuffed with most indigestible dumplings. Point-blank, the range of a carronade does not exceed one hundred and fifty yards, much less than the range of a long-gun. When of large caliber, however, it throws within that limit, Paixhan shot, all manner of shells and combustibles, with great effect, being a very destructive engine at close quarters. This piece is now very generally found mounted in the batteries of the English and American navies. The quarter-deck armaments of most modern frigates wholly consist of carronades. The name is derived from the village of Carron, in Scotland, at whose celebrated foundries this iron Attila was first cast.

quarter-bill. Among our gun's crew, however, it was known as *Black Bet*. This name was bestowed by the captain of the gun—a fine negro—in honor of his sweetheart, a colored lady of Philadelphia. Of Black Bet I was rammer-and-sponger; and ram and sponge I did, like a good fellow. I have no doubt that, had I and my gun been at the battle of the Nile, we would mutually have immortalized ourselves; the ramming-pole would have been hung up in Westminster Abbey; and I, ennobled by the king, besides receiving the illustrious honor of an autograph letter from his majesty through the perfumed right hand of his private secretary.

But it was terrible work to help run in and out of the porthole that amazing mass of metal, especially as the thing must be done in a trice. Then, at the summons of a horrid, rasping rattle, swayed by the Captain in person, we were made to rush from our guns, seize pikes and pistols, and repel an imaginary army of boarders, who, by a fiction of the officers, were supposed to be assailing all sides of the ship at once. After cutting and slashing at them a while, we jumped back to our guns, and again went to jerking our elbows.

Meantime, a loud cry is heard of "Fire! fire! fire!" in the fore-top; and a regular engine, worked by a set of Bowery-boy tars, is forthwith set to playing streams of water aloft. And now it is "Fire! fire! fire!" on the main-deck; and the entire ship is in as great a commotion as if a whole city ward were in a blaze.

Are our officers of the Navy utterly unacquainted with the laws of good health? Do they not know that this violent exercise, taking place just after a hearty dinner, as it generally does, is eminently calculated to breed the dyspepsia? There was no satisfaction in dining; the flavor of every mouthful was destroyed by the thought that the next moment the cannonading drum might be beating to quarters.

Such a sea-martinet was our Captain, that sometimes we were roused from our hammocks at night; when a scene would ensue that it is not in the power of pen and ink to describe. Five hundred men spring to their feet, dress themselves, take up their bedding, and run to the nettings and stow it; then he to their stations—each man jostling his neighbor—some alow, some aloft; some this way, some that; and in less than five minutes the frigate is ready for action, and still as the grave; almost every man precisely where he would be were an enemy actually about to be engaged. The Gunner, like a Cornwall miner in a cave, is burrowing down in the magazine under the Ward-room, which is lighted by battle-lanterns, placed behind glazed glass bull's-eyes inserted in the bulkhead. The *Powder-monkeys*, or boys, who fetch and carry cartridges, are scampering to and fro among the guns; and the *first and second loaders* stand ready to receive their supplies.

These *Powder-monkeys*, as they are called, enact a curious part in time of action. The entrance to the magazine on the berth-deck, where they procure their food for the guns, is guarded by a woolen screen; and a gunner's mate, standing behind it, thrusts out the cartridges through a small arm-hole in this screen. The enemy's shot (perhaps red hot) are flying in all directions; and to protect their cartridges, the powder-monkeys hurriedly wrap them up in their jackets; and with all haste scramble up the ladders to their respective guns, like eating-house waiters hurrying along with hot cakes for breakfast.

At *general quarters* the shot-boxes are uncovered; showing the grape-shot—aptly so called, for they precisely resemble bunches of the fruit; though, to receive a bunch of iron grapes in the abdomen would be but a sorry dessert; and also showing the canister-shot—old iron of various sorts, packed in a tin case, like a tea-caddy.

Imagine some midnight craft sailing down on her enemy thus; twenty-four pounders leveled, matches lighted, and each captain of his gun at his post!

But if verily going into action, then would the *Neversink* have made still further preparations; for however alike in some things, there is always a vast difference—if you sound them—between a reality and a sham. Not to speak of the pale sternness of the men at their guns at such a juncture, and the choked thoughts at their hearts, the ship itself would here and there present a far different appearance. Something like that of an extensive mansion preparing for a grand entertainment, when folding-doors are withdrawn, chambers converted into drawing-rooms, and every inch of available space thrown into one continuous whole. For previous to an action, every bulkhead in a man-of-war is knocked down; great guns are run out of the Commodore's parlor windows; nothing separates the ward-room officers' quarters from those of the men, but an ensign used for a curtain. The sailors' mess-chests are tumbled down into the hold; and the hospital cots—of which all men-of-war carry a large supply—are dragged forth from the sail-room, and piled near at hand to receive the wounded; amputation-tables are ranged in the *cock-pit* or in the *tiers,* whereon to carve the bodies of the maimed. The yards are slung in chains; fire-screens distributed here and there: hillocks of cannon-balls piled between the guns; shot-plugs suspended within easy reach from the beams; and solid masses of wads, big as Dutch cheeses, braced to the cheeks of the gun-carriages.

No small difference, also, would be visible in the wardrobe of both officers and men. The officers generally fight as dandies dance, namely, in silk stockings; inasmuch as, in case of being wounded in the leg, the silk-hose can be more easily drawn off by the Surgeon; cotton sticks, and works into the wound. An economical captain, while taking care to case his legs in silk, might yet see fit to save his best suit, and fight in his old clothes. For, besides that an old garment might much better be cut to pieces than a new one, it must be a mighty disagreeable thing to die in a stiff, tight-breasted coat, not yet worked easy under the arm-pits. At such times, a man should feel free, unencumbered, and perfectly at his ease in point of straps and suspenders. No ill-will concerning his tailor should intrude upon his thoughts of eternity. Seneca understood this, when he chose to die naked in a bath. And men-of-war's men understand it, also; for most of them, in battle, strip to the waist-bands; wearing nothing but a pair of duck trousers, and a handkerchief round their head.

A captain combining a heedful patriotism with economy would probably "bend" his old topsails before going into battle, instead of exposing his best canvas to be riddled to pieces; for it is generally the case that the enemy's shot flies high. Unless allowance is made for it in pointing the tube, at long-gun distance, the slightest roll of the ship, at the time of firing, would send a shot, meant for the hull, high over the top-gallant yards.

But besides these differences between a sham-fight at *general quarters* and a real cannonading, the aspect of the ship, at the beating of the retreat, would, in the latter case, be very dissimilar to the neatness and uniformity in the former.

Then our bulwarks might look like the walls of the houses in West Broadway in New York, after being broken into and burned out by the Negro Mob. Our stout masts and yards might be lying about decks, like tree boughs after a tornado in a piece of woodland; our dangling ropes, cut and sundered in all directions, would be bleeding tar at every yard; and strew with jagged splinters from our wounded planks, the gun-deck might resemble a carpenter's shop. *Then,* when all was over, and all hands would be piped to take down the hammocks from the exposed nettings (where they play the part of the cotton bales at New Orleans), we might find bits of broken shot, iron bolts and bullets in our blankets. And, while smeared with blood like butchers, the surgeon and his mates would be amputating arms and legs on the berth-deck, an underling of the carpenter's gang would be new-legging and arming the broken chairs and tables in the Commodore's cabin; while the rest of his *squad* would be *splicing* and *fishing* the shattered masts and yards. The scupper-holes having discharged the last rivulet of blood, the decks would be washed down; and the galley-cooks would be going fore and aft, sprinkling them with hot vinegar, to take out the shambles' smell from the planks; which, unless some such means are employed, often create a highly offensive effluvia for weeks after a fight.

Then, upon mustering the men, and calling the quarter-bills by the light of a battle-lantern, many a wounded seaman with his arm in a sling, would answer for some poor shipmate who could never more make answer for himself:

"Tom Brown?"

"Killed, sir."

"Jack Jewel?"

"Killed, sir."

"Joe Hardy?"

"Killed, sir."

And opposite all these poor fellows' names, down would go on the quarter-bills the bloody marks of red ink—a murderer's fluid, fitly used on these occasions.

Chapter XVII

AWAY! SECOND, THIRD, AND FOURTH CUTTERS, AWAY!

IT WAS THE MORNING SUCCEEDING ONE OF THESE *GENERAL QUARTERS* THAT WE PICKED UP A LIFE-buoy, descried floating by.

It was a circular mass of cork, about eight inches thick and four feet in diameter, covered with tarred canvas. All round its circumference there trailed a number of knotted ropes'-ends, terminating in fanciful Turks' heads. These were the life-lines, for the drowning to clutch. Inserted into the middle of the cork was an upright, carved pole, somewhat shorter than a pike-staff. The whole buoy was embossed with barnacles, and its sides festooned with sea-weeds. Dolphins were sporting and flashing around it, and one white bird was hovering over the top of the pole. Long ago, this thing must have been thrown over-board to save some poor wretch, who must have been drowned; while even the life-buoy itself had drifted away out of sight.

The forecastle-men fished it up from the bows, and the seamen thronged round it.

"Bad luck! bad luck!" cried the Captain of the Head; "we'll number one less before long."

The ship's cooper strolled by; he, to whose department it belongs to see that the ship's life-buoys are kept in good order.

In men-of-war, night and day, week in and week out, two life-buoys are kept depending from the stern; and two men, with hatchets in their hands, pace up and down, ready at the first cry to cut the cord and drop the buoys overboard. Every two hours they are regularly relieved, like sentinels on guard. No similar precautions are adopted in the merchant or whaling service.

Thus deeply solicitous to preserve human life are the regulations of men-of-war; and seldom has there been a better illustration of this solicitude than at the battle of Trafalgar, when, after "several thousand" French seamen had been destroyed, according to Lord Collingwood, and, by the official returns, sixteen hundred and ninety Englishmen were killed or wounded, the Captains of the surviving ships ordered the life-buoy sentries from their death-dealing guns to their vigilant posts, as officers of the Humane Society.

"There, Bungs!" cried Scrimmage, a sheet-anchor-man,[1] "there's a good pattern for you; make us a brace of life-buoys like that; something that will save a man, and not fill and sink under him, as those leaky quarter-casks of yours will the first time there's occasion to drop 'em. I came near pitching off the bowsprit the other day; and, when I scrambled inboard again, I went aft to get a squint at 'em. Why, Bungs, they are all open between the staves. Shame on you! Suppose you your-

1. In addition to the *Bower-anchors* carried on her bows, a frigate carries large anchors in her fore-chains, called *Sheet-anchors.* Hence, the old seamen stationed in that part of a man-of-war are called *sheet-anchor-men.*

self should fall over-board, and find yourself going down with buoys under you of your own making—what then?"

"I never go aloft, and don't intend to fall overboard," replied Bungs.

"Don't believe it!" cried the sheet-anchor-man; "you lopers that live about the decks here are nearer the bottom of the sea than the light hand that looses the main-royal. Mind your eye, Bungs—mind your eye!"

"I will," retorted Bungs; "and you mind yours!"

Next day, just at dawn, I was startled from my hammock by the cry of *"All hands about ship and shorten sail!"* Springing up the ladders, I found that an unknown man had fallen overboard from the chains; and darting a glance toward the poop, perceived, from their gestures, that the life-sentries there had cut away the buoys.

It was blowing a fresh breeze; the frigate was going fast through the water. But the one thousand arms of five hundred men soon tossed her about on the other tack, and checked her further headway.

"Do you see him?" shouted the officer of the watch through his trumpet, hailing the main-mast-head. "Man or *buoy,* do you see either?"

"See nothing, sir," was the reply.

"Clear away the cutters!" was the next order. "Bugler! call away the second, third, and fourth cutters' crews. Hands by the tackles!"

In less than three minutes the three boats were down. More hands were wanted in one of them, and, among others, I jumped in to make up the deficiency.

"Now, men, give way! and each man look out along his oar, and look sharp!" cried the officer of our boat. For a time, in perfect silence, we slid up and down the great seething swells of the sea, but saw nothing.

"There, it's no use," cried the officer; "he's gone, whoever he is. Pull away, men—pull away! they'll be recalling us soon."

"Let him drown!" cried the strokesman; "he's spoiled my watch below for me."

"Who the devil is he?" cried another.

"He's one who'll never have a coffin!" replied a third.

"No, no! they'll never sing out, *'All hands bury the dead!'* for him, my hearties!" cried a fourth.

"Silence," said the officer, "and look along your oars." But the sixteen oarsmen still continued their talk; and, after pulling about for two or three hours, we spied the recall-signal at the frigate's fore-t'-gallant-mast-head, and returned on board, having seen no sign even of the life-buoys.

The boats were hoisted up, the yards braced forward, and away we bowled—one man less.

"Muster all hands!" was now the order; when, upon calling the roll, the cooper was the only man missing.

"I told you so, men," cried the Captain of the Head; "I said we would lose a man before long."

"Bungs, is it?" cried Scrimmage, the sheet-anchor-man; "I told him his buoys wouldn't save a drowning man; and now he has proved it!"

Chapter XVIII

A MAN-OF-WAR FULL AS A NUT

IT WAS NECESSARY TO SUPPLY THE LOST COOPER'S PLACE; ACCORDINGLY, WORD WAS PASSED FOR all who belonged to that calling to muster at the main-mast, in order that one of them might be selected. Thirteen men obeyed the summons—a circumstance illustrative of the fact that many good handicrafts-men are lost to their trades and the world by serving in men-of-war. Indeed, from a frigate's crew might be culled out men of all callings and vocations, from a backslidden parson to a broken-down comedian. The Navy is the asylum for the perverse, the home of the unfortunate. Here the sons of adversity meet the children of calamity, and here the children of calamity meet the offspring of sin. Bankrupt brokers, boot-blacks, blacklegs, and blacksmiths here assemble together; and castaway tinkers, watch-makers, quill-drivers, cobblers, doctors, farmers, and lawyers compare past experiences and talk of old times. Wrecked on a desert shore, a man-of-war's crew could quickly found an Alexandria by themselves, and fill it with all the things which go to make up a capital.

Frequently, at one and the same time, you see every trade in operation on the gun-deck—coopering, carpentering, tailoring, tinkering, blacksmithing, rope-making, preaching, gambling, and fortune-telling.

In truth, a man-of-war is a city afloat, with long avenues set out with guns instead of trees, and numerous shady lanes, courts, and by-ways. The quarter-deck is a grand square, park, or parade ground, with a great Pittsfield elm, in the shape of the main-mast, at one end, and fronted at the other by the palace of the Commodore's cabin.

Or, rather, a man-of-war is a lofty, walled, and garrisoned town, like Quebec, where the thoroughfares and mostly ramparts, and peaceable citizens meet armed sentries at every corner.

Or it is like the lodging-houses in Paris, turned upside down; the first floor, or deck, being rented by a lord; the second, by a select club of gentlemen; the third, by crowds of artisans; and the fourth, by a whole rabble of common people.

For even thus is it in a frigate, where the commander has a whole cabin to himself and the spar-deck, the lieutenants their ward-room underneath, and the mass of sailors swing their hammocks under all.

And with its long rows of port-hole casements, each revealing the muzzle of a cannon, a man-of-war resembles a three-story house in a suspicions part of the town, with a basement of indefinite depth, and ugly-looking fellows gazing out at the windows.

Chapter XIX

THE JACKET ALOFT

AGAIN MUST I CALL ATTENTION TO MY WHITE JACKET, WHICH, ABOUT THIS TIME CAME NEAR being the death of me.

I am of a meditative humor, and at sea used often to mount aloft at night, and seating myself on one of the upper yards, tuck my jacket about me and give loose to reflection. In some ships in which I have done this, the sailors used to fancy that I must be studying astronomy—which, indeed, to some extent, was the case—and that my object in mounting aloft was to get a nearer view of the stars, supposing me, of course, to be short-sighted. A very silly conceit of theirs, some may say, but not so silly after all; for surely the advantage of getting nearer an object by two hundred feet is not to be underrated. Then, to study the stars upon the wide, boundless sea, is divine as it was to the Chaldean Magi, who observed their revolutions from the plains.

And it is a very fine feeling, and one that fuses us into the universe of things, and makes us a part of the All, to think that, wherever we ocean-wanderers rove, we have still the same glorious old stars to keep us company; that they still shine onward and on, forever beautiful and bright, and luring us, by every ray, to die and be glorified with them.

Ay, ay! we sailors sail not in vain. We expatriate ourselves to nationalize with the universe; and in all our voyages round the world, we are still accompanied by those old circumnavigators, the stars, who are shipmates and fellow-sailors of ours—sailing in heaven's blue, as we on the azure main. Let genteel generations scoff at our hardened hands, and finger-nails tipped with tar—did they ever clasp truer palms than ours? Let them feel of our sturdy hearts, beating like sledge-hammers in those hot smithies, our bosoms; with their amber-headed canes, let them feel of our generous pulses, and swear that they go off like thirty-two-pounders.

Oh, give me again the rover's life—the joy, the thrill, the whirl! Let me feel thee again, old sea! let me leap into thy saddle once more. I am sick of these terra firma toils and cares; sick of the dust and reek of towns. Let me hear the clatter of hail-stones on icebergs, and not the dull tramp of these plodders, plodding their dull way from their cradles to their graves. Let me snuff thee up, sea-breeze! and whinny in thy spray. Forbid it, sea-gods! intercede for me with Neptune, O sweet Amphitrite, that no dull clod may fall on my coffin! Be mine the tomb that swallowed up Pharaoh and all his hosts; let me lie down with Drake, where he sleeps in the sea.

But when White-Jacket speaks of the rover's life, he means not life in a man-of-war, which, with its martial formalities and thousand vices, stabs to the heart the soul of all free-and-easy honorable rovers.

I have said that I was wont to mount up aloft and muse; and thus was it with me the night following the loss of the cooper. Ere my watch in the top had expired, high up on the main-royal-yard I reclined, the white jacket folded around me like Sir John Moore in his frosted cloak.

Eight bells had struck, and my watchmates had hied to their hammocks, and the other watch had gone to their stations, and the *top* below me was full of strangers, and still one hundred feet above even *them* I lay entranced; now dozing, now dreaming; now thinking of things past, and anon of the life to come. Well-timed was the latter thought, for the life to come was much nearer overtaking me than I then could imagine. Perhaps I was half conscious at last of a tremulous voice hailing the main-royal-yard from the *top*. But if so, the consciousness glided away from me, and left me in Lethe. But when, like lightning, the yard dropped under me, and instinctively I clung with both hands to the "*tie*," then I came to myself with a rush, and felt something like a choking hand at my throat. For an instant I thought the Gulf Stream in my head was whirling me away to eternity; but the next moment I found myself standing; the yard had descended to the *cup*; and shaking myself in my jacket, I felt that I was unharmed and alive.

Who had done this? who had made this attempt on my life? thought I, as I ran down the rigging.

"Here it comes!—Lord! Lord! here it comes! See, see! it is white as a hammock."

"Who's coming?" I shouted, springing down into the top; "who's white as a hammock?"

"Bless my soul, Bill it's only White-Jacket—that infernal White-Jacket again!"

It seems they had spied a moving white spot there aloft, and, sailor-like, had taken me for the ghost of the cooper; and after hailing me, and bidding me descend, to test my corporeality, and getting no answer, they had lowered the halyards in affright.

In a rage I tore off the jacket, and threw it on the deck.

"Jacket," cried I, "you must change your complexion! you must hie to the dyers and be dyed, that I may live. I have but one poor life, White-Jacket, and that life I cannot spare. I cannot consent to die for *you,* but be dyed you must for me. You can dye many times without injury; but I cannot die without irreparable loss, and running the eternal risk."

So in the morning, jacket in hand, I repaired to the First Lieutenant, and related the narrow escape I had had during the night. I enlarged upon the general perils I ran in being taken for a ghost, and earnestly besought him to relax his commands for once, and give me an order on Brush, the captain of the paint-room, for some black paint, that my jacket might be painted of that color.

"Just look at it, sir," I added, holding it up; "did you ever see anything whiter? Consider how it shines of a night, like a bit of the Milky Way. A little paint, sir, you cannot refuse."

"The ship has no paint to spare," he said; "you must get along without it."

"Sir, every rain gives me a soaking;—Cape Horn is at hand—six brushes-full would make it waterproof; and no longer would I be in peril of my life!"

"Can't help it, sir; depart!"

I fear it will not be well with me in the end; for if my own sins are to be forgiven only as I forgive that hard-hearted and unimpressible First Lieutenant, then pardon there is none for me.

What! when but one dab of paint would make a man of a ghost, and a Mackintosh of a herring-net—to refuse it!

I am full. I can say no more.

Chapter XX

How They Sleep in a Man-of-War

NO MORE OF MY LUCKLESS JACKET FOR A WHILE; LET ME SPEAK OF MY HAMMOCK, AND THE TRIBUlations I endured therefrom.

Give me plenty of room to swing it in; let me swing it between two date-trees on an Arabian plain; or extend it diagonally from Moorish pillar to pillar, in the open marble Court of the Lions in Granada's Alhambra: let me swing it on a high bluff of the Mississippi—one swing in the pure ether for every swing over the green grass; or let me oscillate in it beneath the cool dome of St. Peter's; or drop me in it, as in a balloon, from the zenith, with the whole firmament to rock and expatiate in; and I would not exchange my coarse canvas hammock for the grand state-bed, like a stately coach-and-four, in which they tuck in a king when he passes a night at Blenheim Castle.

When you have the requisite room, you always have "spreaders" in your hammock; that is, two horizontal sticks, one at each end, which serve to keep the sides apart, and create a wide vacancy between, wherein you can turn over and over—lay on this side or that; on your back, if you please; stretch out your legs; in short, take your ease in your hammock; for of all inns, your bed is the best.

But when, with five hundred other hammocks, yours is crowded and jammed on all sides, on a frigate berth-deck; the third from above, when *"spreaders"* are prohibited by an express edict from the Captain's cabin; and every man about you is jealously watchful of the rights and privileges of his own proper hammock, as settled by law and usage; *then* your hammock is your Bastille and canvas jug; into which, or out of which, it is very hard to get; and where sleep is but a mockery and a name.

Eighteen inches a man is all they allow you; eighteen inches in width; in *that* you must swing. Dreadful! they give you more swing than that at the gallows.

During warm nights in the Tropics, your hammock is as a stew-pan; where you stew and stew, till you can almost hear yourself hiss. Vain are all stratagems to widen your accommodations. Let them catch you insinuating your boots or other articles in the head of your hammock, by way of a "spreader." Near and far, the whole rank and file of the row to which you belong feel the encroachment in an instant, and are clamorous till the guilty one is found out, and his pallet brought back to its bearings.

In platoons and squadrons, they all lie on a level; their hammock *clews* crossing and recrossing in all directions, so as to present one vast field-bed, midway between the ceiling and the floor; which are about five feet asunder.

One extremely warm night, during a calm, when it was so hot that only a skeleton could keep cool (from the free current of air through its bones), after being drenched in my own perspiration, I managed to wedge myself out of my hammock; and with what little strength I had left, lowered myself gently to the deck. Let me see now, thought I, whether my ingenuity cannot devise some method whereby I can have room to breathe and sleep at the same time. I have it. I will lower my hammock underneath all these others; and then—upon that separate and independent level, at least—I shall have the whole berth-deck to myself. Accordingly, I lowered away my pallet to the desired point—about three inches from the floor—and crawled into it again.

But, alas! this arrangement made such a sweeping semi-circle of my hammock, that, while my head and feet were at par, the small of my back was settling down indefinitely; I felt as if some gigantic archer had hold of me for a bow.

But there was another plan left. I triced up my hammock with all my strength, so as to bring it wholly *above* the tiers of pallets around me. This done, by a last effort, I hoisted myself into it; but, alas! it was much worse than before. My luckless hammock was stiff and straight as a board; and there I was—laid out in it, with my nose against the ceiling, like a dead man's against the lid of his coffin.

So at last I was fain to return to my old level, and moralize upon the folly, in all arbitrary governments, of striving to get either *below* or *above* those whom legislation has placed upon an equality with yourself.

Speaking of hammocks, recalls a circumstance that happened one night in the *Neversink*. It was three or four times repeated, with various but not fatal results.

The watch below was fast asleep on the berth-deck, where perfect silence was reigning, when a sudden shock and a groan roused up all hands; and the hem of a pair of white trousers vanished up one of the ladders at the fore-hatchway.

We ran toward the groan, and found a man lying on the deck; one end of his hammock having given way, pitching his head close to three twenty-four pound cannon shot, which must have been purposely placed in that position. When it was discovered that this man had long been suspected of being an *informer* among the crew, little surprise and less pleasure were evinced at his narrow escape.

Chapter XXI

ONE REASON WHY MEN-OF-WAR'S MEN ARE, GENERALLY, SHORT-LIVED

I CANNOT QUIT THIS MATTER OF THE HAMMOCKS WITHOUT MAKING MENTION OF A GRIEVANCE among the sailors that ought to be redressed.

In a man-of-war at sea, the sailors have *watch and watch*; that is, through every twenty-four hours, they are on and off duty every four hours. Now, the hammocks are piped down from the nettings (the open space for stowing them, running round the top of the bulwarks) a little after sunset, and piped up again when the forenoon watch is called, at eight o'clock in the morning; so that during the daytime they are inaccessible as pallets. This would be all well enough, did the sailors have a complete night's rest; but every other night at sea, one watch have only four hours in their hammocks. Indeed, deducting the time allowed for the other watch to turn out; for yourself to arrange your hammock, get into it, and fairly get asleep; it maybe said that, every other night, you have but three hours' sleep in your hammock. Having then been on deck for twice four hours, at eight o'clock in the morning your *watch-below* comes round, and you are not liable to duty until noon. Under like circumstances, a merchant seaman goes to his *bunk*, and has the benefit of a good long sleep. But in a man-of-war you can do no such thing; your hammock is very neatly stowed in the nettings, and there it must remain till nightfall.

But perhaps there is a corner for you somewhere along the batteries on the gun-deck, where you may enjoy a snug nap. But as no one is allowed to recline on the larboard side of the gun-deck (which is reserved as a corridor for the officers when they go forward to their smoking-room at the *bridle-port*), the starboard side only is left to the seaman. But most of this side, also, is occupied by the carpenters, sail-makers, barbers, and coopers. In short, so few are the corners where you can snatch a nap during daytime in a frigate, that not one in ten of the watch, who have been on deck eight hours, can get a wink of sleep till the following night. Repeatedly, after by good fortune securing a corner, I have been roused from it by some functionary commissioned to keep it clear.

Off Cape Horn, what before had been very uncomfortable became a serious hardship. Drenched through and through by the spray of the sea at night, I have sometimes slept standing on the spar-deck—and shuddered as I slept—for the want of sufficient sleep in my hammock.

During three days of the stormiest weather, we were given the privilege of the *berth-deck* (at other times strictly interdicted), where we were permitted to spread our jackets, and take a nap in the morning after the eight hours' night exposure. But this privilege was but a beggarly one, indeed. Not to speak of our jackets—used for blankets—being soaking wet, the spray, coming down the hatchways, kept the planks of the berth-deck itself constantly wet; whereas, had we been permitted our hammocks, we might have swung dry over all this deluge. But we endeavored to make ourselves as warm and comfortable as possible, chiefly by close stowing, so as to generate a little steam, in the absence of any fire-side warmth. You have seen, perhaps, the way in which they box up subjects intended to illustrate the winter lectures of a professor of surgery. Just so we laid; heel and point, face to back, dove-tailed into each other at every ham and knee. The wet of our jackets, thus densely packed, would soon begin to distill. But it was like pouring hot water on you to keep you from freezing. It was like being "packed" between the soaked sheets in a Water-cure Establishment.

Such a posture could not be preserved for any considerable period without shifting side for side. Three or four times during the four hours I would be startled from a wet doze by the hoarse cry of a fellow who did the duty of a corporal at the after-end of my file. *"Sleepers ahoy! stand by to slew round!*" and, with a double shuffle, we all rolled in concert, and found ourselves facing the taffrail instead of the bowsprit. But, however you turned, your nose was sure to stick to one or other of the steaming backs on your two flanks. There was some little relief in the change of odor consequent upon this.

But what is the reason that, after battling out eight stormy hours on deck at night, men-of-war's-men are not allowed the poor boon of a dry four hours' nap during the day following? What is the reason? The Commodore, Captain, and first Lieutenant, Chaplain, Purser, and scores of others, have *all night in,* just as if they were staying at a hotel on shore. And the junior Lieutenants not only have their cots to go to at any time: but as only one of them is required to head the watch, and there are so many of them among whom to divide that duty, they are only on deck four hours to twelve hours below. In some cases the proportion is still greater. Whereas, with *the people* it is four hours in and four hours off continually.

What is the reason, then, that the common seamen should fare so hard in this matter? It would seem but a simple thing to let them get down their hammocks during the day for a nap. But no; such a proceeding would mar the uniformity of daily events in a man-of-war. It seems indispensable to the picturesque effect of the spar-deck, that the hammocks should invariably remain stowed in the nettings between sunrise and sundown. But the chief reason is this—a reason which has sanctioned many an abuse in this world—*precedents are against it*; such a thing as sailors sleeping in their hammocks in the daytime, after being eight hours exposed to a night-storm, was hardly ever heard of in the navy. Though, to the immortal honor of some captains be it said, the fact is upon navy record, that off Cape Horn, they *have* vouchsafed the morning hammocks to their crew. Heaven bless such tender-hearted officers; and may they and their descendants—ashore or afloat—have sweet and pleasant slumbers while they live, and an undreaming siesta when they die.

It is concerning such things as the subject of this chapter that special enactments of Congress are demanded. Health and comfort—so far as duly attainable under the circumstances—should be legally guaranteed to the man-of-war's-men; and not left to the discretion or caprice of their commanders.

Chapter XXII

Wash-Day and House-Cleaning in a Man-of-War

Besides the other tribulations connected with your hammock, you must keep it snow-white and clean; who has not observed the long rows of spotless hammocks exposed in a frigate's nettings, where, through the day, their outsides, at least, are kept airing?

Hence it comes that there are regular mornings appointed for the scrubbing of hammocks; and such mornings are called *scrub-hammock-mornings*; and desperate is the scrubbing that ensues.

Before daylight the operation begins. All hands are called, and at it they go. Every deck is spread with hammocks, fore and aft; and lucky are you if you can get sufficient superfices to spread your own hammock in. Down on their knees are five hundred men, scrubbing away with brushes and brooms; jostling, and crowding, and quarreling about using each other's suds; when all their Purser's soap goes to create one indiscriminate yeast.

Sometimes you discover that, in the dark, you have been all the while scrubbing your next neighbor's hammock instead of your own. But it is too late to begin over again; for now the word is passed for every man to advance with his hammock, that it may be tied to a net-like frame-work of clothes-lines, and hoisted aloft to dry.

That done, without delay you get together your frocks and trousers, and on the already flooded deck embark in the laundry business. You have no special bucket or basin to yourself—the ship being one vast wash-tub, where all hands wash and rinse out, and rinse out and wash, till at last the word is passed again, to make fast your clothes, that they, also, may be elevated to dry.

Then on all three decks the operation of holy-stoning begins, so called from the queer name bestowed upon the principal instruments employed. These are ponderous flat stones with long ropes at each end, by which the stones are slidden about, to and fro, over the wet and sanded decks; a most wearisome, dog-like, galley-slave employment. For the by-ways and corners about the masts and guns, smaller stones are used, called *prayer-books*; inasmuch as the devout operator has to down with them on his knees.

Finally, a grand flooding takes place, and the decks are remorselessly thrashed with dry swabs. After which an extraordinary implement—a sort of leathern hoe called a *"squilgee"*—is used to scrape and squeeze the last dribblings of water from the planks. Concerning this "squilgee," I think something of drawing up a memoir, and reading it before the Academy of Arts and Sciences. It is a most curious affair.

By the time all these operations are concluded it is *eight bells,* and all hands are piped to breakfast upon the damp and every-way disagreeable decks.

Now, against this invariable daily flooding of the three decks of a frigate, as a man-of-war's-man, White-Jacket most earnestly protests. In sunless weather it keeps the sailors' quarters perpetually damp; so much so, that you can scarce sit down without running the risk of getting the lumbago. One rheumatic old sheet-anchor-man among us was driven to the extremity of sewing a piece of tarred canvas on the seat of his trousers.

Let those neat and tidy officers who so love to see a ship kept spick and span clean; who institute vigorous search after the man who chances to drop the crumb of a biscuit on deck, when the ship is rolling in a sea-way; let all such swing their hammocks with the sailors; and they would soon get sick of this daily damping of the decks.

Is a ship a wooden platter, that is to be scrubbed out every morning before breakfast, even if the thermometer be at zero, and every sailor goes barefooted through the flood with the chilblains? And all the while the ship carries a doctor, well aware of Boerhaave's great maxim *"keep the feet dry."* He has plenty of pills to give you when you are down with a fever, the consequence of these things; but enters no protest at the outset—as it is his duty to do—against the cause that induces the fever.

During the pleasant night watches, the promenading officers, mounted on their high-heeled boots, pass dry-shod, like the Israelites, over the decks; but by daybreak the roaring tide sets back, and the poor sailors are almost overwhelmed in it, like the Egyptians in the Red Sea.

Oh! the chills, colds, and agues that are caught. No snug stove, grate, or fireplace to go to; no, your only way to keep warm is to keep in a blazing passion, and anathematize the custom that every morning makes a wash-house of a man-of-war.

Look at it. Say you go on board a line-of-battle-ship: you see everything scrupulously neat; you see all the decks clear and unobstructed as the sidewalks of Wall Street of a Sunday morning; you see no trace of a sailor's dormitory; you marvel by what magic all this is brought about. And well you may. For consider, that in this unobstructed fabric nearly one thousand mortal men have to sleep, eat, wash, dress, cook, and perform all the ordinary functions of humanity. The same number of men ashore would expand themselves into a township. Is it credible, then, that this extraordinary neatness, and especially this *unobstructedness* of a man-of-war, can be brought about, except by the most rigorous edicts, and a very serious sacrifice, with respect to the sailors, of the domestic comforts of life? To be sure, sailors themselves do not often complain of these things; they are used to them; but man can become used even to the hardest usage. And it is because he is used to it, that sometimes he does not complain of it.

Of all men-of-war, the American ships are the most excessively neat, and have the greatest reputation for it. And of all men-of-war the general discipline of the American ships is the most arbitrary.

In the English navy, the men liberally mess on tables, which, between meals, are triced up out of the way. The American sailors mess on deck, and pick up their broken biscuit, or *midshipman's nuts,* like fowls in a barn-yard.

But if this unobstructedness in an American fighting-ship be, at all hazards, so desirable, why not imitate the Turks? In the Turkish navy they have no mess-chests; the sailors roll their mess things up in a rug, and thrust them under a gun. Nor do they have any hammocks; they sleep anywhere about the decks in their *gregoes.* Indeed, come to look at it, what more does a man-of-war's-man absolutely require to live in than his own skin? That's room enough; and room enough to turn in, if he but knew how to shift his spine, end for end, like a ramrod, without disturbing his next neighbor.

Among all men-of-war's-men, it is a maxim that over-neat vessels are Tartars to the crew: and perhaps it may be safely laid down that, when you see such a ship, some sort of tyranny is not very far off.

In the *Neversink,* as in other national ships, the business of *holy-stoning* the decks was often prolonged, by way of punishment to the men, particularly of a raw, cold morning. This is one of the punishments which a lieutenant of the watch may easily inflict upon the crew, without infringing the statute which places the power of punishment solely in the hands of the Captain.

The abhorrence which men-of-war's-men have for this protracted *holy-stoning* in cold, comfortless weather—with their bare feet exposed to the splashing inundations—is shown in a strange story, rife among them, curiously tinctured with their proverbial superstitions.

The First Lieutenant of an English sloop of war, a severe disciplinarian, was uncommonly particular concerning the whiteness of the quarter-deck. One bitter winter morning at sea, when the crew had washed that part of the vessel, as usual, and put away their holy-stones, this officer came on deck, and after inspecting it, ordered the *holy-stones* and *prayer-books* up again. Once more slipping off the shoes from their frosted feet, and rolling up their trousers, the crew kneeled down to their task; and in that suppliant posture, silently invoked a curse upon their tyrant; praying, as he went below, that he might never more come out of the ward-room alive. The prayer seemed answered: for shortly after being visited with a paralytic stroke at his breakfast-table, the First Lieutenant next morning was carried out of the ward-room feet foremost, dead. As they dropped him over the side—so goes the story—the marine sentry at the gangway turned his back upon the corpse.

To the credit of the humane and sensible portion of the roll of American navy-captains, be it added, that *they* are not so particular in keeping the decks spotless at all times, and in all weathers; nor do they torment the men with scraping bright-wood and polishing ring-bolts; but give all such gingerbread-work a hearty coat of black paint, which looks more war-like, is a better preservative, and exempts the sailors from a perpetual annoyance.

Chapter XXIII

THEATRICALS IN A MAN-OF-WAR

THE *NEVERSINK* HAD SUMMERED OUT HER LAST CHRISTMAS ON THE EQUATOR; SHE WAS NOW DEStined to winter out the Fourth of July not very far from the frigid latitudes of Cape Horn.

It is sometimes the custom in the American Navy to celebrate this national holiday by doubling the allowance of spirits to the men; that is, if the ship happen to be lying in harbor. The effects of this patriotic plan may be easily imagined: the whole ship is converted into a dram-shop; and the intoxicated sailors reel about, on all three decks, singing, howling, and fighting. This is the time that, owing to the relaxed discipline of the ship, old and almost forgotten quarrels are revived, under the stimulus of drink; and, fencing themselves up between the guns—so as to be sure of a clear space with at least three walls—the combatants, two and two, fight out their hate, cribbed and cabined like soldiers dueling in a sentry-box. In a word, scenes ensue which would not for a single instant be tolerated by the officers upon any other occasion. This is the time that the most venerable of quarter-gunners and quarter-masters, together with the smallest apprentice boys, and men never known to have been previously intoxicated during the cruise—this is the time that they all roll together in the same muddy trough of drunkenness.

In emulation of the potentates of the Middle Ages, some Captains augment the din by authorizing a grand jail-delivery of all the prisoners who, on that auspicious Fourth of the month, may happen to be confined in the ship's prison—*"the brig."*

But from scenes like these the *Neversink* was happily delivered. Besides that she was now approaching a most perilous part of the ocean—which would have made it madness to intoxicate the sailors—her complete destitution of *grog*, even for ordinary consumption, was an obstacle altogether insuperable, even had the Captain felt disposed to indulge his man-of-war's-men by the most copious libations.

For several days previous to the advent of the holiday, frequent conferences were held on the gun-deck touching the melancholy prospects before the ship.

"Too bad—too bad!" cried a top-man. "Think of it, shipmates—a Fourth of July without grog!"

"I'll hoist the Commodore's pennant at half-mast that day," sighed the signal-quarter-master.

"And I'll turn my best uniform jacket wrong side out, to keep company with the pennant, old Ensign," sympathetically responded an after-guard's-man.

"Ay, do!" cried a forecastle-man. "I could almost pipe my eye to think on't."

"No grog on de day dat tried men's souls!" blubbered Sunshine, the galley-cook.

"Who would be a *Jankee* now?" roared a Hollander of the fore-top, more Dutch than sour-crout.

"Is this the *riglar* fruits of liberty?" touchingly inquired an Irish waister of an old Spanish sheet-anchor-man.

You will generally observe that, of all Americans, your foreign-born citizens are the most patriotic—especially toward the Fourth of July.

But how could Captain Claret, the father of his crew, behold the grief of his ocean children with indifference? He could not. Three days before the anniversary—it still continuing very pleasant weather for these latitudes—it was publicly announced that free permission was given to the sailors to get up any sort of theatricals they desired, wherewith to honor the Fourth.

Now, some weeks prior to the *Neversink*'s sailing from home—nearly three years before the time here spoken of—some of the seamen had clubbed together, and made up a considerable purse, for the purpose of purchasing a theatrical outfit; having in view to diversify the monotony of lying in foreign harbors for weeks together, by an occasional display on the boards—though if ever there was a continual theatre in the world, playing by night and by day, and without intervals between the acts, a man-of-war is that theatre, and her planks are the *boards* indeed.

The sailors who originated this scheme had served in other American frigates, where the privilege of having theatricals was allowed to the crew. What was their chagrin, then, when, upon making an application to the Captain, in a Peruvian harbor, for permission to present the much-admired drama of *"The Ruffian Boy,"* under the Captain's personal patronage, that dignitary assured them that there were already enough *ruffian boys* on board, without conjuring up any more from the green-room.

The theatrical outfit, therefore, was stowed down in the bottom of the sailors' bags, who little anticipated *then* that it would ever be dragged out while Captain Claret had the sway.

But immediately upon the announcement that the embargo was removed, vigorous preparations were at once commenced to celebrate the Fourth with unwonted spirit. The half-deck was set apart for the theatre, and the signal-quarter-master was commanded to loan his flags to decorate it in the most patriotic style.

As the stage-struck portion of the crew had frequently during the cruise rehearsed portions of various plays, to while away the tedium of the night-watches, they needed no long time now to perfect themselves in their parts.

Accordingly, on the very next morning after the indulgence had been granted by the Captain, the following written placard, presenting a broadside of staring capitals, was found tacked against the main-mast on the gun-deck. It was as if a Drury-Lane bill had been posted upon the London Monument.

CAPE HORN THEATRE.

Grand Celebration of the Fourth of July.

DAY PERFORMANCE.

UNCOMMON ATTRACTION.

THE OLD WAGON PAID OFF!

JACK CHASE. . . . PERCY ROYAL-MAST.

STARS OF THE FIRST MAGNITUDE.

For this time only.

THE TRUE YANKEE SAILOR.

The managers of the Cape Horn Theatre beg leave to inform the inhabitants of the Pacific and Southern Oceans that, on the afternoon of the Fourth of July, 184—, they will have the honor to present the admired drama of

THE OLD WAGON PAID OFF!

Commodore Bougee . . . . *Tom Brown, of the Fore-top.*
Captain Spy-glass . . . . *Ned Brace, of the After-Guard.*
Commodore's Cockswain . . . . *Joe Bunk, of the Launch.*
Old Luff . . . . *Quarter-master Coffin.*
Mayor . . . . *Seafull, of the Forecastle.*
PERCY ROYAL-MAST . . . . JACK CHASE.
Mrs. Lovelorn . . . . *Long-locks, of the After-Guard.*
Toddy Moll . . . . Frank Jones.
Gin and Sugar Sall . . . . *Dick Dash.*

Sailors, Mariners, Bar-keepers, Crimps, Aldermen, Police-officers, Soldiers, Landsmen generally.

Long live the Commodore! || Admission Free.

To conclude with the much-admired song by Dibdin,
altered to suit all American Tars, entitled
THE TRUE YANKEE SAILOR.
True Yankee Sailor (in costume), Patrick Flinegan, Captain of the Head.

Performance to commence with "Hail Columbia," by the Brass Band. Ensign rises at three bells, P.M. No sailor permitted to enter in his shirt-sleeves. Good order is expected to be maintained. The Master-at-arms and Ship's Corporals to be in attendance to keep the peace.

At the earnest entreaties of the seamen, Lemsford, the gun-deck poet, had been prevailed upon to draw up this bill. And upon this one occasion his literary abilities were far from being underrated, even by the least intellectual person on board. Nor must it be omitted that, before the bill was placarded, Captain Claret, enacting the part of censor and grand chamberlain ran over a manuscript copy of *"The Old Wagon Paid Off,"* to see whether it contained anything calculated to breed disaffection against lawful authority among the crew. He objected to some parts, but in the end let them all pass.

The morning of The Fourth—most anxiously awaited—dawned clear and fair. The breeze was steady; the air bracing cold; and one and all the sailors anticipated a gleeful afternoon. And thus was falsified the prophecies of certain old growlers averse to theatricals, who had predicted a gale of wind that would squash all the arrangements of the green-room.

As the men whose regular turns, at the time of the performance, would come round to be stationed in the tops, and at the various halyards and running ropes about the spar-deck, could not be permitted to partake in the celebration, there accordingly ensued, during the morning, many amusing scenes of tars who were anxious to procure substitutes at their posts. Through the day, many anxious glances were cast to windward; but the weather still promised fair.

At last *the people* were piped to dinner; two bells struck; and soon after, all who could be spared from their stations hurried to the half-deck. The capstan-bars were placed on shot-boxes, as at prayers on Sundays, furnishing seats for the audience, while a low stage, rigged by the carpenter's gang, was built at one end of the open space. The curtain was composed of a large ensign, and the bulwarks round about were draperied with the flags of all nations. The ten or twelve members of the brass band were ranged in a row at the foot of the stage, their polished instruments in their hands, while the consequential Captain of the Band himself was elevated upon a gun carriage.

At three bells precisely a group of ward-room officers emerged from the after-hatchway, and seated themselves upon camp-stools, in a central position, with the stars and stripes for a canopy. *That* was the royal box. The sailors looked round for the Commodore but neither Commodore nor Captain honored *the people* with their presence.

At the call of a bugle the band struck up *Hail Columbia*, the whole audience keeping time, as at Drury Lane, when *God Save The King* is played after a great national victory.

At the discharge of a marine's musket the curtain rose, and four sailors, in the picturesque garb of Maltese mariners, staggered on the stage in a feigned state of intoxication. The truthfulness of the representation was much heightened by the roll of the ship.

"The Commodore," "Old Luff," "The Mayor," and "Gin and Sugar Sall," were played to admiration, and received great applause. But at the first appearance of that universal favorite, Jack

Chase, in the chivalric character of *Percy Royal-Mast,* the whole audience simultaneously rose to their feet, and greeted him with three hearty cheers, that almost took the main-top-sail aback.

Matchless Jack, *in full fig,* bowed again and again, with true quarter-deck grace and self possession; and when five or six untwisted strands of rope and bunches of oakum were thrown to him, as substitutes for bouquets, he took them one by one, and gallantly hung them from the buttons of his jacket.

"Hurrah! hurrah! hurrah!—go on! go on!—stop hollering—hurrah!—go on!—stop hollering—hurrah!" was now heard on all sides, till at last, seeing no end to the enthusiasm of his ardent admirers, Matchless Jack stepped forward, and, with his lips moving in pantomime, plunged into the thick of the part. Silence soon followed, but was fifty times broken by uncontrollable bursts of applause. At length, when that heart-thrilling scene came on, where Percy Royal-Mast rescues fifteen oppressed sailors from the watch-house, in the teeth of a posse of constables, the audience leaped to their feet, overturned the capstan-bars, and to a man hurled their hats on the stage in a delirium of delight. Ah Jack, that was a ten-stroke indeed!

The commotion was now terrific; all discipline seemed gone for ever; the Lieutenants ran in among the men, the Captain darted from his cabin, and the Commodore nervously questioned the armed sentry at his door as to what the deuce *the people* were about. In the midst of all this, the trumpet of the officer-of-the-deck, commanding the top-gallant sails to be taken in, was almost completely drowned. A black squall was coming down on the weather-bow, and the boat-swain's mates bellowed themselves hoarse at the main-hatchway. There is no knowing what would have ensued, had not the bass drum suddenly been heard, calling all hands to quarters, a summons not to be withstood. The sailors pricked their ears at it, as horses at the sound of a cracking whip, and confusedly stumbled up the ladders to their stations. The next moment all was silent but the wind, howling like a thousand devils in the cordage.

"Stand by to reef all three top-sails!—settle away the halyards!—haul out—so: make fast!—aloft, top-men! and reef away!"

Thus, in storm and tempest terminated that day's theatricals. But the sailors never recovered from the disappointment of not having the *"True Yankee Sailor"* sung by the Irish Captain of the Head.

And here White-Jacket must moralize a bit. The unwonted spectacle of the row of gun-room officers mingling with "the people" in applauding a mere seaman like Jack Chase, filled me at the time with the most pleasurable emotions. It is a sweet thing, thought I, to see these officers confess a human brotherhood with us, after all; a sweet thing to mark their cordial appreciation of the manly merits of my matchless Jack. Ah! they are noble fellows all round, and I do not know but I have wronged them sometimes in my thoughts.

Nor was it without similar pleasurable feelings that I witnessed the temporary rupture of the ship's stern discipline, consequent upon the tumult of the theatricals. I thought to myself, this now is as it should be. It is good to shake off, now and then, this iron yoke round our necks. And after having once permitted us sailors to be a little noisy, in a harmless way—somewhat merrily turbulent—the officers cannot, with any good grace, be so excessively stern and unyielding as before. I began to think a man-of-war a man-of-peace-and-good-will, after all. But, alas! disappointment came.

Next morning the same old scene was enacted at the gang-way. And beholding the row of uncompromising-looking-officers there assembled with the Captain, to witness punishment—the same officers who had been so cheerfully disposed over night—an old sailor touched my shoulder and said, "See, White-Jacket, all round they have *shipped their quarter-deck faces again.* But this is the way."

I afterward learned that this was an old man-of-war's-man's phrase, expressive of the facility with which a sea-officer falls back upon all the severity of his dignity, after a temporary suspension of it.

Chapter XXIV

INTRODUCTORY TO CAPE HORN

AND NOW, THROUGH DRIZZLING FOGS AND VAPORS, AND UNDER DAMP, DOUBLE-REEFED TOP-sails, our wet-decked frigate drew nearer and nearer to the squally Cape.

Who has not heard of it? Cape Horn, Cape Horn—a *horn* indeed, that has tossed many a good ship. Was the descent of Orpheus, Ulysses, or Dante into Hell, one whit more hardy and sublime than the first navigator's weathering of that terrible Cape?

Turned on her heel by a fierce West Wind, many an outward-bound ship has been driven across the Southern Ocean to the Cape of Good Hope—*that* way to seek a passage to the Pacific. And that stormy Cape, I doubt not, has sent many a fine craft to the bottom, and told no tales. At those ends of the earth are no chronicles. What signify the broken spars and shrouds that, day after day, are driven before the prows of more fortunate vessels? or the tall masts, imbedded in icebergs, that are found floating by? They but hint the old story—of ships that have sailed from their ports, and never more have been heard of.

Impracticable Cape! You may approach it from this direction or that—in any way you please—from the east or from the west; with the wind astern, or abeam, or on the quarter; and still Cape Horn is Cape Horn. Cape Horn it is that takes the conceit out of fresh-water sailors, and steeps in a still salter brine the saltest. Woe betide the tyro; the fool-hardy, Heaven preserve!

Your Mediterranean captain, who with a cargo of oranges has hitherto made merry runs across the Atlantic, without so much as furling a t'-gallant-sail, oftentimes, off Cape Horn, receives a lesson which he carries to the grave; though the grave—as is too often the case—follows so hard on the lesson that no benefit comes from the experience.

Other strangers who draw nigh to this Patagonia termination of our Continent, with their souls full of its shipwrecks and disasters—top-sails cautiously reefed, and everything guardedly snug—these strangers at first unexpectedly encountering a tolerably smooth sea, rashly conclude that the Cape, after all, is but a bugbear; they have been imposed upon by fables, and founderings and sinkings hereabouts are all cock-and-bull stories.

"Out reefs, my hearties; fore and aft set t'-gallant-sails! stand by to give her the fore-top-mast stun'-sail!"

But, Captain Rash, those sails of yours were much safer in the sail-maker's loft. For now, while the heedless craft is bounding over the billows, a black cloud rises out of the sea; the sun drops down from the sky; a horrible mist far and wide spreads over the water.

"Hands by the halyards! Let go! Clew up!"

Too late.

For ere the ropes' ends can be the east off from the pins, the tornado is blowing down to the bottom of their throats. The masts are willows, the sails ribbons, the cordage wool; the whole ship is brewed into the yeast of the gale.

And now, if, when the first green sea breaks over him, Captain Rash is not swept overboard, he has his hands full be sure. In all probability his three masts have gone by the board, and, ravelled into list, his sails are floating in the air. Or, perhaps, the ship *broaches to*, or is *brought by the lee*. In either ease, Heaven help the sailors, their wives and their little ones; and heaven help the underwriters.

Familiarity with danger makes a brave man braver, but less daring. Thus with seamen: he who goes the oftenest round Cape Horn goes the most circumspectly. A veteran mariner is never deceived by the treacherous breezes which sometimes waft him pleasantly toward the latitude of the Cape. No sooner does he come within a certain distance of it—previously fixed in his own mind—than all hands are turned to setting the ship in storm-trim; and never mind how light the breeze, down come his t'-gallant-yards. He "bends" his strongest storm-sails, and lashes everything on deck securely. The ship is then ready for the worst; and if, in reeling round the headland, she receives a broadside, it generally goes well with her. If ill, all hands go to the bottom with quiet consciences.

Among sea-captains, there are some who seem to regard the genius of the Cape as a willful, capricious jade, that must be courted and coaxed into complaisance. First, they come along under easy sails; do not steer boldly for the headland, but tack this way and that—sidling up to it. Now they woo the Jezebel with a t'-gallant-studding-sail; anon, they deprecate her wrath with double-reefed-topsails. When, at length, her unappeasable fury is fairly aroused, and all round the dismantled ship the storm howls and howls for days together, they still persevere in their efforts. First, they try unconditional submission; furling every rag and *heaving to*; laying like a log, for the tempest to toss wheresoever it pleases.

This failing, they set a *spencer* or *try-sail*, and shift on the other tack. Equally vain! The gale sings as hoarsely as before. At last, the wind comes round fair; they drop the fore-sail; square the yards, and scud before it; their implacable foe chasing them with tornadoes, as if to show her insensibility to the last.

Other ships, without encountering these terrible gales, spend week after week endeavoring to turn this boisterous world-corner against a continual head-wind. Tacking hither and thither, in the language of sailors they *polish* the Cape by beating about its edges so long.

Le Mair and Schouten, two Dutchmen, were the first navigators who weathered Cape Horn. Previous to this, passages had been made to the Pacific by the Straits of Magellan; nor, indeed, at that period, was it known to a certainty that there was any other route, or that the land now called Terra del Fuego was an island. A few leagues southward from Terra del Fuego is a cluster of small islands, the Diegoes; between which and the former island are the Straits of Le Mair, so called in honor of their discoverer, who first sailed through them into the Pacific. Le Mair and Schouten, in their small, clumsy vessels, encountered a series of tremendous gales, the prelude to the long train of similar hardships which most of their followers have experienced. It is a significant fact, that Schouten's vessel, the *Horne*, which gave its name to the Cape, was almost lost in weathering it.

The next navigator round the Cape was Sir Francis Drake, who, on Raleigh's Expedition, beholding for the first time, from the Isthmus of Darien, the "goodlie South Sea," like a true-born Englishman, vowed, please God, to sail an English ship thereon; which the gallant sailor did, to the sore discomfiture of the Spaniards on the coasts of Chile and Peru.

But perhaps the greatest hardships on record, in making this celebrated passage, were those experienced by Lord Anson's squadron in 1736. Three remarkable and most interesting narratives record their disasters and sufferings. The first, jointly written by the carpenter and gunner of the *Wager*; the second by young Byron, a midshipman in the same ship; the third, by the chaplain of the *Centurion*. White-Jacket has them all; and they are fine reading of a boisterous March night, with the casement rattling in your ear, and the chimney-stacks blowing down upon the pavement, bubbling with rain-drops.

But if you want the best idea of Cape Horn, get my friend Dana's unmatchable *Two Years Before the Mast*. But you can read, and so you must have read it. His chapters describing Cape Horn must have been written with an icicle.

At the present day the horrors of the Cape have somewhat abated. This is owing to a growing familiarity with it; but, more than all, to the improved condition of ships in all respects, and the means now generally in use of preserving the health of the crews in times of severe and prolonged exposure.

Chapter XXV

THE DOG-DAYS OFF CAPE HORN

COLDER AND COLDER; WE ARE DRAWING NIGH TO THE CAPE. NOW GREGOES, PEA JACKETS, MONkey jackets reefing jackets, storm jackets, oil jackets, paint jackets, round jackets short jackets, long jackets, and all manner of jackets, are the order of the day, not excepting the immortal white jacket, which begins to be sturdily buttoned up to the throat, and pulled down vigorously at the skirts, to bring them well over the loins.

But, alas! those skirts were lamentably scanty; and though, with its quiltings, the jacket was stuffed out about the breasts like a Christmas turkey, and of a dry cold day kept the wearer warm enough in that vicinity, yet about the loins it was shorter than ballet-dancer's skirts; so that while my chest was in the temperate zone close adjoining the torrid, my hapless thighs were in Nova Zembla, hardly an icicle's toss from the Pole.

Then, again, the repeated soakings and dryings it had undergone, had by this time made it shrink woefully all over, especially in the arms, so that the wristbands had gradually crawled up near to the elbows; and it required an energetic thrust to push the arm through, in drawing the jacket on.

I endeavored to amend these misfortunes by sewing a sort of canvas ruffle round the skirts, by way of a continuation or supplement to the original work, and by doing the same with the wristbands.

This is the time for oil-skin suits, dreadnaughts, tarred trousers and overalls, sea-boots, comforters, mittens, woolen socks, Guernsey frocks, Havre shirts, buffalo-robe shirts, and moose-skin drawers. Every man's jacket is his wigwam, and every man's hat his caboose.

Perfect license is now permitted to the men respecting their clothing. Whatever they can rake and scrape together they put on—swaddling themselves in old sails, and drawing old socks over their heads for night-caps. This is the time for smiting your chest with your hand, and talking loud to keep up the circulation.

Colder, and colder, and colder, till at last we spoke a fleet of icebergs bound North. After that, it was one incessant *"cold snap,"* that almost snapped off our fingers and toes. Cold! It was cold as *Blue Flujin*, where sailors say fire freezes.

And now coming up with the latitude of the Cape, we stood southward to give it a wide berth, and while so doing were becalmed; ay, becalmed off Cape Horn, which is worse, far worse, than being becalmed on the Line.

Here we lay forty-eight hours, during which the cold was intense. I wondered at the liquid sea, which refused to freeze in such a temperature. The clear, cold sky overhead looked like a steel-blue cymbal, that might ring, could you smite it. Our breath came and went like puffs of smoke from pipe-bowls. At first there was a long gauky swell, that obliged us to furl most of the sails, and even send down t'-gallant-yards, for fear of pitching them overboard.

Out of sight of land, at this extremity of both the inhabitable and uninhabitable world, our peopled frigate, echoing with the voices of men, the bleating of lambs, the cackling of fowls, the gruntings of pigs, seemed like Noah's old ark itself, becalmed at the climax of the Deluge.

There was nothing to be done but patiently to await the pleasure of the elements, and "whistle for a wind," the usual practice of seamen in a calm. No fire was allowed, except for the indispensable purpose of cooking, and heating bottles of water to toast Selvagee's feet. He who possessed the largest stock of vitality, stood the best chance to escape freezing. It was horrifying. In such weather any man could have undergone amputation with great ease, and helped take up the arteries himself.

Indeed, this state of affairs had not lasted quite twenty-four hours, when the extreme frigidity of the air, united to our increased tendency to inactivity, would very soon have rendered some of us subjects for the surgeon and his mates, had not a humane proceeding of the Captain suddenly impelled us to vigorous exercise.

And here be it said, that the appearance of the Boat-swain, with his silver whistle to his mouth, at the main hatchway of the gun-deck, is always regarded by the crew with the utmost curiosity, for this betokens that some general order is about to be promulgated through the ship. What now? is the question that runs on from man to man. A short preliminary whistle is then given by "Old Yarn," as they call him, which whistle serves to collect round him, from their various stations, his four mates. Then Yarn, or Pipes, as leader of the orchestra, begins a peculiar call, in which his assistants join. This over, the order, whatever it may be, is loudly sung out and prolonged, till the remotest corner echoes again. The Boatswain and his mates are the town-criers of a man-of-war.

The calm had commenced in the afternoon: and the following morning the ship's company were electrified by a general order, thus set forth and declared: *"D'ye hear there, fore and aft! all hands skylark!"*

This mandate, nowadays never used except upon very rare occasions, produced the same effect upon the men that Exhilarating Gas would have done, or an extra allowance of "grog." For a time, the wonted discipline of the ship was broken through, and perfect license allowed. It was a Babel here, a Bedlam there, and a Pandemonium everywhere. The Theatricals were nothing compared with it. Then the faint-hearted and timorous crawled to their hiding-places, and the lusty and bold shouted forth their glee. Gangs of men, in all sorts of outlandish habiliments, wild as those worn at some crazy carnival, rushed to and fro, seizing upon whomsoever they pleased—warrant-officers and dangerous pugilists excepted—pulling and hauling the luckless tars about, till fairly baited into a genial warmth. Some were made fast to and hoisted aloft with a will: others, mounted upon oars, were ridden fore and aft on a rail, to the boisterous mirth of the spectators, any one of whom might be the next victim. Swings were rigged from the tops, or the masts; and the most reluctant wights being purposely selected, spite of all struggles, were swung from east to west, in vast arcs of circles, till almost breathless. Hornpipes, fandangoes, Donnybrook-jigs, reels, and quadrilles, were danced under the very nose of the most mighty captain, and upon the very quarter-deck and poop. Sparring and wrestling, too, were all the vogue; *Kentucky bites* were given, and the *Indian hug* exchanged. The din frightened the sea-fowl, that flew by with accelerated wing.

It is worth mentioning that several casualties occurred, of which, however, I will relate but one. While the "skylarking" was at its height, one of the fore-top-men—an ugly-tempered devil of a Portuguese, looking on—swore that he would be the death of any man who laid violent hands upon his inviolable person. This threat being overheard, a band of desperadoes, coming up from behind, tripped him up in an instant, and in the twinkling of an eye the Portuguese was straddling an oar, borne aloft by an uproarious multitude, who rushed him along the deck at a railroad gallop. The living mass of arms all round and beneath him was so dense, that every time he inclined one side he was instantly pushed upright, but only to fall over again, to receive another push from the contrary direction. Presently, disengaging his hands from those who held them, the enraged seaman drew from his bosom an iron belaying-pin, and recklessly laid about him to right and left. Most of his persecutors fled; but some eight or ten still stood their ground, and, while bearing him aloft, endeavored to wrest the weapon from his hands. In this attempt, one man was struck on the head, and dropped insensible. He was taken up for dead, and carried below to Cuticle, the surgeon, while the

Portuguese was put under guard. But the wound did not prove very serious; and in a few days the man was walking about the deck, with his head well bandaged.

This occurrence put an end to the "skylarking," further head-breaking being strictly prohibited. In due time the Portuguese paid the penalty of his rashness at the gangway; while once again the officers *shipped their quarter-deck faces.*

Chapter XXVI

THE PITCH OF THE CAPE

ERE THE CALM HAD YET LEFT US, A SAIL HAD BEEN DISCERNED FROM THE FORE-TOP-MAST-HEAD, at a great distance, probably three leagues or more. At first it was a mere speck, altogether out of sight from the deck. By the force of attraction, or something else equally inscrutable, two ships in a calm, and equally affected by the currents, will always approximate, more or less. Though there was not a breath of wind, it was not a great while before the strange sail was descried from our bulwarks; gradually, it drew still nearer.

What was she, and whence? There is no object which so excites interest and conjecture, and, at the same time, baffles both, as a sail, seen as a mere speck on these remote seas off Cape Horn.

A breeze! a breeze! for lo! the stranger is now perceptibly nearing the frigate; the officer's spy-glass pronounces her a full-rigged ship, with all sail set, and coming right down to us, though in our own vicinity the calm still reigns.

She is bringing the wind with her. Hurrah! Ay, there it is! Behold how mincingly it creeps over the sea, just ruffling and crisping it.

Our top-men were at once sent aloft to loose the sails, and presently they faintly began to distend. As yet we hardly had steerage-way. Toward sunset the stranger bore down before the wind, a complete pyramid of canvas. Never before, I venture to say, was Cape Horn so audaciously insulted. Stun'-sails alow and aloft; royals, moon-sails, and everything else. She glided under our stern, within hailing distance, and the signal-quarter-master ran up our ensign to the gaff.

"Ship ahoy!" cried the Lieutenant of the Watch, through his trumpet.

"Halloa!" bawled an old fellow in a green jacket, clapping one hand to his mouth, while he held on with the other to the mizzen-shrouds.

"What ship's that?"

"The *Sultan,* Indiaman, from New York, and bound to Callao and Canton, sixty days out, all well. What frigate's that?"

"The United States ship *Neversink,* homeward bound."

"Hurrah! hurrah! hurrah!" yelled our enthusiastic countryman, transported with patriotism.

By this time the *Sultan* had swept past, but the Lieutenant of the Watch could not withhold a parting admonition.

"D'ye hear? You'd better take in some of your flying-kites there. Look out for Cape Horn!"

But the friendly advice was lost in the now increasing wind. With a suddenness by no means unusual in these latitudes, the light breeze soon became a succession of sharp squalls, and our sail-proud braggadacio of an Indiaman was observed to let everything go by the run, his t'-gallant stun'-sails and flying-jib taking quick leave of the spars; the flying-jib was swept into the air, rolled together for a few minutes, and tossed about in the squalls like a foot-ball. But the wind played no such pranks with the more prudently managed canvas of the *Neversink*, though before many hours it was stirring times with us.

About midnight, when the starboard watch, to which, I belonged, was below, the boatswain's whistle was heard, followed by the shrill cry of "*All hands take in sail!* jump, men, and save ship!"

Springing from our hammocks, we found the frigate leaning over to it so steeply, that it was with difficulty we could climb the ladders leading to the upper deck.

Here the scene was awful. The vessel seemed to be sailing on her side. The main-deck guns had several days previous been run in and housed, and the port-holes closed, but the lee carronades on the quarter-deck and forecastle were plunging through the sea, which undulated over them in milk-white billows of foam. With every lurch to leeward the yard-arm-ends seemed to dip in the sea, while forward the spray dashed over the bows in cataracts, and drenched the men who were on the fore-yard. By this time the deck was alive with the whole strength of the ship's company, five hundred men, officers and all, mostly clinging to the weather bulwarks. The occasional phosphorescence of the yeasting sea cast a glare upon their uplifted faces, as a night fire in a populous city lights up the panic-stricken crowd.

In a sudden gale, or when a large quantity of sail is suddenly to be furled, it is the custom for the First Lieutenant to take the trumpet from whoever happens then to be officer of the deck. But Mad Jack had the trumpet that watch; nor did the First Lieutenant now seek to wrest it from his hands. Every eye was upon him, as if we had chosen him from among us all, to decide this battle with the elements, by single combat with the spirit of the Cape; for Mad Jack was the saving genius of the ship, and so proved himself that night. I owe this right hand, that is this moment flying over my sheet, and all my present being to Mad Jack. The ship's bows were now butting, battering, ramming, and thundering over and upon the head seas, and with a horrible wallowing sound our whole hull was rolling in the trough of the foam. The gale came athwart the deck, and every sail seemed bursting with its wild breath.

All the quarter-masters, and several of the forecastle-men, were swarming round the double-wheel on the quarter-deck. Some jumping up and down, with their hands upon the spokes; for the whole helm and galvanized keel were fiercely feverish, with the life imparted to them by the tempest.

"Hard *up* the helm!" shouted Captain Claret, bursting from his cabin like a ghost in his night-dress.

"Damn you!" raged Mad Jack to the quarter-masters; "hard *down*—hard *down*, I say, and be damned to you!"

Contrary orders! but Mad Jack's were obeyed. His object was to throw the ship into the wind, so as the better to admit of close-reefing the top-sails. But though the halyards were let go, it was impossible to clew down the yards, owing to the enormous horizontal strain on the canvas. It now blew a hurricane. The spray flew over the ship in floods. The gigantic masts seemed about to snap under the world-wide strain of the three entire top-sails.

"Clew down! clew down!" shouted Mad Jack, husky with excitement, and in a frenzy, beating his trumpet against one of the shrouds. But, owing to the slant of the ship, the thing could not be done. It was obvious that before many minutes something must go—either sails, rigging, or sticks; perhaps the hull itself, and all hands.

Presently a voice from the top exclaimed that there was a rent in the main-top-sail. And instantly we heard a report like two or three muskets discharged together; the vast sail was rent up and down like the Vail of the Temple. This saved the main-mast; for the yard was now clewed down with comparative ease, and the top-men laid out to stow the shattered canvas. Soon, the two remaining top-sails were also clewed down and close-reefed.

Above all the roar of the tempest and the shouts of the crew, was heard the dismal tolling of the ship's bell—almost as large as that of a village church—which the violent rolling of the ship was occasioning. Imagination cannot conceive the horror of such a sound in a night-tempest at sea.

"Stop that ghost!" roared Mad Jack; "away, one of you, and wrench off the clapper!"

But no sooner was this ghost gagged, than a still more appalling sound was heard, the rolling to and fro of the heavy shot, which, on the gun-deck, had broken loose from the gun-racks, and converted that part of the ship into an immense bowling-alley. Some hands were sent down to secure them; but it was as much as their lives were worth. Several were maimed; and the midshipmen who were ordered to see the duty performed reported it impossible, until the storm abated.

The most terrific job of all was to furl the main-sail, which, at the commencement of the squalls, had been clewed up, coaxed and quieted as much as possible with the bunt-lines and slab-lines. Mad Jack waited some time for a lull, ere he gave an order so perilous to be executed. For to furl this enormous sail, in such a gale, required at least fifty men on the yard; whose weight, superadded to that of the ponderous stick itself, still further jeopardized their lives. But there was no prospect of a cessation of the gale, and the order was at last given.

At this time a hurricane of slanting sleet and hail was descending upon us; the rigging was coated with a thin glare of ice, formed within the hour.

"Aloft, main-yard-men! and all you main-top-men! and furl the main-sail!" cried Mad Jack.

I dashed down my hat, slipped out of my quilted jacket in an instant, kicked the shoes from my feet, and, with a crowd of others, sprang for the rigging. Above the bulwarks (which in a frigate are so high as to afford much protection to those on deck) the gale was horrible. The sheer force of the wind flattened us to the rigging as we ascended, and every hand seemed congealing to the icy shrouds by which we held.

"Up—up, my brave hearties!" shouted Mad Jack; and up we got, some way or other, all of us, and groped our way out on the yard-arms.

"Hold on, every mother's son!" cried an old quarter-gunner at my side. He was bawling at the top of his compass; but in the gale, he seemed to be whispering; and I only heard him from his being right to windward of me.

But his hint was unnecessary; I dug my nails into the *jack-stays,* and swore that nothing but death should part me and them until I was able to turn round and look to windward. As yet, this was impossible; I could scarcely hear the man to leeward at my elbow; the wind seemed to snatch the words from his mouth and fly away with them to the South Pole.

All this while the sail itself was flying about, sometimes catching over our heads, and threatening to tear us from the yard in spite of all our hugging. For about three-quarters of an hour we thus hung suspended right over the rampant billows, which curled their very crests under the feet of some four or five of us clinging to the lee-yard-arm, as if to float us from our place.

Presently, the word passed along the yard from wind-ward, that we were ordered to come down and leave the sail to blow, since it could not be furled. A midshipman, it seemed, had been sent up by the officer of the deck to give the order, as no trumpet could be heard where we were.

Those on the weather yard-arm managed to crawl upon the spar and scramble down the rigging; but with us, upon the extreme leeward side, this feat was out of the question; it was, literary, like climbing a precipice to get to windward in order to reach the shrouds: besides, the entire yard was now encased in ice, and our hands and feet were so numb that we dared not trust our lives to them. Nevertheless, by assisting each other, we contrived to throw ourselves prostrate along the yard, and embrace it with our arms and legs. In this position, the stun'-sail-booms greatly assisted in securing our hold. Strange as it may appear, I do not suppose that, at this moment, the slightest sensation of fear was felt by one man on that yard. We clung to it with might and main; but this was instinct. The truth is, that, in circumstances like these, the sense of fear is annihilated in the unutterable sights that fill all the eye, and the sounds that fill all the ear. You become identified with the tempest; your insignificance is lost in the riot of the stormy universe around.

Below us, our noble frigate seemed thrice its real length—a vast black wedge, opposing its widest end to the combined fury of the sea and wind.

At length the first fury of the gale began to abate, and we at once fell to pounding our hands, as a preliminary operation to going to work; for a gang of men had now ascended to help secure what was left of the sail; we somehow packed it away, at last, and came down.

About noon the next day, the gale so moderated that we shook two reefs out of the top-sails, set new courses, and stood due east, with the wind astern.

Thus, all the fine weather we encountered after first weighing anchor on the pleasant Spanish coast, was but the prelude to this one terrific night; more especially, that treacherous calm immediately preceding it. But how could we reach our long-promised homes without encountering Cape Horn? by what possibility avoid it? And though some ships have weathered it without these perils, yet by far the greater part must encounter them. Lucky it is that it comes about midway in the homeward-bound passage, so that the sailors have time to prepare for it, and time to recover from it after it is astern.

But, sailor or landsman, there is some sort of a Cape Horn for all. Boys! beware of it; prepare for it in time. Gray-beards! thank God it is passed. And ye lucky livers, to whom, by some rare fatality, your Cape Horns are placid as Lake Lemans, flatter not yourselves that good luck is judgment and discretion; for all the yolk in your eggs, you might have foundered and gone down, had the Spirit of the Cape said the word.

Chapter XXVII

Some Thoughts Growing out of Mad Jack's Countermanding His Superior's Order

In time of peril, like the needle to the load-stone, obedience, irrespective of rank, generally flies to him who is best fitted to command. The truth of this seemed evinced in the case of Mad Jack, during the gale, and especially at that perilous moment when he countermanded the Captain's order at the helm. But every seaman knew, at the time, that the Captain's order was an unwise one in the extreme; perhaps worse than unwise.

These two orders given, by the Captain and his Lieutenant, exactly contrasted their characters. By putting the helm *hard up,* the Captain was for *scudding*; that is, for flying away from the gale. Whereas, Mad Jack was for running the ship into its teeth. It is needless to say that, in almost all cases of similar hard squalls and gales, the latter step, though attended with more appalling appearances is, in reality, the safer of the two, and the most generally adopted.

Scudding makes you a slave to the blast, which drives you headlong before it; but *running up into the wind's eye* enables you, in a degree, to hold it at bay. Scudding exposes to the gale your stern, the weakest part of your hull; the contrary course presents to it your bows, your strongest part. As with ships, so with men; he who turns his back to his foe gives him an advantage. Whereas, our ribbed chests, like the ribbed bows of a frigate, are as bulkheads to dam off an onset.

That night, off the pitch of the Cape, Captain Claret was hurried forth from his disguises, and, at a manhood-testing conjuncture, appeared in his true colors. A thing which every man in the ship had long suspected that night was proved true. Hitherto, in going about the ship, and casting his glances among the men, the peculiarly lusterless repose of the Captain's eye—his slow, even, unnecessarily methodical step, and the forced firmness of his whole demeanor—though, to a casual observer, expressive of the consciousness of command and a desire to strike subjection among the crew—all this, to some minds, had only been deemed indications of the fact that Captain Claret, while carefully shunning positive excesses, continually kept himself in an uncertain equilibrio between soberness and its reverse; which equilibrio might be destroyed by the first sharp vicissitude of events.

And though this is only a surmise, nevertheless, as having some knowledge of brandy and mankind, White-Jacket will venture to state that, had Captain Claret been an out-and-out temperance man, he would never have given that most imprudent order to *hard up* the helm. He would either have held his peace, and stayed in his cabin, like his gracious majesty the Commodore, or else have anticipated Mad Jack's order, and thundered forth "Hard down the helm!"

To show how little real sway at times have the severest restrictive laws, and how spontaneous is the instinct of discretion in some minds, it must here be added, that though Mad Jack, under a hot impulse, had countermanded an order of his superior officer before his very face, yet that severe Article of War, to which he thus rendered himself obnoxious, was never enforced against him. Nor, so far as any of the crew ever knew, did the Captain even venture to reprimand him for his temerity.

It has been said that Mad Jack himself was a lover of strong drink. So he was. But here we only see the virtue of being placed in a station constantly demanding a cool head and steady nerves, and the misfortune of filling a post that does *not* at all times demand these qualities. So exact and methodical in most things was the discipline of the frigate, that, to a certain extent, Captain Claret was exempted from personal interposition in many of its current events, and thereby, perhaps, was he lulled into security, under the enticing lee of his decanter.

But as for Mad Jack, he must stand his regular watches, and pace the quarter-deck at night, and keep a sharp eye to windward. Hence, at sea, Mad Jack tried to make a point of keeping sober, though in very fine weather he was sometimes betrayed into a glass too many. But with Cape Horn before him, he took the temperance pledge outright, till that perilous promontory should be far astern.

The leading incident of the gale irresistibly invites the question: Are there incompetent officers in the American navy?—that is, incompetent to the due performance of whatever duties may devolve upon them. But in that gallant marine, which, during the late war, gained so much of what is called *glory*, can there possibly be to-day incompetent officers?

As in the camp ashore, so on the quarter-deck at sea—the trumpets of one victory drown the muffled drums of a thousand defeats. And, in degree, this holds true of those events of war which are neuter in their character, neither making renown nor disgrace. Besides, as a long array of ciphers, led by but one solitary numeral, swell, by mere force of aggregation, into an immense arithmetical sum, even so, in some brilliant actions, do a crowd of officers, each inefficient in himself, aggregate renown when banded together, and led by a numeral Nelson or a Wellington. And the renown of such heroes, by outliving themselves, descends as a heritage to their subordinate survivors. One large brain and one large heart have virtue sufficient to magnetize a whole fleet or an army. And if all the men who, since the beginning of the world, have mainly contributed to the warlike successes or reverses of nations, were now mustered together, we should be amazed to behold but a handful of heroes. For there is no heroism in merely running in and out a gun at a port-hole, enveloped in smoke or vapor, or in firing off muskets in platoons at the word of command. This kind of merely manual valor is often born of trepidation at the heart. There may be men, individually craven, who, united, may display even temerity. Yet it would be false to deny that, in some instances, the lowest privates have acquitted themselves with even more gallantry than their commodores. True heroism is not in the hand, but in the heart and the head.

But are there incompetent officers in the gallant American navy? For an American, the question is of no grateful cast. White-Jacket must again evade it, by referring to an historical fact in the history of a kindred marine, which, from its long standing and magnitude, furnishes many more examples of all kinds than our own. And this is the only reason why it is ever referred to in this narrative. I thank God I am free from all national invidiousness.

It is indirectly on record in the books of the English Admiralty, that in the year 1808—after the death of Lord Nelson—when Lord Collingwood commanded on the Mediterranean station, and his broken health induced him to solicit a furlough, that out of a list of upward of one hundred admirals, not a single officer was found who was deemed qualified to relieve the applicant with credit to the country. This fact Collingwood sealed with his life; for, hopeless of being recalled, he shortly after died, worn out, at his post. Now, if this was the case in so renowned a marine as England's, what must be inferred with respect to our own? But herein no special disgrace is involved. For the truth is, that to be an accomplished and skillful naval generalissimo needs natural capabilities of an uncommon order. Still more, it may safely be asserted, that, worthily to command even a frigate, requires a degree of natural heroism, talent, judgment, and integrity, that is denied to mediocrity. Yet these qualifications are not only required, but demanded; and no one has a right to be a naval captain unless he possesses them.

Regarding Lieutenants, there are not a few Selvagees and Paper Jacks in the American navy. Many Commodores know that they have seldom taken a line-of-battle ship to sea, without feeling more or less nervousness when some of the Lieutenants have the deck at night.

According to the last Navy Register (1849), there are now 68 Captains in the American navy, collectively drawing about $300,000 annually from the public treasury; also, 297 Commanders, drawing about $200,000; and 377 Lieutenants, drawing about half a million; and 451 Midshipmen (including Passed-midshipmen), also drawing nearly half a million. Considering the known facts, that some of these officers are seldom or never sent to sea, owing to the Navy Department being well aware of their inefficiency; that others are detailed for pen-and-ink work at observatories, and solvers of logarithms in the Coast Survey; while the really meritorious officers, who are accomplished practical seamen, are known to be sent from ship to ship, with but small interval of a furlough; considering all this, it is not too much to say, that no small portion of the million and a half of money above mentioned is annually paid to national pensioners in disguise, who live on the navy without serving it.

Nothing like this can be even insinuated against the "*forward officers*"—Boatswains, Gunners, etc.; nor against the *petty officers*—Captains of the Tops, etc.; nor against the able-seamen in the navy. For if any of *these* are found wanting, they are forthwith disrated or discharged.

True, all experience teaches that, whenever there is a great national establishment, employing large numbers of officials, the public must be reconciled to support many incompetent men; for such is the favoritism and nepotism always prevailing in the purlieus of these establishments, that some incompetent persons are always admitted, to the exclusion of many of the worthy.

Nevertheless, in a country like ours, boasting of the political equality of all social conditions, it is a great reproach that such a thing as a common seaman rising to the rank of a commissioned officer in our navy, is nowadays almost unheard-of. Yet, in former times, when officers have so risen to rank, they have generally proved of signal usefulness in the service, and sometimes have reflected solid honor upon the country. Instances in point might be mentioned.

Is it not well to have our institutions of a piece? Any American landsman may hope to become President of the Union—commodore of our squadron of states. And every American sailor should be placed in such a position, that he might freely aspire to command a squadron of frigates.

Chapter XXVIII

EDGING AWAY

RIGHT BEFORE THE WIND! AY, BLOW, BLOW, YE BREEZES; SO LONG as *YE* STAY FAIR, AND *WE* ARE homeward bound, what care the jolly crew?

It is worth mentioning here that, in nineteen cases out of twenty, a passage from the Pacific round the Cape is almost sure to be much shorter, and attended with less hardship, than a passage undertaken from the Atlantic. The reason is, that the gales are mostly from the westward, also the currents.

But, after all, going before the wind in a frigate, in such a tempest, has its annoyances and drawbacks, as well as many other blessings. The disproportionate weight of metal upon the spar and gun decks induces a violent rolling, unknown to merchant ships. We rolled and rolled on our way, like the world in its orbit, shipping green seas on both sides, until the old frigate dipped and went into it like a diving-bell.

The hatchways of some armed vessels are but poorly secured in bad weather. This was peculiarly the ease with those of the *Neversink*. They were merely spread over with an old tarpaulin, cracked and rent in every direction.

In fair weather, the ship's company messed on the gun-deck; but as this was now flooded almost continually, we were obliged to take our meals upon the berth-deck, the next one below. One day, the messes of the starboard-watch were seated here at dinner; forming little groups, twelve or fifteen men in each, reclining about the beef-kids and their pots and pans; when all of a sudden the ship was seized with such a paroxysm of rolling that, in a single instant, everything on the berth-deck—pots, kids, sailors, pieces of beef, bread-bags, clothes-bags, and barges—were tossed indiscriminately from side to side. It was impossible to stay one's self; there was nothing but the bare deck to cling to, which was slippery with the contents of the kids, and heaving under us as if there were a volcano in the frigate's hold. While we were yet sliding in uproarious crowds—all seated—the windows of the deck opened, and floods of brine descended, simultaneously with a violent lee-roll. The shower was hailed by the reckless tars with a hurricane of yells; although, for an instant, I really imagined we were about being swamped in the sea, such volumes of water came cascading down.

A day or two after, we had made sufficient Easting to stand to the northward, which we did, with the wind astern; thus fairly turning the corner without abating our rate of progress. Though we had seen no land since leaving Callao, Cape Horn was said to be somewhere to the west of us; and though there was no positive evidence of the fact, the weather encountered might be accounted pretty good presumptive proof.

The land near Cape Horn, however, is well worth seeing, especially Staten Land. Upon one occasion, the ship in which I then happened to be sailing drew near this place from the northward, with a fair, free wind, blowing steadily, through a bright translucent day, whose air was almost musical with the clear, glittering cold. On our starboard beam, like a pile of glaciers in Switzerland, lay this Staten Land, gleaming in snow-white barrenness and solitude. Unnumbered white albatross were skimming the sea nearby, and clouds of smaller white wings fell through the air like snowflakes. High, towering in their own turbaned snows, the far-inland pinnacles loomed up, like the border of some other world. Flashing walls and crystal battlements, like the diamond watch-towers along heaven's furthest frontier.

After leaving the latitude of the Cape, we had several storms of snow; one night a considerable quantity laid upon the decks, and some of the sailors enjoyed the juvenile diversion of snow-balling. Woe unto the "middy" who that night went forward of the booms. Such a target for snow-balls! The throwers could never be known. By some curious sleight in hurling the missiles, they seemed to be thrown on board by some hoydenish sea-nymphs outside the frigate.

At daybreak Midshipman Pert went below to the surgeon with an alarming wound, gallantly received in discharging his perilous duty on the forecastle. The officer of the deck had sent him on an errand, to tell the boatswain that he was wanted in the captain's cabin. While in the very act of performing the exploit of delivering the message, Mr. Pert was struck on the nose with a snow-ball of wondrous compactness. Upon being informed of the disaster, the rogues expressed the liveliest sympathy. Pert was no favorite.

After one of these storms, it was a curious sight to see the men relieving the uppermost deck of its load of snow. It became the duty of the captain of each gun to keep his own station clean; accordingly, with an old broom, or "squilgee," he proceeded to business, often quarreling with his next-door neighbors about their scraping their snow on his premises. It was like Broadway in winter, the morning after a storm, when rival shop-boys are at work cleaning the sidewalk.

Now and then, by way of variety, we had a fall of hail-stones, so big that sometimes we found ourselves dodging them.

The Commodore had a Polynesian servant on board, whose services he had engaged at the Society Islands. Unlike his countrymen, Wooloo was of a sedate, earnest, and philosophic temperament. Having never been outside of the tropics before, he found many phenomena off Cape Horn, which absorbed his attention, and set him, like other philosophers, to feign theories corresponding to the marvels he beheld. At the first snow, when he saw the deck covered all over with a white powder, as it were, he expanded his eyes into stewpans; but upon examining the strange substance, he decided that this must be a species of super-fine flour, such as was compounded into his master's *"duffs,"* and other dainties. In vain did an experienced natural philosopher belonging to the foretop maintain before his face, that in this hypothesis Wooloo was mistaken. Wooloo's opinion remained unchanged for some time.

As for the hail-stones, they transported him; he went about with a bucket, making collections, and receiving contributions, for the purpose of carrying them home to his sweethearts for glass beads; but having put his bucket away, and returning to it again, and finding nothing but a little water, he accused the bystanders of stealing his precious stones.

This suggests another story concerning him. The first time he was given a piece of "duff" to eat, he was observed to pick out very carefully every raisin, and throw it away, with a gesture indicative of the highest disgust. It turned out that he had taken the raisins for bugs.

In our man-of-war, this semi-savage, wandering about the gun-deck in his barbaric robe, seemed a being from some other sphere. His tastes were our abominations: ours his. Our creed he rejected: his we. We thought him a loon: he fancied us fools. Had the case been reversed; had we been Polynesians and he an American, our mutual opinion of each other would still have remained the same. A fact proving that neither was wrong, but both right.

Chapter XXIX

THE NIGHT-WATCHES

THOUGH LEAVING THE CAPE BEHIND US, THE SEVERE COLD STILL CONTINUED, AND ONE OF ITS worst consequences was the almost incurable drowsiness induced thereby during the long night-watches. All along the decks, huddled between the guns, stretched out on the carronade-slides, and in every accessible nook and corner, you would see the sailors wrapped in their monkey jackets, in a state of half-conscious torpidity, lying still and freezing alive, without the power to rise and shake themselves.

"Up—up, you lazy dogs!" our good-natured Third Lieutenant, a Virginian, would cry, rapping them with his speaking trumpet. "Get up, and stir about."

But in vain. They would rise for an instant, and as soon as his back was turned, down they would drop, as if shot through the heart.

Often I have lain thus when the fact, that if I laid much longer I would actually freeze to death, would come over me with such overpowering force as to break the icy spell, and starting to my feet, I would endeavor to go through the combined manual and pedal exercise to restore the circulation. The first fling of my benumbed arm generally struck me in the face, instead of smiting my chest, its true destination. But in these cases one's muscles have their own way.

In exercising my other extremities, I was obliged to hold on to something, and leap with both feet; for my limbs seemed as destitute of joints as a pair of canvas pants spread to dry, and frozen stiff.

When an order was given to haul the braces—which required the strength of the entire watch, some two hundred men—a spectator would have supposed that all hands had received a stroke of the palsy. Roused from their state of enchantment, they came halting and limping across the decks, falling against each other, and, for a few moments, almost unable to handle the ropes. The slightest exertion seemed intolerable; and frequently a body of eighty or a hundred men summoned to brace the main-yard, would hang over the rope for several minutes, waiting for some active fellow to pick it up and put it into their hands. Even then, it was some time before they were able to do anything. They made all the motions usual in hauling a rope, but it was a long time before the yard budged an inch. It was to no purpose that the officers swore at them, or sent the midshipmen among them to find out who those *"horse-marines"* and *"sogers"* were. The sailors were so enveloped in monkey jackets, that in the dark night there was no telling one from the other.

"Here, *you*, sir!" cries little Mr. Pert eagerly catching hold of the skirts of an old sea-dog, and trying to turn him round, so as to peer under his tarpaulin. "Who are *you*, sir? What's your name?"

"Find out, Milk-and-Water," was the impertinent rejoinder.

"Blast you! you old rascal; I'll have you licked for that! Tell me his name, some of you!" turning round to the bystanders.

"Gammon!" cries a voice at a distance.

"Hang me, but I know *you*, sir! and here's at you!" and, so saying, Mr. Pert drops the impenetrable unknown, and makes into the crowd after the bodiless voice. But the attempt to find an owner for that voice is quite as idle as the effort to discover the contents of the monkey jacket.

And here sorrowful mention must be made of something which, during this state of affairs, most sorely afflicted me. Most monkey jackets are of a dark hue; mine, as I have fifty times repeated, and say again, was white. And thus, in those long, dark nights, when it was my quarter-watch on deck, and not in the top, and others went skulking and "sogering" about the decks, secure from detection—their identity undiscoverable—my own hapless jacket forever proclaimed the name of its wearer. It gave me many a hard job, which otherwise I should have escaped. When an officer wanted a man for any particular duty—running aloft, say, to communicate some slight order to the captains of the tops—how easy, in that mob of incognitoes, to individualize *"that white jacket,"* and dispatch him on the errand. Then, it would never do for me to hang back when the ropes were being pulled.

Indeed, upon all these occasions, such alacrity and cheerfulness was I obliged to display, that I was frequently held up as an illustrious example of activity, which the rest were called upon to emulate. "Pull—pull! you lazy lubbers! Look at White-Jacket, there; pull like him!"

Oh! how I execrated my luckless garment; how often I scoured the deck with it to give it a tawny hue; how often I supplicated the inexorable Brush, captain of the paint-room, for just one brushful of his invaluable pigment. Frequently, I meditated giving it a toss overboard; but I had not the resolution. Jacketless at sea! Jacketless so near Cape Horn! The thought was unendurable. And, at least, my garment was a jacket in name, if not in utility.

At length I essayed a "swap." "Here, Bob," said I, assuming all possible suavity, and accosting a mess-mate with a sort of diplomatic assumption of superiority, "suppose I was ready to part with this 'grego' of mine, and take yours in exchange—what would you give me to boot?"

"Give you to *boot?*" he exclaimed, with horror; "I wouldn't take your infernal jacket for a gift!"

How I hailed every snow-squall; for then—blessings on them!—many of the men became *white-jackets* along with myself; and, powdered with the flakes, we all looked like millers.

We had six lieutenants, all of whom, with the exception of the First Lieutenant, by turns headed the watches. Three of these officers, including Mad Jack, were strict disciplinarians, and never permitted us to lay down on deck during the night. And, to tell the truth, though it caused much growling, it was far better for our health to be thus kept on our feet. So promenading was all the vogue. For some of us, however, it was like pacing in a dungeon; for, as we had to keep at our stations—some at the halyards, some at the braces, and elsewhere—and were not allowed to stroll about indefinitely, and fairly take the measure of the ship's entire keel, we were fain to confine ourselves to the space of a very few feet. But the worse of this was soon over. The suddenness of the change in the temperature consequent on leaving Cape Horn, and steering to the northward with a ten-knot breeze, is a noteworthy thing. To-day, you are assailed by a blast that seems to have edged itself on icebergs; but in a little more than a week, your jacket may be superfluous.

One word more about Cape Horn, and we have done with it.

Years hence, when a ship-canal shall have penetrated the Isthmus of Darien, and the traveler be taking his seat in the ears at Cape Cod for Astoria, it will be held a thing almost incredible that, for so long a period, vessels bound to the Nor'-west Coast from New York should, by going round Cape Horn, have lengthened their voyages some thousands of miles. "In those unenlightened days" (I quote, in advance, the language of some future philosopher), "entire years were frequently consumed in making the voyage to and from the Spice Islands, the present fashionable watering-place of the beau-monde of Oregon." Such must be our national progress.

Why, sir, that boy of yours will, one of these days, be sending your grandson to the salubrious city of Jeddo to spend his summer vacations.

Chapter XXX

A Peep through a Port-Hole at the Subterranean Parts of a Man-of-War

WHILE NOW RUNNING RAPIDLY AWAY FROM THE BITTER COAST OF PATAGONIA, BATTLING WITH the night-watches—still cold—as best we may; come under the lee of my white-jacket, reader, while I tell of the less painful sights to be seen in a frigate.

A hint has already been conveyed concerning the subterranean depths of the *Neversink*'s hold. But there is no time here to speak of the *spirit-room,* a cellar down in the after-hold, where the sailor's "grog" is kept; nor of the *cabletiers,* where the great hawsers and chains are piled, as you see them at a large ship-chandler's on shore; nor of the grocer's vaults, where tierces of sugar, molasses, vinegar, rice, and flour are snugly stowed; nor of the *sail-room,* full as a sail-maker's loft ashore—piled up with great top-sails and top-gallant-sails, all ready-folded in their places, like so many white vests in a gentleman's wardrobe; nor of the copper and copper-fastened *magazine,* closely packed with kegs of powder, great-gun and small-arm cartridges; nor of the immense *shot-lockers,* or subterranean arsenals, full as a bushel of apples with twenty-four-pound balls; nor of the *bread-room,* a large apartment, tinned all round within to keep out the mice, where the hard biscuit destined for the consumption of five hundred men on a long voyage is stowed away by the cubic yard; nor of the vast iron *tanks* for fresh water in the hold, like the reservoir lakes at Fairmount, in Philadelphia; nor of the *paint-room,* where the kegs of white-lead, and casks of linseed oil, and all sorts of pots and brushes, are kept; nor of the *armoror's smithy,* where the ship's forges and anvils may be heard ringing at times; I say I have no time to speak of these things, and many more places of note.

But there is one very extensive warehouse among the rest that needs special mention—*the ship's Yeoman's store-room.* In the *Neversink* it was down in the ship's basement, beneath the berth-deck, and you went to it by way of the *Fore-passage,* a very dim, devious corridor, indeed. Entering—say at noonday—you find yourself in a gloomy apartment, lit by a solitary lamp. On one side are shelves, filled with balls of *marline, ratlin-stuff, seizing-stuff, spun-yarn,* and numerous twines of assorted sizes. In another direction you see large cases containing heaps of articles, reminding one of a shoemaker's furnishing-store—wooden *serving-mallets, fids, toggles,* and *heavers*: iron *prickers* and *marling-spikes*; in a third quarter you see a sort of hardware shop—shelves piled with all manner of hooks, bolts, nails, screws, and *thimbles*; and, in still another direction, you see a block-maker's store, heaped up with lignum-vitae sheeves and wheels.

Through low arches in the bulkhead beyond, you peep in upon distant vaults and catacombs, obscurely lighted in the far end, and showing immense coils of new ropes, and other bulky articles, stowed in tiers, all savoring of tar.

But by far the most curious department of these mysterious store-rooms is the armory, where the spikes, cutlasses, pistols, and belts, forming the arms of the boarders in time of action, are hung against the walls, and suspended in thick rows from the beams overhead. Here, too, are to be seen scores of Colt's patent revolvers, which, though furnished with but one tube, multiply the fatal bullets, as the naval cat-o'-nine-tails, with a cannibal cruelty, in one blow nine times multiplies a culprit's lashes; so that when a sailor is ordered one dozen lashes, the sentence should read one hundred and eight. All these arms are kept in the brightest order, wearing a fine polish, and may truly be said to *reflect* credit on the Yeoman and his mates.

Among the lower grade of officers in a man-of-war, that of Yeoman is not the least important. His responsibilities are denoted by his pay. While the *petty officers,* quarter-gunners, captains of the tops, and others, receive but fifteen and eighteen dollars a month—but little more than a mere able-seamen—the Yeoman in an American line-of-battle ship receives forty dollars, and in a frigate thirty-five dollars per month.

He is accountable for all the articles under his charge, and on no account must deliver a yard of twine or a ten-penny nail to the boatswain or carpenter, unless shown a written requisition and order from the Senior Lieutenant. The Yeoman is to be found burrowing in his underground store-rooms all the day long, in readiness to serve licensed customers. But in the counter, behind which he usually stands, there is no place for a till to drop the shillings in, which takes away not a little from the most agreeable part of a storekeeper's duties. Nor, among the musty, old account-books in his desk, where he registers all expenditures of his stuffs, is there any cash or check-book.

The Yeoman of the *Neversink* was a somewhat odd specimen of a Troglodyte. He was a little old man, round-shouldered, bald-headed, with great goggle-eyes, looking through portentous round spectacles, which he called his *barnacles.* He was imbued with a wonderful zeal for the naval service, and seemed to think that, in keeping his pistols and cutlasses free from rust, he preserved the national honor untarnished.

After *general quarters,* it was amusing to watch his anxious air as the various *petty officers* restored to him the arms used at the martial exercises of the crew. As successive bundles would be deposited on his counter, he would count over the pistols and cutlasses, like an old housekeeper telling over her silver forks and spoons in a pantry before retiring for the night. And often, with a sort of dark lantern in his hand, he might be seen poking into his furthest vaults and cellars, and counting over his great coils of ropes, as if they were all jolly puncheons of old Port and Madeira.

By reason of his incessant watchfulness and unaccountable bachelor oddities, it was very difficult for him to retain in his employment the various sailors who, from time to time, were billeted with him to do the duty of subalterns. In particular, he was always desirous of having at least one steady, faultless young man, of a literary taste, to keep an eye to his account-books, and swab out the armory every morning. It was an odious business this, to be immured all day in such a bottomless hole, among tarry old ropes and villainous guns and pistols. It was with peculiar dread that I one day noticed the goggle-eyes of *Old Revolver,* as they called him, fastened upon me with a fatal glance of good-will and approbation. He had somehow heard of my being a very learned person, who could both read and write with extraordinary facility; and moreover that I was a rather reserved youth, who kept his modest, unassuming merits in the background. But though, from the keen sense of my situation as a man-of-war's-man all this about my keeping myself in the *back* ground was true enough, yet I had no idea of hiding my diffident merits *under* ground. I became alarmed at the old Yeoman's goggling glances, lest he should drag me down into tarry perdition in his hideous store-rooms. But this fate was providentially averted, owing to mysterious causes which I never could fathom.

Chapter XXXI

THE GUNNER UNDER HATCHES

AMONG SUCH A CROWD OF MARKED CHARACTERS AS WERE TO BE MET WITH ON BOARD OUR frigate, many of whom moved in mysterious circles beneath the lowermost deck, and at long intervals flitted into sight like apparitions, and disappeared again for whole weeks together, there were some who inordinately excited my curiosity, and whose names, callings, and precise abodes I industriously sought out, in order to learn something satisfactory concerning them.

While engaged in these inquiries, often fruitless, or but partially gratified, I could not but regret that there was no public printed Directory for the *Neversink,* such as they have in large towns, containing an alphabetic list of all the crew, and where they might be found. Also, in losing myself in some remote, dark corner of the bowels of the frigate, in the vicinity of the various store-rooms, shops, and warehouses, I much lamented that no enterprising tar had yet thought of compiling a *Hand-book of the Neversink,* so that the tourist might have a reliable guide.

Indeed, there were several parts of the ship under hatches shrouded in mystery, and completely inaccessible to the sailor. Wondrous old doors, barred and bolted in dingy bulkheads, must have opened into regions full of interest to a successful explorer.

They looked like the gloomy entrances to family vaults of buried dead; and when I chanced to see some unknown functionary insert his key, and enter these inexplicable apartments with a battle-lantern, as if on solemn official business, I almost quaked to dive in with him, and satisfy myself whether these vaults indeed contained the moldering relics of by-gone old Commodores and Post-captains. But the habitations of the living commodore and captain—their spacious and curtained cabins—were themselves almost as sealed volumes, and I passed them in hopeless wonderment, like a peasant before a prince's palace. Night and day armed sentries guarded their sacred portals, cutlass in hand; and had I dared to cross their path, I would infallibly have been cut down, as if in battle. Thus, though for a period of more than a year I was an inmate of this floating box of live-oak, yet there were numberless things in it that, to the last, remained wrapped in obscurity, or concerning which I could only lose myself in vague speculations. I was as a Roman Jew of the Middle Ages, confined to the Jews' quarter of the town, and forbidden to stray beyond my limits. Or I was as a modern traveler in the same famous city, forced to quit it at last without gaining ingress to the most mysterious haunts—the innermost shrine of the Pope, and the dungeons and cells of the Inquisition.

But among all the persons and things on board that puzzled me, and filled me most with strange emotions of doubt, misgivings and mystery, was the Gunner—a short, square, grim man, his hair and beard grizzled and singed, as if with gunpowder. His skin was of a flecky brown, like the stained barrel of a fowling-piece, and his hollow eyes burned in his head like blue-lights. He it was who had access to many of those mysterious vaults I have spoken of. Often he might be seen groping his way into them, followed by his subalterns, the old quarter-gunners, as if intent upon laying a train of powder to blow up the ship. I remembered Guy Fawkes and the Parliament-house, and made earnest inquiry whether this gunner was a Roman Catholic. I felt relieved when informed that he was not.

A little circumstance which one of his *mates* once told me heightened the gloomy interest with which I regarded his chief. He told me that, at periodical intervals, his master the Gunner, accompanied by his phalanx, entered into the great Magazine under the Gun-room, of which he had sole custody and kept the key, nearly as big as the key of the Bastille, and provided with lanterns, something like Sir Humphrey Davy's Safety-lamp for coal mines, proceeded to turn, end for end, all the kegs of powder and packages of cartridges stored in this innermost explosive vault, lined throughout with sheets of copper. In the vestibule of the Magazine, against the paneling, were several pegs for slippers, and, before penetrating further than that vestibule, every man of the gunner's gang silently removed his shoes, for fear that the nails in their heels might possibly create a spark, by striking against the coppered floor within. Then, with slippered feet and with hushed whispers, they stole into the heart of the place.

This turning of the powder was to preserve its inflammability. And surely it was a business full of direful interest, to be buried so deep below the sun, handling whole barrels of powder, any one of which, touched by the smallest spark, was powerful enough to blow up a whole street of warehouses.

The gunner went by the name of *Old Combustibles,* though I thought this an undignified name for so momentous a personage, who had all our lives in his hand.

While we lay in Callao, we received from shore several barrels of powder. So soon as the *launch* came alongside with them, orders were given to extinguish all lights and all fires in the ship; and the master-at-arms and his corporals inspected every deck to see that this order was obeyed; a very prudent precaution, no doubt, but not observed at all in the Turkish navy. The Turkish sailors will sit on their gun-carriages, tranquilly smoking, while kegs of powder are being rolled under their ignited pipe-bowls. This shows the great comfort there is in the doctrine of these Fatalists, and how such a doctrine, in some things at least, relieves men from nervous anxieties. But we all are Fatalists at bottom. Nor need we so much marvel at the heroism of that army officer, who challenged his personal foe to bestride a barrel of powder with him—the match to be placed between them—and be blown up in good company, for it is pretty certain that the whole earth itself is a vast hogshead, full of inflammable materials, and which we are always bestriding; at the same time, that all good Christians believe that at any minute the last day may come and the terrible combustion of the entire planet ensue.

As if impressed with a befitting sense of the awfulness of his calling, our gunner always wore a fixed expression of solemnity, which was heightened by his grizzled hair and beard. But what imparted such a sinister look to him, and what wrought so upon my imagination concerning this man, was a frightful scar crossing his left cheek and forehead. He had been almost mortally wounded, they said, with a saber-cut, during a frigate engagement in the last war with Britain.

He was the most methodical, exact, and punctual of all the forward officers. Among his other duties, it pertained to him, while in harbor, to see that at a certain hour in the evening one of the great guns was discharged from the forecastle, a ceremony only observed in a flag-ship. And always at the precise moment you might behold him blowing his match, then applying it; and with that booming thunder in his ear, and the smell of the powder in his hair, he retired to his hammock for the night. What dreams he must have had!

The same precision was observed when ordered to fire a gun to *bring to* some ship at sea; for, true to their name, and preserving its applicability, even in times of peace, all men-of-war are great bullies on the high seas. They domineer over the poor merchantmen, and with a hissing hot ball sent bowling across the ocean, compel them to stop their headway at pleasure.

It was enough to make you a man of method for life, to see the gunner superintending his subalterns, when preparing the main-deck batteries for a great national salute. While lying in harbor, intelligence reached us of the lamentable casualty that befell certain high officers of state, including the acting Secretary of the Navy himself, some other member of the President's cabinet, a Commodore, and others, all engaged in experimenting upon a new-fangled engine of war. At the same time with the receipt of this sad news, orders arrived to fire minute-guns for the deceased head of the naval department. Upon this occasion the gunner was more than usually ceremonious, in seeing that the long twenty-fours were thoroughly loaded and rammed down, and then accurately marked with chalk, so as to be discharged in undeviating rotation, first from the larboard side, and then from the starboard.

But as my ears hummed, and all my bones danced in me with the reverberating din, and my eyes and nostrils were almost suffocated with the smoke, and when I saw this grim old gunner firing away so solemnly, I thought it a strange mode of honoring a man's memory who had himself been slaughtered by a cannon. Only the smoke, that, after rolling in at the port-holes, rapidly drifted away to leeward, and was lost to view, seemed truly emblematical touching the personage thus honored, since that great non-combatant, the Bible, assures us that our life is but a vapor, that quickly passeth away.

Chapter XXXII

A DISH OF DUNDERFUNK

IN MEN-OF-WAR, THE SPACE ON THE UPPERMOST DECK, ROUND ABOUT THE MAIN-MAST, IS THE Police-office, Court-house, and yard of execution, where all charges are lodged, causes tried, and punishment administered. In frigate phrase, to be *brought up to the mast,* is equivalent to being presented before the grand-jury, to see whether a true bill will be found against you.

From the merciless, inquisitorial *baiting,* which sailors, charged with offenses, too often experience *at the mast,* that vicinity is usually known among them as the *bull-ring.*

The main-mast, moreover, is the only place where the sailor can hold formal communication with the captain and officers. If anyone has been robbed; if anyone has been evilly entreated; if anyone's character has been defamed; if anyone has a request to present; if anyone has aught important for the executive of the ship to know—straight to the main-mast he repairs; and stands there—generally with his hat off—waiting the pleasure of the officer of the deck, to advance and communicate with him. Often, the most ludicrous scenes occur, and the most comical complaints are made.

One clear, cold morning, while we were yet running away from the Cape, a raw-boned, crack-pated Down Easter, belonging to the Waist, made his appearance at the mast, dolefully exhibiting a blackened tin pan, bearing a few crusty traces of some sort of a sea-pie, which had been cooked in it.

"Well, sir, what now?" said the Lieutenant of the Deck, advancing.

"They stole it, sir; all my nice *dunderfunk,* sir; they did, sir," whined the Down Easter, ruefully holding up his pan.

"Stole your *dunderfunk!* what's that?"

"*Dunderfunk,* sir, *dunderfunk*; a cruel nice dish as ever man put into him."

"Speak out, sir; what's the matter?"

"My *dunderfunk,* sir—as elegant a dish of *dunderfunk* as you ever see, sir—they stole it, sir!"

"Go forward, you rascal!" cried the Lieutenant, in a towering rage, "or else stop your whining. Tell me, what's the matter?"

"Why, sir, them 'ere two fellows, Dobs and Hodnose, stole my *dunderfunk.*"

"Once more, sir, I ask what that *dundledunk* is? Speak!"

"As cruel a nice——"

"Be off, sir! sheer!" and muttering something about *non compos mentis,* the Lieutenant stalked away; while the Down Easter beat a melancholy retreat, holding up his pan like a tambourine, and making dolorous music on it as he went.

"Where are you going with that tear in your eye, like a traveling rat?" cried a top-man.

"Oh! he's going home to Down East," said another; "so far eastward, you know, *shippy,* that they have to pry up the sun with a handspike."

To make this anecdote plainer, be it said that, at sea, the monotonous round of salt beef and pork at the messes of the sailors—where but very few of the varieties of the season are to be found—induces them to adopt many contrivances in order to diversify their meals. Hence the various sea-rolls, made dishes, and Mediterranean pies, well known by men-of-war's-men—*Scouse, Lob-scouse, Soft-Tack, Soft-Tommy, Skillagalee, Burgoo, Dough-boys, Lob-Dominion, Dog's-Body,* and lastly, and least known, *Dunderfunk*; all of which come under the general denomination of *Manavalins.*

Dunderfunk is made of hard biscuit, hashed and pounded, mixed with beef fat, molasses, and water, and baked brown in a pan. And to those who are beyond all reach of shore delicacies, this *dunderfunk,* in the feeling language of the Down Easter, is certainly "*a cruel nice dish.*"

Now the only way that a sailor, after preparing his *dunderfunk,* could get it cooked on board the *Neversink,* was by slyly going to *Old Coffee,* the ship's cook, and bribing him to put it into his oven. And as some such dishes or other are well known to be all the time in the oven, a set of unprincipled gourmands are constantly on the look-out for the chance of stealing them. Generally, two or three league together, and while one engages *Old Coffee* in some interesting conversation touching his wife and family at home, another snatches the first thing he can lay hands on in the oven, and rapidly passes it to the third man, who at his earliest leisure disappears with it.

In this manner had the Down Easter lost his precious pie, and afterward found the empty pan knocking about the forecastle.

Chapter XXXIII

A FLOGGING

IF YOU BEGIN THE DAY WITH A LAUGH, YOU MAY, NEVERTHELESS, END IT WITH A SOB AND A SIGH.

Among the many who were exceedingly diverted with the scene between the Down Easter and the Lieutenant, none laughed more heartily than John, Peter, Mark, and Antone—four sailors of the starboard-watch. The same evening these four found themselves prisoners in the "brig," with a sentry standing over them. They were charged with violating a well-known law of the ship—having been engaged in one of those tangled, general fights sometimes occurring among sailors. They had nothing to anticipate but a flogging, at the captain's pleasure.

Toward evening of the next day, they were startled by the dread summons of the boatswain and his mates at the principal hatchway—a summons that ever sends a shudder through every manly heart in a frigate:

"All hands witness punishment, ahoy!"

The hoarseness of the cry, its unrelenting prolongation, its being caught up at different points, and sent through the lowermost depths of the ship; all this produces a most dismal effect upon every heart not calloused by long habituation to it.

However much you may desire to absent yourself from the scene that ensues, yet behold it you must; or, at least, stand near it you must; for the regulations enjoin the attendance of the entire ship's company, from the corpulent Captain himself to the smallest boy who strikes the bell.

"All hands witness punishment, ahoy!"

To the sensitive seaman that summons sounds like a doom. He knows that the same law which impels it—the same law by which the culprits of the day must suffer; that by that very law he also is liable at any time to be judged and condemned. And the inevitableness of his own presence at the scene; the strong arm that drags him in view of the scourge, and holds him there till all is over; forcing upon his loathing eye and soul the sufferings and groans of men who have familiarly consorted with him, eaten with him, battled out watches with him—men of his own type and badge—all this conveys a terrible hint of the omnipotent authority under which he lives. Indeed, to such a man the naval summons to witness punishment carries a thrill, somewhat akin to what we may impute to the quick and the dead, when they shall hear the Last Trump, that is to bid them all arise in their ranks, and behold the final penalties inflicted upon the sinners of our race.

But it must not be imagined that to all men-of-war's-men this summons conveys such poignant emotions; but it is hard to decide whether one should be glad or sad that this is not the case; whether it is grateful to know that so much pain is avoided, or whether it is far sadder to think that, either from constitutional hard-heartedness or the multiplied searings of habit, hundreds of men-of-war's-men have been made proof against the sense of degradation, pity, and shame.

As if in sympathy with the scene to be enacted, the sun, which the day previous had merrily flashed upon the tin pan of the disconsolate Down Easter, was now setting over the dreary waters, veiling itself in vapors. The wind blew hoarsely in the cordage; the seas broke heavily against the bows; and the frigate, staggering under whole top-sails, strained as in agony on her way.

"All hands witness punishment, ahoy!"

At the summons the crew crowded round the main-mast; multitudes eager to obtain a good place on the booms, to overlook the scene; many laughing and chatting, others canvassing the case of the culprits; some maintaining sad, anxious countenances, or carrying a suppressed indignation in their eyes; a few purposely keeping behind to avoid looking on; in short, among five hundred men, there was every possible shade of character.

All the officers—midshipmen included—stood together in a group on the starboard side of the main-mast; the First Lieutenant in advance, and the surgeon, whose special duty it is to be present at such times, standing close by his side.

Presently the Captain came forward from his cabin, and stood in the center of this solemn group, with a small paper in his hand. That paper was the daily report of offenses, regularly laid upon his table every morning or evening, like the day's journal placed by a bachelor's napkin at breakfast.

"Master-at-arms, bring up the prisoners," he said.

A few moments elapsed, during which the Captain, now clothed in his most dreadful attributes, fixed his eyes severely upon the crew, when suddenly a lane formed through the crowd of seamen, and the prisoners advanced—the master-at-arms, rattan in hand, on one side, and an armed marine on the other—and took up their stations at the mast.

"You John, you Peter, you Mark, you Antone," said the Captain, "were yesterday found fighting on the gun-deck. Have you anything to say?"

Mark and Antone, two steady, middle-aged men, whom I had often admired for their sobriety, replied that they did not strike the first blow; that they had submitted to much before they had yielded to their passions; but as they acknowledged that they had at last defended themselves, their excuse was overruled.

John—a brutal bully, who, it seems, was the real author of the disturbance—was about entering into a long extenuation, when he was cut short by being made to confess, irrespective of circumstances, that he had been in the fray.

Peter, a handsome lad about nineteen years old, belonging to the mizzen-top, looked pale and tremulous. He was a great favorite in his part of the ship, and especially in his own mess, principally composed of lads of his own age. That morning two of his young mess-mates had gone to his bag, taken out his best clothes, and, obtaining the permission of the marine sentry at the "brig," had handed them to him, to be put on against being summoned to the mast. This was done to propitiate the Captain, as most captains love to see a tidy sailor. But it would not do. To all his supplications the Captain turned a deaf ear. Peter declared that he had been struck twice before he had returned a blow. "No matter," said the Captain, "you struck at last, instead of reporting the case to an officer. I allow no man to fight on board here but myself. *I* do the fighting."

"Now, men," he added, "you all admit the charge; you know the penalty. Strip! Quarter-masters, are the gratings rigged?"

The gratings are square frames of barred wood-work, sometimes placed over the hatchways. One of these squares was now laid on the deck, close to the ship's bulwarks, and while the remaining preparations were being made, the master-at-arms assisted the prisoners in removing their jackets and shirts. This done, their shirts were loosely thrown over their shoulders.

At a sign from the Captain, John, with a shameless leer, advanced, and stood passively upon the grating, while the bare-headed old quarter-master, with gray hair streaming in the wind, bound his feet to the cross-bars, and, stretching out his arms over his head, secured them to the hammock-nettings above. He then retreated a little space, standing silent.

Meanwhile, the boatswain stood solemnly on the other side, with a green bag in his hand, from which, taking four instruments of punishment, he gave one to each of his mates; for a fresh "cat" applied by a fresh hand, is the ceremonious privilege accorded to every man-of-war culprit.

At another sign from the Captain, the master-at-arms, stepping up, removed the shirt from the prisoner. At this juncture a wave broke against the ship's side, and clashed the spray over his exposed back. But though the air was piercing cold, and the water drenched him, John stood still, without a shudder.

The Captain's finger was now lifted, and the first boatswain's-mate advanced, combing out the nine tails of his *cat* with his hand, and then, sweeping them round his neck, brought them with the whole force of his body upon the mark. Again, and again, and again; and at every blow, higher and higher rose the long, purple bars on the prisoner's back. But he only bowed over his head, and stood still. Meantime, some of the crew whispered among themselves in applause of their ship-mate's nerve; but the greater part were breathlessly silent as the keen scourge hissed through the wintry air, and fell with a cutting, wiry sound upon the mark. One dozen lashes being applied, the man was taken down, and went among the crew with a smile, saying, "D—n me! it's nothing when you're used to it! Who wants to fight?"

The next was Antone, the Portuguese. At every blow he surged from side to side, pouring out a torrent of involuntary blasphemies. Never before had he been heard to curse. When cut down, he went among the men, swearing to have the life of the Captain. Of course, this was unheard by the officers.

Mark, the third prisoner, only cringed and coughed under his punishment. He had some pulmonary complaint. He was off duty for several days after the flogging; but this was partly to be imputed to his extreme mental misery. It was his first scourging, and he felt the insult more than the injury. He became silent and sullen for the rest of the cruise.

The fourth and last was Peter, the mizzen-top lad. He had often boasted that he had never been degraded at the gangway. The day before his cheek had worn its usual red but now no ghost was whiter. As he was being secured to the gratings, and the shudderings and creepings of his dazzlingly white back were revealed, he turned round his head imploringly; but his weeping entreaties and vows of contrition were of no avail. "I would not forgive God Almighty!" cried the Captain. The fourth boatswain's-mate advanced, and at the first blow, the boy, shouting *"My God! Oh! my God!"* writhed and leaped so as to displace the gratings, and scatter the nine tails of the scourge all over his person. At the next blow he howled, leaped, and raged in unendurable torture.

"What are you stopping for, boatswain's-mate?" cried the Captain. "Lay on!" and the whole dozen was applied.

"I don't care what happens to me now!" wept Peter, going among the crew, with blood-shot eyes, as he put on his shirt. "I have been flogged once, and they may do it again, if they will. Let them look for me now!"

"Pipe down!" cried the Captain, and the crew slowly dispersed.

Let us have the charity to believe them—as we do—when some Captains in the Navy say, that the thing of all others most repulsive to them, in the routine of what they consider their duty, is the administration of corporal punishment upon the crew; for, surely, not to feel scarified to the quick at these scenes would argue a man but a beast.

You see a human being, stripped like a slave; scourged worse than a hound. And for what? For things not essentially criminal, but only made so by arbitrary laws.

Chapter XXXIV

SOME OF THE EVIL EFFECTS OF FLOGGING

THERE ARE INCIDENTAL CONSIDERATIONS TOUCHING THIS MATTER OF FLOGGING, WHICH EXAGgerate the evil into a great enormity. Many illustrations might be given, but let us be content with a few.

One of the arguments advanced by officers of the Navy in favor of corporal punishment is this: it can be inflicted in a moment; it consumes no valuable time; and when the prisoner's shirt is put on, *that* is the last of it. Whereas, if another punishment were substituted, it would probably occasion a great waste of time and trouble, besides thereby begetting in the sailor an undue idea of his importance.

Absurd, or worse than absurd, as it may appear, all this is true; and if you start from the same premises with these officers, you must admit that they advance an irresistible argument. But in accordance with this principle, captains in the Navy, to a certain extent, inflict the scourge—which is ever at hand—for nearly all degrees of transgression. In offenses not cognizable by a court-martial, little, if any, discrimination is shown. It is of a piece with the penal laws that prevailed in England some sixty years ago, when one hundred and sixty different offenses were declared by the statute-book to be capital, and the servant-maid who but pilfered a watch was hung beside the murderer of a family.

It is one of the most common punishments for very trivial offenses in the Navy, to "stop" a seaman's *grog* for a day or a week. And as most seamen so cling to their *grog*, the loss of it is generally deemed by them a very serious penalty. You will sometimes hear them say, "I would rather have my wind *stopped* than my *grog!*"

But there are some sober seamen that would much rather draw the money for it, instead of the grog itself, as provided by law; but they are too often deterred from this by the thought of receiving a scourging for some inconsiderable offense, as a substitute for the stopping of their spirits. This is a most serious obstacle to the cause of temperance in the Navy. But, in many cases, even the reluctant drawing of his grog cannot exempt a prudent seaman from ignominy; for besides the formal administering of the *"cat"* at the gangway for petty offenses, he is liable to the "colt," or rope's-end, a bit of *ratlin-stuff,* indiscriminately applied—without stripping the victim—at any time, and in any part of the ship, at the merest wink from the Captain. By an express order of that officer, most boatswain's mates carry the "colt" coiled in their hats, in readiness to be administered at a minute's warning upon any offender. This was the custom in the *Neversink*. And until so recent a period as the administration of President Polk, when the historian Bancroft, Secretary of the Navy, officially interposed, it was an almost universal thing for the officers of the watch, at their own discretion, to inflict chastisement upon a sailor, and this, too, in the face of the ordinance restricting the power of flogging solely to Captains and Courts Martial. Nor was it a thing unknown for a Lieutenant, in a sudden outburst of passion, perhaps inflamed by brandy, or smarting under the sense of being disliked or hated by the seamen, to order a whole watch of two hundred and fifty men, at dead of night, to undergo the indignity of the "colt."

It is believed that, even at the present day, there are instances of Commanders still violating the law, by delegating the power of the colt to subordinates. At all events, it is certain that, almost to a man, the Lieutenants in the Navy bitterly rail against the officiousness of Bancroft, in so materially abridging their usurped functions by snatching the colt from their hands. At the time, they predicted that this rash and most ill-judged interference of the Secretary would end in the breaking up of all discipline in the Navy. But it has not so proved. These officers *now* predict that, if the "cat" be abolished, the same unfulfilled prediction would be verified.

Concerning the license with which many captains violate the express laws laid down by Congress for the government of the Navy, a glaring instance may be quoted. For upward of forty years there has been on the American Statute-book a law prohibiting a captain from inflicting, on his own authority, more than twelve lashes at one time. If more are to be given, the sentence must be passed by a Court-martial. Yet, for nearly half a century, this law has been frequently, and with almost perfect impunity, set at naught: though of late, through the exertions of Bancroft and others, it has been much better observed than formerly; indeed, at the present day, it is generally respected. Still, while the *Neversink* was lying in a South American port, on the cruise now written of, the seamen belonging to another American frigate informed us that their captain sometimes inflicted, upon his own authority, eighteen and twenty lashes. It is worthwhile to state that this frigate was vastly admired by the shore ladies for her wonderfully neat appearance. One of her forecastle-men told me that he had used up three jack-knives (charged to him on the books of the purser) in scraping the belaying-pins and the combings of the hatchways.

It is singular that while the Lieutenants of the watch in American men-of-war so long usurped the power of inflicting corporal punishment with the *colt,* few or no similar abuses were known in the English Navy. And though the captain of an English armed ship is authorized to inflict, at his own discretion, *more* than a dozen lashes (I think three dozen), yet it is to be doubted whether, upon the whole, there is as much flogging at present in the English Navy as in the American. The chivalric Virginian, John Randolph of Roanoke, declared, in his place in Congress, that on board of the American man-of-war that carried him out Ambassador to Russia he had witnessed more flogging than had taken place on his own plantation of five hundred African slaves in ten years. Certain it is, from what I have personally seen, that the English officers, as a general thing, seem to be less disliked by their crews than the American officers by theirs. The reason probably is, that many of them, from their station in life, have been more accustomed to social command; hence, quarter-deck authority sits more naturally on them. A coarse, vulgar man, who happens to rise to high naval rank by the exhibition of talents not incompatible with vulgarity, invariably proves a tyrant to his crew. It is a thing that American men-of-war's-men have often observed, that the Lieutenants from the Southern States, the descendants of the old Virginians, are much less severe, and much more gentle and gentlemanly in command, than the Northern officers, as a class.

According to the present laws and usages of the Navy, a seaman, for the most trivial alleged offenses, of which he may be entirely innocent, must, without a trial, undergo a penalty the traces whereof he carries to the grave; for to a man-of-war's-man's experienced eye the marks of a naval scourging with the *"cat"* are through life discernible. And with these marks on his back, this image of his Creator must rise at the Last Day. Yet so untouchable is true dignity, that there are cases wherein to be flogged at the gangway is no dishonor; though, to abase and hurl down the last pride of some sailor who has piqued him, be sometimes the secret motive, with some malicious officer, in procuring him to be condemned to the lash. But this feeling of the innate dignity remaining untouched, though outwardly the body be scarred for the whole term of the natural life, is one of the hushed things, buried among the holiest privacies of the soul; a thing between a man's God and himself; and forever undiscernible by our fellow-men, who account *that* a degradation which seems so to the corporal eye. But what torments must that seaman undergo who, while his back bleeds at the gangway, bleeds agonized drops of shame from his soul! Are we not justified in immeasurably denouncing this thing? Join hands with me, then; and, in the name of that Being in whose image the flogged sailor is made, let us demand of Legislators, by what right they dare profane what God himself accounts sacred.

Is it lawful for you to scourge a man that is a Roman? asks the intrepid Apostle, well knowing, as a Roman citizen, that it was not. And now, eighteen hundred years after, is it lawful for you, my countrymen, to scourge a man that is an American? to scourge him round the world in your frigates?

It is to no purpose that you apologetically appeal to the general depravity of the man-of-war's-man. Depravity in the oppressed is no apology for the oppressor; but rather an additional stigma to him, as being, in a large degree, the effect, and not the cause and justification of oppression.

Chapter XXXV

FLOGGING NOT LAWFUL

IT IS NEXT TO IDLE, AT THE PRESENT DAY, MERELY TO DENOUNCE AN INIQUITY. BE OURS, THEN, A different task.

If there are any three things opposed to the genius of the American Constitution, they are these: irresponsibility in a judge, unlimited discretionary authority in an executive, and the union of an irresponsible judge and an unlimited executive in one person.

Yet by virtue of an enactment of Congress, all the Commodores in the American navy are obnoxious to these three charges, so far as concerns the punishment of the sailor for alleged misdemeanors not particularly set forth in the Articles of War.

Here is the enactment in question.

XXXII. *Of the Articles of War.*—"All crimes committed by persons belonging to the Navy, which are not specified in the foregoing articles, shall be punished according to the laws and customs in such cases at sea."

This is the article that, above all others, puts the scourge into the hands of the Captain, calls him to no account for its exercise, and furnishes him with an ample warrant for inflictions of cruelty upon the common sailor, hardly credible to landsmen.

By this article the Captain is made a legislator, as well as a judge and an executive. So far as it goes, it absolutely leaves to his discretion to decide what things shall be considered crimes, and what shall be the penalty; whether an accused person has been guilty of actions by him declared to be crimes; and how, when, and where the penalty shall be inflicted.

In the American Navy there is an everlasting suspension of the Habeas Corpus. Upon the bare allegation of misconduct there is no law to restrain the Captain from imprisoning a seaman, and keeping him confined at his pleasure. While I was in the *Neversink*, the Captain of an American sloop of war, from undoubted motives of personal pique, kept a seaman confined in the brig for upward of a month.

Certainly the necessities of navies warrant a code for their government more stringent than the law that governs the land; but that code should conform to the spirit of the political institutions of the country that ordains it. It should not convert into slaves some of the citizens of a nation of freemen. Such objections cannot be urged against the laws of the Russian navy (not essentially different from our own), because the laws of that navy, creating the absolute one-man power in the Captain, and vesting in him the authority to scourge, conform in spirit to the territorial laws of Russia, which is ruled by an autocrat, and whose courts inflict the *knout* upon the subjects of the land. But with us it is different. Our institutions claim to be based upon broad principles of political liberty and equality. Whereas, it would hardly affect one iota the condition on shipboard of an American man-of-war's-man, were he transferred to the Russian navy and made a subject of the Czar.

As a sailor, he shares none of our civil immunities; the law of our soil in no respect accompanies the national floating timbers grown thereon, and to which he clings as his home. For him our Revolution was in vain; to him our *Declaration of Independence* is a lie.

It is not sufficiently borne in mind, perhaps, that though the naval code comes under the head of the martial law, yet, in time of peace, and in the thousand questions arising between man and man on board ship, this code, to a certain extent, may not improperly be deemed municipal. With its crew of 800 or 1,000 men, a three-decker is a city on the sea. But in most of these matters between man and man, the Captain instead of being a magistrate, dispensing what the law promulgates, is an absolute ruler, making and unmaking law as he pleases.

It will be seen that the XXth of the *Articles of War* provides, that if any person in the Navy negligently perform the duties assigned him, he shall suffer such punishment as a court-martial shall adjudge; but if the offender be a private (common sailor) he may, at the discretion of the Captain, be put in irons or flogged. It is needless to say, that in cases where an officer commits a trivial violation of this law, a court-martial is seldom or never called to sit upon his trial; but in the sailor's case, he is at once condemned to the lash. Thus, one set of sea-citizens is exempted from a law that is hung in terror over others. What would landsmen think, were the State of New York to pass a law against some offense, affixing a fine as a penalty, and then add to that law a section restricting its penal operation to mechanics and day laborers, exempting all gentlemen with an income of one thousand dollars? Yet thus, in the spirit of its practical operation, even thus, stands a good part of the naval laws wherein naval flogging is involved.

But a law should be "universal," and include in its possible penal operations the very judge himself who gives decisions upon it; nay, the very judge who expounds it. Had Sir William Blackstone violated the laws of England, he would have been brought before the bar over which he had presided, and would there have been tried, with the counsel for the crown reading to him, perhaps, from a copy of his own *Commentaries.* And should he have been found guilty, he would have suffered like the meanest subject, "according to law."

How is it in an American frigate? Let one example suffice. By the Articles of War, and especially by Article I, an American Captain may, and frequently does, inflict a severe and degrading punishment upon a sailor, while he himself is forever removed from the possibility of undergoing the like disgrace; and, in all probability, from undergoing any punishment whatever, even if guilty of the same thing—contention with his equals, for instance—for which he punishes another. Yet both sailor and captain are American citizens.

Now, in the language of Blackstone, again, there is a law, "coeval with mankind, dictated by God himself, superior in obligation to any other, and no human laws are of any validity if contrary to this." That law is the Law of Nature; among the three great principles of which Justinian includes "that to every man should be rendered his due." But we have seen that the laws involving flogging in the Navy do *not* render to every man his due, since in some cases they indirectly exclude the officers from any punishment whatever, and in all cases protect them from the scourge, which is inflicted upon the sailor. Therefore, according to Blackstone and Justinian, those laws have no binding force; and every American man-of-war's-man would be morally justified in resisting the scourge to the uttermost; and, in so resisting, would be religiously justified in what would be judicially styled "the act of mutiny" itself.

If, then, these scourging laws be for any reason necessary, make them binding upon all who of right come under their sway; and let us see an honest Commodore, duly authorized by Congress, condemning to the lash a transgressing Captain by the side of a transgressing sailor. And if the Commodore himself prove a transgressor, let us see one of his brother Commodores take up the lash against *him,* even as the boatswain's mates, the navy executioners, are often called upon to scourge each other.

Or will you say that a navy officer is a man, but that an American-born citizen, whose grandsire may have ennobled him by pouring out his blood at Bunker Hill—will you say that, by entering the service of his country as a common seaman, and standing ready to fight her foes, he thereby loses his manhood at the very time he most asserts it? Will you say that, by so doing, he degrades himself to the liability of the scourge, but if he tarries ashore in time of danger, he is safe from that indignity? All our linked states, all four continents of mankind, unite in denouncing such a thought.

We plant the question, then, on the topmost argument of all. Irrespective of incidental considerations, we assert that flogging in the navy is opposed to the essential dignity of man, which no legislator has a right to violate; that it is oppressive, and glaringly unequal in its operations; that it is utterly repugnant to the spirit of our democratic institutions; indeed, that it involves a lingering trait of the worst times of a barbarous feudal aristocracy; in a word, we denounce it as religiously, morally, and immutably *wrong*.

No matter, then, what may be the consequences of its abolition; no matter if we have to dismantle our fleets, and our unprotected commerce should fall a prey to the spoiler, the awful admonitions of justice and humanity demand that abolition without procrastination; in a voice that is not to be mistaken, demand that abolition to-day. It is not a dollar-and-cent question of expediency; it is a matter of *right and wrong*. And if any man can lay his hand on his heart, and solemnly say that this scourging is right, let that man but once feel the lash on his own back, and in his agony you will hear the apostate call the seventh heavens to witness that it is *wrong*. And, in the name of immortal manhood, would to God that every man who upholds this thing were scourged at the gangway till he recanted.

Chapter XXXVI

FLOGGING NOT NECESSARY

BUT WHITE-JACKET IS READY TO COME DOWN FROM THE LOFTY MAST-HEAD OF AN ETERNAL PRINciple, and fight you—Commodores and Captains of the navy—on your own quarter-deck, with your own weapons, at your own paces.

Exempt yourselves from the lash, you take Bible oaths to it that it is indispensable for others; you swear that, without the lash, no armed ship can be kept in suitable discipline. Be it proved to you, officers, and stamped upon your foreheads, that herein you are utterly wrong.

"Send them to Collingwood," said Lord Nelson, "and *he* will bring them to order." This was the language of that renowned Admiral, when his officers reported to him certain seamen of the fleet as wholly ungovernable. "Send them to Collingwood." And who was Collingwood, that, after these navy rebels had been imprisoned and scourged without being brought to order, Collingwood could convert them to docility?

Who Admiral Colllngwood was, as an historical hero, history herself will tell you; nor, in whatever triumphal hall they may be hanging, will the captured flags of Trafalgar fail to rustle at the mention of that name. But what Collingwood was as a disciplinarian on board the ships he commanded perhaps needs to be said. He was an officer, then, who held in abhorrence all corporal punishment; who, though seeing more active service than any sea-officer of his time, yet, for years together, governed his men without inflicting the lash.

But these seaman of his must have been most exemplary saints to have proved docile under so lenient a sway. Were they saints? Answer, ye jails and alms-houses throughout the length and breadth of Great Britain, which, in Collingwood's time, were swept clean of the last lingering villain and pauper to man his majesty's fleets.

Still more, *that* was a period when the uttermost resources of England were taxed to the quick; when the masts of her multiplied fleets almost transplanted her forests, all standing to the sea; when British press-gangs not only boarded foreign ships on the high seas, and boarded foreign pier-heads, but boarded their own merchantmen at the mouth of the Thames, and boarded the very fire-sides along its banks; when Englishmen were knocked down and dragged into the navy, like cattle into the slaughter-house, with every mortal provocation to a mad desperation against the service that thus ran their unwilling heads into the muzzles of the enemy's cannon. *This* was the time, and *these* the men that Collingwood governed without the lash.

I know it has been said that Lord Collingwood began by inflicting severe punishments, and afterward ruling his sailors by the mere memory of a by-gone terror, which he could at pleasure revive; and that his sailors knew this, and hence their good behavior under a lenient sway. But, granting the quoted assertion to be true, how comes it that many American Captains, who, after inflicting as severe punishment as ever Collingwood could have authorized—how comes it that *they*, also, have not been able to maintain good order without subsequent floggings, after once showing to the crew with what terrible attributes they were invested? But it is notorious, and a thing that I myself, in several instances, *know* to have been the case, that in the American navy, where corporal punishment has been most severe, it has also been most frequent.

But it is incredible that, with such crews as Lord Collingwood's—composed, in part, of the most desperate characters, the rakings of the jails—it is incredible that such a set of men could have been governed by the mere *memory* of the lash. Some other influence must have been brought to bear; mainly, no doubt, the influence wrought by a powerful brain, and a determined, intrepid spirit over a miscellaneous rabble.

It is well known that Lord Nelson himself, in point of policy, was averse to flogging; and that, too, when he had witnessed the mutinous effects of government abuses in the navy—unknown in our times—and which, to the terror of all England, developed themselves at the great mutiny of the Nore: an outbreak that for several weeks jeopardized the very existence of the British navy.

But we may press this thing nearly two centuries further back, for it is a matter of historical doubt whether, in Robert Blake's time, Cromwell's great admiral, such a thing as flogging was known at the gangways of his victorious fleets. And as in this matter we cannot go further back than to Blake, so we cannot advance further than to our own time, which shows Commodore Stockton, during the recent war with Mexico, governing the American squadron in the Pacific without employing the scourge.

But if of three famous English Admirals one has abhorred flogging, another almost governed his ships without it, and to the third it may be supposed to have been unknown, while an American Commander has, within the present year almost, been enabled to sustain the good discipline of an entire squadron in time of war without having an instrument of scourging on board, what inevitable inferences must be drawn, and how disastrous to the mental character of all advocates of navy flogging, who may happen to be navy officers themselves.

It cannot have escaped the discernment of any observer of mankind, that, in the presence of its conventional inferiors, conscious imbecility in power often seeks to carry off that imbecility by assumptions of lordly severity. The amount of flogging on board an American man-of-war is, in many cases, in exact proportion to the professional and intellectual incapacity of her officers to command. Thus, in these cases, the law that authorizes flogging does but put a scourge into the hand of a fool. In most calamitous instances this has been shown.

It is a matter of record, that some English ships of war have fallen a prey to the enemy through the insubordination of the crew, induced by the witless cruelty of their officers; officers so armed by the law that they could inflict that cruelty without restraint. Nor have there been wanting instances where the seamen have ran away with their ships, as in the case of the Hermione and Danaë, and forever rid themselves of the outrageous inflictions of their officers by sacrificing their lives to their fury.

Events like these aroused the attention of the British public at the time. But it was a tender theme, the public agitation of which the government was anxious to suppress. Nevertheless, whenever the thing was privately discussed, these terrific mutinies, together with the then prevailing insubordination of the men in the navy, were almost universally attributed to the exasperating system of flogging. And the necessity for flogging was generally believed to be directly referable to the impressment of such crowds of dissatisfied men. And in high quarters it was held that if, by any mode, the English fleet could be manned without resource to coercive measures, then the necessity of flogging would cease.

"If we abolish either impressment or flogging, the abolition of the other will follow as a matter of course." This was the language of the *Edinburgh Review* at a still later period, 1824.

If, then, the necessity of flogging in the British armed marine was solely attributed to the impressment of the seamen, what faintest shadow of reason is there for the continuance of this barbarity in the American service, which is wholly freed from the reproach of impressment?

It is true that, during a long period of non-impressment, and even down to the present day, flogging has been, and still is, the law of the English navy. But in things of this kind England should be nothing to us, except an example to be shunned. Nor should wise legislators wholly govern themselves by precedents, and conclude that, since scourging has so long prevailed, some virtue must reside in it. Not so. The world has arrived at a period which renders it the part of Wisdom to pay homage to the prospective precedents of the Future in preference to those of the Past. The Past is dead, and has no resurrection; but the Future is endowed with such a life, that it lives to us even in anticipation. The Past is, in many things, the foe of mankind; the Future is, in all things, our friend. In the Past is no hope; the Future is both hope and fruition. The Past is the text-book of tyrants; the Future the Bible of the Free. Those who are solely governed by the Past stand like Lot's wife, crystallized in the act of looking backward, and forever incapable of looking before.

Let us leave the Past, then, to dictate laws to immovable China; let us abandon it to the Chinese Legitimists of Europe. But for us, we will have another captain to rule over us—that captain who ever marches at the head of his troop and beckons them forward, not lingering in the rear, and impeding their march with lumbering baggage-wagons of old precedents. *This* is the Past.

But in many things we Americans are driven to a rejection of the maxims of the Past, seeing that, ere long, the van of the nations must, of right, belong to ourselves. There are occasions when it is for America to make precedents, and not to obey them. We should, if possible, prove a teacher to posterity, instead of being the pupil of by-gone generations. More shall come after us than have gone before; the world is not yet middle-aged.

Escaped from the house of bondage, Israel of old did not follow after the ways of the Egyptians. To her was given an express dispensation; to her were given new things under the sun. And we Americans are the peculiar, chosen people—the Israel of our time; we bear the ark of the liberties of the world. Seventy years ago we escaped from thrall; and, besides our first birthright—embracing one continent of earth—God has given to us, for a future inheritance, the broad domains of the political pagans, that shall yet come and lie down under the shade of our ark, without bloody hands being lifted. God has predestinated, mankind expects, great things from our race; and great things we feel in our souls. The rest of the nations must soon be in our rear. We are the pioneers of the world; the advance-guard, sent on through the wilderness of untried things, to break a new path in the New World that is ours. In our youth is our strength; in our inexperience, our wisdom. At a period when other nations have but lisped, our deep voice is heard afar. Long enough, have we been skeptics with regard to ourselves, and doubted whether, indeed, the political Messiah had come. But he has come in *us,* if we would but give utterance to his promptings. And let us always remember that with ourselves, almost for the first time in the history of earth, national selfishness is unbounded philanthropy; for we can not do a good to America but we give alms to the world.

Chapter XXXVII

Some Superior Old "London Dock" from the Wine-Coolers of Neptune

We had just slid into pleasant weather, drawing near to the tropics, when all hands were thrown into a wonderful excitement by an event that eloquently appealed to many palates.

A man at the fore-top-sail-yard sung out that there were eight or ten dark objects floating on the sea, some three points off our lee-bow.

"Keep her off three points!" cried Captain Claret, to the quarter-master at the *cun*.

And thus, with all our batteries, store-rooms, and five hundred men, with their baggage, and beds, and provisions, at one move of a round bit of mahogany, our great-embattled ark edged away for the strangers, as easily as a boy turns to the right or left in pursuit of insects in the field.

Directly the man on the top-sail-yard reported the dark objects to be hogsheads. Instantly all the top-men were straining their eyes, in delirious expectation of having their long *grog-fast* broken at last, and that, too, by what seemed an almost miraculous intervention. It was a curious circumstance that, without knowing the contents of the hogsheads, they yet seemed certain that the staves encompassed the thing they longed for.

Sail was now shortened, our headway was stopped, and a cutter was lowered, with orders to tow the fleet of strangers alongside. The men sprang to their oars with a will, and soon five goodly puncheons lay wallowing in the sea, just under the main-chains. We got overboard the slings, and hoisted them out of the water.

It was a sight that Bacchus and his bacchanals would have gloated over. Each puncheon was of a deep-green color, so covered with minute barnacles and shell-fish, and streaming with sea-weed, that it needed long searching to find out their bung-holes; they looked like venerable old *loggerhead-turtles*. How long they had been tossing about, and making voyages for the benefit of the flavor of their contents, no one could tell. In trying to raft them ashore, or on board of some merchant-ship, they must have drifted off to sea. This we inferred from the ropes that length-wise united them, and which, from one point of view, made them resemble a long sea-serpent. They were *struck* into the gun-deck, where, the eager crowd being kept off by sentries, the cooper was called with his tools.

"Bung up, and bilge free!" he cried, in an ecstasy, flourishing his driver and hammer.

Upon clearing away the barnacles and moss, a flat sort of shell-fish was found, closely adhering, like a California-shell, right over one of the bungs. Doubtless this shell-fish had there taken up his quarters, and thrown his own body into the breach, in order the better to preserve the precious contents of the cask. The bystanders were breathless, when at last this puncheon was canted over and a tin-pot held to the orifice. What was to come forth? salt-water or wine? But a rich purple tide soon settled the question, and the lieutenant assigned to taste it, with a loud and satisfactory smack of his lips, pronounced it Port!

"Oporto!" cried Mad Jack, "and no mistake!"

But, to the surprise, grief, and consternation of the sailors, an order now came from the quarter-deck to strike the "strangers down into the main-hold!" This proceeding occasioned all sorts of censorious observations upon the Captain, who, of course, had authorized it.

It must be related here that, on the passage out from home, the *Neversink* had touched at Madeira; and there, as is often the case with men-of-war, the Commodore and Captain had laid in a goodly stock of wines for their own private tables, and the benefit of their foreign visitors. And although the Commodore was a small, spare man, who evidently emptied but few glasses, yet Captain Claret was a portly gentleman, with a crimson face, whose father had fought at the battle of the Brandywine, and whose brother had commanded the well-known frigate named in honor of that engagement. And his whole appearance evinced that Captain Claret himself had fought many Brandywine battles ashore in honor of his sire's memory, and commanded in many bloodless Brandywine actions at sea.

It was therefore with some savor of provocation that the sailors held forth on the ungenerous conduct of Captain Claret, in stepping in between them and Providence, as it were, which by this lucky windfall, they held, seemed bent upon relieving their necessities; while Captain Claret himself, with an inexhaustible cellar, emptied his Madeira decanters at his leisure.

But next day all hands were electrified by the old familiar sound—so long hushed—of the drum rolling to grog.

After that the port was served out twice a day, till all was expended.

Chapter XXXVIII

THE CHAPLAIN AND CHAPEL IN A MAN-OF-WAR

THE NEXT DAY WAS SUNDAY; A FACT SET DOWN IN THE ALMANAC, SPITE OF MERCHANT SEAMEN'S maxim, that *there are no Sundays off soundings.*

No Sundays off soundings, indeed! No Sundays on shipboard! You may as well say there should be no Sundays in churches; for is not a ship modeled after a church? has it not three spires—three steeples? yea, and on the gun-deck, a bell and a belfry? And does not that bell merrily peal every Sunday morning, to summon the crew to devotions?

At any rate, there were Sundays on board this particular frigate of ours, and a clergyman also. He was a slender, middle-aged man, of an amiable deportment and irreproachable conversation; but I must say, that his sermons were but ill calculated to benefit the crew. He had drank at the mystic fountain of Plato; his head had been turned by the Germans; and this I will say, that White-Jacket himself saw him with Coleridge's *Biographia Literaria* in his hand.

Fancy, now, this transcendental divine standing behind a gun-carriage on the main-deck, and addressing five hundred salt-sea sinners upon the psychological phenomena of the soul, and the ontological necessity of every sailor's saving it at all hazards. He enlarged upon the follies of the ancient philosophers; learnedly alluded to the Phædon of Plato; exposed the follies of Simplicius's Commentary on Aristotle's *De Coelo,* by arraying against that clever Pagan author the admired tract of Tertullian—*De Prœscriptionibus Hœreticorum*—and concluded by a Sanscrit invocation. He was particularly hard upon the Gnostics and Marcionites of the second century of the Christian era; but he never, in the remotest manner, attacked the everyday vices of the nineteenth century, as eminently illustrated in our man-of-war world. Concerning drunkenness, fighting, flogging, and oppression—things expressly or impliedly prohibited by Christianity—he never said aught. But the most mighty Commodore and Captain sat before him; and in general, if, in a monarchy, the state form the audience of the church, little evangelical piety will be preached. Hence, the harmless, non-committal abstrusities of our Chaplain were not to be wondered at. He was no Massillon, to thunder forth his ecclesiastical rhetoric, even when a Louis le Grand was enthroned among his congregation. Nor did the chaplains who preached on the quarter-deck of Lord Nelson ever allude to the guilty Felix, nor to Delilah, nor practically reason of righteousness, temperance, and judgment to come, when that renowned Admiral sat, sword-belted, before them.

During these Sunday discourses, the officers always sat in a circle round the Chaplain, and, with a business-like air, steadily preserved the utmost propriety. In particular, our old Commodore himself made a point of looking intensely edified; and not a sailor on board but believed that the Commodore, being the greatest man present, must alone comprehend the mystic sentences that fell from our parson's lips.

Of all the noble lords in the ward-room, this lord-spiritual, with the exception of the Purser, was in the highest favor with the Commodore, who frequently conversed with him in a close and confidential manner. Nor, upon reflection, was this to be marveled at, seeing how efficacious, in all despotic governments, it is for the throne and altar to go hand-in-hand.

The accommodations of our chapel were very poor. We had nothing to sit on but the great gun-rammers and capstan-bars, placed horizontally upon shot-boxes. These seats were exceedingly uncomfortable, wearing out our trousers and our tempers, and, no doubt, impeded the conversion of many valuable souls.

To say the truth, men-of-war's-men, in general, make but poor auditors upon these occasions, and adopt every possible means to elude them. Often the boatswain's-mates were obliged to drive the men to service, violently swearing upon these occasions, as upon every other.

"Go to prayers, d—n you! To prayers, you rascals—to prayers!" In this clerical invitation Captain Claret would frequently unite.

At this Jack Chase would sometimes make merry. "Come, boys, don't hang back," he would say; "come, let us go hear the parson talk about his Lord High Admiral Plato, and Commodore Socrates."

But, in one instance, grave exception was taken to this summons. A remarkably serious, but bigoted seaman, a sheet-anchor-man—whose private devotions may hereafter be alluded to—once touched his hat to the Captain, and respectfully said, "Sir, I am a Baptist; the chaplain is an Episcopalian; his form of worship is not mine; I do not believe with him, and it is against my conscience to be under his ministry. May I be allowed, sir, *not* to attend service on the half-deck?"

"You will be allowed, sir!" said the Captain, haughtily, "to obey the laws of the ship. If you absent yourself from prayers on Sunday mornings, you know the penalty."

According to the *Articles of War,* the Captain was perfectly right; but if any law requiring an American to attend divine service against his will be a law respecting the establishment of religion, then the *Articles of War* are, in this one particular, opposed to the American Constitution, which expressly says, "Congress shall make no law respecting the establishment of religion, or the free exercise thereof." But this is only one of several things in which the *Articles of War* are repugnant to that instrument. They will be glanced at in another part of the narrative.

The motive which prompts the introduction of chaplains into the Navy cannot but be warmly responded to by every Christian. But it does not follow, that because chaplains are to be found in men-of-war, that, under the present system, they achieve much good, or that, under any other, they ever will.

How can it be expected that the religion of peace should flourish in an oaken castle of war? How can it be expected that the clergyman, whose pulpit is a forty-two-pounder, should convert sinners to a faith that enjoins them to turn the right cheek when the left is smitten? How is it to be expected that when, according to the XLII of the *Articles of War,* as they now stand unrepealed on the Statute-book, "a bounty shall be paid" (to the officers and crew) "by the United States government of $20 for each person on board any ship of an enemy which shall be sunk or destroyed by any United States ship"; and when, by a subsequent section (vii), it is provided, among other apportionings, that the chaplain shall receive "two twentieths" of this price paid for sinking and destroying ships full of human beings? How is it to be expected that a clergyman, thus provided for, should prove efficacious in enlarging upon the criminality of Judas, who, for thirty pieces of silver, betrayed his Master?

Although, by the regulations of the Navy, each seaman's mess on board the *Neversink* was furnished with a Bible, these Bibles were seldom or never to be seen, except on Sunday mornings, when usage demands that they shall be exhibited by the cooks of the messes, when the master-at-arms goes his rounds on the berth-deck. At such times, they usually surmounted a highly-polished tin-pot placed on the lid of the chest.

Yet, for all this, the Christianity of men-of-war's men, and their disposition to contribute to pious enterprises, are often relied upon. Several times subscription papers were circulated among the crew of the *Neversink*, while in harbor, under the direct patronage of the Chaplain. One was for the purpose of building a seaman's chapel in China; another to pay the salary of a tract-distributor in Greece; a third to raise a fund for the benefit of an African Colonization Society.

Where the Captain himself is a moral man, he makes a far better chaplain for his crew than any clergyman can be. This is sometimes illustrated in the case of sloops of war and armed brigs, which are not allowed a regular chaplain. I have known one crew, who were warmly attached to a naval commander worthy of their love, who have mustered even with alacrity to the call to prayer; and when their Captain would read the Church of England service to them, would present a congregation not to be surpassed for earnestness and devotion by any Scottish Kirk. It seemed like family devotions, where the head of the house is foremost in confessing himself before his Maker. But our own hearts are our best prayer-rooms, and the chaplains who can most help us are ourselves.

Chapter XXXIX

The Frigate in Harbor—The Boats—Grand State Receptions of the Commodore

In good time we were up with the parallel of Rio de Janeiro, and, standing in for the land, the mist soon cleared; and high aloft the famed Sugar Loaf pinnacle was seen, our bowsprit pointing for it straight as a die.

As we glided on toward our anchorage, the bands of the various men-of-war in harbor saluted us with national airs, and gallantly lowered their ensigns. Nothing can exceed the courteous etiquette of these ships, of all nations, in greeting their brethren. Of all men, your accomplished duelist is generally the most polite.

We lay in Rio some weeks, lazily taking in stores and otherwise preparing for the passage home. But though Rio is one of the most magnificent bays in the world; though the city itself contains many striking objects; and though much might be said of the Sugar Loaf and Signal Hill heights; and the little islet of Lucia; and the fortified Ihla Dos Cobras, or Isle of the Snakes (though the only anacondas and adders now found in the arsenals there are great guns and pistols); and Lord Wood's Nose—a lofty eminence said by seamen to resemble his lordship's conch-shell; and the Prays do Flamingo—a noble tract of beach, so called from its having been the resort, in olden times, of those gorgeous birds; and the charming Bay of Botofogo, which, spite of its name, is fragrant as the neighboring Larangieros, or Valley of the Oranges; and the green Gloria Hill, surmounted by the belfries of the queenly Church of Nossa Señora de Gloria; and the iron-gray Benedictine convent nearby; and the fine drive and promenade, Passeo Publico; and the massive arch-over-arch aqueduct, Arcos de Carico; and the Emperor's Palace; and the Empress's Gardens; and the fine Church de Candelaria; and the gilded throne on wheels, drawn by eight silken, silver-belled mules, in which, of pleasant evenings, his Imperial Majesty is driven out of town to his

Moorish villa of St. Christova—ay, though much might be said of all this, yet must I forbear, if I may, and adhere to my one proper object, *the world in a man-of-war.*

Behold, now, the *Neversink* under a new aspect. With all her batteries, she is tranquilly lying in harbor, surrounded by English, French, Dutch, Portuguese, and Brazilian seventy-fours, moored in the deep-green water, close under the lee of that oblong, castellated mass of rock, Ilha Dos Cobras, which, with its port-holes and lofty flag-staffs, looks like another man-of-war, fast anchored in the way. But what is an insular fortress, indeed, but an embattled land-slide into the sea from the world Gibraltars and Quebecs? And what a main-land fortress but a few decks of a line-of-battle ship transplanted ashore? They are all one—all, as King David, men-of-war from their youth.

Ay, behold now the *Neversink* at her anchors, in many respects presenting a different appearance from what she presented at sea. Nor is the routine of life on board the same.

At sea there is more to employ the sailors, and less temptation to violations of the law. Whereas, in port, unless some particular service engages them, they lead the laziest of lives, beset by all the allurements of the shore, though perhaps that shore they may never touch.

Unless you happen to belong to one of the numerous boats, which, in a man-of-war in harbor, are continually plying to and from the land, you are mostly thrown upon your own resources to while away the time. Whole days frequently pass without your being individually called upon to lift a finger; for though, in the merchant-service, they make a point of keeping the men always busy about something or other, yet, to employ five hundred sailors when there is nothing definite to be done wholly surpasses the ingenuity of any First Lieutenant in the Navy.

As mention has just been made of the numerous boats employed in harbor, something more may as well be put down concerning them. Our frigate carried a very large boat—as big as a small sloop—called a *launch,* which was generally used for getting off wood, water, and other bulky articles. Besides this, she carried four boats of an arithmetical progression in point of size—the largest being known as the first cutter, the next largest the second cutter, then the third and fourth cutters. She also carried a Commodore's Barge, a Captain's Gig, and a "dingy," a small yawl, with a crew of apprentice boys. All these boats, except the "dingy," had their regular crews, who were subordinate to their cockswains—*petty officers,* receiving pay in addition to their seaman's wages.

The *launch* was manned by the old Tritons of the forecastle, who were no ways particular about their dress, while the other boats—commissioned for genteeler duties—were rowed by young fellows, mostly, who had a dandy eye to their personal appearance. Above all, the officers see to it that the Commodore's Barge and the Captain's Gig are manned by gentlemanly youths, who may do credit to their country, and form agreeable objects for the eyes of the Commodore or Captain to repose upon as he tranquilly sits in the stern, when pulled ashore by his barge-men or gig-men, as the case may be. Some sailors are very fond of belonging to the boats, and deem it a great honor to be a *Commodore's barge-man*; but others, perceiving no particular distinction in that office, do not court it so much.

On the second day after arriving at Rio, one of the gig-men fell sick, and, to my no small concern, I found myself temporarily appointed to his place.

"Come, White-Jacket, rig yourself in white—that's the gig's uniform to-day; you are a gigman, my boy—give ye joy!" This was the first announcement of the fact that I heard; but soon after it was officially ratified.

I was about to seek the First Lieutenant, and plead the scantiness of my wardrobe, which wholly disqualified me to fill so distinguished a station, when I heard the bugler call away the "gig"; and, without more ado, I slipped into a clean frock, which a messmate doffed for my benefit, and soon after found myself pulling off his High Mightiness, the Captain, to an English seventy-four.

As we were bounding along, the cockswain suddenly cried "Oars!" At the word every oar was suspended in the air, while our Commodore's barge floated by, bearing that dignitary himself. At the sight, Captain Claret removed his chapeau, and saluted profoundly, our boat lying motionless on the water. But the barge never stopped; and the Commodore made but a slight return to the obsequious salute he had received.

We then resumed rowing, and presently I heard "Oars!" again; but from another boat, the second cutter, which turned out to be carrying a Lieutenant ashore. It was now Captain Claret's turn to be honored. The cutter lay still, and the Lieutenant off hat; while the Captain only nodded, and we kept on our way.

This naval etiquette is very much like the etiquette at the Grand Porte of Constantinople, where, after washing the Sublime Sultan's feet, the Grand Vizier avenges himself on an Emir, who does the same office for him.

When we arrived aboard the English seventy-four, the Captain was received with the usual honors, and the gig's crew were conducted below, and hospitably regaled with some spirits, served out by order of the officer of the deck.

Soon after, the English crew went to quarters; and as they stood up at their guns, all along the main-deck, a row of beef-fed Britons, stalwart-looking fellows, I was struck with the contrast they afforded to similar sights on board of the *Neversink*.

For on board of us our *"quarters"* showed an array of rather slender, lean-cheeked chaps. But then I made no doubt, that, in a sea-tussle, these lantern-jawed varlets would have approved themselves as slender Damascus blades, nimble and flexible; whereas these Britons would have been, perhaps, as sturdy broadswords. Yet everyone remembers that story of Saladin and Richard trying their respective blades; how gallant Richard clove an anvil in twain, or something quite as ponderous, and Saladin elegantly severed a cushion; so that the two monarchs were even—each excelling in his way—though, unfortunately for my simile, in a patriotic point of view, Richard whipped Saladin's armies in the end.

There happened to be a lord on board of this ship—the younger son of an earl, they told me. He was a fine-looking fellow. I chanced to stand by when he put a question to an Irish captain of a gun; upon the seaman's inadvertently saying *sir* to him, his lordship looked daggers at the slight; and the sailor touching his hat a thousand times, said, "Pardon, your honor; I meant to say *my lord,* sir!"

I was much pleased with an old white-headed musician, who stood at the main hatchway, with his enormous bass drum full before him, and thumping it sturdily to the tune of *"God Save the King!"* though small mercy did he have on his drum-heads. Two little boys were clashing cymbals, and another was blowing a fife, with his cheeks puffed out like the plumpest of his country's plum-puddings.

When we returned from this trip, there again took place that ceremonious reception of our captain on board the vessel he commanded, which always had struck me as exceedingly diverting.

In the first place, while in port, one of the quarter-masters is always stationed on the poop with a spy-glass, to look out for all boats approaching, and report the same to the officer of the deck; also, who it is that may be coming in them; so that preparations may be made accordingly. As soon, then, as the gig touched the side, a mighty shrill piping was heard, as if some boys were celebrating the Fourth of July with penny whistles. This proceeded from a boatswain's mate, who, standing at the gangway, was thus honoring the Captain's return after his long and perilous absence.

The Captain then slowly mounted the ladder, and gravely marching through a lane of *"side-boys,"* so called—all in their best bibs and tuckers, and who stood making sly faces behind his back—was received by all the Lieutenants in a body, their hats in their hands, and making a prodigious scraping and bowing, as if they had just graduated at a French dancing-school. Meanwhile, preserving an erect, inflexible, and ram-rod carriage, and slightly touching his chapeau, the Captain made his ceremonious way to the cabin, disappearing behind the scenes, like the pasteboard ghost in Hamlet.

But these ceremonies are nothing to those in homage of the Commodore's arrival, even should he depart and arrive twenty times a day. Upon such occasions, the whole marine guard, except the sentries on duty, are marshalled on the quarter-deck, presenting arms as the Commodore passes them; while their commanding officer gives the military salute with his sword, as if making masonic signs. Meanwhile, the boatswain himself—not a *boatswain's mate*—is keeping up a persevering whistling with his silver pipe; for the Commodore is never greeted with the rude whistle of a boatswain's subaltern; *that* would be positively insulting. All the Lieutenants and Midshipmen, besides the Captain himself, are drawn up in a phalanx, and off hat together; and the *side-boys,* whose number is now increased to ten or twelve, make an imposing display at the gangway; while the whole brass band, elevated upon the poop, strike up *"See! the Conquering Hero Comes!"* At least, this was the tune that our Captain always hinted, by a gesture, to the captain of the band, whenever the Commodore arrived from shore. It conveyed a complimentary appreciation, on the Captain's part, of the Commodore's heroism during the late war.

To return to the gig. As I did not relish the idea of being a sort of body-servant to Captain Claret—since his gig-men were often called upon to scrub his cabin floor, and perform other duties for him—I made it my particular business to get rid of my appointment in his boat as soon as possible, and the next day after receiving it, succeeded in procuring a substitute, who was glad of the chance to fill the position I so much undervalued.

And thus, with our counterlikes and dislikes, most of us men-of-war's-men harmoniously dove-tail into each other, and, by our very points of opposition, unite in a clever whole, like the parts of a Chinese puzzle. But as, in a Chinese puzzle, many pieces are hard to place, so there are some unfortunate fellows who can never slip into their proper angles, and thus the whole puzzle becomes a puzzle indeed, which is the precise condition of the greatest puzzle in the world—this man-of-war world itself.

Chapter XL

Some of the Ceremonies in a Man-of-War Unnecessary and Injurious

THE CEREMONIALS OF A MAN-OF-WAR, SOME OF WHICH HAVE BEEN DESCRIBED IN THE PRECEDing chapter, may merit a reflection or two.

The general usages of the American Navy are founded upon the usages that prevailed in the navy of monarchical England more than a century ago; nor have they been materially altered since. And while both England and America have become greatly liberalized in the interval; while shore pomp in high places has come to be regarded by the more intelligent masses of men as belonging to the absurd, ridiculous, and mock-heroic; while that most truly august of all the majesties of earth, the President of the United States, may be seen entering his residence with his umbrella under his arm, and no brass band or military guard at his heels, and unostentatiously taking his seat by the side of the meanest citizen in a public conveyance; while this is the case, there still lingers in American men-of-war all the stilted etiquette and childish parade of the old-fashioned Spanish court of Madrid. Indeed, so far as the things that meet the eye are concerned, an American Commodore is by far a greater man than the President of twenty millions of freemen.

But we plain people ashore might very willingly be content to leave these commodores in the unmolested possession of their gilded penny whistles, rattles, and gewgaws, since they seem to take so much pleasure in them, were it not that all this is attended by consequences to their subordinates in the last degree to be deplored.

While hardly anyone will question that a naval officer should be surrounded by circumstances calculated to impart a requisite dignity to his position, it is not the less certain that, by the excessive pomp he at present maintains, there is naturally and unavoidably generated a feeling of servility and debasement in the hearts of most of the seamen who continually behold a fellow-mortal flourishing over their heads like the archangel Michael with a thousand wings. And as, in degree, this same pomp is observed toward their inferiors by all the grades of commissioned officers, even down to a midshipman, the evil is proportionately multiplied.

It would not at all diminish a proper respect for the officers, and subordination to their authority among the seamen, were all this idle parade—only ministering to the arrogance of the officers, without at all benefiting the state—completely done away. But to do so, we voters and lawgivers ourselves must be no respecters of persons.

That saying about *leveling upward, and not downward,* may seem very fine to those who cannot see its self-involved absurdity. But the truth is, that, to gain the true level, in some things, we *must* cut downward; for how can you make every sailor a commodore? or how raise the valleys, without filling them up with the superfluous tops of the hills?

Some discreet, but democratic, legislation in this matter is much to be desired. And by bringing down naval officers, in these things at least, without affecting their legitimate dignity and authority, we shall correspondingly elevate the common sailor, without relaxing the subordination, in which he should by all means be retained.

Chapter XLI

A MAN-OF-WAR LIBRARY

NOWHERE DOES TIME PASS MORE HEAVILY THAN WITH MOST MEN-OF-WAR'S-MEN ON BOARD THEIR craft in harbor.

One of my principal antidotes against *ennui* in Rio, was reading. There was a public library on board, paid for by government, and entrusted to the custody of one of the marine corporals, a little, dried-up man, of a somewhat literary turn. He had once been a clerk in a post-office ashore; and, having been long accustomed to hand over letters when called for, he was now just the man to hand over books. He kept them in a large cask on the berth-deck, and, when seeking a particular volume, had to capsize it like a barrel of potatoes. This made him very cross and irritable, as most all librarians are. Who had the selection of these books, I do not know, but some of them must have been selected by our Chaplain, who so pranced on Coleridge's "*High German horse.*"

Mason Good's *Book of Nature*—a very good book, to be sure, but not precisely adapted to tarry tastes—was one of these volumes; and Machiavelli's *Art of War*—which was very dry fighting; and a folio of Tillotson's *Sermons*—the best of reading for divines, indeed, but with little relish for a main-top-man; and Locke's *Essays*—incomparable essays, everybody knows, but miserable reading at sea; and Plutarch's *Lives*—super-excellent biographies, which pit Greek against Roman in beautiful style, but then, in a sailor's estimation, not to be mentioned with the *Lives of the Admirals*; and Blair's *Lectures,* University Edition—a fine treatise on rhetoric, but having nothing to say about nautical phrases, such as *"splicing the main-brace," "passing a gammoning," "puddinging the dolphin,"* and "*making a Carrick-bend*"; besides numerous invaluable but unreadable tomes, that might have been purchased cheap at the auction of some college-professor's library.

But I found ample entertainment in a few choice old authors, whom I stumbled upon in various parts of the ship, among the inferior officers. One was Morgan's *History of Algiers*, a famous old quarto, abounding in picturesque narratives of corsairs, captives, dungeons, and sea-fights; and making mention of a cruel old Dey, who, toward the latter part of his life, was so filled with remorse for his cruelties and crimes that he could not stay in bed after four o'clock in the morning, but had to rise in great trepidation and walk off his bad feelings till breakfast time. And another venerable octavo, containing a certificate from Sir Christopher Wren to its authenticity, entitled *Knox's Captivity in Ceylon, 1681*—abounding in stories about the Devil, who was superstitiously supposed to tyrannize over that unfortunate land: to mollify him, the priests offered up buttermilk, red cocks, and sausages; and the Devil ran roaring about in the woods, frightening travelers out of their wits; insomuch that the islanders bitterly lamented to Knox that their country was full of devils, and consequently, there was no hope for their eventual well-being. Knox swears that he himself heard the Devil roar, though he did not see his horns; it was a terrible noise, he says, like the baying of a hungry mastiff.

Then there was Walpole's *Letters*—very witty, pert, and polite—and some odd volumes of plays, each of which was a precious casket of jewels of good things, shaming the trash nowadays passed off for dramas, containing *The Jew of Malta, Old Fortunatus, The City Madam. Volpone, The Alchymist*, and other glorious old dramas of the age of Marlowe and Jonson, and that literary Damon and Pythias, the magnificent, mellow old Beaumont and Fletcher, who have sent the long shadow of their reputation, side by side with Shakespeare's, far down the endless vale of posterity. And may that shadow never be less! but as for St. Shakespeare may his never be more, lest the commentators arise, and settling upon his sacred text like unto locusts, devour it clean up, leaving never a dot over an I.

I diversified this reading of mine, by borrowing Moore's *"Loves of the Angels"* from Rose-water, who recommended it as *"de charmingest of wolumes"*; and a Negro Song-book, containing *Sittin' on a Rail, Gumbo Squash,* and *Jim along Josey,* from Broadbit, a sheet-anchor-man. The sad taste of this old tar, in admiring such vulgar stuff, was much denounced by Rose-water, whose own predilections were of a more elegant nature, as evinced by his exalted opinion of the literary merits of the *Loves of the Angels.*

I was by no means the only reader of books on board the *Neversink*. Several other sailors were diligent readers, though their studies did not lie in the way of belles-lettres. Their favorite authors were such as you may find at the book-stalls around Fulton Market; they were slightly physiological in their nature. My book experiences on board of the frigate proved an example of a fact which every book-lover must have experienced before me, namely, that though public libraries have an imposing air, and doubtless contain invaluable volumes, yet, somehow, the books that prove most agreeable, grateful, and companionable, are those we pick up by chance here and there; those which seem put into our hands by Providence; those which pretend to little, but abound in much.

Chapter XLII

KILLING TIME IN A MAN-OF-WAR IN HARBOR

READING WAS BY NO MEANS THE ONLY METHOD ADOPTED BY MY SHIPMATES IN WHILING AWAY the long, tedious hours in harbor. In truth, many of them could not have read, had they wanted to ever so much; in early youth their primers had been sadly neglected. Still, they had other pursuits; some were experts at the needle, and employed their time in making elaborate shirts, stitching picturesque eagles, and anchors, and all the stars of the federated states in the collars thereof; so that when they at last completed and put on these shirts, they may be said to have hoisted the American colors.

Others excelled in *tattooing* or *pricking*, as it is called in a man-of-war. Of these prickers, two had long been celebrated, in their way, as consummate masters of the art. Each had a small box full of tools and coloring matter; and they charged so high for their services, that at the end of the cruise they were supposed to have cleared upward of four hundred dollars. They would *prick* you to order a palm-tree, or an anchor, a crucifix, a lady, a lion, an eagle, or anything else you might want.

The Roman Catholic sailors on board had at least the crucifix pricked on their arms, and for this reason: If they chanced to die in a Catholic land, they would be sure of a decent burial in consecrated ground, as the priest would be sure to observe the symbol of Mother Church on their persons. They would not fare as Protestant sailors dying in Callao, who are shoved under the sands of St. Lorenzo, a solitary, volcanic island in the harbor, overrun with reptiles, their heretical bodies not being permitted to repose in the more genial loam of Lima.

And many sailors not Catholics were anxious to have the crucifix painted on them, owing to a curious superstition of theirs. They affirm—some of them—that if you have that mark tattooed upon all four limbs, you might fall overboard among seven hundred and seventy-five thousand white sharks, all dinnerless, and not one of them would so much as dare to smell at your little finger.

We had one fore-top-man on board, who, during the entire cruise, was having an endless cable *pricked* round and round his waist, so that, when his frock was off, he looked like a capstan with a hawser coiled round about it. This fore-top-man paid eighteen pence per link for the cable, besides being on the smart the whole cruise, suffering the effects of his repeated puncturings; so he paid very dear for his cable.

One other mode of passing time while in port was cleaning and polishing your *bright-work*; for it must be known that, in men-of-war, every sailor has some brass or steel of one kind or other to keep in high order—like housemaids, whose business it is to keep well-polished the knobs on the front door railing and the parlor-grates.

Excepting the ring-bolts, eye-bolts, and belaying-pins scattered about the decks, this bright-work, as it is called, is principally about the guns, embracing the *"monkey-tails"* of the carronades, the screws, *prickers,* little irons, and other things.

The portion that fell to my own share I kept in superior order, quite equal in polish to Rogers's best cutlery. I received the most extravagant encomiums from the officers; one of whom offered to match me against any brazier or brass-polisher in her British Majesty's Navy. Indeed, I devoted myself to the work body and soul, and thought no pains too painful, and no labour too laborious, to achieve the highest attainable polish possible for us poor lost sons of Adam to reach.

Upon one occasion, even, when woolen rags were scarce, and no burned-brick was to be had from the ship's Yeoman, I sacrificed the corners of my woolen shirt, and used some dentrifice I had, as substitutes for the rags and burned-brick. The dentrifice operated delightfully, and made the threading of my carronade screw shine and grin again, like a set of false teeth in an eager heiress-hunter's mouth.

Still another mode of passing time, was arraying yourself in your best "*togs*" and promenading up and down the gun-deck, admiring the shore scenery from the port-holes, which, in an amphitheatrical bay like Rio—belted about by the most varied and charming scenery of hill, dale, moss, meadow, court, castle, tower, grove, vine, vineyard, aqueduct, palace, square, island, fort—is very much like lounging round a circular cosmorama, and ever and anon lazily peeping through the glasses here and there. Oh! there is something worth living for, even in our man-of-war world; and one glimpse of a bower of grapes, though a cable's-length off, is almost satisfaction for dining off a shank-bone salted down.

This promenading was chiefly patronized by the marines, and particularly by Colbrook, a remarkably handsome and very gentlemanly corporal among them. He was a complete lady's man; with fine black eyes, bright red cheeks, glossy jet whiskers, and a refined organization of the whole man. He used to array himself in his regimentals, and saunter about like an officer of the Coldstream Guards, strolling down to his club in St. James's. Every time he passed me, he would heave a sentimental sigh, and hum to himself *"The Girl I Left Behind Me."* This fine corporal afterward became a representative in the Legislature of the State of New Jersey; for I saw his name returned about a year after my return home.

But, after all, there was not much room, while in port, for promenading, at least on the gundeck, for the whole larboard side is kept clear for the benefit of the officers, who appreciate the advantages of having a clear stroll fore and aft; and they well know that the sailors had much better be crowded together on the other side than that the set of their own coat-tails should be impaired by brushing against their tarry trousers.

One other way of killing time while in port is playing checkers; that is, when it is permitted; for it is not every navy captain who will allow such a scandalous proceeding. But, as for Captain Claret, though he *did* like his glass of Madeira uncommonly well, and was an undoubted descendant from the hero of the Battle of the Brandywine, and though he sometimes showed a suspiciously flushed face when superintending in person the flogging of a sailor for getting intoxicated against his particular orders, yet I will say for Captain Claret that, upon the whole, he was rather indulgent to his crew, so long as they were perfectly docile. He allowed them to play checkers as much as they pleased. More than once I have known him, when going forward to the forecastle, pick his way carefully among scores of canvas checker-cloths spread upon the deck, so as not to tread upon the men—the checker-men and man-of-war's-men included; but, in a certain sense, they were both one; for, as the sailors used their checker-men, so, at quarters, their officers used these man-of-war's men.

But Captain Claret's leniency in permitting checkers on board his ship might have arisen from the following little circumstance, confidentially communicated to me. Soon after the ship had sailed from home, checkers were prohibited; whereupon the sailors were exasperated against the Captain, and one night, when he was walking round the forecastle, bim! came an iron belaying-pin past his ears; and while he was dodging that, bim! came another, from the other side; so that, it being a very dark night, and nobody to be seen, and it being impossible to find out the trespassers, he thought it best to get back into his cabin as soon as possible. Some time after—just as if the belaying-pins had nothing to do with it—it was indirectly rumored that the checker-boards might be brought out again, which—as a philosophical shipmate observed—showed that Captain Claret was a man of a ready understanding, and could understand a hint as well as any other man, even when conveyed by several pounds of iron.

Some of the sailors were very precise about their checker-cloths, and even went so far that they would not let you play with them unless you first washed your hands, especially if so be you had just come from tarring down the rigging.

Another way of beguiling the tedious hours, is to get a cozy seat somewhere, and fall into as snug a little reverie as you can. Or if a seat is not to be had—which is frequently the case—then get a tolerably comfortable *stand-up* against the bulwarks, and begin to think about home and bread and butter—always inseparably connected to a wanderer—which will very soon bring delicious tears into your eyes; for everyone knows what a luxury is grief, when you can get a private closet to enjoy it in, and no Paul Prys intrude. Several of my shore friends, indeed, when suddenly overwhelmed by some disaster, always make a point of flying to the first oyster-cellar, and shutting themselves up in a box with nothing but a plate of stewed oysters, some crackers, the castor, and a decanter of old port.

Still another way of killing time in harbor, is to lean over the bulwarks, and speculate upon where, under the sun, you are going to be that day next year, which is a subject full of interest to every living soul; so much so, that there is a particular day of a particular month of the year, which, from my earliest recollections, I have always kept the run of, so that I can even now tell just where I was on that identical day of every year past since I was twelve years old. And, when I am all alone, to run over this almanac in my mind is almost as entertaining as to read your own diary, and far more interesting than to peruse a table of logarithms on a rainy afternoon. I always keep the anniversary of that day with lamb and peas, and a pint of sherry, for it comes in Spring. But when it came round in the *Neversink,* I could get neither lamb, peas, nor sherry.

But perhaps the best way to drive the hours before you four-in-hand, is to select a soft plank on the gun-deck, and go to sleep. A fine specific, which seldom fails, unless, to be sure, you have been sleeping all the twenty-four hours beforehand.

Whenever employed in killing time in harbor, I have lifted myself up on my elbow and looked around me, and seen so many of my shipmates all employed at the same common business; all under lock and key; all hopeless prisoners like myself; all under martial law; all dieting on salt beef and biscuit; all in one uniform; all yawning, gaping, and stretching in concert, it was then that I used to feel a certain love and affection for them, grounded, doubtless, on a fellow-feeling.

And though, in a previous part of this narrative, I have mentioned that I used to hold myself somewhat aloof from the mass of seamen on board the *Neversink*; and though this was true, and my real acquaintances were comparatively few, and my intimates still fewer, yet, to tell the truth, it is quite impossible to live so long with five hundred of your fellow-beings, even if not of the best families in the land, and with morals that would not be spoiled by further cultivation; it is quite impossible, I say, to live with five hundred of your fellow-beings, be they who they may, without feeling a common sympathy with them at the time, and ever after cherishing some sort of interest in their welfare.

The truth of this was curiously corroborated by a rather equivocal acquaintance of mine, who, among the men, went by the name of *"Shakings."* He belonged to the fore-hold, whence, of a dark night, he would sometimes emerge to chat with the sailors on deck. I never liked the man's looks; I protest it was a mere accident that gave me the honor of his acquaintance, and generally I did my best to avoid him, when he would come skulking, like a jail-bird, out of his den into the liberal, open air of the sky. Nevertheless, the anecdote this *holder* told me is well worth preserving, more especially the extraordinary frankness evinced in his narrating such a thing to a comparative stranger.

The substance of his story was as follows: Shakings, it seems, had once been a convict in the New York State's Prison at Sing Sing, where he had been for years confined for a crime, which he gave me his solemn word of honor he was wholly innocent of. He told me that, after his term had expired, and he went out into the world again, he never could stumble upon any of his old Sing Sing associates without dropping into a public-house and talking over old times. And when fortune would go hard with him, and he felt out of sorts, and incensed at matters and things in general, he told me that, at such time, he almost wished he was back again in Sing Sing, where he was relieved from all anxieties about what he should eat and drink, and was supported, like the President of the United States and Prince Albert, at the public charge. He used to have such a snug little cell, he said, all to himself, and never felt afraid of house-breakers, for the walls were uncommonly thick, and his door was securely bolted for him, and a watchman was all the time walking up and down in the passage, while he himself was fast asleep and dreaming. To this, in substance, the *holder* added, that he narrated this anecdote because he thought it applicable to a man-of-war, which he scandalously asserted to be a sort of State Prison afloat.

Concerning the curious disposition to fraternize and be sociable, which this Shakings mentioned as characteristic of the convicts liberated from his old homestead at Sing Sing, it may well be asked, whether it may not prove to be some feeling, somehow akin to the reminiscent impulses which influenced them, that shall hereafter fraternally reunite all us mortals, when we shall have exchanged this State's Prison man-of-war world of ours for another and a better.

From the foregoing account of the great difficulty we had in killing time while in port, it must not be inferred that on board of the *Neversink* in Rio there was literally no work to be done, at long intervals the *launch* would come alongside with water-casks, to be emptied into iron tanks in the hold. In this way nearly fifty thousand gallons, as chronicled in the books of the master's mate, were decanted into the ship's bowels—a ninety day's allowance. With this huge Lake Ontario in us, the mighty *Neversink* might be said to resemble the united continent of the Eastern Hemisphere—floating in a vast ocean herself, and having a Mediterranean floating in her.

Chapter XLIII

Smuggling in a Man-of-War

It is in a good degree owing to the idleness just described, that, while lying in harbor, the man-of-war's-man is exposed to the most temptations and gets into his saddest scrapes. For though his vessel be anchored a mile from the shore, and her sides are patrolled by sentries night and day, yet these things cannot entirely prevent the seductions of the land from reaching him. The prime agent in working his calamities in port is his old arch-enemy, the ever-devilish god of grog.

Immured as the man-of-war's-man is, serving out his weary three years in a sort of sea-Newgate, from which he cannot escape, either by the roof or burrowing underground, he too often flies to the bottle to seek relief from the intolerable ennui of nothing to do, and nowhere to go. His ordinary government allowance of spirits, one gill per diem, is not enough to give a sufficient filip to his listless senses; he pronounces his grog basely *watered*; he scouts at it as *thinner than muslin*; he craves a more vigorous *nip at the cable,* a more sturdy *swig at the halyards*; and if opium were to be had, many would steep themselves a thousand fathoms down in the densest fumes of that oblivious drug. Tell him that the delirium tremens and the mania-a-potu lie in ambush for drunkards, he will say to you, "Let them bear down upon me, then, before the wind; anything that smacks of life is better than to feel Davy Jones's chest-lid on your nose." He is reckless as an avalanche; and though his fall destroy himself and others, yet a ruinous commotion is better than being frozen fast in unendurable solitudes. No wonder, then, that he goes all lengths to procure the thing he craves; no wonder that he pays the most exorbitant prices, breaks through all law, and braves the ignominious lash itself, rather than be deprived of his stimulus.

Now, concerning no one thing in a man-of-war, are the regulations more severe than respecting the smuggling of grog, and being found intoxicated. For either offense there is but one penalty, invariably enforced; and that is the degradation of the gangway.

All conceivable precautions are taken by most frigate-executives to guard against the secret admission of spirits into the vessel. In the first place, no shore-boat whatever is allowed to approach a man-of-war in a foreign harbor without permission from the officer of the deck. Even the *bum-boats,* the small craft licensed by the officers to bring off fruit for the sailors, to be bought out of their own money—these are invariably inspected before permitted to hold intercourse with the ship's company. And not only this, but every one of the numerous ship's boats—kept almost continually plying to and from the shore—are similarly inspected, sometimes each boat twenty times in the day.

This inspection is thus performed: The boat being descried by the quarter-master from the poop, she is reported to the deck officer, who thereupon summons the master-at-arms, the ship's chief of police. This functionary now stations himself at the gangway, and as the boat's crew, one by one, come up the side, he personally overhauls them, making them take off their hats, and then, placing both hands upon their heads, draws his palms slowly down to their feet, carefully feeling all unusual protuberances. If nothing suspicious is felt, the man is let pass; and so on, till the whole boat's crew, averaging about sixteen men, are examined. The chief of police then descends into the boat, and walks from stem to stern, eyeing it all over, and poking his long rattan into every nook and cranny. This operation concluded, and nothing found, he mounts the ladder, touches his hat to the deck-officer, and reports the boat *clean*; whereupon she is hauled out to the booms.

Thus it will be seen that not a man of the ship's company ever enters the vessel from shore without it being rendered next to impossible, apparently, that he should have succeeded in smuggling anything. Those individuals who are permitted to board the ship without undergoing this ordeal, are only persons whom it would be preposterous to search—such as the Commodore himself, the Captain, Lieutenants, etc., and gentlemen and ladies coming as visitors.

For anything to be clandestinely thrust through the lower port-holes at night, is rendered very difficult, from the watchfulness of the quarter-master in hailing all boats that approach, long before they draw alongside, and the vigilance of the sentries, posted on platforms overhanging the water, whose orders are to fire into a strange boat which, after being warned to withdraw, should still persist in drawing nigh. Moreover, thirty-two-pound shots are slung to ropes, and suspended over the bows, to drop a hole into and sink any small craft, which, spite of all precautions, by strategy should succeed in getting under the bows with liquor by night. Indeed, the whole power of martial law is enlisted in this matter; and every one of the numerous officers of the ship, besides his general zeal in enforcing the regulations, adds to that a personal feeling, since the sobriety of the men abridges his own cares and anxieties.

How then, it will be asked, in the face of an argus-eyed police, and in defiance even of bayonets and bullets, do men-of-war's-men contrive to smuggle their spirits? Not to enlarge upon minor stratagems—every few days detected, and rendered naught (such as rolling up, in a handkerchief, a long, slender "skin" of grog, like a sausage, and in that manner ascending to the deck out of a boat just from shore; or openly bringing on board cocoanuts and melons, procured from a knavish bumboat filled with spirits, instead of milk or water)—we will only mention here two or three other modes, coming under my own observation.

While in Rio, a fore-top-man, belonging to the second cutter, paid down the money, and made an arrangement with a person encountered at the Palace-landing ashore, to the following effect. Of a certain moonless night, he was to bring off three gallons of spirits, *in skins*, and moor them to the frigate's anchor-buoy—some distance from the vessel—attaching something heavy, to sink them out of sight. In the middle watch of the night, the fore-top-man slips out of his hammock, and by creeping along in the shadows, eludes the vigilance of the master-at-arms and his mates, gains a port-hole, and softly lowers himself into the water, almost without creating a ripple—the sentries marching to and fro on their overhanging platform above him. He is an expert swimmer, and paddles along under the surface, every now and then rising a little, and lying motionless on his back to breathe—little but his nose exposed. The buoy gained, he cuts the skins adrift, ties them round his body, and in the same adroit manner makes good his return.

This feat is very seldom attempted, for it needs the utmost caution, address, and dexterity; and no one but a super-expert burglar, and faultless Leander of a swimmer, could achieve it.

From the greater privileges which they enjoy, the "*forward officers,*" that is, the Gunner, Boatswain, etc., have much greater opportunities for successful smuggling than the common seamen. Coming alongside one night in a cutter, Yarn, our boatswain, in some inexplicable way, contrived to slip several skins of brandy through the air-port of his own state-room. The feat, however, must have been perceived by one of the boat's crew, who immediately, on gaining the deck, sprung down the ladders, stole into the boatswain's room, and made away with the prize, not three minutes before the rightful owner entered to claim it. Though, from certain circumstances, the thief was known to the aggrieved party, yet the latter could say nothing, since he himself had infringed the law. But the next day, in the capacity of captain of the ship's executioners, Yarn had the satisfaction (it was so to him) of standing over the robber at the gangway; for, being found intoxicated with the very liquor the boatswain himself had smuggled, the man had been condemned to a flogging.

This recalls another instance, still more illustrative of the knotted, trebly intertwisted villainy, accumulating at a sort of compound interest in a man-of-war. The cockswain of the Commodore's barge takes his crew apart, one by one, and cautiously sounds them as to their fidelity—not to the United States of America, but to himself. Three individuals, whom he deems doubtful—that is, faithful to the United States of America—he procures to be discharged from the barge, and men of his own selection are substituted; for he is always an influential character, this cockswain of the Commodore's barge. Previous to this, however, he has seen to it well, that no Temperance men—that is, sailors who do not draw their government ration of grog, but take the money for it—he has seen to it, that none of these *balkers* are numbered among his crew. Having now proved his men, he divulges his plan to the assembled body; a solemn oath of secrecy is obtained, and he waits the first fit opportunity to carry into execution his nefarious designs.

At last it comes. One afternoon the barge carries the Commodore across the Bay to a fine water-side settlement of noblemen's seats, called Praya Grande. The Commodore is visiting a Portuguese marquis, and the pair linger long over their dinner in an arbor in the garden. Meanwhile, the cockswain has liberty to roam about where he pleases. He searches out a place where some choice *red-eye* (brandy) is to be had, purchases six large bottles, and conceals them among the trees. Under the pretense of filling the boat-keg with water, which is always kept in the barge to refresh the crew, he now carries it off into the grove, knocks out the head, puts the bottles inside, reheads the keg, fills it with water, carries it down to the boat, and audaciously restores it to its conspicuous position in the middle, with its bung-hole up. When the Commodore comes down to the beach, and they pull off for the ship, the cockswain, in a loud voice, commands the nearest man to take that bung out of the keg—that precious water will spoil. Arrived alongside the frigate, the boat's crew are overhauled, as usual, at the gangway; and nothing being found on them, are passed. The master-at-arms now descending into the barge, and finding nothing suspicious, reports it *clean*, having put his finger into the open bung of the keg and tasted that the water was pure. The barge is ordered out to the booms, and deep night is waited for, ere the cockswain essays to snatch the bottles from the keg.

But, unfortunately for the success of this masterly smuggler, one of his crew is a weak-pated fellow, who, having drank somewhat freely ashore, goes about the gun-deck throwing out profound, tipsy hints concerning some unutterable proceeding on the ship's anvil. A knowing old sheet-anchor-man, an unprincipled fellow, putting this, that, and the other together, ferrets out the mystery; and straightway resolves to reap the goodly harvest which the cockswain has sowed. He seeks him out, takes him to one side, and addresses him thus:

"Cockswain, you have been smuggling off some *red-eye*, which at this moment is in your barge at the booms. Now, cockswain, I have stationed two of my mess-mates at the port-holes, on that side of the ship; and if they report to me that you, or any of your bargemen, offer to enter that barge before morning, I will immediately report you as a smuggler to the officer of the deck."

The cockswain is astounded; for, to be reported to the deck-officer as a smuggler, would inevitably procure him a sound flogging, and be the disgraceful *breaking* of him as a petty officer, receiving four dollars a month beyond his pay as an able-seaman. He attempts to bribe the other to secrecy, by promising half the profits of the enterprise; but the sheet-anchor-man's integrity is like a rock; he is no mercenary, to be bought up for a song. The cockswain, therefore, is forced to swear that neither himself, nor any of his crew, shall enter the barge before morning. This done, the sheet-anchor-man goes to his confidants, and arranges his plans. In a word, he succeeds in introducing the six brandy bottles into the ship; five of which he sells at eight dollars a bottle; and then, with the sixth, between two guns, he secretly regales himself and confederates; while the helpless cockswain, stifling his rage, bitterly eyes them from afar.

Thus, though they say that there is honor among thieves, there is little among man-of-war smugglers.

Chapter XLIV

A Knave in Office in a Man-of-War

THE LAST SMUGGLING STORY NOW ABOUT TO BE RELATED ALSO OCCURRED WHILE WE LAY IN Rio. It is the more particularly presented, since it furnishes the most curious evidence of the almost incredible corruption pervading nearly all ranks in some men-of-war.

For some days, the number of intoxicated sailors collared and brought up to the mast by the master-at-arms, to be reported to the deck-officers—previous to a flogging at the gangway—had, in the last degree, excited the surprise and vexation of the Captain and senior officers. So strict were the Captain's regulations concerning the suppression of grog-smuggling, and so particular had he been in charging the matter upon all the Lieutenants, and every understrapper official in the frigate, that he was wholly at a loss how so large a quantity of spirits could have been spirited into the ship, in the face of all these checks, guards, and precautions.

Still additional steps were adopted to detect the smugglers; and Bland, the master-at-arms, together with his corporals, were publicly harangued at the mast by the Captain in person, and charged to exert their best powers in suppressing the traffic. Crowds were present at the time, and saw the master-at-arms touch his cap in obsequious homage, as he solemnly assured the Captain that he would still continue to do his best; as, indeed, he said he had always done. He concluded with a pious ejaculation expressive of his personal abhorrence of smuggling and drunkenness, and his fixed resolution, so help him Heaven, to spend his last wink in sitting up by night, to spy out all deeds of darkness.

"I do not doubt you, master-at-arms," returned the Captain; "now go to your duty." This master-at-arms was a favorite of the Captain's.

The next morning, before breakfast, when the market-boat came off (that is, one of the ship's boats regularly deputed to bring off the daily fresh provisions for the officers)—when this boat came off, the master-at-arms, as usual, after carefully examining both her and her crew, reported them to the deck-officer to be free from suspicion. The provisions were then hoisted out, and among them came a good-sized wooden box, addressed to "Mr.——, Purser of the United States ship *Neversink*." Of course, any private matter of this sort, destined for a gentleman of the ward-room, was sacred from examination, and the master-at-arms commanded one of his corporals to carry it down into the Purser's state-room. But recent occurrences had sharpened the vigilance of the deck-officer to an unwonted degree, and seeing the box going down the hatchway, he demanded what that was, and whom it was for.

"All right, sir," said the master-at-arms, touching his cap; "stores for the Purser, sir."

"Let it remain on deck," said the Lieutenant. "Mr. Montgomery!" calling a midshipman, "ask the Purser whether there is any box coming off for him this morning."

"Ay, ay, sir," said the middy, touching his cap.

Presently he returned, saying that the Purser was ashore.

"Very good, then; Mr. Montgomery, have that box put into the 'brig,' with strict orders to the sentry not to suffer anyone to touch it."

"Had I not better take it down into my mess, sir, till the Purser comes off?" said the master-at-arms, deferentially.

"I have given my orders, sir!" said the Lieutenant, turning away.

When the Purser came on board, it turned out that he knew nothing at all about the box. He had never so much as heard of it in his life. So it was again brought up before the deck-officer, who immediately summoned the master-at-arms.

"Break open that box!"

"Certainly, sir!" said the master-at-arms; and, wrenching off the cover, twenty-five brown jugs like a litter of twenty-five brown pigs, were found snugly nestled in a bed of straw.

"The smugglers are at work, sir," said the master-at-arms, looking up.

"Uncork and taste it," said the officer.

The master-at-arms did so; and, smacking his lips after a puzzled fashion, was a little doubtful whether it was American whisky or Holland gin; but he said he was not used to liquor.

"Brandy; I know it by the smell," said the officer; "return the box to the brig."

"Ay, ay, sir," said the master-at-arms, redoubling his activity.

The affair was at once reported to the Captain, who, incensed at the audacity of the thing, adopted every plan to detect the guilty parties. Inquiries were made ashore; but by whom the box had been brought down to the market-boat there was no finding out. Here the matter rested for a time.

Some days after, one of the boys of the mizzen-top was flogged for drunkenness, and, while suspended in agony at the gratings, was made to reveal from whom he had procured his spirits. The man was called, and turned out to be an old superannuated marine, one Scriggs, who did the cooking for the marine-sergeants and masters-at-arms' mess. This marine was one of the most villainous-looking fellows in the ship, with a squinting, pick-lock, gray eye, and hang-dog gallows gait. How such a most unmartial vagabond had insinuated himself into the honorable marine corps was a perfect mystery. He had always been noted for his personal uncleanliness, and among all hands, fore and aft, had the reputation of being a notorious old miser, who denied himself the few comforts, and many of the common necessaries of a man-of-war life.

Seeing no escape, Scriggs fell on his knees before the Captain, and confessed the charge of the boy. Observing the fellow to be in an agony of fear at the sight of the boat-swain's mates and their lashes, and all the striking parade of public punishment, the Captain must have thought this a good opportunity for completely pumping him of all his secrets. This terrified marine was at length forced to reveal his having been for some time an accomplice in a complicated system of underhand villainy, the head of which was no less a personage than the indefatigable chief of police, the master-at-arms himself. It appeared that this official had his confidential agents ashore, who supplied him with spirits, and in various boxes, packages, and bundles—addressed to the Purser and others—brought them down to the frigate's boats at the landing. Ordinarily, the appearance of these things for the Purser and other ward-room gentlemen occasioned no surprise; for almost every day some bundle or other is coming off for them, especially for the Purser; and, as the master-at-arms was always present on these occasions, it was an easy matter for him to hurry the smuggled liquor out of sight, and, under pretense of carrying the box or bundle down to the Purser's room, hide it away upon his own premises.

The miserly marine, Scriggs, with the pick-lock eye, was the man who clandestinely sold the spirits to the sailors, thus completely keeping the master-at-arms in the background. The liquor sold at the most exorbitant prices; at one time reaching twelve dollars the bottle in cash, and thirty dollars a bottle in orders upon the Purser, to be honored upon the frigate's arrival home. It may seem incredible that such prices should have been given by the sailors; but when some man-of-war's-men crave liquor, and it is hard to procure, they would almost barter ten years of their life-time for but one solitary "*tot*" if they could.

The sailors who became intoxicated with the liquor thus smuggled on board by the master-at-arms, were, in almost numberless instances, officially seized by that functionary and scourged at the gangway. In a previous place it has been shown how conspicuous a part the master-at-arms enacts at this scene.

The ample profits of this iniquitous business were divided, between all the parties concerned in it; Scriggs, the marine, coming in for one third. His cook's mess-chest being brought on deck, four canvas bags of silver were found in it, amounting to a sum something short of as many hundred dollars.

The guilty parties were scourged, double-ironed, and for several weeks were confined in the "brig" under a sentry; all but the master-at-arms, who was merely cashiered and imprisoned for a time; with bracelets at his wrists. Upon being liberated, he was turned adrift among the ship's company; and by way of disgracing him still more, was thrust into the *waist,* the most inglorious division of the ship.

Upon going to dinner one day, I found him soberly seated at my own mess; and at first I could not but feel some very serious scruples about dining with him. Nevertheless, he was a man to study and digest; so, upon a little reflection; I was not displeased at his presence. It amazed me, however, that he had wormed himself into the mess, since so many of the other messes had declined the honor, until at last, I ascertained that he had induced a mess-mate of ours, a distant relation of his, to prevail upon the cook to admit him.

Now it would not have answered for hardly any other mess in the ship to have received this man among them, for it would have torn a huge rent in their reputation; but our mess, A. No. 1—the Forty-two-pounder Club—was composed of so fine a set of fellows; so many captains of tops, and quarter-masters—men of undeniable mark on board ship—of long-established standing and consideration on the gun-deck; that, with impunity, we could do so many equivocal things, utterly inadmissible for messes of inferior pretension. Besides, though we all abhorred the monster of Sin itself, yet, from our social superiority, highly rarified education in our lofty top, and large and liberal sweep of the aggregate of things, we were in a good degree free from those useless, personal prejudices, and galling hatreds against conspicuous *sinners,* not *Sin*—which so widely prevail among men of warped understandings and unchristian and uncharitable hearts. No; the superstitions and dogmas concerning Sin had not laid their withering maxims upon our hearts. We perceived how that evil was but good disguised, and a knave a saint in his way; how that in other planets, perhaps, what we deem wrong, may there be deemed right; even as some substances, without undergoing any mutations in themselves utterly change their color, according to the light thrown upon them. We perceived that the anticipated millennium must have begun upon the morning the first worlds were created; and that, taken all in all, our man-of-war world itself was as eligible a round-sterned craft as any to be found in the Milky Way. And we fancied that though some of us, of the gun-deck, were at times condemned to sufferings and slights, and all manner of tribulation and anguish, yet, no doubt, it was only our misapprehension of these things that made us take them for woeful pains instead of the most agreeable pleasures. I have dreamed of a sphere, says Pinzella, where to break a man on the wheel is held the most exquisite of delights you can confer upon him; where for one gentleman in any way to vanquish another is accounted an everlasting dishonor; where to tumble one into a pit after death, and then throw cold clods upon his upturned face, is a species of contumely, only inflicted upon the most notorious criminals.

But whatever we mess-mates thought, in whatever circumstances we found ourselves, we never forgot that our frigate, bad as it was, was homeward-bound. Such, at least, were our reveries at times, though sorely jarred, now and then, by events that took our philosophy aback. For after all, philosophy—that is, the best wisdom that has ever in any way been revealed to our man-of-war world—is but a slough and a mire, with a few tufts of good footing here and there.

But there was one man in the mess who would have naught to do with our philosophy—a churlish, ill-tempered, unphilosophical, superstitious old bear of a quarter-gunner; a believer in Tophet, for which he was accordingly preparing himself. Priming was his name; but methinks I have spoken of him before.

Besides, this Bland, the master-at-arms, was no vulgar, dirty knave. In him—to modify Burke's phrase—vice *seemed,* but only seemed, to lose half its seeming evil by losing all its apparent grossness. He was a neat and gentlemanly villain, and broke his biscuit with a dainty hand. There was a fine polish about his whole person, and a pliant, insinuating style in his conversation, that was, socially, quite irresistible. Save my noble captain, Jack Chase, he proved himself the most entertaining, I had almost said the most companionable man in the mess. Nothing but his mouth, that was somewhat small, Moorish-arched, and wickedly delicate, and his snaky, black eye, that at times shone like a dark-lantern in a jeweler-shop at midnight, betokened the accomplished scoundrel within. But in his conversation there was no trace of evil; nothing equivocal; he studiously shunned an indelicacy, never swore, and chiefly abounded in passing puns and witticisms, varied with humorous contrasts between ship and shore life, and many agreeable and racy anecdotes, very tastefully narrated. In short—in a merely psychological point of view, at least—he was a charming blackleg. Ashore, such a man might have been an irreproachable mercantile swindler, circulating in polite society.

But he was still more than this. Indeed, I claim for this master-at-arms a lofty and honorable niche in the Newgate Calendar of history. His intrepidity, coolness, and wonderful self-possession in calmly resigning himself to a fate that thrust him from an office in which he had tyrannized over five hundred mortals, many of whom hated and loathed him, passed all belief; his intrepidity, I say, in now fearlessly gliding among them, like a disarmed swordfish among ferocious white-sharks; this, surely, bespoke no ordinary man. While in office, even, his life had often been secretly attempted by the seamen whom he had brought to the gangway. Of dark nights they had dropped shot down the hatchways, destined "to damage his pepper-box," as they phrased it; they had made ropes with a hangman's noose at the end and tried to *lasso* him in dark corners. And now he was adrift among them, under notorious circumstances of superlative villainy, at last dragged to light; and yet he blandly smiled, politely offered his cigar-holder to a perfect stranger, and laughed and chatted to right and left, as if springy, buoyant, and elastic, with an angelic conscience, and sure of kind friends wherever he went, both in this life and the life to come.

While he was lying ironed in the "brig," gangs of the men were sometimes overheard whispering about the terrible reception they would give him when he should be set at large. Nevertheless, when liberated, they seemed confounded by his erect and cordial assurance, his gentlemanly sociability and fearless companionableness. From being an implacable policeman, vigilant, cruel, and remorseless in his office, however polished in his phrases, he was now become a disinterested, sauntering man of leisure, winking at all improprieties, and ready to laugh and make merry with anyone. Still, at first, the men gave him a wide berth, and returned scowls for his smiles; but who can forever resist the very Devil himself, when he comes in the guise of a gentleman, free, fine, and frank? Though Goethe's pious Margaret hates the Devil in his horns and harpooner's tail, yet she smiles and nods to the engaging fiend in the persuasive, winning, oily, wholly harmless Mephistopheles. But, however it was, I, for one, regarded this master-at-arms with mixed feelings of detestation, pity, admiration, and something opposed to enmity. I could not but abominate him when I thought of his conduct; but I pitied the continual gnawing which, under all his deftly-donned disguises, I saw lying at the bottom of his soul. I admired his heroism in sustaining himself so well under such reverses. And when I thought how arbitrary the *Articles of War* are in defining a man-of-war villain; how much undetected guilt might be sheltered by the aristocratic awning of our quarter-deck; how many florid pursers, ornaments of the ward-room, had been legally protected in defrauding *the people,* I could not but say to myself: Well, after all, though this man is a most wicked one indeed, yet is he even more luckless than depraved.

Besides, a studied observation of Bland convinced me that he was an organic and irreclaimable scoundrel, who did wicked deeds as the cattle browse the herbage, because wicked deeds seemed the legitimate operation of his whole infernal organization. Phrenologically, he was without a soul. Is it to be wondered at, that the devils are irreligious? What, then, thought I, who is to blame in this matter? For one, I will not take the Day of Judgment upon me by authoritatively pronouncing upon the essential criminality of any man-of-war's-man; and Christianity has taught me that, at the last day, man-of-war's-men will not be judged by the *Articles of War,* nor by the *United States Statutes at Large,* but by immutable laws, ineffably beyond the comprehension of the honorable Board of Commodores and Navy Commissioners. But though I will stand by even a man-of-war thief, and defend him from being seized up at the gangway, if I can—remembering that my Savior once hung between two thieves, promising one life eternal—yet I would not, after the plain conviction of a villain, again let him entirely loose to prey upon honest seamen, fore and aft all three decks. But this did Captain Claret; and though the thing may not perhaps be credited, nevertheless, here it shall be recorded.

After the master-at-arms had been adrift among the ship's company for several weeks, and we were within a few days' sail of home, he was summoned to the mast, and publicly reinstated in his office as the ship's chief of police. Perhaps Captain Claret had read the Memoirs of Vidocq, and believed in the old saying, *set a rogue to catch a rogue.* Or, perhaps, he was a man of very tender feelings, highly susceptible to the soft emotions of gratitude, and could not bear to leave in disgrace a person who, out of the generosity of his heart, had, about a year previous, presented him with a rare snuff-box, fabricated from a sperm-whale's tooth, with a curious silver hinge, and cunningly wrought in the shape of a whale; also a splendid gold-mounted cane, of a costly Brazilian wood, with a gold plate, bearing the Captain's name and rank in the service, the place and time of his birth, and with a vacancy underneath—no doubt providentially left for his heirs to record his decease.

Certain it was that, some months previous to the master-at-arms' disgrace, he had presented these articles to the Captain, with his best love and compliments; and the Captain had received them, and seldom went ashore without the cane, and never took snuff but out of that box. With some Captains, a sense of propriety might have induced them to return these presents, when the generous donor had proved himself unworthy of having them retained; but it was not Captain Claret who would inflict such a cutting wound upon any officer's sensibilities, though long-established naval customs had habituated him to scourging *the people* upon an emergency.

Now had Captain Claret deemed himself constitutionally bound to decline all presents from his subordinates, the sense of gratitude would not have operated to the prejudice of justice. And, as some of the subordinates of a man-of-war captain are apt to invoke his good wishes and mollify his conscience by making him friendly gifts, it would perhaps have been an excellent thing for him to adopt the plan pursued by the President of the United States, when he received a present of lions and Arabian chargers from the Sultan of Muscat. Being forbidden by his sovereign lords and masters, the imperial people, to accept of any gifts from foreign powers, the President sent them to an auctioneer, and the proceeds were deposited in the Treasury. In the same manner, when Captain Claret received his snuff-box and cane, he might have accepted them very kindly, and then sold them off to the highest bidder, perhaps to the donor himself, who in that case would never have tempted him again.

Upon his return home, Bland was paid off for his full term, not deducting the period of his suspension. He again entered the service in his old capacity.

As no further allusion will be made to this affair, it may as well be stated now that, for the very brief period elapsing between his restoration and being paid off in port by the Purser, the master-at-arms conducted himself with infinite discretion, artfully steering between any relaxation of discipline—which would have awakened the displeasure of the officers—and any unwise severity—which would have revived, in tenfold force, all the old grudges of the seamen under his command.

Never did he show so much talent and tact as when vibrating in this his most delicate predicament; and plenty of cause was there for the exercise of his cunningest abilities; for, upon the discharge of our man-of-war's-men at home, should he *then* be held by them as an enemy, as free and independent citizens they would waylay him in the public streets, and take purple vengeance for all his iniquities, past, present, and possible in the future. More than once a master-at-arms ashore has been seized by night by an exasperated crew, and served as Origen served himself, or as his enemies served Abelard.

But though, under extreme provocation, *the people* of a man-of-war have been guilty of the maddest vengeance, yet, at other times, they are very placable and milky-hearted, even to those who may have outrageously abused them; many things in point might be related, but I forbear.

This account of the master-at-arms cannot better be concluded than by denominating him, in the vivid language of the Captain of the Fore-top, as "*the two ends and middle of the thrice-laid strand of a bloody rascal,*" which was intended for a terse, well-knit, and all-comprehensive assertion, without omission or reservation. It was also asserted that, had Tophet itself been raked with a fine-tooth comb, such another ineffable villain could not by any possibility have been caught.

Chapter XLV

PUBLISHING POETRY IN A MAN-OF-WAR

A DAY OR TWO AFTER OUR ARRIVAL IN RIO, A RATHER AMUSING INCIDENT OCCURRED TO A PARticular acquaintance of mine, young Lemsford, the gun-deck bard.

The great guns of an armed ship have blocks of wood, called *tompions,* painted black, inserted in their muzzles, to keep out the spray of the sea. These tompions slip in and out very handily, like covers to butter firkins.

By advice of a friend, Lemsford, alarmed for the fate of his box of poetry, had latterly made use of a particular gun on the main-deck, in the tube of which he thrust his manuscripts, by simply crawling partly out of the port-hole, removing the tompion, inserting his papers, tightly rolled, and making all snug again.

Breakfast over, he and I were reclining in the main-top—where, by permission of my noble master, Jack Chase, I had invited him—when, of a sudden, we heard a cannonading. It was our own ship.

"Ah!" said a top-man, "returning the shore salute they gave us yesterday."

"O Lord!" cried Lemsford, "my *Songs of the Sirens!*" and he ran down the rigging to the batteries; but just as he touched the gun-deck, gun No. 20—his literary strong-box—went off with a terrific report.

"Well, my after-guard Virgil," said Jack Chase to him, as he slowly returned up the rigging, "did you get it? You need not answer; I see you were too late. But never mind, my boy: no printer could do the business for you better. That's the way to publish, White-Jacket," turning to me—"fire it right into 'em; every canto a twenty-four-pound shot; *hull* the blockheads, whether they will or no. And mind you, Lemsford, when your shot does the most execution, your hear the least from the foe. A killed man cannot even lisp."

"Glorious Jack!" cried Lemsford, running up and snatching him by the hand, "say that again, Jack! look me in the eyes. By all the Homers, Jack, you have made my soul mount like a balloon! Jack, I'm a poor devil of a poet. Not two months before I shipped aboard here, I published a volume of poems, very aggressive on the world, Jack. Heaven knows what it cost me. I published it, Jack, and the cursed publisher sued me for damages; my friends looked sheepish; one or two who liked it were non-committal; and as for the addle-pated mob and rabble, they thought they had found out a fool. Blast them, Jack, what they call the public is a monster, like the idol we saw in Owhyhee, with the head of a jackass, the body of a baboon, and the tail of a scorpion!"

"I don't like that," said Jack; "when I'm ashore, I myself am part of the public."

"Your pardon, Jack; you are not, you are then a part of the people, just as you are aboard the frigate here. The public is one thing, Jack, and the people another."

"You are right," said Jack; "right as this leg. Virgil, you are a trump; you are a jewel, my boy. The public and the people! Ay, ay, my lads, let us hate the one and cleave to the other."

Chapter XLVI

The Commodore on the Poop, and One of "The People" under the Hands of the Surgeon

A DAY OR TWO AFTER THE PUBLICATION OF LEMSFORD'S *SONGS OF THE SIRENS*, A SAD ACCIDENT befell a mess-mate of mine, one of the captains of the mizzen-top. He was a fine little Scot, who, from the premature loss of the hair on the top of his head, always went by the name of *Baldy*. This baldness was no doubt, in great part, attributable to the same cause that early thins the locks of most man-of-war's-men—namely, the hard, unyielding, and ponderous man-of-war and navy-regulation tarpaulin hat, which, when new, is stiff enough to sit upon, and indeed, in lieu of his thumb, sometimes serves the common sailor for a bench.

Now, there is nothing upon which the Commodore of a squadron more prides himself than upon the celerity with which his men can handle the sails, and go through with all the evolutions pertaining thereto. This is especially manifested in harbor, when other vessels of his squadron are near, and perhaps the armed ships of rival nations.

Upon these occasions, surrounded by his post-captain satraps—each of whom in his own floating island is king—the Commodore domineers over all—emperor of the whole oaken archipelago; yea, magisterial and magnificent as the Sultan of the Isles of Sooloo.

But, even as so potent an emperor and Cæsar to boot as the great Don of Germany, Charles the Fifth, was used to divert himself in his dotage by watching the gyrations of the springs and cogs of a long row of clocks, even so does an elderly Commodore while away his leisure in harbor, by what is called *"exercising guns,"* and also *"exercising yards and sails"*; causing the various spars of all the ships under his command to be "braced," "topped," and "cock billed" in concert, while the Commodore himself sits, something like King Canute, on an arm-chest on the poop of his flag-ship.

But far more regal than any descendant of Charlemagne, more haughty than any Mogul of the East, and almost mysterious and voiceless in his authority as the Great Spirit of the Five Nations, the Commodore deigns not to verbalize his commands; they are imparted by signal.

And as for old Charles the Fifth, again, the gay-pranked, colored suits of cards were invented, to while away his dotage, even so, doubtless, must these pretty little signals of blue and red spotted *bunting* have been devised to cheer the old age of all Commodores.

By the Commodore's side stands the signal-midshipman, with a sea-green bag swung on his shoulder (as a sportsman bears his game-bag), the signal-book in one hand, and the signal spy-glass in the other. As this signal-book contains the Masonic signs and tokens of the navy, and would therefore be invaluable to an enemy, its binding is always bordered with lead, so as to insure its sinking in case the ship should be captured. Not the only book this, that might appropriately be bound in lead, though there be many where the author, and not the bookbinder, furnishes the metal.

As White-Jacket understands it, these signals consist of variously-colored flags, each standing for a certain number. Say there are ten flags, representing the cardinal numbers—the red flag, No. 1; the blue flag, No. 2; the green flag, No. 3, and so forth; then, by mounting the blue flag over the red, that would stand for No. 21: if the green flag were set underneath, it would then stand for 213. How easy, then, by endless transpositions, to multiply the various numbers that may be exhibited at the mizzen-peak, even by only three or four of these flags.

To each number a particular meaning is applied. No. 100, for instance, may mean, *"Beat to quarters."* No. 150, *"All hands to grog."* No. 2000, *"Strike top-gallant-yards."* No. 2110, *"See anything to windward?"* No. 2800, *"No."*

And as every man-of-war is furnished with a signal-book, where all these things are set down in order, therefore, though two American frigates—almost perfect strangers to each other—came from the opposite Poles, yet at a distance of more than a mile they could carry on a very liberal conversation in the air.

When several men-of-war of one nation lie at anchor in one port, forming a wide circle round their lord and master, the flag-ship, it is a very interesting sight to see them all obeying the Commodore's orders, who meanwhile never opens his lips.

Thus was it with us in Rio, and hereby hangs the story of my poor mess-mate Baldy.

One morning, in obedience to a signal from our flag-ship, the various vessels belonging to the American squadron then in harbor simultaneously loosened their sails to dry. In the evening, the signal was set to furl them. Upon such occasions, great rivalry exists between the First Lieutenants of the different ships; they vie with each other who shall first have his sails stowed on the yards. And this rivalry is shared between all the officers of each vessel, who are respectively placed over the different top-men; so that the main-mast is all eagerness to vanquish the fore-mast, and the mizzen-mast to vanquish them both. Stimulated by the shouts of their officers, the sailors throughout the squadron exert themselves to the utmost.

"Aloft, top-men! lay out! furl!" cried the First Lieutenant of the *Neversink*.

At the word the men sprang into the rigging, and on all three masts were soon climbing about the yards, in reckless haste, to execute their orders.

Now, in furling top-sails or courses, the point of honor, and the hardest work, is in the *bunt*, or middle of the yard; this post belongs to the first captain of the top.

"What are you 'bout there, mizzen-top-men?" roared the First Lieutenant, through his trumpet. "D—n you, you are clumsy as Russian bears! don't you see the main-top-men are nearly off the yard? Bear a hand, bear a hand, or I'll stop your grog all round! You, Baldy! are you going to sleep there in the bunt?"

While this was being said, poor Baldy—his hat off, his face streaming with perspiration—was frantically exerting himself, piling up the ponderous folds of canvas in the middle of the yard; ever and anon glancing at victorious Jack Chase, hard at work at the main-top-sail-yard before him.

At last, the sail being well piled up, Baldy jumped with both feet into the *bunt*, holding on with one hand to the chain *"tie,"* and in that manner was violently treading down the canvas, to pack it close.

"D—n you, Baldy, why don't you move, you crawling caterpillar"; roared the First Lieutenant.

Baldy brought his whole weight to bear on the rebellious sail, and in his frenzied heedlessness let go his hold on the *tie*.

"You, Baldy! are you afraid of falling?" cried the First Lieutenant.

At that moment, with all his force, Baldy jumped down upon the sail; the *bunt gasket* parted; and a dark form dropped through the air. Lighting upon the *top-rim*, it rolled off; and the next instant, with a horrid crash of all his bones, Baldy came, like a thunderbolt, upon the deck.

Aboard of most large men-of-war there is a stout oaken platform, about four feet square, on each side of the quarter-deck. You ascend to it by three or four steps; on top, it is railed in at the sides, with horizontal brass bars. It is called *the Horse Block*; and there the officer of the deck usually stands, in giving his orders at sea.

It was one of these horse blocks, now unoccupied, that broke poor Baldy's fall. He fell lengthwise across the brass bars, bending them into elbows, and crushing the whole oaken platform, steps and all, right down to the deck in a thousand splinters.

He was picked up for dead, and carried below to the surgeon. His bones seemed like those of a man broken on the wheel, and no one thought he would survive the night. But with the surgeon's skillful treatment he soon promised recovery. Surgeon Cuticle devoted all his science to this case.

A curious frame-work of wood was made for the maimed man; and placed in this, with all his limbs stretched out, Baldy lay flat on the floor of the Sick-bay, for many weeks. Upon our arrival home, he was able to hobble ashore on crutches; but from a hale, hearty man, with bronzed cheeks, he was become a mere dislocated skeleton, white as foam; but ere this, perhaps, his broken bones are healed and whole in the last repose of the man-of-war's-man.

Not many days after Baldy's accident in furling sails—in this same frenzied manner, under the stimulus of a shouting officer—a seaman fell from the main-royal-yard of an English line-of-battle ship near us, and buried his ankle-bones in the deck, leaving two indentations there, as if scooped out by a carpenter's gouge.

The royal-yard forms a cross with the mast, and falling from that lofty cross in a line-of-battle ship is almost like falling from the cross of St. Paul's; almost like falling as Lucifer from the well-spring of morning down to the Phlegethon of night.

In some cases, a man, hurled thus from a yard, has fallen upon his own shipmates in the tops, and dragged them down with him to the same destruction with himself.

Hardly ever will you hear of a man-of-war returning home after a cruise, without the loss of some of her crew from aloft, whereas similar accidents in the merchant service—considering the much greater number of men employed in it—are comparatively few.

Why mince the matter? The death of most of these man-of-war's-men lies at the door of the souls of those officers, who, while safely standing on deck themselves, scruple not to sacrifice an immortal man or two, in order to show off the excelling discipline of the ship. And thus do *the people* of the gun-deck suffer, that the Commodore on the poop may be glorified.

Chapter XLVII

An Auction in a Man-of-War

Some allusion has been made to the weariness experienced by the man-of-war's-men while lying at anchor; but there are scenes now and then that serve to relieve it. Chief among these are the Purser's auctions, taking place while in harbor. Some weeks, or perhaps months, after a sailor dies in an armed vessel, his bag of clothes is in this manner sold, and the proceeds transferred to the account of his heirs or executors.

One of these auctions came off in Rio, shortly after the sad accident of Baldy.

It was a dreamy, quiet afternoon, and the crew were listlessly lying around, when suddenly the Boatswain's whistle was heard, followed by the announcement, "D'ye hear there, fore and aft? Purser's auction on the spar-deck!"

At the sound, the sailors sprang to their feet and mustered round the main-mast. Presently up came the Purser's steward, marshalling before him three or four of his subordinates, carrying several clothes' bags, which were deposited at the base of the mast.

Our Purser's steward was a rather gentlemanly man in his way. Like many young Americans of his class, he had at various times assumed the most opposite functions for a livelihood, turning from one to the other with all the facility of a light-hearted, clever adventurer. He had been a clerk in a steamer on the Mississippi River; an auctioneer in Ohio; a stock actor at the Olympic Theatre in New York; and now he was Purser's steward in the Navy. In the course of this diversified career his natural wit and waggery had been highly spiced, and every way improved; and he had acquired the last and most difficult art of the joker, the art of lengthening his own face while widening those of his hearers, preserving the utmost solemnity while setting them all in a roar. He was quite a favorite with the sailors, which, in a good degree, was owing to his humor; but likewise to his off-hand, irresistible, romantic, theatrical manner of addressing them.

With a dignified air, he now mounted the pedestal of the main-top-sail sheet-bitts, imposing silence by a theatrical wave of his hand; meantime, his subordinates were rummaging the bags, and assorting their contents before him.

"Now, my noble hearties," he began, "we will open this auction by offering to your impartial competition a very superior pair of old boots"; and so saying, he dangled aloft one clumsy cowhide cylinder, almost as large as a fire bucket, as a specimen of the complete pair.

"What shall I have now, my noble tars, for this superior pair of sea-boots?"

"Where's t'other boot?" cried a suspicious-eyed waister. "I remember them 'ere boots. They were old Bob's the quarter-gunner's; there was two on 'em, too. I want to see t'other boot."

"My sweet and pleasant fellow," said the auctioneer, with his blandest accents, "the other boot is not just at hand, but I give you my word of honor that it in all respects corresponds to the one you here see—it does, I assure you. And I solemnly guarantee, my noble sea-faring fencibles," he added, turning round upon all, "that the other boot is the exact counterpart of this. Now, then, say the word, my fine fellows. What shall I have? Ten dollars, did you say?" politely bowing toward some indefinite person in the background.

"No; ten cents," responded a voice.

"Ten cents! ten cents! gallant sailors, for this noble pair of boots," exclaimed the auctioneer, with affected horror; "I must close the auction, my tars of Columbia; this will never do. But let's have another bid; now, come," he added, coaxingly and soothingly. "What is it? One dollar, one dollar then—one dollar; going at one dollar; going, going—going. Just see how it vibrates"—swinging the boot to and fro—"this superior pair of sea-boots vibrating at one dollar; wouldn't pay for the nails in their heels; going, going—*gone!*" And down went the boots.

"Ah, what a sacrifice! what a sacrifice!" he sighed, tearfully eyeing the solitary fire-bucket, and then glancing round the company for sympathy.

"A sacrifice, indeed!" exclaimed Jack Chase, who stood by; "Purser's Steward, you are Mark Antony over the body of Julius Cæsar."

"So I am, so I am," said the auctioneer, without moving a muscle. "And look!" he exclaimed, suddenly seizing the boot, and exhibiting it on high, "look, my noble tars, if you have tears, prepare to shed them now. You all do know this boot. I remember the first time ever old Bob put it on. 'Twas on a winter evening, off Cape Horn, between the starboard carronades—that day his precious grog was stopped. Look! in this place a mouse has nibbled through; see what a rent some envious rat has made, through this another filed, and, as he plucked his cursed rasp away, mark how the boot-leg gaped. This was the unkindest cut of all. But whose are the boots?" suddenly assuming a business-like air; "yours? yours? yours?"

But not a friend of the lamented Bob stood by.

"Tars of Columbia," said the auctioneer, imperatively, "these boots must be sold; and if I can't sell them one way, I must sell them another. How much *a pound*, now, for this superior pair of old boots? going by *the pound* now, remember, my gallant sailors! what shall I have? one cent, do I hear? going now at one cent a pound—going—going—going—*gone!*"

"Whose are they? Yours, Captain of the Waist? Well, my sweet and pleasant friend, I will have them weighed out to you when the auction is over."

In like manner all the contents of the bags were disposed of, embracing old frocks, trousers, and jackets, the various sums for which they went being charged to the bidders on the books of the Purser.

Having been present at this auction, though not a purchaser, and seeing with what facility the most dismantled old garments went off, through the magical cleverness of the accomplished auctioneer, the thought occurred to me, that if ever I calmly and positively decided to dispose of my famous white jacket, this would be the very way to do it. I turned the matter over in my mind a long time.

The weather in Rio was genial and warm, and that I would ever again need such a thing as a heavy quilted jacket—and such a jacket as the white one, too—seemed almost impossible. Yet I remembered the American coast, and that it would probably be Autumn when we should arrive there. Yes, I thought of all that, to be sure; nevertheless, the ungovernable whim seized me to sacrifice my jacket and recklessly abide the consequences. Besides, was it not a horrible jacket? To how many annoyances had it subjected me? How many scrapes had it dragged me into? Nay, had it not once jeopardized my very existence? And I had a dreadful presentiment that, if I persisted in retaining it, it would do so again. Enough! I will sell it, I muttered; and so muttering, I thrust my hands further down in my waistband, and walked the main-top in the stern concentration of an inflexible purpose. Next day, hearing that another auction was shortly to take place, I repaired to the office of the Purser's steward, with whom I was upon rather friendly terms. After vaguely and delicately hinting at the object of my visit, I came roundly to the point, and asked him whether he could slip my jacket into one of the bags of clothes next to be sold, and so dispose of it by public auction. He kindly acquiesced and the thing was done.

In due time all hands were again summoned round the main-mast; the Purser's steward mounted his post, and the ceremony began. Meantime, I lingered out of sight, but still within hearing, on the gun-deck below, gazing up, unperceived, at the scene.

As it is now so long ago, I will here frankly make confession that I had privately retained the services of a friend—Williams, the Yankee pedagogue and peddler—whose business it would be to linger near the scene of the auction, and, if the bids on the jacket loitered, to start it roundly himself; and if the bidding then became brisk, he was continually to strike in with the most pertinacious and infatuated bids, and so exasperate competition into the maddest and most extravagant overtures.

A variety of other articles having been put up, the white jacket was slowly produced, and, held high aloft between the auctioneer's thumb and forefinger, was submitted to the inspection of the discriminating public.

Here it behooves me once again to describe my jacket; for, as a portrait taken at one period of life will not answer for a later stage; much more this jacket of mine, undergoing so many changes, needs to be painted again and again, in order truly to present its actual appearance at any given period.

A premature old age had now settled upon it; all over it bore melancholy sears of the masoned-up pockets that had once trenched it in various directions. Some parts of it were slightly mildewed from dampness; on one side several of the buttons were gone, and others were broken or cracked; while, alas! my many mad endeavors to rub it black on the decks had now imparted to the whole garment an exceedingly untidy appearance. Such as it was, with all its faults, the auctioneer displayed it.

"You, venerable sheet-anchor-men! and you, gallant fore-top-men! and you, my fine waisters! what do you say now for this superior old jacket? Buttons and sleeves, lining and skirts, it must this day be sold without reservation. How much for it, my gallant tars of Columbia? say the word, and how much?"

"My eyes!" exclaimed a fore-top-man, "don't that 'ere bunch of old swabs belong to Jack Chase's pet? Aren't that *the white jacket?*"

"The white jacket!" cried fifty voices in response; *"the white jacket!"* The cry ran fore and aft the ship like a slogan, completely overwhelming the solitary voice of my private friend Williams, while all hands gazed at it with straining eyes, wondering how it came among the bags of deceased mariners.

"Ay, noble tars," said the auctioneer, "you may well stare at it; you will not find another jacket like this on either side of Cape Horn, I assure you. Why, just look at it! How much, now? Give me a bid—but don't be rash; be prudent, be prudent, men; remember your Purser's accounts, and don't be betrayed into extravagant bids."

"Purser's Steward!" cried Grummet, one of the quarter-gunners, slowly shifting his quid from one cheek to the other, like a ballast-stone, "I won't bid on that 'ere bunch of old swabs, unless you put up ten pounds of soap with it."

"Don't mind that old fellow," said the auctioneer. "How much for the jacket, my noble tars?"

"Jacket"; cried a dandy *bone polisher* of the gun-room. "The sail-maker was the tailor, then. How many fathoms of canvas in it, Purser's Steward?"

"How much for this *jacket?*" reiterated the auctioneer, emphatically.

"*Jacket,* do you call it!" cried a captain of the hold.

"Why not call it a white-washed man-of-war schooner? Look at the port-holes, to let in the air of cold nights."

"A reg'lar herring-net," chimed in Grummet.

"Gives me the *fever nagur* to look at it," echoed a mizzen-top-man.

"Silence!" cried the auctioneer. "Start it now—start it, boys; anything you please, my fine fellows! it *must* be sold. Come, what ought I to have on it, now?"

"Why, Purser's Steward," cried a waister, "you ought to have new sleeves, a new lining, and a new body on it, afore you try to shove it off on a greenhorn."

"What are you, 'busin' that 'ere garment for?" cried an old sheet-anchor-man. "Don't you see it's a 'uniform mustering jacket'—three buttons on one side, and none on t'other?"

"Silence!" again cried the auctioneer. "How much, my sea-fencibles, for this superior old jacket?"

"Well," said Grummet, "I'll take it for cleaning-rags at one cent."

"Oh, come, give us a bid! say something, Columbians."

"Well, then," said Grummet, all at once bursting into genuine indignation, "if you want us to say something, then heave that bunch of old swabs overboard, *say I,* and show us something worth looking at."

"No one will give me a bid, then? Very good; here, shove it aside. Let's have something else there."

While this scene was going forward, and my white jacket was thus being abused, how my heart swelled within me! Thrice was I on the point of rushing out of my hiding-place, and bearing it off from derision; but I lingered, still flattering myself that all would be well, and the jacket find a purchaser at last. But no, alas! there was no getting rid of it, except by rolling a forty-two-pound shot in it, and committing it to the deep. But though, in my desperation, I had once contemplated something of that sort, yet I had now become unaccountably averse to it, from certain involuntary superstitious considerations. If I sink my jacket, thought I, it will be sure to spread itself into a bed at the bottom of the sea, upon which I shall sooner or later recline, a dead man. So, unable to conjure it into the possession of another, and withheld from burying it out of sight for ever, my jacket stuck to me like the fatal shirt on Nessus.

Chapter XLVIII

PURSER, PURSER'S STEWARD, AND POSTMASTER IN A MAN-OF-WAR

AS THE PURSER'S STEWARD SO CONSPICUOUSLY FIGURED AT THE UNSUCCESSFUL AUCTION OF MY jacket, it reminds me of how important a personage that official is on board of all men-of-war. He is the right-hand man and confidential deputy and clerk of the Purser, who entrusts to him all his accounts with the crew, while, in most cases, he himself, snug and comfortable in his state-room, glances over a file of newspapers instead of overhauling his ledgers.

Of all the non-combatants of a man-of-war, the Purser, perhaps, stands foremost in importance. Though he is but a member of the gun-room mess, yet usage seems to assign him a conventional station somewhat above that of his equals in navy rank—the Chaplain, Surgeon, and Professor. Moreover, he is frequently to be seen in close conversation with the Commodore, who, in the *Neversink,* was more than once known to be slightly jocular with our Purser. Upon several occasions, also, he was called into the Commodore's cabin, and remained closeted there for several minutes together. Nor do I remember that there ever happened a cabinet meeting of the ward-room barons, the Lieutenants, in the Commodore's cabin, but the Purser made one of the party. Doubtless the important fact of the Purser having under his charge all the financial affairs of a man-of-war, imparts to him the great importance he enjoys. Indeed, we find in every government—monarchies and republics alike—that the personage at the head of the finances invariably occupies a commanding position. Thus, in point of station, the Secretary of the Treasury of the United States is deemed superior to the other heads of departments. Also, in England, the real office held by the great Premier himself is—as everyone knows—that of First Lord of the Treasury.

Now, under this high functionary of state, the official known as the Purser's Steward was head clerk of the frigate's fiscal affairs. Upon the berth-deck he had a regular counting-room, full of ledgers, journals, and day-books. His desk was as much littered with papers as any Pearl Street merchant's, and much time was devoted to his accounts. For hours together you would see him, through the window of his subterranean office, writing by the light of his perpetual lamp.

Ex-officio, the Purser's Steward of most ships is a sort of postmaster, and his office the post-office. When the letter-bags for the squadron—almost as large as those of the United States mail—arrived on board the *Neversink,* it was the Purser's Steward that sat at his little window on the berth-deck and handed you your letter or paper—if any there were to your address. Some disappointed applicants among the sailors would offer to buy the epistles of their more fortunate shipmates, while yet the seal was unbroken—maintaining that the sole and confidential reading of a fond, long, domestic letter from any man's home, was far better than no letter at all.

In the vicinity of the office of the Purser's Steward are the principal store-rooms of the Purser, where large quantities of goods of every description are to be found. On board of those ships where goods are permitted to be served out to the crew for the purpose of selling them ashore, to raise money, more business is transacted at the office of a Purser's Steward in one *Liberty-day* morning than all the dry goods shops in a considerable village would transact in a week.

Once a month, with undeviating regularity, this official has his hands more than usually full. For, once a month, certain printed bills, called Mess-bills, are circulated among the crew, and whatever you may want from the Purser—be it tobacco, soap, duck, dungaree, needles, thread, knives, belts, calico, ribbon, pipes, paper, pens, hats, ink, shoes, socks, or whatever it may be—down it goes on the mess-bill, which, being the next day returned to the office of the Steward, the "slops," as they are called, are served out to the men and charged to their accounts.

Lucky is it for man-of-war's-men that the outrageous impositions to which, but a very few years ago, they were subjected from the abuses in this department of the service, and the unscrupulous cupidity of many of the pursers—lucky is it for them that *now* these things are in a great degree done away. The Pursers, instead of being at liberty to make almost what they pleased from the sale of their wares, are now paid by regular stipends laid down by law.

Under the exploded system, the profits of some of these officers were almost incredible. In one cruise up the Mediterranean, the Purser of an American line-of-battle ship was, on good authority, said to have cleared the sum of $50,000. Upon that he quitted the service, and retired into the country. Shortly after, his three daughters—not very lovely—married extremely well.

The ideas that sailors entertain of Pursers is expressed in a rather inelegant but expressive saying of theirs: "The Purser is a conjurer; he can make a dead man chew tobacco"—insinuating that the accounts of a dead man are sometimes subjected to post-mortem charges. Among sailors, also, Pursers commonly go by the name of *nip-cheeses.*

No wonder that on board of the old frigate *Java,* upon her return from a cruise extending over a period of more than four years, one thousand dollars paid off eighty of her crew, though the aggregate wages of the eighty for the voyage must have amounted to about sixty thousand dollars. Even under the present system, the Purser of a line-of-battle ship, for instance, is far better paid than any other officer, short of Captain or Commodore. While the Lieutenant commonly receives but eighteen hundred dollars, the Surgeon of the fleet but fifteen hundred, the Chaplain twelve hundred, the Purser of a line-of-battle ship receives thirty-five hundred dollars. In considering his salary, however, his responsibilities are not to be overlooked; they are by no means insignificant.

There are Pursers in the Navy whom the sailors exempt from the insinuations above mentioned, nor, as a class, are they so obnoxious to them now as formerly; for one, the florid old Purser of the *Neversink*—never coming into disciplinary contact with the seamen, and being withal a jovial and apparently good-hearted gentleman—was something of a favorite with many of the crew.

Chapter XLIX

Rumors of a War, and How They Were Received by the Population of the Neversink

While lying in the harbor of Callao, in Peru, certain rumors had come to us touching a war with England, growing out of the long-vexed Northeastern Boundary Question. In Rio these rumors were increased; and the probability of hostilities induced our Commodore to authorize proceedings that closely brought home to every man on board the *Neversink* his liability at any time to be killed at his gun.

Among other things, a number of men were detailed to pass up the rusty cannon-balls from the shot-lockers in the hold, and scrape them clean for service. The Commodore was a very neat gentleman, and would not fire a dirty shot into his foe.

It was an interesting occasion for a tranquil observer; nor was it altogether neglected. Not to recite the precise remarks made by the seamen while pitching the shot up the hatchway from hand to hand, like schoolboys playing ball ashore, it will be enough to say that, from the general drift of their discourse—jocular as it was—it was manifest that, almost to a man, they abhorred the idea of going into action.

And why should they desire a war? Would their wages be raised? Not a cent. The prize-money, though, ought to have been an inducement. But of all the "rewards of virtue," prize-money is the most uncertain; and this the man-of-war's-man knows. What, then, has he to expect from war? What but harder work, and harder usage than in peace; a wooden leg or arm; mortal wounds, and death? Enough, however, that by far the majority of the common sailors of the *Neversink* were plainly concerned at the prospect of war, and were plainly averse to it.

But with the officers of the quarter-deck it was just the reverse. None of them, to be sure, in my hearing at least, verbally expressed their gratification; but it was unavoidably betrayed by the increased cheerfulness of their demeanor toward each other, their frequent fraternal conferences, and their unwonted animation for several days in issuing their orders. The voice of Mad Jack—always a belfry to hear—now resounded like that famous bell of England, Great Tom of Oxford. As for Selvagee, he wore his sword with a jaunty air, and his servant daily polished the blade.

But why this contrast between the forecastle and the quarter-deck, between the man-of-war's-man and his officer? Because, though war would equally jeopardize the lives of both, yet, while it held out to the sailor no promise of promotion, and what is called *glory*, these things fired the breast of his officers.

It is no pleasing task, nor a thankful one, to dive into the souls of some men; but there are occasions when, to bring up the mud from the bottom, reveals to us on what soundings we are, on what coast we adjoin.

How were these officers to gain glory? How but by a distinguished slaughtering of their fellow-men. How were they to be promoted? How but over the buried heads of killed comrades and mess-mates.

This hostile contrast between the feelings with which the common seamen and the officers of the *Neversink* looked forward to this more than possible war, is one of many instances that might be quoted to show the antagonism of their interests, the incurable antagonism in which they dwell. But can men, whose interests are diverse, ever hope to live together in a harmony uncoerced? Can the brotherhood of the race of mankind ever hope to prevail in a man-of-war, where one man's bane is almost another's blessing? By abolishing the scourge, shall we do away tyranny; *that* tyranny which must ever prevail, where of two essentially antagonistic classes in perpetual contact, one is immeasurably the stronger? Surely it seems all but impossible. And as the very object of a man-of-war, as its name implies, is to fight the very battles so naturally averse to the seamen; so long as a man-of-war exists, it must ever remain a picture of much that is tyrannical and repelling in human nature.

Being an establishment much more extensive than the American Navy, the English armed marine furnishes a yet more striking example of this thing, especially as the existence of war produces so vast an augmentation of her naval force compared with what it is in time of peace. It is well known what joy the news of Bonaparte's sudden return from Elba created among crowds of British naval officers, who had previously been expecting to be sent ashore on half-pay. Thus, when all the world wailed, these officers found occasion for thanksgiving. I urge it not against them as *men*—their feelings belonged to their profession. Had they not been naval officers, they had not been rejoicers in the midst of despair.

When shall the time come, how much longer will God postpone it, when the clouds, which at times gather over the horizons of nations, shall not be hailed by any class of humanity, and invoked to burst as a bomb? Standing navies, as well as standing armies, serve to keep alive the spirit of war even in the meek heart of peace. In its very embers and smolderings, they nourish that fatal fire, and half-pay officers, as the priests of Mars, yet guard the temple, though no god be there.

Chapter L

THE BAY OF ALL BEAUTIES

I HAVE SAID THAT I MUST PASS OVER RIO WITHOUT A DESCRIPTION; BUT JUST NOW SUCH A FLOOD of scented reminiscences steals over me, that I must needs yield and recant, as I inhale that musky air.

More than one hundred and fifty miles' circuit of living green hills embosoms a translucent expanse, so gemmed in by sierras of grass, that among the Indian tribes the place was known as "The Hidden Water." On all sides, in the distance, rise high conical peaks, which at sunrise and sunset burn like vast tapers; and down from the interior, through vineyards and forests, flow radiating streams, all emptying into the harbor.

Talk not of Bahia de Todos os Santos—the Bay of All Saints; for though that be a glorious haven, yet Rio is the Bay of all Rivers—the Bay of all Delights—the Bay of all Beauties. From circumjacent hill-sides, untiring summer hangs perpetually in terraces of vivid verdure; and, embossed with old mosses, convent and castle nestle in valley and glen.

All round, deep inlets run into the green mountain land, and, overhung with wild Highlands, more resemble Loch Katrines than Lake Lemans. And though Loch Katrine has been sung by the bonneted Scott, and Lake Leman by the coroneted Byron; yet here, in Rio, both the loch and the lake are but two wild flowers in a prospect that is almost unlimited. For, behold! far away and away, stretches the broad blue of the water, to yonder soft-swelling hills of light green, backed by the purple pinnacles and pipes of the grand Organ Mountains; fitly so called, for in thunder-time they roll cannonades down the bay, drowning the blended bass of all the cathedrals in Rio. Shout amain, exalt your voices, stamp your feet, jubilate, Organ Mountains! and roll your Te Deums round the world!

What though, for more than five thousand five hundred years, this grand harbor of Rio lay hid in the hills, unknown by the Catholic Portuguese? Centuries ere Haydn performed before emperors and kings, these Organ Mountains played his *Oratorio of the Creation*, before the Creator himself. But nervous Haydn could not have endured that cannonading choir, since this composer of thunderbolts himself died at last through the crashing commotion of Napoleon's bombardment of Vienna.

But all mountains are Organ Mountains: the Alps and the Himalayas; the Appalachian Chain, the Ural, the Andes, the Green Hills and the White. All of them play anthems forever: The Messiah, and Samson, and Israel in Egypt, and Saul, and Judas Maccabeus, and Solomon.

Archipelago Rio! ere Noah on old Ararat anchored his ark, there lay anchored in you all these green, rocky isles I now see. But God did not build on you, isles! those long lines of batteries; nor did our blessed Savior stand godfather at the christening of yon frowning fortress of Santa Cruz, though named in honor of himself, the divine Prince of Peace!

Amphitheatrical Rio! in your broad expanse might be held the Resurrection and Judgment-day of the whole world's men-of-war, represented by the flag-ships of fleets—the flag-ships of the

Phœnician armed galleys of Tyre and Sidon; of King Solomon's annual squadrons that sailed to Ophir; whence in after times, perhaps, sailed the Acapulco fleets of the Spaniards, with golden ingots for ballasting; the flag-ships of all the Greek and Persian craft that exchanged the war-hug at Salamis; of all the Roman and Egyptian galleys that, eagle-like, with blood-dripping prows, beaked each other at Actium; of all the Danish keels of the Vikings; of all the musquito craft of Abba Thule, king of the Pelaws, when he went to vanquish Artinsall; of all the Venetian, Genoese, and Papal fleets that came to the shock at Lepanto; of both horns of the crescent of the Spanish Armada; of the Portuguese squadron that, under the gallant Gama, chastised the Moors, and discovered the Moluccas; of all the Dutch navies led by Van Tromp, and sunk by Admiral Hawke; of the forty-seven French and Spanish sail-of-the-line that, for three months, essayed to batter down Gibraltar; of all Nelson's seventy-fours that thunder-bolted off St. Vincent's, at the Nile, Copenhagen, and Trafalgar; of all the frigate-merchantmen of the East India Company; of Perry's war-brigs, sloops, and schooners that scattered the British armament on Lake Erie; of all the Barbary corsairs captured by Bainbridge; of the war-canoes of the Polynesian kings, Tammahammaha and Pomare—ay! one and all, with Commodore Noah for their Lord High Admiral—in this abounding Bay of Rio these flag-ships might all come to anchor, and swing round in concert to the first of the flood.

Rio is a small Mediterranean; and what was fabled of the entrance to that sea, in Rio is partly made true; for here, at the mouth, stands one of Hercules' Pillars, the Sugar-Loaf Mountain, one thousand feet high, inclining over a little, like the Leaning Tower of Pisa. At its base crouch, like mastiffs, the batteries of Jose and Theodosia; while opposite, you are menaced by a rock-founded fort.

The channel between—the sole inlet to the bay—seems but a biscuit's toss over; you see naught of the land-locked sea within till fairly in the strait. But, then, what a sight is beheld! Diversified as the harbor of Constantinople, but a thousand-fold grander. When the *Neversink* swept in, word was passed, "Aloft, top-men! and furl t'-gallant-sails and royals!"

At the sound I sprang into the rigging, and was soon at my perch. How I hung over that main-royal-yard in a rapture! High in air, poised over that magnificent bay, a new world to my ravished eyes, I felt like the foremost of a flight of angels, new-lighted upon earth, from some star in the Milky Way.

Chapter LI

ONE OF "THE PEOPLE" HAS AN AUDIENCE WITH THE COMMODORE AND THE CAPTAIN ON THE QUARTER-DECK

WE HAD NOT LAIN IN RIO LONG, WHEN IN THE INNERMOST RECESSES OF THE MIGHTY SOUL OF my noble Captain of the Top—incomparable Jack Chase—the deliberate opinion was formed, and rock-founded, that our ship's company must have at least one day's *"liberty"* to go ashore ere we weighed anchor for home.

Here it must be mentioned that, concerning anything of this kind, no sailor in a man-of-war ever presumes to be an agitator, unless he is of a rank superior to a mere able-seaman; and no one short of a petty officer—that is, a captain of the top, a quarter-gunner, or boatswain's mate—ever dreams of being a spokesman to the supreme authority of the vessel in soliciting any kind of favor for himself and shipmates.

After canvassing the matter thoroughly with several old quarter-masters and other dignified sea-fencibles, Jack, hat in hand, made his appearance, one fine evening, at the mast, and, waiting till Captain Claret drew nigh, bowed, and addressed him in his own off-hand, polished, and poetical style. In his intercourse with the quarter-deck, he always presumed upon his being such a universal favorite.

"Sir, this Rio is a charming harbor, and we poor mariners—your trusty sea-warriors, valiant Captain! who, with *you* at their head, would board the Rock of Gibraltar itself, and carry it by storm—we poor fellows, valiant Captain! have gazed round upon this ravishing landscape till we can gaze no more. Will Captain Claret vouchsafe one day's liberty, and so assure himself of eternal felicity, since, in our flowing cups, he will be ever after freshly remembered?"

As Jack thus rounded off with a snatch from Shakespeare, he saluted the Captain with a gallant flourish of his tarpaulin, and then, bringing the rim to his mouth, with his head bowed, and his body thrown into a fine negligent attitude, stood a picture of eloquent but passive appeal. He seemed to say, Magnanimous Captain Claret, we fine fellows, and hearts of oak, throw ourselves upon your unparalleled goodness.

"And what do you want to go ashore for?" asked the Captain, evasively, and trying to conceal his admiration of Jack by affecting some haughtiness.

"Ah! sir," sighed Jack, "why do the thirsty camels of the desert desire to lap the waters of the fountain and roll in the green grass of the oasis? Are we not but just from the ocean Sahara? and is not this Rio a verdant spot, noble Captain? Surely you will not keep us always tethered at anchor, when a little more cable would admit of our cropping the herbage! And it is a weary thing, Captain Claret, to be imprisoned month after month on the gun-deck, without so much as smelling a citron. Ah! Captain Claret, what sings sweet Waller:

But who can always on the billows lie?
The watery wilderness yields no supply.

compared with such a prisoner, noble Captain,

Happy, thrice happy, who, in battle slain,
Press'd in Atrides' cause the Trojan pain!

Pope's version, sir, not the original Greek."

And so saying, Jack once more brought his hat-rim to his mouth, and slightly bending forward, stood mute.

At this juncture the Most Serene Commodore himself happened to emerge from the after-gangway, his gilded buttons, epaulets, and the gold lace on his chapeau glittering in the flooding sunset. Attracted by the scene between Captain Claret and so well-known and admired a commoner as Jack Chase he approached, and assuming for the moment an air of pleasant condescension—never shown to his noble barons the officers of the ward-room—he said, with a smile, "Well, Jack, you and your shipmates are after some favor, I suppose—a day's liberty, is it not?"

Whether it was the horizontal setting sun, streaming along the deck, that blinded Jack, or whether it was in sun-worshiping homage of the mighty Commodore, there is no telling; but just at this juncture noble Jack was standing reverentially holding his hat to his brow, like a man with weak eyes.

"Valiant Commodore," said he, at last, "this audience is indeed an honor undeserved. I almost sink beneath it. Yes, valiant Commodore, your sagacious mind has truly divined our object. Liberty, sir; liberty is, indeed, our humble prayer. I trust your honorable wound, received in glorious battle, valiant Commodore, pains you less to-day than common."

"Ah! cunning Jack!" cried the Commodore, by no means blind to the bold sortie of his flattery, but not at all displeased with it. In more respects than one, our Commodore's wound was his weak side.

"I think we must give them liberty," he added, turning to Captain Claret; who thereupon, waving Jack further off, fell into confidential discourse with his superior.

"Well, Jack, we will see about it," at last cried the Commodore, advancing. "I think we must let you go."

"To your duty, captain of the main-top!" said the Captain, rather stiffly. He wished to neutralize somewhat the effect of the Commodore's condescension. Besides, he had much rather the Commodore had been in his cabin. His presence, for the time, affected his own supremacy in his ship. But Jack was nowise cast down by the Captain's coldness; he felt safe enough; so he proceeded to offer his acknowledgments.

" 'Kind gentlemen,' " he sighed, " 'your pains are registered where every day I turn the leaf to read'—*Macbeth,* valiant Commodore and Captain!—what the Thane says to the noble lords, Ross and Angus."

And long and lingeringly bowing to the two noble officers, Jack backed away from their presence, still shading his eyes with the broad rim of his hat.

"Jack Chase for ever!" cried his shipmates, as he carried the grateful news of liberty to them on the forecastle. "Who can talk to Commodores like our matchless Jack!"

Chapter LII

SOMETHING CONCERNING MIDSHIPMEN

IT WAS THE NEXT MORNING AFTER MATCHLESS JACK'S INTERVIEW WITH THE COMMODORE AND Captain, that a little incident occurred, soon forgotten by the crew at large, but long remembered by the few seamen who were in the habit of closely scrutinizing every-day proceedings. Upon the face of it, it was but a common event—at least in a man-of-war—the flogging of a man at the gangway. But the under-current of circumstances in the case were of a nature that magnified this particular flogging into a matter of no small importance. The story itself cannot here be related; it would not well bear recital: enough that the person flogged was a middle-aged man of the Waist—a forlorn, broken-down, miserable object, truly; one of those wretched landsmen sometimes driven into the Navy by their unfitness for all things else, even as others are driven into the workhouse. He was flogged at the complaint of a midshipman; and hereby hangs the drift of the thing. For though this waister was so ignoble a mortal, yet his being scourged on this one occasion indirectly proceeded from the mere wanton spite and unscrupulousness of the midshipman in question—a youth, who was apt to indulge at times in undignified familiarities with some of the men, who, sooner or later, almost always suffered from his capricious preferences.

But the leading principle that was involved in this affair is far too mischievous to be lightly dismissed.

In most cases, it would seem to be a cardinal principle with a Navy Captain that his subordinates are disintegrated parts of himself, detached from the main body on special service, and that the order of the minutest midshipman must be as deferentially obeyed by the seamen as if proceeding from the Commodore on the poop. This principle was once emphasized in a remarkable manner by the valiant and handsome Sir Peter Parker, upon whose death, on a national arson expedition on the shores of Chesapeake Bay, in 1812 or 1813, Lord Byron wrote his well-known stanzas. "By the god of war!" said Sir Peter to his sailors, "I'll make you touch your hat to a midshipman's coat, if it's only hung on a broomstick to dry!"

That the king, in the eye of the law, can do no wrong, is the well-known fiction of despotic states; but it has remained for the navies of Constitutional Monarchies and Republics to magnify this fiction, by indirectly extending it to all the quarter-deck subordinates of an armed ship's chief magistrate. And though judicially unrecognized, and unacknowledged by the officers themselves, yet this is the principle that pervades the fleet; this is the principle that is every hour acted upon, and to sustain which, thousands of seamen have been flogged at the gangway.

However childish, ignorant, stupid, or idiotic a midshipman, if he but orders a sailor to perform even the most absurd action, that man is not only bound to render instant and unanswering obedience, but he would refuse at his peril. And if, having obeyed, he should then complain to the Captain, and the Captain, in his own mind, should be thoroughly convinced of the impropriety, perhaps of the illegality of the order, yet, in nine cases out of ten, he would not publicly reprimand the midshipman, nor by the slightest token admit before the complainant that, in this particular thing, the midshipman had done otherwise than perfectly right.

Upon a midshipman's complaining of a seaman to Lord Collingwood, when Captain of a line-of-battle ship, he ordered the man for punishment; and, in the interval, calling the midshipman aside, said to him, "In all probability, now, the fault is yours—you know; therefore, when the man is brought to the mast, you had better ask for his pardon."

Accordingly, upon the lad's public intercession, Collingwood, turning to the culprit, said, "This young gentleman has pleaded so humanely for you, that, in hope you feel a due gratitude to him for his benevolence, I will, for this time, overlook your offense." This story is related by the editor of the Admiral's *Correspondence*, to show the Admiral's kind-heartedness.

Now Collingood was, in reality, one of the most just, humane, and benevolent admirals that ever hoisted a flag. For a sea-officer, Collingwood was a man in a million. But if a man like him, swayed by old usages, could thus violate the commonest principle of justice—with however good motives at bottom—what must be expected from other Captains not so eminently gifted with noble traits as Collingwood?

And if the corps of American midshipmen is mostly replenished from the nursery, the counter, and the lap of unrestrained indulgence at home: and if most of them at least, by their impotency as officers, in all important functions at sea, by their boyish and overweening conceit of their gold lace, by their overbearing manner toward the seamen, and by their peculiar aptitude to construe the merest trivialities of manner into set affronts against their dignity; if by all this they sometimes contract the ill-will of the seamen; and if, in a thousand ways, the seamen cannot but betray it—how easy for any of these midshipmen, who may happen to be unrestrained by moral principle, to resort to spiteful practices in procuring vengeance upon the offenders, in many instances to the extremity of the lash; since, as we have seen, the tacit principle in the Navy seems to be that, in his ordinary intercourse with the sailors, a midshipman can do nothing obnoxious to the public censure of his superiors.

"You fellow, I'll get you *licked* before long," is often heard from a midshipman to a sailor who, in some way not open to the judicial action of the Captain, has chanced to offend him.

At times you will see one of these lads, not five feet high, gazing up with inflamed eye at some venerable six-footer of a forecastle man, cursing and insulting him by every epithet deemed most scandalous and unendurable among men. Yet that man's indignant tongue is treble-knotted by the law, that suspends death itself over his head should his passion discharge the slightest blow at the boy-worm that spits at his feet.

But since what human nature is, and what it must forever continue to be, is well enough understood for most practical purposes, it needs no special example to prove that, where the merest boys, indiscriminately snatched from the human family, are given such authority over mature men, the results must be proportionable in monstrousness to the custom that authorizes this worse than cruel absurdity.

Nor is it unworthy of remark that, while the noblest-minded and most heroic sea-officers—men of the topmost stature, including Lord Nelson himself—have regarded flogging in the Navy with the deepest concern, and not without weighty scruples touching its general necessity, still, one who has seen much of midshipmen can truly say that he has seen but few midshipmen who were not enthusiastic advocates and admirers of scourging. It would almost seem that they themselves, having so recently escaped the posterior discipline of the nursery and the infant-school, are impatient to recover from those smarting reminiscences by mincing the backs of full-grown American freemen.

It should not to be omitted here, that the midshipmen in the English Navy are not permitted to be quite so imperious as in the American ships. They are divided into three (I think) probationary classes of "volunteers," instead of being at once advanced to a warrant. Nor will you fail to remark, when you see an English cutter officered by one of those volunteers, that the boy does not so strut and slap his dirk-hilt with a Bobadil air, and anticipatingly feel of the place where his war-like whiskers are going to be, and sputter out oaths so at the men, as is too often the case with the little boys wearing best-bower anchors on their lapels in the American Navy.

Yet it must be confessed that at times you see midshipmen who are noble little fellows, and not at all disliked by the crew. Besides three gallant youths, one black-eyed little lad in particular, in the *Neversink*, was such a one. From his diminutiveness, he went by the name of *Boat Plug* among the seamen. Without being exactly familiar with them, he had yet become a general favorite, by reason of his kindness of manner, and never cursing them. It was amusing to hear some of the older Tritons invoke blessings upon the youngster, when his kind tones fell on their weather-beaten ears. "Ah, good luck to you, sir!" touching their hats to the little man; "you have a soul to be saved, sir!" There was a wonderful deal of meaning involved in the latter sentence. *You have a soul to be saved,* is the phrase which a man-of-war's-man peculiarly applies to a humane and kind-hearted officer. It also implies that the majority of quarter-deck officers are regarded by them in such a light that they deny to them the possession of souls. Ah! but these plebeians sometimes have a sublime vengeance upon patricians. Imagine an outcast old sailor seriously cherishing the purely speculative conceit that some bully in epaulets, who orders him to and fro like a slave, is of an organization immeasurably inferior to himself; must at last perish with the brutes, while he goes to his immortality in heaven.

But from what has been said in this chapter, it must not be inferred that a midshipman leads a lord's life in a man-of-war. Far from it. He lords it over those below him, while lorded over himself by his superiors. It is as if with one hand a school-boy snapped his fingers at a dog, and at the same time received upon the other the discipline of the usher's ferule. And though, by the American *Articles of War,* a Navy Captain cannot, of his own authority, legally punish a midshipman, otherwise than by suspension from duty (the same as with respect to the Ward-room officers), yet this is one of those sea-statutes which the Captain, to a certain extent, observes or disregards at his pleasure. Many instances might be related of the petty mortifications and official insults inflicted by some Captains upon their midshipmen; far more severe, in one sense, than the old-fashioned punishment of sending them to the mast-head, though not so arbitrary as sending them before the mast, to do duty with the common sailors—a custom, in former times, pursued by Captains in the English Navy.

Captain Claret himself had no special fondness for midshipmen. A tall, overgrown young midshipman, about sixteen years old, having fallen under his displeasure, he interrupted the humble apologies he was making, by saying, "Not a word, sir! I'll not hear a word! Mount the netting, sir, and stand there till you are ordered to come down!"

The midshipman obeyed; and, in full sight of the entire ship's company, Captain Claret promenaded to and fro below his lofty perch, reading him a most aggravating lecture upon his alleged misconduct. To a lad of sensibility, such treatment must have been almost as stinging as the lash itself would have been.

It is to be remembered that, wherever these chapters treat of midshipmen, the officers known as passed-midshipmen are not at all referred to. In the American Navy, these officers form a class of young men, who, having seen sufficient service at sea as midshipmen to pass an examination before a Board of Commodores, are promoted to the rank of passed-midshipmen, introductory to that of lieutenant. They are supposed to be qualified to do duty as lieutenants, and in some cases temporarily serve as such. The difference between a passed-midshipman and a midshipman may be also inferred from their respective rates of pay. The former, upon sea-service, receives $750 a year; the latter, $400. There were no passed-midshipmen in the *Neversink*.

Chapter LIII

Sea-faring Persons Peculiarly Subject to Being Under the Weather—The Effects of This upon a Man-of-War Captain

It has been said that some midshipmen, in certain cases, are guilty of spiteful practices against the man-of-war's-man. But as these midshipmen are presumed to have received the liberal and lofty breeding of gentlemen, it would seem all but incredible that any of their corps could descend to the paltriness of cherishing personal malice against so conventionally degraded a being as a sailor. So, indeed, it would seem. But when all the circumstances are considered, it will not appear extraordinary that some of them should thus cast discredit upon the warrants they wear. Title, and rank, and wealth, and education cannot unmake human nature; the same in cabin-boy and commodore, its only differences lie in the different modes of development.

At sea, a frigate houses and homes five hundred mortals in a space so contracted that they can hardly so much as move but they touch. Cut off from all those outward passing things which ashore employ the eyes, tongues, and thoughts of landsmen, the inmates of a frigate are thrown upon themselves and each other, and all their ponderings are introspective. A morbidness of mind is often the consequence, especially upon long voyages, accompanied by foul weather, calms, or head-winds. Nor does this exempt from its evil influence any rank on board. Indeed, high station only ministers to it the more, since the higher the rank in a man-of-war, the less companionship.

It is an odious, unthankful, repugnant thing to dwell upon a subject like this; nevertheless, be it said, that, through these jaundiced influences, even the captain of a frigate is, in some cases, indirectly induced to the infliction of corporal punishment upon a seaman. Never sail under a navy captain whom you suspect of being dyspeptic, or constitutionally prone to hypochondria..

The manifestation of these things is sometimes remarkable. In the earlier part of the cruise, while making a long, tedious run from Mazatlan to Callao on the Main, baffled by light head-winds and frequent intermitting calms, when all hands were heartily wearied by the torrid, monotonous sea, a good-natured fore-top-man, by the name of Candy—quite a character in his way—standing in the waist among a crowd of seamen, touched me, and said, "D'ye see the old man there, White-Jacket, walking the poop? Well, don't he look as if he wanted to flog someone? Look at him once."

But to me, at least, no such indications were visible in the deportment of the Captain, though his thrashing the arm-chest with the slack of the spanker-out-haul looked a little suspicious. But anyone might have been doing that to pass away a calm.

"Depend on it," said the top-man, "he must somehow have thought I was making sport of *him* a while ago, when I was only taking off old Priming, the gunner's mate. Just look at him once, White-Jacket, while I make believe coil this here rope; if there arn't a dozen in that 'ere Captain's top-lights, my name is *horse-marine.* If I could only touch my tile to him now, and take my Bible oath on it, that I was only taking off Priming, and not *him,* he wouldn't have such hard thoughts of me. But that can't be done; he'd think I meant to insult him. Well, it can't be helped; I suppose I must look out for a baker's dozen afore long."

I had an incredulous laugh at this. But two days afterward, when we were hoisting the main-top-mast stun'-sail, and the Lieutenant of the Watch was reprimanding the crowd of seamen at the halyards for their laziness—for the sail was but just crawling up to its place, owing to the languor of the men, induced by the heat—the Captain, who had been impatiently walking the deck, suddenly stopped short, and darting his eyes among the seamen, suddenly fixed them, crying out, "You, Candy, and be damned to you, you don't pull an ounce, you blackguard! Stand up to that gun, sir; I'll teach you to be grinning over a rope that way, without lending your pound of beef to it. Boatswain's mate, where's your *colt?* Give that man a dozen."

Removing his hat, the boatswain's mate looked into the crown aghast; the coiled rope, usually worn there, was not to be found; but the next instant it slid from the top of his head to the deck. Picking it up, and straightening it out, he advanced toward the sailor.

"Sir," said Candy, touching and retouching his cap to the Captain, "I was pulling, sir, as much as the rest, sir; I was, indeed, sir."

"Stand up to that gun," cried the Captain. "Boatswain's mate, do your duty."

Three stripes were given, when the Captain raised his finger. "You——[1] do you dare stand up to be flogged with your hat on! Take it off, sir, instantly."

Candy dropped it on deck.

"Now go on, boatswain's mate." And the sailor received his dozen.

With his hand to his back he came up to me, where I stood among the bystanders, saying, "O Lord, O Lord! that boatswain's mate, too, had a spite agin me; he always thought it was *me* that set afloat that yarn about his wife in Norfolk. O Lord! just run your hand under my shirt will you, White-Jacket? There! didn't he have a spite agin me, to raise such bars as them? And my shirt all cut to pieces, too—arn't it, White-Jacket? Damn me, but these coltings puts the tin in the Purser's pocket. O Lord! my back feels as if there was a red-hot gridiron lashed to it. But I told you so—a widow's curse on him, say I—he thought I meant *him,* and not Priming."

1. The phrase here used I have never seen either written or printed, and should not like to be the first person to introduce it to the public.

Chapter LIV

"THE PEOPLE" ARE GIVEN "LIBERTY"

WHENEVER, IN INTERVALS OF MILD BENEVOLENCE, OR YIELDING TO MERE POLITIC DICTATES, Kings and Commodores relax the yoke of servitude, they should see to it well that the concession seem not too sudden or unqualified; for, in the commoner's estimation, that might argue feebleness or fear.

Hence it was, perhaps, that, though noble Jack had carried the day captive in his audience at the mast, yet more than thirty-six hours elapsed ere anything official was heard of the "liberty" his shipmates so earnestly coveted. Some of the people began to growl and grumble.

"It's turned out all gammon, Jack," said one.

"Blast the Commodore!" cried another, "he bamboozled you, Jack."

"Lay on your oars a while," answered Jack, "and we shall see; we've struck for liberty, and liberty we'll have! I'm your tribune, boys; I'm your Rienzi. The Commodore must keep his word."

Next day, about breakfast-time, a mighty whistling and piping was heard at the main-hatchway, and presently the boatswain's voice was heard: "D'ye hear there, fore and aft! all you starboard-quarter watch! get ready to go ashore on liberty!"

In a paroxysm of delight, a young mizzen-top-man, standing by at the time, whipped the tarpaulin from his head, and smashed it like a pancake on the deck. "Liberty!" he shouted, leaping down into the berth-deck after his bag.

At the appointed hour, the quarter-watch mustered round the capstan, at which stood our old First Lord of the Treasury and Pay-Master-General, the Purser, with several goodly buck-skin bags of dollars, piled up on the capstan. He helped us all round to half a handful or so, and then the boats were manned, and, like so many Esterhazys, we were pulled ashore by our shipmates. All their lives lords may live in listless state; but give the commoners a holiday, and they outlord the Commodore himself.

The ship's company were divided into four sections or quarter-watches, only one of which were on shore at a time, the rest remaining to garrison the frigate—the term of liberty for each being twenty-four hours.

With Jack Chase and a few other discreet and gentlemanly top-men, I went ashore on the first day, with the first quarter-watch. Our own little party had a charming time; we saw many fine sights; fell in—as all sailors must—with dashing adventures. But, though not a few good chapters might be written on this head, I must again forbear; for in this book I have nothing to do with the shore further than to glance at it, now and then, from the water; my man-of-war world alone must supply me with the staple of my matter; I have taken an oath to keep afloat to the last letter of my narrative.

Had they all been as punctual as Jack Chase's party, the whole quarter-watch of liberty-men had been safe on board the frigate at the expiration of the twenty-four hours. But this was not the case; and during the entire day succeeding, the midshipmen and others were engaged in ferreting them out of their hiding-places on shore, and bringing them off in scattered detachments to the ship.

They came in all imaginable stages of intoxication; some with blackened eyes and broken heads; some still more severely injured, having been stabbed in frays with the Portuguese soldiers. Others, unharmed, were immediately dropped on the gun-deck, between the guns, where they lay snoring for the rest of the day. As a considerable degree of license is invariably permitted to man-of-war's-men just "off liberty," and as man-of-war's-men well know this to be the case, they occasionally avail themselves of the privilege to talk very frankly to the officers when they first cross the gangway, taking care, meanwhile, to reel about very industriously, so that there shall be no doubt about their being seriously intoxicated, and altogether *non compos* for the time. And though but few of them have cause to feign intoxication, yet some individuals may be suspected of enacting a studied part upon these occasions. Indeed—judging by certain symptoms—even when really inebriated, some of the sailors must have previously determined upon their conduct; just as some persons who, before taking the exhilarating gas, secretly make up their minds to perform certain mad feats while under its influence, which feats consequently come to pass precisely as if the actors were not accountable for them.

For several days, while the other quarter-watches were given liberty, the *Neversink* presented a sad scene. She was more like a madhouse than a frigate; the gun-deck resounded with frantic fights, shouts, and songs. All visitors from shore were kept at a cable's-length.

These scenes, however, are nothing to those which have repeatedly been enacted in American men-of-war upon other stations. But the custom of introducing women on board, in harbor, is now pretty much discontinued, both in the English and American Navy, unless a ship, commanded by some dissolute Captain, happens to lie in some far away, outlandish port, in the Pacific or Indian Ocean.

The British line-of-battle ship, *Royal George,* which in 1782 sunk at her anchors at Spithead, carried down three hundred English women among the one thousand souls that were drowned on that memorable morning.

When, at last, after all the mad tumult and contention of "Liberty," the reaction came, our frigate presented a very different scene. The men looked jaded and wan, lethargic and lazy; and many an old mariner, with hand upon abdomen, called upon the Flag-staff to witness that there were more *hot coppers* in the *Neversink* than those in the ship's galley.

Such are the lamentable effects of suddenly and completely releasing *"the people"* of a man-of-war from arbitrary discipline. It shows that, to such, "liberty," at first, must be administered in small and moderate quantities, increasing with the patient's capacity to make good use of it.

Of course while we lay in Rio, our officers frequently went ashore for pleasure, and, as a general thing, conducted themselves with propriety. But it is a sad thing to say, that, as for Lieutenant Mad Jack, he enjoyed himself so delightfully for three consecutive days in the town, that, upon returning to the ship, he sent his card to the Surgeon, with his compliments, begging him to drop into his state-room the first time he happened to pass that way in the ward-room.

But one of our Surgeon's mates, a young medico of fine family but slender fortune, must have created by far the strongest impression among the hidalgoes of Rio. He had read *Don Quixote,* and, instead of curing him of his Quixotism, as it ought to have done, it only made him still more Quixotic. Indeed, there are some natures concerning whose moral maladies the grand maxim of Mr. Similia Similibus Curantur Hahneman does not hold true, since, with them, *like cures* not *like,* but only aggravates *like.* Though, on the other hand, so incurable are the moral maladies of such persons, that the antagonist maxim, *contraria contrariis curantur,* often proves equally false.

Of a warm tropical day, this Surgeon's mate must needs go ashore in his blue cloth boat-cloak, wearing it, with a gallant Spanish toss, over his cavalier shoulder. By noon, he perspired very freely; but then his cloak attracted all eyes, and that was huge satisfaction. Nevertheless, his being knock-kneed, and spavined of one leg, sorely impaired the effect of this hidalgo cloak, which, by-the-way, was somewhat rusty in front, where his chin rubbed against it, and a good deal bedraggled all over, from his having used it as a counterpane off Cape Horn.

As for the midshipmen, there is no knowing what their mammas would have said to their conduct in Rio. Three of them drank a good deal too much; and when they came on board, the Captain ordered them to be sewed up in their hammocks, to cut short their obstreperous capers till sober.

This shows how unwise it is to allow children yet in their teens to wander so far from home. It more especially illustrates the folly of giving them long holidays in a foreign land, full of seductive dissipation. Port for men, claret for boys, cried Dr. Johnson. Even so, men only should drink the strong drink of travel; boys should still be kept on milk and water at home. Middies! you may despise your mother's leading-strings, but they are the *man-ropes* my lads, by which many youngsters have steadied the giddiness of youth, and saved themselves from lamentable falls. And middies! know this, that as infants, being too early put on their feet, grow up bandy-legged, and curtailed of their fair proportions, even so, my dear middies, does it morally prove with some of you, who prematurely are sent off to sea.

These admonitions are solely addressed to the more diminutive class of midshipmen—those under five feet high, and under seven stone in weight.

Truly, the records of the steerages of men-of-war are full of most melancholy examples of early dissipation, disease, disgrace, and death. Answer, ye shades of fine boys, who in the soils of all climes, the round world over, far away sleep from your homes.

Mothers of men! If your hearts have been cast down when your boys have fallen in the way of temptations ashore, how much more bursting your grief, did you know that those boys were far from your arms, cabined and cribbed in by all manner of iniquities. But this some of you cannot believe. It is, perhaps, well that it is so.

But hold them fast—all those who have not yet weighed their anchors for the Navy—round and round, hitch over hitch, bind your leading-strings on them, and clinching a ring-bolt into your chimmey-jam, moor your boys fast to that best of harbors, the hearth-stone.

But if youth be giddy, old age is staid; even as young saplings, in the litheness of their limbs, toss to their roots in the fresh morning air; but, stiff and unyielding with age, mossy trunks never bend. With pride and pleasure be it said, that, as for our old Commodore, though he might treat himself to as many *"liberty days"* as he pleased, yet throughout our stay in Rio he conducted himself with the utmost discretion.

But he was an old, old man; physically, a very small man; his spine was as an unloaded musket-barrel—not only attenuated, but destitute of a solitary cartridge, and his ribs were as the ribs of a weasel.

Besides, he was Commodore of the fleet, supreme lord of the Commons in Blue. It beseemed him, therefore, to erect himself into an ensample of virtue, and show the gun-deck what virtue was. But alas! when Virtue sits high aloft on a frigate's poop, when Virtue is crowned in the cabin a Commodore, when Virtue rules by compulsion, and domineers over Vice as a slave, then Virtue, though her mandates be outwardly observed, bears little interior sway. To be efficacious, Virtue must come down from aloft, even as our blessed Redeemer came down to redeem our whole man-of-war world; to that end, mixing with its sailors and sinners as equals.

Chapter LV

MIDSHIPMEN ENTERING THE NAVY EARLY

THE ALLUSION IN THE PRECEDING CHAPTER TO THE EARLY AGE AT WHICH SOME OF THE MIDshipmen enter the Navy, suggests some thoughts relative to more important considerations.

A very general modern impression seems to be, that, in order to learn the profession of a sea-officer, a boy can hardly be sent to sea too early. To a certain extent, this may be a mistake. Other professions, involving a knowledge of technicalities and things restricted to one particular field of action, are frequently mastered by men who begin after the age of twenty-one, or even at a later period of life. It was only about the middle of the seventeenth century that the British military and naval services were kept distinct. Previous to that epoch the king's officers commanded indifferently either by sea or by land.

Robert Blake, perhaps one of the most accomplished, and certainly one of the most successful Admirals that ever hoisted a flag, was more than half a century old (fifty-one years) before he entered the naval service, or had aught to do, professionally, with a ship. He was of a studious turn, and, after leaving Oxford, resided quietly on his estate, a country gentleman, till his forty-second year, soon after which he became connected with the Parliamentary army.

The historian Clarendon says of him, "He was the first man that made it manifest that the science (seamanship) might be attained in less time than was imagined." And doubtless it was to his shore sympathies that the well-known humanity and kindness which Blake evinced in his intercourse with the sailors is in a large degree to be imputed.

Midshipmen sent into the Navy at a very early age are exposed to the passive reception of all the prejudices of the quarter-deck in favor of ancient usages, however useless or pernicious; those prejudices grow up with them, and solidify with their very bones. As they rise in rank, they naturally carry them up, whence the inveterate repugnance of many Commodores and Captains to the slightest innovations in the service, however salutary they may appear to landsmen.

It is hardly to be doubted that, in matters connected with the general welfare of the Navy, government has paid rather too much deference to the opinions of the officers of the Navy, considering them as men almost born to the service, and therefore far better qualified to judge concerning any and all questions touching it than people on shore. But in a nation under a liberal Constitution, it must ever be unwise to make too distinct and peculiar the profession of either branch of its military men. True, in a country like ours, nothing is at present to be apprehended of their gaining political rule; but not a little is to be apprehended concerning their perpetuating or creating abuses among their subordinates, unless civilians have full cognizance of their administrative affairs, and account themselves competent to the complete overlooking and ordering them.

We do wrong when we in any way contribute to the prevailing mystification that has been thrown about the internal affairs of the national sea-service. Hitherto those affairs have been regarded even by some high state functionaries as things beyond their insight—altogether too technical and mysterious to be fully comprehended by landsmen. And this it is that has perpetuated in the Navy many evils that otherwise would have been abolished in the general amelioration of other things. The army is sometimes remodeled, but the Navy goes down from generation to generation almost untouched and unquestioned, as if its code were infallible, and itself a piece of perfection that no statesman could improve. When a Secretary of the Navy ventures to innovate upon its established customs, you hear some of the Navy officers say, "What does this landsman know about our affairs? Did he ever head a watch? He does not know starboard from larboard, girt-line from back-stay."

While we deferentially and cheerfully leave to Navy officers the sole conduct of making and shortening sail, tacking ship, and performing other nautical maneuvers, as may seem to them best; let us beware of abandoning to their discretion those general municipal regulations touching the well-being of the great body of men before the mast; let us beware of being too much influenced by their opinions in matters where it is but natural to suppose that their long-established prejudices are enlisted.

Chapter LVI

A Shore Emperor On Board a Man-of-War

WHILE WE LAY IN RIO, WE SOMETIMES HAD COMPANY FROM SHORE; BUT AN UNFORESEEN HONOR awaited us. One day, the young Emperor, Don Pedro II, and suite—making a circuit of the harbor, and visiting all the men-of-war in rotation—at last condescendingly visited the *Neversink*.

He came in a splendid barge, rowed by thirty African slaves, who, after the Brazilian manner, in concert rose upright to their oars at every stroke; then sank backward again to their seats with a simultaneous groan.

He reclined under a canopy of yellow silk, looped with tassels of green, the national colors. At the stern waved the Brazilian flag, bearing a large diamond figure in the center, emblematical, perhaps, of the mines of precious stones in the interior; or, it may be, a magnified portrait of the famous "Portuguese diamond" itself, which was found in Brazil, in the district of Tejuco, on the banks of the Rio Belmonte.

We gave them a grand salute, which almost made the ship's live-oak *knees* knock together with the tremendous concussions. We manned the yards, and went through a long ceremonial of paying the Emperor homage. Republicans are often more courteous to royalty than royalists themselves. But doubtless this springs from a noble magnanimity.

At the gangway, the Emperor was received by our Commodore in person, arrayed in his most resplendent coat and finest French epaulets. His servant had devoted himself to polishing every button that morning with rotten-stone and rags—your sea air is a sworn foe to metallic glosses; whence it comes that the swords of sea-officers have, of late, so rusted in their scabbards that they are with difficulty drawn.

It was a fine sight to see this Emperor and Commodore complimenting each other. Both were *chapeaux-de-bras*, and both continually waved them. By instinct, the Emperor knew that the venerable personage before him was as much a monarch afloat as he himself was ashore. Did not our Commodore carry the sword of state by his side? For though not borne before him, it must have been a sword of state, since it looked far too lustrous to have been his fighting sword. *That* was naught but a limber steel blade, with a plain, serviceable handle, like the handle of a slaughter-house knife.

Who ever saw a star when the noon sun was in sight? But you seldom see a king without satellites. In the suite of the youthful Emperor came a princely train; so brilliant with gems, that they seemed just emerged from the mines of the Rio Belmonte.

You have seen cones of crystallized salt? Just so flashed these Portuguese Barons, Marquises, Viscounts, and Counts. Were it not for their titles, and being seen in the train of their lord, you would have sworn they were eldest sons of jewelers all, who had run away with their fathers' cases on their backs.

Contrasted with these lamp-lusters of Barons of Brazil, how waned the gold lace of our barons of the frigate, the officers of the gun-room! and compared with the long, jewel-hilted rapiers of the Marquises, the little dirks of our cadets of noble houses—the middies—looked like gilded tenpenny nails in their girdles.

But there they stood! Commodore and Emperor, Lieutenants and Marquises, middies and pages! The brazen band on the poop struck up; the marine guard presented arms; and high aloft, looking down on this scene, all *the people* vigorously hurraed. A top-man next me on the main-royal-yard removed his hat, and diligently manipulated his head in honor of the event; but he was so far out of sight in the clouds, that this ceremony went for nothing.

A great pity it was, that in addition to all these honors, that admirer of Portuguese literature, Viscount Strangford, of Great Britain—who, I believe, once went out Ambassador Extraordinary to the Brazils—it was a pity that he was not present on this occasion, to yield his tribute of *A Stanza to Braganza!* For our royal visitor was an undoubted Braganza, allied to nearly all the great families of Europe. His grandfather, John VI, had been King of Portugal; his own sister, Maria, was now its queen. He was, indeed, a distinguished young gentleman, entitled to high consideration, and that consideration was most cheerfully accorded him.

He wore a green dress-coat, with one regal morning-star at the breast, and white pantaloons. In his chapeau was a single, bright, golden-hued feather of the Imperial Toucan fowl, a magnificent, omnivorous, broad-billed bandit bird of prey, a native of Brazil. Its perch is on the loftiest trees, whence it looks down upon all humbler fowls, and, hawk-like, flies at their throats. The Toucan once formed part of the savage regalia of the Indian caciques of the country, and upon the establishment of the empire, was symbolically retained by the Portuguese sovereigns.

His Imperial Majesty was yet in his youth; rather corpulent, if anything, with a care-free, pleasant face, and a polite, indifferent, and easy address. His manners, indeed, were entirely unexceptionable.

Now here, thought I, is a very fine lad, with very fine prospects before him. He is supreme Emperor of all these Brazils; he has no stormy night-watches to stand; he can lay abed of mornings just as long as he pleases. Any gentleman in Rio would be proud of his personal acquaintance, and the prettiest girl in all South America would deem herself honored with the least glance from the acutest angle of his eye.

Yes: this young Emperor will have a fine time of this life, even so long as he condescends to exist. Everyone jumps to obey him; and see, as I live, there is an old nobleman in his suit—the Marquis d'Acarty they call him, old enough to be his grandfather—who, in the hot sun, is standing bareheaded before him, while the Emperor carries his hat on his head.

"I suppose that old gentleman, now," said a young New England tar beside me, "would consider it a great honor to put on his Royal Majesty's boots; and yet, White-Jacket, if yonder Emperor and I were to strip and jump overboard for a bath, it would be hard telling which was of the blood royal when we should once be in the water. Look you, Don Pedro II," he added, "how do you come to be Emperor? Tell me that. You cannot pull as many pounds as I on the main-topsail-halyards; you are not as tall as I: your nose is a pug, and mine is a cut-water; and how do you come to be a '*brigand,*' with that thin pair of spars? A *brigand,* indeed!"

"*Braganza,* you mean," said I, willing to correct the rhetoric of so fierce a republican, and, by so doing, chastise his censoriousness.

"Braganza! *bragger* it is," he replied; "and a bragger, indeed. See that feather in his cap! See how he struts in that coat! He may well wear a green one, top-mates—he's a green-looking swab at the best."

"Hush, Jonathan," said I; "there's the *First Luff* looking up. Be still! the Emperor will hear you"; and I put my hand on his mouth.

"Take your hand away, White-Jacket," he cried; "there's no law up aloft here. I say, you Emperor—you greenhorn in the green coat, there—look you, you can't raise a pair of whiskers yet; and see what a pair of homeward-bounders I have on my jowls! *Don Pedro,* eh? What's that, after all, but plain Peter—reckoned a shabby name in my country. Damn me, White-Jacket, I wouldn't call my dog Peter!"

"Clap a stopper on your jaw-tackle, will you?" cried Ringbolt, the sailor on the other side of him. "You'll be getting us all into darbies for this."

"I won't trice up my red rag for nobody," retorted Jonathan. "So you had better take a round turn with yours, Ringbolt, and let me alone, or I'll fetch you such a swat over your figure-head, you'll think a Long Wharf truck-horse kicked you with all four shoes on one hoof! You Emperor—

you counter-jumping son of a gun—cock your weather eye up aloft here, and see your betters! I say, top-mates, he ain't any Emperor at all—*I'm* the rightful Emperor. Yes, by the Commodore's boots! they stole me out of my cradle here in the palace of Rio, and put that greenhorn in my place. Ay, you timber-head, you, I'm Don Pedro II, and by good rights you ought to be a main-top-man here, with your fist in a tar-bucket! Look you, I say, that crown of yours ought to be on my head; or, if you don't believe *that*, just heave it into the ring once, and see who's the best man."

"What's this hurra's nest here aloft?" cried Jack Chase, coming up the t'-gallant rigging from the top-sail yard. "Can't you behave yourself, royal-yard-men, when an Emperor's on board?"

"It's this here Jonathan," answered Ringbolt; "he's been blackguarding the young nob in the green coat, there. He says Don Pedro stole his hat."

"How?"

"Crown, he means, noble Jack," said a top-man.

"Jonathan don't call himself an Emperor, does he?" asked Jack.

"Yes," cried Jonathan; "that greenhorn, standing there by the Commodore, is sailing under false colors; he's an impostor, I say; he wears my crown."

"Ha! ha!" laughed Jack, now seeing into the joke, and willing to humor it; "though I'm born a Briton, boys, yet, by the mast! these Don Pedros are all Perkin Warbecks. But I say, Jonathan, my lad, don't pipe your eye now about the loss of your crown; for, look you, we all wear crowns, from our cradles to our graves, and though in *double-darbies* in the *brig*, the Commodore himself can't unking us."

"A riddle, noble Jack."

"Not a bit; every man who has a sole to his foot has a crown to his head. Here's mine"; and so saying, Jack, removing his tarpaulin, exhibited a bald spot, just about the bigness of a crown-piece, on the summit of his curly and classical head.

Chapter LVII

The Emperor Reviews the People at Quarters

I BEG THEIR ROYAL HIGHNESSES' PARDONS ALL ROUND, BUT I HAD ALMOST FORGOTTEN TO CHRONicle the fact, that with the Emperor came several other royal Princes—kings for aught we knew—since it was just after the celebration of the nuptials of a younger sister of the Brazilian monarch to some European royalty. Indeed, the Emperor and his suite formed a sort of bridal party, only the bride herself was absent.

The first reception over, the smoke of the cannonading salute having cleared away, and the martial outburst of the brass band having also rolled off to leeward, the people were called down from the yards, and the drum beat to quarters.

To quarters we went; and there we stood up by our iron bull-dogs, while our royal and noble visitors promenaded along the batteries, breaking out into frequent exclamations at our war-like array, the extreme neatness of our garments, and, above all, the extraordinary polish of the *bright-work* about the great guns, and the marvelous whiteness of the decks.

"Que gosto!" cried a Marquis, with several dry goods samples of ribbon, tallied with bright buttons, hanging from his breast.

"Que gloria!" cried a crooked, coffee-colored Viscount, spreading both palms.

"Que alegria!" cried a little Count, mincingly circumnavigating a shot-box.

"Que contentamento he o meu!" cried the Emperor himself, complacently folding his royal arms, and serenely gazing along our ranks.

Pleasure, *Glory*, and *Joy*—this was the burden of the three noble courtiers. *And very pleasing indeed*—was the simple rendering of Don Pedro's imperial remark.

"Ay, ay," growled a grim rammer-and-sponger behind me; "it's all devilish fine for you nobs to look at; but what would you say if you had to holy-stone the deck yourselves, and wear out your elbows in polishing this cursed old iron, besides getting a dozen at the gangway, if you dropped a grease-spot on deck in your mess? Ay, ay, devilish fine for you, but devilish dull for us!"

In due time the drums beat the retreat, and the ship's company scattered over the decks.

Some of the officers now assumed the part of cicerones, to show the distinguished strangers the bowels of the frigate, concerning which several of them showed a good deal of intelligent curiosity. A guard of honor, detached from the marine corps, accompanied them, and they made the circuit of the berth-deck, where, at a judicious distance, the Emperor peeped down into the cable-tier, a very subterranean vault.

The Captain of the Main-Hold, who there presided, made a polite bow in the twilight, and respectfully expressed a desire for His Royal Majesty to step down and honor him with a call; but, with his handkerchief to his Imperial nose, his Majesty declined. The party then commenced the ascent to the spar-deck; which, from so great a depth in a frigate, is something like getting up to the top of Bunker Hill Monument from the basement.

While a crowd of people was gathered about the forward part of the booms, a sudden cry was heard from below; a lieutenant came running forward to learn the cause, when an old sheet-anchor-man, standing by, after touching his hat hitched up his waistbands, and replied, "I don't know, sir, but I'm thinking as how one o' them 'ere kings has been tumblin' down the hatchway."

And something like this it turned out. In ascending one of the narrow ladders leading from the berth-deck to the gun-deck, the Most Noble Marquis of Silva, in the act of elevating the Imperial coat-tails, so as to protect them from rubbing against the newly-painted combings of the hatchway, this noble marquis's sword, being an uncommonly long one, had caught between his legs, and tripped him head over heels down into the fore-passage.

"Onde ides?" (where are you going?) said his royal master, tranquilly peeping down toward the falling Marquis; "and what did you let go of my coat-tails for?" he suddenly added, in a passion, glancing round at the same time, to see if they had suffered from the unfaithfulness of his train bearer.

"Oh, Lord!" sighed the Captain of the Fore-top, "who would be a Marquis of Silva?"

Upon being assisted to the spar-deck, the unfortunate Marquis was found to have escaped without serious harm; but, from the marked coolness of his royal master, when the Marquis drew near to apologize for his awkwardness, it was plain that he was condemned to languish for a time under the royal displeasure.

Shortly after, the Imperial party withdrew, under another grand national salute.

Chapter LVIII

A Quarter-Deck Officer Before the Mast

As we were somewhat short-handed while we lay in Rio, we received a small draft of men from a United States sloop of war, whose three years' term of service would expire about the time of our arrival in America.

Under guard of an armed Lieutenant and four midshipmen, they came on board in the afternoon. They were immediately mustered in the starboard gangway, that Mr. Bridewell, our First Lieutenant, might take down their names, and assign them their stations.

They stood in a mute and solemn row; the officer advanced, with his memorandum-book and pencil.

My casual friend, Shakings, the holder, happened to be by at the time. Touching my arm, he said, "White-Jacket, this here reminds me of Sing-Sing, when a draft of fellows in darbies, came on from the State Prison at Auburn for a change of scene like, you know!"

After taking down four or five names, Mr. Bridewell accosted the next man, a rather good-looking person, but, from his haggard cheek and sunken eye, he seemed to have been in the sad habit, all his life, of sitting up rather late at night; and though all sailors do certainly keep late hours enough—standing watches at midnight—yet there is no small difference between keeping late hours at sea and keeping late hours ashore.

"What's your name?" asked the officer, of this rather rakish-looking recruit.

"Mandeville, sir," said the man, courteously touching his cap. "You must remember me, sir," he added, in a low, confidential tone, strangely dashed with servility; "we sailed together once in the old *Macedonian*, sir. I wore an epaulet then; we had the same state-room, you know, sir. I'm your old chum, Mandeville, sir," and he again touched his cap.

"I remember an *officer* by that name," said the First Lieutenant, emphatically, "and I know *you*, fellow. But I know you henceforth for a common sailor. I can show no favoritism here. If you ever violate the ship's rules, you shall be flogged like any other seaman. I place you in the fore-top; go forward to your duty."

It seemed this Mandeville had entered the Navy when very young, and had risen to be a lieutenant, as he said. But brandy had been his bane. One night, when he had the deck of a line-of-battle ship, in the Mediterranean, he was seized with a fit of mania-a-potu, and being out of his senses for the time, went below and turned into his berth, leaving the deck without a commanding officer. For this unpardonable offense he was broken.

Having no fortune, and no other profession than the sea, upon his disgrace he entered the merchant-service as a chief mate; but his love of strong drink still pursuing him, he was again cashiered at sea, and degraded before the mast by the Captain. After this, in a state of intoxication, he re-entered the Navy at Pensacola as a common sailor. But all these lessons, so biting-bitter to learn, could not cure him of his sin. He had hardly been a week on board the *Neversink*, when he was found intoxicated with smuggled spirits. They lashed him to the gratings, and ignominiously scourged him under the eye of his old friend and comrade, the First Lieutenant.

This took place while we lay in port, which reminds me of the circumstance, that when punishment is about to be inflicted in harbor, all strangers are ordered ashore; and the sentries at the side have it in strict charge to waive off all boats drawing near.

Chapter LIX

A MAN-OF-WAR BUTTON DIVIDES TWO BROTHERS

THE CONDUCT OF MANDEVILLE, IN CLAIMING THE ACQUAINTANCE OF THE FIRST LIEUTENANT under such disreputable circumstances was strongly contrasted by the behavior of another person on board, placed for a time in a somewhat similar situation.

Among the genteel youths of the after-guard was a lad of about sixteen, a very handsome young fellow, with starry eyes, curly hair of a golden color, and a bright, sunshiny complexion: he must have been the son of some goldsmith. He was one of the few sailors—not in the main-top—whom I used to single out for occasional conversation. After several friendly interviews he became quite frank, and communicated certain portions of his history. There is some charm in the sea, which induces most persons to be very communicative concerning themselves.

We had lain in Rio but a day, when I observed that this lad—whom I shall here call Frank—wore an unwonted expression of sadness, mixed with apprehension. I questioned him as to the cause, but he chose to conceal it. Not three days after, he abruptly accosted me on the gun-deck, where I happened to be taking a promenade.

"I can't keep it to myself anymore," he said; "I must have a confidant, or I shall go mad!"

"What is the matter?" said I, in alarm.

"Matter enough—look at this!" and he handed me a torn half sheet of an old New York *Herald*, putting his finger upon a particular word in a particular paragraph. It was the announcement of the sailing from the Brooklyn Navy-yard of a United States store ship, with provisions for the squadron in Rio. It was upon a particular name, in the list of officers and midshipmen, that Frank's fingers was placed.

"That is my own brother," said he; "he must have got a reefer's warrant since I left home. Now, White-Jacket, what's to be done? I have calculated that the store ship may be expected here every day; my brother will then see me—he an officer and I a miserable sailor that any moment may be flogged at the gangway, before his very eyes. Heavens! White-Jacket, what shall I do? Would you run? Do you think there is any chance to desert? I won't see him, by Heaven, with this sailor's frock on, and he with the anchor button!"

"Why, Frank," said I, "I do not really see sufficient cause for this fit you are in. Your brother is an officer—very good; and you are nothing but a sailor—but that is no disgrace. If he comes on board here, go up to him, and take him by the hand; believe me, he will be glad enough to see you!"

Frank started from his desponding attitude, and fixing his eyes full upon mine, with clasped hands exclaimed, "White-Jacket, I have been from home nearly three years; in that time I have never heard one word from my family, and, though God knows how I love them, yet I swear to you, that though my brother can tell me whether my sisters are still alive, yet, rather than accost him in this *lined-frock*, I would go ten centuries without hearing one syllable from home?"

Amazed at his earnestness, and hardly able to account for it altogether, I stood silent a moment; then said, "Why, Frank, this midshipman is your own brother, you say; now, do you really think that your own flesh and blood is going to give himself airs over you, simply because he sports large brass buttons on his coat? Never believe it. If he does, he can be no brother, and ought to be hanged—that's all!"

"Don't say that again," said Frank, resentfully; "my brother is a noble-hearted fellow; I love him as I do myself. You don't understand me, White-Jacket; don't you see, that when my brother arrives, he must consort more or less with our chuckle-headed reefers on board here? There's that namby-pamby Miss Nancy of a white-face, Stribbles, who, the other day, when Mad Jack's back was turned, ordered me to hand him the spy-glass, as if he were a Commodore. Do you suppose, now, I want my brother to see me a lackey abroad here? By Heaven it is enough to drive one distracted! What's to be done?" he cried, fiercely.

Much more passed between us, but all my philosophy was in vain, and at last Frank departed, his head hanging down in despondency.

For several days after, whenever the quarter-master reported a sail entering the harbor, Frank was foremost in the rigging to observe it. At length, one afternoon, a vessel drawing near was reported to be the long-expected store ship. I looked round for Frank on the spar-deck, but he was nowhere to be seen. He must have been below, gazing out of a port-hole. The vessel was hailed from our poop, and came to anchor within a biscuit's toss of our batteries.

That evening I heard that Frank had ineffectually endeavored to get removed from his place as an oarsman in the *First-Cutter*—a boat which, from its size, is generally employed with the *launch* in carrying ship-stores. When I thought that, the very next day, perhaps, this boat would be plying between the store ship and our frigate, I was at no loss to account for Frank's attempts to get rid of his oar, and felt heartily grieved at their failure.

Next morning the bugler called away the *First-Cutter*'s crew, and Frank entered the boat with his hat slouched over his eyes. Upon his return, I was all eagerness to learn what had happened, and, as the communication of his feelings was a grateful relief, he poured his whole story into my ear.

It seemed that, with his comrades, he mounted the store ship's side, and hurried forward to the forecastle. Then, turning anxiously toward the quarter-deck, he spied two midshipmen leaning against the bulwarks, conversing. One was the officer of his boat—was the other his brother? No; he was too tall—too large. Thank Heaven! it was *not* him. And perhaps his brother had not sailed from home, after all; there might have been some mistake. But suddenly the strange midshipman laughed aloud, and that laugh Frank had heard a thousand times before. It was a free, hearty laugh—a brother's laugh; but it carried a pang to the heart of poor Frank.

He was now ordered down to the main-deck to assist in removing the stores. The boat being loaded, he was ordered into her, when, looking toward the gangway, he perceived the two midshipmen lounging upon each side of it, so that no one could pass them without brushing their persons. But again pulling his hat over his eyes, Frank, darting between them, gained his oar. "How my heart thumped," he said, "when I actually *felt* him so near me; but I wouldn't look at him—no! I'd have died first!"

To Frank's great relief, the store ship at last moved further up the bay, and it fortunately happened that he saw no more of his brother while in Rio; and while there, he never in any way made himself known to him.

Chapter LX

A Man-of-War's Man Shot At

There was a seaman belonging to the fore-top—a mess-mate, though not a top-mate of mine, and no favorite of the Captain's—who, for certain venial transgressions, had been prohibited from going ashore on liberty when the ship's company went. Enraged at the deprivation—for he had not touched earth in upward of a year—he, some nights after, lowered himself overboard, with the view of gaining a canoe, attached by a robe to a Dutch galiot some cables'-

lengths distant. In this canoe he proposed paddling himself ashore. Not being a very expert swimmer, the commotion he made in the water attracted the ear of the sentry on that side of the ship, who, turning about in his walk, perceived the faint white spot where the fugitive was swimming in the frigate's shadow. He hailed it; but no reply.

"Give the word, or I fire!"

Not a word was heard.

The next instant there was a red flash, and, before it had completely ceased illuminating the night the white spot was changed into crimson. Some of the officers, returning from a party at the Beach of the Flamingoes, happened to be drawing near the ship in one of her cutters. They saw the flash, and the bounding body it revealed. In a moment the top-man was dragged into the boat, a handkerchief was used for a tourniquet, and the wounded fugitive was soon on board the frigate, when, the surgeon being called, the necessary attentions were rendered.

Now, it appeared, that at the moment the sentry fired, the top-man—in order to elude discovery, by manifesting the completest quietude—was floating on the water, straight and horizontal, as if reposing on a bed. As he was not far from the ship at the time, and the sentry was considerably elevated above him—pacing his platform, on a level with the upper part of the hammock-nettings—the ball struck with great force, with a downward obliquity, entering the right thigh just above the knee, and, penetrating some inches, glanced upward along the bone, burying itself somewhere, so that it could not be felt by outward manipulation. There was no dusky discoloration to mark its internal track, as in the case when a partly-spent ball—obliquely hitting—after entering the skin, courses on, just beneath the surface, without penetrating further. Nor was there any mark on the opposite part of the thigh to denote its place, as when a ball forces itself straight through a limb, and lodges, perhaps, close to the skin on the other side. Nothing was visible but a small, ragged puncture, bluish about the edges, as if the rough point of a tenpenny nail had been forced into the flesh, and withdrawn. It seemed almost impossible, that through so small an aperture, a musket-bullet could have penetrated.

The extreme misery and general prostration of the man, caused by the great effusion of blood—though, strange to say, at first he said he felt no pain from the wound itself—induced the Surgeon, very reluctantly, to forego an immediate search for the ball, to extract it, as that would have involved the dilating of the wound by the knife; an operation which, at that juncture, would have been almost certainly attended with fatal results. A day or two, therefore, was permitted to pass, while simple dressings were applied.

The Surgeon of the other American ships of war in harbor occasionally visited the *Neversink*, to examine the patient, and incidentally to listen to the expositions of our own Surgeon, their senior in rank. But Cadwallader Cuticle, who, as yet, has been but incidentally alluded to, now deserves a chapter by himself.

Chapter LXI

The Surgeon of the Fleet

Cadwallader Cuticle, M. D., and honorary member of the most distinguished colleges of Surgeons both in Europe and America, was our Surgeon of the Fleet. Nor was he at all blind to the dignity of his position; to which, indeed, he was rendered peculiarly competent, if the reputation he enjoyed was deserved. He had the name of being the foremost Surgeon in the Navy, a gentleman of remarkable science, and a veteran practitioner.

He was a small, withered man, nearly, perhaps quite, sixty years of age. His chest was shallow, his shoulders bent, his pantaloons hung round skeleton legs, and his face was singularly attenuated. In truth, the corporeal vitality of this man seemed, in a good degree, to have died out of him. He walked abroad, a curious patch-work of life and death, with a wig, one glass eye, and a set of false teeth, while his voice was husky and thick; but his mind seemed undebilitated as in youth; it shone out of his remaining eye with basilisk brilliancy.

Like most old physicians and surgeons who have seen much service, and have been promoted to high professional place for their scientific attainments, this Cuticle was an enthusiast in his calling. In private, he had once been heard to say, confidentially, that he would rather cut off a man's arm than dismember the wing of the most delicate pheasant. In particular, the department of Morbid Anatomy was his peculiar love; and in his state-room below he had a most unsightly collection of Parisian casts, in plaster and wax, representing all imaginable malformations of the human members, both organic and induced by disease. Chief among these was a cast, often to be met with in the Anatomical Museums of Europe, and no doubt an unexaggerated copy of a genuine original; it was the head of an elderly woman, with an aspect singularly gentle and meek, but at the same time wonderfully expressive of a gnawing sorrow, never to be relieved. You would almost have thought it the face of some abbess, for some unspeakable crime voluntarily sequestered from human society, and leading a life of agonized penitence without hope; so marvelously sad and tearfully pitiable was this head. But when you first beheld it, no such emotions ever crossed your mind. All your eyes and all your horrified soul were fast fascinated and frozen by the sight of a hideous, crumpled horn, like that of a ram, downward growing out from the forehead, and partly shadowing the face; but as you gazed, the freezing fascination of its horribleness gradually waned, and then your whole heart burst with sorrow, as you contemplated those aged features, ashy pale and wan. The horn seemed the mark of a curse for some mysterious sin, conceived and committed before the spirit had entered the flesh. Yet that sin seemed something imposed, and not voluntarily sought; some sin growing out of the heartless necessities of the predestination of things; some sin under which the sinner sank in sinless woe.

But no pang of pain, not the slightest touch of concern, ever crossed the bosom of Cuticle when he looked on this cast. It was immovably fixed to a bracket, against the partition of his state-room, so that it was the first object that greeted his eyes when he opened them from his nightly sleep. Nor was it to hide the face, that upon retiring, he always hung his Navy cap upon the upward curling extremity of the horn, for that obscured it but little.

The Surgeon's cot-boy, the lad who made up his swinging bed and took care of his room, often told us of the horror he sometimes felt when he would find himself alone in his master's retreat. At times he was seized with the idea that Cuticle was a preternatural being; and once entering his room in the middle watch of the night, he started at finding it enveloped in a thick, bluish vapor, and stifling with the odors of brimstone. Upon hearing a low groan from the smoke, with a wild cry he darted from the place, and, rousing the occupants of the neighboring state-rooms, it was found that the vapor proceeded from smoldering bunches of lucifer matches, which had become ignited through the carelessness of the Surgeon. Cuticle, almost dead, was dragged from the suffocating atmosphere, and it was several days ere he completely recovered from its effects. This accident took place immediately over the powder magazine; but as Cuticle, during his sickness, paid dearly enough for transgressing the laws prohibiting combustibles in the gun-room, the Captain contented himself with privately remonstrating with him.

Well knowing the enthusiasm of the Surgeon for all specimens of morbid anatomy, some of the ward-room officers used to play upon his credulity, though, in every case, Cuticle was not long in discovering their deceptions. Once, when they had some sago pudding for dinner, and Cuticle chanced to be ashore, they made up a neat parcel of this bluish-white, firm, jelly-like preparation, and placing it in a tin box, carefully sealed with wax, they deposited it on the gun-room table, with a note, purporting to come from an eminent physician in Rio, connected with the Grand National Museum on the Praca d' Acclamacao, begging leave to present the scientific Señor Cuticle—with the donor's compliments—an uncommonly fine specimen of a cancer.

Descending to the ward-room, Cuticle spied the note, and no sooner read it, than, clutching the case, he opened it, and exclaimed, "Beautiful! splendid! I have never seen a finer specimen of this most interesting disease."

"What have you there, Surgeon Cuticle?" said a Lieutenant, advancing.

"Why, sir, look at it; did you ever see anything more exquisite?"

"Very exquisite indeed; let me have a bit of it, will you, Cuticle?"

"Let you have a bit of it!" shrieked the Surgeon, starting back. "Let you have one of my limbs! I wouldn't mar so large a specimen for a hundred dollars; but what can you want of it? You are not making collections!"

"I'm fond of the article," said the Lieutenant; "it's a fine cold relish to bacon or ham. You know, I was in New Zealand last cruise, Cuticle, and got into sad dissipation there among the cannibals; come, let's have a bit, if it's only a mouthful."

"Why, you infernal Fiji!" shouted Cuticle, eyeing the other with a confounded expression; "you don't really mean to eat a piece of this cancer?"

"Hand it to me, and see whether I will not," was the reply.

"In God's name, take it!" cried the Surgeon, putting the case into his hands, and then standing with his own uplifted.

"Steward!" cried the Lieutenant, "the castor—quick! I always use plenty of pepper with this dish, Surgeon; it's oystery. Ah! this is really delicious," he added, smacking his lips over a mouthful. "Try it now, Surgeon, and you'll never keep such a fine dish as this, lying uneaten on your hands, as a mere scientific curiosity."

Cuticle's whole countenance changed; and, slowly walking up to the table, he put his nose close to the tin case, then touched its contents with his finger and tasted it. Enough. Buttoning up his coat, in all the tremblings of an old man's rage he burst from the ward-room, and, calling for a boat, was not seen again for twenty-four hours.

But though, like all other mortals, Cuticle was subject at times to these fits of passion—at least under outrageous provocation—nothing could exceed his coolness when actually employed in his imminent vocation. Surrounded by moans and shrieks, by features distorted with anguish inflicted by himself, he yet maintained a countenance almost supernaturally calm; and unless the intense interest of the operation flushed his wan face with a momentary tinge of professional enthusiasm, he toiled away, untouched by the keenest misery coming under a fleet-surgeon's eye. Indeed, long habituation to the dissecting-room and the amputation-table had made him seemingly impervious to the ordinary emotions of humanity. Yet you could not say that Cuticle was essentially a cruel-hearted man. His apparent heartlessness must have been of a purely scientific origin. It is not to be imagined even that Cuticle would have harmed a fly, unless he could procure a microscope powerful enough to assist him in experimenting on the minute vitals of the creature.

But notwithstanding his marvelous indifference to the sufferings of his patients, and spite even of his enthusiasm in his vocation—not cooled by frosting old age itself—Cuticle, on some occasions, would effect a certain disrelish of his profession, and declaim against the necessity that forced a man of his humanity to perform a surgical operation. Especially was it apt to be thus with him, when the case was one of more than ordinary interest. In discussing it previous to setting about it, he would veil his eagerness under an aspect of great circumspection, curiously marred, however, by continual sallies of unsuppressible impatience. But the knife once in his hand, the compassionless surgeon himself, undisguised, stood before you. Such was Cadwallader Cuticle, our Surgeon of the Fleet.

Chapter LXII

A CONSULTATION OF MAN-OF-WAR SURGEONS

IT SEEMS CUSTOMARY FOR THE SURGEON OF THE FLEET, WHEN ANY IMPORTANT OPERATION IN HIS department is on the anvil, and there is nothing to absorb professional attention from it, to invite his brother surgeons, if at hand at the time, to a ceremonious consultation upon it. And this, in courtesy, his brother surgeons expect.

In pursuance of this custom, then, the surgeons of the neighboring American ships of war were requested to visit the *Neversink* in a body, to advise concerning the case of the top-man, whose situation had now become critical. They assembled on the half-deck, and were soon joined by their respected senior, Cuticle. In a body they bowed as he approached, and accosted him with deferential regard.

"Gentlemen," said Cuticle, unostentatiously seating himself on a camp-stool, handed him by his cot-boy, "we have here an extremely interesting case. You have all seen the patient, I believe. At first I had hopes that I should have been able to cut down to the ball, and remove it; but the state of the patient forbade. Since then, the inflammation and sloughing of the part has been attended with a copious suppuration, great loss of substance, extreme debility and emaciation. From this, I am convinced that the ball has shattered and deadened the bone, and now lies impacted in the medullary canal. In fact, there can be no doubt that the wound is incurable, and that amputation is the only resource. But, gentlemen, I find myself placed in a very delicate predicament. I assure you I feel no professional anxiety to perform the operation. I desire your advice, and if you will now again visit the patient with me, we can then return here and decide what is best to be done. Once more, let me say, that I feel no personal anxiety whatever to use the knife."

The assembled surgeons listened to this address with the most serious attention, and, in accordance with their superior's desire, now descended to the sick-bay, where the patient was languishing. The examination concluded, they returned to the half-deck, and the consultation was renewed.

"Gentlemen," began Cuticle, again seating himself, "you have now just inspected the limb; you have seen that there is no resource but amputation; and now, gentlemen, what do you say? Surgeon Bandage, of the *Mohawk,* will you express your opinion?"

"The wound is a very serious one," said Bandage—a corpulent man, with a high German forehead—shaking his head solemnly.

"Can anything save him but amputation?" demanded Cuticle.

"His constitutional debility is extreme," observed Bandage, "but I have seen more dangerous cases."

"Surgeon Wedge, of the *Malay,*" said Cuticle, in a pet, "be pleased to give *your* opinion; and let it be definitive, I entreat:" this was said with a severe glance toward Bandage.

"If I thought," began Wedge, a very spare, tall man, elevating himself still higher on his toes, "that the ball had shattered and divided the whole *femur,* including the *Greater* and *Lesser Trochanter* the *Linear aspera* the *Digital fossa,* and the *Intertrochanteric,* I should certainly be in favor of amputation; but that, sir, permit me to observe, is not my opinion."

"Surgeon Sawyer, of the *Buccaneer,*" said Cuticle, drawing in his thin lower lip with vexation, and turning to a round-faced, florid, frank, sensible-looking man, whose uniform coat very handsomely fitted him, and was adorned with an unusual quantity of gold lace; "Surgeon Sawyer, of the Buccaneer, let us now hear *your* opinion, if you please. Is not amputation the only resource, sir?"

"Excuse me," said Sawyer, "I am decidedly opposed to it; for if hitherto the patient has not been strong enough to undergo the extraction of the ball, I do not see how he can be expected to endure a far more severe operation. As there is no immediate danger of mortification, and you say the ball cannot be reached without making large incisions, I should support him, I think, for the present, with tonics, and gentle antiphlogistics, locally applied. On no account would I proceed to amputation until further symptoms are exhibited."

"Surgeon Patella, of the *Algerine*," said Cuticle, in an ill-suppressed passion, abruptly turning round on the person addressed, "will *you* have the kindness to say whether *you* do not think that amputation is the only resource?"

Now Patella was the youngest of the company, a modest man, filled with a profound reverence for the science of Cuticle, and desirous of gaining his good opinion, yet not wishing to commit himself altogether by a decided reply, though, like Surgeon Sawyer, in his own mind he might have been clearly against the operation.

"What you have remarked, Mr. Surgeon of the Fleet," said Patella, respectfully hemming, "concerning the dangerous condition of the limb, seems obvious enough; amputation would certainly be a cure to the wound; but then, as, notwithstanding his present debility, the patient seems to have a strong constitution, he might rally as it is, and by your scientific treatment, Mr. Surgeon of the Fleet"— bowing—"be entirely made whole, without risking an amputation. Still, it is a very critical case, and amputation may be indispensable; and if it *is* to be performed, there ought to be no delay whatever. That is my view of the case, Mr. Surgeon of the Fleet."

"Surgeon Patella, then, gentlemen," said Cuticle, turning round triumphantly, "is clearly of opinion that amputation should be immediately performed. For my own part—individually, I mean, and without respect to the patient—I am sorry to have it so decided. But this settles the question, gentlemen—in my own mind, however, it was settled before. At ten o'clock to-morrow morning the operation will be performed. I shall be happy to see you all on the occasion, and also your juniors" (alluding to the absent *Assistant Surgeons*). "Good-morning, gentlemen; at ten o'clock, remember."

And Cuticle retreated to the Ward-room.

Chapter LXIII

THE OPERATION

NEXT MORNING, AT THE APPOINTED HOUR, THE SURGEONS ARRIVED IN A BODY. THEY WERE ACcompanied by their juniors, young men ranging in age from nineteen years to thirty. Like the senior surgeons, these young gentlemen were arrayed in their blue navy uniforms, displaying a profusion of bright buttons, and several broad bars of gold lace about the wristbands. As in honor of the occasion, they had put on their best coats; they looked exceedingly brilliant.

The whole party immediately descended to the half-deck, where preparations had been made for the operation. A large garrison-ensign was stretched across the ship by the main-mast, so as completely to screen the space behind. This space included the whole extent aft to the bulkhead of the Commodore's cabin, at the door of which the marine-orderly paced, in plain sight, cutlass in hand.

Upon two gun-carriages, dragged amidships, the Death-board (used for burials at sea) was horizontally placed, covered with an old royal-stun'-sail. Upon this occasion, to do duty as an amputation-table, it was widened by an additional plank. Two match-tubs, nearby, placed one upon another, at either end supported another plank, distinct from the table, whereon was exhibited an array of saws and knives of various and peculiar shapes and sizes; also, a sort of steel, something like the dinner-table implement, together with long needles, crooked at the end for taking up the arteries, and large darning-needles, thread and bee's-wax, for sewing up a wound.

At the end nearest the larger table was a tin basin of water, surrounded by small sponges, placed at mathematical intervals. From the long horizontal pole of a great-gun rammer—fixed in its usual place overhead—hung a number of towels, with "U.S." marked in the corners.

All these arrangements had been made by the "Surgeon's steward," a person whose important functions in a man-of-war will, in a future chapter, be entered upon at large. Upon the present occasion, he was bustling about, adjusting and readjusting the knives, needles, and carver, like an over-conscientious butler fidgeting over a dinner-table just before the convivialists enter.

But by far the most striking object to be seen behind the ensign was a human skeleton, whose every joint articulated with wires. By a rivet at the apex of the skull, it hung dangling from a hammock-hook fixed in a beam above. Why this object was here, will presently be seen; but why it was placed immediately at the foot of the amputation-table, only Surgeon Cuticle can tell.

While the final preparations were being made, Cuticle stood conversing with the assembled Surgeons and Assistant Surgeons, his invited guests.

"Gentlemen," said he, taking up one of the glittering knives and artistically drawing the steel across it; "Gentlemen, though these scenes are very unpleasant, and in some moods, I may say, repulsive to me—yet how much better for our patient to have the contusions and lacerations of his present wound—with all its dangerous symptoms—converted into a clean incision, free from these objections, and occasioning so much less subsequent anxiety to himself and the Surgeon. Yes," he added, tenderly feeling the edge of his knife, "amputation is our only resource. Is it not so, Surgeon Patella?" turning toward that gentleman, as if relying upon some sort of an assent, however clogged with conditions.

"Certainly," said Patella, "amputation is your only resource, Mr. Surgeon of the Fleet; that is, I mean, if you are fully persuaded of its necessity."

The other surgeons said nothing, maintaining a somewhat reserved air, as if conscious that they had no positive authority in the case, whatever might be their own private opinions; but they seemed willing to behold, and, if called upon, to assist at the operation, since it could not now be averted.

The young men, their Assistants, looked very eager, and cast frequent glances of awe upon so distinguished a practitioner as the venerable Cuticle.

"They say he can drop a leg in one minute and ten seconds from the moment the knife touches it," whispered one of them to another.

"We shall see," was the reply, and the speaker clapped his hand to his fob, to see if his watch would be forthcoming when wanted.

"Are you all ready here?" demanded Cuticle, now advancing to his steward; "have not those fellows got through yet?" pointing to three men of the carpenter's gang, who were placing bits of wood under the gun-carriages supporting the central table.

"They are just through, sir," respectfully answered the steward, touching his hand to his forehead, as if there were a cap-front there.

"Bring up the patient, then," said Cuticle.

"Young gentlemen," he added, turning to the row of Assistant Surgeons, "seeing you here reminds me of the classes of students once under my instruction at the Philadelphia College of Physicians and Surgeons. Ah, those were happy days!" he sighed, applying the extreme corner of his handkerchief to his glass-eye. "Excuse an old man's emotions, young gentlemen; but when I think of the numerous rare cases that then came under my treatment, I cannot but give way to my feelings. The town, the city, the metropolis, young gentlemen, is the place for you students; at least in these dull times of peace, when the army and navy furnish no inducements for a youth ambitious of rising in our honorable profession. Take an old man's advice, and if the war now threatening between the States and Mexico should break out, exchange your navy commissions for commissions in the army. From having no military marine herself, Mexico has always been backward in furnishing subjects for the amputation-tables of foreign navies. The cause of science has languished in her hands. The army, young gentlemen, is your best school; depend upon it. You will hardly believe it, Surgeon Bandage," turning to that gentleman, "but this is my first important case of surgery in a nearly three years' cruise. I have been almost wholly confined in this ship to doctor's practice—prescribing for fevers and fluxes. True, the other day a man fell from the mizzen-top-sail-yard; but that was merely an aggravated case of dislocations and bones splintered and broken. No one, sir, could have made an amputation of it, without severely contusing his conscience. And mine—I may say it, gentlemen, without ostentation is—peculiarly susceptible."

And so saying, the knife and carver touchingly dropped to his sides, and he stood for a moment fixed in a tender reverie. But a commotion being heard beyond the curtain, he started, and, briskly crossing and recrossing the knife and carver, exclaimed, "Ah, here comes our patient; surgeons, this side of the table, if you please; young gentlemen, a little further off, I beg. Steward, take off my coat—so; my neckerchief now; I must be perfectly unencumbered, Surgeon Patella, or I can do nothing whatever."

These articles being removed, he snatched off his wig, placing it on the gun-deck capstan; then took out his set of false teeth, and placed it by the side of the wig; and, lastly, putting his forefinger to the inner angle of his blind eye, spirited out the glass optic with professional dexterity, and deposited that, also, next to the wig and false teeth.

Thus divested of nearly all inorganic appurtenances, what was left of the Surgeon slightly shook itself, to see whether anything more could be spared to advantage.

"Carpenter's mates," he now cried, "will you never get through with that job?"

"Almost through, sir—just through," they replied, staring round in search of the strange, unearthly voice that addressed them; for the absence of his teeth had not at all improved the conversational tones of the Surgeon of the Fleet.

With natural curiosity, these men had purposely been lingering, to see all they could; but now, having no further excuse, they snatched up their hammers and chisels, and—like the stage-builders decamping from a public meeting at the eleventh hour, after just completing the rostrum in time for the first speaker—the Carpenter's gang withdrew.

The broad ensign now lifted, revealing a glimpse of the crowd of man-of-war's-men outside, and the patient, borne in the arms of two of his mess-mates, entered the place. He was much emaciated, weak as an infant, and every limb visibly trembled, or rather jarred, like the head of a man with the palsy. As if an organic and involuntary apprehension of death had seized the wounded leg, its nervous motions were so violent that one of the mess-mates was obliged to keep his hand upon it.

The top-man was immediately stretched upon the table, the attendants steadying his limbs, when, slowly opening his eyes, he glanced about at the glittering knives and saws, the towels and sponges, the armed sentry at the Commodore's cabin-door, the row of eager-eyed students, the meager death's-head of a Cuticle, now with his shirt sleeves rolled up upon his withered arms, and knife in hand, and, finally, his eyes settled in horror upon the skeleton, slowly vibrating and jingling before him, with the slow, slight roll of the frigate in the water.

"I would advise perfect repose of your every limb, my man," said Cuticle, addressing him; "the precision of an operation is often impaired by the inconsiderate restlessness of the patient. But if you consider, my good fellow," he added, in a patronizing and almost sympathetic tone, and slightly pressing his hand on the limb, "if you consider how much better it is to live with three limbs than to die with four, and especially if you but knew to what torments both sailors and soldiers were subjected before the time of Celsus, owing to the lamentable ignorance of surgery then prevailing, you would certainly thank God from the bottom of your heart that *your* operation has been postponed to the period of this enlightened age, blessed with a Bell, a Brodie, and a Lally. My man, before Celsus's time, such was the general ignorance of our noble science, that, in order to prevent the excessive effusion of blood, it was deemed indispensable to operate with a red-hot knife"—making a professional movement toward the thigh—"and pour scalding oil upon the parts"—elevating his elbow, as if with a tea-pot in his hand—"still further to sear them, after amputation had been performed."

"He is fainting!" said one of his mess-mates; "quick! some water!" The steward immediately hurried to the top-man with the basin.

Cuticle took the top-man by the wrist, and feeling it a while, observed, "Don't be alarmed, men," addressing the two mess-mates; "he'll recover presently; this fainting very generally takes place." And he stood for a moment, tranquilly eyeing the patient.

Now the Surgeon of the Fleet and the top-man presented a spectacle which, to a reflecting mind, was better than a church-yard sermon on the mortality of man.

Here was a sailor, who four days previous, had stood erect—a pillar of life—with an arm like a royal-mast and a thigh like a windlass. But the slightest conceivable finger-touch of a bit of crooked trigger had eventuated in stretching him out, more helpless than an hour-old babe, with a blasted thigh, utterly drained of its brawn. And who was it that now stood over him like a superior being, and, as if clothed himself with the attributes of immortality, indifferently discoursed of carving up his broken flesh, and thus piecing out his abbreviated days. Who was it, that in capacity of Surgeon, seemed enacting the part of a Regenerator of life? The withered, shrunken, one-eyed, toothless, hairless Cuticle; with a trunk half dead—a *memento mori* to behold!

And while, in those soul-sinking and panic-striking premonitions of speedy death which almost invariably accompany a severe gun-shot wound, even with the most intrepid spirits; while thus drooping and dying, this once robust top-man's eye was now waning in his head like a Lapland moon being eclipsed in clouds—Cuticle, who for years had still lived in his withered tabernacle of a body—Cuticle, no doubt sharing in the common self-delusion of old age—Cuticle must have felt his hold of life as secure as the grim hug of a grizzly bear. Verily, Life is more awful than Death; and let no man, though his live heart beat in him like a cannon—let him not hug his life to himself; for, in the predestinated necessities of things, that bounding life of his is not a whit more secure than the life of a man on his death-bed. To-day we inhale the air with expanding lungs, and life runs through us like a thousand Niles; but to-morrow we may collapse in death, and all our veins be dry as the Brook Kedron in a drought.

"And now, young gentlemen," said Cuticle, turning to the Assistant Surgeons, "while the patient is coming to, permit me to describe to you the highly-interesting operation I am about to perform."

"Mr. Surgeon of the Fleet," said Surgeon Bandage, "if you are about to lecture, permit me to present you with your teeth; they will make your discourse more readily understood." And so saying, Bandage, with a bow, placed the two semicircles of ivory into Cuticle's hands.

"Thank you, Surgeon Bandage," said Cuticle, and slipped the ivory into its place.

"In the first place, now, young gentlemen, let me direct your attention to the excellent preparation before you. I have had it unpacked from its case, and set up here from my state-room, where it occupies the spare berth; and all this for your express benefit, young gentlemen. This skeleton I procured in person from the Hunterian department of the Royal College of Surgeons in London. It is a masterpiece of art. But we have no time to examine it now. Delicacy forbids that I should amplify at a juncture like this"—casting an almost benignant glance toward the patient, now beginning to open his eyes; "but let me point out to you upon this thigh-bone"—disengaging it from the skeleton, with a gentle twist—"the precise place where I propose to perform the operation. *Here,* young gentlemen, *here* is the place. You perceive it is very near the point of articulation with the trunk."

"Yes," interposed Surgeon Wedge, rising on his toes, "yes, young gentlemen, the point of articulation with the *acetabulum* of the *os innominatum*."

"Where's your Bell on Bones, Dick?" whispered one of the assistants to the student next him. "Wedge has been spending the whole morning over it, getting out the hard names."

"Surgeon Wedge," said Cuticle, looking round severely, "we will dispense with your commentaries, if you please, at present. Now, young gentlemen, you cannot but perceive, that the point of operation being so near the trunk and the vitals, it becomes an unusually beautiful one, demanding a steady hand and a true eye; and, after all, the patient may die under my hands."

"Quick, Steward! water, water; he's fainting again!" cried the two mess-mates.

"Don't be alarmed for your comrade, men," said Cuticle, turning round. "I tell you it is not an uncommon thing for the patient to betray some emotion upon these occasions—most usually manifested by swooning; it is quite natural it should be so. But we must not delay the operation. Steward, that knife—no, the next one—there, that's it. He is coming to, I think"—feeling the top-man's wrist. "Are you all ready, sir?"

This last observation was addressed to one of the *Neversink*'s assistant surgeons, a tall, lank, cadaverous young man, arrayed in a sort of shroud of white canvas, pinned about his throat, and completely enveloping his person. He was seated on a match-tub—the skeleton swinging near his head—at the foot of the table, in readiness to grasp the limb, as when a plank is being severed by a carpenter and his apprentice.

"The sponges, Steward," said Cuticle, for the last time taking out his teeth, and drawing up his shirt sleeves still further. Then, taking the patient by the wrist, "Stand by, now, you mess-mates; keep hold of his arms; pin him down. Steward, put your hand on the artery; I shall commence as soon as his pulse begins to—*now, now!*" Letting fall the wrist, feeling the thigh carefully, and bowing over it an instant, he drew the fatal knife unerringly across the flesh. As it first touched the part, the row of surgeons simultaneously dropped their eyes to the watches in their hands while the patient lay, with eyes horribly distended, in a kind of waking trance. Not a breath was heard; but as the quivering flesh parted in a long, lingering gash, a spring of blood welled up between the living walls of the wounds, and two thick streams, in opposite directions, coursed down the thigh. The sponges were instantly dipped in the purple pool; every face present was pinched to a point with suspense; the limb writhed; the man shrieked; his mess-mates pinioned him; while round and round the leg went the unpitying cut.

"The saw!" said Cuticle.

Instantly it was in his hand.

Full of the operation, he was about to apply it, when, looking up, and turning to the assistant surgeons, he said, "Would any of you young gentlemen like to apply the saw? A splendid subject!"

Several volunteered; when, selecting one, Cuticle surrendered the instrument to him, saying, "Don't be hurried, now; be steady."

While the rest of the assistants looked upon their comrade with glances of envy, he went rather timidly to work; and Cuticle, who was earnestly regarding him, suddenly snatched the saw from his hand. "Away, butcher! you disgrace the profession. Look at *me!*"

For a few moments the thrilling, rasping sound was heard; and then the top-man seemed parted in twain at the hip, as the leg slowly slid into the arms of the pale, gaunt man in the shroud, who at once made away with it, and tucked it out of sight under one of the guns.

"Surgeon Sawyer," now said Cuticle, courteously turning to the surgeon of the *Mohawk*, "would you like to take up the arteries? They are quite at your service, sir."

"Do, Sawyer; be prevailed upon," said Surgeon Bandage.

Sawyer complied; and while, with some modesty he was conducting the operation, Cuticle, turning to the row of assistants said, "Young gentlemen, we will now proceed with our illustration. Hand me that bone, Steward." And taking the thigh-bone in his still bloody hands, and holding it conspicuously before his auditors, the Surgeon of the Fleet began:

"Young gentlemen, you will perceive that precisely at this spot—*here*—to which I previously directed your attention—at the corresponding spot precisely—the operation has been performed. About here, young gentlemen, here"—lifting his hand some inches from the bone—"about *here* the great artery was. But you noticed that I did not use the tourniquet; I never do. The forefinger of my steward is far better than a tourniquet, being so much more manageable, and leaving the smaller veins uncompressed. But I have been told, young gentlemen, that a certain Seignior Seignioroni, a surgeon of Seville, has recently invented an admirable substitute for the clumsy, old-fashioned tourniquet. As I understand it, it is something like a pair of *calipers,* working with a small Archimedes screw—a very clever invention, according to all accounts. For the padded points at the end of the arches"—arching his forefinger and thumb—"can be so worked as to approximate in such a way, as to—but you don't attend to me, young gentlemen," he added, all at once starting.

Being more interested in the active proceedings of Surgeon Sawyer, who was now threading a needle to sew up the overlapping of the stump, the young gentlemen had not scrupled to turn away their attention altogether from the lecturer.

A few moments more, and the top-man, in a swoon, was removed below into the sick-bay. As the curtain settled again after the patient had disappeared, Cuticle, still holding the thigh-bone of the skeleton in his ensanguined hands, proceeded with his remarks upon it; and having concluded them, added, "Now, young gentlemen, not the least interesting consequence of this operation will be the finding of the ball, which, in case of non-amputation, might have long eluded the most careful search. That ball, young gentlemen, must have taken a most circuitous route. Nor, in cases where the direction is oblique, is this at all unusual. Indeed, the learned Henner gives us a most remarkable—I had almost said an incredible—case of a soldier's neck, where the bullet, entering at the part called Adam's Apple—"

"Yes," said Surgeon Wedge, elevating himself, "the *pomum Adami.*"

"Entering the point called *Adam's Apple,*" continued Cuticle, severely emphasizing the last two words, "ran completely round the neck, and, emerging at the same hole it had entered, shot the next man in the ranks. It was afterward extracted, says Henner, from the second man, and pieces of the other's skin were found adhering to it. But examples of foreign substances being received into the body with a ball, young gentlemen, are frequently observed. Being attached to a United States ship at the time, I happened to be near the spot of the battle of Ayacucho, in Peru. The day after the action, I saw in the barracks of the wounded a trooper, who, having been severely injured in the brain, went crazy, and, with his own holster-pistol, committed suicide in the hospital. The ball drove inward a portion of his woolen night-cap—"

"In the form of a *cul-de-sac,* doubtless," said the undaunted Wedge.

"For once, Surgeon Wedge, you use the only term that can be employed; and let me avail myself of this opportunity to say to you, young gentlemen, that a man of true science"—expanding his shallow chest a little—"uses but few hard words, and those only when none other will answer his purpose; whereas the smatterer in science"—slightly glancing toward Wedge—"thinks, that by mouthing hard words, he proves that he understands hard things. Let this sink deep in your minds, young gentlemen; and, Surgeon Wedge"—with a stiff bow—"permit me to submit the reflection to yourself. Well, young gentlemen, the bullet was afterward extracted by pulling upon the external parts of the *cul-de-sac*—a simple, but exceedingly beautiful operation. There is a fine example, somewhat similar, related in Guthrie; but, of course, you must have met with it, in so well-known a work as his *Treatise upon Gun-shot Wounds.* When, upward of twenty years ago, I was with Lord Cochrane, then Admiral of the fleets of this very country"—pointing shoreward, out of a port-hole—"a sailor of the vessel to which I was attached, during the blockade of Bahia, had his leg—" But by this time the fidgets had completely taken possession of his auditors, especially of the senior surgeons; and turning upon them abruptly, he added, "But I will not detain you longer, gentlemen"—turning round upon all the surgeons—"your dinners must be waiting you on board your respective ships. But, Surgeon Sawyer, perhaps you may desire to wash your hands before you go. There is the basin, sir; you will find a clean towel on the rammer. For myself, I seldom use them"—taking out his handkerchief. "I must leave you now, gentlemen"—bowing. "To-morrow, at ten, the limb will be upon the table, and I shall be happy to see you all upon the occasion. Who's there?" turning to the curtain, which then rustled.

"Please, sir," said the Steward, entering, "the patient is dead."

"The body also, gentlemen, at ten precisely," said Cuticle, once more turning round upon his guests. "I predicted that the operation might prove fatal; he was very much run down. Good-morning"; and Cuticle departed.

"He does not, surely, mean to touch the body?" exclaimed Surgeon Sawyer, with much excitement.

"Oh, no!" said Patella, "that's only his way; he means, doubtless, that it may be inspected previous to being taken ashore for burial."

The assemblage of gold-laced surgeons now ascended to the quarter-deck; the second cutter was called away by the bugler, and, one by one, they were dropped aboard of their respective ships.

The following evening the mess-mates of the top-man rowed his remains ashore, and buried them in the ever-vernal Protestant cemetery, hard by the Beach of the Flamingoes, in plain sight from the bay.

Chapter LXIV

MAN-OF-WAR TROPHIES

WHEN THE SECOND CUTTER PULLED ABOUT AMONG THE SHIPS, DROPPING THE SURGEONS aboard the American men-of-war here and there—as a pilot-boat distributes her pilots at the mouth of the harbor—she passed several foreign frigates, two of which, an Englishman and a Frenchman, had excited not a little remark on board the *Neversink*. These vessels often loosed their sails and exercised yards simultaneously with ourselves, as if desirous of comparing the respective efficiency of the crews.

When we were nearly ready for sea, the English frigate, weighing her anchor, made all sail with the sea-breeze, and began showing off her paces by gliding about among all the men-of-war in harbor, and particularly by running down under the *Neversink*'s stern. Every time she drew near, we complimented her by lowering our ensign a little, and invariably she courteously returned the salute. She was inviting us to a sailing-match; and it was rumored that, when we should leave the bay, our Captain would have no objections to gratify her; for, be it known, the *Neversink* was accounted the fleetest keeled craft sailing under the American long-pennant. Perhaps this was the reason why the stranger challenged us.

It may have been that a portion of our crew were the more anxious to race with this frigate, from a little circumstance which a few of them deemed rather galling. Not many cables'-length distant from our Commodore's cabin lay the frigate *President*, with the red cross of *St. George* flying from her peak. As its name imported, this fine craft was an American born; but having been captured during the last war with Britain, she now sailed the salt seas as a trophy.

Think of it, my gallant countrymen, one and all, down the sea-coast and along the endless banks of the Ohio and Columbia—think of the twinges we sea-patriots must have felt to behold the live-oak of the Floridas and the pines of green Maine built into the oaken walls of Old England!

But, to some of the sailors, there was a counterbalancing thought, as grateful as the other was galling, and that was, that somewhere, sailing under the stars and stripes, was the frigate *Macedonian,* a British-born craft which had once sported the battle-banner of Britain.

It has ever been the custom to spend almost any amount of money in repairing a captured vessel, in order that she may long survive to commemorate the heroism of the conqueror. Thus, in the English Navy, there are many Monsieurs of seventy-fours won from the Gaul. But we Americans can show but few similar trophies, though, no doubt, we would much like to be able so to do.

But I never have beheld any of these floating trophies without being reminded of a scene once witnessed in a pioneer village on the western bank of the Mississippi. Not far from this village, where the stumps of aboriginal trees yet stand in the market-place, some years ago lived a portion of the remnant tribes of the Sioux Indians, who frequently visited the white settlements to purchase trinkets and cloths.

One florid crimson evening in July, when the red-hot sun was going down in a blaze, and I was leaning against a corner in my huntsman's frock, lo! there came stalking out of the crimson west a gigantic red-man, erect as a pine, with his glittering tomahawk, big as a broad-ax, folded in martial repose across his chest. Moodily wrapped in his blanket, and striding like a king on the stage, he promenaded up and down the rustic streets, exhibiting on the back of his blanket a crowd of human hands, rudely delineated in red; one of them seemed recently drawn.

"Who is this warrior?" asked I; "and why marches he here? and for what are these bloody hands?"

"That warrior is the *Red-hot Coal,*" said a pioneer in moccasins, by my side. "He marches here to show-off his last trophy; every one of those hands attests a foe scalped by his tomahawk; and he has just emerged from Ben Brown's, the painter, who has sketched the last red hand that you see; for last night this *Red-hot Coal* outburned the *Yellow Torch,* the chief of a band of the Foxes."

Poor savage thought I; and is this the cause of your lofty gait? Do you straighten yourself to think that you have committed a murder, when a chance-falling stone has often done the same? Is it a proud thing to topple down six feet perpendicular of immortal manhood, though that lofty living tower needed perhaps thirty good growing summers to bring it to maturity? Poor savage! And you account it so glorious, do you, to mutilate and destroy what God himself was more than a quarter of a century in building?

And yet, fellow-Christians, what is the American frigate *Macedonian,* or the English frigate *President,* but as two bloody red hands painted on this poor savage's blanket?

Are there no Moravians in the Moon, that not a missionary has yet visited this poor pagan planet of ours, to civilize civilization and christianize Christendom?

Chapter LXV

A Man-of-War Race

WE LAY IN RIO SO LONG—FOR WHAT REASON THE COMMODORE ONLY KNOWS—THAT A SAYING went abroad among the impatient sailors that our frigate would at last ground on the beef-bones daily thrown overboard by the cooks.

But at last good tidings came. "All hands up anchor, ahoy!" And bright and early in the morning up came our old iron, as the sun rose in the East.

The land-breezes at Rio—by which alone vessels may emerge from the bay—is ever languid and faint. It comes from gardens of citrons and cloves, spiced with all the spices of the Tropic of

Capricorn. And, like that old exquisite, Mohammed, who so much loved to snuff perfumes and essences, and used to lounge out of the conservatories of Khadija, his wife, to give battle to the robust sons of Koriesh; even so this Rio land-breeze comes jaded with sweet-smelling savors, to wrestle with the wild Tartar breezes of the sea.

Slowly we dropped and dropped down the bay, glided like a stately swan through the outlet, and were gradually rolled by the smooth, sliding billows broad out upon the deep. Straight in our wake came the tall main-mast of the English fighting-frigate, terminating, like a steepled cathedral, in the bannered cross of the religion of peace; and straight after *her* came the rainbow banner of France, sporting God's token that no more would he make war on the earth.

Both Englishmen and Frenchmen were resolved upon a race; and we Yankees swore by our top-sails and royals to sink their blazing banners that night among the Southern constellations we should daily be extinguishing behind us in our run to the North.

"Ay," said Mad Jack, "*St. George*'s banner shall be as the *Southern Cross,* out of sight, leagues down the horizon, while our gallant stars, my brave boys, shall burn all alone in the North, like the Great Bear at the Pole! Come on, Rainbow and Cross!"

But the wind was long languid and faint, not yet recovered from its night's dissipation ashore, and noon advanced, with the Sugar-Loaf pinnacle in sight.

Now it is not with ships as with horses; for though, if a horse walk well and fast, it generally furnishes good token that he is not bad at a gallop, yet the ship that in a light breeze is outstripped, may sweep the stakes, so soon as a t'gallant breeze enables her to strike into a canter. Thus fared it with us. First, the Englishman glided ahead, and bluffly passed on; then the Frenchman politely bade us adieu, while the old *Neversink* lingered behind, railing at the effeminate breeze. At one time, all three frigates were irregularly abreast, forming a diagonal line; and so near were all three, that the stately officers on the poops stiffly saluted by touching their caps, though refraining from any further civilities. At this juncture, it was a noble sight to behold those fine frigates, with dripping breast-hooks, all rearing and nodding in concert, and to look through their tall spars and wilderness of rigging, that seemed like inextricably-entangled, gigantic cobwebs against the sky.

Toward sundown the ocean pawed its white hoofs to the spur of its helter-skelter rider, a strong blast from the Eastward, and, giving three cheers from decks, yards, and tops, we crowded all sail on *St. George* and *St. Denis*.

But it is harder to overtake than outstrip; night fell upon us, still in the rear—still where the little boat was, which, at the eleventh hour, according to a Rabbinical tradition, pushed after the ark of old Noah.

It was a misty, cloudy night; and though at first our look-outs kept the chase in dim sight, yet at last so thick became the atmosphere, that no sign of a strange spar was to be seen. But the worst of it was that, when last discerned, the Frenchman was broad on our weather-bow, and the Englishman gallantly leading his van.

The breeze blew fresher and fresher; but, with even our main-royal set, we dashed along through a cream-colored ocean of illuminated foam. White-Jacket was then in the top; and it was glorious to look down and see our black hull butting the white sea with its broad bows like a ram.

"We must beat them with such a breeze, dear Jack," said I to our noble Captain of the Top.

"But the same breeze blows for John Bull, remember," replied Jack, who, being a Briton, perhaps favored the Englishman more than the *Neversink*.

"But how we boom through the billows!" cried Jack, gazing over the top-rail; then, flinging forth his arm, recited,

Aslope, and gliding on the leeward side,
The bounding vessel cuts the roaring tide.

Camoens! White-Jacket, Camoens! Did you ever read him? The *Lusiad,* I mean? It's the man-of-war epic of the world, my lad. Give me Gama for a Commodore, say I—Noble Gama! And Mickle, White-Jacket, did you ever read of him? William Julius Mickle? Camoens's Translator? A disappointed man though, White-Jacket. Besides his version of the *Lusiad,* he wrote many forgotten things. Did you ever see his ballad of Cumnor Hall?—No?—Why, it gave Sir Walter Scott the hint of Kenilworth. My father knew Mickle when he went to sea on board the old Romney man-of-war. How many great men have been sailors, White-Jacket! They say Homer himself was once a tar, even as his hero, Ulysses, was both a sailor and a shipwright. I'll swear Shakspeare was once a captain of the forecastle. Do you mind the first scene in *The Tempest,* White-Jacket? And the world-finder, Christopher Columbus, was a sailor! and so was Camoens, who went to sea with Gama, else we had never had the *Lusiad,* White-Jacket. Yes, I've sailed over the very track that Camoens sailed—round the East Cape into the Indian Ocean. I've been in Don Jose's garden, too, in Macao, and bathed my feet in the blessed dew of the walks where Camoens wandered before me. Yes, White-Jacket, and I have seen and sat in the cave at the end of the flowery, winding way, where Camoens, according to tradition, composed certain parts of his *Lusiad.* Ay, Camoens was a sailor once! Then, there's Falconer, whose 'Ship-wreck' will never founder, though he himself, poor fellow, was lost at sea in the Aurora frigate. Old Noah was the first sailor. And St. Paul, too, knew how to box the compass, my lad! mind you that chapter in *Acts*? I couldn't spin the yarn better myself. Were you ever in Malta? They called it Melita in the Apostle's day. I have been in Paul's cave there, White-Jacket. They say a piece of it is good for a charm against shipwreck; but I never tried it. There's Shelley, he was quite a sailor. Shelley—poor lad! a Percy, too—but they ought to have let him sleep in his sailor's grave—he was drowned in the Mediterranean, you know, near Leghorn—and not burn his body, as they did, as if he had been a bloody Turk. But many people thought him so, White-Jacket, because he didn't go to mass, and because he wrote *Queen Mab.* Trelawney was by at the burning; and he was an ocean-rover, too! Ay, and Byron helped put a piece of a keel on the fire; for it was made of bits of a wreck, they say; one wreck burning another! And was not Byron a sailor? an amateur forecastle-man, White-Jacket, so he was; else how bid the ocean heave and fall in that grand, majestic way? I say, White-Jacket, d'ye mind me? there never was a very great man yet who spent all his life inland. A snuff of the sea, my boy, is inspiration; and having been once out of sight of land, has been the making of many a true poet and the blasting of many pretenders; for, d'ye see, there's no gammon about the ocean; it knocks the false keel right off a pretender's bows; it tells him just what he is, and makes him feel it, too. A sailor's life, I say, is the thing to bring us mortals out. What does the blessed Bible say? Don't it say that we main-top-men alone see the marvelous sights and wonders? Don't deny the blessed Bible, now! don't do it! How it rocks up here, my boy!" holding on to a shroud; "but it only proves what I've been saying—the sea is the place to cradle genius! Heave and fall, old sea!"

"And *you,* also, noble Jack," said I, "what are you but a sailor?"

"You're merry, my boy," said Jack, looking up with a glance like that of a sentimental archangel doomed to drag out his eternity in disgrace. "But mind you, White-Jacket, there are many great men in the world besides Commodores and Captains. I've that here, White-Jacket"—touching his forehead—"which, under happier skies—perhaps in yon solitary star there, peeping down from those clouds—might have made a Homer of me. But Fate is Fate, White-Jacket; and we Homers who happen to be captains of tops must write our odes in our hearts, and publish them in our heads. But look! the Captain's on the poop."

It was now midnight; but all the officers were on deck.

"Jib-boom, there!" cried the Lieutenant of the Watch, going forward and hailing the headmost look-out. "D'ye see anything of those fellows now?"

"See nothing, sir."

"See nothing, sir," said the Lieutenant, approaching the Captain, and touching his cap.

"Call all hands!" roared the Captain. "This keel sha'n't be beat while I stride it."

All hands were called, and the hammocks stowed in the nettings for the rest of the night, so that no one could lie between blankets.

Now, in order to explain the means adopted by the Captain to ensure us the race, it needs to be said of the *Neversink*, that, for some years after being launched, she was accounted one of the slowest vessels in the American Navy. But it chanced upon a time, that, being on a cruise in the Mediterranean, she happened to sail out of Port Mahon in what was then supposed to be very bad trim for the sea. Her bows were rooting in the water, and her stern kicking up its heels in the air. But, wonderful to tell, it was soon discovered that in this comical posture she sailed like a shooting-star; she outstripped every vessel on the station. Thenceforward all her Captains, on all cruises, *trimmed her by the head*; and the *Neversink* gained the name of a clipper.

To return. All hands being called, they were now made use of by Captain Claret as make-weights, to trim the ship, scientifically, to her most approved bearings. Some were sent forward on the spar-deck, with twenty-four-pound shot in their hands, and were judiciously scattered about here and there, with strict orders not to budge an inch from their stations, for fear of marring the Captain's plans. Others were distributed along the gun and berth-decks, with similar orders; and, to crown all, several carronade-guns were unshipped from their carriages, and swung in their breechings from the beams of the main-deck, so as to impart a sort of vibratory briskness and oscillating buoyancy to the frigate.

And thus we five hundred make-weights stood out that whole night, some of us exposed to a drenching rain, in order that the *Neversink* might not be beaten. But the comfort and consolation of all make-weights is as dust in the balance in the estimation of the rulers of our man-of-war world.

The long, anxious night at last came to an end, and, with the first peep of day, the look-out on the jib-boom was hailed; but nothing was in sight. At last it was broad day; yet still not a bow was to be seen in our rear, nor a stern in our van.

"Where are they?" cried the Captain.

"Out of sight, astern, to be sure, sir," said the officer of the deck.

"Out of sight, *ahead*, to be sure, sir," muttered Jack Chase, in the top.

Precisely thus stood the question: whether we beat them, or whether they beat us, no mortal can tell to this hour, since we never saw them again; but for one, White-Jacket will lay his two hands on the bow chasers of the *Neversink*, and take his ship's oath that we Yankees carried the day.

Chapter LXVI

FUN IN A MAN-OF-WAR

AFTER THE RACE (OUR MAN-OF-WAR DERBY) WE HAD MANY DAYS FINE WEATHER, DURING WHICH we continued running before the Trades toward the north. Exhilarated by the thought of being homeward-bound, many of the seamen became joyous, and the discipline of the ship, if anything, became a little relaxed. Many pastimes served to while away the *Dog-Watches* in particular. These *Dog-Watches* (embracing two hours in the early part of the evening) form the only authorized play-time for the crews of most ships at sea.

Among other diversions at present licensed by authority in the *Neversink*, were those of single-stick, sparring, hammer-and-anvil, and head-bumping. All these were under the direct patronage of the Captain, otherwise—seeing the consequences they sometimes led to—they would undoubtedly have been strictly prohibited. It is a curious coincidence, that when a navy captain does not happen to be an admirer of the *Fistiana* his crew seldom amuse themselves in that way.

Single-stick, as everyone knows, is a delightful pastime, which consists in two men standing a few feet apart, and rapping each other over the head with long poles. There is a good deal of fun in it, so long as you are not hit; but a hit—in the judgment of discreet persons—spoils the sport completely. When this pastime is practiced by connoisseurs ashore, they wear heavy, wired helmets, to break the force of the blows. But the only helmets of our tars were those with which nature had furnished them. They played with great gun-rammers.

Sparring consists in playing single-stick with bone poles instead of wooden ones. Two men stand apart, and pommel each other with their fists (a hard bunch of knuckles permanently attached to the arms, and made globular, or extended into a palm, at the pleasure of the proprietor), till one of them, finding himself sufficiently thrashed, cries *enough*.

Hammer-and-anvil is thus practiced by amateurs: Patient No. 1 gets on all-fours, and stays so; while patient No. 2 is taken up by his arms and legs, and his base is swung against the base of patient No. 1, till patient No. 1, with the force of the final blow, is sent flying along the deck.

Head-bumping, as patronized by Captain Claret, consists in two negroes (whites will not answer) butting at each other like rams. This pastime was an especial favorite with the Captain. In the dog-watches, Rose-water and May-day were repeatedly summoned into the lee waist to tilt at each other, for the benefit of the Captain's health.

May-day was a full-blooded "*bull-negro*," so the sailors called him, with a skull like an iron tea-kettle, wherefore May-day much fancied the sport. But Rose-water, he was a slender and rather handsome mulatto, and abhorred the pastime. Nevertheless, the Captain must be obeyed; so at the word poor Rose-water was fain to put himself in a posture of defense, else May-day would incontinently have bumped him out of a port-hole into the sea. I used to pity poor Rose-water from the bottom of my heart. But my pity was almost aroused into indignation at a sad sequel to one of these gladiatorial scenes.

It seems that, lifted up by the unaffected, though verbally unexpressed applause of the Captain, May-day had begun to despise Rose-water as a poltroon—a fellow all brains and no skull; whereas he himself was a great warrior, all skull and no brains.

Accordingly, after they had been bumping one evening to the Captain's content, May-day confidentially told Rose-water that he considered him a *"nigger,"* which, among some blacks, is held a great term of reproach. Fired at the insult, Rose-water gave May-day to understand that he utterly erred; for his mother, a black slave, had been one of the mistresses of a Virginia planter belonging to one of the oldest families in that state. Another insulting remark followed this innocent disclosure; retort followed retort; in a word, at last they came together in mortal combat.

The master-at-arms caught them in the act, and brought them up to the mast. The Captain advanced.

"Please, sir," said poor Rose-water, "it all came of dat 'ar bumping; May-day, here, aggrawated me 'bout it."

"Master-at-arms," said the Captain, "did you see them fighting?"

"Ay, sir," said the master-at-arms, touching his cap.

"Rig the gratings," said the Captain. "I'll teach you two men that, though I now and then permit you to *play*, I will have no *fighting*. Do your duty, boatswain's mate!" And the negroes were flogged.

Justice commands that the fact of the Captain's not showing any leniency to May-day—a decided favorite of his, at least while in the ring—should not be passed over. He flogged both culprits in the most impartial manner.

As in the matter of the scene at the gangway, shortly after the Cape Horn theatricals, when my attention had been directed to the fact that the officers had *shipped their quarter-deck faces*—upon that occasion, I say, it was seen with what facility a sea-officer assumes his wonted severity of demeanor after a casual relaxation of it. This was especially the case with Captain Claret upon the present occasion. For any landsman to have beheld him in the lee waist, of a pleasant dog-watch, with a genial, good-humored countenance, observing the gladiators in the ring, and now and then indulging in a playful remark—that landsman would have deemed Captain Claret the indulgent father of his crew, perhaps permitting the excess of his kind-heartedness to encroach upon the appropriate dignity of his station. He would have deemed Captain Claret a fine illustration of those two well-known poetical comparisons between a sea-captain and a father, and between a sea-captain and the master of apprentices, instituted by those eminent maritime jurists, the noble Lords Tenterden and Stowell.

But surely, if there is anything hateful, it is this *shipping of the quarter-deck face* after wearing a merry and good-natured one. How can they have the heart? Methinks, if but once I smiled upon a man—never mind how much beneath me—I could not bring myself to condemn him to the shocking misery of the lash. Oh officers! all round the world, if this quarter-deck face you wear at all, then never unship it for another, to be merely sported for a moment. Of all insults, the temporary condescension of a master to a slave is the most outrageous and galling. That potentate who most condescends, mark him well; for that potentate, if occasion come, will prove your uttermost tyrant.

Chapter LXVII

WHITE-JACKET ARRAIGNED AT THE MAST

WHEN WITH FIVE HUNDRED OTHERS I MADE ONE OF THE COMPELLED SPECTATORS AT THE scourging of poor Rose-water, I little thought what Fate had ordained for myself the next day.

Poor mulatto! thought I, one of an oppressed race, they degrade you like a hound. Thank God! I am a white. Yet I had seen whites also scourged; for, black or white, all my shipmates were liable to that. Still, there is something in us, somehow, that in the most degraded condition, we snatch at a chance to deceive ourselves into a fancied superiority to others, whom we suppose lower in the scale than ourselves.

Poor Rose-water! thought I; poor mulatto! Heaven send you a release from your humiliation!

To make plain the thing about to be related, it needs to repeat what has somewhere been previously mentioned, that in *tacking ship* every seaman in a man-of-war has a particular station assigned him. What that station is, should be made known to him by the First Lieutenant; and when the word is passed to *tack* or *wear*, it is every seaman's duty to be found at his post. But among the various *numbers* and *stations* given to me by the senior Lieutenant, when I first came on board the frigate, he had altogether omitted informing me of my particular place at those times, and, up to the precise period now written of, I had hardly known that I should have had any special place then at all. For the rest of the men, they seemed to me to catch hold of the first rope that offered, as in a merchant-man upon similar occasions. Indeed, I subsequently discovered, that such was the state of discipline—in this one particular, at least—that very few of the seamen could tell where their proper stations were, at *tacking* or *wearing*.

"All hands tack ship, ahoy!" such was the announcement made by the boatswain's mates at the hatchways the morning after the hard fate of Rose-water. It was just eight bells—noon, and springing from my white jacket, which I had spread between the guns for a bed on the main-deck, I ran up the ladders, and, as usual, seized hold of the main-brace, which fifty hands were streaming along forward. When *main-top-sail haul!* was given through the trumpet, I pulled at this brace with such heartiness and good-will, that I almost flattered myself that my instrumentality in getting the frigate round on the other tack, deserved a public vote of thanks, and a silver tankard from Congress.

But something happened to be in the way aloft when the yards swung round; a little confusion ensued; and, with anger on his brow, Captain Claret came forward to see what occasioned it. No one to let go the weather-lift of the main-yard! The rope was cast off, however, by a hand, and the yards unobstructed, came round.

When the last rope was coiled, away, the Captain desired to know of the First Lieutenant who it might be that was stationed at the weather (then the starboard) main-lift. With a vexed expression of countenance the First Lieutenant sent a midshipman for the Station Bill, when, upon glancing it over, my own name was found put down at the post in question.

At the time I was on the gun-deck below, and did not know of these proceedings; but a moment after, I heard the boatswain's mates bawling my name at all the hatch-ways, and along all three decks. It was the first time I had ever heard it so sent through the furthest recesses of the ship, and well knowing what this generally betokened to other seamen, my heart jumped to my throat, and I hurriedly asked Flute, the boatswain's-mate at the fore-hatchway, what was wanted of me.

"Captain wants ye at the mast," he replied. "Going to flog ye, I guess."

"What for?"

"My eyes! you've been chalking your face, hain't ye?"

"What am I wanted for?" I repeated.

But at that instant my name was again thundered forth by the other boatswain's mate, and Flute hurried me away, hinting that I would soon find out what the Captain desired of me.

I swallowed down my heart in me as I touched the spar-deck, for a single instant balanced myself on my best center, and then, wholly ignorant of what was going to be alleged against me, advanced to the dread tribunal of the frigate.

As I passed through the gangway, I saw the quarter-master rigging the gratings; the boatswain with his green bag of scourges; the master-at-arms ready to help off someone's shirt.

Again I made a desperate swallow of my whole soul in me, and found myself standing before Captain Claret. His flushed face obviously showed him in ill-humor. Among the group of officers by his side was the First Lieutenant, who, as I came aft, eyed me in such a manner, that I plainly perceived him to be extremely vexed at me for having been the innocent means of reflecting upon the manner in which he kept up the discipline of the ship.

"Why were you not at your station, sir?" asked the Captain.

"What station do you mean, sir?" said I.

It is generally the custom with man-of-war's-men to stand obsequiously touching their hat at every sentence they address to the Captain. But as this was not obligatory upon me by the *Articles of War,* I did not do so upon the present occasion, and previously, I had never had the dangerous honor of a personal interview with Captain Claret.

He quickly noticed my omission of the homage usually rendered him, and instinct told me, that to a certain extent, it set his heart against me.

"What station, sir, do you mean?" said I.

"You pretend ignorance," he replied; "it will not help you, sir."

Glancing at the Captain, the First Lieutenant now produced the Station Bill, and read my name in connection with that of the starboard main-lift.

"Captain Claret," said I, "it is the first time I ever heard of my being assigned to that post."

"How is this, Mr. Bridewell?" he said, turning to the First Lieutenant, with a fault-finding expression.

"It is impossible, sir," said that officer, striving to hide his vexation, "but this man must have known his station."

"I have never known it before this moment, Captain Claret," said I.

"Do you contradict my officer?" he returned. "I shall flog you."

I had now been on board the frigate upward of a year, and remained unscourged; the ship was homeward-bound, and in a few weeks, at most, I would be a free man. And now, after making a hermit of myself in some things, in order to avoid the possibility of the scourge, here it was hanging over me for a thing utterly unforeseen, for a crime of which I was as utterly innocent. But all that was as naught. I saw that my case was hopeless; my solemn disclaimer was thrown in my teeth, and the boatswain's mate stood curling his fingers through the *cat*.

There are times when wild thoughts enter a man's heart, when he seems almost irresponsible for his act and his deed. The Captain stood on the weather-side of the deck. Sideways, on an unobstructed line with him, was the opening of the lee-gangway, where the side-ladders are suspended in port. Nothing but a slight bit of sinnate-stuff served to rail in this opening, which was cut right down to the level of the Captain's feet, showing the far sea beyond. I stood a little to windward of him, and, though he was a large, powerful man, it was certain that a sudden rush against him, along the slanting deck, would infallibly pitch him head-foremost into the ocean, though he who so rushed must needs go over with him. My blood seemed clotting in my veins; I felt icy cold at the tips of my fingers, and a dimness was before my eyes. But through that dimness the boatswain's mate, scourge in hand, loomed like a giant, and Captain Claret, and the blue sea seen through the opening at the gangway, showed with an awful vividness. I cannot analyze my heart, though it then stood still within me. But the thing that swayed me to my purpose was not altogether the thought that Captain Claret was about to degrade me, and that I had taken an oath with my soul that he should not. No, I felt my man's manhood so bottomless within me, that no word, no blow, no scourge of Captain Claret could cut me deep enough for that. I but swung to an instinct in me—the instinct diffused through all animated nature, the same that prompts even a worm to turn under the heel. Locking souls with him, I meant to drag Captain Claret from this earthly tribunal of his to that of Jehovah and let Him decide between us. No other way could I escape the scourge.

Nature has not implanted any power in man that was not meant to be exercised at times, though too often our powers have been abused. The privilege, inborn and inalienable, that every man has of dying himself, and inflicting death upon another, was not given to us without a purpose. These are the last resources of an insulted and unendurable existence.

"To the gratings, sir!" said Captain Claret; "do you hear?"

My eye was measuring the distance between him and the sea.

"Captain Claret," said a voice advancing from the crowd. I turned to see who this might be, that audaciously interposed at a juncture like this. It was the same remarkably handsome and gentlemanly corporal of marines, Colbrook, who has been previously alluded to, in the chapter describing killing time in a man-of-war.

"I know that man," said Colbrook, touching his cap, and speaking in a mild, firm, but extremely deferential manner; "and I know that he would not be found absent from his station, if he knew where it was."

This speech was almost unprecedented. Seldom or never before had a marine dared to speak to the Captain of a frigate in behalf of a seaman at the mast. But there was something so unostentatiously commanding in the calm manner of the man, that the Captain, though astounded, did not in any way reprimand him. The very unusualness of his interference seemed Colbrook's protection.

Taking heart, perhaps, from Colbrook's example, Jack Chase interposed, and in a manly but carefully respectful manner, in substance repeated the corporal's remark, adding that he had never found me wanting in the top.

The Captain looked from Chase to Colbrook, and from Colbrook to Chase—one the foremost man among the seamen, the other the foremost man among the soldiers—then all round upon the packed and silent crew, and, as if a slave to Fate, though supreme Captain of a frigate, he turned to the First Lieutenant, made some indifferent remark, and saying to me *you may go,* sauntered aft into his cabin; while I, who, in the desperation of my soul, had but just escaped being a murderer and a suicide, almost burst into tears of thanksgiving where I stood.

Chapter LXVIII

A Man-of-War Fountain, and Other Things

Let us forget the scourge and the gangway a while, and jot down in our memories a few little things pertaining to our man-of-war world. I let nothing slip, however small; and feel myself actuated by the same motive which has prompted many worthy old chroniclers, to set down the merest trifles concerning things that are destined to pass away entirely from the earth, and which, if not preserved in the nick of time, must infallibly perish from the memories of man. Who knows that this humble narrative may not hereafter prove the history of an obsolete barbarism? Who knows that, when men-of-war shall be no more, "White-Jacket" may not be quoted to show to the people in the Millennium what a man-of-war was? God hasten the time! Lo! ye years, escort it hither, and bless our eyes ere we die.

There is no part of a frigate where you will see more going and coming of strangers, and overhear more greetings and gossipings of acquaintances, than in the immediate vicinity of the scuttle-butt, just forward of the main-hatchway, on the gun-deck.

The scuttle-butt is a goodly, round, painted cask, standing on end, and with its upper head removed, showing a narrow, circular shelf within, where rest a number of tin cups for the accommodation of drinkers. Central, within the scuttle-butt itself, stands an iron pump, which, connecting with the immense water-tanks in the hold, furnishes an unfailing supply of the much-admired Pale Ale, first brewed in the brooks of the garden of Eden, and stamped with the *brand* of our old father Adam, who never knew what wine was. We are indebted to the old vintner Noah for that. The scuttle-butt is the only fountain in the ship; and here alone can you drink, unless at your meals. Night and day an armed sentry paces before it, bayonet in hand, to see that no water is taken away, except according to law. I wonder that they station no sentries at the port-holes, to see that no air is breathed, except according to Navy regulations.

As five hundred men come to drink at this scuttle-butt; as it is often surrounded by officers' servants drawing water for their masters to wash; by the cooks of the range, who hither come to fill their coffee-pots; and by the cooks of the ship's messes to procure water for their *duffs*; the scuttle-butt may be denominated the town-pump of the ship. And would that my fine countryman, Hawthorne of Salem, had but served on board a man-of-war in his time, that he might give us the reading of a *"rill"* from the scuttle-butt.

* * * * *

As in all extensive establishments—abbeys, arsenals, colleges, treasuries, metropolitan post-offices, and monasteries—there are many snug little niches, wherein are ensconced certain superannuated old pensioner officials; and, more especially, as in most ecclesiastical establishments, a few choice prebendary stalls are to be found, furnished with well-filled mangers and racks; so, in a man-of-war, there are a variety of similar snuggeries for the benefit of decrepit or rheumatic old tars. Chief among these is the office of *mast-man*.

There is a stout rail on deck, at the base of each mast, where a number of *braces, lifts,* and *bunt-lines* are belayed to the pins. It is the sole duty of the mast-man to see that these ropes are always kept clear, to preserve his premises in a state of the greatest attainable neatness, and every Sunday morning to dispose his ropes in neat *Flemish coils*.

The *main-mast-man* of the *Neversink* was a very aged seaman, who well deserved his comfortable berth. He had seen more than half a century of the most active service, and, through all, had proved himself a good and faithful man. He furnished one of the very rare examples of a sailor in a green old age; for, with most sailors, old age comes in youth, and Hardship and Vice carry them on an early bier to the grave.

As in the evening of life, and at the close of the day, old Abraham sat at the door of his tent, biding his time to die, so sits our old mast-man on the *coat of the mast*, glancing round him with patriarchal benignity. And that mild expression of his sets off very strangely a face that has been burned almost black by the torrid suns that shone fifty years ago—a face that is seamed with three saber cuts. You would almost think this old mast-man had been blown out of Vesuvius, to look alone at his scarred, blackened forehead, chin, and cheeks. But gaze down into his eye, and though all the snows of Time have drifted higher and higher upon his brow, yet deep down in that eye you behold an infantile, sinless look, the same that answered the glance of this old man's mother when first she cried for the babe to be laid by her side. That look is the fadeless, ever infantile immortality within.

* * * * *

The Lord Nelsons of the sea, though but Barons in the state, yet oftentimes prove more potent than their royal masters; and at such scenes as Trafalgar—dethroning this Emperor and reinstating that—enact on the ocean the proud part of mighty Richard Neville, the king-making Earl of the land. And as Richard Neville entrenched himself in his moated old man-of-war castle of Warwick, which, underground, was traversed with vaults, hewn out of the solid rock, and intricate as the wards of the old keys of Calais surrendered to Edward III; even so do these King-Commodores house themselves in their water-rimmed, cannon-sentried frigates, oaken dug, deck under deck, as cell under cell. And as the old Middle-Age warders of Warwick, every night at curfew, patrolled the battlements, and dove down into the vaults to see that all lights were extinguished, even so do the master-at-arms and ship's corporals of a frigate perambulate all the decks of a man-of-war, blowing out all tapers but those burning in the legalized battle-lanterns. Yea, in these things, so potent is the authority of these sea-wardens, that, though almost the lowest subalterns in the ship, yet should they find the Senior Lieutenant himself sitting up late in his state-room, reading Bowditch's *Navigator,* or D'Anton *On Gunpowder and Fire-arms,* they would infallibly blow the light out under his very nose; nor durst that Grand-Vizier resent the indignity.

But, unwittingly, I have ennobled, by grand historical comparisons, this prying, pettifogging, Irish-informer of a master-at-arms.

You have seen some slim, slip-shod housekeeper, at midnight ferreting over a rambling old house in the country, startling at fancied witches and ghosts, yet intent on seeing every door bolted, every smoldering ember in the fireplaces smothered, every loitering domestic abed, and every light made dark. This is the master-at-arms taking his night-rounds in a frigate.

* * * * *

It may be thought that but little is seen of the Commodore in these chapters, and that, since he so seldom appears on the stage, he cannot be so august a personage, after all. But the mightiest potentates keep the most behind the veil. You might tarry in Constantinople a month, and never catch a glimpse of the Sultan. The grand Lama of Thibet, according to some accounts, is never beheld by the people. But if anyone doubts the majesty of a Commodore, let him know that, according to XLII of the *Articles of War,* he is invested with a prerogative which, according to monarchical jurists, is inseparable from the throne—the plenary pardoning power. He may pardon all offenses committed in the squadron under his command.

But this prerogative is only his while at sea, or on a foreign station. A circumstance peculiarly significant of the great difference between the stately absolutism of a Commodore enthroned on his poop in a foreign harbor, and an unlaced Commodore negligently reclining in an easy-chair in the bosom of his family at home.

Chapter LXIX

Prayers at the Guns

The training-days, or general quarters, now and then taking place in our frigate, have already been described, also the Sunday devotions on the half-deck; but nothing has yet been said concerning the daily morning and evening quarters, when the men silently stand at their guns, and the chaplain simply offers up a prayer.

Let us now enlarge upon this matter. We have plenty of time; the occasion invites; for behold! the homeward-bound *Neversink* bowls along over a jubilant sea.

Shortly after breakfast the drum beats to quarters; and among five hundred men, scattered over all three decks, and engaged in all manner of ways, that sudden rolling march is magical as the monitory sound to which every good Mussulman at sunset drops to the ground whatsoever his hands might have found to do, and, throughout all Turkey, the people in concert kneel toward their holy Mecca.

The sailors run to and fro—some up the deck-ladders, some down—to gain their respective stations in the shortest possible time. In three minutes all is composed. One by one, the various officers stationed over the separate divisions of the ship then approach the First Lieutenant on the quarter-deck, and report their respective men at their quarters. It is curious to watch their countenances at this time. A profound silence prevails; and, emerging through the hatchway, from one of the lower decks, a slender young officer appears, hugging his sword to his thigh, and advances through the long lanes of sailors at their guns, his serious eye all the time fixed upon the First Lieutenant's—his polar star. Sometimes he essays a stately and graduated step, an erect and martial bearing, and seems full of the vast national importance of what he is about to communicate.

But when at last he gains his destination, you are amazed to perceive that all he has to say is imparted by a Freemason touch of his cap, and a bow. He then turns and makes off to his division, perhaps passing several brother Lieutenants, all bound on the same errand he himself has just achieved. For about five minutes these officers are coming and going, bringing in thrilling intelligence from all quarters of the frigate; most stoically received, however, by the First Lieutenant. With his legs apart, so as to give a broad foundation for the superstructure of his dignity, this gentleman stands stiff as a pike-staff on the quarter-deck. One hand holds his saber—an appurtenance altogether unnecessary at the time; and which he accordingly tucks, point backward, under his arm, like an umbrella on a sunshiny day. The other hand is continually bobbing up and down to the leather front of his cap, in response to the reports and salute of his subordinates, to whom he never deigns to vouchsafe a syllable, merely going through the motions of accepting their news, without bestowing thanks for their pains.

This continual touching of caps between officers on board a man-of-war is the reason why you invariably notice that the glazed fronts of their caps look jaded, lack-luster, and worn; sometimes slightly oleaginous—though, in other respects, the cap may appear glossy and fresh. But as for the First Lieutenant, he ought to have extra pay allowed to him, on account of his extraordinary outlays in cap fronts; for he it is to whom, all day long, reports of various kinds are incessantly being made by the junior Lieutenants; and no report is made by them, however trivial, but caps are touched on the occasion. It is obvious that these individual salutes must be greatly multiplied and aggregated upon the senior Lieutenant, who must return them all. Indeed, when a subordinate officer is first promoted to that rank, he generally complains of the same exhaustion about the shoulder and elbow that La Fayette mourned over, when, in visiting America, he did little else but shake the sturdy hands of patriotic farmers from sunrise to sunset.

The various officers of divisions having presented their respects, and made good their return to their stations, the First Lieutenant turns round, and, marching aft, endeavors to catch the eye of the Captain, in order to touch his own cap to that personage, and thereby, without adding a word of explanation, communicate the fact of all hands being at their guns. He is a sort of retort, or receiver-general, to concentrate the whole sum of the information imparted to him, and discharge it upon his superior at one touch of his cap front.

But sometimes the Captain feels out of sorts, or in ill-humor, or is pleased to be somewhat capricious, or has a fancy to show a touch of his omnipotent supremacy; or, peradventure, it has so happened that the First Lieutenant has, in some way, piqued or offended him, and he is not unwilling to show a slight specimen of his dominion over him, even before the eyes of all hands; at all events, only by some one of these suppositions can the singular circumstance be accounted for, that frequently Captain Claret would pertinaciously promenade up and down the poop, purposely averting his eye from the First Lieutenant, who would stand below in the most awkward suspense, waiting the first wink from his superior's eye.

"Now I have him!" he must have said to himself, as the Captain would turn toward him in his walk; "now's my time!" and up would go his hand to his cap; but, alas! the Captain was off again; and the men at the guns would cast sly winks at each other as the embarrassed Lieutenant would bite his lips with suppressed vexation.

Upon some occasions this scene would be repeated several times, till at last Captain Claret, thinking, that in the eyes of all hands, his dignity must by this time be pretty well bolstered, would stalk towards his subordinate, looking him full in the eyes; whereupon up goes his hand to the cap front, and the Captain, nodding his acceptance of the report, descends from his perch to the quarter-deck.

By this time the stately Commodore slowly emerges from his cabin, and soon stands leaning alone against the brass rails of the after-hatchway. In passing him, the Captain makes a profound salutation, which his superior returns, in token that the Captain is at perfect liberty to proceed with the ceremonies of the hour.

Marching on, Captain Claret at last halts near the main-mast, at the head of a group of the ward-room officers, and by the side of the Chaplain. At a sign from his finger, the brass band strikes up the Portuguese hymn. This over, from Commodore to hammock-boy, all hands uncover, and the Chaplain reads a prayer. Upon its conclusion, the drum beats the retreat, and the ship's company disappear from the guns. At sea or in harbor, this ceremony is repeated every morning and evening.

By those stationed on the quarter-deck the Chaplain is distinctly heard; but the quarter-deck gun division embraces but a tenth part of the ship's company, many of whom are below, on the main-deck, where not one syllable of the prayer can be heard. This seemed a great misfortune; for I well knew myself how blessed and soothing it was to mingle twice every day in these peaceful devotions, and, with the Commodore, and Captain, and smallest boy, unite in acknowledging Almighty God. There was also a touch of the temporary equality of the Church about it, exceedingly grateful to a man-of-war's-man like me.

My carronade-gun happened to be directly opposite the brass railing against which the Commodore invariably leaned at prayers. Brought so close together, twice every day, for more than a year, we could not but become intimately acquainted with each other's faces. To this fortunate circumstance it is to be ascribed, that some time after reaching home, we were able to recognize each other when we chanced to meet in Washington, at a ball given by the Russian Minister, the Baron de Bodisco. And though, while on board the frigate, the Commodore never in any manner personally addressed me—nor did I him—yet, at the Minister's social entertainment, we *there* became exceedingly chatty; nor did I fail to observe, among that crowd of foreign dignitaries and magnates from all parts of America, that my worthy friend did not appear so exalted as when leaning, in solitary state, against the brass railing of the *Neversink*'s quarter-deck. Like many other gentlemen, he appeared to the best advantage, and was treated with the most deference in the bosom of his home, the frigate.

Our morning and evening quarters were agreeably diversified for some weeks by a little circumstance, which to some of us at least, always seemed very pleasing.

At Callao, half of the Commodore's cabin had been hospitably yielded to the family of a certain aristocratic-looking magnate, who was going ambassador from Peru to the Court of the Brazils, at Rio. This dignified diplomatist sported a long, twirling mustache, that almost enveloped his mouth. The sailors said he looked like a rat with his teeth through a bunch of oakum, or a St. Jago monkey peeping through a prickly-pear bush.

He was accompanied by a very beautiful wife, and a still more beautiful little daughter, about six years old. Between this dark-eyed little gypsy and our chaplain there soon sprung up a cordial love and good feeling, so much so, that they were seldom apart. And whenever the drum beat to quarters, and the sailors were hurrying to their stations, this little signorita would outrun them all to gain her own quarters at the capstan, where she would stand by the chaplain's side, grasping his hand, and looking up archly in his face.

It was a sweet relief from the domineering sternness of our martial discipline—a sternness not relaxed even at our devotions before the altar of the common God of commodore and cabin-boy—to see that lovely little girl standing among the thirty-two pounders, and now and then casting a wondering, commiserating glance at the array of grim seamen around her.

Chapter LXX

MONTHLY MUSTER ROUND THE CAPSTAN

BESIDES GENERAL QUARTERS, AND THE REGULAR MORNING AND EVENING QUARTERS FOR PRAYERS on board the *Neversink*, on the first Sunday of every month we had a grand *"muster round the capstan,"* when we passed in solemn review before the Captain and officers, who closely scanned our frocks and trousers, to see whether they were according to the Navy cut. In some ships, every man is required to bring his bag and hammock along for inspection.

This ceremony acquires its chief solemnity, and, to a novice, is rendered even terrible, by the reading of the *Articles of War* by the Captain's clerk before the assembled ship's company, who in testimony of their enforced reverence for the code, stand bareheaded till the last sentence is pronounced.

To a mere amateur reader the quiet perusal of these *Articles of War* would be attended with some nervous emotions. Imagine, then, what *my* feelings must have been, when, with my hat deferentially in my hand, I stood before my lord and master, Captain Claret, and heard these *Articles* read as the law and gospel, the infallible, unappealable dispensation and code, whereby I lived, and moved, and had my being on board of the United States ship *Neversink*.

Of some twenty offenses—made penal—that a seaman may commit, and which are specified in this code, thirteen are punishable by death.

"*Shall suffer death!*" This was the burden of nearly every *Article* read by the Captain's clerk; for he seemed to have been instructed to omit the longer *Articles*, and only present those which were brief and to the point.

"*Shall suffer death!*" The repeated announcement falls on your ear like the intermitting discharge of artillery. After it has been repeated again and again, you listen to the reader as he deliberately begins a new paragraph; you hear him reciting the involved, but comprehensive and clear arrangement of the sentence, detailing all possible particulars of the offense described, and you breathlessly await, whether *that* clause also is going to be concluded by the discharge of the terrible minute-gun. When, lo! it again booms on your ear—*shall suffer death!* No reservations, no contingencies; not the remotest promise of pardon or reprieve; not a glimpse of commutation of the sentence; all hope and consolation is shut out—*shall suffer death!* that is the simple fact for you to digest; and it is a tougher morsel, believe White-Jacket when he says it, than a forty-two-pound cannon-ball.

But there is a glimmering of an alternative to the sailor who infringes these *Articles*. Some of them thus terminates: "*Shall suffer death, or such punishment as a court-martial shall adjudge.*" But hints this at a penalty still more serious? Perhaps it means "*death, or worse punishment.*"

Your honors of the Spanish Inquisition, Loyola and Torquemada! produce, reverend gentlemen, your most secret code, and match these *Articles of War*, if you can. Jack Ketch, *you* also are experienced in these things! Thou most benevolent of mortals, who standest by us, and hangest round our necks, when all the rest of this world are against us—tell us, hangman, what punishment is this, horribly hinted at as being worse than death? Is it, upon an empty stomach, to read the *Articles of War* every morning, for the term of one's natural life? Or is it to be imprisoned in a cell, with its walls papered from floor to ceiling with printed copies, in italics, of these *Articles of War*?

But it needs not to dilate upon the pure, bubbling milk of human kindness, and Christian charity, and forgiveness of injuries which pervade this charming document, so thoroughly imbued, as a Christian code, with the benignant spirit of the Sermon on the Mount. But as it is very nearly alike in the foremost states of Christendom, and as it is nationally set forth by those states, it indirectly becomes an index to the true condition of the present civilization of the world.

As, month after month, I would stand bareheaded among my shipmates, and hear this document read, I have thought to myself, Well, well, White-Jacket, you are in a sad box, indeed. But prick your ears, there goes another minute-gun. It admonishes you to take all bad usage in good part, and never to join in any public meeting that may be held on the gun-deck for a redress of grievances. Listen:

Art. XIII. "If any person in the navy shall make, or attempt to make, any mutinous assembly, he shall, on conviction thereof by a court-martial, suffer death."

Bless me, White-Jacket, are you a great gun yourself, that you so recoil, to the extremity of your breechings, at that discharge?

But give ear again. Here goes another minute-gun. It indirectly admonishes you to receive the grossest insult, and stand still under it:

Art. XIV. "No private in the navy shall disobey the lawful orders of his superior officer, or strike him, or draw, or offer to draw, or raise any weapon against him, while in the execution of the duties of his office, on pain of death."

Do not hang back there by the bulwarks, White-Jacket; come up to the mark once more; for here goes still another minute-gun, which admonishes you never to be caught napping:

Part of *Art. XX*. "If any person in the navy shall sleep upon his watch, he shall suffer death."

Murderous! But then, in time of peace, they do not enforce these blood-thirsty laws? Do they not, indeed? What happened to those three sailors on board an American armed vessel a few years ago, quite within your memory, White-Jacket; yea, while you yourself were yet serving on board this very frigate, the *Neversink*? What happened to those three Americans, White-Jacket—those three sailors, even as you, who once were alive, but now are dead? *"Shall suffer death!"* those were the three words that hung those three sailors.

Have a care, then, have a care, lest you come to a sad end, even the end of a rope; lest, with a black-and-blue throat, you turn a dumb diver after pearl-shells; put to bed for ever, and tucked in, in your own hammock, at the bottom of the sea. And there you will lie, White-Jacket, while hostile navies are playing cannon-ball billiards over your grave.

By the main-mast! then, in a time of profound peace, I am subject to the cut-throat martial law. And when my own brother, who happens to be dwelling ashore, and does not serve his country as I am now doing—when *he* is at liberty to call personally upon the President of the United States, and express his disapprobation of the whole national administration, here am *I*, liable at any time to be run up at the yard-arm, with a necklace, made by no jeweler, round my neck!

A hard case, truly, White-Jacket; but it cannot be helped. Yes; you live under this same martial law. Does not everything around you din the fact in your ears? Twice every day do you not jump to your quarters at the sound of a drum? Every morning, in port, are you not roused from your hammock by the *reveille,* and sent to it again at nightfall by the *tattoo?* Every Sunday are you not commanded in the mere matter of the very dress you shall wear through that blessed day? Can your shipmates so much as drink their "tot of grog?" nay, can they even drink but a cup of water at the scuttle-butt, without an armed sentry standing over them? Does not every officer wear a sword instead of a cane? You live and move among twenty-four-pounders. White-Jacket; the very cannon-balls are deemed an ornament around you, serving to embellish the hatchways; and should you come to die at sea, White-Jacket, still two cannon-balls would bear you company when you would be committed to the deep. Yea, by all methods, and devices, and inventions, you are momentarily admonished of the fact that you live under the *Articles of War*. And by virtue of them it is, White-Jacket, that, without a hearing and without a trial, you may, at a wink from the Captain, be condemned to the scourge.

Speak you true? Then let me fly!

Nay, White-Jacket, the landless horizon hoops you in.

Some tempest, then, surge all the sea against us! hidden reefs and rocks, arise and dash the ships to chips! I was not born a serf, and will not live a slave! Quick! cork-screw whirlpools, suck us down! world's end whelm us!

Nay, White-Jacket, though this frigate laid her broken bones upon the Antarctic shores of Palmer's Land; though not two planks adhered; though all her guns were spiked by sword-fish blades, and at her yawning hatchways mouth-yawning sharks swam in and out; yet, should you escape the wreck and scramble to the beach, this Martial Law would meet you still, and snatch you by the throat. Hark!

Art. XLII. Part of Sec. 3.—"In all cases where the crews of the ships or vessels of the United States shall be separated from their vessels by the latter being wrecked, lost, or destroyed, all the command, power, and authority given to the officers of such ships or vessels shall remain, and be in full force, as effectually as if such ship or vessel were not so wrecked, lost or destroyed."

Hear you that, White-Jacket! I tell you there is no escape. Afloat or wrecked the Martial Law relaxes not its gripe. And though, by that self-same warrant, for some offense therein set down, you were indeed to "suffer death," even then the Martial Law might hunt you straight through the other world, and out again at its other end, following you through all eternity, like an endless thread on the inevitable track of its own point, passing unnumbered needles through.

Chapter LXXI

THE GENEALOGY OF THE ARTICLES OF WAR

AS THE *ARTICLES OF WAR* FORM THE ARK AND CONSTITUTION OF THE PENAL LAWS OF THE AMERican Navy, in all sobriety and earnestness it may be well to glance at their origin. Whence came they? And how is it that one arm of the national defenses of a Republic comes to be ruled by a Turkish code, whose every section almost, like each of the tubes of a revolving pistol, fires nothing short of death into the heart of an offender? How comes it that, by virtue of a law solemnly ratified by a Congress of freemen, the representatives of freemen, thousands of Americans are subjected to the most despotic usages, and, from the dockyards of a republic, absolute monarchies are launched, with the "glorious stars and stripes" for an ensign? By what unparalleled anomaly, by what monstrous grafting of tyranny upon freedom did these *Articles of War* ever come to be so much as heard of in the American Navy?

Whence came they? They cannot be the indigenous growth of those political institutions, which are based upon that arch-democrat Thomas Jefferson's Declaration of Independence? No; they are an importation from abroad, even from Britain, whose laws we Americans hurled off as tyrannical, and yet retained the most tyrannical of all.

But we stop not here; for these *Articles of War* had their congenial origin in a period of the history of Britain when the Puritan Republic had yielded to a monarchy restored; when a hangman Judge Jeffreys sentenced a world's champion like Algernon Sidney to the block; when one of a race—by some deemed accursed of God—even a Stuart, was on the throne; and a Stuart, also, was at the head of the Navy, as Lord High Admiral. One, the son of a King beheaded for encroachments upon the rights of his people, and the other, his own brother, afterward a king, James II, who was hurled from the throne for his tyranny. This is the origin of the *Articles of War*; and it carries with it an unmistakable clue to their despotism.[1]

Nor is it a dumb thing that the men who, in democratic Cromwell's time, first proved to the nations the toughness of the British oak and the hardihood of the British sailor—that in Cromwell's

1. The first Naval *Articles of War* in the English language were passed in the thirteenth year of the reign of Charles the Second, under the title of "*An act for establishing Articles and Orders for the regulating and better Government of his Majesty's Navies, Ships-of-War, and Forces by Sea.*" This act was repealed, and, so far as concerned the officers, a modification of it substituted, in the twenty-second year of the reign of Geroge the Second, shortly after the Peace of Aix la Chapelle, just one century ago. This last act, it is believed, comprises, in substance, the *Articles of War* at this day in force in the British Navy. It is not a little curious, nor without meaning, that neither of these acts explicity empowers an officer to inflict the lash. It would almost seem as if, in this case, the British lawgivers were willing to leave such a stigma out of an organic statute, and bestow the power of the lash in some less solemn, and perhaps less public manner. Indeed, the only broad enactments directly sanctioning naval scourging at sea are to be found in the *United States Statute Book* and in the "Sea Laws" of the abolute monarch, Louis le Grand, of France.*

Taking for their basis the above-mentioned British Naval Code, and imgrafting upon it the positive scourging laws, which Britain was loth to recognize as organic statues, our American lawgivers, in the year 1800, framed the Articles of War now governing the American Navy. They may be found in the second volume of the "United States Statues at Large," under chapter xxxiii.—"An act for the *better* government of the Navy of the United States."

*For reference to the latter (L'Ord. de la Marine), *vide* Curtis's *Treatise on the Rights and Duties of Merchant-Seamen, according to the General Maritime Law,* Part ii, c. i.

time, whose fleets struck terror into the cruisers of France, Spain, Portugal, and Holland, and the corsairs of Algiers and the Levant; in Cromwell's time, when Robert Blake swept the Narrow Seas of all the keels of a Dutch Admiral who insultingly carried a broom at his fore-mast; it is not a dumb thing that, at a period deemed so glorious to the British Navy, these *Articles of War* were unknown.

Nevertheless, it is granted that some laws or other must have governed Blake's sailors at that period; but they must have been far less severe than those laid down in the written code which superseded them, since, according to the father-in-law of James II, the Historian of the Rebellion, the English Navy, prior to the enforcement of the new code, was full of officers and sailors who, of all men, were the most republican. Moreover, the same author informs us that the first work undertaken by his respected son-in-law, then Duke of York, upon entering on the duties of Lord High Admiral, was to have a grand rechristening of the men-of-war, which still carried on their sterns names too democratic to suit his high-tory ears.

But if these *Articles of War* were unknown in Blake's time, and also during the most brilliant period of Admiral Benbow's career, what inference must follow? That such tyrannical ordinances are not indispensable—even during war—to the highest possible efficiency of a military marine.

Chapter LXXII

"Herein Are the Good Ordinances of the Sea, Which Wise Men, Who Voyaged Round the World, Gave to Our Ancestors, And Which Constitute the Books of the Science of Good Customs."—The Consulate of the Sea

THE PRESENT USAGES OF THE AMERICAN NAVY ARE SUCH THAT, THOUGH THERE IS NO GOVERNMENT enactment to that effect, yet, in many respect, its Commanders seem virtually invested with the power to observe or violate, as seems to them fit, several of the *Articles of War.*

According to Article XV, *"No person in the Navy shall quarrel with any other person in the Navy, nor use provoking or reproachful words, gestures, or menaces, on pain of such punishment as a court-martial shall adjudge."*

"Provoking or reproachful words!" Officers of the Navy, answer me! Have you not, many of you, a thousand times violated this law, and addressed to men, whose tongues were tied by this very *Article,* language which no landsman would ever hearken to without flying at the throat of his insulter? I know that worse words than *you* ever used are to be heard addressed by a merchant-captain to his crew; but the merchant-captain does not live under this XVth *Article of War.*

Not to make an example of him, nor to gratify any personal feeling, but to furnish one certain illustration of what is here asserted, I honestly declare that Captain Claret, of the *Neversink,* repeatedly violated this law in his own proper person.

According to Article III, no officer, or other person in the Navy, shall be guilty of "oppression, fraud, profane swearing, drunkenness, or any other scandalous conduct."

Again let me ask you, officers of the Navy, whether many of you have not repeatedly, and in more than one particular, violated this law? And here, again, as a certain illustration, I must once more cite Captain Claret as an offender, especially in the matter of profane swearing. I must also cite four of the lieutenants, some eight of the midshipmen, and nearly all the seamen.

Additional *Articles* might be quoted that are habitually violated by the officers, while nearly all those *exclusively* referring to the sailors are unscrupulously enforced. Yet those *Articles,* by which the sailor is scourged at the gangway, are not one whit more laws than those *other Articles,* binding upon the officers, that have become obsolete from immemorial disuse; while still other *Articles,* to which the sailors alone are obnoxious, are observed or violated at the caprice of the Captain. Now, if it be not so much the severity as the certainty of punishment that deters from transgression, how fatal to all proper reverence for the enactments of Congress must be this disregard of its statutes.

Still more. This violation of the law, on the part of the officers, in many cases involves oppression to the sailor. But throughout the whole naval code, which so hems in the mariner by law upon law, and which invests the Captain with so much judicial and administrative authority over him—in most cases entirely discretionary—not one solitary clause is to be found which in any way provides means for a seaman deeming himself aggrieved to obtain redress. Indeed, both the written and unwritten laws of the American Navy are as destitute of individual guarantees to the mass of seamen as the Statute Book of the despotic Empire of Russia.

Who put this great gulf between the American Captain and the American sailor? Or is the Captain a creature of like passions with ourselves? Or is he an infallible archangel, incapable of the shadow of error? Or has a sailor no mark of humanity, no attribute of manhood, that, bound hand and foot, he is cast into an American frigate shorn of all rights and defenses, while the notorious lawlessness of the Commander has passed into a proverb, familiar to man-of-war's-men, *the law was not made for the Captain!* Indeed, he may almost be said to put off the citizen when he touches his quarter-deck; and, almost exempt from the law of the land himself, he comes down upon others with a judicial severity unknown on the national soil. With the *Articles of War* in one hand, and the cat-o'-nine-tails in the other, he stands an undignified parody upon Mohammed enforcing Moslemism with the sword and the Koran.

The concluding sections of the *Articles of War* treat of the naval courts-martial before which officers are tried for serious offenses as well as the seamen. The oath administered to members of these courts—which sometimes sit upon matters of life and death—explicitly enjoins that the members shall not "at any time divulge the vote or opinion of any particular member of the court, unless required so to do before a court of justice in due course of law."

Here, then, is a Council of Ten and a Star Chamber indeed! Remember, also, that though the sailor is sometimes tried for his life before a tribunal like this, in no case do his fellow-sailors, his peers, form part of the court. Yet that a man should be tried by his peers is the fundamental principle of all civilized jurisprudence. And not only tried by his peers, but his peers must be unanimous to render a verdict; whereas, in a court-martial, the concurrence of a majority of conventional and social superiors is all that is requisite.

In the English Navy, it is said, they had a law which authorized the sailor to appeal, if he chose, from the decision of the Captain—even in a comparatively trivial case—to the higher tribunal of a court-martial. It was an English seaman who related this to me. When I said that such a law must be a fatal clog to the exercise of the penal power in the Captain, he, in substance, told me the following story.

A top-man guilty of drunkenness being sent to the gratings, and the scourge about to be inflicted, he turned round and demanded a court-martial. The Captain smiled, and ordered him to be taken down and put into the "brig." There he was kept in irons some weeks, when, despairing of being liberated, he offered to compromise at two dozen lashes. "Sick of your bargain, then, are you?" said the Captain. "No, no! a court-martial you demanded, and a court-martial you shall have!" Being at last tried before the bar of quarter-deck officers, he was condemned to two hundred lashes. What for? for his having been drunk? No! for his having had the insolence to appeal from an authority, in maintaining which the men who tried and condemned him had so strong a sympathetic interest.

Whether this story be wholly true or not, or whether the particular law involved prevails, or ever did prevail, in the English Navy, the thing, nevertheless, illustrates the ideas that man-of-war's-men themselves have touching the tribunals in question.

What can be expected from a court whose deeds are done in the darkness of the recluse courts of the Spanish Inquisition? when that darkness is solemnized by an oath on the Bible? when an oligarchy of epaulets sits upon the bench, and a plebeian top-man, without a jury, stands judicially naked at the bar?

In view of these things, and especially in view of the fact that, in several cases, the degree of punishment inflicted upon a man-of-war's-man is absolutely left to the discretion of the court, what shame should American legislators take to themselves, that with perfect truth we may apply to the entire body of the American man-of-war's-men that infallible principle of Sir Edward Coke: "It is one of the genuine marks of servitude to have the law either concealed or precarious." But still better may we subscribe to the saying of Sir Matthew Hale in his *History of the Common Law,* that "the Martial Law, being based upon no settled principles, is, in truth and reality, no law, but something indulged rather than allowed as a law."

I know it may be said that the whole nature of this naval code is purposely adapted to the war exigencies of the Navy. But waiving the grave question that might be raised concerning the moral, not judicial, lawfulness of this arbitrary code, even in time of war; be it asked, why it is in force during a time of peace? The United States has now existed as a nation upward of seventy years, and in all that time the alleged necessity for the operation of the naval code—in cases deemed capital—has only existed during a period of two or three years at most.

Some may urge that the severest operations of the code are tacitly made null in time of peace. But though with respect to several of the *Articles* this holds true, yet at any time any and all of them may be legally enforced. Nor have there been wanting recent instances, illustrating the spirit of this code, even in cases where the letter of the code was not altogether observed. The well-known case of a United States brig furnishes a memorable example, which at any moment may be repeated. Three men, in a time of peace, were then hung at the yard-arm, merely because, in the Captain's judgment, it became necessary to hang them. To this day the question of their complete guilt is socially discussed.

How shall we characterize such a deed? Says Blackstone, "If anyone that hath commission of martial authority doth, in time of peace, hang, or otherwise execute any man by color of martial law, this is murder; for it is against Magna Charta."[1]

Magna Charta! We moderns, who may be landsmen, may justly boast of civil immunities not possessed by our forefathers; but our remoter forefathers who happened to be mariners may straighten themselves even in their ashes to think that their lawgivers were wiser and more humane in their generation than our lawgivers in ours. Compare the sea-laws of our Navy with the Roman and Rhodian ocean ordinances; compare them with the "Consulate of the Sea"; compare them with the Laws of the Hanse Towns; compare them with the ancient Wisbury laws. In the last we find that they were ocean democrats in those days. "If he strikes, he ought to receive blow for blow." Thus speak out the Wisbury laws concerning a Gothland sea-captain.

In final reference to all that has been said in previous chapters touching the severity and unusualness of the laws of the American Navy, and the large authority vested in its commanding officers, be it here observed, that White-Jacket is not unaware of the fact, that the responsibility of an officer commanding at sea—whether in the merchant service or the national marine—is unparalleled by that of any other relation in which man may stand to man. Nor is he unmindful that both wisdom and humanity dictate that, from the peculiarity of his position, a sea-officer in command should be clothed with a degree of authority and discretion inadmissible in any master ashore. But, at the same time, these principles—recognized by all writers on maritime law—have undoubtedly

1. *Commentaries,* b. i., c. xiii.

furnished warrant for clothing modern sea-commanders and naval courts-martial with powers which exceed the due limits of reason and necessity. Nor is this the only instance where right and salutary principles, in themselves almost self-evident and infallible, have been advanced in justification of things, which in themselves are just as self-evidently wrong and pernicious.

Be it here, once and for all, understood, that no sentimental and theoretic love for the common sailor; no romantic belief in that peculiar noble-heartedness and exaggerated generosity of disposition fictitiously imputed to him in novels; and no prevailing desire to gain the reputation of being his friend, have actuated me in anything I have said, in any part of this work, touching the gross oppression under which I know that the sailors suffers. Indifferent as to who may be the parties concerned, I but desire to see wrong things righted, and equal justice administered to all.

Nor, as has been elsewhere hinted, is the general ignorance or depravity of any race of men to be alleged as an apology for tyranny over them. On the contrary, it cannot admit of a reasonable doubt, in any unbiased mind conversant with the interior life of a man-of-war, that most of the sailor iniquities practiced therein are indirectly to be ascribed to the morally debasing effects of the unjust, despotic, and degrading laws under which the man-of-war's-man lives.

Chapter LXXIII

Night and Day Gambling in a Man-of-War

Mention has been made that the game of drafts, or checkers, was permitted to be played on board the *Neversink*. At the present time, while there was little or no shipwork to be done, and all hands, in high spirits, were sailing homeward over the warm smooth sea of the tropics; so numerous became the players, scattered about the decks, that our First Lieutenant used ironically to say that it was a pity they were not tesselated with squares of white and black marble, for the express benefit and convenience of the players. Had this gentleman had his way, our checker-boards would very soon have been pitched out of the ports. But the Captain—usually lenient in some things—permitted them, and so Mr. Bridewell was fain to hold his peace.

But, although this one game was allowable in the frigate, all kinds of gambling were strictly interdicted, under the penalty of the gangway; nor were cards or dice tolerated in any way whatever. This regulation was indispensable, for, of all human beings, man-of-war's-men are perhaps the most inclined to gambling. The reason must be obvious to anyone who reflects upon their condition on shipboard. And gambling—the most mischievous of vices anywhere—in a man-of-war operates still more perniciously than on shore. But quite as often as the law against smuggling spirits is transgressed by the unscrupulous sailors, the statutes against cards and dice are evaded.

Sable night, which, since the beginning of the world, has winked and looked on at so many deeds of iniquity—night is the time usually selected for their operations by man-of-war gamblers. The place pitched upon is generally the berth-deck, where the hammocks are swung, and which is lighted so stintedly as not to disturb the sleeping seamen with any obtruding glare. In so spacious an area the two lanterns swinging from the stanchions diffuse a subdued illumination, like a night-taper in the apartment of some invalid. Owing to their position, also, these lanterns are far from shedding an impartial light, however dim, but fling long angular rays here and there, like burglar's dark-lanterns in the fifty-acre vaults of the West India Docks on the Thames.

It may well be imagined, therefore, how well adapted is this mysterious and subterranean Hall of Eblis to the clandestine proceedings of gamblers, especially as the hammocks not only hang thickly, but many of them swing very low, within two feet of the floor, thus forming innumerable little canvas glens, grottoes, nooks, corners, and crannies, where a good deal of wickedness may be practiced by the wary with considerable impunity.

Now the master-at-arms, assisted by his mates, the ship's corporals, reigns supreme in these bowels of the ship. Throughout the night these policemen relieve each other at standing guard over the premises; and, except when the watches are called, they sit in the midst of a profound silence, only invaded by trumpeters' snores, or the ramblings of some old sheet-anchor-man in his sleep.

The two ship's corporals went among the sailors by the names of Leggs and Pounce; Pounce had been a policeman, it was said, in Liverpool; Leggs, a turnkey attached to "The Tombs" in New York. Hence their education eminently fitted them for their stations; and Bland, the master-at-arms, ravished with their dexterity in prying out offenders, used to call them his two right hands.

When man-of-war's-men desire to gamble, they appoint the hour, and select some certain corner, in some certain shadow, behind some certain hammock. They then contribute a small sum toward a joint fund, to be invested in a bribe for some argus-eyed shipmate, who shall play the part of a spy upon the master-at-arms and corporals while the gaming is in progress. In nine cases out of ten these arrangements are so cunning and comprehensive, that the gamblers, eluding all vigilance, conclude their game unmolested. But now and then, seduced into unwariness, or perhaps, from parsimony, being unwilling to employ the services of a spy, they are suddenly lighted upon by the constables, remorselessly collared, and dragged into the *brig*, there to await a dozen lashes in the morning.

Several times at midnight I have been startled out of a sound sleep by a sudden, violent rush under my hammock, caused by the abrupt breaking up of some nest of gamblers, who have scattered in all directions, brushing under the tiers of swinging pallets, and setting them all in a rocking commotion.

It is, however, while laying in port that gambling most thrives in a man-of-war. Then the men frequently practice their dark deeds in the light of the day, and the additional guards which, at such times, they deem indispensable, are not unworthy of note. More especially, their extra precautions in engaging the services of several spies, necessitate a considerable expenditure, so that, in port, the diversion of gambling rises to the dignity of a nabob luxury.

During the day the master-at-arms and his corporals are continually prowling about on all three decks, eager to spy out iniquities. At one time, for example, you see Leggs switching his magisterial rattan, and lurking round the fore-mast on the spar-deck; the next moment, perhaps, he is three decks down, out of sight, prowling among the cable-tiers. Just so with his master, and Pounce his coadjutor; they are here, there, and everywhere, seemingly gifted with ubiquity.

In order successfully to carry on their proceedings by day, the gamblers must see to it that each of these constables is relentlessly dogged wherever he goes; so that, in case of his approach toward the spot where themselves are engaged, they may be warned of the fact in time to make good their escape. Accordingly, light and active scouts are selected to follow the constable about. From their youthful alertness and activity, the boys of the mizzen-top are generally chosen for this purpose.

But this is not all. Onboard of most men-of-war there is a set of sly, knavish foxes among the crew, destitute of every principle of honor, and on a par with Irish informers. In man-of-war parlance, they come under the denomination of *fancy-men* and *white-mice*. They are called *fancy-men*, because, from their zeal in craftily reporting offenders, they are presumed to be regarded with high favor by some of the officers. Though it is seldom that these informers can be certainly individualized, so secret and subtle are they in laying their information, yet certain of the crew, and especially certain of the marines, are invariably suspected to be *fancy-men* and *white-mice*, and are accordingly more or less hated by their comrades.

Now, in addition to having an eye on the master-at-arms and his aids, the day-gamblers must see to it, that every person suspected of being a *white-mouse* or *fancy-man*, is like-wise dogged wherever he goes. Additional scouts are retained constantly to snuff at their trail. But the mysteries of man-of-war vice are wonderful; and it is now to be recorded, that, from long habit and observation, and familiarity with the *guardo moves* and *maneuvers* of a frigate, the master-at-arms and his aids can almost invariably tell when any gambling is going on by day; though, in the crowded vessel, abounding in decks, tops, dark places, and outlandish corners of all sorts, they may not be able to pounce upon the identical spot where the gamblers are hidden.

During the period that Bland was suspended from his office as master-at-arms, a person who, among the sailors, went by the name of Sneak, having been long suspected to have been a *white-mouse,* was put in Bland's place. He proved a hangdog, sidelong catch-thief, but gifted with a marvelous perseverance in ferreting out culprits; following in their track like an inevitable Cuba blood-hound, with his noiseless nose. When disconcerted, however, you sometimes heard his bay.

"The muffled dice are somewhere around," Sneak would say to his aids; "there are them three chaps, there, been dogging me about for the last half-hour. I say, Pounce, has anyone been scouting around *you* this morning?"

"Four on 'em," says Pounce. "I know'd it; I know'd the muffled dice was rattlin'!"

"Leggs!" says the master-at-arms to his other aid, "Leggs, how is it with *you*—any spies?"

"Ten on 'em," says Leggs. "There's one on 'em now—that fellow stitching a hat."

"Halloo, you, sir!" cried the master-at-arms, "top your boom and sail large, now. If I see you about me again, I'll have you up to the mast."

"What am I a-doin' now?" says the hat-stitcher, with a face as long as a rope-walk. "Can't a feller be workin' here, without being 'spected of Tom Coxe's traverse, up one ladder and down t'other?"

"Oh, I know the moves, sir; I have been on board a *guardo.* Top your boom, I say, and be off, or I'll have you hauled up and riveted in a clinch—both fore-tacks over the main-yard, and no bloody knife to cut the seizing. Sheer! or I'll pitch into you like a shin of beef into a beggar's wallet."

It is often observable, that, in vessels of all kinds, the men who talk the most sailor lingo are the least sailor-like in reality. You may sometimes hear even marines jerk out more salt phrases than the Captain of the Forecastle himself. On the other hand, when not actively engaged in his vocation, you would take the best specimen of a seaman for a landsman. When you see a fellow yawning about the docks like a homeward-bound Indiaman, a long Commodore's pennant of black ribbon flying from his mast-head, and fetching up at a grog-shop with a slew of his hull, as if an Admiral were coming alongside a three-decker in his barge; you may put that man down for what man-of-war's-men call a *damn-my-eyes-tar,* that is, a humbug. And many damn-my-eyes humbugs there are in this man-of-war world of ours.

Chapter LXXIV

THE MAIN-TOP AT NIGHT

THE WHOLE OF OUR RUN FROM RIO TO THE LINE WAS ONE DELIGHTFUL YACHTING, SO FAR AS FINE weather and the ship's sailing were concerned. It was especially pleasant when our quarter-watch lounged in the main-top, diverting ourselves in many agreeable ways. Removed from the immediate presence of the officers, we there harmlessly enjoyed ourselves, more than in any other part of the ship. By day, many of us were very industrious, making hats or mending our clothes. But by night we became more romantically inclined.

Often Jack Chase, an enthusiastic admirer of sea-scenery, would direct our attention to the moonlight on the waves, by fine snatches from his catalogue of poets. I shall never forget the lyric air with which, one morning, at dawn of day, when all the East was flushed with red and gold, he stood leaning against the top-mast shrouds, and stretching his bold hand over the sea, exclaimed, "Here comes Aurora: top-mates, see!" And, in a liquid, long-lingering tone, he recited the lines,

With gentle hand, as seeming oft to pause,
The purple curtains of the morn she draws.

"Commodore Camoens, White-Jacket.—But bear a hand there; we must rig out that stun'-sail boom—the wind is shifting."

From our lofty perch, of a moonlight night, the frigate itself was a glorious sight. She was going large before the wind, her stun'-sails set on both sides, so that the canvas on the main-mast and fore-mast presented the appearance of majestic, tapering pyramids, more than a hundred feet broad at the base, and terminating in the clouds with the light copestone of the royals. That immense area of snow-white canvas sliding along the sea was indeed a magnificent spectacle. The three shrouded masts looked like the apparitions of three gigantic Turkish Emirs striding over the ocean.

Nor, at times, was the sound of music wanting, to augment the poetry of the scene. The whole band would be assembled on the poop, regaling the officers, and incidentally ourselves, with their fine old airs. To these, some of us would occasionally dance in the *top,* which was almost as large as an ordinary sized parlor. When the instrumental melody of the band was not to be had, our nightingales mustered their voices, and gave us a song.

Upon these occasions Jack Chase was often called out, and regaled us, in his own free and noble style, with the *Spanish Ladies*— a favorite thing with British man-of-war's-men—and many other salt-sea ballads and ditties, including,

Sir Patrick Spens was the best sailor
That ever sailed the sea.

also,

And three times around spun our gallant ship;
Three times around spun she;
Three times around spun our gallant ship,
And she went to the bottom of the sea—
The sea, the sea, the sea,
And she went to the bottom of the sea!

These songs would be varied by sundry *yarns* and *twisters* of the top-men. And it was at these times that I always endeavored to draw out the oldest Tritons into narratives of the war-service they had seen. There were but few of them, it is true, who had been in action; but that only made their narratives the more valuable.

There was an old negro, who went by the name of Tawney, a sheet-anchor-man, whom we often invited into our top of tranquil nights, to hear him discourse. He was a staid and sober sea-man, very intelligent, with a fine, frank bearing, one of the best men in the ship, and held in high estimation by everyone.

It seems that, during the last war between England and America, he had, with several others, been "impressed" upon the high seas, out of a New England merchantman. The ship that impressed him was an English frigate, the *Macedonian,* afterward taken by the *Neversink,* the ship in which we were sailing.

It was the holy Sabbath, according to Tawney, and, as the Briton bore down on the American—her men at their quarters—Tawney and his countrymen, who happened to be stationed at the quarter-deck battery, respectfully accosted the captain—an old man by the name of Cardan—as he passed them, in his rapid promenade, his spy-glass under his arm. Again they assured him that they were not Englishmen, and that it was a most bitter thing to lift their hands against the flag of that country which harbored the mothers that bore them. They conjured him to release them from their guns, and allow them to remain neutral during the conflict. But when a ship of any nation is running into action, it is no time for argument, small time for justice, and not much time for humanity. Snatching a pistol from the belt of a boarder standing by, the Captain leveled it at the heads of the three sailors, and commanded them instantly to their quarters, under penalty of being shot on the spot. So, side by side with his country's foes, Tawney and his companions toiled at the guns, and fought out the fight to the last; with the exception of one of them, who was killed at his post by one of his own country's balls.

At length, having lost her fore and main-top-masts, and her mizzen-mast having been shot away to the deck, and her fore-yard lying in two pieces on her shattered forecastle, and in a hundred places having been *hulled* with round shot, the English frigate was reduced to the last extremity. Captain Cardan ordered his signal quarter-master to strike the flag.

Tawney was one of those who, at last, helped pull him on board the *Neversink.* As he touched the deck, Cardan saluted Decatur, the hostile commander, and offered his sword; but it was courteously declined. Perhaps the victor remembered the dinner parties that he and the Englishman had enjoyed together in Norfolk, just previous to the breaking out of hostilities—and while both were in command of the very frigates now crippled on the sea. The *Macedonian,* it seems, had gone into Norfolk with dispatches. *Then* they had laughed and joked over their wine, and a wager of a beaver hat was said to have been made between them upon the event of the hostile meeting of their ships.

Gazing upon the heavy batteries before him, Cardan said to Decatur, "This is a seventy-four, not a frigate; no wonder the day is yours!"

This remark was founded upon the *Neversink*'s superiority in guns. The *Neversink*'s main-deck-batteries then consisted, as now, of twenty-four-pounders; the Macedonian's of only eighteens. In all, the *Neversink* numbered fifty-four guns and four hundred and fifty men; the *Macedonian,* forty-nine guns and three hundred men; a very great disparity, which, united to the other circumstances of this action, deprives the victory of all claims to glory beyond those that might be set up by a river-horse getting the better of a seal.

But if Tawney spoke truth—and he was a truth-telling man—this fact seemed counterbalanced by a circumstance he related. When the guns of the Englishman were examined, after the engagement, in more than one instance the wad was found rammed against the cartridge, without intercepting the ball. And though, in a frantic sea-fight, such a thing might be imputed to hurry and remissness, yet Tawney, a stickler for his tribe, always ascribed it to quite a different and less honorable cause. But, even granting the cause he assigned to have been the true one, it does not involve anything inimical to the general valor displayed by the British crew. Yet, from all that may be learned from candid persons who have been in sea-fights, there can be but little doubt that on board of all ships, of whatever nation, in time of action, no very small number of the men are exceedingly nervous, to say the least, at the guns; ramming and sponging at a venture. And what special patriotic interest could an impressed man, for instance, take in a fight, into which he had been dragged from the arms of his wife? Or is it to be wondered at that impressed English seamen have not scrupled, in time of war, to cripple the arm that has enslaved them?

During the same general war which prevailed at and previous to the period of the frigate-action here spoken of, a British flag-officer, in writing to the Admiralty, said, "Everything appears to be quiet in the fleet; but, in preparing for battle last week, several of the guns in the after part of the ship were found to be spiked"; that is to say, rendered useless. Who had spiked them? The dissatisfied seamen. Is it altogether improbable, then, that the guns to which Tawney referred were manned by men who purposely refrained from making them tell on the foe; that, in this one action, the victory America gained was partly won for her by the sulky insubordination of the enemy himself?

During this same period of general war, it was frequently the case that the guns of English armed ships were found in the mornings with their breechings cut over night. This maiming of the guns, and for the time incapacitating them, was only to be imputed to that secret spirit of hatred to the service which induced the spiking above referred to. But even in cases where no deep-seated dissatisfaction was presumed to prevail among the crew, and where a seaman, in time of action, impelled by pure fear, "shirked from his gun"; it seems but flying in the face of Him who made such a seaman what he constitutionally was, to sew *coward* upon his back, and degrade and agonize the already trembling wretch in numberless other ways. Nor seems it a practice warranted by the Sermon on the Mount, for the officer of a battery, in time of battle, to stand over the men with his drawn sword (as was done in the *Macedonian*), and run through on the spot the first seaman who showed a semblance of fear. Tawney told me that he distinctly heard this order given by the English Captain to his officers of divisions. Were the secret history of all sea-fights written, the laurels of sea-heroes would turn to ashes on their brows.

And how nationally disgraceful, in every conceivable point of view, is the IV of our American *Articles of War*: "If any person in the Navy shall pusillanimously cry for quarter, he shall suffer death." Thus, with death before his face from the foe, and death behind his back from his countrymen, the best valor of a man-of-war's-man can never assume the merit of a noble spontaneousness. In this, as in every other case, the *Articles of War* hold out no reward for good conduct, but only compel the sailor to fight, like a hired murderer, for his pay, by digging his grave before his eyes if he hesitates.

But this Article IV is open to still graver objections. Courage is the most common and vulgar of the virtues; the only one shared with us by the beasts of the field; the one most apt, by excess, to run into viciousness. And since Nature generally takes away with one hand to counter-balance her gifts with the other, excessive animal courage, in many cases, only finds room in a character vacated of loftier things. But in a naval officer, animal courage is exalted to the loftiest merit, and often procures him a distinguished command.

Hence, if some brainless bravo be Captain of a frigate in action, he may fight her against invincible odds, and seek to crown himself with the glory of the shambles, by permitting his hopeless crew to be butchered before his eyes, while at the same time that crew must consent to be slaughtered by the foe, under penalty of being murdered by the law. Look at the engagement between the American frigate *Essex* with the two English cruisers, the *Phœbe* and *Cherub*, off the Bay of Valparaiso, during the late war. It is admitted on all hands that the American Captain continued to fight his crippled ship against a greatly superior force; and when, at last, it became physically impossible that he could ever be otherwise than vanquished in the end; and when, from peculiarly unfortunate circumstances, his men merely stood up to their nearly useless batteries to be dismembered and blown to pieces by the incessant fire of the enemy's long guns. Nor, by thus continuing to fight, did this American frigate, one iota, promote the true interests of her country. I seek not to underrate any reputation which the American Captain may have gained by this battle. He was a brave man; *that* no sailor will deny. But the whole world is made up of brave men. Yet I would not be at all understood as impugning his special good name. Nevertheless, it is not to be doubted, that if there were any common-sense sailors at the guns of the *Essex*, however valiant they may have been, those common-sense sailors must have greatly preferred to strike their flag, when they saw the day was fairly lost, than postpone that inevitable act till there were few American arms left to assist in hauling it down. Yet had these men, under these circumstances, "pusillanimously cried for quarter," by the IV *Article of War* they might have been legally hung.

According to the negro, Tawney, when the Captain of the *Macedonian*—seeing that the *Neversink* had his vessel completely in her power—gave the word to strike the flag, one of his officers, a man hated by the seamen for his tyranny, howled out the most terrific remonstrances, swearing that, for his part, he would not give up, but was for sinking the *Macedonian* alongside the enemy. Had he been Captain, doubtless he would have done so; thereby gaining the name of a hero in this world;—but what would they have called him in the next?

But as the whole matter of war is a thing that smites common-sense and Christianity in the face; so everything connected with it is utterly foolish, unchristian, barbarous, brutal, and savoring of the Fiji Islands, cannibalism, saltpeter, and the devil.

It is generally the case in a man-of-war when she strikes her flag that all discipline is at an end, and the men for a time are ungovernable. This was so on board of the English frigate. The spirit-room was broken open, and buckets of grog were passed along the decks, where many of the wounded were lying between the guns. These mariners seized the buckets, and, spite of all remonstrances, gulped down the burning spirits, till, as Tawney said, the blood suddenly spirted out of their wounds, and they fell dead to the deck.

The negro had many more stories to tell of this fight; and frequently he would escort me along our main-deck batteries—still mounting the same guns used in the battle—pointing out their ineffaceable indentations and scars. Coated over with the accumulated paint of more than thirty years, they were almost invisible to a casual eye; but Tawney knew them all by heart; for he had returned home in the *Neversink*, and had beheld these scars shortly after the engagement.

One afternoon, I was walking with him along the gun-deck, when he paused abreast of the main-mast. "This part of the ship," said he, "we called the *slaughter-house* on board the *Macedonian*. Here the men fell, five and six at a time. An enemy always directs its shot here, in order to hurl over the mast, if possible. The beams and carlines overhead in the *Macedonian slaughter-house* were spattered with blood and brains. About the hatchways it looked like a butcher's stall; bits of human flesh sticking in the ring-bolts. A pig that ran about the decks escaped unharmed, but his hide was so clotted with blood, from rooting among the pools of gore, that when the ship struck the sailors hove the animal overboard, swearing that it would be rank cannibalism to eat him."

Another quadruped, a goat, lost its forelegs in this fight.

The sailors who were killed—according to the usual custom—were ordered to be thrown overboard as soon as they fell; no doubt, as the negro said, that the sight of so many corpses lying around might not appall the survivors at the guns. Among other instances, he related the following. A shot entering one of the port-holes, dashed dead two-thirds of a gun's crew. The captain of the next gun, dropping his lock-string, which he had just pulled, turned over the heap of bodies to see who they were; when, perceiving an old mess-mate, who had sailed with him in many cruises, he burst into tears, and, taking the corpse up in his arms, and going with it to the side, held it over the water a moment, and eyeing it, cried, "Oh God! Tom!"— "D—n your prayers over that thing! overboard with it, and down to your gun!" roared a wounded Lieutenant. The order was obeyed, and the heart-stricken sailor returned to his post.

Tawney's recitals were enough to snap this man-of-war world's sword in its scabbard. And thinking of all the cruel carnal glory wrought out by naval heroes in scenes like these, I asked myself whether, indeed, that was a glorious coffin in which Lord Nelson was entombed—a coffin presented to him, during life, by Captain Hallowell; it had been dug out of the main-mast of the French line-of-battle ship *L'Orient*, which, burning up with British fire, destroyed hundreds of Frenchmen at the battle of the Nile.

Peace to Lord Nelson where he sleeps in his moldering mast! but rather would I be urned in the trunk of some green tree, and even in death have the vital sap circulating round me, giving of my dead body to the living foliage that shaded my peaceful tomb.

Chapter LXXV

"SINK, BURN, AND DESTROY"

Printed Admiralty orders in time of war

AMONG INNUMERABLE "YARNS AND TWISTERS" REELED OFF IN OUR MAIN-TOP DURING OUR pleasant run to the North, none could match those of Jack Chase, our captain.

Never was there better company than ever-glorious Jack. The things which most men only read of, or dream about, he had seen and experienced. He had been a dashing smuggler in his day, and could tell of a long nine-pounder rammed home with wads of French silks; of cartridges stuffed with the finest gunpowder tea; of cannister-shot full of West India sweetmeats; of sailor frocks and trousers, quilted inside with costly laces; and table legs, hollow as musket barrels, compactly stowed with rare drugs and spices. He could tell of a wicked widow, too—a beautiful receiver of smuggled goods upon the English coast—who smiled so sweetly upon the smugglers when they sold her silks and laces, cheap as tape and ginghams. She called them gallant fellows, hearts of game; and bade them bring her more.

He could tell of desperate fights with his British majesty's cutters, in midnight coves upon a stormy coast; of the capture of a reckless band, and their being drafted on board a man-of-war; of their swearing that their chief was slain; of a writ of habeas corpus sent on board for one of them for a debt—a reserved and handsome man—and his going ashore, strongly suspected of being the slaughtered captain, and this a successful scheme for his escape.

But more than all, Jack could tell of the battle of Navarino, for he had been a captain of one of the main-deck guns on board Admiral Codrington's flag-ship, the *Asia*. Were mine the style of stout old Chapman's Homer, even then I would scarce venture to give noble Jack's own version of this fight, wherein, on the 20th of October, A.D. 1827, thirty-two sail of Englishmen, Frenchmen, and Russians, attacked and vanquished in the *Levant* an Ottoman fleet of three ships-of-the line, twenty-five frigates, and a swarm of fire ships and hornet craft.

"We bayed to be at them," said Jack; "and when we *did* open fire, we were like dolphin among the flying-fish. 'Every man take his bird' was the cry, when we trained our guns. And those guns all smoked like rows of Dutch pipe-bowls, my hearties! My gun's crew carried small flags in their bosoms, to nail to the mast in case the ship's colors were shot away. Stripped to the waistbands, we fought like skinned tigers, and bowled down the Turkish frigates like nine-pins. Among their shrouds—swarming thick with small-arm men, like flights of pigeons lighted on pine-trees—our marines sent their leaden pease and goose-berries, like a shower of hail-stones in Labrador. It was a stormy time, my hearties! The blasted Turks pitched into the old *Asia*'s hull a whole quarry of marble shot, each ball one hundred and fifty pounds. They knocked three port-holes into one. But we gave them better than they sent. 'Up and at them, my bull-dog!' said I, patting my gun on the breech; 'tear open hatchways in their Moslem sides!' White-Jacket, my lad, you ought to have been there. The bay was covered with masts and yards, as I have seen a raft of snags in the Arkansas River. Showers of burned rice and olives from the exploding foe fell upon us like manna in the wilderness. *'Allah! Allah! Mohammed! Mohammed!'* split the air; some cried it out from the Turkish port-holes; others shrieked it forth from the drowning waters, their top-knots floating on their shaven skulls, like black snakes on half-tide rocks. By those top-knots they believed that their Prophet would drag them up to Paradise, but they sank fifty fathoms, my hearties, to the bottom of the bay. 'Ain't the bloody 'Hometons going to strike yet?' cried my first loader, a Guernsey man, thrusting his neck out of the port-hole, and looking at the Turkish line-of-battle-ship nearby.

That instant his head blew by me like a bursting Paixhan shot, and the flag of Neb Knowles himself was hauled down for ever. We dragged his hull to one side, and avenged him with the cooper's anvil, which, endways, we rammed home; a mess-mate shoved in the dead man's bloody Scotch cap for the wad, and sent it flying into the line-of-battle ship. By the god of war! boys, we hardly left enough of that craft to boil a pot of water with. It was a hard day's work—a sad day's work, my hearties. That night, when all was over, I slept sound enough, with a box of cannister shot for my pillow! But you ought to have seen the boat-load of Turkish flags one of our captains carried home; he swore to dress his father's orchard in colors with them, just as our spars are dressed for a gala day."

"Though you tormented the Turks at Navarino, noble Jack, yet you came off yourself with only the loss of a splinter, it seems," said a top-man, glancing at our captain's maimed hand.

"Yes; but I and one of the Lieutenants had a narrower escape than that. A shot struck the side of my port-hole, and sent the splinters right and left. One took off my hat rim clean to my brow; another *razed* the Lieutenant's left boot, by slicing off the heel; a third shot killed my powder-monkey without touching him."

"How, Jack?"

"It *whizzed* the poor babe dead. He was seated on a *cheese of wads* at the time, and after the dust of the powdered bulwarks had blown away, I noticed he yet sat still, his eyes wide open. *'My little hero!'* cried I, and I clapped him on the back; but he fell on his face at my feet. I touched his heart, and found he was dead. There was not a little finger mark on him."

Silence now fell upon the listeners for a time, broken at last by the Second Captain of the Top.

"Noble Jack, I know you never brag, but tell us what you did yourself that day?"

"Why, my hearties, I did not do quite as much as my gun. But I flatter myself it was that gun that brought clown the Turkish Admiral's main-mast; and the stump left wasn't long enough to make a wooden leg for Lord Nelson."

"How? but I thought, by the way you pull a lock-string on board here, and look along the sight, that you can steer a shot about right—hey, Jack?"

"It was the Admiral of the fleet—God Almighty—who directed the shot that dismasted the Turkish Admiral," said Jack; "I only pointed the gun."

"But how did you feel, Jack, when the musket-ball carried away one of your hooks there?"

"Feel! only a finger the lighter. I have seven more left, besides thumbs; and they did good service, too, in the torn rigging the day after the fight; for you must know, my hearties, that the hardest work comes after the guns are run in. Three days I helped work, with one hand, in the rigging, in the same trousers that I wore in the action; the blood had dried and stiffened; they looked like glazed red morocco."

Now, this Jack Chase had a heart in him like a mastodon's. I have seen him weep when a man has been flogged at the gangway; yet, in relating the story of the Battle of Navarino, he plainly showed that he held the God of the blessed Bible to have been the British Commodore in the *Levant,* on the bloody 20th of October, A.D. 1827. And thus it would seem that war almost makes blasphemers of the best of men, and brings them all down to the Fiji standard of humanity. Some man-of-war's-men have confessed to me, that as a battle has raged more and more, their hearts have hardened in infernal harmony; and, like their own guns, they have fought without a thought.

Soldier or sailor, the fighting man is but a fiend; and the staff and body-guard of the Devil musters many a baton. But war at times is inevitable. Must the national honor be trampled under foot by an insolent foe?

Say on, say on; but know you this, and lay it to heart, war-voting Bench of Bishops, that He on whom we believe *himself* has enjoined us to turn the left cheek if the right be smitten. Never mind what follows. That passage you can not expunge from the Bible; that passage is as binding upon us as any other; that passage embodies the soul and substance of the Christian faith; without it, Christianity were like any other faith. And that passage will yet, by the blessing of God, turn the world. But in some things we must turn Quakers first.

But though unlike most scenes of carnage, which have proved useless murders of men, Admiral Codrington's victory undoubtedly achieved the emancipation of Greece, and terminated the Turkish atrocities in that tomahawked state, yet who shall lift his hand and swear that a Divine Providence led the van of the combined fleets of England, France, and Russia at the battle of Navarino? For if this be so, then it led the van against the Church's own elect—the persecuted Waldenses in Switzerland—and kindled the Smithfield fires in bloody Mary's time.

But all events are mixed in a fusion indistinguishable. What we call Fate is even, heartless, and impartial; not a fiend to kindle bigot flames, nor a philanthropist to espouse the cause of Greece. We may fret, fume, and fight; but the thing called Fate everlastingly sustains an armed neutrality.

Yet though all this be so, nevertheless, in our own hearts, we mold the whole world's hereafters; and in our own hearts we fashion our own gods. Each mortal casts his vote for whom he will to rule the worlds; I have a voice that helps to shape eternity; and my volitions stir the orbits of the furthest suns. In two senses, we are precisely what we worship. Ourselves are Fate.

Chapter LXXVI

THE CHAINS

WHEN WEARIED WITH THE TUMULT AND OCCASIONAL CONTENTION OF THE GUN-DECK OF OUR frigate, I have often retreated to a port-hole, and calmed myself down by gazing broad off upon a placid sea. After the battle-din of the last two chapters, let us now do the like, and, in the sequestered fore-chains of the *Neversink*, tranquilize ourselves, if we may.

Notwithstanding the domestic communism to which the seamen in a man-of-war are condemned, and the publicity in which actions the most diffident and retiring in their nature must be performed, there is yet an odd corner or two where you may sometimes steal away, and, for a few moments, almost be private.

Chief among these places is the *chains*, to which I would sometimes hie during our pleasant homeward-bound glide over those pensive tropical latitudes. After hearing my fill of the wild yarns of our top, here would I recline—if not disturbed—serenely concocting information into wisdom.

The chains designates the small platform outside of the hull, at the base of the large shrouds leading down from the three mast-heads to the bulwarks. At present they seem to be getting out of vogue among merchant-vessels, along with the fine, old-fashioned quarter-galleries, little turret-like appurtenances, which, in the days of the old Admirals, set off the angles of an armed ship's stern. Here a naval officer might lounge away an hour after action, smoking a cigar, to drive out of his whiskers the villainous smoke of the gun-powder. The picturesque, delightful stern-gallery, also, a broad balcony overhanging the sea, and entered from the Captain's cabin, much as you might enter a bower from a lady's chamber; this charming balcony, where, sailing over summer seas in the days of *Neversink*, the old Peruvian viceroys, the Spanish cavalier Mendanna, of Lima, made love to the Lady Isabella, as they voyaged in quest of the Solomon Islands, the fabulous Ophir, the Grand Cyclades; and the Lady Isabella, at sunset, blushed like the Orient, and gazed down to the gold-fish and silver-hued flying-fish, that wove the woof and warp of their wakes in bright, scaly tartans and plaids underneath where the Lady reclined; this charming balcony—exquisite retreat—has been cut away by

Vandalic innovations. Ay, that claw-footed old gallery is no longer in fashion; in Commodore's eyes, is no longer genteel.

Out on all furniture fashions but those that are past! Give me my grandfather's old arm-chair, planted upon four carved frogs, as the Hindoos fabled the world to be supported upon four tortoises; give me his cane, with the gold-loaded top—a cane that, like the musket of General Washington's father and the broadsword of William Wallace, would break down the back of the switch-carrying dandies of these spindle-shank days; give me his broad-breasted vest, coming bravely down over the hips, and furnished with two strong-boxes of pockets to keep guineas in; toss this toppling cylinder of a beaver overboard, and give me my grandfather's gallant, gable-ended, cocked hat.

But though the quarter-galleries and the stern-gallery of a man-of-war are departed, yet the *chains* still linger; nor can there be imagined a more agreeable retreat. The huge blocks and lanyards forming the pedestals of the shrouds divide the chains into numerous little chapels, alcoves, niches, and altars, where you lazily lounge—outside of the ship, though on board. But there are plenty to divide a good thing with you in this man-of-war world. Often, when snugly seated in one of these little alcoves, gazing off to the horizon, and thinking of Cathay, I have been startled from my repose by some old quarter-gunner, who, having newly painted a parcel of match-tubs, wanted to set them to dry.

At other times, one of the tattooing artists would crawl over the bulwarks, followed by his sitter; and then a bare arm or leg would be extended, and the disagreeable business of "*pricking*" commence, right under my eyes; or an irruption of tars, with ditty-bags or sea-reticules, and piles of old trousers to mend, would break in upon my seclusion, and, forming a sewing-circle, drive me off with their chatter.

But once—it was a Sunday afternoon—I was pleasantly reclining in a particularly shady and secluded little niche between two lanyards, when I heard a low, supplicating voice. Peeping through the narrow space between the ropes, I perceived an aged seaman on his knees, his face turned seaward, with closed eyes, buried in prayer. Softly rising, I stole through a port-hole, and left the venerable worshipper alone.

He was a sheet-anchor-man, an earnest Baptist, and was well known, in his own part of the ship, to be constant in his solitary devotions in the *chains*. He reminded me of St. Anthony going out into the wilderness to pray.

This man was captain of the starboard bow-chaser, one of the two long twenty-four-pounders on the forecastle. In time of action, the command of that iron Thalaba the Destroyer would devolve upon *him*. It would be his business to "train" it properly; to see it well loaded; the grape and cannister rammed home; also, to "prick the cartridge," "take the sight," and give the word for the match-man to apply his wand; bidding a sudden hell to flash forth from the muzzle, in wide combustion and death.

Now, this captain of the bow-chaser was an upright old man, a sincere, humble believer, and he but earned his bread in being captain of that gun; but how, with those hands of his begrimed with powder, could he break that *other* and most peaceful and penitent bread of the Supper? though in that hallowed sacrament, it seemed, he had often partaken ashore. The omission of this rite in a man-of-war—though there is a chaplain to preside over it, and at least a few communicants to partake—must be ascribed to a sense of religious propriety, in the last degree to be commended.

Ah! the best righteousness of our man-of-war world seems but an unrealized ideal, after all; and those maxims which, in the hope of bringing about a Millennium, we busily teach to the heathen, we Christians ourselves disregard. In view of the whole present social frame-work of our world, so ill adapted to the practical adoption of the meekness of Christianity, there seems almost some ground for the thought, that although our blessed Savior was full of the wisdom of heaven, yet his gospel seems lacking in the practical wisdom of earth—in a due appreciation of the necessities of nations at times demanding bloody massacres and wars; in a proper estimation of the value of rank, title, and money. But all this only the more crowns the divine consistency of Jesus; since Burnet and the best theologians demonstrate, that his nature was not merely human—was not that of a mere man of the world.

Chapter LXXVII

The Hospital in a Man-of-War

After running with a fine steady breeze up to the line, it fell calm, and there we lay, three days enchanted on the sea. We were a most puissant man-of-war, no doubt, with our five hundred men, Commodore and Captain, backed by our long batteries of thirty-two and twenty-four pounders; yet, for all that, there we lay rocking, helpless as an infant in the cradle. Had it only been a gale instead of a calm, gladly would we have charged upon it with our gallant bowsprit, as with a stout lance in rest; but, as with man-kind, this serene, passive foe—unresisting and irresistible—lived it out, unconquered to the last.

All these three days the heat was excessive; the sun drew the tar from the seams of the ship; the awnings were spread fore and aft; the decks were kept constantly sprinkled with water. It was during this period that a sad event occurred, though not an unusual one on shipboard. But in order to prepare for its narration, some account of a part of the ship called the "*sick-bay*" must needs be presented.

The "*sick-bay*" is that part of a man-of-war where the invalid seamen are placed; in many respects it answers to a public hospital ashore. As with most frigates, the sick-bay of the *Neversink* was on the berth-deck—the third deck from above. It was in the extreme forward part of that deck, embracing the triangular area in the bows of the ship. It was, therefore, a subterranean vault, into which scarce a ray of heaven's glad light ever penetrated, even at noon.

In a sea-going frigate that has all her armament and stores on board, the floor of the berth-deck is partly below the surface of the water. But in a smooth harbor, some circulation of air is maintained by opening large auger-holes in the upper portion of the sides, called "air-ports," not much above the water level. Before going to sea, however, these air-ports must be closed, caulked, and the seams hermetically sealed with pitch. These places for ventilation being shut, the sick-bay is entirely barred against the free, natural admission of fresh air. In the *Neversink* a few lungsful were forced down by artificial means. But as the ordinary *wind-sail* was the only method adopted, the quantity of fresh air sent down was regulated by the force of the wind. In a calm there was none to be had, while in a severe gale the wind-sail had to be hauled up, on account of the violent draft flowing full upon the cots of the sick. An open-work partition divided our sick-bay from the rest of the deck, where the hammocks of the watch were slung; it, therefore, was exposed to all the uproar that ensued upon the watches being relieved.

An official, called the surgeon's steward, assisted by subordinates, presided over the place. He was the same individual alluded to as officiating at the amputation of the top-man. He was always to be found at his post, by night and by day.

This surgeon's steward deserves a description. He was a small, pale, hollow-eyed young man, with that peculiar Lazarus-like expression so often noticed in hospital attendants. Seldom or never did you see him on deck, and when he *did* emerge into the light of the sun, it was with an abashed look, and an uneasy, winking eye. The sun was not made for *him*. His nervous organization was confounded by the sight of the robust old sea-dogs on the forecastle and the general tumult of the spar-deck, and he mostly buried himself below in an atmosphere which long habit had made congenial.

This young man never indulged in frivolous conversation; he only talked of the surgeon's prescriptions; his every word was a bolus. He never was known to smile; nor did he even look sober in the ordinary way; but his countenance ever wore an aspect of cadaverous resignation to his fate. Strange! that so many of those who would fain minister to our own health should look so much like invalids themselves.

Connected with the sick-bay, over which the surgeon's steward presided—but removed from it in place, being next door to the counting-room of the purser's steward—was a regular apothecary's shop, of which he kept the key. It was fitted up precisely like an apothecary's on shore, displaying tiers of shelves on all four sides filled with green bottles and gallipots; beneath were multitudinous drawers bearing incomprehensible gilded inscriptions in abbreviated Latin.

He generally opened his shop for an hour or two every morning and evening. There was a Venetian blind in the upper part of the door, which he threw up when inside so as to admit a little air. And there you would see him, with a green shade over his eyes, seated on a stool, and pounding his pestle in a great iron mortar that looked like a howitzer, mixing some jallapy compound. A smoky lamp shed a flickering, yellow-fever tinge upon his pallid face and the closely-packed regiments of gallipots.

Several times when I felt in need of a little medicine, but was not ill enough to report myself to the surgeon at his levees, I would call of a morning upon his steward at the Sign of the Mortar, and beg him to give me what I wanted; when, without speaking a word, this cadaverous young man would mix me my potion in a tin cup, and hand it out through the little opening in his door, like the boxed-up treasurer giving you your change at the ticket-office of a theater.

But there was a little shelf against the wall of the door, and upon this I would set the tin cup for a while, and survey it; for I never was a Julius Cæsar at taking medicine; and to take it in this way, without a single attempt at disguising it; with no counteracting little morsel to hurry down after it; in short to go to the very apothecary's in person, and there, at the counter, swallow down your dose, as if it were a nice mint-julep taken at the bar of a hotel—*this* was a bitter bolus indeed. But, then, this pallid young apothecary charged nothing for it, and *that* was no small satisfaction; for is it not remarkable, to say the least, that a shore apothecary should actually charge you money—round dollars and cents—for giving you a horrible nausea?

My tin cup would wait a long time on that little shelf; yet "Pills," as the sailors called him, never heeded my lingering, but in sober, silent sadness continued pounding his mortar or folding up his powders; until at last some other customer would appear, and then in a sudden frenzy of resolution, I would gulp clown my sherry-cobbler, and carry its unspeakable flavor with me far up into the frigate's main-top. I do not know whether it was the wide roll of the ship, as felt in that giddy perch, that occasioned it, but I always got sea-sick after taking medicine and going aloft with it. Seldom or never did it do me any lasting good.

Now the Surgeon's steward was only a subordinate of Surgeon Cuticle himself, who lived in the ward-room among the Lieutenants, Sailing-master, Chaplain, and Purser.

The Surgeon is, by law, charged with the business of overlooking the general sanitary affairs of the ship. If anything is going on in any of its departments which he judges to be detrimental to the healthfulness of the crew, he has a right to protest against it formally to the Captain. When a man is being scourged at the gangway, the Surgeon stands by; and if he thinks that the punishment is becoming more than the culprit's constitution can well bear, he has a right to interfere and demand its cessation for the time.

But though the Navy regulations nominally vest him with this high discretionary authority over the very Commodore himself, how seldom does he exercise it in cases where humanity demands it? Three years is a long time to spend in one ship, and to be at swords' points with its Captain and Lieutenants during such a period, must be very unsocial and every way irksome. No otherwise than thus, at least, can the remissness of some surgeons in remonstrating against cruelty be accounted for.

Not to speak again of the continual dampness of the decks consequent upon flooding them with salt water, when we were driving near to Cape Horn, it needs only to be mentioned that, on board of the *Neversink,* men known to be in consumptions gasped under the scourge of the boatswain's mate, when the Surgeon and his two attendants stood by and never interposed. But where the unscrupulousness of martial discipline is maintained, it is in vain to attempt softening its rigor by the ordaining of humanitarian laws. Sooner might you tame the grizzly bear of Missouri than humanize a thing so essentially cruel and heartless.

But the Surgeon has yet other duties to perform. Not a seaman enters the Navy without undergoing a corporal examination, to test his soundness in wind and limb.

One of the first places into which I was introduced when I first entered on board the *Neversink* was the sick-bay, where I found one of the Assistant Surgeons seated at a green-baize table. It was his turn for visiting the apartment. Having been commanded by the deck officer to report my business to the functionary before me, I accordingly hemmed, to attract his attention, and then catching his eye, politely intimated that I called upon him for the purpose of being accurately laid out and surveyed.

"Strip!" was the answer, and, rolling up his gold-laced cuff, he proceeded to manipulate me. He punched me in the ribs, smote me across the chest, commanded me to stand on one leg and hold out the other horizontally. He asked me whether any of my family were consumptive; whether I ever felt a tendency to a rush of blood to the head; whether I was gouty; how often I had been bled during my life; how long I had been ashore; how long I had been afloat; with several other questions which have altogether slipped my memory. He concluded his interrogatories with this extraordinary and unwarranted one—"Are you pious?"

It was a leading question which somewhat staggered me, but I said not a word; when, feeling of my calves, he looked up and incomprehensibly said, "I am afraid you are not."

At length he declared me a sound animal, and wrote a certificate to that effect, with which I returned to the deck.

This Assistant Surgeon turned out to be a very singular character, and when I became more acquainted with him, I ceased to marvel at the curious question with which he had concluded his examination of my person.

He was a thin, knock-kneed man, with a sour, saturnine expression, rendered the more peculiar from his shaving his beard so remorselessly, that his chin and cheeks always looked blue, as if pinched with cold. His long familiarity with nautical invalids seemed to have filled him full of theological hypoes concerning the state of their souls. He was at once the physician and priest of the sick, washing down his boluses with ghostly consolation, and among the sailors went by the name of The Pelican, a fowl whose hanging pouch imparts to it a most chop-fallen, lugubrious expression.

The privilege of going off duty and lying by when you are sick, is one of the few points in which a man-of-war is far better for the sailor than a merchantman. But, as with every other matter in the Navy, the whole thing is subject to the general discipline of the vessel, and is conducted with a severe, unyielding method and regularity, making no allowances for exceptions to rules.

During the half-hour preceding morning quarters, the Surgeon of a frigate is to be found in the sick-bay, where, after going his rounds among the invalids, he holds a levee for the benefit of all new candidates for the sick-list. If, after looking at your tongue, and feeling of your pulse, he pronounces you a proper candidate, his secretary puts you down on his books, and you are thenceforth relieved from all duty, and have abundant leisure in which to recover your health. Let the boatswain blow; let the deck officer bellow; let the captain of your gun hunt you up; yet, if it can be answered by your mess-mates that you are *"down on the list,"* you ride it all out with impunity. The Commodore himself has then no authority over you. But you must not be too much elated, for your immunities are only secure while you are immured in the dark hospital below. Should you venture to get a mouthful of fresh air on the spar-deck, and be there discovered by an officer, you will in vain plead your illness; for it is quite impossible, it seems, that any true man-of-war invalid can be hearty enough to crawl up the ladders. Besides, the raw sea air, as they will tell you, is not good for the sick.

But, notwithstanding all this, notwithstanding the darkness and closeness of the sick-bay, in which an alleged invalid must be content to shut himself up till the Surgeon pronounces him cured, many instances occur, especially in protracted bad weather, where pretended invalids will submit to this dismal hospital durance, in order to escape hard work and wet jackets.

There is a story told somewhere of the Devil taking down the confessions of a woman on a strip of parchment, and being obliged to stretch it longer and longer with his teeth, in order to find room for all the lady had to say. Much thus was it with our Purser's steward, who had to lengthen out his manuscript sick-list, in order to accommodate all the names which were presented to him while we were off the pitch of Cape Horn. What sailors call the *"Cape Horn fever,"* alarmingly prevailed; though it disappeared altogether when we got into the weather, which, as with many other invalids, was solely to be imputed to the wonder-working effects of an entire change of climate.

It seems very strange, but it is really true, that off Cape Horn some *"sogers"* of sailors will stand cupping, and bleeding, and blistering, before they will budge. On the other hand, there are cases where a man actually sick and in need of medicine will refuse to go on the sick-list, because in that case his allowance of *grog* must be stopped.

On board of every American man-of-war, bound for sea, there is a goodly supply of wines and various delicacies put on board—according to law—for the benefit of the sick, whether officers or sailors. And one of the chicken-coops is always reserved for the Government chickens, destined for a similar purpose. But, on board of the *Neversink,* the only delicacies given to invalid sailors was a little sago or arrow-root, and they did not get *that* unless severely ill; but, so far as I could learn, no wine, in any quantity, was ever prescribed for them, though the Government bottles often went into the ward-room, for the benefit of indisposed officers.

And though the Government chicken-coop was replenished at every port, yet not four pair of drum-sticks were ever boiled into broth for sick sailors. Where the chickens went, someone must have known; but, as I cannot vouch for it myself, I will not here back the hardy assertion of the men, which was that the pious Pelican—true to his name—was extremely fond of poultry. I am the still less disposed to believe this scandal, from the continued leanness of the Pelican, which could hardly have been the case did he nourish himself by so nutritious a dish as the drum-sticks of fowls, a diet prescribed to pugilists in training. But who can avoid being suspicious of a very suspicious person? Pelican! I rather suspect you still.

Chapter LXXVIII

DISMAL TIMES IN THE MESS

IT WAS ON THE FIRST DAY OF THE LONG, HOT CALM WHICH WE HAD ON THE EQUATOR, THAT A mess-mate of mine, by the name of Shenly, who had been for some weeks complaining, at length went on the sick-list.

An old gunner's mate of the mess—Priming, the man with the hare-lip, who, true to his tribe, was charged to the muzzle with bile, and, moreover, rammed home on top of it a wad of sailor superstition—this gunner's mate indulged in some gloomy and savage remarks—strangely tinged with genuine feeling and grief—at the announcement of the sickness of Shenly, coming as it did not long after the almost fatal accident befalling poor Baldy, captain of the mizzen-top, another mess-mate of ours, and the dreadful fate of the amputated fore-top-man whom we buried in Rio, also our mess-mate.

We were cross-legged seated at dinner, between the guns, when the sad news concerning Shenly was first communicated.

"I know'd it, I know'd it," said Priming, through his nose. "Blast ye, I told ye so; poor fellow! But dam'me, I know'd it. This comes of having *thirteen* in the mess. I hope he arn't dangerous, men? Poor Shenly! But, blast it, it warn't till White-Jacket there comed into the mess that these here things began. I don't believe there'll be more nor three of us left by the time we strike soundings, men. But how is he now? Have you been down to see him, any on ye? Damn you, you Jonah! I don't see how you can sleep in your hammock, knowing as you do that by making an odd number in the mess you have been the death of one poor fellow, and ruined Baldy for life, and here's poor Shenly keeled up. Blast you, and your jacket, say I."

"My dear mess-mate," I cried, "don't blast me anymore, for Heaven's sale. Blast my jacket you may, and I'll join you in *that*; but don't blast *me*; for if you do, I shouldn't wonder if I myself was the next man to keel up."

"Gunner's mate!" said Jack Chase, helping himself to a slice of beef, and sandwiching it between two large biscuits—"Gunner's mate! White-Jacket there is my particular friend, and I would take it as a particular favor if you would *knock off* blasting him. It's in bad taste, rude, and unworthy a gentleman."

"Take your back away from that 'ere gun-carriage, will ye now, Jack Chase?" cried Priming, in reply, just then Jack happening to lean up against it. "Must I be all the time cleaning after you fellows? Blast ye! I spent an hour on that 'ere gun-carriage this very mornin'. But it all comes of White-Jacket there. If it warn't for having one too many, there wouldn't be any crowding and jamming in the mess. I'm blessed if we ar'n't about chock a' block here! Move further up there, I'm sitting on my leg!"

"For God's sake, gunner's mate," cried I, "if it will content you, I and my jacket will leave the mess."

"I wish you would, and be——to you!" he replied.

"And if he does, you will mess alone, gunner's mate," said Jack Chase.

"That you will," cried all.

"And I wish to the Lord you'd let me!" growled Priming, irritably rubbing his head with the handle of his sheath-knife.

"You are an old bear, gunner's mate," said Jack Chase.

"I am an old Turk," he replied, drawing the flat blade of his knife between his teeth, thereby producing a whetting, grating sound.

"Let him alone, let him alone, men," said Jack Chase. "Only keep off the tail of a rattlesnake, and he'll not rattle."

"Look out he don't bite, though," said Priming, snapping his teeth; and with that he rolled off, growling as he went.

Though I did my best to carry off my vexation with an air of indifference, need I say how I cursed my jacket, that it thus seemed the means of fastening on me the murder of one of my shipmates, and the probable murder of two more. For, had it not been for my jacket, doubtless, I had yet been a member of my old mess, and so have escaped making the luckless odd number among my present companions.

All I could say in private to Priming had no effect; though I often took him aside, to convince him of the philosophical impossibility of my having been accessary to the misfortunes of Baldy, the buried sailor in Rio, and Shenly. But Priming knew better; nothing could move him; and he ever afterward eyed me as virtuous citizens do some notorious underhand villain going unhung of justice.

Jacket! jacket! thou hast much to answer for, jacket!

Chapter LXXIX

How Man-of-War's-Men Die at Sea

SHENLY, MY SICK MESS-MATE, WAS A MIDDLE-AGED, HANDSOME, INTELLIGENT SEAMAN, WHOM some hard calamity, or perhaps some unfortunate excess, must have driven into the Navy. He told me he had a wife and two children in Portsmouth, in the state of New Hampshire. Upon being examined by Cuticle, the surgeon, he was, on purely scientific grounds, reprimanded by that functionary for not having previously appeared before him. He was immediately consigned to one of the invalid cots as a serious case. His complaint was of long standing; a pulmonary one, now attended with general prostration.

The same evening he grew so much worse, that according to man-of-war usage, we, his messmates, were officially notified that we must take turns at sitting up with him through the night. We at once made our arrangements, allotting two hours for a watch. Not till the third night did my own turn come round. During the day preceding, it was stated at the mess that our poor mess-mate was run down completely; the surgeon had given him up.

At four bells (two o'clock in the morning), I went down to relieve one of my mess-mates at the sick man's cot. The profound quietude of the calm pervaded the entire frigate through all her decks. The watch on duty were dozing on the carronade-slides, far above the sick-bay; and the watch below were fast asleep in their hammocks, on the same deck with the invalid.

Groping my way under these two hundred sleepers, I entered the hospital. A dim lamp was burning on the table, which was screwed down to the floor. This light shed dreary shadows over the white-washed walls of the place, making it look look a whited sepulchre underground. The windsail had collapsed, and lay motionless on the deck. The low groans of the sick were the only sounds to be heard; and as I advanced, some of them rolled upon me their sleepless, silent, tormented eyes.

"Fan him, and keep his forehead wet with this sponge," whispered my mess-mate, whom I came to relieve, as I drew near to Shenly's cot, "and wash the foam from his mouth; nothing more can be done for him. If he dies before your watch is out, call the Surgeon's steward; he sleeps in that hammock," pointing it out. "Good-bye, good-bye, mess-mate," he then whispered, stooping over the sick man; and so saying, he left the place.

Shenly was lying on his back. His eyes were closed, forming two dark-blue pits in his face; his breath was coming and going with a slow, long-drawn, mechanical precision. It was the mere foundering hull of a man that was before me; and though it presented the well-known features of my mess-mate, yet I knew that the living soul of Shenly never more would look out of those eyes.

So warm had it been during the day, that the Surgeon himself, when visiting the sick-bay, had entered it in his shirt-sleeves; and so warm was now the night that even in the lofty top I had worn but a loose linen frock and trousers. But in this subterranean sick-bay, buried in the very bowels of the ship, and at sea cut off from all ventilation, the heat of the night calm was intense. The sweat dripped from me as if I had just emerged from a bath; and stripping myself naked to the waist, I sat by the side of the cot, and with a bit of crumpled paper—put into my hand by the sailor I had relieved—kept fanning the motionless white face before me.

I could not help thinking, as I gazed, whether this man's fate had not been accelerated by his confinement in this heated furnace below; and whether many a sick man round me might not soon improve, if but permitted to swing his hammock in the airy vacancies of the half-deck above, open to the port-holes, but reserved for the promenade of the officers.

At last the heavy breathing grew more and more irregular, and gradually dying away, left forever the unstirring form of Shenly.

Calling the Surgeon's steward, he at once told me to rouse the master-at-arms, and four or five of my mess-mates. The master-at-arms approached, and immediately demanded the dead man's bag, which was accordingly dragged into the bay. Having been laid on the floor, and washed with a bucket of water which I drew from the ocean, the body was then dressed in a white frock, trousers, and neckerchief, taken out of the bag. While this was going on, the master-at-arms—standing over the operation with his rattan, and directing myself and mess-mates—indulged in much discursive levity, intended to manifest his fearlessness of death.

Pierre, who had been a *"chummy"* of Shenly's, spent much time in tying the neckerchief in an elaborate bow, and affectionately adjusting the white frock and trousers; but the master-at-arms put an end to this by ordering us to carry the body up to the gun-deck. It was placed on the death-board (used for that purpose), and we proceeded with it toward the main hatchway, awkwardly crawling under the tiers of hammocks, where the entire watch-below was sleeping. As, unavoidably, we rocked their pallets, the man-of-war's-men would cry out against us; through the mutterings of curses, the corpse reached the hatchway. Here the board slipped, and some time was spent in readjusting the body. At length we deposited it on the gun-deck, between two guns, and a union-jack being thrown over it for a pall, I was left again to watch by its side.

I had not been seated on my shot-box three minutes, when the messenger-boy passed me on his way forward; presently the slow, regular stroke of the ship's great bell was heard, proclaiming through the calm the expiration of the watch; it was four o'clock in the morning.

Poor Shenly! thought I, that sounds like your knell! and here you lie becalmed, in the last calm of all!

Hardly had the brazen din died away, when the Boatswain and his mates mustered round the hatchway, within a yard or two of the corpse, and the usual thundering call was given for the watch below to turn out.

"All the starboard-watch, ahoy! On deck there, below! Wide awake there, sleepers!"

But the dreamless sleeper by my side, who had so often sprung from his hammock at that summons, moved not a limb; the blue sheet over him lay unwrinkled.

A mess-mate of the other watch now came to relieve me; but I told him I chose to remain where I was till daylight came.

Chapter LXXX

THE LAST STITCH

JUST BEFORE DAYBREAK, TWO OF THE SAIL-MAKER'S GANG DREW NEAR, EACH WITH A LANTERN, carrying some canvas, two large shot, needles, and twine. I knew their errand; for in men-of-war the sail-maker is the undertaker.

They laid the body on deck, and, after fitting the canvas to it, seated themselves, cross-legged like tailors, one on each side, and, with their lanterns before them, went to stitching away, as if mending an old sail. Both were old men, with grizzled hair and beard, and shrunken faces. They belonged to that small class of aged seamen who, for their previous long and faithful services, are retained in the Navy more as pensioners upon its merited bounty than anything else. They are set to light and easy duties.

"Ar'n't this the fore-top-man, Shenly?" asked the foremost, looking full at the frozen face before him.

"Ay, ay, old Ringrope," said the other, drawing his hand far back with a long thread, "I thinks it's him; and he's further aloft now, I hope, than ever he was at the fore-truck. But I only hopes; I'm afeard this ar'n't the last on him!"

"His hull here will soon be going out of sight below hatches, though, old Thrummings," replied Ringrope, placing two heavy cannon-balls in the foot of the canvas shroud.

"I don't know that, old man; I never yet sewed up a ship-mate but he spooked me arterward. I tell ye, Ringrope, these 'ere corpses is cunning. You think they sinks deep, but they comes up again as soon as you sails over 'em. They lose the number of their mess, and their mess-mates sticks the spoons in the rack; but no good—no good, old Ringrope; they ar'n't dead yet. I tell ye, now, ten best-bower-anchors wouldn't sink this 'ere top-man. He'll be soon coming in the wake of the thirty-nine spooks what spooks me every night in my hammock—jist afore the mid-watch is called. Small thanks I gets for my pains; and every one on 'em looks so 'proachful-like, with a sail-maker's needle through his nose. I've been thinkin', old Ringrope, it's all wrong that 'ere last stitch we takes. Depend on't, they don't like it—none on 'em."

I was standing leaning over a gun, gazing at the two old men. The last remark reminded me of a superstitious custom generally practiced by most sea-undertakers upon these occasions. I resolved that, if I could help it, it should not take place upon the remains of Shenly.

"Thrummings," said I, advancing to the last speaker, "you are right. That last thing you do to the canvas is the very reason, be sure of it, that brings the ghosts after you, as you say. So don't do it to this poor fellow, I entreat. Try once, now, how it goes not to do it."

"What do you say to the youngster, old man?" said Thrummings, holding up his lantern into his comrade's wrinkled face, as if deciphering some ancient parchment.

"I'm agin all innowations," said Ringrope; "it's a good old fashion, that last stitch; it keeps 'em snug, d'ye see, youngster. I'm blessed if they could sleep sound, if it wa'n't for that. No, no, Thrummings! no innowations; I won't hear on't. I goes for the last stitch!"

"S'pose you was going to be sewed up yourself, old Ringrope, would you like the last stitch then! You are an old, gun, Ringrope; you can't stand looking out at your port-hole much longer," said Thrummings, as his own palsied hands were quivering over the canvas.

"Better say that to yourself, old man," replied Ringrope, stooping close to the light to thread his coarse needle, which trembled in his withered hands like the needle, in a compass of a Greenland ship near the Pole. "You ain't long for the sarvice. I wish I could give you some o' the blood in my veins, old man!"

"Ye ain't got ne'er a teaspoonful to spare," said Thrummings. "It will go hard, and I wouldn't want to do it; but I'm afeard I'll have the sewing on ye up afore long!"

"Sew *me* up? Me dead and you alive, old man?" shrieked Ringrope. "Well, I've he'rd the parson of the old *Independence* say as how old age was deceitful; but I never seed it so true afore this blessed night. I'm sorry for ye, old man—to see you so innocent-like, and Death all the while turning in and out with you in your hammock, for all the world like a hammock-mate."

"You lie! old man," cried Thrummings, shaking with rage. "It's *you* that have Death for a hammock-mate; it's *you* that will make a hole in the shot-locker soon."

"Take that back!" cried Ringrope, huskily, leaning far over the corpse, and, needle in hand, menacing his companion with his aguish fist. "Take that back, or I'll throttle your lean bag of wind fer ye!"

"Blast ye! old chaps, ain't ye any more manners than to be fighting over a dead man?" cried one of the sail-maker's mates, coming down from the spar-deck. "Bear a hand!—bear a hand! and get through with that job!"

"Only one more stitch to take," muttered Ringrope, creeping near the face.

"Drop your *'palm,'* then and let Thrummings take it; follow me—the foot of the main-sail wants mending—must do it afore a breeze springs up. D'ye hear, old chap! I say, drop your *palm*, and follow me."

At the reiterated command of his superior, Ringrope rose, and, turning to his comrade, said, "I take it all back, Thrummings, and I'm sorry for it, too. But mind ye, take that 'ere last stitch, now; if ye don't, there's no tellin' the consekenses."

As the mate and his man departed, I stole up to Thrummings. "Don't do it—don't do it, now, Thrummings—depend on it, it's wrong!"

"Well, youngster, I'll try this here one without it for jist this here once; and if, arter that, he don't spook me, I'll be dead agin the last stitch as long as my name is Thrummings."

So, without mutilation, the remains were replaced between the guns, the union jack again thrown over them, and I reseated myself on the shot-box.

Chapter LXXXI

How They Bury a Man-of-War's-Man at Sea

QUARTERS OVER IN THE MORNING, THE BOATSWAIN AND HIS FOUR MATES STOOD ROUND THE main hatchway, and after giving the usual whistle, made the customary announcement—*"All hands bury the dead, ahoy!"*

In a man-of-war, every thing, even to a man's funeral and burial, proceeds with the unrelenting promptitude of the martial code. And whether it is *all hands bury the dead!* or *all hands splice the main-brace,* the order is given in the same hoarse tones.

Both officers and men assembled in the lee waist, and through that bareheaded crowd the mess-mates of Shenly brought his body to the same gangway where it had thrice winced under the scourge. But there is something in death that ennobles even a pauper's corpse; and the Captain himself stood bareheaded before the remains of a man whom, with his hat on, he had sentenced to the ignominious gratings when alive.

"I am the resurrection and the life!" solemnly began the Chaplain, in full canonicals, the prayer-book in his hand.

"Damn you! off those booms!" roared a boatswain's mate to a crowd of top-men, who had elevated themselves to gain a better view of the scene.

"We commit this body to the deep!" At the word, Shenly's mess-mates tilted the board, and the dead sailor sank in the sea.

"Look aloft," whispered Jack Chase. "See that bird! it is the spirit of Shenly."

Gazing upward, all beheld a snow-white, solitary fowl, which—whence coming no one could tell—had been hovering over the main-mast during the service, and was now sailing far up into the depths of the sky.

Chapter LXXXII

What Remains of a Man-of-War's-Man after His Burial at Sea

Upon examining Shenly's bag, a will was found, scratched in pencil, upon a blank leaf in the middle of his Bible; or, to use the phrase of one of the seamen, in the midships, atween the Bible and Testament, where the Pothecary (Apocrypha) uses to be.

The will was comprised in one solitary sentence, exclusive of the dates and signatures: *"In case I die on the voyage, the Purser will please pay over my wages to my wife, who lives in Portsmouth, New Hampshire."*

Besides the testator's, there were two signatures of witnesses.

This last will and testament being shown to the Purser, who, it seems, had been a notary, or surrogate, or some sort of cozy chamber practitioner in his time, he declared that it must be "proved." So the witnesses were called, and after recognizing their hands to the paper; for the purpose of additionally testing their honesty, they were interrogated concerning the day on which they had signed—whether it was *Banyan Day*, or *Duff Day*, or *Swampseed Day*; for among the sailors on board a man-of-war, the land terms, *Monday, Tuesday, Wednesday*, are almost unknown. In place of these they substitute nautical names, some of which are significant of the daily bill of fare at dinner for the week.

The two witnesses were somewhat puzzled by the attorney-like questions of the Purser, till a third party came along, one of the ship's barbers, and declared, of his own knowledge, that Shenly executed the instrument on a *Shaving Day*; for the deceased seaman had informed him of the circumstance, when he came to have his beard reaped on the morning of the event.

In the Purser's opinion, this settled the question; and it is to be hoped that the widow duly received her husband's death-earned wages.

Shenly was dead and gone; and what was Shenly's epitaph?

—"D.D."—

opposite his name in the Purser's books, in *"Black's best Writing Fluid"*—funereal name and funereal hue—meaning "Discharged, Dead."

Chapter LXXXIII

A MAN-OF-WAR COLLEGE

IN OUR MAN-OF-WAR WORLD, LIFE COMES IN AT ONE GANGWAY AND DEATH GOES OVERBOARD AT the other. Under the man-of-war scourge, curses mix with tears; and the sigh and the sob furnish the bass to the shrill octave of those who laugh to drown buried griefs of their own. Checkers were played in the waist at the time of Shenly's burial; and as the body plunged, a player swept the board. The bubbles had hardly burst, when all hands were *piped down* by the Boatswain, and the old jests were heard again, as if Shenly himself were there to hear.

This man-of-war life has not left me unhardened. I cannot stop to weep over Shenly now; that would be false to the life I depict; wearing no mourning weeds, I resume the task of portraying our man-of-war world.

Among the various other vocations, all driven abreast on board of the *Neversink,* was that of the schoolmaster. There were two academies in the frigate. One comprised the apprentice boys, who, upon certain days of the week, were indoctrinated in the mysteries of the primer by an invalid corporal of marines, a slender, wizzen-cheeked man, who had received a liberal infant-school education.

The other school was a far more pretentious affair—a sort of army and navy seminary combined, where mystical mathematical problems were solved by the midshipmen, and great ships-of-the-line were navigated over imaginary shoals by unimaginable observations of the moon and the stars, and learned lectures were delivered upon great guns, small arms, and the curvilinear lines described by bombs in the air.

"The Professor" was the title bestowed upon the erudite gentleman who conducted this seminary, and by that title alone was he known throughout the ship. He was domiciled in the Ward-room, and circulated there on a social par with the Purser, Surgeon, and other *non-combatants* and Quakers. By being advanced to the dignity of a peerage in the Ward-room, Science and Learning were ennobled in the person of this Professor, even as divinity was honored in the Chaplain enjoying the rank of a spiritual peer.

Every other afternoon, while at sea, the Professor assembled his pupils on the half-deck, near the long twenty-four pounders. A bass drum-head was his desk, his pupils forming a semicircle around him, seated on shot-boxes and match-tubs.

They were in the jelly of youth, and this learned Professor poured into their susceptible hearts all the gentle gunpowder maxims of war. Presidents of Peace Societies and Superintendents of Sabbath-schools, must it not have been a most interesting sight?

But the Professor himself was a noteworthy person. A tall, thin, spectacled man, about forty years old, with a student's stoop in his shoulders, and wearing uncommonly scanty pantaloons, exhibiting an undue proportion of his boots. In early life he had been a cadet in the military academy of West Point; but, becoming very weak-sighted, and thereby in a good manner disqualified for active service in the field, he had declined entering the army, and accepted the office of Professor in the Navy.

His studies at West Point had thoroughly grounded him in a knowledge of gunnery; and, as he was not a little of a pedant, it was sometimes amusing, when the sailors were at quarters, to hear him criticize their evolutions at the batteries. He would quote Dr. Hutton's *Tracts* on the subject, also, in the original, *The French Bombardier,* and wind up by Italian passages from the *Prattica Manuale dell' Artiglieria.*

Though not required by the Navy regulations to instruct his scholars in aught but the application of mathematics to navigation, yet besides this, and besides instructing them in the theory of gunnery, he also sought to root them in the theory of frigate and fleet tactics. To be sure, he himself did not know how to splice a rope or furl a sail; and, owing to his partiality for strong coffee, he was apt to be nervous when we fired salutes; yet all this did not prevent him from delivering lectures on cannonading and "breaking the enemy's line."

He had arrived at his knowledge of tactics by silent, solitary study, and earnest meditation in the sequestered retreat of his state-room. His case was somewhat parallel to the Scotchman's—John. Clerk, Esq., of Eldin—who, though he had never been to sea, composed a quarto treatise on fleet-fighting, which to this day remains a text-book; and he also originated a nautical maneuver, which has given to England many a victory over her foes.

Now there was a large black-board, something like a great-gun target—only it was square—which during the professor's lectures was placed upright on the gun-deck, supported behind by three boarding-pikes. And here he would chalk out diagrams of great fleet engagements; making marks, like the soles of shoes, for the ships, and drawing a dog-vane in one corner to denote the assumed direction of the wind. This done, with a cutlass he would point out every spot of interest.

"Now, young gentlemen, the board before you exhibits the disposition of the British West Indian squadron under Rodney, when, early on the morning of the 9th of April, in the year of our blessed Lord 1782, he discovered part of the French fleet, commanded by the Count de Grasse, lying under the north end of the Island of Dominica. It was at this juncture that the Admiral gave the signal for the British line to prepare for battle, and stand on. D'ye understand, young gentlemen? Well, the British van having nearly fetched up with the center of the enemy—who, be it remembered, were then on the starboard tack—and Rodney's center and rear being yet becalmed under the lee of the land—the question I ask you is: What should Rodney now do?"

"Blaze away, by all means!" responded a rather confident reefer, who had zealously been observing the diagram.

"But, sir, his center and rear are still becalmed, and his van has not yet closed with the enemy."

"Wait till he *does* come in range, and *then* blaze away," said the reefer.

"Permit me to remark, Mr. Pert, that *'blaze away'* is not a strictly technical term; and also permit me to hint, Mr. Pert, that you should consider the subject rather more deeply before you hurry forward your opinion."

This rebuke not only abashed Mr. Pert, but for a time intimidated the rest; and the professor was obliged to proceed, and extricate the British fleet by himself. He concluded by awarding Admiral Rodney the victory, which must have been exceedingly gratifying to the family pride of the surviving relatives and connections of that distinguished hero.

"Shall I clean the board, sir?" now asked Mr. Pert, brightening up.

"No, sir; not till you have saved that crippled French ship in the corner. That ship, young gentlemen, is the *Glorieuse*: you perceive she is cut off from her consorts, and the whole British fleet is giving chase to her. Her bowsprit is gone; her rudder is torn away; she has one hundred round shot in her hull, and two thirds of her men are dead or dying. What's to be done? the wind being at northeast by north?"

"Well, sir," said Mr. Dash, a chivalric young gentleman from Virginia, "I wouldn't strike yet; I'd nail my colors to the main-royal-mast! I would, by Jove!"

"That would not save your ship, sir; besides, your main-mast has gone by the board."

"I think, sir," said Mr. Slim, a diffident youth, "I think, sir, I would haul back the fore-top-sail."

"And why so? of what service would *that* be, I should like to know, Mr. Slim?"

"I can't tell exactly; but I think it would help her a little," was the timid reply.

"Not a whit, sir—not one particle; besides, you can't haul back your fore-top-sail—your fore-mast is lying across your forecastle."

"Haul back the main-top-sail, then," suggested another.

"Can't be done; your main-mast, also, has gone by the board!"

"Mizzen-top-sail?" meekly suggested little Boat-Plug.

"Your mizzen-top-mast, let me inform you, sir, was shot down in the first of the fight!"

"Well, sir," cried Mr. Dash, "I'd tack ship, anyway; bid 'em good-bye with a broadside; nail my flag to the keel, if there was no other place; and blow my brains out on the poop!"

"Idle, idle, sir! worse than idle! you are carried away, Mr. Dash, by your ardent Southern temperament! Let me inform you, young gentlemen, that this ship," touching it with his cutlass, "can*not* be saved."

Then, throwing down his cutlass, "Mr. Pert, have the goodness to hand me one of those cannon-balls from the rack."

Balancing the iron sphere in one hand, the learned professor began fingering it with the other, like Columbus illustrating the rotundity of the globe before the Royal Commission of Castilian Ecclesiastics.

"Young gentlemen, I resume my remarks on the passage of a shot *in vacuo,* which remarks were interrupted yesterday by general quarters. After quoting that admirable passage in *Spearman's British Gunner,* I then laid it down, you remember, that the path of a shot *in vacuo* describes a parabolic curve. I now add that, agreeably to the method pursued by the illustrious Newton in treating the subject of curvilinear motion, I consider the *trajectory* or curve described by a moving body in space as consisting of a series of right lines, described in successive intervals of time, and constituting the diagonals of parallelograms formed in a vertical plane between the vertical deflections caused by gravity and the production of the line of motion which has been described in each preceding interval of time. This must be obvious; for, if you say that the passage *in vacuo* of this cannon-ball, now held in my hand, would describe otherwise than a series of right lines, etc., then you are brought to the *Reductio ad Absurdum,* that the diagonals of parallelograms are—"

"All hands reef top-sail!" was now thundered forth by the boatswain's mates. The shot fell from the professor's palm; his spectacles dropped on his nose, and the school tumultuously broke up, the pupils scrambling up the ladders with the sailors, who had been overhearing the lecture.

Chapter LXXXIV

MAN-OF-WAR BARBERS

THE ALLUSION TO ONE OF THE SHIP'S BARBERS IN A PREVIOUS CHAPTER, TOGETHER WITH THE RECollection of how conspicuous a part they enacted in a tragical drama soon to be related, leads me now to introduce them to the reader.

Among the numerous artists and professors of polite trades in the Navy, none are held in higher estimation or drive a more profitable business than these barbers. And it may well be imagined that the five hundred heads of hair and five hundred beards of a frigate should furnish no small employment for those to whose faithful care they may be entrusted. As everything connected with the domestic affairs of a man-of-war comes under the supervision of the martial executive, so certain barbers are formally licensed by the First Lieutenant. The better to attend to the profitable duties of their calling, they are exempted from all ship's duty except that of standing night-watches at sea, mustering at quarters, and coming on deck when all hands are called. They are rated as *able-seamen* or *ordinary seamen,* and receive their wages as such; but in addition to this, they are liberally recompensed for their professional services. Herein their rate of pay is fixed for every sailor manipulated—so much per quarter, which is charged to the sailor, and credited to his barber on the books of the Purser.

It has been seen that while a man-of-war barber is shaving his customers at so much per chin, his wages as a seaman are still running on, which makes him a sort of *sleeping partner* of a sailor; nor are the sailor wages he receives altogether to be reckoned as earnings. Considering the circumstances, however, not much objection can be made to the barbers on this score. But there were instances of men in the *Neversink* receiving government money in part pay for work done for private individuals. Among these were several accomplished tailors, who nearly the whole cruise sat cross-legged on the half deck, making coats, pantaloons, and vests for the quarter-deck officers. Some of these men, though knowing little or nothing about sailor duties, and seldom or never performing them, stood upon the ship's books as ordinary seamen, entitled to ten dollars a month. Why was this? Previous to shipping they had divulged the fact of their being tailors. True, the officers who employed them upon their wardrobes paid them for their work, but some of them in such a way as to elicit much grumbling from the tailors. At any rate, these makers and menders of clothes did not receive from some of these officers an amount equal to what they could have fairly earned ashore by doing the same work. It was a considerable saving to the officers to have their clothes made on board.

The men belonging to the carpenter's gang furnished another case in point. There were some six or eight allotted to this department. All the cruise they were hard at work. At what? Mostly making chests of drawers, canes, little ships and schooners, swifts, and other elaborated trifles, chiefly for the Captain. What did the Captain pay them for their trouble? Nothing. But the United States government paid them; two of them (the mates) at nineteen dollars a month, and the rest receiving the pay of able-seamen, twelve dollars.

To return.

The regular days upon which the barbers shall exercise their vocation are set down on the ship's calendar, and known as *shaving days.* On board of the *Neversink* these days are Wednesdays and Saturdays; when, immediately after breakfast, the barbers' shops were opened to customers. They were in different parts of the gun-deck, between the long twenty-four pounders. Their furniture, however, was not very elaborate, hardly equal to the sumptuous appointments of metropolitan barbers. Indeed, it merely consisted of a match-tub, elevated upon a shot-box, as a barber's chair for the patient. No Psyche glasses; no hand-mirror; no ewer and basin; no comfortable padded footstool; nothing, in short, that makes a shore "*shave*" such a luxury.

Nor are the implements of these man-of-war barbers out of keeping with the rude appearance of their shops. Their razors are of the simplest patterns, and, from their jaggedness, would seem better fitted for the preparing and harrowing of the soil than for the ultimate reaping of the crop. But this is no matter for wonder, since so many chins are to be shaven, and a razor-case holds but two razors. For only two razors does a man-of-war barber have, and, like the marine sentries at the gangway in port, these razors go off and on duty in rotation. One brush, too, brushes every chin, and one lather lathers them all. No private brushes and boxes; no reservations whatever.

As it would be altogether too much trouble for a man-of-war's-man to keep his own shaving-tools and shave himself at sea, and since, therefore, nearly the whole ship's company patronize the ship's barbers, and as the seamen must be shaven by evening quarters of the days appointed for the business, it may be readily imagined what a scene of bustle and confusion there is when the razors are being applied. First come, first served, is the motto; and often you have to wait for hours together, sticking to your position (like one of an Indian file of merchants' clerks getting letters out of the post-office), ere you have a chance to occupy the pedestal of the match-tub. Often the crowd of quarrelsome candidates wrangle and fight for precedency, while at all times the interval is employed by the garrulous in every variety of ship-gossip.

As the shaving days are unalterable, they often fall upon days of high seas and tempestuous winds, when the vessel pitches and rolls in a frightful manner. In consequence, many valuable lives are jeopardized from the razor being plied under such untoward circumstances. But these sea-barbers pride themselves upon their sea-legs, and often you will see them standing over their patients with their feet wide apart, and scientifically swaying their bodies to the motion of the ship, as they flourish their edge-tools about the lips, nostrils, and jugular.

As I looked upon the practitioner and patient at such times, I could not help thinking that, if the sailor had any insurance on his life, it would certainly be deemed forfeited should the president of the company chance to lounge by and behold him in that imminent peril. For myself, I accounted it an excellent preparation for going into a sea-fight, where fortitude in standing up to your gun and running the risk of all splinters, comprise part of the practical qualities that make up an efficient man-of-war's man.

It remains to be related, that these barbers of ours had their labors considerably abridged by a fashion prevailing among many of the crew, of wearing very large whiskers; so that, in most cases, the only parts needing a shave were the upper lip and suburbs of the chin. This had been more or less the custom during the whole three years' cruise; but for some time previous to our weathering Cape Horn, very many of the seamen had redoubled their assiduity in cultivating their beards preparatory to their return to America. There they anticipated creating no small impression by their immense and magnificent *homeward-bounders*—so they called the long fly-brushes at their chins. In particular, the more aged sailors, embracing the Old Guard of sea grenadiers on the forecastle, and the begrimed gunner's mates and quarter-gunners, sported most venerable beards of an exceeding length and hoariness, like long, trailing moss hanging from the bough of some aged oak. Above all, the Captain of the Forecastle, old Ushant—a fine specimen of a sea sexagenarian—wore a wide, spreading beard, gizzled and gray, that flowed over his breast and often became tangled and knotted with tar. This Ushant, in all weathers, was ever alert at his duty; intrepidly mounting the fore-yard in a gale, his long beard streaming like Neptune's. Off Cape Horn it looked like a miller's, being all over powdered with frost; sometimes it glittered with minute icicles in the pale, cold, moonlit Patagonian nights. But though he was so active in time of tempest, yet when his duty did not call for exertion, he was a remarkably staid, reserved, silent, and majestic old man, holding himself aloof from noisy revelry, and never participating in the boisterous sports of the crew. He resolutely set his beard against their boyish frolickings, and often held forth like an oracle concerning the vanity thereof. Indeed, at times he was wont to talk philosophy to his ancient companions—the old sheet-anchor-men around him—as well as to the hare-brained tenants of the fore-top, and the giddy lads in the mizzen.

Nor was his philosophy to be despised; it abounded in wisdom. For this Ushant was an old man, of strong natural sense, who had seen nearly the whole terraqueous globe, and could reason of civilized and savage, of Gentile and Jew, of Christian and Moslem. The long night-watches of the sailor are eminently adapted to draw out the reflective faculties of any serious-minded man, however humble or uneducated. Judge, then, what half a century of battling out watches on the ocean must have done for this fine old tar. He was a sort of a sea-Socrates, in his old age "pouring out his last philosophy and life," as sweet Spenser has it; and I never could look at him, and survey his right reverend beard, without bestowing upon him that title which, in one of his satires, Persius gives to the immortal quaffer of the hemlock—*Magister Barbatus*—the bearded master.

Not a few of the ship's company had also bestowed great pains upon their hair, which some of them—especially the genteel young sailor bucks of the After-guard—wore over their shoulders like the ringleted Cavaliers. Many sailors, with naturally tendril locks, prided themselves upon what they call *love curls*, worn at the side of the head, just before the ear—a custom peculiar to tars, and which seems to have filled the vacated place of the old-fashioned Lord Rodney cue, which they used to wear some fifty years ago.

But there were others of the crew laboring under the misfortune of long, lank, Winnebago locks, carroty bunches of hair, or rebellious bristles of a sandy hue. Ambitious of redundant mops, these still suffered their carrots to grow, spite of all ridicule. They looked like Huns and Scandinavians; and one of them, a young Down Easter, the unenvied proprietor of a thick crop of inflexible yellow bamboos, went by the name of *Peter the Wild Boy*; for, like Peter the Wild Boy in France, it was supposed that he must have been caught like a catamount in the pine woods of Maine. But there were many fine, flowing heads of hair to counter-balance such sorry exhibitions as Peter's.

What with long whiskers and venerable beards, then, of every variety of cut—Charles the Fifth's and Aurelian's—and endless *goatees* and *imperials*; and what with abounding locks, our crew seemed a company of Merovingians or Long-haired kings, mixed with savage Lombards or Longobardi, so called from their lengthy beards.

Chapter LXXXV

The Great Massacre of the Beards

The preceding chapter fitly paves the way for the present, wherein it sadly befalls White-Jacket to chronicle a calamitous event, which filled the *Neversink* with long lamentations, that echo through all her decks and tops. After dwelling upon our redundant locks and thrice-noble beards, fain would I cease, and let the sequel remain undisclosed, but truth and fidelity forbid.

As I now deviously hover and lingeringly skirmish about the frontiers of this melancholy recital, a feeling of sadness comes over me that I cannot withstand. Such a heartless massacre of hair! Such a Bartholomew's Day and Sicilian Vespers of assassinated beards! Ah! who would believe it! With intuitive sympathy I feel of my own brown beard while I write, and thank my kind stars that each precious hair is forever beyond the reach of the ruthless barbers of a man-of-war!

It needs that this sad and most serious matter should be faithfully detailed. Throughout the cruise, many of the officers had expressed their abhorrence of the impunity with which the most extensive plantations of hair were cultivated under their very noses; and they frowned upon every beard with even greater dislike. They said it was unseamanlike; not *ship-shape*; in short, it was disgraceful to the Navy. But as Captain Claret said nothing, and as the officers, of themselves, had no authority to preach a crusade against whiskerandoes, the Old Guard on the forecastle still complacently stroked their beards, and the sweet youths of the After-guard still lovingly threaded their fingers through their curls.

Perhaps the Captain's generosity in thus far permitting our beards sprung from the fact that he himself wore a small speck of a beard upon his own imperial cheek; which if rumor said true, was to hide something, as Plutarch relates of the Emperor Adrian. But, to do him justice—as I always have done—the Captain's beard did not exceed the limits prescribed by the Navy Department.

According to a then recent ordinance at Washington, the beards of both officers and seamen were to be accurately laid out and surveyed, and on no account must come lower than the mouth, so as to correspond with the Army standard—a regulation directly opposed to the theocratical law laid down in the nineteenth chapter and twenty-seventh verse of Leviticus, where it is expressly ordained, *"Thou shalt not mar the corners of thy beard."* But legislators do not always square their statutes by those of the Bible.

At last, when we had crossed the Northern Tropic, and were standing up to our guns at evening quarters, and when the setting sun, streaming in at the port-holes, lit up every hair, till to an observer on the quarter-deck, the two long, even lines of beards seemed one dense grove; in that evil hour it must have been, that a cruel thought entered into the heart of our Captain.

A pretty set of savages, thought he, am I taking home to America; people will think them all catamounts and Turks. Besides, now that I think of it, it's against the law. It will never do. They must be shaven and shorn—that's flat.

There is no knowing, indeed, whether these were the very words in which the Captain meditated that night; for it is yet a mooted point among metaphysicians, whether we think in words or whether we think in thoughts. But something like the above must have been the Captain's cogitations. At any rate, that very evening the ship's company were astounded by an extraordinary announcement made at the main-hatch-way of the gun-deck, by the Boatswain's mate there stationed. He was afterwards discovered to have been tipsy at the time.

"D'ye hear there, fore and aft? All you that have hair on your heads, shave them off; and all you that have beards, trim 'em small!"

Shave off our Christian heads! And then, placing them between our knees, trim small our worshiped beards! The Captain was mad.

But directly the Boatswain came rushing to the hatchway, and, after soundly rating his tipsy mate, thundered forth a true version of the order that had issued from the quarter-deck. As amended, it ran thus:

"D'ye hear there, fore and aft? All you that have long hair, cut it short; and all you that have large whiskers, trim them down, according to the Navy regulations."

This was an amendment, to be sure; but what barbarity, after all! What! not thirty days' run from home, and lose our magnificent homeward-bounders! The homeward-bounders we had been cultivating so long! Lose them at one fell swoop? Were the vile barbers of the gun-deck to reap our long, nodding harvests, and expose our innocent chins to the chill air of the Yankee coast! And our viny locks! were they also to be shorn? Was a grand sheep-shearing, such as they annually have at Nantucket, to take place; and our ignoble barbers to carry off the fleece?

Captain Claret! in cutting our beards and our hair, you cut us the unkindest cut of all! Were we going into action, Captain Claret—going to fight the foe with our hearts of flame and our arms of steel, then would we gladly offer up our beards to the terrific God of War, and *that* we would account but a wise precaution against having them tweaked by the foe. *Then,* Captain Claret, you would but be imitating the example of Alexander, who had his Macedonians all shaven, that in the hour of battle their beards might not be handles to the Persians. But *now,* Captain Claret! when after our long, long cruise, we are returning to our homes, tenderly stroking the fine tassels on our chins, and thinking of father or mother, or sister or brother, or daughter or son; to cut off our beards *now*—the very beards that were frosted white off the pitch of Patagonia—*this* is too bitterly bad, Captain Claret! and, by Heaven, we will not submit. Train your guns inboard, let the marines fix their bayonets, let the officers draw their swords; we *will not* let our beards be reaped—the last insult inflicted upon a vanquished foe in the East!

Where are you, sheet-anchor-men! Captains of the tops! gunner's mates! mariners, all! Muster round the capstan your venerable beards, and while you braid them together in token of brotherhood, cross hands and swear that we will enact over again the mutiny of the *Nore*, and sooner perish than yield up a hair!

The excitement was intense throughout that whole evening. Groups of tens and twenties were scattered about all the decks, discussing the mandate, and inveighing against its barbarous author. The long area of the gun-deck was something like a populous street of brokers, when some terrible commercial tidings have newly arrived. One and all, they resolved not to succumb, and every man swore to stand by his beard and his neighbor.

Twenty-four hours after—at the next evening quarters—the Captain's eye was observed to wander along the men at their guns—not a beard was shaven!

When the drum beat the retreat, the Boatswain—now attended by all four of his mates, to give additional solemnity to the announcement—repeated the previous day's order, and concluded by saying, that twenty-four hours would be given for all to acquiesce.

But the second day passed, and at quarters, untouched, every beard bristled on its chin. Forthwith Captain Claret summoned the midshipmen, who, receiving his orders, hurried to the various divisions of the guns, and communicated them to the Lieutenants respectively stationed over divisions.

The officer commanding mine turned upon us, and said, "Men, if to-morrow night I find any of you with long hair, or whiskers of a standard violating the Navy regulations, the names of such offenders shall be put down on the report."

The affair had now assumed a most serious aspect. The Captain was in earnest. The excitement increased ten-fold; and a great many of the older seamen, exasperated to the uttermost, talked about *knocking off duty* till the obnoxious mandate was revoked. I thought it impossible that they would seriously think of such a folly; but there is no knowing what man-of-war's-men will sometimes do, under provocation—witness Parker and the *Nore*.

That same night, when the first watch was set, the men in a body drove the two boatswain's mates from their stations at the fore and main hatchways, and unshipped the ladders; thus cutting off all communication between the gun and spar decks, forward of the main-mast.

Mad Jack had the trumpet; and no sooner was this incipient mutiny reported to him, than he jumped right down among the mob, and fearlessly mingling with them, exclaimed, "What do you mean, men? don't be fools! This is no way to get what you want. Turn to, my lads, turn to! Boatswain's mate, ship that ladder! So! up you tumble, now, my hearties! away you go!"

His gallant, off-handed, confident manner, recognizing no attempt at mutiny, operated upon the sailors like magic.

They *tumbled up*, as commanded; and for the rest of that night contented themselves with privately fulminating their displeasure against the Captain, and publicly emblazoning every anchor-button on the coat of admired Mad Jack.

Captain Claret happened to be taking a nap in his cabin at the moment of the disturbance; and it was quelled so soon that he knew nothing of it till it was officially reported to him. It was afterward rumored through the ship that he reprimanded Mad Jack for acting as he did. He maintained that he should at once have summoned the marines, and charged upon the "mutineers." But if the sayings imputed to the Captain were true, he nevertheless refrained from subsequently noticing the disturbance, or attempting to seek out and punish the ringleaders. This was but wise; for there are times when even the most potent governor must wink at transgression in order to preserve the laws inviolate for the future. And great care is to be taken, by timely management, to avert an incontestable act of mutiny, and so prevent men from being roused, by their own consciousness of transgression, into all the fury of an unbounded insurrection. *Then* for the time, both soldiers and sailors are irresistible; as even the valor of Cæsar was made to know, and the prudence of Germanicus, when their legions rebelled. And not all the concessions of Earl Spencer, as First lord of the Admiralty, nor the threats and entreaties of Lord Bridport, the Admiral of the Fleet—no, nor his gracious Majesty's plenary pardon in prospective, could prevail upon the Spithead mutineers (when at last fairly lashed up to the mark) to succumb, until deserted by their own mess-mates, and a handful was left in the breach.

Therefore, Mad Jack! you did right, and no one else could have acquitted himself better. By your crafty simplicity, good-natured daring, and off-handed air (as if nothing was happening) you perhaps quelled a very serious affair in the bud, and prevented the disgrace to the American Navy of a tragical mutiny, growing out of whiskers, soap-suds, and razors. Think of it, if future historians should devote a long chapter to the great *Rebellion of the Beards* on board the United States ship *Neversink*. Why, through all time thereafter, barbers would cut down their spiralized poles, and substitute miniature main-masts for the emblems of their calling.

And here is ample scope for some pregnant instruction, how that events of vast magnitude in our man-of-war world may originate in the pettiest of trifles. But that is an old theme; we waive it, and proceed.

On the morning following, though it was not a regular shaving day, the gun-deck barbers were observed to have their shops open, their match-tub accommodations in readiness, and their razors displayed. With their brushes, raising a mighty lather in their tin pots, they stood eyeing the passing throng of seamen, silently inviting them to walk in and be served. In addition to their usual implements, they now flourished at intervals a huge pair of sheep-shears, by way of more forcibly reminding the men of the edict which that day must be obeyed, or woe betide them.

For some hours the seamen paced to and fro in no very good humor, vowing not to sacrifice a hair. Beforehand, they denounced that man who should abase himself by compliance. But habituation to discipline is magical; and ere long an old forecastle-man was discovered elevated upon a match-tub, while, with a malicious grin, his barber—a fellow who, from his merciless rasping, was called Blue-Skin—seized him by his long beard, and at one fell stroke cut it off and tossed it out of the port-hole behind him. This forecastle-man was ever afterwards known by a significant title—in the main equivalent to that name of reproach fastened upon that Athenian who, in Alexander's time, previous to which all the Greeks sported beards, first submitted to the deprivation of his own. But, spite of all the contempt hurled on our forecastle-man, so prudent an example was soon followed; presently all the barbers were busy.

Sad sight! at which anyone but a barber or a Tartar would have wept! Beards three years old; *goatees* that would have graced a Chamois of the Alps; *imperials* that Count D'Orsay would have envied; and *love-curls* and man-of-war ringlets that would have measured, inch for inch, with the longest tresses of The Fair One with the Golden Locks—all went by the board! Captain Claret! how can you rest in your hammock! by this brown beard which now waves from my chin—the illustrious successor to that first, young, vigorous beard I yielded to your tyranny—by this manly beard, I swear, it was barbarous!

My noble captain, Jack Chase, was indignant. Not even all the special favors he had received from Captain Claret and the plenary pardon extended to him for his desertion into the Peruvian service, could restrain the expression of his feelings. But in his cooler moments, Jack was a wise man; he at last deemed it but wisdom to succumb.

When he went to the barber he almost drew tears from his eyes. Seating himself mournfully on the match-tub, he looked sideways, and said to the barber, who was *slithering* his sheep-shears in readiness to begin: "My friend, I trust your scissors are consecrated. Let them not touch this beard if they have yet to be dipped in holy water; beards are sacred things, barber. Have you no feeling for beards, my friend? think of it"; and mournfully he laid his deep-dyed, russet cheek upon his hand. "Two summers have gone by since my chin has been reaped. I was in Coquimbo then, on the Spanish Main; and when the husbandman was sowing his Autumnal grain on the Vega, I started this blessed beard; and when the vine-dressers were trimming their vines in the vineyards, I first trimmed it to the sound of a flute. Ah! barber, have you no heart? This beard has been caressed by the snow-white hand of the lovely Tomasita of Tombez—the Castilian belle of all lower Peru. Think of *that,* barber! I have worn it as an officer on the quarter-deck of a Peruvian man-of-war. I have sported it at brilliant fandangoes in Lima. I have been alow and aloft with it at sea. Yea, barber! it has streamed like an Admiral's pennant at the mast-head of this same gallant frigate, the *Neversink*! Oh! barber, barber! it stabs me to the heart. Talk not of hauling down your ensigns and standards when vanquished—what is *that,* barber! to striking the flag that Nature herself has nailed to the mast!"

Here noble Jack's feelings overcame him: he dropped from the animated attitude into which his enthusiasm had momentarily transported him; his proud head sunk upon his chest, and his long, sad beard almost grazed the deck.

"Ay! trail your beards in grief and dishonor, oh crew of the *Neversink*!" sighed Jack. "Barber, come closer—now, tell me, my friend, have you obtained absolution for this deed you are about to commit? You have not? Then, barber, I will absolve you; your hands shall be washed of this sin; it is not you, but another; and though you are about to shear off my manhood, yet, barber, I freely forgive you; kneel, kneel, barber! that I may bless you, in token that I cherish no malice!"

So when this barber, who was the only tender-hearted one of his tribe, had kneeled, been absolved, and then blessed, Jack gave up his beard into his hands, and the barber, clipping it off with a sigh, held it high aloft, and, parodying the style of the boatswain's mates, cried aloud, "D'ye hear, fore and aft? This is the beard of our matchless Jack Chase, the noble captain of this frigate's main-top!"

Chapter LXXXVI

The Rebels Brought to the Mast

THOUGH MANY HEADS OF HAIR WERE SHORN, AND MANY FINE BEARDS REAPED THAT DAY, YET several still held out, and vowed to defend their sacred hair to the last gasp of their breath. These were chiefly old sailors—some of them petty officers—who, presuming upon their age or rank, doubtless thought that, after so many had complied with the Captain's commands, *they*, being but a handful, would be exempted from compliance, and remain a monument of our master's clemency.

That same evening, when the drum beat to quarters, the sailors went sullenly to their guns, and the old tars who still sported their beards stood up, grim, defying, and motionless, as the rows of sculptured Assyrian kings, who, with their magnificent beards, have recently been exhumed by Layard.

When the proper time arrived, their names were taken down by the officers of divisions, and they were afterward summoned in a body to the mast, where the Captain stood ready to receive them. The whole ship's company crowded to the spot, and, amid the breathless multitude, the venerable rebels advanced and unhatted.

It was an imposing display. They were old and venerable mariners; their cheeks had been burned brown in all latitudes, wherever the sun sends a tropical ray. Reverend old tars, one and all; some of them might have been grandsires, with grandchildren in every port round the world. They ought to have commanded the veneration of the most frivolous or magisterial beholder. Even Captain Claret they ought to have humiliated into deference. But a Scythian is touched with no reverential promptings; and, as the Roman student well knows, the august Senators themselves, seated in the Senate-house, on the majestic hill of the Capitol, had their holy beards tweaked by the insolent chief of the Goths.

Such an array of beards! spade-shaped, hammer-shaped, dagger-shaped, triangular, square, peaked, round, hemispherical, and forked. But chief among them all, was old Ushant's, the ancient Captain of the Forecastle. Of a Gothic venerableness, it fell upon his breast like a continual iron-gray storm.

Ah! old Ushant, Nestor of the crew! it promoted my longevity to behold you.

He was a man-of-war's-man of the old Benbow school. He wore a short cue, which the wags of the mizzen-top called his *"plug of pig-tail."* About his waist was a broad boarder's belt, which he wore, he said, to brace his main-mast, meaning his backbone; for at times he complained of rheumatic twinges in the spine, consequent upon sleeping on deck, now and then, during the night-watches of upward of half a century. His sheath-knife was an antique—a sort of old-fashioned pruning-hook; its handle—a sperm whale's tooth—was carved all over with ships, cannon, and anchors. It was attached to his neck by a *lanyard,* elaborately worked into "rose-knots" and "Turks' heads" by his own venerable fingers.

Of all the crew, this Ushant was most beloved by my glorious captain, Jack Chase, who one day pointed him out to me as the old man was slowly coming down the rigging from the fore-top.

"There, White-Jacket! isn't that old Chaucer's shipman?

A dagger hanging by a las hadde he,
About his nekke, under his arm adown;
The hote sommer hadde made his beard all brown.
Hardy he is, and wise; I undertake
With many a tempest has his beard be shake.

From the *Canterbury Tales,* White-Jacket! and must not old Ushant have been living in Chaucer's time, that Chaucer could draw his portrait so well?"

Chapter LXXXVII

Old Ushant at the Gangway

The rebel beards, headed by old Ushant's, streaming like a commodore's *bougee,* now stood in silence at the mast.

"You knew the order!" said the Captain, eyeing them severely; "what does that hair on your chins?"

"Sir," said the Captain of the Forecastle, "did old Ushant ever refuse doing his duty? did he ever yet miss his muster? But, sir, old Ushant's beard is his own!"

"What's that, sir? Master-at-arms, put that man into the brig."

"Sir," said the old man, respectfully, "the three years for which I shipped are expired; and though I am perhaps bound to work the ship home, yet, as matters are, I think my beard might be allowed me. It is but a few days, Captain Claret."

"Put him into the brig!" cried the Captain; "and now, you old rascals!" he added, turning round upon the rest, "I give you fifteen minutes to have those beards taken off; if they then remain on your chins, I'll flog you—every mother's son of you—though you were all my own godfathers!"

The band of beards went forward, summoned their barbers, and their glorious pennants were no more. In obedience to orders, they then paraded themselves at the mast, and, addressing the Captain, said, "Sir, our *muzzle-lashings* are cast off!"

Nor is it unworthy of being chronicled, that not a single sailor who complied with the general order but refused to sport the vile *regulation-whiskers* prescribed by the Navy Department. No! like heroes they cried, "Shave me clean! I will not wear a hair, since I cannot wear all!"

On the morrow, after breakfast, Ushant was taken out of irons, and, with the master-at-arms on one side and an armed sentry on the other, was escorted along the gun-deck and up the ladder to the main-mast. There the Captain stood, firm as before. They must have guarded the old man thus to prevent his escape to the shore, something less than a thousand miles distant at the time.

"Well, sir, will you have that beard taken off? you have slept over it a whole night now; what do you say? I don't want to flog an old man like you, Ushant!"

"My beard is my own, sir!" said the old man, lowly.

"Will you take it off?"

"It is mine, sir?" said the old man, tremulously.

"Rig the gratings?" roared the Captain. "Master-at-arms, strip him! quarter-masters, seize him up! boatswain's mates, do your duty!"

While these executioners were employed, the Captain's excitement had a little time to abate; and when, at last, old Ushant was tied up by the arms and legs and his venerable back was exposed—that back which had bowed at the guns of the frigate *Constitution* when she captured the *Guerrière*—the Captain seemed to relent.

"You are a very old man," he said, "and I am sorry to flog you; but my orders must be obeyed. I will give you one more chance; will you have that beard taken off?"

"Captain Claret," said the old man, turning round painfully in his bonds, "you may flog me if you will; but, sir, in this one thing I can*not* obey you."

"Lay on! I'll see his backbone!" roared the Captain in a sudden fury.

"By Heaven!" thrillingly whispered Jack Chase, who stood by, "it's only a halter; I'll strike him!"

"Better not," said a top-mate; "it's death, or worse punishment, remember."

"There goes the lash!" cried Jack. "Look at the old man! By G—d, I can't stand it! Let me go, men!" and with moist eyes Jack forced his way to one side.

"You, boatswain's mate," cried the Captain, "you are favoring that man! Lay on soundly, sir, or I'll have your own *cat* laid soundly on you."

One, two, three, four, five, six, seven, eight, nine, ten, eleven, twelve lashes were laid on the back of that heroic old man. He only bowed over his head, and stood as the Dying Gladiator lies.

"Cut him down," said the Captain.

"And now go and cut your own throat," hoarsely whispered an old sheet-anchor-man, a messmate of Ushant's.

When the master-at-arms advanced with the prisoner's shirt, Ushant waved him off with the dignified air of a Brahim, saying, "Do you think, master-at-arms, that I am hurt? I will put on my own garment. I am never the worse for it, man; and 'tis no dishonor when he who would dishonor you, only dishonors himself."

"What says he?" cried the Captain; "what says that tarry old philosopher with the smoking back? Tell it to me, sir, if you dare! Sentry, take that man back to the brig. Stop! John Ushant, you have been Captain of the Forecastle; I break you. And now you go into the brig, there to remain till you consent to have that beard taken off."

"My beard is my own," said the old man, quietly. "Sentry, I am ready."

And back he went into durance between the guns; but after lying some four or five days in irons, an order came to remove them; but he was still kept confined.

Books were allowed him, and he spent much time in reading. But he also spent many hours in braiding his beard, and interweaving with it strips of red bunting, as if he desired to dress out and adorn the thing which had triumphed over all opposition.

He remained a prisoner till we arrived in America; but the very moment he heard the chain rattle out of the hawse-hole, and the ship swing to her anchor, he started to his feet, dashed the sentry aside, and gaining the deck, exclaimed, "At home, with my beard!"

His term of service having some months previous expired, and the ship being now in harbor, he was beyond the reach of naval law, and the officers durst not molest him. But without unduly availing himself of these circumstances, the old man merely got his bag and hammock together, hired a boat, and throwing himself into the stern, was rowed ashore, amid the unsuppressible cheers of all hands. It was a glorious conquest over the Conqueror himself, as well worthy to be celebrated as the Battle of the Nile.

Though, as I afterward learned, Ushant was earnestly entreated to put the case into some lawyer's hands, he firmly declined, saying, "I have won the battle, my friends, and I do not care for the prize-money." But even had he complied with these entreaties, from precedents in similar cases, it is almost certain that not a sou's worth of satisfaction would have been received.

I know not in what frigate you sail now, old Ushant; but Heaven protect your storied old beard, in whatever Typhoon it may blow. And if ever it must be shorn, old man, may it fare like the royal beard of Henry I, of England, and be clipped by the right reverend hand of some Archbishop of Sees.

As for Captain Claret, let it not be supposed that it is here sought to impale him before the world as a cruel, black-hearted man. Such he was not. Nor was he, upon the whole, regarded by his crew with anything like the feelings which man-of-war's-men sometimes cherish toward signally tyrannical commanders. In truth, the majority of the *Neversink*'s crew—in previous cruises habituated to flagrant misusage—deemed Captain Claret a lenient officer. In many things he certainly refrained from oppressing them. It has been related what privileges he accorded to the seamen respecting the free playing of checkers—a thing almost unheard of in most American men-of-war. In the matter of overseeing the men's clothing, also, he was remarkably indulgent, compared with the conduct of other Navy captains, who, by sumptuary regulations, oblige their sailors to run up large bills with the Purser for clothes. In a word, of whatever acts Captain Claret might have been guilty in the *Neversink*, perhaps none of them proceeded from any personal, organic hard-heartedness. What he was, the usages of the Navy had made him. Had he been a mere landsman—a merchant, say—he would no doubt have been considered a kind-hearted man.

There may be some who shall read of this Bartholomew Massacre of beards who will yet marvel, perhaps, that the loss of a few hairs, more or less, should provoke such hostility from the sailors, lash them into so frothing a rage; indeed, come near breeding a mutiny.

But these circumstances are not without precedent. Not to speak of the riots, attended with the loss of life, which once occurred in Madrid, in resistance to an arbitrary edict of the king's, seeking to suppress the cloaks of the Cavaliers; and, not to make mention of other instances that might be quoted, it needs only to point out the rage of the Saxons in the time of William the Conqueror, when that despot commanded the hair on their upper lips to be shaven off—the hereditary mustaches which whole generations had sported. The multitude of the dispirited vanquished were obliged to acquiesce; but many Saxon Franklins and gentlemen of spirit, choosing rather to lose their castles than their mustaches, voluntarily deserted their firesides, and went into exile. All this is indignantly related by the stout Saxon friar, Matthew Paris, in his *Historia Major*, beginning with the Norman Conquest.

And that our man-of-war's-men were right in desiring to perpetuate their beards, as martial appurtenances, must seem very plain, when it is considered that, as the beard is the token of manhood, so, in some shape or other, has it ever been held the true badge of a warrior. Bonaparte's grenadiers were stout whiskerandoes; and perhaps, in a charge, those fierce whiskers of theirs did as much to appall the foe as the sheen of their bayonets. Most all fighting creatures sport either whiskers or beards; it seems a law of Dame Nature. Witness the boar, the tiger, the cougar, man, the leopard, the ram, the cat—all warriors, and all whiskerandoes. Whereas, the peace-loving tribes have mostly enameled chins.

Chapter LXXXVIII

FLOGGING THROUGH THE FLEET

THE FLOGGING OF AN OLD MAN LIKE USHANT, MOST LANDSMEN WILL PROBABLY REGARD WITH abhorrence. But though, from peculiar circumstances, his case occasioned a good deal of indignation among the people of the *Neversink,* yet, upon its own proper grounds, they did not denounce it. Man-of-war's-men are so habituated to what landsmen would deem excessive cruelties, that they are almost reconciled to inferior severities.

And here, though the subject of punishment in the Navy has been canvassed in previous chapters, and though the thing is every way a most unpleasant and grievous one to enlarge upon, and though I painfully nerve myself to it while I write, a feeling of duty compels me to enter upon a branch of the subject till now undiscussed. I would not be like the man, who, seeing an outcast perishing by the roadside, turned about to his friend, saying, "Let us cross the way; my soul so sickens at this sight, that I cannot endure it."

There are certain enormities in this man-of-war world that often secure impunity by their very excessiveness. Some ignorant people will refrain from permanently removing the cause of a deadly malaria, for fear of the temporary spread of its offensiveness. Let us not be of such. The more repugnant and repelling, the greater the evil. Leaving our women and children behind, let us freely enter this Golgotha.

Years ago there was a punishment inflicted in the English, and I believe in the American Navy, called *keel-hauling*—a phrase still employed by man-of-war's-men when they would express some signal vengeance upon a personal foe. The practice still remains in the French national marine, though it is by no means resorted to so frequently as in times past. It consists of attaching tackles to the two extremities of the main-yard, and passing the rope under the ship's bottom. To one end of this rope the culprit is secured; his own shipmates are then made to run him up and down, first on this side, then on that—now scraping the ship's hull under water—anon, hoisted, stunned and breathless, into the air.

But though this barbarity is now abolished from the English and American navies, there still remains another practice which, if anything, is even worse than *keel-hauling.* This remnant of the Middle Ages is known in the Navy as *"flogging through the fleet."* It is never inflicted except by authority of a court-martial upon some trespasser deemed guilty of a flagrant offense. Never, that I know of, has it been inflicted by an American man-of-war on the home station. The reason, probably, is, that the officers well know that such a spectacle would raise a mob in any American seaport.

By XLI of the *Articles of War,* a court-martial shall not "for any one offense not capital," inflict a punishment beyond one hundred lashes. In cases "not capital" this law may be, and has been, quoted in judicial justification of the infliction of more than one hundred lashes. Indeed, it would cover a thousand. Thus: One act of a sailor may be construed into the commission of ten different transgressions, for each of which he may be legally condemned to a hundred lashes, to be inflicted without intermission. It will be perceived, that in any case deemed "capital," a sailor under the above *Article,* may legally be flogged to the death.

But neither by the *Articles of War,* nor by any other enactment of Congress, is there any direct warrant for the extraordinary cruelty of the mode in which punishment is inflicted, in cases of flogging through the fleet. But as in numerous other instances, the incidental aggravations of this penalty are indirectly covered by other clauses in the *Articles of War*: one of which authorizes the authorities of a ship—in certain indefinite cases—to correct the guilty *"according to the usages of the sea-service."*

One of these "usages" is the following:

All hands being called "to witness punishment" in the ship to which the culprit belongs, the sentence of the court-martial condemning him is read, when, with the usual solemnities, a portion of the punishment is inflicted. In order that it shall not lose in severity by the slightest exhaustion in the arm of the executioner, a fresh boatswain's mate is called out at every dozen.

As the leading idea is to strike terror into the beholders, the greatest number of lashes is inflicted on board the culprit's own ship, in order to render him the more shocking spectacle to the crews of the other vessels.

The first infliction being concluded, the culprit's shirt is thrown over him; he is put into a boat—the *Rogue's March* being played meanwhile—and rowed to the next ship of the squadron. All hands of that ship are then called to man the rigging, and another portion of the punishment is inflicted by the boatswain's mates of that ship. The bloody shirt is again thrown over the seaman; and thus he is carried through the fleet or squadron till the whole sentence is inflicted.

In other cases, the launch—the largest of the boats—is rigged with a platform (like a headsman's scaffold), upon which halberds, something like those used in the English army, are erected. They consist of two stout poles, planted upright. Upon the platform stand a Lieutenant, a Surgeon a Master-at-arms, and the executioners with their "cats." They are rowed through the fleet, stopping at each ship, till the whole sentence is inflicted, as before.

In some cases, the attending surgeon has professionally interfered before the last lash has been given, alleging that immediate death must ensue if the remainder should be administered without a respite. But instead of humanely remitting the remaining lashes, in a case like this, the man is generally consigned to his cot for ten or twelve days; and when the surgeon officially reports him capable of undergoing the rest of the sentence, it is forthwith inflicted. Shylock must have his pound of flesh.

To say, that after being flogged through the fleet, the prisoner's back is sometimes puffed up like a pillow; or to say that in other cases it looks as if burned black before a roasting fire; or to say that you may track him through the squadron by the blood on the bulwarks of every ship, would only be saying what many seamen have seen.

Several weeks, sometimes whole months, elapse before the sailor is sufficiently recovered to resume his duties. During the greater part of that interval he lies in the sick-bay, groaning out his days and nights; and unless he has the hide and constitution of a rhinoceros, he never is the man he was before, but, broken and shattered to the marrow of his bones, sinks into death before his time. Instances have occurred where he has expired the day after the punishment. No wonder that the Englishman, Dr. Granville—himself once a surgeon in the Navy—declares, in his work on Russia, that the barbarian "knout" itself is not a greater torture to undergo than the Navy cat-o'-nine-tails.

Some years ago a fire broke out near the powder magazine in an American national ship, one of the squadron at anchor in the Bay of Naples. The utmost alarm prevailed. A cry went fore and aft that the ship was about to blow up. One of the seamen sprang overboard in affright. At length the fire was got under, and the man was picked up. He was tried before a court-martial, found guilty of cowardice, and condemned to be flogged through the fleet. In due time the squadron made sail for Algiers, and in that harbor, once haunted by pirates, the punishment was inflicted—the Bay of Naples, though washing the shores of an absolute king, not being deemed a fit place for such an exhibition of American naval law.

While the *Neversink* was in the Pacific, an American sailor, who had deposited a vote for General Harrison for President of the United States, was flogged through the fleet.

Chapter LXXXIX

THE SOCIAL STATE IN A MAN-OF-WAR

BUT THE FLOGGINGS AT THE GANGWAY AND THE FLOGGINGS THROUGH THE FLEET, THE STEALings, highway robberies, swearings, gamblings, blasphemings, thimble-riggings, smugglings, and tipplings of a man-of-war, which throughout this narrative have been here and there sketched from the life, by no means comprise the whole catalogue of evil. One single feature is full of significance.

All large ships of war carry soldiers, called marines. In the *Neversink* there was something less than fifty, two thirds of whom were Irishmen. They were officered by a Lieutenant, an Orderly Sergeant, two Sergeants, and two Corporals, with a drummer and fifer. The custom, generally, is to have a marine to each gun; which rule usually furnishes the scale for distributing the soldiers in vessels of different force.

Our marines had no other than martial duty to perform; excepting that, at sea, they stood watches like the sailors, and now and then lazily assisted in pulling the ropes. But they never put foot in rigging or hand in tar-bucket.

On the quarter-bills, these men were stationed at none of the great guns; on the station-bills, they had no posts at the ropes. What, then, were they for? To serve their country in time of battle? Let us see. When a ship is running into action, her marines generally lie flat on their faces behind the bulwarks (the sailors are sometimes ordered to do the same), and when the vessel is fairly engaged, they are usually drawn up in the ship's waist—like a company reviewing in the Park. At close quarters, their muskets may pick off a seaman or two in the rigging, but at long-gun distance they must passively stand in their ranks and be decimated at the enemy's leisure. Only in one case in ten—that is, when their vessel is attempted to be boarded by a large party, are these marines of any essential service as fighting men; with their bayonets they are then called upon to "repel!"

If comparatively so useless as soldiers, why have marines at all in the Navy? Know, then, that what standing armies are to nations, what turnkeys are to jails, these marines are to the seamen in all large men-of-war. Their muskets are their keys. With those muskets they stand guard over the fresh water; over the grog, when doled; over the provisions, when being served out by the Master's mate; over the "brig" or jail; at the Commodore's and Captain's cabin doors; and, in port, at both gangways and forecastle.

Surely, the crowd of sailors, who besides having so many sea-officers over them, are thus additionally guarded by soldiers, even when they quench their thirst—surely these man-of-war's-men must be desperadoes indeed; or else the naval service must be so tyrannical that the worst is feared from their possible insubordination. Either reason holds good, or both, according to the character of the officers and crew.

It must be evident that the man-of-war's-man casts but an evil eye on a marine. To call a man a "horse-marine," is, among seamen, one of the greatest terms of contempt.

But the mutual contempt, and even hatred, subsisting between these two bodies of men—both clinging to one keel, both lodged in one household—is held by most Navy officers as the height of the perfection of Navy discipline. It is regarded as the button that caps the uttermost point on their main-mast.

Thus they reason: Secure of this antagonism between the marine and the sailor, we can always rely upon it, that if the sailor mutinies, it needs no great incitement for the marine to thrust his bayonet through his heart; if the marine revolts, the pike of the sailor is impatient to charge. Checks and balances, blood against blood, *that* is the cry and the argument.

What applies to the relation in which the marine and sailor stand toward each other—the mutual repulsion implied by a system of checks—will, in degree, apply to nearly the entire interior of a man-of-war's discipline. The whole body of this discipline is emphatically a system of cruel cogs and wheels, systematically grinding up in one common hopper all that might minister to the moral well-being of the crew.

It is the same with both officers and men. If a Captain have a grudge against a Lieutenant, or a Lieutenant against a midshipman, how easy to torture him by official treatment, which shall not lay open the superior officer to legal rebuke. And if a midshipman bears a grudge against a sailor, how easy for him, by cunning practices, born of a boyish spite, to have him degraded at the gangway. Through all the endless ramifications of rank and station, in most men-of-war there runs a sinister vein of bitterness, not exceeded by the fireside hatreds in a family of stepsons ashore. It were sickening to detail all the paltry irritabilities, jealousies, and cabals, the spiteful detractions and animosities, that lurk far down, and cling to the very kelson of the ship. It is unmanning to think of. The immutable ceremonies and iron etiquette of a man-of-war; the spiked barriers separating the various grades of rank; the delegated absolutism of authority on all hands; the impossibility, on the part of the common seaman, of appeal from incidental abuses, and many more things that might be enumerated, all tend to beget in most armed ships a general social condition which is the precise reverse of what any Christian could desire. And though there are vessels, that in some measure furnish exceptions to this; and though, in other ships, the thing may be glazed over by a guarded, punctilious exterior, almost completely hiding the truth from casual visitors, while the worst facts touching the common sailor are systematically kept in the background, yet it is certain that what has here been said of the domestic interior of a man-of-war will, in a greater or less degree, apply to most vessels in the Navy. It is not that the officers are so malevolent, nor, altogether, that the man-of-war's-man is so vicious. Some of these evils are unavoidably generated through the operation of the Naval code; others are absolutely organic to a Navy establishment, and, like other organic evils, are incurable, except when they dissolve with the body they live in.

Chapter XC

THE MANNING OF NAVIES

"THE GALLOWS AND THE SEA REFUSE NOTHING," IS A VERY OLD SEA SAYING; AND, AMONG ALL THE wondrous prints of Hogarth, there is none remaining more true at the present day than that dramatic boat-scene, where after consorting with harlots and gambling on tomb-stones, the Idle Apprentice, with the villainous low forehead, is at last represented as being pushed off to sea, with a ship and a gallows in the distance. But Hogarth should have converted the ship's masts themselves into Tyburn-trees, and thus, with the ocean for a background, closed the career of his hero. It would then have had all the dramatic force of the opera of *Don Juan*, who, after running his impious courses, is swept from our sight in a tornado of devils.

For the sea is the true Tophet and bottomless pit of many workers of iniquity; and, as the German mystics feign Gehennas within Gehennas, even so are men-of-war familiarly known among sailors as "Floating Hells." And as the sea, according to old Fuller, is the stable of brute monsters, gliding hither and thither in unspeakable swarms, even so is it the home of many moral monsters, who fitly divide its empire with the snake, the shark, and the worm.

Nor are sailors, and man-of-war's-men especially, at all blind to a true sense of these things.

"Purser rigged and parish damned," is the sailor saying in the American Navy, when the tyro first mounts the lined frock and blue jacket, aptly manufactured for him in a State Prison ashore.

No wonder, that lured by some *crimp* into a service so galling, and, perhaps, persecuted by a vindictive lieutenant, some repentant sailors have actually jumped into the sea to escape from their fate, or set themselves adrift on the wide ocean on the gratings without compass or rudder.

In one case, a young man, after being nearly cut into dog's meat at the gangway, loaded his pockets with shot and walked overboard.

Some years ago, I was in a whaling ship lying in a harbor of the Pacific, with three French men-of-war alongside. One dark, moody night, a suppressed cry was heard from the face of the waters, and, thinking it was someone drowning, a boat was lowered, when two French sailors were picked up, half dead from exhaustion, and nearly throttled by a bundle of their clothes tied fast to their shoulders. In this manner they had attempted their escape from their vessel. When the French officers came in pursuit, these sailors, rallying from their exhaustion, fought like tigers to resist being captured. Though this story concerns a French armed ship, it is not the less applicable, in degree, to those of other nations.

Mix with the men in an American armed ship, mark how many foreigners there are, though it is against the law to enlist them. Nearly one third of the petty officers of the *Neversink* were born east of the Atlantic. Why is this? Because the same principle that operates in hindering Americans from hiring themselves out as menial domestics also restrains them, in a great measure, from voluntarily assuming a far worse servitude in the Navy. *"Sailors wanted for the Navy"* is a common announcement along the wharves of our sea-ports. They are always *"wanted."* It may have been, in part, owing to this scarcity man-of-war's men, that not many years ago, black slaves were frequently to be found regularly enlisted with the crew of an American frigate, their masters receiving their pay. This was in the teeth of a law of Congress expressly prohibiting slaves in the Navy. This law, indirectly, means black slaves, nothing being said concerning white ones. But in view of what John Randolph of Roanoke said about the frigate that carried him to Russia, and in view of what most armed vessels actually are at present, the American Navy is not altogether an inappropriate place for hereditary bondmen. Still, the circumstance of their being found in it is of such a nature, that to some it may hardly appear credible. The incredulity of such persons, nevertheless, must yield to the fact, that on board of the United States ship *Neversink,* during the present cruise, there was a Virginian slave regularly shipped as a seaman, his owner receiving his wages. Guinea—such was his name among the crew—belonged to the Purser, who was a Southern gentleman; he was employed as his body servant. Never did I feel my condition as a man-of-war's-man so keenly as when seeing this Guinea freely circulating about the decks in citizen's clothes, and through the influence of his master, almost entirely exempted from the disciplinary degradation of the Caucasian crew. Faring sumptuously in the ward-room; sleek and round, his ebon face fairly polished with content: ever gay and hilarious; ever ready to laugh and joke, that African slave was actually envied by many of the seamen. There were times when I almost envied him myself. Lemsford once envied him outright, "Ah, Guinea!" he sighed, "you have peaceful times; you never opened the book I read in."

One morning, when all hands were called to witness punishment, the Purser's slave, as usual, was observed to be hurrying down the ladders toward the ward-room, his face wearing that peculiar, pinched blueness, which, in the negro, answers to the paleness caused by nervous agitation in the white. "Where are you going, Guinea?" cried the deck-officer, a humorous gentleman, who sometimes diverted himself with the Purser's slave, and well knew what answer he would now receive from him. "Where are you going, Guinea?" said this officer; "turn about; don't you hear the call, sir?" " *'Scuse* me, massa!" said the slave, with a low salutation; "I can't 'tand it; I can't, indeed, massa!" and, so saying, he disappeared beyond the hatchway. He was the only person on board, except the hospital-steward and the invalids of the sick-bay, who was exempted from being present at the administering of the scourge. Accustomed to light and easy duties from his birth, and so fortunate as to meet with none but gentle masters, Guinea, though a bondman, liable to be saddled with a mortgage, like a horse—Guinea, in India-rubber manacles, enjoyed the liberties of the world.

Though his body-and-soul proprietor, the Purser, never in any way individualized me while I served on board the frigate, and never did me a good office of any kind (it was hardly in his power), yet, from his pleasant, kind, indulgent manner toward his slave, I always imputed to him a generous heart, and cherished an involuntary friendliness toward him. Upon our arrival home, his treatment of Guinea, under circumstances peculiarly calculated to stir up the resentment of a slave-owner, still more augmented my estimation of the Purser's good heart.

Mention has been made of the number of foreigners in the American Navy; but it is not in the American Navy alone that foreigners bear so large a proportion to the rest of the crew, though in no navy, perhaps, have they ever borne so large a proportion as in our own. According to an English estimate, the foreigners serving in the King's ships at one time amounted to one eighth of the entire body of seamen. How it is in the French Navy, I cannot with certainty say; but I have repeatedly sailed with English seamen who have served in it.

One of the effects of the free introduction of foreigners into any Navy cannot be sufficiently deplored. During the period I lived in the *Neversink,* I was repeatedly struck by the lack of patriotism in many of my shipmates. True, they were mostly foreigners who unblushingly avowed, that were it not for the difference of pay, they would as lief man the guns of an English ship as those of an American or Frenchman. Nevertheless, it was evident, that as for any high-toned patriotic feeling, there was comparatively very little—hardly any of it—evinced by our sailors as a body. Upon reflection, this was not to be wondered at. From their roving career, and the sundering of all domestic ties, many sailors, all the world over, are like the "Free Companions," who some centuries ago wandered over Europe, ready to fight the battles of any prince who could purchase their swords. The only patriotism is born and nurtured in a stationary home, and upon an immovable hearth-stone; but the man-of-war's-man, though in his voyagings he weds the two Poles and brings both Indies together, yet, let him wander where he will, he carries his one only home along with him: that home is his hammock. *"Born under a gun, and educated on the bowsprit,"* according to a phrase of his own, the man-of-war-man rolls round the world like a billow, ready to mix with any sea, or be sucked down to death in the maelstrom of any war.

Yet more. The dread of the general discipline of a man-of-war; the special obnoxiousness of the gangway; the protracted confinement on board ship, with so few "liberty days"; and the pittance of pay (much less than what can always be had in the Merchant Service), these things contrive to deter from the navies of all countries by far the majority of their best seamen. This will be obvious, when the following statistical facts, taken from Macpherson's *Annals of Commerce,* are considered. At one period, upon the Peace Establishment, the number of men employed in the English Navy was 25,000; at the same time, the English Merchant Service was employing 118,952. But while the necessities of a merchantman render it indispensable that the greater part of her crew be able-seamen, the circumstances of a man-of-war admit of her mustering a crowd of landsmen, soldiers, and boys in her service. By a statement of Captain Marryat's, in his pamphlet (A.D. 1822) *On the Abolition of Impressment,* it appears that, at the close of the Bonaparte wars, a full third of all the crews of his Majesty's fleets consisted of landsmen and boys.

Far from entering with enthusiasm into the king's ships when their country were menaced, the great body of English seamen, appalled at the discipline of the Navy, adopted unheard-of devices to escape its press-gangs. Some even hid themselves in caves, and lonely places inland, fearing to run the risk of seeking a berth in an outward-bound merchantman, that might have carried them beyond sea. In the true narrative of *John Nichol, Mariner,* published in 1822 by Blackwood in Edinburgh, and Cadell in London, and which everywhere bears the spontaneous impress of truth, the old sailor, in the most artless, touching, and almost uncomplaining manner, tells of his "skulking like a thief" for whole years in the country round about Edinburgh, to avoid the press-gangs, prowling through the land like bandits and Burkers. At this time (Bonaparte's wars), according to "Steel's List," there were forty-five regular press-gang stations in Great Britain.[1]

In a later instance, a large body of British seamen solemnly assembled upon the eve of an anticipated war, and together determined, that in case of its breaking out, they would at once flee to America, to avoid being pressed into the service of their country—a service which degraded her own guardians at the gangway.

At another time, long previous to this, according to an English Navy officer, Lieutenant Tomlinson, three thousand seamen, impelled by the same motive, fled ashore in a panic from the colliers between Yarmouth Roads and the *Nore*. Elsewhere, he says, in speaking of some of the men on board the king's ships, that "they were most miserable objects." This remark is perfectly corroborated by other testimony referring to another period. In alluding to the lamented scarcity of good English seamen during the wars of 1808, etc., the author of a pamphlet on "Naval Subjects" says, that all the best seamen, the steadiest and best-behaved men, generally succeeded in avoiding the impress. This writer was, or had been, himself a Captain in the British fleet.

Now it may be easily imagined who are the men, and of what moral character they are, who, even at the present day, are willing to enlist as full-grown adults in a service so galling to all shore-manhood as the Navy. Hence it comes that the skulkers and scoundrels of all sorts in a man-of-war are chiefly composed not of regular seamen, but of these "dock-lopers" of landsmen, men who enter the Navy to draw their grog and murder their time in the notorious idleness of a frigate. But if so idle, why not reduce the number of a man-of-war's crew, and reasonably keep employed the rest? It cannot be done. In the first place, the magnitude of most of these ships requires a large number of hands to brace the heavy yards, hoist the enormous top-sails, and weigh the ponderous anchor. And though the occasion for the employment of so many men comes but seldom, it is true, yet when that occasion *does* come—and come it may at any moment—this multitude of men are indispensable.

But besides this, and to crown all, the batteries must be manned. There must be enough men to work all the guns at one time. And thus, in order to have a sufficiency of mortals at hand to "sink, burn and destroy"; a man-of-war—besides, through her vices, hopelessly depraving the volunteer landsmen and ordinary seamen of good habits, who occasionally enlist—must feed at the public cost a multitude of persons, who, if they did not find a home in the Navy, would probably fall on the parish, or linger out their days in a prison.

Among others, these are the men into whose mouths Dibdin puts his patriotic verses, full of sea-chivalry and romance. With an exception in the last line, they might be sung with equal propriety by both English and American man-of-war's-men.

As for me, in all weathers, all times, tides, and ends,
Naught's a trouble from duty that springs;
For my heart is my Poll's, and my rhino's my friends,
And as for my life, it's the king's.

To rancor unknown, to no passion a slave,
Nor unmanly, nor mean, nor a railer, etc.

1. Besides this domestic kidnapping, British frigates, in friendly or neutral harbors, in some instances pressed into their service foreign sailors of all nations from the public wharves. In certain cases, where Americans were concerned, when "*protections*" were found upon their persons, these were destroyed; and to prevent the American consul from claiming his sailor countrymen, the press-gang generally went on shore the night previous to the sailing of the frigate, so that the kidnapped seamen were far out to sea before they could be missed by their friends. These things should be known; for in case the English government again goes to war with its fleets, and should again resort to indiscriminate impressment to man them, it is well that both Englishmen and Americans, that all the world be prepared to put down an iniquity outrageous and insulting to God and man.

I do not unite with a high critical authority in considering Dibdin's ditties as "slang songs," for most of them breathe the very poetry of the ocean. But it is remarkable that those songs—which would lead one to think that man-of-war's-men are the most care-free, contented, virtuous, and patriotic of mankind—were composed at a time when the English Navy was principally manned by felons and paupers, as mentioned in a former chapter. Still more, these songs are pervaded by a true Mohammedan sensualism; a reckless acquiescence in fate, and an implicit, unquestioning, dog-like devotion to whoever may be lord and master. Dibdin was a man of genius; but no wonder Dibdin was a government pensioner at £200 per annum.

But notwithstanding the iniquities of a man-of-war, men are to be found in them, at times, so used to a hard life; so drilled and disciplined to servitude, that, with an incomprehensible philosophy, they seem cheerfully to resign themselves to their fate. They have plenty to eat; spirits to drink; clothing to keep them warm; a hammock to sleep in; tobacco to chew; a doctor to medicine them; a parson to pray for them; and, to a penniless castaway, must not all this seem as a luxurious Bill of Fare?

There was on board of the *Neversink* a fore-top-man by the name of Landless, who, though his back was cross-barred, and plaided with the ineffaceable scars of all the floggings accumulated by a reckless tar during a ten years' service in the Navy, yet he perpetually wore a hilarious face, and at joke and repartee was a very Joe Miller.

That man, though a sea-vagabond, was not created in vain. He enjoyed life with the zest of everlasting adolescence; and, though cribbed in an oaken prison, with the turnkey sentries all round him, yet he paced the gun-deck as if it were broad as a prairie, and diversified in landscape as the hills and valleys of the Tyrol. Nothing ever disconcerted him; nothing could transmute his laugh into anything like a sigh. Those glandular secretions, which in other captives sometimes go to the formation of tears, in *him* were expectorated from the mouth, tinged with the golden juice of a weed, wherewith he solaced and comforted his ignominious days.

"Rum and tobacco!" said Landless, "what more does a sailor want?"

His favorite song was *Dibdin's True English Sailor*, beginning,

Jack dances and sings, and is always content,
In his vows to his lass he'll ne'er fail her;
His anchor's atrip when his money's all spent,
And this is the life of a sailor.

But poor Landless danced quite as often at the gangway, under the lash, as in the sailor dance-houses ashore.

Another of his songs, also set to the significant tune of *The King, God Bless Him!* mustered the following lines among many similar ones:

Oh, when safely landed in Boston or 'York,
Oh how I will tipple and jig it;
And toss off my glass while my rhino holds out,
In drinking success to our frigate!

During the many idle hours when our frigate was lying in harbor, this man was either merrily playing at checkers, or mending his clothes, or snoring like a trumpeter under the lee of the booms. When fast asleep, a national salute from our batteries could hardly move him. Whether ordered to the main-truck in a gale; or rolled by the drum to the grog-tub; or commanded to walk up to the gratings and be lashed, Landless always obeyed with the same invincible indifference.

His advice to a young lad, who shipped with us at Valparaiso, embodies the pith and marrow of that philosophy which enables some man-of-war's-men to wax jolly in the service.

"Shippy!" said Landless, taking the pale lad by his neckerchief, as if he had him by the halter; "Shippy, I've seen sarvice with Uncle Sam—I've sailed in many *Andrew Millers.* Now take my advice, and steer clear of all trouble. D'ye see, touch your tile whenever a swob (officer) speaks to you. And never mind how much they rope's-end you, keep your red-rag belayed; for you must know as how they don't fancy sea-lawyers; and when the sarving out of slops comes round, stand up to it stiffly; it's only an oh Lord! or two, and a few oh my Gods!—that's all. And what then? Why, you sleeps it off in a few nights, and turn out at last all ready for your grog."

This Landless was a favorite with the officers, among whom he went by the name of *"Happy Jack."* And it is just such Happy Jacks as Landless that most sea-officers profess to admire; a fellow without shame, without a soul, so dead to the least dignity of manhood that he could hardly be called a man. Whereas, a seaman who exhibits traits of moral sensitiveness, whose demeanor shows some dignity within; this is the man they, in many cases, instinctively dislike. The reason is, they feel such a man to be a continual reproach to them, as being mentally superior to their power. He has no business in a man-of-war; they do not want such men. To them there is an insolence in his manly freedom, contempt in his very carriage. He is unendurable, as an erect, lofty-minded African would be to some slave-driving planter.

Let it not be supposed, however, that the remarks in this and the preceding chapter apply to *all* men-of-war. There are some vessels blessed with patriarchal, intellectual Captains, gentlemanly and brotherly officers, and docile and Christianized crews. The peculiar usages of such vessels insensibly softens the tyrannical rigour of the *Articles of War*; in them, scourging is unknown. To sail in such ships is hardly to realize that you live under the martial law, or that the evils above mentioned can anywhere exist.

And Jack Chase, old Ushant, and several more fine tars that might be added, sufficiently attest, that in the *Neversink* at least, there was more than one noble man-of-war's-man who almost redeemed all the rest.

Wherever, throughout this narrative, the American Navy, in any of its bearings, has formed the theme of a general discussion, hardly one syllable of admiration for what is accounted illustrious in its achievements has been permitted to escape me. The reason is this: I consider, that so far as what is called military renown is concerned, the American Navy needs no eulogist but History. It were superfluous for White-Jacket to tell the world what it knows already. The office imposed upon me is of another cast; and, though I foresee and feel that it may subject me to the pillory in the hard thoughts of some men, yet, supported by what God has given me, I tranquilly abide the event, whatever it may prove.

Chapter XCI

Smoking-Club in a Man-of-War, with Scenes on the Gun-Deck Drawing Near Home

THERE IS A FABLE ABOUT A PAINTER MOVED BY JOVE TO THE PAINTING OF THE HEAD OF MEDUSA. Though the picture was true to the life, yet the poor artist sickened at the sight of what his forced pencil had drawn. Thus, borne through my task toward the end, my own soul now sinks at what I myself have portrayed. But let us forget past chapters, if we may, while we paint less repugnant things.

Metropolitan gentlemen have their club; provincial gossipers their news-room; village quidnuncs their barber's shop; the Chinese their opium-houses; American Indians their council-fire; and even cannibals their *Noojona,* or Talk-Stone, where they assemble at times to discuss the affairs of the day. Nor is there any government, however despotic, that ventures to deny to the least of its subjects the privilege of a sociable chat. Not the Thirty Tyrants even—the clubbed post-captains of old Athens—could stop the wagging tongues at the street-corners. For chat man must; and by our immortal Bill of Rights, that guarantees to us liberty of speech, chat we Yankees will, whether on board a frigate, or on board our own terra-firma plantations.

In men-of-war, the Galley, or Cookery, on the gun-deck, is the grand center of gossip and news among the sailors. Here crowds assemble to chat away the half-hour elapsing after every meal. The reason why this place and these hours are selected rather than others is this: in the neighborhood of the galley alone, and only after meals, is the man-of-war's-man permitted to regale himself with a smoke.

A sumptuary edict, truly, that deprived White-Jacket, for one, of a luxury to which he had long been attached. For how can the mystical motives, the capricious impulses of a luxurious smoker go and come at the beck of a Commodore's command? No! when I smoke, be it because of my sovereign good pleasure I choose so to do, though at so unseasonable an hour that I send round the town for a brasier of coals. What! smoke by a sun-dial? Smoke on compulsion? Make a trade, a business, a vile recurring calling of smoking? And, perhaps, when those sedative fumes have steeped you in the grandest of reveries, and, circle over circle, solemnly rises some immeasurable dome in your soul—far away, swelling and heaving into the vapor you raise—as if from one Mozart's grandest marches of a temple were rising, like Venus from the sea—at such a time, to have your whole Parthenon tumbled about your ears by the knell of the ship's bell announcing the expiration of the half-hour for smoking! Whip me, ye Furies! toast me in saltpeter! smite me, some thunderbolt! charge upon me, endless squadrons of Mamalukes! devour me, Fijis! but preserve me from a tyranny like this!

No! though I smoked like an Indian summer ere I entered the *Neversink*, so abhorrent was this sumptuary law that I altogether abandoned the luxury rather than enslave it to a time and a place. Herein did I not right, Ancient and Honorable Old Guard of Smokers all round the world?

But there were others of the crew not so fastidious as myself. After every meal, they hied to the galley and solaced their souls with a whiff.

Now a bunch of cigars, all banded together, is a type and a symbol of the brotherly love between smokers. Likewise, for the time, in a community of pipes is a community of hearts! Nor was it an ill thing for the Indian Sachems to circulate their calumet tobacco-bowl—even as our own forefathers circulated their punch-bowl—in token of peace, charity, and good-will, friendly feelings, and sympathizing souls. And this it was that made the gossipers of the galley so loving a club, so long as the vapory bond united them.

It was a pleasant sight to behold them. Grouped in the recesses between the guns, they chatted and laughed like rows of convivialists in the boxes of some vast dining-saloon. Take a Flemish kitchen full of good fellows from Teniers; add a fireside group from Wilkie; throw in a naval sketch from Cruickshank; and then stick a short pipe into every mother's son's mouth, and you have the smoking scene at the galley of the *Neversink*.

Not a few were politicians; and, as there were some thoughts of a war with England at the time, their discussions waxed warm.

"I tell you what it is, *shippies!*" cried the old captain of gun No. 1 on the forecastle, "if that 'ere President of ourn don't luff up into the wind, by the Battle of the Nile! he'll be getting us into a grand fleet engagement afore the Yankee nation has rammed home her cartridges—let alone blowing the match!"

"Who talks of luffing?" roared a roystering fore-top-man. "Keep our Yankee nation large before the wind, say I, till you come plump on the enemy's bows, and then board him in the smoke," and with that, there came forth a mighty blast from his pipe.

"Who says the old man at the helm of the Yankee nation can't steer his *trick* as well as George Washington himself?" cried a sheet-anchor-man.

"But they say he's a cold-water customer, Bill," cried another; "and sometimes o' nights I somehow has a presentation that he's goin' to stop our grog."

"D'ye hear there, fore and aft!" roared the boatswain's mate at the gangway, "all hands tumble up, and 'bout ship!"

"That's the talk!" cried the captain of gun No. 1, as, in obedience to the summons, all hands dropped their pipes and crowded toward the ladders, "and that's what the President must do—go in stays, my lads, and put the Yankee nation on the other tack."

But these political discussions by no means supplied the staple of conversation for the gossiping smokers of the galley. The interior affairs of the frigate itself formed their principal theme. Rumors about the private life of the Commodore in his cabin; about the Captain, in his; about the various officers in the ward-room; about the *reefers* in the steerage, and their madcap frolickings, and about a thousand other matters touching the crew themselves; all these—forming the eternally shifting, domestic by-play of a man-of-war—proved inexhaustible topics for our quidnuncs.

The animation of these scenes was very much heightened as we drew nearer and nearer our port; it rose to a climax when the frigate was reported to be only twenty-four hours' sail from the land. What they should do when they landed; how they should invest their wages; what they should eat; what they should drink; and what lass they should marry—these were the topics which absorbed them.

"Sink the sea!" cried a forecastle man. "Once more ashore, and you'll never again catch old Boombolt afloat. I mean to settle down in a sail-loft."

"Cable-tier pinchers blister all tarpaulin hats!" cried a young after-guard's-man; "I mean to go back to the counter."

"Shipmates! take me by the arms, and swab up the lee-scuppers with me, but I mean to steer a clam-cart before I go again to a ship's wheel. Let the Navy go by the board—to sea again, I won't!"

"Start my soul-bolts, maties, if any more Blue Peters and sailing signals fly at my fore!" cried the Captain of the Head. "My wages will buy a wheelbarrow, if nothing more."

"I have taken my last dose of salts," said the Captain of the Waist, "and after this mean to stick to fresh water. Ay, maties, ten of us Waisters mean to club together and buy a *serving-mallet boat*, d'ye see; and if ever we drown, it will be in the 'raging canal!' Blast the sea, shipmates! say I."

"Profane not the holy element!" said Lemsford, the poet of the gun-deck, leaning over a cannon. "Know ye not, man-of-war's-men! that by the Parthian magi the ocean was held sacred? Did not Tiridates, the eastern monarch, take an immense land circuit to avoid desecrating the Mediterranean, in order to reach his imperial master, Nero, and do homage for his crown?"

"What lingo is that?" cried the Captain of the Waist.

"Who's Commodore Tiddery-eye?" cried the forecastle-man.

"Hear me out," resumed Lemsford. "Like Tiridates, I venerate the sea, and venerate it so highly, shipmates, that evermore I shall abstain from crossing it. In *that* sense, Captain of the Waist, I echo your cry."

It was, indeed, a remarkable fact, that nine men out of every ten of the *Neversink*'s crew had formed some plan or other to keep themselves ashore for life, or, at least, on fresh water, after the expiration of the present cruise. With all the experiences of that cruise accumulated in one intense recollection of a moment; with the smell of tar in their nostrils; out of sight of land; with a stout ship under foot, and snuffing the ocean air; with all the things of the sea surrounding them; in their cool, sober moments of reflection; in the silence and solitude of the deep, during the long night-watches, when all their holy home associations were thronging round their hearts; in the spontaneous piety and devotion of the last hours of so long a voyage; in the fullness and the frankness of their souls; when there was naught to jar the well-poised equilibrium of their judgment—under all these circumstances, at least nine tenths of a crew of five hundred man-of-war's-men resolved forever to turn their backs on the sea. But do men ever hate the thing they love? Do men forswear the hearth and the homestead? What, then, must the Navy be?

But, alas for the man-of-war's-man, who, though he may take a Hannibal oath against the service; yet, cruise after cruise, and after forswearing it again and again, he is driven back to the spirit-tub and the gun-deck by his old hereditary foe, the ever-devilish god of grog.

On this point, let some of the crew of the *Neversink* be called to the stand.

You, Captain of the Waist! and you, seamen of the fore-top! and you, after-guard's-men and others! how came you here at the guns of the *North Carolina,* after registering your solemn vows at the galley of the *Neversink?*

They all hang their heads. I know the cause; poor fellows! perjure yourselves not again; swear not at all hereafter.

Ay, these very tars—the foremost in denouncing the Navy; who had bound themselves by the most tremendous oaths—these very men, not three days after getting ashore, were rolling round the streets in penniless drunkenness; and next day many of them were to be found on board of the *guardo* or receiving-ship. Thus, in part, is the Navy manned.

But what was still more surprising, and tended to impart a new and strange insight into the character of sailors, and overthrow some long-established ideas concerning them as a class, was this: numbers of men who, during the cruise, had passed for exceedingly prudent, nay, parsimonious persons, who would even refuse you a patch, or a needleful of thread, and, from their stinginess, procured the name of *Ravelings*—no sooner were these men fairly adrift in harbor, and under the influence of frequent quaffings, than their three-years'-earned wages flew right and left; they summoned whole boarding-houses of sailors to the bar, and treated them over and over again. Fine fellows! generous-hearted tars! Seeing this sight, I thought to myself, Well, these generous-hearted tars on shore were the greatest curmudgeons afloat! it's the bottle that's generous, not they! Yet the popular conceit concerning a sailor is derived from his behavior ashore; whereas, ashore he is no longer a sailor, but a landsman for the time. A man-of-war's-man is only a man-of-war's-man at sea; and the sea is the place to learn what he is. But we have seen that a man-of-war is but this old-fashioned world of ours afloat, full of all manner of characters—full of strange contradictions; and though boasting some fine fellows here and there, yet, upon the whole, charged to the combings of her hatchways with the spirit of Belial and all unrighteousness.

Chapter XCII

THE LAST OF THE JACKET

ALREADY HAS WHITE-JACKET CHRONICLED THE MISHAPS AND INCONVENIENCES, TROUBLES AND tribulations of all sorts brought upon him by that unfortunate but indispensable garment of his. But now it befalls him to record how this jacket, for the second and last time, came near proving his shroud.

Of a pleasant midnight, our good frigate, now somewhere off the Capes of Virginia, was running on bravely, when the breeze, gradually dying, left us slowly gliding toward our still invisible port.

Headed by Jack Chase, the quarter-watch were reclining in the top, talking about the shore delights into which they intended to plunge, while our captain often broke in with allusions to similar conversations when he was on board the English line-of-battle ship, the *Asia,* drawing nigh to Portsmouth, in England, after the battle of Navarino.

Suddenly an order was given to set the main-top-gallant-stun'-sail, and the halyards not being rove, Jack Chase assigned to me that duty. Now this reeving of the halyards of a main-top-gallant-stun'-sail is a business that eminently demands sharpsightedness, skill, and celerity.

Consider that the end of a line, some two hundred feet long, is to be carried aloft, in your teeth, if you please, and dragged far out on the giddiest of yards, and after being wormed and twisted about through all sorts of intricacies—turning abrupt corners at the abruptest of angles—is to be dropped, clear of all obstructions, in a straight plumb-line right down to the deck. In the course of this business, there is a multitude of sheeve-holes and blocks, through which you must pass it; often the rope is a very tight fit, so as to make it like threading a fine cambric needle with rather coarse thread. Indeed, it is a thing only deftly to be done, even by day. Judge, then, what it must be to be threading cambric needles by night, and at sea, upward of a hundred feet aloft in the air.

With the end of the line in one hand, I was mounting the top-mast shrouds, when our Captain of the Top told me that I had better off jacket; but though it was not a very cold night, I had been reclining so long in the top, that I had become somewhat chilly, so I thought best not to comply with the hint.

Having reeved the line through all the inferior blocks, I went out with it to the end of the weather-top-gallant-yard-arm, and was in the act of leaning over and passing it through the suspended jewel-block there, when the ship gave a plunge in the sudden swells of the calm sea, and pitching me still further over the yard, threw the heavy skirts of my jacket right over my head, completely muffling me. Somehow I thought it was the sail that had flapped, and, under that impression, threw up my hands to drag it from my head, relying upon the sail itself to support me meanwhile. Just then the ship gave another sudden jerk, and, head-foremost, I pitched from the yard. I knew where I was, from the rush of the air by my ears, but all else was a nightmare. A bloody film was before my eyes, through which, ghost-like, passed and repassed my father, mother, and sisters. An utterable nausea oppressed me; I was conscious of gasping; there seemed no breath in my body. It was over one hundred feet that I fell—down, down, with lungs collapsed as in death. Ten thousand pounds of shot seemed tied to my head, as the irresistible law of gravitation dragged me, head-foremost and straight as a die, toward the infallible center of this terraqueous globe. All I had seen, and read, and heard, and all I had thought and felt in my life, seemed intensified in one fixed idea in my soul. But dense as this idea was, it was made up of atoms. Having fallen from the projecting yard-arm end, I was conscious of a collected satisfaction in feeling, that I should not be dashed on the deck, but would sink into the speechless profound of the sea.

With the bloody, blind film before my eyes, there was a still stranger hum in my head, as if a hornet were there; and I thought to myself, Great God! this is Death! Yet these thoughts were unmixed with alarm. Like frost-work that flashes and shifts its scared hues in the sun, all my braided, blended emotions were in themselves icy cold and calm.

So protracted did my fall seem, that I can even now recall the feeling of wondering how much longer it would be, ere all was over and I struck. Time seemed to stand still, and all the worlds seemed poised on their poles, as I fell, soul-becalmed, through the eddying whirl and swirl of the maelstrom air.

At first, as I have said, I must have been precipitated head-foremost; but I was conscious, at length, of a swift, flinging motion of my limbs, which involuntarily threw themselves out, so that at last I must have fallen in a heap. This is more likely, from the circumstance, that when I struck the sea, I felt as if someone had smote me slantingly across the shoulder and along part of my right side.

As I gushed into the sea, a thunder-boom sounded in my ear; my soul seemed flying from my mouth. The feeling of death flooded over me with the billows. The blow from the sea must have turned me, so that I sank almost feet-foremost through a soft, seething foamy lull. Some current seemed hurrying me away; in a trance I yielded, and sank deeper down with a glide. Purple and pathless was the deep calm now around me, flecked by summer lightnings in an azure afar. The horrible nausea was gone; the bloody, blind film turned a pale green; I wondered whether I was yet dead, or still dying. But of a sudden some fashionless form brushed my side—some inert, coiled fish of the sea; the thrill of being alive again tingled in my nerves, and the strong shunning of death shocked me through.

For one instant an agonizing revulsion came over me as I found myself utterly sinking. Next moment the force of my fall was expanded; and there I hung, vibrating in the mid-deep. What wild sounds then rang in my ear! One was a soft moaning, as of low waves on the beach; the other wild and heartlessly jubilant, as of the sea in the height of a tempest. Oh soul! thou then heardest life and death: as he who stands upon the Corinthian shore hears both the Ionian and the Ægean waves. The life-and-death poise soon passed; and then I found myself slowly ascending, and caught a dim glimmering of light.

Quicker and quicker I mounted; till at last I bounded up like a buoy, and my whole head was bathed in the blessed air.

I had fallen in a line with the main-mast; I now found myself nearly abreast of the mizzen-mast, the frigate slowly gliding by like a black world in the water. Her vast hull loomed out of the night, showing hundreds of seamen in the hammock-nettings, some tossing over ropes, others madly flinging overboard the hammocks; but I was too far out from them immediately to reach what they threw. I essayed to swim toward the ship; but instantly I was conscious of a feeling like being pinioned in a feather-bed, and, moving my hands, felt my jacket puffed out above my tight girdle with water. I strove to tear it off; but it was looped together here and there, and the strings were not then to be sundered by hand. I whipped out my knife, that was tucked at my belt, and ripped my jacket straight up and down, as if I were ripping open myself. With a violent struggle I then burst out of it, and was free. Heavily soaked, it slowly sank before my eyes.

Sink! sink! oh shroud! thought I; sink forever! accursed jacket that thou art!

"See that white shark!" cried a horrified voice from the taffrail; "he'll have that man down his hatchway! Quick! the *grains!* the *grains!*"

The next instant that barbed bunch of harpoons pierced through and through the unfortunate jacket, and swiftly sped down with it out of sight.

Being now astern of the frigate, I struck out boldly toward the elevated pole of one of the life-buoys which had been cut away. Soon after, one of the cutters picked me up. As they dragged me out of the water into the air, the sudden transition of elements made my every limb feel like lead, and I helplessly sunk into the bottom of the boat.

Ten minutes after, I was safe on board, and, springing aloft, was ordered to reeve anew the stun'-sail-halyards, which, slipping through the blocks when I had let go the end, had unrove and fallen to the deck.

The sail was soon set; and, as if purposely to salute it, a gentle breeze soon came, and the *Neversink* once more glided over the water, a soft ripple at her bows, and leaving a tranquil wake behind.

Chapter XCIII

CABLE AND ANCHOR ALL CLEAR

AND NOW THAT THE WHITE JACKET HAS SUNK TO THE BOTTOM OF THE SEA, AND THE BLESSED Capes of Virginia are believed to be broad on our bow—though still out of sight—our five hundred souls are fondly dreaming of home, and the iron throats of the guns round the galley re-echo with their songs and hurras—what more remains?

Shall I tell what conflicting and almost crazy surmisings prevailed concerning the precise harbor for which we were bound? For, according to rumor, our Commodore had received sealed orders touching that matter, which were not to be broken open till we gained a precise latitude of the coast. Shall I tell how, at last, all this uncertainty departed, and many a foolish prophecy was proved false, when our noble frigate—her longest pennant at her main—wound her stately way into the innermost harbor of Norfolk, like a plumed Spanish Grandee threading the corridors of the Escurial toward the throne-room within? Shall I tell how we kneeled upon the holy soil? How I begged a blessing of old Ushant, and one precious hair of his beard for a keepsake? How Lemsford, the gun-deck bard, offered up a devout ode as a prayer of thanksgiving? How saturnine Nord, the magnifico in disguise, refusing all companionship, stalked off into the woods, like the ghost of an old Calif of Bagdad? How I swayed and swung the hearty hand of Jack Chase, and nipped it to mine with a Carrick bend; yea, and kissed that noble hand of my liege lord and captain of my top, my sea-tutor and sire?

Shall I tell how the grand Commodore and Captain drove off from the pier-head? How the Lieutenants, in undress, sat down to their last dinner in the ward-room, and the champagne, packed in ice, spirted and sparkled like the Hot Springs out of a snow-drift in Iceland? How the Chaplain went off in his cassock, without bidding the people adieu? How shrunken Cuticle, the Surgeon, stalked over the side, the wired skeleton carried in his wake by his cot-boy? How the Lieutenant of Marines sheathed his sword on the poop, and, calling for wax and a taper, sealed the end of the scabbard with his family crest and motto—*Denique Cœlum?* How the Purser in due time mustered his money-bags, and paid us all off on the quarter-deck—good and bad, sick and well, all receiving their wages; though, truth to tell, some reckless, improvident seamen, who had lived too fast during the cruise, had little or nothing now standing on the credit side of their Purser's accounts?

Shall I tell of the Retreat of the Five Hundred inland; not, alas! in battle-array, as at quarters, but scattered broadcast over the land?

Shall I tell how the *Neversink* was at last stripped of spars, shrouds, and sails—had her guns hoisted out—her powder-magazine, shot-lockers, and armories discharged—till not one vestige of a fighting thing was left in her, from furthest stem to uttermost stern?

No! let all this go by; for our anchor still hangs from our bows, though its eager flukes dip their points in the impatient waves. Let us leave the ship on the sea—still with the land out of sight—still with brooding darkness on the face of the deep. I love an indefinite, infinite background—a vast, heaving, rolling, mysterious rear!

It is night. The meager moon is in her last quarter—that betokens the end of a cruise that is passing. But the stars look forth in their everlasting brightness—and *that* is the everlasting, glorious Future, forever beyond us.

We main-top-men are all aloft in the top; and round our mast we circle, a brother-band, hand in hand, all spliced together. We have reefed the last top-sail; trained the last gun; blown the last match; bowed to the last blast; been tranced in the last calm. We have mustered our last round the capstan; been rolled to grog the last time; for the last time swung in our hammocks; for the last time turned out at the sea-gull call of the watch. We have seen our last man scourged at the gangway; our last man gasp out the ghost in the stifling Sick-bay; our last man tossed to the sharks. Our last death-denouncing *Article of War* has been read; and far inland, in that blessed clime whither-ward our frigate now glides, the last wrong in our frigate will be remembered no more; when down from our main-mast comes our Commodore's pennant, when down sinks its shooting stars from the sky.

"By the mark, nine!" sings the hoary old leadsman, in the chains. And thus, the mid-world Equator passed, our frigate strikes soundings at last.

Hand in hand we top-mates stand, rocked in our Pisgah top. And over the starry waves, and broad out into the blandly blue and boundless night, spiced with strange sweets from the long-sought land—the whole long cruise predestinated ours, though often in tempest-time we almost refused to believe in that far-distant shore—straight out into that fragrant night, ever-noble Jack Chase, matchless and unmatchable Jack Chase stretches forth his bannered hand, and, pointing shoreward, cries: "For the last time, hear Camoens, boys!"

How calm the waves, how mild the balmy gale!
The Halcyons call, ye Lusians spread the sail!
Appeased, old Ocean now shall rage no more;
Haste, point our bowsprit for yon shadowy shore.
Soon shall the transports of your natal soil
O'erwhelm in bounding joy the thoughts of every toil.

The End

As a man-of-war that sails through the sea, so this earth that sails through the air. We mortals are all on board a fast-sailing, never-sinking world-frigate, of which God was the shipwright; and she is but one craft in a Milky-Way fleet, of which God is the Lord High Admiral. The port we sail from is forever astern. And though far out of sight of land, for ages and ages we continue to sail with sealed orders, and our last destination remains a secret to ourselves and our officers; yet our final haven was predestinated ere we slipped from the stocks at Creation.

Thus sailing with sealed orders, we ourselves are the repositories of the secret packet, whose mysterious contents we long to learn. There are no mysteries out of ourselves. But let us not give ear to the superstitious, gun-deck gossip about whither we may be gliding, for, as yet, not a soul on board of us knows—not even the Commodore himself; assuredly not the Chaplain; even our Professor's scientific surmisings are vain. On that point, the smallest cabin-boy is as wise as the Captain. And believe not the hypochondriac dwellers below hatches, who will tell you, with a sneer, that our world-frigate is bound to no final harbor whatever; that our voyage will prove an endless circumnavigation of space. Not so. For how can this world-frigate prove our eventual abiding place, when upon our first embarkation, as infants in arms, her violent rolling—in after-life unperceived—makes every soul of us sea-sick? Does not this show, too, that the very air we here inhale is uncongenial, and only becomes endurable at last through gradual habituation, and that some blessed, placid haven, however remote at present, must be in store for us all?

Glance fore and aft our flush decks. What a swarming crew! All told, they muster hard upon eight hundred millions of souls. Over these we have authoritative Lieutenants, a sword-belted Officer of Marines, a Chaplain, a Professor, a Purser, a Doctor, a Cook, a Master-at-arms.

Oppressed by illiberal laws, and partly oppressed by themselves, many of our people are wicked, unhappy, inefficient. We have skulkers and idlers all round, and brow-beaten waisters, who, for a pittance, do our craft's shabby work. Nevertheless, among our people we have gallant fore, main, and mizzen top-men aloft, who, well treated or ill, still trim our craft to the last.

We have a *brig* for trespassers; a bar by our main-mast, at which they are arraigned; a cat-o'-nine-tails and a gangway, to degrade them in their own eyes and in ours. These are not always employed to convert Sin to Virtue, but to divide them, and protect Virtue and legalized Sin from unlegalized Vice.

We have a Sick-bay for the smitten and helpless, whither we hurry them out of sight, and however they may groan beneath hatches, we hear little of their tribulations on deck; we still sport our gay streamer aloft. Outwardly regarded, our craft is a lie; for all that is outwardly seen of it is the clean-swept deck, and oft-painted planks comprised above the waterline; whereas, the vast mass of our fabric, with all its store-rooms of secrets, forever slides along far under the surface.

When a shipmate dies, straightway we sew him up, and overboard he goes; our world-frigate rushes by, and never more do we behold him again; though, sooner or later, the everlasting under-tow sweeps him toward our own destination.

We have both a quarter-deck to our craft and a gun-deck; subterranean shot-lockers and gun-powder magazines; and the *Articles of War* form our domineering code.

Oh, shipmates and world-mates, all round! we the people suffer many abuses. Our gun-deck is full of complaints. In vain from Lieutenants do we appeal to the Captain; in vain—while on board our world-frigate—to the indefinite Navy Commissioners, so far out of sight aloft. Yet the worst of our evils we blindly inflict upon ourselves; our officers cannot remove them, even if they would. From the last ills no being can save another; therein each man must be his own savior. For the rest, whatever befall us, let us never train our murderous guns inboard; let us not mutiny with bloody pikes in our hands. Our Lord High Admiral will yet interpose; and though long ages should elapse, and leave our wrongs unredressed, yet, shipmates and world-mates! let us never forget, that,

Whoever afflict us, whatever surround,
Life is a voyage that's homeward-bound!

MOBY-DICK

OR THE WHALE

In token of my admiration for his genius this book is inscribed to
NATHANIEL HAWTHORNE

Contents

ETYMOLOGY

(SUPPLIED BY A LATE CONSUMPTIVE USHER TO A GRAMMAR SCHOOL)

The pale Usher—threadbare in coat, heart, body, and brain; I see him now. He was ever dusting his old lexicons and grammars, with a queer handkerchief, mockingly embellished with all the gay flags of all the known nations of the world. He loved to dust his old grammars; it somehow mildly reminded him of his mortality.

"While you take in hand to school others, and to teach them by what name a whale-fish is to be called in our tongue, leaving out, through ignorance, the letter H, which almost alone maketh up the signification of the word, you deliver that which is not true." HACKLUYT

"WHALE.***Sw. and Dan. *hval.* This animal is named from roundness or rolling; for in Dan. *hvalt* is arched or vaulted." WEBSTER'S *Dictionary*

"WHALE.***It is more immediately from the Dut. and Ger. *Wallen*; A.S. *Walw-ian*, to roll, to wallow." RICHARDON'S *Dictionary*

χητος	Greek
CETUS,	Latin
WHŒL,	Anglo-Saxon
HVALT,	Danish
WAL,	Dutch
HWAL,	Swedish
WHALE,	Icelandic
WHALE,	English
BALEINE,	French
BALLENA,	Spanish
PEKEE-NUEE-NUEE,	Fiji
PEKEE-NUEE-NUEE,	Erromangoan

EXTRACTS

(SUPPLIED BY A SUB-SUB-LIBRARIAN)

It will be seen that this mere painstaking burrower and grub-worm of a poor devil of a Sub-Sub appears to have gone through the long Vaticans and street-stalls of the earth, picking up whatever random allusions to whales he could anyways find in any book whatsoever, sacred or profane. Therefore you must not, in every case at least, take the higgledy-piggledy whale statement, however authentic, in these extracts, for veritable gospel cetology. Far from it. As touching the ancient authors generally, as well as the poets here appearing, these extracts are solely valuable or entertaining, as affording a glancing bird's-eye view of what has been promiscuously said, thought, fancied, and sung of Leviathan, by many nations and generations, including our own.

So fare thee well, poor devil of a Sub-Sub, whose commentator I am. Thou belongest to that hopeless, sallow tribe which no wine of this world will ever warm; and for whom even Pale Sherry would be too rosy-strong; but with whom one sometimes loves to sit, and feel poor-devilish, too; and grow convivial upon tears; and say to them bluntly, with full eyes and empty glasses, and in not altogether unpleasant sadness—Give it up, Sub-Subs! For by how much more pains ye take to please the world, by so much the more shall ye forever go thankless! Would that I could clear out Hampton Court and the Tuileries for ye! But gulp down your tears and hie aloft to the royalmast with your hearts; for your friends who have gone before are clearing out the seven-storied heavens, and making refugees of long pampered Gabriel, Michael, and Raphael, against your coming. Here ye strike but splintered hearts together—there, ye shall strike unsplinterable glasses!

"And God created great whales." *Genesis*

"Leviathan maketh a path to shine after him;
One would think the deep to be hoary." *Job*

"Now the Lord had prepared a great fish to swallow up Jonah." *Jonah*

"There go the ships; there is that Leviathan whom thou hast made to play therein." *Psalms*

"In that day, the Lord with his sore, and great, and strong sword, shall punish Leviathan the piercing serpent, even Leviathan that crooked serpent; and he shall slay the dragon that is in the sea." *Isaiah*

"And what thing soever besides cometh within the chaos of this monster's mouth, be it beast, boat, or stone, down it goes all incontinently that foul great swallow of his, and perisheth in the bottomless gulf of his paunch." Holland's *Plutarch's Morals*

"The Indian Sea breedeth the most and the biggest fishes that are: among which the Whales and Whirlpooles called Balæne, take up as much in length as four acres or arpens of land." Holland's *Pliny*

"Scarcely had we proceeded two days on the sea, when about sunrise a great many Whales and other monsters of the sea, appeared. Among the former, one was of a most monstrous size. * * This came towards us, openmouthed, raising the waves on all sides, and beating the sea before him into a foam."

Tooke's *Lucian*. "The True History"

"He visited this country also with a view of catching horse-whales, which had bones of very great value for their teeth, of which he brought some to the king. * * * The best whales were catched in his own country, of which some were forty-eight, some fifty yards long. He said that he was one of six who had killed sixty in two days."

Other or Octher's verbal narrative taken down from his mouth by King Alfred A.D. 890

"And whereas all the other things, whether beast or vessel, that enter into the dreadful gulf of this monster's (whale's) mouth, are immediately lost and swallowed up, the sea-gudgeon retires into it in great security, and there sleeps."

Montaigne.—*Apology for Raimond Sebond*

"Let us fly, let us fly! Old Nick take me if is not Leviathan described by the noble prophet Moses in the life of patient Job."

Rabelais

"This whale's liver was two cart-loads."

Stowe's *Annals*

"The great Leviathan that maketh the seas to seethe like boiling pan."

Lord Bacon's *Version of the Psalms*

"Touching that monstrous bulk of the whale or ork we have received nothing certain. They grow exceeding fat, insomuch that an incredible quantity of oil will be extracted out of one whale."

Ibid. *History of Life and Death*

"The sovereignest thing on earth is parmacetti for an inward bruise."

King Henry

"Very like a whale."

Hamlet

"Which to secure, no skill of leach's art
Mote him availle, but to returne againe
To his wound's worker, that with lowly dart,
Dinting his breast, had bred his restless paine,
Like as the wounded whale to shore flies thro' the maine."

The Faerie Queen

"Immense as whales, the motion of whose vast bodies can in a peaceful calm trouble the ocean til it boil."

Sir William Davenant. *Preface to Gondibert*

"What spermacetti is, men might justly doubt, since the learned Hosmannus in his work of thirty years, saith plainly, *Nescio quid sit.*"

Sir T. Browne. *Of Sperma Ceti and the Sperma Ceti Whale. Vide his V.E.*

"Like Spencer's Talus with his modern flail
He threatens ruin with his ponderous tail.
* * * * *
Their fixed jav'lins in his side he wears,
And on his back a grove of pikes appears."
Waller's *Battle of the Summer Islands*

"By art is created that great Leviathan, called a Commonwealth or State—(in Latin, *Civitas*) which is but an artificial man." Opening sentence of Hobbe's *Leviathan*

"Silly Mansoul swallowed it without chewing, as if it had been a sprat in the mouth of a whale." *Pilgrim's Progress*

"That sea beast
Leviathan, which God of all his works
Created hugest that swim the ocean stream."
Paradise Lost

—"There Leviathan,
Hugest of living creatures, in the deep
Stretched like a promontory sleeps or swims,
And seems a moving land; and at his gills
Draws in, and at his breath spouts out a sea."
Ibid

"The mighty whales which swim in a sea of water, and have a sea of oil swimming in them." Fuller's *Profane and Holy State*

"So close behind some promontory lie
The huge Leviathans to attend their prey,
And give no chance, but swallow in the fry,
Which through their gaping jaws mistake the way."
Dryden's *Annus Mirabilis*

"While the whale is floating at the stern of the ship, they cut off his head, and tow it with a boat as near the shore as it will come; but it will be aground in twelve or thirteen feet water." Thomas Edge's *Ten Voyages to Spitzbergen, in Purchass*

"In their way they saw many whales sporting in the ocean, and in wantonness fuzzing up the water through their pipes and vents, which nature has placed on their shoulders."
Sir T. Herbert's *Voyages into Asia and Africa. Harris Coll.*

"Here they saw such huge troops of whales, that they were forced to proceed with a great deal of caution for fear they should run their ship upon them."
Schouten's *Sixth Circumnavigation*

"We set sail from the Elbe, wind N. E. in the ship called the *Jonas-in-the-Whale*. ***
"Some say the whale can't open his mouth, but that is a fable. ***

"They frequently climb up the masts to see whether they can see a whale, for the first discoverer has a ducat for his pains. * * *

"I was told of a whale taken near Shetland, that had above a barrel of herrings in his belly. * * *

"One of our harpooneers told me that he caught once a whale in Spitzbergen that was white all over." *A Voyage to Greenland, A.D. 1671. Harris Coll.*

"Several whales have come in upon this coast (Fife) Anno 1652, one eighty feet in length of the whale-bone kind came in, which (as I was informed) besides a vast quantity of oil, did afford 500 weight of baleen. The jaws of it stand for a gate in the garden of Pitferren." Sibbald's *Fife and Kinross*

"Myself have agreed to try whether I can master and kill this Sperma-ceti whale, for I could never hear of any of that sort that was killed by any man, such is his fierceness and swiftness." Richard Strafford's *Letter from the Bermudas. Phil. Trans A.D.1668*

"Whales in the sea
God's voice obey."
N. E. Primer

"We saw also abundance of large whales, there being more in those southern seas, as I may say, by a hundred to one; than we have to the northward of us."
Captain Cowley's *Voyage Round the Globe. A.D.1729*

* * * * * "and the breath of the whale is frequently attended with such an insupportable smell, as to bring on a disorder of the brain." Ulloa's *South America*

"To fifty chosen sylphs of special note,
We trust the important charge, the petticoat.
Oft have we known that seven-fold fence to fail,
Tho' stuffed with hoops and armed with ribs of whale."
Rape of the Lock

"If we compare land animals in respect to magnitude, with those that take up their abode in the deep, we shall find they will appear contemptible in the comparison. The whale is doubtless the largest animal in creation." Goldsmith, *Nat. Hist.*

"If you should write a fable for little fishes, you would make them speak like great wales."
Goldsmith to Johnson

"In the afternoon we saw what was supposed to be a rock, but it was found to be a dead whale, which some Asiatics had killed, and were then towing ashore. They seemed to endeavor to conceal themselves behind the whale, in order to avoid being seen by us."
Cook's *Voyages*

"The larger whales, they seldom venture to attack. They stand in so great dread of some of them, that when out at sea they are afraid to mention even their names, and carry dung, lime-stone, juniper-wood, and some other articles of the same nature in their boats, in order to terrify and prevent their too near approach."
Uno Von Troil's *Letters on Banks's and Solander's Voyage to Iceland in 1772*

"The Spermacetti Whale found by the Nantuckois, is an active, fierce animal, and requires vast address and boldness in the fishermen."

Thomas Jefferson's *Whale Memorial to the French Minister in 1778*

"And pray, sir, what in the world is equal to it?"

Edmund Burke's reference in Parliament to the Nantucket Whale-Fishery

"Spain—a great whale stranded on the shores of Europe."

Edmund Burke. (somewhere.)

"A tenth branch of the king's ordinary revenue, said to be grounded on the consideration of his guarding and protecting the seas from pirates and robbers, is the right to *royal* fish, which are whale and sturgeon. And these, when either thrown ashore or caught near the coast, are the property of the king." Blackstone

"Soon to the sport of death the crews repair:
Rodmond unerring o'er his head suspends
The barbed steel, and every turn attends."

Falconer's *Shipwreck*

"Bright shone the roofs, the domes, the spires,
And rockets blew self driven,
To hang their momentary fire
Around the vault of heaven.

"So fire with water to compare,
The ocean serves on high,
Up-spouted by a whale in air,
To express unwieldy joy."

Cowper, on the Queen's Visit to London

"Ten or fifteen gallons of blood are thrown out of the heart at a stroke, with immense velocity." John Hunter's *Account of the dissection of a whale. (A small sized one.)*

"The aorta of a whale is larger in the bore than the main pipe of the water-works at London Bridge, and the water roaring in its passage through that pipe is inferior in impetus and velocity to the blood gushing from the whale's heart." Paley's *Theology*

"The whale is a mammiferous animal without hind feet." Baron Cuvier

"In 40 degrees south, we saw Spermacetti Whales, but did not take any till the first of May, the sea being then covered with them."

Colnett's *Voyage for the Purpose of Extending the Spermacetti Whale Fishery*

"In the free element beneath me swam,
Floundered and dived, in play, in chace, in battle,
Fishes of every color, form, and kind;
Which language cannot paint, and mariner
Had never seen; from dread Leviathan
To insect millions peopling every wave:

Gather'd in shoals immense, like floating islands,
Led by mysterious instincts through that waste
And trackless region, though on every side
Assaulted by voracious enemies,
Whales, sharks, and monsters, arm'd in front or jaw,
With swords, saws, spiral horns, or hooked fangs."
Montgomery's *World before the Flood*

"Io! Pæan! Io! sing.
To the finny people's king.
Not a mightier whale than this
In the vast Atlantic is;
Not a fatter fish than he,
Flounders round the Polar Sea."
Charles Lamb's *Triumph of the Whale*

"In the year 1690 some persons were on a high hill observing the whales spouting and sporting with each other, when one observed; there—pointing to the sea—is a green pasture where our children's grand-children will go for bread."
Obed Macy's *History of Nantucket*

"I built a cottage for Susan and myself and made a gateway in the form of a Gothic Arch, by setting up a whale's jaw bones." Hawthorne's *Twice Told Tales*

"She came to bespeak a monument for her first love, who had been killed by a whale in the Pacific Ocean, no less than forty years ago." Ibid

"No, Sir, 'tis a Right Whale," answered Tom; "I saw his sprout; he threw up a pair of as pretty rainbows as a Christian would wish to look at. He's a raal oil-butt, that fellow!"
Cooper's *Pilot*

"The papers were brought in, and we saw in the *Berlin Gazette* that whales had been introduced on the stage there." Eckermann's *Conversations with Goethe*

"My God! Mr. Chace, what is the matter?" I answered, "we have been stove by a whale."
Narrative of the Shipwreck of the Whale-Ship Essex *of Nantucket, which was attacked and finally destroyed by a large Sperm Whale in the Pacific Ocean.* By Owen Chace of Nantucket, first mate of said vessel. New York, 1821

"A mariner sat in the shrouds one night,
The wind was piping free;
Now bright, now dimmed, was the moonlight pale,
And the phospher gleamed in the wake of the whale,
As it floundered in the sea."
Elizabeth Oakes Smith

"The quantity of line withdrawn from the boats engaged in the capture of this one whale, amounted altogether to 10,440 yards or nearly six English miles. * * *

"Sometimes the whale shakes its tremendous tail in the air, which, cracking like a whip, resounds to the distance of three or four miles." Scoresby

"Mad with the agonies he endures from these fresh attacks, the infuriated Sperm Whale rolls over and over; he rears his enormous head, and with wide expanded jaws snaps at everything around him; he rushes at the boats with his head; they are propelled before him with vast swiftness, and sometimes utterly destroyed.
* * * It is a matter of great astonishment that the consideration of the habits of so interesting, and, in a commercial point of view, so important an animal (as the Sperm Whale) should have been so entirely neglected, or should have excited so little curiosity among the numerous, and many of them competent observers, that of late years must have possessed the most abundant and the most convenient opportunities of witnessing their habitudes."

Thomas Beale's *History of the Sperm Whale,* 1839

"The Cachalot" (Sperm Whale) "is not only better armed than the True Whale" (Greenland or Right Whale) "in possessing a formidable weapon at either extremity of its body, but also more frequently displays a disposition to employ these weapons offensively, and in manner at once so artful, bold, and mischievous, as to lead to its being regarded as the most dangerous to attack of all the known species of the whale tribe."

Frederick Debell Bennett's *Whaling Voyage Round the Globe.* 1840

"Nantucket itself," said Mr. Webster, "is a very striking and peculiar portion of the National interest. There is a population of eight or nine thousand persons, living here in the sea, adding largely every year to the National wealth by the boldest and most persevering industry."

Report of Daniel Webster's Speech in the U.S. Senate, on the application of the Erection of a Breakwater at Nantucket. 1828

October 13. "There she blows," was sung out from the mast-head.

"Where away?" demanded the captain.

"Three points off the lee bow, sir."

"Raise up your wheel. Steady!"

"Steady, sir."

"Mast-head ahoy! Do you see that whale now?"

"Ay ay, sir! A shoal of Sperm Whales! There she blows! There she breaches!"

"Sing out! sing out every time!"

"Ay ay, sir! There she blows! there—there—*thar* she blows—bowes—bo-o-o-s!"

"How far off?"

"Two miles and a half."

"Thunder and lightning! so near! Call all hands."

J. Ross Browne's *Etchings of a Whaling Cruize.* 1846

"The Whale-ship *Globe,* on board of which vessel occurred the horrid transactions we are about to relate, belonged to the island of Nantucket."

Narrative of the Globe Mutiny, by Lay and Hussey, survivors. A.D.1828

"Being once pursued by a whale which he had wounded, he parried the assault for some time with a lance; but the furious monster at length rushed on the boat; himself and comrades only being preserved by leaping into the water when they saw the onset was inevitable."

Missionary Journal of Tyerman and Bennett

"The whale fell directly over him, and probably killed him in a moment."

The Whale and his Captors, or The Whaleman's Adventures and the Whale's Biography, gathered on the Homeward Cruise of the Commodore Preble. By Rev. Henry T. Cheever

"If you make the least damn bit of noise," replied Samuel, "I will send you to hell."

Life of Samuel Comstock (the mutineer), by his brother, William Comstock. Another Version of the whale-ship *Globe* narrative.

"The voyages of the Dutch and English to the Northern Ocean, in order, if possible, to discover a passage through it to India, though they failed of their main object, laid open the haunts of the whale." McCulloch's *Commercial Dictionary*

"These things are reciprocal; the ball rebounds, only to bound forward again; for now in laying open the haunts of the whale, the whalemen seem to have indirectly hit upon new clews to that same mystic North-West Passage." From "Something" unpublished

"It is impossible to meet a whale-ship on the ocean without being struck by her near appearance. The vessel under short sail, with look-outs at the mast-heads, eagerly scanning the wide expanse around them, has a totally different air from those engaged in a regular voyage." *Currents and Whaling. U. S. Ex. Ex.*

"Pedestrians in the vicinity of London and elsewhere may recollect having seen large curved bones set upright in the earth, either to form arches over gateways, or entrances to alcoves, and they may perhaps have been told that these were the ribs of whales."

Tales of a Whale Voyager to the Arctic Ocean

"It was not till the boats returned from the pursuit of these whales, that the whites saw their ship in bloody possession of the savages enrolled among the crew."

Newspaper Account of the Taking and Retaking of the Whale-ship *Hobomack*

"It is generally well known that out of the crews of Whaling vessels (American) few ever return in the ships on board of which they departed." *Cruise in a Whale Boat*

"Suddenly a mighty mass emerged from the water, and shot up perpendicularly into the air. It was the whale." *Miriam Coffin or the Whale Fisherman*

"The Whale is harpooned to be sure; but bethink you, how you would manage a powerful unbroken colt, with the mere appliance of a rope tied to the root of his tail."

A Chapter on Whaling in *Ribs and Trucks*

"On one occasion I saw two of these monsters (whales) probably male and female, slowly swimming, one after the other, within less than a stone's throw of the shore" (Terra Del Fuego), "over which the beech tree extended its branches."

Darwin's *Voyage of a Naturalist*

" 'Stern all!' exclaimed the mate, as upon turning his head, he saw the distended jaws of a large Sperm Whale close to the head of the boat, threatening it with instant destruction;—'Stern all, for your lives!' " *Wharton the Whale Killer*

"So be cheery, my lads, let your hearts never fail,
While the bold harpooneer is striking the whale!"
Nantucket Song

"Oh, the rare old Whale, mid storm and gale
In his ocean home will be
A giant in might, where might is right,
And King of the boundless sea."

Whale Song

Chapter I

Loomings

CALL ME ISHMAEL. SOME YEARS AGO—NEVER MIND HOW LONG PRECISELY—HAVING LITTLE or no money in my purse, and nothing particular to interest me on shore, I thought I would sail about a little and see the watery part of the world. It is a way I have of driving off the spleen, and regulating the circulation. Whenever I find myself growing grim about the mouth; whenever it is a damp, drizzly November in my soul; whenever I find myself involuntarily pausing before coffin warehouses, and bringing up the rear of every funeral I meet; and especially whenever my hypos get such an upper hand of me, that it requires a strong moral principle to prevent me from deliberately stepping into the street, and methodically knocking people's hats off—then, I account it high time to get to sea as soon as I can. This is my substitute for pistol and ball. With a philosophical flourish Cato throws himself upon his sword; I quietly take to the ship. There is nothing surprising in this. If they but knew it, almost all men in their degree, some time or other, cherish very nearly the same feelings towards the ocean with me.

There now is your insular city of the Manhattoes, belted round by wharves as Indian isles by coral reefs—commerce surrounds it with her surf. Right and left, the streets take you waterward. Its extreme downtown is the battery, where that noble mole is washed by waves, and cooled by breezes, which a few hours previous were out of sight of land. Look at the crowds of water-gazers there.

Circumambulate the city of a dreamy Sabbath afternoon. Go from Corlears Hook to Coenties Slip, and from thence, by Whitehall, northward. What do you see?—Posted like silent sentinels all around the town, stand thousands upon thousands of mortal men fixed in ocean reveries. Some leaning against the spiles; some seated upon the pier-heads; some looking over the bulwarks of ships from China; some high aloft in the rigging, as if striving to get a still better seaward peep. But these are all landsmen; of week-days pent up in lath and plaster—tied to counters, nailed to benches, clinched to desks. How then is this? Are the green fields gone? What do they here?

But look! here come more crowds, pacing straight for the water, and seemingly bound for a dive. Strange! Nothing will content them but the extremest limit of the land; loitering under the shady lee of yonder warehouses will not suffice. No. They must get just as nigh the water as they possibly can without falling in. And there they stand—miles of them—leagues. Inlanders all, they come from lanes and alleys, streets and avenues—north, east, south, and west. Yet here they all unite. Tell me, does the magnetic virtue of the needles of the compasses of all those ships attract them thither?

Once more. Say, you are in the country; in some high land of lakes. Take almost any path you please, and ten to one it carries you down in a dale, and leaves you there by a pool in the stream. There is magic in it. Let the most absent-minded of men be plunged in his deepest reveries—stand that man on his legs, set his feet a-going, and he will infallibly lead you to water, if water there be in all that region. Should you ever be athirst in the great American desert, try this experiment, if your caravan happen to be supplied with a metaphysical professor. Yes, as everyone knows, meditation and water are wedded forever.

But here is an artist. He desires to paint you the dreamiest, shadiest, quietest, most enchanting bit of romantic landscape in all the valley of the Saco. What is the chief element he employs? There stand his trees, each with a hollow trunk, as if a hermit and a crucifix were within; and here sleeps his meadow, and there sleep his cattle; and up from yonder cottage goes a sleepy smoke. Deep into distant woodlands winds a mazy way, reaching to overlapping spurs of mountains bathed in their hill-side blue. But though the picture lies thus tranced, and though this pine-tree shakes down its sighs like leaves upon his shepherd's head, yet all were vain, unless the shepherd's eye were fixed upon the magic stream before him. Go visit the Prairies in June, when for scores on scores of miles you wade knee-deep among Tiger-lilies—what is the one charm wanting?—Water—there is not a drop of water there! Were Niagara but a cataract of sand, would you travel your thousand miles to see it? Why did the poor poet of Tennessee, upon suddenly receiving two handfuls of silver, deliberate whether to buy him a coat, which he sadly needed, or invest his money in a pedestrian trip to Rockaway Beach? Why is almost every robust healthy boy with a robust healthy soul in him, at some time or other crazy to go to sea? Why upon your first voyage as a passenger, did you yourself feel such a mystical vibration, when first told that you and your ship were now out of sight of land? Why did the old Persians hold the sea holy? Why did the Greeks give it a separate deity, and own brother of Jove? Surely all this is not without meaning. And still deeper the meaning of that story of Narcissus, who because he could not grasp the tormenting, mild image he saw in the fountain, plunged into it and was drowned. But that same image, we ourselves see in all rivers and oceans. It is the image of the ungraspable phantom of life; and this is the key to it all.

Now, when I say that I am in the habit of going to sea whenever I begin to grow hazy about the eyes, and begin to be over conscious of my lungs, I do not mean to have it inferred that I ever go to sea as a passenger. For to go as a passenger you must needs have a purse, and a purse is but a rag unless you have something in it. Besides, passengers get sea-sick—grow quarrelsome—don't sleep of nights—do not enjoy themselves much, as a general thing;—no, I never go as a passenger; nor, though I am something of a salt, do I ever go to sea as a Commodore, or a Captain, or a Cook. I abandon the glory and distinction of such offices to those who like them. For my part, I abominate all honorable respectable toils, trials, and tribulations of every kind whatsoever. It is quite as much as I can do to take care of myself, without taking care of ships, barques, brigs, schooners, and what not. And as for going as cook—though I confess there is considerable glory in that, a cook being a sort of officer on shipboard—yet, somehow, I never fancied broiling fowls;—though once broiled, judiciously buttered, and judgmatically salted and peppered, there is no one who will speak more respectfully, not to say reverentially, of a broiled fowl than I will. It is out of the idolatrous dotings of the old Egyptians upon broiled ibis and roasted river horse, that you see the mummies of those creatures in their huge bake-houses the pyramids.

No, when I go to sea, I go as a simple sailor, right before the mast, plumb down into the forecastle, aloft there to the royal mast-head. True, they rather order me about some, and make me jump from spar to spar, like a grasshopper in a May meadow. And at first, this sort of thing is unpleasant enough. It touches one's sense of honor, particularly if you come of an old established family in the land, the Van Rensselaers, or Randolphs, or Hardicanutes. And more than all, if just previous to putting your hand into the tar-pot, you have been lording it as a country schoolmaster, making the tallest boys stand in awe of you. The transition is a keen one, I assure you, from a schoolmaster to a sailor, and requires a strong decoction of Seneca and the Stoics to enable you to grin and bear it. But even this wears off in time.

What of it, if some old hunks of a sea-captain orders me to get a broom and sweep down the decks? What does that indignity amount to, weighed, I mean, in the scales of the New Testament? Do you think the archangel Gabriel thinks anything the less of me, because I promptly and respectfully obey that old hunks in that particular instance? Who ain't a slave? Tell me that. Well, then, however the old sea-captains may order me about—however they may thump and punch me about, I have the satisfaction of knowing that it is all right; that everybody else is one way or other served in much the same way—either in a physical or metaphysical point of view, that is; and so the universal thump is passed round, and all hands should rub each other's shoulder-blades, and be content.

Again, I always go to sea as a sailor, because they make a point of paying me for my trouble, whereas they never pay passengers a single penny that I ever heard of. On the contrary, passengers themselves must pay. And there is all the difference in the world between paying and being paid. The act of paying is perhaps the most uncomfortable infliction that the two orchard thieves entailed upon us. But *being paid*—what will compare with it? The urbane activity with which a man receives money is really marvelous, considering that we so earnestly believe money to be the root of all earthly ills, and that on no account can a monied man enter heaven. Ah! how cheerfully we consign ourselves to perdition!

Finally, I always go to sea as a sailor, because of the wholesome exercise and pure air of the forecastle deck. For as in this world, head-winds are far more prevalent than winds from astern (that is, if you never violate the Pythagorean maxim), so for the most part the Commodore on the quarter-deck gets his atmosphere at second hand from the sailors on the forecastle. He thinks he breathes it first; but not so. In much the same way do the commonalty lead their leaders in many other things, at the same time that the leaders little suspect it. But wherefore it was that after having repeatedly smelled the sea as a merchant sailor, I should now take it into my head to go on a whaling voyage; this the invisible police-officer of the Fates, who has the constant surveillance of me, and secretly dogs me, and influences me in some unaccountable way—he can better answer than anyone else. And, doubtless, my going on this whaling voyage, formed part of the grand program of Providence that was drawn up a long time ago. It came in as a sort of brief interlude and solo between more extensive performances. I take it that this part of the bill must have run something like this:

Grand Contested Election for the Presidency of the United States

WHALING VOYAGE BY ONE ISHMAEL

BLOODY BATTLE IN AFGHANISTAN

Though I cannot tell why it was exactly that those stage managers, the Fates, put me down for this shabby part of a whaling voyage, when others were set down for magnificent parts in high tragedies, and short and easy parts in genteel comedies, and jolly parts in farces—though I cannot tell why this was exactly; yet, now that I recall all the circumstances, I think I can see a little into the springs and motives which being cunningly presented to me under various disguises, induced me to set about performing the part I did, besides cajoling me into the delusion that it was a choice resulting from my own unbiased freewill and discriminating judgment.

Chief among these motives was the overwhelming idea of the great whale himself. Such a portentous and mysterious monster roused all my curiosity. Then the wild and distant seas where he rolled his island bulk; the undeliverable, nameless perils of the whale; these, with all the attending marvels of a thousand Patagonian sights and sounds, helped to sway me to my wish. With other men, perhaps, such things would not have been inducements; but as for me, I am tormented with an everlasting itch for things remote. I love to sail forbidden seas, and land on barbarous coasts. Not ignoring what is good, I am quick to perceive a horror, and could still be social with it—would they let me—since it is but well to be on friendly terms with all the inmates of the place one lodges in.

By reason of these things, then, the whaling voyage was welcome; the great flood-gates of the wonder-world swung open, and in the wild conceits that swayed me to my purpose, two and two there floated into my inmost soul, endless processions of the whale, and, mid most of them all, one grand hooded phantom, like a snow hill in the air.

Chapter II

THE CARPET-BAG

I STUFFED A SHIRT OR TWO INTO MY OLD CARPET-BAG, TUCKED IT UNDER MY ARM, AND STARTED for Cape Horn and the Pacific. Quitting the good city of old Manhatto, I duly arrived in New Bedford. It was on a Saturday night in December. Much was I disappointed upon learning that the little packet for Nantucket had already sailed, and that no way of reaching that place would offer, till the following Monday.

As most young candidates for the pains and penalties of whaling stop at this same New Bedford, thence to embark on their voyage, it may as well be related that I, for one, had no idea of so doing. For my mind was made up to sail in no other than a Nantucket craft, because there was a fine, boisterous something about everything connected with that famous old island, which amazingly pleased me. Besides though New Bedford has of late been gradually monopolizing the business of whaling, and though in this matter poor old Nantucket is now much behind her, yet Nantucket was her great original—the Tyre of this Carthage;—the place where the first dead American whale was stranded. Where else but from Nantucket did those aboriginal whalemen, the Red-Men, first sally out in canoes to give chase to the Leviathan? And where but from Nantucket, too, did that first adventurous little sloop put forth, partly laden with imported cobble-stones—so goes the story—to throw at the whales, in order to discover when they were nigh enough to risk a harpoon from the bowsprit?

Now having a night, a day, and still another night following before me in New Bedford, ere I could embark for my destined port, it became a matter of concernment where I was to eat and sleep meanwhile. It was a very dubious-looking, nay, a very dark and dismal night, bitingly cold and cheerless. I knew no one in the place. With anxious grapnels I had sounded my pocket, and only brought up a few pieces of silver—So, wherever you go, Ishmael, said I to myself, as I stood in the middle of a dreary street shouldering my bag, and comparing the gloom towards the north with the darkness towards the south—wherever in your wisdom you may conclude to lodge for the night, my dear Ishmael, be sure to inquire the price, and don't be too particular.

With halting steps I paced the streets, and passed the sign of "The Crossed Harpoons"—but it looked too expensive and jolly there. Further on, from the bright red windows of the "Sword-Fish Inn," there came such fervent rays, that it seemed to have melted the packed snow and ice from before the house, for everywhere else the congealed frost lay ten inches thick in a hard, asphaltic pavement—rather weary for me, when I struck my foot against the flinty projections, because from hard, remorseless service the soles of my boots were in a most miserable plight. Too expensive and jolly, again thought I, pausing one moment to watch the broad glare in the street, and hear the sounds of the tinkling glasses within. But go on, Ishmael, said I at last; don't you hear? get away from before the door; your patched boots are stopping the way. So on I went. I now by instinct followed the streets that took me waterward, for there, doubtless, were the cheapest, if not the cheeriest inns.

Such dreary streets! blocks of blackness, not houses on either hand, and here and there a candle, like a candle moving about in a tomb. At this hour of the night, of the last day of the week, that quarter of the town proved all but deserted. But presently I came to a smoky light proceeding from a low, wide building, the door of which stood invitingly open. It had a careless look, as if it were meant for the uses of the public; so, entering, the first thing I did was to stumble over an ash-box in the porch. Ha! thought I, ha, as the flying particles almost choked me, are these ashes from that destroyed city, Gomorrah? But "The Crossed Harpoons," and the "The Sword-Fish?"—this, then must needs be the sign of "The Trap." However, I picked myself up and hearing a loud voice within, pushed on and opened a second, interior door.

It seemed the great Black Parliament sitting in Tophet. A hundred black faces turned round in their rows to peer; and beyond, a black Angel of Doom was beating a book in a pulpit. It was a negro church; and the preacher's text was about the blackness of darkness, and the weeping and wailing and teeth-gnashing there. Ha, Ishmael, muttered I, backing out, Wretched entertainment at the sign of "The Trap!"

Moving on, I at last came to a dim sort of light not far from the docks, and heard a forlorn creaking in the air; and looking up, saw a swinging sign over the door with a white painting upon it, faintly representing a tall straight jet of misty spray, and these words underneath—"The Spouter-Inn:—Peter Coffin."

Coffin?—Spouter?—Rather ominous in that particular connection, thought I. But it is a common name in Nantucket, they say, and I suppose this Peter here is an emigrant from there. As the light looked so dim, and the place, for the time, looked quiet enough, and the dilapidated little wooden house itself looked as if it might have been carted here from the ruins of some burned district, and as the swinging sign had a poverty-stricken sort of creak to it, I thought that here was the very spot for cheap lodgings, and the best of pea coffee.

It was a queer sort of place—a gable-ended old house, one side palsied as it were, and leaning over sadly. It stood on a sharp bleak corner, where that tempestuous wind Euroclydon kept up a worse howling than ever it did about poor Paul's tossed craft. Euroclydon, nevertheless, is a mighty pleasant zephyr to anyone indoors, with his feet on the hob quietly toasting for bed. "In judging of that tempestuous wind called Euroclydon," says an old writer—of whose works I possess the only copy extant—"it maketh a marvelous difference, whether thou lookest out at it from a glass window where the frost is all on the outside, or whether thou observest it from that sashless window, where the frost is on both sides, and of which the wight Death is the only glazier." True enough, thought I, as this passage occurred to my mind—old blackletter, thou reasonest well. Yes, these eyes are windows, and this body of mine is the house. What a pity they didn't stop up the chinks and the crannies though, and thrust in a little lint here and there. But it's too late to make any improvements now. The universe is finished; the cope-stone is on, and the chips were carted off a million years ago. Poor Lazarus there, chattering his teeth against the curb-stone for his pillow, and shaking off his tatters with his shiverings, he might plug up both ears with rags, and put a corn-cob into his mouth, and yet that would not keep out the tempestuous Euroclydon. Euroclydon! says old Dives, in his red silken wrapper—(he had a redder one afterwards) pooh, pooh! What a fine frosty night; how Orion glitters; what northern lights! Let them talk of their oriental summer climes of everlasting conservatories; give me the privilege of making my own summer with my own coals.

But what thinks Lazarus? Can he warm his blue hands by holding them up to the grand northern lights? Would not Lazarus rather be in Sumatra than here? Would he not far rather lay him down lengthwise along the line of the equator; yea, ye gods! go down to the fiery pit itself, in order to keep out this frost?

Now, that Lazarus should lie stranded there on the curb-stone before the door of Dives, this is more wonderful than that an iceberg should be moored to one of the Moluccas. Yet Dives himself, he too lives like a Czar in an ice palace made of frozen sighs, and being a president of a temperance society, he only drinks the tepid tears of orphans.

But no more of this blubbering now, we are going a-whaling, and there is plenty of that yet to come. Let us scrape the ice from our frosted feet, and see what sort of a place this "Spouter" may be.

Chapter III

THE SPOUTER-INN

ENTERING THAT GABLE-ENDED SPOUTER-INN, YOU FOUND YOURSELF IN A WIDE, LOW, STRAGgling entry with old-fashioned wainscots, reminding one of the bulwarks of some condemned old craft. On one side hung a very large oil painting so thoroughly besmoked, and every way defaced, that in the unequal cross-lights by which you viewed it, it was only by diligent study and a series of systematic visits to it, and careful inquiry of the neighbors, that you could any way arrive at an understanding of its purpose. Such unaccountable masses of shades and shadows, that at first you almost thought some ambitious young artist, in the time of the New England hags, had endeavored to delineate chaos bewitched. But by dint of much and earnest contemplation, and oft repeated ponderings, and especially by throwing open the little window towards the back of the entry, you at last come to the conclusion that such an idea, however wild, might not be altogether unwarranted.

But what most puzzled and confounded you was a long, limber, portentous, black mass of something hovering in the center of the picture over three blue, dim, perpendicular lines floating in a nameless yeast. A boggy, soggy, squitchy picture truly, enough to drive a nervous man distracted. Yet was there a sort of indefinite, half-attained, unimaginable sublimity about it that fairly froze you to it, till you involuntarily took an oath with yourself to find out what that marvelous painting meant. Ever and anon a bright, but, alas, deceptive idea would dart you through.—It's the Black Sea in a midnight gale.—It's the unnatural combat of the four primal elements.—It's a blasted heath.—It's a Hyperborean winter scene.—It's the breaking-up of the ice-bound stream of Time. But at last all these fancies yielded to that one portentous something in the picture's midst. *That* once found out, and all the rest were plain. But stop; does it not bear a faint resemblance to a gigantic fish? even the great leviathan himself?

In fact, the artist's design seemed this: a final theory of my own, partly based upon the aggregated opinions of many aged persons with whom I conversed upon the subject. The picture represents a Cape-Horner in a great hurricane; the half-foundered ship weltering there with its three dismantled masts alone visible; and an exasperated whale, purposing to spring clean over the craft, is in the enormous act of impaling himself upon the three mast-heads.

The opposite wall of this entry was hung all over with a heathenish array of monstrous clubs and spears. Some were thickly set with glittering teeth resembling ivory saws; others were tufted with knots of human hair; and one was sickle-shaped, with a vast handle sweeping round like the segment made in the new-mown grass by a long-armed mower. You shuddered as you gazed, and wondered what monstrous cannibal and savage could ever have gone a death-harvesting with such a hacking, horrifying implement. Mixed with these were rusty old whaling lances and harpoons all broken and deformed. Some were storied weapons. With this once long lance, now wildly elbowed, fifty years ago did Nathan Swain kill fifteen whales between a sunrise and a sunset. And that harpoon—so like a corkscrew now—was flung in Javan seas, and run away with by a whale, years afterwards slain off the Cape of Blanco. The original iron entered nigh the tail, and, like a restless needle sojourning in the body of a man, traveled full forty feet, and at last was found imbedded in the hump.

Crossing this dusky entry, and on through yon low-arched way—cut through what in old times must have been a great central chimney with fireplaces all round—you enter the public room. A still duskier place is this, with such low ponderous beams above, and such old wrinkled planks beneath, that you would almost fancy you trod some old craft's cock-pits, especially of such a howling night, when this corner-anchored old ark rocked so furiously. On one side stood a long, low, shelf-like table covered with cracked glass cases, filled with dusty rarities gathered from this wide world's remotest nooks. Projecting from the further angle of the room stands a dark-looking den—the bar—a rude attempt at a right whale's head. Be that how it may, there stands the vast arched bone of the whale's jaw, so wide, a coach might almost drive beneath it. Within are shabby shelves, ranged round with old decanters, bottles, flasks; and in those jaws of swift destruction, like another cursed Jonah (by which name indeed they called him), bustles a little withered old man, who, for their money, dearly sells the sailors deliriums and death.

Abominable are the tumblers into which he pours his poison. Though true cylinders without—within, the villainous green goggling glasses deceitfully tapered downwards to a cheating bottom. Parallel meridians rudely pecked into the glass, surround these foot-pads' goblets. Fill to *this* mark, and your charge is but a penny; to *this* a penny more; and so on to the full glass—the Cape Horn measure, which you may gulp down for a shilling.

Upon entering the place I found a number of young seamen gathered about a table, examining by a dim light divers specimens of *skrimshander*. I sought the landlord, and telling him I desired to be accommodated with a room, received for answer that his house was full—not a bed unoccupied. "But avast," he added, tapping his forehead, "you haint no objections to sharing a harpooneer's blanket, have ye? I s'pose you are goin' a-whalin', so you'd better get used to that sort of thing."

I told him that I never liked to sleep two in a bed; that if I should ever do so, it would depend upon who the harpooneer might be, and that if he (the landlord) really had no other place for me, and the harpooneer was not decidedly objectionable, why rather than wander further about a strange town on so bitter a night, I would put up with the half of any decent man's blanket.

"I thought so. All right; take a seat. Supper?—you want supper? Supper'll be ready directly."

I sat down on an old wooden settle, carved all over like a bench on the Battery. At one end a ruminating tar was still further adorning it with his jack-knife, stooping over and diligently working away at the space between his legs. He was trying his hand at a ship under full sail, but he didn't make much headway, I thought.

At last some four or five of us were summoned to our meal in an adjoining room. It was cold as Iceland—no fire at all—the landlord said he couldn't afford it. Nothing but two dismal tallow candles, each in a winding sheet. We were fain to button up our monkey jackets, and hold to our lips cups of scalding tea with our half frozen fingers. But the fare was of the most substantial kind—not only meat and potatoes, but dumplings; good heavens! dumplings for supper! One young fellow in a green box coat, addressed himself to these dumplings in a most direful manner.

"My boy," said the landlord, "you'll have the nightmare to a dead sartainty."

"Landlord," I whispered, "that ain't the harpooneer is it?"

"Oh, no," said he, looking a sort of diabolically funny, "the harpooneer is a dark complexioned chap. He never eats dumplings, he don't—he eats nothing but steaks, and he likes 'em rare."

"The devil he does," says I. "Where is that harpooneer? Is he here?"

"He'll be here afore long," was the answer.

I could not help it, but I began to feel suspicious of this "dark complexioned" harpooneer. At any rate, I made up my mind that if it so turned out that we should sleep together, he must undress and get into bed before I did.

Supper over, the company went back to the bar-room, when, knowing not what else to do with myself, I resolved to spend the rest of the evening as a looker on.

Presently a rioting noise was heard without. Starting up, the landlord cried, "That's the *Grampus's* crew. I seed her reported in the offing this morning; a three years' voyage, and a full ship. Hurrah, boys; now we'll have the latest news from the Fijis."

A tramping of sea-boots was heard in the entry; the door was flung open, and in rolled a wild set of mariners enough. Enveloped in their shaggy watch coats, and with their heads muffled in woolen comforters, all bedarned and ragged, and their beards stiff with icicles, they seemed an eruption of bears from Labrador. They had just landed from their boat, and this was the first house they entered. No wonder, then, that they made a straight wake for the whale's mouth—the bar—when the wrinkled little old Jonah, there officiating, soon poured them out brimmers all round. One complained of a bad cold in his head, upon which Jonah mixed him a pitch-like potion of gin and molasses, which he swore was a sovereign cure for all colds and catarrhs whatsoever, never mind of how long standing, or whether caught off the coast of Labrador, or on the weather side of an ice-island.

The liquor soon mounted into their heads, as it generally does even with the arrantest topers newly landed from sea, and they began capering about most obstreperously.

I observed, however, that one of them held somewhat aloof, and though he seemed desirous not to spoil the hilarity of his shipmates by his own sober face, yet upon the whole he refrained from making as much noise as the rest. This man interested me at once; and since the sea-gods had ordained that he should soon become my shipmate (though but a sleeping-partner one, so far as this narrative is concerned), I will here venture upon a little description of him. He stood full six feet in height, with noble shoulders, and a chest like a coffer-dam. I have seldom seen such brawn in a man. His face was deeply brown and burned, making his white teeth dazzling by the contrast; while in the deep shadows of his eyes floated some reminiscences that did not seem to give him much joy. His voice at once announced that he was a Southerner, and from his fine stature, I thought he must be one of those tall mountaineers from the Alleghanian Ridge in Virginia. When the revelry of his companions had mounted to its height, this man slipped away unobserved, and I saw no more of him till he became my comrade on the sea. In a few minutes, however, he was missed by his shipmates, and being, it seems, for some reason a huge favorite with them, they raised a cry of "Bulkington! Bulkington! where's Bulkington?" and darted out of the house in pursuit of him.

It was now about nine o'clock, and the room seeming almost supernaturally quiet after these orgies, I began to congratulate myself upon a little plan that had occurred to me just previous to the entrance of the seamen.

No man prefers to sleep two in a bed. In fact, you would a good deal rather not sleep with your own brother. I don't know how it is, but people like to be private when they are sleeping. And when it comes to sleeping with an unknown stranger, in a strange inn, in a strange town, and that stranger a harpooneer, then your objections indefinitely multiply. Nor was there any earthly reason why I as a sailor should sleep two in a bed, more than anybody else; for sailors no more sleep two in a bed at sea, than bachelor Kings do ashore. To be sure they all sleep together in one apartment, but you have your own hammock, and cover yourself with your own blanket, and sleep in your own skin.

The more I pondered over this harpooneer, the more I abominated the thought of sleeping with him. It was fair to presume that being a harpooneer, his linen or woolen, as the case might be, would not be of the tidiest, certainly none of the finest. I began to twitch all over. Besides, it was getting late, and my decent harpooneer ought to be home and going bedwards. Suppose now, he should tumble in upon me at midnight—how could I tell from what vile hole he had been coming?

"Landlord! I've changed my mind about that harpooneer—I shan't sleep with him. I'll try the bench here."

"Just as you please; I'm sorry I can't spare ye a tablecloth for a mattress, and it's a plaguy rough board here"—feeling of the knots and notches. "But wait a bit, Skrimshander; I've got a carpenter's plane there in the bar—wait, I say, and I'll make ye snug enough." So saying he procured the plane; and with his old silk handkerchief first dusting the bench, vigorously set to planing away at my bed, the while grinning like an ape. The shavings flew right and left; till at last the plane-iron came bump against an indestructible knot. The landlord was near spraining his wrist, and I told him for heaven's sake to quit—the bed was soft enough to suit me, and I did not know how all the planning in the world could make eider down of a pine plank. So gathering up the shavings with another grin, and throwing them into the great stove in the middle of the room, he went about his business, and left me in a brown study.

I now took the measure of the bench, and found that it was a foot too short; but that could be mended with a chair. But it was a foot too narrow, and the other bench in the room was about four inches higher than the planed one—so there was no yoking them. I then placed the first bench lengthwise along the only clear space against the wall, leaving a little interval between, for my back to settle down in. But I soon found that there came such a draft of cold air over me from under the sill of the window, that this plan would never do at all, especially as another current from the rickety door met the one from the window, and both together formed a series of small whirlwinds in the immediate vicinity of the spot where I had thought to spend the night.

The devil fetch that harpooneer, thought I; but stop, couldn't I steal a march on him—bolt his door inside, and jump into his bed, not to be wakened by the most violent knockings? It seemed no bad idea; but upon second thoughts I dismissed it. For who could tell but what the next morning, so soon as I popped out of the room, the harpooneer might be standing in the entry, all ready to knock me down!

Still, looking round me again, and seeing no possible chance of spending a sufferable night unless in some other person's bed, I began to think that after all I might be cherishing unwarrantable prejudices against this unknown harpooneer. Thinks I, I'll wait awhile; he must be dropping in before long. I'll have a good look at him then, and perhaps we may become jolly good bedfellows after all—there's no telling.

But though the other boarders kept coming in by ones, twos, and threes, and going to bed, yet no sign of my harpooneer.

"Landlord!" said I, "what sort of a chap is he—does he always keep such late hours?" It was now hard upon twelve o'clock.

The landlord chuckled again with his lean chuckle, and seemed to be mightily tickled at something beyond my comprehension. "No," he answered, "generally he's an early bird—airley to bed and airley to rise—yea, he's the bird what catches the worm. But to-night he went out a-peddling, you see, and I don't see what on airth keeps him so late, unless, may be, he can't sell his head."

"Can't sell his head?—What sort of a bamboozing story is this you are telling me?" getting into a towering rage. "Do you pretend to say, landlord, that this harpooneer is actually engaged this blessed Saturday night, or rather Sunday morning, in peddling his head around this town?"

"That's precisely it," said the landlord, "and I told him he couldn't sell it here, the market's overstocked."

"With what?" shouted I.

"With heads to be sure; ain't there too many heads in the world?"

"I tell you what it is, landlord," said I quite calmly, "you'd better stop spinning that yarn to me—I'm not green."

"May be not," taking out a stick and whittling a toothpick, "but I rayther guess you'll be done *brown* if that ere harpooneer hears you a slanderin' his head."

"I'll break it for him," said I, now flying into a passion again at this unaccountable farrago of the landlord's.

"It's broke a'ready," said he.

"Broke," said I—"*broke*, do you mean?"

"Sartain, and that's the very reason he can't sell it, I guess."

"Landlord," said I, going up to him as cool as Mt. Hecla in a snow-storm—"landlord, stop whittling. You and I must understand one another, and that too without delay. I come to your house and want a bed; you tell me you can only give me half a one; that the other half belongs to a certain harpooneer. And about this harpooneer, whom I have not yet seen, you persist in telling me the most mystifying and exasperating stories, tending to beget in me an uncomfortable feeling towards the man whom you design for my bedfellow—a sort of connection, landlord, which is an intimate and confidential one in the highest degree. I now demand of you to speak out and tell me who and what this harpooneer is, and whether I shall be in all respects safe to spend the night with him. And in the first place, you will be so good as to unsay that story about selling his head, which if true I take to be good evidence that this harpooneer is stark mad, and I've no idea of sleeping with a madman; and you, sir, *you* I mean, landlord, *you*, sir, by trying to induce me to do so knowingly, would thereby render yourself liable to a criminal prosecution."

"Wall," said the landlord, fetching a long breath, "that's a purty long sarmon for a chap that rips a little now and then. But be easy, be easy, this here harpooneer I have been tellin' you of has just arrived from the south seas, where he bought up a lot of 'balmed New Zealand heads (great curios, you know), and he's sold all on 'em but one, and that one he's trying to sell to-night, cause to-morrow's Sunday, and it would not do to be sellin' human heads about the streets when folks is goin' to churches. He wanted to, last Sunday, but I stopped him just as he was goin' out of the door with four heads strung on a string, for all the airth like a string of inions."

This account cleared up the otherwise unaccountable mystery, and showed that the landlord, after all, had had no idea of fooling me—but at the same time what could I think of a harpooneer who stayed out of a Saturday night clean into the holy Sabbath, engaged in such a cannibal business as selling the heads of dead idolators?

"Depend upon it, landlord, that harpooneer is a dangerous man."

"He pays reg'lar," was the rejoinder. "But come, it's getting dreadful late, you had better be turning flukes—it's a nice bed: Sal and me slept in that ere bed the night we were spliced. There's plenty room for two to kick about in that bed; it's an almighty big bed that. Why, afore we give it up, Sal used to put our Sam and little Johnny in the foot of it. But I got a dreaming and sprawling about one night, and somehow, Sam got pitched on the floor, and came near breaking his arm. After that, Sal said it wouldn't do. Come along here, I'll give ye a glim in a jiffy"; and so saying he lighted a candle and held it towards me, offering to lead the way. But I stood irresolute; when looking at a clock in the corner, he exclaimed "I vum it's Sunday—you won't see that harpooneer to-night; he's come to anchor somewhere—come along then; *do* come; *won't* ye come?"

I considered the matter a moment, and then up stairs we went, and I was ushered into a small room, cold as a clam, and furnished, sure enough, with a prodigious bed, almost big enough indeed for any four harpooneers to sleep abreast.

"There," said the landlord, placing the candle on a crazy old sea chest that did double duty as a wash-stand and center table; "there, make yourself comfortable now; and good-night to ye." I turned round from eyeing the bed, but he had disappeared.

Folding back the counterpane, I stooped over the bed. Though none of the most elegant, it yet stood the scrutiny tolerably well. I then glanced round the room; and besides the bedstead and center table, could see no other furniture belonging to the place, but a rude shelf, the four walls, and a papered fire-board representing a man striking a whale. Of things not properly belonging to the room, there was a hammock lashed up, and thrown upon the floor in one corner; also a large seaman's bag, containing the harpooneer's wardrobe, no doubt in lieu of a land trunk. Likewise, there was a parcel of outlandish bone fish hooks on the shelf over the fireplace, and a tall harpoon standing at the head of the bed.

But what is this on the chest? I took it up, and held it close to the light, and felt it, and smelled it, and tried every way possible to arrive at some satisfactory conclusion concerning it. I can compare it to nothing but a large door mat, ornamented at the edges with little tinkling tags something like the stained porcupine quills round an Indian moccasin. There was a hole or slit in the middle of this mat, as you see the same in South American ponchos. But could it be possible that any sober harpooneer would get into a door mat, and parade the streets of any Christian town in that sort of guise? I put it on, to try it, and it weighed me down like a hamper, being uncommonly shaggy and thick, and I thought a little damp, as though this mysterious harpooneer had been wearing it of a rainy day. I went up in it to a bit of glass stuck against the wall, and I never saw such a sight in my life. I tore myself out of it in such a hurry that I gave myself a kink in the neck.

I sat down on the side of the bed, and commenced thinking about this head-peddling harpooneer, and his door mat. After thinking some time on the bed-side, I got up and took off my monkey jacket, and then stood in the middle of the room thinking. I then took off my coat, and thought a little more in my shirt sleeves. But beginning to feel very cold now, half undressed as I was, and remembering what the landlord said about the harpooneer's not coming home at all that night, it being so very late, I made no more ado, but jumped out of my pantaloons and boots, and then blowing out the light tumbled into bed, and commended myself to the care of heaven.

Whether that mattress was stuffed with corncobs or broken crockery, there is no telling, but I rolled about a good deal, and could not sleep for a long time. At last I slid off into a light doze, and had pretty nearly made a good offing towards the land of Nod, when I heard a heavy footfall in the passage, and saw a glimmer of light come into the room from under the door.

Lord save me, thinks I, that must be the harpooneer, the infernal head-peddler. But I lay perfectly still, and resolved not to say a word till spoken to. Holding a light in one hand, and that identical New Zealand head in the other, the stranger entered the room, and without looking towards the bed, placed his candle a good way off from me on the floor in one corner, and then began working away at the knotted cords of the large bag I before spoke of as being in the room. I was all eagerness to see his face, but he kept it averted for some time while employed in unlacing the bag's mouth. This accomplished, however, he turned round—when, good heavens! what a sight! Such a face! It was of a dark, purplish, yellow color, here and there stuck over with large, blackish looking squares. Yes, it's just as I thought, he's a terrible bedfellow; he's been in a fight, got dreadfully cut, and here he is, just from the surgeon. But at that moment he chanced to turn his face so towards the light, that I plainly saw they could not be sticking-plasters at all, those black squares on his cheeks. They were stains of some sort or other. At first I knew not what to make of this; but soon an inkling of the truth occurred to me. I remembered a story of a white man—a whaleman too—who, falling among the cannibals, had been tattooed by them. I concluded that this harpooneer, in the course of his distant voyages, must have met with a similar adventure. And what is it, thought I, after all! It's only his outside; a man can be honest in any sort of skin. But then, what to make of his unearthly complexion, that part of it, I mean, lying round about, and completely independent of the squares of tattooing. To be sure, it might be nothing but a good coat of tropical tanning; but I never heard of a hot sun's tanning a white man into a purplish yellow one. However, I had never been in the South Seas; and perhaps the sun there produced these extraordinary effects upon the skin. Now, while all these ideas were passing through me like lightning, this harpooneer never noticed me at all. But, after some difficulty having opened his bag, he commenced fumbling in it, and presently pulled out a sort of tomahawk, and a seal-skin wallet with the hair on. Placing these on the old chest in the middle of the room, he then took the New Zealand head—a ghastly thing enough—and crammed it down into the bag. He now took off his hat—a new beaver hat—when I came nigh singing out with fresh surprise. There was no hair on his head—none to speak of at least—nothing but a small scalp-knot twisted up on his forehead. His bald purplish head now looked for all the world like a mildewed skull. Had not the stranger stood between me and the door, I would have bolted out of it quicker than ever I bolted a dinner.

Even as it was, I thought something of slipping out of the window, but it was the second floor back. I am no coward, but what to make of this head-peddling purple rascal altogether passed my comprehension. Ignorance is the parent of fear, and being completely nonplussed and confounded about the stranger, I confess I was now as much afraid of him as if it was the devil himself who had thus broken into my room at the dead of night. In fact, I was so afraid of him that I was not game enough just then to address him, and demand a satisfactory answer concerning what seemed inexplicable in him.

Meanwhile, he continued the business of undressing, and at last showed his chest and arms. As I live, these covered parts of him were checkered with the same squares as his face; his back, too, was all over the same dark squares; he seemed to have been in a Thirty Years' War, and just escaped from it with a sticking-plaster shirt. Still more, his very legs were marked, as if a parcel of dark green frogs were running up the trunks of young palms. It was now quite plain that he must be some abominable savage or other shipped aboard of a whaleman in the South Seas, and so landed in this Christian country. I quaked to think of it. A peddler of heads too—perhaps the heads of his own brothers. He might take a fancy to mine—heavens! look at that tomahawk!

But there was no time for shuddering, for now the savage went about something that completely fascinated my attention, and convinced me that he must indeed be a heathen. Going to his heavy grego, or wrapall, or dreadnaught, which he had previously hung on a chair, he fumbled in the pockets, and produced at length a curious little deformed image with a hunch on its back, and exactly the color of a three days' old Congo baby. Remembering the embalmed head, at first I almost thought that this black manikin was a real baby preserved in some similar manner. But seeing that it was not at all limber, and that it glistened a good deal like polished ebony, I concluded that it must be nothing but a wooden idol, which indeed it proved to be. For now the savage goes up to the empty fireplace, and removing the papered fire-board, sets up this little hunch-backed image, like a tenpin, between the andirons. The chimney-jams and all the bricks inside were very sooty, so that I thought this fireplace made a very appropriate little shrine or chapel for his Congo idol.

I now screwed my eyes hard towards the half hidden image, feeling but ill at ease meantime—to see what was next to follow. First he takes about a double handful of shavings out of his grego pocket, and places them carefully before the idol; then laying a bit of ship biscuit on top and applying the flame from the lamp, he kindled the shavings into a sacrificial blaze. Presently, after many hasty snatches into the fire, and still hastier withdrawals of his fingers (whereby he seemed to be scorching them badly), he at last succeeded in drawing out the biscuit; then blowing off the heat and ashes a little, he made a polite offer of it to the little negro. But the little devil did not seem to fancy such dry sort of fare at all; he never moved his lips. All these strange antics were accompanied by still stranger guttural noises from the devotee, who seemed to be praying in a sing-song or else singing some pagan psalmody or other, during which his face twitched about in the most unnatural manner. At last extinguishing the fire, he took the idol up very unceremoniously, and bagged it again in his grego pocket as carelessly as if he were a sportsman bagging a dead woodcock.

All these queer proceedings increased my uncomfortableness, and seeing him now exhibiting strong symptoms of concluding his business operations, and jumping into bed with me, I thought it was high time, now or never, before the light was put out, to break the spell in which I had so long been bound.

But the interval I spent in deliberating what to say, was a fatal one. Taking up his tomahawk from the table, he examined the head of it for an instant, and then holding it to the light, with his mouth at the handle, he puffed out great clouds of tobacco smoke. The next moment the light was extinguished, and this wild cannibal, tomahawk between his teeth, sprang into bed with me. I sang out, I could not help it now; and giving a sudden grunt of astonishment he began feeling me.

Stammering out something, I know not what, I rolled away from him against the wall, and then conjured him, whoever or whatever he might be, to keep quiet, and let me get up and light the lamp again. But his guttural responses satisfied me at once that he but ill comprehended my meaning.

"Who-e debel you?"—he at last said—"you no speak-e, dam-me, I kill-e." And so saying the lighted tomahawk began flourishing about me in the dark.

"Landlord, for God's sake, Peter Coffin!" shouted I. "Landlord! Watch! Coffin! Angels! save me!"

"Speak-e! tell-ee me who-ee be, or dam-me, I kill-e!" again growled the cannibal, while his horrid flourishings of the tomahawk scattered the hot tobacco ashes about me till I thought my linen would get on fire. But thank heaven, at that moment the landlord came into the room light in hand, and leaping from the bed I ran up to him.

"Don't be afraid now," said he, grinning again, "Queequeg here wouldn't harm a hair of your head."

"Stop your grinning," shouted I, "and why didn't you tell me that that infernal harpooneer was a cannibal?"

"I thought ye know'd it;—didn't I tell ye, he was a-peddlin' heads around town?—but turn flukes again and go to sleep. Queequeg, look here—you sabbee me, I sabbee you—this man sleepe you—you sabbee?"

"Me sabbee plenty," grunted Queequeg, puffing away at his pipe and sitting up in bed.

"You gettee in," he added, motioning to me with his tomahawk, and throwing the clothes to one side. He really did this in not only a civil but a really kind and charitable way. I stood looking at him a moment. For all his tattooings he was on the whole a clean, comely looking cannibal. What's all this fuss I have been making about, thought I to myself—the man's a human being just as I am: he has just as much reason to fear me, as I have to be afraid of him. Better sleep with a sober cannibal than a drunken Christian.

"Landlord," said I, "tell him to stash his tomahawk there, or pipe, or whatever you call it; tell him to stop smoking, in short, and I will turn in with him. But I don't fancy having a man smoking in bed with me. It's dangerous. Besides, I ain't insured."

This being told to Queequeg, he at once complied, and again politely motioned me to get into bed—rolling over to one side as much as to say—I won't touch a leg of ye."

"Good-night, landlord," said I, "you may go."

I turned in, and never slept better in my life.

Chapter IV

THE COUNTERPANE

UPON WAKING NEXT MORNING ABOUT DAYLIGHT, I FOUND QUEEQUEG'S ARM THROWN OVER ME in the most loving and affectionate manner. You had almost thought I had been his wife. The counterpane was of patch-work, full of odd little parti-colored squares and triangles; and this arm of his tattooed all over with an interminable Cretan labyrinth of a figure, no two parts of which were of one precise shade—owing I suppose to his keeping his arm at sea unmethodically in sun and shade, his shirt sleeves irregularly rolled up at various times—this same arm of his, I say, looked for all the world like a strip of that same patch-work quilt. Indeed, partly lying on it as the arm did when I first awoke, I could hardly tell it from the quilt, they so blended their hues together; and it was only by the sense of weight and pressure that I could tell that Queequeg was hugging me.

My sensations were strange. Let me try to explain them. When I was a child, I well remember a somewhat similar circumstance that befell me; whether it was a reality or a dream, I never could entirely settle. The circumstance was this. I had been cutting up some caper or other—I think it was trying to crawl up the chimney, as I had seen a little sweep do a few days previous; and my stepmother who, somehow or other, was all the time whipping me, or sending me to bed supperless—my mother dragged me by the legs out of the chimney and packed me off to bed, though it was only two o'clock in the afternoon of the 21st June, the longest day in the year in our hemisphere. I felt dreadfully. But there was no help for it, so up stairs I went to my little room in the third floor, undressed myself as slowly as possible so as to kill time, and with a bitter sigh got between the sheets.

I lay there dismally calculating that sixteen entire hours must elapse before I could hope for a resurrection. Sixteen hours in bed! the small of my back ached to think of it. And it was so light too; the sun shining in at the window, and a great rattling of coaches in the streets, and the sound of gay voices all over the house. I felt worse and worse—at last I got up, dressed, and softly going down in my stockinged feet, sought out my stepmother, and suddenly threw myself at her feet, beseeching her as a particular favor to give me a good slippering for my misbehavior; anything indeed but condemning me to lie abed such an unendurable length of time. But she was the best and most conscientious of stepmothers, and back I had to go to my room. For several hours I lay there broad awake, feeling a great deal worse than I have ever done since, even from the greatest subsequent misfortunes. At last I must have fallen into a troubled nightmare of a doze; and slowly waking from it—half steeped in dreams—I opened my eyes, and the before sunlit room was now wrapped in outer darkness. Instantly I felt a shock running through all my frame; nothing was to be seen, and nothing was to be heard; but a supernatural hand seemed placed in mine. My arm hung over the counterpane, and the nameless, unimaginable, silent form or phantom, to which the hand belonged, seemed closely seated by my bedside. For what seemed ages piled on ages, I lay there, frozen with the most awful fears, not daring to drag away my hand; yet ever thinking that if I could but stir it one single inch, the horrid spell would be broken. I knew not how this consciousness at last glided away from me; but waking in the morning, I shudderingly remembered it all, and for days and weeks and months afterwards I lost myself in confounding attempts to explain the mystery. Nay, to this very hour, I often puzzle myself with it.

Now, take away the awful fear, and my sensations at feeling the supernatural hand in mine were very similar, in their strangeness, to those which I experienced on waking up and seeing Queequeg's pagan arm thrown round me. But at length all the past night's events soberly recurred, one by one, in fixed reality, and then I lay only alive to the comical predicament. For though I tried to move his arm—unlock his bridegroom clasp—yet, sleeping as he was, he still hugged me tightly, as though naught but death should part us twain. I now strove to rouse him—"Queequeg!"—but his only answer was a snore. I then rolled over, my neck feeling as if it were in a horse-collar; and suddenly felt a slight scratch. Throwing aside the counterpane, there lay the tomahawk sleeping by the savage's side, as if it were a hatchet-faced baby. A pretty pickle, truly, thought I; abed here in a strange house in the broad day, with a cannibal and a tomahawk! "Queequeg!—in the name of goodness, Queequeg, wake!" At length, by dint of much wriggling, and loud and incessant expostulations upon the unbecomingness of his hugging a fellow-male in that matrimonial sort of style, I succeeded in extracting a grunt; and presently, he drew back his arm, shook himself all over like a Newfoundland dog just from the water, and sat up in bed, stiff as a pike-staff, looking at me, and rubbing his eyes as if he did not altogether remember how I came to be there, though a dim consciousness of knowing something about me seemed slowly dawning over him. Meanwhile, I lay quietly eyeing him, having no serious misgivings now, and bent upon narrowly observing so curious a creature. When, at last, his mind seemed made up touching the character of his bedfellow, and he became, as it were, reconciled to the fact; he jumped out upon the floor, and by certain signs and sounds gave me to understand that, if it pleased me, he would dress first and then leave me to dress afterwards, leaving the whole apartment to myself. Thinks I, Queequeg, under the circumstances, this is a very civilized overture; but, the truth is, these savages have an innate sense of delicacy, say what you will; it is marvelous how essentially polite they are. I pay this particular compliment to Queequeg, because he treated me with so much civility and consideration, while I was guilty of great rudeness; staring at him from the bed, and watching all his toilette motions; for the time my curiosity getting the better of my breeding. Nevertheless, a man like Queequeg you don't see every day, he and his ways were well worth unusual regarding.

He commenced dressing at top by donning his beaver hat, a very tall one, by the by, and then—still minus his trousers—he hunted up his boots. What under the heavens he did it for, I cannot tell, but his next movement was to crush himself—boots in hand, and hat on—under the bed; when, from sundry violent gaspings and strainings, I inferred he was hard at work booting himself; though by no law of propriety that I ever heard of, is any man required to be private when putting on his boots. But Queequeg, do you see, was a creature in the transition state—neither caterpillar nor butterfly. He was just enough civilized to show off his outlandishness in the strangest possible manner. His education was not yet completed. He was an undergraduate. If he had not been a small degree civilized, he very probably would not have troubled himself with boots at all; but then, if he had not been still a savage, he never would have dreamed of getting under the bed to put them on. At last, he emerged with his hat very much dented and crushed down over his eyes, and began creaking and limping about the room, as if, not being much accustomed to boots, his pair of damp, wrinkled cowhide ones—probably not made to order either—rather pinched and tormented him at the first go off of a bitter cold morning.

Seeing, now, that there were no curtains to the window, and that the street being very narrow, the house opposite commanded a plain view into the room, and observing more and more the indecorous figure that Queequeg made, staving about with little else but his hat and boots on; I begged him as well as I could, to accelerate his toilette somewhat, and particularly to get into his pantaloons as soon as possible. He complied, and then proceeded to wash himself. At that time in the morning any Christian would have washed his face; but Queequeg, to my amazement, contented himself with restricting his ablutions to his chest, arms, and hands. He then donned his waistcoat, and taking up a piece of hard soap on the wash-stand center-table, dipped it into water and commenced lathering his face. I was watching to see where he kept his razor, when lo and behold, he takes the harpoon from the bed corner, slips out the long wooden stock, unsheathes the head, whets it a little on his boot, and striding up to the bit of mirror against the wall, begins a vigorous scraping, or rather harpooning of his cheeks. Thinks I, Queequeg, this is using Rogers's best cutlery with a vengeance. Afterwards I wondered the less at this operation when I came to know of what fine steel the head of a harpoon is made, and how exceedingly sharp the long straight edges are always kept.

The rest of his toilette was soon achieved, and he proudly marched out of the room, wrapped up in his great pilot monkey jacket, and sporting his harpoon like a marshal's baton.

Chapter V

BREAKFAST

I QUICKLY FOLLOWED SUIT, AND DESCENDING INTO THE BAR-ROOM ACCOSTED THE GRINNING landlord very pleasantly. I cherished no malice towards him, though he had been skylarking with me not a little in the matter of my bedfellow.

However, a good laugh is a mighty good thing, and rather too scarce a good thing; the more's the pity. So, if any one man, in his own proper person, afford stuff for a good joke to anybody, let him not be backward, but let him cheerfully allow himself to spend and to be spent in that way. And the man that has anything bountifully laughable about him, be sure there is more in that man than you perhaps think for.

The bar-room was now full of the boarders who had been dropping in the night previous, and whom I had not as yet had a good look at. They were nearly all whalemen; chief mates, and second mates, and third mates, and sea carpenters, and sea coopers, and sea blacksmiths, and harpooneers, and ship keepers; a brown and brawny company, with bosky beards; an unshorn, shaggy set, all wearing monkey jackets for morning gowns.

You could pretty plainly tell how long each one had been ashore. This young fellow's healthy cheek is like a sun-toasted pear in hue, and would seem to smell almost as musky; he cannot have been three days landed from his Indian voyage. That man next him looks a few shades lighter; you might say a touch of satin wood is in him. In the complexion of a third still lingers a tropic tawn, but slightly bleached withal; *he* doubtless has tarried whole weeks ashore. But who could show a cheek like Queequeg? which, barred with various tints, seemed like the Andes' western slope, to show forth in one array, contrasting climates, zone by zone.

"Grub, ho!" now cried the landlord, flinging open a door, and in we went to breakfast.

They say that men who have seen the world, thereby become quite at ease in manner, quite self-possessed in company. Not always, though: Ledyard, the great New England traveler, and Mungo Park, the Scotch one; of all men, they possessed the least assurance in the parlor. But perhaps the mere crossing of Siberia in a sledge drawn by dogs as Ledyard did, or the taking a long solitary walk on an empty stomach, in the negro heart of Africa, which was the sum of poor Mungo's performances—this kind of travel, I say, may not be the very best mode of attaining a high social polish. Still, for the most part, that sort of thing is to be had anywhere.

These reflections just here are occasioned by the circumstance that after we were all seated at the table, and I was preparing to hear some good stories about whaling; to my no small surprise nearly every man maintained a profound silence. And not only that, but they looked embarrassed. Yes, here were a set of sea-dogs, many of whom without the slightest bashfulness had boarded great whales on the high seas—entire strangers to them—and dueled them dead without winking; and yet, here they sat at a social breakfast table—all of the same calling, all of kindred tastes—looking round as sheepishly at each other as though they had never been out of sight of some sheepfold among the Green Mountains. A curious sight; these bashful bears, these timid warrior whalemen!

But as for Queequeg—why, Queequeg sat there among them—at the head of the table, too, it so chanced; as cool as an icicle. To be sure I cannot say much for his breeding. His greatest admirer could not have cordially justified his bringing his harpoon into breakfast with him, and using it there without ceremony; reaching over the table with it, to the imminent jeopardy of many heads, and grappling the beefsteaks towards him. But *that* was certainly very coolly done by him, and everyone knows that in most people's estimation, to do anything coolly is to do it genteelly.

We will not speak of all Queequeg's peculiarities here; how he eschewed coffee and hot rolls, and applied his undivided attention to beefsteaks, done rare. Enough, that when breakfast was over he withdrew like the rest into the public room, lighted his tomahawk-pipe, and was sitting there quietly digesting and smoking with his inseparable hat on, when I sallied out for a stroll.

Chapter VI

THE STREET

IF I HAD BEEN ASTONISHED AT FIRST CATCHING A GLIMPSE OF SO OUTLANDISH AN INDIVIDUAL AS Queequeg circulating among the polite society of a civilized town, that astonishment soon departed upon taking my first daylight stroll through the streets of New Bedford.

In thoroughfares nigh the docks, any considerable seaport will frequently offer to view the queerest looking nondescripts from foreign parts. Even in Broadway and Chestnut streets, Mediterranean mariners will sometimes jostle the affrighted ladies. Regent Street is not unknown to Lascars and Malays; and at Bombay, in the Apollo Green, live Yankees have often scared the natives. But New Bedford beats all Water Street and Wapping. In these last-mentioned haunts you see only sailors; but in New Bedford, actual cannibals stand chatting at street corners; savages outright; many of whom yet carry on their bones unholy flesh. It makes a stranger stare.

But, besides the Fijians, Tongatobooarrs, Erromangoans, Pannangians, and Brighggians, and, besides the wild specimens of the whaling-craft which unheeded reel about the streets, you will see other sights still more curious, certainly more comical. There weekly arrive in this town scores of green Vermonters and New Hampshire men, all athirst for gain and glory in the fishery. They are mostly young, of stalwart frames; fellows who have felled forests, and now seek to drop the ax and snatch the whale-lance. Many are as green as the Green Mountains whence they came. In some things you would think them but a few hours old. Look there! that chap strutting round the corner. He wears a beaver hat and swallow-tailed coat, girdled with a sailor-belt and a sheath-knife. Here comes another with a sou'-wester and a bombazine cloak.

No town-bred dandy will compare with a country-bred one—I mean a downright bumpkin dandy—a fellow that, in the dog-days, will mow his two acres in buck-skin gloves for fear of tanning his hands. Now when a country dandy like this takes it into his head to make a distinguished reputation, and joins the great whale-fishery, you should see the comical things he does upon reaching the seaport. In bespeaking his sea-outfit, he orders bell-buttons to his waistcoats; straps to his canvas trousers. Ah, poor Hay-Seed! how bitterly will burst those straps in the first howling gale, when thou art driven, straps, buttons, and all, down the throat of the tempest.

But think not that this famous town has only harpooneers, cannibals, and bumpkins to show her visitors. Not at all. Still New Bedford is a queer place. Had it not been for us whalemen, that tract of land would this day perhaps have been in as howling condition as the coast of Labrador. As it is, parts of her back country are enough to frighten one, they look so bony. The town itself is perhaps the dearest place to live in, in all New England. It is a land of oil, true enough: but not like Canaan; a land, also, of corn and wine. The streets do not run with milk; nor in the spring-time do they pave them with fresh eggs. Yet, in spite of this, nowhere in all America will you find more patrician-like houses; parks and gardens more opulent, than in New Bedford. Whence came they? how planted upon this once scraggy scoria of a country?

Go and gaze upon the iron emblematical harpoons round yonder lofty mansion, and your question will be answered. Yes; all these brave houses and flowery gardens came from the Atlantic, Pacific, and Indian Oceans. One and all, they were harpooned and dragged up hither from the bottom of the sea. Can Herr Alexander perform a feat like that?

In New Bedford, fathers, they say, give whales for dowers to their daughters, and portion off their nieces with a few porpoises apiece. You must go to New Bedford to see a brilliant wedding;

for, they say, they have reservoirs of oil in every house, and every night recklessly burn their lengths in spermaceti candles.

In summer time, the town is sweet to see; full of fine maples—long avenues of green and gold. And in August, high in air, the beautiful and bountiful horse-chestnuts, candelabra-wise, proffer the passer-by their tapering upright cones of congregated blossoms. So omnipotent is art; which in many a district of New Bedford has superinduced bright terraces of flowers upon the barren refuse rocks thrown aside at creation's final day.

And the women of New Bedford, they bloom like their own red roses. But roses only bloom in summer; whereas the fine carnation of their cheeks is perennial as sunlight in the seventh heavens. Elsewhere match that bloom of theirs, ye cannot, save in Salem, where they tell me the young girls breathe such musk, their sailor sweethearts smell them miles off-shore, as though they were drawing nigh the odorous Moluccas instead of the Puritanic sands.

Chapter VII

THE CHAPEL

IN THIS SAME NEW BEDFORD THERE STANDS A WHALEMAN'S CHAPEL, AND FEW ARE THE MOODY fishermen, shortly bound for the Indian Ocean or Pacific, who fail to make a Sunday visit to the spot. I am sure that I did not.

Returning from my first morning stroll, I again sallied out upon this special errand. The sky had changed from clear, sunny cold, to driving sleet and mist. Wrapping myself in my shaggy jacket of the cloth called bear-skin, I fought my way against the stubborn storm. Entering, I found a small scattered congregation of sailors, and sailors' wives and widows. A muffled silence reigned, only broken at times by the shrieks of the storm. Each silent worshiper seemed purposely sitting apart from the other, as if each silent grief were insular and incommunicable. The chaplain had not yet arrived; and there these silent islands of men and women sat steadfastly eyeing several marble tablets, with black borders, masoned into the wall on either side the pulpit. Three of them ran something like the following, but I do not pretend to quote:

SACRED
In the Memory
OF
JOHN TALBOT,
Who, at the age of eighteen, was lost overboard,
Near the Isle of Desolation, off Patagonia,
November 1st, 1836.
THIS TABLET
Is erected to his Memory
BY HIS SISTER.

SACRED
In the Memory
OF
ROBERT LONG, WILLIS ELLERY,

NATHAN COLEMAN, WALTER CANNY, SETH MACY,
AND SAMUEL GLEIG,
Forming one of the boats' crews
OF
THE SHIP *ELIZA*
Who were towed out of sight by a Whale,
On the Off-shore Ground in the
PACIFIC,
December 31st, 1839.
THIS MARBLE
Is here placed by their surviving
Shipmates.

SACRED
In the Memory
OF
The late
CAPTAIN EZEKIEL HARDY,
Who in the bows of his boat was killed by a
Sperm Whale on the coast of Japan,
August 3rd, 1833.
THIS TABLET
Is erected to his Memory
BY
HIS WIDOW.

Shaking off the sleet from my ice-glazed hat and jacket, I seated myself near the door, and turning sideways was surprised to see Queequeg near me. Affected by the solemnity of the scene, there was a wondering gaze of incredulous curiosity in his countenance. This savage was the only person present who seemed to notice my entrance; because he was the only one who could not read, and, therefore, was not reading those frigid inscriptions on the wall. Whether any of the relatives of the seamen whose names appeared there were now among the congregation, I knew not; but so many are the unrecorded accidents in the fishery, and so plainly did several women present wear the countenance if not the trappings of some unceasing grief, that I feel sure that here before me were assembled those, in whose unhealing hearts the sight of those bleak tablets sympathetically caused the old wounds to bleed afresh.

Oh! ye whose dead lie buried beneath the green grass; who standing among flowers can say—here, *here* lies my beloved; ye know not the desolation that broods in bosoms like these. What bitter blanks in those black-bordered marbles which cover no ashes! What despair in those immovable inscriptions! What deadly voids and unbidden infidelities in the lines that seem to gnaw upon all Faith, and refuse resurrections to the beings who have placelessly perished without a grave. As well might those tablets stand in the cave of Elephanta as here.

In what census of living creatures, the dead of mankind are included; why it is that a universal proverb says of them, that they tell no tales, though containing more secrets than the Goodwin Sands; how it is that to his name who yesterday departed for the other world, we prefix so significant and infidel a word, and yet do not thus entitle him, if he but embarks for the remotest Indies of this living earth; why the Life Insurance Companies pay death-forfeitures upon immortals; in what eternal, unstirring paralysis, and deadly, hopeless trance, yet lies antique Adam who died sixty round centuries ago; how it is that we still refuse to be comforted for those who we nevertheless maintain are dwelling in unspeakable bliss; why all the living so strive to hush all the dead; wherefore but the rumor of a knocking in a tomb will terrify a whole city. All these things are not without their meanings.

But Faith, like a jackal, feeds among the tombs, and even from these dead doubts she gathers her most vital hope.

It needs scarcely to be told, with what feelings, on the eve of a Nantucket voyage, I regarded those marble tablets, and by the murky light of that darkened, doleful day read the fate of the whalemen who had gone before me. Yes, Ishmael, the same fate may be thine. But somehow I grew merry again. Delightful inducements to embark, fine chance for promotion, it seems—aye, a stove boat will make me an immortal by brevet. Yes, there is death in this business of whaling—a speechlessly quick chaotic bundling of a man into Eternity. But what then? Methinks we have hugely mistaken this matter of Life and Death. Methinks that what they call my shadow here on earth is my true substance. Methinks that in looking at things spiritual, we are too much like oysters observing the sun through the water, and thinking that thick water the thinnest of air. Methinks my body is but the lees of my better being. In fact take my body who will, take it I say, it is not me. And therefore three cheers for Nantucket; and come a stove boat and stove body when they will, for stave my soul, Jove himself cannot.

Chapter VIII

THE PULPIT

I HAD NOT BEEN SEATED VERY LONG ERE A MAN OF A CERTAIN VENERABLE ROBUSTNESS ENTERED; immediately as the storm-pelted door flew back upon admitting him, a quick regardful eyeing of him by all the congregation, sufficiently attested that this fine old man was the chaplain. Yes, it was the famous Father Mapple, so called by the whalemen, among whom he was a very great favorite. He had been a sailor and a harpooneer in his youth, but for many years past had dedicated his life to the ministry. At the time I now write of, Father Mapple was in the hardy winter of a healthy old age; that sort of old age which seems merging into a second flowering youth, for among all the fissures of his wrinkles, there shone certain mild gleams of a newly developing bloom—the spring verdure peeping forth even beneath February's snow. No one having previously heard his history, could for the first time behold Father Mapple without the utmost interest, because there were certain engrafted clerical peculiarities about him, imputable to that adventurous maritime life he had led. When he entered I observed that he carried no umbrella, and certainly had not come in his carriage, for his tarpaulin hat ran down with melting sleet, and his great pilot cloth jacket seemed almost to drag him to the floor with the weight of the water it had absorbed. However, hat and coat and overshoes were one by one removed, and hung up in a little space in an adjacent corner; when, arrayed in a decent suit, he quietly approached the pulpit.

Like most old-fashioned pulpits, it was a very lofty one, and since a regular stairs to such a height would, by its long angle with the floor, seriously contract the already small area of the chapel, the architect, it seemed, had acted upon the hint of Father Mapple, and finished the pulpit without a stairs, substituting a perpendicular side ladder, like those used in mounting a ship from a boat at sea. The wife of a whaling captain had provided the chapel with a handsome pair of red worsted man-ropes for this ladder, which, being itself nicely headed, and stained with a mahogany color, the whole contrivance, considering what manner of chapel it was, seemed by no means in bad taste. Halting for an instant at the foot of the ladder, and with both hands grasping the ornamental knobs of the man-ropes, Father Mapple cast a look upwards, and then with a truly sailor-like but still reverential dexterity, hand over hand, mounted the steps as if ascending the main-top of his vessel.

The perpendicular parts of this side ladder, as is usually the case with swinging ones, were of cloth-covered rope, only the rounds were of wood, so that at every step there was a joint. At my first glimpse of the pulpit, it had not escaped me that however convenient for a ship, these joints in the present instance seemed unnecessary. For I was not prepared to see Father Mapple after gaining the height, slowly turn round, and stooping over the pulpit, deliberately drag up the ladder step by step, till the whole was deposited within, leaving him impregnable in his little Quebec.

I pondered some time without fully comprehending the reason for this. Father Mapple enjoyed such a wide reputation for sincerity and sanctity, that I could not suspect him of courting notoriety by any mere tricks of the stage. No, thought I, there must be some sober reason for this thing; furthermore, it must symbolize something unseen. Can it be, then, that by that act of physical isolation, he signifies his spiritual withdrawal for the time, from all outward worldly ties and connections? Yes, for replenished with the meat and wine of the word, to the faithful man of God, this pulpit, I see, is a self-containing stronghold—a lofty Ehrenbreitstein, with a perennial well of water within the walls.

But the side ladder was not the only strange feature of the place, borrowed from the chaplain's former sea-farings. Between the marble cenotaphs on either hand of the pulpit, the wall which formed its back was adorned with a large painting representing a gallant ship beating against a terrible storm off a lee coast of black rocks and snowy breakers. But high above the flying scud and dark-rolling clouds, there floated a little isle of sunlight, from which beamed forth an angel's face; and this bright face shed a distant spot of radiance upon the ship's tossed deck, something like that silver plate now inserted into the *Victory*'s plank where Nelson fell. "Ah, noble ship," the angel seemed to say, "beat on, beat on, thou noble ship, and bear a hardy helm; for lo! the sun is breaking through; the clouds are rolling off—serenest azure is at hand."

Nor was the pulpit itself without a trace of the same sea-taste that had achieved the ladder and the picture. Its paneled front was in the likeness of a ship's bluff bows, and the Holy Bible rested on a projecting piece of scroll work, fashioned after a ship's fiddle-headed beak.

What could be more full of meaning?—for the pulpit is ever this earth's foremost part; all the rest comes in its rear; the pulpit leads the world. From thence it is the storm of God's quick wrath is first descried, and the bow must bear the earliest brunt. From thence it is the God of breezes fair or foul is first invoked for favorable winds. Yes, the world's a ship on its passage out, and not a voyage complete; and the pulpit is its prow.

Chapter IX

THE SERMON

FATHER MAPPLE ROSE, AND IN A MILD VOICE OF UNASSUMING AUTHORITY ORDERED THE SCATtered people to condense. "Starboard gangway, there! side away to larboard—larboard gangway to starboard! Midships! midships!"

There was a low rumbling of heavy sea-boots among the benches, and a still slighter shuffling of women's shoes, and all was quiet again, and every eye on the preacher.

He paused a little; then kneeling in the pulpit's bows, folded his large brown hands across his chest, uplifted his closed eyes, and offered a prayer so deeply devout that he seemed kneeling and praying at the bottom of the sea.

This ended, in prolonged solemn tones, like the continual tolling of a bell in a ship that is foundering at sea in a fog—in such tones he commenced reading the following hymn; but changing his manner towards the concluding stanzas, burst forth with a pealing exultation and joy—

The ribs and terrors in the whale,
Arched over me a dismal gloom,
While all God's sun-lit waves rolled by,
And left me deepening down to doom.

I saw the opening maw of hell,
With endless pains and sorrows there;
Which none but they that feel can tell—
Oh, I was plunging to despair.

In black distress, I called my God,
When I could scarce believe him mine,
He bowed his ear to my complaints—
No more the whale did me confine.

With speed he flew to my relief,
As on a radiant dolphin borne;
Awful, yet bright, as lightning shone
The face of my Deliverer God.

My song for ever shall record
That terrible, that joyful hour;
I give the glory to my God,
His all the mercy and the power.

Nearly all joined in singing this hymn, which swelled high above the howling of the storm. A brief pause ensued; the preacher slowly turned over the leaves of the Bible, and at last, folding his hand down upon the proper page, said: "Beloved shipmates, clinch the last verse of the first chapter of Jonah—'And God had prepared a great fish to swallow up Jonah.' "

"Shipmates, this book, containing only four chapters—four yarns—is one of the smallest strands in the mighty cable of the Scriptures. Yet what depths of the soul does Jonah's deep sealine sound! what a pregnant lesson to us is this prophet! What a noble thing is that canticle in the fish's belly! How billow-like and boisterously grand! We feel the floods surging over us, we sound with him to the kelpy bottom of the waters; sea-weed and all the slime of the sea is about us! But *what* is this lesson that the book of Jonah teaches? Shipmates, it is a two-stranded lesson; a lesson to us all as sinful men, and a lesson to me as a pilot of the living God. As sinful men, it is a lesson to us all, because it is a story of the sin, hard-heartedness, suddenly awakened fears, the swift punishment, repentance, prayers, and finally the deliverance and joy of Jonah. As with all sinners among men, the sin of this son of Amittai was in his willful disobedience of the command of God—never mind now what that command was, or how conveyed—which he found a hard command. But all the things that God would have us do are hard for us to do—remember that—and hence, he oftener commands us than endeavors to persuade. And if we obey God, we must disobey ourselves; and it is in this disobeying ourselves, wherein the hardness of obeying God consists.

"With this sin of disobedience in him, Jonah still further flouts at God, by seeking to flee from Him. He thinks that a ship made by men, will carry him into countries where God does not reign, but only the Captains of this earth. He skulks about the wharves of Joppa, and seeks a ship that's bound for Tarshish. There lurks, perhaps, a hitherto unheeded meaning here. By all accounts Tarshish could have been no other city than the modern Cadiz. That's the opinion of learned men. And where is Cadiz, shipmates? Cadiz is in Spain; as far by water, from Joppa, as Jonah could possibly have sailed in those ancient days, when the Atlantic was an almost unknown sea. Because Joppa, the modern Jaffa, shipmates, is on the most easterly coast of the Mediterranean, the Syrian; and Tarshish or Cadiz more than two thousand miles to the westward from that, just outside the Straits of Gibraltar. See ye not then, shipmates, that Jonah sought to flee world-wide from God? Miserable man! Oh! most contemptible and worthy of all scorn; with slouched hat and guilty eye, skulking from his God; prowling among the shipping like a vile burglar hastening to cross the seas. So disordered, self-condemning is his look, that had there been policemen in those days, Jonah, on the mere suspicion of something wrong, had been arrested ere he touched a deck. How plainly he's a fugitive! no baggage, not a hat-box, valise, or carpet-bag—no friends accompany him to the wharf with their adieux. At last, after much dodging search, he finds the Tarshish ship receiving the last items of her cargo; and as he steps on board to see its Captain in the cabin, all the sailors for the moment desist from hoisting in the goods, to mark the stranger's evil eye. Jonah sees this; but in vain he tries to look all ease and confidence; in vain essays his wretched smile. Strong intuitions of the man assure the mariners he can be no innocent. In their gamesome but still serious way, one whispers to the other—'Jack, he's robbed a widow'; or, 'Joe, do you mark him; he's a bigamist'; or, 'Harry lad, I guess he's the adulterer that broke jail in old Gomorrah, or belike, one of the missing murderers from Sodom.' Another runs to read the bill that's stuck against the spile upon the wharf to which the ship is moored, offering five hundred gold coins for the apprehension of a parricide, and containing a description of his person. He reads, and looks from Jonah to the bill; while all his sympathetic shipmates now crowd round Jonah, prepared to lay their hands upon him. Frighted Jonah trembles, and summoning all his boldness to his face, only looks so much the more a coward. He will not confess himself suspected; but that itself is strong suspicion. So he makes the best of it; and when the sailors find him not to be the man that is advertised, they let him pass, and he descends into the cabin.

" 'Who's there?' cries the Captain at his busy desk, hurriedly making out his papers for the Customs—'Who's there?' Oh! how that harmless question mangles Jonah! For the instant he almost turns to flee again. But he rallies. 'I seek a passage in this ship to Tarshish; how soon sail ye, sir?' Thus far the busy Captain had not looked up to Jonah, though the man now stands before him; but no sooner does he hear that hollow voice, than he darts a scrutinizing glance. 'We sail with the next coming tide,' at last he slowly answered, still intently eyeing him. 'No sooner, sir?'—'Soon enough for any honest man that goes a passenger.' Ha! Jonah, that's another stab. But he swiftly calls away the Captain from that scent. 'I'll sail with ye'—he says—'the passage money how much is that?—I'll pay now.' For it is particularly written, shipmates, as if it were a thing not to be overlooked in this history, 'that he paid the fare thereof' ere the craft did sail. And taken with the context, this is full of meaning.

"Now Jonah's Captain, shipmates, was one whose discernment detects crime in any, but whose cupidity exposes it only in the penniless. In this world, shipmates, sin that pays its way can travel freely and without a passport; whereas Virtue, if a pauper, is stopped at all frontiers. So Jonah's Captain prepares to test the length of Jonah's purse, ere he judge him openly. He charges him thrice the usual sum; and it's assented to. Then the Captain knows that Jonah is a fugitive; but at the same time resolves to help a flight that paves its rear with gold. Yet when Jonah fairly takes out his purse, prudent suspicions still molest the Captain. He rings every coin to find a counterfeit. Not a forger, any way, he mutters; and Jonah is put down for his passage. 'Point out my state-room, Sir,' says Jonah now, 'I'm travel-weary; I need sleep.' 'Thou look'st like it,' says the Captain, 'there's thy room.' Jonah enters, and would lock the door, but the lock contains no key. Hearing him foolishly fumbling there, the Captain laughs lowly to himself, and mutters something about the doors of convicts' cells being never allowed to be locked within. All dressed and dusty as he is, Jonah throws himself into his berth, and finds the little state-room ceiling almost resting on his forehead. The air is close, and Jonah gasps. Then, in that contracted hole, sunk, too, beneath the ship's water-line, Jonah feels the heralding presentiment of that stifling hour, when the whale shall hold him in the smallest of his bowels' wards.

"Screwed at its axis against the side, a swinging lamp slightly oscillates in Jonah's room; and the ship, heeling over towards the wharf with the weight of the last bales received, the lamp, flame and all, though in slight motion, still maintains a permanent obliquity with reference to the room; though, in truth, infallibly straight itself, it but made obvious the false, lying levels among which it hung. The lamp alarms and frightens Jonah; as lying in his berth his tormented eyes roll round the place, and this thus far successful fugitive finds no refuge for his restless glance. But that contradiction in the lamp more and more appalls him. The floor, the ceiling, and the side, are all awry. 'Oh! so my conscience hangs in me!' he groans, "straight upward, so it burns; but the chambers of my soul are all in crookedness!'

"Like one who after a night of drunken revelry hies to his bed, still reeling, but with conscience yet pricking him, as the plungings of the Roman race-horse but so much the more strike his steel tags into him; as one who in that miserable plight still turns and turns in giddy anguish, praying God for annihilation until the fit be passed; and at last amid the whirl of woe he feels, a deep stupor steals over him, as over the man who bleeds to death, for conscience is the wound, and there's naught to staunch it; so, after sore wrestling in his berth, Jonah's prodigy of ponderous misery drags him drowning down to sleep.

"And now the time of tide has come; the ship casts off her cable; and from the deserted wharf the uncheered ship for Tarshish, all careening, glides to sea. That ship, my friends, was the first of recorded smugglers! the contraband was Jonah. But the sea rebels; he will not bear the wicked burden. A dreadful storm comes on, the ship is like to break. But now when the boatswain calls all hands to lighten her; when boxes, bales, and jars are clattering overboard; when the wind is shrieking, and the men are yelling, and every plank thunders with trampling feet right over Jonah's head; in all this raging tumult, Jonah sleeps his hideous sleep. He sees no black sky and raging sea, feels not the reeling timbers, and little hears he or heeds he the far rush of the mighty whale, which even now with open mouth is cleaving the seas after him. Ay, shipmates, Jonah was gone down into the sides of the ship—a berth in the cabin as I have taken it, and was fast asleep. But the frightened master comes to him, and shrieks in his dead ear, 'What meanest thou, O sleeper! arise!' Startled from his lethargy by that direful cry, Jonah staggers to his feet, and stumbling to the deck, grasps a shroud, to look out upon the sea. But at that moment he is sprung upon by a panther billow leaping over the bulwarks. Wave after wave thus leaps into the ship, and finding no speedy vent runs roaring fore and aft, till the mariners come nigh to drowning while yet afloat. And ever, as the white moon shows her affrighted face from the steep gullies in the blackness overhead, aghast Jonah sees the rearing bowsprit pointing high upward, but soon beat downward again towards the tormented deep.

"Terrors upon terrors run shouting through his soul. In all his cringing attitudes, the God-fugitive is now too plainly known. The sailors mark him; more and more certain grow their suspicions of him, and at last, fully to test the truth, by referring the whole matter to high Heaven, they fall to casting lots, to see for whose cause this great tempest was upon them. The lot is Jonah's; that discovered, then how furiously they mob him with their questions. 'What is thine occupation? Whence comest thou? Thy country? What people?' But mark now, my shipmates, the behavior of poor Jonah. The eager mariners but ask him who he is, and where from; whereas, they not only receive an answer to those questions, but likewise another answer to a question not put by them, but the unsolicited answer is forced from Jonah by the hard hand of God that is upon him.

" 'I am a Hebrew,' he cries—and then—'I fear the Lord the God of Heaven who hath made the sea and the dry land!' Fear him, O Jonah? Ay, well mightest thou fear the Lord God *then*! Straightway, he now goes on to make a full confession; whereupon the mariners became more and more appalled, but still are pitiful. For when Jonah, not yet supplicating God for mercy, since he but too well knew the darkness of his deserts—when wretched Jonah cries out to them to take him and cast him forth into the sea, for he knew that for *his* sake this great tempest was upon them, they mercifully turn from him, and seek by other means to save the ship. But all in vain; the indignant gale howls louder; then, with one hand raised invokingly to God, with the other they not unreluctantly lay hold of Jonah.

"And now behold Jonah taken up as an anchor and dropped into the sea; when instantly an oily calmness floats out from the east, and the sea is still, as Jonah carries down the gale with him, leaving smooth water behind. He goes down in the whirling heart of such a masterless commotion that he scarce heeds the moment when he drops seething into the yawning jaws awaiting him; and the whale shoots-to all his ivory teeth, like so many white bolts, upon his prison. Then Jonah prayed unto the Lord out of the fish's belly. But observe his prayer, and learn a weighty lesson. For sinful as he is, Jonah does not weep and wail for direct deliverance. He feels that his dreadful punishment is just. He leaves all his deliverance to God, contenting himself with this, that spite of all his pains and pangs, he will still look towards His holy temple. And here, shipmates, is true and faithful repentance; not clamorous for pardon, but grateful for punishment. And how pleasing to God was this conduct in Jonah, is shown in the eventual deliverance of him from the sea and the whale. Shipmates, I do not place Jonah before you to be copied for his sin but I do place him before you as a model for repentance. Sin not; but if you do, take heed to repent of it like Jonah."

While he was speaking these words, the howling of the shrieking, slanting storm without seemed to add new power to the preacher, who, when describing Jonah's sea-storm, seemed tossed by a storm himself. His deep chest heaved as with a ground-swell; his tossed arms seemed the warring elements at work; and the thunders that rolled away from off his swarthy brow, and the light leaping from his eye, made all his simple hearers look on him with a quick fear that was strange to them.

There now came a lull in his look, as he silently turned over the leaves of the Book once more; and, at last, standing motionless, with closed eyes, for the moment, seemed communing with God and himself.

But again he leaned over towards the people, and bowing his head lowly, with an aspect of the deepest yet manliest humility, he spake these words:

"Shipmates, God has laid but one hand upon you; both his hands press upon me. I have read ye by what murky light may be mine the lesson that Jonah teaches to all sinners; and therefore to ye, and still more to me, for I am a greater sinner than ye. And now how gladly would I come down from this mast-head and sit on the hatches there where you sit, and listen as you listen, while some one of you reads *me* that other and more awful lesson which Jonah teaches to *me*, as a pilot of the living God. How being an anointed pilot-prophet, or speaker of true things, and bidden by the Lord to sound those unwelcome truths in the ears of a wicked Nineveh, Jonah, appalled at the hostility he should raise, fled from his mission, and sought to escape his duty and his God by taking ship at Joppa. But God is everywhere; Tarshish he never reached. As we have seen, God came upon him in the whale, and swallowed him down to living gulfs of doom, and with swift slantings tore him along 'into the midst of the seas,' where the eddying depths sucked him ten thousand fathoms down, and 'the weeds were wrapped about his head,' and all the watery world of woe bowled over him. Yet even then beyond the reach of any plummet—'out of the belly of hell'—when the whale grounded upon the ocean's utmost bones, even then, God heard the engulphed, repenting prophet when he cried. Then God spake unto the fish; and from the shuddering cold and blackness of the sea, the whale came breeching up towards the warm and pleasant sun, and all the delights of air and earth; and 'vomited out Jonah upon the dry land'; when the word of the Lord came a second time; and Jonah, bruised and beaten—his ears, like two sea-shells, still multitudinously murmuring of the ocean—Jonah did the Almighty's bidding. And what was that, shipmates? To preach the Truth to the face of Falsehood! That was it!

"This, shipmates, this is that other lesson; and woe to that pilot of the living God who slights it. Woe to him whom this world charms from Gospel duty! Woe to him who seeks to pour oil upon the waters when God has brewed them into a gale! Woe to him who seeks to please rather than to appall! Woe to him whose good name is more to him than goodness! Woe to him who, in this world, courts not dishonor! Woe to him who would not be true, even though to be false were salvation! Yea, woe to him who as the great Pilot Paul has it, while preaching to others is himself a castaway!"

He drooped and fell away from himself for a moment; then lifting his face to them again, showed a deep joy in his eyes, as he cried out with a heavenly enthusiasm—"But oh! shipmates! on the starboard hand of every woe, there is a sure delight; and higher the top of that delight, than the bottom of the woe is deep. Is not the main-truck higher than the kelson is low? Delight is to him—a far, far upward, and inward delight—who against the proud gods and commodores of this earth, ever stands forth his own inexorable self. Delight is to him whose strong arms yet support him, when the ship of this base treacherous world has gone down beneath him. Delight is to him, who gives no quarter in the truth, and kills, burns, and destroys all sin though he pluck it out from under the robes of Senators and Judges. Delight—top-gallant delight is to him, who acknowledges no law or lord, but the Lord his God, and is only a patriot to heaven. Delight is to him, whom all the waves of the billows of the seas of the boisterous mob can never shake from this sure Keel of the Ages. And eternal delight and deliciousness will be his, who coming to lay him down, can say with his final breath—O Father!—chiefly known to me by Thy rod—mortal or immortal, here I die. I have striven to be Thine, more than to be this world's or mine own. Yet this is nothing: I leave eternity to Thee; for what is man that he should live out the lifetime of his God?"

He said no more, but slowly waving a benediction, covered his face with his hands, and so remained kneeling, till all the people had departed, and he was left alone in the place.

Chapter X

A Bosom Friend

Returning to the Spouter-Inn from the Chapel, I found Queequeg there quite alone; he having left the Chapel before the benediction some time. He was sitting on a bench before the fire, with his feet on the stove hearth, and in one hand was holding close up to his face that little negro idol of his; peering hard into its face, and with a jack-knife gently whittling away at its nose, meanwhile humming to himself in his heathenish way.

But being now interrupted, he put up the image; and pretty soon, going to the table, took up a large book there, and placing it on his lap began counting the pages with deliberate regularity; at every fiftieth page—as I fancied—stopping for a moment, looking vacantly around him, and giving utterance to a long-drawn gurgling whistle of astonishment. He would then begin again at the next fifty; seeming to commence at number one each time, as though he could not count more than fifty, and it was only by such a large number of fifties being found together, that his astonishment at the multitude of pages was excited.

With much interest I sat watching him. Savage though he was, and hideously marred about the face—at least to my taste—his countenance yet had a something in it which was by no means disagreeable. You cannot hide the soul. Through all his unearthly tattooings, I thought I saw the traces of a simple honest heart; and in his large, deep eyes, fiery black and bold, there seemed tokens of a spirit that would dare a thousand devils. And besides all this, there was a certain lofty bearing about the Pagan, which even his uncouthness could not altogether maim. He looked like a man who had never cringed and never had had a creditor. Whether it was, too, that his head being shaved, his forehead was drawn out in freer and brighter relief, and looked more expansive than it otherwise would, this I will not venture to decide; but certain it was his head was phrenologically an excellent one. It may seem ridiculous, but it reminded me of General Washington's head, as seen in the popular busts of him. It had the same long regularly graded retreating slope from above the brows, which were likewise very projecting, like two long promontories thickly wooded on top. Queequeg was George Washington cannibalistically developed.

Whilst I was thus closely scanning him, half-pretending meanwhile to be looking out at the storm from the casement, he never heeded my presence, never troubled himself with so much as a single glance; but appeared wholly occupied with counting the pages of the marvelous book. Considering how sociably we had been sleeping together the night previous, and especially considering the affectionate arm I had found thrown over me upon waking in the morning, I thought this indifference of his very strange. But savages are strange beings; at times you do not know exactly how to take them. At first they are overawing; their calm self-collectedness of simplicity seems as Socratic wisdom. I had noticed also that Queequeg never consorted at all, or but very little, with the other seamen in the inn. He made no advances whatever; appeared to have no desire to enlarge the circle of his acquaintances. All this struck me as mighty singular; yet, upon second thoughts, there was something almost sublime in it. Here was a man some twenty thousand miles from home, by the way of Cape Horn, that is—which was the only way he could get there—thrown among people as strange to him as though he were in the planet Jupiter; and yet he seemed entirely at his ease; preserving the utmost serenity; content with his own companionship; always equal to himself. Surely this was a touch of fine philosophy; though no doubt he had never heard there was such a thing as that. But, perhaps, to be true philosophers, we mortals should not be conscious of so living or so striving. So soon as I hear that such or such a man gives himself out for a philosopher, I conclude that, like the dyspeptic old woman, he must have "broken his digester."

As I sat there in that now lonely room; the fire burning low, in that mild stage when, after its first intensity has warmed the air, it then only glows to be looked at; the evening shades and phantoms gathering round the casements, and peering in upon us silent, solitary twain; the storm booming without in solemn swells; I began to be sensible of strange feelings. I felt a melting in me. No more my splintered heart and maddened hand were turned against the wolfish world. This soothing savage had redeemed it. There he sat, his very indifference speaking a nature in which there lurked no civilized hypocrisies and bland deceits. Wild he was; a very sight of sights to see; yet I began to feel myself mysteriously drawn towards him. And those same things that would have repelled most others, they were the very magnets that thus drew me. I'll try a pagan friend, thought I, since Christian kindness has proved but hollow courtesy. I drew my bench near him, and made some friendly signs and hints, doing my best to talk with him meanwhile. At first he little noticed these advances; but presently, upon my referring to his last night's hospitalities, he made out to ask me whether we were again to be bedfellows. I told him yes; whereat I thought he looked pleased, perhaps a little complimented.

We then turned over the book together, and I endeavored to explain to him the purpose of the printing, and the meaning of the few pictures that were in it. Thus I soon engaged his interest; and from that we went to jabbering the best we could about the various outer sights to be seen in this famous town. Soon I proposed a social smoke; and, producing his pouch and tomahawk, he quietly offered me a puff. And then we sat exchanging puffs from that wild pipe of his, and keeping it regularly passing between us.

If there yet lurked any ice of indifference towards me in the Pagan's breast, this pleasant, genial smoke we had, soon thawed it out, and left us cronies. He seemed to take to me quite as naturally and unbiddenly as I to him; and when our smoke was over, he pressed his forehead against mine, clasped me round the waist, and said that henceforth we were married; meaning, in his country's phrase, that we were bosom friends; he would gladly die for me, if need should be. In a countryman, this sudden flame of friendship would have seemed far too premature, a thing to be much distrusted; but in this simple savage those old rules would not apply.

After supper, and another social chat and smoke, we went to our room together. He made me a present of his embalmed head; took out his enormous tobacco wallet, and groping under the tobacco, drew out some thirty dollars in silver; then spreading them on the table, and mechanically dividing them into two equal portions, pushed one of them towards me, and said it was mine. I was going to remonstrate; but he silenced me by pouring them into my trousers' pockets. I let them stay. He then went about his evening prayers, took out his idol, and removed the paper firebrand. By certain signs and symptoms, I thought he seemed anxious for me to join him; but well knowing what was to follow, I deliberated a moment whether, in case he invited me, I would comply or otherwise.

I was a good Christian; born and bred in the bosom of the infallible Presbyterian Church. How then could I unite with this wild idolator in worshiping his piece of wood? But what is worship? thought I. Do you suppose now, Ishmael, that the magnanimous God of heaven and earth—pagans and all included—can possibly be jealous of an insignificant bit of black wood? Impossible! But what is worship?—to do the will of God?—*that* is worship. And what is the will of God?—to do to my fellow-man what I would have my fellow-man to do to me—*that* is the will of God. Now, Queequeg is my fellow-man. And what do I wish that this Queequeg would do to me? Why, unite with me in my particular Presbyterian form of worship. Consequently, I must then unite with him in his; ergo, I must turn idolator. So I kindled the shavings; helped prop up the innocent little idol; offered him burned biscuit with Queequeg; salaamed before him twice or thrice; kissed his nose; and that done, we undressed and went to bed, at peace with our own consciences and all the world. But we did not go to sleep without some little chat.

How it is I know not; but there is no place like a bed for confidential disclosures between friends. Man and wife, they say, there open the very bottom of their souls to each other; and some old couples often lie and chat over old times till nearly morning. Thus, then, in our hearts' honeymoon, lay I and Queequeg—a cozy, loving pair.

Chapter XI

NIGHTGOWN

WE HAD LAIN THUS IN BED, CHATTING AND NAPPING AT SHORT INTERVALS, AND QUEEQUEG now and then affectionately throwing his brown tattooed legs over mine, and then drawing them back; so entirely sociable and free and easy were we; when, at last, by reason of our confabulations, what little nappishness remained in us altogether departed, and we felt like getting up again, though day-break was yet some way down the future.

Yes, we became very wakeful; so much so that our recumbent position began to grow wearisome, and by little and little we found ourselves sitting up; the clothes well tucked around us, leaning against the headboard with our four knees drawn up close together, and our two noses bending over them, as if our knee-pans were warming-pans. We felt very nice and snug, the more so since it was so chilly out of doors; indeed out of bed-clothes too, seeing that there was no fire in the room. The more so, I say, because truly to enjoy bodily warmth, some small part of you must be cold, for there is no quality in this world that is not what it is merely by contrast. Nothing exists in itself. If you flatter yourself that you are all over comfortable, and have been so a long time, then you cannot be said to be comfortable any more. But if, like Queequeg and me in the bed, the tip of your nose or the crown of your head be slightly chilled, why then, indeed, in the general consciousness you feel most delightfully and unmistakably warm. For this reason a sleeping apartment should never be furnished with a fire, which is one of the luxurious discomforts of the rich. For the height of this sort of deliciousness is to have nothing but the blankets between you and your snugness and the cold of the outer air. Then there you lie like the one warm spark in the heart of an arctic crystal.

We had been sitting in this crouching manner for some time, when all at once I thought I would open my eyes; for when between sheets, whether by day or by night, and whether asleep or awake, I have a way of always keeping my eyes shut, in order the more to concentrate the snugness of being in bed. Because no man can ever feel his own identity aright except his eyes be closed; as if, darkness were indeed the proper element of our essences, though light be more congenial to our clayey part. Upon opening my eyes then, and coming out of my own pleasant and self-created darkness into the imposed and coarse outer gloom of the unilluminated twelve-o'clock-at-night, I experienced a disagreeable revulsion. Nor did I at all object to the hint from Queequeg that perhaps it were best to strike a light, seeing that we were so wide awake; and besides he felt a strong desire to have a few quiet puffs from his Tomahawk. Be it said, that though I had felt such a strong repugnance to his smoking in the bed the night before, yet see how elastic our stiff prejudices grow when love once comes to bend them. For now I liked nothing better than to have Queequeg smoking by me, even in bed, because he seemed to be full of such serene household joy then. I no more felt unduly concerned for the landlord's policy of insurance. I was only alive to the condensed confidential comfortableness of sharing a pipe and a blanket with a real friend. With our shaggy jackets drawn about our shoulders, we now passed the Tomahawk from one to the other, till slowly there grew over us a blue hanging tester of smoke, illuminated by the flame of the new-lit lamp.

Whether it was that this undulating tester rolled the savage away to far distant scenes, I know not, but he now spoke of his native island; and, eager to hear his history, I begged him to go on and tell it. He gladly complied. Though at the time I but ill comprehended not a few of his words, yet subsequent disclosures, when I had become more familiar with his broken phraseology, now enable me to present the whole story such as it may prove in the mere skeleton I give.

Chapter XII

BIOGRAPHICAL

QUEEQUEG WAS A NATIVE OF KOKOVOKO, AN ISLAND FAR AWAY TO THE WEST AND SOUTH. IT IS not down on any map; true places never are.

When a new-hatched savage running wild about his native woodlands in a grass clout, followed by the nibbling goats, as if he were a green sapling; even then, in Queequeg's ambitious soul, lurked a strong desire to see something more of Christendom than a specimen whaler or two. His father was a High-Chief, a King; his uncle a High-Priest; and on the maternal side he boasted aunts who were the wives of unconquerable warriors. There was excellent blood in his veins—royal stuff; though sadly vitiated, I fear, by the cannibal propensity he nourished in his untutored youth.

A Sag Harbor ship visited his father's bay, and Queequeg sought a passage to Christian lands. But the ship, having her full complement of seamen, spurned his suit; and not all the King his father's influence could prevail. But Queequeg vowed a vow. Alone in his canoe, he paddled off to a distant strait, which he knew the ship must pass through when she quitted the island. On one side was a coral reef; on the other a low tongue of land, covered with mangrove thickets that grew out into the water. Hiding his canoe, still afloat, among these thickets, with its prow seaward, he sat down in the stern, paddle low in hand; and when the ship was gliding by, like a flash he darted out; gained her side; with one backward dash of his foot capsized and sank his canoe; climbed up the chains; and throwing himself at full length upon the deck, grappled a ring-bolt there, and swore not to let it go, though hacked in pieces.

In vain the captain threatened to throw him overboard; suspended a cutlass over his naked wrists; Queequeg was the son of a King, and Queequeg budged not. Struck by his desperate dauntlessness, and his wild desire to visit Christendom, the captain at last relented, and told him he might make himself at home. But this fine young savage—this sea Prince of Wales, never saw the Captain's cabin. They put him down among the sailors, and made a whaleman of him. But like Czar Peter content to toil in the shipyards of foreign cities, Queequeg disdained no seeming ignominy, if thereby he might happily gain the power of enlightening his untutored countrymen. For at bottom—so he told me—he was actuated by a profound desire to learn among the Christians, the arts whereby to make his people still happier than they were; and more than that, still better than they were. But, alas! the practices of whalemen soon convinced him that even Christians could be both miserable and wicked; infinitely more so, than all his father's heathens. Arrived at last in old Sag Harbor; and seeing what the sailors did there; and then going on to Nantucket, and seeing how they spent their wages in *that* place also, poor Queequeg gave it up for lost. Thought he, it's a wicked world in all meridians; I'll die a pagan.

And thus an old idolator at heart, he yet lived among these Christians, wore their clothes, and tried to talk their gibberish. Hence the queer ways about him, though now some time from home.

By hints I asked him whether he did not propose going back, and having a coronation; since he might now consider his father dead and gone, he being very old and feeble at the last accounts. He answered no, not yet; and added that he was fearful Christianity, or rather Christians, had unfitted him for ascending the pure and undefiled throne of thirty pagan Kings before him. But by and by, he said, he would return—as soon as he felt himself baptized again. For the nonce, however, he proposed to sail about, and sow his wild oats in all four oceans. They had made a harpooneer of him, and that barbed iron was in lieu of a scepter now.

I asked him what might be his immediate purpose, touching his future movements. He answered, to go to sea again, in his old vocation. Upon this, I told him that whaling was my own design, and informed him of my intention to sail out of Nantucket, as being the most promising port for an adventurous whaleman to embark from. He at once resolved to accompany me to that island, ship aboard the same vessel, get into the same watch, the same boat, the same mess with me, in short to share my every hap; with both my hands in his, boldly dip into the Potluck of both worlds. To all this I joyously assented; for besides the affection I now felt for Queequeg, he was an experienced harpooneer, and as such, could not fail to be of great usefulness to one who, like me, was wholly ignorant of the mysteries of whaling, though well acquainted with the sea, as known to merchant seamen.

His story being ended with his pipe's last dying puff, Queequeg embraced me, pressed his forehead against mine, and blowing out the light, we rolled over from each other, this way and that, and very soon were sleeping.

Chapter XIII

WHEELBARROW

NEXT MORNING, MONDAY, AFTER DISPOSING OF THE EMBALMED HEAD TO A BARBER, FOR A BLOCK, I settled my own and comrade's bill; using, however, my comrade's money. The grinning landlord, as well as the boarders, seemed amazingly tickled at the sudden friendship which had sprung up between me and Queequeg—especially as Peter Coffin's cock and bull stories about him had previously so much alarmed me concerning the very person whom I now companied with.

We borrowed a wheelbarrow, and embarking our things, including my own poor carpet-bag, and Queequeg's canvas sack and hammock, away we went down to the *Moss,* the little Nantucket packet schooner moored at the wharf. As we were going along the people stared; not at Queequeg so much—for they were used to seeing cannibals like him in their streets—but at seeing him and me upon such confidential terms. But we heeded them not, going along wheeling the barrow by turns, and Queequeg now and then stopping to adjust the sheath on his harpoon barbs. I asked him why he carried such a troublesome thing with him ashore, and whether all whaling ships did not find their own harpoons. To this, in substance, he replied, that though what I hinted was true enough, yet he had a particular affection for his own harpoon, because it was of assured stuff, well tried in many a mortal combat, and deeply intimate with the hearts of whales. In short, like many inland reapers and mowers, who go into the farmer's meadows armed with their own scythes—though in nowise obliged to furnish them—even so, Queequeg, for his own private reasons, preferred his own harpoon.

Shifting the barrow from my hand to his, he told me a funny story about the first wheelbarrow he had ever seen. It was in Sag Harbor. The owners of his ship, it seems, had lent him one, in which to carry his heavy chest to his boarding-house. Not to seem ignorant about the thing—though in truth he was entirely so, concerning the precise way in which to manage the barrow—Queequeg puts his chest upon it; lashes it fast; and then shoulders the barrow and marches up the wharf. "Why," said I, "Queequeg, you might have known better than that, one would think. Didn't the people laugh?"

Upon this, he told me another story. The people of his island of Rokovoko, it seems, at their wedding feasts express the fragrant water of young cocoanuts into a large stained calabash like a punch-bowl; and this punch-bowl always forms the great central ornament on the braided mat where the feast is held. Now a certain grand merchant-ship once touched at Rokovoko, and its commander—from all accounts a very stately punctilious gentleman, at least for a sea-captain—this commander was invited to the wedding feast of Queequeg's sister, a pretty young princess just turned of ten. Well; when all the wedding guests were assembled at the bride's bamboo cottage, this Captain marches in, and being assigned the post of honor, placed himself over against the punch-bowl, and between the High-Priest and his majesty the King, Queequeg's father. Grace being said—for those people have their grace as well as we—though Queequeg told me that unlike us, who at such times look downwards to our platters, they, on the contrary, copying the ducks, glance upwards to the great Giver of all feasts—Grace, I say, being said, the High-Priest opens the banquet by the immemorial ceremony of the island; that is, dipping his consecrated and consecrating fingers into the bowl before the blessed beverage circulates. Seeing himself placed next the Priest, and noting the ceremony, and thinking himself—being Captain of a ship—as having plain precedence over a mere island King, especially in the King's own house—the Captain coolly proceeds to wash his hands in the punch-bowl;—taking it I suppose for a huge finger-glass. "Now," said Queequeg, "what you tink now?—Didn't our people laugh?"

At last, passage paid, and luggage safe, we stood on board the schooner. Hoisting sail, it glided down the Acushnet river. On one side, New Bedford rose in terraces of streets, their ice-covered trees all glittering in the clear, cold air. Huge hills and mountains of casks on casks were piled upon her wharves, and side by side the world-wandering whale-ships lay silent and safely moored at last; while from others came a sound of carpenters and coopers, with blended noises of fires and forges to melt the pitch, all betokening that new cruises were on the start; that one most perilous and long voyage ended, only begins a second! and a second ended, only begins a third, and so on, forever and for aye. Such is the endlessness, yea, the intolerableness of all earthly effort.

Gaining the more open water, the bracing breeze waxed fresh; the little *Moss* tossed the quick foam from her bows, as a young colt his snortings. How I snuffed that Tartar air!—how I spurned that turnpike earth!—that common highway all over dented with the marks of slavish heels and hoofs; and turned me to admire the magnanimity of the sea which will permit no records.

At the same foam-fountain, Queequeg seemed to drink and reel with me. His dusky nostrils swelled apart; he showed his filed and pointed teeth. On, on we flew; and our offing gained, the *Moss* did homage to the blast; ducked and dived her bows as a slave before the Sultan. Sideways leaning, we sideways darted; every ropeyarn tingling like a wire; the two tall masts buckling like Indian canes in land tornadoes. So full of this reeling scene were we, as we stood by the plunging bowsprit, that for some time we did not notice the jeering glances of the passengers, a lubber-like assembly, who marveled that two fellow-beings should be so companionable; as though a white man were anything more dignified than a white-washed negro. But there were some boobies and bumpkins there, who, by their intense greenness, must have come from the heart and center of all verdure. Queequeg caught one of these young saplings mimicking him behind his back. I thought the bumpkin's hour of doom was come. Dropping his harpoon, the brawny savage caught him in his arms, and by an almost miraculous dexterity and strength, sent him high up bodily into the air; then slightly tapping his stern in mid-somerset, the fellow landed with bursting lungs upon his feet, while Queequeg, turning his back upon him, lighted his tomahawk pipe and passed it to me for a puff.

"Capting! Capting!" yelled the bumpkin, running towards that officer; "Capting, Capting, here's the devil."

"Hallo, *you* sir," cried the Captain, a gaunt rib of the sea, stealing up to Queequeg, "what in thunder do you mean by that? Don't you know you might have killed that chap?"

"What him say?" said Queequeg, as he mildly turned to me.

"He say," said I, "that you came near kill-e that man there," pointing to the still shivering greenhorn.

"Kill-e," cried Queequeg, twisting his tattooed face into an unearthly expression of disdain, "ah! him bevy small-e fish-e; Queequeg no kill-e so small-e fish-e; Queequeg kill-e big whale!"

"Look you," roared the Captain, "I'll kill-e *you*, you cannibal, if you try any more of your tricks here; so mind your eye."

But it so happened just then, that it was high time for the Captain to mind his own eye. The prodigious strain upon the main-sail had parted the weather-sheet, and the tremendous boom was now flying from side to side, completely sweeping the entire after part of the deck. The poor fellow whom Queequeg had handled so roughly, was swept overboard; all hands were in a panic; and to attempt snatching at the boom to stay it, seemed madness. It flew from right to left, and back again, almost in one ticking of a watch, and every instant seemed on the point of snapping into splinters. Nothing was done, and nothing seemed capable of being done; those on deck rushed toward the bows, and stood eyeing the boom as if it were the lower jaw of an exasperated whale. In the midst of this consternation, Queequeg dropped deftly to his knees, and crawling under the path of the boom, whipped hold of a rope, secured one end to the bulwarks, and then flinging the other like a lasso, caught it round the boom as it swept over his head, and at the next jerk, the spar was that way trapped, and all was safe. The schooner was run into the wind, and while the hands were clearing away the stern boat, Queequeg, stripped to the waist, darted from the side with a long living arc of a leap. For three minutes or more he was seen swimming like a dog, throwing his long arms straight out before him, and by turns revealing his brawny shoulders through the freezing foam. I looked at the grand and glorious fellow, but saw no one to be saved. The greenhorn had gone down. Shooting himself perpendicularly from the water, Queequeg now took an instant's glance around him, and seeming to see just how matters were, dived down and disappeared. A few minutes more, and he rose again, one arm still striking out, and with the other dragging a lifeless form. The boat soon picked them up. The poor bumpkin was restored. All hands voted Queequeg a noble trump; the captain begged his pardon. From that hour I clove to Queequeg like a barnacle; yea, till poor Queequeg took his last long dive.

Was there ever such unconsciousness? He did not seem to think that he at all deserved a medal from the Humane and Magnanimous Societies. He only asked for water—fresh water—something to wipe the brine off; that done, he put on dry clothes, lighted his pipe, and leaning against the bulwarks, and mildly eyeing those around him, seemed to be saying to himself—"It's a mutual, joint-stock world, in all meridians. We cannibals must help these Christians."

Chapter XIV

NANTUCKET

NOTHING MORE HAPPENED ON THE PASSAGE WORTHY THE MENTIONING; SO, AFTER A FINE RUN, we safely arrived in Nantucket.

Nantucket! Take out your map and look at it. See what a real corner of the world it occupies; how it stands there, away off-shore, more lonely than the Eddystone light-house. Look at it—a mere hillock, and elbow of sand; all beach, without a background. There is more sand there than you would use in twenty years as a substitute for blotting paper. Some gamesome wights will tell you that they have to plant weeds there, they don't grow naturally; that they import Canada thistles; that they have to send beyond seas for a spile to stop a leak in an oil cask; that pieces of wood in Nantucket are carried about like bits of the true cross in Rome; that people there plant toadstools before their houses, to get under the shade in summer time; that one blade of grass makes an oasis, three blades in a day's walk a prairie; that they wear quicksand shoes, something like Laplander snow-shoes; that they are so shut up, belted about, every way enclosed, surrounded, and made an utter island of by the ocean, that to their very chairs and tables small clams will sometimes be found adhering, as to the backs of sea turtles. But these extravaganzas only show that Nantucket is no Illinois.

Look now at the wondrous traditional story of how this island was settled by the red-men. Thus goes the legend. In olden times an eagle swooped down upon the New England coast, and carried off an infant Indian in his talons. With loud lament the parents saw their child borne out of sight over the wide waters. They resolved to follow in the same direction. Setting out in their canoes, after a perilous passage they discovered the island, and there they found an empty ivory casket—the poor little Indian's skeleton.

What wonder, then, that these Nantucketers, born on a beach, should take to the sea for a livelihood! They first caught crabs and quahogs in the sand; grown bolder, they waded out with nets for mackerel; more experienced, they pushed off in boats and captured cod; and at last, launching a navy of great ships on the sea, explored this watery world; put an incessant belt of circumnavigations round it; peeped in at Behring's Straits; and in all seasons and all oceans declared everlasting war with the mightiest animated mass that has survived the flood; most monstrous and most mountainous! That Himalayan, salt-sea Mastodon, clothed with such portentousness of unconscious power, that his very panics are more to be dreaded than his most fearless and malicious assaults!

And thus have these naked Nantucketers, these sea hermits, issuing from their ant-hill in the sea, overrun and conquered the watery world like so many Alexanders; parcelling out among them the Atlantic, Pacific, and Indian oceans, as the three pirate powers did Poland. Let America add Mexico to Texas, and pile Cuba upon Canada; let the English overswarm all India, and hang out their blazing banner from the sun; two thirds of this terraqueous globe are the Nantucketer's. For the sea is his; he owns it, as Emperors own empires; other seamen having but a right of way through it. Merchant-ships are but extension bridges; armed ones but floating forts; even pirates and privateers, though following the sea as highwaymen the road, they but plunder other ships, other fragments of the land like themselves, without seeking to draw their living from the bottomless deep itself. The Nantucketer, he alone resides and riots on the sea; he alone, in Bible language, goes down to it in ships; to and fro plowing it as his own special plantation. *There* is his home; *there* lies his business which a Noah's flood would not interrupt, though it overwhelmed all the millions in China. He lives on the sea, as prairie cocks in the prairie; he hides among the waves, he climbs them as chamois hunters climb the Alps. For years he knows not the land; so that when he comes to it at last, it smells like another world, more strangely than the moon would to an Earthsman. With the landless gull, that at sunset folds her wings and is rocked to sleep between billows; so at nightfall, the Nantucketer, out of sight of land, furls his sails, and lays him to his rest, while under his very pillow rush herds of walruses and whales.

Chapter XV

CHOWDER

It was quite late in the evening when the little *Moss* came snugly to anchor, and Queequeg and I went ashore; so we could attend to no business that day, at least none but a supper and a bed. The landlord of the Spouter-Inn had recommended us to his cousin Hosea Hussey of the Try Pots, whom he asserted to be the proprietor of one of the best kept hotels in all Nantucket, and moreover he had assured us that Cousin Hosea, as he called him, was famous for his chowders. In short, he plainly hinted that we could not possibly do better than try pot-luck at the Try Pots. But the directions he had given us about keeping a yellow warehouse on our starboard hand till we opened a white church to the larboard, and then keeping that on the larboard hand till we made a corner three points to the starboard, and that done, then ask the first man we met where the place was: these crooked directions of his very much puzzled us at first, especially as, at the outset, Queequeg insisted that the yellow warehouse—our first point of departure—must be left on the larboard hand, whereas I had understood Peter Coffin to say it was on the starboard. However, by dint of beating about a little in the dark, and now and then knocking up a peaceful inhabitant to inquire the way, we at last came to something which there was no mistaking.

Two enormous wooden pots painted black, and suspended by asses' ears, swung from the cross-trees of an old top-mast, planted in front of an old doorway. The horns of the cross-trees were sawed off on the other side, so that this old top-mast looked not a little like a gallows. Perhaps I was over sensitive to such impressions at the time, but I could not help staring at this gallows with a vague misgiving. A sort of crick was in my neck as I gazed up to the two remaining horns; yes, *two* of them, one for Queequeg, and one for me. It's ominous, thinks I. A. Coffin my Innkeeper upon landing in my first whaling port; tomb-stones staring at me in the whalemen's chapel, and here a gallows! A pair of prodigious black pots too! Are these last throwing out oblique hints touching Tophet?

I was called from these reflections by the sight of a freckled woman with yellow hair and a yellow gown, standing in the porch of the inn, under a dull red lamp swinging there, that looked much like an injured eye, and carrying on a brisk scolding with a man in a purple woolen shirt.

"Get along with ye," said she to the man, "or I'll be combing ye!"

"Come on, Queequeg," said I, "all right. There's Mrs. Hussey."

And so it turned out; Mr. Hosea Hussey being from home, but leaving Mrs. Hussey entirely competent to attend to all his affairs. Upon making known our desires for a supper and a bed, Mrs. Hussey, postponing further scolding for the present, ushered us into a little room, and seating us at a table spread with the relics of a recently concluded repast, turned round to us and said—"Clam or Cod?"

"What's that about Cods, ma'am?" said I, with much politeness.

"Clam or Cod?" she repeated.

"A clam for supper? a cold clam; is *that* what you mean, Mrs. Hussey?" says I; "but that's a rather cold and clammy reception in the winter time, ain't it, Mrs. Hussey?"

But being in a great hurry to resume scolding the man in the purple shirt, who was waiting for it in the entry, and seeming to hear nothing but the word "clam," Mrs. Hussey hurried towards an open door leading to the kitchen, and bawling out "clam for two," disappeared.

"Queequeg," said I, "do you think that we can make out a supper for us both on one clam?"

However, a warm savory steam from the kitchen served to belie the apparently cheerless prospect before us. But when that smoking chowder came in, the mystery was delightfully explained. Oh! sweet friends, hearken to me. It was made of small juicy clams, scarcely bigger than hazel nuts, mixed with pounded ship biscuits, and salted pork cut up into little flakes; the whole enriched with butter, and plentifully seasoned with pepper and salt. Our appetites being sharpened by the frosty voyage, and in particular, Queequeg seeing his favorite fishing food before him, and the chowder being surpassingly excellent, we dispatched it with great expedition: when leaning back a moment and bethinking me of Mrs. Hussey's clam and cod announcement, I thought I would try a little experiment. Stepping to the kitchen door, I uttered the word "cod" with great emphasis, and resumed my seat. In a few moments the savory steam came forth again, but with a different flavor, and in good time a fine cod-chowder was placed before us.

We resumed business; and while plying our spoons in the bowl, thinks I to myself, I wonder now if this here has any effect on the head? What's that stultifying saying about chowder-headed people? "But look, Queequeg, ain't that a live eel in your bowl? Where's your harpoon?"

Fishiest of all fishy places was the Try Pots, which well deserved its name; for the pots there were always boiling chowders. Chowder for breakfast, and chowder for dinner, and chowder for supper, till you began to look for fish-bones coming through your clothes. The area before the house was paved with clam-shells. Mrs. Hussey wore a polished necklace of codfish vertebra; and Hosea Hussey had his account books bound in superior old shark-skin. There was a fishy flavor to the milk, too, which I could not at all account for, till one morning happening to take a stroll along the beach among some fishermen's boats, I saw Hosea's brindled cow feeding on fish remnants, and marching along the sand with each foot in a cod's decapitated head, looking very slip-shod, I assure ye.

Supper concluded, we received a lamp, and directions from Mrs. Hussey concerning the nearest way to bed; but, as Queequeg was about to precede me up the stairs, the lady reached forth her arm, and demanded his harpoon; she allowed no harpoon in her chambers. "Why not? said I;

"every true whaleman sleeps with his harpoon—but why not?" "Because it's dangerous," says she. "Ever since young Stiggs coming from that unfort'nt v'y'ge of his, when he was gone four years and a half, with only three barrels of *ile*, was found dead in my first floor back, with his harpoon in his side; ever since then I allow no boarders to take sich dangerous weepons in their rooms at night. So, Mr. Queequeg (for she had learned his name), I will just take this here iron, and keep it for you till morning. But the chowder; clam or cod to-morrow for breakfast, men?"

"Both," says I; "and let's have a couple of smoked herring by way of variety."

Chapter XVI

THE SHIP

IN BED WE CONCOCTED OUR PLANS FOR THE MORROW. BUT TO MY SURPRISE AND NO SMALL CONcern, Queequeg now gave me to understand that he had been diligently consulting Yojo—the name of his black little god—and Yojo had told him two or three times over, and strongly insisted upon it every way, that instead of our going together among the whaling-fleet in harbor, and in concert selecting our craft; instead of this, I say, Yojo earnestly enjoined that the selection of the ship should rest wholly with me, inasmuch as Yojo purposed befriending us; and, in order to do so, had already pitched upon a vessel, which, if left to myself, I, Ishmael, should infallibly light upon, for all the world as though it had turned out by chance; and in that vessel I must immediately ship myself, for the present irrespective of Queequeg.

I have forgotten to mention that, in many things, Queequeg placed great confidence in the excellence of Yojo's judgment and surprising forecast of things; and cherished Yojo with considerable esteem, as a rather good sort of god, who perhaps meant well enough upon the whole, but in all cases did not succeed in his benevolent designs.

Now, this plan of Queequeg's, or rather Yojo's, touching the selection of our craft; I did not like that plan at all. I had not a little relied on Queequeg's sagacity to point out the whaler best fitted to carry us and our fortunes securely. But as all my remonstrances produced no effect upon Queequeg, I was obliged to acquiesce; and accordingly prepared to set about this business with a determined rushing sort of energy and vigor, that should quickly settle that trifling little affair. Next morning early, leaving Queequeg shut up with Yojo in our little bed-room—for it seemed that it was some sort of Lent or Ramadan, or day of fasting, humiliation, and prayer with Queequeg and Yojo that day; *how* it was I never could find out, for, though I applied myself to it several times, I never could master his liturgies and XXXIX Articles—leaving Queequeg, then, fasting on his tomahawk pipe, and Yojo warming himself at his sacrificial fire of shavings, I sallied out among the shipping. After much prolonged sauntering, and many random inquiries, I learned that there were three ships up for three-years' voyages—the *Devil-Dam*, the *Tit-bit*, and the *Pequod*. *Devil-Dam*, I do not know the origin of; *Tit-bit* is obvious; *Pequod* you will no doubt remember, was the name of a celebrated tribe of Massachusetts Indians, now extinct as the ancient Medes. I peered and pryed about the *Devil-Dam*; from her, hopped over to the *Tit-bit*; and finally, going on board the *Pequod*, looked around her for a moment, and then decided that this was the very ship for us.

You may have seen many a quaint craft in your day, for aught I know;—square-toed luggers; mountainous Japanese junks; butter-box galliots, and what not; but take my word for it, you never saw such a rare old craft as this same rare old *Pequod*. She was a ship of the old school, rather small if anything; with an old-fashioned clawfooted look about her. Long seasoned and weather-stained in the typhoons and calms of all four oceans, her old hull's complexion was darkened like a French grenadier's, who has alike fought in Egypt and Siberia. Her venerable bows looked bearded. Her masts—cut somewhere on the coast of Japan, where her original ones were lost overboard in a gale—her masts stood stiffly up like the spines of the three old kings of Cologne. Her ancient decks were worn and wrinkled, like the pilgrim-worshiped flag-stone in Canterbury Cathedral where Becket bled. But to all these her old antiquities, were added new and marvelous features, pertaining to the wild business that for more than half a century she had followed. Old Captain Peleg, many years her chief-mate, before he commanded another vessel of his own, and now a retired seaman, and one of the principal owners of the *Pequod*—this old Peleg, during the term of his chief-mateship, had built upon her original grotesqueness, and inlaid it, all over, with a quaintness both of material and device, unmatched by anything except it be Thorkill-Hake's carved buckler or bed-stead. She was apparelled like any barbaric Ethiopian emperor, his neck heavy with pendants of polished ivory. She was a thing of trophies. A cannibal of a craft, tricking herself forth in the chased bones of her enemies. All round, her unpaneled, open bulwarks were garnished like one continuous jaw, with the long sharp teeth of the sperm whale, inserted there for pins, to fasten her old hempen thews and tendons to. Those thews ran not through base blocks of land wood, but deftly traveled over sheaves of sea-ivory. Scorning a turnstile wheel at her reverend helm, she sported there a tiller; and that tiller was in one mass, curiously carved from the long narrow lower jaw of her hereditary foe. The helmsman who steered by that tiller in a tempest, felt like the Tartar, when he holds back his fiery steed by clutching its jaw. A noble craft, but somehow a most melancholy! All noble things are touched with that.

Now when I looked about the quarter-deck, for someone having authority, in order to propose myself as a candidate for the voyage, at first I saw nobody; but I could not well overlook a strange sort of tent, or rather wigwam, pitched a little behind the main-mast. It seemed only a temporary erection used in port. It was of a conical shape, some ten feet high; consisting of the long, huge slabs of limber black bone taken from the middle and highest part of the jaws of the right-whale. Planted with their broad ends on the deck, a circle of these slabs laced together, mutually sloped towards each other, and at the apex united in a tufted point, where the loose hairy fibers waved to and fro like a top-knot on some old Pottowottamie Sachem's head. A triangular opening faced towards the bows of the ship, so that the insider commanded a complete view forward.

And half concealed in this queer tenement, I at length found one who by his aspect seemed to have authority; and who, it being noon, and the ship's work suspended, was now enjoying respite from the burden of command. He was seated on an old-fashioned oaken chair, wriggling all over with curious carving; and the bottom of which was formed of a stout interlacing of the same elastic stuff of which the wigwam was constructed.

There was nothing so very particular, perhaps, about the appearance of the elderly man I saw; he was brown and brawny, like most old seamen, and heavily rolled up in blue pilot-cloth, cut in the Quaker style; only there was a fine and almost microscopic net-work of the minutest wrinkles interlacing round his eyes, which must have arisen from his continual sailings in many hard gales, and always looking to windward;—for this causes the muscles about the eyes to become pursed together. Such eye-wrinkles are very effectual in a scowl.

"Is this the Captain of the *Pequod?*" said I, advancing to the door of the tent.

"Supposing it be the Captain of the *Pequod*, what dost thou want of him?" he demanded.

"I was thinking of shipping."

"Thou wast, wast thou? I see thou art no Nantucketer—ever been in a stove boat?"

"No, Sir, I never have."

"Dost know nothing at all about whaling, I dare-say—eh?"

"Nothing, Sir; but I have no doubt I shall soon learn. I've been several voyages in the merchant service, and I think that—"

"Marchant service be damned. Talk not that lingo to me. Dost see that leg?—I'll take that leg away from thy stern, if ever thou talkest of the marchant service to me again. Marchant service indeed! I suppose now ye feel considerable proud of having served in those marchant ships. But flukes! man, what makes thee want to go a-whaling, eh?—it looks a little suspicious, don't it, eh?—Hast not been a pirate, hast thou?—Didst not rob thy last Captain, didst thou?—Dost not think of murdering the officers when thou gettest to sea?"

I protested my innocence of these things. I saw that under the mask of these half humorous innuendoes, this old seaman, as an insulated Quakerish Nantucketer, was full of his insular prejudices, and rather distrustful of all aliens, unless they hailed from Cape Cod or the Vineyard.

"But what takes thee a-whaling? I want to know that before I think of shipping ye."

"Well, sir, I want to see what whaling is. I want to see the world."

"Want to see what whaling is, eh? Have ye clapped eye on Captain Ahab?"

"Who is Captain Ahab, sir?"

"Ay, ay, I thought so. Captain Ahab is the Captain of this ship."

"I am mistaken then. I thought I was speaking to the Captain himself."

"Thou art speaking to Captain Peleg—that's who ye are speaking to, young man. It belongs to me and Captain Bildad to see the *Pequod* fitted out for the voyage, and supplied with all her needs, including crew. We are part owners and agents. But as I was going to say, if thou wantest to know what whaling is, as thou tellest ye do, I can put ye in a way of finding it out before ye bind yourself to it, past backing out. Clap eye on Captain Ahab, young man, and thou wilt find that he has only one leg."

"What do you mean, sir? Was the other one lost by a whale?"

"Lost by a whale! Young man, come nearer to me: it was devoured, chewed up, crunched by the monstrousest parmacetty that ever chipped a boat!—ah, ah!"

I was a little alarmed by his energy, perhaps also a little touched at the hearty grief in his concluding exclamation, but said as calmly as I could, "What you say is no doubt true enough, sir; but how could I know there was any peculiar ferocity in that particular whale, though indeed I might have inferred as much from the simple fact of the accident."

"Look ye now, young man, thy lungs are a sort of soft, d'ye see; thou dost not talk shark a bit. *Sure,* ye've been to sea before now; sure of that?"

"Sir," said I, "I thought I told you that I had been four voyages in the merchant—"

"Hard down out of that! Mind what I said about the marchant service—don't aggravate me—I won't have it. But let us understand each other. I have given thee a hint about what whaling is; do ye yet feel inclined for it?"

"I do, sir."

"Very good. Now, art thou the man to pitch a harpoon down a live whale's throat, and then jump after it? Answer, quick!"

"I am, sir, if it should be positively indispensable to do so; not to be got rid of, that is; which I don't take to be the fact."

"Good again. Now then, thou not only wantest to go a-whaling, to find out by experience what whaling is, but ye also want to go in order to see the world? Was not that what ye said? I thought so. Well then, just step forward there, and take a peep over the weather-bow, and then back to me and tell me what ye see there."

For a moment I stood a little puzzled by this curious request, not knowing exactly how to take it, whether humorously or in earnest. But concentrating all his crow's feet into one scowl, Captain Peleg started me on the errand.

Going forward and glancing over the weather-bow, I perceived that the ship swinging to her anchor with the flood-tide, was now obliquely pointing towards the open ocean. The prospect was unlimited, but exceedingly monotonous and forbidding; not the slightest variety that I could see.

"Well, what's the report?" said Peleg when I came back; "what did ye see?"

"Not much," I replied—"nothing but water; considerable horizon though, and there's a squall coming up, I think."

"Well, what dost thou think then of seeing the world? Do ye wish to go round Cape Horn to see any more of it, eh? Can't ye see the world where you stand?"

I was a little staggered, but go a-whaling I must, and I would; and the *Pequod* was as good a ship as any—I thought the best—and all this I now repeated to Peleg. Seeing me so determined, he expressed his willingness to ship me.

"And thou mayest as well sign the papers right off," he added—"come along with ye." And so saying, he led the way below deck into the cabin.

Seated on the transom was what seemed to me a most uncommon and surprising figure. It turned out to be Captain Bildad, who along with Captain Peleg was one of the largest owners of the vessel; the other shares, as is sometimes the case in these ports, being held by a crowd of old annuitants; widows, fatherless children, and chancery wards; each owning about the value of a timber-head, or a foot of plank, or a nail or two in the ship. People in Nantucket invest their money in whaling vessels, the same way that you do yours in approved state stocks bringing in good interest.

Now, Bildad, like Peleg, and indeed many other Nantucketers, was a Quaker, the island having been originally settled by that sect; and to this day its inhabitants in general retain in an uncommon measure the peculiarities of the Quaker, only variously and anomalously modified by things altogether alien and heterogeneous. For some of these same Quakers are the most sanguinary of all sailors and whale-hunters. They are fighting Quakers; they are Quakers with a vengeance.

So that there are instances among them of men, who, named with Scripture names—a singularly common fashion on the island—and in childhood naturally imbibing the stately dramatic thee and thou of the Quaker idiom; still, from the audacious, daring, and boundless adventure of their subsequent lives, strangely blend with these unoutgrown peculiarities, a thousand bold dashes of character, not unworthy a Scandinavian sea-king, or a poetical Pagan Roman. And when these things unite in a man of greatly superior natural force, with a globular brain and a ponderous heart; who has also by the stillness and seclusion of many long night-watches in the remotest waters, and beneath constellations never seen here at the north, been led to think untraditionally and independently; receiving all nature's sweet or savage impressions fresh from her own virgin voluntary and confiding breast, and thereby chiefly, but with some help from accidental advantages, to learn a bold and nervous lofty language—that man makes one in a whole nation's census—a mighty pageant creature, formed for noble tragedies. Nor will it at all detract from him, dramatically regarded, if either by birth or other circumstances, he have what seems a half willful over-ruling morbidness at the bottom of his nature. For all men tragically great are made so through a certain morbidness. Be sure of this, O young ambition, all mortal greatness is but disease. But, as yet we have not to do with such an one, but with quite another; and still a man, who, if indeed peculiar, it only results again from another phase of the Quaker, modified by individual circumstances.

Like Captain Peleg, Captain Bildad was a well-to-do, retired whaleman. But unlike Captain Peleg—who cared not a rush for what are called serious things, and indeed deemed those selfsame serious things the veriest of all trifles—Captain Bildad had not only been originally educated according to the strictest sect of Nantucket Quakerism, but all his subsequent ocean life, and the sight of many unclad, lovely island creatures, round the Horn—all that had not moved this native born Quaker one single jot, had not so much as altered one angle of his vest. Still, for all this immutableness, was there some lack of common consistency about worthy Captain Bildad. Though refusing, from conscientious scruples, to bear arms against land invaders, yet himself had illimitably invaded the Atlantic and Pacific; and though a sworn foe to human bloodshed, yet had he in his straight-bodied coat, spilled tuns upon tuns of leviathan gore. How now in the contemplative evening of his days, the pious Bildad reconciled these things in the reminiscence, I do not know; but it did not seem to concern him much, and very probably he had long since come to the sage and sensible conclusion that a man's religion is one thing, and this practical world quite another. This world pays dividends. Rising from a little cabin-boy in short clothes of the drabbest drab, to a harpooneer in a broad shad-bellied waistcoat; from that becoming boat-header, chief-mate, and captain, and finally a ship-owner; Bildad, as I hinted before, had concluded his adventurous career by wholly retiring from active life at the goodly age of sixty, and dedicating his remaining days to the quiet receiving of his well-earned income.

Now Bildad, I am sorry to say, had the reputation of being an incorrigible old hunks, and in his sea-going days, a bitter, hard task-master. They told me in Nantucket, though it certainly seems a curious story, that when he sailed the old *Categut* whaleman, his crew, upon arriving home, were mostly all carried ashore to the hospital, sore exhausted and worn out. For a pious man, especially for a Quaker, he was certainly rather hard-hearted, to say the least. He never used to swear, though, at his men, they said; but somehow he got an inordinate quantity of cruel, unmitigated hard work out of them. When Bildad was a chief-mate, to have his drab-colored eye intently looking at you, made you feel completely nervous, till you could clutch something—a hammer or a marling-spike, and go to work like mad, at something or other, never mind what. Indolence and idleness perished from before him. His own person was the exact embodiment of his utilitarian character. On his long, gaunt body, he carried no spare flesh, no superfluous beard, his chin having a soft, economical nap to it, like the worn nap of his broad-brimmed hat.

Such, then, was the person that I saw seated on the transom when I followed Captain Peleg down into the cabin. The space between the decks was small; and there, bolt upright, sat old Bildad, who always sat so, and never leaned, and this to save his coat-tails. His broad-brim was placed beside him; his legs were stiffly crossed; his drab vesture was buttoned up to his chin; and spectacles on nose, he seemed absorbed in reading from a ponderous volume.

"Bildad," cried Captain Peleg, "at it again, Bildad, eh? Ye have been studying those Scriptures, now, for the last thirty years, to my certain knowledge. How far ye got, Bildad?"

As if long habituated to such profane talk from his old shipmate, Bildad, without noticing his present irreverence, quietly looked up, and seeing me, glanced again inquiringly towards Peleg.

"He says he's our man, Bildad," said Peleg, "he wants to ship."

"Dost thee?" said Bildad, in a hollow tone, and turning round to me.

"I *dost*," said I unconsciously, he was so intense a Quaker.

"What do ye think of him, Bildad?" said Peleg.

"He'll do," said Bildad, eyeing me, and then went on spelling away at his book in a mumbling tone quite audible.

I thought him the queerest old Quaker I ever saw, especially as Peleg, his friend and old shipmate, seemed such a blusterer. But I said nothing, only looking round me sharply. Peleg now threw open a chest, and drawing forth the ship's articles, placed pen and ink before him, and seated himself at a little table. I began to think it was high time to settle with myself at what terms I would be willing to engage for the voyage. I was already aware that in the whaling business they paid no wages; but all hands, including the captain, received certain shares of the profits called lays, and that these lays were proportioned to the degree of importance pertaining to the respective duties of the ship's company. I was also aware that being a green hand at whaling, my own lay would not be very large; but considering that I was used to the sea, could steer a ship, splice a rope, and all that, I made no doubt that from all I had heard I should be offered at least the 275th lay—that is, the 275th part of the clear net proceeds of the voyage, whatever that might eventually amount to. And though the 275th lay was what they call a rather *long lay*, yet it was better than nothing; and if we had a lucky voyage, might pretty nearly pay for the clothing I would wear out on it, not to speak of my three years' beef and board, for which I would not have to pay one stiver.

It might be thought that this was a poor way to accumulate a princely fortune—and so it was, a very poor way indeed. But I am one of those that never take on about princely fortunes, and I am quite content if the world is ready to board and lodge me, while I am putting up at this grim sign of the Thunder Cloud. Upon the whole, I thought that the 275th lay would be about the fair thing, but would not have been surprised had I been offered the 200th, considering I was of a broad-shouldered make.

But one thing, nevertheless, that made me a little distrustful about receiving a generous share of the profits was this: Ashore, I had heard something of both Captain Peleg and his unaccountable old crony Bildad; how that they being the principal proprietors of the *Pequod*, therefore the other and more inconsiderable and scattered owners, left nearly the whole management of the ship's affairs to these two. And I did not know but what the stingy old Bildad might have a mighty deal to say about shipping hands, especially as I now found him on board the *Pequod*, quite at home there in the cabin, and reading his Bible as if at his own fireside. Now while Peleg was vainly trying to mend a pen with his jack-knife, old Bildad, to my no small surprise, considering that he was such an interested party in these proceedings; Bildad never heeded us, but went on mumbling to himself out of his book, " '*Lay* not up for yourselves treasures upon earth, where moth—' "

"Well, Captain Bildad," interrupted Peleg, "what d'ye say, what lay shall we give this young man?"

"Thou knowest best," was the sepulchral reply, "the seven hundred and seventy-seventh wouldn't be too much, would it?—'where moth and rust do corrupt, but *lay*—' "

Lay, indeed, thought I, and such a lay! the seven hundred and seventy-seventh! Well, old Bildad, you are determined that I, for one, shall not *lay* up many *lays* here below, where moth and rust do corrupt. It was an exceedingly *long lay* that, indeed; and though from the magnitude of the figure it might at first deceive a landsman, yet the slightest consideration will show that though seven hundred and seventy-seven is a pretty large number, yet, when you come to make a *tenth* of it, you will then see, I say, that the seven hundred and seventy-seventh part of a farthing is a good deal less than seven hundred and seventy-seven gold doubloons; and so I thought at the time.

"Why, blast your eyes, Bildad," cried Peleg, "thou dost not want to swindle this young man! he must have more than that."

"Seven hundred and seventy-seventh," again said Bildad, without lifting his eyes; and then went on mumbling—"for where your treasure is, there will your heart be also."

"I am going to put him down for the three hundredth," said Peleg, "do ye hear that, Bildad! The three hundredth lay, I say."

Bildad laid down his book, and turning solemnly towards him said, "Captain Peleg, thou hast a generous heart; but thou must consider the duty thou owest to the other owners of this ship—widows and orphans, many of them—and that if we too abundantly reward the labors of this young man, we may be taking the bread from those widows and those orphans. The seven hundred and seventy-seventh lay, Captain Peleg."

"Thou Bildad!" roared Peleg, starting up and clattering about the cabin. "Blast ye, Captain Bildad, if I had followed thy advice in these matters, I would afore now had a conscience to lug about that would be heavy enough to founder the largest ship that ever sailed round Cape Horn."

"Captain Peleg," said Bildad steadily, "thy conscience may be drawing ten inches of water, or ten fathoms, I can't tell; but as thou art still an impenitent man, Captain Peleg, I greatly fear lest thy conscience be but a leaky one; and will in the end sink thee foundering down to the fiery pit, Captain Peleg."

"Fiery pit! fiery pit! ye insult me, man; past all natural bearing, ye insult me. It's an all-fired outrage to tell any human creature that he's bound to hell. Flukes and flames! Bildad, say that again to me, and start my soul-bolts, but I'll—yes, I'll swallow a live goat with all his hair and horns on. Out of the cabin, ye canting, drab-colored son of a wooden gun—a straight wake with ye!"

As he thundered out this he made a rush at Bildad, but with a marvelous oblique, sliding celerity, Bildad for that time eluded him.

Alarmed at this terrible outburst between the two principal and responsible owners of the ship, and feeling half a mind to give up all idea of sailing in a vessel so questionably owned and temporarily commanded, I stepped aside from the door to give egress to Bildad, who, I made no doubt, was all eagerness to vanish from before the awakened wrath of Peleg. But to my astonishment, he sat down again on the transom very quietly, and seemed to have not the slightest intention of withdrawing. He seemed quite used to impenitent Peleg and his ways. As for Peleg, after letting off his rage as he had, there seemed no more left in him, and he, too, sat down like a lamb, though he twitched a little as if still nervously agitated. "Whew!" he whistled at last—"the squall's gone off to leeward, I think. Bildad, thou used to be good at sharpening a lance, mend that pen, will ye. My jack-knife here needs the grind-stone. That's he; thank ye, Bildad. Now then, my young man, Ishmael's thy name, didn't ye say? Well then, down ye go here, Ishmael, for the three hundredth lay."

"Captain Peleg," said I, "I have a friend with me who wants to ship too—shall I bring him down to-morrow?"

"To be sure," said Peleg. "Fetch him along, and we'll look at him."

"What lay does he want?" groaned Bildad, glancing up from the Book in which he had again been burying himself.

"Oh! never thee mind about that, Bildad," said Peleg. "Has he ever whaled it any?" turning to me.

"Killed more whales than I can count, Captain Peleg."

"Well, bring him along then."

And, after signing the papers, off I went; nothing doubting but that I had done a good morning's work, and that the *Pequod* was the identical ship that Yojo had provided to carry Queequeg and me round the Cape.

But I had not proceeded far, when I began to bethink me that the Captain with whom I was to sail yet remained unseen by me; though, indeed, in many cases, a whale-ship will be completely fitted out, and receive all her crew on board, ere the captain makes himself visible by arriving to take command; for sometimes these voyages are so prolonged, and the shore intervals at home so exceedingly brief, that if the captain have a family, or any absorbing concernment of that sort, he does not trouble himself much about his ship in port, but leaves her to the owners till all is ready for sea. However, it is always as well to have a look at him before irrevocably committing yourself into his hands. Turning back I accosted Captain Peleg, inquiring where Captain Ahab was to be found.

"And what dost thou want of Captain Ahab? It's all right enough; thou art shipped."

"Yes, but I should like to see him."

"But I don't think thou wilt be able to at present. I don't know exactly what's the matter with him; but he keeps close inside the house; a sort of sick, and yet he don't look so. In fact, he ain't sick; but no, he isn't well either. Anyhow, young man, he won't always see me, so I don't suppose he will thee. He's a queer man, Captain Ahab—so some think—but a good one. Oh, thou'lt like him well enough; no fear, no fear. He's a grand, ungodly, god-like man, Captain Ahab; doesn't speak much; but, when he does speak, then you may well listen. Mark ye, be forewarned; Ahab's above the common; Ahab's been in colleges, as well as 'mong the cannibals; been used to deeper wonders than the waves; fixed his fiery lance in mightier, stranger foes than whales. His lance! aye, the keenest and the surest that out of all our isle! Oh! he ain't Captain Bildad; no, and he ain't Captain Peleg; *he's Ahab*, boy; and Ahab of old, thou knowest, was a crowned king!"

"And a very vile one. When that wicked king was slain, the dogs, did they not lick his blood?"

"Come hither to me—hither, hither," said Peleg, with a significance in his eye that almost startled me. "Look ye, lad; never say that on board the *Pequod*. Never say it anywhere. Captain Ahab did not name himself. 'Twas a foolish, ignorant whim of his crazy widowed mother, who died when he was only a twelvemonth old. And yet the old squaw Tistig, at Gayhead, said that the name would somehow prove prophetic. And, perhaps, other fools like her may tell thee the same. I wish to warn thee. It's a lie. I know Captain Ahab well; I sailed with him as mate years ago; I know what he is—a good man—not a pious, good man, like Bildad, but a swearing good man—something like me—only there's a good deal more of him. Ay, ay, I know that he was never very jolly; and I know that on the passage home he was a little out of his mind for a spell; but it was the sharp shooting pains in his bleeding stump that brought that about, as anyone might see. I know, too, that ever since he lost his leg last voyage by that accursed whale, he's been a kind of moody—desperate moody, and savage sometimes; but that will all pass off. And once for all, let me tell thee and assure thee, young man, it's better to sail with a moody good captain than a laughing bad one. So good-bye to thee—and wrong not Captain Ahab, because he happens to have a wicked name. Besides, my boy, he has a wife—not three voyages wedded—a sweet, resigned girl. Think of that; by that sweet girl that old man had a child; hold ye then there can be any utter, hopeless harm in Ahab? No, no, my lad; stricken, blasted, if he be, Ahab has his humanities!"

As I walked away, I was full of thoughtfulness; what had been incidentally revealed to me of Captain Ahab, filled me with a certain wild vagueness of painfulness concerning him. And somehow, at the time, I felt a sympathy and a sorrow for him, but for I don't know what, unless it was the cruel loss of his leg. And yet I also felt a strange awe of him; but that sort of awe, which I cannot at all describe, was not exactly awe; I do not know what it was. But I felt it; and it did not disincline me towards him; though I felt impatience at what seemed like mystery in him, so imperfectly as he was known to me then. However, my thoughts were at length carried in other directions, so that for the present dark Ahab slipped my mind.

Chapter XVII

THE RAMADAN

As QUEEQUEG'S RAMADAN, OR FASTING AND HUMILIATION, WAS TO CONTINUE ALL DAY, I DID not choose to disturb him till towards nightfall; for I cherish the greatest respect towards everybody's religious obligations, never mind how comical, and could not find it in my heart to undervalue even a congregation of ants worshiping a toadstool; or those other creatures in certain parts of our earth, who with a degree of footmanism quite unprecedented in other planets, bow down before the torso of a deceased landed proprietor merely on account of the inordinate possessions yet owned and rented in his name.

I say, we good Presbyterian Christians should be charitable in these things, and not fancy ourselves so vastly superior to other mortals, pagans and what not, because of their half-crazy conceits on these subjects. There was Queequeg, now, certainly entertaining the most absurd notions about Yojo and his Ramadan;—but what of that? Queequeg thought he knew what he was about, I suppose; he seemed to be content; and there let him rest. All our arguing with him would not avail; let him be, I say: and Heaven have mercy on us all—Presbyterians and Pagans alike—for we are all somehow dreadfully cracked about the head, and sadly need mending.

Towards evening, when I felt assured that all his performances and rituals must be over, I went up to his room and knocked at the door; but no answer. I tried to open it, but it was fastened inside. "Queequeg," said I softly through the key-hole—all silent. "I say, Queequeg! why don't you speak? It's I—Ishmael." But all remained still as before. I began to grow alarmed. I had allowed him such abundant time; I thought he might have had an apoplectic fit. I looked through the key-hole; but the door opening into an odd corner of the room, the key-hole prospect was but a crooked and sinister one. I could only see part of the foot-board of the bed and a line of the wall, but nothing more. I was surprised to behold resting against the wall the wooden shaft of Queequeg's harpoon, which the landlady the evening previous had taken from him, before our mounting to the chamber. That's strange, thought I; but at any rate, since the harpoon stands yonder, and he seldom or never goes abroad without it, therefore he must be inside here, and no possible mistake.

"Queequeg!—Queequeg!"—all still. Something must have happened. Apoplexy! I tried to burst open the door; but it stubbornly resisted. Running down stairs, I quickly stated my suspicions to the first person I met—the chambermaid. "La! la!" she cried, "I thought something must be the matter. I went to make the bed after breakfast, and the door was locked; and not a mouse to be heard; and it's been just so silent ever since. But I thought, maybe, you had both gone off and locked your baggage in for safe keeping. La! La, ma'am!—Mistress! murder! Mrs. Hussey! apoplexy!"—and with these cries she ran towards the kitchen, I following.

Mrs. Hussey soon appeared, with a mustard-pot in one hand and a vinegar-cruet in the other, having just broken away from the occupation of attending to the castors, and scolding her little black boy meantime.

"Wood-house!" cried I, "which way to it? Run for God's sake, and fetch something to pry open the door—the ax!—the ax!—he's had a stroke; depend upon it!"—and so saying I was unmethodically rushing up stairs again empty-handed, when Mrs. Hussey interposed the mustard-pot and vinegar-cruet, and the entire castor of her countenance.

"What's the matter with you, young man?"

"Get the ax! For God's sake, run for the doctor, someone, while I pry it open!"

"Look here," said the landlady, quickly putting down the vinegar-cruet, so as to have one hand free; "look here; are you talking about prying open any of my doors?"—and with that she seized my arm. "What's the matter with you? What's the matter with you, shipmate?"

In as calm, but rapid a manner as possible, I gave her to understand the whole case. Unconsciously clapping the vinegar-cruet to one side of her nose, she ruminated for an instant; then exclaimed—"No! I haven't seen it since I put it there." Running to a little closet under the landing of the stairs, she glanced in, and returning, told me that Queequeg's harpoon was missing. "He's killed himself," she cried. "It's unfort'nate Stiggs done over again—there goes another counterpane—God pity his poor mother!—it will be the ruin of my house. Has the poor lad a sister? Where's that girl?—there, Betty, go to Snarles the Painter, and tell him to paint me a sign, with—'no suicides permitted here, and no smoking in the parlor';—might as well kill both birds at once. Kill? The Lord be merciful to his ghost! What's that noise there? You, young man, avast there!"

And running up after me, she caught me as I was again trying to force open the door.

"I won't allow it; I won't have my premises spoiled. Go for the locksmith, there's one about a mile from here. But avast!" putting her hand in her side pocket, "here's a key that'll fit, I guess; let's see." And with that, she turned it in the lock; but alas! Queequeg's supplemental bolt remained unwithdrawn within.

"Have to burst it open," said I, and was running down the entry a little, for a good start, when the landlady caught at me, again vowing I should not break down her premises; but I tore from her and with a sudden bodily rush dashed myself full against the mark.

With a prodigious noise the door flew open, and the knob slamming against the door, sent the plaster to the ceiling; and there, good heavens! there sat Queequeg, altogether cool and self-collected; right in the middle of the room; squatting on his hams, and holding Yojo on top of his head. He looked neither one way nor the other way, but sat like a carved image with scarce a sign of active life.

"Queequeg," said I, going up to him, "Queequeg, what's the matter with you?"

"He hain't been a sittin' so all day, has he?" said the landlady.

But all we said, not a word could we drag out of him; I almost felt like pushing him over, so as to change his position, for it was almost intolerable, it seemed so painfully and unnaturally constrained; especially, as in all probability he had been sitting so for upwards of eight or ten hours, going too without his regular meals.

"Mrs. Hussey," said I, "he's *alive* at all events; so leave us, if you please, and I will see to this strange affair myself."

Closing the door upon the landlady, I endeavored to prevail upon Queequeg to take a chair; but in vain. There he sat; and all he could do—for all my polite arts and blandishments—he would not move a peg, nor say a single word, nor even look at me, nor notice my presence in any the slightest way.

I wonder, thought I, if this can possibly be a part of his Ramadan; do they fast on their hams that way in his native island. It must be so; yes, it's a part of his creed, I suppose; well, then, let him rest; he'll get up sooner or later, no doubt. It can't last forever, thank God, and his Ramadan only comes once a year; and I don't believe it's very punctual then.

I went down to supper. After sitting a long time listening to the long stories of some sailors who had just come from a plum-pudding voyage, as they called it (that is, a short whaling voyage in a schooner or brig, confined to the north of the line, in the Atlantic Ocean only); after listening to these plum-puddingers till nearly eleven o'clock, I went up stairs to go to bed, feeling quite sure by this time Queequeg must certainly have brought his Ramadan to a termination. But no; there he was just where I had left him; he had not stirred an inch. I began to grow vexed with him; it seemed so downright senseless and insane to be sitting there all day and half the night on his hams in a cold room, holding a piece of wood on his head.

"For heaven's sake, Queequeg, get up and shake yourself; get up and have some supper. You'll starve; you'll kill yourself, Queequeg." But not a word did he reply.

Despairing of him, therefore, I determined to go to bed and to sleep; and no doubt, before a great while, he would follow me. But previous to turning in, I took my heavy bear-skin jacket, and threw it over him, as it promised to be a very cold night; and he had nothing but his ordinary round jacket on. For some time, do all I would, I could not get into the faintest doze. I had blown out the candle; and the mere thought of Queequeg—not four feet off—sitting there in that uneasy position, stark alone in the cold and dark; this made me really wretched. Think of it; sleeping all night in the same room with a wide awake pagan on his hams in this dreary, unaccountable Ramadan!

But somehow I dropped off at last, and knew nothing more till break of day; when, looking over the bedside, there squatted Queequeg, as if he had been screwed down to the floor. But as soon as the first glimpse of sun entered the window, up he got, with stiff and grating joints, but with a cheerful look; limped towards me where I lay; pressed his forehead again against mine; and said his Ramadan was over.

Now, as I before hinted, I have no objection to any person's religion, be it what it may, so long as that person does not kill or insult any other person, because that other person don't believe it also. But when a man's religion becomes really frantic; when it is a positive torment to him; and, in fine, makes this earth of ours an uncomfortable inn to lodge in; then I think it high time to take that individual aside and argue the point with him.

And just so I now did with Queequeg. "Queequeg," said I, "get into bed now, and lie and listen to me." I then went on, beginning with the rise and progress of the primitive religions, and coming down to the various religions of the present time, during which time I labored to show Queequeg that all these Lents, Ramadans, and prolonged ham-squattings in cold, cheerless rooms were stark nonsense; bad for the health; useless for the soul; opposed, in short, to the obvious laws of Hygiene and common sense. I told him, too, that he being in other things such an extremely sensible and sagacious savage, it pained me, very badly pained me, to see him now so deplorably foolish about this ridiculous Ramadan of his. Besides, argued I, fasting makes the body cave in; hence the spirit caves in; and all thoughts born of a fast must necessarily be half-starved. This is the reason why most dyspeptic religionists cherish such melancholy notions about their hereafters. In one word, Queequeg, said I, rather digressively; hell is an idea first born on an undigested apple-dumpling; and since then perpetuated through the hereditary dyspepsias nurtured by Ramadans.

I then asked Queequeg whether he himself was ever troubled with dyspepsia; expressing the idea very plainly, so that he could take it in. He said no; only upon one memorable occasion. It was after a great feast given by his father the king, on the gaining of a great battle wherein fifty of the enemy had been killed by about two o'clock in the afternoon, and all cooked and eaten that very evening.

"No more, Queequeg," said I, shuddering; "that will do"; for I knew the inferences without his further hinting them. I had seen a sailor who had visited that very island, and he told me that it was the custom, when a great battle had been gained there, to barbecue all the slain in the yard or garden of the victor; and then, one by one, they were placed in great wooden trenchers, and garnished round like a pilau, with bread-fruit and cocoanuts; and with some parsley in their mouths, were sent round with the victor's compliments to all his friends, just as though these presents were so many Christmas turkeys.

After all, I do not think that my remarks about religion made much impression upon Queequeg. Because, in the first place, he somehow seemed dull of hearing on that important subject, unless considered from his own point of view; and, in the second place, he did not more than one third understand me, couch my ideas simply as I would; and, finally, he no doubt thought he knew a good deal more about the true religion than I did. He looked at me with a sort of condescending concern and compassion, as though he thought it a great pity that such a sensible young man should be so hopelessly lost to evangelical pagan piety.

At last we rose and dressed; and Queequeg, taking a prodigiously hearty breakfast of chowders of all sorts, so that the landlady should not make much profit by reason of his Ramadan, we sallied out to board the *Pequod,* sauntering along, and picking our teeth with halibut bones.

Chapter XVIII

His Mark

As we were walking down the end of the wharf towards the ship, Queequeg carrying his harpoon, Captain Peleg in his gruff voice loudly hailed us from his wigwam, saying he had not suspected my friend was a cannibal, and furthermore announcing that he let no cannibals on board that craft, unless they previously produced their papers.

"What do you mean by that, Captain Peleg?" said I, now jumping on the bulwarks, and leaving my comrade standing on the wharf.

"I mean," he replied, "he must show his papers."

"Yes," said Captain Bildad in his hollow voice, sticking his head from behind Peleg's, out of the wigwam. "He must show that he's converted. Son of darkness," he added, turning to Queequeg, "art thou at present in communion with any Christian church?"

"Why," said I, "he's a member of the First Congregational Church." Here be it said, that many tattooed savages sailing in Nantucket ships at last come to be converted into the churches.

"First Congregational Church," cried Bildad, "what! that worships in Deacon Deuteronomy Coleman's meeting-house?" and so saying, taking out his spectacles, he rubbed them with his great yellow bandana handkerchief, and putting them on very carefully, came out of the wigwam, and leaning stiffly over the bulwarks, took a good long look at Queequeg.

"How long hath he been a member?" he then said, turning to me; "not very long, I rather guess, young man."

"No," said Peleg, "and he hasn't been baptized right either, or it would have washed some of that devil's blue off his face."

"Do tell, now," cried Bildad, "is this Philistine a regular member of Deacon Deuteronomy's meeting? I never saw him going there, and I pass it every Lord's day."

"I don't know anything about Deacon Deuteronomy or his meeting," said I, "all I know is, that Queequeg here is a born member of the First Congregational Church. He is a deacon himself, Queequeg is."

"Young man," said Bildad sternly, "thou art skylarking with me—explain thyself, thou young Hittite. What church dost thee mean? answer me."

Finding myself thus hard pushed, I replied, "I mean, sir, the same ancient Catholic Church to which you and I, and Captain Peleg there, and Queequeg here, and all of us, and every mother's son and soul of us belong; the great and everlasting First Congregation of this whole worshiping world; we all belong to that; only some of us cherish some crotchets no-ways touching the grand belief; in *that* we all join hands."

"Splice, thou mean'st *splice* hands," cried Peleg, drawing nearer. "Young man, you'd better ship for a missionary, instead of a fore-mast hand; I never heard a better sermon. Deacon Deuteronomy—why Father Mapple himself couldn't beat it, and he's reckoned something. Come aboard, come aboard; never mind about the papers. I say, tell Quohog there—what's that you call him? tell Quohog to step along. By the great anchor, what a harpoon he's got there! looks like good stuff that; and he handles it about right. I say, Quohog, or whatever your name is, did you ever stand in the head of a whale-boat? did you ever strike a fish?"

Without saying a word, Queequeg, in his wild sort of way, jumped upon the bulwarks, from thence into the bows of one of the whale-boats hanging to the side; and then bracing his left knee, and poising his harpoon, cried out in some such way as this:

"Cap'ain, you see him small drop tar on water dere? You see him? well, spose him one whale eye, well, den!" and taking sharp aim at it, he darted the iron right over old Bildad's broad brim, clean across the ship's decks, and struck the glistening tar spot out of sight.

"Now," said Queequeg, quietly hauling in the line, "spose-ee him whale-e eye; why, dad whale dead."

"Quick, Bildad," said Peleg, his partner, who, aghast at the close vicinity of the flying harpoon, had retreated towards the cabin gangway. "Quick, I say, you Bildad, and get the ship's papers. We must have Hedgehog there, I mean Quohog, in one of our boats. Look ye, Quohog, we'll give ye the ninetieth lay, and that's more than ever was given a harpooneer yet out of Nantucket."

So down we went into the cabin, and to my great joy Queequeg was soon enrolled among the same ship's company to which I myself belonged.

When all preliminaries were over and Peleg had got everything ready for signing, he turned to me and said, "I guess, Quohog there don't know how to write, does he? I say, Quohog, blast ye! dost thou sign thy name or make thy mark?

But at this question, Queequeg, who had twice or thrice before taken part in similar ceremonies, looked noways abashed; but taking the offered pen, copied upon the paper, in the proper place, an exact counterpart of a queer round figure which was tattooed upon his arm; so that through Captain Peleg's obstinate mistake touching his appellative, it stood something like this:

Quohog.
his ✠ mark.

Meanwhile Captain Bildad sat earnestly and steadfastly eyeing Queequeg, and at last rising solemnly and fumbling in the huge pockets of his broad-skirted drab coat, took out a bundle of tracts, and selecting one entitled *The Latter Day Coming; or No Time to Lose,* placed it in Queequeg's hands, and then grasping them and the book with both his, looked earnestly into his eyes, and said, "Son of darkness, I must do my duty by thee; I am part owner of this ship, and feel concerned for the souls of all its crew; if thou still clingest to thy Pagan ways, which I sadly fear, I beseech thee, remain not for aye a Belial bondsman. Spurn the idol Bell, and the hideous dragon; turn from the wrath to come; mind thine eye, I say; oh! goodness gracious! steer clear of the fiery pit!"

Something of the salt sea yet lingered in old Bildad's language, heterogeneously mixed with Scriptural and domestic phrases.

"Avast there, avast there, Bildad, avast now spoiling our harpooneer," cried Peleg. "Pious harpooneers never make good voyagers—it takes the shark out of 'em; no harpooneer is worth a straw who ain't pretty sharkish. There was young Nat Swaine, once the bravest boat-header out of all Nantucket and the Vineyard; he joined the meeting, and never came to good. He got so frightened about his plaguey soul, that he shrinked and sheered away from whales, for fear of after-claps, in case he got stove and went to Davy Jones."

"Peleg! Peleg!" said Bildad, lifting his eyes and hands, "thou thyself, as I myself, hast seen many a perilous time; thou knowest, Peleg, what it is to have the fear of death; how, then, canst thou prate in this ungodly guise? Thou beliest thine own heart, Peleg. Tell me, when this same *Pequod* here had her three masts overboard in that typhoon on Japan, that same voyage when thou went mate with Captain Ahab, did'st thou not think of Death and the Judgment then?"

"Hear him, hear him now," cried Peleg, marching across the cabin, and thrusting his hands far down into his pockets—"hear him, all of ye. Think of that! When every moment we thought the ship would sink! Death and the Judgment then? What? With all three masts making such an everlasting thundering against the side; and every sea breaking over us, fore and aft. Think of Death and the Judgment then? No! no time to think about Death then. Life was what Captain Ahab and I was thinking of; and how to save all hands—how to rig jury-masts—how to get into the nearest port; that was what I was thinking of."

Bildad said no more, but buttoning up his coat, stalked on deck, where we followed him. There he stood, very quietly overlooking some sail-makers who were mending a top-sail in the waist. Now and then he stooped to pick up a patch, or save an end of tarred twine, which otherwise might have been wasted.

Chapter XIX

The Prophet

"Shipmates, have ye shipped in that ship?"

Queequeg and I had just left the *Pequod*, and were sauntering away from the water, for the moment each occupied with his own thoughts, when the above words were put to us by a stranger, who, pausing before us, leveled his massive forefinger at the vessel in question. He was but shabbily apparelled in faded jacket and patched trousers; a rag of a black handkerchief investing his neck. A confluent small-pox had in all directions flowed over his face, and left it like the complicated ribbed bed of a torrent, when the rushing waters have been dried up.

"Have ye shipped in her?" he repeated.

"You mean the ship *Pequod,* I suppose," said I, trying to gain a little more time for an uninterrupted look at him.

"Ay, the *Pequod*—that ship there," he said, drawing back his whole arm and then rapidly shoving it straight out from him, with the fixed bayonet of his pointed finger darted full at the object.

"Yes," said I, "we have just signed the articles."

"Anything down there about your souls?"

"About what?"

"Oh, perhaps you hav'n't got any," he said quickly. "No matter though, I know many chaps that hav'n't got any—good luck to 'em; and they are all the better off for it. A soul's a sort of a fifth wheel to a wagon."

"What are you jabbering about, shipmate?" said I.

"*He's* got enough, though, to make up for all deficiencies of that sort in other chaps," abruptly said the stranger, placing a nervous emphasis upon the word *he.*

"Queequeg," said I, "let's go; this fellow has broken loose from somewhere; he's talking about something and somebody we don't know."

"Stop!" cried the stranger. "Ye said true—ye hav'n't seen Old Thunder yet, have ye?"

"Who's Old Thunder?" said I, again riveted with the insane earnestness of his manner.

"Captain Ahab."

"What! the captain of our ship, the *Pequod?*"

"Ay, among some of us old sailor chaps, he goes by that name. Ye hav'n't seen him yet, have ye?"

"No, we hav'n't. He's sick they say, but is getting better, and will be all right again before long."

"All right again before long!" laughed the stranger, with a solemnly derisive sort of laugh. "Look ye; when Captain Ahab is all right, then this left arm of mine will be all right; not before."

"What do you know about him?"

"What did they *tell* you about him? Say that!"

"They didn't tell much of anything about him; only I've heard that he's a good whale-hunter, and a good captain to his crew."

"That's true, that's true—yes, both true enough. But you must jump when he gives an order. Step and growl; growl and go—that's the word with Captain Ahab. But nothing about that thing that happened to him off Cape Horn, long ago, when he lay like dead for three days and nights; nothing about that deadly skrimmage with the Spaniard afore the altar in Santa?—heard nothing about that, eh? Nothing about the silver calabash he spat into? And nothing about his losing his leg last voyage, according to the prophecy. Didn't ye hear a word about them matters and something more, eh? No, I don't think ye did; how could ye? Who knows it? Not all Nantucket, I guess. But hows'ever, mayhap, ye've heard tell about the leg, and how he lost it; ay, ye have heard of that, I dare-say. Oh, yes, *that* everyone knows a'most—I mean they know he's only one leg; and that a parmacetti took the other off."

"My friend," said I, "what all this gibberish of yours is about, I don't know, and I don't much care; for it seems to me that you must be a little damaged in the head. But if you are speaking of Captain Ahab, of that ship there, the *Pequod,* then let me tell you, that I know all about the loss of his leg."

"*All* about it, eh—sure you do?—all?

"Pretty sure."

With finger pointed and eye leveled at the *Pequod,* the beggar-like stranger stood a moment, as if in a troubled reverie; then starting a little, turned and said—"Ye've shipped, have ye? Names down on the papers? Well, well, what's signed, is signed; and what's to be, will be; and then again, perhaps it won't be, after all. Anyhow, it's all fixed and arranged a'ready; and some sailors or other must go with him, I suppose; as well these as any other men, God pity 'em! Morning to ye, shipmates, morning; the ineffable heavens bless ye; I'm sorry I stopped ye."

"Look here, friend," said I, "if you have anything important to tell us, out with it; but if you are only trying to bamboozle us, you are mistaken in your game; that's all I have to say."

"And it's said very well, and I like to hear a chap talk up that way; you are just the man for him—the likes of ye. Morning to ye, shipmates, morning! Oh! when ye get there, tell 'em I've concluded not to make one of 'em."

"Ah, my dear fellow, you can't fool us that way—you can't fool us. It is the easiest thing in the world for a man to look as if he had a great secret in him."

"Morning to ye, shipmates, morning."

"Morning it is," said I. "Come along, Queequeg, let's leave this crazy man. But stop, tell me your name, will you?"

"Elijah."

Elijah! thought I, and we walked away, both commenting, after each other's fashion, upon this ragged old sailor; and agreed that he was nothing but a humbug, trying to be a bugbear. But we had not gone perhaps above a hundred yards, when chancing to turn a corner, and looking back as I did so, who should be seen but Elijah following us, though at a distance. Somehow, the sight of him struck me so, that I said nothing to Queequeg of his being behind, but passed on with my comrade, anxious to see whether the stranger would turn the same corner that we did. He did; and then it seemed to me that he was dogging us, but with what intent I could not for the life of me imagine. This circumstance, coupled with his ambiguous, half-hinting, half-revealing, shrouded sort of talk, now begat in me all kinds of vague wonderments and half-apprehensions, and all connected with the *Pequod*; and Captain Ahab; and the leg he had lost; and the Cape Horn fit; and the silver calabash; and what Captain Peleg had said of him, when I left the ship the day previous; and the prediction of the squaw Tistig; and the voyage we had bound ourselves to sail; and a hundred other shadowy things.

I was resolved to satisfy myself whether this ragged Elijah was really dogging us or not, and with that intent crossed the way with Queequeg, and on that side of it retraced our steps. But Elijah passed on, without seeming to notice us. This relieved me; and once more, and finally as it seemed to me, I pronounced him in my heart, a humbug.

Chapter XX

All Astir

A day or two passed, and there was great activity aboard the *Pequod*. Not only were the old sails being mended, but new sails were coming on board, and bolts of canvas, and coils of rigging; in short, everything betokened that the ship's preparations were hurrying to a close. Captain Peleg seldom or never went ashore, but sat in his wigwam keeping a sharp look-out upon the hands: Bildad did all the purchasing and providing at the stores; and the men employed in the hold and on the rigging were working till long after nightfall.

On the day following Queequeg's signing the articles, word was given at all the inns where the ship's company were stopping, that their chests must be on board before night, for there was no telling how soon the vessel might be sailing. So Queequeg and I got down our traps, resolving, however, to sleep ashore till the last. But it seems they always give very long notice in these cases, and the ship did not sail for several days. But no wonder; there was a good deal to be done, and there is no telling how many things to be thought of, before the *Pequod* was fully equipped.

Everyone knows what a multitude of things—beds, saucepans, knives and forks, shovels and tongs, napkins, nut-crackers, and what not, are indispensable to the business of housekeeping. Just so with whaling, which necessitates a three-years' housekeeping upon the wide ocean, far from all grocers, costermongers, doctors, bakers, and bankers. And though this also holds true of merchant-vessels, yet not by any means to the same extent as with whalemen. For besides the great length of the whaling voyage, the numerous articles peculiar to the prosecution of the fishery, and the impossibility of replacing them at the remote harbors usually frequented, it must be remembered, that of all ships, whaling vessels are the most exposed to accidents of all kinds, and especially to the destruction and loss of the very things upon which the success of the voyage most depends. Hence, the spare boats, spare spars, and spare lines and harpoons, and spare everything, almost, but a spare Captain and duplicate ship.

At the period of our arrival at the Island, the heaviest storage of the *Pequod* had been almost completed; comprising her beef, bread, water, fuel, and iron hoops and staves. But, as before hinted, for some time there was a continual fetching and carrying on board of divers odds and ends of things, both large and small.

Chief among those who did this fetching and carrying was Captain Bildad's sister, a lean old lady of a most determined and indefatigable spirit, but withal very kindhearted, who seemed resolved that, if *she* could help it, nothing should be found wanting in the *Pequod,* after once fairly getting to sea. At one time she would come on board with a jar of pickles for the steward's pantry; another time with a bunch of quills for the chief mate's desk, where he kept his log; a third time with a roll of flannel for the small of someone's rheumatic back. Never did any woman better deserve her name, which was Charity—Aunt Charity, as everybody called her. And like a sister of charity did this charitable Aunt Charity bustle about hither and thither, ready to turn her hand and heart to anything that promised to yield safety, comfort, and consolation to all on board a ship in which her beloved brother Bildad was concerned, and in which she herself owned a score or two of well-saved dollars.

But it was startling to see this excellent hearted Quakeress coming on board, as she did the last day, with a long oil-ladle in one hand, and a still longer whaling lance in the other. Nor was Bildad himself nor Captain Peleg at all backward. As for Bildad, he carried about with him a long list of the articles needed, and at every fresh arrival, down went his mark opposite that article upon the paper. Every once in a while Peleg came hobbling out of his whale-bone den, roaring at the men down the hatchways, roaring up to the riggers at the mast-head, and then concluded by roaring back into his wigwam.

During these days of preparation, Queequeg and I often visited the craft, and as often I asked about Captain Ahab, and how he was, and when he was going to come on board his ship. To these questions they would answer, that he was getting better and better, and was expected aboard every day; meantime, the two Captains, Peleg and Bildad, could attend to everything necessary to fit the vessel for the voyage. If I had been downright honest with myself, I would have seen very plainly in my heart that I did but half fancy being committed this way to so long a voyage, without once laying my eyes on the man who was to be the absolute dictator of it, so soon as the ship sailed out upon the open sea. But when a man suspects any wrong, it sometimes happens that if he be already involved in the matter, he insensibly strives to cover up his suspicions even from himself. And much this way it was with me. I said nothing, and tried to think nothing.

At last it was given out that some time next day the ship would certainly sail. So next morning, Queequeg and I took a very early start.

Chapter XXI

GOING ABOARD

IT WAS NEARLY SIX O'CLOCK, BUT ONLY GRAY IMPERFECT MISTY DAWN, WHEN WE DREW NIGH THE wharf.

"There are some sailors running ahead there, if I see right," said I to Queequeg, "it can't be shadow; she's off by sunrise, I guess; come on!"

"Avast!" cried a voice, whose owner at the same time coming close behind us, laid a hand upon both our shoulders, and then insinuating himself between us, stood stooping forward a little, in the uncertain twilight, strangely peering from Queequeg to me. It was Elijah.

"Going aboard?"

"Hands off, will you," said I.

"Lookee here," said Queequeg, shaking himself, "go 'way!"

"Ain't going aboard, then?"

"Yes, we are," said I, "but what business is that of yours? Do you know, Mr. Elijah, that I consider you a little impertinent?"

"No, no, no; I wasn't aware of that," said Elijah, slowly and wonderingly looking from me to Queequeg, with the most unaccountable glances.

"Elijah," said I, "you will oblige my friend and me by withdrawing. We are going to the Indian and Pacific Oceans, and would prefer not to be detained."

"Ye be, be ye? Coming back afore breakfast?"

"He's cracked, Queequeg," said I, "come on."

"Holloa!" cried stationary Elijah, hailing us when we had removed a few paces.

"Never mind him," said I, "Queequeg, come on."

But he stole up to us again, and suddenly clapping his hand on my shoulder, said, "Did ye see anything looking like men going towards that ship a while ago?"

Struck by this plain matter-of-fact question, I answered, saying, "Yes, I thought I did see four or five men; but it was too dim to be sure."

"Very dim, very dim," said Elijah. "Morning to ye."

Once more we quitted him; but once more he came softly after us; and touching my shoulder again, said, "See if you can find 'em now, will ye?

"Find who?"

"Morning to ye! morning to ye!" he rejoined, again moving off. "Oh! I was going to warn ye against—but never mind, never mind—it's all one, all in the family too;—sharp frost this morning, ain't it? Good-bye to ye. Shan't see ye again very soon, I guess; unless it's before the Grand-Jury." And with these cracked words he finally departed, leaving me, for the moment, in no small wonderment at his frantic impudence.

At last, stepping on board the *Pequod,* we found everything in profound quiet, not a soul moving. The cabin entrance was locked within; the hatches were all on, and lumbered with coils of rigging. Going forward to the forecastle, we found the slide of the scuttle open. Seeing a light, we went down, and found only an old rigger there, wrapped in a tattered pea-jacket. He was thrown at whole length upon two chests, his face downwards and enclosed in his folded arms. The profoundest slumber slept upon him.

"Those sailors we saw, Queequeg, where can they have gone to?" said I, looking dubiously at the sleeper. But it seemed that, when on the wharf, Queequeg had not at all noticed what I now alluded to; hence I would have thought myself to have been optically deceived in that matter, were it not for Elijah's otherwise inexplicable question. But I beat the thing down; and again marking the sleeper, jocularly hinted to Queequeg that perhaps we had best sit up with the body; telling him to establish himself accordingly. He put his hand upon the sleeper's rear, as though feeling if it was soft enough; and then, without more ado, sat quietly down there.

"Gracious! Queequeg, don't sit there," said I.

"Oh; perry dood seat," said Queequeg, "my country way; won't hurt him face."

"Face!" said I, "call that his face? very benevolent countenance then; but how hard he breathes, he's heaving himself; get off, Queequeg, you are heavy, it's grinding the face of the poor. Get off, Queequeg! Look, he'll twitch you off soon. I wonder he don't wake."

Queequeg removed himself to just beyond the head of the sleeper, and lighted his tomahawk pipe. I sat at the feet. We kept the pipe passing over the sleeper, from one to the other. Meanwhile, upon questioning him in his broken fashion, Queequeg gave me to understand that, in his land, owing to the absence of settees and sofas of all sorts, the king, chiefs, and great people generally, were in the custom of fattening some of the lower orders for ottomans; and to furnish a house comfortably in that respect, you had only to buy up eight or ten lazy fellows, and lay them round in the piers and alcoves. Besides, it was very convenient on an excursion; much better than those garden-chairs which are convertible into walking-sticks; upon occasion, a chief calling his attendant, and desiring him to make a settee of himself under a spreading tree, perhaps in some damp marshy place.

While narrating these things, every time Queequeg received the tomahawk from me, he flourished the hatchet-side of it over the sleeper's head.

"What's that for, Queequeg?"

"Perry easy, kill-e; oh! perry easy!

He was going on with some wild reminiscences about his tomahawk-pipe which, it seemed, had in its two uses both brained his foes and soothed his soul, when we were directly attracted to the sleeping rigger. The strong vapor now completely filling the contracted hole, it began to tell upon him. He breathed with a sort of muffledness; then seemed troubled in the nose; then revolved over once or twice; then sat up and rubbed his eyes.

"Holloa!" he breathed at last, "who be ye smokers?"

"Shipped men," answered I, "when does she sail?"

"Ay, ay, ye are going in her, be ye? She sails to-day. The Captain came aboard last night."

"What Captain?—Ahab?"

"Who but him indeed?"

I was going to ask him some further questions concerning Ahab, when we heard a noise on deck.

"Holloa! Starbuck's astir," said the rigger. "He's a lively chief mate, that; good man, and a pious; but all alive now, I must turn to." And so saying he went on deck, and we followed.

It was now clear sunrise. Soon the crew came on board in twos and threes; the riggers bestirred themselves; the mates were actively engaged; and several of the shore people were busy in bringing various last things on board. Meanwhile Captain Ahab remained invisibly enshrined within his cabin.

Chapter XXII

MERRY CHRISTMAS

AT LENGTH, TOWARDS NOON, UPON THE FINAL DISMISSAL OF THE SHIP'S RIGGERS, AND AFTER THE *Pequod* had been hauled out from the wharf, and after the ever-thoughtful Charity had come off in a whale-boat, with her last gift—a nightcap for Stubb, the second mate, her brother-in-law, and a spare Bible for the steward—after all this, the two Captains, Peleg and Bildad, issued from the cabin, and turning to the chief mate, Peleg said:

"Now, Mr. Starbuck, are you sure everything is right? Captain Ahab is all ready—just spoke to him—nothing more to be got from shore, eh? Well, call all hands, then. Muster 'em aft here—blast 'em!"

"No need of profane words, however great the hurry, Peleg," said Bildad, "but away with thee, friend Starbuck, and do our bidding."

How now! Here upon the very point of starting for the voyage, Captain Peleg and Captain Bildad were going it with a high hand on the quarter-deck, just as if they were to be joint-commanders at sea, as well as to all appearances in port. And, as for Captain Ahab, no sign of him was yet to be seen; only, they said he was in the cabin. But then, the idea was, that his presence was by no means necessary in getting the ship under weigh, and steering her well out to sea. Indeed, as that was not at all his proper business, but the pilot's; and as he was not yet completely recovered—so they said—therefore, Captain Ahab stayed below. And all this seemed natural enough; especially as in the merchant service many captains never show themselves on deck for a considerable time after heaving up the anchor, but remain over the cabin table, having a farewell merry-making with their shore friends, before they quit the ship for good with the pilot.

But there was not much chance to think over the matter, for Captain Peleg was now all alive. He seemed to do most of the talking and commanding, and not Bildad.

"Aft here, ye sons of bachelors," he cried, as the sailors lingered at the main-mast. "Mr. Starbuck, drive 'em aft."

"Strike the tent there!"—was the next order. As I hinted before, this whalebone marquee was never pitched except in port; and on board the *Pequod,* for thirty years, the order to strike the tent was well known to be the next thing to heaving up the anchor.

"Man the capstan! Blood and thunder!—jump!"—was the next command, and the crew sprang for the handspikes.

Now in getting under weigh, the station generally occupied by the pilot is the forward part of the ship. And here Bildad, who, with Peleg, be it known, in addition to his other offices, was one of the licensed pilots of the port—he being suspected to have got himself made a pilot in order to save the Nantucket pilot-fee to all the ships he was concerned in, for he never piloted any other craft—Bildad, I say, might now be seen actively engaged in looking over the bows for the approaching anchor, and at intervals singing what seemed a dismal stave of psalmody, to cheer the hands at the windlass, who roared forth some sort of a chorus about the girls in Booble Alley, with hearty good-will. Nevertheless, not three days previous, Bildad had told them that no profane songs would be allowed on board the *Pequod,* particularly in getting under weigh; and Charity, his sister, had placed a small choice copy of Watts in each seaman's berth.

Meantime, overseeing the other part of the ship, Captain Peleg ripped and swore astern in the most frightful manner. I almost thought he would sink the ship before the anchor could be got up; involuntarily I paused on my handspike, and told Queequeg to do the same, thinking of the perils we both ran, in starting on the voyage with such a devil for a pilot. I was comforting myself, however, with the thought that in pious Bildad might be found some salvation, spite of his seven hundred and seventy-seventh lay; when I felt a sudden sharp poke in my rear, and turning round, was horrified at the apparition of Captain Peleg in the act of withdrawing his leg from my immediate vicinity. That was my first kick.

"Is that the way they heave in the marchant service?" he roared. "Spring, thou sheep-head; spring, and break thy backbone! Why don't ye spring, I say, all of ye—spring! Quohog! spring, thou chap with the red whiskers; spring there, Scotch-cap; spring, thou green pants. Spring, I say, all of ye, and spring your eyes out!" And so saying, he moved along the windlass, here and there using his leg very freely, while imperturbable Bildad kept leading off with his psalmody. Thinks I, Captain Peleg must have been drinking something to-day.

At last the anchor was up, the sails were set, and off we glided. It was a short, cold Christmas; and as the short northern day merged into night, we found ourselves almost broad upon the wintry ocean, whose freezing spray cased us in ice, as in polished armor. The long rows of teeth on the bulwarks glistened in the moonlight; and like the white ivory tusks of some huge elephant, vast curving icicles depended from the bows.

Lank Bildad, as pilot, headed the first watch, and ever and anon, as the old craft deep dived into the green seas, and sent the shivering frost all over her, and the winds howled, and the cordage rang, his steady notes were heard—

Sweet fields beyond the swelling flood,
Stand dressed in living green.
So to the Jews old Canaan stood,
While Jordan rolled between.

Never did those sweet words sound more sweetly to me than then. They were full of hope and fruition. Spite of this frigid winter night in the boisterous Atlantic, spite of my wet feet and wetter jacket, there was yet, it then seemed to me, many a pleasant haven in store; and meads and glades so eternally vernal, that the grass shot up by the spring, untrodden, unwilted, remains at midsummer.

At last we gained such an offing, that the two pilots were needed no longer. The stout sail-boat that had accompanied us began ranging alongside.

It was curious and not unpleasing, how Peleg and Bildad were affected at this juncture, especially Captain Bildad. For loath to depart, yet; very loath to leave, for good, a ship bound on so long and perilous a voyage—beyond both stormy Capes; a ship in which some thousands of his hard earned dollars were invested; a ship, in which an old shipmate sailed as captain; a man almost as old as he, once more starting to encounter all the terrors of the pitiless jaw; loath to say good-bye to a thing so every way brimful of every interest to him—poor old Bildad lingered long; paced the deck with anxious strides; ran down into the cabin to speak another farewell word there; again came on deck, and looked to windward; looked towards the wide and endless waters, only bounded by the far-off unseen Eastern Continents; looked towards the land; looked aloft; looked right and left; looked everywhere and nowhere; and at last, mechanically coiling a rope upon its pin, convulsively grasped stout Peleg by the hand, and holding up a lantern, for a moment stood gazing heroically in his face, as much as to say, "Nevertheless, friend Peleg, I can stand it; yes, I can."

As for Peleg himself, he took it more like a philosopher; but for all his philosophy, there was a tear twinkling in his eye, when the lantern came too near. And he, too, did not a little run from the cabin to deck—now a word below, and now a word with Starbuck, the chief mate.

But, at last, he turned to his comrade, with a final sort of look about him—"Captain Bildad—

come, old shipmate, we must go. Back the main-yard there! Boat ahoy! Stand by to come close alongside, now! Careful, careful!—come, Bildad, boy—say your last. Luck to ye, Starbuck—luck to ye, Mr. Stubb—luck to ye, Mr. Flask—good-bye, and good luck to ye all—and this day three years I'll have a hot supper smoking for ye in old Nantucket. Hurrah and away!"

"God bless ye, and have ye in His holy keeping, men," murmured old Bildad, almost incoherently. "I hope ye'll have fine weather now, so that Captain Ahab may soon be moving among ye—a pleasant sun is all he needs, and ye'll have plenty of them in the tropic voyage ye go. Be careful in the hunt, ye mates. Don't stave the boats needlessly, ye harpooneers; good white cedar plank is raised full three per cent within the year. Don't forget your prayers, either. Mr. Starbuck, mind that cooper don't waste the spare staves. Oh! the sail-needles are in the green locker. Don't whale it too much a' Lord's days, men; but don't miss a fair chance either, that's rejecting Heaven's good gifts. Have an eye to the molasses tierce, Mr. Stubb; it was a little leaky, I thought. If ye touch at the islands, Mr. Flask, beware of fornication. Good-bye, good-bye! Don't keep that cheese too long down in the hold, Mr. Starbuck; it'll spoil. Be careful with the butter—twenty cents the pound it was, and mind ye, if—"

"Come, come, Captain Bildad; stop palavering—away!" and with that, Peleg hurried him over the side, and both dropped into the boat.

Ship and boat diverged; the cold, damp night breeze blew between; a screaming gull flew overhead; the two hulls wildly rolled; we gave three heavy-hearted cheers, and blindly plunged like fate into the lone Atlantic.

Chapter XXIII

The Lee Shore

Some chapters back, one Bulkington was spoken of, a tall, newlanded mariner, encountered in New Bedford at the inn.

When on that shivering winter's night, the *Pequod* thrust her vindictive bows into the cold malicious waves, who should I see standing at her helm but Bulkington! I looked with sympathetic awe and fearfulness upon the man, who in mid-winter just landed from a four years' dangerous voyage, could so unrestingly push off again for still another tempestuous term. The land seemed scorching to his feet. Wonderfullest things are ever the unmentionable; deep memories yield no epitaphs; this six-inch chapter is the stoneless grave of Bulkington. Let me only say that it fared with him as with the storm-tossed ship, that miserably drives along the leeward land. The port would fain give succor; the port is pitiful; in the port is safety, comfort, hearth-stone, supper, warm blankets, friends, all that's kind to our mortalities. But in that gale, the port, the land, is that ship's direst jeopardy; she must fly all hospitality; one touch of land, though it but graze the keel, would make her shudder through and through. With all her might she crowds all sail off-shore; in so doing, fights 'gainst the very winds that fain would blow her homeward; seeks all the lashed sea's landlessness again; for refuge's sake forlornly rushing into peril; her only friend her bitterest foe!

Know ye now, Bulkington? Glimpses do ye seem to see of that mortally intolerable truth; that all deep, earnest thinking is but the intrepid effort of the soul to keep the open independence of her sea; while the wildest winds of heaven and earth conspire to cast her on the treacherous, slavish shore?

But as in landlessness alone resides the highest truth, shoreless, indefinite as God—so, better is it to perish in that howling infinite, than be ingloriously dashed upon the lee, even if that were safety! For worm-like, then, oh! who would craven crawl to land! Terrors of the terrible! is all this agony so vain? Take heart, take heart, O Bulkington! Bear thee grimly, demi-god! Up from the spray of thy ocean-perishing—straight up, leaps thy apotheosis!

Chapter XXIV

THE ADVOCATE

AS QUEEQUEG AND I ARE NOW FAIRLY EMBARKED IN THIS BUSINESS OF WHALING; AND AS THIS business of whaling has somehow come to be regarded among landsmen as a rather unpoetical and disreputable pursuit; therefore, I am all anxiety to convince ye, ye landsmen, of the injustice hereby done to us hunters of whales.

In the first place, it may be deemed almost superfluous to establish the fact, that among people at large, the business of whaling is not accounted on a level with what are called the liberal professions. If a stranger were introduced into any miscellaneous metropolitan society, it would but slightly advance the general opinion of his merits, were he presented to the company as a harpooneer, say; and if in emulation of the naval officers he should append the initials S.W.F. (Sperm-Whale Fishery) to his visiting card, such a procedure would be deemed pre-eminently presuming and ridiculous.

Doubtless one leading reason why the world declines honoring us whalemen, is this: they think that, at best, our vocation amounts to a butchering sort of business; and that when actively engaged therein, we are surrounded by all manner of defilements. Butchers we are, that is true. But butchers, also, and butchers of the bloodiest badge have been all Martial Commanders whom the world invariably delights to honor. And as for the matter of the alleged uncleanliness of our business, ye shall soon be initiated into certain facts hitherto pretty generally unknown, and which, upon the whole, will triumphantly plant the sperm whale-ship at least among the cleanliest things of this tidy earth. But even granting the charge in question to be true; what disordered slippery decks of a whale-ship are comparable to the unspeakable carrion of those battle-fields from which so many soldiers return to drink in all ladies' plaudits? And if the idea of peril so much enhances the popular conceit of the soldier's profession; let me assure ye that many a veteran who has freely marched up to a battery, would quickly recoil at the apparition of the sperm whale's vast tail, fanning into eddies the air over his head. For what are the comprehensible terrors of man compared with the interlinked terrors and wonders of God!

But, though the world scouts at us whale hunters, yet does it unwittingly pay us the profoundest homage; yea, an all-abounding adoration! for almost all the tapers, lamps, and candles that burn round the globe, burn, as before so many shrines, to our glory!

But look at this matter in other lights; weigh it in all sorts of scales; see what we whalemen are, and have been.

Why did the Dutch in De Witt's time have admirals of their whaling-fleets? Why did Louis XVI of France, at his own personal expense, fit out whaling ships from Dunkirk, and politely invite to that town some score or two of families from our own island of Nantucket? Why did Britain between the years 1750 and 1788 pay to her whalemen in bounties upwards of £1,000,000? And lastly, how comes it that we whalemen of America now outnumber all the rest of the banded whalemen in the world; sail a navy of upwards of seven hundred vessels; manned by eighteen thousand men; yearly consuming 4,000,000 of dollars; the ships worth, at the time of sailing, $20,000,000; and every year importing into our harbors a well reaped harvest of $7,000,000. How comes all this, if there be not something puissant in whaling?

But this is not the half; look again.

I freely assert that the cosmopolite philosopher cannot, for his life, point out one single peaceful influence, which within the last sixty years has operated more potentially upon the whole broad world, taken in one aggregate, than the high and mighty business of whaling. One way and another, it has begotten events so remarkable in themselves, and so continuously momentous in their sequential issues, that whaling may well be regarded as that Egyptian mother, who bore offspring themselves pregnant from her womb. It would be a hopeless, endless task to catalogue all these things. Let a handful suffice. For many years past the whale-ship has been the pioneer in ferreting out the remotest and least known parts of the earth. She has explored seas and archipelagoes which had no chart, where no Cook or Vancouver had ever sailed. If American and European men-of-war now peacefully ride in once savage harbors, let them fire salutes to the honor and glory of the whale-ship, which originally showed them the way, and first interpreted between them and the savages. They may celebrate as they will the heroes of Exploring Expeditions, your Cooks, your Krusensterns; but I say that scores of anonymous Captains have sailed out of Nantucket, that were as great, and greater, than your Cook and your Krusenstern. For in their succorless empty-handedness, they, in the heathenish sharked waters, and by the beaches of unrecorded, javelin islands, battled with virgin wonders and terrors that Cook with all his marines and muskets would not have willingly dared. All that is made such a flourish of in the old South Sea Voyages, those things were but the life-time commonplaces of our heroic Nantucketers. Often, adventures which Vancouver dedicates three chapters to, these men accounted unworthy of being set down in the ship's common log. Ah, the world! Oh, the world!

Until the whale fishery rounded Cape Horn, no commerce but colonial, scarcely any intercourse but colonial, was carried on between Europe and the long line of the opulent Spanish provinces on the Pacific coast. It was the whalemen who first broke through the jealous policy of the Spanish crown, touching those colonies; and, if space permitted, it might be distinctly shown how from those whalemen at last eventuated the liberation of Peru, Chile, and Bolivia from the yoke of Old Spain, and the establishment of the eternal democracy in those parts.

That great America on the other side of the sphere, Australia, was given to the enlightened world by the whaleman. After its first blunder-born discovery by a Dutchman, all other ships, long shunned those shores as pestiferously barbarous; but the whale-ship touched there. The whale-ship is the true mother of that now mighty colony. Moreover, in the infancy of the first Australian settlement, the emigrants were several times saved from starvation by the benevolent biscuit of the whale-ship luckily dropping an anchor in their waters. The uncounted isles of all Polynesia confess the same truth, and do commercial homage to the whale-ship, that cleared the way for the missionary and the merchant, and in many cases carried the primitive missionaries to their first destinations. If that double-bolted land, Japan, is ever to become hospitable, it is the whale-ship alone to whom the credit will be due; for already she is on the threshold.

But if, in the face of all this, you still declare that whaling has no aesthetically noble associations connected with it, then am I ready to shiver fifty lances with you there, and unhorse you with a split helmet every time.

The whale has no famous author, and whaling no famous chronicler, you will say.

The whale no famous author, and whaling no famous chronicler? Who wrote the first account of our Leviathan? Who but mighty Job? And who composed the first narrative of a whaling voyage? Who, but no less a prince than Alfred the Great, who, with his own royal pen, took down the words from Other, the Norwegian whale-hunter of those times! And who pronounced our glowing eulogy in Parliament? Who, but Edmund Burke!

True enough, but then whalemen themselves are poor devils; they have no good blood in their veins.

No good blood in their veins? They have something better than royal blood there. The grandmother of Benjamin Franklin was Mary Morrel; afterwards, by marriage, Mary Folger, one of the old settlers of Nantucket, and the ancestress to a long line of Folgers and harpooneers—all kith and kin to noble Benjamin—this day darting the barbed iron from one side of the world to the other.

Good again; but then all confess that somehow whaling is not respectable.

Whaling not respectable? Whaling is imperial! By old English statutory law, the whale is declared "a royal fish."[1]

Oh, that's only nominal! The whale himself has never figured in any grand imposing way.

The whale never figured in any grand imposing way? In one of the mighty triumphs given to a Roman general upon his entering the world's capital, the bones of a whale, brought all the way from the Syrian coast, were the most conspicuous object in the cymballed procession.

Grant it, since you cite it; but say what you will, there is no real dignity in whaling.

No dignity in whaling? The dignity of our calling the very heavens attest. Cetus is a constellation in the South! No more! Drive down your hat in presence of the Czar, and take it off to Queequeg! No more! I know a man that, in his lifetime, has taken three hundred and fifty whales. I account that man more honorable than that great captain of antiquity who boasted of taking as many walled towns.

And, as for me, if, by any possibility, there be any as yet undiscovered prime thing in me; if I shall ever deserve any real repute in that small but high hushed world which I might not be unreasonably ambitious of; if hereafter I shall do anything that, upon the whole, a man might rather have done than to have left undone; if, at my death, my executors, or more properly my creditors, find any precious MSS. in my desk, then here I prospectively ascribe all the honor and the glory to whaling; for a whale-ship was my Yale College and my Harvard.

Chapter XXV

POSTSCRIPT

IN BEHALF OF THE DIGNITY OF WHALING, I WOULD FAIN ADVANCE NAUGHT BUT SUBSTANTIATED facts. But after embattling his facts, an advocate who should wholly suppress a not unreasonable surmise, which might tell eloquently upon his cause—such an advocate, would he not be blameworthy?

It is well known that at the coronation of kings and queens, even modern ones, a certain curious process of seasoning them for their functions is gone through. There is a saltcellar of state, so called, and there may be a caster of state. How they use the salt, precisely—who knows? Certain I am, however, that a king's head is solemnly oiled at his coronation, even as a head of salad. Can it be, though, that they anoint it with a view of making its interior run well, as they anoint machinery? Much might be ruminated here, concerning the essential dignity of this regal process, because in common life we esteem but meanly and contemptibly a fellow who anoints his hair, and palpably smells of that anointing. In truth, a mature man who uses hair-oil, unless medicinally, that man has

1. See subsequent chapters for something more on this head.

probably got a quoggy spot in him somewhere. As a general rule, he can't amount to much in his totality.

But the only thing to be considered here, is this—what kind of oil is used at coronations? Certainly it cannot be olive oil, nor macassar oil, nor castor oil, nor bear's oil, nor train oil, nor cod-liver oil. What then can it possibly be, but the sperm oil in its unmanufactured, unpolluted state, the sweetest of all oils?

Think of that, ye loyal Britons! we whalemen supply your kings and queens with coronation stuff!

Chapter XXVI

KNIGHTS AND SQUIRES

THE CHIEF MATE OF THE *PEQUOD* WAS STARBUCK, A NATIVE OF NANTUCKET, AND A QUAKER BY descent. He was a long, earnest man, and though born on an icy coast, seemed well adapted to endure hot latitudes, his flesh being hard as twice-baked biscuit. Transported to the Indies, his live blood would not spoil like bottled ale. He must have been born in some time of general drought and famine, or upon one of those fast days for which his state is famous. Only some thirty arid summers had he seen; those summers had dried up all his physical superfluousness. But this, his thinness, so to speak, seemed no more the token of wasting anxieties and cares, than it seemed the indication of any bodily blight. It was merely the condensation of the man. He was by no means ill-looking; quite the contrary. His pure tight skin was an excellent fit; and closely wrapped up in it, and embalmed with inner health and strength, like a revivified Egyptian, this Starbuck seemed prepared to endure for long ages to come, and to endure always, as now; for be it Polar snow or torrid sun, like a patent chronometer, his interior vitality was warranted to do well in all climates. Looking into his eyes, you seemed to see there the yet lingering images of those thousand-fold perils he had calmly confronted through life. A staid, steadfast man, whose life for the most part was a telling pantomime of action, and not a tame chapter of sounds. Yet, for all his hardy sobriety and fortitude, there were certain qualities in him which at times affected, and in some cases seemed well-nigh to overbalance all the rest. Uncommonly conscientious for a seaman, and endued with a deep natural reverence, the wild watery loneliness of his life did therefore strongly incline him to superstition; but to that sort of superstition, which in some organizations seems rather to spring, somehow, from intelligence than from ignorance. Outward portents and inward presentiments were his. And if at times these things bent the welded iron of his soul, much more did his far-away domestic memories of his young Cape wife and child, tend to bend him still more from the original ruggedness of his nature, and open him still further to those latent influences which, in some honest-hearted men, restrain the gush of dare-devil daring, so often evinced by others in the more perilous vicissitudes of the fishery. "I will have no man in my boat," said Starbuck, "who is not afraid of a whale." By this, he seemed to mean, not only that the most reliable and useful courage was that which arises from the fair estimation of the encountered peril, but that an utterly fearless man is a far more dangerous comrade than a coward.

"Ay, ay," said Stubb, the second mate, "Starbuck, there, is as careful a man as you'll find anywhere in this fishery." But we shall ere long see what that word "careful" precisely means when used by a man like Stubb, or almost any other whale hunter.

Starbuck was no crusader after perils; in him courage was not a sentiment; but a thing simply useful to him, and always at hand upon all mortally practical occasions. Besides, he thought, perhaps, that in this business of whaling, courage was one of the great staple outfits of the ship, like her beef and her bread, and not to be foolishly wasted. Wherefore he had no fancy for lowering for whales after sun-down; nor for persisting in fighting a fish that too much persisted in fighting him. For, thought Starbuck, I am here in this critical ocean to kill whales for my living, and not to be killed by them for theirs; and that hundreds of men had been so killed Starbuck well knew. What doom was his own father's? Where, in the bottomless deeps, could he find the torn limbs of his brother?

With memories like these in him, and, moreover, given to a certain superstitiousness, as has been said; the courage of this Starbuck, which could, nevertheless, still flourish, must indeed have been extreme. But it was not in reasonable nature that a man so organized, and with such terrible experiences and remembrances as he had; it was not in nature that these things should fail in latently engendering an element in him, which, under suitable circumstances, would break out from its confinement, and burn all his courage up. And brave as he might be, it was that sort of bravery chiefly visible in some intrepid men, which, while generally abiding firm in the conflict with seas, or winds, or whales, or any of the ordinary irrational horrors of the world, yet cannot withstand those more terrific, because more spiritual terrors, which sometimes menace you from the concentrating brow of an enraged and mighty man.

But were the coming narrative to reveal in any instance, the complete abasement of poor Starbuck's fortitude, scarce might I have the heart to write it; for it is a thing most sorrowful, nay shocking, to expose the fall of valor in the soul. Men may seem detestable as joint stock-companies and nations; knaves, fools, and murderers there may be; men may have mean and meager faces; but, man, in the ideal, is so noble and so sparkling, such a grand and glowing creature, that over any ignominious blemish in him all his fellows should run to throw their costliest robes. That immaculate manliness we feel within ourselves, so far within us, that it remains intact though all the outer character seem gone; bleeds with keenest anguish at the undraped spectacle of a valor ruined man. Nor can piety itself, at such a shameful sight, completely stifle her upbraidings against the permitting stars. But this august dignity I treat of, is not the dignity of kings and robes, but that abounding dignity which has no robed investiture. Thou shalt see it shining in the arm that wields a pick or drives a spike; that democratic dignity which, on all hands, radiates without end from God; Himself! The great God absolute! The center and circumference of all democracy! His omnipresence, our divine equality!

If, then, to meanest mariners, and renegades and castaways, I shall hereafter ascribe high qualities, though dark; weave round them tragic graces; if even the most mournful, perchance the most abased, among them all, shall at times lift himself to the exalted mounts; if I shall touch that workman's arm with some ethereal light; if I shall spread a rainbow over his disastrous set of sun; then against all mortal critics bear me out in it, thou just Spirit of Equality, which hast spread one royal mantle of humanity over all my kind! Bear me out in it, thou great democratic God! who didst not refuse to the swart convict, Bunyan, the pale, poetic pearl; Thou who didst clothe with doubly hammered leaves of finest gold, the stumped and paupered arm of old Cervantes; Thou who didst pick up Andrew Jackson from the pebbles; who didst hurl him upon a war-horse; who didst thunder him higher than a throne! Thou who, in all Thy mighty, earthly marchings, ever cullest Thy selectest champions from the kingly commoners; bear me out in it, O God!

Chapter XXVII

KNIGHTS AND SQUIRES

STUBB WAS THE SECOND MATE. HE WAS A NATIVE OF CAPE COD; AND HENCE, ACCORDING TO LOCAL usage, was called a Cape-Cod-man. A happy-go-lucky; neither craven nor valiant; taking perils as they came with an indifferent air; and while engaged in the most imminent crisis of the chase, toiling away, calm and collected as a journeyman joiner engaged for the year. Good-humored, easy, and careless, he presided over his whale-boat as if the most deadly encounter were but a dinner, and his crew all invited guests. He was as particular about the comfortable arrangements of his part of the boat as an old stage-driver is about the snugness of his box. When close to the whale, in the very death-lock of the fight, he handled his unpitying lance coolly and off-handedly, as a whistling tinker his hammer. He would hum over his old rigadig tunes while flank and flank with the most exasperated monster. Long usage had, for this Stubb, converted the jaws of death into an easy chair. What he thought of death itself, there is no telling. Whether he ever thought of it at all, might be a question; but, if he ever did chance to cast his mind that way after a comfortable dinner, no doubt, like a good sailor, he took it to be a sort of call of the watch to tumble aloft, and bestir themselves there, about something which he would find out when he obeyed the order, and not sooner.

What, perhaps, with other things, made Stubb such an easy-going, unfearing man, so cheerily trudging off with the burden of life in a world full of grave peddlers, all bowed to the ground with their packs; what helped to bring about that almost impious good-humor of his; that thing must have been his pipe. For, like his nose, his short, black little pipe was one of the regular features of his face. You would almost as soon have expected him to turn out of his bunk without his nose as without his pipe. He kept a whole row of pipes there ready loaded, stuck in a rack, within easy reach of his hand; and, whenever he turned in, he smoked them all out in succession, lighting one from the other to the end of the chapter; then loading them again to be in readiness anew. For, when Stubb dressed, instead of first putting his legs into his trousers, he put his pipe into his mouth.

I say this continual smoking must have been one cause, at least, of his peculiar disposition; for everyone knows that this earthly air, whether ashore or afloat, is terribly infected with the nameless miseries of the numberless mortals who have died exhaling it; and as in time of the cholera, some people go about with a camphorated handkerchief to their mouths; so, likewise, against all mortal tribulations, Stubb's tobacco smoke might have operated as a sort of disinfecting agent.

The third mate was Flask, a native of Tisbury, in Martha's Vineyard. A short, stout, ruddy young fellow, very pugnacious concerning whales, who somehow seemed to think that the great Leviathans had personally and hereditarily affronted him; and therefore it was a sort of point of honor with him to destroy them whenever encountered. So utterly lost was he to all sense of reverence for the many marvels of their majestic bulk and mystic ways; and so dead to anything like an apprehension of any possible danger from encountering them; that in his poor opinion, the wondrous whale was but a species of magnified mouse, or at least water-rat, requiring only a little circumvention and some small application of time and trouble in order to kill and boil. This ignorant, unconscious fearlessness of his made him a little waggish in the matter of whales; he followed these fish for the fun of it; and a three years' voyage round Cape Horn was only a jolly joke that lasted that length of time. As a carpenter's nails are divided into wrought nails and cut nails; so mankind may be similarly divided. Little Flask was one of the wrought ones; made to clinch tight and last long. They called him King-Post on board of the *Pequod*; because, in form, he could be well likened to the short, square timber known by that name in Arctic whalers; and which by the means of many radiating side timbers inserted into it, serves to brace the ship against the icy concussions of those battering seas.

Now these three mates—Starbuck, Stubb, and Flask—were momentous men. They it was who by universal prescription commanded three of the *Pequod*'s boats as headsmen. In that grand order of battle in which Captain Ahab would probably marshal his forces to descend on the whales, these three headsmen were as captains of companies. Or, being armed with their long keen whaling spears, they were as a picked trio of lancers; even as the harpooneers were flingers of javelins.

And since in this famous fishery, each mate or headsman, like a Gothic Knight of old, is always accompanied by his boat-steerer or harpooneer, who in certain conjunctures provides him with a fresh lance, when the former one has been badly twisted, or elbowed in the assault; and moreover, as there generally subsists between the two, a close intimacy and friendliness; it is therefore but meet, that in this place we set down who the *Pequod*'s harpooneers were and to what boats headsman each of them belonged.

First of all was Queequeg, whom Starbuck, the chief mate, had selected for his squire. But Queequeg is already known.

Next was Tashtego, an unmixed Indian from Gay Head, the most westerly promontory of Martha's Vineyard, where there still exists the last remnant of a village of red men, which has long supplied the neighboring island of Nantucket with many of her most daring harpooneers. In the fishery, they usually go by the generic name of Gay-Headers. Tashtego's long, lean, sable hair, his high cheek bones, and black rounding eyes—for an Indian, Oriental in their largeness, but Antarctic in their glittering expression—all this sufficiently proclaimed him an inheritor of the unvitiated blood of those proud warrior hunters, who, in quest of the great New England moose, had scoured, bow in hand, the aboriginal forests of the main. But no longer snuffing in the trail of the wild beasts of the woodland, Tashtego now hunted in the wake of the great whales of the sea; the unerring harpoon of the son fitly replacing the infallible arrow of the sires. To look at the tawny brawn of his lithe snaky limbs, you would almost have credited the superstitions of some of the earlier Puritans and half-believed this wild Indian to be a son of the Prince of the Powers of the Air. Tashtego was Stubb the second mate's squire.

Third among the harpooneers was Daggoo, a gigantic, coal-black negro-savage, with a lion-like tread—an Ahasuerus to behold. Suspended from his ears were two golden hoops, so large that the sailors called them ring-bolts, and would talk of securing the top-sail halyards to them. In his youth Daggoo had voluntarily shipped on board of a whaler, lying in a lonely bay on his native coast. And never having been anywhere in the world but in Africa, Nantucket, and the pagan harbors most frequented by the whalemen; and having now led for many years the bold life of the fishery in the ships of owners uncommonly heedful of what manner of men they shipped; Daggoo retained all his barbaric virtues, and erect as a giraffe, moved about the decks in all the pomp of six feet five in his socks. There was a corporeal humility in looking up at him; and a white man standing before him seemed a white flag come to beg truce of a fortress. Curious to tell, this imperial negro, Ahasuerus Daggoo, was the Squire of little Flask, who looked like a chess-man beside him. As for the residue of the *Pequod*'s company, be it said, that at the present day not one in two of the many thousand men before the mast employed in the American whale fishery, are Americans born, though pretty nearly all the officers are. Herein it is the same with the American whale fishery as with the American army and military and merchant navies, and the engineering forces employed in the construction of the American Canals and Railroads. The same, I say, because in all these cases the native American literally provides the brains, the rest of the world as generously supplying the muscles. No small number of these whaling seamen belong to the Azores, where the outward-bound Nantucket whalers frequently touch to augment their crews from the hardy peasants of those rocky shores. In like manner, the Greenland whalers sailing out of Hull or London, put in at the Shetland Islands, to receive the full complement of their crew. Upon the passage homewards, they drop them there again. How it is, there is no telling, but islanders seem to make the best whalemen. They were nearly all islanders in the *Pequod, Isolatoes* too, I call such, not acknowledging the common continent of men, but each *Isolato* living on a separate continent of his own. Yet now, federated along one keel, what a set these *Isolatoes* were! An Anacharsis Clootz deputation from all the isles of the sea, and all the ends of the earth, accompanying Old Ahab in the *Pequod* to lay the world's grievances before that bar from which not very many of them ever come back. Black Little Pip—he never did—oh, no! he went before. Poor Alabama boy! On the grim *Pequod*'s forecastle, ye shall ere long see him, beating his tambourine; prelusive of the eternal time, when sent for, to the great quarter-deck on high, he was bid strike in with angels, and beat his tambourine in glory; called a coward here, hailed a hero there!

Chapter XXVIII

AHAB

FOR SEVERAL DAYS AFTER LEAVING NANTUCKET, NOTHING ABOVE HATCHES WAS SEEN OF CAPTAIN Ahab. The mates regularly relieved each other at the watches, and for aught that could be seen to the contrary, they seemed to be the only commanders of the ship; only they sometimes issued from the cabin with orders so sudden and peremptory, that after all it was plain they but commanded vicariously. Yes, their supreme lord and dictator was there, though hitherto unseen by any eyes not permitted to penetrate into the now sacred retreat of the cabin.

Every time I ascended to the deck from my watches below, I instantly gazed aft to mark if any strange face were visible; for my first vague disquietude touching the unknown captain, now in the seclusion of the sea became almost a perturbation. This was strangely heightened at times by the ragged Elijah's diabolical incoherences uninvitingly recurring to me, with a subtle energy I could not have before conceived of. But poorly could I withstand them, much as in other moods I was almost ready to smile at the solemn whimsicalities of that outlandish prophet of the wharves. But whatever it was of apprehensiveness or uneasiness—to call it so—which I felt, yet whenever I came to look about me in the ship, it seemed against all warranty to cherish such emotions. For though the harpooneers, with the great body of the crew, were a far more barbaric, heathenish, and motley set than any of the tame merchant-ship companies which my previous experiences had made me acquainted with, still I ascribed this—and rightly ascribed it—to the fierce uniqueness of the very nature of that wild Scandinavian vocation in which I had so abandonedly embarked. But it was especially the aspect of the three chief officers of the ship, the mates, which was most forcibly calculated to allay these colorless misgivings, and induce confidence and cheerfulness in every presentment of the voyage. Three better, more likely sea-officers and men, each in his own different way, could not readily be found, and they were every one of them Americans; a Nantucketer, a Vineyarder, a Cape man. Now, it being Christmas when the ship shot from out her harbor, for a space we had biting Polar weather, though all the time running away from it to the southward; and by every degree and minute of latitude which we sailed, gradually leaving that merciless winter, and all its intolerable weather behind us. It was one of those less lowering, but still gray and gloomy enough mornings of the transition, when with a fair wind the ship was rushing through the water with a vindictive sort of leaping and melancholy rapidity, that as I mounted to the deck at the call of the forenoon watch, so soon as I leveled my glance towards the taffrail, foreboding shivers ran over me. Reality outran apprehension; Captain Ahab stood upon his quarter-deck.

There seemed no sign of common bodily illness about him, nor of the recovery from any. He looked like a man cut away from the stake, when the fire has overrunningly wasted all the limbs without consuming them, or taking away one particle from their compacted aged robustness. His whole high, broad form, seemed made of solid bronze, and shaped in an unalterable mold, like Cellini's cast Perseus. Threading its way out from among his gray hairs, and continuing right down one side of his tawny scorched face and neck, till it disappeared in his clothing, you saw a slender rod-like mark, lividly whitish. It resembled that perpendicular seam sometimes made in the straight, lofty trunk of a great tree, when the upper lightning tearingly darts down it, and without wrenching a single twig, peels and grooves out the bark from top to bottom ere running off into the soil, leaving the tree still greenly alive, but branded. Whether that mark was born with him, or whether it was the scar left by some desperate wound, no one could certainly say. By some tacit consent, throughout the voyage little or no allusion was made to it, especially by the mates. But once Tashtego's senior, an old Gay-Head Indian among the crew, superstitiously asserted that not till he was full forty years old did Ahab become that way branded, and then it came upon him, not in the fury of any mortal fray, but in an elemental strife at sea. Yet, this wild hint seemed inferentially negatived, by what a gray Manxman insinuated, an old sepulchral man, who, having never before sailed out of Nantucket, had never ere this laid eye upon wild Ahab. Nevertheless, the old sea-traditions, the immemorial credulities, popularly invested this old Manxman with preternatural powers of discernment. So that no white sailor seriously contradicted him when he said that if ever Captain Ahab should be tranquilly laid out—which might hardly come to pass, so he muttered—then, whoever should do that last office for the dead, would find a birth-mark on him from crown to sole.

So powerfully did the whole grim aspect of Ahab affect me, and the livid brand which streaked it, that for the first few moments I hardly noted that not a little of this overbearing grimness was owing to the barbaric white leg upon which he partly stood. It had previously come to me that this ivory leg had at sea been fashioned from the polished bone of the sperm whale's jaw. "Ay, he was dismasted off Japan," said the old Gay-Head Indian once; "but like his dismasted craft, he shipped another mast without coming home for it. He has a quiver of 'em."

I was struck with the singular posture he maintained. Upon each side of the *Pequod*'s quarter-deck, and pretty close to the mizzen shrouds, there was an auger hole, bored about half an inch or so, into the plank. His bone leg steadied in that hole; one arm elevated, and holding by a shroud; Captain Ahab stood erect, looking straight out beyond the ship's ever-pitching prow. There was an infinity of firmest fortitude, a determinate, unsurrenderable willfulness, in the fixed and fearless, forward dedication of that glance. Not a word he spoke; nor did his officers say aught to him; though by all their minutest gestures and expressions, they plainly showed the uneasy, if not painful, consciousness of being under a troubled master-eye. And not only that, but moody stricken Ahab stood before them with a crucifixion in his face; in all the nameless regal overbearing dignity of some mighty woe.

Ere long, from his first visit in the air, he withdrew into his cabin. But after that morning, he was every day visible to the crew; either standing in his pivot-hole, or seated upon an ivory stool he had; or heavily walking the deck. As the sky grew less gloomy; indeed, began to grow a little genial, he became still less and less a recluse; as if, when the ship had sailed from home, nothing but the dead wintry bleakness of the sea had then kept him so secluded. And, by and by, it came to pass, that he was almost continually in the air; but, as yet, for all that he said, or perceptibly did, on the at last sunny deck, he seemed as unnecessary there as another mast. But the *Pequod* was only making a passage now; not regularly cruising; nearly all whaling preparatives needing supervision the mates were fully competent to, so that there was little or nothing, out of himself, to employ or excite Ahab, now; and thus chase away, for that one interval, the clouds that layer upon layer were piled upon his brow, as ever all clouds choose the loftiest peaks to pile themselves upon.

Nevertheless, ere long, the warm, warbling persuasiveness of the pleasant, holiday weather we came to, seemed gradually to charm him from his mood. For, as when the red-cheeked, dancing girls, April and May, trip home to the wintry, misanthropic woods; even the barest, ruggedest, most thunder-cloven old oak will at least send forth some few green sprouts, to welcome such glad-hearted visitants; so Ahab did, in the end, a little respond to the playful allurings of that girlish air. More than once did he put forth the faint blossom of a look, which, in any other man, would have soon flowered out in a smile.

Chapter XXIX

Enter Ahab; to Him, Stubb

Some days elapsed and ice and icebergs all astern, the *Pequod* now went rolling through the bright Quito spring, which, at sea, almost perpetually reigns on the threshold of the eternal August of the tropic. The warmly cool, clear, ringing, perfumed, overflowing, redundant days, were as crystal goblets of Persian sherbet, heaped up—flaked up, with rose-water snow. The starred and stately nights seemed haughty dames in jeweled velvets, nursing at home in lonely pride, the memory of their absent conquering Earls, the golden helmeted suns! For sleeping man, 'twas hard to choose between such winsome days and such seducing nights. But all the witcheries of that unwaning weather did not merely lend new spells and potencies to the outward world. Inward they turned upon the soul, especially when the still mild hours of eve came on; then, memory shot her crystals as the clear ice most forms of noiseless twilights. And all these subtle agencies, more and more they wrought on Ahab's texture.

Old age is always wakeful; as if, the longer linked with life, the less man has to do with aught that looks like death. Among sea-commanders, the old graybeards will oftenest leave their berths to visit the night-cloaked deck. It was so with Ahab; only that now, of late, he seemed so much to live in the open air, that truly speaking, his visits were more to the cabin, than from the cabin to the planks. "It feels like going down into one's tomb"—he would mutter to himself—"for an old captain like me to be descending this narrow scuttle, to go to my grave-dug berth."

So, almost every twenty-four hours, when the watches of the night were set, and the band on deck sentinelled the slumbers of the band below; and when if a rope was to be hauled upon the forecastle, the sailors flung it not rudely down, as by day, but with some cautiousness dropped it to its place for fear of disturbing their slumbering shipmates; when this sort of steady quietude would begin to prevail, habitually, the silent steersman would watch the cabin-scuttle; and ere long the old man would emerge, gripping at the iron banister, to help his crippled way. Some considering touch of humanity was in him; for at times like these, he usually abstained from patrolling the quarter-deck, because to his wearied mates, seeking repose within six inches of his ivory heel, such would have been the reverberating crack and din of that bony step, that their dreams would have been of the crunching teeth of sharks. But once, the mood was on him too deep for common regardings; and as with heavy, lumber-like pace he was measuring the ship from taffrail to mainmast, Stubb, the old second mate, came up from below, and with a certain unassured, deprecating humorousness, hinted that if Captain Ahab was pleased to walk the planks, then, no one could say nay; but there might be some way of muffling the noise; hinting something indistinctly and hesitatingly about a globe of tow, and the insertion into it, of the ivory heel. Ah! Stubb, thou did'st not know Ahab then.

"Am I a cannon-ball, Stubb," said Ahab, "that thou wouldst wad me that fashion? But go thy ways; I had forgot. Below to thy nightly grave; where such as ye sleep between shrouds, to use ye to the filling one at last.—Down, dog, and kennel!"

Starting at the unforeseen concluding exclamation of the so suddenly scornful old man, Stubb was speechless a moment; then said excitedly, "I am not used to be spoken to that way, sir; I do but less than half like it, sir."

"Avast!" gritted Ahab between his set teeth, and violently moving away, as if to avoid some passionate temptation.

"No, sir; not yet," said Stubb, emboldened, "I will not tamely be called a dog, sir."

"Then be called ten times a donkey, and a mule, and an ass, and begone, or I'll clear the world of thee!"

As he said this, Ahab advanced upon him with such overbearing terrors in his aspect, that Stubb involuntarily retreated.

"I was never served so before without giving a hard blow for it," muttered Stubb, as he found himself descending the cabin-scuttle. "It's very queer. Stop, Stubb; somehow, now, I don't well know whether to go back and strike him, or—what's that?—down here on my knees and pray for him? Yes, that was the thought coming up in me; but it would be the first time I ever *did* pray. It's queer; very queer; and he's queer too; ay, take him fore and aft, he's about the queerest old man Stubb ever sailed with. How he flashed at me!—his eyes like powder-pans! is he mad? Anyway there's something's on his mind, as sure as there must be something on a deck when it cracks. He ain't in his bed now, either, more than three hours out of the twenty-four; and he don't sleep then. Didn't that Dough-Boy, the steward, tell me that of a morning he always finds the old man's hammock clothes all rumpled and tumbled, and the sheets down at the foot, and the coverlid almost tied into knots, and the pillow a sort of frightful hot, as though a baked brick had been on it? A hot old man! I guess he's got what some folks ashore call a conscience; it's a kind of Tic-Dolly-row they say—worse than a toothache. Well, well; I don't know what it is, but the Lord keep me from catching it. He's full of riddles; I wonder what he goes into the after-hold for, every night, as Dough-Boy tells me he suspects; what's that for, I should like to know? Who's made appointments with him in the hold? Ain't that queer, now? But there's no telling, it's the old game—Here goes for a snooze. Damn me, it's worth a fellow's while to be born into the world, if only to fall right asleep. And now that I think of it, that's about the first thing babies do, and that's a sort of queer, too. Damn me, but all things are queer, come to think of 'em. But that's against my principles. Think not, is my eleventh commandment; and sleep when you can, is my twelfth—So here goes again. But how's that? didn't he call me a dog? blazes! he called me ten times a donkey, and piled a lot of jackasses on top of *that!* He might as well have kicked me, and done with it. Maybe he *did* kick me, and I didn't observe it, I was so taken all aback with his brow, somehow. It flashed like a bleached bone. What the devil's the matter with me? I don't stand right on my legs. Coming afoul of that old man has a sort of turned me wrong side out. By the Lord, I must have been dreaming, though—How? how? how?—but the only way's to stash it; so here goes to hammock again; and in the morning, I'll see how this plaguey juggling thinks over by daylight."

Chapter XXX

THE PIPE

WHEN STUBB HAD DEPARTED, AHAB STOOD FOR A WHILE LEANING OVER THE BULWARKS; AND then, as had been usual with him of late, calling a sailor of the watch, he sent him below for his ivory stool, and also his pipe. Lighting the pipe at the binnacle lamp and planting the stool on the weather side of the deck, he sat and smoked.

In old Norse times, the thrones of the sea-loving Danish kings were fabricated, saith tradition, of the tusks of the narwhale. How could one look at Ahab then, seated on that tripod of bones, without bethinking him of the royalty it symbolized? For a Khan of the plank, and a king of the sea, and a great lord of Leviathans was Ahab.

Some moments passed, during which the thick vapor came from his mouth in quick and constant puffs, which blew back again into his face. "How now," he soliloquized at last, withdrawing the tube, "this smoking no longer soothes. Oh, my pipe! hard must it go with me if thy charm be gone! Here have I been unconsciously toiling, not pleasuring—ay, and ignorantly smoking to windward all the while; to windward, and with such nervous whiffs, as if, like the dying whale, my final jets were the strongest and fullest of trouble. What business have I with this pipe? This thing that is meant for sereneness, to send up mild white vapors among mild white hairs, not among torn iron-gray locks like mine. I'll smoke no more—"

He tossed the still lighted pipe into the sea. The fire hissed in the waves; the same instant the ship shot by the bubble the sinking pipe made. With slouched hat, Ahab lurchingly paced the planks.

Chapter XXXI

QUEEN MAB

NEXT MORNING STUBB ACCOSTED FLASK.

"Such a queer dream, King-Post, I never had. You know the old man's ivory leg, well I dreamed he kicked me with it; and when I tried to kick back, upon my soul, my little man, I kicked my leg right off! And then, presto! Ahab seemed a pyramid, and I, like a blazing fool, kept kicking at it. But what was still more curious, Flask—you know how curious all dreams are—through all this rage that I was in, I somehow seemed to be thinking to myself, that after all, it was not much of an insult, that kick from Ahab. 'Why,' thinks I, 'what's the row? It's not a real leg, only a false one.' And there's a mighty difference between a living thump and a dead thump. That's what makes a blow from the hand, Flask, fifty times more savage to bear than a blow from a cane. The living member—that makes the living insult, my little man. And thinks I to myself all the while, mind, while I was stubbing my silly toes against that cursed pyramid—so confoundedly contradictory was it all, all the while, I say, I was thinking to myself, 'what's his leg now, but a cane—a whale-bone cane. Yes,' thinks I, 'it was only a playful cudgelling—in fact, only a whaleboning that he gave me—not a base kick. Besides,' thinks I, 'look at it once; why, the end of it—the foot part—what a small sort of end it is; whereas, if a broad footed farmer kicked me, *there's* a devilish broad insult. But this insult is whittled down to a point only.' But now comes the greatest joke of the dream, Flask. While I was battering away at the pyramid, a sort of badger-haired old merman, with a hump on his back, takes me by the shoulders, and slews me round. 'What are you 'bout?' says he. Slid! man, but I was frightened. Such a phiz! But, somehow, next moment I was over the fright. 'What am I about?' says I at last. 'And what business is that of yours, I should like to know, Mr. Humpback? Do *you* want a kick?' By the lord, Flask, I had no sooner said that, than he turned round his stern to me, bent over, and dragging up a lot of sea-weed he had for a clout—what do you think, I saw?—why thunder alive, man, his stern was stuck full of marling-spikes, with the points out. Says I on second thought, 'I guess I won't kick you, old fellow.' 'Wise Stubb,' said he, 'wise Stubb'; and kept muttering it all the time, a sort of eating of his own gums like a chimney hag. Seeing he wasn't going to stop saying over his 'wise Stubb, wise Stubb,' I thought I might as well fall to kicking the pyramid again. But I had only just lifted my foot for it, when he roared out, 'Stop that kicking!' 'Halloa,' says I, 'what's the matter now, old fellow?' 'Look ye here,' says he; 'let's argue the insult. Captain Ahab kicked ye, didn't he?' 'Yes, he did,' says I—'right *here* it was.' 'Very good,' says he—'he used his ivory leg, didn't he?' 'Yes, he did,' says I. 'Well then,' says he, 'wise Stubb, what have you to complain of? Didn't he kick with right good-will? it wasn't a common pitch pine leg he kicked with, was it? No, you were kicked by a great man, and with a beautiful ivory leg, Stubb. It's an honor; I consider it an honor. Listen, wise Stubb. In old England the greatest lords think it great glory to be slapped by a queen, and made garter-knights of; but, be *your* boast, Stubb, that ye were kicked by old Ahab, and made a wise man of. Remember what I say; *be* kicked by him; account his kicks honors; and on no account kick back; for you can't help yourself, wise Stubb. Don't you see that pyramid?' With that, he all of a sudden seemed somehow, in some queer fashion, to swim off into the air. I snored; rolled over; and there I was in my hammock! Now, what do you think of that dream, Flask?"

"I don't know; it seems a sort of foolish to me, tho'."

"Maybe; maybe. But it's made a wise man of me, Flask. D'ye see Ahab standing there, sideways looking over the stern? Well, the best thing you can do, Flask, is to let the old man alone; never speak to him, whatever he says. Halloa! What's that he shouts? Hark!"

"Mast-head, there! Look sharp, all of ye! There are whales hereabouts! If ye see a white one, split your lungs for him!"

"What do you think of that now, Flask? ain't there a small drop of something queer about that, eh? A white whale—did ye mark that, man? Look ye—there's something special in the wind. Stand by for it, Flask. Ahab has that that's bloody on his mind. But, mum; he comes this way."

Chapter XXXII

CETOLOGY

ALREADY WE ARE BOLDLY LAUNCHED UPON THE DEEP; BUT SOON WE SHALL BE LOST IN ITS UNshored, harborless immensities. Ere that come to pass; ere the *Pequod*'s weedy hull rolls side by side with the barnacled hulls of the leviathan; at the outset it is but well to attend to a matter almost indispensable to a thorough appreciative understanding of the more special leviathanic revelations and allusions of all sorts which are to follow.

It is some systematized exhibition of the whale in his broad genera, that I would now fain put before you. Yet is it no easy task. The classification of the constituents of a chaos, nothing less is here essayed. Listen to what the best and latest authorities have laid down.

"No branch of Zoology is so much involved as that which is entitled Cetology," says Captain Scoresby, A.D. 1820.

"It is not my intention, were it in my power, to enter into the inquiry as to the true method of dividing the cetacea into groups and families.* * * Utter confusion exists among the historians of this animal" (sperm whale), says Surgeon Beale, A.D. 1839.

"Unfitness to pursue our research in the unfathomable waters." "Impenetrable veil covering our knowledge of the cetacea." "A field strewn with thorns." "All these incomplete indications but serve to torture us naturalists."

Thus speak of the whale, the great Cuvier, and John Hunter, and Lesson, those lights of zoology and anatomy. Nevertheless, though of real knowledge there be little, yet of books there are a plenty; and so in some small degree, with cetology, or the science of whales. Many are the men, small and great, old and new, landsmen and seamen, who have at large or in little, written of the whale. Run over a few:—The Authors of the Bible; Aristotle; Pliny; Aldrovandi; Sir Thomas Browne; Gesner; Ray; Linnæus; Rondeletius; Willoughby; Green; Artedi; Sibbald; Brisson; Marten; Lacépède; Bonneterre; Desmarest; Baron Cuvier; Frederick Cuvier; John Hunter; Owen; Scoresby; Beale; Bennett; J. Ross Browne; the Author of Miriam Coffin; Olmstead; and the Rev. T. Cheever. But to what ultimate generalizing purpose all these have written, the above cited extracts will show.

Of the names in this list of whale authors, only those following Owen ever saw living whales; and but one of them was a real professional harpooneer and whaleman. I mean Captain Scoresby. On the separate subject of the Greenland or right-whale, he is the best existing authority. But Scoresby knew nothing and says nothing of the great sperm whale, compared with which the Greenland whale is almost unworthy mentioning. And here be it said, that the Greenland whale is an usurper upon the throne of the seas. He is not even by any means the largest of the whales. Yet, owing to the long priority of his claims, and the profound ignorance which, till some seventy years back, invested the then fabulous and utterly unknown sperm-whale, and which ignorance to this present day still reigns in all but some few scientific retreats and whale-ports; this usurpation has been every way complete. Reference to nearly all the leviathanic allusions in the great poets of past days, will satisfy you that the Greenland whale, without one rival, was to them the monarch of the seas. But the time has at last come for a new proclamation. This is Charing Cross; hear ye! good people all—the Greenland whale is deposed—the great sperm whale now reigneth!

There are only two books in being which at all pretend to put the living sperm whale before you, and at the same time, in the remotest degree succeed in the attempt. Those books are Beale's and Bennett's; both in their time surgeons to the English South-Sea whale-ships, and both exact and reliable men. The original matter touching the sperm whale to be found in their volumes is necessarily small; but so far as it goes, it is of excellent quality, though mostly confined to scientific description. As yet, however, the sperm whale, scientific or poetic, lives not complete in any literature. Far above all other hunted whales, his is an unwritten life.

Now the various species of whales need some sort of popular comprehensive classification, if only an easy outline one for the present, hereafter to be filled in all its departments by subsequent laborers. As no better man advances to take this matter in hand, I hereupon offer my own poor endeavors. I promise nothing complete; because any human thing supposed to be complete must for that very reason infallibly be faulty. I shall not pretend to a minute anatomical description of the various species, or—in this space at least—to much of any description. My object here is simply to project the draft of a systematization of cetology. I am the architect, not the builder.

But it is a ponderous task; no ordinary letter-sorter in the post-office is equal to it. To grope down into the bottom of the sea after them; to have one's hands among the unspeakable foundations, ribs, and very pelvis of the world; this is a fearful thing. What am I that I should essay to hook the nose of this leviathan! The awful tauntings in Job might well appall me. "Will he (the leviathan) make a covenant with thee? Behold the hope of him is vain!" But I have swam through libraries and sailed through oceans; I have had to do with whales with these visible hands; I am in earnest; and I will try. There are some preliminaries to settle.

First: The uncertain, unsettled condition of this science of Cetology is in the very vestibule attested by the fact, that in some quarters it still remains a moot point whether a whale be a fish. In his System of Nature, A.D. 1776, Linnæus declares, "I hereby separate the whales from the fish." But of my own knowledge, I know that down to the year 1850, sharks and shad, alewives and herring, against Linnæus's express edict, were still found dividing the possession of the same seas with the Leviathan.

The grounds upon which Linnæus would fain have banished the whales from the waters, he states as follows: "On account of their warm bilocular heart, their lungs, their movable eyelids, their hollow ears, *penem intrantem feminam mammis lactantem*," and finally, *"ex lege naturae jure meritoque."* I submitted all this to my friends Simeon Macey and Charley Coffin, of Nantucket, both mess-mates of mine in a certain voyage, and they united in the opinion that the reasons set forth were altogether insufficient. Charley profanely hinted they were humbug.

Be it known that, waiving all argument, I take the good old fashioned ground that the whale is a fish, and call upon holy Jonah to back me. This fundamental thing settled, the next point is, in what internal respect does the whale differ from other fish. Above, Linnæus has given you those items. But in brief they are these: lungs and warm blood; whereas, all other fish are lungless and cold blooded.

Next: how shall we define the whale, by his obvious externals, so as conspicuously to label him for all time to come. To be short, then, a whale is *a spouting fish with a horizontal tail*. There you have him. However contracted, that definition is the result of expanded meditation. A walrus spouts much like a whale, but the walrus is not a fish, because he is amphibious. But the last term of the definition is still more cogent, as coupled with the first. Almost anyone must have noticed that all the fish familiar to landsmen have not a flat, but a vertical, or up-and-down tail. Whereas, among spouting fish the tail, though it may be similarly shaped, invariably assumes a horizontal position.

By the above definition of what a whale is, I do by no means exclude from the leviathanic brotherhood any sea creature hitherto identified with the whale by the best informed Nantucketers; nor, on the other hand, link with it any fish hitherto authoritatively regarded as alien.[1] Hence, all the smaller, spouting, and horizontal tailed fish must be included in this ground-plan of Cetology. Now, then, come the grand divisions of the entire whale host.

First: According to magnitude I divide the whales into three primary BOOKS (subdivisible into CHAPTERS), and these shall comprehend them all, both small and large.

I. THE FOLIO WHALE; II. the OCTAVO WHALE; III. the DUODECIMA WHALE.

As the type of the FOLIO I present the *Sperm Whale*; of the OCTAVO, the *Grampus*; of the DUODECIMO, the *Porpoise*.

FOLIOS. Among these I here include the following chapters: I. The *Sperm Whale*; II. the *Right Whale*; III. the *Fin Back Whale*; IV. the *Hump-backed Whale*; V. the *Razor Back Whale*; VI. the *Sulfur Bottom Whale*.

BOOK I. (*Folio*), CHAPTER I. (*Sperm Whale*).—This whale, among the English of old vaguely known as the Trumpa whale, and the Physeter whale, and the Anvil Headed whale, is the present Cachalot of the French, and the Pottsfich of the Germans, and the Macrocephalus of the

1. I am aware that down to the present time, the fish styled Lamatins and Dugongs (Pig-fish and Sow-fish of the Coffins of Nantucket) are included by many naturalists among the whales. But as these pig-fish are a noisy, contemptible set, mostly lurking in the mouths of rivers, and feeding on wet hay, and especially as they do not spout, I deny their credentials as whales; and have presented them with their passports to quit the Kingdom of Cetology.

Long Words. He is, without doubt, the largest inhabitant of the globe; the most formidable of all whales to encounter; the most majestic in aspect; and lastly, by far the most valuable in commerce; he being the only creature from which that valuable substance, spermaceti, is obtained. All his peculiarities will, in many other places, be enlarged upon. It is chiefly with his name that I now have to do. Philologically considered, it is absurd. Some centuries ago, when the sperm whale was almost wholly unknown in his own proper individuality, and when his oil was only accidentally obtained from the stranded fish; in those days spermaceti, it would seem, was popularly supposed to be derived from a creature identical with the one then known in England as the Greenland or Right Whale. It was the idea also, that this same spermaceti was that quickening humor of the Greenland Whale which the first syllable of the word literally expresses. In those times, also, spermaceti was exceedingly scarce, not being used for light, but only as an ointment and medicament. It was only to be had from the druggists as you nowadays buy an ounce of rhubarb. When, as I opine, in the course of time, the true nature of spermaceti became known, its original name was still retained by the dealers; no doubt to enhance its value by a notion so strangely significant of its scarcity. And so the appellation must at last have come to be bestowed upon the whale from which this spermaceti was really derived.

BOOK I. (*Folio*), CHAPTER II. (*Right Whale*).—In one respect this is the most venerable of the leviathans, being the one first regularly hunted by man. It yields the article commonly known as whalebone or baleen; and the oil specially known as "whale oil," an inferior article in commerce. Among the fishermen, he is indiscriminately designated by all the following titles: The Whale; the Greenland Whale; the Black Whale; the Great Whale; the True Whale; the Right Whale. There is a deal of obscurity concerning the identity of the species thus multitudinously baptized. What then is the whale, which I include in the second species of my Folios? It is the Great Mysticetus of the English naturalists; the Greenland Whale of the English Whalemen; the Baliene Ordinaire of the French whalemen; the Growlands Walfish of the Swedes. It is the whale which for more than two centuries past has been hunted by the Dutch and English in the Arctic seas; it is the whale which the American fishermen have long pursued in the Indian ocean, on the Brazil Banks, on the Nor'West Coast, and various other parts of the world, designated by them Right Whale Cruising-Grounds.

Some pretend to see a difference between the Greenland whale of the English and the right whale of the Americans. But they precisely agree in all their grand features; nor has there yet been presented a single determinate fact upon which to ground a radical distinction. It is by endless subdivisions based upon the most inconclusive differences, that some departments of natural history become so repellingly intricate. The right whale will be elsewhere treated of at some length, with reference to elucidating the sperm whale.

BOOK I. (*Folio*), CHAPTER III. (*Fin-Back*).—Under this head I reckon a monster which, by the various names of Fin-Back, Tall-Spout, and Long-John, has been seen almost in every sea and is commonly the whale whose distant jet is so often descried by passengers crossing the Atlantic, in the New York Packet-tracks. In the length he attains, and in his baleen, the Fin-back resembles the right whale, but is of a less portly girth, and a lighter color, approaching to olive. His great lips present a cable-like aspect, formed by the intertwisting, slanting folds of large wrinkles. His grand distinguishing feature, the fin, from which he derives his name, is often a conspicuous object. This fin is some three or four feet long, growing vertically from the hinder part of the back, of an angular shape, and with a very sharp pointed end. Even if not the slightest other part of the creature be visible, this isolated fin will, at times, be seen plainly projecting from the surface. When the sea is moderately calm, and slightly marked with spherical ripples, and this gnomon-like fin stands up and casts shadows upon the wrinkled surface, it may well be supposed that the watery circle surrounding it somewhat resembles a dial, with its style and wavy hour-lines graved on it. On that Ahaz-dial the shadow often goes back. The Fin-Back is not gregarious. He seems a whale-hater, as some men are man-haters. Very shy; always going solitary; unexpectedly rising to the surface in the remotest and most sullen waters; his straight and single lofty jet rising like a tall misanthropic spear upon a barren plain; gifted with such wondrous power and velocity in swimming, as to defy all present pursuit from man; this leviathan seems the banished and unconquerable Cain of his race, bearing for his mark that style upon his back. From having the baleen in his mouth, the Fin-Back is sometimes included with the right whale, among a theoretic species denominated *Whalebone whales*, that is, whales with baleen. Of these so-called Whalebone whales, there would seem to be several varieties, most of which, however, are little known. Broad-nosed whales and beaked whales; pike-headed whales; bunched whales; under-jawed whales and rostrated whales, are the fisherman's names for a few sorts.

In connection with this appellative of "Whalebone whales," it is of great importance to mention, that however such a nomenclature may be convenient in facilitating allusions to some kind of whales, yet it is in vain to attempt a clear classification of the Leviathan, founded upon either his baleen, or hump, or fin, or teeth; notwithstanding that those marked parts or features very obviously seem better adapted to afford the basis for a regular system of Cetology than any other detached bodily distinctions, which the whale, in his kinds, presents. How then? The baleen, hump, back-fin, and teeth; these are things whose peculiarities are indiscriminately dispersed among all sorts of whales, without any regard to what may be the nature of their structure in other and more essential particulars. Thus, the sperm whale and the humpbacked whale, each has a hump; but there the similitude ceases. Then, this same humpbacked whale and the Greenland whale, each of these has baleen; but there again the similitude ceases. And it is just the same with the other parts abovementioned. In various sorts of whales, they form such irregular combinations; or, in the case of any one of them detached, such an irregular isolation; as utterly to defy all general methodization formed upon such a basis. On this rock every one of the whale-naturalists has split.

But it may possibly be conceived that, in the internal parts of the whale, in his anatomy—there, at least, we shall be able to hit the right classification. Nay; what thing, for example, is there in the Greenland whale's anatomy more striking than his baleen? Yet we have seen that by his baleen it is impossible correctly to classify the Greenland whale. And if you descend into the bowels of the various leviathans, why there you will not find distinctions a fiftieth part as available to the systematizer as those external ones already enumerated. What then remains? nothing but to take hold of the whales bodily, in their entire liberal volume, and boldly sort them that way. And this is the bibliographical system here adopted; and it is the only one that can possibly succeed, for it alone is practicable. To proceed.

BOOK I. (*Folio*) CHAPTER IV. (*Humpback*).—This whale is often seen on the northern American coast. He has been frequently captured there, and towed into harbor. He has a great pack on him like a peddler; or you might call him the Elephant and Castle whale. At any rate, the popular name for him does not sufficiently distinguish him, since the sperm whale also has a hump, though a smaller one. His oil is not very valuable. He has baleen. He is the most gamesome and lighthearted of all the whales, making more gay foam and white water generally than any other of them.

BOOK I. (*Folio*), CHAPTER V. (*Razor Back*).—Of this whale little is known but his name. I have seen him at a distance off Cape Horn. Of a retiring nature, he eludes both hunters and philosophers. Though no coward, he has never yet shown any part of him but his back, which rises in a long sharp ridge. Let him go. I know little more of him, nor does anybody else.

BOOK I. (*Folio*), CHAPTER VI. (*Sulfur Bottom*).—Another retiring gentleman, with a brimstone belly, doubtless got by scraping along the Tartarian tiles in some of his profounder divings. He is seldom seen; at least I have never seen him except in the remoter southern seas, and then always at too great a distance to study his countenance. He is never chased; he would run away with rope-walks of line. Prodigies are told of him. Adieu, Sulfur Bottom! I can say nothing more that is true of ye, nor can the oldest Nantucketer.

Thus ends BOOK I. (*Folio*), and now begins BOOK II. (*Octavo*).

OCTAVOES.[1] These embrace the whales of middling magnitude, among which at present may be numbered: I. the *Grampus*; II. the *Black Fish*; III. the *Narwhale*; IV. the *Thrasher*; V. the *Killer*.

BOOK II. (*Octavo*), CHAPTER I. (*Grampus*).—Though this fish, whose loud sonorous breathing, or rather blowing, has furnished a proverb to landsmen, is so well known a denizen of the deep, yet is he not popularly classed among whales. But possessing all the grand distinctive features of the leviathan, most naturalists have recognized him for one. He is of moderate octavo size, varying from fifteen to twenty-five feet in length, and of corresponding dimensions round the waist. He swims in herds; he is never regularly hunted, though his oil is considerable in quantity, and pretty good for light. By some fishermen his approach is regarded as premonitory of the advance of the great sperm whale.

BOOK II. (*Octavo*), CHAPTER II. (*Black Fish*).—I give the popular fishermen's names for all these fish, for generally they are the best. Where any name happens to be vague or inexpressive, I shall say so, and suggest another. I do so now touching the Black Fish, so called because blackness is the rule among almost all whales. So, call him the Hyena Whale, if you please. His voracity is well known, and from the circumstance that the inner angles of his lips are curved upwards, he carries an everlasting Mephistophelean grin on his face. This whale averages some sixteen or eighteen feet in length. He is found in almost all latitudes. He has a peculiar way of showing his dorsal hooked fin in swimming, which looks something like a Roman nose. When not more profitably employed, the sperm-whale hunters sometimes capture the Hyena Whale, to keep up the supply of cheap oil for domestic employment—as some frugal housekeepers, in the absence of company, and quite alone by themselves, burn unsavory tallow instead of odorous wax. Though their blubber is very thin, some of these whales will yield you upwards of thirty gallons of oil.

BOOK II. (*Octavo*), CHAPTER III. (*Narwhale*), that is, *Nostril Whale*.—Another instance of a curiously named whale, so named I suppose from his peculiar horn being originally mistaken for a peaked nose. The creature is some sixteen feet in length, while its horn averages five feet, though some exceed ten, and even attain to fifteen feet. Strictly speaking, this horn is but a lengthened tusk, growing out from the jaw in a line a little depressed from the horizontal. But it is only found on the sinister side, which has an ill effect, giving its owner something analogous to the aspect of a clumsy left-handed man. What precise purpose this ivory horn or lance answers, it would be hard to say. It does not seem to be used like the blade of the sword-fish and bill-fish; though some sailors tell me that the Narwhale employs it for a rake in turning over the bottom of the sea for food. Charley Coffin said it was used for an ice-piercer; for the Narwhale, rising to the surface of the Polar Sea, and finding it sheeted with ice, thrusts his horn up, and so breaks through. But you cannot prove either of these surmises to be correct. My own opinion is, that however this one-sided horn may really be used by the Narwhale—however that may be—it would certainly be very convenient to him for a folder in reading pamphlets. The Narwhale I have heard called the Tusked whale, the Horned whale, and the Unicorn whale. He is certainly a curious example of the Unicornism to be found in almost every kingdom of animated nature. From certain cloistered old authors I have gathered that this same sea-unicorn's horn was in ancient days regarded as the great antidote against poison, and as such, preparations of it brought immense prices. It was also distilled to a volatile salts for fainting ladies, the same way that the horns of the male deer are manufactured into hartshorn. Originally it was in itself accounted an object of great curiosity. Black Letter tells me that Sir Martin Frobisher on his return from that voyage, when Queen Bess did gallantly wave her jeweled hand to

1. Why this book of whales is not denominated the Quarto is very plain. Because, while the whales of this order, though smaller than those of the former order, nevertheless retain a proportionate likeness to them in figure, yet the bookbinder's Quarto volume in its dimensioned form does not preserve the shape of the Folio volume, but the Octavo volume does.

him from a window of Greenwich Palace, as his bold ship sailed down the Thames; "when Sir Martin returned from that voyage," saith Black Letter, "on bended knees he presented to her highness a prodigious long horn of the Narwhale, which for a long period after hung in the castle at Windsor." An Irish author avers that the Earl of Leicester, on bended knees, did likewise present to her highness another horn, pertaining to a land beast of the unicorn nature.

The Narwhale has a very picturesque, leopard-like look, being of a milk-white ground color, dotted with round and oblong spots of black. His oil is very superior, clear and fine; but there is little of it, and he is seldom hunted. He is mostly found in the circumpolar seas.

BOOK II. (*Octavo*), CHAPTER IV. (*Killer*).—Of this whale little is precisely known to the Nantucketer, and nothing at all to the professed naturalists. From what I have seen of him at a distance, I should say that he was about the bigness of a Grampus. He is very savage—a sort of Fiji fish. He sometimes takes the great Folio whales by the lip, and hangs there like a leech, till the mighty brute is worried to death. The Killer is never hunted. I never heard what sort of oil he has. Exception might be taken to the name bestowed upon this whale, on the ground of its indistinctness. For we are all killers, on land and on sea; Bonapartes and Sharks included.

BOOK II. (*Octavo*), CHAPTER V. (*Thrasher*).—This gentleman is famous for his tail, which he uses for a ferule in thrashing his foes. He mounts the Folio whale's back, and as he swims, he works his passage by flogging him; as some schoolmasters get along in the world by a similar process. Still less is known of the Thrasher than of the Killer. Both are outlaws, even in the lawless seas.

Thus ends BOOK II. (*Octavo*), and begins BOOK III. (*Duodecimo*).

DUODECIMOES.—These include the smaller whales. I. The Huzza Porpoise. II. The Algerine Porpoise. III. The Mealy-mouthed Porpoise.

To those who have not chanced specially to study the subject, it may possibly seem strange, that fishes not commonly exceeding four or five feet should be marshalled among WHALES—a word, which, in the popular sense, always conveys an idea of hugeness. But the creatures set down above as Duodecimoes are infallibly whales, by the terms of my definition of what a whale is—i.e. a spouting fish, with a horizontal tail.

BOOK III. (*Duodecimo*), CHAPTER I. (*Huzza Porpoise*).—This is the common porpoise found almost all over the globe. The name is of my own bestowal; for there are more than one sort of porpoises, and something must be done to distinguish them. I call him thus, because he always swims in hilarious shoals, which upon the broad sea keep tossing themselves to heaven like caps in a Fourth-of-July crowd. Their appearance is generally hailed with delight by the mariner. Full of fine spirits, they invariably come from the breezy billows to windward. They are the lads that always live before the wind. They are accounted a lucky omen. If you yourself can withstand three cheers at beholding these vivacious fish, then heaven help ye; the spirit of godly gamesomeness is not in ye. A well-fed, plump Huzza Porpoise will yield you one good gallon of good oil. But the fine and delicate fluid extracted from his jaws is exceedingly valuable. It is in request among jewelers and watch-makers. Sailors put it on their hones. Porpoise meat is good eating, you know. It may never have occurred to you that a porpoise spouts. Indeed, his spout is so small that it is not very readily discernible. But the next time you have a chance, watch him; and you will then see the great Sperm whale himself in miniature.

BOOK III. (*Duodecimo*), CHAPTER II. (*Algerine Porpoise*).—A pirate. Very savage. He is only found, I think, in the Pacific. He is somewhat larger than the Huzza Porpoise, but much of the same general make. Provoke him, and he will buckle to a shark. I have lowered for him many times, but never yet saw him captured.

BOOK III. (*Duodecimo*), CHAPTER III. (*Mealy-mouthed Porpoise*).—The largest kind of Porpoise; and only found in the Pacific, so far as it is known. The only English name, by which he has hitherto been designated, is that of the fishers—Right-Whale Porpoise, from the circumstance that he is chiefly found in the vicinity of that Folio. In shape, he differs in some degree from the Huzza

Porpoise, being of a less rotund and jolly girth; indeed, he is of quite a neat and gentleman-like figure. He has no fins on his back (most other porpoises have), he has a lovely tail, and sentimental Indian eyes of a hazel hue. But his mealy-mouth spoils him. Though his entire back down to his side fins is of a deep sable, yet a boundary line, distinct as the mark in a ship's hull, called the "bright waist," that line streaks him from stem to stern, with two separate colors, black above and white below. The white comprises part of his head, and the whole of his mouth, which makes him look as if he had just escaped from a felonious visit to a meal-bag. A most mean and mealy aspect! His oil is much like that of the common porpoise.

* * * * *

Beyond the DUODECIMO, this system does not proceed, inasmuch as the Porpoise is the smallest of the whales. Above, you have all the Leviathans of note. But there are a rabble of uncertain, fugitive, half-fabulous whales, which, as an American whaleman, I know by reputation, but not personally. I shall enumerate them by their forecastle appellations; for possibly such a list may be valuable to future investigators, who may complete what I have here but begun. If any of the following whales, shall hereafter be caught and marked, then he can readily be incorporated into this System, according to his Folio, Octavo, or Duodecimo magnitude:—The Bottle-Nose Whale; the Junk Whale; the Pudding-Headed Whale; the Cape Whale; the Leading Whale; the Cannon Whale; the Scragg Whale; the Coppered Whale; the Elephant Whale; the Iseberg Whale; the Quog Whale; the Blue Whale; &c. From Icelandic, Dutch, and old English authorities, there might be quoted other lists of uncertain whales, blessed with all manner of uncouth names. But I omit them as altogether obsolete; and can hardly help suspecting them for mere sounds, full of Leviathanism, but signifying nothing.

Finally: It was stated at the outset, that this system would not be here, and at once, perfected. You cannot but plainly see that I have kept my word. But I now leave my cetological System standing thus unfinished, even as the great Cathedral of Cologne was left, with the cranes still standing upon the top of the uncompleted tower. For small erections may be finished by their first architects; grand ones, true ones, ever leave the cope-stone to posterity. God keep me from ever completing anything. This whole book is but a draft—nay, but the draft of a draft. Oh, Time, Strength, Cash, and Patience!

Chapter XXXIII

THE SPECKSYNDER

CONCERNING THE OFFICERS OF THE WHALE-CRAFT, THIS SEEMS AS GOOD A PLACE AS ANY TO SET down a little domestic peculiarity on shipboard, arising from the existence of the harpooneer class of officers, a class unknown of course in any other marine than the whale-fleet.

The large importance attached to the harpooneer's vocation is evinced by the fact, that originally in the old Dutch Fishery, two centuries and more ago, the command of a whale-ship was not wholly lodged in the person now called the captain, but was divided between him and an officer called the Specksynder. Literally this word means Fat-Cutter; usage, however, in time made it equivalent to Chief Harpooneer. In those days, the captain's authority was restricted to the navigation and general management of the vessel: while over the whale-hunting department and all its concerns, the Specksynder or Chief Harpooneer reigned supreme. In the British Greenland Fishery, under the corrupted title of Specksioneer, this old Dutch official is still retained, but his former dignity is sadly abridged. At present he ranks simply as senior Harpooneer; and as such, is but one of the captain's more inferior subalterns. Nevertheless, as upon the good conduct of the harpooneers the success of a whaling voyage largely depends, and since in the American Fishery he is not only an important officer in the boat, but under certain circumstances (night-watches on a whaling ground) the command of the ship's deck is also his; therefore the grand political maxim of the sea demands, that he should nominally live apart from the men before the mast, and be in some way distinguished as their professional superior; though always, by them, familiarly regarded as their social equal.

Now, the grand distinction drawn between officer and man at sea, is this—the first lives aft, the last forward. Hence, in whale-ships and merchantmen alike, the mates have their quarters with the captain; and so, too, in most of the American whalers the harpooneers are lodged in the after part of the ship. That is to say, they take their meals in the captain's cabin, and sleep in a place indirectly communicating with it.

Though the long period of a Southern whaling voyage (by far the longest of all voyages now or ever made by man), the peculiar perils of it, and the community of interest prevailing among a company, all of whom, high or low, depend for their profits, not upon fixed wages, but upon their common luck, together with their common vigilance, intrepidity, and hard work; though all these things do in some cases tend to beget a less rigorous discipline than in merchantmen generally; yet, never mind how much like an old Mesopotamian family these whalemen may, in some primitive instances, live together; for all that, the punctilious externals, at least, of the quarter-deck are seldom materially relaxed, and in no instance done away. Indeed, many are the Nantucket ships in which you will see the skipper parading his quarter-deck with an elated grandeur not surpassed in any military navy; nay, extorting almost as much outward homage as if he wore the imperial purple, and not the shabbiest of pilot-cloth.

And though of all men the moody captain of the *Pequod* was the least given to that sort of shallowest assumption; and though the only homage he ever exacted, was implicit, instantaneous obedience; though he required no man to remove the shoes from his feet ere stepping upon the quarter-deck; and though there were times when, owing to peculiar circumstances connected with events hereafter to be detailed, he addressed them in unusual terms, whether of condescension or *in terrorem*, or otherwise; yet even Captain Ahab was by no means unobservant of the paramount forms and usages of the sea.

Nor, perhaps, will it fail to be eventually perceived, that behind those forms and usages, as it were, he sometimes masked himself; incidentally making use of them for other and more private ends than they were legitimately intended to subserve. That certain sultanism of his brain, which had otherwise in a good degree remained unmanifested; through those forms that same sultanism became incarnate in an irresistible dictatorship. For be a man's intellectual superiority what it will, it can never assume the practical available supremacy over other men, without the aid of some sort of external arts and entrenchments, always, in themselves, more or less paltry and base. This it is, that forever keeps God's true princes of the Empire from the world's hustings; and leaves the highest honors that this air can give, to those men who become famous more through their infinite inferiority to the choice hidden handful of the Divine Inert, than through their undoubted superiority over the dead level of the mass. Such large virtue lurks in these small things when extreme political superstitions invest them, that in some royal instances even to idiot imbecility they have imparted potency. But when, as in the case of Nicholas the Czar, the ringed crown of geographical empire encircles an imperial brain; then, the plebeian herds crouch abased before the tremendous centralization. Nor will the tragic dramatist who would depict mortal indomitableness in its fullest sweep and direct swing, ever forget a hint, incidentally so important in his art, as the one now alluded to.

But Ahab, my Captain, still moves before me in all his Nantucket grimness and shagginess; and in this episode touching Emperors and Kings, I must not conceal that I have only to do with a poor old whale-hunter like him; and, therefore, all outward majestical trappings and housings are denied me. Oh, Ahab! what shall be grand in thee, it must needs be plucked at from the skies, and dived for in the deep, and featured in the unbodied air!

Chapter XXXIV

The Cabin Table

It is noon; and Dough-Boy, the steward, thrusting his pale loaf-of-bread face from the cabin-scuttle, announces dinner to his lord and master who, sitting in the lee quarter-boat, has just been taking an observation of the sun; and is now mutely reckoning the latitude on the smooth, medallion-shaped tablet, reserved for that daily purpose on the upper part of his ivory leg. From his complete inattention to the tidings, you would think that moody Ahab had not heard his menial. But presently, catching hold of the mizzen shrouds, he swings himself to the deck, and in an even, unexhilarated voice, saying, "Dinner, Mr. Starbuck," disappears into the cabin.

When the last echo of his sultan's step has died away, and Starbuck, the first Emir, has every reason to suppose that he is seated, then Starbuck rouses from his quietude, takes a few turns along the planks, and, after a grave peep into the binnacle, says, with some touch of pleasantness, "Dinner, Mr. Stubb," and descends the scuttle. The second Emir lounges about the rigging awhile, and then slightly shaking the main-brace, to see whether it will be all right with that important rope, he likewise takes up the old burden, and with a rapid "Dinner, Mr. Flask," follows after his predecessors.

But the third Emir, now seeing himself all alone on the quarter-deck, seems to feel relieved from some curious restraint; for, tipping all sorts of knowing winks in all sorts of directions, and kicking off his shoes, he strikes into a sharp but noiseless squall of a hornpipe right over the Grand Turk's head; and then, by a dexterous sleight, pitching his cap up into the mizzen-top for a shelf, he goes down rollicking, so far at least as he remains visible from the deck, reversing all other processions, by bringing up the rear with music. But ere stepping into the cabin-doorway, below, he pauses, ships a new face altogether, and, then, independent, hilarious little Flask enters King Ahab's presence, in the character of Abjectus, or the Slave.

It is not the least among the strange things bred by the intense artificialness of sea-usages, that while in the open air of the deck some officers will, upon provocation, bear themselves boldly and defyingly enough towards their commander; yet, ten to one let those very officers the next moment go down to their customary dinner in that same commander's cabin, and straightway their inoffensive, not to say deprecatory and humble air towards him, as he sits at the head of the table; this is marvelous, sometimes most comical. Wherefore this difference? A problem? Perhaps not. To have been Belshazzar, King of Babylon; and to have been Belshazzar, not haughtily but courteously, therein certainly must have been some touch of mundane grandeur. But he who in the rightly regal and intelligent spirit presides over his own private dinner-table of invited guests, that man's unchallenged power and dominion of individual influence for the time; that man's royalty of state transcends Belshazzar's, for Belshazzar was not the greatest. Who has but once dined his friends, has tasted what it is to be Cæsar. It is a witchery of social czarship which there is no withstanding. Now, if to this consideration you superadd the official supremacy of a ship-master, then, by inference, you will derive the cause of that peculiarity of sea-life just mentioned.

Over his ivory-inlaid table, Ahab presided like a mute, maned sea-lion on the white coral beach, surrounded by his war-like but still deferential cubs. In his own proper turn, each officer waited to be served. They were as little children before Ahab; and yet, in Ahab, there seemed not to lurk the smallest social arrogance. With one mind, their intent eyes all fastened upon the old man's knife, as he carved the chief dish before him. I do not suppose that for the world they would have profaned that moment with the slightest observation, even upon so neutral a topic as the weather. No! And when reaching out his knife and fork, between which the slice of beef was locked, Ahab thereby motioned Starbuck's plate towards him, the mate received his meat as though receiving alms; and cut it tenderly; and a little startled if, perchance, the knife grazed against the plate; and chewed it noiselessly; and swallowed it, not without circumspection. For, like the Coronation banquet at Frankfort, where the German Emperor profoundly dines with the seven Imperial Electors, so these cabin meals were somehow solemn meals, eaten in awful silence; and yet at table old Ahab forbade not conversation; only he himself was dumb. What a relief it was to choking Stubb, when a rat made a sudden racket in the hold below. And poor little Flask, he was the youngest son, and little boy of this weary family party. His were the shin-bones of the saline beef; his would have been the drumsticks. For Flask to have presumed to help himself, this must have seemed to him tantamount to larceny in the first degree. Had he helped himself at that table, doubtless, never more would he have been able to hold his head up in this honest world; nevertheless, strange to say, Ahab never forbade him. And had Flask helped himself, the chances were Ahab had never so much as noticed it. Least of all, did Flask presume to help himself to butter. Whether he thought the owners of the ship denied it to him, on account of its clotting his clear, sunny complexion; or whether he deemed that, on so long a voyage in such marketless waters, butter was at a premium, and therefore was not for him, a subaltern; however it was, Flask, alas! was a butterless man!

Another thing. Flask was the last person down at the dinner and Flask is the first man up. Consider! For hereby Flask's dinner was badly jammed in point of time. Starbuck and Stubb both had the start of him; and yet they also have the privilege of lounging in the rear. If Stubb even, who is but a peg higher than Flask, happens to have but a small appetite, and soon shows symptoms of concluding his repast, then Flask must bestir himself, he will not get more than three mouthfuls that day; for it is against holy usage for Stubb to precede Flask to the deck. Therefore it was that Flask once admitted in private, that ever since he had arisen to the dignity of an officer, from that moment he had never known what it was to be otherwise than hungry, more or less. For what he ate did not so much relieve his hunger, as keep it immortal in him. Peace and satisfaction, thought Flask, have forever departed from my stomach. I am an officer; but, how I wish I could fist a bit of old-fashioned beef in the forecastle, as I used to when I was before the mast. There's the fruits of promotion now; there's the vanity of glory: there's the insanity of life! Besides, if it were so that any mere sailor of the *Pequod* had a grudge against Flask in Flask's official capacity, all that sailor had to do, in order to obtain ample vengeance, was to go aft at dinner-time, and get a peep at Flask through the cabin skylight, sitting silly and dumb-founded before awful Ahab.

Now, Ahab and his three mates formed what may be called the first table in the *Pequod*'s cabin. After their departure, taking place in inverted order to their arrival, the canvas cloth was cleared, or rather was restored to some hurried order by the pallid steward. And then the three harpooneers were bidden to the feast, they being its residuary legatees. They made a sort of temporary servants' hall of the high and mighty cabin.

In strange contrast to the hardly tolerable constraint and nameless invisible domineerings of the captain's table, was the entire care-free license and ease, the almost frantic democracy of those inferior fellows the harpooneers. While their masters, the mates, seemed afraid of the sound of the hinges of their own jaws, the harpooneers chewed their food with such a relish that there was a report to it. They dined like lords; they filled their bellies like Indian ships all day loading with spices. Such portentous appetites had Queequeg and Tashtego, that to fill out the vacancies made by the previous repast, often the pale Dough-Boy was fain to bring on a great baron of salt-junk, seemingly quarried out of the solid ox. And if he were not lively about it, if he did not go with a nimble hop-skip-and-jump, then Tashtego had an ungentlemanly way of accelerating him by darting a fork at his back, harpoonwise. And once Daggoo, seized with a sudden humor, assisted Dough-Boy's memory by snatching him up bodily, and thrusting his head into a great empty wooden trencher, while Tashtego, knife in hand, began laying out the circle preliminary to scalping him. He was naturally a very nervous, shuddering sort of little fellow, this bread-faced steward; the progeny of a bankrupt baker and a hospital nurse. And what with the standing spectacle of the black terrific Ahab, and the periodical tumultuous visitations of these three savages, Dough-Boy's whole life was one continual lip-quiver. Commonly, after seeing the harpooneers furnished with all things they demanded, he would escape from their clutches into his little pantry adjoining, and fearfully peep out at them through the blinds of its door, till all was over.

It was a sight to see Queequeg seated over against Tashtego, opposing his filed teeth to the Indian's; crosswise to them, Daggoo seated on the floor, for a bench would have brought his hearse-plumed head to the low carlines; at every motion of his colossal limbs, making the low cabin frame-work to shake, as when an African elephant goes passenger in a ship. But for all this, the great negro was wonderfully abstemious, not to say dainty. It seemed hardly possible that by such comparatively small mouthfuls he could keep up the vitality diffused through so broad, baronial, and superb a person. But, doubtless, this noble savage fed strong and drank deep of the abounding element of air; and through his dilated nostrils snuffed in the sublime life of the worlds. Not by beef or by bread, are giants made or nourished. But Queequeg, he had a mortal, barbaric smack of the lip in eating—an ugly sound enough—so much so, that the trembling Dough-Boy almost looked to see whether any marks of teeth lurked in his own lean arms. And when he would hear Tashtego singing out for him to produce himself, that his bones might be picked, the simple-witted Steward all but shattered the crockery hanging round him in the pantry, by his sudden fits of the palsy. Nor did the whet-stone which the harpooneers carried in their pockets, for their lances and other weapons; and with which whet-stones, at dinner, they would ostentatiously sharpen their knives; that grating sound did not at all tend to tranquilize poor Dough-Boy. How could he forget that in his Island days, Queequeg, for one, must certainly have been guilty of some murderous, convivial indiscretions. Alas! Dough-Boy! hard fares the white waiter who waits upon cannibals. Not a napkin should he carry on his arm, but a buckler. In good time, though, to his great delight, the three salt-sea warriors would rise and depart; to his credulous, fable-mongering ears, all their martial bones jingling in them at every step, like Moorish scimetars in scabbards.

But, though these barbarians dined in the cabin, and nominally lived there; still, being anything but sedentary in their habits, they were scarcely ever in it except at meal-times, and just before sleeping time, when they passed through it to their own peculiar quarters.

In this one matter, Ahab seemed no exception to most American whale captains, who, as a set, rather incline to the opinion that by rights the ship's cabin belongs to them; and that it is by courtesy alone that anybody else is, at any time, permitted there. So that, in real truth, the mates and harpooneers of the *Pequod* might more properly be said to have lived out of the cabin than in it. For when they did enter it, it was something as a street-door enters a house; turning inwards for a moment, only to be turned out the next; and, as a permanent thing, residing in the open air. Nor did they lose much hereby; in the cabin was no companionship; socially, Ahab was inaccessible. Though nominally included in the census of Christendom, he was still an alien to it. He lived in the world, as the last of the Grisly Bears lived in settled Missouri. And as when Spring and Summer had departed, that wild Logan of the woods, burying himself in the hollow of a tree, lived out the winter there, sucking his own paws; so, in his inclement, howling old age, Ahab's soul, shut up in the caved trunk of his body, there fed upon the sullen paws of its gloom!

Chapter XXXV

The Mast-Head

It was during the more pleasant weather, that in due rotation with the other seamen my first mast-head came round.

In most American whalemen the mast-heads are manned almost simultaneously with the vessel's leaving her port; even though she may have fifteen thousand miles, and more, to sail ere reaching her proper cruising-ground. And if, after a three, four, or five years' voyage she is drawing nigh home with anything empty in her—say, an empty vial even—then, her mast-heads are kept manned to the last; and not till her skysail-poles sail in among the spires of the port, does she altogether relinquish the hope of capturing one whale more.

Now, as the business of standing mast-heads, ashore or afloat, is a very ancient and interesting one, let us in some measure expatiate here. I take it, that the earliest standers of mast-heads were the old Egyptians; because, in all my researches, I find none prior to them. For though their progenitors, the builders of Babel, must doubtless, by their tower, have intended to rear the loftiest mast-head in all Asia, or Africa either; yet (ere the final truck was put to it) as that great stone mast of theirs may be said to have gone by the board, in the dread gale of God's wrath; therefore, we cannot give these Babel builders priority over the Egyptians. And that the Egyptians were a nation of mast-head standers, is an assertion based upon the general belief among archaeologists, that the first pyramids were founded for astronomical purposes; a theory singularly supported by the peculiar stair-like formation of all four sides of those edifices; whereby, with prodigious long upliftings of their legs, those old astronomers were wont to mount to the apex, and sing out for new stars; even as the look-outs of a modern ship sing out for a sail, or a whale just bearing in sight. In Saint Stylites, the famous Christian hermit of old times, who built him a lofty stone pillar in the desert and spent the whole latter portion of his life on its summit, hoisting his food from the ground with a tackle; in him we have a remarkable instance of a dauntless stander-of-mast-heads; who was not to be driven from his place by fogs or frosts, rain, hail, or sleet; but valiantly facing everything out to the last, literally died at his post. Of modern standers-of-mast-heads we have but a lifeless set; mere stone, iron, and bronze men; who, though well capable of facing out a stiff gale, are still entirely incompetent to the business of singing out upon discovering any strange sight. There is Napoleon; who, upon the top of the column of Vendôme, stands with arms folded, some one hundred and fifty feet in the air; careless, now, who rules the decks below; whether Louis Philippe, Louis Blanc, or Louis the Devil. Great Washington, too, stands high aloft on his towering mainmast in Baltimore, and like one of Hercules' pillars, his column marks that point of human grandeur beyond which few mortals will go. Admiral Nelson, also, on a capstan of gun-metal, stands his mast-head in Trafalgar Square; and ever when most obscured by that London smoke, token is yet given that a hidden hero is there; for where there is smoke, must be fire. But neither great Washington, nor Napoleon, nor Nelson, will answer a single hail from below, however madly invoked to befriend by their counsels the distracted decks upon which they gaze; however it may be surmised, that their spirits penetrate through the thick haze of the future, and descry what shoals and what rocks must be shunned.

It may seem unwarrantable to couple in any respect the mast-head standers of the land with those of the sea; but that in truth it is not so, is plainly evinced by an item for which Obed Macy, the sole historian of Nantucket, stands accountable. The worthy Obed tells us, that in the early times of the whale fishery, ere ships were regularly launched in pursuit of the game, the people of that island erected lofty spars along the sea-coast, to which the look-outs ascended by means of nailed cleats, something as fowls go up stairs in a hen-house. A few years ago this same plan was adopted by the Bay whalemen of New Zealand, who, upon descrying the game, gave notice to the ready-manned boats nigh the beach. But this custom has now become obsolete; turn we then to the one proper mast-head, that of a whale-ship at sea. The three mast-heads are kept manned from sun-rise to sun-set; the seamen taking their regular turns (as at the helm), and relieving each other every two hours. In the serene weather of the tropics it is exceedingly pleasant the mast-head: nay, to a dreamy meditative man it is delightful. There you stand, a hundred feet above the silent decks, striding along the deep, as if the masts were gigantic stilts, while beneath you and between your legs, as it were, swim the hugest monsters of the sea, even as ships once sailed between the boots of the famous Colossus at old Rhodes. There you stand, lost in the infinite series of the sea, with nothing ruffled but the waves. The tranced ship indolently rolls; the drowsy trade-winds blow; everything resolves you into languor. For the most part, in this tropic whaling life, a sublime uneventfulness invests you; you hear no news; read no gazettes; extras with startling accounts of commonplaces never delude you into unnecessary excitements; you hear of no domestic afflictions; bankrupt securities; fall of stocks; are never troubled with the thought of what you shall have for dinner—for all your meals for three years and more are snugly stowed in casks, and your bill of fare is immutable.

In one of those southern whalemen, on a long three or four years' voyage, as often happens, the sum of the various hours you spend at the mast-head would amount to several entire months. And it is much to be deplored that the place to which you devote so considerable a portion of the whole term of your natural life, should be so sadly destitute of anything approaching to a cozy inhabitiveness, or adapted to breed a comfortable localness of feeling, such as pertains to a bed, a hammock, a hearse, a sentry box, a pulpit, a coach, or any other of those small and snug contrivances in which men temporarily isolate themselves. Your most usual point of perch is the head of the t' gallant-mast, where you stand upon two thin parallel sticks (almost peculiar to whalemen) called the t' gallant cross trees. Here, tossed about by the sea, the beginner feels about as cozy as he would standing on a bull's horns. To be sure, in cold weather you may carry your house aloft with you in the shape of a watch-coat; but properly speaking the thickest watch-coat is no more of a house than the unclad body; for as the soul is glued inside of its fleshy tabernacle, and cannot freely move about in it, nor even move out of it, without running great risk of perishing (like an ignorant pilgrim crossing the snowy Alps in winter); so a watch-coat is not so much of a house as it is a mere envelope, or additional skin encasing you. You cannot put a shelf or chest of drawers in your body, and no more can you make a convenience closet of your watch-coat.

Concerning all this, it is much to be deplored that the mast-heads of a southern whale-ship are unprovided with those enviable little tents or pulpits, called *crow's nests,* in which the look-outs of a Greenland whaler are protected from the inclement weather of the frozen seas. In the fireside narrative of Captain Sleet, entitled *A Voyage among the Icebergs, in quest of the Greenland Whale, and incidentally for the rediscovery of the Lost Icelandic Colonies of Old Greenland*; in this admirable volume, all standers of mast-heads are furnished with a charmingly circumstantial account of the then recently invented *crow's-nest* of the *Glacier,* which was the name of Captain Sleet's good craft. He called it the *Sleet's crow's-nest,* in honor of himself; he being the original inventor and patentee, and free from all ridiculous false delicacy, and holding that if we call our own children after our own names (we fathers being the original inventors and patentees), so likewise should we denominate after ourselves any other apparatus we may beget. In shape, the Sleet's crow's-nest is something like a large tierce or pipe; it is open above, however, where it is furnished with a movable side-screen to keep to windward of your head in a hard gale. Being fixed on the summit of the mast, you ascend into it through a little trap-hatch in the bottom. On the after side, or side next the stern of the ship, is a comfortable seat, with a locker underneath for umbrellas, comforters, and coats. In front is a leather rack, in which to keep your speaking trumpet, pipe, telescope, and other nautical conveniences. When Captain Sleet in person stood his mast-head in this crow's-nest of his, he tells us that he always had a rifle with him (also fixed in the rack), together with a powder flask and shot, for the purpose of popping off the stray narwhales, or vagrant sea unicorns infesting those waters; for you cannot successfully shoot at them from the deck owing to the resistance of the water, but to shoot down upon them is a very different thing. Now, it was plainly a labor of love for Captain Sleet to describe, as he does, all the little detailed conveniences of his crow's-nest; but though he so enlarges upon many of these, and though he treats us to a very scientific account of his experiments in this crow's-nest, with a small compass he kept there for the purpose of counteracting the errors resulting from what is called the "local attraction" of all binnacle magnets; an error ascribable to the horizontal vicinity of the iron in the ship's planks, and in the *Glacier*'s case, perhaps to there having been so many broken-down blacksmiths among her crew; I say, that though the Captain is very discreet and scientific here, yet, for all his learned "binnacle deviations," "azimuth compass observations," and "approximate errors," he knows very well, Captain Sleet, that he was not so much immersed in those profound magnetic meditations, as to fail being attracted occasionally towards that well replenished little case-bottle, so nicely tucked in on one side of his crow's-nest, within easy reach of his hand. Though, upon the whole, I greatly admire and even love the brave, the honest, and learned Captain; yet I take it very ill of him that he should so utterly ignore that case-bottle, seeing what a faithful friend and comforter it must have been, while with mittened fingers and hooded head he was studying the mathematics aloft there in that bird's nest within three or four perches of the pole.

But if we Southern whale-fishers are not so snugly housed aloft as Captain Sleet and his Greenland-men were; yet that disadvantage is greatly counterbalanced by the widely contrasting serenity of those seductive seas in which we South fishers mostly float. For one, I used to lounge up the rigging very leisurely, resting in the top to have a chat with Queequeg, or anyone else off duty whom I might find there; then ascending a little way further, and throwing a lazy leg over the top-sail yard, take a preliminary view of the watery pastures, and so at last mount to my ultimate destination.

Let me make a clean breast of it here, and frankly admit that I kept but sorry guard. With the problem of the universe revolving in me, how could I—being left completely to myself at such a thought-engendering altitude—how could I but lightly hold my obligations to observe all whale-ships' standing orders, "Keep your weather eye open, and sing out every time."

And let me in this place movingly admonish you, ye ship-owners of Nantucket! Beware of enlisting in your vigilant fisheries any lad with lean brow and hollow eye; given to unseasonable meditativeness; and who offers to ship with the Phædon instead of Bowditch in his head. Beware of such an one, I say; your whales must be seen before they can be killed; and this sunken-eyed young Platonist will tow you ten wakes round the world, and never make you one pint of sperm the richer. Nor are these monitions at all unneeded. For nowadays, the whale-fishery furnishes an asylum for many romantic, melancholy, and absent-minded young men, disgusted with the carking care of earth, and seeking sentiment in tar and blubber. Childe Harold not unfrequently perches himself upon the mast-head of some luckless disappointed whale-ship, and in moody phrase ejaculates:

Roll on, thou deep and dark blue ocean, roll!
Ten thousand blubber-hunters sweep over thee in vain.

Very often do the captains of such ships take those absent-minded young philosophers to task, upbraiding them with not feeling sufficient "interest" in the voyage; half-hinting that they are so hopelessly lost to all honorable ambition, as that in their secret souls they would rather not see whales than otherwise. But all in vain; those young Platonists have a notion that their vision is imperfect; they are short-sighted; what use, then, to strain the visual nerve? They have left their opera-glasses at home.

"Why, thou monkey," said a harpooneer to one of these lads, "we've been cruising now hard upon three years, and thou hast not raised a whale yet. Whales are scarce as hen's teeth whenever thou art up here." Perhaps they were; or perhaps there might have been shoals of them in the far horizon; but lulled into such an opium-like listlessness of vacant, unconscious reverie is this absent-minded youth by the blending cadence of waves with thoughts, that at last he loses his identity; takes the mystic ocean at his feet for the visible image of that deep, blue, bottomless soul, pervading mankind and nature; and every strange, half-seen, gliding, beautiful thing that eludes him; every dimly-discovered, uprising fin of some undiscernible form, seems to him the embodiment of those elusive thoughts that only people the soul by continually flitting through it. In this enchanted mood, thy spirit ebbs away to whence it came; becomes diffused through time and space; like Crammer's sprinkled Pantheistic ashes, forming at last a part of every shore the round globe over.

There is no life in thee, now, except that rocking life imparted by a gently rolling ship; by her, borrowed from the sea; by the sea, from the inscrutable tides of God. But while this sleep, this dream is on ye, move your foot or hand an inch; slip your hold at all; and your identity comes back in horror. Over Descartian vortices you hover. And perhaps, at mid-day, in the fairest weather, with one half-throttled shriek you drop through that transparent air into the summer sea, no more to rise forever. Heed it well, ye Pantheists!

Chapter XXXVI

The Quarter-Deck

(Enter Ahab: Then, all.)

It was not a great while after the affair of the pipe, that one morning shortly after breakfast, Ahab, as was his wont, ascended the cabin-gangway to the deck. There most sea-captains usually walk at that hour, as country gentlemen, after the same meal, take a few turns in the garden.

Soon his steady, ivory stride was heard, as to and fro he paced his old rounds, upon planks so familiar to his tread, that they were all over dented, like geological stones, with the peculiar mark of his walk. Did you fixedly gaze, too, upon that ribbed and dented brow; there also, you would see still stranger foot-prints—the foot-prints of his one unsleeping, ever-pacing thought.

But on the occasion in question, those dents looked deeper, even as his nervous step that morning left a deeper mark. And, so full of his thought was Ahab, that at every uniform turn that he made, now at the main-mast and now at the binnacle, you could almost see that thought turn in him as he turned, and pace in him as he paced; so completely possessing him, indeed, that it all but seemed the inward mold of every outer movement.

"D'ye mark him, Flask?" whispered Stubb; "the chick that's in him pecks the shell. 'Twill soon be out."

The hours wore on;—Ahab now shut up within his cabin; anon, pacing the deck, with the same intense bigotry of purpose in his aspect.

It drew near the close of day. Suddenly he came to a halt by the bulwarks, and inserting his bone leg into the auger-hole there, and with one hand grasping a shroud, he ordered Starbuck to send everybody aft.

"Sir!" said the mate, astonished at an order seldom or never given on shipboard except in some extraordinary case.

"Send everybody aft," repeated Ahab. "Mast-heads, there! come down!"

When the entire ship's company were assembled, and with curious and not wholly unapprehensive faces, were eyeing him, for he looked not unlike the weather horizon when a storm is coming up, Ahab, after rapidly glancing over the bulwarks, and then darting his eyes among the crew, started from his standpoint; and as though not a soul were nigh him resumed his heavy turns upon the deck. With bent head and half-slouched hat he continued to pace, unmindful of the wondering whispering among the men; till Stubb cautiously whispered to Flask, that Ahab must have summoned them there for the purpose of witnessing a pedestrian feat. But this did not last long. Vehemently pausing, he cried:

"What do ye do when ye see a whale, men?"

"Sing out for him!" was the impulsive rejoinder from a score of clubbed voices.

"Good!" cried Ahab, with a wild approval in his tones; observing the hearty animation into which his unexpected question had so magnetically thrown them.

"And what do ye next, men?"

"Lower away, and after him!"

"And what tune is it ye pull to, men?"

"A dead whale or a stove boat!"

More and more strangely and fiercely glad and approving, grew the countenance of the old man at every shout; while the mariners began to gaze curiously at each other, as if marveling how it was that they themselves became so excited at such seemingly purposeless questions.

But, they were all eagerness again, as Ahab, now half-revolving in his pivot-hole, with one hand reaching high up a shroud, and tightly, almost convulsively grasping it, addressed them thus:—

"All ye mast-headers have before now heard me give orders about a white whale. Look ye! d'ye see this Spanish ounce of gold?"—holding up a broad bright coin to the sun—"it is a sixteen dollar piece, men. D'ye see it? Mr. Starbuck, hand me yon top-maul."

While the mate was getting the hammer, Ahab, without speaking, was slowly rubbing the gold piece against the skirts of his jacket, as if to heighten its luster, and without using any words was meanwhile lowly humming to himself, producing a sound so strangely muffled and inarticulate that it seemed the mechanical humming of the wheels of his vitality in him.

Receiving the top-maul from Starbuck, he advanced towards the main-mast with the hammer uplifted in one hand, exhibiting the gold with the other, and with a high raised voice exclaiming: "Whosoever of ye raises me a white-headed whale with a wrinkled brow and a crooked jaw; whosoever of ye raises me that white-headed whale, with three holes punctured in his starboard fluke—look ye, whosoever of ye raises me that same white whale, he shall have this gold ounce, my boys!"

"Huzza! huzza!" cried the seamen, as with swinging tarpaulins they hailed the act of nailing the gold to the mast.

"It's a white whale, I say," resumed Ahab, as he threw down the topmaul: "a white whale. Skin your eyes for him, men; look sharp for white water; if ye see but a bubble, sing out."

All this while Tashtego, Daggoo, and Queequeg had looked on with even more intense interest and surprise than the rest, and at the mention of the wrinkled brow and crooked jaw they had started as if each was separately touched by some specific recollection.

"Captain Ahab," said Tashtego, "that white whale must be the same that some call Moby-Dick."

"Moby-Dick?" shouted Ahab. "Do ye know the White Whale then, Tash?"

"Does he fan-tail a little curious, sir, before he goes down?" said the Gay-Header deliberately.

"And has he a curious spout, too," said Daggoo, "very bushy, even for a parmacetty, and mighty quick, Captain Ahab?"

"And he have one, two, tree—oh! good many iron in him hide, too, Captain," cried Queequeg disjointedly, "all twiske-tee be-twisk, like him—him—" faltering hard for a word, and screwing his hand round and round as though uncorking a bottle—"like him—him—"

"Corkscrew!" cried Ahab, "ay, Queequeg, the harpoons lie all twisted and wrenched in him; ay, Daggoo, his spout is a big one, like a whole shock of wheat, and white as a pile of our Nantucket wool after the great annual sheep-shearing; ay, Tashtego, and he fan-tails like a split jib in a squall. Death and devils! men, it is Moby-Dick ye have seen—Moby-Dick—Moby-Dick!"

"Captain Ahab," said Starbuck, who, with Stubb and Flask, had thus far been eyeing his superior with increasing surprise, but at last seemed struck with a thought which somewhat explained all the wonder. "Captain Ahab, I have heard of Moby-Dick—but it was not Moby-Dick that took off thy leg?"

"Who told thee that?" cried Ahab; then pausing, "Ay, Starbuck; ay, my hearties all round; it was Moby-Dick that dismasted me; Moby-Dick that brought me to this dead stump I stand on now. Ay, ay," he shouted with a terrific, loud, animal sob, like that of a heart-stricken moose; "Ay, ay! it was that accursed White Whale that razeed me; made a poor pegging lubber of me forever and a day!" Then tossing both arms, with measureless imprecations he shouted out: "Ay, ay! and I'll chase him round Good Hope, and round the Horn, and round the Norway Maelstrom, and round perdition's flames before I give him up. And this is what ye have shipped for, men! to chase that White Whale on both sides of land, and over all sides of earth, till he spouts black blood and rolls fin out. What say ye, men, will ye splice hands on it, now? I think ye do look brave."

"Ay, ay!" shouted the harpooneers and seamen, running closer to the excited old man: "A sharp eye for the White Whale; a sharp lance for Moby-Dick!"

"God bless ye," he seemed to half sob and half shout. "God bless ye, men. Steward! go draw the great measure of grog. But what's this long face about, Mr. Starbuck; wilt thou not chase the White Whale? art not game for Moby-Dick?"

"I am game for his crooked jaw, and for the jaws of Death too, Captain Ahab, if it fairly comes in the way of the business we follow; but I came here to hunt whales, not my commander's vengeance. How many barrels will thy vengeance yield thee even if thou gettest it, Captain Ahab? it will not fetch thee much in our Nantucket market."

"Nantucket market! Hoot! But come closer, Starbuck; thou requirest a little lower layer. If money's to be the measurer, man, and the accountants have computed their great counting-house the globe, by girdling it with guineas, one to every three parts of an inch; then, let me tell thee, that my vengeance will fetch a great premium *here!*"

"He smites his chest," whispered Stubb, "what's that for? methinks it rings most vast, but hollow."

"Vengeance on a dumb brute!" cried Starbuck, "that simply smote thee from blindest instinct! Madness! To be enraged with a dumb thing, Captain Ahab, seems blasphemous."

"Hark ye yet again—the little lower layer. All visible objects, man, are but as pasteboard masks. But in each event—in the living act, the undoubted deed—there, some unknown but still reasoning thing puts forth the moldings of its features from behind the unreasoning mask. If man will strike, strike through the mask! How can the prisoner reach outside except by thrusting through the wall? To me, the White Whale is that wall, shoved near to me. Sometimes I think there's naught beyond. But 'tis enough. He tasks me; he heaps me; I see in him outrageous strength, with an inscrutable malice sinewing it. That inscrutable thing is chiefly what I hate; and be the White Whale agent, or be the White Whale principal, I will wreak that hate upon him. Talk not to me of blasphemy, man; I'd strike the sun if it insulted me. For could the sun do that, then could I do the other; since there is ever a sort of fair play herein, jealousy presiding over all creations. But not my master, man, is even that fair play. Who's over me? Truth hath no confines. Take off thine eye! more intolerable than fiends' glarings is a doltish stare! So, so; thou reddenest and palest; my heat has melted thee to anger-glow. But look ye, Starbuck, what is said in heat, that thing unsays itself. There are men from whom warm words are small indignity. I meant not to incense thee. Let it go. Look! see yonder Turkish cheeks of spotted tawn—living, breathing pictures painted by the sun. The Pagan leopards—the unrecking and unworshiping things, that live; and seek, and give no reasons for the torrid life they feel! The crew, man, the crew! Are they not one and all with Ahab, in this matter of the whale? See Stubb! he laughs! See yonder Chilean! he snorts to think of it. Stand up amid the general hurricane, thy one tossed sapling cannot, Starbuck! And what is it? Reckon it. 'Tis but to help strike a fin; no wondrous feat for Starbuck. What is it more? From this one poor hunt, then, the best lance out of all Nantucket, surely he will not hang back, when every fore-mast-hand has clutched a whet-stone. Ah! constrainings seize thee; I see! the billow lifts thee! Speak, but speak!—Ay, ay! thy silence, then, *that* voices thee. (*Aside*) Something shot from my dilated nostrils, he has inhaled it in his lungs. Starbuck now is mine; cannot oppose me now, without rebellion."

"God keep me!—keep us all!" murmured Starbuck, lowly.

But in his joy at the enchanted, tacit acquiescence of the mate, Ahab did not hear his foreboding invocation; nor yet the low laugh from the hold; nor yet the presaging vibrations of the winds in the cordage; nor yet the hollow flap of the sails against the masts, as for a moment their hearts sank in. For again Starbuck's downcast eyes lighted up with the stubbornness of life; the subterranean laugh died away; the winds blew on; the sails filled out; the ship heaved and rolled as before. Ah, ye admonitions and warnings! why stay ye not when ye come? But rather are ye predictions than warnings, ye shadows! Yet not so much predictions from without, as verifications of the foregoing things within. For with little external to constrain us, the innermost necessities in our being, these still drive us on.

"The measure! the measure!" cried Ahab.

Receiving the brimming pewter, and turning to the harpooneers, he ordered them to produce their weapons. Then ranging them before him near the capstan, with their harpoons in their hands, while his three mates stood at his side with their lances, and the rest of the ship's company formed a circle round the group; he stood for an instant searchingly eyeing every man of his crew. But those wild eyes met his, as the blood-shot eyes of the prairie wolves meet the eye of their leader, ere he rushes on at their head in the trail of the bison; but, alas! only to fall into the hidden snare of the Indian.

"Drink and pass!" he cried, handing the heavy charged flagon to the nearest seaman. "The crew alone now drink. Round with it, round! Short drafts—long swallows, men; 'tis hot as Satan's hoof. So, so; it goes round excellently. It spiralizes in ye; forks out at the serpent-snapping eye. Well done; almost drained. That way it went, this way it comes. Hand it me—here's a hollow! Men, ye seem the years; so brimming life is gulped and gone. Steward, refill!

"Attend now, my braves. I have mustered ye all round this capstan; and ye mates, flank me with your lances; and ye harpooneers, stand there with your irons; and ye, stout mariners, ring me in, that I may in some sort revive a noble custom of my fisherman fathers before me. O men, you will yet see that—Ha! boy, come back? bad pennies come not sooner. Hand it me. Why, now, this pewter had run brimming again, wer't not thou St. Vitus' imp—away, thou ague!

"Advance, ye mates! Cross your lances full before me. Well done! Let me touch the axis." So saying, with extended arm, he grasped the three level, radiating lances at their crossed center; while so doing, suddenly and nervously twitched them; meanwhile, glancing intently from Starbuck to Stubb; from Stubb to Flask. It seemed as though, by some nameless, interior volition, he would fain have shocked into them the same fiery emotion accumulated within the Leyden jar of his own magnetic life. The three mates quailed before his strong, sustained, and mystic aspect. Stubb and Flask looked sideways from him; the honest eye of Starbuck fell downright.

"In vain!" cried Ahab; "but, maybe, 'tis well. For did ye three but once take the full-forced shock, then mine own electric thing, *that* had perhaps expired from out me. Perchance, too, it would have dropped ye dead. Perchance ye need it not. Down lances! And now, ye mates, I do appoint ye three cupbearers to my three pagan kinsmen there—yon three most honorable gentlemen and noblemen, my valiant harpooneers. Disdain the task? What, when the great Pope washes the feet of beggars, using his tiara for ewer? Oh, my sweet cardinals! your own condescension, *that* shall bend ye to it. I do not order ye; ye will it. Cut your seizings and draw the poles, ye harpooneers!"

Silently obeying the order, the three harpooneers now stood with the detached iron part of their harpoons, some three feet long, held, barbs up, before him.

"Stab me not with that keen steel! Cant them; cant them over! know ye not the goblet end? Turn up the socket! So, so; now, ye cup-bearers, advance. The irons! take them; hold them while I fill!" Forthwith, slowly going from one officer to the other, he brimmed the harpoon sockets with the fiery waters from the pewter.

"Now, three to three, ye stand. Commend the murderous chalices! Bestow them, ye who are now made parties to this indissoluble league. Ha! Starbuck! but the deed is done! Yon ratifying sun now waits to sit upon it. Drink, ye harpooneers! drink and swear, ye men that man the deathful whale-boat's bow—Death to Moby-Dick! God hunt us all, if we do not hunt Moby-Dick to his death!" The long, barbed steel goblets were lifted; and to cries and maledictions against the White Whale, the spirits were simultaneously quaffed down with a hiss. Starbuck paled, and turned, and shivered. Once more, and finally, the replenished pewter went the rounds among the frantic crew; when, waving his free hand to them, they all dispersed; and Ahab retired within his cabin.

Chapter XXXVII

SUNSET

The cabin; by the stern windows; Ahab sitting alone, and gazing out.

I LEAVE A WHITE AND TURBID WAKE; PALE WATERS, PALER CHEEKS, WHERE'ER I SAIL. THE ENVIOUS billows sidelong swell to whelm my track; let them; but first I pass.

Yonder, by the ever-brimming goblet's rim, the warm waves blush like wine. The gold brow plumbs the blue. The diver sun—slow dived from noon—goes down; my soul mounts up! she wearies with her endless hill. Is, then, the crown too heavy that I wear? this Iron Crown of Lombardy. Yet is it bright with many a gem, I, the wearer, see not its far flashings; but darkly feel that I wear that, that dazzlingly confounds. 'Tis iron—that I know—not gold. 'Tis split, too—that I feel; the jagged edge galls me so, my brain seems to beat against the solid metal; ay, steel skull, mine; the sort that needs no helmet in the most brain-battering fight!

Dry heat upon my brow? Oh! time was, when as the sunrise nobly spurred me, so the sunset soothed. No more. This lovely light, it lights not me; all loveliness is anguish to me, since I can ne'er enjoy. Gifted with the high perception, I lack the low, enjoying power; damned, most subtly and most malignantly! damned in the midst of Paradise! Good-night—good-night! (*waving his hand, he moves from the window.*)

'Twas not so hard a task. I thought to find one stubborn, at the least; but my one cogged circle fits into all their various wheels, and they revolve. Or, if you will, like so many ant-hills of powder, they all stand before me; and I their match. Oh, hard! that to fire others, the match itself must needs be wasting! What I've dared, I've willed; and what I've willed, I'll do! They think me mad—Starbuck does; but I'm demoniac, I am madness maddened! That wild madness that's only calm to comprehend itself! The prophecy was that I should be dismembered; and—Ay! I lost this leg. I now prophesy that I will dismember my dismemberer. Now, then, be the prophet and the fulfiller one. That's more than ye, ye great gods, ever were. I laugh and hoot at ye, ye cricket-players, ye pugilists, ye deaf Burkes and blinded Bendigoes! I will not say as schoolboys do to bullies—Take someone of your own size; don't pommel *me!* No, ye've knocked me down, and I am up again; but *ye* have run and hidden. Come forth from behind your cotton bags! I have no long-gun to reach ye. Come, Ahab's compliments to ye; come and see if ye can swerve me. Swerve me? ye cannot swerve me, else ye swerve yourselves! man has ye there. Swerve me? The path to my fixed purpose is laid with iron rails, whereon my soul is grooved to run. Over unsounded gorges, through the rifled hearts of mountains, under torrents' beds, unerringly I rush! Naught's an obstacle, naught's an angle to the iron way!

Chapter XXXVIII

DUSK

By the Main-mast; Starbuck leaning against it.

MY SOUL IS MORE THAN MATCHED; SHE'S OVERMANNED; AND BY A MADMAN! INSUFFERABLE STING, that sanity should ground arms on such a field! But he drilled deep down, and blasted all my reason out of me! I think I see his impious end; but feel that I must help him to it. Will I, nill I, the ineffable thing has tied me to him; tows me with a cable I have no knife to cut. Horrible old man! Who's over him, he cries;—ay, he would be a democrat to all above; look, how he lords it over all below! Oh! I plainly see my miserable office—to obey, rebelling; and worse yet, to hate with touch of pity! For in his eyes I read some lurid woe would shrivel me up, had I it. Yet is there hope. Time and tide flow wide. The hated whale has the round watery world to swim in, as the small gold-fish has its glassy globe. His heaven-insulting purpose, God may wedge aside. I would up heart, were it not like lead. But my whole clock's run down; my heart the all-controlling weight, I have no key to lift again.

[*A burst of revelry from the forecastle.*]

Oh, God! to sail with such a heathen crew that have small touch of human mothers in them! Whelped somewhere by the sharkish sea. The White Whale is their demigorgon. Hark! the infernal orgies! that revelry is forward! mark the unfaltering silence aft! Methinks it pictures life. Foremost through the sparkling sea shoots on the gay, embattled, bantering bow, but only to drag dark Ahab after it, where he broods within his sternward cabin, builded over the dead water of the wake, and further on, hunted by its wolfish gurglings. The long howl thrills me through! Peace! ye revelers, and set the watch; Oh, life! 'tis in an hour like this, with soul beat down and held to knowledge—as wild, untutored things are forced to feed—Oh, life! 'tis now that I do feel the latent horror in thee! but 'tis not me! that horror's out of me, and with the soft feeling of the human in me, yet will I try to fight ye, ye grim, phantom futures! Stand by me, hold me, bind me, O ye blessed influences!

Chapter XXXIX

First Night-Watch

FORE-TOP

(Stubb solus, and mending a brace.)

HA! HA! HA! HA! HEM! CLEAR MY THROAT!—I'VE BEEN THINKING OVER IT EVER SINCE, AND THAT ha, ha's the final consequence. Why so? Because a laugh's the wisest, easiest answer to all that's queer; and come what will, one comfort's always left—that unfailing comfort is, it's all predestinated. I heard not all his talk with Starbuck; but to my poor eye Starbuck then looked something as I the other evening felt. Be sure the old Mogul has fixed him, too. I twigged it, knew it; had had the gift, might readily have prophesied it—for when I clapped my eye upon his skull I saw it. Well, Stubb, *wise* Stubb—that's my title—well, Stubb, what of it, Stubb? Here's a carcass. I know not all that may be coming, but be it what it will, I'll go to it laughing. Such a waggish leering as lurks in all your horribles! I feel funny. Fa, la! lirra, skirra! What's my juicy little pear at home doing now? Crying its eyes out?—Giving a party to the last arrived harpooneers, I dare-say, gay as a frigate's pennant, and so am I—fa, la! lirra, skirra! Oh—

We'll drink to-night with hearts as light,
To love, as gay and fleeting
As bubbles that swim, on the beaker's brim,
And break on the lips while meeting.

A brave stave that—who calls? Mr. Starbuck? Ay, ay, sir—(*Aside*) he's my superior, he has his too, if I'm not mistaken.—Ay, ay, sir, just through with this job—coming.

Chapter XL

Midnight, Forecastle

HARPOONEERS AND SAILORS

(*Fore-sail rises and discovers the watch standing, lounging, leaning, and lying in various attitudes, all singing in chorus.*)

Farewell and adieu to you, Spanish ladies!
Farewell and adieu to you, ladies of Spain!
Our captain's commanded.—

1ST NANTUCKET SAILOR

Oh, boys, don't be sentimental; it's bad for the digestion! Take a tonic, follow me!

(*Sings, and all follow.*)

Our captain stood upon the deck,
A spy-glass in his hand,
A viewing of those gallant whales
That blew at every strand.
Oh, your tubs in your boats, my boys,
And by your braces stand,
And we'll have one of those fine whales,
Hand, boys, over hand!
So, be cheery, my lads! may your hearts never fail!
While the bold harpooneer is striking the whale!

MATE'S VOICE FROM THE QUARTER-DECK

Eight bells there, forward!

2ND NANTUCKET SAILOR

Avast the chorus! Eight bells there! d'ye hear, bell-boy? Strike the bell eight, thou Pip! thou blackling! and let me call the watch. I've the sort of mouth for that—the hogshead mouth. So, so, (*thrusts his head down the scuttle,*) Star—bo-l-e-e-n-s, a-h-o-y! Eight bells there below! Tumble up!

DUTCH SAILOR

Grand snoozing to-night, maty; fat night for that. I mark this in our old Mogul's wine; it's quite as deadening to some as filliping to others. We sing; they sleep—ay, lie down there, like ground-tier butts. At 'em again! There, take this copper-pump, and hail 'em through it. Tell 'em to avast dreaming of their lassies. Tell 'em it's the resurrection; they must kiss their last, and come to judgment. That's the way—*that's* it; thy throat ain't spoiled with eating Amsterdam butter.

FRENCH SAILOR

Hist, boys! let's have a jig or two before we ride to anchor in Blanket Bay. What say ye? There comes the other watch. Stand by all legs! Pip! little Pip! hurrah with your tambourine!

PIP

(*Sulky and sleepy*)

Don't know where it is.

FRENCH SAILOR

Beat thy belly, then, and wag thy ears. Jig it, men, I say; merry's the word; hurrah! Damn me, won't you dance? Form, now, Indian-file and gallop into the double-shuffle! Throw yourselves! Legs! legs!

ICELAND SAILOR

I don't like your floor, maty; it's too springy to my taste. I'm used to ice-floors. I'm sorry to throw cold water on the subject; but excuse me.

MALTESE SAILOR

Me too; where's your girls? Who but a fool would take his left hand by his right and say to himself, how d'ye do? Partners! I must have partners!

SICILIAN SAILOR

Ay; girls and a green!—then I'll hop with ye; yea, turn grasshopper!

LONG-ISLAND SAILOR

Well, well, ye sulkies, there's plenty more of us. Hoe corn when you may, say I. All legs go to harvest soon. Ah! here comes the music; now for it!

AZORE SAILOR

(*Ascending, and pitching the tambourine up the scuttle.*)

Here you are, Pip; and there's the windlass-bits; up you mount! Now, boys!

(*The half of them dance to the tambourine; some go below; some sleep or lie among the coils of rigging. Oaths aplenty.*)

AZORE SAILOR

(*Dancing*)

Go it, Pip! Bang it, bell-boy! Rig it, dig it, stig it, quig it, bell-boy! Make fire-flies; break the jinglers!

PIP

Jinglers, you say?—there goes another, dropped off; I pound it so.

CHINA SAILOR

Rattle thy teeth, then, and pound away; make a pagoda of thyself.

FRENCH SAILOR

Merry-mad! Hold up thy hoop, Pip, till I jump through it! Split jibs! tear yourselves!

TASHTEGO

(*Quietly smoking*)

That's a white man; he calls that fun: humph! I save my sweat.

OLD MANX SAILOR

I wonder whether those jolly lads bethink them of what they are dancing over. I'll dance over your grave, I will—that's the bitterest threat of your night-women, that beat head-winds round corners. O Christ! to think of the green navies and the green-skulled crews! Well, well; belike the whole world's a ball, as you scholars have it; and so 'tis right to make one ball-room of it. Dance on, lads, you're young; I was once.

3RD NANTUCKET SAILOR

Spell oh!—whew! this is worse than pulling after whales in a calm—give us a whiff, Tash.

(*They cease dancing, and gather in clusters. Meantime the sky darkens—the wind rises.*)

LASCAR SAILOR

By Brahma! boys, it'll be douse sail soon. The sky-born, high-tide Ganges turned to wind! Thou showest thy black brow, Seeva!

MALTESE SAILOR

(*Reclining and shaking his cap*)

It's the waves—the snow's caps turn to jig it now. They'll shake their tassels soon. Now would all the waves were women, then I'd go drown, and chassee with them ever more! There's naught so sweet on earth—heaven may not match it!—as those swift glances of warm, wild bosoms in the dance, when the over-arboring arms hide such ripe, bursting grapes.

SICILIAN SAILOR

(*Reclining*)

Tell me not of it! Hark ye, lad—fleet interlacings of the limbs—lithe swayings—coyings—flutterings! lip! heart! hip! all graze: unceasing touch and go! not taste, observe ye, else come satiety. Eh, Pagan? (*Nudging.*)

TAHITAN SAILOR

(*Reclining on a mat*)

Hail, holy nakedness of our dancing girls!—the Heeva-Heeva! Ah! low veiled, high palmed Tahiti! I still rest me on thy mat, but the soft soil has slid! I saw thee woven in the wood, my mat! green the first day I brought ye thence; now worn and wilted quite. Ah me!—not thou nor I can bear the change! How then, if so be transplanted to yon sky? Hear I the roaring streams from Pirohitee's peak of spears, when they leap down the crags and drown the villages?—The blast! the blast! Up, spine, and meet it! (*Leaps to his feet.*)

PORTUGUESE SAILOR

How the sea rolls swashing 'gainst the side! Stand by for reefing, hearties! the winds are just crossing swords, pell-mell they'll go lunging presently.

DANISH SAILOR

Crack, crack, old ship! so long as thou crackest, thou holdest! Well done! The mate there holds ye to it stiffly. He's no more afraid than the isle fort at Categat, put there to fight the Baltic with storm-lashed guns, on which the sea-salt cakes!

4TH NANTUCKET SAILOR

He has his orders, mind ye that. I heard old Ahab tell him he must always kill a squall, something as they burst a waterspout with a pistol—fire your ship right into it!

ENGLISH SAILOR

Blood! but that old man's a grand old cove! We are the lads to hunt him up his whale!

ALL

Ay! ay!

OLD MANX SAILOR

How the three pines shake! Pines are the hardest sort of tree to live when shifted to any other soil, and here there's none but the crew's cursed clay. Steady, helmsman! steady. This is the sort of weather when brave hearts snap ashore, and keeled hulls split at sea. Our captain has his birth-mark; look yonder, boys, there's another in the sky—lurid-like, ye see, all else pitch black.

DAGGOO

What of that? Who's afraid of black's afraid of me! I'm quarried out of it!

SPANISH SAILOR

(*Aside.*) He wants to bully, ah!—the old grudge makes me touchy. (*Advancing.*) Ay, harpooneer, thy race is the undeniable dark side of mankind—devilish dark at that. No offense.

DAGGOO (*grimly*)

None.

ST. JAGO'S SAILOR

That Spaniard's mad or drunk. But that can't be, or else in his one case our old Mogul's fire-waters are somewhat long in working.

5TH NANTUCKET SAILOR

What's that I saw—lightning? Yes.

SPANISH SAILOR

No; Daggoo showing his teeth.

DAGGOO (*springing*)

Swallow thine, mannikin! White skin, white liver!

SPANISH SAILOR (*meeting him*)

Knife thee heartily! big frame, small spirit!

ALL

A row! a row! a row!

TASHTEGO (*with a whiff*)

A row a'low, and a row aloft—Gods and men—both brawlers! Humph!

BELFAST SAILOR

A row! arrah a row! The Virgin be blessed, a row! Plunge in with ye!

ENGLISH SAILOR

Fair play! Snatch the Spaniard's knife! A ring, a ring!

OLD MANX SAILOR

Ready formed. There! the ringed horizon. In that ring Cain struck Abel. Sweet work, right work! No? Why then, God, mad'st thou the ring?

MATE'S VOICE FROM THE QUARTER-DECK

Hands by the halyards! in top-gallant sails! Stand by to reef top-sails!

ALL

The squall! the squall! jump, my jollies! (*They scatter*)

PIP (*shrinking under the windlass*)

Jollies? Lord help such jollies! Crish, crash! there goes the jib-stay! Blang-whang! God! Duck lower, Pip, here comes the royal yard! It's worse than being in the whirled woods, the last day of the year! Who'd go climbing after chestnuts now? But there they go, all cursing, and here I don't. Fine prospects to 'em; they're on the road to heaven. Hold on hard! Jimmini, what a squall! But those chaps there are worse yet—they are your white squalls, they. White squalls? White Whale, shirr! shirr! Here have I heard all their chat just now, and the White Whale—shirr! shirr!—but spoken of once! and only this evening—it makes me jingle all over like my tambourine—that anaconda of an old man swore 'em in to hunt him! Oh! thou big white God aloft there somewhere in yon darkness, have mercy on this small black boy down here; preserve him from all men that have no bowels to feel fear!

* * * * *

Chapter XLI

MOBY-DICK

I, ISHMAEL, WAS ONE OF THAT CREW; MY SHOUTS HAD GONE UP WITH THE REST; MY OATH HAD BEEN welded with theirs; and stronger I shouted, and more did I hammer and clinch my oath, because of the dread in my soul. A wild, mystical, sympathetical feeling was in me; Ahab's quenchless feud seemed mine. With greedy ears I learned the history of that murderous monster against whom I and all the others had taken our oaths of violence and revenge.

For some time past, though at intervals only, the unaccompanied, secluded White Whale had haunted those uncivilized seas mostly frequented by the Sperm-Whale fishermen. But not all of them knew of his existence; only a few of them, comparatively, had knowingly seen him; while the number who as yet had actually and knowingly given battle to him, was small indeed. For, owing to the large number of whale-cruisers; the disorderly way they were sprinkled over the entire watery circumference, many of them adventurously pushing their quest along solitary latitudes, so as seldom or never for a whole twelvemonth or more on a stretch, to encounter a single news-telling sail of any sort; the inordinate length of each separate voyage; the irregularity of the times of sailing from home; all these, with other circumstances, direct and indirect, long obstructed the spread through the whole world-wide whaling-fleet of the special individualizing tidings concerning Moby-Dick. It was hardly to be doubted, that several vessels reported to have encountered, at such or such a time, or on such or such a meridian, a Sperm Whale of uncommon magnitude and malignity, which whale, after doing great mischief to his assailants, had completely escaped them; to some minds it was not an unfair presumption, I say, that the whale in question must have been no other than Moby-Dick. Yet as of late the Sperm-Whale fishery had been marked by various and not unfrequent instances of great ferocity, cunning, and malice in the monster attacked; therefore it was, that those who by accident ignorantly gave battle to Moby-Dick; such hunters, perhaps, for the most part, were content to ascribe the peculiar terror he bred, more, as it were, to the perils of the Sperm-Whale fishery at large, than to the individual cause. In that way, mostly, the disastrous encounter between Ahab and the whale had hitherto been popularly regarded.

And as for those who, previously hearing of the White Whale, by chance caught sight of him; in the beginning of the thing they had every one of them, almost, as boldly and fearlessly lowered for him, as for any other whale of that species. But at length, such calamities did ensue in these assaults—not restricted to sprained wrists and ankles, broken limbs, or devouring amputations—but fatal to the last degree of fatality; those repeated disastrous repulses, all accumulating and piling their terrors upon Moby-Dick; those things had gone far to shake the fortitude of many brave hunters, to whom the story of the White Whale had eventually come.

Nor did wild rumors of all sorts fail to exaggerate, and still the more horrify the true histories of these deadly encounters. For not only do fabulous rumors naturally grow out of the very body of all surprising terrible events—as the smitten tree gives birth to its fungi; but, in maritime life, far more than in that of terra firma, wild rumors abound, wherever there is any adequate reality for them to cling to. And as the sea surpasses the land in this matter, so the whale fishery surpasses every other sort of maritime life, in the wonderfulness and fearfulness of the rumors which sometimes circulate there. For not only are whalemen as a body unexempt from that ignorance and superstitiousness hereditary to all sailors; but of all sailors, they are by all odds the most directly brought into contact with whatever is appallingly astonishing in the sea; face to face they not only eye its greatest marvels, but, hand to jaw, give battle to them. Alone, in such remotest waters, that though you sailed a thousand miles, and passed a thousand shores, you would not come to any chiseled hearth-stone, or aught hospitable beneath that part of the sun; in such latitudes and longitudes, pursuing too such a calling as he does, the whaleman is wrapped by influences all tending to make his fancy pregnant with many a mighty birth.

No wonder, then, that ever gathering volume from the mere transit over the wildest watery spaces, the outblown rumors of the White Whale did in the end incorporate with themselves all manner of morbid hints, and half-formed foetal suggestions of supernatural agencies, which eventually invested Moby-Dick with new terrors unborrowed from anything that visibly appears. So that in many cases such a panic did he finally strike, that few who by those rumors, at least, had heard of the White Whale, few of those hunters were willing to encounter the perils of his jaw.

But there were still other and more vital practical influences at work. Not even at the present day has the original prestige of the Sperm Whale, as fearfully distinguished from all other species of the leviathan, died out of the minds of the whalemen as a body. There are those this day among them, who, though intelligent and courageous enough in offering battle to the Greenland or Right Whale, would perhaps—either from professional inexperience, or incompetency, or timidity, decline a contest with the Sperm Whale; at any rate, there are plenty of whalemen, especially among those whaling nations not sailing under the American flag, who have never hostilely encountered the Sperm Whale, but whose sole knowledge of the leviathan is restricted to the ignoble monster primitively pursued in the North; seated on their hatches, these men will hearken with a childish fireside interest and awe, to the wild, strange tales of Southern whaling. Nor is the pre-eminent tremendousness of the great Sperm Whale anywhere more feelingly comprehended, than on board of those prows which stem him.

And as if the now tested reality of his might had in former legendary times thrown its shadow before it; we find some book naturalists—Olassen and Povelson—declaring the Sperm Whale not only to be a consternation to every other creature in the sea, but also to be so incredibly ferocious as continually to be athirst for human blood. Nor even down to so late a time as Cuvier's, were these or almost similar impressions effaced. For in his *Natural History,* the Baron himself affirms that at sight of the Sperm Whale, all fish (sharks included) are "struck with the most lively terrors," and "often in the precipitancy of their flight dash themselves against the rocks with such violence as to cause instantaneous death." And however the general experiences in the fishery may amend such reports as these; yet in their full terribleness, even to the blood-thirsty item of Povelson, the superstitious belief in them is, in some vicissitudes of their vocation, revived in the minds of the hunters.

So that overawed by the rumors and portents concerning him, not a few of the fishermen recalled, in reference to Moby-Dick, the earlier days of the Sperm-Whale fishery, when it was oftentimes hard to induce long practiced Right whalemen to embark in the perils of this new and daring warfare; such men protesting that although other leviathans might be hopefully pursued, yet to chase and point lances at such an apparition as the Sperm Whale was not for mortal man. That to attempt it, would be inevitably to be torn into a quick eternity. On this head, there are some remarkable documents that may be consulted.

Nevertheless, some there were, who even in the face of these things were ready to give chase to Moby-Dick; and a still greater number who, chancing only to hear of him distantly and vaguely, without the specific details of any certain calamity, and without superstitious accompaniments, were sufficiently hardy not to flee from the battle if offered.

One of the wild suggestions referred to, as at last coming to be linked with the White Whale in the minds of the superstitiously inclined, was the unearthly conceit that Moby-Dick was ubiquitous; that he had actually been encountered in opposite latitudes at one and the same instant of time.

Nor, credulous as such minds must have been, was this conceit altogether without some faint show of superstitious probability. For as the secrets of the currents in the seas have never yet been divulged, even to the most erudite research; so the hidden ways of the Sperm Whale when beneath the surface remain, in great part, unaccountable to his pursuers; and from time to time have originated the most curious and contradictory speculations regarding them, especially concerning the mystic modes whereby, after sounding to a great depth, he transports himself with such vast swiftness to the most widely distant points.

It is a thing well known to both American and English whale-ships, and as well a thing placed upon authoritative record years ago by Scoresby, that some whales have been captured far north in the Pacific, in whose bodies have been found the barbs of harpoons darted in the Greenland seas. Nor is it to be gainsaid, that in some of these instances it has been declared that the interval of time between the two assaults could not have exceeded very many days. Hence, by inference, it has been believed by some whalemen, that the Nor' West Passage, so long a problem to man, was never a problem to the whale. So that here, in the real living experience of living men, the prodigies related in old times of the inland Strello mountain in Portugal (near whose top there was said to be a lake in which the wrecks of ships floated up to the surface); and that still more wonderful story of the Arethusa fountain near Syracuse (whose waters were believed to have come from the Holy Land by an underground passage); these fabulous narrations are almost fully equaled by the realities of the whaleman.

Forced into familiarity, then, with such prodigies as these; and knowing that after repeated, intrepid assaults, the White Whale had escaped alive; it cannot be much matter of surprise that some whalemen should go still further in their superstitions; declaring Moby-Dick not only ubiquitous, but immortal (for immortality is but ubiquity in time); that though groves of spears should be planted in his flanks, he would still swim away unharmed; or if indeed he should ever be made to spout thick blood, such a sight would be but a ghastly deception; for again in unensanguined billows hundreds of leagues away, his unsullied jet would once more be seen.

But even stripped of these supernatural surmisings, there was enough in the earthly make and incontestable character of the monster to strike the imagination with unwonted power. For, it was not so much his uncommon bulk that so much distinguished him from other sperm whales, but, as was elsewhere thrown out—a peculiar snow-white wrinkled forehead, and a high, pyramidical white hump. These were his prominent features; the tokens whereby, even in the limitless, uncharted seas, he revealed his identity, at a long distance, to those who knew him.

The rest of his body was so streaked, and spotted, and marbled with the same shrouded hue, that, in the end, he had gained his distinctive appellation of the White Whale; a name, indeed, literally justified by his vivid aspect, when seen gliding at high noon through a dark blue sea, leaving a milky-way wake of creamy foam, all spangled with golden gleamings.

Nor was it his unwonted magnitude, nor his remarkable hue, nor yet his deformed lower jaw, that so much invested the whale with natural terror, as that unexampled, intelligent malignity which, according to specific accounts, he had over and over again evinced in his assaults. More than all, his treacherous retreats struck more of dismay than perhaps aught else. For, when swimming before his exulting pursuers, with every apparent symptom of alarm, he had several times been known to turn round suddenly, and, bearing down upon them, either stave their boats to splinters, or drive them back in consternation to their ship.

Already several fatalities had attended his chase. But though similar disasters, however little bruited ashore, were by no means unusual in the fishery; yet, in most instances, such seemed the White Whale's infernal aforethought of ferocity, that every dismembering or death that he caused, was not wholly regarded as having been inflicted by an unintelligent agent.

Judge, then, to what pitches of inflamed, distracted fury the minds of his more desperate hunters were impelled, when amid the chips of chewed boats, and the sinking limbs of torn comrades, they swam out of the white curds of the whale's direful wrath into the serene, exasperating sunlight, that smiled on, as if at a birth or a bridal.

His three boats stove around him, and oars and men both whirling in the eddies; one captain, seizing the line-knife from his broken prow, had dashed at the whale, as an Arkansas duelist at his foe, blindly seeking with a six inch blade to reach the fathom-deep life of the whale. That captain was Ahab. And then it was, that suddenly sweeping his sickle-shaped lower jaw beneath him, Moby-Dick had reaped away Ahab's leg, as a mower a blade of grass in the field. No turbaned Turk, no hired Venetian or Malay, could have smote him with more seeming malice. Small reason was there to doubt, then, that ever since that almost fatal encounter, Ahab had cherished a wild vindictiveness against the whale, all the more fell for that in his frantic morbidness he at last came to identify with him, not only all his bodily woes, but all his intellectual and spiritual exasperations. The White Whale swam before him as the monomaniac incarnation of all those malicious agencies which some deep men feel eating in them, till they are left living on with half a heart and half a lung. That intangible malignity which has been from the beginning; to whose dominion even the modern Christians ascribe one-half of the worlds; which the ancient Ophites of the east reverenced in their statue devil;—Ahab did not fall down and worship it like them; but deliriously transferring its idea to the abhorred White Whale, he pitted himself, all mutilated, against it. All that most maddens and torments; all that stirs up the lees of things; all truth with malice in it; all that cracks the sinews and cakes the brain; all the subtle demonisms of life and thought; all evil, to crazy Ahab, were visibly personified, and made practically assailable in Moby-Dick. He piled upon the whale's white hump the sum of all the general rage and hate felt by his whole race from Adam down; and then, as if his chest had been a mortar, he burst his hot heart's shell upon it.

It is not probable that this monomania in him took its instant rise at the precise time of his bodily dismemberment. Then, in darting at the monster, knife in hand, he had but given loose to a sudden, passionate, corporal animosity; and when he received the stroke that tore him, he probably but felt the agonizing bodily laceration, but nothing more. Yet, when by this collision forced to turn towards home, and for long months of days and weeks, Ahab and anguish lay stretched together in one hammock, rounding in midwinter that dreary, howling Patagonian Cape; then it was, that his torn body and gashed soul bled into one another; and so interfusing, made him mad. That it was only then, on the homeward voyage, after the encounter, that the final monomania seized him, seems all but certain from the fact that, at intervals during the passage, he was a raving lunatic; and though unlimbed of a leg, yet such vital strength yet lurked in his Egyptian chest, and was moreover intensified by his delirium, that his mates were forced to lace him fast, even there, as he sailed, raving in his hammock. In a strait-jacket, he swung to the mad rockings of the gales. And, when running into more sufferable latitudes, the ship, with mild stun-sails spread, floated across the tranquil tropics, and, to all appearances, the old man's delirium seemed left behind him with the Cape Horn swells, and he came forth from his dark den into the blessed light and air; even then, when he bore that firm, collected front, however pale, and issued his calm orders once again; and his mates thanked God the direful madness was now gone; even then, Ahab, in his hidden self, raved on. Human madness is oftentimes a cunning and most feline thing. When you think it fled, it may have but become transfigured into some still subtler form. Ahab's full lunacy subsided not, but deepeningly contracted; like the unabated Hudson, when that noble Northman flows narrowly, but unfathomably through the Highland gorge. But, as in his narrow-flowing monomania, not one jot of Ahab's broad madness had been left behind; so in that broad madness, not one jot of his great natural intellect had perished. That before living agent, now became the living instrument. If such a furious trope may stand, his special lunacy stormed his general sanity, and carried it, and turned all its concentered cannon upon its own mad mark; so that far from having lost his strength, Ahab, to that one end, did now possess a thousandfold more potency than ever he had sanely brought to bear upon any one reasonable object.

This is much; yet Ahab's larger, darker, deeper part remains unhinted. But vain to popularize profundities, and all truth is profound. Winding far down from within the very heart of this spiked Hotel de Cluny where we here stand—however grand and wonderful, now quit it;—and take your way, ye nobler, sadder souls, to those vast Roman halls of Thermes; where far beneath the fantastic towers of man's upper earth, his root of grandeur, his whole awful essence sits in bearded state; an antique buried beneath antiquities, and throned on torsoes! So with a broken throne, the great gods mock that captive king; so like a Caryatid, he patient sits, upholding on his frozen brow the piled entablatures of ages. Wind ye down there, ye prouder, sadder souls! question that proud, sad king! A family likeness! ay, he did beget ye, ye young exiled royalties; and from your grim sire only will the old State-secret come.

Now, in his heart, Ahab had some glimpse of this, namely: all my means are sane, my motive and my object mad. Yet without power to kill, or change, or shun the fact; he likewise knew that to mankind he did now long dissemble; in some sort, did still. But that thing of his dissembling was only subject to his perceptibility, not to his will determinate. Nevertheless, so well did he succeed in that dissembling, that when with ivory leg he stepped ashore at last, no Nantucketer thought him otherwise than but naturally grieved, and that to the quick, with the terrible casualty which had overtaken him.

The report of his undeniable delirium at sea was likewise popularly ascribed to a kindred cause. And so too, all the added moodiness which always afterwards, to the very day of sailing in the *Pequod* on the present voyage, sat brooding on his brow. Nor is it so very unlikely, that far from distrusting his fitness for another whaling voyage, on account of such dark symptoms, the calculating people of that prudent isle were inclined to harbor the conceit, that for those very reasons he was all the better qualified and set on edge, for a pursuit so full of rage and wildness as the bloody hunt of whales. Gnawed within and scorched without, with the infixed, unrelenting fangs of some incurable idea; such an one, could he be found, would seem the very man to dart his iron and lift his lance against the most appalling of all brutes. Or, if for any reason thought to be corporeally incapacitated for that, yet such an one would seem superlatively competent to cheer and howl on his underlings to the attack. But be all this as it may, certain it is, that with the mad secret of his unabated rage bolted up and keyed in him, Ahab had purposely sailed upon the present voyage with the one only and all-engrossing object of hunting the White Whale. Had any one of his old acquaintances on shore but half dreamed of what was lurking in him then, how soon would their aghast and righteous souls have wrenched the ship from such a fiendish man! They were bent on profitable cruises, the profit to be counted down in dollars from the mint. He was intent on an audacious, immitigable, and supernatural revenge.

Here, then, was this gray-headed, ungodly old man, chasing with curses a Job's whale round the world, at the head of a crew, too, chiefly made up of mongrel renegades, and castaways, and cannibals—morally enfeebled also, by the incompetence of mere unaided virtue or right-mindedness in Starbuck, the invulnerable jollity of indifference and recklessness in Stubb, and the pervading mediocrity in Flask. Such a crew, so officered, seemed specially picked and packed by some infernal fatality to help him to his monomaniac revenge. How it was that they so aboundingly responded to the old man's ire—by what evil magic their souls were possessed, that at times his hate seemed almost theirs; the White Whale as much their insufferable foe as his; how all this came to be—what the White Whale was to them, or how to their unconscious understandings, also, in some dim, unsuspected way, he might have seemed the gliding great demon of the seas of life—all this to explain, would be to dive deeper than Ishmael can go. The subterranean miner that works in us all, how can one tell whither leads his shaft by the ever shifting, muffled sound of his pick? Who does not feel the irresistible arm drag? What skiff in tow of a seventy-four can stand still? For one, I gave myself up to the abandonment of the time and the place; but while yet all a-rush to encounter the whale, could see naught in that brute but the deadliest ill.

Chapter XLII

The Whiteness of the Whale

What the White Whale was to Ahab, has been hinted; what, at times, he was to me, as yet remains unsaid.

Aside from those more obvious considerations touching Moby-Dick, which could not but occasionally awaken in any man's soul some alarm, there was another thought, or rather vague, nameless horror concerning him, which at times by its intensity completely overpowered all the rest; and yet so mystical and well-nigh ineffable was it, that I almost despair of putting it in a comprehensible form. It was the whiteness of the whale that above all things appalled me. But how can I hope to explain myself here; and yet, in some dim, random way, explain myself I must, else all these chapters might be naught.

Though in many natural objects, whiteness refiningly enhances beauty, as if imparting some special virtue of its own, as in marbles, japonicas, and pearls; and though various nations have in some way recognized a certain royal pre-eminence in this hue; even the barbaric, grand old kings of Pegu placing the title "Lord of the White Elephants" above all their other magniloquent ascriptions of dominion; and the modern kings of Siam unfurling the same snow-white quadruped in the royal standard; and the Hanoverian flag bearing the one figure of a snow-white charger; and the great Austrian Empire, Cæsarian, heir to overlording Rome, having for the imperial color the same imperial hue; and though this pre-eminence in it applies to the human race itself, giving the white man ideal mastership over every dusky tribe; and though, besides all this, whiteness has been even made significant of gladness, for among the Romans a white stone marked a joyful day; and though in other mortal sympathies and symbolizings, this same hue is made the emblem of many touching, noble things—the innocence of brides, the benignity of age; though among the Red Men of America the giving of the white belt of wampum was the deepest pledge of honor; though in many climes, whiteness typifies the majesty of Justice in the ermine of the Judge, and contributes to the daily state of kings and queens drawn by milk-white steeds; though even in the higher mysteries of the most august religions it has been made the symbol of the divine spotlessness and power; by the Persian fire worshipers, the white forked flame being held the holiest on the altar; and in the Greek mythologies, Great Jove himself being made incarnate in a snow-white bull; and though to the noble Iroquois, the midwinter sacrifice of the sacred White Dog was by far the holiest festival of their theology, that spotless, faithful creature being held the purest envoy they could send to the Great Spirit with the annual tidings of their own fidelity; and though directly from the Latin word for white, all Christian priests derive the name of one part of their sacred vesture, the alb or tunic, worn beneath the cassock; and though among the holy pomps of the Romish faith, white is specially employed in the celebration of the Passion of our Lord; though in the Vision of St. John, white robes are given to the redeemed, and the four-and-twenty elders stand clothed in white before the great white throne, and the Holy One that sitteth there white like wool; yet for all these accumulated associations, with whatever is sweet, and honorable, and sublime, there yet lurks an elusive something in the innermost idea of this hue, which strikes more of panic to the soul than that redness which affrights in blood.

This elusive quality it is, which causes the thought of whiteness, when divorced from more kindly associations, and coupled with any object terrible in itself, to heighten that terror to the furthest bounds. Witness the white bear of the poles, and the white shark of the tropics; what but their smooth, flaky whiteness makes them the transcendent horrors they are? That ghastly whiteness it is which imparts such an abhorrent mildness, even more loathsome than terrific, to the dumb bloating of their aspect. So that not the fierce-fanged tiger in his heraldic coat can so stagger courage as the white-shrouded bear or shark.[1]

Bethink thee of the albatross, whence come those clouds of spiritual wonderment and pale dread, in which that white phantom sails in all imaginations? Not Coleridge first threw that spell; but God's great, unflattering laureate, Nature.[2]

1. With reference to the Polar bear, it may possibly be urged by him who would fain go still deeper into this matter, that it is not the whiteness, separately regarded, which heightens the intolerable hideousness of that brute; for, analyzed, that heightened hideousness, it might be said, only rises from the circumstance, that the irresponsible ferociousness of the creature stands invested in the fleece of celestial innocence and love; and hence, by bringing together two such opposite emotions in our minds, the Polar bear frightens us with so unnatural a contrast. But even assuming all this to be true; yet, were it not for the whiteness, you would not have that intensified terror.

As for the white shark, the white gliding ghostliness of repose in that creature, when beheld in his ordinary moods, strangely tallies with the same quality in the Polar quadruped. This peculiarity is most vividly hit by the French in the name they bestow upon that fish. The Romish mass for the dead begins with "Requiem eternam" (eternal rest), whence *Requiem* denominating the mass itself, and any other funereal music. Now, in allusion to the white, silent stillness of death in this shark, and the mild deadliness of his habits, the French call him *Requin*.

2. I remember the first albatross I ever saw. It was during a prolonged gale, in waters hard upon the Antarctic seas. From my forenoon watch below, I ascended to the overclouded deck; and there, dashed upon the main hatches, I saw a regal, feathery thing of unspotted whiteness, and with a hooked, Roman bill sublime. At intervals, it arched forth its vast archangel wings, as if to embrace some holy ark. Wondrous flutterings and throbbings shook it. Though bodily unharmed, it uttered cries, as some king's ghost in supernatural distress. Through its inexpressible, strange eyes, methought I peeped to secrets which took hold of God. As Abraham before the angels, I bowed myself; the white thing was so white, its wings so wide, and in those forever exiled waters, I had lost the miserable warping memories of traditions and of towns. Long I gazed at the prodigy of plumage. I cannot tell, can only hint, the things that darted through me then. But at last I awoke; and turning, asked a sailor what bird was this. A goney, he replied. Goney! never had heard that name before; is it conceivable that this glorious thing is utterly unknown to men ashore! never! But some time after, I learned that goney was some seaman's name for albatross. So that by no possibility could Coleridge's wild *Rhyme* have had aught to do with those mystical impressions which were mine, when I saw that bird upon our deck. For neither had I then read the *Rhyme,* nor knew the bird to be an albatross. Yet, in saying this, I do but indirectly burnish a little brighter the noble merit of the poem and the poet.

I assert, then, that in the wondrous bodily whiteness of the bird chiefly lurks the secret of the spell; a truth the more evinced in this, that by a solecism of terms there are birds called gray albatrosses; and these I have frequently seen, but never with such emotions as when I beheld the Antarctic fowl.

But how had the mystic thing been caught? Whisper it not, and I will tell; with a treacherous hook and line, as the fowl floated on the sea. At last the Captain made a postman of it; tying a lettered, leathern tally round its neck, with the ship's time and place; and then letting it escape. But I doubt not, that leathern tally, meant for man, was taken off in Heaven, when the white fowl flew to join the wing-folding, the invoking, and adoring cherubim!

Most famous in our Western annals and Indian traditions is that of the White Steed of the Prairies; a magnificent milk-white charger, large-eyed, small-headed, bluff-chested, and with the dignity of a thousand monarchs in his lofty, overscorning carriage. He was the elected Xerxes of vast herds of wild horses, whose pastures in those days were only fenced by the Rocky Mountains and the Alleghanies. At their flaming head he westward trooped it like that chosen star which every evening leads on the hosts of light. The flashing cascade of his mane, the curving comet of his tail, invested him with housings more resplendent than gold and silver-beaters could have furnished him. A most imperial and archangelical apparition of that unfallen western world, which to the eyes of the old trappers and hunters revived the glories of those primeval times when Adam walked majestic as a god, bluff-bowed and fearless as this mighty steed. Whether marching amid his aides and marshals in the van of countless cohorts that endlessly streamed it over the plains, like an Ohio; or whether with his circumambient subjects browsing all around at the horizon, the White Steed gallopingly reviewed them with warm nostrils reddening through his cool milkiness; in whatever aspect he presented himself, always to the bravest Indians he was the object of trembling reverence and awe. Nor can it be questioned from what stands on legendary record of this noble horse, that it was his spiritual whiteness chiefly, which so clothed him with divineness; and that this divineness had that in it which, though commanding worship, at the same time enforced a certain nameless terror.

But there are other instances where this whiteness loses all that accessory and strange glory which invests it in the White Steed and Albatross.

What is it that in the Albino man so peculiarly repels and often shocks the eye, as that sometimes he is loathed by his own kith and kin! It is that whiteness which invests him, a thing expressed by the name he bears. The Albino is as well made as other men—has no substantive deformity—and yet this mere aspect of all-pervading whiteness makes him more strangely hideous than the ugliest abortion. Why should this be so?

Nor, in quite other aspects, does Nature in her least palpable but not the less malicious agencies, fail to enlist among her forces this crowning attribute of the terrible. From its snowy aspect, the gauntleted ghost of the Southern Seas has been denominated the White Squall. Nor, in some historic instances, has the art of human malice omitted so potent an auxiliary. How wildly it heightens the effect of that passage in Froissart, when, masked in the snowy symbol of their faction, the desperate White Hoods of Ghent murder their bailiff in the market-place!

Nor, in some things, does the common, hereditary experience of all mankind fail to bear witness to the supernaturalism of this hue. It cannot well be doubted, that the one visible quality in the aspect of the dead which most appals the gazer, is the marble pallor lingering there; as if indeed that pallor were as much like the badge of consternation in the other world, as of mortal trepidation here. And from that pallor of the dead, we borrow the expressive hue of the shroud in which we wrap them. Nor even in our superstitions do we fail to throw the same snowy mantle round our phantoms; all ghosts rising in a milk-white fog—Yea, while these terrors seize us, let us add, that even the king of terrors, when personified by the evangelist, rides on his pallid horse.

Therefore, in his other moods, symbolize whatever grand or gracious thing he will by whiteness, no man can deny that in its profoundest idealized significance it calls up a peculiar apparition to the soul.

But though without dissent this point be fixed, how is mortal man to account for it? To analyze it, would seem impossible. Can we, then, by the citation of some of those instances wherein this thing of whiteness—though for the time either wholly or in great part stripped of all direct associations calculated to impart to it aught fearful, but nevertheless, is found to exert over us the same sorcery, however modified;—can we thus hope to light upon some chance clue to conduct us to the hidden cause we seek?

Let us try. But in a matter like this, subtlety appeals to subtlety, and without imagination no man can follow another into these halls. And though, doubtless, some at least of the imaginative impressions about to be presented may have been shared by most men, yet few perhaps were entirely conscious of them at the time, and therefore may not be able to recall them now.

Why to the man of untutored ideality, who happens to be but loosely acquainted with the peculiar character of the day, does the bare mention of Whitsuntide marshal in the fancy of such long, dreary speechless processions of slow-pacing pilgrims, downcast and hooded with new-fallen snow. Or to the unread, unsophisticated Protestant of the Middle American States, why does the passing mention of a White Friar or a White Nun evoke such an eyeless statue in the soul?

Or what is there apart from the traditions of dungeoned warriors and kings (which will not wholly account for it) that makes the White Tower of London tell so much more strongly on the imagination of an untraveled American, than those other storied structures, its neighbors—the Byward Tower, or even the Bloody? And those sublimer towers, the White Mountains of New Hampshire, whence, in peculiar moods, comes that gigantic ghostliness over the soul at the bare mention of that name, while the thought of Virginia's Blue Ridge is full of a soft, dewy, distant dreaminess? Or why, irrespective of all latitudes and longitudes, does the name of the White Sea exert such a spectralness over the fancy, while that of the Yellow Sea lulls us with mortal thoughts of long lacquered mild afternoons on the waves, followed by the gaudiest and yet sleepiest of sunsets? Or, to choose a wholly unsubstantial instance, purely addressed to the fancy, why, in reading the old fairy tales of Central Europe, does "the tall pale man" of the Hartz forests, whose changeless pallor unrestingly glides through the green of the groves—why is this phantom more terrible than all the whooping imps of the Blocksburg?

Nor is it, altogether, the remembrance of her cathedral-toppling earthquakes; nor the stampedoes of her frantic seas; nor the tearlessness of arid skies that never rain; nor the sight of her wide field of leaning spires, wrenched cope-stones, and crosses all adroop (like canted yards of anchored fleets); and her suburban avenues of house-walls lying over upon each other, as a tossed pack of cards;—it is not these things alone which make tearless Lima, the strangest, saddest city thou can'st see. For Lima has taken the white veil; and there is a higher horror in this whiteness of her woe. Old as Pizarro, this whiteness keeps her ruins forever new; admits not the cheerful greenness of complete decay; spreads over her broken ramparts the rigid pallor of an apoplexy that fixes its own distortions.

I know that, to the common apprehension, this phenomenon of whiteness is not confessed to be the prime agent in exaggerating the terror of objects otherwise terrible; nor to the unimaginative mind is there aught of terror in those appearances whose awfulness to another mind almost solely consists in this one phenomenon, especially when exhibited under any form at all approaching to muteness or universality. What I mean by these two statements may perhaps be respectively elucidated by the following examples.

First: The mariner, when drawing nigh the coasts of foreign lands, if by night he hear the roar of breakers, starts to vigilance, and feels just enough of trepidation to sharpen all his faculties; but under precisely similar circumstances, let him be called from his hammock to view his ship sailing through a midnight sea of milky whiteness—as if from encircling headlands shoals of combed white bears were swimming round him, then he feels a silent, superstitious dread; the shrouded phantom of the whitened waters is horrible to him as a real ghost; in vain the lead assures him he is still off soundings; heart and helm they both go down; he never rests till blue water is under him again. Yet where is the mariner who will tell thee, "Sir, it was not so much the fear of striking hidden rocks, as the fear of that hideous whiteness that so stirred me?"

Second: To the native Indian of Peru, the continual sight of the snow-howdahed Andes conveys naught of dread, except, perhaps in the mere fancying of the eternal frosted desolateness reigning at such vast altitudes, and the natural conceit of what a fearfulness it would be to lose oneself in such inhuman solitude. Much the same is it with the backwoodsman of the West, who with comparative indifference views an unbounded prairie sheeted with driven snow, no shadow of tree or twig to break the fixed trance of whiteness. Not so the sailor, beholding the scenery of the Antarctic seas; where at times, by some infernal trick of legerdemain in the powers of frost and air, he, shivering and half shipwrecked, instead of rainbows speaking hope and solace to his misery, views what seems a boundless church-yard grinning upon him with its lean ice monuments and splintered crosses.

But thou sayest, methinks this white-lead chapter about whiteness is but a white flag hung out from a craven soul; thou surrenderest to a hypo, Ishmael.

Tell me, why this strong young colt, foaled in some peaceful valley of Vermont, far removed from all beasts of prey—why is it that upon the sunniest day, if you but shake a fresh buffalo robe behind him, so that he cannot even see it, but only smells its wild animal muskiness—why will he start, snort, and with bursting eyes paw the ground in phrensies of affright? There is no remembrance in him of any gorings of wild creatures in his green northern home, so that the strange muskiness he smells cannot recall to him anything associated with the experience of former perils; for what knows he, this New England colt, of the black bisons of distant Oregon?

No: but here thou beholdest even in a dumb brute, the instinct of the knowledge of the demonism in the world. Though thousands of miles from Oregon, still when he smells that savage musk, the rending, goring bison herds are as present as to the deserted wild foal of the prairies, which this instant they may be trampling into dust.

Thus, then, the muffled rollings of a milky sea; the bleak rustlings of the festooned frosts of mountains; the desolate shiftings of the windrowed snows of prairies; all these, to Ishmael, are as the shaking of that buffalo robe to the frightened colt!

Though neither knows where lie the nameless things of which the mystic sign gives forth such hints; yet with me, as with the colt, somewhere those things must exist. Though in many of its aspects this visible world seems formed in love, the invisible spheres were formed in fright.

But not yet have we solved the incantation of this whiteness, and learned why it appeals with such power to the soul; and more strange and far more portentous—why, as we have seen, it is at once the most meaning symbol of spiritual things, nay, the very veil of the Christian's Deity; and yet should be as it is, the intensifying agent in things the most appalling to mankind.

Is it that by its indefiniteness it shadows forth the heartless voids and immensities of the universe, and thus stabs us from behind with the thought of annihilation, when beholding the white depths of the milky way? Or is it, that as in essence whiteness is not so much a color as the visible absence of color; and at the same time the concrete of all colors; is it for these reasons that there is such a dumb blackness, full of meaning, in a wide landscape of snows—a colorless, all-color of atheism from which we shrink? And when we consider that other theory of the natural philosophers, that all other earthly hues—every stately or lovely emblazoning—the sweet tinges of sunset skies and woods; yea, and the gilded velvets of butterflies, and the butterfly cheeks of young girls; all these are but subtle deceits, not actually inherent in substances, but only laid on from without; so that all deified Nature absolutely paints like the harlot, whose allurements cover nothing but the charnel-house within; and when we proceed further, and consider that the mystical cosmetic which produces every one of her hues, the great principle of light, forever remains white or colorless in itself, and if operating without medium upon matter, would touch all objects, even tulips and roses, with its own blank tinge—pondering all this, the palsied universe lies before us a leper; and like willful travelers in Lapland, who refuse to wear colored and coloring glasses upon their eyes, so the wretched infidel gazes himself blind at the monumental white shroud that wraps all the prospect around him. And of all these things the Albino whale was the symbol. Wonder ye then at the fiery hunt?

Chapter XLIII

HARK!

"HIST! DID YOU HEAR THAT NOISE, CABACO?"

It was the middle-watch: a fair moonlight; the seamen were standing in a cordon, extending from one of the fresh-water butts in the waist, to the scuttle-butt near the taffrail. In this manner, they passed the buckets to fill the scuttle-butt. Standing, for the most part on the hallowed precincts of the quarter-deck, they were careful not to speak or rustle their feet. From hand to hand, the buckets went in the deepest silence, only broken by the occasional flap of a sail, and the steady hum of the unceasingly advancing keel.

It was in the midst of this repose, that Archy, one of the cordon, whose post was near the after-hatches, whispered to his neighbor, a Cholo, the words above.

"Hist! did you hear that noise, Cabaco?"

"Take the bucket, will ye, Archy? what noise d'ye mean?"

"There it is again—under the hatches—don't you hear it—a cough—it sounded like a cough."

"Cough be damned! Pass along that return bucket."

"There again—there it is!—it sounds like two or three sleepers turning over, now!"

"Caramba! have done, shipmate, will ye? It's the three soaked biscuits ye eat for supper turning over inside of ye—nothing else. Look to the bucket!"

"Say what ye will, shipmate: I've sharp ears."

"Ay, you are the chap, ain't ye, that heard the hum of the old Quakeress's knitting-needles fifty miles at sea from Nantucket; you're the chap."

"Grin away; we'll see what turns up. Hark ye, Cabaco, there is somebody down in the after-hold that has not yet been seen on deck; and I suspect our old Mogul knows something of it too. I heard Stubb tell Flask, one morning watch, that there was something of that sort in the wind."

"Tish! the bucket!"

Chapter XLIV

THE CHART

HAD YOU FOLLOWED CAPTAIN AHAB DOWN INTO HIS CABIN AFTER THE SQUALL THAT TOOK PLACE on the night succeeding that wild ratification of his purpose with his crew, you would have seen him go to a locker in the transom, and bringing out a large wrinkled roll of yellowish sea charts, spread them before him on his screwed-down table. Then seating himself before it, you would have seen him intently study the various lines and shadings which there met his eye; and with slow but steady pencil trace additional courses over spaces that before were blank. At intervals, he would refer to piles of old log-books beside him, wherein were set down the seasons and places in which, on various former voyages of various ships, sperm whales had been captured or seen.

While thus employed, the heavy pewter lamp suspended in chains over his head, continually rocked with the motion of the ship, and forever threw shifting gleams and shadows of lines upon his wrinkled brow, till it almost seemed that while he himself was marking out lines and courses on the wrinkled charts, some invisible pencil was also tracing lines and courses upon the deeply marked chart of his forehead.

But it was not this night in particular that, in the solitude of his cabin, Ahab thus pondered over his charts. Almost every night they were brought out; almost every night some pencil marks were effaced, and others were substituted. For with the charts of all four oceans before him, Ahab was threading a maze of currents and eddies, with a view to the more certain accomplishment of that monomaniac thought of his soul.

Now, to anyone not fully acquainted with the ways of the leviathans, it might seem an absurdly hopeless task thus to seek out one solitary creature in the unhooped oceans of this planet. But not so did it seem to Ahab, who knew the sets of all tides and currents; and thereby calculating the driftings of the sperm whale's food; and, also calling to mind the regular, ascertained seasons for hunting him in particular latitudes; could arrive at reasonable surmises, almost approaching to certainties, concerning the timeliest day to be upon this or that ground in search of his prey.

So assured, indeed, is the fact concerning the periodicalness of the sperm whale's resorting to given waters, that many hunters believe that, could he be closely observed and studied throughout the world; were the logs for one voyage of the entire whale fleet carefully collated, then the migrations of the sperm whale would be found to correspond in invariability to those of the herring-shoals or the flights of swallows. On this hint, attempts have been made to construct elaborate migratory charts of the sperm whale.[1]

Besides, when making a passage from one feeding-ground to another, the sperm whales, guided by some infallible instinct—say rather, secret intelligence from the Deity—mostly swim in *veins,* as they are called; continuing their way along a given ocean-line with such undeviating exactitude, that no ship ever sailed her course, by any chart, with one tithe of such marvelous precision. Though, in these cases, the direction taken by any one whale be straight as a surveyor's parallel, and though the line of advance be strictly confined to its own unavoidable, straight wake, yet the arbitrary *vein* in which at these times he is said to swim, generally embraces some few miles in width (more or less, as the vein is presumed to expand or contract); but never exceeds the visual sweep from the whale-ship's mast-heads, when circumspectly gliding along this magic zone. The sum is, that at particular seasons within that breadth and along that path, migrating whales may with great confidence be looked for.

And hence not only at substantiated times, upon well known separate feeding-grounds, could Ahab hope to encounter his prey; but in crossing the widest expanses of water between those grounds he could, by his art, so place and time himself on his way, as even then not to be wholly without prospect of a meeting.

There was a circumstance which at first sight seemed to entangle his delirious but still methodical scheme. But not so in the reality, perhaps. Though the gregarious sperm whales have their regular seasons for particular grounds, yet in general you cannot conclude that the herds which haunted such and such a latitude or longitude this year, say, will turn out to be identically the same with those that were found there the preceding season; though there are peculiar and unquestion-

1. Since the above was written, the statement is happily borne out by an official circular, issued by Lieutenant Maury, of the National Observatory, Washington, April 16th, 1851. By that circular, it appears that precisely such a chart is in course of completion; and portions of it are presented in the circular. "This chart divides the ocean into districts of five degrees of latitude by five degrees of longitude; perpendicularly through each of which districts are twelve columns for the twelve months; and horizontally through each of which districts are three lines; one to show the number of days that have been spent in each month in every district, and the two others to show the number of days in which whales, sperm or right, have been seen."

able instances where the contrary of this has proved true. In general, the same remark, only within a less wide limit, applies to the solitaries and hermits among the matured, aged sperm whales. So that though Moby-Dick had in a former year been seen, for example, on what is called the Seychelle ground in the Indian Ocean, or Volcano Bay on the Japanese Coast; yet it did not follow, that were the *Pequod* to visit either of those spots at any subsequent corresponding season, she would infallibly encounter him there. So, too, with some other feeding-grounds, where he had at times revealed himself. But all these seemed only his casual stopping-places and ocean-inns, so to speak, not his places of prolonged abode. And where Ahab's chances of accomplishing his object have hitherto been spoken of, allusion has only been made to whatever way-side, antecedent, extra prospects were his, ere a particular set time or place were attained, when all possibilities would become probabilities, and, as Ahab fondly thought, every possibility the next thing to a certainty. That particular set time and place were conjoined in the one technical phrase—the Season-on-the-Line. For there and then, for several consecutive years, Moby-Dick had been periodically descried, lingering in those waters for awhile, as the sun, in its annual round, loiters for a predicted interval in any one sign of the Zodiac. There it was, too, that most of the deadly encounters with the White Whale had taken place; there the waves were storied with his deeds; there also was that tragic spot where the monomaniac old man had found the awful motive to his vengeance. But in the cautious comprehensiveness and unloitering vigilance with which Ahab threw his brooding soul into this unfaltering hunt, he would not permit himself to rest all his hopes upon the one crowning fact above-mentioned, however flattering it might be to those hopes; nor in the sleeplessness of his vow could he so tranquilize his unquiet heart as to postpone all intervening quest.

Now, the *Pequod* had sailed from Nantucket at the very beginning of the Season-on-the-Line. No possible endeavor then could enable her commander to make the great passage southwards, double Cape Horn, and then running down sixty degrees of latitude arrive in the equatorial Pacific in time to cruise there. Therefore, he must wait for the next ensuing season. Yet the premature hour of the *Pequod*'s sailing had, perhaps, been correctly selected by Ahab, with a view to this very complexion of things. Because, an interval of three hundred and sixty-five days and nights was before him; an interval which, instead of impatiently enduring ashore, he would spend in a miscellaneous hunt; if by chance the White Whale, spending his vacation in seas far remote from his periodical feeding-grounds, should turn up his wrinkled brow off the Persian Gulf, or in the Bengal Bay, or China Seas, or in any other waters haunted by his race. So that Monsoons, Pampas, Nor'Westers, Harmattans, Trades; any wind but the Levanter and Simoon, might blow Moby-Dick into the devious zig-zag world-circle of the *Pequod*'s circumnavigating wake.

But granting all this; yet, regarded discreetly and coolly, seems it not but a mad idea, this; that in the broad boundless ocean, one solitary whale, even if encountered, should be thought capable of individual recognition from his hunter, even as a white-bearded Mufti in the thronged thoroughfares of Constantinople? Yes. For the peculiar snow-white brow of Moby-Dick, and his snow-white hump, could not but be unmistakable. And have I not tallied the whale, Ahab would mutter to himself, as after poring over his charts till long after midnight he would throw himself back in reveries—tallied him, and shall he escape? His broad fins are bored, and scalloped out like a lost sheep's ear! And here, his mad mind would run on in a breathless race; till a weariness and faintness of pondering came over him; and in the open air of the deck he would seek to recover his strength. Ah, God! what trances of torments does that man endure who is consumed with one unachieved revengeful desire. He sleeps with clenched hands; and wakes with his own bloody nails in his palms.

Often when forced from his hammock by exhausting and intolerably vivid dreams of the night, which, resuming his own intense thoughts through the day, carried them on amid a clashing of phrensies, and whirled them round and round and round in his blazing brain, till the very throbbing of his life-spot became insufferable anguish; and when, as was sometimes the case, these spiritual throes in him heaved his being up from its base, and a chasm seemed opening in him, from which forked flames and lightnings shot up, and accursed fiends beckoned him to leap down among them; when this hell in himself yawned beneath him, a wild cry would be heard through the ship; and with glaring eyes Ahab would burst from his state-room, as though escaping from a bed that was on fire. Yet these, perhaps, instead of being the unsuppressible symptoms of some latent weakness, or fright at his own resolve, were but the plainest tokens of its intensity. For, at such times, crazy Ahab, the scheming, unappeasedly steadfast hunter of the White Whale; this Ahab that had gone to his hammock, was not the agent that so caused him to burst from it in horror again. The latter was the eternal, living principle or soul in him; and in sleep, being for the time dissociated from the characterizing mind, which at other times employed it for its outer vehicle or agent, it spontaneously sought escape from the scorching contiguity of the frantic thing, of which, for the time, it was no longer an integral. But as the mind does not exist unless leagued with the soul, therefore it must have been that in Ahab's case, yielding up all his thoughts and fancies to his one supreme purpose; that purpose, by its own sheer inveteracy of will, forced itself against gods and devils into a kind of self-assumed, independent being of its own. Nay, could grimly live and burn, while the common vitality to which it was conjoined, fled horror-stricken from the unbidden and unfathered birth. Therefore, the tormented spirit that glared out of bodily eyes, when what seemed Ahab rushed from his room, was for the time but a vacated thing, a formless somnambulistic being, a ray of living light, to be sure, but without an object to color, and therefore a blankness in itself. God help thee, old man, thy thoughts have created a creature in thee; and he whose intense thinking thus makes him a Prometheus; a vulture feeds upon that heart forever; that vulture the very creature he creates.

Chapter XLV

The Affidavit

So far as what there may be of a narrative in this book; and, indeed, as indirectly touching one or two very interesting and curious particulars in the habits of sperm whales, the foregoing chapter, in its earlier part, is as important a one as will be found in this volume; but the leading matter of it requires to be still further and more familiarly enlarged upon, in order to be adequately understood, and moreover to take away any incredulity which a profound ignorance of the entire subject may induce in some minds, as to the natural verity of the main points of this affair.

I care not to perform this part of my task methodically; but shall be content to produce the desired impression by separate citations of items, practically or reliably known to me as a whaleman; and from these citations, I take it—the conclusion aimed at will naturally follow of itself.

First: I have personally known three instances where a whale, after receiving a harpoon, has effected a complete escape; and, after an interval (in one instance of three years), has been again struck by the same hand, and slain; when the two irons, both marked by the same private cipher, have been taken from the body. In the instance where three years intervened between the flinging of the two harpoons; and I think it may have been something more than that; the man who darted them happening, in the interval, to go in a trading ship on a voyage to Africa, went ashore there, joined a discovery party, and penetrated far into the interior, where he traveled for a period of nearly two years, often endangered by serpents, savages, tigers, poisonous miasmas, with all the other common perils incident to wandering in the heart of unknown regions. Meanwhile, the whale he had struck must also have been on its travels; no doubt it had thrice circumnavigated the globe, brushing with its flanks all the coasts of Africa; but to no purpose. This man and this whale again came together, and the one vanquished the other. I say I, myself, have known three instances similar to this; that is in two of them I saw the whales struck; and, upon the second attack, saw the two irons with the respective marks cut in them, afterwards taken from the dead fish. In the three-year instance, it so fell out that I was in the boat both times, first and last, and the last time distinctly recognized a peculiar sort of huge mole under the whale's eye, which I had observed there three years previous. I say three years, but I am pretty sure it was more than that. Here are three instances, then, which I personally know the truth of; but I have heard of many other instances from persons whose veracity in the matter there is no good ground to impeach.

Secondly: It is well known in the Sperm-Whale Fishery, however ignorant the world ashore may be of it, that there have been several memorable historical instances where a particular whale in the ocean has been at distant times and places popularly cognizable. Why such a whale became thus marked was not altogether and originally owing to his bodily peculiarities as distinguished from other whales; for however peculiar in that respect any chance whale may be, they soon put an end to his peculiarities by killing him, and boiling him down into a peculiarly valuable oil. No; the reason was this: that from the fatal experiences of the fishery there hung a terrible prestige of perilousness about such a whale as there did about Rinaldo Rinaldini, insomuch that most fishermen were content to recognize him by merely touching their tarpaulins when he would be discovered lounging by them on the sea, without seeking to cultivate a more intimate acquaintance. Like some poor devils ashore that happen to known an irascible great man, they make distant unobtrusive salutations to him in the street, lest if they pursued the acquaintance further, they might receive a summary thump for their presumption.

But not only did each of these famous whales enjoy great individual celebrity—nay, you may call it an ocean-wide renown; not only was he famous in life and now is immortal in forecastle stories after death, but he was admitted into all the rights, privileges, and distinctions of a name; had as much a name indeed as Cambyses or Cæsar. Was it not so, O Timor Tom! thou famed leviathan, scarred like an iceberg, who so long did'st lurk in the Oriental straits of that name, whose spout was oft seen from the palmy beach of Ombay? Was it not so, O New Zealand Jack! thou terror of all cruisers that crossed their wakes in the vicinity of the Tattoo Land? Was it not so, O Morquan! King of Japan, whose lofty jet they say at times assumed the semblance of a snow-white cross against the sky? Was it not so, O Don Miguel! thou Chilean whale, marked like an old tortoise with mystic hieroglyphics upon the back! In plain prose, here are four whales as well known to the students of Cetacean History as Marius or Sylla to the classic scholar.

But this is not all. New Zealand Tom and Don Miguel, after at various times creating great havoc among the boats of different vessels, were finally gone in quest of, systematically hunted out, chased and killed by valiant whaling captains, who heaved up their anchors with that express object as much in view, as in setting out through the Narragansett Woods, Captain Butler of old had it in his mind to capture that notorious murderous savage Annawon, the headmost warrior of the Indian King Philip.

I do not know where I can find a better place than just here, to make mention of one or two other things, which to me seem important, as in printed form establishing in all respects the reasonableness of the whole story of the White Whale, more especially the catastrophe. For this is one of those disheartening instances where truth requires full as much bolstering as error. So ignorant are most landsmen of some of the plainest and most palpable wonders of the world, that without some hints touching the plain facts, historical and otherwise, of the fishery, they might scout at Moby-Dick as a monstrous fable, or still worse and more detestable, a hideous and intolerable allegory.

First: Though most men have some vague flitting ideas of the general perils of the grand fishery, yet they have nothing like a fixed, vivid conception of those perils, and the frequency with which they recur. One reason perhaps is, that not one in fifty of the actual disasters and deaths by casualties in the fishery, ever finds a public record at home, however transient and immediately forgotten that record. Do you suppose that that poor fellow there, who this moment perhaps caught by the whale-line off the coast of New Guinea, is being carried down to the bottom of the sea by the sounding leviathan—do you suppose that that poor fellow's name will appear in the newspaper obituary you will read to-morrow at your breakfast? No; because the mails are very irregular between here and New Guinea. In fact, did you ever hear what might be called regular news direct or indirect from New Guinea? Yet I will tell you that upon one particular voyage which I made to the Pacific, among many others we spoke thirty different ships, every one of which had had a death by a whale, some of them more than one, and three that had each lost a boat's crew. For God's sake, be economical with your lamps and candles! not a gallon you burn, but at least one drop of man's blood was spilled for it.

Secondly: People ashore have indeed some indefinite idea that a whale is an enormous creature of enormous power; but I have ever found that when narrating to them some specific example of this two-fold enormousness, they have significantly complimented me upon my facetiousness; when, I declare upon my soul, I had no more idea of being facetious than Moses, when he wrote the history of the plagues of Egypt.

But fortunately the special point I here seek can be established upon testimony entirely independent of my own. That point is this: The Sperm Whale is in some cases sufficiently powerful, knowing, and judiciously malicious, as with direct aforethought to stave in, utterly destroy, and sink a large ship; and what is more, the Sperm Whale *has* done it.

First: In the year 1820 the ship *Essex*, Captain Pollard, of Nantucket, was cruising in the Pacific Ocean. One day she saw spouts, lowered her boats, and gave chase to a shoal of sperm whales. Ere long, several of the whales were wounded; when, suddenly, a very large whale escaping from the boats, issued from the shoal, and bore directly down upon the ship. Dashing his forehead against her hull he so stove her in, that in less than "ten minutes" she settled down and fell over. Not a surviving plank of her has been seen since. After the severest exposure, part of the crew reached the land in their boats. Being returned home at last, Captain Pollard once more sailed for the Pacific in command of another ship, but the gods shipwrecked him again upon unknown rocks and breakers; for the second time his ship was utterly lost, and forthwith forswearing the sea, he has never attempted it since. At this day Captain Pollard is a resident of Nantucket. I have seen Owen Chace, who was chief mate of the *Essex* at the time of the tragedy; I have read his plain and faithful narrative; I have conversed with his son; and all this within a few miles of the scene of the catastrophe.[1]

1. The following are extracts from Chace's narrative: "Every fact seemed to warrant me in concluding that it was anything but chance which directed his operations; he made two several attacks upon the ship, at a short interval between them, both of which, according to their direction, were calculated to do us the most injury, by being made ahead, and thereby combining the speed of the two objects for the shock; to effect which, the exact maneuvers which he made were necessary. His aspect was most horrible, and such as indicated resentment and fury. He came directly from the shoal which we had just before entered, and in which we had struck three of his companions, as if fired with revenge for their sufferings." Again: "At all events, the whole circumstances taken together, all happening before my own eyes, and producing, at the time, impressions in my mind of decided, calculating mischief, on the part of the whale (many of which impressions I cannot now recall), induce me to be satisfied that I am correct in my opinion.

Here are his reflections some time after quitting the ship, during a black night in an open boat, when almost despairing of reaching any hospitable shore. "The dark ocean and swelling waters were nothing; the fears of being swallowed up by some dreadful tempest, or dashed upon hidden rocks, with all the other ordinary subjects of fearful contemplation, seemed scarcely entitled to a moment's thought; this dismal looking wreck, and *the horrid aspect and revenge of the whale*, wholly engrossed my reflections, until day again made its appearance."

In another place—p. 45—he speaks of *"the mysterious and mortal attack of the animal."*

Secondly: The ship *Union,* also of Nantucket, was in the year 1807 totally lost off the Azores by a similar onset, but the authentic particulars of this catastrophe I have never chanced to encounter, though from the whale hunters I have now and then heard casual allusions to it.

Thirdly: Some eighteen or twenty years ago Commodore J——— then commanding an American sloop-of-war of the first class, happened to be dining with a party of whaling captains, on board a Nantucket ship in the harbor of Oahu, Sandwich Islands. Conversation turning upon whales, the Commodore was pleased to be skeptical touching the amazing strength ascribed to them by the professional gentlemen present. He peremptorily denied for example, that any whale could so smite his stout sloop-of-war as to cause her to leak so much as a thimbleful. Very good; but there is more coming. Some weeks later, the Commodore set sail in this impregnable craft for Valparaiso. But he was stopped on the way by a portly sperm whale, that begged a few moments' confidential business with him. That business consisted in fetching the Commodore's craft such a thwack, that with all his pumps going he made straight for the nearest port to heave down and repair. I am not superstitious, but I consider the Commodore's interview with that whale as providential. Was not Saul of Tarsus converted from unbelief by a similar fright? I tell you, the sperm whale will stand no nonsense.

I will now refer you to Langsdorff's *Voyages* for a little circumstance in point, peculiarly interesting to the writer hereof. Langsdorff, you must know by the way, was attached to the Russian Admiral Krusenstern's famous Discovery Expedition in the beginning of the present century. Captain Langsdorff thus begins his seventeenth chapter.

"By the thirteenth of May our ship was ready to sail, and the next day we were out in the open sea, on our way to Ochotsh. The weather was very clear and fine, but so intolerably cold that we were obliged to keep on our fur clothing. For some days we had very little wind; it was not till the nineteenth that a brisk gale from the north-west sprang up. An uncommon large whale, the body of which was larger than the ship itself, lay almost at the surface of the water, but was not perceived by anyone on board till the moment when the ship, which was in full sail, was almost upon him, so that it was impossible to prevent its striking against him. We were thus placed in the most imminent danger, as this gigantic creature, setting up its back, raised the ship three feet at least out of the water. The masts reeled, and the sails fell altogether, while we who were below all sprang instantly upon the deck, concluding that we had struck upon some rock; instead of this we saw the monster sailing off with the utmost gravity and solemnity. Captain D'Wolf applied immediately to the pumps to examine whether or not the vessel had received any damage from the shock, but we found that very happily it had escaped entirely uninjured."

Now, the Captain D'Wolf here alluded to as commanding the ship in question, is a New Englander, who, after a long life of unusual adventures as a sea-captain, this day resides in the village of Dorchester, near Boston. I have the honor of being a nephew of his. I have particularly questioned him concerning this passage in Langsdorff. He substantiates every word. The ship, however, was by no means a large one: a Russian craft built on the Siberian coast, and purchased by my uncle after bartering away the vessel in which he sailed from home.

In that up and down manly book of old-fashioned adventure, so full, too, of honest wonders—the voyage of Lionel Wafer, one of ancient Dampier's old chums—I found a little matter set down so like that just quoted from Langsdorff, that I cannot forbear inserting it here for a corroborative example, if such be needed.

Lionel, it seems, was on his way to "John Ferdinando," as he calls the modern Juan Fernandes. "In our way thither," he says, "about four o'clock in the morning, when we were about one hundred and fifty leagues from the Main of America, our ship felt a terrible shock, which put our men in such consternation that they could hardly tell where they were or what to think; but everyone began to prepare for death. And, indeed, the shock was so sudden and violent, that we took it for granted the ship had struck against a rock; but when the amazement was a little over, we cast the lead and sounded, but found no ground. * * * The suddenness of the shock made the guns leap in their carriages, and several of the men were shaken out of their hammocks. Captain Davis, who lay with his head on a gun, was thrown out of his cabin!" Lionel then goes on to impute the shock to an earthquake, and seems to substantiate the imputation by stating that a great earthquake, somewhere about that time, did actually do great mischief along the Spanish land. But I should not much wonder if, in the darkness of that early hour of the morning, the shock was after all caused by an unseen whale vertically bumping the hull from beneath.

I might proceed with several more examples, one way or another known to me, of the great power and malice at times of the sperm whale. In more than one instance, he has been known, not only to chase the assailing boats back to their ships, but to pursue the ship itself, and long withstand all the lances hurled at him from its decks. The English ship *Pusie Hall* can tell a story on that head; and, as for his strength, let me say, that there have been examples where lines attached to a running sperm have, in a calm, been transferred to the ship, and secured there; the whale towing her great hull through the water, as a horse walks off with a cart. Again, it is very often observed that, if the sperm whale, once struck, is allowed time to rally, he then acts, not so often with blind rage, as with willful, deliberate designs of destruction to his pursuers; nor is it without conveying some eloquent indication of his character, that upon being attacked he will frequently open his mouth, and retain it in that dread expansion for several consecutive minutes. But I must be content with only one more and a concluding illustration; a remarkable and most significant one, by which you will not fail to see, that not only is the most marvelous event in this book corroborated by plain facts of the present day, but that these marvels (like all marvels) are mere repetitions of the ages; so that for the millionth time we say amen with Solomon—Verily there is nothing new under the sun.

In the sixth Christian century lived Procopius, a Christian magistrate of Constantinople, in the days when Justinian was Emperor and Belisarius general. As many know, he wrote the history of his own times, a work every way of uncommon value. By the best authorities, he has always been considered a most trustworthy and unexaggerating historian, except in some one or two particulars, not at all affecting the matter presently to be mentioned.

Now, in this history of his, Procopius mentions that, during the term of his prefecture at Constantinople, a great sea-monster was captured in the neighboring Propontis, or Sea of Marmora, after having destroyed vessels at intervals in those waters for a period of more than fifty years. A fact thus set down in substantial history cannot easily be gainsaid. Nor is there any reason it should be. Of what precise species this sea-monster was, is not mentioned. But as he destroyed ships, as well as for other reasons, he must have been a whale; and I am strongly inclined to think a sperm whale. And I will tell you why. For a long time I fancied that the sperm whale had been always unknown in the Mediterranean and the deep waters connecting with it. Even now I am certain that those seas are not, and perhaps never can be, in the present constitution of things, a place for his habitual gregarious resort. But further investigations have recently proved to me, that in modern times there have been isolated instances of the presence of the sperm whale in the Mediterranean. I am told, on good authority, that on the Barbary coast, a Commodore Davis of the British navy found the skeleton of a sperm whale. Now, as a vessel of war readily passes through the Dardanelles, hence a sperm whale could, by the same route, pass out of the Mediterranean into the Propontis.

In the Propontis, as far as I can learn, none of that peculiar substance called *brit* is to be found, the aliment of the right whale. But I have every reason to believe that the food of the sperm whale—squid or cuttle-fish—lurks at the bottom of that sea, because large creatures, but by no means the largest of that sort, have been found at its surface. If, then, you properly put these statements together, and reason upon them a bit, you will clearly perceive that, according to all human reasoning, Procopius's sea-monster, that for half a century stove the ships of a Roman Emperor, must in all probability have been a sperm whale.

Chapter XLVI

Surmises

Though, consumed with the hot fire of his purpose, Ahab in all his thoughts and actions ever had in view the ultimate capture of Moby-Dick; though he seemed ready to sacrifice all mortal interests to that one passion; nevertheless it may have been that he was by nature and long habituation far too wedded to a fiery whaleman's ways, altogether to abandon the collateral prosecution of the voyage. Or at least if this were otherwise, there were not wanting other motives much more influential with him. It would be refining too much, perhaps, even considering his monomania, to hint that his vindictiveness towards the White Whale might have possibly extended itself in some degree to all sperm whales, and that the more monsters he slew by so much the more he multiplied the chances that each subsequently encountered whale would prove to be the hated one he hunted. But if such a hypothesis be indeed exceptionable, there were still additional considerations which, though not so strictly according with the wildness of his ruling passion, yet were by no means incapable of swaying him.

To accomplish his object Ahab must use tools; and of all tools used in the shadow of the moon, men are most apt to get out of order. He knew, for example, that however magnetic his ascendency in some respects was over Starbuck, yet that ascendency did not cover the complete spiritual man any more than mere corporeal superiority involves intellectual mastership; for to the purely spiritual, the intellectual but stand in a sort of corporeal relation. Starbuck's body and Starbuck's coerced will were Ahab's so long as Ahab kept his magnet at Starbuck's brain; still he knew that for all this the chief mate, in his soul, abhorred his captain's quest, and could he, would joyfully disintegrate himself from it, or even frustrate it. It might be that a long interval would elapse ere the White Whale was seen. During that long interval Starbuck would ever be apt to fall into open relapses of rebellion against his captain's leadership, unless some ordinary, prudential, circumstantial influences were brought to bear upon him. Not only that, but the subtle insanity of Ahab respecting Moby-Dick was noways more significantly manifested than in his superlative sense and shrewdness in foreseeing that, for the present, the hunt should in some way be stripped of that strange imaginative impiousness which naturally invested it; that the full terror of the voyage must be kept withdrawn into the obscure background (for few men's courage is proof against protracted meditation unrelieved by action); that when they stood their long night-watches, his officers and men must have some nearer things to think of than Moby-Dick. For however eagerly and impetuously the savage crew had hailed the announcement of his quest; yet all sailors of all sorts are more or less capricious and unreliable—they live in the varying outer weather, and they inhale its fickleness—and when retained for any object remote and blank in the pursuit, however promissory of life and passion in the end, it is above all things requisite that temporary interests and employments should intervene and hold them healthily suspended for the final dash.

Nor was Ahab unmindful of another thing. In times of strong emotion mankind disdain all base considerations; but such times are evanescent. The permanent constitutional condition of the manufactured man, thought Ahab, is sordidness. Granting that the White Whale fully incites the hearts of this my savage crew, and playing round their savageness even breeds a certain generous knight-errantism in them, still, while for the love of it they give chase to Moby-Dick, they must also have food for their more common, daily appetites. For even the high lifted and chivalric Crusaders of old times were not content to traverse two thousand miles of land to fight for their holy sepulchre, without committing burglaries, picking pockets, and gaining other pious perquisites by the way. Had they been strictly held to their one final and romantic object—that final and romantic object, too many would have turned from in disgust. I will not strip these men, thought Ahab, of all hopes of cash—ay, cash. They may scorn cash now; but let some months go by, and no perspective promise of it to them, and then this same quiescent cash all at once mutinying in them, this same cash would soon cashier Ahab.

Nor was there wanting still another precautionary motive more related to Ahab personally. Having impulsively, it is probable, and perhaps somewhat prematurely revealed the prime but private purpose of the *Pequod*'s voyage, Ahab was now entirely conscious that, in so doing, he had indirectly laid himself open to the unanswerable charge of usurpation; and with perfect impunity, both moral and legal, his crew if so disposed, and to that end competent, could refuse all further obedience to him, and even violently wrest from him the command. From even the barely hinted imputation of usurpation, and the possible consequences of such a suppressed impression gaining ground, Ahab must of course have been most anxious to protect himself. That protection could only consist in his own predominating brain and heart and hand, backed by a heedful, closely calculating attention to every minute atmospheric influence which it was possible for his crew to be subjected to.

For all these reasons then, and others perhaps too analytic to be verbally developed here, Ahab plainly saw that he must still in a good degree continue true to the natural, nominal purpose of the *Pequod*'s voyage; observe all customary usages; and not only that, but force himself to evince all his well known passionate interest in the general pursuit of his profession.

Be all this as it may, his voice was now often heard hailing the three mast-heads and admonishing them to keep a bright look-out, and not omit reporting even a porpoise. This vigilance was not long without reward.

Chapter XLVII

The Mat-Maker

It was a cloudy, sultry afternoon; the seamen were lazily lounging about the decks, or vacantly gazing over into the lead-colored waters. Queequeg and I were mildly employed weaving what is called a sword-mat, for an additional lashing to our boat. So still and subdued and yet somehow preluding was all the scene, and such an incantation of revelry lurked in the air, that each silent sailor seemed resolved into his own invisible self.

I was the attendant or page of Queequeg, while busy at the mat. As I kept passing and repassing the filling or woof of marline between the long yarns of the warp, using my own hand for the shuttle, and as Queequeg, standing sideways, ever and anon slid his heavy oaken sword between the threads, and idly looking off upon the water, carelessly and unthinkingly drove home every yarn: I say so strange a dreaminess did there then reign all over the ship and all over the sea, only broken by the intermitting dull sound of the sword, that it seemed as if this were the Loom of Time, and I myself were a shuttle mechanically weaving and weaving away at the Fates. There lay the fixed threads of the warp subject to but one single, ever returning, unchanging vibration, and that vibration merely enough to admit of the crosswise interblending of other threads with its own. This warp seemed necessity; and here, thought I, with my own hand I ply my own shuttle and weave my own destiny into these unalterable threads. Meantime, Queequeg's impulsive, indifferent sword, sometimes hitting the woof slantingly, or crookedly, or strongly, or weakly, as the case might be;

and by this difference in the concluding blow producing a corresponding contrast in the final aspect of the completed fabric; this savage's sword, thought I, which thus finally shapes and fashions both warp and woof; this easy, indifferent sword must be chance—ay, chance, free will, and necessity—no wise incompatible—all interweavingly working together. The straight warp of necessity, not to be swerved from its ultimate course—its every alternating vibration, indeed, only tending to that; free will still free to ply her shuttle between given threads; and chance, though restrained in its play within the right lines of necessity, and sideways in its motions directed by free will, though thus prescribed to by both, chance by turns rules either, and has the last featuring blow at events.

* * * * *

Thus we were weaving and weaving away when I started at a sound so strange, long-drawn, and musically wild and unearthly, that the ball of free will dropped from my hand, and I stood gazing up at the clouds whence that voice dropped like a wing. High aloft in the cross-trees was that mad Gay-Header, Tashtego. His body was reaching eagerly forward, his hand stretched out like a wand, and at brief sudden intervals he continued his cries. To be sure the same sound was that very moment perhaps being heard all over the seas, from hundreds of whalemen's look-outs perched as high in the air; but from few of those lungs could that accustomed old cry have derived such a marvelous cadence as from Tashtego the Indian's.

As he stood hovering over you half suspended in air, so wildly and eagerly peering towards the horizon, you would have thought him some prophet or seer beholding the shadows of Fate, and by those wild cries announcing their coming.

"There she blows! there! there! there! she blows! she blows!"

"Where-away?"

"On the lee-beam, about two miles off! a school of them!"

Instantly all was commotion.

The Sperm Whale blows as a clock ticks, with the same undeviating and reliable uniformity. And thereby whalemen distinguish this fish from other tribes of his genus.

"There go flukes!" was now the cry from Tashtego; and the whales disappeared.

"Quick, steward!" cried Ahab. "Time! time!"

Dough-Boy hurried below, glanced at the watch, and reported the exact minute to Ahab.

The ship was now kept away from the wind, and she went gently rolling before it. Tashtego reporting that the whales had gone down heading to leeward, we confidently looked to see them again directly in advance of our bows. For that singular craft at times evinced by the Sperm Whale when, sounding with his head in one direction, he nevertheless, while concealed beneath the surface, mills around, and swiftly swims off in the opposite quarter—this deceitfulness of his could not now be in action; for there was no reason to suppose that the fish seen by Tashtego had been in any way alarmed, or indeed knew at all of our vicinity. One of the men selected for shipkeepers—that is, those not appointed to the boats, by this time relieved the Indian at the main-mast-head. The sailors at the fore and mizzen had come down; the line-tubs were fixed in their places; the cranes were thrust out; the main-yard was backed, and the three boats swung over the sea like three samphire baskets over high cliffs. Outside of the bulwarks their eager crews with one hand clung to the rail, while one foot was expectantly poised on the gunwale. So look the long line of man-of-war's men about to throw themselves on board an enemy's ship.

But at this critical instant a sudden exclamation was heard that took every eye from the whale. With a start all glared at dark Ahab, who was surrounded by five dusky phantoms that seemed fresh formed out of air.

Chapter XLVIII

THE FIRST LOWERING

THE PHANTOMS, FOR SO THEY THEN SEEMED, WERE FLITTING ON THE OTHER SIDE OF THE DECK, and, with a noiseless celerity, were casting loose the tackles and bands of the boat which swung there. This boat had always been deemed one of the spare boats, though technically called the captain's, on account of its hanging from the starboard quarter. The figure that now stood by its bows was tall and swart, with one white tooth evilly protruding from its steel-like lips. A rumpled Chinese jacket of black cotton funereally invested him, with wide black trousers of the same dark stuff. But strangely crowning this ebonness was a glistening white plaited turban, the living hair braided and coiled round and round upon his head. Less swart in aspect, the companions of this figure were of that vivid, tiger-yellow complexion peculiar to some of the aboriginal natives of the Manilas;—a race notorious for a certain diabolism of subtility, and by some honest white mariners supposed to be the paid spies and secret confidential agents on the water of the devil, their lord, whose counting-room they suppose to be elsewhere.

While yet the wondering ship's company were gazing upon these strangers, Ahab cried out to the white-turbaned old man at their head, "All ready there, Fedallah?"

"Ready," was the half-hissed reply.

"Lower away then; d'ye hear?" shouting across the deck. "Lower away there, I say."

Such was the thunder of his voice, that spite of their amazement the men sprang over the rail; the sheaves whirled round in the blocks; with a wallow, the three boats dropped into the sea; while, with a dexterous, off-handed daring, unknown in any other vocation, the sailors, goat-like, leaped down the rolling ship's side into the tossed boats below.

Hardly had they pulled out from under the ship's lee, when a fourth keel, coming from the windward side, pulled round under the stern, and showed the five strangers rowing Ahab, who, standing erect in the stern, loudly hailed Starbuck, Stubb, and Flask, to spread themselves widely, so as to cover a large expanse of water. But with all their eyes again riveted upon the swart Fedallah and his crew, the inmates of the other boats obeyed not the command.

"Captain Ahab?—" said Starbuck.

"Spread yourselves," cried Ahab; "give way, all four boats. Thou, Flask, pull out more to leeward!"

"Ay, ay, sir," cheerily cried little King-Post, sweeping round his great steering oar. "Lay back!" addressing his crew. "There!—there!—there again! There she blows right ahead, boys!—lay back!"

"Never heed yonder yellow boys, Archy."

"Oh, I don't mind 'em, sir," said Archy; "I knew it all before now. Didn't I hear 'em in the hold? And didn't I tell Cabaco here of it? What say ye, Cabaco? They are stowaways, Mr. Flask."

"Pull, pull, my fine hearts-alive; pull, my children; pull, my little ones," drawlingly and soothingly sighed Stubb to his crew, some of whom still showed signs of uneasiness. "Why don't you break your backbones, my boys? What is it you stare at? Those chaps in yonder boat? Tut! They are only five more hands come to help us—never mind from where—the more the merrier. Pull, then, do pull; never mind the brim-stone—devils are good fellows enough. So, so; there you are now; that's the stroke for a thousand pounds; that's the stroke to sweep the stakes! Hurrah for the gold cup of sperm oil, my heroes! Three cheers, men—all hearts alive! Easy, easy; don't be in a hurry—don't be in a hurry. Why don't you snap your oars, you rascals? Bite something, you dogs!

So, so, so, then;—softly, softly! That's it—that's it! long and strong. Give way there, give way! The devil fetch ye, ye ragamuffin rapscallions; ye are all asleep. Stop snoring, ye sleepers, and pull. Pull, will ye? pull, can't ye? pull, won't ye? Why in the name of gudgeons and ginger-cakes don't ye pull?—pull and break something! pull, and start your eyes out! Here!" whipping out the sharp knife from his girdle; "every mother's son of ye draw his knife, and pull with the blade between his teeth. That's it—that's it. Now ye do something; that looks like it, my steel-bits. Start her—start her, my silver-spoons! Start her, marling-spikes!"

Stubb's exordium to his crew is given here at large, because he had rather a peculiar way of talking to them in general, and especially in inculcating the religion of rowing. But you must not suppose from this specimen of his sermonizings that he ever flew into downright passions with his congregation. Not at all; and therein consisted his chief peculiarity. He would say the most terrific things to his crew, in a tone so strangely compounded of fun and fury, and the fury seemed so calculated merely as a spice to the fun, that no oarsman could hear such queer invocations without pulling for dear life, and yet pulling for the mere joke of the thing. Besides he all the time looked so easy and indolent himself, so loungingly managed his steering-oar, and so broadly gaped—open-mouthed at times—that the mere sight of such a yawning commander, by sheer force of contrast, acted like a charm upon the crew. Then again, Stubb was one of those old sort of humorists, whose jollity is sometimes so curiously ambiguous, as to put all inferiors on their guard in the matter of obeying them.

In obedience to a sign from Ahab, Starbuck was now pulling obliquely across Stubb's bow; and when for a minute or so the two boats were pretty near to each other, Stubb hailed the mate.

"Mr. Starbuck! larboard boat there, ahoy! a word with ye, sir, if ye please!"

"Halloa!" returned Starbuck, turning round not a single inch as he spoke; still earnestly but whisperingly urging his crew; his face set like a flint from Stubb's.

"What think ye of those yellow boys, sir!"

"Smuggled on board, somehow, before the ship sailed. (Strong, strong, boys!)" in a whisper to his crew, then speaking out loud again: "A sad business, Mr. Stubb! (Seethe her, seethe her, my lads!) but never mind, Mr. Stubb, all for the best. Let all your crew pull strong, come what will. (Spring, my men, spring!) There's hogsheads of sperm ahead, Mr. Stubb, and that's what ye came for. (Pull, my boys!) Sperm, sperm's the play! This at least is duty; duty and profit hand in hand."

"Ay, ay, I thought as much," soliloquized Stubb, when the boats diverged, "as soon as I clapped eye on 'em, I thought so. Ay, and that's what he went into the after-hold for, so often, as Dough-Boy long suspected. They were hidden down there. The White Whale's at the bottom of it. Well, well, so be it! Can't be helped! All right! Give way, men! It ain't the White Whale to-day! Give way!"

Now the advent of these outlandish strangers at such a critical instant as the lowering of the boats from the deck, this had not unreasonably awakened a sort of superstitious amazement in some of the ship's company; but Archy's fancied discovery having some time previous got abroad among them, though indeed not credited then, this had in some small measure prepared them for the event. It took off the extreme edge of their wonder; and so what with all this and Stubb's confident way of accounting for their appearance, they were for the time freed from superstitious surmisings; though the affair still left abundant room for all manner of wild conjectures as to dark Ahab's precise agency in the matter from the beginning. For me, I silently recalled the mysterious shadows I had seen creeping on board the *Pequod* during the dim Nantucket dawn, as well as the enigmatical hintings of the unaccountable Elijah.

Meantime, Ahab, out of hearing of his officers, having sided the furthest to windward, was still ranging ahead of the other boats; a circumstance bespeaking how potent a crew was pulling him. Those tiger yellow creatures of his seemed all steel and whalebone; like five trip-hammers they rose and fell with regular strokes of strength, which periodically started the boat along the water like a horizontal burst boiler out of a Mississippi steamer. As for Fedallah, who was seen pulling the harpooneer oar, he had thrown aside his black jacket, and displayed his naked chest with the whole part of his body above the gunwale, clearly cut against the alternating depressions of the watery horizon; while at the other end of the boat Ahab, with one arm, like a fencer's, thrown half backward into the air, as if to counterbalance any tendency to trip; Ahab was seen steadily managing his steering oar as in a thousand boat lowerings ere the White Whale had torn him. All at once the outstretched arm gave a peculiar motion and then remained fixed, while the boat's five oars were seen simultaneously peaked. Boat and crew sat motionless on the sea. Instantly the three spread boats in the rear paused on their way. The whales had irregularly settled bodily down into the blue, thus giving no distantly discernible token of the movement, though from his closer vicinity Ahab had observed it.

"Every man look out along his oars!" cried Starbuck. "Thou Queequeg, stand up!"

Nimbly, springing up on the triangular raised box in the bow, the savage stood erect there, and with intensely eager eyes gazed off towards the spot where the chase had last been descried. Likewise upon the extreme stern of the boat where it was also triangularly platformed level with the gunwale, Starbuck himself was seen coolly and adroitly balancing himself to the jerking tossings of his chip of a craft, and silently eyeing the vast blue eye of the sea.

Not very far distant Flask's boat was also lying breathlessly still; its commander recklessly standing upon the top of the loggerhead, a stout sort of post rooted in the keel, and rising some two feet above the level of the stern platform. It is used for catching turns with the whale-line. Its top is not more spacious than the palm of a man's hand, and standing upon such a base as that, Flask seemed perched at the mast-head of some ship which had sunk to all but her trucks. But little King-Post was small and short, and at the same time little King-Post was full of a large and tall ambition, so that this loggerhead stand-point of his did by no means satisfy King-Post.

"I can't see three seas off; tip us up an oar there, and let me on to that."

Upon this, Daggoo, with either hand upon the gunwale to steady his way, swiftly slid aft, and then erecting himself volunteered his lofty shoulders for a pedestal.

"Good a mast-head as any, sir. Will you mount?"

"That I will, and thank ye very much, my fine fellow; only I wish you fifty feet taller."

Whereupon planting his feet firmly against two opposite planks of the boat, the gigantic negro, stooping a little, presented his flat palm to Flask's foot, and then putting Flask's hand on his hearse-plumed head and bidding him spring as he himself should toss, with one dexterous fling landed the little man high and dry on his shoulders. And here was Flask now standing, Daggoo with one lifted arm furnishing him with a breastband to lean against and steady himself by.

At any time it is a strange sight to the tyro to see with what wondrous habitude of unconscious skill the whaleman will maintain an erect posture in his boat, even when pitched about by the most riotously perverse and cross-running seas. Still more strange to see him giddily perched upon the loggerhead itself, under such circumstances. But the sight of little Flask mounted upon gigantic Daggoo was yet more curious; for sustaining himself with a cool, indifferent, easy, unthought of, barbaric majesty, the noble negro to every roll of the sea harmoniously rolled his fine form. On his broad back, flaxen-haired Flask seemed a snow-flake. The bearer looked nobler than the rider. Though truly vivacious, tumultuous, ostentatious little Flask would now and then stamp with impatience; but not one added heave did he thereby give to the negro's lordly chest. So have I seen Passion and Vanity stamping the living magnanimous earth, but the earth did not alter her tides and her seasons for that.

Meanwhile Stubb, the third mate, betrayed no such far-gazing solicitudes. The whales might have made one of their regular soundings, not a temporary dive from mere fright; and if that were the case, Stubb, as his wont in such cases, it seems, was resolved to solace the languishing interval with his pipe. He withdrew it from his hatband, where he always wore it aslant like a feather. He loaded it, and rammed home the loading with his thumb-end; but hardly had he ignited his match across the rough sandpaper of his hand, when Tashtego, his harpooneer, whose eyes had been setting to windward like two fixed stars, suddenly dropped like light from his erect attitude to his seat, crying out in a quick phrensy of hurry, "Down, down all, and give way!—there they are!"

To a landsman, no whale, nor any sign of a herring, would have been visible at that moment; nothing but a troubled bit of greenish white water, and thin scattered puffs of vapor hovering over it, and suffusingly blowing off to leeward, like the confused scud from white rolling billows. The air around suddenly vibrated and tingled, as it were, like the air over intensely heated plates of iron. Beneath this atmospheric waving and curling, and partially beneath a thin layer of water, also, the whales were swimming. Seen in advance of all the other indications, the puffs of vapor they spouted, seemed their forerunning couriers and detached flying outriders.

All four boats were now in keen pursuit of that one spot of troubled water and air. But it bade far to outstrip them; it flew on and on, as a mass of interblending bubbles borne down a rapid stream from the hills.

"Pull, pull, my good boys," said Starbuck, in the lowest possible but intensest concentrated whisper to his men; while the sharp fixed glance from his eyes darted straight ahead of the bow, almost seemed as two visible needles in two unerring binnacle compasses. He did not say much to his crew, though, nor did his crew say anything to him. Only the silence of the boat was at intervals startlingly pierced by one of his peculiar whispers, now harsh with command, now soft with entreaty.

How different the loud little King-Post. "Sing out and say something, my hearties. Roar and pull, my thunderbolts! Beach me, beach me on their black backs, boys; only do that for me, and I'll sign over to you my Martha's Vineyard plantation, boys; including wife and children, boys. Lay me on—lay me on! O Lord, Lord! but I shall go stark, staring mad! See! see that white water!" And so shouting, he pulled his hat from his head, and stamped up and down on it; then picking it up, flirted it far off upon the sea; and finally fell to rearing and plunging in the boat's stern like a crazed colt from the prairie.

"Look at that chap now," philosophically drawled Stubb, who, with his unlighted short pipe, mechanically retained between his teeth, at a short distance, followed after—"He's got fits, that Flask has. Fits? yes, give him fits—that's the very word—pitch fits into 'em. Merrily, merrily, hearts-alive. Pudding for supper, you know;—merry's the word. Pull, babes—pull, sucklings—pull, all. But what the devil are you hurrying about? Softly, softly, and steadily, my men. Only pull, and keep pulling; nothing more. Crack all your backbones, and bite your knives in two—that's all. Take it easy—why don't ye take it easy, I say, and burst all your livers and lungs!"

But what it was that inscrutable Ahab said to that tiger-yellow crew of his—these were words best omitted here; for you live under the blessed light of the evangelical land. Only the infidel sharks in the audacious seas may give ear to such words, when, with tornado brow, and eyes of red murder, and foam-glued lips, Ahab leaped after his prey.

Meanwhile, all the boats tore on. The repeated specific allusions of Flask to "that whale," as he called the fictitious monster which he declared to be incessantly tantalizing his boat's bow with its tail—these allusions of his were at times so vivid and life-like, that they would cause some one or two of his men to snatch a fearful look over his shoulder. But this was against all rule; for the oarsmen must put out their eyes, and ram a skewer through their necks; usages pronouncing that they must have no organs but ears, and no limbs but arms, in these critical moments.

It was a sight full of quick wonder and awe! The vast swells of the omnipotent sea; the surging, hollow roar they made, as they rolled along the eight gunwales, like gigantic bowls in a boundless bowling-green; the brief suspended agony of the boat, as it would tip for an instant on the knife-like edge of the sharper waves, that almost seemed threatening to cut it in two; the sudden profound dip into the watery glens and hollows; the keen spurrings and goadings to gain the top of the opposite hill; the headlong, sled-like slide down its other side;—all these, with the cries of the headsmen and harpooneers, and the shuddering gasps of the oarsmen, with the wondrous sight of the ivory *Pequod* bearing down upon her boats with outstretched sails, like a wild hen after her screaming brood;—all this was thrilling. Not the raw recruit, marching from the bosom of his wife into the fever heat of his first battle; not the dead man's ghost encountering the first unknown phantom in the other world;—neither of these can feel stranger and stronger emotions than that man does, who for the first time finds himself pulling into the charmed, churned circle of the hunted sperm whale.

The dancing white water made by the chase was now becoming more and more visible, owing to the increasing darkness of the dun cloud-shadows flung upon the sea. The jets of vapor no longer blended, but tilted everywhere to right and left; the whales seemed separating their wakes. The boats were pulled more apart; Starbuck giving chase to three whales running dead to leeward. Our sail was now set, and, with the still rising wind, we rushed along; the boat going with such madness through the water, that the lee oars could scarcely be worked rapidly enough to escape being torn from the row-locks.

Soon we were running through a suffusing wide veil of mist; neither ship nor boat to be seen.

"Give way, men," whispered Starbuck, drawing still further aft the sheet of his sail; "there is time to kill a fish yet before the squall comes. There's white water again!—close to! Spring!"

Soon after, two cries in quick succession on each side of us denoted that the other boats had got fast; but hardly were they overheard, when with a lightning-like hurtling whisper Starbuck said: "Stand up!" and Queequeg, harpoon in hand, sprang to his feet.

Though not one of the oarsmen was then facing the life and death peril so close to them ahead, yet with their eyes on the intense countenance of the mate in the stern of the boat, they knew that the imminent instant had come; they heard, too, an enormous wallowing sound as of fifty elephants stirring in their litter. Meanwhile the boat was still booming through the mist, the waves curling and hissing around us like the erected crests of enraged serpents.

"That's his hump. *There, there,* give it to him!" whispered Starbuck.

A short rushing sound leaped out of the boat; it was the darted iron of Queequeg. Then all in one welded commotion came an invisible push from astern, while forward the boat seemed striking on a ledge; the sail collapsed and exploded; a gush of scalding vapor shot up nearby; something rolled and tumbled like an earthquake beneath us. The whole crew were half suffocated as they were tossed helter-skelter into the white curdling cream of the squall. Squall, whale, and harpoon had all blended together; and the whale, merely grazed by the iron, escaped.

Though completely swamped, the boat was nearly unharmed. Swimming round it we picked up the floating oars, and lashing them across the gunwale, tumbled back to our places. There we sat up to our knees in the sea, the water covering every rib and plank, so that to our downward gazing eyes the suspended craft seemed a coral boat grown up to us from the bottom of the ocean.

The wind increased to a howl; the waves dashed their bucklers together; the whole squall roared, forked, and crackled around us like a white fire upon the prairie, in which, unconsumed, we were burning; immortal in these jaws of death! In vain we hailed the other boats; as well roar to the live coals down the chimney of a flaming furnace as hail those boats in that storm. Meanwhile the driving scud, rack, and mist, grew darker with the shadows of night; no sign of the ship could be seen. The rising sea forbade all attempts to bale out the boat. The oars were useless as propellers, performing now the office of life-preservers. So, cutting the lashing of the water-proof match keg, after many failures Starbuck contrived to ignite the lamp in the lantern; then stretching it on a waif pole, handed it to Queequeg as the standard-bearer of this forlorn hope. There, then, he sat, holding up that imbecile candle in the heart of that almighty forlornness. There, then, he sat, the sign and symbol of a man without faith, hopelessly holding up hope in the midst of despair.

Wet, drenched through, and shivering cold, despairing of ship or boat, we lifted up our eyes as the dawn came on. The mist still spread over the sea, the empty lantern lay crushed in the bottom of the boat. Suddenly Queequeg started to his feet, hollowing his hand to his ear. We all heard a faint creaking, as of ropes and yards hitherto muffled by the storm. The sound came nearer and nearer; the thick mists were dimly parted by a huge, vague form. Affrighted, we all sprang into the sea as the ship at last loomed into view, bearing right down upon us within a distance of not much more than its length.

Floating on the waves we saw the abandoned boat, as for one instant it tossed and gaped beneath the ship's bows like a chip at the base of a cataract; and then the vast hull rolled over it, and it was seen no more till it came up weltering astern. Again we swam for it, were dashed against it by the seas, and were at last taken up and safely landed on board. Ere the squall came close to, the other boats had cut loose from their fish and returned to the ship in good time. The ship had given us up, but was still cruising, if haply it might light upon some token of our perishing—an oar or a lance pole.

Chapter XLIX

The Hyena

There are certain queer times and occasions in this strange mixed affair we call life when a man takes this whole universe for a vast practical joke, though the wit thereof he but dimly discerns, and more than suspects that the joke is at nobody's expense but his own. However, nothing dispirits, and nothing seems worthwhile disputing. He bolts down all events, all creeds, and beliefs, and persuasions, all hard things visible and invisible, never mind how knobby; as an ostrich of potent digestion gobbles down bullets and gun flints. And as for small difficulties and worryings, prospects of sudden disaster, peril of life and limb; all these, and death itself, seem to him only sly, good-natured hits, and jolly punches in the side bestowed by the unseen and unaccountable old joker. That odd sort of wayward mood I am speaking of, comes over a man only in some time of extreme tribulation; it comes in the very midst of his earnestness, so that what just before might have seemed to him a thing most momentous, now seems but a part of the general joke. There is nothing like the perils of whaling to breed this free and easy sort of genial, desperado philosophy; and with it I now regarded this whole voyage of the *Pequod*, and the great White Whale its object.

"Queequeg," said I, when they had dragged me, the last man, to the deck, and I was still shaking myself in my jacket to fling off the water; "Queequeg, my fine friend does this sort of thing often happen?" Without much emotion, though soaked through just like me, he gave me to understand that such things did often happen.

"Mr. Stubb," said I, turning to that worthy, who, buttoned up in his oil-jacket, was now calmly smoking his pipe in the rain; "Mr. Stubb, I think I have heard you say that of all whalemen you ever met, our chief mate, Mr. Starbuck, is by far the most careful and prudent. I suppose then, that going plump on a flying whale with your sail set in a foggy squall is the height of a whaleman's discretion?"

"Certain. I've lowered for whales from a leaking ship in a gale off Cape Horn."

"Mr. Flask," said I, turning to little King-Post, who was standing close by; "you are experienced in these things, and I am not. Will you tell me whether it is an unalterable law in this fishery, Mr. Flask, for an oarsman to break his own back pulling himself back-foremost into death's jaws?"

"Can't you twist that smaller?" said Flask. "Yes, that's the law. I should like to see a boat's crew backing water up to a whale face-foremost. Ha, ha! the whale would give them squint for squint, mind that!"

Here then, from three impartial witnesses, I had a deliberate statement of the entire case. Considering, therefore, that squalls and capsizings in the water and consequent bivouacks on the deep, were matters of common occurrence in this kind of life; considering that at the superlatively critical instant of going on to the whale I must resign my life into the hands of him who steered the boat—oftentimes a fellow who at that very moment is in his impetuousness upon the point of scuttling the craft with his own frantic stampings; considering that the particular disaster to our own particular boat was chiefly to be imputed to Starbuck's driving on to his whale almost in the teeth of a squall, and considering that Starbuck, notwithstanding, was famous for his great heedfulness in the fishery; considering that I belonged to this uncommonly prudent Starbuck's boat; and finally considering in what a devil's chase I was implicated, touching the White Whale: taking all things together, I say, I thought I might as well go below and make a rough draft of my will. "Queequeg," said I, "come along, you shall be my lawyer, executor, and legatee."

It may seem strange that of all men sailors should be tinkering at their last wills and testaments, but there are no people in the world more fond of that diversion. This was the fourth time in my nautical life that I had done the same thing. After the ceremony was concluded upon the present occasion, I felt all the easier; a stone was rolled away from my heart. Besides, all the days I should now live would be as good as the days that Lazarus lived after his resurrection; a supplementary clean gain of so many months or weeks as the case may be. I survived myself; my death and burial were locked up in my chest. I looked round me tranquilly and contentedly, like a quiet ghost with a clean conscience sitting inside the bars of a snug family vault.

Now then, thought I, unconsciously rolling up the sleeves of my frock, here goes for a cool, collected dive at death and destruction, and the devil fetch the hindmost.

Chapter L

AHAB'S BOAT AND CREW. FEDALLAH

"WHO WOULD HAVE THOUGHT IT, FLASK!" CRIED STUBB; "IF I HAD BUT ONE LEG YOU WOULD not catch me in a boat, unless maybe to stop the plug-hole with my timber toe. Oh! he's a wonderful old man!"

"I don't think it so strange, after all, on that account," said Flask. "If his leg were off at the hip, now, it would be a different thing. That would disable him; but he has one knee, and good part of the other left, you know."

"I don't know that, my little man; I never yet saw him kneel."

* * * * *

Among whale-wise people it has often been argued whether, considering the paramount importance of his life to the success of the voyage, it is right for a whaling captain to jeopardize that life in the active perils of the chase. So Tamerlane's soldiers often argued with tears in their eyes, whether that invaluable life of his ought to be carried into the thickest of the fight.

But with Ahab the question assumed a modified aspect. Considering that with two legs man is but a hobbling wight in all times of danger; considering that the pursuit of whales is always under great and extraordinary difficulties; that every individual moment, indeed, then comprises a peril; under these circumstances is it wise for any maimed man to enter a whale-boat in the hunt? As a general thing, the joint-owners of the *Pequod* must have plainly thought not.

Ahab well knew that although his friends at home would think little of his entering a boat in certain comparatively harmless vicissitudes of the chase, for the sake of being near the scene of action and giving his orders in person, yet for Captain Ahab to have a boat actually apportioned to him as a regular headsman in the hunt—above all for Captain Ahab to be supplied with five extra men, as that same boat's crew, he well knew that such generous conceits never entered the heads of the owners of the *Pequod*. Therefore he had not solicited a boat's crew from them, nor had he in any way hinted his desires on that head. Nevertheless he had taken private measures of his own touching all that matter. Until Cabaco's published discovery, the sailors had little foreseen it, though to be sure when, after being a little while out of port, all hands had concluded the customary business of fitting the whale-boats for service; when some time after this Ahab was now and then found bestirring himself in the matter of making thole-pins with his own hands for what was thought to be one of the spare boats, and even solicitously cutting the small wooden skewers, which when the line is running out are pinned over the groove in the bow: when all this was observed in him, and particularly his solicitude in having an extra coat of sheathing in the bottom of the boat, as if to make it better withstand the pointed pressure of his ivory limb; and also the anxiety he evinced in exactly shaping the thigh board, or clumsy cleat, as it is sometimes called, the horizontal piece in the boat's bow for bracing the knee against in darting or stabbing at the whale; when it was observed how often he stood up in that boat with his solitary knee fixed in the semi-circular depression in the cleat, and with the carpenter's chisel gouged out a little here and straightened it a little there; all these things, I say, had awakened much interest and curiosity at the time. But almost everybody supposed that this particular preparative heedfulness in Ahab must only be with a view to the ultimate chase of Moby-Dick; for he had already revealed his intention to hunt that mortal monster in person. But such a supposition did by no means involve the remotest suspicion as to any boat's crew being assigned to that boat.

Now, with the subordinate phantoms, what wonder remained soon waned away; for in a whaler wonders soon wane. Besides, now and then such unaccountable odds and ends of strange nations come up from the unknown nooks and ash-holes of the earth to man these floating outlaws of whalers; and the ships themselves often pick up such queer castaway creatures found tossing about the open sea on planks, bits of wreck, oars, whale-boats, canoes, blown-off Japanese junks, and what not; that Beelzebub himself might climb up the side and step down into the cabin to chat with the captain, and it would not create any unsubduable excitement in the forecastle.

But be all this as it may, certain it is that while the subordinate phantoms soon found their place among the crew, though still as it were somehow distinct from them, yet that hair-turbaned Fedallah remained a muffled mystery to the last. Whence he came in a mannerly world like this, by what sort of unaccountable tie he soon evinced himself to be linked with Ahab's peculiar fortunes; nay, so far as to have some sort of a half-hinted influence; Heaven knows, but it might have been even authority over him; all this none knew. But one cannot sustain an indifferent air concerning Fedallah. He was such a creature as civilized, domestic people in the temperate zone only see in their dreams, and that but dimly; but the like of whom now and then glide among the unchanging Asiatic communities, especially the Oriental isles to the east of the continent—those insulated, immemorial, unalterable countries, which even in these modern days still preserve much of the ghostly aboriginalness of earth's primal generations, when the memory of the first man was a distinct recollection, and all men his descendants, unknowing whence he came, eyed each other as real phantoms, and asked of the sun and the moon why they were created and to what end; when though, according to Genesis, the angels indeed consorted with the daughters of men, the devils also, add the uncanonical Rabbins, indulged in mundane amours.

Chapter LI

THE SPIRIT-SPOUT

DAYS, WEEKS PASSED, AND UNDER EASY SAIL, THE IVORY *PEQUOD* HAD SLOWLY SWEPT ACROSS four several cruising-grounds; that off the Azores; off the Cape de Verdes; on the Plate (so-called), being off the mouth of the Rio de la Plata; and the Carrol Ground, an unstaked, watery locality, southerly from St. Helena.

It was while gliding through these latter waters that one serene and moonlight night, when all the waves rolled by like scrolls of silver; and, by their soft, suffusing seethings, made what seemed a silvery silence, not a solitude; on such a silent night a silvery jet was seen far in advance of the white bubbles at the bow. Lit up by the moon, it looked celestial; seemed some plumed and glittering god uprising from the sea. Fedallah first descried this jet. For of these moonlight nights, it was his wont to mount to the main-mast-head, and stand a look-out there, with the same precision as if it had been day. And yet, though herds of whales were seen by night, not one whaleman in a hundred would venture a lowering for them. You may think with what emotions, then, the seamen beheld this old Oriental perched aloft at such unusual hours; his turban and the moon, companions in one sky. But when, after spending his uniform interval there for several successive nights without uttering a single sound; when, after all this silence, his unearthly voice was heard announcing that silvery, moon-lit jet, every reclining mariner started to his feet as if some winged spirit had lighted in the rigging, and hailed the mortal crew. "There she blows!" Had the trump of judgment blown, they could not have quivered more; yet still they felt no terror; rather pleasure. For though it was a most unwonted hour, yet so impressive was the cry, and so deliriously exciting, that almost every soul on board instinctively desired a lowering.

Walking the deck with quick, side-lunging strides, Ahab commanded the t'gallant sails and royals to be set, and every stun-sail spread. The best man in the ship must take the helm. Then, with every mast-head manned, the piled-up craft rolled down before the wind. The strange, upheaving, lifting tendency of the taffrail breeze filling the hollows of so many sails, made the buoyant, hovering deck to feel like air beneath the feet; while still she rushed along, as if two antagonistic influences were struggling in her—one to mount direct to heaven, the other to drive yawningly to some horizontal goal. And had you watched Ahab's face that night, you would have thought that in him also two different things were warring. While his one live leg made lively echoes along the deck, every stroke of his dead limb sounded like a coffin-tap. On life and death this old man walked. But though the ship so swiftly sped, and though from every eye, like arrows, the eager glances shot, yet the silvery jet was no more seen that night. Every sailor swore he saw it once, but not a second time.

This midnight-spout had almost grown a forgotten thing, when, some days after, lo! at the same silent hour, it was again announced: again it was descried by all; but upon making sail to overtake it, once more it disappeared as if it had never been. And so it served us night after night, till no one heeded it but to wonder at it. Mysteriously jetted into the clear moonlight, or starlight, as the case might be; disappearing again for one whole day, or two days, or three; and somehow seeming at every distinct repetition to be advancing still further and further in our van, this solitary jet seemed forever alluring us on.

Nor with the immemorial superstition of their race, and in accordance with the preternaturalness, as it seemed, which in many things invested the *Pequod*, were there wanting some of the seamen who swore that whenever and wherever descried; at however remote times, or in however far apart latitudes and longitudes, that unnearable spout was cast by one selfsame whale; and that whale, Moby-Dick. For a time, there reigned, too, a sense of peculiar dread at this flitting apparition, as if it were treacherously beckoning us on and on, in order that the monster might turn round upon us, and rend us at last in the remotest and most savage seas.

These temporary apprehensions, so vague but so awful, derived a wondrous potency from the contrasting serenity of the weather, in which, beneath all its blue blandness, some thought there lurked a devilish charm, as for days and days we voyaged along, through seas so wearily, lonesomely mild, that all space, in repugnance to our vengeful errand, seemed vacating itself of life before our urn-like prow.

But, at last, when turning to the eastward, the Cape winds began howling around us, and we rose and fell upon the long, troubled seas that are there; when the ivory-tusked *Pequod* sharply bowed to the blast, and gored the dark waves in her madness, till, like showers of silver chips, the foam-flakes flew over her bulwarks; then all this desolate vacuity of life went away, but gave place to sights more dismal than before.

Close to our bows, strange forms in the water darted hither and thither before us; while thick in our rear flew the inscrutable sea-ravens. And every morning, perched on our stays, rows of these birds were seen; and spite of our hootings, for a long time obstinately clung to the hemp, as though they deemed our ship some drifting, uninhabited craft; a thing appointed to desolation, and therefore fit roosting-place for their homeless selves. And heaved and heaved, still unrestingly heaved the black sea, as if its vast tides were a conscience; and the great mundane soul were in anguish and remorse for the long sin and suffering it had bred.

Cape of Good Hope, do they call ye? Rather Cape Tormentoto, as called of yore; for long allured by the perfidious silences that before had attended us, we found ourselves launched into this tormented sea, where guilty beings transformed into those fowls and these fish, seemed condemned to swim on everlastingly without any haven in store, or beat that black air without any horizon. But calm, snow-white, and unvarying; still directing its fountain of feathers to the sky; still beckoning us on from before, the solitary jet would at times be descried.

During all this blackness of the elements, Ahab, though assuming for the time the almost continual command of the drenched and dangerous deck, manifested the gloomiest reserve; and more seldom than ever addressed his mates. In tempestuous times like these, after everything above and aloft has been secured, nothing more can be done but passively to await the issue of the gale. Then Captain and crew become practical fatalists. So, with his ivory leg inserted into its accustomed hole, and with one hand firmly grasping a shroud, Ahab for hours and hours would stand gazing dead to windward, while an occasional squall of sleet or snow would all but congeal his very eyelashes together. Meantime, the crew driven from the forward part of the ship by the perilous seas that burstingly broke over its bows, stood in a line along the bulwarks in the waist; and the better to guard against the leaping waves, each man had slipped himself into a sort of bowline secured to the rail, in which he swung as in a loosened belt. Few or no words were spoken; and the silent ship, as if manned by painted sailors in wax, day after day tore on through all the swift madness and gladness of the demoniac waves. By night the same muteness of humanity before the shrieks of the ocean prevailed; still in silence the men swung in the bowlines; still wordless Ahab stood up to the blast. Even when wearied nature seemed demanding repose he would not seek that repose in his hammock. Never could Starbuck forget the old man's aspect, when one night going down into the cabin to mark how the barometer stood, he saw him with closed eyes sitting straight in his floor-screwed chair; the rain and half-melted sleet of the storm from which he had some time before emerged, still slowly dripping from the unremoved hat and coat. On the table beside him lay unrolled one of those charts of tides and currents which have previously been spoken of. His lantern swung from his tightly clenched hand.

Though the body was erect, the head was thrown back so that the closed eyes were pointed towards the needle of the tell-tale that swung from a beam in the ceiling.[1]

Terrible old man! thought Starbuck with a shudder, sleeping in this gale, still thou steadfastly eyest thy purpose.

Chapter LII

The Albatross

South-eastward from the Cape, off the distant Crozetts, a good cruising-ground for Right Whalemen, a sail loomed ahead, the *Goney* (Albatross) by name. As she slowly drew nigh, from my lofty perch at the fore-mast-head, I had a good view of that sight so remarkable to a tyro in the far ocean fisheries—a whaler at sea, and long absent from home.

As if the waves had been fullers, this craft was bleached like the skeleton of a stranded walrus. All down her sides, this spectral appearance was traced with long channels of reddened rust, while all her spars and her rigging were like the thick branches of trees furred over with hoar-frost. Only her lower sails were set. A wild sight it was to see her long-bearded look-outs at those three mast-heads. They seemed clad in the skins of beasts, so torn and bepatched the raiment that had survived nearly four years of cruising. Standing in iron hoops nailed to the mast, they swayed and swung over a fathomless sea; and though, when the ship slowly glided close under our stern, we six men in the air came so nigh to each other that we might almost have leaped from the mast-heads of one ship to those of the other; yet, those forlorn-looking fishermen, mildly eyeing us as they passed, said not one word to our own look-outs, while the quarter-deck hail was being heard from below.

"Ship ahoy! Have ye seen the White Whale?"

But as the strange captain, leaning over the pallid bulwarks, was in the act of putting his trumpet to his mouth, it somehow fell from his hand into the sea; and the wind now rising amain, he in vain strove to make himself heard without it. Meantime his ship was still increasing the distance between us. While in various silent ways the seamen of the *Pequod* were evincing their observance of this ominous incident at the first mere mention of the White Whale's name to another ship, Ahab for a moment paused; it almost seemed as though he would have lowered a boat to board the stranger, had not the threatening wind forbade. But taking advantage of his windward position, he again seized his trumpet, and knowing by her aspect that the stranger vessel was a Nantucketer and shortly bound home, he loudly hailed—"Ahoy there! This is the *Pequod*, bound round the world! Tell them to address all future letters to the Pacific ocean! and this time three years, if I am not at home, tell them to address them to—"

At that moment the two wakes were fairly crossed, and instantly, then, in accordance with their singular ways, shoals of small harmless fish, that for some days before had been placidly swimming by our side, darted away with what seemed shuddering fins, and ranged themselves fore and aft with the stranger's flanks. Though in the course of his continual voyagings Ahab must often before have noticed a similar sight, yet, to any monomaniac man, the veriest trifles capriciously carry meanings.

"Swim away from me, do ye?" murmured Ahab, gazing over into the water. There seemed but

1. The cabin-compass is called the tell-tale, because without going to the compass at the helm, the Captain, while below, can inform himself of the course of the ship

little in the words, but the tone conveyed more of deep helpless sadness than the insane old man had ever before evinced. But turning to the steersman, who thus far had been holding the ship in the wind to diminish her headway, he cried out in his old lion voice—"Up helm! Keep her off round the world!"

Round the world! There is much in that sound to inspire proud feelings; but whereto does all that circumnavigation conduct? Only through numberless perils to the very point whence we started, where those that we left behind secure, were all the time before us.

Were this world an endless plain, and by sailing eastward we could forever reach new distances, and discover sights more sweet and strange than any Cyclades or Islands of King Solomon, then there were promise in the voyage. But in pursuit of those far mysteries we dream of, or in tormented chase of that demon phantom that, some time or other, swims before all human hearts; while chasing such over this round globe, they either lead us on in barren mazes or midway leave us whelmed.

Chapter LIII

THE GAM

THE OSTENSIBLE REASON WHY AHAB DID NOT GO ON BOARD OF THE WHALER WE HAD SPOKEN was this: the wind and sea betokened storms. But even had this not been the case, he would not after all, perhaps, have boarded her—judging by his subsequent conduct on similar occasions—if so it had been that, by the process of hailing, he had obtained a negative answer to the question he put. For, as it eventually turned out, he cared not to consort, even for five minutes, with any stranger captain, except he could contribute some of that information he so absorbingly sought. But all this might remain inadequately estimated, were not something said here of the peculiar usages of whaling-vessels when meeting each other in foreign seas, and especially on a common cruising-ground.

If two strangers crossing the Pine Barrens in New York State, or the equally desolate Salisbury Plain in England; if casually encountering each other in such inhospitable wilds, these twain, for the life of them, cannot well avoid a mutual salutation; and stopping for a moment to interchange the news; and, perhaps, sitting down for a while and resting in concert: then, how much more natural that upon the illimitable Pine Barrens and Salisbury Plains of the sea, two whaling vessels descrying each other at the ends of the earth—off lone Fanning's Island, or the far away King's Mills; how much more natural, I say, that under such circumstances these ships should not only interchange hails, but come into still closer, more friendly and sociable contact. And especially would this seem to be a matter of course, in the case of vessels owned in one seaport, and whose captains, officers, and not a few of the men are personally known to each other; and consequently, have all sorts of dear domestic things to talk about.

For the long absent ship, the outward-bounder, perhaps, has letters on board; at any rate, she will be sure to let her have some papers of a date a year or two later than the last one on her blurred and thumb-worn files. And in return for that courtesy, the outward-bound ship would receive the latest whaling intelligence from the cruising-ground to which she may be destined, a thing of the utmost importance to her. And in degree, all this will hold true concerning whaling-vessels crossing each other's track on the cruising-ground itself, even though they are equally long absent from home. For one of them may have received a transfer of letters from some third, and now far remote vessel; and some of those letters may be for the people of the ship she now meets. Besides, they would exchange the whaling news, and have an agreeable chat. For not only would they meet with all the sympathies of sailors, but likewise with all the peculiar congenialities arising from a common pursuit and mutually shared privations and perils.

Nor would difference of country make any very essential difference; that is, so long as both parties speak one language, as is the case with Americans and English. Though, to be sure, from the small number of English whalers, such meetings do not very often occur, and when they do occur there is too apt to be a sort of shyness between them; for your Englishman is rather reserved, and your Yankee, he does not fancy that sort of thing in anybody but himself. Besides, the English whalers sometimes affect a kind of metropolitan superiority over the American whalers; regarding the long, lean Nantucketer, with his nondescript provincialisms, as a sort of sea-peasant. But where this superiority in the English whaleman does really consist, it would be hard to say, seeing that the Yankees in one day, collectively, kill more whales than all the English, collectively, in ten years. But this is a harmless little foible in the English whale-hunters, which the Nantucketer does not take much to heart; probably, because he knows that he has a few foibles himself.

So, then, we see that of all ships separately sailing the sea, the whalers have most reason to be sociable—and they are so. Whereas, some merchant-ships crossing each other's wake in the mid-Atlantic, will oftentimes pass on without so much as a single word of recognition, mutually cutting each other on the high seas, like a brace of dandies in Broadway; and all the time indulging, perhaps, in finical criticism upon each other's rig. As for Men-of-War, when they chance to meet at sea, they first go through such a string of silly bowings and scrapings, such a ducking of ensigns, that there does not seem to be much right-down hearty good-will and brotherly love about it at all. As touching Slave-ships meeting, why, they are in such a prodigious hurry, they run away from each other as soon as possible. And as for Pirates, when they chance to cross each other's cross-bones, the first hail is—"How many skulls?"—the same way that whalers hail—"How many barrels?" And that question once answered, pirates straightway steer apart, for they are infernal villains on both sides, and don't like to see overmuch of each other's villainous likenesses.

But look at the godly, honest, unostentatious, hospitable, sociable, free-and-easy whaler! What does the whaler do when she meets another whaler in any sort of decent weather? She has a *"Gam,"* a thing so utterly unknown to all other ships that they never heard of the name even; and if by chance they should hear of it, they only grin at it, and repeat gamesome stuff about "spouters" and "blubber-boilers," and such like pretty exclamations. Why it is that all Merchant-seamen, and also all Pirates and Man-of-War's men, and Slave-ship sailors, cherish such a scornful feeling towards Whale-ships; this is a question it would be hard to answer. Because, in the case of pirates, say, I should like to know whether that profession of theirs has any peculiar glory about it. It sometimes ends in uncommon elevation, indeed; but only at the gallows. And besides, when a man is elevated in that odd fashion, he has no proper foundation for his superior altitude. Hence, I conclude, that in boasting himself to be high lifted above a whaleman, in that assertion the pirate has no solid basis to stand on.

But what is a *Gam?* You might wear out your index-finger running up and down the columns of dictionaries, and never find the word. Dr. Johnson never attained to that erudition; Noah Webster's ark does not hold it. Nevertheless, this same expressive word has now for many years been in constant use among some fifteen thousand true born Yankees. Certainly, it needs a definition, and should be incorporated into the Lexicon. With that view, let me learnedly define it.

GAM. NOUN—*A social meeting of two (or more) Whale-ships, generally on a cruising-ground; when, after exchanging hails, they exchange visits by boats' crews: the two captains remaining, for the time, on board of one ship, and the two chief mates on the other.*

There is another little item about Gamming which must not be forgotten here. All professions have their own little peculiarities of detail; so has the whale fishery. In a pirate, man-of-war, or slave-ship, when the captain is rowed anywhere in his boat, he always sits in the stern sheets on a comfortable, sometimes cushioned seat there, and often steers himself with a pretty little milliner's tiller decorated with gay cords and ribbons. But the whale-boat has no seat astern, no sofa of that sort whatever, and no tiller at all. High times indeed, if whaling captains were wheeled about the water on castors like gouty old aldermen in patent chairs. And as for a tiller, the whale-boat never admits of any such effeminacy; and therefore as in gamming a complete boat's crew must leave the ship, and hence as the boat steerer or harpooneer is of the number, that subordinate is the steersman upon the occasion, and the captain, having no place to sit in, is pulled off to his visit all standing like a pine-tree. And often you will notice that being conscious of the eyes of the whole visible world resting on him from the sides of the two ships, this standing captain is all alive to the importance of sustaining his dignity by maintaining his legs. Nor is this any very easy matter; for in his rear is the immense projecting steering oar hitting him now and then in the small of his back, the after-oar reciprocating by rapping his knees in front. He is thus completely wedged before and behind, and can only expand himself sideways by settling down on his stretched legs; but a sudden, violent pitch of the boat will often go far to topple him, because length of foundation is nothing without corresponding breadth. Merely make a spread angle of two poles, and you cannot stand them up. Then, again, it would never do in plain sight of the world's riveted eyes, it would never do, I say, for this straddling captain to be seen steadying himself the slightest particle by catching hold of anything with his hands; indeed, as token of his entire, buoyant self-command, he generally carries his hands in his trousers' pockets; but perhaps being generally very large, heavy hands, he carries them there for ballast. Nevertheless there have occurred instances, well authenticated ones too, where the captain has been known for an uncommonly critical moment or two, in a sudden squall say—to seize hold of the nearest oarsman's hair, and hold on there like grim death.

Chapter LIV

The Town-Ho's Story

(As told at the Golden Inn)

THE CAPE OF GOOD HOPE, AND ALL THE WATERY REGION ROUNDABOUT THERE, IS MUCH LIKE some noted four corners of a great highway, where you meet more travelers than in any other part.

It was not very long after speaking the *Goney* that another homeward-bound whaleman, the *Town-Ho,*[1] was encountered. She was manned almost wholly by Polynesians. In the short gam that ensued she gave us strong news of Moby-Dick. To some the general interest in the White Whale was now wildly heightened by a circumstance of the *Town-Ho*'s story, which seemed obscurely to involve with the whale a certain wondrous, inverted visitation of one of those so called judgments of God which at times are said to overtake some men. This latter circumstance, with its own particular accompaniments, forming what may be called the secret part of the tragedy about to be narrated, never reached the ears of Captain Ahab or his mates. For that secret part of the story was unknown to the captain of the *Town-Ho* himself. It was the private property of three confederate

1. The ancient whale-cry upon first sighting a whale from the mast-head, still used by whalemen in hunting the famous Gallipagos terrapin.

white seamen of that ship, one of whom it seems, communicated it to Tashtego with Romish injunctions of secrecy, but the following night Tashtego rambled in his sleep, and revealed so much of it in that way, that when he was wakened he could not well withhold the rest. Nevertheless, so potent an influence did this thing have on those seamen in the *Pequod* who came to the full knowledge of it, and by such a strange delicacy, to call it so, were they governed in this matter, that they kept the secret among themselves so that it never transpired abaft the *Pequod*'s main-mast. Interweaving in its proper place this darker thread with the story as publicly narrated on the ship, the whole of this strange affair I now proceed to put on lasting record.

For my humor's sake, I shall preserve the style in which I once narrated it at Lima, to a lounging circle of my Spanish friends, one saint's eve, smoking upon the thick-gilt tiled piazza of the Golden Inn. Of those fine cavaliers, the young Dons, Pedro and Sebastian, were on the closer terms with me; and hence the interluding questions they occasionally put, and which are duly answered at the time.

"Some two years prior to my first learning the events which I am about rehearsing to you, gentlemen, the *Town-Ho*, Sperm Whaler of Nantucket, was cruising in your Pacific here, not very many days' sail eastward from the eaves of this good Golden Inn. She was somewhere to the northward of the Line. One morning upon handling the pumps according to daily usage, it was observed that she made more water in her hold than common. They supposed a sword-fish had stabbed her, gentlemen. But the captain, having some unusual reason for believing that rare good luck awaited him in those latitudes; and therefore being very averse to quit them, and the leak not being then considered at all dangerous, though, indeed, they could not find it after searching the hold as low down as was possible in rather heavy weather, the ship still continued her cruisings, the mariners working at the pumps at wide and easy intervals; but no good luck came; more days went by and not only was the leak yet undiscovered, but it sensibly increased. So much so, that now taking some alarm, the captain, making all sail, stood away for the nearest harbor among the islands, there to have his hull hove out and repaired.

"Though no small passage was before her, yet, if the commonest chance favored, he did not at all fear that his ship would founder by the way, because his pumps were of the best, and being periodically relieved at them, those six-and-thirty men of his could easily keep the ship free; never mind if the leak should double on her. In truth, well-nigh the whole of this passage being attended by very prosperous breezes, the *Town-Ho* had all but certainly arrived in perfect safety at her port without the occurrence of the least fatality, had it not been for the brutal overbearing of Radney, the mate, a Vineyarder, and the bitterly provoked vengeance of Steelkilt, a Lakeman and desperado from Buffalo.

" 'Lakeman!—Buffalo! Pray, what is a Lakeman, and where is Buffalo?' said Don Sebastian, rising in his swinging mat of grass.

"On the eastern shore of our Lake Erie, Don; but—I crave your courtesy—maybe, you shall soon hear further of all that. Now, gentlemen, in square-sail brigs and three-masted ships, well-nigh as large and stout as any that ever sailed out of your old Callao to far Manila; this Lakeman, in the land-locked heart of our America, had yet been nurtured by all those agrarian freebooting impressions popularly connected with the open ocean. For in their interflowing aggregate, those grand fresh-water seas of ours—Erie, and Ontario, and Huron, and Superior, and Michigan—possess an ocean-like expansiveness, with many of the ocean's noblest traits; with many of its rimmed varieties of races and of climes. They contain round archipelagoes of romantic isles, even as the Polynesian waters do; in large part, are shored by two great contrasting nations, as the Atlantic is; they furnish long maritime approaches to our numerous territorial colonies from the east, dotted all round their banks; here and there are frowned upon by batteries, and by the goat-like craggy guns of lofty Mackinaw; they have heard the fleet thunderings of naval victories; at intervals, they yield their beaches to wild barbarians, whose red painted faces flash from out their peltry wigwams; for leagues and leagues are flanked by ancient and unentered forests, where the gaunt pines stand like serried lines of kings in Gothic genealogies; those same woods harboring wild Afric beasts of prey, and silken creatures whose exported furs give robes to Tartar Emperors; they mirror the paved capitals of Buffalo and Cleveland, as well as Winnebago villages; they float alike the full-rigged merchant-ship, the armed cruiser of the State, the steamer, and the beech canoe; they are swept by Borean and dismasting blasts as direful as any that lash the salted wave; they know what shipwrecks are, for out of sight of land, however inland, they have drowned full many a midnight ship with all its shrieking crew. Thus, gentlemen, though an inlander, Steelkilt was wild-ocean born, and wild-ocean nurtured; as much of an audacious mariner as any. And for Radney, though in his infancy he may have laid him down on the lone Nantucket beach, to nurse at his maternal sea; though in after life he had long followed our austere Atlantic and your contemplative Pacific; yet was he quite as vengeful and full of social quarrel as the backwoods seaman, fresh from the latitudes of buckhorn handled Bowie-knives. Yet was this Nantucketer a man with some good-hearted traits; and this Lakeman, a mariner, who though a sort of devil indeed, might yet by inflexible firmness, only tempered by that common decency of human recognition which is the meanest slave's right; thus treated, Steelkilt had long been retained harmless and docile. At all events, he had proved so thus far; but Radney was doomed and made mad, and Steelkilt—but, gentlemen, you shall hear.

"It was not more than a day or two at the furthest after pointing her prow for her island haven, that the *Town-Ho*'s leak seemed again increasing, but only so as to require an hour or more at the pumps every day. You must know that in a settled and civilized ocean like our Atlantic, for example, some skippers think little of pumping their whole way across it; though of a still, sleepy night should the officer of the deck happen to forget his duty in that respect, the probability would be that he and his shipmates would never again remember it, on account of all hands gently subsiding to the bottom. Nor in the solitary and savage seas far from you to the westward, gentlemen, is it altogether unusual for ships to keep clanging at their pump-handles in full chorus even for a voyage of considerable length; that is, if it lie along a tolerably accessible coast, or if any other reasonable retreat is afforded them. It is only when a leaky vessel is in some very out of the way part of those waters, some really landless latitude, that her captain begins to feel a little anxious.

"Much this way had it been with the *Town-Ho*; so when her leak was found gaining once more, there was in truth some small concern manifested by several of her company; especially by Radney the mate. He commanded the upper sails to be well hoisted, sheeted home anew, and every way expanded to the breeze. Now this Radney, I suppose, was as little of a coward, and as little inclined to any sort of nervous apprehensiveness touching his own person as any fearless, unthinking creature on land or on sea that you can conveniently imagine, gentlemen. Therefore when he betrayed this solicitude about the safety of the ship, some of the seamen declared that it was only on account of his being a part owner in her. So when they were working that evening at the pumps, there was on this head no small gamesomeness slyly going on among them, as they stood with their feet continually overflowed by the rippling clear water; clear as any mountain spring, gentlemen—that bubbling from the pumps ran across the deck, and poured itself out in steady spouts at the lee scupper-holes.

"Now, as you well know, it is not seldom the case in this conventional world of ours—watery or otherwise; that when a person placed in command over his fellow-men finds one of them to be very significantly his superior in general pride of manhood, straightway against that man he conceives an unconquerable dislike and bitterness; and if he had a chance he will pull down and pulverize that subaltern's tower, and make a little heap of dust of it. Be this conceit of mine as it may, gentlemen, at all events Steelkilt was a tall and noble animal with a head like a Roman, and a flowing golden beard like the tasseled housings of your last viceroy's snorting charger; and a brain, and a heart, and a soul in him, gentlemen, which had made Steelkilt Charlemagne, had he been born son to Charlemagne's father. But Radney, the mate, was ugly as a mule; yet as hardy, as stubborn, as malicious. He did not love Steelkilt, and Steelkilt knew it.

"Espying the mate drawing near as he was toiling at the pump with the rest, the Lakeman affected not to notice him, but unawed, went on with his gay banterings.

" 'Ay, ay, my merry lads, it's a lively leak this; hold a cannikin, one of ye, and let's have a taste. By the Lord, it's worth bottling! I tell ye what, men, old Rad's investment must go for it! he had best cut away his part of the hull and tow it home. The fact is, boys, that sword-fish only began the job; he's come back again with a gang of ship-carpenters, saw-fish, and file-fish, and what not; and the whole posse of 'em are now hard at work cutting and slashing at the bottom; making improvements, I suppose. If old Rad were here now, I'd tell him to jump overboard and scatter 'em. They're playing the devil with his estate, I can tell him. But he's a simple old soul—Rad, and a beauty too. Boys, they say the rest of his property is invested in looking-glasses. I wonder if he'd give a poor devil like me the model of his nose.'

" 'Damn your eyes! what's that pump stopping for?' roared Radney, pretending not to have heard the sailors' talk. 'Thunder away at it!'

'Ay, ay, sir,' said Steelkilt, merry as a cricket. 'Lively, boys, lively, now!' And with that the pump clanged like fifty fire-engines; the men tossed their hats off to it, and ere long that peculiar gasping of the lungs was heard which denotes the fullest tension of life's utmost energies.

"Quitting the pump at last, with the rest of his band, the Lakeman went forward all panting, and sat himself down on the windlass; his face fiery red, his eyes blood-shot, and wiping the profuse sweat from his brow. Now what cozening fiend it was, gentlemen, that possessed Radney to meddle with such a man in that corporeally exasperated state, I know not; but so it happened. Intolerably striding along the deck, the mate commanded him to get a broom and sweep down the planks, and also a shovel, and remove some offensive matters consequent upon allowing a pig to run at large.

"Now, gentlemen, sweeping a ship's deck at sea is a piece of household work which in all times but raging gales is regularly attended to every evening; it has been known to be done in the case of ships actually foundering at the time. Such, gentlemen, is the inflexibility of sea-usages and the instinctive love of neatness in seamen; some of whom would not willingly drown without first washing their faces. But in all vessels this broom business is the prescriptive province of the boys, if boys there be aboard. Besides, it was the stronger men in the *Town-Ho* that had been divided into gangs, taking turns at the pumps; and being the most athletic seaman of them all, Steelkilt had been regularly assigned captain of one of the gangs; consequently he should have been freed from any trivial business not connected with truly nautical duties, such being the case with his comrades. I mention all these particulars so that you may understand exactly how this affair stood between the two men.

"But there was more than this: the order about the shovel was almost as plainly meant to sting and insult Steelkilt, as though Radney had spat in his face. Any man who has gone sailor in a whale-ship will understand this; and all this and doubtless much more, the Lakeman fully comprehended when the mate uttered his command. But as he sat still for a moment, and as he steadfastly looked into the mate's malignant eye and perceived the stacks of powder-casks heaped up in him and the slow-match silently burning along towards them; as he instinctively saw all this, that strange forbearance and unwillingness to stir up the deeper passionateness in any already ireful being—a repugnance most felt, when felt at all, by really valiant men even when aggrieved—this nameless phantom feeling, gentlemen, stole over Steelkilt.

"Therefore, in his ordinary tone, only a little broken by the bodily exhaustion he was temporarily in, he answered him saying that sweeping the deck was not his business, and he would not do it. And then, without at all alluding to the shovel, he pointed to three lads as the customary sweepers; who, not being billeted at the pumps, had done little or nothing all day. To this, Radney replied with an oath, in a most domineering and outrageous manner unconditionally reiterating his command; meanwhile advancing upon the still seated Lakeman, with an uplifted cooper's club hammer which he had snatched from a cask nearby.

"Heated and irritated as he was by his spasmodic toil at the pumps, for all his first nameless feeling of forbearance the sweating Steelkilt could but ill brook this bearing in the mate; but somehow still smothering the conflagration within him, without speaking he remained doggedly rooted to his seat, till at last the incensed Radney shook the hammer within a few inches of his face, furiously commanding him to do his bidding.

"Steelkilt rose, and slowly retreating round the windlass, steadily followed by the mate with his menacing hammer, deliberately repeated his intention not to obey. Seeing, however, that his forbearance had not the slightest effect, by an awful and unspeakable intimation with his twisted hand he warned off the foolish and infatuated man; but it was to no purpose. And in this way the two went once slowly round the windlass; when, resolved at last no longer to retreat, bethinking him that he had now forborne as much as comported with his humor, the Lakeman paused on the hatches and thus spoke to the officer:

" 'Mr. Radney, I will not obey you. Take that hammer away, or look to yourself.' But the predestinated mate coming still closer to him, where the Lakeman stood fixed, now shook the heavy hammer within an inch of his teeth; meanwhile repeating a string of insufferable maledictions. Retreating not the thousandth part of an inch; stabbing him in the eye with the unflinching poniard of his glance, Steelkilt, clenching his right hand behind him and creepingly drawing it back, told his persecutor that if the hammer but grazed his cheek he (Steelkilt) would murder him. But, gentlemen, the fool had been branded for the slaughter by the gods. Immediately the hammer touched the cheek; the next instant the lower jaw of the mate was stove in his head; he fell on the hatch spouting blood like a whale.

"Ere the cry could go aft Steelkilt was shaking one of the back-stays leading far aloft to where two of his comrades were standing their mast-heads. They were both Canallers.

" 'Canallers!' cried Don Pedro. 'We have seen many whale-ships in our harbors, but never heard of your Canallers. Pardon: who and what are they?'

" 'Canallers, Don, are the boatmen belonging to our grand Erie Canal. You must have heard of it.'

" 'Nay, Senor: hereabouts in this dull, warm, most lazy, and hereditary land, we know but little of your vigorous North.'

" 'Ay? Well then, Don, refill my cup. Your chicha's very fine; and ere proceeding further I will tell ye what our Canallers are; for such information may throw side-light upon my story.'

"For three hundred and sixty miles, gentlemen, through the entire breadth of the state of New York; through numerous populous cities and most thriving villages; through long, dismal, uninhabited swamps, and affluent, cultivated fields, unrivaled for fertility; by billiard-room and bar-room; through the holy-of-holies of great forests; on Roman arches over Indian rivers; through sun and shade; by happy hearts or broken; through all the wide contrasting scenery of those noble Mohawk counties; and especially, by rows of snow-white chapels, whose spires stand almost like milestones, flows one continual stream of Venetianly corrupt and often lawless life. There's your true Ashantee, gentlemen; there howl your pagans; where you ever find them, next door to you; under the long-flung shadow, and the snug patronizing lee of churches. For by some curious fatality, as it is often noted of your metropolitan freebooters that they ever encamp around the halls of justice, so sinners, gentlemen, most abound in holiest vicinities.

" 'Is that a friar passing?' said Don Pedro, looking downwards into the crowded plaza, with humorous concern.

" 'Well for our northern friend, Dame Isabella's Inquisition wanes in Lima,' laughed Don Sebastian. 'Proceed, Senor.'

" 'A moment! Pardon!' cried another of the company. 'In the name of all us Limeese, I but desire to express to you, sir sailor, that we have by no means overlooked your delicacy in not substituting present Lima for distant Venice in your corrupt comparison. Oh! do not bow and look surprised; you know the proverb all along this coast—"Corrupt as Lima." It but bears out your saying, too; churches more plentiful than billiard-tables, and forever open—and "Corrupt as Lima." So, too, Venice; I have been there; the holy city of the blessed evangelist, St. Mark!—St. Dominic, purge it! Your cup! Thanks: here I refill; now, you pour out again.'

"Freely depicted in his own vocation, gentlemen, the Canaller would make a fine dramatic hero, so abundantly and picturesquely wicked is he. Like Mark Antony, for days and days along his green-turfed, flowery Nile, he indolently floats, openly toying with his red-cheeked Cleopatra, ripening his apricot thigh upon the sunny deck. But ashore, all this effeminacy is dashed. The brigandish guise which the Canaller so proudly sports; his slouched and gaily-ribboned hat betoken his grand features. A terror to the smiling innocence of the villages through which he floats; his swart visage and bold swagger are not unshunned in cities. Once a vagabond on his own canal, I have received good turns from one of these Canallers; I thank him heartily; would fain be not ungrateful; but it is often one of the prime redeeming qualities of your man of violence, that at times he has as stiff an arm to back a poor stranger in a strait, as to plunder a wealthy one. In sum, gentlemen, what the wildness of this canal life is, is emphatically evinced by this; that our wild whale-fishery contains so many of its most finished graduates, and that scarce any race of mankind, except Sydney men, are so much distrusted by our whaling captains. Nor does it at all diminish the curiousness of this matter, that to many thousands of our rural boys and young men born along its line, the probationary life of the Grand Canal furnishes the sole transition between quietly reaping in a Christian corn-field, and recklessly plowing the waters of the most barbaric seas.

" 'I see! I see!' impetuously exclaimed Don Pedro, spilling his chicha upon his silvery ruffles. 'No need to travel! The world's one Lima. I had thought, now, that at your temperate North the generations were cold and holy as the hills.—But the story.'

"I left off, gentlemen, where the Lakeman shook the back-stay. Hardly had he done so, when he was surrounded by the three junior mates and the four harpooneers, who all crowded him to the deck. But sliding down the ropes like baleful comets, the two Canallers rushed into the uproar, and sought to drag their man out of it towards the forecastle. Others of the sailors joined with them in this attempt, and a twisted turmoil ensued; while standing out of harm's way, the valiant captain danced up and down with a whale-pike, calling upon his officers to man-handle that atrocious scoundrel, and smoke him along to the quarter-deck. At intervals, he ran close up to the revolving border of the confusion, and prying into the heart of it with his pike, sought to prick out the object of his resentment. But Steelkilt and his desperadoes were too much for them all; they succeeded in gaining the forecastle deck, where, hastily slewing about three or four large casks in a line with the windlass, these sea-Parisians entrenched themselves behind the barricade.

" 'Come out of that, ye pirates!' roared the captain, now menacing them with a pistol in each hand, just brought to him by the steward. 'Come out of that, ye cut-throats!'

"Steelkilt leaped on the barricade, and striding up and down there, defied the worst the pistols could do; but gave the captain to understand distinctly, that his (Steelkilt's) death would be the signal for a murderous mutiny on the part of all hands. Fearing in his heart lest this might prove but too true, the captain a little desisted, but still commanded the insurgents instantly to return to their duty.

" 'Will you promise not to touch us, if we do?' demanded their ringleader.

" 'Turn to! turn to!—I make no promise;—to your duty! Do you want to sink the ship, by knocking off at a time like this? Turn to!' and he once more raised a pistol.

" 'Sink the ship?' cried Steelkilt. 'Ay, let her sink. Not a man of us turns to, unless you swear not to raise a rope-yarn against us. What say ye, men?' turning to his comrades. A fierce cheer was their response.

"The Lakeman now patrolled the barricade, all the while keeping his eye on the Captain, and jerking out such sentences as these:—'It's not our fault; we didn't want it; I told him to take his hammer away; it was boy's business; he might have known me before this; I told him not to prick the Buffalo; I believe I have broken a finger here against his cursed jaw; ain't those mincing knives down in the forecastle there, men? look to those handspikes, my hearties. Captain, by God, look to yourself; say the word; don't be a fool; forget it all; we are ready to turn to! treat us decently, and we're your men; but we won't be flogged.'

" 'Turn to! I make no promises, turn to, I say!'

" 'Look ye, now,' cried the Lakeman, flinging out his arm towards him, 'there are a few of us here (and I am one of them) who have shipped for the cruise, d'ye see; now as you well know, sir, we can claim our discharge as soon as the anchor is down; so we don't want a row; it's not our interest; we want to be peaceable; we are ready to work, but we won't be flogged.'

" 'Turn to!' roared the Captain.

"Steelkilt glanced round him a moment, and then said: 'I tell you what it is now, Captain, rather than kill ye, and be hung for such a shabby rascal, we won't lift a hand against ye unless ye attack us; but till you say the word about not flogging us, we don't do a hand's turn.'

" 'Down into the forecastle then, down with ye, I'll keep ye there till ye're sick of it. Down ye go.'

" 'Shall we?' cried the ringleader to his men. Most of them were against it; but at length, in obedience to Steelkilt, they preceded him down into their dark den, growlingly disappearing, like bears into a cave.

"As the Lakeman's bare head was just level with the planks, the Captain and his posse leaped the barricade, and rapidly drawing over the slide of the scuttle, planted their group of hands upon it, and loudly called for the steward to bring the heavy brass padlock belonging to the companionway. Then opening the slide a little, the Captain whispered something down the crack, closed it, and turned the key upon them—ten in number—leaving on deck some twenty or more, who thus far had remained neutral.

"All night a wide-awake watch was kept by all the officers, forward and aft, especially about the forecastle scuttle and fore-hatchway; at which last place it was feared the insurgents might emerge, after breaking through the bulkhead below. But the hours of darkness passed in peace; the men who still remained at their duty toiling hard at the pumps, whose clinking and clanking at intervals through the dreary night dismally resounded through the ship.

"At sunrise the Captain went forward, and knocking on the deck, summoned the prisoners to work; but with a yell they refused. Water was then lowered down to them, and a couple of handfuls of biscuit were tossed after it; when again turning the key upon them and pocketing it, the Captain returned to the quarter-deck. Twice every day for three days this was repeated; but on the fourth morning a confused wrangling, and then a scuffling was heard, as the customary summons was delivered; and suddenly four men burst up from the forecastle, saying they were ready to turn to. The fetid closeness of the air, and a famishing diet, united perhaps to some fears of ultimate retribution, had constrained them to surrender at discretion. Emboldened by this, the Captain reiterated his demand to the rest, but Steelkilt shouted up to him a terrific hint to stop his babbling and betake himself where he belonged. On the fifth morning three others of the mutineers bolted up into the air from the desperate arms below that sought to restrain them. Only three were left.

" 'Better turn to, now?' said the Captain with a heartless jeer.

" 'Shut us up again, will ye!' cried Steelkilt.

" 'Oh! certainly,' " said the Captain, and the key clicked.

"It was at this point, gentlemen, that enraged by the defection of seven of his former associates, and stung by the mocking voice that had last hailed him, and maddened by his long entombment in a place as black as the bowels of despair; it was then that Steelkilt proposed to the two Canallers, thus far apparently of one mind with him, to burst out of their hole at the next summoning of the garrison; and armed with their keen mincing knives (long, crescentic, heavy implements with a handle at each end) run amuck from the bowsprit to the taffrail; and if by any devilishness of desperation possible, seize the ship. For himself, he would do this, he said, whether they joined him or not. That was the last night he should spend in that den. But the scheme met with no opposition on the part of the other two; they swore they were ready for that, or for any other mad thing, for anything in short but a surrender. And what was more, they each insisted upon being the first man on deck, when the time to make the rush should come. But to this their leader as fiercely objected, reserving that priority for himself; particularly as his two comrades would not yield, the one to the other, in the matter; and both of them could not be first, for the ladder would but admit one man at a time. And here, gentlemen, the foul play of these miscreants must come out.

"Upon hearing the frantic project of their leader, each in his own separate soul had suddenly lighted, it would seem, upon the same piece of treachery, namely: to be the foremost in breaking out, in order to be the first of the three, though the last of the ten, to surrender; and thereby secure whatever small chance of pardon such conduct might merit. But when Steelkilt made known his determination still to lead them to the last, they in some way, by some subtle chemistry of villainy, mixed their before secret treacheries together; and when their leader fell into a doze, verbally opened their souls to each other in three sentences; and bound the sleeper with cords, and gagged him with cords; and shrieked out for the Captain at midnight.

"Thinking murder at hand, and smelling in the dark for the blood, he and all his armed mates and harpooneers rushed for the forecastle. In a few minutes the scuttle was opened, and, bound hand and foot, the still struggling ringleader was shoved up into the air by his perfidious allies, who at once claimed the honor of securing a man who had been fully ripe for murder. But all these were collared, and dragged along the deck like dead cattle; and, side by side, were seized up into the mizzen rigging, like three quarters of meat, and there they hung till morning. 'Damn ye,' cried the Captain, pacing to and fro before them, 'the vultures would not touch ye, ye villains!'

"At sunrise he summoned all hands; and separating those who had rebelled from those who had taken no part in the mutiny, he told the former that he had a good mind to flog them all round—thought, upon the while, he would do so—he ought to—justice demanded it; but for the present, considering their timely surrender, he would let them go with a reprimand, which he accordingly administered in the vernacular.

" 'But as for you, ye carrion rogues,' turning to the three men in the rigging—'for you, I mean to mince ye up for the try-pots'; and, seizing a rope, he applied it with all his might to the backs of the two traitors, till they yelled no more, but lifelessly hung their heads sideways, as the two crucified thieves are drawn.

" 'My wrist is sprained with ye!' he cried, at last; 'but there is still rope enough left for you, my fine bantam, that wouldn't give up. Take that gag from his mouth, and let us hear what he can say for himself.'

"For a moment the exhausted mutineer made a tremulous motion of his cramped jaws, and then painfully twisting round his head, said in a sort of hiss, 'What I say is this—and mind it well—if you flog me, I murder you!'

" 'Say ye so? then see how ye frighten me'—and the Captain drew off with the rope to strike.

" 'Best not,' hissed the Lakeman.

" 'But I must'—and the rope was once more drawn back for the stroke.

"Steelkilt here hissed out something, inaudible to all but the Captain; who, to the amazement of all hands, started back, paced the deck rapidly two or three times, and then suddenly throwing down his rope said, 'I won't do it—let him go—cut him down: d'ye hear?'

"But as the junior mates were hurrying to execute the order, a pale man, with a bandaged head, arrested them—Radney the chief mate. Ever since the blow, he had lain in his berth; but that morning hearing the tumult on the deck, he had crept out, and thus far had watched the whole scene. Such was the state of his mouth, that he could hardly speak; but mumbling something about *his* being willing and able to do what the captain dared not attempt, he snatched the rope and advanced to his pinioned foe.

" 'You are a coward!' hissed the Lakeman.

" 'So I am, but take that.' The mate was in the very act of striking, when another hiss stayed his uplifted arm. He paused: and then pausing no more, made good his word, spite of Steelkilt's threat, whatever that might have been. The three men were then cut down, all hands were turned to, and, sullenly worked by the moody seamen, the iron pumps clanged as before.

"Just after dark that day, when one watch had retired below, a clamor was heard in the forecastle; and the two trembling traitors running up, besieged the cabin-door, saying they durst not consort with the crew. Entreaties, cuffs, and kicks could not drive them back, so at their own instance they were put down in the ship's run for salvation. Still, no sign of mutiny reappeared among the rest. On the contrary, it seemed, that mainly at Steelkilt's instigation, they had resolved to maintain the strictest peacefulness, obey all orders to the last, and, when the ship reached port, desert her in a body. But in order to ensure the speediest end to the voyage, they all agreed to another thing—namely, not to sing out for whales, in case any should be discovered. For, spite of her leak, and spite of all her other perils, the *Town-Ho* still maintained her mast-heads, and her captain was just as willing to lower for a fish that moment, as on the day his craft first struck the cruising-ground; and Radney the mate was quite as ready to change his berth for a boat, and with his bandaged mouth seek to gag in death the vital jaw of the whale.

"But though the Lakeman had induced the seamen to adopt this sort of passiveness in their conduct, he kept his own counsel (at least till all was over) concerning his own proper and private revenge upon the man who had stung him in the ventricles of his heart. He was in Radney the chief mate's watch; and as if the infatuated man sought to run more than half-way to meet his doom, after the scene at the rigging, he insisted, against the express counsel of the captain, upon resuming the head of his watch at night. Upon this, and one or two other circumstances, Steelkilt systematically built the plan of his revenge.

"During the night, Radney had an unseaman-like way of sitting on the bulwarks of the quarter-deck, and leaning his arm upon the gunwale of the boat which was hoisted up there, a little above the ship's side. In this attitude, it was well known, he sometimes dozed. There was a considerable vacancy between the boat and the ship, and down between this was the sea. Steelkilt calculated his time, and found that his next trick at the helm would come round at two o'clock, in the morning of the third day from that in which he had been betrayed. At his leisure, he employed the interval in braiding something very carefully in his watches below.

" 'What are you making there?' said a shipmate.

" 'What do you think? what does it look like?'

" 'Like a lanyard for your bag; but it's an odd one, seems to me.'

" 'Yes, rather oddish,' said the Lakeman, holding it at arm's length before him; 'but I think it will answer. Shipmate, I haven't enough twine—have you any?'

"But there was none in the forecastle.

" 'Then I must get some from old Rad'; and he rose to go aft.

" 'You don't mean to go a begging to *him!*' said a sailor.

" 'Why not? Do you think he won't do me a turn, when it's to help himself in the end, shipmate?' and going to the mate, he looked at him quietly, and asked him for some twine to mend his hammock. It was given him—neither twine nor lanyard were seen again; but the next night an iron ball, closely netted, partly rolled from the pocket of the Lakeman's monkey jacket, as he was tucking the coat into his hammock for a pillow. Twenty-four hours after, his trick at the silent helm—nigh to the man who was apt to doze over the grave always ready dug to the seaman's hand—that fatal hour was then to come; and in the fore-ordaining soul of Steelkilt, the mate was already stark and stretched as a corpse, with his forehead crushed in.

"But, gentlemen, a fool saved the would-be murderer from the bloody deed he had planned. Yet complete revenge he had, and without being the avenger. For by a mysterious fatality,

Heaven itself seemed to step in to take out of his hands into its own the damning thing he would have done.

"It was just between daybreak and sunrise of the morning of the second day, when they were washing down the decks, that a stupid Teneriffe man, drawing water in the main-chains, all at once shouted out, 'There she rolls! there she rolls! Jesu, what a whale!' It was Moby-Dick.

" 'Moby-Dick!' cried Don Sebastian; 'St. Dominic! Sir sailor, but do whales have christenings? Whom call you Moby-Dick?'

" 'A very white, and famous, and most deadly immortal monster, Don;—but that would be too long a story.'

" 'How? how?' cried all the young Spaniards, crowding.

" 'Nay, Dons, Dons—nay, nay! I cannot rehearse that now. Let me get more into the air, Sirs.'

" 'The chicha! the chicha!' cried Don Pedro; 'our vigorous friend looks faint;—fill up his empty glass!'

"No need, gentlemen; one moment, and I proceed.—Now, gentlemen, so suddenly perceiving the snowy whale within fifty yards of the ship—forgetful of the compact among the crew—in the excitement of the moment, the Teneriffe man had instinctively and involuntarily lifted his voice for the monster, though for some little time past it had been plainly beheld from the three sullen mast-heads. All was now a phrensy. 'The White Whale—the White Whale!' was the cry from captain, mates, and harpooneers, who, undeterred by fearful rumors, were all anxious to capture so famous and precious a fish; while the dogged crew eyed askance, and with curses, the appalling beauty of the vast milky mass, that lit up by a horizontal spangling sun, shifted and glistened like a living opal in the blue morning sea. Gentlemen, a strange fatality pervades the whole career of these events, as if verily mapped out before the world itself was charted. The mutineer was the bowsman of the mate, and when fast to a fish, it was his duty to sit next him, while Radney stood up with his lance in the prow, and haul in or slacken the line, at the word of command. Moreover, when the four boats were lowered, the mate's got the start; and none howled more fiercely with delight than did Steelkilt, as he strained at his oar. After a stiff pull, their harpooneer got fast, and, spear in hand, Radney sprang to the bow. He was always a furious man, it seems, in a boat. And now his bandaged cry was, to beach him on the whale's topmost back. Nothing loath, his bowsman hauled him up and up, through a blinding foam that blent two whitenesses together; till of a sudden the boat struck as against a sunken ledge, and keeling over, spilled out the standing mate. That instant, as he fell on the whale's slippery back, the boat righted, and was dashed aside by the swell, while Radney was tossed over into the sea, on the other flank of the whale. He struck out through the spray, and, for an instant, was dimly seen through that veil, wildly seeking to remove himself from the eye of Moby-Dick. But the whale rushed round in a sudden maelstrom; seized the swimmer between his jaws; and rearing high up with him, plunged headlong again, and went down.

"Meantime, at the first tap of the boat's bottom, the Lakeman had slackened the line, so as to drop astern from the whirlpool; calmly looking on, he thought his own thoughts. But a sudden, terrific, downward jerking of the boat, quickly brought his knife to the line. He cut it; and the whale was free. But, at some distance, Moby-Dick rose again, with some tatters of Radney's red woolen shirt, caught in the teeth that had destroyed him. All four boats gave chase again; but the whale eluded them, and finally wholly disappeared.

"In good time, the *Town-Ho* reached her port—a savage, solitary place—where no civilized creature resided. There, headed by the Lakeman, all but five or six of the fore-mast-men deliberately deserted among the palms; eventually, as it turned out, seizing a large double war-canoe of the savages, and setting sail for some other harbor.

"The ship's company being reduced to but a handful, the captain called upon the islanders to assist him in the laborious business of heaving down the ship to stop the leak. But to such unresting vigilance over their dangerous allies was this small band of whites necessitated, both by night and by day, and so extreme was the hard work they underwent, that upon the vessel being ready again for sea, they were in such a weakened condition that the captain durst not put off with them in so heavy a vessel. After taking counsel with his officers, he anchored the ship as far off-shore as possible; loaded and ran out his two cannon from the bows; stacked his muskets on the poop; and warning the islanders not to approach the ship at their peril, took one man with him, and setting the sail of his best whale-boat, steered straight before the wind for Tahiti, five hundred miles distant, to procure a reinforcement to his crew.

"On the fourth day of the sail, a large canoe was descried, which seemed to have touched at a low isle of corals. He steered away from it; but the savage craft bore down on him; and soon the voice of Steelkilt hailed him to heave to, or he would run him under water. The captain presented a pistol. With one foot on each prow of the yoked war-canoes, the Lakeman laughed him to scorn; assuring him that if the pistol so much as clicked in the lock, he would bury him in bubbles and foam.

" 'What do you want of me?' cried the captain.

" 'Where are you bound? and for what are you bound?' demanded Steelkilt; 'no lies.'

" 'I am bound to Tahiti for more men.'

" 'Very good. Let me board you a moment—I come in peace.' With that he leaped from the canoe, swam to the boat; and climbing the gunwale, stood face to face with the captain.

" 'Cross your arms, sir; throw back your head. Now, repeat after me. As soon as Steelkilt leaves me, I swear to beach this boat on yonder island, and remain there six days. If I do not, may lightnings strike me!'

" 'A pretty scholar,' laughed the Lakeman. 'Adios, Señor!' and leaping into the sea, he swam back to his comrades.

"Watching the boat till it was fairly beached, and drawn up to the roots of the cocoanut-trees, Steelkilt made sail again, and in due time arrived at Tahiti, his own place of destination. There, luck befriended him; two ships were about to sail for France, and were providentially in want of precisely that number of men which the sailor headed. They embarked, and so forever got the start of their former captain, had he been at all minded to work them legal retribution.

"Some ten days after the French ships sailed, the whale-boat arrived, and the captain was forced to enlist some of the more civilized Tahitians, who had been somewhat used to the sea. Chartering a small native schooner, he returned with them to his vessel; and finding all right there, again resumed his cruisings.

"Where Steelkilt now is, gentlemen, none know; but upon the island of Nantucket, the widow of Radney still turns to the sea which refuses to give up its dead; still in dreams sees the awful White Whale that destroyed him.

* * * * *

" 'Are you through?' said Don Sebastian, quietly.

" 'I am, Don.'

" 'Then I entreat you, tell me if to the best of your own convictions, this your story is in substance really true? It is so passing wonderful! Did you get it from an unquestionable source? Bear with me if I seem to press.'

" 'Also bear with all of us, sir sailor; for we all join in Don Sebastian's suit,' cried the company, with exceeding interest.

" 'Is there a copy of the Holy Evangelists in the Golden Inn, gentlemen?'

" 'Nay,' said Don Sebastian; 'but I know a worthy priest nearby, who will quickly procure one for me. I go for it; but are you well advised? this may grow too serious.'

" 'Will you be so good as to bring the priest also, Don?'

" 'Though there are no Auto-da-Fé's in Lima now,' said one of the company to another; 'I fear our sailor friend runs risk of the archiepiscopacy. Let us withdraw more out of the moonlight. I see no need of this.'

" 'Excuse me for running after you, Don Sebastian; but may I also beg that you will be particular in procuring the largest sized Evangelists you can.'

" 'This is the priest, he brings you the Evangelists,' said Don Sebastian, gravely, returning with a tall and solemn figure.

" 'Let me remove my hat. Now, venerable priest, further into the light, and hold the Holy Book before me that I may touch it.

" 'So help me Heaven, and on my honor the story I have told ye, gentlemen, is in substance and its great items, true. I know it to be true; it happened on this ball; I trod the ship; I knew the crew; I have seen and talked with Steelkilt since the death of Radney.' "

Chapter LV

OF THE MONSTROUS PICTURES OF WHALES

I SHALL ERE LONG PAINT TO YOU AS WELL AS ONE CAN WITHOUT CANVAS, SOMETHING LIKE THE true form of the whale as he actually appears to the eye of the whaleman when in his own absolute body the whale is moored alongside the whale-ship so that he can be fairly stepped upon there. It may be worthwhile, therefore, previously to advert to those curious imaginary portraits of him which even down to the present day confidently challenge the faith of the landsman. It is time to set the world right in this matter, by proving such pictures of the whale all wrong.

It may be that the primal source of all those pictorial delusions will be found among the oldest Hindoo, Egyptian, and Grecian sculptures. Forever since those inventive but unscrupulous times when on the marble panelings of temples, the pedestals of statues, and on shields, medallions, cups, and coins, the dolphin was drawn in scales of chain-armor like Saladin's, and a helmeted head like St. George's; ever since then has something of the same sort of license prevailed, not only in most popular pictures of the whale, but in many scientific presentations of him.

Now, by all odds, the most ancient extant portrait anyways purporting to be the whale's, is to be found in the famous cavern-pagoda of Elephants, in India. The Brahmins maintain that in the almost endless sculptures of that immemorial pagoda, all the trades and pursuits, every conceivable avocation of man, were prefigured ages before any of them actually came into being. No wonder then, that in some sort our noble profession of whaling should have been there shadowed forth. The Hindoo whale referred to, occurs in a separate department of the wall, depicting the incarnation of Vishnu in the form of leviathan, learnedly known as the Matse Avatar. But though this sculpture is half man and half whale, so as only to give the tail of the latter, yet that small section of him is all wrong. It looks more like the tapering tail of an anaconda, than the broad palms of the true whale's majestic flukes.

But go to the old Galleries, and look now at a great Christian painter's portrait of this fish; for he succeeds no better than the antediluvian Hindoo. It is Guido's picture of Perseus rescuing Andromeda from the sea-monster or whale. Where did Guido get the model of such a strange creature as that? Nor does Hogarth, in painting the same scene in his own *Perseus Descending*, make out one whit better. The huge corpulence of that Hogarthian monster undulates on the surface, scarcely drawing one inch of water. It has a sort of howdah on its back, and its distended tusked mouth into which the billows are rolling, might be taken for the Traitors' Gate leading from the Thames by water into the Tower. Then, there are the Prodromus whales of the old Scotch Sibbald, and Jonah's whale, as depicted in the prints of old Bibles and the cuts of old primers. What shall be said of these? As for the bookbinder's whale winding like a vine-stalk round the stock of a descending anchor—as stamped and gilded on the backs and title-pages of many books both old and new—that is a very picturesque but purely fabulous creature, imitated, I take it, from the like figures on antique vases. Though universally denominated a dolphin, I nevertheless call this bookbinder's fish an attempt at a whale; because it was so intended when the device was first introduced. It was introduced by an old Italian publisher somewhere about the 15th century, during the Revival of Learning; and in those days, and even down to a comparatively late period, dolphins were popularly supposed to be a species of the Leviathan.

In the vignettes and other embellishments of some ancient books you will at times meet with very curious touches at the whale, where all manner of spouts, jets d'eau, hot-springs and cold, Saratoga and Baden-Baden, come bubbling up from his unexhausted brain. In the title-page of the original edition of the *Advancement of Learning* you will find some curious whales.

But quitting all these unprofessional attempts, let us glance at those pictures of leviathan purporting to be sober, scientific delineations, by those who know. In old Harris's collection of voyages there are some plates of whales extracted from a Dutch book of voyages, A.D. 1671, entitled *A Whaling Voyage to Spitzbergen in the ship Jonas in the Whale, Peter Peterson of Friesland, master.* In one of those plates the whales, like great rafts of logs, are represented lying among ice-isles, with white bears running over their living backs. In another plate, the prodigious blunder is made of representing the whale with perpendicular flukes.

Then again, there is an imposing quarto, written by one Captain Colnett, a Post Captain in the English navy, entitled *A Voyage round Cape Horn into the South Seas, for the purpose of extending the Spermaceti Whale Fisheries.* In this book is an outline purporting to be a *Picture of a Physeter or Spermaceti whale, drawn by scale from one killed on the coast of Mexico, August, 1793, and hoisted on deck.* I doubt not the captain had this veracious picture taken for the benefit of his marines. To mention but one thing about it, let me say that it has an eye which applied, according to the accompanying scale, to a full grown sperm whale, would make the eye of that whale a bow-window some five feet long. Ah, my gallant captain, why did ye not give us Jonah looking out of that eye!

Nor are the most conscientious compilations of Natural History for the benefit of the young and tender, free from the same heinousness of mistake. Look at that popular work *Goldsmith's Animated Nature.* In the abridged London edition of 1807, there are plates of an alleged "whale" and a "narwhale." I do not wish to seem inelegant, but this unsightly whale looks much like an amputated sow; and, as for the narwhale, one glimpse at it is enough to amaze one, that in this nineteenth century such a hippogriff could be palmed for genuine upon any intelligent public of schoolboys.

Then, again, in 1825, Bernard Germain, Count de Lacépède, a great naturalist, published a scientific systemized whale book, wherein are several pictures of the different species of the Leviathan. All these are not only incorrect, but the picture of the Mysticetus or Greenland whale (that is to say, the Right whale), even Scoresby, a long experienced man as touching that species, declares not to have its counterpart in nature.

But the placing of the cap-sheaf to all this blundering business was reserved for the scientific Frederick Cuvier, brother to the famous Baron. In 1836, he published a *Natural History of Whales*, in which he gives what he calls a picture of the Sperm Whale. Before showing that picture to any Nantucketer, you had best provide for your summary retreat from Nantucket. In a word, Frederick Cuvier's Sperm Whale is not a Sperm Whale, but a squash. Of course, he never had the benefit of a whaling voyage (such men seldom have), but whence he derived that picture, who can tell? Perhaps he got it as his scientific predecessor in the same field, Desmarest, got one of his authentic abortions; that is, from a Chinese drawing. And what sort of lively lads with the pencil those Chinese are, many queer cups and saucers inform us.

As for the sign-painters' whales seen in the streets hanging over the shops of oil-dealers, what shall be said of them? They are generally Richard III whales, with dromedary humps, and very savage; breakfasting on three or four sailor tarts, that is whale-boats full of mariners: their deformities floundering in seas of blood and blue paint.

But these manifold mistakes in depicting the whale are not so very surprising after all. Consider! Most of the scientific drawings have been taken from the stranded fish; and these are about as correct as a drawing of a wrecked ship, with broken back, would correctly represent the noble animal itself in all its undashed pride of hull and spars. Though elephants have stood for their full-lengths, the living Leviathan has never yet fairly floated himself for his portrait. The living whale, in his full majesty and significance, is only to be seen at sea in unfathomable waters; and afloat the vast bulk of him is out of sight, like a launched line-of-battle-ship; and out of that element it is a thing eternally impossible for mortal man to hoist him bodily into the air, so as to preserve all his mighty swells and undulations. And, not to speak of the highly presumable difference of contour between a young suckling whale and a full-grown Platonian Leviathan; yet, even in the case of one of those young sucking whales hoisted to a ship's deck, such is then the outlandish, eel-like, limbered, varying shape of him, that his precise expression the devil himself could not catch.

But it may be fancied, that from the naked skeleton of the stranded whale, accurate hints may be derived touching his true form. Not at all. For it is one of the more curious things about this Leviathan, that his skeleton gives very little idea of his general shape. Though Jeremy Bentham's skeleton, which hangs for candelabra in the library of one of his executors, correctly conveys the idea of a burly-browed utilitarian old gentleman, with all Jeremy's other leading personal characteristics; yet nothing of this kind could be inferred from any leviathan's articulated bones. In fact, as the great Hunter says, the mere skeleton of the whale bears the same relation to the fully invested and padded animal as the insect does to the chrysalis that so roundingly envelopes it. This peculiarity is strikingly evinced in the head, as in some part of this book will be incidentally shown. It is also very curiously displayed in the side fin, the bones of which almost exactly answer to the bones of the human hand, minus only the thumb. This fin has four regular bone-fingers, the index, middle, ring and little finger. But all these are permanently lodged in their fleshy covering, as the human fingers in an artificial covering. "However recklessly the whale may sometimes serve us," said humorous Stubb one day, "he can never be truly said to handle us without mittens."

For all these reasons, then, any way you may look at it, you must needs conclude that the great Leviathan is that one creature in the world which must remain unpainted to the last. True, one portrait may hit the mark much nearer than another, but none can hit it with any very considerable degree of exactness. So there is no earthly way of finding out precisely what the whale really looks like. And the only mode in which you can derive even a tolerable idea of his living contour, is by going a-whaling yourself; but by so doing, you run no small risk of being eternally stove and sunk by him. Wherefore, it seems to me you had best not be too fastidious in your curiosity touching this Leviathan.

Chapter LVI

OF THE LESS ERRONEOUS PICTURES OF WHALES, AND THE TRUE PICTURES OF WHALING SCENES

IN CONNECTION WITH THE MONSTROUS PICTURES OF WHALES, I AM STRONGLY TEMPTED HERE TO enter upon those still more monstrous stories of them which are to be found in certain books, both ancient and modern, especially in Pliny, Purchas, Hackluyt, Harris, Cuvier, &c. But I pass that matter by.

I know of only four published outlines of the great Sperm Whale; Colnett's, Huggins's, Frederick Cuvier's, and Beale's. In the previous chapter Colnett and Cuvier have been referred to. Huggins's is far better than theirs; but, by great odds, Beale's is the best. All Beale's drawings of this whale are good, excepting the middle figure in the picture of three whales in various attitudes, capping his second chapter. His frontispiece, boats attacking Sperm Whales, though no doubt calculated to excite the civil skepticism of some parlor men, is admirably correct and life-like in its general effect. Some of the Sperm Whale drawings in J. Ross Browne are pretty correct in contour; but they are wretchedly engraved. That is not his fault though.

Of the Right Whale, the best outline pictures are in Scoresby; but they are drawn on too small a scale to convey a desirable impression. He has but one picture of whaling scenes, and this is a sad deficiency, because it is by such pictures only, when at all well done, that you can derive anything like a truthful idea of the living whale as seen by his living hunters.

But, taken for all in all, by far the finest, though in some details not the most correct, presentations of whales and whaling scenes to be anywhere found, are two large French engravings, well executed, and taken from paintings by one Garnery. Respectively, they represent attacks on the Sperm and Right Whale. In the first engraving a noble Sperm Whale is depicted in full majesty of might, just risen beneath the boat from the profundities of the ocean, and bearing high in the air upon his back the terrific wreck of the stoven planks. The prow of the boat is partially unbroken, and is drawn just balancing upon the monster's spine; and standing in that prow, for that one single incomputable flash of time, you behold an oarsman, half shrouded by the incensed boiling spout of the whale, and in the act of leaping, as if from a precipice. The action of the whole thing is wonderfully good and true. The half-emptied line-tub floats on the whitened sea; the wooden poles of the spilled harpoons obliquely bob in it; the heads of the swimming crew are scattered about the whale in contrasting expressions of affright; while in the black stormy distance the ship is bearing down upon the scene. Serious fault might be found with the anatomical details of this whale, but let that pass; since, for the life of me, I could not draw so good a one.

In the second engraving, the boat is in the act of drawing alongside the barnacled flank of a large running Right Whale, that rolls his black weedy bulk in the sea like some mossy rock-slide from the Patagonian cliffs. His jets are erect, full, and black like soot; so that from so abounding a smoke in the chimney, you would think there must be a brave supper cooking in the great bowels below. Sea-fowls are pecking at the small crabs, shell-fish, and other sea candies and maccaroni, which the Right Whale sometimes carries on his pestilent back. And all the while the thick-lipped leviathan is rushing through the deep, leaving tons of tumultuous white curds in his wake, and causing the slight boat to rock in the swells like a skiff caught nigh the paddle-wheels of an ocean steamer. Thus, the foreground is all raging commotion; but behind, in admirable artistic contrast, is the glassy level of a sea becalmed, the drooping unstarched sails of the powerless ship, and the inert mass of a dead whale, a conquered fortress, with the flag of capture lazily hanging from the whale-pole inserted into his spout-hole.

Who Garnery the painter is, or was, I know not. But my life for it he was either practically conversant with his subject, or else marvelously tutored by some experienced whaleman. The French are the lads for painting action. Go and gaze upon all the paintings in Europe, and where will you find such a gallery of living and breathing commotion on canvas, as in that triumphal hall at Versailles; where the beholder fights his way, pell-mell through the consecutive great battles of France; where every sword seems a flash of the Northern Lights, and the successive armed kings and Emperors dash by, like a charge of crowned centaurs? Not wholly unworthy of a place in that gallery, are these sea-battle-pieces of Garnery.

The natural aptitude of the French for seizing the picturesqueness of things seems to be peculiarly evinced in what paintings and engravings they have of their whaling scenes. With not one tenth of England's experience in the fishery, and not the thousandth part of that of the Americans, they have nevertheless furnished both nations with the only finished sketches at all capable of conveying the real spirit of the whale hunt. For the most part, the English and American whale draftsmen seem entirely content with presenting the mechanical outline of things, such as the vacant profile of the whale; which, so far as picturesqueness of effect is concerned, is about tantamount to sketching the profile of a pyramid. Even Scoresby, the justly renowned Right whaleman, after giving us a stiff full length of the Greenland whale, and three or four delicate miniatures of narwhales and porpoises, treats us to a series of classical engravings of boat hooks, chopping knives, and grapnels; and with the microscopic diligence of a Leuwenhoeck submits to the inspection of a shivering world ninety-six fac-similes of magnified Arctic snow crystals. I mean no disparagement to the excellent voyager (I honor him for a veteran), but in so important a matter it was certainly an oversight not to have procured for every crystal a sworn affidavit taken before a Greenland Justice of the Peace.

In addition to those fine engravings from Garnery, there are two other French engravings worthy of note, by someone who subscribes himself "H. Durand." One of them, though not precisely adapted to our present purpose, nevertheless deserves mention on other accounts. It is a quiet noon-scene among the isles of the Pacific; a French whaler anchored, inshore, in a calm, and lazily taking water on board; the loosened sails of the ship, and the long leaves of the palms in the background, both drooping together in the breezeless air. The effect is very fine, when considered with reference to its presenting the hardy fishermen under one of their few aspects of oriental repose. The other engraving is quite a different affair: the ship hove-to upon the open sea, and in the very heart of the Leviathanic life, with a Right Whale alongside; the vessel (in the act of cutting-in) hove over to the monster as if to a quay; and a boat, hurriedly pushing off from this scene of activity, is about giving chase to whales in the distance. The harpoons and lances lie leveled for use; three oarsmen are just setting the mast in its hole; while from a sudden roll of the sea, the little craft stands half-erect out of the water, like a rearing horse. From that ship, the smoke of the torments of the boiling whale is going up like the smoke over a village of smithies; and to windward, a black cloud, rising up with earnest of squalls and rains, seems to quicken the activity of the excited seamen.

Chapter LVII

OF WHALES IN PAINT; IN TEETH; IN WOOD; IN SHEET-IRON; IN STONE; IN MOUNTAINS; IN STARS

ON TOWER-HILL, AS YOU GO DOWN TO THE LONDON DOCKS, YOU MAY HAVE SEEN A CRIPPLED beggar (or *kedger*, as the sailors say) holding a painted board before him, representing the tragic scene in which he lost his leg. There are three whales and three boats; and one of the boats (presumed to contain the missing leg in all its original integrity) is being crunched by the jaws of the foremost whale. Any time these ten years, they tell me, has that man held up that picture, and exhibited that stump to an incredulous world. But the time of his justification has now come. His three whales are as good whales as were ever published in Wapping, at any rate; and his stump as unquestionable a stump as any you will find in the western clearings. But, though forever mounted on that stump, never a stump-speech does the poor whaleman make; but, with downcast eyes, stands ruefully contemplating his own amputation.

Throughout the Pacific, and also in Nantucket, and New Bedford, and Sag Harbor, you will come across lively sketches of whales and whaling-scenes, graven by the fishermen themselves on Sperm Whale-teeth, or ladies' busks wrought out of the Right Whale-bone, and other like skrimshander articles, as the whalemen call the numerous little ingenious contrivances they elaborately carve out of the rough material, in their hours of ocean leisure. Some of them have little boxes of dentistical-looking implements, specially intended for the skrimshandering business. But, in general, they toil with their jack-knives alone; and, with that almost omnipotent tool of the sailor, they will turn you out anything you please, in the way of a mariner's fancy.

Long exile from Christendom and civilization inevitably restores a man to that condition in which God placed him, *i.e.* what is called savagery. Your true whale-hunter is as much a savage as an Iroquois. I myself am a savage, owning no allegiance but to the King of the Cannibals; and ready at any moment to rebel against him.

Now, one of the peculiar characteristics of the savage in his domestic hours, is his wonderful patience of industry. An ancient Hawaiian war-club or spear-paddle, in its full multiplicity and elaboration of carving, is as great a trophy of human perseverance as a Latin lexicon. For, with but a bit of broken sea-shell or a shark's tooth, that miraculous intricacy of wooden net-work has been achieved; and it has cost steady years of steady application.

As with the Hawaiian savage, so with the white sailor-savage. With the same marvelous patience, and with the same single shark's tooth, of his one poor jack-knife, he will carve you a bit of bone sculpture, not quite as workman-like, but as close packed in its maziness of design, as the Greek savage, Achilles's shield; and full of barbaric spirit and suggestiveness, as the prints of that fine old Dutch savage, Albert Dürer.

Wooden whales, or whales cut in profile out of the small dark slabs of the noble South Sea warwood, are frequently met with in the forecastles of American whalers. Some of them are done with much accuracy.

At some old gable-roofed country houses you will see brass whales hung by the tail for knockers to the road-side door. When the porter is sleepy, the anvil-headed whale would be best. But these knocking whales are seldom remarkable as faithful essays. On the spires of some old-fashioned churches you will see sheet-iron whales placed there for weather-cocks; but they are so elevated, and besides that are to all intents and purposes so labeled with *"Hands off!"* you cannot examine them closely enough to decide upon their merit.

In bony, ribby regions of the earth, where at the base of high broken cliffs masses of rock lie strewn in fantastic groupings upon the plain, you will often discover images as of the petrified forms of the Leviathan partly merged in grass, which of a windy day breaks against them in a surf of green surges.

Then, again, in mountainous countries where the traveler is continually girdled by amphitheatrical heights; here and there from some lucky point of view you will catch passing glimpses of the profiles of whales defined along the undulating ridges. But you must be a thorough whaleman, to see these sights; and not only that, but if you wish to return to such a sight again, you must be sure and take the exact intersecting latitude and longitude of your first stand-point, else so chance-like are such observations of the hills, that your precise, previous stand-point would require a laborious rediscovery; like the Solomon islands, which still remain incognita, though once high-ruffed Mendanna trod them and old Figuera chronicled them.

Nor when expandingly lifted by your subject, can you fail to trace out great whales in the starry heavens, and boats in pursuit of them; as when long filled with thoughts of war the Eastern nations saw armies locked in battle among the clouds. Thus at the north have I chased Leviathan round and round the Pole with the revolutions of the bright points that first defined him to me. And beneath the effulgent Antarctic skies I have boarded the Argo-Navis, and joined the chase against the starry Cetus far beyond the utmost stretch of Hydrus and the Flying Fish.

With a frigate's anchors for my bridle-bitts and fasces of harpoons for spurs, would I could mount that whale and leap the topmost skies, to see whether the fabled heavens with all their countless tents really lie encamped beyond my mortal sight!

Chapter LVIII

BRIT

STEERING NORTH-EASTWARD FROM THE CROZETTS, WE FELL IN WITH VAST MEADOWS OF BRIT, THE minute yellow substance, upon which the Right Whale largely feeds. For leagues and leagues it undulated round us, so that we seemed to be sailing through boundless fields of ripe and golden wheat.

On the second day, numbers of Right Whales were seen, who, secure from the attack of a Sperm Whaler like the *Pequod,* with open jaws sluggishly swam through the brit, which, adhering to the fringing fibers of that wondrous Venetian blind in their mouths, was in that manner separated from the water that escaped at the lip.

As morning mowers, who side by side slowly and seethingly advance their scythes through the long wet grass of marshy meads; even so these monsters swam, making a strange, grassy, cutting sound; and leaving behind them endless swaths of blue upon the yellow sea.[1]

But it was only the sound they made as they parted the brit which at all reminded one of mowers. Seen from the mast-heads, especially when they paused and were stationary for a while, their vast black forms looked more like lifeless masses of rock than anything else. And as in the great

1. That part of the sea known among whalemen as the "Brazil Banks" does not bear that name as the Banks of Newfoundland do, because of there being shallows and soundings there, but because of this remarkable meadow-like appearance, caused by the vast drifts of brit continually floating in those latitudes, where the Right Whale is often chased.

hunting countries of India, the stranger at a distance will sometimes pass on the plains recumbent elephants without knowing them to be such, taking them for bare, blackened elevations of the soil; even so, often, with him, who for the first time beholds this species of the leviathans of the sea. And even when recognized at last, their immense magnitude renders it very hard really to believe that such bulky masses of overgrowth can possibly be instinct, in all parts, with the same sort of life that lives in a dog or a horse.

Indeed, in other respects, you can hardly regard any creatures of the deep with the same feelings that you do those of the shore. For though some old naturalists have maintained that all creatures of the land are of their kind in the sea; and though taking a broad general view of the thing, this may very well be; yet coming to specialties, where, for example, does the ocean furnish any fish that in disposition answers to the sagacious kindness of the dog? The accursed shark alone can in any generic respect be said to bear comparative analogy to him.

But though, to landsmen in general, the native inhabitants of the seas have ever been regarded with emotions unspeakably unsocial and repelling; though we know the sea to be an everlasting terra incognita, so that Columbus sailed over numberless unknown worlds to discover his one superficial western one; though, by vast odds, the most terrific of all mortal disasters have immemorially and indiscriminately befallen tens and hundreds of thousands of those who have gone upon the waters; though but a moment's consideration will teach, that however baby man may brag of his science and skill, and however much, in a flattering future, that science and skill may augment; yet forever and forever, to the crack of doom, the sea will insult and murder him, and pulverize the stateliest, stiffest frigate he can make; nevertheless, by the continual repetition of these very impressions, man has lost that sense of the full awfulness of the sea which aboriginally belongs to it.

The first boat we read of, floated on an ocean, that with Portuguese vengeance had whelmed a whole world without leaving so much as a widow. That same ocean rolls now; that same ocean destroyed the wrecked ships of last year. Yea, foolish mortals, Noah's flood is not yet subsided; two thirds of the fair world it yet covers.

Wherein differ the sea and the land, that a miracle upon one is not a miracle upon the other? Preternatural terrors rested upon the Hebrews, when under the feet of Korah and his company the live ground opened and swallowed them up forever; yet not a modern sun ever sets, but in precisely the same manner the live sea swallows up ships and crews.

But not only is the sea such a foe to man who is an alien to it, but it is also a fiend to its own offspring; worse than the Persian host who murdered his own guests; sparing not the creatures which itself hath spawned. Like a savage tigress that tossing in the jungle overlays her own cubs, so the sea dashes even the mightiest whales against the rocks, and leaves them there side by side with the split wrecks of ships. No mercy, no power but its own controls it. Panting and snorting like a mad battle steed that has lost its rider, the masterless ocean overruns the globe.

Consider the subtleness of the sea; how its most dreaded creatures glide under water, unapparent for the most part, and treacherously hidden beneath the loveliest tints of azure. Consider also the devilish brilliance and beauty of many of its most remorseless tribes, as the dainty embellished shape of many species of sharks. Consider, once more, the universal cannibalism of the sea; all whose creatures prey upon each other, carrying on eternal war since the world began.

Consider all this; and then turn to this green, gentle, and most docile earth; consider them both, the sea and the land; and do you not find a strange analogy to something in yourself? For as this appalling ocean surrounds the verdant land, so in the soul of man there lies one insular Tahiti, full of peace and joy, but encompassed by all the horrors of the half known life. God keep thee! Push not off from that isle, thou canst never return!

Chapter LIX

SQUID

SLOWLY WADING THROUGH THE MEADOWS OF BRIT, THE *PEQUOD* STILL HELD ON HER WAY NORTH-eastward towards the island of Java; a gentle air impelling her keel, so that in the surrounding serenity her three tall tapering masts mildly waved to that languid breeze, as three mild palms on a plain. And still at wide intervals in the silvery night, the lonely, alluring jet would be seen.

But one transparent blue morning, when a stillness almost preternatural spread over the sea, however unattended with any stagnant calm; when the long burnished sun-glade on the waters seemed a golden finger laid across them, enjoining some secrecy; when the slippered waves whispered together as they softly ran on; in this profound hush of the visible sphere a strange specter was seen by Daggoo from the main-mast-head.

In the distance, a great white mass lazily rose, and rising higher and higher, and disentangling itself from the azure, at last gleamed before our prow like a snow-slide, new slid from the hills. Thus glistening for a moment, as slowly it subsided, and sank. Then once more arose, and silently gleamed. It seemed not a whale; and yet is this Moby-Dick? thought Daggoo. Again the phantom went down, but on reappearing once more, with a stiletto-like cry that startled every man from his nod, the negro yelled out—"There! there again! there she breaches! right ahead! The White Whale, the White Whale!"

Upon this, the seamen rushed to the yard-arms, as in swarming-time the bees rush to the boughs. Bare-headed in the sultry sun, Ahab stood on the bowsprit, and with one hand pushed far behind in readiness to wave his orders to the helmsman, cast his eager glance in the direction indicated aloft by the outstretched motionless arm of Daggoo.

Whether the flitting attendance of the one still and solitary jet had gradually worked upon Ahab, so that he was now prepared to connect the ideas of mildness and repose with the first sight of the particular whale he pursued; however this was, or whether his eagerness betrayed him; whichever way it might have been, no sooner did he distinctly perceive the white mass than with a quick intensity he instantly gave orders for lowering.

The four boats were soon on the water; Ahab's in advance, and all swiftly pulling towards their prey. Soon it went down, and while, with oars suspended, we were awaiting its reappearance, lo! in the same spot where it sank, once more it slowly rose. Almost forgetting for the moment all thoughts of Moby-Dick, we now gazed at the most wondrous phenomenon which the secret seas have hitherto revealed to mankind. A vast pulpy mass, furlongs in length and breadth, of a glancing cream-color, lay floating on the water, innumerable long arms radiating from its center, and curling and twisting like a nest of anacondas, as if blindly to catch at any hapless object within reach. No perceptible face or front did it have; no conceivable token of either sensation or instinct; but undulated there on the billows, an unearthly, formless, chance-like apparition of life.

As with a low sucking sound it slowly disappeared again, Starbuck still gazing at the agitated waters where it had sunk, with a wild voice exclaimed—"Almost rather had I seen Moby-Dick and fought him, than to have seen thee, thou white ghost!"

"What was it, Sir?" said Flask.

"The great live squid, which, they say, few whale-ships ever beheld, and returned to their ports to tell of it."

But Ahab said nothing; turning his boat, he sailed back to the vessel; the rest as silently following.

Whatever superstitions the sperm whalemen in general have connected with the sight of this object, certain it is, that a glimpse of it being so very unusual, that circumstance has gone far to invest it with portentousness. So rarely is it beheld, that though one and all of them declare it to be the largest animated thing in the ocean, yet very few of them have any but the most vague ideas concerning its true nature and form; notwithstanding, they believe it to furnish to the sperm whale his only food. For though other species of whales find their food above water, and may be seen by man in the act of feeding, the spermaceti whale obtains his whole food in unknown zones below the surface; and only by inference is it that anyone can tell of what, precisely, that food consists. At times, when closely pursued, he will disgorge what are supposed to be the detached arms of the squid; some of them thus exhibited exceeding twenty and thirty feet in length. They fancy that the monster to which these arms belonged ordinarily clings by them to the bed of the ocean; and that the sperm whale, unlike other species, is supplied with teeth in order to attack and tear it.

There seems some ground to imagine that the great Kraken of Bishop Pontoppodan may ultimately resolve itself into Squid. The manner in which the Bishop describes it, as alternately rising and sinking, with some other particulars he narrates, in all this the two correspond. But much abatement is necessary with respect to the incredible bulk he assigns it.

By some naturalists who have vaguely heard rumors of the mysterious creature, here spoken of, it is included among the class of cuttle-fish, to which, indeed, in certain external respects it would seem to belong, but only as the Anak of the tribe.

Chapter LX

The Line

With reference to the whaling scene shortly to be described, as well as for the better understanding of all similar scenes elsewhere presented, I have here to speak of the magical, sometimes horrible whale-line.

The line originally used in the fishery was of the best hemp, slightly vapored with tar, not impregnated with it, as in the case of ordinary ropes; for while tar, as ordinarily used, makes the hemp more pliable to the rope-maker, and also renders the rope itself more convenient to the sailor for common ship use; yet, not only would the ordinary quantity too much stiffen the whale-line for the close coiling to which it must be subjected; but as most seamen are beginning to learn, tar in general by no means adds to the rope's durability or strength, however much it may give it compactness and gloss.

Of late years the Manila rope has in the American fishery almost entirely superseded hemp as a material for whale-lines; for, though not so durable as hemp, it is stronger, and far more soft and elastic; and I will add (since there is an aesthetics in all things), is much more handsome and becoming to the boat, than hemp. Hemp is a dusky, dark fellow, a sort of Indian; but Manila is as a golden-haired Circassian to behold.

The whale-line is only two thirds of an inch in thickness. At first sight, you would not think it so strong as it really is. By experiment its one and fifty yarns will each suspend a weight of one hundred and twenty pounds; so that the whole rope will bear a strain nearly equal to three tons. In length, the common sperm whale-line measures something over two hundred fathoms. Towards the stern of the boat it is spirally coiled away in the tub, not like the worm-pipe of a still though, but so as to form one round, cheese-shaped mass of densely bedded "sheaves," or layers of concentric spiralizations, without any hollow but the "heart," or minute vertical tube formed at the axis of the cheese. As the least tangle or kink in the coiling would, in running out, infallibly take somebody's arm, leg, or entire body off, the utmost precaution is used in stowing the line in its tub. Some harpooneers will consume almost an entire morning in this business, carrying the line high aloft and then reeving it downwards through a block towards the tub, so as in the act of coiling to free it from all possible wrinkles and twists.

In the English boats two tubs are used instead of one; the same line being continuously coiled in both tubs. There is some advantage in this; because these twin-tubs being so small they fit more readily into the boat, and do not strain it so much; whereas, the American tub, nearly three feet in diameter and of proportionate depth, makes a rather bulky freight for a craft whose planks are but one half-inch in thickness; for the bottom of the whale-boat is like critical ice, which will bear up a considerable distributed weight, but not very much of a concentrated one. When the painted canvas cover is clapped on the American, tub-line, the boat looks as if it were pulling off with a prodigious great wedding-cake to present to the whales.

Both ends of the line are exposed; the lower end terminating in an eye-splice or loop coming up from the bottom against the side of the tub, and hanging over its edge completely disengaged from everything. This arrangement of the lower end is necessary on two accounts. First: In order to facilitate the fastening to it of an additional line from a neighboring boat, in case the stricken whale should sound so deep as to threaten to carry off the entire line originally attached to the harpoon. In these instances, the whale of course is shifted like a mug of ale, as it were, from the one boat to the other; though the first boat always hovers at hand to assist its consort. Second: This arrangement is indispensable for common safety's sake; for were the lower end of the line in any way attached to the boat, and were the whale then to run the line out to the end almost in a single, smoking minute as he sometimes does, he would not stop there, for the doomed boat would infallibly be dragged down after him into the profundity of the sea; and in that case no town-crier would ever find her again.

Before lowering the boat for the chase, the upper end of the line is taken aft from the tub, and passing round the loggerhead there, is again carried forward the entire length of the boat, resting crosswise upon the loom or handle of every man's oar, so that it jogs against his wrist in rowing; and also passing between the men, as they alternately sit at the opposite gunwales, to the leaded chocks or grooves in the extreme pointed prow of the boat, where a wooden pin or skewer the size of a common quill, prevents it from slipping out. From the chocks it hangs in a slight festoon over the bows, and is then passed inside the boat again; and some ten or twenty fathoms (called box-line) being coiled upon the box in the bows, it continues its way to the gunwale still a little further aft, and is then attached to the short-warp—the rope which is immediately connected with the harpoon; but previous to that connection, the short-warp goes through sundry mystifications too tedious to detail.

Thus the whale-line folds the whole boat in its complicated coils, twisting and writhing around it in almost every direction. All the oarsmen are involved in its perilous contortions; so that to the timid eye of the landsman, they seem as Indian jugglers, with the deadliest snakes sportively festooning their limbs. Nor can any son of mortal woman, for the first time, seat himself amid those hempen intricacies, and while straining his utmost at the oar, bethink him that at any unknown instant the harpoon may be darted, and all these horrible contortions be put in play like ringed lightnings; he cannot be thus circumstanced without a shudder that makes the very marrow in his bones to quiver in him like a shaken jelly. Yet habit—strange thing! what cannot habit accomplish?—Gayer sallies, more merry mirth, better jokes, and brighter repartees, you never heard over your mahogany, than you will hear over the half-inch white cedar of the whale-boat, when thus hung in hangman's nooses; and, like the six burghers of Calais before King Edward, the six men composing the crew pull into the jaws of death, with a halter around every neck, as you may say.

Perhaps a very little thought will now enable you to account for those repeated whaling disasters—some few of which are casually chronicled—of this man or that man being taken out of the boat by the line, and lost. For, when the line is darting out, to be seated then in the boat, is like being seated in the midst of the manifold whizzings of a steam-engine in full play, when every flying beam, and shaft, and wheel, is grazing you. It is worse; for you cannot sit motionless in the heart of these perils, because the boat is rocking like a cradle, and you are pitched one way and the other, without the slightest warning; and only by a certain self-adjusting buoyancy and simultaneousness of volition and action, can you escape being made a Mazeppa of, and run away with where the all-seeing sun himself could never pierce you out.

Again: as the profound calm which only apparently precedes and prophesies of the storm, is perhaps more awful than the storm itself; for, indeed, the calm is but the wrapper and envelope of the storm; and contains it in itself, as the seemingly harmless rifle holds the fatal powder, and the ball, and the explosion; so the graceful repose of the line, as it silently serpentines about the oarsmen before being brought into actual play—this is a thing which carries more of true terror than any other aspect of this dangerous affair. But why say more? All men live enveloped in whale-lines. All are born with halters round their necks; but it is only when caught in the swift, sudden turn of death, that mortals realize the silent, subtle, ever-present perils of life. And if you be a philosopher, though seated in the whale-boat, you would not at heart feel one whit more of terror, than though seated before your evening fire with a poker, and not a harpoon, by your side.

Chapter LXI

Stubb Kills a Whale

If to Starbuck the apparition of the squid was a thing of portents, to Queequeg it was quite a different object.

"When you see him 'quid," said the savage, honing his harpoon in the bow of his hoisted boat, "then you quick see him 'parm whale."

The next day was exceedingly still and sultry, and with nothing special to engage them, the *Pequod*'s crew could hardly resist the spell of sleep induced by such a vacant sea. For this part of the Indian Ocean through which we then were voyaging is not what whalemen call a lively ground; that is, it affords fewer glimpses of porpoises, dolphins, flying-fish, and other vivacious denizens of more stirring waters, than those off the Rio de la Plata, or the in-shore ground off Peru.

It was my turn to stand at the fore-mast-head; and with my shoulders leaning against the slackened royal shrouds, to and fro I idly swayed in what seemed an enchanted air. No resolution could withstand it; in that dreamy mood losing all consciousness, at last my soul went out of my body; though my body still continued to sway as a pendulum will, long after the power which first moved it is withdrawn.

Ere forgetfulness altogether came over me, I had noticed that the seamen at the main and mizzen mast-heads were already drowsy. So that at last all three of us lifelessly swung from the spars, and for every swing that we made there was a nod from below from the slumbering helmsman. The waves, too, nodded their indolent crests; and across the wide trance of the sea, east nodded to west, and the sun over all.

Suddenly bubbles seemed bursting beneath my closed eyes; like vices my hands grasped the shrouds; some invisible, gracious agency preserved me; with a shock I came back to life. And lo!

close under our lee, not forty fathoms off, a gigantic Sperm Whale lay rolling in the water like the capsized hull of a frigate, his broad, glossy back, of an Ethiopian hue, glistening in the sun's rays like a mirror. But lazily undulating in the trough of the sea, and ever and anon tranquilly spouting his vapory jet, the whale looked like a portly burgher smoking his pipe of a warm afternoon. But that pipe, poor whale, was thy last. As if struck by some enchanter's wand, the sleepy ship and every sleeper in it all at once started into wakefulness; and more than a score of voices from all parts of the vessel, simultaneously with the three notes from aloft, shouted forth the accustomed cry, as the great fish slowly and regularly spouted the sparkling brine into the air.

"Clear away the boats! Luff!" cried Ahab. And obeying his own order, he dashed the helm down before the helmsman could handle the spokes.

The sudden exclamations of the crew must have alarmed the whale; and ere the boats were down, majestically turning, he swam away to the leeward, but with such a steady tranquility, and making so few ripples as he swam, that thinking after all he might not as yet be alarmed, Ahab gave orders that not an oar should be used, and no man must speak but in whispers. So seated like Ontario Indians on the gunwales of the boats, we swiftly but silently paddled along; the calm not admitting of the noiseless sails being set. Presently, as we thus glided in chase, the monster perpendicularly flitted his tail forty feet into the air, and then sank out of sight like a tower swallowed up.

"There go flukes!" was the cry, an announcement immediately followed by Stubb's producing his match and igniting his pipe, for now a respite was granted. After the full interval of his sounding had elapsed, the whale rose again, and being now in advance of the smoker's boat, and much nearer to it than to any of the others, Stubb counted upon the honor of the capture. It was obvious, now, that the whale had at length become aware of his pursuers. All silence of cautiousness was therefore no longer of use. Paddles were dropped, and oars came loudly into play. And still puffing at his pipe, Stubb cheered on his crew to the assault.

Yes, a mighty change had come over the fish. All alive to his jeopardy, he was going "head out"; that part obliquely projecting from the mad yeast which he brewed.[1]

"Start her, start her, my men! Don't hurry yourselves; take plenty of time—but start her; start her like thunder-claps, that's all," cried Stubb, spluttering out the smoke as he spoke. "Start her, now; give 'em the long and strong stroke, Tashtego. Start her, Tash, my boy—start her, all; but keep cool, keep cool—cucumbers is the word—easy, easy—only start her like grim death and grinning devils, and raise the buried dead perpendicular out of their graves, boys—that's all. Start her!"

"Woo-hoo! Wa-hee!" screamed the Gay-Header in reply, raising some old war-whoop to the skies; as every oarsman in the strained boat involuntarily bounced forward with one tremendous leading stroke which the eager Indian gave.

But his wild screams were answered by others quite as wild. "Kee-hee! Kee-hee!" yelled Daggoo, straining forwards and backwards on his seat, like a pacing tiger in his cage.

"Ka-la! Koo-loo!" howled Queequeg, as if smacking his lips over a mouthful of Grenadier's steak. And thus with oars and yells the keels cut the sea. Meanwhile, Stubb retaining his place in the van, still encouraged his men to the onset, all the while puffing the smoke from his mouth. Like desperadoes they tugged and they strained, till the welcome cry was heard—"Stand up, Tashtego!—give it to him!" The harpoon was hurled. "Stern all!" The oarsmen backed water; the same moment

1. It will be seen in some other place of what a very light substance the entire interior of the sperm whale's enormous head consists. Though apparently the most massive, it is by far the most buoyant part about him. So that with ease he elevates it in the air, and invariably does so when going at his utmost speed. Besides, such is the breadth of the upper part of the front of his head, and such the tapering cut-water formation of the lower part, that by obliquely elevating his head, he thereby may be said to transform himself from a bluff-bowed sluggish galliot into a sharp-pointed New York pilot-boat.

something went hot and hissing along every one of their wrists. It was the magical line. An instant before, Stubb had swiftly caught two additional turns with it round the loggerhead, whence, by reason of its increased rapid circlings, a hempen blue smoke now jetted up and mingled with the steady fumes from his pipe. As the line passed round and round the loggerhead; so also, just before reaching that point, it blisteringly passed through and through both of Stubb's hands, from which the hand-cloths, or squares of quilted canvas sometimes worn at these times, had accidentally dropped. It was like holding an enemy's sharp two-edged sword by the blade, and that enemy all the time striving to wrest it out of your clutch.

"Wet the line! wet the line!" cried Stubb to the tub oarsman (him seated by the tub) who, snatching off his hat, dashed the sea-water into it.[1] More turns were taken, so that the line began holding its place. The boat now flew through the boiling water like a shark all fins. Stubb and Tashtego here changed places—stem for stern—a staggering business truly in that rocking commotion.

From the vibrating line extending the entire length of the upper part of the boat, and from its now being more tight than a harp-string, you would have thought the craft had two keels—one cleaving the water, the other the air—as the boat churned on through both opposing elements at once. A continual cascade played at the bows; a ceaseless whirling eddy in her wake; and, at the slightest motion from within, even but of a little finger, the vibrating, cracking craft canted over her spasmodic gunwale into the sea. Thus they rushed; each man with might and main clinging to his seat, to prevent being tossed to the foam; and the tall form of Tashtego at the steering oar crouching almost double, in order to bring down his center of gravity. Whole Atlantics and Pacifics seemed passed as they shot on their way, till at length the whale somewhat slackened his flight.

"Haul in—haul in!" cried Stubb to the bowsman! and, facing round towards the whale, all hands began pulling the boat up to him, while yet the boat was being towed on. Soon ranging up by his flank, Stubb, firmly planting his knee in the clumsy cleat, darted dart after dart into the flying fish; at the word of command, the boat alternately sterning out of the way of the whale's horrible wallow, and then ranging up for another fling.

The red tide now poured from all sides of the monster like brooks down a hill. His tormented body rolled not in brine but in blood, which bubbled and seethed for furlongs behind in their wake. The slanting sun playing upon this crimson pond in the sea, sent back its reflection into every face, so that they all glowed to each other like red men. And all the while, jet after jet of white smoke was agonizingly shot from the spiracle of the whale, and vehement puff after puff from the mouth of the excited headsman; as at every dart, hauling in upon his crooked lance (by the line attached to it), Stubb straightened it again and again, by a few rapid blows against the gunwale, then again and again sent it into the whale.

"Pull up—pull up!" he now cried to the bowsman, as the waning whale relaxed in his wrath. "Pull up!—close to!" and the boat ranged along the fish's flank. When reaching far over the bow, Stubb slowly churned his long sharp lance into the fish, and kept it there, carefully churning and churning, as if cautiously seeking to feel after some gold watch that the whale might have swallowed, and which he was fearful of breaking ere he could hook it out. But that gold watch he sought was the innermost life of the fish. And now it is struck; for, starting from his trance into that unspeakable thing called his "flurry," the monster horribly wallowed in his blood, overwrapped himself in impenetrable, mad, boiling spray, so that the imperilled craft, instantly dropping astern, had much ado blindly to struggle out from that phrensied twilight into the clear air of the day.

And now abating in his flurry, the whale once more rolled out into view; surging from side to side; spasmodically dilating and contracting his spout-hole, with sharp, cracking, agonized respira-

1. Partly to show the indispensableness of this act, it may here be stated, that, in the old Dutch fishery, a mop was used to dash the running line with water; in many other ships, a wooden piggin, or bailer, is set apart for that purpose. Your hat, however, is the most convenient.

tions. At last, gush after gush of clotted red gore, as if it had been the purple lees of red wine, shot into the frighted air; and falling back again, ran dripping down his motionless flanks into the sea. His heart had burst!

"He's dead, Mr. Stubb," said Daggoo.

"Yes; both pipes smoked out!" and withdrawing his own from his mouth, Stubb scattered the dead ashes over the water; and, for a moment, stood thoughtfully eyeing the vast corpse he had made.

Chapter LXII

The Dart

A WORD CONCERNING AN INCIDENT IN THE LAST CHAPTER.

According to the invariable usage of the fishery, the whale-boat pushes off from the ship, with the headsman or whale-killer as temporary steersman, and the harpooneer or whale-fastener pulling the foremost oar, the one known as the harpooneer-oar. Now it needs a strong, nervous arm to strike the first iron into the fish; for often, in what is called a long dart, the heavy implement has to be flung to the distance of twenty or thirty feet. But however prolonged and exhausting the chase, the harpooneer is expected to pull his oar meanwhile to the uttermost; indeed, he is expected to set an example of superhuman activity to the rest, not only by incredible rowing, but by repeated loud and intrepid exclamations; and what it is to keep shouting at the top of one's compass, while all the other muscles are strained and half started—what that is none know but those who have tried it. For one, I cannot bawl very heartily and work very recklessly at one and the same time. In this straining, bawling state, then, with his back to the fish, all at once the exhausted harpooneer hears the exciting cry—"Stand up, and give it to him!" He now has to drop and secure his oar, turn round on his center half-way, seize his harpoon from the crotch, and with what little strength may remain, he essays to pitch it somehow into the whale. No wonder, taking the whole fleet of whalemen in a body, that out of fifty fair chances for a dart, not five are successful; no wonder that so many hapless harpooneers are madly cursed and disrated; no wonder that some of them actually burst their blood-vessels in the boat; no wonder that some sperm whalemen are absent four years with four barrels; no wonder that to many shipowners, whaling is but a losing concern; for it is the harpooneer that makes the voyage, and if you take the breath out of his body how can you expect to find it there when most wanted!

Again, if the dart be successful, then at the second critical instant, that is, when the whale starts to run, the boat-header and harpooneer likewise start to running fore and aft, to the imminent jeopardy of themselves and everyone else. It is then they change places; and the headsman, the chief officer of the little craft, takes his proper station in the bows of the boat.

Now, I care not who maintains the contrary, but all this is both foolish and unnecessary. The headsman should stay in the bows from first to last; he should both dart the harpoon and the lance, and no rowing whatever should be expected of him, except under circumstances obvious to any fisherman. I know that this would sometimes involve a slight loss of speed in the chase; but long experience in various whalemen of more than one nation has convinced me that in the vast majority of failures in the fishery, it has not by any means been so much the speed of the whale as the before described exhaustion of the harpooneer that has caused them.

To ensure the greatest efficiency in the dart, the harpooneers of this world must start to their feet from out of idleness, and not from out of toil.

Chapter LXIII

The Crotch

Out of the trunk, the branches grow; out of them, the twigs. So, in productive subjects, grow the chapters.

The crotch alluded to on a previous page deserves independent mention. It is a notched stick of a peculiar form, some two feet in length, which is perpendicularly inserted into the starboard gunwale near the bow, for the purpose of furnishing a rest for the wooden extremity of the harpoons, whose other naked, barbed end slopingly projects from the prow. Thereby the weapon is instantly at hand to its hurler, who snatches it up as readily from its rest as a backwoodsman swings his rifle from the wall. It is customary to have two harpoons reposing in the crotch, respectively called the first and second irons.

But these two harpoons, each by its own cord, are both connected with the line; the object being this: to dart them both, if possible, one instantly after the other into the same whale; so that if, in the coming drag, one should draw out, the other may still retain a hold. It is a doubling of the chances. But it very often happens that owing to the instantaneous, violent, convulsive running of the whale upon receiving the first iron, it becomes impossible for the harpooneer, however lightning-like in his movements, to pitch the second iron into him. Nevertheless, as the second iron is already connected with the line, and the line is running, hence that weapon must, at all events, be anticipatingly tossed out of the boat, somehow and somewhere; else the most terrible jeopardy would involve all hands. Tumbled into the water, it accordingly is in such cases; the spare coils of box line (mentioned in a preceding chapter) making this feat, in most instances, prudently practicable. But this critical act is not always unattended with the saddest and most fatal casualties.

Furthermore: you must know that when the second iron is thrown overboard, it thenceforth becomes a dangling, sharp-edged terror, skittishly curvetting about both boat and whale, entangling the lines, or cutting them, and making a prodigious sensation in all directions. Nor, in general, is it possible to secure it again until the whale is fairly captured and a corpse.

Consider, now, how it must be in the case of four boats all engaging one unusually strong, active, and knowing whale; when owing to these qualities in him, as well as to the thousand concurring accidents of such an audacious enterprise, eight or ten loose second irons may be simultaneously dangling about him. For, of course, each boat is supplied with several harpoons to bend on to the line should the first one be ineffectually darted without recovery. All these particulars are faithfully narrated here, as they will not fail to elucidate several most important, however intricate passages, in scenes hereafter to be painted.

Chapter LXIV

STUBB'S SUPPER

STUBB'S WHALE HAD BEEN KILLED SOME DISTANCE FROM THE SHIP. IT WAS A CALM; SO, FORMING a tandem of three boats, we commenced the slow business of towing the trophy to the *Pequod*. And now, as we eighteen men with our thirty-six arms, and one hundred and eighty thumbs and fingers, slowly toiled hour after hour upon that inert, sluggish corpse in the sea; and it seemed hardly to budge at all, except at long intervals; good evidence was hereby furnished of the enormousness of the mass we moved. For, upon the great canal of Hang-Ho, or whatever they call it, in China, four or five laborers on the foot-path will draw a bulky freighted junk at the rate of a mile an hour; but this grand argosy we towed heavily forged along, as if laden with pig-lead in bulk.

Darkness came on; but three lights up and down in the *Pequod*'s main-rigging dimly guided our way; till drawing nearer we saw Ahab dropping one of several more lanterns over the bulwarks. Vacantly eyeing the heaving whale for a moment, he issued the usual orders for securing it for the night, and then handing his lantern to a seaman, went his way into the cabin, and did not come forward again until morning.

Though, in overseeing the pursuit of this whale, Captain Ahab had evinced his customary activity, to call it so; yet now that the creature was dead, some vague dissatisfaction, or impatience, or despair, seemed working in him; as if the sight of that dead body reminded him that Moby-Dick was yet to be slain; and though a thousand other whales were brought to his ship, all that would not one jot advance his grand, monomaniac object. Very soon you would have thought from the sound on the *Pequod*'s decks, that all hands were preparing to cast anchor in the deep; for heavy chains are being dragged along the deck, and thrust rattling out of the port-holes. But by those clanking links, the vast corpse itself, not the ship, is to be moored. Tied by the head to the stern, and by the tail to the bows, the whale now lies with its black hull close to the vessel's, and seen through the darkness of the night, which obscured the spars and rigging aloft, the two—ship and whale, seemed yoked together like colossal bullocks, whereof one reclines while the other remains standing.[1]

If moody Ahab was now all quiescence, at least so far as could be known on deck, Stubb, his second mate, flushed with conquest, betrayed an unusual but still good-natured excitement. Such an unwonted bustle was he in that the staid Starbuck, his official superior, quietly resigned to him for the time the sole management of affairs. One small, helping cause of all this liveliness in Stubb, was soon made strangely manifest. Stubb was a high-liver; he was somewhat intemperately fond of the whale as a flavorish thing to his palate.

"A steak, a steak, ere I sleep! You, Daggoo! overboard you go, and cut me one from his small!"

Here be it known, that though these wild fishermen do not, as a general thing, and according to the great military maxim, make the enemy defray the current expenses of the war (at least before

1. A little item may as well be related here. The strongest and most reliable hold which the ship has upon the whale when moored alongside, is by the flukes or tail; and as from its greater density that part is relatively heavier than any other (excepting the side-fins), its flexibility even in death causes it to sink low beneath the surface; so that with the hand you cannot get at it from the boat, in order to put the chain around it. But this difficulty is ingeniously overcome: a small, strong line is prepared with a wooden float at its outer end, and a weight in its middle, while the other end is secured to the ship. By adroit management the wooden float is made to rise on the other side of the mass, so that now having girdled the whale, the chain is readily made to follow suit; and being slipped along the body, is at last locked fast round the smallest part of the tail, at the point of junction with its broad flukes or lobes.

realizing the proceeds of the voyage), yet now and then you find some of these Nantucketers who have a genuine relish for that particular part of the Sperm Whale designated by Stubb; comprising the tapering extremity of the body.

About midnight that steak was cut and cooked; and lighted by two lanterns of sperm oil, Stubb stoutly stood up to his spermaceti supper at the capstan-head, as if that capstan were a sideboard. Nor was Stubb the only banqueter on whale's flesh that night. Mingling their mumblings with his own mastications, thousands on thousands of sharks, swarming round the dead leviathan, smackingly feasted on its fatness. The few sleepers below in their bunks were often startled by the sharp slapping of their tails against the hull within a few inches of the sleepers' hearts. Peering over the side you could just see them (as before you heard them) wallowing in the sullen, black waters, and turning over on their backs as they scooped out huge globular pieces of the whale of the bigness of a human head. This particular feat of the shark seems all but miraculous. How, at such an apparently unassailable surface, they contrive to gouge out such symmetrical mouthfuls, remains a part of the universal problem of all things. The mark they thus leave on the whale, may best be likened to the hollow made by a carpenter in countersinking for a screw.

Though amid all the smoking horror and diabolism of a sea-fight, sharks will be seen longingly gazing up to the ship's decks, like hungry dogs round a table where red meat is being carved, ready to bolt down every killed man that is tossed to them; and though, while the valiant butchers over the deck-table are thus cannibally carving each other's live meat with carving-knives all gilded and tasseled, the sharks, also, with their jewel-hilted mouths, are quarrelsomely carving away under the table at the dead meat; and though, were you to turn the whole affair upside down, it would still be pretty much the same thing, that is to say, a shocking sharkish business enough for all parties; and though sharks also are the invariable outriders of all slave ships crossing the Atlantic, systematically trotting alongside, to be handy in case a parcel is to be carried anywhere, or a dead slave to be decently buried; and though one or two other like instances might be set down, touching the set terms, places, and occasions, when sharks do most socially congregate, and most hilariously feast; yet is there no conceivable time or occasion when you will find them in such countless numbers, and in gayer or more jovial spirits, than around a dead sperm whale, moored by night to a whale-ship at sea. If you have never seen that sight, then suspend your decision about the propriety of devil-worship, and the expediency of conciliating the devil.

But, as yet, Stubb heeded not the mumblings of the banquet that was going on so nigh him, no more than the sharks heeded the smacking of his own epicurean lips.

"Cook, cook!—where's that old Fleece?" he cried at length, widening his legs still further, as if to form a more secure base for his supper; and, at the same time darting his fork into the dish, as if stabbing with his lance; "cook, you cook!—sail this way, cook!"

The old black, not in any very high glee at having been previously routed from his warm hammock at a most unseasonable hour, came shambling along from his galley, for, like many old blacks, there was something the matter with his knee-pans, which he did not keep well-scoured like his other pans; this old Fleece, as they called him, came shuffling and limping along, assisting his step with his tongs, which, after a clumsy fashion, were made of straightened iron hoops; this old Ebony floundered along, and in obedience to the word of command, came to a dead stop on the opposite side of Stubb's sideboard; when, with both hands folded before him, and resting on his two-legged cane, he bowed his arched back still further over, at the same time sideways inclining his head, so as to bring his best ear into play.

"Cook," said Stubb, rapidly lifting a rather reddish morsel to his mouth, "don't you think this steak is rather overdone? You've been beating this steak too much, cook; it's too tender. Don't I always say that to be good, a whale-steak must be tough? There are those sharks now over the side, don't you see they prefer it tough and rare? What a shindy they are kicking up! Cook, go and talk to 'em; tell 'em they are welcome to help themselves civilly, and in moderation, but they must keep quiet. Blast me, if I can hear my own voice. Away, cook, and deliver my message. Here, take this lantern," snatching one from his sideboard; "now then, go and preach to them!"

Sullenly taking the offered lantern, old Fleece limped across the deck to the bulwarks; and then, with one hand drooping his light low over the sea, so as to get a good view of his congregation, with the other hand he solemnly flourished his tongs, and leaning far over the side in a mumbling voice began addressing the sharks, while Stubb, softly crawling behind, overheard all that was said.

"Fellow-critters: I'se ordered here to say dat you must stop dat dam noise dare. You hear? Stop dat dam smackin' ob de lips! Massa Stubb say dat you can fill your dam bellies up to de hatchings, but by Gor! you must stop dat dam racket!"

"Cook," here interposed Stubb, accompanying the word with a sudden slap on the shoulder—"Cook! why, damn your eyes, you mustn't swear that way when you're preaching. That's no way to convert sinners, Cook!"

"Who dat? Den preach to him yourself," sullenly turning to go.

"No, Cook; go on, go on."

"Well, den Belubed fellow-critters:"

"Right!" exclaimed Stubb, approvingly, "coax 'em to it; try that," and Fleece continued.

"Do you is all sharks, and by natur wery woracious, yet I zay to you, fellow-critters, dat dat woraciousness—'top dat dam slappin' ob de tail! How you tink to hear, 'spose you keep up such a dam slapping and bitin' dare?"

"Cook," cried Stubb, collaring him, "I won't have that swearing. Talk to 'em gentlemanly."

Once more the sermon proceeded.

"Your woraciousness, fellow-critters, I don't blame ye so much for; dat is natur, and can't be helped; but to gobern dat wicked natur, dat is de pint. You is sharks, sartin; but if you gobern de shark in you, why den you be angel; for all angel is not'ing more dan de shark well goberned. Now, look here, bred'ren, just try wonst to be cibil, a helping yourselbs from dat whale. Don't be tearin' de blubber out your neighbor's mout, I say. Is not one shark dood right as toder to dat whale? And, by Gor, none on you has de right to dat whale; dat whale belong to someone else. I know some o' you has berry brig mout, brigger dan oders; but den the brig mouts sometimes has de small bellies; so dat de brigness ob de mout is not to swaller wid, but to bite off de blubber for de small fry ob sharks, dat can't get into de scrouge to help demselves."

"Well done, old Fleece!" cried Stubb, "that's Christianity; go on."

"No use goin' on; de dam willains will keep a scrougin' and slappin' each oder, Massa Stubb; dey don't hear one word; no use a-preaching to such dam g'uttons as you call 'em, till dare bellies is full, and dare bellies is bottomless; and when dey do get 'em full, dey wont hear you den; for den dey sink in de sea, go fast to sleep on de coral, and can't hear not'ing at all, no more, for eber and eber."

"Upon my soul, I am about of the same opinion; so give the benediction, Fleece, and I'll away to my supper."

Upon this, Fleece, holding both hands over the fishy mob, raised his shrill voice, and cried—

"Cussed fellow-critters! Kick up de damdest row as ever you can; fill your dam bellies 'till dey bust—and den die."

"Now, cook," said Stubb, resuming his supper at the capstan; "stand just where you stood before, there, over against me, and pay particular attention."

"All dention," said Fleece, again stooping over upon his tongs in the desired position.

"Well," said Stubb, helping himself freely meanwhile; "I shall now go back to the subject of this steak. In the first place, how old are you, cook?"

"What dat do wid de 'teak," said the old black, testily.

"Silence! How old are you, cook?"

"'Bout ninety, dey say," he gloomily muttered.

"And have you have lived in this world hard upon one hundred years, cook, and don't know yet how to cook a whale-steak?" rapidly bolting another mouthful at the last word, so that that morsel seemed a continuation of the question. "Where were you born, cook?"

" 'Hind de hatchway, in ferry-boat, goin' ober de Roanoke."

"Born in a ferry-boat! That's queer, too. But I want to know what country you were born in, cook?"

"Didn't I say de Roanoke country?" he cried, sharply.

"No, you didn't, cook; but I'll tell you what I'm coming to, cook. You must go home and be born over again; you don't know how to cook a whale-steak yet."

"Bress my soul, if I cook noder one," he growled, angrily, turning round to depart.

"Come back here, cook;—here, hand me those tongs;—now take that bit of steak there, and tell me if you think that steak cooked as it should be? Take it, I say"—holding the tongs towards him—"take it, and taste it."

Faintly smacking his withered lips over it for a moment, the old negro muttered, "Best cooked 'teak I eber taste; joosy berry, joosy."

"Cook," said Stubb, squaring himself once more; "do you belong to the church?"

"Passed one once in Cape-Down," said the old man sullenly.

"And you have once in your life passed a holy church in Cape-Town, where you doubtless overheard a holy parson addressing his hearers as his beloved fellow-creatures, have you cook! And yet you come here, and tell me such a dreadful lie as you did just now, eh?" said Stubb. "Where do you expect to go to, cook?"

"Go to bed berry soon," he mumbled, half-turning as he spoke.

"Avast! heave to! I mean when you die, cook. It's an awful question. Now what's your answer?"

"When dis old brack man dies," said the negro slowly, changing his whole air and demeanor, "he hisself won't go nowhere; but some bressed angel will come and fetch him."

"Fetch him? How? In a coach and four, as they fetched Elijah? And fetch him where?"

"Up dere," said Fleece, holding his tongs straight over his head, and keeping it there very solemnly.

"So, then, you expect to go up into our main-top, do you, cook, when you are dead? But don't you know the higher you climb, the colder it gets? Main-top eh?"

"Didn't say dat t'all," said Fleece, again in the sulks.

"You said up there, didn't you? and now look yourself, and see where your tongs are pointing. But, perhaps you expect to get into heaven by crawling through the lubber's hole, cook; but, no, no, cook, you don't get there, except you go the regular way, round by the rigging. It's a ticklish business, but must be done, or else it's no go. But none of us are in heaven yet. Drop your tongs, cook, and hear my orders. Do ye hear? Hold your hat in one hand, and clap t'other a'top of your heart, when I'm giving my orders, cook. What! that your heart, there?—that's your gizzard! Aloft! aloft!—that's it—now you have it. Hold it there now, and pay attention."

"All 'dention," said the old black, with both hands placed as desired, vainly wriggling his grizzled head, as if to get both ears in front at one and the same time.

"Well then, cook, you see this whale-steak of yours was so very bad, that I have put it out of sight as soon as possible; you see that, don't you? Well, for the future, when you cook another whale-steak for my private table here, the capstan, I'll tell you what to do so as not to spoil it by overdoing. Hold the steak in one hand, and show a live coal to it with the other; that done, dish it; d'ye hear? And now to-morrow, cook, when we are cutting in the fish, be sure you stand by to get the tips of his fins; have them put in pickle. As for the ends of the flukes, have them soused, cook. There, now ye may go."

But Fleece had hardly got three paces off, when he was recalled.

"Cook, give me cutlets for supper to-morrow night in the mid-watch. D'ye hear? away you sail, then.—Halloa! stop! make a bow before you go.—Avast heaving again! Whale-balls for breakfast—don't forget."

"Wish, by gor! whale eat him, 'stead of him eat whale. I'm bressed if he ain't more of shark dan Massa Shark hisself," muttered the old man, limping away; with which sage ejaculation he went to his hammock.

Chapter LXV

The Whale as a Dish

That mortal man should feed upon the creature that feeds his lamp, and, like Stubb, eat him by his own light, as you may say; this seems so outlandish a thing that one must needs go a little into the history and philosophy of it.

It is upon record, that three centuries ago the tongue of the Right Whale was esteemed a great delicacy in France, and commanded large prices there. Also, that in Henry VIIIth's time, a certain cook of the court obtained a handsome reward for inventing an admirable sauce to be eaten with barbacued porpoises, which, you remember, are a species of whale. Porpoises, indeed, are to this day considered fine eating. The meat is made into balls about the size of billiard balls, and being well seasoned and spiced might be taken for turtle-balls or veal balls. The old monks of Dunfermline were very fond of them. They had a great porpoise grant from the crown.

The fact is, that among his hunters at least, the whale would by all hands be considered a noble dish, were there not so much of him; but when you come to sit down before a meat-pie nearly one hundred feet long, it takes away your appetite. Only the most unprejudiced of men like Stubb, nowadays partake of cooked whales; but the Esquimaux are not so fastidious. We all know how they live upon whales, and have rare old vintages of prime old train oil. Zogranda, one of their most famous doctors, recommends strips of blubber for infants, as being exceedingly juicy and nourishing. And this reminds me that certain Englishmen, who long ago were accidentally left in Greenland by a whaling vessel—that these men actually lived for several months on the moldy scraps of whales which had been left ashore after trying out the blubber. Among the Dutch whalemen these scraps are called "fritters"; which, indeed, they greatly resemble, being brown and crisp, and smelling something like old Amsterdam housewives' dough-nuts or oly-cooks, when fresh. They have such an eatable look that the most self-denying stranger can hardly keep his hands off.

But what further depreciates the whale as a civilized dish, is his exceeding richness. He is the great prize ox of the sea, too fat to be delicately good. Look at his hump, which would be as fine eating as the buffalo's (which is esteemed a rare dish), were it not such a solid pyramid of fat. But the spermaceti itself, how bland and creamy that is; like the transparent, half jellied, white meat of a cocoanut in the third month of its growth, yet far too rich to supply a substitute for butter. Nevertheless, many whalemen have a method of absorbing it into some other substance, and then partaking of it. In the long try watches of the night it is a common thing for the seamen to dip their ship-biscuit into the huge oil-pots and let them fry there awhile. Many a good supper have I thus made.

In the case of a small Sperm Whale the brains are accounted a fine dish. The casket of the skull is broken into with an ax, and the two plump, whitish lobes being withdrawn (precisely resembling two large puddings), they are then mixed with flour, and cooked into a most delectable mess, in flavor somewhat resembling calves' head which is quite a dish among some epicures; and everyone knows that some young bucks among the epicures, by continually dining upon calves' brains, by and by get to have a little brains of their own, so as to be able to tell a calf's head from their own heads; which, indeed, requires uncommon discrimination. And that is the reason why a young buck with an intelligent looking calf's head before him, is somehow one of the saddest sights you can see. The head looks a sort of reproachfully at him, with an "Et tu Brute!" expression.

It is not, perhaps, entirely because the whale is so excessively unctuous that landsmen seem to regard the eating of him with abhorrence; that appears to result, in some way, from the consideration before mentioned: i.e. that a man should eat a newly murdered thing of the sea, and eat it too by its own light. But no doubt the first man that ever murdered an ox was regarded as a murderer; perhaps he was hung; and if he had been put on his trial by oxen, he certainly would have been; and he certainly deserved it if any murderer does. Go to the meat-market of a Saturday night and see the crowds of live bipeds staring up at the long rows of dead quadrupeds. Does not that sight take a tooth out of the cannibal's jaw? Cannibals? who is not a cannibal? I tell you it will be more tolerable for the Fiji that salted down a lean missionary in his cellar against a coming famine; it will be more tolerable for that provident Fiji, I say, in the day of judgment, than for thee, civilized and enlightened gourmand, who nailest geese to the ground and feastest on their bloated livers in thy paté-de-foie-gras.

But Stubb, he eats the whale by its own light, does he? and that is adding insult to injury, is it? Look at your knife-handle, there, my civilized and enlightened gourmand dining off that roast beef, what is that handle made of?—what but the bones of the brother of the very ox you are eating? And what do you pick your teeth with, after devouring that fat goose? With a feather of the same fowl. And with what quill did the Secretary of the Society for the Suppression of Cruelty to Ganders formally indite his circulars? It is only within the last month or two that that society passed a resolution to patronize nothing but steel pens.

Chapter LXVI

The Shark Massacre

When in the southern fishery, a captured sperm whale, after long and weary toil, is brought alongside late at night, it is not, as a general thing at least, customary to proceed at once to the business of cutting him in. For that business is an exceedingly laborious one; is not very soon completed; and requires all hands to set about it. Therefore, the common usage is to take in all sail; lash the helm a'lee; and then send everyone below to his hammock till daylight, with the reservation that, until that time, anchor-watches shall be kept; that is, two and two for an hour, each couple, the crew in rotation shall mount the deck to see that all goes well.

But sometimes, especially upon the Line in the Pacific, this plan will not answer at all; because such incalculable hosts of sharks gather round the moored carcass, that were he left so for six hours, say, on a stretch, little more than the skeleton would be visible by morning. In most other parts of the ocean, however, where these fish do not so largely abound, their wondrous voracity can be at times considerably diminished, by vigorously stirring them up with sharp whaling-spades, a procedure notwithstanding, which, in some instances, only seems to tickle them into still greater activity. But it was not thus in the present case with the *Pequod*'s sharks; though to be sure, any man unaccustomed to such sights, to have looked over her side that night, would have almost thought the whole round sea was one huge cheese, and those sharks the maggots in it.

Nevertheless, upon Stubb setting the anchor-watch after his supper was concluded; and when, accordingly, Queequeg and a forecastle seaman came on deck, no small excitement was created among the sharks; for immediately suspending the cutting stages over the side, and lowering three lanterns, so that they cast long gleams of light over the turbid sea, these two mariners, darting their long whaling-spades, kept up an incessant murdering of the sharks,[1] by striking the keen steel deep into their skulls, seemingly their only vital part. But in the foamy confusion of their mixed and struggling hosts, the marksmen could not always hit their mark; and this brought about new revelations of the incredible ferocity of the foe. They viciously snapped, not only at each other's disembowelments, but like flexible bows, bent round, and bit their own; till those entrails seemed swallowed over and over again by the same mouth, to be oppositely voided by the gaping wound. Nor was this all. It was unsafe to meddle with the corpses and ghosts of these creatures. A sort of generic or Pantheistic vitality seemed to lurk in their very joints and bones, after what might be called the individual life had departed. Killed and hoisted on deck for the sake of his skin, one of these sharks almost took poor Queequeg's hand off, when he tried to shut down the dead lid of his murderous jaw.

"Queequeg no care what god made him shark," said the savage, agonizingly lifting his hand up and down; "wedder Fiji god or Nantucket god; but de god wat made shark must be one dam Ingin."

Chapter LXVII

CUTTING-IN

IT WAS A SATURDAY NIGHT, AND SUCH A SABBATH AS FOLLOWED! EX OFFICIO PROFESSORS OF SABbath breaking are all whalemen. The ivory *Pequod* was turned into what seemed a shamble; every sailor a butcher. You would have thought we were offering up ten thousand red oxen to the sea gods.

In the first place, the enormous cutting tackles, among other ponderous things comprising a cluster of blocks generally painted green, and which no single man can possibly lift—this vast bunch of grapes was swayed up to the main-top and firmly lashed to the lower mast-head, the strongest point anywhere above a ship's deck. The end of the hawser-like rope winding through these intricacies, was then conducted to the windlass, and the huge lower block of the tackles was swung over the whale; to this block the great blubber hook, weighing some one hundred pounds, was attached. And now suspended in stages over the side, Starbuck and Stubb, the mates, armed with their long spades, began cutting a hole in the body for the insertion of the hook just above the nearest of the two side-fins. This done, a broad, semicircular line is cut round the hole, the hook is inserted, and the main body of the crew striking up a wild chorus, now commence heaving in one dense crowd at the windlass. When instantly, the entire ship careens over on her side; every bolt in her starts like the nail-heads of an old house in frosty weather; she trembles, quivers, and nods her frighted mast-heads to the sky. More and more she leans over to the whale, while

1. The whaling-spade used for cutting-in is made of the very best steel; is about the bigness of a man's spread hand; and in general shape corresponds to the garden implement after which it is named; only its sides are perfectly flat, and its upper edge considerably narrower than the lower. This weapon is always kept as sharp as possible; and when being used is occasionally honed, just like a razor. In its socket, a stiff pole, from twenty to thirty feet long, is inserted for a handle.

every gasping heave of the windlass is answered by a helping heave from the billows; till at last, a swift, startling snap is heard; with a great swash the ship rolls upwards and backwards from the whale, and the triumphant tackle rises into sight dragging after it the disengaged semicircular end of the first strip of blubber. Now as the blubber envelopes the whale precisely as the rind does an orange, so is it stripped off from the body precisely as an orange is sometimes stripped by spiralizing it. For the strain constantly kept up by the windlass continually keeps the whale rolling over and over in the water, and as the blubber in one strip uniformly peels off along the line called the "scarf," simultaneously cut by the spades of Starbuck and Stubb, the mates; and just as fast as it is thus peeled off, and indeed by that very act itself, it is all the time being hoisted higher and higher aloft till its upper end grazes the main-top; the men at the windlass then cease heaving, and for a moment or two the prodigious blood-dripping mass sways to and fro as if let down from the sky, and everyone present must take good heed to dodge it when it swings, else it may box his ears and pitch him headlong overboard.

One of the attending harpooneers now advances with a long, keen weapon called a boarding-sword, and watching his chance he dexterously slices out a considerable hole in the lower part of the swaying mass. Into this hole, the end of the second alternating great tackle is then hooked so as to retain a hold upon the blubber, in order to prepare for what follows. Whereupon, this accomplished swordsman, warning all hands to stand off, once more makes a scientific dash at the mass, and with a few sidelong, desperate, lunging slicings, severs it completely in twain; so that while the short lower part is still fast, the long upper strip, called a blanket-piece, swings clear, and is all ready for lowering. The heavers forward now resume their song, and while the one tackle is peeling and hoisting a second strip from the whale, the other is slowly slackened away, and down goes the first strip through the main hatchway right beneath, into an unfurnished parlor called the blubber-room. Into this twilight apartment sundry nimble hands keep coiling away the long blanket-piece as if it were a great live mass of plaited serpents. And thus the work proceeds; the two tackles hoisting and lowering simultaneously; both whale and windlass heaving, the heavers singing, the blubber-room gentlemen coiling, the mates scarfing, the ship straining, and all hands swearing occasionally, by way of assuaging the general friction.

Chapter LXVIII

The Blanket

I HAVE GIVEN NO SMALL ATTENTION TO THAT NOT UNVEXED SUBJECT, THE SKIN OF THE WHALE. I have had controversies about it with experienced whalemen afloat, and learned naturalists ashore. My original opinion remains unchanged; but it is only an opinion.

The question is, what and where is the skin of the whale? Already you know what his blubber is. That blubber is something of the consistence of firm, close-grained beef, but tougher, more elastic and compact, and ranges from eight or ten to twelve and fifteen inches in thickness.

Now, however preposterous it may at first seem to talk of any creature's skin as being of that sort of consistence and thickness, yet in point of fact these are no arguments against such a presumption; because you cannot raise any other dense enveloping layer from the whale's body but that same blubber; and the outermost enveloping layer of any animal, if reasonably dense, what can that be but the skin? True, from the unmarred dead body of the whale, you may scrape off with your hand an infinitely thin, transparent substance, somewhat resembling the thinnest shreds of isinglass, only it is almost as flexible and soft as satin; that is, previous to being dried, when it not only contracts and thickens, but becomes rather hard and brittle. I have several such dried bits, which I use for marks in my whale-books. It is transparent, as I said before; and being laid upon the printed page, I have sometimes pleased myself with fancying it exerted a magnifying influence. At any rate, it is pleasant to read about whales through their own spectacles, as you may say. But what I am driving at here is this. That same infinitely thin, isinglass substance, which, I admit, invests the entire body of the whale, is not so much to be regarded as the skin of the creature, as the skin of the skin, so to speak; for it were simply ridiculous to say, that the proper skin of the tremendous whale is thinner and more tender than the skin of a new-born child. But no more of this.

Assuming the blubber to be the skin of the whale; then, when this skin, as in the case of a very large Sperm Whale, will yield the bulk of one hundred barrels of oil; and, when it is considered that, in quantity, or rather weight, that oil, in its expressed state, is only three fourths, and not the entire substance of the coat; some idea may hence be had of the enormousness of that animated mass, a mere part of whose mere integument yields such a lake of liquid as that. Reckoning ten barrels to the ton, you have ten tons for the net weight of only three quarters of the stuff of the whale's skin.

In life, the visible surface of the Sperm Whale is not the least among the many marvels he presents. Almost invariably it is all over obliquely crossed and recrossed with numberless straight marks in thick array, something like those in the finest Italian line engravings. But these marks do not seem to be impressed upon the isinglass substance above-mentioned, but seem to be seen through it, as if they were engraved upon the body itself. Nor is this all. In some instances, to the quick, observant eye, those linear marks, as in a veritable engraving, but afford the ground for far other delineations. These are hieroglyphical; that is, if you call those mysterious ciphers on the walls of pyramids hieroglyphics then that is the proper word to use in the present connection. By my retentive memory of the hieroglyphics upon one Sperm Whale in particular, I was much struck with a plate representing the old Indian characters chiselled on the famous hieroglyphic palisades on the banks of the Upper Mississippi. Like those mystic rocks, too, the mystic-marked whale remains undecipherable. This allusion to the Indian rocks reminds me of another thing. Besides all the other phenomena which the exterior of the Sperm Whale presents, he not seldom displays the back, and more especially his flanks, effaced in great part of the regular linear appearance, by reason of numerous rude scratches, altogether of an irregular, random aspect. I should say that those New England rocks on the sea-coast, which Agassiz imagines to bear the marks of violent scraping contact with vast floating icebergs—I should say, that those rocks must not a little resemble the Sperm Whale in this particular. It also seems to me that such scratches in the whale are probably made by hostile contact with other whales; for I have most remarked them in the large, full-grown bulls of the species.

A word or two more concerning this matter of the skin or blubber of the whale. It has already been said, that it is stripped from him in long pieces, called blanket-pieces. Like most sea-terms, this one is very happy and significant. For the whale is indeed wrapped up in his blubber as in a real blanket or counterpane; or, still better, an Indian poncho slipped over his head, and skirting his extremity. It is by reason of this cozy blanketing of his body, that the whale is enabled to keep himself comfortable in all weathers, in all seas, times, and tides. What would become of a Greenland whale, say, in those shuddering, icy seas of the North, if unsupplied with his cozy surtout? True, other fish are found exceedingly brisk in those Hyperborean waters; but these, be it observed, are your cold-blooded, lungless fish, whose very bellies are refrigerators; creatures, that warm themselves under the lee of an iceberg, as a traveler in winter would bask before an inn fire; whereas, like man, the whale has lungs and warm blood. Freeze his blood, and he dies. How wonderful is it then—except after explanation—that this great monster, to whom corporeal warmth is as indispensable as it is to man; how wonderful that he should be found at home, immersed to his lips for life in those Arctic waters! where, when seamen fall overboard, they are sometimes found, months afterwards, perpendicularly frozen into the hearts of fields of ice, as a fly is found glued in amber. But more surprising is it to know, as has been proved by experiment, that the blood of a Polar whale is warmer than that of a Borneo negro in summer.

It does seem to me, that herein we see the rare virtue of a strong individual vitality, and the rare virtue of thick walls, and the rare virtue of interior spaciousness. Oh, man! admire and model thyself after the whale! Do thou, too, remain warm among ice. Do thou, too, live in this world without being of it. Be cool at the equator; keep thy blood fluid at the Pole. Like the great dome of St. Peter's, and like the great whale, retain, O man! in all seasons a temperature of thine own.

But how easy and how hopeless to teach these fine things! Of erections, how few are domed like St. Peter's! of creatures, how few vast as the whale!

Chapter LXIX

THE FUNERAL

HAUL IN THE CHAINS! LET THE CARCASS GO ASTERN!"

The vast tackles have now done their duty. The peeled white body of the beheaded whale flashes like a marble sepulchre; though changed in hue, it has not perceptibly lost anything in bulk. It is still colossal. Slowly it floats more and more away, the water round it torn and splashed by the insatiate sharks, and the air above vexed with rapacious flights of screaming fowls, whose beaks are like so many insulting poniards in the whale.The vast white headless phantom floats further and further from the ship, and every rod that it so floats, what seem square roods of sharks and cubic roods of fowls, augment the murderous din. For hours and hours from the almost stationary ship that hideous sight is seen. Beneath the unclouded and mild azure sky, upon the fair face of the pleasant sea, wafted by the joyous breezes, that great mass of death floats on and on, till lost in infinite perspectives.

There's a most doleful and most mocking funeral! The sea-vultures all in pious mourning, the air-sharks all punctiliously in black or speckled. In life but few of them would have helped the whale, I ween, if peradventure he had needed it; but upon the banquet of his funeral they most piously do pounce. Oh, horrible vulturism of earth! from which not the mightiest whale is free.

Nor is this the end. Desecrated as the body is, a vengeful ghost survives and hovers over it to scare. Espied by some timid man-of-war or blundering discovery-vessel from afar, when the distance obscuring the swarming fowls, nevertheless still shows the white mass floating in the sun, and the white spray heaving high against it; straightway the whale's unharming corpse, with trembling fingers is set down in the log—*shoals, rocks, and breakers hereabouts: beware!* And for years afterwards, perhaps, ships shun the place; leaping over it as silly sheep leap over a vacuum, because their leader originally leaped there when a stick was held. There's your law of precedents; there's your utility of traditions; there's the story of your obstinate survival of old beliefs never bottomed on the earth, and now not even hovering in the air! There's orthodoxy!

Thus, while in the life the great whale's body may have been a real terror to his foes, in his death his ghost becomes a powerless panic to a world.

Are you a believer in ghosts, my friend? There are other ghosts than the Cock-Lane one, and far deeper men than Doctor Johnson who believe in them.

Chapter LXX

THE SPHYNX

IT SHOULD NOT HAVE BEEN OMITTED THAT PREVIOUS TO COMPLETELY STRIPPING THE BODY OF THE leviathan, he was beheaded. Now, the beheading of the Sperm Whale is a scientific anatomical feat, upon which experienced whale surgeons very much pride themselves: and not without reason.

Consider that the whale has nothing that can properly be called a neck; on the contrary, where his head and body seem to join, there, in that very place, is the thickest part of him. Remember, also, that the surgeon must operate from above, some eight or ten feet intervening between him and his subject, and that subject almost hidden in a discolored, rolling, and oftentimes tumultuous and bursting sea. Bear in mind, too, that under these untoward circumstances he has to cut many feet deep in the flesh; and in that subterraneous manner, without so much as getting one single peep into the ever-contracting gash thus made, he must skillfully steer clear of all adjacent, interdicted parts, and exactly divide the spine at a critical point hard by its insertion into the skull. Do you not marvel, then, at Stubb's boast, that he demanded but ten minutes to behead a sperm whale?

When first severed, the head is dropped astern and held there by a cable till the body is stripped. That done, if it belong to a small whale it is hoisted on deck to be deliberately disposed of. But, with a full grown leviathan this is impossible; for the sperm whale's head embraces nearly one third of his entire bulk, and completely to suspend such a burden as that, even by the immense tackles of a whaler, this were as vain a thing as to attempt weighing a Dutch barn in jewelers' scales.

The *Pequod*'s whale being decapitated and the body stripped, the head was hoisted against the ship's side—about half-way out of the sea, so that it might yet in great part be buoyed up by its native element. And there with the strained craft steeply leaning over to it, by reason of the enormous downward drag from the lower mast-head, and every yard-arm on that side projecting like a crane over the waves; there, that blood-dripping head hung to the *Pequod*'s waist like the giant Holofernes's from the girdle of Judith.

When this last task was accomplished it was noon, and the seamen went below to their dinner. Silence reigned over the before tumultuous but now deserted deck. An intense copper calm, like a universal yellow lotus, was more and more unfolding its noiseless measureless leaves upon the sea.

A short space elapsed, and up into this noiselessness came Ahab alone from his cabin. Taking a few turns on the quarter-deck, he paused to gaze over the side, then slowly getting into the main-chains he took Stubb's long spade—still remaining there after the whale's decapitation—and striking it into the lower part of the half-suspended mass, placed its other end crutch-wise under one arm, and so stood leaning over with eyes attentively fixed on this head.

It was a black and hooded head; and hanging there in the midst of so intense a calm, it seemed the Sphynx's in the desert. "Speak, thou vast and venerable head," muttered Ahab, "which, though ungarnished with a beard, yet here and there lookest hoary with mosses; speak, mighty head, and tell us the secret thing that is in thee. Of all divers, thou hast dived the deepest. That head upon which the upper sun now gleams, has moved amid this world's foundations. Where unrecorded names and navies rust, and untold hopes and anchors rot; where in her murderous hold this frigate earth is ballasted with bones of millions of the drowned; there, in that awful water-land, there was thy most familiar home. Thou hast been where bell or diver never went; hast slept by many a sailor's side, where sleepless mothers would give their lives to lay them down. Thou saw'st the locked lovers when leaping from their flaming ship; heart to heart they sank beneath the exulting wave; true to each other, when heaven seemed false to them. Thou saw'st the murdered mate when tossed by pirates from the midnight deck; for hours he fell into the deeper midnight of the insatiate maw; and his murderers still sailed on unharmed—while swift lightnings shivered the neighboring ship that would have borne a righteous husband to outstretched, longing arms. O head! thou hast seen enough to split the planets and make an infidel of Abraham, and not one syllable is thine!"

"Sail ho!" cried a triumphant voice from the main-mast-head.

"Ay? Well, now, that's cheering," cried Ahab, suddenly erecting himself, while whole thunder-clouds swept aside from his brow. "That lively cry upon this deadly calm might almost convert a better man.—Where away?"

"Three points on the starboard bow, sir, and bringing down her breeze to us!"

"Better and better, man. Would now St. Paul would come along that way, and to my breezelessness bring his breeze! O Nature, and O soul of man! how far beyond all utterance are your linked analogies! not the smallest atom stirs or lives on matter, but has its cunning duplicate in mind."

Chapter LXXI

THE JEROBOAM'S STORY

HAND IN HAND, SHIP AND BREEZE BLEW ON; BUT THE BREEZE CAME FASTER THAN THE SHIP, AND soon the *Pequod* began to rock.

By and by, through the glass the stranger's boats and manned mast-heads proved her a whale-ship. But as she was so far to windward, and shooting by, apparently making a passage to some other ground, the *Pequod* could not hope to reach her. So the signal was set to see what response would be made.

Here be it said, that like the vessels of military marines, the ships of the American Whale Fleet have each a private signal; all which signals being collected in a book with the names of the respective vessels attached, every captain is provided with it. Thereby, the whale commanders are enabled to recognize each other upon the ocean, even at considerable distances, and with no small facility.

The *Pequod*'s signal was at last responded to by the stranger's setting her own; which proved the ship to be the *Jeroboam* of Nantucket. Squaring her yards, she bore down, ranged abeam under the *Pequod*'s lee, and lowered a boat; it soon drew nigh; but, as the side-ladder was being rigged by Starbuck's order to accommodate the visiting captain, the stranger in question waved his hand from his boat's stern in token of that proceeding being entirely unnecessary. It turned out that the *Jeroboam* had a malignant epidemic on board, and that Mayhew, her captain, was fearful of infecting the *Pequod*'s company. For, though himself and the boat's crew remained untainted, and though his ship was half a rifle-shot off, and an incorruptible sea and air rolling and flowing between; yet conscientiously adhering to the timid quarantine of the land, he peremptorily refused to come into direct contact with the *Pequod*.

But this did by no means prevent all communications. Preserving an interval of some few yards between itself and the ship, the *Jeroboam*'s boat by the occasional use of its oars contrived to keep parallel to the *Pequod*, as she heavily forged through the sea (for by this time it blew very fresh), with her main-top-sail aback; though, indeed, at times by the sudden onset of a large rolling wave, the boat would be pushed some way ahead; but would be soon skillfully brought to her proper bearings again. Subject to this, and other the like interruptions now and then, a conversation was sustained between the two parties; but at intervals not without still another interruption of a very different sort.

Pulling an oar in the *Jeroboam*'s boat, was a man of a singular appearance, even in that wild whaling life where individual notabilities make up all totalities. He was a small, short, youngish man, sprinkled all over his face with freckles, and wearing redundant yellow hair. A long-skirted cabalistically-cut coat of a faded walnut tinge enveloped him; the overlapping sleeves of which were rolled up on his wrists. A deep, settled, fanatic delirium was in his eyes.

So soon as this figure had been first descried, Stubb had exclaimed—"That's he! that's he!—the long-togged scaramouch the *Town-Ho*'s company told us of!" Stubb here alluded to a strange story told of the *Jeroboam*, and a certain man among her crew, some time previous when the *Pequod* spoke the *Town-Ho*. According to this account and what was subsequently learned, it seemed that the scaramouch in question had gained a wonderful ascendency over almost everybody in the *Jeroboam*. His story was this:

He had been originally nurtured among the crazy society of Neskyeuna Shakers, where he had been a great prophet; in their cracked, secret meetings having several times descended from heaven by the way of a trap-door, announcing the speedy opening of the seventh vial, which he carried in his vest-pocket; but, which, instead of containing gunpowder, was supposed to be charged with laudanum. A strange, apostolic whim having seized him, he had left Neskyeuna for Nantucket, where, with that cunning peculiar to craziness, he assumed a steady, common sense exterior, and offered himself as a green-hand candidate for the *Jeroboam*'s whaling voyage. They engaged him; but straightway upon the ship's getting out of sight of land, his insanity broke out in a freshet. He announced himself as the archangel Gabriel, and commanded the captain to jump overboard. He published his manifesto, whereby he set himself forth as the deliverer of the isles of the sea and vicar-general of all Oceanica. The unflinching earnestness with which he declared these things;—the dark, daring play of his sleepless, excited imagination, and all the preternatural terrors of real delirium, united to invest this Gabriel in the minds of the majority of the ignorant crew, with an atmosphere of sacredness. Moreover, they were afraid of him. As such a man, however, was not of much practical use in the ship, especially as he refused to work except when he pleased, the incredulous captain would fain have been rid of him; but apprised that that individual's intention was to land him in the first convenient port, the archangel forthwith opened all his seals and vials—devoting the ship and all hands to unconditional perdition, in case this intention was carried out. So strongly did he work upon his disciples among the crew, that at last in a body they went to the captain and told him if Gabriel was sent from the ship, not a man of them would remain. He was therefore forced to relinquish his plan. Nor would they permit Gabriel to be any way maltreated, say or do what he would; so that it came to pass that Gabriel had the complete freedom of the ship. The consequence of all this was, that the archangel cared little or nothing for the captain and mates; and since the epidemic had broken out, he carried a higher hand than ever; declaring that the plague, as he called it, was at his sole command; nor should it be stayed but according to his good pleasure. The sailors, mostly poor devils, cringed and some of them fawned before him; in obedience to his instructions, sometimes rendering him personal homage, as to a god. Such things may seem incredible; but, however wondrous, they are true. Nor is the history of fanatics half so striking in respect to the measureless self-deception of the fanatic himself, as his measureless power of deceiving and bedeviling so many others. But it is time to return to the *Pequod*.

"I fear not thy epidemic, man," said Ahab from the bulwarks, to Captain Mayhew, who stood in the boat's stern; "come on board."

But now Gabriel started to his feet.

"Think, think of the fevers, yellow and bilious! Beware of the horrible plague!"

"Gabriel! Gabriel!" cried Captain Mayhew; "thou must either—" But that instant a headlong wave shot the boat far ahead, and its seethings drowned all speech.

"Hast thou seen the White Whale?" demanded Ahab, when the boat drifted back.

"Think, think of thy whale-boat, stoven and sunk! Beware of the horrible tail!"

"I tell thee again, Gabriel, that—" But again the boat tore ahead as if dragged by fiends. Nothing was said for some moments, while a succession of riotous waves rolled by, which by one of those occasional caprices of the seas were tumbling, not heaving it. Meantime, the hoisted sperm whale's head jogged about very violently, and Gabriel was seen eyeing it with rather more apprehensiveness than his archangel nature seemed to warrant.

When this interlude was over, Captain Mayhew began a dark story concerning Moby-Dick; not, however, without frequent interruptions from Gabriel, whenever his name was mentioned, and the crazy sea that seemed leagued with him.

It seemed that the *Jeroboam* had not long left home, when upon speaking a whale-ship, her people were reliably apprised of the existence of Moby-Dick, and the havoc he had made. Greedily sucking in this intelligence, Gabriel solemnly warned the captain against attacking the White Whale, in case the monster should be seen; in his gibbering insanity, pronouncing the White Whale to be no less a being than the Shaker God incarnated; the Shakers receiving the Bible. But when, some year or two afterwards, Moby-Dick was fairly sighted from the mast-heads, Macey, the chief mate, burned with ardor to encounter him; and the captain himself being not unwilling to let him have the opportunity, despite all the archangel's denunciations and forewarnings, Macey succeeded in persuading five men to man his boat. With them he pushed off; and, after much weary pulling, and many perilous, unsuccessful onsets, he at last succeeded in getting one iron fast. Meantime, Gabriel, ascending to the main-royal mast-head, was tossing one arm in frantic gestures, and hurling forth prophecies of speedy doom to the sacrilegious assailants of his divinity. Now, while Macey, the mate, was standing up in his boat's bow, and with all the reckless energy of his tribe was venting his wild exclamations upon the whale, and essaying to get a fair chance for his poised lance, lo! a broad white shadow rose from the sea; by its quick, fanning motion, temporarily taking the breath out of the bodies of the oarsmen. Next instant, the luckless mate, so full of furious life, was smitten bodily into the air, and making a long arc in his descent, fell into the sea at the distance of about fifty yards. Not a chip of the boat was harmed, nor a hair of any oarsman's head; but the mate forever sank.

It is well to parenthesize here, that of the fatal accidents in the Sperm-Whale Fishery, this kind is perhaps almost as frequent as any. Sometimes, nothing is injured but the man who is thus annihilated; oftener the boat's bow is knocked off, or the thigh-board, in which the headsman stands, is torn from its place and accompanies the body. But strangest of all is the circumstance, that in more instances than one, when the body has been recovered, not a single mark of violence is discernible; the man being stark dead.

The whole calamity, with the falling form of Macey, was plainly descried from the ship. Raising a piercing shriek—"The vial! the vial!" Gabriel called off the terror-stricken crew from the further hunting of the whale. This terrible event clothed the archangel with added influence; because his credulous disciples believed that he had specifically fore-announced it, instead of only making a general prophecy, which anyone might have done, and so have chanced to hit one of many marks in the wide margin allowed. He became a nameless terror to the ship.

Mayhew having concluded his narration, Ahab put such questions to him, that the stranger captain could not forbear inquiring whether he intended to hunt the White Whale, if opportunity should offer. To which Ahab answered—"Ay." Straightway, then, Gabriel once more started to his feet, glaring upon the old man, and vehemently exclaimed, with downward pointed finger—"Think, think of the blasphemer—dead, and down there!—beware of the blasphemer's end!"

Ahab stolidly turned aside; then said to Mayhew, "Captain, I have just bethought me of my letter-bag; there is a letter for one of thy officers, if I mistake not. Starbuck, look over the bag."

Every whale-ship takes out a goodly number of letters for various ships, whose delivery to the persons to whom they may be addressed, depends upon the mere chance of encountering them in the four oceans. Thus, most letters never reach their mark; and many are only received after attaining an age of two or three years or more.

Soon Starbuck returned with a letter in his hand. It was sorely tumbled, damp, and covered with a dull, spotted, green mold, in consequence of being kept in a dark locker of the cabin. Of such a letter, Death himself might well have been the post-boy.

"Can'st not read it?" cried Ahab. "Give it me, man. Ay, ay, it's but a dim scrawl;—what's this?" As he was studying it out, Starbuck took a long cutting-spade pole, and with his knife slightly split the end, to insert the letter there, and in that way, hand it to the boat, without its coming any closer to the ship.

Meantime, Ahab, holding the letter, muttered, "Mr. Har—yes, Mr. Harry—(a woman's pinny hand—the man's wife, I'll wager)—Ay—Mr. Harry Macey, Ship *Jeroboam*;—why it's Macey, and he's dead!"

"Poor fellow! poor fellow! and from his wife," sighed Mayhew; "but let me have it."

"Nay, keep it thyself," cried Gabriel to Ahab; "thou art soon going that way."

"Curses throttle thee!" yelled Ahab. "Captain Mayhew, stand by now to receive it"; and taking the fatal missive from Starbuck's hands, he caught it in the slit of the pole, and reached it over towards the boat. But as he did so, the oarsmen expectantly desisted from rowing; the boat drifted a little towards the ship's stern; so that, as if by magic, the letter suddenly ranged along with Gabriel's eager hand. He clutched it in an instant, seized the boat-knife, and impaling the letter on it, sent it thus loaded back into the ship. It fell at Ahab's feet. Then Gabriel shrieked out to his comrades to give way with their oars, and in that manner the mutinous boat rapidly shot away from the *Pequod*.

As, after this interlude, the seamen resumed their work upon the jacket of the whale, many strange things were hinted in reference to this wild affair.

Chapter LXXII

THE MONKEY-ROPE

IN THE TUMULTUOUS BUSINESS OF CUTTING-IN AND ATTENDING TO A WHALE, THERE IS MUCH RUNning backwards and forwards among the crew. Now hands are wanted here, and then again hands are wanted there. There is no staying in any one place; for at one and the same time everything has to be done everywhere. It is much the same with him who endeavors the description of the scene. We must now retrace our way a little. It was mentioned that upon first breaking ground in the whale's back, the blubber-hook was inserted into the original hole there cut by the spades of the mates. But how did so clumsy and weighty a mass as that same hook get fixed in that hole! It was inserted there by my particular friend Queequeg, whose duty it was, as harpooneer, to descend upon the monster's back for the special purpose referred to. But in very many cases, circumstances require that the harpooneer shall remain on the whale till the whole flensing or stripping operation is concluded. The whale, be it observed, lies almost entirely submerged, excepting the immediate parts operated upon. So down there, some ten feet below the level of the deck, the poor harpooneer flounders about, half on the whale and half in the water, as the vast mass revolves like a tread-mill beneath him. On the occasion in question, Queequeg figured in the Highland costume—a shirt and socks—in which to my eyes, at least, he appeared to uncommon advantage; and no one had a better chance to observe him, as will presently be seen.

Being the savage's bowsman, that is, the person who pulled the bow-oar in his boat (the second one from forward), it was my cheerful duty to attend upon him while taking that hard-scrabble scramble upon the dead whale's back. You have seen Italian organ-boys holding a dancing-ape by a long cord. Just so, from the ship's steep side, did I hold Queequeg down there in the sea, by what is technically called in the fishery a monkey-rope, attached to a strong strip of canvas belted round his waist.

It was a humorously perilous business for both of us. For, before we proceed further, it must be said that the monkey-rope was fast at both ends; fast to Queequeg's broad canvas belt, and fast to my narrow leather one. So that for better or for worse, we two, for the time, were wedded; and should poor Queequeg sink to rise no more, then both usage and honor demanded, that instead of cutting the cord, it should drag me down in his wake. So, then, an elongated Siamese ligature united us. Queequeg was my own inseparable twin-brother; nor could I any way get rid of the dangerous liabilities which the hempen bond entailed.

So strongly and metaphysically did I conceive of my situation then, that while earnestly watching his motions, I seemed distinctly to perceive that my own individuality was now merged in a joint stock company of two: that my free will had received a mortal wound; and that another's mistake or misfortune might plunge innocent me into unmerited disaster and death. Therefore, I saw that here was a sort of interregnum in Providence; for its even-handed equity never could have sanctioned so gross an injustice. And yet still further pondering—while I jerked him now and then from between the whale and ship, which would threaten to jam him—still further pondering, I say, I saw that this situation of mine was the precise situation of every mortal that breathes; only, in most cases, he, one way or other, has this Siamese connection with a plurality of other mortals. If your banker breaks, you snap; if your apothecary by mistake sends you poison in your pills, you die. True, you may say that, by exceeding caution, you may possibly escape these and the multitudinous other evil chances of life. But handle Queequeg's monkey-rope heedfully as I would, sometimes he jerked it so, that I came very near sliding overboard. Nor could I possibly forget that, do what I would, I only had the management of one end of it.[1]

I have hinted that I would often jerk poor Queequeg from between the whale and the ship—where he would occasionally fall, from the incessant rolling and swaying of both. But this was not the only jamming jeopardy he was exposed to. Unappalled by the massacre made upon them during the night, the sharks now freshly and more keenly allured by the before pent blood which began to flow from the carcass—the rabid creatures swarmed round it like bees in a beehive.

And right in among those sharks was Queequeg; who often pushed them aside with his floundering feet. A thing altogether incredible were it not that attracted by such prey as a dead whale, the otherwise miscellaneously carnivorous shark will seldom touch a man.

Nevertheless, it may well be believed that since they have such a ravenous finger in the pie, it is deemed but wise to look sharp to them. Accordingly, besides the monkey-rope, with which I now and then jerked the poor fellow from too close a vicinity to the maw of what seemed a peculiarly ferocious shark—he was provided with still another protection. Suspended over the side in one of the stages, Tashtego and Daggoo continually flourished over his head a couple of keen whale-spades, wherewith they slaughtered as many sharks as they could reach. This procedure of theirs, to be sure, was very disinterested and benevolent of them. They meant Queequeg's best happiness, I admit; but in their hasty zeal to befriend him, and from the circumstance that both he and the sharks were at times half hidden by the blood-muddled water, those indiscreet spades of theirs

1. The monkey-rope is found in all whalers; but it was only in the *Pequod* that the monkey and his holder were ever tied together. This improvement upon the original usage was introduced by no less a man than Stubb, in order to afford to the imperiled harpooneer the strongest possible guarantee for the faithfulness and vigilance of his monkey-rope holder.

would come nearer amputating a leg than a tail. But poor Queequeg, I suppose, straining and gasping there with that great iron hook—poor Queequeg, I suppose, only prayed to his Yojo, and gave up his life into the hands of his gods.

Well, well, my dear comrade and twin-brother, thought I, as I drew in and then slacked off the rope to every swell of the sea—what matters it, after all? Are you not the precious image of each and all of us men in this whaling world? That unsounded ocean you gasp in, is Life; those sharks, your foes; those spades, your friends; and what between sharks and spades you are in a sad pickle and peril, poor lad.

But courage! there is good cheer in store for you, Queequeg. For now, as with blue lips and blood-shot eyes the exhausted savage at last climbs up the chains and stands all dripping and involuntarily trembling over the side; the steward advances, and with a benevolent, consolatory glance hands him—what? Some hot Cognac? No! hands him, ye gods! hands him a cup of tepid ginger and water!

"Ginger? Do I smell ginger?" suspiciously asked Stubb, coming near. "Yes, this must be ginger," peering into the as yet untasted cup. Then standing as if incredulous for a while, he calmly walked towards the astonished steward slowly saying, "Ginger? ginger? and will you have the goodness to tell me, Mr. Dough-Boy, where lies the virtue of ginger? Ginger! is ginger the sort of fuel you use, Dough-Boy, to kindle a fire in this shivering cannibal? Ginger!—what the devil is ginger? sea-coal?—firewood?—lucifer matches?—tinder?—gunpowder?—what the devil is ginger, I say, that you offer this cup to our poor Queequeg here."

"There is some sneaking Temperance Society movement about this business," he suddenly added, now approaching Starbuck, who had just come from forward. "Will you look at that kannakin, sir: smell of it, if you please." Then watching the mate's countenance, he added, "The steward, Mr. Starbuck, had the face to offer that calomel and jalap to Queequeg, there, this instant off the whale. Is the steward an apothecary, sir? and may I ask whether this is the sort of bitters by which he blows back the life into a half-drowned man?"

"I trust not," said Starbuck, "it is poor stuff enough."

"Aye, aye, steward," cried Stubb, "we'll teach you to drug a harpooneer; none of your apothecary's medicine here; you want to poison us, do ye? You have got out insurances on our lives and want to murder us all, and pocket the proceeds, do ye?"

"It was not me," cried Dough-Boy, "it was Aunt Charity that brought the ginger on board; and bade me never give the harpooneers any spirits, but only this ginger-jub—so she called it."

"Ginger-jub! you gingerly rascal! take that! and run along with ye to the lockers, and get something better. I hope I do no wrong, Mr. Starbuck. It is the captain's orders—grog for the harpooneer on a whale."

"Enough," replied Starbuck, "only don't hit him again, but—"

"Oh, I never hurt when I hit, except when I hit a whale or something of that sort; and this fellow's a weasel. What were you about saying, sir?"

"Only this: go down with him, and get what thou wantest thyself."

When Stubb reappeared, he came with a dark flask in one hand, and a sort of tea-caddy in the other. The first contained strong spirits, and was handed to Queequeg; the second was Aunt Charity's gift, and that was freely given to the waves.

Chapter LXXIII

STUBB AND FLASK KILL A RIGHT WHALE; AND THEN HAVE A TALK OVER HIM

IT MUST BE BORNE IN MIND THAT ALL THIS TIME WE HAVE A SPERM WHALE'S PRODIGIOUS HEAD hanging to the *Pequod*'s side. But we must let it continue hanging there a while till we can get a chance to attend to it. For the present other matters press, and the best we can do now for the head, is to pray heaven the tackles may hold.

Now, during the past night and forenoon, the *Pequod* had gradually drifted into a sea, which, by its occasional patches of yellow brit, gave unusual tokens of the vicinity of Right Whales, a species of the Leviathan that but few supposed to be at this particular time lurking anywhere near. And though all hands commonly disdained the capture of those inferior creatures; and though the *Pequod* was not commissioned to cruise for them at all, and though she had passed numbers of them near the Crozetts without lowering a boat; yet now that a Sperm Whale had been brought alongside and beheaded, to the surprise of all, the announcement was made that a Right Whale should be captured that day, if opportunity offered.

Nor was this long wanting. Tall spouts were seen to leeward; and two boats, Stubb's and Flask's, were detached in pursuit. Pulling further and further away, they at last became almost invisible to the men at the mast-head. But suddenly in the distance, they saw a great heap of tumultuous white water, and soon after news came from aloft that one or both the boats must be fast. An interval passed and the boats were in plain sight, in the act of being dragged right towards the ship by the towing whale. So close did the monster come to the hull, that at first it seemed as if he meant it malice; but suddenly going down in a maelstrom, within three rods of the planks, he wholly disappeared from view, as if diving under the keel. "Cut, cut!" was the cry from the ship to the boats, which, for one instant, seemed on the point of being brought with a deadly dash against the vessel's side. But having plenty of line yet in the tubs, and the whale not sounding very rapidly, they paid out abundance of rope, and at the same time pulled with all their might so as to get ahead of the ship. For a few minutes the struggle was intensely critical; for while they still slacked out the tightened line in one direction, and still plied their oars in another, the contending strain threatened to take them under. But it was only a few feet advance they sought to gain. And they stuck to it till they did gain it; when instantly, a swift tremor was felt running like lightning along the keel, as the strained line, scraping beneath the ship, suddenly rose to view under her bows, snapping and quivering; and so flinging off its drippings, that the drops fell like bits of broken glass on the water, while the whale beyond also rose to sight and once more the boats were free to fly. But the fagged whale abated his speed, and blindly altering his course, went round the stern of the ship towing the two boats after him, so that they performed a complete circuit.

Meantime, they hauled more and more upon their lines, till close flanking him on both sides, Stubb answered Flask with lance for lance; and thus round and round the *Pequod* the battle went, while the multitudes of sharks that had before swum round the Sperm Whale's body, rushed to the fresh blood that was spilled, thirstily drinking at every new gash, as the eager Israelites did at the new bursting fountains that poured from the smitten rock.

At last his spout grew thick, and with a frightful roll and vomit, he turned upon his back a corpse.

While the two headsmen were engaged in making fast cords to his flukes, and in other ways getting the mass in readiness for towing, some conversation ensued between them.

"I wonder what the old man wants with this lump of foul lard," said Stubb, not without some disgust at the thought of having to do with so ignoble a leviathan.

"Wants with it?" said Flask, coiling some spare line in the boat's bow, "did you never hear that the ship which but once has a Sperm Whale's head hoisted on her starboard side, and at the same time a Right Whale's on the larboard; did you never hear, Stubb, that that ship can never afterwards capsize?"

"Why not?"

"I don't know, but I heard that gamboge ghost of a Fedallah saying so, and he seems to know all about ships' charms. But I sometimes think he'll charm the ship to no good at last. I don't half like that chap, Stubb. Did you ever notice how that tusk of his is a sort of carved into a snake's head, Stubb?"

"Sink him! I never look at him at all; but if ever I get a chance of a dark night, and he standing hard by the bulwarks, and no one by; look down there, Flask"—pointing into the sea with a peculiar motion of both hands—"Ay, will I! Flask, I take that Fedallah to be the devil in disguise. Do you believe that cock and bull story about his having been stowed away on board ship? He's the devil, I say. The reason why you don't see his tail, is because he tucks it up out of sight; he carries it coiled away in his pocket, I guess. Blast him! now that I think of it, he's always wanting oakum to stuff into the toes of his boots."

"He sleeps in his boots, don't he? He hasn't got any hammock; but I've seen him lay of nights in a coil of rigging."

"No doubt, and it's because of his cursed tail; he coils it down, do ye see, in the eye of the rigging."

"What's the old man have so much to do with him for?"

"Striking up a swap or a bargain, I suppose."

"Bargain?—about what?"

"Why, do ye see, the old man is hard bent after that White Whale, and the devil there is trying to come round him, and get him to swap away his silver watch, or his soul, or something of that sort, and then he'll surrender Moby-Dick."

"Pooh! Stubb, you are skylarking; how can Fedallah do that?"

"I don't know, Flask, but the devil is a curious chap, and a wicked one, I tell ye. Why, they say as how he went a sauntering into the old flag-ship once, switching his tail about devilish easy and gentleman-like, and inquiring if the old governor was at home. Well, he was at home, and asked the devil what he wanted. The devil, switching his hoofs up and says, 'I want John.' 'What for?' says the old governor. 'What business is that of yours,' says the devil, getting mad—'I want to use him.' 'Take him,' says the governor—and by the Lord, Flask, if the devil didn't give John the Asiatic cholera before he got through with him, I'll eat this whale in one mouthful. But look sharp—ain't you all ready there? Well, then, pull ahead, and let's get the whale alongside."

"I think I remember some such story as you were telling," said Flask, when at last the two boats were slowly advancing with their burden towards the ship, "but I can't remember where."

"Three Spaniards? Adventures of those three bloody-minded soldadoes? Did ye read it there, Flask? I guess ye did?"

"No: never saw such a book; heard of it, though. But now tell me, Stubb, do you suppose that that devil you was speaking of just now, was the same you say is now on board the *Pequod?*"

"Am I the same man that helped kill this whale? Doesn't the devil live forever; who ever heard that the devil was dead? Did you ever see any parson a-wearing mourning for the devil? And if the devil has a latch-key to get into the admiral's cabin, don't you suppose he can crawl into a port-hole? Tell me that, Mr. Flask?"

"How old do you suppose Fedallah is, Stubb?"

"Do you see that main-mast there?" pointing to the ship; "well, that's the figure one; now take all the hoops in the *Pequod*'s hold, and string 'em along in a row with that mast, for oughts, do you see; well, that wouldn't begin to be Fedallah's age. Nor all the coopers in creation couldn't show hoops enough to make oughts enough."

"But see here, Stubb, I thought you a little boasted just now, that you meant to give Fedallah a sea-toss, if you got a good chance. Now, if he's so old as all those hoops of yours come to, and if he is going to live forever, what good will it do to pitch him overboard—tell me that?"

"Give him a good ducking, anyhow."

"But he'd crawl back."

"Duck him again; and keep ducking him."

"Suppose he should take it into his head to duck you, though—yes, and drown you—what then?"

"I should like to see him try it; I'd give him such a pair of black eyes that he wouldn't dare to show his face in the admiral's cabin again for a long while, let alone down in the orlop there, where he lives, and hereabouts on the upper decks where he sneaks so much. Damn the devil, Flask; so you suppose I'm afraid of the devil? Who's afraid of him, except the old governor who daresn't catch him and put him in double-darbies, as he deserves, but lets him go about kidnapping people; ay, and signed a bond with him, that all the people the devil kidnapped, he'd roast for him? There's a governor!"

"Do you suppose Fedallah wants to kidnap Captain Ahab?"

"Do I suppose it? You'll know it before long, Flask. But I am going now to keep a sharp look-out on him; and if I see anything very suspicious going on, I'll just take him by the nape of his neck, and say—Look here, Beelzebub, you don't do it; and if he makes any fuss, by the Lord I'll make a grab into his pocket for his tail, take it to the capstan, and give him such a wrenching and heaving, that his tail will come short off at the stump—do you see; and then, I rather guess when he finds himself docked in that queer fashion, he'll sneak off without the poor satisfaction of feeling his tail between his legs."

"And what will you do with the tail, Stubb?"

"Do with it? Sell it for an ox whip when we get home;—what else?"

"Now, do you mean what you say, and have been saying all along, Stubb?"

"Mean or not mean, here we are at the ship."

The boats were here hailed, to tow the whale on the larboard side, where fluke chains and other necessaries were already prepared for securing him.

"Didn't I tell you so?" said Flask; "yes, you'll soon see this right whale's head hoisted up opposite that parmacetti's."

In good time, Flask's saying proved true. As before, the *Pequod* steeply leaned over towards the sperm whale's head, now, by the counterpoise of both heads, she regained her even keel; though sorely strained, you may well believe. So, when on one side you hoist in Locke's head, you go over that way; but now, on the other side, hoist in Kant's and you come back again; but in very poor plight. Thus, some minds forever keep trimming boat. Oh, ye foolish! throw all these thunder-heads overboard, and then you will float light and right.

In disposing of the body of a right whale, when brought alongside the ship, the same preliminary proceedings commonly take place as in the case of a sperm whale; only, in the latter instance, the head is cut off whole, but in the former the lips and tongue are separately removed and hoisted on deck, with all the well known black bone attached to what is called the crown-piece. But nothing like this, in the present case, had been done. The carcasses of both whales had dropped astern; and the head-laden ship not a little resembled a mule carrying a pair of overburdening panniers.

Meantime, Fedallah was calmly eyeing the right whale's head, and ever and anon glancing from the deep wrinkles there to the lines in his own hand. And Ahab chanced so to stand, that the Parsee occupied his shadow; while, if the Parsee's shadow was there at all it seemed only to blend with, and lengthen Ahab's. As the crew toiled on, Laplandish speculations were bandied among them, concerning all these passing things.

Chapter LXXIV

THE SPERM WHALE'S HEAD—CONTRASTED VIEW

HERE, NOW, ARE TWO GREAT WHALES, LAYING THEIR HEADS TOGETHER; LET US JOIN THEM, AND lay together our own.

Of the grand order of folio leviathans, the Sperm Whale and the Right Whale are by far the most noteworthy. They are the only whales regularly hunted by man. To the Nantucketer, they present the two extremes of all the known varieties of the whale. As the external difference between them is mainly observable in their heads; and as a head of each is this moment hanging from the *Pequod*'s side; and as we may freely go from one to the other, by merely stepping across the deck: where, I should like to know, will you obtain a better chance to study practical cetology than here?

In the first place, you are struck by the general contrast between these heads. Both are massive enough in all conscience; but there is a certain mathematical symmetry in the Sperm Whale's which the Right Whale's sadly lacks. There is more character in the Sperm Whale's head. As you behold it, you involuntarily yield the immense superiority to him, in point of pervading dignity. In the present instance, too, this dignity is heightened by the pepper and salt color of his head at the summit, giving token of advanced age and large experience. In short, he is what the fishermen technically call a "gray-headed whale."

Let us now note what is least dissimilar in these heads—namely, the two most important organs, the eye and the ear. Far back on the side of the head, and low down, near the angle of either whale's jaw, if you narrowly search, you will at last see a lashless eye, which you would fancy to be a young colt's eye; so out of all proportion is it to the magnitude of the head.

Now, from this peculiar sideway position of the whale's eyes, it is plain that he can never see an object which is exactly ahead, no more than he can one exactly astern. In a word, the position of the whale's eyes corresponds to that of a man's ears; and you may fancy, for yourself, how it would fare with you, did you sideways survey objects through your ears. You would find that you could only command some thirty degrees of vision in advance of the straight side-line of sight; and about thirty more behind it. If your bitterest foe were walking straight towards you, with dagger uplifted in broad day, you would not be able to see him, any more than if he were stealing upon you from behind. In a word, you would have two backs, so to speak; but, at the same time, also, two fronts (side fronts): for what is it that makes the front of a man—what, indeed, but his eyes?

Moreover, while in most other animals that I can now think of, the eyes are so planted as imperceptibly to blend their visual power, so as to produce one picture and not two to the brain; the peculiar position of the whale's eyes, effectually divided as they are by many cubic feet of solid head, which towers between them like a great mountain separating two lakes in valleys; this, of course, must wholly separate the impressions which each independent organ imparts. The whale, therefore, must see one distinct picture on this side, and another distinct picture on that side; while all between must be profound darkness and nothingness to him. Man may, in effect, be said to look out on the world from a sentry-box with two joined sashes for his window. But with the whale, these two sashes are separately inserted, making two distinct windows, but sadly impairing the view. This peculiarity of the whale's eyes is a thing always to be borne in mind in the fishery; and to be remembered by the reader in some subsequent scenes.

A curious and most puzzling question might be started concerning this visual matter as touching the Leviathan. But I must be content with a hint. So long as a man's eyes are open in the light, the act of seeing is involuntary; that is, he cannot then help mechanically seeing whatever objects are before him. Nevertheless, anyone's experience will teach him, that though he can take in an undiscriminating sweep of things at one glance, it is quite impossible for him, attentively, and completely, to examine any two things—however large or however small—at one and the same instant of time; never mind if they lie side by side and touch each other. But if you now come to separate these two objects, and surround each by a circle of profound darkness; then, in order to see one of them, in such a manner as to bring your mind to bear on it, the other will be utterly excluded from your contemporary consciousness. How is it, then, with the whale? True, both his eyes, in themselves, must simultaneously act; but is his brain so much more comprehensive, combining, and subtle than man's, that he can at the same moment of time attentively examine two distinct prospects, one on one side of him, and the other in an exactly opposite direction? If he can, then is it as marvelous a thing in him, as if a man were able simultaneously to go through the demonstrations of two distinct problems in Euclid. Nor, strictly investigated, is there any incongruity in this comparison.

It may be but an idle whim, but it has always seemed to me, that the extraordinary vacillations of movement displayed by some whales when beset by three or four boats; the timidity and liability to queer frights, so common to such whales; I think that all this indirectly proceeds from the helpless perplexity of volition, in which their divided and diametrically opposite powers of vision must involve them.

But the ear of the whale is full as curious as the eye. If you are an entire stranger to their race, you might hunt over these two heads for hours, and never discover that organ. The ear has no external leaf whatever; and into the hole itself you can hardly insert a quill, so wondrously minute is it. It is lodged a little behind the eye. With respect to their ears, this important difference is to be observed between the sperm whale and the right. While the ears of the former has an external opening, that of the latter is entirely and evenly covered over with a membrane, so as to be quite imperceptible from without.

Is it not curious, that so vast a being as the whale should see the world through so small an eye, and hear the thunder through an ear which is smaller than a hare's? But if his eyes were broad as the lens of Herschel's great telescope; and his ears capacious as the porches of cathedrals; would that make him any longer of sight, or sharper of hearing? Not at all.—Why then do you try to "enlarge" your mind? Subtilize it.

Let us now with whatever levers and steam-engines we have at hand, cant over the sperm whale's head, so that it may lie bottom up; then, ascending by a ladder to the summit, have a peep down the mouth; and were it not that the body is now completely separated from it, with a lantern we might descend into the great Kentucky Mammoth Cave of his stomach. But let us hold on here by this tooth, and look about us where we are. What a really beautiful and chaste-looking mouth! from floor to ceiling, lined, or rather papered with a glistening white membrane, glossy as bridal satins.

But come out now, and look at this portentous lower jaw, which seems like the long narrow lid of an immense snuff-box, with the hinge at one end, instead of one side. If you pry it up, so as to get it overhead, and expose its rows of teeth, it seems a terrific portcullis; and such, alas! it proves to many a poor wight in the fishery, upon whom these spikes fall with impaling force. But far more terrible is it to behold, when fathoms down in the sea, you see some sulky whale, floating there suspended, with his prodigious jaw, some fifteen feet long, hanging straight down at right-angles with his body, for all the world like a ship's jib-boom. This whale is not dead; he is only dispirited; out of sorts, perhaps; hypochondriac; and so supine, that the hinges of his jaw have relaxed, leaving him there in that ungainly sort of plight, a reproach to all his tribe, who must, no doubt, imprecate lockjaws upon him.

In most cases this lower jaw—being easily unhinged by a practiced artist—is disengaged and hoisted on deck for the purpose of extracting the ivory teeth, and furnishing a supply of that hard white whalebone with which the fishermen fashion all sorts of curious articles, including canes, umbrella-sticks, and handles to riding-whips.

With a long, weary hoist the jaw is dragged on board, as if it were an anchor; and when the proper time comes—some few days after the other work—Queequeg, Daggoo, and Tashtego, being all accomplished dentists, are set to drawing teeth. With a keen cutting-spade, Queequeg lances the gums; then the jaw is lashed down to ring-bolts, and a tackle being rigged from aloft, they drag out these teeth, as Michigan oxen drag stumps of old oaks out of wild woodlands. There are generally forty-two teeth in all; in old whales, much worn down, but undecayed; nor filled after our artificial fashion. The jaw is afterwards sawn into slabs, and piled away like joists for building houses.

Chapter LXXV

The Right Whale's Head—Contrasted View

CROSSING THE DECK, LET US NOW HAVE A GOOD LONG LOOK AT THE THE RIGHT WHALE'S HEAD.

As in general shape the noble Sperm Whale's head may be compared to a Roman war-chariot (especially in front, where it is so broadly rounded); so, at a broad view, the Right Whale's head bears a rather inelegant resemblance to a gigantic galliot-toed shoe. Two hundred years ago an old Dutch voyager likened its shape to that of a shoemaker's last. And in this same last or shoe, that old woman of the nursery tale with the swarming brood, might very comfortably be lodged, she and all her progeny.

But as you come nearer to this great head it begins to assume different aspects, according to your point of view. If you stand on its summit and look at these two *f*-shaped spout-holes, you would take the whole head for an enormous bass-viol, and these spiracles, the apertures in its sounding-board. Then, again, if you fix your eye upon this strange, crested, comb-like encrustation on the top of the mass—this green, barnacled thing, which the Greenlanders call the "crown," and the Southern fishers the "bonnet" of the Right Whale; fixing your eyes solely on this, you would take the head for the trunk of some huge oak, with a bird's nest in its crotch. At any rate, when you watch those live crabs that nestle here on this bonnet, such an idea will be almost sure to occur to you; unless, indeed, your fancy has been fixed by the technical term "crown" also bestowed upon it; in which case you will take great interest in thinking how this mighty monster is actually a diademed king of the sea, whose green crown has been put together for him in this marvelous manner. But if this whale be a king, he is a very sulky looking fellow to grace a diadem. Look at that hanging lower lip! what a huge sulk and pout is there! a sulk and pout, by carpenter's measurement, about twenty feet long and five feet deep; a sulk and pout that will yield you some 500 gallons of oil and more.

A great pity, now, that this unfortunate whale should be hare-lipped. The fissure is about a foot across. Probably the mother during an important interval was sailing down the Peruvian coast when earthquakes caused the beach to gape. Over this lip, as over a slippery threshold, we now slide into the mouth. Upon my word were I at Mackinaw, I should take this to be the inside of an Indian wigwam. Good Lord! is this the road that Jonah went? The roof is about twelve feet high, and runs to a pretty sharp angle, as if there were a regular ridge-pole there; while these ribbed, arched, hairy sides, present us with those wondrous, half vertical, scimetar-shaped slats of whalebone, say three hundred on a side, which depending from the upper part of the head or crown bone, form those Venetian blinds which have elsewhere been cursorily mentioned. The edges of these bones are fringed with hairy fibers, through which the Right Whale strains the water, and in whose intricacies he retains the small fish, when open-mouthed he goes through the seas of brit in feeding time. In the central blinds of bone, as they stand in their natural order, there are certain curious marks, curves, hollows, and ridges, whereby some whalemen calculate the creature's age, as the age of an oak by its circular rings. Though the certainty of this criterion is far from demonstrable, yet it has the savor of analogical probability. At any rate, if we yield to it, we must grant a far greater age to the Right Whale than at first glance will seem reasonable.

In old times, there seem to have prevailed the most curious fancies concerning these blinds. One voyager in Purchas calls them the wondrous "whiskers" inside of the whale's mouth;[1] another, "hogs' bristles"; a third old gentleman in Hakluyt uses the following elegant language: "There are about two hundred and fifty fins growing on each side of his upper *chop*, which arch over his tongue on each side of his mouth."

As everyone knows, these same "hogs' bristles," "fins," "whiskers," "blinds," or whatever you please, furnish to the ladies their busks and other stiffening contrivances. But in this particular, the demand has long been on the decline. It was in Queen Anne's time that the bone was in its glory, the farthingale being then all the fashion. And as those ancient dames moved about gaily, though in the jaws of the whale, as you may say; even so, in a shower, with the like thoughtlessness, do we nowadays fly under the same jaws for protection; the umbrella being a tent spread over the same bone.

But now forget all about blinds and whiskers for a moment, and, standing in the Right Whale's mouth, look around you afresh. Seeing all these colonnades of bone so methodically ranged about, would you not think you were inside of the great Haarlem organ, and gazing upon its thousand pipes? For a carpet to the organ we have a rug of the softest Turkey—the tongue, which is glued, as it were, to the floor of the mouth. It is very fat and tender, and apt to tear in pieces in hoisting it on deck. This particular tongue now before us; at a passing glance I should say it was a six-barreler; that is, it will yield you about that amount of oil.

Ere this, you must have plainly seen the truth of what I started with—that the Sperm Whale and the Right Whale have almost entirely different heads. To sum up, then: in the Right Whale's there is no great well of sperm; no ivory teeth at all; no long, slender mandible of a lower jaw, like the Sperm Whale's. Nor in the Sperm Whale are there any of those blinds of bone; no huge lower lip; and scarcely anything of a tongue. Again, the Right Whale has two external spout-holes, the Sperm Whale only one.

Look your last now, on these venerable hooded heads, while they yet lie together; for one will soon sink, unrecorded, in the sea; the other will not be very long in following.

Can you catch the expression of the Sperm Whale's there? It is the same he died with, only some of the longer wrinkles in the forehead seem now faded away. I think his broad brow to be full of a prairie-like placidity, born of a speculative indifference as to death. But mark the other head's expression. See that amazing lower lip, pressed by accident against the vessel's side, so as firmly to embrace the jaw. Does not this whole head seem to speak of an enormous practical resolution in facing death? This Right Whale I take to have been a Stoic; the Sperm Whale, a Platonian, who might have taken up Spinoza in his latter years.

1. This reminds us that the Right Whale really has a sort of whisker, or rather a mustache, consisting of a few scattered white hairs on the upper part of the outer end of the lower jaw. Sometimes these tufts impart a rather brigandish expression to his otherwise solemn countenance.

Chapter LXXVI

THE BATTERING-RAM

Ere quitting, for the nonce, the Sperm Whale's head, I would have you, as a sensible physiologist, simply—particularly remark its front aspect, in all its compacted collectedness. I would have you investigate it now with the sole view of forming to yourself some unexaggerated, intelligent estimate of whatever battering-ram power may be lodged there. Here is a vital point; for you must either satisfactorily settle this matter with yourself, or forever remain an infidel as to one of the most appalling, but not the less true events, perhaps anywhere to be found in all recorded history.

You observe that in the ordinary swimming position of the Sperm Whale, the front of his head presents an almost wholly vertical plane to the water; you observe that the lower part of that front slopes considerably backwards, so as to furnish more of a retreat for the long socket which receives the boom-like lower jaw; you observe that the mouth is entirely under the head, much in the same way, indeed, as though your own mouth were entirely under your chin. Moreover you observe that the whale has no external nose; and that what nose he has—his spout-hole—is on the top of his head; you observe that his eyes and ears are at the sides of his head; nearly one third of his entire length from the front. Wherefore, you must now have perceived that the front of the Sperm Whale's head is a dead, blind wall, without a single organ or tender prominence of any sort whatsoever. Furthermore, you are now to consider that only in the extreme, lower, backward sloping part of the front of the head, is there the slightest vestige of bone; and not till you get near twenty feet from the forehead do you come to the full cranial development. So that this whole enormous boneless mass is as one wad. Finally, though, as will soon be revealed, its contents partly comprise the most delicate oil; yet, you are now to be apprised of the nature of the substance which so impregnably invests all that apparent effeminacy. In some previous place I have described to you how the blubber wraps the body of the whale, as the rind wraps an orange. Just so with the head; but with this difference: about the head this envelope, though not so thick, is of a boneless toughness, inestimable by any man who has not handled it. The severest pointed harpoon, the sharpest lance darted by the strongest human arm, impotently rebounds from it. It is as though the forehead of the Sperm Whale were paved with horses' hoofs. I do not think that any sensation lurks in it.

Bethink yourself also of another thing. When two large, loaded Indiamen chance to crowd and crush towards each other in the docks, what do the sailors do? They do not suspend between them, at the point of coming contact, any merely hard substance, like iron or wood. No, they hold there a large, round wad of tow and cork, enveloped in the thickest and toughest of ox-hide. That bravely and uninjured takes the jam which would have snapped all their oaken handspikes and iron crow-bars. By itself this sufficiently illustrates the obvious fact I drive at. But supplementary to this, it has hypothetically occurred to me, that as ordinary fish possess what is called a swimming bladder in them, capable, at will, of distension or contraction; and as the Sperm Whale, as far as I know, has no such provision in him; considering, too, the otherwise inexplicable manner in which he now depresses his head altogether beneath the surface, and anon swims with it high elevated out of the water; considering the unobstructed elasticity of its envelope; considering the unique interior of his head; it has hypothetically occurred to me, I say, that those mystical lung-celled honey-combs there may possibly have some hitherto unknown and unsuspected connection with the outer air, so as to be susceptible to atmospheric distension and contraction. If this be so, fancy the irresistibleness of that might, to which the most impalpable and destructive of all elements contributes.

Now, mark. Unerringly impelled this dead, impregnable, uninjurable wall, and this most buoyant thing within; there swims behind it all a mass of tremendous life, only to be adequately estimated as piled wood is—by the cord; and all obedient to one volition, as the smallest insect. So that when I shall hereafter detail to you all the specialities and concentrations of potency everywhere lurking in this expansive monster; when I shall show you some of his more inconsiderable braining feats; I trust you will have renounced all ignorant incredulity, and be ready to abide by this; that though the Sperm Whale stove a passage through the Isthmus of Darien, and mixed the Atlantic with the Pacific, you would not elevate one hair of your eye-brow. For unless you own the whale, you are but a provincial and sentimentalist in Truth. But clear Truth is a thing for salamander giants only to encounter; how small the chances for the provincials then? What befell the weakling youth lifting the dread goddess's veil at Lais?

Chapter LXXVII

The Great Heidelburgh Tun

Now comes the baling of the case. But to comprehend it aright, you must know something of the curious internal structure of the thing operated upon.

Regarding the Sperm Whale's head as a solid oblong, you may, on an inclined plane, sideways divide it into two quoins,[1] whereof the lower is the bony structure, forming the cranium and jaws, and the upper an unctuous mass wholly free from bones; its broad forward end forming the expanded vertical apparent forehead of the whale. At the middle of the forehead horizontally subdivide this upper quoin, and then you have two almost equal parts, which before were naturally divided by an internal wall of a thick tendinous substance.

The lower subdivided part, called the junk, is one immense honey-comb of oil, formed by the crossing and recrossing, into ten thousand infiltrated cells, of tough elastic white fibers throughout its whole extent. The upper part, known as the Case, may be regarded as the great Heidelburgh Tun of the Sperm Whale. And as that famous great tierce is mystically carved in front, so the whale's vast plaited forehead forms innumerable strange devices for the emblematical adornment of his wondrous tun. Moreover, as that of Heidelburgh was always replenished with the most excellent of the wines of the Rhenish valleys, so the tun of the whale contains by far the most precious of all his oily vintages; namely, the highly-prized spermaceti, in its absolutely pure, limpid, and odoriferous state. Nor is this precious substance found unalloyed in any other part of the creature. Though in life it remains perfectly fluid, yet, upon exposure to the air, after death, it soon begins to concrete; sending forth beautiful crystalline shoots, as when the first thin delicate ice is just forming in water. A large whale's case generally yields about five hundred gallons of sperm, though from unavoidable circumstances, considerable of it is spilled, leaks, and dribbles away, or is otherwise irrevocably lost in the ticklish business of securing what you can.

I know not with what fine and costly material the Heidelburgh Tun was coated within, but in

1. Quoin is not a Euclidean term. It belongs to the pure nautical mathematics. I know not that it has been defined before. A quoin is a solid which differs from a wedge in having its sharp end formed by the steep inclination of one side, instead of the mutual tapering of both sides.

superlative richness that coating could not possibly have compared with the silken pearl-colored membrane, like the lining of a fine pelisse, forming the inner surface of the Sperm Whale's case.

It will have been seen that the Heidelburgh Tun of the Sperm Whale embraces the entire length of the entire top of the head; and since—as has been elsewhere set forth—the head embraces one third of the whole length of the creature, then setting that length down at eighty feet for a good sized whale, you have more than twenty-six feet for the depth of the tun, when it is lengthwise hoisted up and down against a ship's side.

As in decapitating the whale, the operator's instrument is brought close to the spot where an entrance is subsequently forced into the spermaceti magazine; he has, therefore, to be uncommonly heedful, lest a careless, untimely stroke should invade the sanctuary and wastingly let out its invaluable contents. It is this decapitated end of the head, also, which is at last elevated out of the water, and retained in that position by the enormous cutting tackles, whose hempen combinations, on one side, make quite a wilderness of ropes in that quarter.

Thus much being said, attend now, I pray you, to that marvelous and—in this particular instance—almost fatal operation whereby the Sperm Whale's great Heidelburgh Tun is tapped.

Chapter LXXVIII

CISTERN AND BUCKETS

NIMBLE AS A CAT, TASHTEGO MOUNTS ALOFT; AND WITHOUT ALTERING HIS ERECT POSTURE, runs straight out upon the overhanging main-yard-arm, to the part where it exactly projects over the hoisted Tun. He has carried with him a light tackle called a whip, consisting of only two parts, traveling through a single-sheaved block. Securing this block, so that it hangs down from the yard-arm, he swings one end of the rope, till it is caught and firmly held by a hand on the deck. Then hand-over-hand, down the other part, the Indian drops through the air, till dexterously he lands on the summit of the head. There—still high elevated above the rest of the company, to whom he vivaciously cries—he seems some Turkish Muezzin calling the good people to prayers from the top of a tower. A short-handled sharp spade being sent up to him, he diligently searches for the proper place to begin breaking into the Tun. In this business he proceeds very heedfully, like a treasure-hunter in some old house, sounding the walls to find where the gold is masoned in. By the time this cautious search is over, a stout iron-bound bucket, precisely like a well-bucket, has been attached to one end of the whip; while the other end, being stretched across the deck, is there held by two or three alert hands. These last now hoist the bucket within grasp of the Indian, to whom another person has reached up a very long pole. Inserting this pole into the bucket, Tashtego downward guides the bucket into the Tun, till it entirely disappears; then giving the word to the seamen at the whip, up comes the bucket again, all bubbling like a dairy-maid's pail of new milk. Carefully lowered from its height, the full-freighted vessel is caught by an appointed hand, and quickly emptied into a large tub. Then remounting aloft, it again goes through the same round until the deep cistern will yield no more. Towards the end, Tashtego has to ram his long pole harder and harder, and deeper and deeper into the Tun, until some twenty feet of the pole have gone down.

Now, the people of the *Pequod* had been baling some time in this way; several tubs had been filled with the fragrant sperm; when all at once a queer accident happened. Whether it was that Tashtego, that wild Indian, was so heedless and reckless as to let go for a moment his one-handed hold on the great cabled tackles suspending the head; or whether the place where he stood was so treacherous and oozy; or whether the Evil One himself would have it to fall out so, without stating his particular reasons; how it was exactly, there is no telling now; but, on a sudden, as the eightieth or ninetieth bucket came suckingly up—my God! poor Tashtego—like the twin reciprocating bucket in a veritable well, dropped head-foremost down into this great Tun of Heidelburgh, and with a horrible oily gurgling, went clean out of sight!

"Man overboard!" cried Daggoo, who amid the general consternation first came to his senses. "Swing the bucket this way!" and putting one foot into it, so as the better to secure his slippery handhold on the whip itself, the hoisters ran him high up to the top of the head, almost before Tashtego could have reached its interior bottom. Meantime, there was a terrible tumult. Looking over the side, they saw the before lifeless head throbbing and heaving just below the surface of the sea, as if that moment seized with some momentous idea; whereas it was only the poor Indian unconsciously revealing by those struggles the perilous depth to which he had sunk.

At this instant, while Daggoo, on the summit of the head, was clearing the whip—which had somehow got foul of the great cutting tackles—a sharp cracking noise was heard; and to the unspeakable horror of all, one of the two enormous hooks suspending the head tore out, and with a vast vibration the enormous mass sideways swung, till the drunk ship reeled and shook as if smitten by an iceberg. The one remaining hook, upon which the entire strain now depended, seemed every instant to be on the point of giving way; an event still more likely from the violent motions of the head.

"Come down, come down!" yelled the seamen to Daggoo, but with one hand holding on to the heavy tackles, so that if the head should drop, he would still remain suspended; the negro having cleared the foul line, rammed down the bucket into the now collapsed well, meaning that the buried harpooneer should grasp it, and so be hoisted out.

"In heaven's name, man," cried Stubb, "are you ramming home a cartridge there?—Avast! How will that help him; jamming that iron-bound bucket on top of his head? Avast, will ye!"

"Stand clear of the tackle!" cried a voice like the bursting of a rocket.

Almost in the same instant, with a thunder-boom, the enormous mass dropped into the sea, like Niagara's Table-Rock into the whirlpool; the suddenly relieved hull rolled away from it, to far down her glittering copper; and all caught their breath, as half swinging—now over the sailors' heads, and now over the water—Daggoo, through a thick mist of spray, was dimly beheld clinging to the pendulous tackles, while poor, buried-alive Tashtego was sinking utterly down to the bottom of the sea! But hardly had the blinding vapor cleared away, when a naked figure with a boarding-sword in his hand, was for one swift moment seen hovering over the bulwarks. The next, a loud splash announced that my brave Queequeg had dived to the rescue. One packed rush was made to the side, and every eye counted every ripple, as moment followed moment, and no sign of either the sinker or the diver could be seen. Some hands now jumped into a boat alongside, and pushed a little off from the ship.

"Ha! ha!" cried Daggoo, all at once, from his now quiet, swinging perch overhead; and looking further off from the side, we saw an arm thrust upright from the blue waves; a sight strange to see, as an arm thrust forth from the grass over a grave.

"Both! both!—it is both!"—cried Daggoo again with a joyful shout; and soon after, Queequeg was seen boldly striking out with one hand, and with the other clutching the long hair of the Indian. Drawn into the waiting boat, they were quickly brought to the deck; but Tashtego was long in coming to, and Queequeg did not look very brisk.

Now, how had this noble rescue been accomplished? Why, diving after the slowly descending head, Queequeg with his keen sword had made side lunges near its bottom, so as to scuttle a large hole there; then dropping his sword, had thrust his long arm far inwards and upwards, and so hauled out our poor Tash by the head. He averred, that upon first thrusting in for him, a leg was presented; but well knowing that that was not as it ought to be, and might occasion great trouble;—he had thrust back the leg, and by a dexterous heave and toss, had wrought a somerset upon the Indian; so that with the next trial, he came forth in the good old way—head-foremost. As for the great head itself, that was doing as well as could be expected.

And thus, through the courage and great skill in obstetrics of Queequeg, the deliverance, or rather, delivery of Tashtego, was successfully accomplished, in the teeth, too, of the most untoward and apparently hopeless impediments; which is a lesson by no means to be forgotten. Midwifery should be taught in the same course with fencing and boxing, riding and rowing.

I know that this queer adventure of the Gay-Header's will be sure to seem incredible to some landsmen, though they themselves may have either seen or heard of someone's falling into a cistern ashore; an accident which not seldom happens, and with much less reason too than the Indian's, considering the exceeding slipperiness of the curb of the Sperm Whale's well.

But, peradventure, it may be sagaciously urged, how is this? We thought the tissued, infiltrated head of the Sperm Whale, was the lightest and most corky part about him; and yet thou makest it sink in an element of a far greater specific gravity than itself. We have thee there. Not at all, but I have ye; for at the time poor Tash fell in, the case had been nearly emptied of its lighter contents, leaving little but the dense tendinous wall of the well—a double welded, hammered substance, as I have before said, much heavier than the sea-water, and a lump of which sinks in it like lead almost. But the tendency to rapid sinking in this substance was in the present instance materially counteracted by the other parts of the head remaining undetached from it, so that it sank very slowly and deliberately indeed, affording Queequeg a fair chance for performing his agile obstetrics on the run, as you may say. Yes, it was a running delivery, so it was.

Now, had Tashtego perished in that head, it had been a very precious perishing; smothering in the very whitest and daintiest of fragrant spermaceti; coffined, hearsed, and tombed in the secret inner chamber and sanctum sanctorum of the whale. Only one sweeter end can readily be recalled—the delicious death of an Ohio honey-hunter, who seeking honey in the crotch of a hollow tree, found such exceeding store of it, that leaning too far over, it sucked him in, so that he died embalmed. How many, think ye, have likewise fallen into Plato's honey head, and sweetly perished there?

Chapter LXXIX

THE PRAIRIE

TO SCAN THE LINES OF HIS FACE, OR FEEL THE BUMPS ON THE HEAD OF THIS LEVIATHAN; THIS IS a thing which no Physiognomist or Phrenologist has as yet undertaken. Such an enterprise would seem almost as hopeful as for Lavater to have scrutinized the wrinkles on the Rock of Gibraltar, or for Gall to have mounted a ladder and manipulated the dome of the Pantheon. Still, in that famous work of his, Lavater not only treats of the various faces of men, but also attentively studies the faces of horses, birds, serpents, and fish; and dwells in detail upon the modifications of expression discernible therein. Nor have Gall and his disciple Spurzheim failed to throw out some hints touching the phrenological characteristics of other beings than man. Therefore, though I am but ill qualified for a pioneer, in the application of these two semi-sciences to the whale, I will do my endeavor. I try all things; I achieve what I can.

Physiognomically regarded, the Sperm Whale is an anomalous creature. He has no proper nose. And since the nose is the central and most conspicuous of the features; and since it perhaps most modifies and finally controls their combined expression; hence it would seem that its entire absence, as an external appendage, must very largely affect the countenance of the whale. For as in landscape gardening, a spire, cupola, monument, or tower of some sort, is deemed almost indispensable to the completion of the scene; so no face can be physiognomically in keeping without the elevated open-work belfry of the nose. Dash the nose from Phidias's marble Jove, and what a sorry remainder! Nevertheless, Leviathan is of so mighty a magnitude, all his proportions are so stately, that the same deficiency which in the sculptured Jove were hideous, in him is no blemish at all. Nay, it is an added grandeur. A nose to the whale would have been impertinent. As on your physiognomical voyage you sail round his vast head in your jolly-boat, your noble conceptions of him are never insulted by the reflection that he has a nose to be pulled. A pestilent conceit, which so often will insist upon obtruding even when beholding the mightiest royal beadle on his throne.

In some particulars, perhaps the most imposing physiognomical view to be had of the Sperm Whale, is that of the full front of his head. This aspect is sublime.

In thought, a fine human brow is like the east when troubled with the morning. In the repose of the pasture, the curled brow of the bull has a touch of the grand in it. Pushing heavy cannon up mountain defiles, the elephant's brow is majestic. Human or animal, the mystical brow is as that great golden seal affixed by the German Emperors to their decrees. It signifies—"God: done this day by my hand." But in most creatures, nay in man himself, very often the brow is but a mere strip of alpine land lying along the snow line. Few are the foreheads which like Shakespeare's or Melancthon's rise so high, and descend so low, that the eyes themselves seem clear, eternal, tideless mountain lakes; and all above them in the forehead's wrinkles, you seem to track the antlered thoughts descending there to drink, as the Highland hunters track the snow prints of the deer. But in the great Sperm Whale, this high and mighty god-like dignity inherent in the brow is so immensely amplified, that gazing on it, in that full front view, you feel the Deity and the dread powers more forcibly than in beholding any other object in living nature. For you see no one point precisely; not one distinct feature is revealed; no nose, eyes, ears, or mouth; no face; he has none, proper; nothing but that one broad firmament of a forehead, pleated with riddles; dumbly lowering with the doom of boats, and ships, and men. Nor, in profile, does this wondrous brow diminish; though that way viewed, its grandeur does not domineer upon you so. In profile, you plainly perceive that horizontal, semi-crescentic depression in the forehead's middle, which, in a man, is Lavater's mark of genius.

But how? Genius in the Sperm Whale? Has the Sperm Whale ever written a book, spoken a speech? No, his great genius is declared in his doing nothing particular to prove it. It is moreover declared in his pyramidical silence. And this reminds me that had the great Sperm Whale been known to the young Orient World, he would have been deified by their child-magian thoughts. They deified the crocodile of the Nile, because the crocodile is tongueless; and the Sperm Whale has no tongue, or at least it is so exceedingly small, as to be incapable of protrusion. If hereafter any highly cultured, poetical nation shall lure back to their birth-right, the merry May-day gods of old; and livingly enthrone them again in the now egotistical sky; in the now unhaunted hill; then be sure, exalted to Jove's high seat, the great Sperm Whale shall lord it.

Champollion deciphered the wrinkled granite hieroglyphics. But there is no Champollion to decipher the Egypt of every man's and every being's face. Physiognomy, like every other human science, is but a passing fable. If then, Sir William Jones, who read in thirty languages, could not read the simplest peasant's face in its profounder and more subtle meanings, how may unlettered Ishmael hope to read the awful Chaldee of the Sperm Whale's brow? I but put that brow before you. Read if it if you can.

Chapter LXXX

THE NUT

IF THE SPERM WHALE BE PHYSIOGNOMICALLY A SPHINX, TO THE PHRENOLOGIST HIS BRAIN SEEMS that geometrical circle which it is impossible to square.

In the full-grown creature the skull will measure at least twenty feet in length. Unhinge the lower jaw, and the side view of this skull is as the side view of a moderately inclined plane resting throughout on a level base. But in life—as we have elsewhere seen—this inclined plane is angularly filled up, and almost squared by the enormous super-encumbent mass of the junk and sperm. At the high end the skull forms a crater to bed that part of the mass; while under the long floor of this crater—in another cavity seldom exceeding ten inches in length and as many in depth—reposes the mere handful of this monster's brain. The brain is at least twenty feet from his apparent forehead in life; it is hidden away behind its vast outworks, like the innermost citadel within the amplified fortifications of Quebec. So like a choice casket is it secreted in him, that I have known some whalemen who peremptorily deny that the Sperm Whale has any other brain than that palpable semblance of one formed by the cubic-yards of his sperm magazine. Lying in strange folds, courses, and convolutions, to their apprehensions, it seems more in keeping with the idea of his general might to regard that mystic part of him as the seat of his intelligence.

It is plain, then, that phrenologically the head of this Leviathan, in the creature's living intact state, is an entire delusion. As for his true brain, you can then see no indications of it, nor feel any. The whale, like all things that are mighty, wears a false brow to the common world.

If you unload his skull of its spermy heaps and then take a rear view of its rear end, which is the high end, you will be struck by its resemblance to the human skull, beheld in the same situation, and from the same point of view. Indeed, place this reversed skull (scaled down to the human magnitude) among a plate of men's skulls, and you would involuntarily confound it with them; and remarking the depressions on one part of its summit, in phrenological phrase you would say—This man had no self-esteem, and no veneration. And by those negations, considered along with the affirmative fact of his prodigious bulk and power, you can best form to yourself the truest, though not the most exhilarating conception of what the most exalted potency is.

But if from the comparative dimensions of the whale's proper brain, you deem it incapable of being adequately charted, then I have another idea for you. If you attentively regard almost any quadruped's spine, you will be struck with the resemblance of its vertebrae to a strung necklace of dwarfed skulls, all bearing rudimental resemblance to the skull proper. It is a German conceit, that the vertebrae are absolutely undeveloped skulls. But the curious external resemblance, I take it the Germans were not the first men to perceive. A foreign friend once pointed it out to me, in the skeleton of a foe he had slain, and with the vertebrae of which he was inlaying, in a sort of basso-relievo, the beaked prow of his canoe. Now, I consider that the phrenologists have omitted an important thing in not pushing their investigations from the cerebellum through the spinal canal. For I believe that much of a man's character will be found betokened in his backbone. I would rather feel your spine than your skull, whoever you are. A thin joist of a spine never yet upheld a full and noble soul. I rejoice in my spine, as in the firm audacious staff of that flag which I fling half out to the world.

Apply this spinal branch of phrenology to the Sperm Whale. His cranial cavity is continuous with the first neck-vertebra; and in that vertebra the bottom of the spinal canal will measure ten inches across, being eight in height, and of a triangular figure with the base downwards. As it passes through the remaining vertebrae the canal tapers in size, but for a considerable distance remains of large capacity. Now, of course, this canal is filled with much the same strangely fibrous substance—the spinal cord—as the brain; and directly communicates with the brain. And what is still more, for many feet after emerging from the brain's cavity, the spinal cord remains of an undecreasing girth, almost equal to that of the brain. Under all these circumstances, would it be unreasonable to survey and map out the whale's spine phrenologically? For, viewed in this light, the wonderful comparative smallness of his brain proper is more than compensated by the wonderful comparative magnitude of his spinal cord.

But leaving this hint to operate as it may with the phrenologists, I would merely assume the spinal theory for a moment, in reference to the Sperm Whale's hump. This august hump, if I mistake not, rises over one of the larger vertebrae, and is, therefore, in some sort, the outer convex mold of it. From its relative situation then, I should call this high hump the organ of firmness or indomitableness in the Sperm Whale. And that the great monster is indomitable, you will yet have reason to know.

Chapter LXXXI

THE PEQUOD MEETS THE VIRGIN

THE PREDESTINATED DAY ARRIVED, AND WE DULY MET THE SHIP *JUNGFRAU*, DERICK DE DEER, master, of Bremen.

At one time the greatest whaling people in the world, the Dutch and Germans are now among the least; but here and there at very wide intervals of latitude and longitude, you still occasionally meet with their flag in the Pacific.

For some reason, the *Jungfrau* seemed quite eager to pay her respects. While yet some distance from the *Pequod,* she rounded to, and dropping a boat, her captain was impelled towards us, impatiently standing in the bows instead of the stern.

"What has he in his hand there?" cried Starbuck, pointing to something wavingly held by the German. "Impossible!—a lamp-feeder!"

"Not that," said Stubb, "no, no, it's a coffee-pot, Mr. Starbuck; he's coming off to make us our coffee, is the Yarman; don't you see that big tin can there alongside of him?—that's his boiling water. Oh! he's all right, is the Yarman."

"Go along with you," cried Flask, "it's a lamp-feeder and an oil-can. He's out of oil, and has come a-begging."

However curious it may seem for an oil-ship to be borrowing oil on the whale-ground, and however much it may invertedly contradict the old proverb about carrying coals to Newcastle, yet sometimes such a thing really happens; and in the present case Captain Derick De Deer did indubitably conduct a lamp-feeder as Flask did declare.

As he mounted the deck, Ahab abruptly accosted him, without at all heeding what he had in his hand; but in his broken lingo, the German soon evinced his complete ignorance of the White Whale; immediately turning the conversation to his lamp-feeder and oil-can, with some remarks touching his having to turn into his hammock at night in profound darkness—his last drop of Bremen oil being gone, and not a single flying-fish yet captured to supply the deficiency; concluding by hinting that his ship was indeed what in the Fishery is technically called a *clean* one (that is, an empty one), well deserving the name of *Jungfrau* or the *Virgin*.

His necessities supplied, Derick departed; but he had not gained his ship's side, when whales were almost simultaneously raised from the mast-heads of both vessels; and so eager for the chase was Derick, that without pausing to put his oil-can and lamp-feeder aboard, he slewed round his boat and made after the leviathan lamp-feeders.

Now, the game having risen to leeward, he and the other three German boats that soon followed him, had considerably the start of the *Pequod*'s keels. There were eight whales, an average pod. Aware of their danger, they were going all abreast with great speed straight before the wind, rubbing their flanks as closely as so many spans of horses in harness. They left a great, wide wake, as though continually unrolling a great wide parchment upon the sea.

Full in this rapid wake, and many fathoms in the rear, swam a huge, humped old bull, which by his comparatively slow progress, as well as by the unusual yellowish encrustations overgrowing him, seemed afflicted with the jaundice, or some other infirmity. Whether this whale belonged to the pod in advance, seemed questionable; for it is not customary for such venerable leviathans to be at all social. Nevertheless, he stuck to their wake, though indeed their back water must have retarded him, because the white-bone or swell at his broad muzzle was a dashed one, like the swell formed when two hostile currents meet. His spout was short, slow, and laborious; coming forth with a choking sort of gush, and spending itself in torn shreds, followed by strange subterranean commotions in him, which seemed to have egress at his other buried extremity, causing the waters behind him to upbubble.

"Who's got some paregoric?" said Stubb, "he has the stomach-ache, I'm afraid. Lord, think of having half an acre of stomach-ache! Adverse winds are holding mad Christmas in him, boys. It's the first foul wind I ever knew to blow from astern; but look, did ever whale yaw so before? it must be, he's lost his tiller."

As an overladen Indiaman bearing down the Hindostan coast with a deck load of frightened horses, careens, buries, rolls, and wallows on her way; so did this old whale heave his aged bulk, and now and then partly turning over on his cumbrous rib-ends, expose the cause of his devious wake in the unnatural stump of his starboard fin. Whether he had lost that fin in battle, or had been born without it, it were hard to say.

"Only wait a bit, old chap, and I'll give ye a sling for that wounded arm," cried cruel Flask, pointing to the whale-line near him.

"Mind he don't sling thee with it," cried Starbuck. "Give way, or the German will have him."

With one intent all the combined rival boats were pointed for this one fish, because not only was he the largest, and therefore the most valuable whale, but he was nearest to them, and the other whales were going with such great velocity, moreover, as almost to defy pursuit for the time. At this juncture, the *Pequod*'s keels had shot by the three German boats last lowered; but from the great start he had had, Derick's boat still led the chase, though every moment neared by his foreign rivals. The only thing they feared, was that from being already so nigh to his mark, he would be enabled to dart his iron before they could completely overtake and pass him. As for Derick, he seemed quite confident that this would be the case, and occasionally with a deriding gesture shook his lamp-feeder at the other boats.

"The ungracious and ungrateful dog!" cried Starbuck; "he mocks and dares me with the very poor-box I filled for him not five minutes ago!"—then in his old intense whisper—"give way, greyhounds! Dog to it!"

"I tell ye what it is, men"—cried Stubb to his crew—"it's against my religion to get mad; but I'd like to eat that villainous Yarman—Pull—won't ye? Are ye going to let that rascal beat ye? Do ye love brandy? A hogshead of brandy, then, to the best man. Come, why don't some of ye burst a blood-vessel? Who's that been dropping an anchor overboard—we don't budge an inch—we're becalmed. Halloo, here's grass growing in the boat's bottom—and by the Lord, the mast there's budding. This won't do, boys. Look at that Yarman! The short and long of it is, men, will ye spit fire or not?"

"Oh! see the suds he makes!" cried Flask, dancing up and down—"What a hump—Oh, *do* pile on the beef—lays like a log! Oh! my lads, *do* spring—slap-jacks and quohogs for supper, you know, my lads—baked clams and muffins—ho, *do, do,* spring—he's a hundred barreler—don't lose him now—don't oh, *don't!*—see that Yarman—Oh, won't ye pull for your duff, my lads—such a sog! such a sogger! Don't ye love sperm? There goes three thousand dollars, men!—a bank!—a whole bank! The bank of England!—Oh, *do, do, do!*—What's that Yarman about now?"

At this moment Derick was in the act of pitching his lamp-feeder at the advancing boats, and also his oil-can; perhaps with the double view of retarding his rivals' way, and at the same time economically accelerating his own by the momentary impetus of the backward toss.

"The unmannerly Dutch dogger!" cried Stubb. "Pull now, men, like fifty thousand line-of-battle-ship loads of red-haired devils. What d'ye say, Tashtego; are you the man to snap your spine in two-and-twenty pieces for the honor of old Gayhead? What d'ye say?"

"I say, pull like god-dam"—cried the Indian.

Fiercely, but evenly incited by the taunts of the German, the *Pequod*'s three boats now began ranging almost abreast; and, so disposed, momentarily neared him. In that fine, loose, chivalrous attitude of the headsman when drawing near to his prey, the three mates stood up proudly, occasionally backing the after oarsman with an exhilarating cry of, "There she slides, now! Hurrah for the white-ash breeze! Down with the Yarman! Sail over him!"

But so decided an original start had Derick had, that spite of all their gallantry, he would have proved the victor in this race had not a righteous judgment descended upon him in a crab which caught the blade of his midship oarsman. While this clumsy lubber was striving to free his white-ash, and while, in consequence, Derick's boat was nigh to capsizing, and he thundering away at his men in a mighty rage;—that was a good time for Starbuck, Stubb, and Flask. With a shout, they took a mortal start forwards, and slantingly ranged up on the German's quarter. An instant more, and all four boats were diagonically in the whale's immediate wake, while stretching from them, on both sides, was the foaming swell that he made.

It was a terrific, most pitiable, and maddening sight. The whale was now going head out, and sending his spout before him in a continual tormented jet; while his one poor fin beat his side in an agony of fright. Now to this hand, now to that, he yawed in his faltering flight, and still at every billow that he broke, he spasmodically sank in the sea, or sideways rolled towards the sky his one beating fin. So have I seen a bird with clipped wing, making affrighted broken circles in the air, vainly striving to escape the piratical hawks. But the bird has a voice, and with plaintive cries will make known her fear; but the fear of this vast dumb brute of the sea, was chained up and enchanted in him; he had no voice, save that choking respiration through his spiracle, and this made the sight of him unspeakably pitiable; while still, in his amazing bulk, portcullis jaw, and omnipotent tail, there was enough to appall the stoutest man who so pitied.

Seeing now that but a very few moments more would give the *Pequod*'s boats the advantage, and rather than be thus foiled of his game, Derick chose to hazard what to him must have seemed a most unusually long dart, ere the last chance would forever escape.

But no sooner did his harpooneer stand up for the stroke, than all three tigers—Queequeg, Tashtego, Daggoo—instinctively sprang to their feet, and standing in a diagonal row, simultaneously pointed their barbs; and darted over the head of the German harpooneer, their three Nantucket irons entered the whale. Blinding vapors of foam and white-fire! The three boats, in the first fury of the whale's headlong rush, bumped the Germans aside with such force, that both Derick and his baffled harpooneer were spilled out, and sailed over by the three flying keels.

"Don't be afraid, my butter-boxes," cried Stubb, casting a passing glance upon them as he shot by; "ye'll be picked up presently—all right—I saw some sharks astern—St. Bernard's dogs, you know—relieve distressed travelers. Hurrah! this is the way to sail now. Every keel a sun-beam! Hurrah!—Here we go like three tin kettles at the tail of a mad cougar! This puts me in mind of fastening to an elephant in a tilbury on a plain—makes the wheel-spokes fly, boys, when you fasten to him that way; and there's danger of being pitched out too, when you strike a hill. Hurrah! this is the way a fellow feels when he's going to Davy Jones—all a-rush down an endless inclined plane! Hurrah! this whale carries the everlasting mail!"

But the monster's run was a brief one. Giving a sudden gasp, he tumultuously sounded. With a grating rush, the three lines flew round the loggerheads with such a force as to gouge deep grooves in them; while so fearful were the harpooneers that this rapid sounding would soon exhaust the lines, that using all their dexterous might, they caught repeated smoking turns with the rope to hold on; till at last—owing to the perpendicular strain from the lead-lined chocks of the boats, whence the three ropes went straight down into the blue—the gunwales of the bows were almost even with the water, while the three sterns tilted high in the air. And the whale soon ceasing to sound, for some time they remained in that attitude, fearful of expending more line, though the position was a little ticklish. But though boats have been taken down and lost in this way, yet it is this "holding on," as it is called; this hooking up by the sharp barbs of his live flesh from the back; this it is that often torments the Leviathan into soon rising again to meet the sharp lance of his foes. Yet not to speak of the peril of the thing, it is to be doubted whether this course is always the best; for it is but reasonable to presume, that the longer the stricken whale stays under water, the more he is exhausted. Because, owing to the enormous surface of him—in a full grown sperm whale something less than 2000 square feet—the pressure of the water is immense. We all know what an astonishing atmospheric weight we ourselves stand up under; even here, above-ground, in the air; how vast, then, the burden of a whale, bearing on his back a column of two hundred fathoms of ocean! It must at least equal the weight of fifty atmospheres. One whaleman has estimated it at the weight of twenty line-of-battle-ships, with all their guns, and stores, and men on board.

As the three boats lay there on that gently rolling sea, gazing down into its eternal blue noon; and as not a single groan or cry of any sort, nay, not so much as a ripple or a bubble came up from its depths; what landsman would have thought, that beneath all that silence and placidity, the utmost monster of the seas was writhing and wrenching in agony! Not eight inches of perpendicular rope were visible at the bows. Seems it credible that by three such thin threads the great Leviathan was suspended like the big weight to an eight day clock? Suspended? and to what? To three bits of board. Is this the creature of whom it was once so triumphantly said—"Canst thou fill his skin with barbed irons? or his head with fish-spears? The sword of him that layeth at him cannot hold, the spear, the dart, nor the habergeon: he esteemeth iron as straw; the arrow cannot make him flee; darts are counted as stubble; he laugheth at the shaking of a spear!" This the creature? this he? Oh! that unfulfillments should follow the prophets. For with the strength of a thousand thighs in his tail, Leviathan had run his head under the mountains of the sea, to hide him from the *Pequod*'s fish-spears!

In that sloping afternoon sunlight, the shadows that the three boats sent down beneath the surface, must have been long enough and broad enough to shade half Xerxes' army. Who can tell how appalling to the wounded whale must have been such huge phantoms flitting over his head!

"Stand by, men; he stirs," cried Starbuck, as the three lines suddenly vibrated in the water, distinctly conducting upwards to them, as by magnetic wires, the life and death throbs of the whale, so that every oarsman felt them in his seat. The next moment, relieved in a great part from the downward strain at the bows, the boats gave a sudden bounce upwards, as a small icefield will, when a dense herd of white bears are scared from it into the sea.

"Haul in! Haul in!" cried Starbuck again; "he's rising."

The lines, of which, hardly an instant before, not one hand's breadth could have been gained, were now in long quick coils flung back all dripping into the boats, and soon the whale broke water within two ship's length of the hunters.

His motions plainly denoted his extreme exhaustion. In most land animals there are certain valves or flood-gates in many of their veins, whereby when wounded, the blood is in some degree at least instantly shut off in certain directions. Not so with the whale; one of whose peculiarities it is, to have an entire non-valvular structure of the blood-vessels, so that when pierced even by so small a point as a harpoon, a deadly drain is at once begun upon his whole arterial system; and when this is heightened by the extraordinary pressure of water at a great distance below the surface, his life may be said to pour from him in incessant streams. Yet so vast is the quantity of blood in him, and so distant and numerous its interior fountains, that he will keep thus bleeding and bleeding for a considerable period; even as in a drought a river will flow, whose source is in the well-springs of far-off and indiscernible hills. Even now, when the boats pulled upon this whale, and perilously drew over his swaying flukes, and the lances were darted into him, they were followed by steady jets from the new made wound, which kept continually playing, while the natural spout-hole in his head was only at intervals, however rapid, sending its affrighted moisture into the air. From this last vent no blood yet came, because no vital part of him had thus far been struck. His life, as they significantly call it, was untouched.

As the boats now more closely surrounded him, the whole upper part of his form, with much of it that is ordinarily submerged, was plainly revealed. His eyes, or rather the places where his eyes had been, were beheld. As strange misgrown masses gather in the knot-holes of the noblest oaks when prostrate, so from the points which the whale's eyes had once occupied, now protruded blind bulbs, horribly pitiable to see. But pity there was none. For all his old age, and his one arm, and his blind eyes he must die the death and be murdered, in order to light the gay bridals and other merry-makings of men, and also to illuminate the solemn churches that preach unconditional inoffensiveness by all to all. Still rolling in his blood, at last he partially disclosed a strangely discolored bunch or protuberance, the size of a bushel, low down on the flank.

"A nice spot," cried Flask; "just let me prick him there once."

"Avast!" cried Starbuck, "there's no need of that!"

But humane Starbuck was too late. At the instant of the dart an ulcerous jet shot from this cruel wound, and goaded by it into more than sufferable anguish, the whale now spouting thick blood, with swift fury blindly darted at the craft, bespattering them and their glorying crews all over with showers of gore, capsizing Flask's boat and marring the bows. It was his death stroke. For, by this time, so spent was he by loss of blood, that he helplessly rolled away from the wreck he had made; lay panting on his side, impotently flapped with his stumped fin, then over and over slowly revolved like a waning world; turned up the white secrets of his belly; lay like a log, and died. It was most piteous, that last expiring spout. As when by unseen hands the water is gradually drawn off from some mighty fountain, and with half-stifled melancholy gurglings the spray-column lowers and lowers to the ground—so the last long dying spout of the whale.

Soon, while the crews were awaiting the arrival of the ship, the body showed symptoms of sinking with all its treasures unrifled. Immediately, by Starbuck's orders, lines were secured to it at different points, so that ere long every boat was a buoy; the sunken whale being suspended a few inches beneath them by the cords. By very heedful management, when the ship drew nigh, the whale was transferred to her side, and was strongly secured there by the stiffest fluke-chains, for it was plain that unless artificially upheld, the body would at once sink to the bottom.

It so chanced that almost upon first cutting into him with the spade, the entire length of a corroded harpoon was found imbedded in his flesh, on the lower part of the bunch before described. But as the stumps of harpoons are frequently found in the dead bodies of captured whales, with the flesh perfectly healed around them and no prominence of any kind to denote their place; therefore, there must needs have been some other unknown reason in the present case fully to account for the ulceration alluded to. But still more curious was the fact of a lance-head of stone being found in him, not far from the buried iron, the flesh perfectly firm about it. Who had darted that stone lance? And when? It might have been darted by some Nor' West Indian long before America was discovered.

What other marvels might have been rummaged out of this monstrous cabinet there is no telling. But a sudden stop was put to further discoveries, by the ship's being unprecedentedly dragged over sideways to the sea, owing to the body's immensely increasing tendency to sink. However, Starbuck, who had the ordering of affairs, hung on to it to the last; hung on to it so resolutely, indeed, that when at length the ship would have been capsized, if still persisting in locking arms with the body; then, when the command was given to break clear from it, such was the immovable strain upon the timber-heads to which the fluke-chains and cables were fastened, that it was impossible to cast them off. Meantime everything in the *Pequod* was aslant. To cross to the other side of the deck was like walking up the steep gabled roof of a house. The ship groaned and gasped. Many of the ivory inlayings of her bulwarks and cabins were started from their places, by the unnatural dislocation. In vain handspikes and crows were brought to bear upon the immovable fluke-chains, to pry them adrift from the timber-heads; and so low had the whale now settled that the submerged ends could not be at all approached, while every moment whole tons of ponderosity seemed added to the sinking bulk, and the ship seemed on the point of going over.

"Hold on, hold on, won't ye?" cried Stubb to the body, "don't be in such a devil of a hurry to sink! By thunder, men, we must do something or go for it. No use prying there; avast, I say with your handspikes, and run one of ye for a prayer-book and a pen-knife, and cut the big chains."

"Knife? Ay, ay," cried Queequeg, and seizing the carpenter's heavy hatchet, he leaned out of a port-hole, and steel to iron, began slashing at the largest fluke-chains. But a few strokes, full of sparks, were given, when the exceeding strain effected the rest. With a terrific snap, every fastening went adrift; the ship righted, the carcass sank.

Now, this occasional inevitable sinking of the recently killed Sperm Whale is a very curious thing; nor has any fisherman yet adequately accounted for it. Usually the dead Sperm Whale floats with great buoyancy, with its side or belly considerably elevated above the surface. If the only whales that thus sank were old, meager, and broken-hearted creatures, their pads of lard diminished and all their bones heavy and rheumatic; then you might with some reason assert that this sinking is caused by an uncommon specific gravity in the fish so sinking, consequent upon this absence of buoyant matter in him. But it is not so. For young whales, in the highest health, and swelling with noble aspirations, prematurely cut off in the warm flush and May of life, with all their panting lard about them; even these brawny, buoyant heroes do sometimes sink.

Be it said, however, that the Sperm Whale is far less liable to this accident than any other species. Where one of that sort go down, twenty Right Whales do. This difference in the species is no doubt imputable in no small degree to the greater quantity of bone in the Right Whale; his Venetian blinds alone sometimes weighing more than a ton; from this encumbrance the Sperm Whale is wholly free. But there are instances where, after the lapse of many hours or several days, the sunken whale again rises, more buoyant than in life. But the reason of this is obvious. Gases are generated in him; he swells to a prodigious magnitude; becomes a sort of animal balloon. A line-of-battle-ship could hardly keep him under then. In the Shore Whaling, on soundings, among the Bays of New Zealand, when a Right Whale gives token of sinking, they fasten buoys to him, with plenty of rope; so that when the body has gone down, they know where to look for it when it shall have ascended again.

It was not long after the sinking of the body that a cry was heard from the *Pequod*'s mast-heads, announcing that the *Jungfrau* was again lowering her boats; though the only spout in sight was that of a Fin-Back, belonging to the species of uncapturable whales, because of its incredible power of swimming. Nevertheless, the Fin-Back's spout is so similar to the Sperm Whale's, that by unskillful fishermen it is often mistaken for it. And consequently Derick and all his host were now in valiant chase of this unnearable brute. The *Virgin* crowding all sail, made after her four young keels, and thus they all disappeared far to leeward, still in bold, hopeful chase.

Oh! many are the Fin-Backs, and many are the Dericks, my friend.

Chapter LXXXII

THE HONOR AND GLORY OF WHALING

THERE ARE SOME ENTERPRISES IN WHICH A CAREFUL DISORDERLINESS IS THE TRUE METHOD.

The more I dive into this matter of whaling, and push my researches up to the very spring-head of it, so much the more am I impressed with its great honorableness and antiquity; and especially when I find so many great demi-gods and heroes, prophets of all sorts, who one way or other have shed distinction upon it, I am transported with the reflection that I myself belong, though but subordinately, to so emblazoned a fraternity.

The gallant Perseus, a son of Jupiter, was the first whaleman; and to the eternal honor of our calling be it said, that the first whale attacked by our brotherhood was not killed with any sordid intent. Those were the knightly days of our profession, when we only bore arms to succor the distressed, and not to fill men's lamp-feeders. Everyone knows the fine story of Perseus and Andromeda; how the lovely Andromeda, the daughter of a king, was tied to a rock on the sea-coast, and as Leviathan was in the very act of carrying her off, Perseus, the prince of whalemen, intrepidly advancing, harpooned the monster, and delivered and married the maid. It was an admirable artistic exploit, rarely achieved by the best harpooneers of the present day; inasmuch as this Leviathan was slain at the very first dart. And let no man doubt this Arkite story; for in the ancient Joppa, now Jaffa, on the Syrian coast, in one of the Pagan temples, there stood for many ages the vast skeleton of a whale, which the city's legends and all the inhabitants asserted to be the identical bones of the monster that Perseus slew. When the Romans took Joppa, the same skeleton was carried to Italy in triumph. What seems most singular and suggestively important in this story, is this: it was from Joppa that Jonah set sail.

Akin to the adventure of Perseus and Andromeda—indeed, by some supposed to be indirectly derived from it—is that famous story of St. George and the Dragon; which dragon I maintain to have been a whale; for in many old chronicles whales and dragons are strangely jumbled together, and often stand for each other. "Thou art as a lion of the waters, and as a dragon of the sea," said Ezekiel; hereby, plainly meaning a whale; in truth, some versions of the Bible use that word itself. Besides, it would much subtract from the glory of the exploit had St. George but encountered a crawling reptile of the land, instead of doing battle with the great monster of the deep. Any man may kill a snake, but only a Perseus, a St. George, a Coffin, have the heart in them to march boldly up to a whale.

Let not the modern paintings of this scene mislead us; for though the creature encountered by that valiant whaleman of old is vaguely represented of a griffin-like shape, and though the battle is depicted on land and the saint on horseback, yet considering the great ignorance of those times, when the true form of the whale was unknown to artists; and considering that as in Perseus' case, St. George's whale might have crawled up out of the sea on the beach; and considering that the animal ridden by St. George might have been only a large seal, or sea-horse; bearing all this in mind, it will not appear altogether incompatible with the sacred legend and the ancientest drafts of the scene, to hold this so-called dragon no other than the great Leviathan himself. In fact, placed before the strict and piercing truth, this whole story will fare like that fish, flesh, and fowl idol of the Philistines, Dagon by name; who being planted before the ark of Israel, his horse's head and both the palms of his hands fell off from him, and only the stump or fishy part of him remained. Thus, then, one of our own noble stamp, even a whaleman, is the tutelary guardian of England; and by good rights, we harpooneers of Nantucket should be enrolled in the most noble order of St.

George. And therefore, let not the knights of that honorable company (none of whom, I venture to say, have ever had to do with a whale like their great patron), let them never eye a Nantucketer with disdain, since even in our woolen frocks and tarred trousers we are much better entitled to St. George's decoration than they.

Whether to admit Hercules among us or not, concerning this I long remained dubious: for though according to the Greek mythologies, that antique Crockett and Kit Carson—that brawny doer of rejoicing good deeds, was swallowed down and thrown up by a whale; still, whether that strictly makes a whaleman of him, that might be mooted. It nowhere appears that he ever actually harpooned his fish, unless, indeed, from the inside. Nevertheless, he may be deemed a sort of involuntary whaleman; at any rate the whale caught him, if he did not the whale. I claim him for one of our clan.

But, by the best contradictory authorities, this Grecian story of Hercules and the whale is considered to be derived from the still more ancient Hebrew story of Jonah and the whale; and vice versa; certainly they are very similar. If I claim the demi-god then, why not the prophet?

Nor do heroes, saints, demi-gods, and prophets alone comprise the whole roll of our order. Our grand master is still to be named; for like royal kings of old times, we find the head-waters of our fraternity in nothing short of the great gods themselves. That wondrous oriental story is now to be rehearsed from the Shaster, which gives us the dread Vishnoo, one of the three persons in the godhead of the Hindoos; gives us this divine Vishnoo himself for our Lord;—Vishnoo, who, by the first of his ten earthly incarnations, has forever set apart and sanctified the whale. When Brahma, or the God of Gods, saith the Shaster, resolved to recreate the world after one of its periodical dissolutions, he gave birth to Vishnoo, to preside over the work; but the Vedas, or mystical books, whose perusal would seem to have been indispensable to Vishnoo before beginning the creation, and which therefore must have contained something in the shape of practical hints to young architects, these Vedas were lying at the bottom of the waters; so Vishnoo became incarnate in a whale, and sounding down in him to the uttermost depths, rescued the sacred volumes. Was not this Vishnoo a whaleman, then? even as a man who rides a horse is called a horseman?

Perseus, St. George, Hercules, Jonah, and Vishnoo! there's a member-roll for you! What club but the whaleman's can head off like that?

Chapter LXXXIII

JONAH HISTORICALLY REGARDED

REFERENCE WAS MADE TO THE HISTORICAL STORY OF JONAH AND THE WHALE IN THE PRECEDING chapter. Now some Nantucketers rather distrust this historical story of Jonah and the whale. But then there were some skeptical Greeks and Romans, who, standing out from the orthodox pagans of their times, equally doubted the story of Hercules and the whale, and Arion and the dolphin; and yet their doubting those traditions did not make those traditions one whit the less facts, for all that.

One old Sag-Harbor whaleman's chief reason for questioning the Hebrew story was this: He had one of those quaint old-fashioned Bibles, embellished with curious, unscientific plates; one of which represented Jonah's whale with two spouts in his head—a peculiarity only true with respect to a species of the Leviathan (the Right Whale, and the varieties of that order), concerning which the fishermen have this saying, "A penny roll would choke him"; his swallow is so very small. But, to this, Bishop Jebb's anticipative answer is ready. It is not necessary, hints the Bishop, that we consider Jonah as tombed in the whale's belly, but as temporarily lodged in some part of his mouth. And this seems reasonable enough in the good Bishop. For truly, the Right Whale's mouth would accommodate a couple of whist-tables, and comfortably seat all the players. Possibly, too, Jonah might have ensconced himself in a hollow tooth; but, on second thoughts, the Right Whale is toothless.

Another reason which Sag-Harbor (he went by that name) urged for his want of faith in this matter of the prophet, was something obscurely in reference to his incarcerated body and the whale's gastric juices. But this objection likewise falls to the ground, because a German exegist supposes that Jonah must have taken refuge in the floating body of a *dead* whale—even as the French soldiers in the Russian campaign turned their dead horses into tents, and crawled into them. Besides, it has been divined by other continental commentators, that when Jonah was thrown overboard from the Joppa ship, he straightway effected his escape to another vessel nearby, some vessel with a whale for a figure-head; and, I would add, possibly called *The Whale,* as some craft are nowadays christened the *Shark,* the *Gull,* the *Eagle.* Nor have there been wanting learned exegetists who have opined that the whale mentioned in the book of Jonah merely meant a life-preserver—an inflated bag of wind—which the endangered prophet swam to, and so was saved from a watery doom. Poor Sag-Harbor, therefore, seems worsted all round. But he had still another reason for his want of faith. It was this, if I remember right: Jonah was swallowed by the whale in the Mediterranean Sea, and after three days he was vomited up somewhere within three days' journey of Nineveh, a city on the Tigris, very much more than three days' journey across from the nearest point of the Mediterranean coast. How is that?

But was there no other way for the whale to land the prophet within that short distance of Nineveh? Yes. He might have carried him round by the way of the Cape of Good Hope. But not to speak of the passage through the whole length of the Mediterranean, and another passage up the Persian Gulf and Red Sea, such a supposition would involve the complete circumnavigation of all Africa in three days, not to speak of the Tigris waters, near the site of Nineveh, being too shallow for any whale to swim in. Besides, this idea of Jonah's weathering the Cape of Good Hope at so early a day would wrest the honor of the discovery of that great headland from Bartholomew Diaz, its reputed discoverer, and so make modern history a liar.

But all these foolish arguments of old Sag-Harbor only evinced his foolish pride of reason—a thing still more reprehensible in him, seeing that he had but little learning except what he had picked up from the sun and the sea. I say it only shows his foolish, impious pride, and abominable, devilish rebellion against the reverend clergy. For by a Portuguese Catholic priest, this very idea of Jonah's going to Nineveh via the Cape of Good Hope was advanced as a signal magnification of the general miracle. And so it was. Besides, to this day, the highly enlightened Turks devoutly believe in the historical story of Jonah. And some three centuries ago, an English traveler in old Harris's *Voyages,* speaks of a Turkish Mosque built in honor of Jonah, in which Mosque was a miraculous lamp that burned without any oil.

Chapter LXXXIV

PITCHPOLING

TO MAKE THEM RUN EASILY AND SWIFTLY, THE AXLES OF CARRIAGES ARE ANOINTED; AND FOR much the same purpose, some whalers perform an analogous operation upon their boat; they grease the bottom. Nor is it to be doubted that as such a procedure can do no harm, it may possibly be of no contemptible advantage; considering that oil and water are hostile; that oil is a sliding thing, and that the object in view is to make the boat slide bravely. Queequeg believed strongly in anointing his boat, and one morning not long after the German ship *Jungfrau* disappeared, took more than customary pains in that occupation; crawling under its bottom, where it hung over the side, and rubbing in the unctuousness as though diligently seeking to insure a crop of hair from the craft's bald keel. He seemed to be working in obedience to some particular presentiment. Nor did it remain unwarranted by the event.

Towards noon whales were raised; but so soon as the ship sailed down to them, they turned and fled with swift precipitancy; a disordered flight, as of Cleopatra's barges from Actium.

Nevertheless, the boats pursued, and Stubb's was foremost. By great exertion, Tashtego at last succeeded in planting one iron; but the stricken whale, without at all sounding, still continued his horizontal flight, with added fleetness. Such unintermitted strainings upon the planted iron must sooner or later inevitably extract it. It became imperative to lance the flying whale, or be content to lose him. But to haul the boat up to his flank was impossible, he swam so fast and furious. What then remained?

Of all the wondrous devices and dexterities, the sleights of hand and countless subtleties, to which the veteran whaleman is so often forced, none exceed that fine maneuver with the lance called pitchpoling. Small sword, or broad sword, in all its exercises boasts nothing like it. It is only indispensable with an inveterate running whale; its grand fact and feature is the wonderful distance to which the long lance is accurately darted from a violently rocking, jerking boat, under extreme headway. Steel and wood included, the entire spear is some ten or twelve feet in length; the staff is much slighter than that of the harpoon, and also of a lighter material—pine. It is furnished with a small rope called a warp, of considerable length, by which it can be hauled back to the hand after darting.

But before going further, it is important to mention here, that though the harpoon may be pitchpoled in the same way with the lance, yet it is seldom done; and when done, is still less frequently successful, on account of the greater weight and inferior length of the harpoon as compared with the lance, which in effect become serious drawbacks. As a general thing, therefore, you must first get fast to a whale, before any pitchpoling comes into play.

Look now at Stubb; a man who from his humorous, deliberate coolness and equanimity in the direst emergencies, was specially qualified to excel in pitchpoling. Look at him; he stands upright in the tossed bow of the flying boat; wrapped in fleecy foam, the towing whale is forty feet ahead. Handling the long lance lightly, glancing twice or thrice along its length to see if it be exactly straight Stubb whistlingly gathers up the coil of the warp in one hand, so as to secure its free end in his grasp, leaving the rest unobstructed. Then holding the lance full before his waistband's middle, he levels it at the whale; when, covering him with it, he steadily depresses the butt-end in his hand, thereby elevating the point till the weapon stands fairly balanced upon his palm, fifteen feet in the air. He minds you somewhat of a juggler, balancing a long staff on his chin. Next moment with a rapid, nameless impulse, in a superb lofty arch the bright steel spans the foaming distance, and quivers in the life spot of the whale. Instead of sparkling water, he now spouts red blood.

"That drove the spigot out of him!" cries Stubb. " 'Tis July's immortal Fourth; all fountains must run wine to-day! Would now, it were old Orleans whiskey, or old Ohio, or unspeakable old Monongahela! Then, Tashtego, lad, I'd have ye hold a canakin to the jet, and we'd drink round it! Yea, verily, hearts alive, we'd brew choice punch in the spread of his spout-hole there, and from that live punch-bowl quaff the living stuff."

Again and again to such gamesome talk, the dexterous dart is repeated, the spear returning to its master like a greyhound held in skillful leash. The agonized whale goes into his flurry; the tow-line is slackened, and the pitchpoler dropping astern, folds his hands, and mutely watches the monster die.

Chapter LXXXV

THE FOUNTAIN

THAT FOR SIX THOUSAND YEARS—AND NO ONE KNOWS HOW MANY MILLIONS OF AGES BEFORE—the great whales should have been spouting all over the sea, and sprinkling and mistifying the gardens of the deep, as with so many sprinkling or mistifying pots; and that for some centuries back, thousands of hunters should have been close by the fountain of the whale, watching these sprinklings and spoutings—that all this should be, and yet, that down to this blessed minute (fifteen and a quarter minutes past one o'clock P.M. of this sixteenth day of December, A.D. 1851), it should still remain a problem, whether these spoutings are, after all, really water, or nothing but vapor—this is surely a noteworthy thing.

Let us, then, look at this matter, along with some interesting items contingent. Everyone knows that by the peculiar cunning of their gills, the finny tribes in general breathe the air which at all times is combined with the element in which they swim; hence, a herring or a cod might live a century, and never once raise its head above the surface. But owing to his marked internal structure which gives him regular lungs, like a human being's, the whale can only live by inhaling the disengaged air in the open atmosphere. Wherefore the necessity for his periodical visits to the upper world. But he cannot in any degree breathe through his mouth, for, in his ordinary attitude, the Sperm Whale's mouth is buried at least eight feet beneath the surface; and what is still more, his windpipe has no connection with his mouth. No, he breathes through his spiracle alone; and this is on the top of his head.

If I say, that in any creature breathing is only a function indispensable to vitality, inasmuch as it withdraws from the air a certain element, which being subsequently brought into contact with the blood imparts to the blood its vivifying principle, I do not think I shall err; though I may possibly use some superfluous scientific words. Assume it, and it follows that if all the blood in a man could be aerated with one breath, he might then seal up his nostrils and not fetch another for a considerable time. That is to say, he would then live without breathing. Anomalous as it may seem, this is precisely the case with the whale, who systematically lives, by intervals, his full hour and more (when at the bottom) without drawing a single breath, or so much as in any way inhaling a particle of air; for, remember, he has no gills. How is this? Between his ribs and on each side of his spine he is supplied with a remarkable involved Cretan labyrinth of vermicelli-like vessels, which vessels, when he quits the surface, are completely distended with oxygenated blood. So that for an hour or more, a thousand fathoms in the sea, he carries a surplus stock of vitality in him, just as the camel crossing the waterless desert carries a surplus supply of drink for future use in its four supplementary stomachs. The anatomical fact of this labyrinth is indisputable; and that the supposition founded upon it is reasonable and true, seems the more cogent to me, when I consider the otherwise inexplicable obstinacy of that leviathan in *having his spoutings out,* as the fishermen phrase it. This is what I mean. If unmolested, upon rising to the surface, the Sperm Whale will continue there for a period of time exactly uniform with all his other unmolested risings. Say he stays eleven minutes, and jets seventy times, that is, respires seventy breaths; then whenever he rises again, he will be sure to have his seventy breaths over again, to a minute. Now, if after he fetches a few breaths you alarm him, so that he sounds, he will be always dodging up again to make good his regular allowance of air. And not till those seventy breaths are told, will he finally go down to stay out his full term below. Remark, however, that in different individuals these rates are different; but in any one they are alike. Now, why should the whale thus insist upon having his spoutings out, unless it be to replenish his reservoir of air, ere descending for good? How obvious is it, too, that this necessity for the whale's rising exposes him to all the fatal hazards of the chase. For not by hook or by net could this vast leviathan be caught, when sailing a thousand fathoms beneath the sunlight. Not so much thy skill, then, O hunter, as the great necessities that strike the victory to thee!

In man, breathing is incessantly going on—one breath only serving for two or three pulsations; so that whatever other business he has to attend to, waking or sleeping, breathe he must, or die he will. But the Sperm Whale only breathes about one seventh or Sunday of his time.

It has been said that the whale only breathes through his spout-hole; if it could truthfully be added that his spouts are mixed with water, then I opine we should be furnished with the reason why his sense of smell seems obliterated in him; for the only thing about him that at all answers to his nose is that identical spout-hole; and being so clogged with two elements, it could not be expected to have the power of smelling. But owing to the mystery of the spout—whether it be water or whether it be vapor—no absolute certainty can as yet be arrived at on this head. Sure it is, nevertheless, that the Sperm Whale has no proper olfactories. But what does he want of them? No roses, no violets, no Cologne-water in the sea.

Furthermore, as his windpipe solely opens into the tube of his spouting canal, and as that long canal—like the grand Erie Canal—is furnished with a sort of locks (that open and shut) for the downward retention of air or the upward exclusion of water, therefore the whale has no voice; unless you insult him by saying, that when he so strangely rumbles, he talks through his nose. But then again, what has the whale to say? Seldom have I known any profound being that had anything to say to this world, unless forced to stammer out something by way of getting a living. Oh! happy that the world is such an excellent listener!

Now, the spouting canal of the Sperm Whale, chiefly intended as it is for the conveyance of air, and for several feet laid along, horizontally, just beneath the upper surface of his head, and a little to one side; this curious canal is very much like a gas-pipe laid down in a city on one side of a street. But the question returns whether this gas-pipe is also a water-pipe; in other words, whether the spout of the Sperm Whale is the mere vapor of the exhaled breath, or whether that exhaled breath is mixed with water taken in at the mouth, and discharged through the spiracle. It is certain that the mouth indirectly communicates with the spouting canal; but it cannot be proved that this is for the purpose of discharging water through the spiracle. Because the greatest necessity for so doing would seem to be, when in feeding he accidentally takes in water. But the Sperm Whale's food is far beneath the surface, and there he cannot spout even if he would. Besides, if you regard him very closely, and time him with your watch, you will find that when unmolested, there is an undeviating rhyme between the periods of his jets and the ordinary periods of respiration.

But why pester one with all this reasoning on the subject? Speak out! You have seen him spout; then declare what the spout is; can you not tell water from air? My dear sir, in this world it is not so easy to settle these plain things. I have ever found your plain things the knottiest of all. And as for this whale spout, you might almost stand in it, and yet be undecided as to what it is precisely.

The central body of it is hidden in the snowy sparkling mist enveloping it; and how can you certainly tell whether any water falls from it, when, always, when you are close enough to a whale to get a close view of his spout, he is in a prodigious commotion, the water cascading all around him. And if at such times you should think that you really perceived drops of moisture in the spout, how do you know that they are not merely condensed from its vapor; or how do you know that they are not those identical drops superficially lodged in the spout-hole fissure, which is countersunk into the summit of the whale's head? For even when tranquilly swimming through the mid-day sea in a calm, with his elevated hump sun-dried as a dromedary's in the desert; even then, the whale always carries a small basin of water on his head, as under a blazing sun you will sometimes see a cavity in a rock filled up with rain.

Nor is it at all prudent for the hunter to be overcurious touching the precise nature of the whale spout. It will not do for him to be peering into it, and putting his face in it. You cannot go with your pitcher to this fountain and fill it, and bring it away. For even when coming into slight contact with the outer, vapory shreds of the jet, which will often happen, your skin will feverishly smart, from the acridness of the thing so touching it. And I know one, who coming into still closer contact with the spout, whether with some scientific object in view, or otherwise, I cannot say, the skin peeled off from his cheek and arm. Wherefore, among whalemen, the spout is deemed poisonous; they try to evade it. Another thing; I have heard it said, and I do not much doubt it, that if the jet is fairly spouted into your eyes, it will blind you. The wisest thing the investigator can do then, it seems to me, is to let this deadly spout alone.

Still, we can hypothesize, even if we cannot prove and establish. My hypothesis is this: that the spout is nothing but mist. And besides other reasons, to this conclusion I am impelled, by considerations touching the great inherent dignity and sublimity of the Sperm Whale; I account him no common, shallow being, inasmuch as it is an undisputed fact that he is never found on soundings, or near shores; all other whales sometimes are. He is both ponderous and profound. And I am convinced that from the heads of all ponderous profound beings, such as Plato, Pyrrho, the Devil, Jupiter, Dante, and so on, there always goes up a certain semi-visible steam, while in the act of thinking deep thoughts. While composing a little treatise on Eternity, I had the curiosity to place a mirror before me; and ere long saw reflected there, a curious involved worming and undulation in the atmosphere over my head. The invariable moisture of my hair, while plunged in deep thought, after six cups of hot tea in my thin shingled attic, of an August noon; this seems an additional argument for the above supposition.

And how nobly it raises our conceit of the mighty, misty monster, to behold him solemnly sailing through a calm tropical sea; his vast, mild head overhung by a canopy of vapor, engendered by his incommunicable contemplations, and that vapor—as you will sometimes see it—glorified by a rainbow, as if Heaven itself had put its seal upon his thoughts. For, d'ye see, rainbows do not visit the clear air; they only irradiate vapor. And so, through all the thick mists of the dim doubts in my mind, divine intuitions now and then shoot, enkindling my fog with a heavenly ray. And for this I thank God; for all have doubts; many deny; but doubts or denials, few along with them, have intuitions. Doubts of all things earthly, and intuitions of some things heavenly; this combination makes neither believer nor infidel, but makes a man who regards them both with equal eye.

Chapter LXXXVI

The Tail

Other poets have warbled the praises of the soft eye of the antelope, and the lovely plumage of the bird that never alights; less celestial, I celebrate a tail.

Reckoning the largest sized Sperm Whale's tail to begin at that point of the trunk where it tapers to about the girth of a man, it comprises upon its upper surface alone, an area of at least fifty square feet. The compact round body of its root expands into two broad, firm, flat palms or flukes, gradually shoaling away to less than an inch in thickness. At the crotch or junction, these flukes slightly overlap, then sideways recede from each other like wings, leaving a wide vacancy between. In no living thing are the lines of beauty more exquisitely defined than in the crescentic borders of these flukes. At its utmost expansion in the full grown whale, the tail will considerably exceed twenty feet across.

The entire member seems a dense webbed bed of welded sinews; but cut into it, and you find that three distinct strata compose it: upper, middle, and lower. The fibers in the upper and lower layers, are long and horizontal; those of the middle one, very short, and running crosswise between the outside layers. This triune structure, as much as anything else, imparts power to the tail. To the student of old Roman walls, the middle layer will furnish a curious parallel to the thin course of tiles always alternating with the stone in those wonderful relics of the antique, and which undoubtedly contribute so much to the great strength of the masonry.

But as if this vast local power in the tendinous tail were not enough, the whole bulk of the leviathan is knit over with a warp and woof of muscular fibers and filaments, which passing on either side the loins and running down into the flukes, insensibly blend with them, and largely contribute to their might; so that in the tail the confluent measureless force of the whole whale seems concentrated to a point. Could annihilation occur to matter, this were the thing to do it.

Nor does this—its amazing strength, at all tend to cripple the graceful flexion of its motions; where infantileness of ease undulates through a Titanism of power. On the contrary, those motions derive their most appalling beauty from it. Real strength never impairs beauty or harmony, but it often bestows it; and in everything imposingly beautiful, strength has much to do with the magic. Take away the tied tendons that all over seem bursting from the marble in the carved Hercules, and its charm would be gone. As devout Eckerman lifted the linen sheet from the naked corpse of Goethe, he was overwhelmed with the massive chest of the man, that seemed as a Roman triumphal arch. When Angelo paints even God the Father in human form, mark what robustness is there. And whatever they may reveal of the divine love in the Son, the soft, curled, hermaphroditical Italian pictures, in which his idea has been most successfully embodied; these pictures, so destitute as they are of all brawniness, hint nothing of any power, but the mere negative, feminine one of submission and endurance, which on all hands it is conceded, form the peculiar practical virtues of his teachings.

Such is the subtle elasticity of the organ I treat of, that whether wielded in sport, or in earnest, or in anger, whatever be the mood it be in, its flexions are invariably marked by exceeding grace. Therein no fairy's arm can transcend it.

Five great motions are peculiar to it. First, when used as a fin for progression; Second, when used as a mace in battle; Third, in sweeping; Fourth, in lobtailing; Fifth, in peaking flukes.

First: Being horizontal in its position, the Leviathan's tail acts in a different manner from the tails of all other sea creatures. It never wriggles. In man or fish, wriggling is a sign of inferiority.

To the whale, his tail is the sole means of propulsion. Scroll-wise coiled forwards beneath the body, and then rapidly sprung backwards, it is this which gives that singular darting, leaping motion to the monster when furiously swimming. His side-fins only serve to steer by.

Second: It is a little significant, that while one sperm whale only fights another sperm whale with his head and jaw, nevertheless, in his conflicts with man, he chiefly and contemptuously uses his tail. In striking at a boat, he swiftly curves away his flukes from it, and the blow is only inflicted by the recoil. If it be made in the unobstructed air, especially if it descend to its mark, the stroke is then simply irresistible. No ribs of man or boat can withstand it. Your only salvation lies in eluding it; but if it comes sideways through the opposing water, then partly owing to the light buoyancy of the whale-boat, and the elasticity of its materials, a cracked rib or a dashed plank or two, a sort of stitch in the side, is generally the most serious result. These submerged side blows are so often received in the fishery, that they are accounted mere child's play. Someone strips off a frock, and the hole is stopped.

Third: I cannot demonstrate it, but it seems to me, that in the whale the sense of touch is concentrated in the tail; for in this respect there is a delicacy in it only equaled by the daintiness of the elephant's trunk. This delicacy is chiefly evinced in the action of sweeping, when in maidenly gentleness the whale with a certain soft slowness moves his immense flukes from side to side upon the surface of the sea; and if he feel but a sailor's whisker, woe to that sailor, whiskers and all. What tenderness there is in that preliminary touch! Had this tail any prehensile power, I should straightway bethink me of Darmonodes' elephant that so frequented the flower-market, and with low salutations presented nosegays to damsels, and then caressed their zones. On more accounts than one, a pity it is that the whale does not possess this prehensile virtue in his tail; for I have heard of yet another elephant, that when wounded in the fight, curved round his trunk and extracted the dart.

Fourth: Stealing unawares upon the whale in the fancied security of the middle of solitary seas, you find him unbent from the vast corpulence of his dignity, and kitten-like, he plays on the ocean as if it were a hearth. But still you see his power in his play. The broad palms of his tail are flirted high into the air; then smiting the surface, the thunderous concussion resounds for miles. You would almost think a great gun had been discharged; and if you noticed the light wreath of vapor from the spiracle at his other extremity, you would think that that was the smoke from the touch-hole.

Fifth: As in the ordinary floating posture of the leviathan the flukes lie considerably below the level of his back, they are then completely out of sight beneath the surface; but when he is about to plunge into the deeps, his entire flukes with at least thirty feet of his body are tossed erect in the air, and so remain vibrating a moment, till they downwards shoot out of view. Excepting the sublime *breach*—somewhere else to be described—this peaking of the whale's flukes is perhaps the grandest sight to be seen in all animated nature. Out of the bottomless profundities the gigantic tail seems spasmodically snatching at the highest heaven. So in dreams, have I seen majestic Satan thrusting forth his tormented colossal claw from the flame Baltic of Hell. But in gazing at such scenes, it is all in all what mood you are in; if in the Dantean, the devils will occur to you; if in that of Isaiah, the archangels. Standing at the mast-head of my ship during a sunrise that crimsoned sky and sea, I once saw a large herd of whales in the east, all heading towards the sun, and for a moment vibrating in concert with peaked flukes. As it seemed to me at the time, such a grand embodiment of adoration of the gods was never beheld, even in Persia, the home of the fire worshipers. As Ptolemy Philopater testified of the African elephant, I then testified of the whale, pronouncing him the most devout of all beings. For according to King Juba, the military elephants of antiquity often hailed the morning with their trunks uplifted in the profoundest silence.

The chance comparison in this chapter, between the whale and the elephant, so far as some aspects of the tail of the one and the trunk of the other are concerned, should not tend to place those two opposite organs on an equality, much less the creatures to which they respectively belong. For as the mightiest elephant is but a terrier to Leviathan, so, compared with Leviathan's tail, his trunk is but the stalk of a lily. The most direful blow from the elephant's trunk were as the playful tap of a fan, compared with the measureless crush and crash of the sperm whale's ponderous flukes, which in repeated instances have one after the other hurled entire boats with all their oars and crews into the air, very much as an Indian juggler tosses his balls.[1]

The more I consider this mighty tail, the more do I deplore my inability to express it. At times there are gestures in it, which, though they would well grace the hand of man, remain wholly inexplicable. In an extensive herd, so remarkable, occasionally, are these mystic gestures, that I have heard hunters who have declared them akin to Free-Mason signs and symbols; that the whale, indeed, by these methods intelligently conversed with the world. Nor are there wanting other motions of the whale in his general body, full of strangeness, and unaccountable to his most experienced assailant. Dissect him how I may, then, I but go skin deep. I know him not, and never will. But if I know not even the tail of this whale, how understand his head? much more, how comprehend his face, when face he has none? Thou shalt see my back parts, my tail, he seems to say, but my face shall not be seen. But I cannot completely make out his back parts; and hint what he will about his face, I say again he has no face.

Chapter LXXXVII

The Grand Armada

The long and narrow peninsula of Malacca, extending south-eastward from the territories of Burmah, forms the most southerly point of all Asia. In a continuous line from that peninsula stretch the long islands of Sumatra, Java, Bally, and Timor; which, with many others, form a vast mole, or rampart, lengthwise connecting Asia with Australia, and dividing the long unbroken Indian Ocean from the thickly studded oriental archipelagoes. This rampart is pierced by several sally-ports for the convenience of ships and whales; conspicuous among which are the straits of Sunda and Malacca. By the straits of Sunda, chiefly, vessels bound to China from the west, emerge into the China seas.

Those narrow straits of Sunda divide Sumatra from Java; and standing midway in that vast rampart of islands, buttressed by that bold green promontory, known to seamen as Java Head; they not a little correspond to the central gateway opening into some vast walled empire; and considering the inexhaustible wealth of spices, and silks, and jewels, and gold, and ivory, with which the thousand islands of that oriental sea are enriched, it seems a significant provision of nature, that such treasures, by the very formation of the land, should at least bear the appearance, however ineffectual, of being guarded from the all-grasping western world. The shores of the Straits of Sunda are unsupplied with those domineering fortresses which guard the entrances to the Mediterranean, the Baltic, and the Propontis. Unlike the Danes, these Orientals do not demand the obsequious homage of lowered top-sails from the endless procession of ships before the wind, which for centuries past, by night and by day, have passed between the islands of Sumatra and Java, freighted

1. Though all comparison in the way of general bulk between the whale and the elephant is preposterous, inasmuch as in that particular the elephant stands in much the same respect to the whale that a dog does to the elephant; nevertheless, there are not wanting some points of curious similitude; among these is the spout. It is well known that the elephant will often draw up water or dust in his trunk, and then elevating it, jet it forth in a stream.

with the costliest cargoes of the east. But while they freely waive a ceremonial like this, they do by no means renounce their claim to more solid tribute.

Time out of mind the piratical proas of the Malays, lurking among the low shaded coves and islets of Sumatra, have sallied out upon the vessels sailing through the straits, fiercely demanding tribute at the point of their spears. Though by the repeated bloody chastisements they have received at the hands of European cruisers, the audacity of these corsairs has of late been somewhat repressed; yet, even at the present day, we occasionally hear of English and American vessels, which, in those waters, have been remorselessly boarded and pillaged.

With a fair, fresh wind, the *Pequod* was now drawing nigh to these straits; Ahab purposing to pass through them into the Javan sea, and thence, cruising northwards, over waters known to be frequented here and there by the Sperm Whale, sweep inshore by the Philippine Islands, and gain the far coast of Japan, in time for the great whaling season there. By these means, the circumnavigating *Pequod* would sweep almost all the known Sperm-Whale cruising-grounds of the world, previous to descending upon the Line in the Pacific; where Ahab, though everywhere else foiled in his pursuit, firmly counted upon giving battle to Moby-Dick, in the sea he was most known to frequent; and at a season when he might most reasonably be presumed to be haunting it.

But how now? in this zoned quest, does Ahab touch no land? does his crew drink air? Surely, he will stop for water. Nay. For a long time, now, the circus-running sun has raced within his fiery ring, and needs no sustenance but what's in himself. So Ahab. Mark this, too, in the whaler. While other hulls are loaded down with alien stuff, to be transferred to foreign wharves; the world-wandering whale-ship carries no cargo but herself and crew, their weapons and their wants. She has a whole lake's contents bottled in her ample hold. She is ballasted with utilities; not altogether with unusable pig-lead and kent-ledge. She carries years' water in her. Clear old prime Nantucket water; which, when three years afloat, the Nantucketer, in the Pacific, prefers to drink before the brackish fluid, but yesterday rafted off in casks, from the Peruvian or Indian streams. Hence it is, that, while other ships may have gone to China from New York, and back again, touching at a score of ports, the whale-ship, in all that interval, may not have sighted one grain of soil; her crew having seen no man but floating seamen like themselves. So that did you carry them the news that another flood had come; they would only answer—"Well, boys, here's the ark!"

Now, as many Sperm Whales had been captured off the western coast of Java, in the near vicinity of the Straits of Sunda; indeed, as most of the ground, roundabout, was generally recognized by the fishermen as an excellent spot for cruising; therefore, as the *Pequod* gained more and more upon Java Head, the look-outs were repeatedly hailed, and admonished to keep wide awake. But though the green palmy cliffs of the land soon loomed on the starboard bow, and with delighted nostrils the fresh cinnamon was snuffed in the air, yet not a single jet was descried. Almost renouncing all thought of falling in with any game hereabouts, the ship had well-nigh entered the straits, when the customary cheering cry was heard from aloft, and ere long a spectacle of singular magnificence saluted us.

But here be it premised, that owing to the unwearied activity with which of late they have been hunted over all four oceans, the Sperm Whales, instead of almost invariably sailing in small detached companies, as in former times, are now frequently met with in extensive herds, sometimes embracing so great a multitude, that it would almost seem as if numerous nations of them had sworn solemn league and covenant for mutual assistance and protection. To this aggregation of the Sperm Whale into such immense caravans, may be imputed the circumstance that even in the best cruising-grounds, you may now sometimes sail for weeks and months together, without being greeted by a single spout; and then be suddenly saluted by what sometimes seems thousands on thousands.

Broad on both bows, at the distance of some two or three miles, and forming a great semicircle, embracing one half of the level horizon, a continuous chain of whale-jets were up-playing and sparkling in the noon-day air. Unlike the straight perpendicular twin-jets of the Right Whale, which, dividing at top, falls over in two branches, like the cleft drooping boughs of a willow, the single forward-slanting spout of the Sperm Whale presents a thick curled bush of white mist, continually rising and falling away to leeward. Seen from the *Pequod*'s deck, then, as she would rise on a high hill of the sea, this host of vapory spouts, individually curling up into the air, and beheld through a blending atmosphere of bluish haze, showed like the thousand cheerful chimneys of some dense metropolis, descried of a balmy autumnal morning, by some horseman on a height.

As marching armies approaching an unfriendly defile in the mountains, accelerate their march, all eagerness to place that perilous passage in their rear, and once more expand in comparative security upon the plain; even so did this vast fleet of whales now seem hurrying forward through the straits; gradually contracting the wings of their semicircle, and swimming on, in one solid, but still crescentic center.

Crowding all sail the *Pequod* pressed after them; the harpooneers handling their weapons, and loudly cheering from the heads of their yet suspended boats. If the wind only held, little doubt had they, that chased through these Straits of Sunda, the vast host would only deploy into the Oriental seas to witness the capture of not a few of their number. And who could tell whether, in that congregated caravan, Moby-Dick himself might not temporarily be swimming, like the worshiped white-elephant in the coronation procession of the Siamese! So with stun-sail piled on stun-sail, we sailed along, driving these leviathans before us; when, of a sudden, the voice of Tashtego was heard, loudly directing attention to something in our wake.

Corresponding to the crescent in our van, we beheld another in our rear. It seemed formed of detached white vapors, rising and falling something like the spouts of the whales; only they did not so completely come and go; for they constantly hovered, without finally disappearing. Leveling his glass at this sight, Ahab quickly revolved in his pivot-hole, crying, "Aloft there, and rig whips and buckets to wet the sails;—Malays, sir, and after us!"

As if too long lurking behind the headlands, till the *Pequod* should fairly have entered the straits, these rascally Asiatics were now in hot pursuit, to make up for their over-cautious delay. But when the swift *Pequod*, with a fresh leading wind, was herself in hot chase; how very kind of these tawny philanthropists to assist in speeding her on to her own chosen pursuit—mere riding-whips and rowels to her, that they were. As with glass under arm, Ahab to-and-fro paced the deck; in his forward turn beholding the monsters he chased, and in the after one the blood-thirsty pirates chasing *him*; some such fancy as the above seemed his. And when he glanced upon the green walls of the watery defile in which the ship was then sailing, and bethought him that through that gate lay the route to his vengeance, and beheld, how that through that same gate he was now both chasing and being chased to his deadly end; and not only that, but a herd of remorseless wild pirates and inhuman atheistical devils were infernally cheering him on with their curses;—when all these conceits had passed through his brain, Ahab's brow was left gaunt and ribbed, like the black sand beach after some stormy tide has been gnawing it, without being able to drag the firm thing from its place.

But thoughts like these troubled very few of the reckless crew; and when, after steadily dropping and dropping the pirates astern, the *Pequod* at last shot by the vivid green Cockatoo Point on the Sumatra side, emerging at last upon the broad waters beyond; then, the harpooneers seemed more to grieve that the swift whales had been gaining upon the ship, than to rejoice that the ship had so victoriously gained upon the Malays. But still driving on in the wake of the whales, at length they seemed abating their speed; gradually the ship neared them; and the wind now dying away, word was passed to spring to the boats. But no sooner did the herd, by some presumed wonderful instinct of the Sperm Whale, become notified of the three keels that were after them—though as yet a mile in their rear—than they rallied again, and forming in close ranks and battalions, so that their spouts all looked like flashing lines of stacked bayonets, moved on with redoubled velocity.

Stripped to our shirts and drawers, we sprang to the white-ash, and after several hours' pulling were almost disposed to renounce the chase, when a general pausing commotion among the whales gave animating tokens that they were now at last under the influence of that strange perplexity of inert irresolution, which, when the fishermen perceive it in the whale, they say he is gallied.[1] The compact martial columns in which they had been hitherto rapidly and steadily swimming, were now broken up in one measureless rout; and like King Porus' elephants in the Indian battle with Alexander, they seemed going mad with consternation. In all directions expanding in vast irregular circles, and aimlessly swimming hither and thither, by their short thick spoutings, they plainly betrayed their distraction of panic. This was still more strangely evinced by those of their number, who, completely paralyzed as it were, helplessly floated like water-logged dismantled ships on the sea. Had these Leviathans been but a flock of simple sheep, pursued over the pasture by three fierce wolves, they could not possibly have evinced such excessive dismay. But this occasional timidity is characteristic of almost all herding creatures. Though banding together in tens of thousands, the lion-maned buffaloes of the West have fled before a solitary horseman. Witness, too, all human beings, how when herded together in the sheepfold of a theater's pit, they will, at the slightest alarm of fire, rush helter-skelter for the outlets, crowding, trampling, jamming, and remorselessly dashing each other to death. Best, therefore, withhold any amazement at the strangely gallied whales before us, for there is no folly of the beasts of the earth which is not infinitely outdone by the madness of men.

Though many of the whales, as has been said, were in violent motion, yet it is to be observed that as a whole the herd neither advanced nor retreated, but collectively remained in one place. As is customary in those cases, the boats at once separated, each making for some one lone whale on the outskirts of the shoal. In about three minutes' time, Queequeg's harpoon was flung; the stricken fish darted blinding spray in our faces, and then running away with us like light, steered straight for the heart of the herd. Though such a movement on the part of the whale struck under such circumstances, is in no wise unprecedented; and indeed is almost always more or less anticipated; yet does it present one of the more perilous vicissitudes of the fishery. For as the swift monster drags you deeper and deeper into the frantic shoal, you bid adieu to circumspect life and only exist in a delirious throb.

As, blind and deaf, the whale plunged forward, as if by sheer power of speed to rid himself of the iron leech that had fastened to him; as we thus tore a white gash in the sea, on all sides menaced as we flew, by the crazed creatures to and fro rushing about us; our beset boat was like a ship mobbed by ice-isles in a tempest, and striving to steer through their complicated channels and straits, knowing not at what moment it may be locked in and crushed.

But not a bit daunted, Queequeg steered us manfully; now sheering off from this monster directly across our route in advance; now edging away from that, whose colossal flukes were suspended overhead, while all the time, Starbuck stood up in the bows, lance in hand, pricking out of

1. To *gally*, or *gallow*, is to frighten excessively—to confound with fright. It is an old Saxon word. It occurs once in Shakespeare:

> The wrathful skies
> *Gallow* the very wanderers of the dark,
> And make them keep their caves.
> *Lear*, Act III. sc. ii.

To common land usage, the word is now completely obsolete. When the polite landsman first hears it from the gaunt Nantucketer, he is apt to set it down as one of the whaleman's self-derived savageries. Much the same is it with many other sinewy Saxonisms of this sort, which emigrated to the New–England rocks with the noble brawn of the old English emigrants in the time of the Commonwealth. Thus, some of the best and furthest–descended English words—the etymological Howards and Percys—are now democratzed, nay, plebeianized—so to speak—in the New World.

our way whatever whales he could reach by short darts, for there was no time to make long ones. Nor were the oarsmen quite idle, though their wonted duty was now altogether dispensed with. They chiefly attended to the shouting part of the business. "Out of the way, Commodore!" cried one, to a great dromedary that of a sudden rose bodily to the surface, and for an instant threatened to swamp us. "Hard down with your tail, there!" cried a second to another, which, close to our gunwale, seemed calmly cooling himself with his own fan-like extremity.

All whale-boats carry certain curious contrivances, originally invented by the Nantucket Indians, called druggs. Two thick squares of wood of equal size are stoutly clenched together, so that they cross each other's grain at right angles; a line of considerable length is then attached to the middle of this block, and the other end of the line being looped, it can in a moment be fastened to a harpoon. It is chiefly among gallied whales that this drugg is used. For then, more whales are close round you than you can possibly chase at one time. But sperm whales are not every day encountered; while you may, then, you must kill all you can. And if you cannot kill them all at once, you must wing them, so that they can be afterwards killed at your leisure. Hence it is, that at times like these the drugg comes into requisition. Our boat was furnished with three of them. The first and second were successfully darted, and we saw the whales staggeringly running off, fettered by the enormous sidelong resistance of the towing drugg. They were cramped like malefactors with the chain and ball. But upon flinging the third, in the act of tossing overboard the clumsy wooden block, it caught under one of the seats of the boat, and in an instant tore it out and carried it away, dropping the oarsman in the boat's bottom as the seat slid from under him. On both sides the sea came in at the wounded planks, but we stuffed two or three drawers and shirts in, and so stopped the leaks for the time.

It had been next to impossible to dart these drugged-harpoons, were it not that as we advanced into the herd, our whale's way greatly diminished; moreover, that as we went still further and further from the circumference of commotion, the direful disorders seemed waning. So that when at last the jerking harpoon drew out, and the towing whale sideways vanished; then, with the tapering force of his parting momentum, we glided between two whales into the innermost heart of the shoal, as if from some mountain torrent we had slid into a serene valley lake. Here the storms in the roaring glens between the outermost whales, were heard but not felt. In this central expanse the sea presented that smooth satin-like surface, called a sleek, produced by the subtle moisture thrown off by the whale in his more quiet moods. Yes, we were now in that enchanted calm which they say lurks at the heart of every commotion. And still in the distracted distance we beheld the tumults of the outer concentric circles, and saw successive pods of whales, eight or ten in each, swiftly going round and round, like multiplied spans of horses in a ring; and so closely shoulder to shoulder that a Titanic circus-rider might easily have over-arched the middle ones, and so have gone round on their backs. Owing to the density of the crowd of reposing whales, more immediately surrounding the embayed axis of the herd, no possible chance of escape was at present afforded us. We must watch for a breach in the living wall that hemmed us in; the wall that had only admitted us in order to shut us up. Keeping at the center of the lake, we were occasionally visited by small tame cows and calves; the women and children of this routed host.

Now, inclusive of the occasional wide intervals between the revolving outer circles, and inclusive of the spaces between the various pods in any one of those circles, the entire area at this juncture, embraced by the whole multitude, must have contained at least two or three square miles. At any rate—though indeed such a test at such a time might be deceptive—spoutings might be discovered from our low boat that seemed playing up almost from the rim of the horizon. I mention this circumstance, because, as if the cows and calves had been purposely locked up in this innermost fold; and as if the wide extent of the herd had hitherto prevented them from learning the precise cause of its stopping; or, possibly, being so young, unsophisticated, and every way innocent and inexperienced; however it may have been, these smaller whales—now and then visiting our becalmed boat from the margin of the lake—evinced a wondrous fearlessness and confidence, or else a still becharmed panic which it was impossible not to marvel at. Like household dogs they came snuffling round us, right up to our gunwales, and touching them; till it almost seemed that some spell had suddenly domesticated them. Queequeg patted their foreheads; Starbuck scratched their backs with his lance; but fearful of the consequences, for the time refrained from darting it.

But far beneath this wondrous world upon the surface, another and still stranger world met our eyes as we gazed over the side. For, suspended in those watery vaults, floated the forms of the nursing mothers of the whales, and those that by their enormous girth seemed shortly to become mothers. The lake, as I have hinted, was to a considerable depth exceedingly transparent; and as human infants while suckling will calmly and fixedly gaze away from the breast, as if leading two different lives at the time; and while yet drawing mortal nourishment, be still spiritually feasting upon some unearthly reminiscence;—even so did the young of these whales seem looking up towards us, but not at us, as if we were but a bit of Gulf-weed in their new-born sight. Floating on their sides, the mothers also seemed quietly eyeing us. One of these little infants, that from certain queer tokens seemed hardly a day old, might have measured some fourteen feet in length, and some six feet in girth. He was a little frisky; though as yet his body seemed scarce yet recovered from that irksome position it had so lately occupied in the maternal reticule; where, tail to head, and all ready for the final spring, the unborn whale lies bent like a Tartar's bow. The delicate side-fins, and the palms of his flukes, still freshly retained the plaited crumpled appearance of a baby's ears newly arrived from foreign parts.

"Line! line!" cried Queequeg, looking over the gunwale; "him fast! him fast!—Who line him! Who struck?—Two whale; one big, one little!"

"What ails ye, man?" cried Starbuck.

"Look-e here," said Queequeg pointing down.

As when the stricken whale, that from the tub has reeled out hundreds of fathoms of rope; as, after deep sounding, he floats up again, and shows the slackened curling line buoyantly rising and spiraling towards the air; so now, Starbuck saw long coils of the umbilical cord of Madame Leviathan, by which the young cub seemed still tethered to its dam. Not seldom in the rapid vicissitudes of the chase, this natural line, with the maternal end loose, becomes entangled with the hempen one, so that the cub is thereby trapped. Some of the subtlest secrets of the seas seemed divulged to us in this enchanted pond. We saw young Leviathan amours in the deep.[1]

And thus, though surrounded by circle upon circle of consternations and affrights, did these inscrutable creatures at the center freely and fearlessly indulge in all peaceful concernments; yea, serenely reveled in dalliance and delight. But even so, amid the tornadoed Atlantic of my being, do I myself still forever centrally disport in mute calm; and while ponderous planets of unwaning woe revolve round me, deep down and deep inland there I still bathe me in eternal mildness of joy.

Meanwhile, as we thus lay entranced, the occasional sudden frantic spectacles in the distance evinced the activity of the other boats, still engaged in drugging the whales on the frontier of the host; or possibly carrying on the war within the first circle, where abundance of room and some convenient retreats were afforded them. But the sight of the enraged drugged whales now and then blindly darting to and fro across the circles, was nothing to what at last met our eyes. It is some-

1. The sperm whale, as with all other species of the Leviathan, but unlike most other fish, breeds indifferently at all seasons; after a gestation which may probably be set down at nine months, producing but one at a time; though in some few known instances giving birth to an Esau and Jacob:—a contingency provided for in suckling by two teats, curiously situated, one on each side of the anus; but the breasts themselves extend upwards from that. When by chance these precious parts in a nursing whale are cut by the hunter's lance, the mother's pouring milk and blood rivalingly discolor the sea for rods. The milk is very sweet and rich; it has been tasted by man; it might do well with strawberries. When overflowing with mutual esteem, the whales salute *more hominum*.

times the custom when fast to a whale more than commonly powerful and alert, to seek to hamstring him, as it were, by sundering or maiming his gigantic tail-tendon. It is done by darting a short-handled cutting-spade, to which is attached a rope for hauling it back again. A whale wounded (as we afterwards learned) in this part, but not effectually, as it seemed, had broken away from the boat, carrying along with him half of the harpoon line; and in the extraordinary agony of the wound, he was now dashing among the revolving circles like the lone, mounted desperado Arnold, at the battle of Saratoga, carrying dismay wherever he went.

But agonizing as was the wound of this whale, and an appalling spectacle enough, anyway; yet the peculiar horror with which he seemed to inspire the rest of the herd, was owing to a cause which at first the intervening distance obscured from us. But at length we perceived that by one of the unimaginable accidents of the fishery, this whale had become entangled in the harpoon-line that he towed; he had also run away with the cutting-spade in him; and while the free end of the rope attached to that weapon, had permanently caught in the coils of the harpoon-line round his tail, the cutting-spade itself had worked loose from his flesh. So that tormented to madness, he was now churning through the water, violently flailing with his flexible tail, and tossing the keen spade about him, wounding and murdering his own comrades.

This terrific object seemed to recall the whole herd from their stationary fright. First, the whales forming the margin of our lake began to crowd a little, and tumble against each other, as if lifted by half spent billows from afar; then the lake itself began faintly to heave and swell; the submarine bridal-chambers and nurseries vanished; in more and more contracting orbits the whales in the more central circles began to swim in thickening clusters. Yes, the long calm was departing. A low advancing hum was soon heard; and then like to the tumultuous masses of block-ice when the great river Hudson breaks up in Spring, the entire host of whales came tumbling upon their inner center, as if to pile themselves up in one common mountain. Instantly Starbuck and Queequeg changed places; Starbuck taking the stern.

"Oars! Oars!" he intensely whispered, seizing the helm—"gripe your oars, and clutch your souls, now! My God, men stand by! Shove him off, you Queequeg—the whale there!—prick him!—hit him! Stand up—stand up, and stay so! Spring, men—pull, men; never mind their backs—scrape them!—scrape away!"

The boat was now all but jammed between two vast black bulks, leaving a narrow Dardanelles between their long lengths. But by desperate endeavor we at last shot into a temporary opening; then giving way rapidly, and at the same time earnestly watching for another outlet. After many similar hair-breadth escapes, we at last swiftly glided into what had just been one of the outer circles, but now crossed by random whales, all violently making for one center. This lucky salvation was cheaply purchased by the loss of Queequeg's hat, who, while standing in the bows to prick the fugitive whales, had his hat taken clean from his head by the air-eddy made by the sudden tossing of a pair of broad flukes close by.

Riotous and disordered as the universal commotion now was, it soon resolved itself into what seemed a systematic movement; for having clumped together at last in one dense body, they then renewed their onward flight with augmented fleetness. Further pursuit was useless; but the boats still lingered in their wake to pick up what drugged whales might be dropped astern, and likewise to secure one which Flask had killed and waifed. The waif is a pennoned pole, two or three of which are carried by every boat; and which, when additional game is at hand, are inserted upright into the floating body of a dead whale, both to mark its place on the sea, and also as token of prior possession, should the boats of any other ship draw near.

The result of this lowering was somewhat illustrative of that sagacious saying in the Fishery—the more whales the less fish. Of all the drugged whales only one was captured. The rest contrived to escape for the time, but only to be taken, as will hereafter be seen, by some other craft than the *Pequod*.

Chapter LXXXVIII

Schools and Schoolmasters

The previous chapter gave account of an immense body or herd of sperm whales, and there was also then given the probable cause inducing those vast aggregations.

Now, though such great bodies are at times encountered, yet, as must have been seen, even at the present day, small detached bands are occasionally observed, embracing from twenty to fifty individuals each. Such bands are known as schools. They generally are of two sorts: those composed almost entirely of females, and those mustering none but young vigorous males, or bulls as they are familiarly designated.

In cavalier attendance upon the school of females, you invariably see a male of full grown magnitude, but not old; who, upon any alarm, evinces his gallantry by falling in the rear and covering the flight of his ladies. In truth, this gentleman is a luxurious Ottoman, swimming about over the watery world, surroundingly accompanied by all the solaces and endearments of the harem. The contrast between this Ottoman and his concubines is striking; because, while he is always of the largest leviathanic proportions, the ladies, even at full growth, are not more than one-third of the bulk of an average-sized male. They are comparatively delicate, indeed; I dare-say, not to exceed half a dozen yards round the waist. Nevertheless, it cannot be denied, that upon the whole they are hereditarily entitled to *en bon point*.

It is very curious to watch this harem and its lord in their indolent ramblings. Like fashionables, they are forever on the move in leisurely search of variety. You meet them on the Line in time for the full flower of the Equatorial feeding season, having just returned, perhaps, from spending the summer in the Northern seas, and so cheating summer of all unpleasant weariness and warmth. By the time they have lounged up and down the promenade of the Equator awhile, they start for the Oriental waters in anticipation of the cool season there, and so evade the other excessive temperature of the year.

When serenely advancing on one of these journeys, if any strange suspicious sights are seen, my lord whale keeps a wary eye on his interesting family. Should any unwarrantably pert young Leviathan coming that way presume to draw confidentially close to one of the ladies, with what prodigious fury the Bashaw assails him, and chases him away! High times, indeed, if unprincipled young rakes like him are to be permitted to invade the sanctity of domestic bliss; though do what the Bashaw will, he cannot keep the most notorious Lothario out of his bed; for alas! all fish bed in common. As ashore, the ladies often cause the most terrible duels among their rival admirers; just so with the whales, who sometimes come to deadly battle, and all for love. They fence with their long lower jaws, sometimes locking them together, and so striving for the supremacy like elks that warringly interweave their antlers. Not a few are captured having the deep scars of these encounters—furrowed heads, broken teeth, scalloped fins; and in some instances, wrenched and dislocated mouths.

But supposing the invader of domestic bliss to betake himself away at the first rush of the harem's lord, then is it very diverting to watch that lord. Gently he insinuates his vast bulk among them again and revels there awhile, still in tantalizing vicinity to young Lothario, like pious Solomon devoutly worshiping among his thousand concubines. Granting other whales to be in sight, the fishermen will seldom give chase to one of these Grand Turks; for these Grand Turks are too lavish of their strength, and hence their unctuousness is small. As for the sons and the daughters they beget, why, those sons and daughters must take care of themselves; at least, with only the maternal help. For like certain other omnivorous roving lovers that might be named, my Lord

Whale has no taste for the nursery, however much for the bower; and so, being a great traveler, he leaves his anonymous babies all over the world; every baby an exotic. In good time, nevertheless, as the ardor of youth declines; as years and dumps increase; as reflection lends her solemn pauses; in short, as a general lassitude overtakes the sated Turk; then a love of ease and virtue supplants the love for maidens; our Ottoman enters upon the impotent, repentant, admonitory stage of life, forswears, disbands the harem, and grown to an exemplary, sulky old soul, goes about all alone among the meridians and parallels saying his prayers, and warning each young Leviathan from his amorous errors.

Now, as the harem of whales is called by the fishermen a school, so is the lord and master of that school technically known as the schoolmaster. It is therefore not in strict character, however admirably satirical, that after going to school himself, he should then go abroad inculcating not what he learned there, but the folly of it. His title, schoolmaster, would very naturally seem derived from the name bestowed upon the harem itself, but some have surmised that the man who first thus entitled this sort of Ottoman whale, must have read the memoirs of Vidocq, and informed himself what sort of a country schoolmaster that famous Frenchman was in his younger days, and what was the nature of those occult lessons he inculcated into some of his pupils.

The same secludedness and isolation to which the schoolmaster whale betakes himself in his advancing years, is true of all aged Sperm Whales. Almost universally, a lone whale—as a solitary Leviathan is called—proves an ancient one. Like venerable moss-bearded Daniel Boone, he will have no one near him but Nature herself; and her he takes to wife in the wilderness of waters, and the best of wives she is, though she keeps so many moody secrets.

The schools composing none but young and vigorous males, previously mentioned, offer a strong contrast to the harem schools. For while those female whales are characteristically timid, the young males, or forty-barrel-bulls, as they call them, are by far the most pugnacious of all Leviathans, and proverbially the most dangerous to encounter; excepting those wondrous gray-headed, grizzled whales, sometimes met, and these will fight you like grim fiends exasperated by a penal gout.

The Forty-barrel-bull schools are larger than the harem schools. Like a mob of young collegians, they are full of fight, fun, and wickedness, tumbling round the world at such a reckless, rollicking rate, that no prudent underwriter would insure them any more than he would a riotous lad at Yale or Harvard. They soon relinquish this turbulence though, and when about three-fourths grown, break up, and separately go about in quest of settlements, that is, harems.

Another point of difference between the male and female schools is still more characteristic of the sexes. Say you strike a Forty-barrel-bull—poor devil! all his comrades quit him. But strike a member of the harem school, and her companions swim around her with every token of concern, sometimes lingering so near her and so long, as themselves to fall a prey.

Chapter LXXXIX

FAST-FISH AND LOOSE-FISH

THE ALLUSION TO THE WAIFS AND WAIF-POLES IN THE LAST CHAPTER BUT ONE, NECESSITATES some account of the laws and regulations of the whale fishery, of which the waif may be deemed the grand symbol and badge.

It frequently happens that when several ships are cruising in company, a whale may be struck by one vessel, then escape, and be finally killed and captured by another vessel; and herein are indirectly comprised many minor contingencies, all partaking of this one grand feature. For example—after a weary and perilous chase and capture of a whale, the body may get loose from the ship by reason of a violent storm; and drifting far away to leeward, be retaken by a second whaler, who, in a calm, snugly tows it alongside, without risk of life or line. Thus the most vexatious and violent disputes would often arise between the fishermen, were there not some written or unwritten, universal, undisputed law applicable to all cases.

Perhaps the only formal whaling code authorized by legislative enactment, was that of Holland. It was decreed by the States-General in A.D. 1695. But though no other nation has ever had any written whaling law, yet the American fishermen have been their own legislators and lawyers in this matter. They have provided a system which for terse comprehensiveness surpasses Justinian's *Pandects* and the *By-laws of the Chinese Society for the Suppression of Meddling with other People's Business*. Yes; these laws might be engraven on a Queen Anne's farthing, or the barb of a harpoon, and worn round the neck, so small are they.

I. A Fast-Fish belongs to the party fast to it.

II. A Loose-Fish is fair game for anybody who can soonest catch it.

But what plays the mischief with this masterly code is the admirable brevity of it, which necessitates a vast volume of commentaries to expound it.

First: What is a Fast-Fish? Alive or dead a fish is technically fast, when it is connected with an occupied ship or boat, by any medium at all controllable by the occupant or occupants—a mast, an oar, a nine-inch cable, a telegraph wire, or a strand of cobweb, it is all the same. Likewise a fish is technically fast when it bears a waif, or any other recognized symbol of possession; so long as the party waifing it plainly evince their ability at any time to take it alongside, as well as their intention so to do.

These are scientific commentaries; but the commentaries of the whalemen themselves sometimes consist in hard words and harder knocks—the Coke-upon-Littleton of the fist. True, among the more upright and honorable whalemen allowances are always made for peculiar cases, where it would be an outrageous moral injustice for one party to claim possession of a whale previously chased or killed by another party. But others are by no means so scrupulous.

Some fifty years ago there was a curious case of whale-trover litigated in England, wherein the plaintiffs set forth that after a hard chase of a whale in the Northern seas; and when indeed they (the plaintiffs) had succeeded in harpooning the fish; they were at last, through peril of their lives, obliged to forsake not only their lines, but their boat itself. Ultimately the defendants (the crew of another ship) came up with the whale, struck, killed, seized, and finally appropriated it before the very eyes of the plaintiffs. And when those defendants were remonstrated with, their captain snapped his fingers in the plaintiffs' teeth, and assured them that by way of doxology to the deed he had done, he would now retain their line, harpoons, and boat, which had remained attached to the whale at the time of the seizure. Wherefore the plaintiffs now sued for the recovery of the value of their whale, line, harpoons, and boat.

Mr. Erskine was counsel for the defendants; Lord Ellenborough was the judge. In the course of the defense, the witty Erskine went on to illustrate his position, by alluding to a recent crim. con. case, wherein a gentleman, after in vain trying to bridle his wife's viciousness, had at last abandoned her upon the seas of life; but in the course of years, repenting of that step, he instituted an action to recover possession of her. Erskine was on the other side; and he then supported it by saying, that though the gentleman had originally harpooned the lady, and had once had her fast, and only by reason of the great stress of her plunging viciousness, had at last abandoned her; yet abandon her he did, so that she became a loose-fish; and therefore when a subsequent gentleman reharpooned her, the lady then became that subsequent gentleman's property, along with whatever harpoon might have been found sticking in her.

Now in the present case Erskine contended that the examples of the whale and the lady were reciprocally illustrative of each other.

Those pleadings, and the counter pleadings, being duly heard, the very learned Judge in set terms decided, to wit—That as for the boat, he awarded it to the plaintiffs, because they had merely abandoned it to save their lives; but that with regard to the controverted whale, harpoons, and line, they belonged to the defendants; the whale, because it was a Loose-Fish at the time of the final capture; and the harpoons and line because when the fish made off with them, it (the fish) acquired a property in those articles; and hence anybody who afterwards took the fish had a right to them. Now the defendants afterwards took the fish; ergo, the aforesaid articles were theirs.

A common man looking at this decision of the very learned Judge, might possibly object to it. But plowed up to the primary rock of the matter, the two great principles laid down in the twin whaling laws previously quoted, and applied and elucidated by Lord Ellenborough in the above cited case; these two laws touching Fast-Fish and Loose-Fish, I say, will, on reflection, be found the fundamentals of all human jurisprudence; for notwithstanding its complicated tracery of sculpture, the Temple of the Law, like the Temple of the Philistines, has but two props to stand on.

Is it not a saying in everyone's mouth, Possession is half of the law: that is, regardless of how the thing came into possession? But often possession is the whole of the law. What are the sinews and souls of Russian serfs and Republican slaves but Fast-Fish, whereof possession is the whole of the law? What to the rapacious landlord is the widow's last mite but a Fast-Fish? What is yonder undetected villain's marble mansion with a door-plate for a waif; what is that but a Fast-Fish? What is the ruinous discount which Mordecai, the broker, gets from poor Woebegone, the bankrupt, on a loan to keep Woebegone's family from starvation; what is that ruinous discount but a Fast-Fish? What is the Archbishop of Savesoul's income of £100,000 seized from the scant bread and cheese of hundreds of thousands of broken-backed laborers (all sure of heaven without any of Savesoul's help) what is that globular 100,000 but a Fast-Fish? What are the Duke of Dunder's hereditary towns and hamlets but Fast-Fish? What to that redoubted harpooneer, John Bull, is poor Ireland, but a Fast-Fish? What to that apostolic lancer, Brother Jonathan, is Texas but a Fast-Fish? And concerning all these, is not Possession the whole of the law?

But if the doctrine of Fast-Fish be pretty generally applicable, the kindred doctrine of Loose-Fish is still more widely so. That is internationally and universally applicable.

What was America in 1492 but a Loose-Fish, in which Columbus struck the Spanish standard by way of waifing it for his royal master and mistress? What was Poland to the Czar? What Greece to the Turk? What India to England? What at last will Mexico be to the United States? All Loose-Fish.

What are the Rights of Man and the Liberties of the World but Loose-Fish? What all men's minds and opinions but Loose-Fish? What is the principle of religious belief in them but a Loose-Fish? What to the ostentatious smuggling verbalists are the thoughts of thinkers but Loose-Fish? What is the great globe itself but a Loose-Fish? And what are you, reader, but a Loose-Fish and a Fast-Fish, too?

Chapter XC

HEADS OR TAILS

"De balena vero sufficit, si rex habeat caput, et regina caudam."
BRACTON, L. 3, C. 3.

LATIN FROM THE BOOKS OF THE *LAWS OF ENGLAND*, WHICH TAKEN ALONG WITH THE CONTEXT, means, that of all whales captured by anybody on the coast of that land, the King, as Honorary Grand Harpooneer, must have the head, and the Queen be respectfully presented with the tail. A division which, in the whale, is much like halving an apple; there is no intermediate remainder. Now as this law, under a modified form, is to this day in force in England; and as it offers in various respects a strange anomaly touching the general law of Fast and Loose-Fish, it is here treated of in a separate chapter, on the same courteous principle that prompts the English railways to be at the expense of a separate car, specially reserved for the accommodation of royalty. In the first place, in curious proof of the fact that the above-mentioned law is still in force, I proceed to lay before you a circumstance that happened within the last two years.

It seems that some honest mariners of Dover, or Sandwich, or someone of the Cinque Ports, had after a hard chase succeeded in killing and beaching a fine whale which they had originally descried afar off from the shore. Now the Cinque Ports are partially or somehow under the jurisdiction of a sort of policeman or beadle, called a Lord Warden. Holding the office directly from the crown, I believe, all the royal emoluments incident to the Cinque Port territories become by assignment his. By some writers this office is called a sinecure. But not so. Because the Lord Warden is busily employed at times in fobbing his perquisites; which are his chiefly by virtue of that same fobbing of them.

Now when these poor sun-burned mariners, barefooted, and with their trousers rolled high up on their eely legs, had wearily hauled their fat fish high and dry, promising themselves a good £150 from the precious oil and bone; and in fantasy sipping rare tea with their wives, and good ale with their cronies, upon the strength of their respective shares, up steps a very learned and most Christian and charitable gentleman, with a copy of Blackstone under his arm; and laying it upon the whale's head, he says—"Hands off! this fish, my masters, is a Fast-Fish. I seize it as the Lord Warden's." Upon this the poor mariners in their respectful consternation—so truly English—knowing not what to say, fall to vigorously scratching their heads all round; meanwhile ruefully glancing from the whale to the stranger. But that did nowise mend the matter, or at all soften the hard heart of the learned gentleman with the copy of Blackstone. At length one of them, after long scratching about for his ideas, made bold to speak.

"Please, sir, who is the Lord Warden?"

"The Duke."

"But the duke had nothing to do with taking this fish?"

"It is his."

"We have been at great trouble, and peril, and some expense, and is all that to go to the Duke's benefit; we getting nothing at all for our pains but our blisters?"

"It is his."

"Is the Duke so very poor as to be forced to this desperate mode of getting a livelihood?"

"It is his."

"I thought to relieve my old bed-ridden mother by part of my share of this whale."

"It is his."

"Won't the Duke be content with a quarter or a half?"

"It is his."

In a word, the whale was seized and sold, and his Grace the Duke of Wellington received the money. Thinking that viewed in some particular lights, the case might by a bare possibility in some small degree be deemed, under the circumstances, a rather hard one, an honest clergyman of the town respectfully addressed a note to his Grace, begging him to take the case of those unfortunate mariners into full consideration. To which my Lord Duke in substance replied (both letters were published) that he had already done so, and received the money, and would be obliged to the reverend gentleman if for the future he (the reverend gentleman) would decline meddling with other people's business. Is this the still militant old man, standing at the corners of the three kingdoms, on all hands coercing alms of beggars?

It will readily be seen that in this case the alleged right of the Duke to the whale was a delegated one from the Sovereign. We must needs inquire then on what principle the Sovereign is originally invested with that right. The law itself has already been set forth. But Plowdon gives us the reason for it. Says Plowdon, the whale so caught belongs to the King and Queen, "because of its superior excellence." And by the soundest commentators this has ever been held a cogent argument in such matters.

But why should the King have the head, and the Queen the tail? A reason for that, ye lawyers!

In his treatise on "Queen-Gold," or Queen-pin-money, an old King's Bench author, one William Prynne, thus discourseth: "Ye tail is ye Queen's, that ye Queen's wardrobe may be supplied with ye whalebone." Now this was written at a time when the black limber bone of the Greenland or Right whale was largely used in ladies' bodices. But this same bone is not in the tail; it is in the head, which is a sad mistake for a sagacious lawyer like Prynne. But is the Queen a mermaid, to be presented with a tail? An allegorical meaning may lurk here.

There are two royal fish so styled by the English law writers—the whale and the sturgeon; both royal property under certain limitations, and nominally supplying the tenth branch of the crown's ordinary revenue. I know not that any other author has hinted of the matter; but by inference it seems to me that the sturgeon must be divided in the same way as the whale, the King receiving the highly dense and elastic head peculiar to that fish, which, symbolically regarded, may possibly be humorously grounded upon some presumed congeniality. And thus there seems a reason in all things even in law.

Chapter XCI

THE PEQUOD MEETS THE ROSE-BUD

"In vain it was to rake for Ambergriese in the paunch of this Leviathan, insufferable fetor denying not inquiry."

SIR T. BROWN, V. E.

IT WAS A WEEK OR TWO AFTER THE LAST WHALING SCENE RECOUNTED, AND WHEN WE WERE slowly sailing over a sleepy, vapory, mid-day sea, that the many noses on the *Pequod*'s deck proved more vigilant discoverers than the three pairs of eyes aloft. A peculiar and not very pleasant smell was smelled in the sea.

"I will bet something now," said Stubb, "that somewhere hereabouts are some of those drugged whales we tickled the other day. I thought they would keel up before long."

Presently, the vapors in advance slid aside; and there in the distance lay a ship, whose furled sails betokened that some sort of whale must be alongside. As we glided nearer, the stranger showed French colors from his peak; and by the eddying cloud of vulture sea-fowl that circled, and hovered, and swooped around him, it was plain that the whale alongside must be what the fishermen call a blasted whale, that is, a whale that has died unmolested on the sea, and so floated an unappropriated corpse. It may well be conceived what an unsavory odor such a mass must exhale; worse than an Assyrian city in the plague, when the living are incompetent to bury the departed. So intolerable indeed is it regarded by some that no cupidity could persuade them to moor alongside of it. Yet are there those who will still do it; notwithstanding the fact that the oil obtained from such subjects is of a very inferior quality, and by no means of the nature of attar-of-rose.

Coming still nearer with the expiring breeze, we saw that the Frenchman had a second whale alongside; and this second whale seemed even more of a nosegay than the first. In truth, it turned out to be one of those problematical whales that seem to dry up and die with a sort of prodigious dyspepsia, or indigestion; leaving their defunct bodies almost entirely bankrupt of anything like oil. Nevertheless, in the proper place we shall see that no knowing fisherman will ever turn up his nose at such a whale as this, however much he may shun blasted whales in general.

The *Pequod* had now swept so nigh to the stranger, that Stubb vowed he recognized his cutting spade-pole entangled in the lines that were knotted round the tail of one of these whales.

"There's a pretty fellow, now," he banteringly laughed, standing in the ship's bows, "there's a jackal for ye! I well know that these Crappoes of Frenchmen are but poor devils in the fishery; sometimes lowering their boats for breakers, mistaking them for Sperm-Whale spouts; yes, and sometimes sailing from their port with their hold full of boxes of tallow candles, and cases of snuffers, foreseeing that all the oil they will get won't be enough to dip the Captain's wick into; ay, we all know these things; but look ye, here's a Crappo that is content with our leavings, the drugged whale there, I mean; ay, and is content too with scraping the dry bones of that other precious fish he has there. Poor devil! I say, pass round a hat, someone, and let's make him a present of a little oil for dear charity's sake. For what oil he'll get from that drugged whale there, wouldn't be fit to burn in a jail; no, not in a condemned cell. And as for the other whale, why, I'll agree to get more oil by chopping up and trying out these three masts of ours, than he'll get from that bundle of bones; though, now that I think of it, it may contain something worth a good deal more than oil; yes, ambergris. I wonder now if our old man has thought of that. It's worth trying. Yes, I'm for it"; and so saying he started for the quarter-deck.

By this time the faint air had become a complete calm; so that whether or no, the *Pequod* was now fairly entrapped in the smell, with no hope of escaping except by its breezing up again. Issuing from the cabin, Stubb now called his boat's crew, and pulled off for the stranger. Drawing across her bow, he perceived that in accordance with the fanciful French taste, the upper part of her stem-piece was carved in the likeness of a huge drooping stalk, was painted green, and for thorns had copper spikes projecting from it here and there; the whole terminating in a symmetrical folded bulb of a bright red color. Upon her head boards, in large gilt letters, he read "Bouton de Rose"—Rose-button, or *Rose-bud*; and this was the romantic name of this aromatic ship.

Though Stubb did not understand the *Bouton* part of the inscription, yet the word *rose*, and the bulbous figure-head put together, sufficiently explained the whole to him.

"A wooden rose-bud, eh?" he cried with his hand to his nose, "that will do very well; but how like all creation it smells!"

Now in order to hold direct communication with the people on deck, he had to pull round the bows to the starboard side, and thus come close to the blasted whale; and so talk over it.

Arrived then at this spot, with one hand still to his nose, he bawled—"Bouton-de-Rose, ahoy! are there any of you Bouton-de-Roses that speak English?"

"Yes," rejoined a Guernsey-man from the bulwarks, who turned out to be the chief-mate.

"Well, then, my Bouton-de-Rose-bud, have you seen the White Whale?"

"*What* whale?"

"The *White* Whale—a Sperm Whale—Moby-Dick, have ye seen him?"

"Never heard of such a whale. Cachalot Blanche! White Whale—no."

"Very good, then; good-bye now, and I'll call again in a minute."

Then rapidly pulling back towards the *Pequod*, and seeing Ahab leaning over the quarter-deck rail awaiting his report, he molded his two hands into a trumpet and shouted—"No, Sir! No!" Upon which Ahab retired, and Stubb returned to the Frenchman.

He now perceived that the Guernsey-man, who had just got into the chains, and was using a cutting-spade, had slung his nose in a sort of bag.

"What's the matter with your nose, there?" said Stubb. "Broke it?"

"I wish it was broken, or that I didn't have any nose at all!" answered the Guernsey-man, who did not seem to relish the job he was at very much. "But what are you holding *yours* for?"

"Oh, nothing! It's a wax nose; I have to hold it on. Fine day, ain't it? Air rather gardenny, I should say; throw us a bunch of posies, will ye, Bouton-de-Rose?"

"What in the devil's name do you want here?" roared the Guernsey-man, flying into a sudden passion.

"Oh! keep cool—cool? yes, that's the word; why don't you pack those whales in ice while you're working at 'em? But joking aside, though; do you know, Rose-bud, that it's all nonsense trying to get any oil out of such whales? As for that dried up one, there, he hasn't a gill in his whole carcass."

"I know that well enough; but, d'ye see, the Captain here won't believe it; this is his first voyage; he was a Cologne manufacturer before. But come aboard, and mayhap he'll believe you, if he won't me; and so I'll get out of this dirty scrape."

"Anything to oblige ye, my sweet and pleasant fellow," rejoined Stubb, and with that he soon mounted to the deck. There a queer scene presented itself. The sailors, in tasseled caps of red worsted, were getting the heavy tackles in readiness for the whales. But they worked rather slow and talked very fast, and seemed in anything but a good humor. All their noses upwardly projected from their faces like so many jib-booms. Now and then pairs of them would drop their work, and run up to the mast-head to get some fresh air. Some thinking they would catch the plague, dipped oakum in coal-tar, and at intervals held it to their nostrils. Others having broken the stems of their pipes almost short off at the bowl, were vigorously puffing tobacco-smoke, so that it constantly filled their olfactories.

Stubb was struck by a shower of outcries and anathemas proceeding from the Captain's round-house abaft; and looking in that direction saw a fiery face thrust from behind the door, which was held ajar from within. This was the tormented surgeon, who, after in vain remonstrating against the proceedings of the day, had betaken himself to the Captain's round-house (*cabinet* he called it) to avoid the pest; but still, could not help yelling out his entreaties and indignations at times.

Marking all this, Stubb argued well for his scheme, and turning to the Guernsey-man had a little chat with him, during which the stranger mate expressed his detestation of his Captain as a conceited ignoramus, who had brought them all into so unsavory and unprofitable a pickle. Sounding him carefully, Stubb further perceived that the Guernsey-man had not the slightest suspicion concerning the ambergris. He therefore held his peace on that head, but otherwise was quite frank and confidential with him, so that the two quickly concocted a little plan for both circumventing and satirizing the Captain, without his at all dreaming of distrusting their sincerity. According to this little plan of theirs, the Guernsey-man, under cover of an interpreter's office, was to tell the Captain what he pleased, but as coming from Stubb; and as for Stubb, he was to utter any nonsense that should come uppermost in him during the interview.

By this time their destined victim appeared from his cabin. He was a small and dark, but rather delicate looking man for a sea-captain, with large whiskers and mustache, however; and wore a red cotton velvet vest with watch-seals at his side. To this gentleman, Stubb was now politely introduced by the Guernsey-man, who at once ostentatiously put on the aspect of interpreting between them. "What shall I say to him first?" said he.

"Why," said Stubb, eyeing the velvet vest and the watch and seals, "you may as well begin by telling him that he looks a sort of babyish to me, though I don't pretend to be a judge."

"He says, Monsieur," said the Guernsey-man, in French, turning to his captain, "that only yesterday his ship spoke a vessel, whose captain and chief-mate, with six sailors, had all died of a fever caught from a blasted whale they had brought alongside."

Upon this the captain started, and eagerly desired to know more.

"What now?" said the Guernsey-man to Stubb.

"Why, since he takes it so easy, tell him that now I have eyed him carefully, I'm quite certain that he's no more fit to command a whale-ship than a St. Jago monkey. In fact, tell him from me he's a baboon."

"He vows and declares, Monsieur, that the other whale, the dried one, is far more deadly than the blasted one; in fine, Monsieur, he conjures us, as we value our lives, to cut loose from these fish."

Instantly the captain ran forward, and in a loud voice commanded his crew to desist from hoisting the cutting-tackles, and at once cast loose the cables and chains confining the whales to the ship.

"What now?" said the Guernsey-man, when the Captain had returned to them.

"Why, let me see; yes, you may as well tell him now that—that—in fact, tell him I've diddled him, and (aside to himself) perhaps somebody else."

"He says, Monsieur, that he's very happy to have been of any service to us."

Hearing this, the captain vowed that they were the grateful parties (meaning himself and mate), and concluded by inviting Stubb down into his cabin to drink a bottle of Bordeaux.

"He wants you to take a glass of wine with him," said the interpreter.

"Thank him heartily; but tell him it's against my principles to drink with the man I've diddled. In fact, tell him I must go."

"He says, Monsieur, that his principles won't admit of his drinking; but that if Monsieur wants to live another day to drink, then Monsieur had best drop all four boats, and pull the ship away from these whales, for it's so calm they won't drift."

By this time Stubb was over the side, and getting into his boat, hailed the Guernsey-man to this effect—that having a long tow-line in his boat, he would do what he could to help them, by pulling out the lighter whale of the two from the ship's side. While the Frenchman's boats, then, were engaged in towing the ship one way, Stubb benevolently towed away at his whale the other way, ostentatiously slacking out a most unusually long tow-line.

Presently a breeze sprang up; Stubb feigned to cast off from the whale; hoisting his boats, the Frenchman soon increased his distance, while the *Pequod* slid in between him and Stubb's whale. Whereupon Stubb quickly pulled to the floating body, and hailing the *Pequod* to give notice of his intentions, at once proceeded to reap the fruit of his unrighteous cunning. Seizing his sharp boat-spade, he commenced an excavation in the body, a little behind the side fin. You would almost have thought he was digging a cellar there in the sea; and when at length his spade struck against the gaunt ribs, it was like turning up old Roman tiles and pottery buried in fat English loam. His boat's crew were all in high excitement, eagerly helping their chief, and looking as anxious as gold-hunters.

And all the time numberless fowls were diving, and ducking, and screaming, and yelling, and fighting around them. Stubb was beginning to look disappointed, especially as the horrible nosegay increased, when suddenly from out the very heart of this plague, there stole a faint stream of perfume, which flowed through the tide of bad smells without being absorbed by it, as one river will flow into and then along with another, without at all blending with it for a time.

"I have it! I have it!" cried Stubb, with delight, striking something in the subterranean regions, "a purse! a purse!"

Dropping his spade, he thrust both hands in, and drew out handfuls of something that looked like ripe Windsor soap, or rich mottled old cheese; very unctuous and savory withal. You might easily dent it with your thumb; it is of a hue between yellow and ash color. And this, good friends, is ambergris, worth a gold guinea an ounce to any druggist. Some six handfuls were obtained; but more was unavoidably lost in the sea, and still more, perhaps, might have been secured were it not for impatient Ahab's loud command to Stubb to desist, and come on board, else the ship would bid them good-bye.

Chapter XCII

AMBERGRIS

NOW THIS AMBERGRIS IS A VERY CURIOUS SUBSTANCE, AND SO IMPORTANT AS AN ARTICLE OF commerce, that in 1791 a certain Nantucket-born Captain Coffin was examined at the bar of the English House of Commons on that subject. For at that time, and indeed until a comparatively late day, the precise origin of ambergris remained, like amber itself a problem to the learned. Though the word ambergris is but the French compound for gray amber, yet the two substances are quite distinct. For amber, though at times found on the sea-coast, is also dug up in some far inland soils, whereas ambergris is never found except upon the sea. Besides, amber is a hard, transparent, brittle, odorless substance, used for mouth-pieces to pipes, for beads and ornaments; but ambergris is soft, waxy, and so highly fragrant and spicy, that it is largely used in perfumery, in pastilles, precious candles, hair-powders, and pomatum. The Turks use it in cooking, and also carry it to Mecca, for the same purpose that frankincense is carried to St. Peter's in Rome. Some wine merchants drop a few grains into claret, to flavor it.

Who would think, then, that such fine ladies and gentlemen should regale themselves with an essence found in the inglorious bowels of a sick whale! Yet so it is. By some, ambergris is supposed to be the cause, and by others the effect, of the dyspepsia in the whale. How to cure such a dyspepsia it were hard to say, unless by administering three or four boat loads of Brandreth's pills, and then running out of harm's way, as laborers do in blasting rocks.

I have forgotten to say that there were found in this ambergris, certain hard, round, bony plates, which at first Stubb thought might be sailors' trousers buttons; but it afterwards turned out that they were nothing more than pieces of small squid bones embalmed in that manner.

Now that the incorruption of this most fragrant ambergris should be found in the heart of such decay; is this nothing? Bethink thee of that saying of St. Paul in Corinthians, about corruption and incorruption; how that we are sown in dishonor, but raised in glory. And likewise call to mind that saying of Paracelsus about what it is that maketh the best musk. Also forget not the strange fact that of all things of ill-savor, Cologne-water, in its rudimental manufacturing stages, is the worst.

I should like to conclude the chapter with the above appeal, but cannot, owing to my anxiety to repel a charge often made against whalemen, and which, in the estimation of some already biased minds, might be considered as indirectly substantiated by what has been said of the Frenchman's two whales. Elsewhere in this volume the slanderous aspersion has been disproved, that the vocation of whaling is throughout a slatternly, untidy business. But there is another thing to rebut. They hint that all whales always smell bad. Now how did this odious stigma originate?

I opine, that it is plainly traceable to the first arrival of the Greenland whaling ships in London, more than two centuries ago. Because those whalemen did not then, and do not now, try out their oil at sea as the Southern ships have always done; but cutting up the fresh blubber in small bits, thrust it through the bung-holes of large casks, and carry it home in that manner; the shortness of the season in those Icy Seas, and the sudden and violent storms to which they are exposed, forbidding any other course. The consequence is, that upon breaking into the hold, and unloading one of these whale cemeteries, in the Greenland dock, a savor is given forth somewhat similar to that arising from excavating an old city grave-yard, for the foundations of a Lying-in Hospital.

I partly surmise also, that this wicked charge against whalers may be likewise imputed to the existence on the coast of Greenland, in former times, of a Dutch village called Schmerenburgh or Smeerenberg, which latter name is the one used by the learned Fogo Von Slack, in his great work on *Smells*, a text-book on that subject. As its name imports (smeer, fat; berg, to put up), this village was founded in order to afford a place for the blubber of the Dutch whale fleet to be tried out, without being taken home to Holland for that purpose. It was a collection of furnaces, fat-kettles, and oil sheds; and when the works were in full operation certainly gave forth no very pleasant savor. But all this is quite different with a South Sea Sperm Whaler; which in a voyage of four years perhaps, after completely filling her hold with oil, does not, perhaps, consume fifty days in the business of boiling out; and in the state that it is casked, the oil is nearly scentless. The truth is, that living or dead, if but decently treated, whales as a species are by no means creatures of ill odor; nor can whalemen be recognized, as the people of the middle ages affected to detect a Jew in the company, by the nose. Nor indeed can the whale possibly be otherwise than fragrant, when, as a general thing, he enjoys such high health; taking abundance of exercise; always out of doors; though, it is true, seldom in the open air. I say, that the motion of a Sperm Whale's flukes above water dispenses a perfume, as when a musk-scented lady rustles her dress in a warm parlor. What then shall I liken the Sperm Whale to for fragrance, considering his magnitude? Must it not be to that famous elephant, with jeweled tusks, and redolent with myrrh, which was led out of an Indian town to do honor to Alexander the Great?

Chapter XCIII

THE CASTAWAY

IT WAS BUT SOME FEW DAYS AFTER ENCOUNTERING THE FRENCHMAN, THAT A MOST SIGNIFICANT event befell the most insignificant of the *Pequod*'s crew; an event most lamentable; and which ended in providing the sometimes madly merry and predestinated craft with a living and ever accompanying prophecy of whatever shattered sequel might prove her own.

Now, in the whale-ship, it is not everyone that goes in the boats. Some few hands are reserved called ship-keepers, whose province it is to work the vessel while the boats are pursuing the whale. As a general thing, these ship-keepers are as hardy fellows as the men comprising the boats' crews. But if there happen to be an unduly slender, clumsy, or timorous wight in the ship, that wight is certain to be made a ship-keeper. It was so in the *Pequod* with the little negro Pippin by nickname, Pip by abbreviation. Poor Pip! ye have heard of him before; ye must remember his tambourine on that dramatic midnight, so gloomy-jolly.

In outer aspect, Pip and Dough-Boy made a match, like a black pony and a white one, of equal developments, though of dissimilar color, driven in one eccentric span. But while hapless Dough-Boy was by nature dull and torpid in his intellects, Pip, though over tender-hearted, was at bottom very bright, with that pleasant, genial, jolly brightness peculiar to his tribe; a tribe, which ever enjoy all holidays and festivities with finer, freer relish than any other race. For blacks, the year's calendar should show naught but three hundred and sixty-five Fourth of Julys and New Year's Days. Nor smile so, while I write that this little black was brilliant, for even blackness has its brilliancy; behold yon lustrous ebony, paneled in king's cabinets. But Pip loved life, and all life's peaceable securities; so that the panic-striking business in which he had somehow unaccountably become entrapped, had most sadly blurred his brightness; though, as ere long will be seen, what was thus temporarily subdued in him, in the end was destined to be luridly illumined by strange wild fires, that fictitiously showed him off to ten times the natural luster with which in his native Tolland County in Connecticut, he had once enlivened many a fiddler's frolic on the green; and at melodious even-tide, with his gay ha-ha! had turned the round horizon into one star-belled tambourine. So, though in the clear air of day, suspended against a blue-veined neck, the pure-watered diamond drop will healthful glow; yet, when the cunning jeweler would show you the diamond in its most impressive luster, he lays it against a gloomy ground, and then lights it up, not by the sun, but by some unnatural gases. Then come out those fiery effulgences, infernally superb; then the evil-blazing diamond, once the divinest symbol of the crystal skies, looks like some crown-jewel stolen from the King of Hell. But let us to the story.

It came to pass, that in the ambergris affair Stubb's after-oarsman chanced so to sprain his hand, as for a time to become quite maimed; and, temporarily, Pip was put into his place.

The first time Stubb lowered with him, Pip evinced much nervousness; but happily, for that time, escaped close contact with the whale; and therefore came off not altogether discreditably; though Stubb observing him, took care, afterwards, to exhort him to cherish his courageousness to the utmost, for he might often find it needful.

Now upon the second lowering, the boat paddled upon the whale; and as the fish received the darted iron, it gave its customary rap, which happened, in this instance, to be right under poor Pip's seat. The involuntary consternation of the moment caused him to leap, paddle in hand, out of the boat; and in such a way, that part of the slack whale-line coming against his chest, he breasted it overboard with him, so as to become entangled in it, when at last plumping into the water. That instant the stricken whale started on a fierce run, the line swiftly straightened; and presto! poor Pip came all foaming up to the chocks of the boat, remorselessly dragged there by the line, which had taken several turns around his chest and neck.

Tashtego stood in the bows. He was full of the fire of the hunt. He hated Pip for a poltroon. Snatching the boat-knife from its sheath, he suspended its sharp edge over the line, and turning towards Stubb, exclaimed interrogatively, "Cut?" Meantime Pip's blue, choked face plainly looked, Do, for God's sake! All passed in a flash. In less than half a minute, this entire thing happened.

"Damn him, cut!" roared Stubb; and so the whale was lost and Pip was saved.

So soon as he recovered himself, the poor little negro was assailed by yells and execrations from the crew. Tranquilly permitting these irregular cursings to evaporate, Stubb then in a plain, business-like, but still half humorous manner, cursed Pip officially; and that done, unofficially gave him much wholesome advice. The substance was, Never jump from a boat, Pip, except—but all the rest was indefinite, as the soundest advice ever is. Now, in general, *Stick to the boat,* is your true motto in whaling; but cases will sometimes happen when *Leap from the boat,* is still better. Moreover, as if perceiving at last that if he should give undiluted conscientious advice to Pip, he would be leaving him too wide a margin to jump in for the future; Stubb suddenly dropped all advice, and concluded with a peremptory command "Stick to the boat, Pip, or by the Lord, I won't pick you up if you jump; mind that. We can't afford to lose whales by the likes of you; a whale would sell for thirty times what you would, Pip, in Alabama. Bear that in mind, and don't jump any more." Hereby perhaps Stubb indirectly hinted, that though man loved his fellow, yet man is a money-making animal, which propensity too often interferes with his benevolence.

But we are all in the hands of the Gods; and Pip jumped again. It was under very similar circumstances to the first performance; but this time he did not breast out the line; and hence, when the whale started to run, Pip was left behind on the sea, like a hurried traveler's trunk. Alas! Stubb was but too true to his word. It was a beautiful, bounteous, blue day; the spangled sea calm and cool, and flatly stretching away, all round, to the horizon, like gold-beater's skin hammered out to the extremest. Bobbing up and down in that sea, Pip's ebon head showed like a head of cloves. No boat-knife was lifted when he fell so rapidly astern. Stubb's inexorable back was turned upon him; and the whale was winged. In three minutes, a whole mile of shoreless ocean was between Pip and Stubb. Out from the center of the sea, poor Pip turned his crisp, curling, black head to the sun, another lonely castaway, though the loftiest and the brightest.

Now, in calm weather, to swim in the open ocean is as easy to the practiced swimmer as to ride in a spring-carriage ashore. But the awful lonesomeness is intolerable. The intense concentration of self in the middle of such a heartless immensity, my God! who can tell it? Mark, how when sailors in a dead calm bathe in the open sea—mark how closely they hug their ship and only coast along her sides.

But had Stubb really abandoned the poor little negro to his fate? No; he did not mean to, at least. Because there were two boats in his wake, and he supposed, no doubt, that they would of course come up to Pip very quickly, and pick him up; though, indeed, such considerations towards oarsmen jeopardized through their own timidity, is not always manifested by the hunters in all similar instances; and such instances not unfrequently occur; almost invariably in the fishery, a coward, so called, is marked with the same ruthless detestation peculiar to military navies and armies.

But it so happened that those boats, without seeing Pip, suddenly spying whales close to them on one side, turned, and gave chase; and Stubb's boat was now so far away, and he and all his crew so intent upon his fish, that Pip's ringed horizon began to expand around him miserably. By merest chance the ship itself at last rescued him; but from that hour the little negro went about the deck an idiot; such, at least, they said he was. The sea had jeeringly kept his finite body up, but drowned the infinite of his soul. Not drowned entirely, though. Rather carried down alive to wondrous depths, where strange shapes of the unwarped primal world glided to and fro before his passive eyes; and the miser-merman, Wisdom, revealed his hoarded heaps; and among the joyous, heartless, ever-juvenile eternities, Pip saw the multitudinous, God-omnipresent, coral insects, that out of the firmament of waters heaved the colossal orbs. He saw God's foot upon the treadle of the loom, and spoke it; and therefore his shipmates called him mad. So man's insanity is heaven's sense; and wandering from all mortal reason, man comes at last to that celestial thought, which, to reason, is absurd and frantic; and weal or woe, feels then uncompromised, indifferent as his God.

For the rest, blame not Stubb too hardly. The thing is common in that fishery; and in the sequel of the narrative, it will then be seen what like abandonment befell myself.

Chapter XCIV

A SQUEEZE OF THE HAND

THAT WHALE OF STUBB'S, SO DEARLY PURCHASED, WAS DULY BROUGHT TO THE *PEQUOD*'S SIDE, where all those cutting and hoisting operations previously detailed, were regularly gone through, even to the baling of the Heidelburgh Tun, or Case.

While some were occupied with this latter duty, others were employed in dragging away the larger tubs, so soon as filled with the sperm; and when the proper time arrived, this same sperm was carefully manipulated ere going to the try-works, of which anon.

It had cooled and crystallized to such a degree, that when, with several others, I sat down before a large Constantine's bath of it, I found it strangely concreted into lumps, here and there rolling about in the liquid part. It was our business to squeeze these lumps back into fluid. A sweet and unctuous duty! No wonder that in old times this sperm was such a favorite cosmetic. Such a clearer! such a sweetener! such a softener! such a delicious mollifier! After having my hands in it for only a few minutes, my fingers felt like eels, and began, as it were, to serpentine and spiralize.

As I sat there at my ease, cross-legged on the deck; after the bitter exertion at the windlass; under a blue tranquil sky; the ship under indolent sail, and gliding so serenely along; as I bathed my hands among those soft, gentle globules of infiltrated tissues, wove almost within the hour; as they richly broke to my fingers, and discharged all their opulence, like fully ripe grapes their wine; as I snuffed up that uncontaminated aroma—literally and truly, like the smell of spring violets; I declare to you, that for the time I lived as in a musky meadow; I forgot all about our horrible oath, in that inexpressible sperm, I washed my hands and my heart of it; I almost began to credit the old Paracelsan superstition that sperm is of rare virtue in allaying the heat of anger: while bathing in that bath, I felt divinely free from all ill-will, or petulance, or malice, of any sort whatsoever.

Squeeze! squeeze! squeeze! all the morning long; I squeezed that sperm till I myself almost melted into it; I squeezed that sperm till a strange sort of insanity came over me; and I found myself unwittingly squeezing my co-laborers' hands in it, mistaking their hands for the gentle globules. Such an abounding, affectionate, friendly, loving feeling did this avocation beget; that at last I was continually squeezing their hands, and looking up into their eyes sentimentally; as much as to say—Oh! my dear fellow-beings, why should we longer cherish any social acerbities, or know the slightest ill-humor or envy! Come; let us squeeze hands all round; nay, let us all squeeze ourselves into each other; let us squeeze ourselves universally into the very milk and sperm of kindness.

Would that I could keep squeezing that sperm forever! For now, since by many prolonged, repeated experiences, I have perceived that in all cases man must eventually lower, or at least shift, his conceit of attainable felicity; not placing it anywhere in the intellect or the fancy; but in the wife, the heart, the bed, the table, the saddle, the fireside; the country; now that I have perceived all this, I am ready to squeeze case eternally. In thoughts of the visions of the night, I saw long rows of angels in paradise, each with his hands in a jar of spermaceti.

* * * * *

Now, while discoursing of sperm, it behooves to speak of other things akin to it, in the business of preparing the sperm whale for the try-works.

First comes white-horse, so called, which is obtained from the tapering part of the fish, and also from the thicker portions of his flukes. It is tough with congealed tendons—a wad of muscle—

but still contains some oil. After being severed from the whale, the white-horse is first cut into portable oblongs ere going to the mincer. They look much like blocks of Berkshire marble.

Plum-pudding is the term bestowed upon certain fragmentary parts of the whale's flesh, here and there adhering to the blanket of blubber, and often participating to a considerable degree in its unctuousness. It is a most refreshing, convivial, beautiful object to behold. As its name imports, it is of an exceedingly rich, mottled tint, with a bestreaked snowy and golden ground, dotted with spots of the deepest crimson and purple. It is plums of rubies, in pictures of citron. Spite of reason, it is hard to keep yourself from eating it. I confess, that once I stole behind the fore-mast to try it. It tasted something as I should conceive a royal cutlet from the thigh of Louis le Gros might have tasted, supposing him to have been killed the first day after the venison season, and that particular venison season contemporary with an unusually fine vintage of the vineyards of Champagne.

There is another substance, and a very singular one, which turns up in the course of this business, but which I feel it to be very puzzling adequately to describe. It is called slobgollion; an appellation original with the whalemen, and even so is the nature of the substance. It is an ineffably oozy, stringy affair, most frequently found in the tubs of sperm, after a prolonged squeezing, and subsequent decanting. I hold it to be the wondrously thin, ruptured membranes of the case, coalescing.

Gurry, so called, is a term properly belonging to right whalemen, but sometimes incidentally used by the sperm fishermen. It designates the dark, glutinous substance which is scraped off the back of the Greenland or right whale, and much of which covers the decks of those inferior souls who hunt that ignoble Leviathan.

Nippers. Strictly this word is not indigenous to the whale's vocabulary. But as applied by whalemen, it becomes so. A whaleman's nipper is a short firm strip of tendinous stuff cut from the tapering part of Leviathan's tail: it averages an inch in thickness, and for the rest, is about the size of the iron part of a hoe. Edgewise moved along the oily deck, it operates like a leathern squilgee; and by nameless blandishments, as of magic, allures along with it all impurities.

But to learn all about these recondite matters, your best way is at once to descend into the blubber-room, and have a long talk with its inmates. This place has previously been mentioned as the receptacle for the blanket-pieces, when stripped and hoisted from the whale. When the proper time arrives for cutting up its contents, this apartment is a scene of terror to all tyros, especially by night. On one side, lit by a dull lantern, a space has been left clear for the workmen. They generally go in pairs—a pike-and-gaff-man and a spade-man. The whaling-pike is similar to a frigate's boarding-weapon of the same name. The gaff is something like a boat-hook. With his gaff, the gaff-man hooks on to a sheet of blubber, and strives to hold it from slipping, as the ship pitches and lurches about. Meanwhile, the spade-man stands on the sheet itself, perpendicularly chopping it into the portable horse-pieces. This spade is sharp as hone can make it; the spade-man's feet are shoeless; the thing he stands on will sometimes irresistibly slide away from him like a sledge. If he cuts off one of his own toes, or one of his assistants', would you be very much astonished? Toes are scarce among veteran blubber-room men.

Chapter XCV

THE CASSOCK

HAD YOU STEPPED ON BOARD THE *PEQUOD* AT A CERTAIN JUNCTURE OF THIS POST-MORTEMIZING of the whale; and had you strolled forward nigh the windlass, pretty sure am I that you would have scanned with no small curiosity a very strange, enigmatical object, which you would have seen there, lying along lengthwise in the lee scuppers. Not the wondrous cistern in the whale's huge head; not the prodigy of his unhinged lower jaw; not the miracle of his symmetrical tail; none of these would so surprise you, as half a glimpse of that unaccountable cone—longer than a Kentuckian is tall, nigh a foot in diameter at the base, and jet-black as Yojo, the ebony idol of Queequeg. And an idol, indeed, it is; or, rather, in old times, its likeness was. Such an idol as that found in the secret groves of Queen Maachah in Judea; and for worshiping which, King Asa, her son, did depose her, and destroyed the idol, and burned it for an abomination at the brook Kedron, as darkly set forth in the 15th chapter of the first book of *Kings*.

Look at the sailor, called the mincer, who now comes along, and assisted by two allies, heavily backs the grandissimus, as the mariners call it, and with bowed shoulders, staggers off with it as if he were a grenadier carrying a dead comrade from the field. Extending it upon the forecastle deck, he now proceeds cylindrically to remove its dark pelt, as an African hunter the pelt of a boa. This done he turns the pelt inside out, like a pantaloon leg; gives it a good stretching, so as almost to double its diameter; and at last hangs it, well spread, in the rigging, to dry. Ere long, it is taken down; when removing some three feet of it, towards the pointed extremity, and then cutting two slits for arm-holes at the other end, he lengthwise slips himself bodily into it. The mincer now stands before you invested in the full canonicals of his calling. Immemorial to all his order, this investiture alone will adequately protect him, while employed in the peculiar functions of his office.

That office consists in mincing the horse-pieces of blubber for the pots; an operation which is conducted at a curious wooden horse, planted endwise against the bulwarks, and with a capacious tub beneath it, into which the minced pieces drop, fast as the sheets from a rapt orator's desk. Arrayed in decent black; occupying a conspicuous pulpit; intent on bible leaves; what a candidate for an archbishopric, what a lad for a Pope were this mincer![1]

Chapter XCVI

THE TRY-WORKS

BESIDES HER HOISTED BOATS, AN AMERICAN WHALER IS OUTWARDLY DISTINGUISHED BY HER TRY-works. She presents the curious anomaly of the most solid masonry joining with oak and hemp in constituting the completed ship. It is as if from the open field a brick-kiln were transported to her planks.

The try-works are planted between the fore-mast and main-mast, the most roomy part of the

1. Bible leaves! Bible leaves! This is the invariable cry from the mates to the mincer. It enjoins him to be careful, and cut his work into as thin slices as possible, inasmuch as by so doing the business of boiling out the oil is much accelerated, and its quantity considerably increased, besides perhaps improving it in quality.

deck. The timbers beneath are of a peculiar strength, fitted to sustain the weight of an almost solid mass of brick and mortar, some ten feet by eight square, and five in height. The foundation does not penetrate the deck, but the masonry is firmly secured to the surface by ponderous knees of iron bracing it on all sides, and screwing it down to the timbers. On the flanks it is cased with wood, and at top completely covered by a large, sloping, battened hatchway. Removing this hatch we expose the great try-pots, two in number, and each of several barrels' capacity. When not in use, they are kept remarkably clean. Sometimes they are polished with soap-stone and sand, till they shine within like silver punch-bowls. During the night-watches some cynical old sailors will crawl into them and coil themselves away there for a nap. While employed in polishing them—one man in each pot, side by side—many confidential communications are carried on, over the iron lips. It is a place also for profound mathematical meditation. It was in the left hand try-pot of the *Pequod*, with the soap-stone diligently circling round me, that I was first indirectly struck by the remarkable fact, that in geometry all bodies gliding along the cycloid, my soap-stone for example, will descend from any point in precisely the same time.

Removing the fire-board from the front of the try-works, the bare masonry of that side is exposed, penetrated by the two iron mouths of the furnaces, directly underneath the pots. These mouths are fitted with heavy doors of iron. The intense heat of the fire is prevented from communicating itself to the deck, by means of a shallow reservoir extending under the entire enclosed surface of the works. By a tunnel inserted at the rear, this reservoir is kept replenished with water as fast as it evaporates. There are no external chimneys; they open direct from the rear wall. And here let us go back for a moment.

It was about nine o'clock at night that the *Pequod*'s try-works were first started on this present voyage. It belonged to Stubb to oversee the business.

"All ready there? Off hatch, then, and start her. You cook, fire the works." This was an easy thing, for the carpenter had been thrusting his shavings into the furnace throughout the passage. Here be it said that in a whaling voyage the first fire in the try-works has to be fed for a time with wood. After that no wood is used, except as a means of quick ignition to the staple fuel. In a word, after being tried out, the crisp, shriveled blubber, now called scraps or fritters, still contains considerable of its unctuous properties. These fritters feed the flames. Like a plethoric burning martyr, or a self-consuming misanthrope, once ignited, the whale supplies his own fuel and burns by his own body. Would that he consumed his own smoke! for his smoke is horrible to inhale, and inhale it you must, and not only that, but you must live in it for the time. It has an unspeakable, wild, Hindoo odor about it, such as may lurk in the vicinity of funereal pyres. It smells like the left wing of the day of judgment; it is an argument for the pit.

By midnight the works were in full operation. We were clear from the carcass; sail had been made; the wind was freshening; the wild ocean darkness was intense. But that darkness was licked up by the fierce flames, which at intervals forked forth from the sooty flues, and illuminated every lofty rope in the rigging, as with the famed Greek fire. The burning ship drove on, as if remorselessly commissioned to some vengeful deed. So the pitch and sulfur-freighted brigs of the bold Hydriote, *Canaris*, issuing from their midnight harbors, with broad sheets of flame for sails, bore down upon the Turkish frigates, and folded them in conflagrations.

The hatch, removed from the top of the works, now afforded a wide hearth in front of them. Standing on this were the Tartarean shapes of the pagan harpooneers, always the whale-ship's stokers. With huge pronged poles they pitched hissing masses of blubber into the scalding pots, or stirred up the fires beneath, till the snaky flames darted, curling, out of the doors to catch them by the feet. The smoke rolled away in sullen heaps. To every pitch of the ship there was a pitch of the boiling oil, which seemed all eagerness to leap into their faces. Opposite the mouth of the works, on the further side of the wide wooden hearth, was the windlass. This served for a sea-sofa. Here lounged the watch, when not otherwise employed, looking into the red heat of the fire, till their eyes felt scorched in their heads. Their tawny features, now all begrimed with smoke and sweat, their matted beards, and the contrasting barbaric brilliancy of their teeth, all these were strangely revealed in the capricious emblazonings of the works. As they narrated to each other their unholy adventures, their tales of terror told in words of mirth; as their uncivilized laughter forked upwards out of them, like the flames from the furnace; as to and fro, in their front, the harpooneers wildly gesticulated with their huge pronged forks and dippers; as the wind howled on, and the sea leaped, and the ship groaned and dived, and yet steadfastly shot her red hell further and further into the blackness of the sea and the night, and scornfully champed the white bone in her mouth, and viciously spat round her on all sides; then the rushing *Pequod,* freighted with savages, and laden with fire, and burning a corpse, and plunging into that blackness of darkness, seemed the material counterpart of her monomaniac commander's soul.

So seemed it to me, as I stood at her helm, and for long hours silently guided the way of this fire-ship on the sea. Wrapped, for that interval, in darkness myself, I but the better saw the redness, the madness, the ghastliness of others. The continual sight of the fiend shapes before me, capering half in smoke and half in fire, these at last begat kindred visions in my soul, so soon as I began to yield to that unaccountable drowsiness which ever would come over me at a midnight helm.

But that night, in particular, a strange (and ever since inexplicable) thing occurred to me. Starting from a brief standing sleep, I was horribly conscious of something fatally wrong. The jaw-bone tiller smote my side, which leaned against it; in my ears was the low hum of sails, just beginning to shake in the wind; I thought my eyes were open; I was half conscious of putting my fingers to the lids and mechanically stretching them still further apart. But, spite of all this, I could see no compass before me to steer by; though it seemed but a minute since I had been watching the card, by the steady binnacle lamp illuminating it. Nothing seemed before me but a jet gloom, now and then made ghastly by flashes of redness. Uppermost was the impression, that whatever swift, rushing thing I stood on was not so much bound to any haven ahead as rushing from all havens astern. A stark, bewildered feeling, as of death, came over me. Convulsively my hands grasped the tiller, but with the crazy conceit that the tiller was, somehow in some enchanted way, inverted. My God! what is the matter with me? thought I. Lo! in my brief sleep I had turned myself about, and was fronting the ship's stern, with my back to her prow and the compass. In an instant I faced back, just in time to prevent the vessel from flying up into the wind, and very probably capsizing her. How glad and how grateful the relief from this unnatural hallucination of the night, and the fatal contingency of being brought by the lee!

Look not too long in the face of the fire, O man! Never dream with thy hand on the helm! Turn not thy back to the compass; accept the first hint of the hitching tiller; believe not the artificial fire, when its redness makes all things look ghastly. To-morrow, in the natural sun, the skies will be bright; those who glared like devils in the forking flames, the morn will show in far other, at least gentler, relief; the glorious, golden, glad sun, the only true lamp—all others but liars!

Nevertheless the sun hides not Virginia's Dismal Swamp, nor Rome's accursed Campagna, nor wide Sahara, nor all the millions of miles of deserts and of griefs beneath the moon. The sun hides not the ocean, which is the dark side of this earth, and which is two thirds of this earth. So, therefore, that mortal man who hath more of joy than sorrow in him, that mortal man cannot be true—not true, or undeveloped. With books the same. The truest of all men was the Man of Sorrows, and the truest of all books is Solomon's, and Ecclesiastes is the fine hammered steel of woe. "All is vanity." ALL. This willful world hath not got hold of unchristian Solomon's wisdom yet. But he who dodges hospitals and jails, and walks fast crossing grave-yards, and would rather talk of operas than hell; calls Cowper, Young, Pascal, Rousseau, poor devils all of sick men; and throughout a care-free lifetime swears by Rabelais as passing wise, and therefore jolly;—not that man is fitted to sit down on tomb-stones, and break the green damp mold with unfathomably wondrous Solomon.

But even Solomon, he says, "the man that wandereth out of the way of understanding shall remain" (*i.e.* even while living) "in the congregation of the dead." Give not thyself up, then, to fire, lest it invert thee, deaden thee; as for the time it did me. There is a wisdom that is woe; but there is a woe that is madness. And there is a Catskill eagle in some souls that can alike dive down into the blackest gorges, and soar out of them again and become invisible in the sunny spaces. And even if he forever flies within the gorge, that gorge is in the mountains; so that even in his lowest swoop the mountain eagle is still higher than other birds upon the plain, even though they soar.

Chapter XCVII

THE LAMP

HAD YOU DESCENDED FROM THE *PEQUOD*'S TRY-WORKS TO THE *PEQUOD*'S FORECASTLE, WHERE the off duty watch were sleeping, for one single moment you would have almost thought you were standing in some illuminated shrine of canonized kings and counselors. There they lay in their triangular oaken vaults, each mariner a chiseled muteness; a score of lamps flashing upon his hooded eyes.

In merchantmen, oil for the sailor is more scarce than the milk of queens. To dress in the dark, and eat in the dark, and stumble in darkness to his pallet, this is his usual lot. But the whaleman, as he seeks the food of light, so he lives in light. He makes his berth an Aladdin's lamp, and lays him down in it; so that in the pitchiest night the ship's black hull still houses an illumination.

See with what entire freedom the whaleman takes his handful of lamps, often but old bottles and vials, though—to the copper cooler at the try-works, and replenishes them there, as mugs of ale at a vat. He burns, too, the purest of oil, in its unmanufactured, and, therefore, unvitiated state; a fluid unknown to solar, lunar, or astral contrivances ashore. It is sweet as early grass butter in April. He goes and hunts for his oil, so as to be sure of its freshness and genuineness, even as the traveler on the prairie hunts up his own supper of game.

Chapter XCVIII

STOWING DOWN AND CLEARING UP

ALREADY HAS IT BEEN RELATED HOW THE GREAT LEVIATHAN IS AFAR OFF DESCRIED FROM THE mast-head; how he is chased over the watery moors, and slaughtered in the valleys of the deep; how he is then towed alongside and beheaded; and how (on the principle which entitled the headsman of old to the garments in which the beheaded was killed) his great padded surtout becomes the property of his executioner; how, in due time, he is condemned to the pots, and, like Shadrach, Meshach, and Abednego, his spermaceti, oil, and bone pass unscathed through the fire;—but now it remains to conclude the last chapter of this part of the description by rehearsing—singing, if I may—the romantic proceeding of decanting off his oil into the casks and striking them down into the hold, where once again leviathan returns to his native profundities, sliding along beneath the surface as before; but, alas! never more to rise and blow.

While still warm, the oil, like hot punch, is received into the six-barrel casks; and while, perhaps, the ship is pitching and rolling this way and that in the midnight sea, the enormous casks are slewed round and headed over, end for end, and sometimes perilously scoot across the slippery deck, like so many land-slides, till at last man-handled and stayed in their course; and all round the hoops, rap, rap, go as many hammers as can play upon them, for now, *ex officio,* every sailor is a cooper.

At length, when the last pint is casked, and all is cool, then the great hatchways are unsealed, the bowels of the ship are thrown open, and down go the casks to their final rest in the sea. This done, the hatches are replaced, and hermetically closed, like a closet walled up.

In the sperm fishery, this is perhaps one of the most remarkable incidents in all the business of whaling. One day the planks stream with freshets of blood and oil; on the sacred quarter-deck enormous masses of the whale's head are profanely piled; great rusty casks lie about, as in a brewery yard; the smoke from the try-works has besooted all the bulwarks; the mariners go about suffused with unctuousness; the entire ship seems great leviathan himself; while on all hands the din is deafening.

But a day or two after, you look about you, and prick your ears in this selfsame ship; and were it not for the tell-tale boats and try-works, you would all but swear you trod some silent merchant-vessel, with a most scrupulously neat commander. The unmanufactured sperm oil possesses a singularly cleansing virtue. This is the reason why the decks never look so white as just after what they call an affair of oil. Besides, from the ashes of the burned scraps of the whale, a potent ley is readily made; and whenever any adhesiveness from the back of the whale remains clinging to the side, that ley quickly exterminates it. Hands go diligently along the bulwarks, and with buckets of water and rags restore them to their full tidiness. The soot is brushed from the lower rigging. All the numerous implements which have been in use are likewise faithfully cleansed and put away. The great hatch is scrubbed and placed upon the try-works, completely hiding the pots; every cask is out of sight; all tackles are coiled in unseen nooks; and when by the combined and simultaneous industry of almost the entire ship's company, the whole of their conscientious duty is at last concluded, then the crew themselves proceed to their own ablutions; shift themselves from top to toe; and finally issue to the immaculate deck, fresh and all aglow, as bridegrooms new-leaped from out the daintiest Holland.

Now, with elated step, they pace the planks in twos and threes, and humorously discourse of parlors, sofas, carpets, and fine cambrics; propose to mat the deck; think of having hangings to the top; object not to taking tea by moonlight on the piazza of the forecastle. To hint to such musked mariners of oil, and bone, and blubber, were little short of audacity. They know not the thing you distantly allude to. Away, and bring us napkins!

But mark: aloft there, at the three mast-heads, stand three men intent on spying out more whales, which, if caught, infallibly will again soil the old oaken furniture, and drop at least one small grease-spot somewhere. Yes; and many is the time, when, after the severest uninterrupted labors, which know no night; continuing straight through for ninety-six hours; when from the boat, where they have swelled their wrists with all day rowing on the Line—they only step to the deck to carry vast chains, and heave the heavy windlass, and cut and slash, yea, and in their very sweatings to be smoked and burned anew by the combined fires of the equatorial sun and the equatorial try-works; when, on the heel of all this, they have finally bestirred themselves to cleanse the ship, and make a spotless dairy room of it; many is the time the poor fellows, just buttoning the necks of their clean frocks, are startled by the cry of "There she blows!" and away they fly to fight another whale, and go through the whole weary thing again. Oh! my friends, but this is man-killing! Yet this is life. For hardly have we mortals by long toilings extracted from this world's vast bulk its small but valuable sperm; and then, with weary patience, cleansed ourselves from its defilements, and learned to live here in clean tabernacles of the soul; hardly is this done, when—*There she blows!*—the ghost is spouted up, and away we sail to fight some other world, and go through young life's old routine again.

Oh! the metempsychosis! Oh! Pythagoras, that in bright Greece, two thousand years ago, did die, so good, so wise, so mild; I sailed with thee along the Peruvian coast last voyage—and, foolish as I am, taught thee, a green simple boy, how to splice a rope.

Chapter XCIX

The Doubloon

Ere now it has been related how Ahab was wont to pace his quarter-deck, taking regular turns at either limit, the binnacle and main-mast; but in the multiplicity of other things requiring narration it has not been added how that sometimes in these walks, when most plunged in his mood, he was wont to pause in turn at each spot and stand there strangely eyeing the particular object before him. When he halted before the binnacle, with his glance fastened on the pointed needle in the compass, that glance shot like a javelin with the pointed intensity of his purpose; and when resuming his walk he again paused before the main-mast, then, as the same riveted glance fastened upon the riveted gold coin there, he still wore the same aspect of nailed firmness, only dashed with a certain wild longing, if not hopefulness.

But one morning, turning to pass the doubloon, he seemed to be newly attracted by the strange figures and inscriptions stamped on it, as though now for the first time beginning to interpret for himself in some monomaniac way whatever significance might lurk in them. And some certain significance lurks in all things, else all things are little worth, and the round world itself but an empty cipher, except to sell by the cartload, as they do hills about Boston, to fill up some morass in the Milky Way.

Now this doubloon was of purest, virgin gold, raked somewhere out of the heart of gorgeous hills, whence, east and west, over golden sands, the head-waters of many a pactolus flows. And though now nailed amidst all the rustiness of iron bolts and the verdigris of copper spikes, yet, untouchable and immaculate to any foulness, it still preserved its Quito glow. Nor, though placed amongst a ruthless crew and every hour passed by ruthless hands, and through the livelong nights shrouded with thick darkness which might cover any pilfering approach, nevertheless every sunrise found the doubloon where the sunset last left it last. For it was set apart and sanctified to one awe-striking end; and however wanton in their sailor ways, one and all, the mariners revered it as the white whale's talisman. Sometimes they talked it over in the weary watch by night, wondering whose it was to be at last, and whether he would ever live to spend it.

Now those noble golden coins of South America are as medals of the sun and tropic token pieces. Here palms, alpacas, and volcanoes; sun's disks and stars; ecliptics, horns-of-plenty, and rich banners waving, are in luxuriant profusion stamped; so that the precious gold seems almost to derive an added preciousness and enhancing glories, by passing through those fancy mints, so Spanishly poetic.

It so chanced that the doubloon of the *Pequod* was a most wealthy example of these things. In its round border it bore the letters, REPUBLICA DEL ECUADOR: QUITO. So this bright coin came from a country planted in the middle of the world, and beneath the great equator, and named after it; and it had been cast midway up the Andes, in the unwaning clime that knows no autumn. Zoned by those letters you saw the likeness of three Andes' summits; from one a flame; a tower on another; on the third a crowing cock; while arching over all was a segment of the partitioned zodiac, the signs all marked with their usual cabalistics, and the key-stone sun entering the equinoctial point at Libra.

Before this equatorial coin, Ahab, not unobserved by others, was now pausing.

"There's something ever egotistical in mountain-tops and towers, and all other grand and lofty things; look here—three peaks as proud as Lucifer. The firm tower, that is Ahab; the volcano, that is Ahab; the courageous, the undaunted, and victorious fowl, that, too, is Ahab; all are Ahab; and this round gold is but the image of the rounder globe, which, like a magician's glass, to each and every man in turn but mirrors back his own mysterious self. Great pains, small gains for those who ask the world to solve them; it cannot solve itself. Methinks now this coined sun wears a ruddy face; but see! ay, he enters the sign of storms, the equinox! and but six months before he wheeled out of a former equinox at Aries! From storm to storm! So be it, then. Born in throes, 'tis fit that man should live in pains and die in pangs! So be it, then! Here's stout stuff for woe to work on. So be it, then."

"No fairy fingers can have pressed the gold, but devil's claws must have left their moldings there since yesterday," murmured Starbuck to himself, leaning against the bulwarks. "The old man seems to read Belshazzar's awful writing. I have never marked the coin inspectingly. He goes below; let me read. A dark valley between three mighty, heaven-abiding peaks, that almost seem the Trinity, in some faint earthly symbol. So in this vale of Death, God girds us round; and over all our gloom, the sun of Righteousness still shines a beacon and a hope. If we bend down our eyes, the dark vale shows her moldy soil; but if we lift them, the bright sun meets our glance half-way, to cheer. Yet, oh, the great sun is no fixture; and if, at midnight, we would fain snatch some sweet solace from him, we gaze for him in vain! This coin speaks wisely, mildly, truly, but still sadly to me. I will quit it, lest Truth shake me falsely."

"There now's the old Mogul," soliloquized Stubb by the try-works, "he's been twigging it; and there goes Starbuck from the same, and both with faces which I should say might be somewhere within nine fathoms long. And all from looking at a piece of gold, which did I have it now on Negro Hill or in Corlaer's Hook, I'd not look at it very long ere spending it. Humph! in my poor, insignificant opinion, I regard this as queer. I have seen doubloons before now in my voyagings; your doubloons of old Spain, your doubloons of Peru, your doubloons of Chile, your doubloons of Bolivia, your doubloons of Popayan; with plenty of gold moidores and pistoles, and joes, and half joes, and quarter joes. What then should there be in this doubloon of the Equator that is so killing wonderful? By Golconda! let me read it once. Halloa! here's signs and wonders truly! That, now, is what old Bowditch in his Epitome calls the zodiac, and what my almanac below calls ditto. I'll get the almanac; and as I have heard devils can be raised with Daboll's arithmetic, I'll try my hand at raising a meaning out of these queer curvicues here with the Massachusetts calendar. Here's the book. Let's see now. Signs and wonders; and the sun, he's always among 'em. Hem, hem, hem; here they are—here they go—all alive—Aries, or the Ram; Taurus, or the Bull and Jimimi! here's Gemini himself, or the Twins. Well; the sun he wheels among 'em. Ay, here on the coin he's just crossing the threshold between two of twelve sitting-rooms all in a ring. Book! you lie there; the fact is, you books must know your places. You'll do to give us the bare words and facts, but we come in to supply the thoughts. That's my small experience, so far as the Massachusetts calendar, and Bowditch's navigator, and Daboll's arithmetic go. Signs and wonders, eh? Pity if there is nothing wonderful in signs, and significant in wonders! There's a clue somewhere; wait a bit; hist—hark! By Jove, I have it! Look you, Doubloon, your zodiac here is the life of man in one round chapter; and now I'll read it off, straight out of the book. Come, Almanac! To begin: there's Aries, or the Ram—lecherous dog, he begets us; then, Taurus, or the Bull—he bumps us the first thing; then Gemini, or the Twins—that is, Virtue and Vice; we try to reach Virtue, when lo! comes Cancer the Crab, and drags us back; and here, going from Virtue, Leo, a roaring Lion, lies in the path—he gives a few fierce bites and surly dabs with his paw; we escape, and hail Virgo, the Virgin! that's our first love; we marry and think to be happy for aye, when pop comes Libra, or the Scales—happiness weighed and found wanting; and while we are very sad about that, Lord! how we suddenly jump, as Scorpio, or the Scorpion, stings us in the rear; we are curing the wound, when whang comes the arrows all round; Sagittarius, or the Archer, is amusing himself. As we pluck out the shafts, stand aside! here's the battering-ram, Capricornus, or the Goat; full tilt, he comes rushing, and headlong we are tossed; when Aquarius, or the Water-bearer, pours out his whole deluge and drowns us; and to wind up with Pisces, or the Fishes, we sleep. There's a sermon now, writ in high heaven, and the sun goes through it every year, and yet comes out of it all alive and hearty. Jollily he, aloft there, wheels through toil and trouble; and so, alow here, does jolly Stubb. Oh, jolly's the word for aye! Adieu, Doubloon! But stop; here comes little King-Post; dodge round the try-works, now, and let's hear what he'll have to say. There; he's before it; he'll out with something presently. So, so; he's beginning."

"I see nothing here, but a round thing made of gold, and whoever raises a certain whale, this round thing belongs to him. So, what's all this staring been about? It is worth sixteen dollars, that's true; and at two cents the cigar, that's nine hundred and sixty cigars. I won't smoke dirty pipes like Stubb, but I like cigars, and here's nine hundred and sixty of them; so here goes Flask aloft to spy 'em out."

"Shall I call that wise or foolish, now; if it be really wise it has a foolish look to it; yet, if it be really foolish, then has it a sort of wiseish look to it. But, avast; here comes our old Manxman—the old hearse-driver, he must have been, that is, before he took to the sea. He luffs up before the doubloon; halloa, and goes round on the other side of the mast; why, there's a horse-shoe nailed on that side; and now he's back again; what does that mean? Hark! he's muttering—voice like an old worn-out coffee-mill. Prick ears, and listen!"

"If the White Whale be raised, it must be in a month and a day, when the sun stands in some one of these signs. I've studied signs, and know their marks; they were taught me two score years ago, by the old witch in Copenhagen. Now, in what sign will the sun then be? The horse-shoe sign; for there it is, right opposite the gold. And what's the horse-shoe sign? The lion is the horse-shoe sign—the roaring and devouring lion. Ship, old ship! my old head shakes to think of thee."

"There's another rendering now; but still one text. All sorts of men in one kind of world, you see. Dodge again! here comes Queequeg—all tattooing—looks like the signs of the Zodiac himself. What says the Cannibal? As I live he's comparing notes; looking at his thigh bone; thinks the sun is in the thigh, or in the calf, or in the bowels, I suppose, as the old women talk Surgeon's Astronomy in the back country. And by Jove, he's found something there in the vicinity of his thigh—I guess it's Sagittarius, or the Archer. No: he don't know what to make of the doubloon; he takes it for an old button off some king's trousers. But, aside again! here comes that ghost-devil, Fedallah; tail coiled out of sight as usual, oakum in the toes of his pumps as usual. What does he say, with that look of his? Ah, only makes a sign to the sign and bows himself; there is a sun on the coin—fire worshiper, depend upon it. Ho! more and more. This way comes Pip—poor boy! would he had died, or I; he's half horrible to me. He too has been watching all of these interpreters—myself included—and look now, he comes to read, with that unearthly idiot face. Stand away again and hear him. Hark!"

"I look, you look, he looks; we look, ye look, they look."

"Upon my soul, he's been studying Murray's *Grammar*! Improving his mind, poor fellow! But what's that he says now—hist!"

"I look, you look, he looks; we look, ye look, they look."

"Why, he's getting it by heart—hist! again."

"I look, you look, he looks; we look, ye look, they look."

"Well, that's funny."

"And I, you, and he; and we, ye, and they, are all bats; and I'm a crow, especially when I stand atop of this pine-tree here. Caw! caw! caw! caw! caw! caw! Ain't I a crow? And where's the scare-crow? There he stands; two bones stuck into a pair of old trousers, and two more poked into the sleeves of an old jacket."

"Wonder if he means me?—complimentary!—poor lad!—I could go hang myself. Anyway, for the present, I'll quit Pip's vicinity. I can stand the rest, for they have plain wits; but he's too crazy-witty for my sanity. So, so, I leave him muttering."

"Here's the ship's navel, this doubloon here, and they are all one fire to unscrew it. But, unscrew your navel, and what's the consequence? Then again, if it stays here, that is ugly, too, for when aught's nailed to the mast it's a sign that things grow desperate. Ha, ha! old Ahab! the White Whale; he'll nail ye! This is a pine-tree. My father, in old Tolland county, cut down a pine-tree once, and found a silver ring grown over in it; some old darkey's wedding ring. How did it get there? And so they'll say in the resurrection when they come to fish up this old mast, and find a doubloon lodged in it, with bedded oysters for the shaggy bark. Oh, the gold! the precious, precious gold!—the green miser 'll hoard ye soon! Hish! hish! God goes 'mong the worlds blackberrying. Cook! ho, cook! and cook us! Jenny hey, hey, hey, hey, hey, Jenny, Jenny! and get your hoe-cake done!"

Chapter C

LEG AND ARM

THE *PEQUOD,* OF NANTUCKET, MEETS THE *SAMUEL ENDERBY,* OF LONDON

SHIP, AHOY! HAST SEEN THE WHITE WHALE?"

So cried Ahab, once more hailing a ship showing English colors, bearing down under the stern. Trumpet to mouth, the old man was standing in his hoisted quarter-deck, his ivory leg plainly revealed to the stranger captain, who was carelessly reclining in his own boat's bow. He was a darkly-tanned, burly, good-natured, fine-looking man, of sixty or thereabouts, dressed in a spacious roundabout, that hung round him in festoons of blue pilot-cloth; and one empty arm of this jacket streamed behind him like the broidered arm of a huzzar's surcoat.

"Hast seen the White Whale?"

"See you this?" and withdrawing it from the folds that had hidden it, he held up a white arm of sperm-whale bone, terminating in a wooden head like a mallet.

"Man my boat!" cried Ahab, impetuously, and tossing about the oars near him—"Stand by to lower!"

In less than a minute, without quitting his little craft, he and his crew were dropped to the water, and were soon alongside of the stranger. But here a curious difficulty presented itself. In the excitement of the moment, Ahab had forgotten that since the loss of his leg he had never once stepped on board of any vessel at sea but his own, and then it was always by an ingenious and very handy mechanical contrivance peculiar to the *Pequod,* and a thing not to be rigged and shipped in any other vessel at a moment's warning. Now, it is no very easy matter for anybody—except those who are almost hourly used to it, like whalemen—to clamber up a ship's side from a boat on the open sea; for the great swells now lift the boat high up towards the bulwarks, and then instantaneously drop it halfway down to the kelson. So, deprived of one leg and the strange ship of course being altogether unsupplied with the kindly invention, Ahab now found himself abjectly reduced to a clumsy landsman again; hopelessly eyeing the uncertain changeful height he could hardly hope to attain.

It has before been hinted, perhaps, that every little untoward circumstance that befell him, and which indirectly sprang from his luckless mishap, almost invariably irritated or exasperated Ahab. And in the present instance, all this was heightened by the sight of the two officers of the strange ship, leaning over the side, by the perpendicular ladder of nailed cleets there, and swinging towards him a pair of tastefully-ornamented man-ropes; for at first they did not seem to bethink them that a one-legged man must be too much of a cripple to use their sea bannisters. But this awkwardness only lasted a minute, because the strange captain, observing at a glance how affairs stood, cried out, "I see, I see!—avast heaving there! Jump, boys, and swing over the cutting-tackle."

As good luck would have it, they had had a whale alongside a day or two previous, and the great tackles were still aloft, and the massive curved blubber-hook, now clean and dry, was still attached to the end. This was quickly lowered to Ahab, who at once comprehending it all, slid his solitary thigh into the curve of the hook (it was like sitting in the fluke of an anchor, or the crotch of an apple tree), and then giving the word, held himself fast, and at the same time also helped to hoist his own weight, by pulling hand-over-hand upon one of the running parts of the tackle. Soon he was carefully swung inside the high bulwarks, and gently landed upon the capstan head. With his ivory arm frankly thrust forth in welcome, the other captain advanced, and Ahab, putting out his ivory leg, and crossing the ivory arm (like two sword-fish blades) cried out in his walrus way, "Ay, ay, hearty! let us shake bones together!—an arm and a leg!—an arm that never can shrink, d'ye see; and a leg that never can run. Where did'st thou see the White Whale?—how long ago?"

"The White Whale," said the Englishman, pointing his ivory arm towards the East, and taking a rueful sight along it, as if it had been a telescope. There I saw him, on the Line, last season."

"And he took that arm off, did he?" asked Ahab, now sliding down from the capstan, and resting on the Englishman's shoulder, as he did so.

"Ay, he was the cause of it, at least; and that leg, too?"

"Spin me the yarn," said Ahab; "how was it?"

"It was the first time in my life that I ever cruised on the Line," began the Englishman. "I was ignorant of the White Whale at that time. Well, one day we lowered for a pod of four or five whales, and my boat fastened to one of them; a regular circus horse he was, too, that went milling and milling round so that my boat's crew could only trim dish, by sitting all their sterns on the outer gunwale. Presently up breaches from the bottom of the sea a bouncing great whale, with a milky-white head and hump, all crows' feet and wrinkles."

"It was he, it was he!" cried Ahab, suddenly letting out his suspended breath.

"And harpoons sticking in near his starboard fin."

"Ay, ay—they were mine—*my* irons," cried Ahab, exultingly—"but on!"

"Give me a chance, then," said the Englishman, good-humoredly. "Well, this old great-grandfather, with the white head and hump, runs all afoam into the pod, and goes to snapping furiously at my fast-line!"

"Ay, I see!—wanted to part it; free the fast-fish—an old trick—I know him."

"How it was exactly," continued the one-armed commander, "I do not know; but in biting the line, it got foul of his teeth, caught there somehow; but we didn't know it then; so that when we afterwards pulled on the line, bounce we came plump on to his hump! instead of the other whale's that went off to windward, all fluking. Seeing how matters stood, and what a noble great whale it was—the noblest and biggest I ever saw, sir, in my life—I resolved to capture him, spite of the boiling rage he seemed to be in. And thinking the haphazard line would get loose, or the tooth it was tangled to might draw (for I have a devil of a boat's crew for a pull on a whale-line); seeing all this, I say, I jumped into my first mate's boat—Mr. Mounttop's here (by the way, Captain—Mounttop; Mounttop—the captain);—as I was saying, I jumped into Mounttop's boat, which, d'ye see, was gunwale and gunwale with mine, then; and snatching the first harpoon, let this old great-grandfather have it. But, Lord, look you, sir—hearts and souls alive, man—the next instant, in a jiff, I was blind as a bat—both eyes out—all befogged and bedeadened with black foam—the whale's tail looming straight up out of it, perpendicular in the air, like a marble steeple. No use sterning all, then; but as I was groping at mid-day, with a blinding sun, all crown-jewels; as I was groping, I say, after the second iron, to toss it overboard—down comes the tail like a Lima tower, cutting my boat in two, leaving each half in splinters; and, flukes first, the white hump backed through the wreck, as though it was all chips. We all struck out. To escape his terrible flailings, I seized hold of my harpoon-pole sticking in him, and for a moment clung to that like a sucking fish. But a combing sea dashed me off, and, at the same instant, the fish, taking one good dart forwards, went down like a flash; and the barb of that cursed second iron towing along near me caught me here" (clapping his hand just below his shoulder); "yes, caught me just here, I say, and bore me down to Hell's flames, I was thinking; when, when, all of a sudden, thank the good God, the barb ripped its way along the flesh—clear along the whole length of my arm—came out nigh my wrist, and up I floated;—and that gentleman there will tell you the rest (by the way, captain—Dr. Bunger, ship's surgeon: Bunger, my lad—the captain). Now, Bunger boy, spin your part of the yarn."

The professional gentleman thus familiarly pointed out, had been all the time standing near them, with nothing specific visible, to denote his gentlemanly rank on board. His face was an exceedingly round but sober one; he was dressed in a faded blue woolen frock or shirt, and patched trousers; and had thus far been dividing his attention between a marling-spike he held in one hand, and a pill-box held in the other, occasionally casting a critical glance at the ivory limbs of the two crippled captains. But, at his superior's introduction of him to Ahab, he politely bowed, and straightway went on to do his captain's bidding.

"It was a shocking bad wound," began the whale-surgeon; "and taking my advice, Captain Boomer here, stood our old *Sammy*—"

"*Samuel Enderby* is the name of my ship," interrupted the one-armed captain, addressing Ahab; "go on, boy."

"Stood our old *Sammy* off to the northward, to get out of the blazing hot weather there on the Line. But it was no use—I did all I could; sat up with him nights; was very severe with him in the matter of diet—"

"Oh, very severe!" chimed in the patient himself; then suddenly altering his voice, "Drinking hot rum toddies with me every night, till he couldn't see to put on the bandages; and sending me to bed, half seas over, about three o'clock in the morning. Oh, ye stars! he sat up with me indeed, and was very severe in my diet. Oh! a great watcher, and very dietetically severe, is Dr. Bunger. (Bunger, you dog, laugh out! why don't ye? You know you're a precious jolly rascal.) But, heave ahead, boy, I'd rather be killed by you than kept alive by any other man."

"My captain, you must have ere this perceived, respected sir"—said the imperturbable godly-looking Bunger, slightly bowing to Ahab—"is apt to be facetious at times; he spins us many clever things of that sort. But I may as well say—en passant, as the French remark—that I myself—that is to say, Jack Bunger, late of the reverend clergy—am a strict total abstinence man; I never drink—"

"Water!" cried the captain; "he never drinks it; it's a sort of fits to him; fresh water throws him into the hydrophobia; but go on—go on with the arm story."

"Yes, I may as well," said the surgeon, coolly. "I was about observing, sir, before Captain Boomer's facetious interruption, that spite of my best and severest endeavors, the wound kept getting worse and worse; the truth was, sir, it was as ugly gaping wound as surgeon ever saw; more than two feet and several inches long. I measured it with the lead line. In short, it grew black; I knew what was threatened, and off it came. But I had no hand in shipping that ivory arm there; that thing is against all rule"—pointing at it with the marling-spike—"that is the captain's work, not mine; he ordered the carpenter to make it; he had that club-hammer there put to the end, to knock someone's brains out with, I suppose, as he tried mine once. He flies into diabolical passions sometimes. Do ye see this dent, sir"—removing his hat, and brushing aside his hair, and exposing a bowl-like cavity in his skull, but which bore not the slightest scarry trace, or any token of ever having been a wound—"Well, the captain there will tell you how that came here; he knows."

"No, I don't," said the captain, "but his mother did; he was born with it. Oh, you solemn rogue, you—you Bunger! was there ever such another Bunger in the watery world? Bunger, when you die, you ought to die in pickle, you dog; you should be preserved to future ages, you rascal."

"What became of the White Whale?" now cried Ahab, who thus far had been impatiently listening to this bye-play between the two Englishmen.

"Oh!" cried the one-armed captain, "oh, yes! Well; after he sounded, we didn't see him again for some time; in fact, as I before hinted, I didn't then know what whale it was that had served me such a trick, till some time afterwards, when coming back to the Line, we heard about Moby-Dick—as some call him—and then I knew it was he."

"Did'st thou cross his wake again?"

"Twice."

"But could not fasten?"

"Didn't want to try to; ain't one limb enough? What should I do without this other arm? And I'm thinking Moby-Dick doesn't bite so much as he swallows."

"Well, then," interrupted Bunger, "give him your left arm for bait to get the right. Do you know, gentlemen"—very gravely and mathematically bowing to each Captain in succession—"do you know, gentlemen, that the digestive organs of the whale are so inscrutably constructed by Divine Providence, that it is quite impossible for him to completely digest even a man's arm? And he knows it, too. So that what you take for the White Whale's malice is only his awkwardness. For he never means to swallow a single limb; he only thinks to terrify by feints. But sometimes he is like the old juggling fellow, formerly a patient of mine in Ceylon, that making believe swallow jack-knives, once upon a time let one drop into him in good earnest, and there it stayed for a twelvemonth or more; when I gave him an emetic, and he heaved it up in small tacks, d'ye see. No possible way for him to digest that jack-knife, and fully incorporate it into his general bodily system. Yes, Captain Boomer, if you are quick enough about it, and have a mind to pawn one arm for the sake of the privilege of giving decent burial to the other, why in that case the arm is yours; only let the whale have another chance at you shortly, that's all."

"No, thank you, Bunger," said the English Captain, "he's welcome to the arm he has, since I can't help it, and didn't know him then; but not to another one. No more White Whales for me; I've lowered for him once, and that has satisfied me. There would be great glory in killing him, I know that; and there is a ship-load of precious sperm in him, but, hark ye, he's best let alone; don't you think so, Captain?"—glancing at the ivory leg.

"He is. But he will still be hunted, for all that. What is best let alone, that accursed thing is not always what least allures. He's all a magnet! How long since thou saw'st him last? Which way heading?"

"Bless my soul, and curse the foul fiend's," cried Bunger, stoopingly walking round Ahab, and like a dog, strangely snuffing; "this man's blood—bring the thermometer!—it's at the boiling point!—his pulse makes these planks beat!—sir!"—taking a lancet from his pocket, and drawing near to Ahab's arm.

"Avast!" roared Ahab, dashing him against the bulwarks—"Man the boat! Which way heading?"

"Good God!" cried the English Captain, to whom the question was put. "What's the matter? He was heading east, I think.—Is your Captain crazy?" whispering Fedallah.

But Fedallah, putting a finger on his lip, slid over the bulwarks to take the boat's steering oar, and Ahab, swinging the cutting-tackle towards him, commanded the ship's sailors to stand by to lower.

In a moment he was standing in the boat's stern, and the Manila men were springing to their oars. In vain the English Captain hailed him. With back to the stranger ship, and face set like a flint to his own, Ahab stood upright till alongside of the *Pequod*.

Chapter CI

THE DECANTER

ERE THE ENGLISH SHIP FADES FROM SIGHT, BE IT SET DOWN HERE, THAT SHE HAILED FROM London, and was named after the late Samuel Enderby, merchant of that city, the original of the famous whaling house of Enderby and Sons; a house which in my poor whaleman's opinion, comes not far behind the united royal houses of the Tudors and Bourbons, in point of real historical interest. How long, prior to the year of our Lord 1775, this great whaling house was in existence, my numerous fish-documents do not make plain; but in that year (1775) it fitted out the first English ships that ever regularly hunted the Sperm Whale; though for some score of years previous (ever since 1726) our valiant Coffins and Maceys of Nantucket and the Vineyard had in large fleets pursued the Leviathan, but only in the North and South Atlantic: not elsewhere. Be it distinctly recorded here, that the Nantucketers were the first among mankind to harpoon with civilized steel the great Sperm Whale; and that for half a century they were the only people of the whole globe who so harpooned him.

In 1778, a fine ship, the *Amelia*, fitted out for the express purpose, and at the sole charge of the vigorous Enderbys, boldly rounded Cape Horn, and was the first among the nations to lower a whale-boat of any sort in the great South Sea. The voyage was a skillful and lucky one; and returning to her berth with her hold full of the precious sperm, the *Amelia*'s example was soon followed by other ships, English and American, and thus the vast Sperm-Whale grounds of the Pacific were thrown open. But not content with this good deed, the indefatigable house again bestirred itself: Samuel and all his Sons—how many, their mother only knows—and under their immediate auspices, and partly, I think, at their expense, the British government was induced to send the sloop-of-war *Rattler* on a whaling voyage of discovery into the South Sea. Commanded by a naval Post-Captain, the *Rattler* made a rattling voyage of it, and did some service; how much does not appear. But this is not all. In 1819, the same house fitted out a discovery whale-ship of their own, to go on a tasting cruise to the remote waters of Japan. That ship—well called the *Syren*—made a noble experimental cruise; and it was thus that the great Japanese Whaling Ground first became generally known. The *Syren* in this famous voyage was commanded by a Captain Coffin, a Nantucketer.

All honor to the Enderbies, therefore, whose house, I think, exists to the present day; though doubtless the original Samuel must long ago have slipped his cable for the great South Sea of the other world.

The ship named after him was worthy of the honor, being a very fast sailer and a noble craft every way. I boarded her once at midnight somewhere off the Patagonian coast, and drank good flip down in the forecastle. It was a fine gam we had, and they were all trumps—every soul on board. A short life to them, and a jolly death. And that fine gam I had—long, very long after old Ahab touched her planks with his ivory heel—it minds me of the noble, solid, Saxon hospitality of that ship; and may my parson forget me, and the devil remember me, if I ever lose sight of it. Flip? Did I say we had flip? Yes, and we flipped it at the rate of ten gallons the hour; and when the squall came (for it's squally off there by Patagonia), and all hands—visitors and all—were called to reef top-sails, we were so top-heavy that we had to swing each other aloft in bowlines; and we ignorantly furled the skirts of our jackets into the sails, so that we hung there, reefed fast in the howling gale, a warning example to all drunken tars. However, the masts did not go overboard; and by and by we scrambled down, so sober that we had to pass the flip again, though the savage salt spray bursting down the forecastle scuttle, rather too much diluted and pickled it for my taste.

The beef was fine—tough, but with body in it. They said it was bull-beef; others, that it was dromedary beef; but I do not know, for certain, how that was. They had dumplings too; small, but substantial, symmetrically globular, and indestructible dumplings. I fancied that you could feel them, and roll them about in you after they were swallowed. If you stooped over too far forward, you risked their pitching out of you like billiard-balls. The bread—but that couldn't be helped; besides, it was an anti-scorbutic; in short, the bread contained the only fresh fare they had. But the forecastle was not very light, and it was very easy to step over into a dark corner when you ate it. But all in all, taking her from truck to helm, considering the dimensions of the cook's boilers, including his own live parchment boilers; fore and aft, I say, the *Samuel Enderby* was a jolly ship; of good fare and plenty; fine flip and strong; crack fellows all, and capital from boot heels to hat-band.

But why was it, think ye, that the *Samuel Enderby,* and some other English whalers I know of—not all though—were such famous, hospitable ships; that passed round the beef, and the bread, and the can, and the joke; and were not soon weary of eating, and drinking, and laughing? I will tell you. The abounding good cheer of these English whalers is matter for historical research. Nor have I been at all sparing of historical whale research, when it has seemed needed.

The English were preceded in the whale fishery by the Hollanders, Zealanders, and Danes; from whom they derived many terms still extant in the fishery; and what is yet more, their fat old fashions, touching plenty to eat and drink. For, as a general thing, the English merchant-ship scrimps her crew; but not so the English whaler. Hence, in the English, this thing of whaling good cheer is not normal and natural, but incidental and particular; and, therefore, must have some special origin, which is here pointed out, and will be still further elucidated.

During my researches in the Leviathanic histories, I stumbled upon an ancient Dutch volume, which, by the musty whaling smell of it, I knew must be about whalers. The title was, *Dan Coopman,* wherefore I concluded that this must be the invaluable memoirs of some Amsterdam cooper in the fishery, as every whale-ship must carry its cooper. I was reinforced in this opinion by seeing that it was the production of one "Fitz Swackhammer." But my friend Dr. Snodhead, a very learned man, professor of Low Dutch and High German in the college of Santa Claus and St. Pott's, to whom I handed the work for translation, giving him a box of sperm candles for his trouble—this same Dr. Snodhead, so soon as he spied the book, assured me that "Dan Coopman" did not mean "The Cooper," but "The Merchant." In short, this ancient and learned Low Dutch book treated of the commerce of Holland; and, among other subjects, contained a very interesting account of its whale fishery. And in this chapter it was, headed, "Smeer," or "Fat," that I found a long detailed list of the outfits for the larders and cellars of 180 sail of Dutch whalemen; from which list, as translated by Dr. Snodhead, I transcribe the following:

400,000 lbs. of beef.
60,000 lbs. Friesland pork.
150,000 lbs. of stock-fish.
550,000 lbs. of biscuit.
72,000 lbs. of soft bread.
2,800 firkins of butter.
20,000 lbs. of Texel & Leyden cheese.
144,000 lbs. cheese (probably an inferior article).
550 ankers of Geneva.
10,800 barrels of beer.

Most statistical tables are parchingly dry in the reading; not so in the present case, however, where the reader is flooded with whole pipes, barrels, quarts, and gills of good gin and good cheer.

At the time, I devoted three days to the studious digesting of all this beer, beef, and bread, during which many profound thoughts were incidentally suggested to me, capable of a transcendental and Platonic application; and, furthermore, I compiled supplementary tables of my own, touching the probable quantity of stock-fish, &c., consumed by every Low Dutch harpooneer in that ancient Greenland and Spitzbergen whale fishery. In the first place, the amount of butter, and Texel and Leyden cheese consumed, seems amazing. I impute it, though, to their naturally unctuous natures, being rendered still more unctuous by the nature of their vocation, and especially by their pursuing their game in those frigid Polar Seas, on the very coasts of that Esquimaux country where the convivial natives pledge each other in bumpers of train oil.

The quantity of the beer, too, is very large, 10,800 barrels. Now, as those polar fisheries could only be prosecuted in the short summer of that climate, so that the whole cruise of one of these Dutch whalemen, including the short voyage to and from the Spitzbergen sea, did not much exceed three months, say, and reckoning 30 men to each of their fleet of 180 sail, we have 5,400 Low Dutch seamen in all; therefore, I say, we have precisely two barrels of beer per man, for a twelve weeks' allowance, exclusive of his fair proportion of that 550 ankers of gin. Now, whether these gin and beer harpooneers, so fuddled as one might fancy them to have been, were the right sort of men to stand up in a boat's head, and take good aim at flying whales; this would seem somewhat improbable. Yet they did aim at them, and hit them too. But this was very far North, be it remembered, where beer agrees well with the constitution; upon the Equator, in our southern fishery, beer would be apt to make the harpooneer sleepy at the mast-head and boozy in his boat; and grievous loss might ensue to Nantucket and New Bedford.

But no more; enough has been said to show that the old Dutch whalers of two or three centuries ago were high-livers; and that the English whalers have not neglected so excellent an example. For, say they, when cruising in an empty ship, if you can get nothing better out of the world, get a good dinner out of it, at least. And this empties the decanter.

Chapter CII

A Bower in the Arsacides

HITHERTO, IN DESCRIPTIVELY TREATING OF THE SPERM WHALE, I HAVE CHIEFLY DWELT UPON THE marvels of his outer aspect; or separately and in detail upon some few interior structural features. But to a large and thorough sweeping comprehension of him, it behooves me now to unbutton him still further, and untagging the points of his hose, unbuckling his garters, and casting loose the hooks and the eyes of the joints of his innermost bones, set him before you in his ultimatum; that is to say, in his unconditional skeleton.

But how now, Ishmael? How is it, that you, a mere oarsman in the fishery, pretend to know aught about the subterranean parts of the whale? Did erudite Stubb, mounted upon your capstan, deliver lectures on the anatomy of the Cetacea; and by help of the windlass, hold up a specimen rib for exhibition? Explain thyself, Ishmael. Can you land a full-grown whale on your deck for examination, as a cook dishes a roast-pig? Surely not. A veritable witness have you hitherto been, Ishmael; but have a care how you seize the privilege of Jonah alone; the privilege of discoursing upon the joists and beams; the rafters, ridge-pole, sleepers, and under-pinnings, making up the frame-work of leviathan; and belike of the tallow-vats, dairy-rooms, butteries, and cheeseries in his bowels.

I confess, that since Jonah, few whalemen have penetrated very far beneath the skin of the adult whale; nevertheless, I have been blessed with an opportunity to dissect him in miniature. In a ship I belonged to, a small cub Sperm Whale was once bodily hoisted to the deck for his poke or bag, to make sheaths for the barbs of the harpoons, and for the heads of the lances. Think you I let that chance go, without using my boat-hatchet and jack-knife, and breaking the seal and reading all the contents of that young cub?

And as for my exact knowledge of the bones of the leviathan in their gigantic, full grown development, for that rare knowledge I am indebted to my late royal friend Tranquo, king of Tranque, one of the Arsacides. For being at Tranque, years ago, when attached to the trading-ship *Dey* of Algiers, I was invited to spend part of the Arsacidean holidays with the lord of Tranque, at his retired palm villa at Pupella; a sea-side glen not very far distant from what our sailors called Bamboo-Town, his capital.

Among many other fine qualities, my royal friend Tranquo, being gifted with a devout love for all matters of barbaric vertu, had brought together in Pupella whatever rare things the more ingenious of his people could invent; chiefly carved woods of wonderful devices, chiseled shells, inlaid spears, costly paddles, aromatic canoes; and all these distributed among whatever natural wonders, the wonder-freighted, tribute-rendering waves had cast upon his shores.

Chief among these latter was a great Sperm Whale, which, after an unusually long raging gale, had been found dead and stranded, with his head against a cocoanut-tree, whose plumage-like, tufted droopings seemed his verdant jet. When the vast body had at last been stripped of its fathom-deep enfoldings, and the bones become dust dry in the sun, then the skeleton was carefully transported up the Pupella glen, where a grand temple of lordly palms now sheltered it.

The ribs were hung with trophies; the vertebrae were carved with Arsacidean animals, in strange hieroglyphics; in the skull, the priests kept up an unextinguished aromatic flame, so that the mystic head again sent forth its vapory spout; while, suspended from a bough, the terrific lower jaw vibrated over all the devotees, like the hair-hung sword that so affrighted Damocles.

It was a wondrous sight. The wood was green as mosses of the Icy Glen; the trees stood high and haughty, feeling their living sap; the industrious earth beneath was as a weaver's loom, with a gorgeous carpet on it, whereof the ground-vine tendrils formed the warp and woof, and the living flowers the figures. All the trees, with all their laden branches; all the shrubs, and ferns, and grasses; the message-carrying air; all these unceasingly were active. Through the lacings of the leaves, the great sun seemed a flying shuttle weaving the unwearied verdure. Oh, busy weaver! unseen weaver!—pause!—one word!—whither flows the fabric? what palace may it deck? wherefore all these ceaseless toilings? Speak, weaver!—stay thy hand!—but one single word with thee! Nay—the shuttle flies—the figures float from forth the loom; the freshet-rushing carpet forever slides away. The weaver-god, he weaves; and by that weaving is he deafened, that he hears no mortal voice; and by that humming, we, too, who look on the loom are deafened; and only when we escape it shall we hear the thousand voices that speak through it. For even so it is in all material factories. The spoken words that are inaudible among the flying spindles; those same words are plainly heard without the walls, bursting from the opened casements. Thereby have villainies been detected. Ah, mortal! then, be heedful; for so, in all this din of the great world's loom, thy subtlest thinkings may be overheard afar.

Now, amid the green life-restless loom of that Arsacidean wood, the great, white, worshiped skeleton lay lounging—a gigantic idler! Yet, as the ever-woven verdant warp and woof intermixed and hummed around him, the mighty idler seemed the cunning weaver; himself all woven over with the vines; every month assuming greener, fresher verdure; but himself a skeleton. Life folded Death; Death trellised Life; the grim god wived with youthful Life, and begat him curly-headed glories.

Now, when with royal Tranquo I visited this wondrous whale, and saw the skull an altar, and the artificial smoke ascending from where the real jet had issued, I marveled that the king should regard a chapel as an object of vertùe. He laughed. But more I marveled that the priests should swear that smoky jet of his was genuine. To and fro I paced before this skeleton—brushed the vines aside—broke through the ribs—and with a ball of Arsacidean twine, wandered, eddied long amid its many winding, shaded colonnades and arbors. But soon my line was out; and following it back, I emerged from the opening where I entered. I saw no living thing within; naught was there but bones.

Cutting me a green measuring-rod, I once more dived within the skeleton. From their arrow-slit in the skull, the priests perceived me taking the altitude of the final rib. "How now!" they shouted; "Dar'st thou measure this our god! That's for us." "Ay, priests—well, how long do ye make him, then?" But hereupon a fierce contest rose among them, concerning feet and inches; they cracked each other's sconces with their yard-sticks—the great skull echoed—and seizing that lucky chance, I quickly concluded my own admeasurements.

These admeasurements I now propose to set before you. But first, be it recorded, that, in this matter, I am not free to utter any fancied measurements I please. Because there are skeleton authorities you can refer to, to test my accuracy. There is a Leviathanic Museum, they tell me, in Hull, England, one of the whaling ports of that country, where they have some fine specimens of fin-backs and other whales. Likewise, I have heard that in the museum of Manchester, in New Hampshire, they have what the proprietors call "the only perfect specimen of a Greenland or River Whale in the United States." Moreover, at a place in Yorkshire, England, Burton Constable by name, a certain Sir Clifford Constable has in his possession the skeleton of a Sperm Whale, but of moderate size, by no means of the full-grown magnitude of my friend King Tranquo's.

In both cases, the stranded whales to which these two skeletons belonged, were originally claimed by their proprietors upon similar grounds. King Tranquo seizing his because he wanted it; and Sir Clifford, because he was lord of the seignories of those parts. Sir Clifford's whale has been articulated throughout; so that, like a great chest of drawers, you can open and shut him, in all his bony cavities—spread out his ribs like a gigantic fan—and swing all day upon his lower jaw. Locks are to be put upon some of his trap-doors and shutters; and a footman will show round future visitors with a bunch of keys at his side. Sir Clifford thinks of charging twopence for a peep at the whispering gallery in the spinal column; threepence to hear the echo in the hollow of his cerebellum; and sixpence for the unrivaled view from his forehead.

The skeleton dimensions I shall now proceed to set down are copied verbatim from my right arm, where I had them tattooed; as in my wild wanderings at that period, there was no other secure way of preserving such valuable statistics. But as I was crowded for space, and wished the other parts of my body to remain a blank page for a poem I was then composing—at least, what untattooed parts might remain—I did not trouble myself with the odd inches; nor, indeed, should inches at all enter into a congenial admeasurement of the whale.

Chapter CIII

MEASUREMENT OF THE WHALE'S SKELETON

IN THE FIRST PLACE, I WISH TO LAY BEFORE YOU A PARTICULAR, PLAIN STATEMENT, TOUCHING THE living bulk of this leviathan, whose skeleton we are briefly to exhibit. Such a statement may prove useful here.

According to a careful calculation I have made, and which I partly base upon Captain Scoresby's estimate, of seventy tons for the largest sized Greenland whale of sixty feet in length;

according to my careful calculation, I say, a Sperm Whale of the largest magnitude, between eighty-five and ninety feet in length, and something less than forty feet in its fullest circumference, such a whale will weigh at least ninety tons; so that, reckoning thirteen men to a ton, he would considerably outweigh the combined population of a whole village of one thousand one hundred inhabitants.

Think you not then that brains, like yoked cattle, should be put to this leviathan, to make him at all budge to any landsman's imagination.

Having already in various ways put before you his skull, spout-hole, jaw, teeth, tail, forehead, fins, and divers other parts, I shall now simply point out what is most interesting in the general bulk of his unobstructed bones. But as the colossal skull embraces so very large a proportion of the entire extent of the skeleton; as it is by far the most complicated part; and as nothing is to be repeated concerning it in this chapter, you must not fail to carry it in your mind, or under your arm, as we proceed, otherwise you will not gain a complete notion of the general structure we are about to view.

In length, the Sperm Whale's skeleton at Tranque measured seventy-two feet: so that when fully vested and extended in life, he must have been ninety feet long; for in the whale, the skeleton loses about one fifth in length compared with the living body. Of this seventy-two feet, his skull and jaw comprised some twenty feet, leaving some fifty feet of plain backbone. Attached to this backbone, for something less than a third of its length, was the mighty circular basket of ribs which once enclosed his vitals.

To me this vast ivory-ribbed chest, with the long, unrelieved spine, extending far away from it in a straight line, not a little resembled the hull of a great ship new-laid upon the stocks, when only some twenty of her naked bow-ribs are inserted, and the keel is otherwise, for the time, but a long, disconnected timber.

The ribs were ten on a side. The first, to begin from the neck, was nearly six feet long; the second, third, and fourth were each successively longer, till you came to the climax of the fifth, or one of the middle ribs, which measured eight feet and some inches. From that part, the remaining ribs diminished, till the tenth and last only spanned five feet and some inches. In general thickness, they all bore a seemly correspondence to their length. The middle ribs were the most arched. In some of the Arsacides they are used for beams whereon to lay footpath bridges over small streams.

In considering these ribs, I could not but be struck anew with the circumstance, so variously repeated in this book, that the skeleton of the whale is by no means the mold of his invested form. The largest of the Tranque ribs, one of the middle ones, occupied that part of the fish which, in life, is greatest in depth. Now, the greatest depth of the invested body of this particular whale must have been at least sixteen feet; whereas, the corresponding rib measured but little more than eight feet. So that this rib only conveyed half of the true notion of the living magnitude of that part. Besides, for some way, where I now saw but a naked spine, all that had been once wrapped round with tons of added bulk in flesh, muscle, blood, and bowels. Still more, for the ample fins, I here saw but a few disordered joints; and in place of the weighty and majestic, but boneless flukes, an utter blank!

How vain and foolish, then, thought I, for timid untraveled man to try to comprehend aright this wondrous whale, by merely poring over his dead attenuated skeleton, stretched in this peaceful wood. No. Only in the heart of quickest perils; only when within the eddyings of his angry flukes; only on the profound unbounded sea, can the fully invested whale be truly and livingly found out.

But the spine. For that, the best way we can consider it is, with a crane, to pile its bones high up on end. No speedy enterprise. But now it's done, it looks much like Pompey's Pillar.

There are forty and odd vertebrae in all, which in the skeleton are not locked together. They mostly lie like the great knobbed blocks on a Gothic spire, forming solid courses of heavy masonry. The largest, a middle one, is in width something less than three feet, and in depth more than four. The smallest, where the spine tapers away into the tail, is only two inches in width, and looks something like a white billiard-ball. I was told that there were still smaller ones, but they had been lost by some little cannibal urchins, the priest's children, who had stolen them to play marbles with. Thus we see how that the spine of even the hugest of living things tapers off at last into simple child's play.

Chapter CIV

The Fossil Whale

FROM HIS MIGHTY BULK THE WHALE AFFORDS A MOST CONGENIAL THEME WHEREON TO ENLARGE, amplify, and generally expatiate. Would you, you could not compress him. By good rights he should only be treated of in imperial folio. Not to tell over again his furlongs from spiracle to tail, and the yards he measures about the waist; only think of the gigantic involutions of his intestines, where they lie in him like great cables and hawsers coiled away in the subterranean orlop-deck of a line-of-battle-ship.

Since I have undertaken to man-handle this Leviathan, it behooves me to approve myself omnisciently exhaustive in the enterprise; not overlooking the minutest seminal germs of his blood, and spinning him out to the uttermost coil of his bowels. Having already described him in most of his present habitatory and anatomical peculiarities, it now remains to magnify him in an archaeological, fossiliferous, and antediluvian point of view. Applied to any other creature than the Leviathan—to an ant or a flea—such portly terms might justly be deemed unwarrantably grandiloquent. But when Leviathan is the text, the case is altered. Fain am I to stagger to this emprise under the weightiest words of the dictionary. And here be it said, that whenever it has been convenient to consult one in the course of these dissertations, I have invariably used a huge quarto edition of Johnson, expressly purchased for that purpose; because that famous lexicographer's uncommon personal bulk more fitted him to compile a lexicon to be used by a whale author like me.

One often hears of writers that rise and swell with their subject, though it may seem but an ordinary one. How, then, with me, writing of this Leviathan? Unconsciously my chirography expands into placard capitals. Give me a condor's quill! Give me Vesuvius' crater for an inkstand! Friends, hold my arms! For in the mere act of penning my thoughts of this Leviathan, they weary me, and make me faint with their outreaching comprehensiveness of sweep, as if to include the whole circle of the sciences, and all the generations of whales, and men, and mastodons, past, present, and to come, with all the revolving panoramas of empire on earth, and throughout the whole universe, not excluding its suburbs. Such, and so magnifying, is the virtue of a large and liberal theme! We expand to its bulk. To produce a mighty book, you must choose a mighty theme. No great and enduring volume can ever be written on the flea, though many there be who have tried it.

Ere entering upon the subject of Fossil Whales, I present my credentials as a geologist, by stating that in my miscellaneous time I have been a stone-mason, and also a great digger of ditches, canals and wells, wine-vaults, cellars, and cisterns of all sorts. Likewise, by way of preliminary, I desire to remind the reader, that while in the earlier geological strata there are found the fossils of monsters now almost completely extinct; the subsequent relics discovered in what are called the Tertiary formations seem the connecting, or at any rate intercepted links, between the antichronical creatures, and those whose remote posterity are said to have entered the Ark; all the Fossil Whales hitherto discovered belong to the Tertiary period, which is the last preceding the superficial formations. And though none of them precisely answer to any known species of the present time, they are yet sufficiently akin to them in general respects, to justify their taking ranks as Cetacean fossils.

Detached broken fossils of pre-adamite whales, fragments of their bones and skeletons, have within thirty years past, at various intervals, been found at the base of the Alps, in Lombardy, in France, in England, in Scotland and in the States of Louisiana, Mississippi, and Alabama. Among the more curious of such remains is part of a skull, which in the year 1779 was disinterred in the Rue Dauphiné in Paris, a short street opening almost directly upon the palace of the Tuileries; and bones disinterred in excavating the great docks of Antwerp, in Napoleon's time. Cuvier pronounced these fragments to have belonged to some utterly unknown Leviathanic species.

But by far the most wonderful of all Cetacean relics was the almost complete vast skeleton of an extinct monster, found in the year 1842, on the plantation of Judge Creagh, in Alabama. The awe-stricken credulous slaves in the vicinity took it for the bones of one of the fallen angels. The Alabama doctors declared it a huge reptile, and bestowed upon it the name of Basilosaurus. But some specimen bones of it being taken across the sea to Owen, the English Anatomist, it turned out that this alleged reptile was a whale, though of a departed species. A significant illustration of the fact, again and again repeated in this book, that the skeleton of the whale furnishes but little clue to the shape of his fully invested body. So Owen rechristened the monster Zeuglodon; and in his paper read before the London Geological Society, pronounced it, in substance, one of the most extraordinary creatures which the mutations of the globe have blotted out of existence.

When I stand among these mighty Leviathan skeletons, skulls, tusks, jaws, ribs, and vertebrae, all characterized by partial resemblances to the existing breeds of sea-monsters; but at the same time bearing on the other hand similar affinities to the annihilated antichronical Leviathans, their incalculable seniors; I am, by a flood, borne back to that wondrous period, ere time itself can be said to have begun; for time began with man. Here Saturn's gray chaos rolls over me, and I obtain dim, shuddering glimpses into those Polar eternities; when wedged bastions of ice pressed hard upon what are now the tropics; and in all the 25,000 miles of this world's circumference, not an inhabitable hand's breadth of land was visible. Then the whole world was the whale's; and, king of creation, he left his wake along the present lines of the Andes and the Himalayas. Who can show a pedigree like Leviathan? Ahab's harpoon had shed older blood than the Pharaoh's. Methuselah seems a schoolboy. I look round to shake hands with Shem. I am horror-struck at this antemosaic, unsourced existence of the unspeakable terrors of the whale, which, having been before all time, must needs exist after all humane ages are over.

But not alone has this Leviathan left his preadamite traces in the stereotype plates of nature, and in limestone and marl bequeathed his ancient bust; but upon Egyptian tablets, whose antiquity seems to claim for them an almost fossiliferous character, we find the unmistakable print of his fin. In an apartment of the great temple of Denderah, some fifty years ago, there was discovered upon the granite ceiling a sculptured and painted planisphere, abounding in centaurs, griffins, and dolphins, similar to the grotesque figures on the celestial globe of the moderns. Gliding among them, old Leviathan swam as of yore; was there swimming in that planisphere, centuries before Solomon was cradled?

Nor must there be omitted another strange attestation of the antiquity of the whale, in his own osseous post-diluvian reality, as set down by the venerable John Leo, the old Barbary traveler.

"Not far from the Sea-side, they have a Temple, the Rafters and Beams of which are made of Whale-Bones; for Whales of a monstrous size are oftentimes cast up dead upon that shore. The Common People imagine, that by a secret Power bestowed by God upon the Temple, no Whale can pass it without immediate death. But the truth of the matter is, that on either side of the Temple, there are Rocks that shoot two Miles into the Sea, and wound the Whales when they light upon 'em. They keep a Whale's Rib of an incredible length for a Miracle, which lying upon the Ground with its convex part uppermost, makes an Arch, the Head of which cannot be reached by a Man upon a

Camel's Back. This Rib (says John Leo) is said to have layn there a hundred Years before I saw it. Their Historians affirm, that a Prophet who prophesy'd of Mahomet, came from this Temple, and some do not stand to assert, that the Prophet Jonas was cast forth by the Whale at the Base of the Temple."

In this Afric Temple of the Whale I leave you, reader, and if you be a Nantucketer, and a whaleman, you will silently worship there.

Chapter CV

DOES THE WHALE'S MAGNITUDE DIMINISH?—WILL HE PERISH?

INASMUCH, THEN, AS THIS LEVIATHAN COMES FLOUNDERING DOWN UPON US FROM THE HEAD-waters of the Eternities, it may be fitly inquired, whether, in the long course of his generations, he has not degenerated from the original bulk of his sires.

But upon investigation we find, that not only are the whales of the present day superior in magnitude to those whose fossil remains are found in the Tertiary system (embracing a distinct geological period prior to man), but of the whales found in that Tertiary system, those belonging to its latter formations exceed in size those of its earlier ones.

Of all the preadamite whales yet exhumed, by far the largest is the Alabama one mentioned in the last chapter, and that was less than seventy feet in length in the skeleton. Whereas, we have already seen, that the tape-measure gives seventy-two feet for the skeleton of a large sized modern whale. And I have heard, on whalemen's authority, that Sperm Whales have been captured near a hundred feet long at the time of capture.

But may it not be, that while the whales of the present hour are an advance in magnitude upon those of all previous geological periods; may it not be, that since Adam's time they have degenerated?

Assuredly, we must conclude so, if we are to credit the accounts of such gentlemen as Pliny, and the ancient naturalists generally. For Pliny tells us of Whales that embraced acres of living bulk, and Aldrovandus of others which measured eight hundred feet in length—Rope Walks and Thames Tunnels of Whales! And even in the days of Banks and Solander, Cooke's naturalists, we find a Danish member of the Academy of Sciences setting down certain Iceland Whales (reydansiskur, or Wrinkled Bellies) at one hundred and twenty yards; that is, three hundred and sixty feet. And Lacépède, the French naturalist, in his elaborate history of whales, in the very beginning of his work (page 3), sets down the Right Whale at one hundred meters, three hundred and twenty-eight feet. And this work was published so late as A.D. 1825.

But will any whaleman believe these stories? No. The whale of to-day is as big as his ancestors in Pliny's time. And if ever I go where Pliny is, I, a whaleman (more than he was), will make bold to tell him so. Because I cannot understand how it is, that while the Egyptian mummies that were buried thousands of years before even Pliny was born, do not measure so much in their coffins as a modern Kentuckian in his socks; and while the cattle and other animals sculptured on the oldest Egyptian and Nineveh tablets, by the relative proportions in which they are drawn, just as plainly prove that the high-bred, stall-fed, prize cattle of Smithfield, not only equal, but far exceed in magnitude the fattest of Pharaoh's fat kine; in the face of all this, I will not admit that of all animals the whale alone should have degenerated.

But still another inquiry remains; one often agitated by the more recondite Nantucketers.

Whether owing to the almost omniscient look-outs at the mast-heads of the whale-ships, now penetrating even through Behring's straits, and into the remotest secret drawers and lockers of the world; and the thousand harpoons and lances darted along all continental coasts; the moot point is, whether Leviathan can long endure so wide a chase, and so remorseless a havoc; whether he must not at last be exterminated from the waters, and the last whale, like the last man, smoke his last pipe, and then himself evaporate in the final puff.

Comparing the humped herds of whales with the humped herds of buffalo, which, not forty years ago, overspread by tens of thousands the prairies of Illinois and Missouri, and shook their iron manes and scowled with their thunder-clotted brows upon the sites of populous river-capitals, where now the polite broker sells you land at a dollar an inch; in such a comparison an irresistible argument would seem furnished, to show that the hunted whale cannot now escape extinction.

But you must look at this matter in every light. Though so short a period ago—not a good lifetime—the census of the buffalo in Illinois exceeded the census of men now in London, and though at the present day not one horn or hoof of them remains in all that region; and though the cause of this wondrous extermination was the spear of man; yet the far different nature of the whale-hunt peremptorily forbids so inglorious an end to the Leviathan. Forty men in one ship hunting the Sperm Whale for forty-eight months think they have done extremely well, and thank God, if at last they carry home the oil of forty fish. Whereas, in the days of the old Canadian and Indian hunters and trappers of the West, when the far west (in whose sunset suns still rise) was a wilderness and a virgin, the same number of moccasined men, for the same number of months, mounted on horse instead of sailing in ships, would have slain not forty, but forty thousand and more buffaloes; a fact that if need were, could be statistically stated.

Nor considered aright, does it seem any argument in favor of the gradual extinction of the Sperm Whale, for example, that in former years (the latter part of the last century, say) these Leviathans, in small pods, were encountered much oftener than at present, and, in consequence, the voyages were not so prolonged, and were also much more remunerative. Because, as has been elsewhere noticed, those whales, influenced by some views to safety, now swim the seas in immense caravans, so that to a large degree the scattered solitaries, yokes, and pods, and schools of other days are now aggregated into vast but widely separated, unfrequent armies. That is all. And equally fallacious seems the conceit, that because the so-called whale-bone whales no longer haunt many grounds in former years abounding with them, hence that species also is declining. For they are only being driven from promontory to cape; and if one coast is no longer enlivened with their jets, then, be sure, some other and remoter strand has been very recently startled by the unfamiliar spectacle.

Furthermore: concerning these last mentioned Leviathans, they have two firm fortresses, which in all human probability, will forever remain impregnable. And as upon the invasion of their valleys the frosty Swiss have retreated to their mountains; so, hunted from the savannas and glades of the middle seas, the whale-bone whales can at last resort to their Polar citadels, and diving under the ultimate glassy barriers and walls there, come up among icy fields and floes; and in a charmed circle of everlasting December bid defiance to all pursuit from man.

But as perhaps fifty of these whale-bone whales are harpooned for one cachalot, some philosophers of the forecastle have concluded that this positive havoc has already very seriously diminished their battalions. But though for some time past a number of these whales, not less than 13,000, have been annually slain on the nor'west coast by the Americans alone; yet there are considerations which render even this circumstance of little or no account as an opposing argument in this matter.

Natural as it is to be somewhat incredulous concerning the populousness of the more enormous creatures of the globe, yet what shall we say to Harto, the historian of Goa, when he tells us that at one hunting the King of Siam took 4,000 elephants; that in those regions elephants are numerous as droves of cattle in the temperate climes. And there seems no reason to doubt that if these elephants, which have now been hunted for thousands of years, by Semiramis, by Porus, by Hannibal, and by all the successive monarchs of the east—if they still survive there in great numbers, much more may the great whale outlast all hunting, since he has a pasture to expatiate in, which is precisely twice as large as all Asia, both Americas, Europe and Africa, New Holland, and all the Isles of the sea combined.

Moreover: we are to consider, that from the presumed great longevity of whales, their probably attaining the age of a century and more, therefore at any one period of time, several distinct adult generations must be contemporary. And what this is, we may soon gain some idea of, by imagining all the grave-yards, cemeteries, and family vaults of creation yielding up the live bodies of all the men, women, and children who were alive seventy-five years ago; and adding this countless host to the present human population of the globe.

Wherefore, for all these things, we account the whale immortal in his species, however perishable in his individuality. He swam the seas before the continents broke water; he once swam over the site of the Tuileries, and Windsor Castle, and the Kremlin. In Noah's flood he despised Noah's Ark; and if ever the world is to be again flooded, like the Netherlands, to kill off its rats, then the eternal whale will still survive, and rearing upon the topmost crest of the equatorial flood, spout his frothed defiance to the skies.

Chapter CVI

AHAB'S LEG

THE PRECIPITATING MANNER IN WHICH CAPTAIN AHAB HAD QUITTED THE *SAMUEL ENDERBY* OF London, had not been unattended with some small violence to his own person. He had lighted with such energy upon a thwart of his boat that his ivory leg had received a half-splintering shock. And when after gaining his own deck, and his own pivot-hole there, he so vehemently wheeled round with an urgent command to the steersman (it was, as ever, something about his not steering inflexibly enough); then, the already shaken ivory received such an additional twist and wrench, that though it still remained entire, and to all appearances lusty, yet Ahab did not deem it entirely trustworthy. And, indeed, it seemed small matter for wonder, that for all his pervading, mad recklessness, Ahab did at times give careful heed to the condition of that dead bone upon which he partly stood. For it had not been very long prior to the *Pequod*'s sailing from Nantucket, that he had been found one night lying prone upon the ground, and insensible; by some unknown, and seemingly inexplicable, unimaginable casualty, his ivory limb having been so violently displaced, that it had stake-wise smitten, and all but pierced his groin; nor was it without extreme difficulty that the agonizing wound was entirely cured.

Nor, at the time, had it failed to enter his monomaniac mind, that all the anguish of that then present suffering was but the direct issue of a former woe; and he too plainly seemed to see, that as the most poisonous reptile of the marsh perpetuates his kind as inevitably as the sweetest songster of the grove; so, equally with every felicity, all miserable events do naturally beget their like. Yea, more than equally, thought Ahab; since both the ancestry and posterity of Grief go further than the ancestry and posterity of Joy. For, not to hint of this: that it is an inference from certain canonic teachings, that while some natural enjoyments here shall have no children born to them for the other world, but, on the contrary, shall be followed by the joy-childlessness of all hell's despair; whereas, some guilty mortal miseries shall still fertilely beget to themselves an eternally progressive progeny of griefs beyond the grave; not at all to hint of this, there still seems an inequality in the deeper analysis of the thing. For, thought Ahab, while even the highest earthly felicities ever have a certain unsignifying pettiness lurking in them, but, at bottom, all heart-woes, a mystic significance, and, in some men, an archangelic grandeur; so do their diligent tracings-out not belie the obvious deduction. To trail the genealogies of these high mortal miseries, carries us at last among the sourceless primogenitures of the gods; so that, in the face of all the glad, hay-making suns, and soft-cymbaling, round harvest-moons, we must needs give in to this: that the gods themselves are not forever glad. The ineffaceable, sad birth-mark in the brow of man, is but the stamp of sorrow in the signers.

Unwittingly here a secret has been divulged, which perhaps might more properly, in set way, have been disclosed before. With many other particulars concerning Ahab, always had it remained a mystery to some, why it was, that for a certain period, both before and after the sailing of the *Pequod*, he had hidden himself away with such Grand-Lama-like exclusiveness; and, for that one interval, sought speechless refuge, as it were, among the marble senate of the dead. Captain Peleg's bruited reason for this thing appeared by no means adequate; though, indeed, as touching all Ahab's deeper part, every revelation partook more of significant darkness than of explanatory light. But, in the end, it all came out; this one matter did, at least. That direful mishap was at the bottom of his temporary recluseness. And not only this, but to that ever-contracting, dropping circle ashore, who, for any reason, possessed the privilege of a less banned approach to him; to that timid circle the above hinted casualty—remaining, as it did, moodily unaccounted for by Ahab—invested itself with terrors, not entirely underived from the land of spirits and of wails. So that, through their zeal for him, they had all conspired, so far as in them lay, to muffle up the knowledge of this thing from others; and hence it was, that not till a considerable interval had elapsed, did it transpire upon the *Pequod*'s decks.

But be all this as it may; let the unseen, ambiguous synod in the air, or the vindictive princes and potentates of fire, have to do or not with earthly Ahab, yet, in this present matter of his leg, he took plain practical procedures;—he called the carpenter.

And when that functionary appeared before him, he bade him without delay set about making a new leg, and directed the mates to see him supplied with all the studs and joists of jaw-ivory (Sperm Whale) which had thus far been accumulated on the voyage, in order that a careful selection of the stoutest, clearest-grained stuff might be secured. This done, the carpenter received orders to have the leg completed that night; and to provide all the fittings for it, independent of those pertaining to the distrusted one in use. Moreover, the ship's forge was ordered to be hoisted out of its temporary idleness in the hold; and, to accelerate the affair, the blacksmith was commanded to proceed at once to the forging of whatever iron contrivances might be needed.

Chapter CVII

THE CARPENTER

SEAT THYSELF SULTANICALLY AMONG THE MOONS OF SATURN, AND TAKE HIGH ABSTRACTED MAN alone; and he seems a wonder, a grandeur and a woe. But from the same point, take mankind in mass, and for the most part, they seem a mob of unnecessary duplicates, both contemporary and hereditary. But most humble though he was, and far from furnishing an example of the high, humane abstraction; the *Pequod*'s carpenter was no duplicate; hence, he now comes in person on this stage.

Like all sea-going ship carpenters, and more especially those belonging to whaling vessels, he was, to a certain off-handed, practical extent, alike experienced in numerous trades and callings collateral to his own; the carpenter's pursuit being the ancient and outbranching trunk of all those numerous handicrafts which more or less have to do with wood as an auxiliary material. But, besides the application to him of the generic remark above, this carpenter of the *Pequod* was singularly efficient in those thousand nameless mechanical emergencies continually recurring in a large ship, upon a three or four years' voyage, in uncivilized and far-distant seas. For not to speak of his readiness in ordinary duties—repairing stove boats, sprung spars, reforming the shape of clumsy-bladed oars, inserting bull's-eyes in the deck, or new tree-nails in the side planks, and other miscellaneous matters more directly pertaining to his special business; he was moreover unhesitatingly expert in all manner of conflicting aptitudes, both useful and capricious.

The one grand stage where he enacted all his various parts so manifold, was his vice-bench; a long rude ponderous table furnished with several vices, of different sizes, and both of iron and of wood. At all times except when whales were alongside, this bench was securely lashed athwart ships against the rear of the try-works.

A belaying-pin is found too large to be easily inserted into its hole: the carpenter claps it into one of his ever-ready vices, and straightway files it smaller. A lost land-bird of strange plumage strays on board, and is made a captive: out of clean shaved rods of right-whale bone, and cross-beams of sperm-whale ivory, the carpenter makes a pagoda-looking cage for it. An oarsman sprains his wrist: the carpenter concocts a soothing lotion. Stubb longed for vermilion stars to be painted upon the blade of his every oar; screwing each oar in his big vice of wood, the carpenter symmetrically supplies the constellation. A sailor takes a fancy to wear shark-bone ear-rings: the carpenter drills his ears. Another has the toothache: the carpenter out pincers, and clapping one hand upon his bench bids him be seated there; but the poor fellow unmanageably winces under the unconcluded operation; whirling round the handle of his wooden vice, the carpenter signs him to clap his jaw in that, if he would have him draw the tooth.

Thus, this carpenter was prepared at all points, and alike indifferent and without respect in all. Teeth he accounted bits of ivory; heads he deemed but top-blocks; men themselves he lightly held for capstans. But while now upon so wide a field thus variously accomplished, and with such liveliness of expertness in him, too; all this would seem to argue some uncommon vivacity of intelligence. But not precisely so. For nothing was this man more remarkable, than for a certain impersonal stolidity as it were; impersonal, I say; for it so shaded off into the surrounding infinite of things, that it seemed one with the general stolidity discernible in the whole visible world; which while pauselessly active in uncounted modes, still eternally holds its peace, and ignores you, though you dig foundations for cathedrals. Yet was this half-horrible stolidity in him, involving, too, as it appeared, an all-ramifying heartlessness;—yet was it oddly dashed at times, with an old, crutch-like, antediluvian, wheezing humorousness, not unstreaked now and then with a certain grizzled wittiness; such as might have served to pass the time during the midnight watch on the bearded forecastle of Noah's ark. Was it that this old carpenter had been a life-long wanderer, whose much rolling, to and fro, not only had gathered no moss; but what is more, had rubbed off whatever small outward clingings might have originally pertained to him? He was a stripped abstract; an unfractioned integral; uncompromised as a new-born babe; living without premeditated reference to this world or the next. You might almost say, that this strange uncompromisedness in him involved a sort of unintelligence; for in his numerous trades, he did not seem to work so much by reason or by instinct, or simply because he had been tutored to it, or by any intermixture of all these, even or uneven; but merely by a kind of deaf and dumb, spontaneous literal process. He was a pure manipulator; his brain, if he had ever had one, must have early oozed along into the muscles of his fingers. He was like one of those unreasoning but still highly useful, *multum in parvo,* Sheffield contrivances, assuming the exterior—though a little swelled—of a common pocket-knife; but containing, not only blades of various sizes, but also screw-drivers, cork-screws, tweezers, awls, pens, rulers, nail-filers, countersinkers. So, if his superiors wanted to use the carpenter for a screw-driver, all they had to do was to open that part of him, and the screw was fast: or if for tweezers, take him up by the legs, and there they were.

Yet, as previously hinted, this omnitooled, open-and-shut carpenter, was, after all, no mere machine of an automaton. If he did not have a common soul in him, he had a subtle something that somehow anomalously did its duty. What that was, whether essence of quicksilver, or a few drops of hartshorn, there is no telling. But there it was; and there it had abided for now some sixty years or more. And this it was, this same unaccountable, cunning life-principle in him; this it was, that kept him a great part of the time soliloquizing; but only like an unreasoning wheel, which also hummingly soliloquizes; or rather, his body was a sentry-box and this soliloquizer on guard there, and talking all the time to keep himself awake.

Chapter CVIII

AHAB AND THE CARPENTER

THE DECK—FIRST NIGHT-WATCH

(Carpenter standing before his vice-bench, and by the light of two lanterns busily filing the ivory joist for the leg, which joist is firmly fixed in the vice. Slabs of ivory, leather straps, pads, screws, and various tools of all sorts lying about the bench. Forward, the red flame of the forge is seen, where the blacksmith is at work.)

DRAT THE FILE, AND DRAT THE BONE! THAT IS HARD WHICH SHOULD BE SOFT, AND THAT IS SOFT which should be hard. So we go, who file old jaws and shin bones. Let's try another. Ay, now, this works better (*sneezes*). Halloa, this bone dust is (*sneezes*)—why it's (*sneezes*)—yes, it's (*sneezes*)—bless my soul, it won't let me speak! This is what an old fellow gets now for working in dead lumber. Saw a live tree, and you don't get this dust; amputate a live bone, and you don't get it (*sneezes*). Come, come, you old Smut, there, bear a hand, and let's have that ferule and buckle-screw; I'll be ready for them presently. Lucky now (*sneezes*) there's no knee-joint to make; that might puzzle a little; but a mere shin-bone—why it's easy as making hop-poles; only I should like to put a good finish on. Time, time; if I but only had the time, I could turn him out as neat a leg now as ever (*sneezes*) scraped to a lady in a parlor. Those buck-skin legs and calves of legs I've seen in shop windows wouldn't compare at all. They soak water, they do; and of course get rheumatic, and have to be doctored (*sneezes*) with washes and lotions, just like live legs. There; before I saw it off; now, I must call his old Mogulship, and see whether the length will be all right; too short, if anything, I guess. Ha! that's the heel; we are in luck; here he comes, or it's somebody else, that's certain.

AHAB (*advancing*)

(*During the ensuing scene, the carpenter continues sneezing at times*)

Well, manmaker!

Just in time, sir. If the captain pleases, I will now mark the length. Let me measure, sir.

Measured for a leg! good. Well, it's not the first time. About it! There; keep thy finger on it. This is a cogent vice thou hast here, carpenter; let me feel its grip once. So, so; it does pinch some.

Oh, sir, it will break bones—beware, beware!

No fear; I like a good grip; I like to feel something in this slippery world that can hold, man. What's Prometheus about there?—the blacksmith, I mean—what's he about?

He must be forging the buckle-screw, sir, now.

Right. It's a partnership; he supplies the muscle part. He makes a fierce red flame there!

Ay, sir; he must have the white heat for this kind of fine work.

Um-m. So he must. I do deem it now a most meaning thing, that that old Greek, Prometheus, who made men, they say, should have been a blacksmith, and animated them with fire; for what's made in fire must properly belong to fire; and so hell's probable. How the soot flies! This must be the remainder the Greek made the Africans of. Carpenter, when he's through with that buckle, tell him to forge a pair of steel shoulder-blades; there's a pedlar aboard with a crushing pack.

Sir?

Hold; while Prometheus is about it, I'll order a complete man after a desirable pattern. Imprimis, fifty feet high in his socks; then, chest modeled after the Thames Tunnel; then, legs with roots to 'em, to stay in one place; then, arms three feet through the wrist; no heart at all, brass forehead, and about a quarter of an acre of fine brains; and let me see—shall I order eyes to see outwards? No, but put a skylight on top of his head to illuminate inwards. There, take the order, and away.

Now, what's he speaking about, and who's he speaking to, I should like to know? Shall I keep standing here? (*Aside*.)

'Tis but indifferent architecture to make a blind dome; here's one. No, no, no; I must have a lantern.

Ho, ho! That's it, hey? Here are two, sir; one will serve my turn.

What art thou thrusting that thief-catcher into my face for, man? Thrusted light is worse than presented pistols.

I thought, sir, that you spoke to carpenter.

Carpenter? why that's—but no;—a very tidy, and, I may say, an extremely gentleman-like sort of business thou art in here, carpenter;—or would'st thou rather work in clay?

Sir?—Clay? clay, sir? That's mud; we leave clay to ditchers, sir.

The fellow's impious! What art thou sneezing about?

Bone is rather dusty, sir.

Take the hint, then; and when thou art dead, never bury thyself under living people's noses.

Sir?—oh! ah!—I guess so;—yes—oh, dear!

Look, ye, carpenter, I dare-say thou callest thyself a right good workman-like workman, eh? Well, then, will it speak thoroughly well for thy work, if, when I come to mount this leg thou makest, I shall nevertheless feel another leg in the same identical place with it; that is, carpenter, my old lost leg; the flesh and blood one, I mean. Canst thou not drive that old Adam away?

Truly, sir, I begin to understand somewhat now. Yes, I have heard something curious on that score, sir; how that a dismasted man never entirely loses the feeling of his old spar, but it will be still pricking him at times. May I humbly ask if it be really so, sir?

It is, man. Look, put thy live leg here in the place where mine once was; so, now, here is only one distinct leg to the eye, yet two to the soul. Where thou feelest tingling life; there, exactly there, there to a hair, do I. Is't a riddle?

I should humbly call it a poser, sir.

Hist, then. How dost thou know that some entire, living, thinking thing may not be invisibly and uninterpenetratingly standing precisely where thou now standest; aye, and standing there in thy spite? In thy most solitary hours, then, dost thou not fear eavesdroppers? Hold, don't speak! And if I still feel the smart of my crushed leg, though it be now so long dissolved; then, why mayest not thou, carpenter, feel the fiery pains of hell forever, and without a body? Hah!

Good Lord! Truly, sir, if it comes to that, I must calculate over again; I think I didn't carry a small figure, sir.

Look ye, pudding-heads should never grant premises.—How long before this leg is done?

Perhaps an hour, sir.

Bungle away at it then, and bring it to me (*turns to go*). Oh, Life! Here I am, proud as Greek god, and yet standing debtor to this blockhead for a bone to stand on! Cursed be that mortal inter-indebtedness which will not do away with ledgers. I would be free as air; and I'm down in the whole world's books. I am so rich, I could have given bid for bid with the wealthiest Prætorians at the auction of the Roman empire (which was the world's); and yet I owe for the flesh in the tongue I brag with. By heavens! I'll get a crucible, and into it, and dissolve myself down to one small, compendious vertebra. So.

CARPENTER (*resuming his work*)

Well, well, well! Stubb knows him best of all, and Stubb always says he's queer; says nothing but that one sufficient little word queer; he's queer, says Stubb; he's queer—queer, queer; and keeps dinning it into Mr. Starbuck all the time—queer, sir—queer, queer, very queer. And here's his leg! Yes, now that I think of it, here's his bed-fellow! has a stick of whale's jaw-bone for a wife! And this is his leg; he'll stand on this. What was that now about one leg standing in three places, and all three places standing in one hell—how was that? Oh! I don't wonder he looked so scornful at me! I'm a sort of strange-thoughted sometimes, they say; but that's only haphazard-like. Then, a short, little old body like me, should never undertake to wade out into deep waters with tall, heron-built captains; the water chucks you under the chin pretty quick, and there's a great cry for life-boats. And here's the heron's leg! long and slim, sure enough! Now, for most folks one pair of legs lasts a lifetime, and that must be because they use them mercifully, as a tender-hearted old lady uses her roly-poly old coach-horses. But Ahab; oh he's a hard driver. Look, driven one leg to death, and spavined the other for life, and now wears out bone legs by the cord. Halloa, there, you Smut! bear a hand there with those screws, and let's finish it before the resurrection fellow comes a-calling with his horn for all legs, true or false, as brewery men go round collecting old beer barrels, to fill 'em up again. What a leg this is! It looks like a real live leg, filed down to nothing but the core; he'll be standing on this to-morrow; he'll be taking altitudes on it. Halloa! I almost forgot the little oval slate, smoothed ivory, where he figures up the latitude. So, so; chisel, file, and sand-paper, now!

Chapter CIX

AHAB AND STARBUCK IN THE CABIN

ACCORDING TO USAGE THEY WERE PUMPING THE SHIP NEXT MORNING; AND LO! NO INCONSIDerable oil came up with the water; the casks below must have sprung a bad leak. Much concern was shown; and Starbuck went down into the cabin to report this unfavorable affair.[1]

Now, from the south and west the *Pequod* was drawing nigh to Formosa and the Bashee Isles, between which lies one of the tropical outlets from the China waters into the Pacific. And so Star-

1. In Sperm-whalemen with any considerable quantity of oil on board, it is a regular semi-weekly duty to conduct a hose into the hold, and drench the casks with sea-water; which afterwards, at varying intervals, is removed by the ship's pumps. Hereby the casks are sought to be kept damply tight; while by the changed character of the withdrawn water, the mariners readily detect any serious leakage in the precious cargo.

buck found Ahab with a general chart of the oriental archipelagoes spread before him; and another separate one representing the long eastern coasts of the Japanese islands—Niphon, Matsmai, and Sikoke. With his snow-white new ivory leg braced against the screwed leg of his table, and with a long pruning-hook of a jack-knife in his hand, the wondrous old man, with his back to the gangway door, was wrinkling his brow, and tracing his old courses again.

"Who's there?" hearing the footstep at the door, but not turning round to it. "On deck! Begone!"

"Captain Ahab mistakes; it is I. The oil in the hold is leaking, sir. We must up Burtons and break out."

"Up Burtons and break out? Now that we are nearing Japan; heave-to here for a week to tinker a parcel of old hoops?"

"Either do that, sir, or waste in one day more oil than we may make good in a year. What we come twenty thousand miles to get is worth saving, sir."

"So it is, so it is; if we get it."

"I was speaking of the oil in the hold, sir."

"And I was not speaking or thinking of that at all. Begone! Let it leak! I'm all aleak myself. Ay! leaks in leaks! not only full of leaky casks, but those leaky casks are in a leaky ship; and that's a far worse plight than the *Pequod*'s, man. Yet I don't stop to plug my leak; for who can find it in the deep-loaded hull; or how hope to plug it, even if found, in this life's howling gale? Starbuck! I'll not have the Burtons hoisted."

"What will the owners say, sir?"

"Let the owners stand on Nantucket beach and outyell the Typhoons. What cares Ahab? Owners, owners? Thou art always prating to me, Starbuck, about those miserly owners, as if the owners were my conscience. But look ye, the only real owner of anything is its commander; and hark ye, my conscience is in this ship's keel.—On deck!"

"Captain Ahab," said the reddening mate, moving further into the cabin, with a daring so strangely respectful and cautious that it almost seemed not only every way seeking to avoid the slightest outward manifestation of itself, but within also seemed more than half distrustful of itself; "A better man than I might well pass over in thee what he would quickly enough resent in a younger man; ay, and in a happier, Captain Ahab."

"Devils! Dost thou then so much as dare to critically think of me?—On deck!"

"Nay, sir, not yet; I do entreat. And I do dare, sir—to be forbearing! Shall we not understand each other better than hitherto, Captain Ahab?"

Ahab seized a loaded musket from the rack (forming part of most South-Sea-men's cabin furniture), and pointing it towards Starbuck, exclaimed: "There is one God that is Lord over the earth, and one Captain that is lord over the *Pequod*.—On deck!"

For an instant in the flashing eyes of the mate, and his fiery cheeks, you would have almost thought that he had really received the blaze of the leveled tube. But, mastering his emotion, he half calmly rose, and as he quitted the cabin, paused for an instant and said: "Thou hast outraged, not insulted me, sir; but for that I ask thee not to beware of Starbuck; thou wouldst but laugh; but let Ahab beware of Ahab; beware of thyself, old man."

"He waxes brave, but nevertheless obeys; most careful bravery that!" murmured Ahab, as Starbuck disappeared. "What's that he said—Ahab beware of Ahab—there's something there!" Then unconsciously using the musket for a staff, with an iron brow he paced to and fro in the little cabin; but presently the thick plaits of his forehead relaxed, and returning the gun to the rack, he went to the deck.

"Thou art but too good a fellow, Starbuck," he said lowly to the mate; then raising his voice to the crew: "Furl the t'gallant-sails, and close-reef the top-sails, fore and aft; back the main-yard up Burtons, and break out in the main-hold."

It were perhaps vain to surmise exactly why it was, that as respecting Starbuck, Ahab thus acted. It may have been a flash of honesty in him; or mere prudential policy which, under the circumstance, imperiously forbade the slightest symptom of open disaffection, however transient, in the important chief officer of his ship. However it was, his orders were executed; and the Burtons were hoisted.

Chapter CX

QUEEQUEG IN HIS COFFIN

UPON SEARCHING, IT WAS FOUND THAT THE CASKS LAST STRUCK INTO THE HOLD WERE PERFECTLY sound, and that the leak must be further off. So, it being calm weather, they broke out deeper and deeper, disturbing the slumbers of the huge ground-tier butts; and from that black midnight sending those gigantic moles into the daylight above. So deep did they go; and so ancient, and corroded, and weedy the aspect of the lowermost puncheons, that you almost looked next for some moldy corner-stone cask containing coins of Captain Noah, with copies of the posted placards, vainly warning the infatuated old world from the flood. Tierce after tierce, too, of water, and bread, and beef, and shooks of staves, and iron bundles of hoops, were hoisted out, till at last the piled decks were hard to get about; and the hollow hull echoed under foot, as if you were treading over empty catacombs, and reeled and rolled in the sea like an air-freighted demijohn. Top-heavy was the ship as a dinnerless student with all Aristotle in his head. Well was it that the Typhoons did not visit them then.

Now, at this time it was that my poor pagan companion, and fast bosom-friend, Queequeg, was seized with a fever, which brought him nigh to his endless end.

Be it said, that in this vocation of whaling, sinecures are unknown; dignity and danger go hand in hand; till you get to be Captain, the higher you rise the harder you toil. So with poor Queequeg, who, as harpooneer, must not only face all the rage of the living whale, but—as we have elsewhere seen—mount his dead back in a rolling sea; and finally descend into the gloom of the hold, and bitterly sweating all day in that subterraneous confinement, resolutely man-handle the clumsiest casks and see to their stowage. To be short, among whalemen, the harpooneers are the holders, so called.

Poor Queequeg! when the ship was about half disemboweled, you should have stooped over the hatchway, and peered down upon him there; where, stripped to his woolen drawers, the tattooed savage was crawling about amid that dampness and slime, like a green spotted lizard at the bottom of a well. And a well, or an ice-house, it somehow proved to him, poor pagan; where, strange to say, for all the heat of his sweatings, he caught a terrible chill which lapsed into a fever; and at last, after some days' suffering, laid him in his hammock, close to the very sill of the door of death. How he wasted and wasted away in those few long-lingering days, till there seemed but little left of him but his frame and tattooing. But as all else in him thinned, and his cheek-bones grew sharper, his eyes, nevertheless, seemed growing fuller and fuller; they became of a strange softness of luster; and mildly but deeply looked out at you there from his sickness, a wondrous testimony to that immortal health in him which could not die, or be weakened. And like circles on the water, which, as they grow fainter, expand; so his eyes seemed rounding and rounding, like the rings of Eternity. An awe that cannot be named would steal over you as you sat by the side of this waning savage, and saw as strange things in his face, as any beheld who were bystanders when Zoroaster died. For whatever is truly wondrous and fearful in man, never yet was put into words or books. And the drawing near of Death, which alike levels all, alike impresses all with a last revelation, which only an author from the dead could adequately tell. So that—let us say it again—no dying Chaldee or Greek had higher and holier thoughts than those, whose mysterious shades you saw creeping over the face of poor Queequeg, as he quietly lay in his swaying hammock, and the rolling sea seemed gently rocking him to his final rest, and the ocean's invisible floodtide lifted him higher and higher towards his destined heaven.

Not a man of the crew but gave him up; and, as for Queequeg himself, what he thought of his case was forcibly shown by a curious favor he asked. He called one to him in the gray morning watch, when the day was just breaking, and taking his hand, said that while in Nantucket he had chanced to see certain little canoes of dark wood, like the rich war-wood of his native isle; and upon inquiry, he had learned that all whalemen who died in Nantucket, were laid in those same dark canoes, and that the fancy of being so laid had much pleased him; for it was not unlike the custom of his own race, who, after embalming a dead warrior, stretched him out in his canoe, and so left him to be floated away to the starry archipelagoes; for not only do they believe that the stars are isles, but that far beyond all visible horizons, their own mild, uncontinented seas, interflow with the blue heavens; and so form the white breakers of the milky way. He added, that he shuddered at the thought of being buried in his hammock, according to the usual sea-custom, tossed like something vile to the death-devouring sharks. No: he desired a canoe like those of Nantucket, all the more congenial to him, being a whaleman, that like a whale-boat these coffin-canoes were without a keel; though that involved but uncertain steering, and much lee-way adown the dim ages.

Now, when this strange circumstance was made known aft, the carpenter was at once commanded to do Queequeg's bidding, whatever it might include. There was some heathenish, coffin-colored old lumber aboard, which upon a long previous voyage, had been cut from the aboriginal groves of the Lackaday islands, and from these dark planks the coffin was recommended to be made. No sooner was the carpenter apprised of the order, than taking his rule, he forthwith with all the indifferent promptitude of his character, proceeded into the forecastle and took Queequeg's measure with great accuracy, regularly chalking Queequeg's person as he shifted the rule.

"Ah! poor fellow! he'll have to die now," ejaculated the Long Island sailor.

Going to his vice-bench, the carpenter for convenience sake and general reference, now transferringly measured on it the exact length the coffin was to be, and then made the transfer permanent by cutting two notches at its extremities. This done, he marshalled the planks and his tools, and to work.

When the last nail was driven, and the lid duly planed and fitted, he lightly shouldered the coffin and went forward with it, inquiring whether they were ready for it yet in that direction.

Overhearing the indignant but half-humorous cries with which the people on deck began to drive the coffin away, Queequeg, to everyone's consternation, commanded that the thing should be instantly brought to him, nor was there any denying him; seeing that, of all mortals, some dying men are the most tyrannical; and certainly, since they will shortly trouble us so little forever more, the poor fellows ought to be indulged.

Leaning over in his hammock, Queequeg long regarded the coffin with an attentive eye. He then called for his harpoon, had the wooden stock drawn from it, and then had the iron part placed in the coffin along with one of the paddles of his boat. All by his own request, also, biscuits were then ranged round the sides within: a flask of fresh water was placed at the head, and a small bag of woody earth scraped up in the hold at the foot; and a piece of sail-cloth being rolled up for a pillow, Queequeg now entreated to be lifted into his final bed, that he might make trial of its comforts, if any it had. He lay without moving a few minutes, then told one to go to his bag and bring out his little god, Yojo. Then crossing his arms on his breast with Yojo between, he called for the coffin lid (hatch he called it) to be placed over him. The head part turned over with a leather hinge, and there lay Queequeg in his coffin with little but his composed countenance in view. "Rarmai" (it will do; it is easy), he murmured at last, and signed to be replaced in his hammock.

But ere this was done, Pip, who had been slyly hovering nearby all this while, drew nigh to him where he lay, and with soft sobbings, took him by the hand; in the other, holding his tambourine.

"Poor rover! will ye never have done with all this weary roving? where go ye now? But if the currents carry ye to those sweet Antilles where the beaches are only beat with water-lilies, will ye do one little errand for me? Seek out one Pip, who's now been missing long: I think he's in those far Antilles. If ye find him, then comfort him; for he must be very sad; for look! he's left his tambourine behind;—I found it. Rig-a-dig, dig, dig! Now, Queequeg, die; and I'll beat ye your dying march."

"I have heard," murmured Starbuck, gazing down the scuttle, "that in violent fevers, men, all ignorance, have talked in ancient tongues; and that when the mystery is probed, it turns out always that in their wholly forgotten childhood those ancient tongues had been really spoken in their hearing by some lofty scholars. So, to my fond faith, poor Pip, in this strange sweetness of his lunacy, brings heavenly vouchers of all our heavenly homes. Where learned he that, but there?—Hark! he speaks again: but more wildly now."

"Form two and two! Let's make a General of him! Ho, where's his harpoon? Lay it across here.—Rig-a-dig, dig, dig! huzza! Oh for a game cock now to sit upon his head and crow! Queequeg dies game!—mind ye that; Queequeg dies game!—take ye good heed of that; Queequeg dies game! I say; game, game, game! but base little Pip, he died a coward; died all a'shiver;—out upon Pip! Hark ye; if ye find Pip, tell all the Antilles he's a runaway; a coward, a coward, a coward! Tell them he jumped from a whale-boat! I'd never beat my tambourine over base Pip, and hail him General, if he were once more dying here. No, no! shame upon all cowards—shame upon them! Let 'em go drown like Pip, that jumped from a whale-boat. Shame! shame!"

During all this, Queequeg lay with closed eyes, as if in a dream. Pip was led away, and the sick man was replaced in his hammock.

But now that he had apparently made every preparation for death; now that his coffin was proved a good fit, Queequeg suddenly rallied; soon there seemed no need of the carpenter's box: and thereupon, when some expressed their delighted surprise, he, in substance, said, that the cause of his sudden convalescence was this;—at a critical moment, he had just recalled a little duty ashore, which he was leaving undone; and therefore had changed his mind about dying: he could not die yet, he averred. They asked him, then, whether to live or die was a matter of his own sovereign will and pleasure. He answered, certainly. In a word, it was Queequeg's conceit, that if a man made up his mind to live, mere sickness could not kill him: nothing but a whale, or a gale, or some violent, ungovernable, unintelligent destroyer of that sort.

Now, there is this noteworthy difference between savage and civilized; that while a sick, civilized man may be six months convalescing, generally speaking, a sick savage is almost half-well again in a day. So, in good time my Queequeg gained strength; and at length after sitting on the windlass for a few indolent days (but eating with a vigorous appetite) he suddenly leaped to his feet, threw out his arms and legs, gave himself a good stretching, yawned a little bit, and then springing into the head of his hoisted boat, and poising a harpoon, pronounced himself fit for a fight.

With a wild whimsiness, he now used his coffin for a sea-chest; and emptying into it his canvas bag of clothes, set them in order there. Many spare hours he spent, in carving the lid with all manner of grotesque figures and drawings; and it seemed that hereby he was striving, in his rude way, to copy parts of the twisted tattooing on his body. And this tattooing had been the work of a departed prophet and seer of his island, who, by those hieroglyphic marks, had written out on his body a complete theory of the heavens and the earth, and a mystical treatise on the art of attaining truth; so that Queequeg in his own proper person was a riddle to unfold; a wondrous work in one volume; but whose mysteries not even himself could read, though his own live heart beat against them; and these mysteries were therefore destined in the end to molder away with the living parchment whereon they were inscribed, and so be unsolved to the last. And this though it must have been which suggested to Ahab that wild exclamation of his, when one morning turning away from surveying poor Queequeg—"Oh, devilish tantalization of the gods!"

Chapter CXI

The Pacific

When gliding by the Bashee isles we emerged at last upon the great South Sea; were it not for other things I could have greeted my dear Pacific with uncounted thanks, for now the long supplication of my youth was answered; that serene ocean rolled eastwards from me a thousand leagues of blue.

There is, one knows not what sweet mystery about this sea, whose gently awful stirrings seems to speak of some hidden soul beneath; like those fabled undulations of the Ephesian sod over the buried Evangelist St. John. And meet it is, that over these sea-pastures, wide-rolling watery prairies and Potters' Fields of all four continents, the waves should rise and fall, and ebb and flow unceasingly; for here, millions of mixed shades and shadows, drowned dreams, somnambulisms, reveries; all that we call lives and souls, lie dreaming, dreaming, still; tossing like slumberers in their beds; the ever-rolling waves but made so by their restlessness.

To any meditative Magian rover, this serene Pacific, once beheld, must ever after be the sea of his adoption. It rolls the midmost waters of the world, the Indian ocean and Atlantic being but its arms. The same waves wash the moles of the new-built California towns, but yesterday planted by the recentest race of men, and lave the faded but still gorgeous skirts of Asiatic lands, older than Abraham; while all between float milky-ways of coral isles, and low-lying, endless, unknown Archipelagoes, and impenetrable Japans. Thus this mysterious, divine Pacific zones the world's whole bulk about; makes all coasts one bay to it; seems the tide-beating heart of earth. Lifted by those eternal swells, you needs must own the seductive god, bowing your head to Pan.

But few thoughts of Pan stirred Ahab's brain, as standing like an iron statue at his accustomed place beside the mizzen rigging, with one nostril he unthinkingly snuffed the sugary musk from the Bashee isles (in whose sweet woods mild lovers must be walking), and with the other consciously inhaled the salt breath of the new found sea; that sea in which the hated White Whale must even then be swimming. Launched at length upon these almost final waters, and gliding towards the Japanese cruising-ground, the old man's purpose intensified itself. His firm lips met like the lips of a vice; the Delta of his forehead's veins swelled like overladen brooks; in his very sleep, his ringing cry ran through the vaulted hull "Stern all! the White Whale spouts thick blood!"

Chapter CXII

THE BLACKSMITH

AVAILING HIMSELF OF THE MILD, SUMMER-COOL WEATHER THAT NOW REIGNED IN THESE LATItudes, and in preparation for the peculiarly active pursuits shortly to be anticipated, Perth, the begrimed, blistered old blacksmith, had not removed his portable forge to the hold again, after concluding his contributory work for Ahab's leg, but still retained it on deck, fast lashed to ring-bolts by the fore-mast; being now almost incessantly invoked by the headsmen, and harpooneers, and bowsmen to do some little job for them; altering, or repairing, or new shaping their various weapons and boat furniture. Often he would be surrounded by an eager circle, all waiting to be served; holding boat-spades, pike-heads, harpoons, and lances, and jealously watching his every sooty movement, as he toiled. Nevertheless, this old man's was a patient hammer wielded by a patient arm. No murmur, no impatience, no petulance did come from him. Silent, slow, and solemn; bowing over still further his chronically broken back, he toiled away, as if toil were life itself, and the heavy beating of his hammer the heavy beating of his heart. And so it was.—Most miserable!

A peculiar walk in this old man, a certain slight but painful appearing yawing in his gait, had at an early period of the voyage excited the curiosity of the mariners. And to the importunity of their persisted questionings he had finally given in; and so it came to pass that everyone now knew the shameful story of his wretched fate.

Belated, and not innocently, one bitter winter's midnight, on the road running between two country towns, the blacksmith half-stupidly felt the deadly numbness stealing over him, and sought refuge in a leaning, dilapidated barn. The issue was, the loss of the extremities of both feet. Out of this revelation, part by part, at last came out the four acts of the gladness, and the one long, and as yet uncatastrophied fifth act of the grief of his life's drama.

He was an old man, who, at the age of nearly sixty, had postponedly encountered that thing in sorrow's technicals called ruin. He had been an artisan of famed excellence, and with plenty to do; owned a house and garden; embraced a youthful, daughter-like, loving wife, and three blithe, ruddy children; every Sunday went to a cheerful-looking church, planted in a grove. But one night, under cover of darkness, and further concealed in a most cunning disguisement, a desperate burglar slid into his happy home, and robbed them all of everything. And darker yet to tell, the blacksmith himself did ignorantly conduct this burglar into his family's heart. It was the Bottle Conjuror! Upon the opening of that fatal cork, forth flew the fiend, and shriveled up his home. Now, for prudent, most wise, and economic reasons, the blacksmith's shop was in the basement of his dwelling, but with a separate entrance to it; so that always had the young and loving healthy wife listened with no unhappy nervousness, but with vigorous pleasure, to the stout ringing of her young-armed old husband's hammer; whose reverberations, muffled by passing through the floors and walls, came up to her, not unsweetly, in her nursery; and so, to stout Labor's iron lullaby, the blacksmith's infants were rocked to slumber.

Oh, woe on woe! Oh, Death, why canst thou not sometimes be timely? Hadst thou taken this old blacksmith to thyself ere his full ruin came upon him, then had the young widow had a delicious grief, and her orphans a truly venerable, legendary sire to dream of in their after years; and all of them a care-killing competency. But Death plucked down some virtuous elder brother, on whose whistling daily toil solely hung the responsibilities of some other family, and left the worse than useless old man standing, till the hideous rot of life should make him easier to harvest.

Why tell the whole? The blows of the basement hammer every day grew more and more between; and each blow every day grew fainter than the last; the wife sat frozen at the window, with tearless eyes, glitteringly gazing into the weeping faces of her children; the bellows fell; the forge choked up with cinders; the house was sold; the mother dived down into the long church-yard grass; her children twice followed her thither; and the houseless, familyless old man staggered off a vagabond in crape; his every woe unreverenced; his gray head a scorn to flaxen curls!

Death seems the only desirable sequel for a career like this; but Death is only a launching into the region of the strange Untried; it is but the first salutation to the possibilities of the immense Remote, the Wild, the Watery, the Unshored; therefore, to the death-longing eyes of such men, who still have left in them some interior compunctions against suicide, does the all-contributed and all-receptive ocean alluringly spread forth his whole plain of unimaginable, taking terrors, and wonderful, new-life adventures; and from the hearts of infinite Pacifics, the thousand mermaids sing to them—"Come hither, broken-hearted; here is another life without the guilt of intermediate death; here are wonders supernatural, without dying for them. Come hither! bury thyself in a life which, to your now equally abhorred and abhorring, landed world, is more oblivious than death. Come hither! put up *thy* grave-stone, too, within the church-yard, and come hither, till we marry thee!"

Hearkening to these voices, East and West, by early sunrise, and by fall of eve, the blacksmith's soul responded, Ay, I come! And so Perth went a-whaling.

Chapter CXIII

The Forge

With matted beard, and swathed in a bristling shark-skin apron, about mid-day, Perth was standing between his forge and anvil, the latter placed upon an iron-wood log, with one hand holding a pike-head in the coals, and with the other at his forge's lungs, when Captain Ahab came along, carrying in his hand a small rusty-looking leathern bag. While yet a little distance from the forge, moody Ahab paused; till at last, Perth, withdrawing his iron from the fire, began hammering it upon the anvil—the red mass sending off the sparks in thick hovering flights, some of which flew close to Ahab.

"Are these thy Mother Carey's chickens, Perth? they are always flying in thy wake; birds of good omen, too, but not to all;—look here, they burn; but thou—thou liv'st among them without a scorch."

"Because I am scorched all over, Captain Ahab," answered Perth, resting for a moment on his hammer; "I am past scorching; not easily can'st thou scorch a scar."

"Well, well; no more. Thy shrunk voice sounds too calmly, sanely woeful to me. In no Paradise myself, I am impatient of all misery in others that is not mad. Thou should'st go mad, blacksmith; say, why dost thou not go mad? How can'st thou endure without being mad? Do the heavens yet hate thee, that thou can'st not go mad?—What wert thou making there?"

"Welding an old pike-head, sir; there were seams and dents in it."

"And can'st thou make it all smooth again, blacksmith, after such hard usage as it had?"

"I think so, sir."

"And I suppose thou can'st smoothe almost any seams and dents; never mind how hard the metal, blacksmith?"

"Ay, sir, I think I can; all seams and dents but one."

"Look ye here, then," cried Ahab, passionately advancing, and leaning with both hands on

Perth's shoulders; "look ye here—*here*—can ye smoothe out a seam like this, blacksmith," sweeping one hand across his ribbed brow; "if thou could'st, blacksmith, glad enough would I lay my head upon thy anvil, and feel thy heaviest hammer between my eyes. Answer! Can'st thou smoothe this seam?"

"Oh! that is the one, sir! Said I not all seams and dents but one?"

"Ay, blacksmith, it is the one; ay, man, it is unsmoothable; for though thou only see'st it here in my flesh, it has worked down into the bone of my skull—*that* is all wrinkles! But, away with child's play; no more gaffs and pikes to-day. Look ye here!" jingling the leathern bag, as if it were full of gold coins. "I, too, want a harpoon made; one that a thousand yoke of fiends could not part, Perth; something that will stick in a whale like his own fin-bone. There's the stuff," flinging the pouch upon the anvil. "Look ye, blacksmith, these are the gathered nail-stubbs of the steel shoes of racing horses."

"Horse-shoe stubbs, sir? Why, Captain Ahab, thou hast here, then, the best and stubbornest stuff we blacksmiths ever work."

"I know it, old man; these stubbs will weld together like glue from the melted bones of murderers. Quick! forge me the harpoon. And forge me first, twelve rods for its shank; then wind, and twist, and hammer these twelve together like the yarns and strands of a tow-line. Quick! I'll blow the fire."

When at last the twelve rods were made, Ahab tried them, one by one, by spiraling them, with his own hand, round a long, heavy iron bolt. "A flaw!" rejecting the last one. "Work that over again, Perth."

This done, Perth was about to begin welding the twelve into one, when Ahab stayed his hand, and said he would weld his own iron. As, then, with regular, gasping hems, he hammered on the anvil, Perth passing to him the glowing rods, one after the other, and the hard pressed forge shooting up its intense straight flame, the Parsee passed silently, and bowing over his head towards the fire, seemed invoking some curse or some blessing on the toil. But, as Ahab looked up, he slid aside.

"What's that bunch of lucifers dodging about there for?" muttered Stubb, looking on from the forecastle. "That Parsee smells fire like a fusee; and smells of it himself, like a hot musket's powder-pan."

At last the shank, in one complete rod, received its final heat; and as Perth, to temper it, plunged it all hissing into the cask of water nearby, the scalding steam shot up into Ahab's bent face.

"Would'st thou brand me, Perth?" wincing for a moment with the pain; "have I been but forging my own branding-iron, then?"

"Pray God, not that; yet I fear something, Captain Ahab. Is not this harpoon for the White Whale?"

"For the white fiend! But now for the barbs; thou must make them thyself, man. Here are my razors—the best of steel; here, and make the barbs sharp as the needle-sleet of the Icy Sea."

For a moment, the old blacksmith eyed the razors as though he would fain not use them.

"Take them, man, I have no need for them; for I now neither shave, sup, nor pray till—but here—to work!"

Fashioned at last into an arrowy shape, and welded by Perth to the shank, the steel soon pointed the end of the iron; and as the blacksmith was about giving the barbs their final heat, prior to tempering them, he cried to Ahab to place the water-cask near.

"No, no—no water for that; I want it of the true death-temper. Ahoy, there! Tashtego, Queequeg, Daggoo! What say ye, pagans! Will ye give me as much blood as will cover this barb?" holding it high up. A cluster of dark nods replied, Yes. Three punctures were made in the heathen flesh, and the White Whale's barbs were then tempered.

"Ego non baptizo te in nomine patris, sed in nomine diaboli!" deliriously howled Ahab, as the malignant iron scorchingly devoured the baptismal blood.

Now, mustering the spare poles from below, and selecting one of hickory, with the bark still investing it, Ahab fitted the end to the socket of the iron. A coil of new tow-line was then unwound, and some fathoms of it taken to the windlass, and stretched to a great tension. Pressing his foot upon it, till the rope hummed like a harpstring, then eagerly bending over it, and seeing no strandings, Ahab exclaimed, "Good! and now for the seizings."

At one extremity the rope was unstranded, and the separate spread yarns were all braided and woven round the socket of the harpoon; the pole was then driven hard up into the socket; from the lower end the rope was traced half-way along the pole's length, and firmly secured so, with intertwistings of twine. This done, pole, iron, and rope—like the Three Fates—remained inseparable, and Ahab moodily stalked away with the weapon; the sound of his ivory leg, and the sound of the hickory pole, both hollowly ringing along every plank. But ere he entered his cabin, a light, unnatural, half-bantering, yet most piteous sound was heard. Oh! Pip, thy wretched laugh, thy idle but unresting eye; all thy strange mummeries not unmeaningly blended with the black tragedy of the melancholy ship, and mocked it!

Chapter CXIV

The Gilder

Penetrating further and further into the heart of the Japanese cruising-ground, the *Pequod* was soon all astir in the fishery. Often, in mild, pleasant weather, for twelve, fifteen, eighteen, and twenty hours on the stretch, they were engaged in the boats, steadily pulling, or sailing, or paddling after the whales, or for an interlude of sixty or seventy minutes calmly awaiting their uprising; though with but small success for their pains.

At such times, under an abated sun; afloat all day upon smooth, slow heaving swells; seated in his boat, light as a birch canoe; and so sociably mixing with the soft waves themselves, that like hearth-stone cats they purr against the gunwale; these are the times of dreamy quietude, when beholding the tranquil beauty and brilliancy of the ocean's skin, one forgets the tiger heart that pants beneath it; and would not willingly remember, that this velvet paw but conceals a remorseless fang.

These are the times, when in his whale-boat the rover softly feels a certain filial, confident, land-like feeling towards the sea; that he regards it as so much flowery earth; and the distant ship revealing only the tops of her masts, seems struggling forward, not through high rolling waves, but through the tall grass of a rolling prairie: as when the western emigrants' horses only show their erected ears, while their hidden bodies widely wade through the amazing verdure.

The long-drawn virgin vales; the mild blue hill-sides; as over these there steals the hush, the hum; you almost swear that play-wearied children lie sleeping in these solitudes, in some glad May-time, when the flowers of the woods are plucked. And all this mixes with your most mystic mood; so that fact and fancy, half-way meeting, inter-penetrate, and form one seamless whole.

Nor did such soothing scenes, however temporary, fail of at least as temporary an effect on Ahab. But if these secret golden keys did seem to open in him his own secret golden treasuries, yet did his breath upon them prove but tarnishing.

Oh, grassy glades! oh ever vernal endless landscapes in the soul; in ye—though long parched by the dead drought of the earthly life—in ye, men yet may roll, like young horses in new morning clover; and for some few fleeting moments, feel the cool dew of the life immortal on them. Would to God these blessed calms would last. But the mingled, mingling threads of life are woven by warp and woof: calms crossed by storms, a storm for every calm. There is no steady unretracing progress in this life; we do not advance through fixed gradations, and at the last one pause:—through infancy's unconscious spell, boyhood's thoughtless faith, adolescences doubt (the common doom), then skepticism, then disbelief, resting at last in manhood's pondering repose of If. But once gone through, we trace the round again; and are infants, boys, and men, and Ifs eternally. Where lies the final harbor, whence we unmoor no more? In what rapt ether sails the world, of which the weariest will never weary? Where is the foundling's father hidden? Our souls are like those orphans whose unwedded mothers die in bearing them: the secret of our paternity lies in their grave, and we must there to learn it.

And that same day, too, gazing far down from his boat's side into that same golden sea, Starbuck lowly murmured:

"Loveliness unfathomable, as ever lover saw in his young bride's eyes!—Tell me not of thy teeth-tiered sharks, and thy kidnapping cannibal ways. Let faith oust fact; let fancy oust memory; I look deep down and do believe."

And Stubb, fish-like, with sparkling scales, leaped up in that same golden light:

"I am Stubb, and Stubb has his history; but here Stubb takes oaths that he has always been jolly!"

Chapter CXV

The Pequod Meets the Bachelor

AND JOLLY ENOUGH WERE THE SIGHTS AND THE SOUNDS THAT CAME BEARING DOWN BEFORE THE wind, some few weeks after Ahab's harpoon had been welded.

It was a Nantucket ship, the *Bachelor,* which had just wedged in her last cask of oil, and bolted down her bursting hatches; and now, in glad holiday apparel, was joyously, though somewhat vain-gloriously, sailing round among the widely-separated ships on the ground, previous to pointing her prow for home.

The three men at her mast-head wore long streamers of narrow red bunting at their hats; from the stern, a whale-boat was suspended, bottom down; and hanging captive from the bowsprit was seen the long lower jaw of the last whale they had slain. Signals, ensigns, and jacks of all colors were flying from her rigging, on every side. Sideways lashed in each of her three basketed tops were two barrels of sperm; above which, in her top-mast cross-trees, you saw slender breakers of the same precious fluid; and nailed to her main truck was a brazen lamp.

As was afterwards learned, the *Bachelor* had met with the most surprising success; all the more wonderful, for that while cruising in the same seas numerous other vessels had gone entire months without securing a single fish. Not only had barrels of beef and bread been given away to make room for the far more valuable sperm, but additional supplemental casks had been bartered for, from the ships she had met; and these were stowed along the deck, and in the captain's and officers' state-rooms. Even the cabin table itself had been knocked into kindling-wood; and the cabin mess dined off the broad head of an oil-butt, lashed down to the floor for a centerpiece. In the forecastle, the sailors had actually caulked and pitched their chests, and filled them; it was humorously added, that the cook had clapped a head on his largest boiler, and filled it; that the steward had plugged his spare coffee-pot and filled it; that the harpooneers had headed the sockets of their irons and filled them; that indeed everything was filled with sperm, except the captain's pantaloons pockets, and those he reserved to thrust his hands into, in self-complacent testimony of his entire satisfaction.

As this glad ship of good luck bore down upon the moody *Pequod*, the barbarian sound of enormous drums came from her forecastle; and drawing still nearer, a crowd of her men were seen standing round her huge try-pots, which, covered with the parchment-like *poke* or stomach skin of the black fish, gave forth a loud roar to every stroke of the clenched hands of the crew. On the quarter-deck, the mates and harpooneers were dancing with the olive-hued girls who had eloped with them from the Polynesian Isles; while suspended in an ornamented boat, firmly secured aloft between the fore-mast and main-mast, three Long Island negroes, with glittering fiddle-bows of whale ivory, were presiding over the hilarious jig. Meanwhile, others of the ship's company were tumultuously busy at the masonry of the try-works, from which the huge pots had been removed. You would have almost thought they were pulling down the cursed Bastille, such wild cries they raised, as the now useless brick and mortar were being hurled into the sea.

Lord and master over all this scene, the captain stood erect on the ship's elevated quarter-deck, so that the whole rejoicing drama was full before him, and seemed merely contrived for his own individual diversion.

And Ahab, he too was standing on his quarter-deck, shaggy and black, with a stubborn gloom; and as the two ships crossed each other's wakes—one all jubilations for things passed, the other all forebodings as to things to come—their two captains in themselves impersonated the whole striking contrast of the scene.

"Come aboard, come aboard!" cried the gay *Bachelor*'s commander, lifting a glass and a bottle in the air.

"Hast seen the White Whale?" gritted Ahab in reply.

"No; only heard of him; but don't believe in him at all," said the other good-humoredly. "Come aboard!"

"Thou art too damned jolly. Sail on. Hast lost any men?"

"Not enough to speak of—two islanders, that's all;—but come aboard, old hearty, come along. I'll soon take that black from your brow. Come along, will ye (merry's the play); a full ship and homeward-bound."

"How wondrous familiar is a fool!" muttered Ahab; then aloud, "Thou art a full ship and homeward-bound, thou sayest; well, then, call me an empty ship, and outward-bound. So go thy ways, and I will mine. Forward there! Set all sail, and keep her to the wind!"

And thus, while the one ship went cheerily before the breeze, the other stubbornly fought against it; and so the two vessels parted; the crew of the *Pequod* looking with grave, lingering glances towards the receding *Bachelor*; but the *Bachelor*'s men never heeding their gaze for the lively revelry they were in. And as Ahab, leaning over the taffrail, eyed the homeward-bound craft, he took from his pocket a small vial of sand, and then looking from the ship to the vial, seemed thereby bringing two remote associations together, for that vial was filled with Nantucket soundings.

Chapter CXVI

THE DYING WHALE

NOT SELDOM IN THIS LIFE, WHEN, ON THE RIGHT SIDE, FORTUNE'S FAVORITES SAIL CLOSE BY US, we, though all adroop before, catch somewhat of the rushing breeze, and joyfully feel our bagging sails fill out. So seemed it with the *Pequod*. For next day after encountering the gay *Bachelor,* whales were seen and four were slain; and one of them by Ahab.

It was far down the afternoon; and when all the spearings of the crimson fight were done; and floating in the lovely sunset sea and sky, sun and whale both stilly died together; then, such a sweetness and such plaintiveness, such inwreathing orisons curled up in that rosy air, that it almost seemed as if far over from the deep green convent valleys of the Manila isles, the Spanish land-breeze, wantonly turned sailor, had gone to sea, freighted with these vesper hymns.

Soothed again, but only soothed to deeper gloom, Ahab, who had sterned off from the whale, sat intently watching his final wanings from the now tranquil boat. For that strange spectacle observable in all sperm whales dying—the turning sunwards of the head, and so expiring—that strange spectacle, beheld of such a placid evening, somehow to Ahab conveyed a wondrousness unknown before.

"He turns and turns him to it—how slowly, but how steadfastly, his homage-rendering and invoking brow, with his last dying motions. He too worships fire; most faithful, broad, baronial vassal of the sun!—Oh that these too-favoring eyes should see these too-favoring sights. Look! here, far water-locked; beyond all hum of human weal or woe; in these most candid and impartial seas; where to traditions no rocks furnish tablets; where for long Chinese ages, the billows have still rolled on speechless and unspoken to, as stars that shine upon the Niger's unknown source; here, too, life dies sunwards full of faith; but see! no sooner dead, than death whirls round the corpse, and it heads some other way.—

"Oh, thou dark Hindoo half of nature, who of drowned bones hast builded thy separate throne somewhere in the heart of these unverdured seas; thou art an infidel, thou queen, and too truly speakest to me in the wide-slaughtering Typhoon, and the hushed burial of its after calm. Nor has this thy whale sunwards turned his dying head, and then gone round again, without a lesson to me.

"Oh, trebly hooped and welded hip of power! Oh, high aspiring, rainbowed jet!—that one strivest, this one jettest all in vain! In vain, oh whale, dost thou seek intercedings with yon all-quickening sun, that only calls forth life, but gives it not again. Yet dost thou, darker half, rock me with a prouder, if a darker faith. All thy unnamable imminglings float beneath me here; I am buoyed by breaths of once living things, exhaled as air, but water now.

"Then hail, forever hail, O sea, in whose eternal tossings the wild fowl finds his only rest. Born of earth, yet suckled by the sea; though hill and valley mothered me, ye billows are my foster-brothers!"

Chapter CXVII

THE WHALE WATCH

THE FOUR WHALES SLAIN THAT EVENING HAD DIED WIDE APART; ONE, FAR TO WINDWARD; ONE, less distant, to leeward; one ahead; one astern. These last three were brought alongside ere nightfall; but the windward one could not be reached till morning; and the boat that had killed it lay by its side all night; and that boat was Ahab's.

The waif-pole was thrust upright into the dead whale's spout-hole and the lantern hanging from its top, cast a troubled flickering glare upon the black, glossy back, and far out upon the midnight waves, which gently chafed the whale's broad flank, like soft surf upon a beach.

Ahab and all his boat's crew seemed asleep but the Parsee; who crouching in the bow, sat watching the sharks, that spectrally played round the whale, and tapped the light cedar planks with their tails. A sound like the moaning in squadrons over Asphaltites of unforgiven ghosts of Gomorrah, ran shuddering through the air.

Started from his slumbers, Ahab, face to face, saw the Parsee; and hooped round by the gloom of the night they seemed the last men in a flooded world. "I have dreamed it again," said he.

"Of the hearses? Have I not said, old man, that neither hearse nor coffin can be thine?"

"And who are hearsed that die on the sea?"

"But I said, old man, that ere thou couldst die on this voyage, two hearses must verily be seen by thee on the sea; the first not made by mortal hands; and the visible wood of the last one must be grown in America."

"Ay, ay! a strange sight that, Parsee:—a hearse and its plumes floating over the ocean with the waves for the pall-bearers. Ha! Such a sight we shall not soon see."

"Believe it or not, thou canst not die till it be seen, old man."

"And what was that saying about thyself?"

"Though it come to the last, I shall still go before thee thy pilot."

"And when thou art so gone before—if that ever befall—then ere I can follow, thou must still appear to me, to pilot me still?—Was it not so? Well, then, did I believe all ye say, oh my pilot! I have here two pledges that I shall yet slay Moby-Dick and survive it."

"Take another pledge, old man," said the Parsee, as his eyes lighted up like fire-flies in the gloom—"Hemp only can kill thee."

"The gallows, ye mean.—I am immortal then, on land and on sea," cried Ahab, with a laugh of derision: "Immortal on land and on sea!"

Both were silent again, as one man. The gray dawn came on, and the slumbering crew arose from the boat's bottom, and ere noon the dead whale was brought to the ship.

Chapter CXVIII

THE QUADRANT

THE SEASON FOR THE LINE AT LENGTH DREW NEAR; AND EVERY DAY WHEN AHAB, COMING FROM his cabin cast his eyes aloft, the vigilant helmsman would ostentatiously handle his spokes, and the eager mariners quickly run to the braces, and would stand there with all their eyes centrally fixed on the nailed doubloon; impatient for the order to point the ship's prow for the equator. In good time the order came. It was hard upon high noon; and Ahab, seated in the bows of his high-hoisted boat, was about taking his wonted daily observation of the sun to determine his latitude.

Now, in that Japanese sea, the days in summer are as freshets of effulgences. That unblinkingly vivid Japanese sun seems the blazing focus of the glassy ocean's immeasurable burning-glass. The sky looks lacquered; clouds there are none; the horizon floats; and this nakedness of unrelieved radiance is as the insufferable splendors of God's throne. Well that Ahab's quadrant was furnished with colored glasses, through which to take sight of that solar fire. So, swinging his seated form to the roll of the ship, and with his astrological-looking instrument placed to his eye, he remained in that posture for some moments to catch the precise instant when the sun should gain its precise meridian. Meantime while his whole attention was absorbed, the Parsee was kneeling beneath him on the ship's deck, and with face thrown up like Ahab's, was eyeing the same sun with him; only the lids of his eyes half hooded their orbs, and his wild face was subdued to an earthly passionlessness. At length the desired observation was taken; and with his pencil upon his ivory leg, Ahab soon calculated what his latitude must be at that precise instant. Then falling into a moment's reverie, he again looked up towards the sun and murmured to himself: "Thou sea-mark! thou high and mighty Pilot! thou tellest me truly where I *am*—but canst thou cast the least hint where I *shall* be? Or canst thou tell where some other thing besides me is this moment living? Where is Moby-Dick? This instant thou must be eyeing him. These eyes of mine look into the very eye that is even now beholding him; ay, and into the eye that is even now equally beholding the objects on the unknown, thither side of thee, thou sun!"

Then gazing at his quadrant, and handling one after the other, its numerous cabalistical contrivances, he pondered again, and muttered: "Foolish toy! babies' plaything of haughty Admirals, and Commodores, and Captains; the world brags of thee, of thy cunning and might; but what after all canst thou do, but tell the poor, pitiful point, where thou thyself happenest to be on this wide planet, and the hand that holds thee: no! not one jot more! Thou canst not tell where one drop of water or one grain of sand will be to-morrow noon; and yet with thy impotence thou insultest the sun! Science! Curse thee, thou vain toy; and cursed be all the things that cast man's eyes aloft to that heaven, whose live vividness but scorches him, as these old eyes are even now scorched with thy light, O sun! Level by nature to this earth's horizon are the glances of man's eyes; not shot from the crown of his head, as if God had meant him to gaze on his firmament. Curse thee, thou quadrant!" dashing it to the deck, "no longer will I guide my earthly way by thee; the level ship's compass, and the level dead-reckoning, by log and by line; *these* shall conduct me, and show me my place on the sea. Ay," lighting from the boat to the deck, "thus I trample on thee, thou paltry thing that feebly pointest on high; thus I split and destroy thee!"

As the frantic old man thus spoke and thus trampled with his live and dead feet, a sneering triumph that seemed meant for Ahab, and a fatalistic despair that seemed meant for himself—these passed over the mute, motionless Parsee's face. Unobserved he rose and glided away; while, awestruck by the aspect of their commander, the seamen clustered together on the forecastle, till Ahab, troubledly pacing the deck, shouted out—"To the braces! Up helm!—square in!"

In an instant the yards swung round; and as the ship half-wheeled upon her heel, her three firm-seated graceful masts erectly poised upon her long, ribbed hull, seemed as the three Horatii pirouetting on one sufficient steed.

Standing between the knight-heads, Starbuck watched the *Pequod*'s tumultuous way, and Ahab's also, as he went lurching along the deck.

"I have sat before the dense coal fire and watched it all aglow, full of its tormented flaming life; and I have seen it wane at last, down, down, to dumbest dust. Old man of oceans! of all this fiery life of thine, what will at length remain but one little heap of ashes!"

"Ay," cried Stubb, "but sea-coal ashes—mind ye that, Mr. Starbuck—sea-coal, not your common charcoal. Well, well; I heard Ahab mutter, 'Here someone thrusts these cards into these old hands of mine; swears that I must play them, and no others.' And damn me, Ahab, but thou actest right; live in the game, and die in it!"

Chapter CXIX

The Candles

Warmest climes but nurse the cruelest fangs: the tiger of Bengal crouches in spiced groves of ceaseless verdure. Skies the most effulgent but basket the deadliest thunders: gorgeous Cuba knows tornadoes that never swept tame northern lands. So, too, it is, that in these resplendent Japanese seas the mariner encounters the direst of all storms, the Typhoon. It will sometimes burst from out that cloudless sky, like an exploding bomb upon a dazed and sleepy town.

Towards evening of that day, the *Pequod* was torn of her canvas, and bare-poled was left to fight a Typhoon which had struck her directly ahead. When darkness came on, sky and sea roared and split with the thunder, and blazed with the lightning, that showed the disabled mast fluttering here and there with the rags which the first fury of the tempest had left for its after sport.

Holding by a shroud, Starbuck was standing on the quarter-deck; at every flash of the lightning glancing aloft, to see what additional disaster might have befallen the intricate hamper there; while Stubb and Flask were directing the men in the higher hoisting and firmer lashing of the boats. But all their pains seemed naught. Though lifted to the very top of the cranes, the windward quarter boat (Ahab's) did not escape. A great rolling sea, dashing high up against the reeling ship's high teetering side, stove in the boat's bottom at the stern, and left it again, all dripping through like a sieve.

"Bad work, bad work! Mr. Starbuck," said Stubb, regarding the wreck, "but the sea will have its way. Stubb, for one, can't fight it. You see, Mr. Starbuck, a wave has such a great long start before it leaps, all round the world it runs, and then comes the spring! But as for me, all the start I have to meet it, is just across the deck here. But never mind; it's all in fun: so the old song says";—(*sings*.)

Oh! jolly is the gale,
And a joker is the whale,
A' flourishin' his tail—
Such a funny, sporty, gamy, jesty, joky, hoky-poky lad, is the Ocean, oh!
The scud all a-flyin',
That's his flip only foamin';
When he stirs in the spicin'—
Such a funny, sporty, gamy, jesty, joky, hoky-poky lad, is the Ocean, oh!

Thunder splits the ships,
But he only smacks his lips,
A tastin' of this flip—
Such a funny, sporty, gamy, jesty, joky, hoky-poky lad, is the Ocean, oh!

"Avast Stubb," cried Starbuck, "let the Typhoon sing, and strike his harp here in our rigging; but if thou art a brave man thou wilt hold thy peace."

"But I am not a brave man; never said I was a brave man; I am a coward; and I sing to keep up my spirits. And I tell you what it is, Mr. Starbuck, there's no way to stop my singing in this world but to cut my throat. And when that's done, ten to one I sing ye the doxology for a wind-up."

"Madman! look through my eyes if thou hast none of thine own."

"What how can you see better of a dark night than anybody else, never mind how foolish?"

"Here!" cried Starbuck, seizing Stubb by the shoulder, and pointing his hand towards the weather-bow, "markest thou not that the gale comes from the eastward, the very course Ahab is to run for Moby-Dick? the very course he swung to this day noon? now mark his boat there; where is that stove? In the stern-sheets, man; where he is wont to stand—his stand-point is stove, man! Now jump overboard, and sing away if thou must!"

"I don't half understand ye: what's in the wind?"

"Yes, yes, round the Cape of Good Hope is the shortest way to Nantucket," soliloquized Starbuck suddenly, heedless of Stubb's question. "The gale that now hammers at us to stave us, we can turn it into a fair wind that will drive us towards home. Yonder, to windward, all is blackness of doom; but to leeward, homeward—I see it lightens up there; but not with the lightning."

At that moment in one of the intervals of profound darkness, following the flashes, a voice was heard at his side; and almost at the same instant a volley of thunder peals rolled overhead.

"Who's there?"

"Old Thunder!" said Ahab, groping his way along the bulwarks to his pivot-hole; but suddenly finding his path made plain to him by elbowed lances of fire.

Now, as the lightning rod to a spire on shore is intended to carry off the perilous fluid into the soil; so the kindred rod which at sea some ships carry to each mast, is intended to conduct into the water. But as this conductor must descend to considerable depth, that its end may avoid all contact with the hull; and as moreover, if kept constantly towing there, it would be liable to many mishaps, besides interfering not a little with some of the rigging, and more or less impeding the vessel's way in the water; because of all this, the lower parts of a ship's lightning-rods are not always overboard; but are generally made in long slender links, so as to be the more readily hauled up into the chains outside, or thrown down into the sea, as occasion may require.

"The rods! the rods!" cried Starbuck to the crew, suddenly admonished to vigilance by the vivid lightning that had just been darting flambeaux, to light Ahab to his post. "Are they overboard? drop them over, fore and aft. Quick!"

"Avast!" cried Ahab; "let's have fair play here, though we be the weaker side. Yet I'll contribute to raise rods on the Himalayas and Andes, that all the world may be secured; but out on privileges! Let them be, sir."

"Look aloft!" cried Starbuck. "The corpusants! the corpusants!

All the yard-arms were tipped with a pallid fire; and touched at each tri-pointed lightning-rod-end with three tapering white flames, each of the three tall masts was silently burning in that sulfurous air, like three gigantic wax tapers before an altar.

"Blast the boat! let it go!" cried Stubb at this instant, as a swashing sea heaved up under his own little craft, so that its gunwale violently jammed his hand, as he was passing a lashing. "Blast it!"—but slipping backward on the deck, his uplifted eyes caught the flames; and immediately shifting his tone, he cried—"The corpusants have mercy on us all!"

To sailors, oaths are household words; they will swear in the trance of the calm, and in the teeth of the tempest; they will imprecate curses from the top-sail-yard-arms, when most they teeter over to a seething sea; but in all my voyagings, seldom have I heard a common oath when God's burning finger has been laid on the ship; when His "Mene, Mene, Tekel, Upharsin" has been woven into the shrouds and the cordage.

While this pallidness was burning aloft, few words were heard from the enchanted crew; who in one thick cluster stood on the forecastle, all their eyes gleaming in that pale phosphorescence, like a far away constellation of stars. Relieved against the ghostly light, the gigantic jet negro, Daggoo, loomed up to thrice his real stature, and seemed the black cloud from which the thunder had come. The parted mouth of Tashtego revealed his shark-white teeth, which strangely gleamed as if they too had been tipped by corpusants; while lit up by the preternatural light, Queequeg's tattooing burned like Satanic blue flames on his body.

The tableau all waned at last with the pallidness aloft; and once more the *Pequod* and every soul on her decks were wrapped in a pall. A moment or two passed, when Starbuck, going forward, pushed against someone. It was Stubb. "What thinkest thou now, man; I heard thy cry; it was not the same in the song."

"No, no, it wasn't; I said the corpusants have mercy on us all; and I hope they will, still. But do they only have mercy on long faces?—have they no bowels for a laugh? And look ye, Mr. Starbuck—but it's too dark to look. Hear me, then: I take that mast-head flame we saw for a sign of good luck; for those masts are rooted in a hold that is going to be chock a' block with sperm oil, d'ye see; and so, all that sperm will work up into the masts, like sap in a tree. Yes, our three masts will yet be as three spermaceti candles—that's the good promise we saw."

At that moment Starbuck caught sight of Stubb's face slowly beginning to glimmer into sight. Glancing upwards, he cried: "See! see!" and once more the high tapering flames were beheld with what seemed redoubled supernaturalness in their pallor.

"The corpusants have mercy on us all," cried Stubb, again.

At the base of the main-mast, full beneath the doubloon and the flame, the Parsee was kneeling in Ahab's front, but with his head bowed away from him; while nearby, from the arched and overhanging rigging, where they had just been engaged securing a spar, a number of the seamen, arrested by the glare, now cohered together, and hung pendulous, like a knot of numbered wasps from a drooping orchard twig. In various enchanted attitudes, like the standing, or stepping or running skeletons in Herculaneum, others remained rooted to the deck; but all their eyes upcast.

"Ay, ay, men!" cried Ahab. "Look up at it; mark it well; the white flame but lights the way to the White Whale! Hand me those main-mast links there; I would fain feel this pulse, and let mine beat against it; blood against fire! So."

Then turning—the last link held fast in his left hand, he put his foot upon the Parsee; and with fixed upward eye, and high-flung right arm, he stood erect before the lofty tri-pointed trinity of flames.

"Oh! thou clear spirit of clear fire, whom on these seas I as Persian once did worship, till in the sacramental act so burned by thee, that to this hour I bear the scar; I now know thee, thou clear spirit, and I now know that thy right worship is defiance. To neither love nor reverence wilt thou be kind; and e'en for hate thou canst but kill; and all are killed. No fearless fool now fronts thee. I own thy speechless, placeless power; but to the last gasp of my earthquake life will dispute its unconditional, unintegral mastery in me. In the midst of the personified impersonal, a personality stands here. Though but a point at best; whencesoe'er I came; wheresoe'er I go; yet while I earthly live, the queenly personality lives in me, and feels her royal rights. But war is pain, and hate is woe. Come in thy lowest form of love, and I will kneel and kiss thee; but at thy highest, come as mere supernal power; and though thou launchest navies of full-freighted worlds, there's that in here that still remains indifferent. Oh, thou clear spirit, of thy fire thou madest me, and like a true child of fire, I breathe it back to thee."

[*Sudden, repeated flashes of lightning; the nine flames leap lengthwise to thrice their previous height; Ahab, with the rest, closes his eyes, his right hand pressed hard upon them.*]

"I own thy speechless, placeless power; said I not so? Nor was it wrung from me; nor do I now drop these links. Thou canst blind; but I can then grope. Thou canst consume; but I can then be ashes. Take the homage of these poor eyes, and shutter-hands. I would not take it. The lightning flashes through my skull; mine eye-balls ache and ache; my whole beaten brain seems as beheaded, and rolling on some stunning ground. Oh, oh! Yet blindfold, yet will I talk to thee. Light though thou be, thou leapest out of darkness; but I am darkness leaping out of light, leaping out of thee! The javelins cease; open eyes; see, or not? There burn the flames! Oh, thou magnanimous! now I do glory in my genealogy. But thou art but my fiery father; my sweet mother, I know not. Oh, cruel! what hast thou done with her? There lies my puzzle; but thine is greater. Thou knowest not how came ye, hence callest thyself unbegotten; certainly knowest not thy beginning, hence callest thyself unbegun. I know that of me, which thou knowest not of thyself, oh, thou omnipotent. There is some unsuffusing thing beyond thee, thou clear spirit, to whom all thy eternity is but time, all thy creativeness mechanical. Through thee, thy flaming self, my scorched eyes do dimly see it. Oh, thou foundling fire, thou hermit immemorial, thou too hast thy incommunicable riddle, thy unparticipated grief. Here again with haughty agony, I read my sire. Leap! leap up, and lick the sky! I leap with thee; I burn with thee; would fain be welded with thee; defyingly I worship thee!"

"The boat! the boat!" cried Starbuck, "look at thy boat, old man!"

Ahab's harpoon, the one forged at Perth's fire, remained firmly lashed in its conspicuous crotch, so that it projected beyond his whale-boat's bow; but the sea that had stove its bottom had caused the loose leather sheath to drop off; and from the keen steel barb there now came a leveled flame of pale, forked fire. As the silent harpoon burned there like a serpent's tongue, Starbuck grasped Ahab by the arm—"God, God is against thee, old man; forbear! 'tis an ill voyage! ill begun, ill continued; let me square the yards, while we may, old man, and make a fair wind of it homewards, to go on a better voyage than this."

Overhearing Starbuck, the panic-stricken crew instantly ran to the braces though not a sail was left aloft. For the moment all the aghast mate's thoughts seemed theirs; they raised a half mutinous cry. But dashing the rattling lightning links to the deck, and snatching the burning harpoon, Ahab waved it like a torch among them; swearing to transfix with it the first sailor that but cast loose a rope's end. Petrified by his aspect, and still more shrinking from the fiery dart that he held, the men fell back in dismay, and Ahab again spoke:

"All your oaths to hunt the White Whale are as binding as mine; and heart, soul, and body, lungs and life, Old Ahab is bound. And that ye may know to what tune this heart beats: look ye here; thus I blow out the last fear!" And with one blast of his breath he extinguished the flame.

As in the hurricane that sweeps the plain, men fly the neighborhood of some lone, gigantic elm, whose very height and strength but render it so much the more unsafe, because so much the more a mark for thunderbolts; so at those last words of Ahab's many of the mariners did run from him in a terror of dismay.

Chapter CXX

THE DECK TOWARDS THE END OF THE FIRST NIGHT-WATCH

Ahab standing by the helm. Starbuck approaching him

WE MUST SEND DOWN THE MAIN-TOP-SAIL YARD, SIR. THE BAND IS WORKING LOOSE AND THE lee lift is half-stranded. Shall I strike it, sir?"

"Strike nothing; lash it. If I had sky-sail poles, I'd sway them up now."

"Sir!—in God's name!—sir?"

"Well."

"The anchors are working, sir. Shall I get them inboard?"

"Strike nothing, and stir nothing but lash everything. The wind rises, but it has not got up to my table-lands yet. Quick, and see to it.—By masts and keels! he takes me for the hunch-backed skipper of some coasting smack. Send down my main-top-sail yard! Ho, gluepots! Loftiest trucks were made for wildest winds, and this brain-truck of mine now sails amid the cloud-scud. Shall I strike that? Oh, none but cowards send down their brain-trucks in tempest time. What a hooroosh aloft there! I would e'en take it for sublime, did I not know that the colic is a noisy malady. Oh, take medicine, take medicine!"

Chapter CXXI

MIDNIGHT—THE FORECASTLE BULWARKS

Stubb and Flask mounted on them, and passing additional lashings over the anchors there hanging

NO, STUBB! YOU MAY POUND THAT KNOT THERE AS MUCH AS YOU PLEASE, BUT YOU WILL NEVER pound into me what you were just now saying. And how long ago is it since you said the very contrary? Didn't you once say that whatever ship Ahab sails in, that ship should pay something extra on its insurance policy, just as though it were loaded with powder barrels aft and boxes of lucifers forward? Stop, now; didn't you say so?"

"Well, suppose I did? What then? I've part changed my flesh since that time, why not my mind? Besides, supposing we *are* loaded with powder barrels aft and lucifers forward; how the devil could the lucifers get afire in this drenching spray here? Why, my little man, you have pretty red hair, but you couldn't get afire now. Shake yourself; you're Aquarius, or the water-bearer, Flask; might fill pitchers at your coat collar. Don't you see, then, that for these extra risks the Marine Insurance companies have extra guarantees? Here are hydrants, Flask. But hark, again, and I'll answer ye the other thing. First take your leg off from the crown of the anchor here, though, so I can pass the rope; now listen. What's the mighty difference between holding a mast's lightning-rod in the storm, and standing close by a mast that hasn't got any lightning-rod at all in a storm? Don't you see, you timber-head, that no harm can come to the holder of the rod, unless the mast is first struck? What are you talking about, then? Not one ship in a hundred carries rods, and Ahab—ay, man, and all of us—were in no more danger then, in my poor opinion, than all the crews in ten thousand ships now sailing the seas. Why, you King-Post, you, I suppose you would have every man in the world go about with a small lightning-rod running up the corner of his hat, like a militia officer's skewered feather, and trailing behind like his sash. Why don't ye be sensible, Flask? it's easy to be sensible; why don't ye, then? any man with half an eye can be sensible."

"I don't know that, Stubb. You sometimes find it rather hard."

"Yes, when a fellow's soaked through, it's hard to be sensible, that's a fact. And I am about drenched with this spray. Never mind; catch the turn there, and pass it. Seems to me we are lashing down these anchors now as if they were never going to be used again. Tying these two anchors here, Flask, seems like tying a man's hands behind him. And what big generous hands they are, to be sure. These are your iron fists, hey? What a hold they have, too! I wonder, Flask, whether the world is anchored anywhere; if she is, she swings with an uncommon long cable, though. There, hammer that knot down, and we've done. So; next to touching land, lighting on deck is the most satisfactory. I say, just wring out my jacket skirts, will ye? Thank ye. They laugh at long-togs so, Flask; but seems to me, a long tailed coat ought always to be worn in all storms afloat. The tails tapering down that way, serve to carry off the water, d'ye see. Same with cocked hats; the cocks form gable-end eave-troughs, Flask. No more monkey-jackets and tarpaulins for me; I must mount a swallow-tail, and drive down a beaver; so. Halloa! whew! there goes my tarpaulin overboard; Lord, Lord, that the winds that come from heaven should be so unmannerly! This is a nasty night, lad."

Chapter CXXII

MIDNIGHT ALOFT—THUNDER AND LIGHTNING

The Main-top-sail yard.—Tashtego passing new lashings around it

UM, UM, UM. STOP THAT THUNDER! PLENTY TOO MUCH THUNDER UP HERE. WHAT'S THE USE OF thunder? Um, um, um. We don't want thunder; we want rum; give us a glass of rum. Um, um, um!"

Chapter CXXIII

THE MUSKET

DURING THE MOST VIOLENT SHOCKS OF THE TYPHOON, THE MAN AT THE *PEQUOD*'S JAW-BONE tiller had several times been reelingly hurled to the deck by its spasmodic motions even though preventer tackles had been attached to it—for they were slack—because some play to the tiller was indispensable.

In a severe gale like this, while the ship is but a tossed shuttlecock to the blast, it is by no means uncommon to see the needles in the compasses, at intervals, go round and round. It was thus with the *Pequod*'s; at almost every shock the helmsman had not failed to notice the whirling velocity with which they revolved upon the cards; it is a sight that hardly anyone can behold without some sort of unwonted emotion.

Some hours after midnight, the Typhoon abated so much, that through the strenuous exertions of Starbuck and Stubb—one engaged forward and the other aft—the shivered remnants of the jib and fore and main-top-sails were cut adrift from the spars, and went eddying away to leeward, like the feathers of an albatross, which sometimes are cast to the winds when that storm-tossed bird is on the wing.

The three corresponding new sails were now bent and reefed, and a storm-trysail was set further aft; so that the ship soon went through the water with some precision again; and the course—for the present, East-south-east—which he was to steer, if practicable, was once more given to the helmsman. For during the violence of the gale, he had only steered according to its vicissitudes. But as he was now bringing the ship as near her course as possible, watching the compass meanwhile, lo! a good sign! the wind seemed coming round astern; ay, the foul breeze became fair!

Instantly the yards were squared, to the lively song of *"Ho! the fair wind! oh-ye-ho cheerly, men!"* the crew singing for joy, that so promising an event should so soon have falsified the evil portents preceding it.

In compliance with the standing order of his commander—to report immediately, and at any one of the twenty-four hours, any decided change in the affairs of the deck—Starbuck had no sooner trimmed the yards to the breeze—however reluctantly and gloomily—than he mechanically went below to appraise Captain Ahab of the circumstance.

Ere knocking at his state-room, he involuntarily paused before it a moment. The cabin lamp—taking long swings this way and that—was burning fitfully, and casting fitful shadows upon the old man's bolted door—a thin one, with fixed blinds inserted, in place of upper panels. The isolated subterraneousness of the cabin made a certain humming silence to reign there, though it was hooped round by all the roar of the elements. The loaded muskets in the rack were shiningly revealed, as they stood upright against the forward bulkhead. Starbuck was an honest, upright man; but out of Starbuck's heart, at that instant when he saw the muskets, there strangely evolved an evil thought; but so blent with its neutral or good accompaniments that for the instant he hardly knew it for itself.

"He would have shot me once," he murmured, "yes, there's the very musket that he pointed at me;—that one with the studded stock; let me touch it—lift it. Strange, that I, who have handled so many deadly lances, strange, that I should shake so now. Loaded? I must see. Ay, ay; and powder in the pan;—that's not good. Best spill it?—wait. I'll cure myself of this. I'll hold the musket boldly while I think.—I come to report a fair wind to him. But how fair? Fair for death and doom—*that's* fair for Moby-Dick. It's a fair wind that's only fair for that accursed fish.—The very tube he pointed at me!—the very one; *this* one—I hold it here; he would have killed me with the very thing I handle now.—Ay and he would fain kill all his crew. Does he not say he will not strike his spars to any gale? Has he not dashed his heavenly quadrant? and in these same perilous seas, gropes he not his way by mere dead reckoning of the error-abounding log? and in this very Typhoon, did he not swear that he would have no lightning-rods? But shall this crazed old man be tamely suffered to drag a whole ship's company down to doom with him?—Yes, it would make him the willful murderer of thirty men and more, if this ship come to any deadly harm; and come to deadly harm, my soul swears this ship will, if Ahab have his way. If, then, he were this instant—put aside, that crime would not be his. Ha! is he muttering in his sleep? Yes, just there—in there he's sleeping. Sleeping? ay, but still alive, and soon awake again. I can't withstand thee, then, old man. Not reasoning; not remonstrance; not entreaty wilt thou hearken to; all this thou scornest. Flat obedience to thy own flat commands, this is all thou breathest. Ay, and say'st the men have vow'd thy vow; say'st all of us are Ahabs? Great God forbid!—But is there no other way? no lawful way?—Make him a prisoner to be taken home? What! hope to wrest this old man's living power from his own living hands? Only a fool would try it. Say he were pinioned even; knotted all over with ropes and hawsers;

chained down to ring-bolts on this cabin floor; he would be more hideous than a caged tiger, then. I could not endure the sight; could not possibly fly his howlings; all comfort, sleep itself, inestimable reason would leave me on the long intolerable voyage. What, then, remains? The land is hundreds of leagues away, and locked Japan the nearest. I stand alone here upon an open sea, with two oceans and a whole continent between me and law.—Ay, ay, 'tis so.—Is heaven a murderer when its lightning strikes a would-be murderer in his bed, tindering sheets and skin together?—And would I be a murderer, then, if"—and slowly, stealthily, and half sideways looking, he placed the loaded musket's end against the door.

"On this level, Ahab's hammock swings within; his head this way. A touch, and Starbuck may survive to hug his wife and child again.—Oh Mary! Mary!—boy! boy! boy!—But if I wake thee not to death, old man, who can tell to what unsounded deeps Starbuck's body this day week may sink, with all the crew! Great God, where art Thou? Shall I? shall I?—The wind has gone down and shifted, sir; the fore and main-top-sails are reefed and set; she heads her course."

"Stern all! Oh Moby-Dick, I clutch thy heart at last!"

Such were the sounds that now came hurtling from out the old man's tormented sleep, as if Starbuck's voice had caused the long dumb dream to speak.

The yet leveled musket shook like a drunkard's arm against the panel; Starbuck seemed wrestling with an angel, but turning from the door, he placed the death-tube in its rack, and left the place.

"He's too sound asleep, Mr. Stubb; go thou down, and wake him, and tell him. I must see to the deck here. Thou know'st what to say."

Chapter CXXIV

The Needle

Next morning the not-yet-subsided sea rolled in long slow billows of mighty bulk, and striving in the *Pequod*'s gurgling track, pushed her on like giants' palms outspread. The strong, unstaggering breeze abounded so, that sky and air seemed vast outbellying sails; the whole world boomed before the wind. Muffled in the full morning light, the invisible sun was only known by the spread intensity of his place; where his bayonet rays moved on in stacks. Emblazonings, as of crowned Babylonian kings and queens, reigned over everything. The sea was as a crucible of molten gold, that bubblingly leaps with light and heat.

Long maintaining an enchanted silence, Ahab stood apart; and every time the teetering ship loweringly pitched down her bowsprit, he turned to eye the bright sun's rays produced ahead; and when she profoundly settled by the stern, he turned behind, and saw the sun's rearward place, and how the same yellow rays were blending with his undeviating wake.

"Ha, ha, my ship! thou mightest well be taken now for the sea-chariot of the sun. Ho, ho! all ye nations before my prow, I bring the sun to ye! Yoke on the further billows; hallo! a tandem, I drive the sea!"

But suddenly reined back by some counter thought, he hurried towards the helm, huskily demanding how the ship was heading.

"East-sou-east, sir," said the frightened steersman.

"Thou liest!" smiting him with his clenched fist. "Heading east at this hour in the morning, and the sun astern?"

Upon this every soul was confounded; for the phenomenon just then observed by Ahab had unaccountably escaped everyone else; but its very blinding palpableness must have been the cause.

Thrusting his head half-way into the binnacle, Ahab caught one glimpse of the compasses; his uplifted arm slowly fell; for a moment he almost seemed to stagger. Standing behind him Starbuck looked, and lo! the two compasses pointed east, and the *Pequod* was as infallibly going west.

But ere the first wild alarm could get out abroad among the crew, the old man with a rigid laugh exclaimed, "I have it! It has happened before. Mr. Starbuck, last night's thunder turned our compasses—that's all. Thou hast before now heard of such a thing, I take it."

"Ay; but never before has it happened to me, sir," said the pale mate, gloomily.

Here, it must needs be said, that accidents like this have in more than one case occurred to ships in violent storms. The magnetic energy, as developed in the mariner's needle, is, as all know, essentially one with the electricity beheld in heaven; hence it is not to be much marveled at, that such things should be. In instances where the lightning has actually struck the vessel, so as to smite down some of the spars and rigging, the effect upon the needle has at times been still more fatal; all its load-stone virtue being annihilated, so that the before magnetic steel was of no more use than an old wife's knitting needle. But in either case, the needle never again, of itself, recovers the original virtue thus marred or lost; and if the binnacle compasses be affected, the same fate reaches all the others that may be in the ship; even were the lowermost one inserted into the kelson.

Deliberately standing before the binnacle, and eyeing the transpointed compasses, the old man, with the sharp of his extended hand, now took the precise bearing of the sun, and satisfied that the needles were exactly inverted, shouted out his orders for the ship's course to be changed accordingly. The yards were hard up; and once more the *Pequod* thrust her undaunted bows into the opposing wind, for the supposed fair one had only been juggling her.

Meanwhile, whatever were his own secret thoughts, Starbuck said nothing, but quietly he issued all requisite orders; while Stubb and Flask—who in some small degree seemed then to be sharing his feelings—likewise unmurmuringly acquiesced. As for the men, though some of them lowly rumbled, their fear of Ahab was greater than their fear of Fate. But, as ever before, the pagan harpooneers remained almost wholly unimpressed; or if impressed, it was only with a certain magnetism shot into their congenial hearts from inflexible Ahab's.

For a space the old man walked the deck in rolling reveries. But chancing to slip with his ivory heel, he saw the crushed copper sight-tubes of the quadrant he had the day before dashed to the deck.

"Thou poor, proud heaven-gazer and sun's pilot! yesterday I wrecked thee, and to-day the compasses would fain have wrecked me. So, so. But Ahab is lord over the level load-stone yet. Mr. Starbuck—a lance without the pole; a top-maul, and the smallest of the sail-maker's needles. Quick!"

Accessory, perhaps, to the impulse dictating the thing he was now about to do, were certain prudential motives, whose object might have been to revive the spirits of his crew by a stroke of his subtle skill, in a matter so wondrous as that of the inverted compasses. Besides, the old man well knew that to steer by transpointed needles, though clumsily practicable, was not a thing to be passed over by superstitious sailors, without some shudderings and evil portents.

"Men," said he, steadily turning upon the crew, as the mate handed him the things he had demanded, "my men, the thunder turned old Ahab's needles; but out of this bit of steel Ahab can make one of his own, that will point as true as any."

Abashed glances of servile wonder were exchanged by the sailors, as this was said; and with fascinated eyes they awaited whatever magic might follow. But Starbuck looked away.

With a blow from the top-maul Ahab knocked off the steel head of the lance, and then handing to the mate the long iron rod remaining, bade him hold it upright, without its touching the deck. Then, with the maul, after repeatedly smiting the upper end of this iron rod, he placed the blunted needle endwise on the top of it, and less strongly hammered that, several times, the mate still holding the rod as before. Then going through some small strange motions with it—whether indispensable to the magnetizing of the steel, or merely intended to augment the awe of the crew, is uncertain—he called for linen thread; and moving to the binnacle, slipped out the two reversed needles there, and horizontally suspended the sail-needle by its middle, over one of the compass cards. At first, the steel went round and round, quivering and vibrating at either end; but at last it settled to its place, when Ahab, who had been intently watching for this result, stepped frankly back from the binnacle, and pointing his stretched arm towards it, exclaimed—"Look ye, for yourselves, if Ahab be not the lord of the level load-stone! The sun is east, and that compass swears it!"

One after another they peered in, for nothing but their own eyes could persuade such ignorance as theirs, and one after another they slunk away. In his fiery eyes of scorn and triumph, you then saw Ahab in all his fatal pride.

Chapter CXXV

The Log and Line

WHILE NOW THE FATED *PEQUOD* HAD BEEN SO LONG AFLOAT THIS VOYAGE, THE LOG AND LINE had but very seldom been in use. Owing to a confident reliance upon other means of determining the vessel's place, some merchantmen, and many whalemen, especially when cruising, wholly neglect to heave the log; though at the same time, and frequently more for form's sake than anything else, regularly putting down the customary slate the course steered by the ship, as well as the presumed average rate of progression every hour. It had been thus with the *Pequod.* The wooden reel and angular log attached hung, long untouched, just beneath the railing of the after bulwarks. Rains and spray had damped it; the sun and wind had warped it; all the elements had combined to rot a thing that hung so idly. But heedless of all this, his mood seized Ahab, as he happened to glance upon the reel, not many hours after the magnet scene, and he remembered how his quadrant was no more, and recalled his frantic oath about the level log and line. The ship was sailing plungingly; astern the billows rolled in riots.

"Forward, there! Heave the log!"

Two seamen came. The golden-hued Tahitian and the grizzly Manxman. "Take the reel, one of ye, I'll heave."

They went towards the extreme stern, on the ship's lee side, where the deck, with the oblique energy of the wind, was now almost dipping into the creamy, sidelong-rushing sea.

The Manxman took the reel, and holding it high up, by the projecting handle-ends of the spindle, round which the spool of line revolved, so stood with the angular log hanging downwards, till Ahab advanced to him.

Ahab stood before him, and was lightly unwinding some thirty or forty turns to form a preliminary hand-coil to toss overboard, when the old Manxman, who was intently eyeing both him and the line, made bold to speak.

"Sir, I mistrust it; this line looks far gone, long heat and wet have spoiled it."

" 'Twill hold, old gentleman. Long heat and wet, have they spoiled thee? Thou seem'st to hold. Or, truer perhaps, life holds thee; not thou it."

"I hold the spool, sir. But just as my captain says. With these gray hairs of mine 'tis not worthwhile disputing, 'specially with a superior, who'll ne'er confess."

"What's that? There now's a patched professor in Queen Nature's granite-founded College; but methinks he's too subservient. Where wert thou born?"

"In the little rocky Isle of Man, sir."

"Excellent! Thou'st hit the world by that."

"I know not, sir, but I was born there."

"In the Isle of Man, hey? Well, the other way, it's good. Here's a man from Man; a man born in once independent Man, and now unmanned of Man; which is sucked in—by what? Up with the reel! The dead, blind wall butts all inquiring heads at last. Up with it! So."

The log was heaved. The loose coils rapidly straightened out in a long dragging line astern, and then, instantly, the reel began to whirl. In turn, jerkingly raised and lowered by the rolling billows, the towing resistance of the log caused the old reelman to stagger strangely.

"Hold hard!"

Snap! the overstrained line sagged down in one long festoon; the tugging log was gone.

"I crush the quadrant, the thunder turns the needles, and now the mad sea parts the log-line. But Ahab can mend all. Haul in here, Tahitian, reel up, Manxman. And look ye, let the carpenter make another log, and mend thou the line. See to it."

"There he goes now; to him nothing's happened; but to me, the skewer seems loosening out of the middle of the world. Haul in, haul in, Tahitian! These lines run whole, and whirling out: come in broken, and dragging slow. Ha, Pip? come to help; eh, Pip?"

"Pip? whom call ye Pip? Pip jumped from the whale-boat. Pip's missing. Let's see now if ye haven't fished him up here, fisherman. It drags hard; I guess he's holding on. Jerk him, Tahiti! Jerk him off; we haul in no cowards here. Ho! there's his arm just breaking water. A hatchet! a hatchet! cut it off—we haul in no cowards here. Captain Ahab! sir, sir! here's Pip, trying to get on board again."

"Peace, thou crazy loon," cried the Manxman, seizing him by the arm. "Away from the quarter-deck!"

"The greater idiot ever scolds the lesser," muttered Ahab, advancing. "Hands off from that holiness! Where sayest thou Pip was, boy?"

"Astern there, sir, astern! Lo! lo!"

"And who art thou, boy? I see not my reflection in the vacant pupils of thy eyes. Oh God! that man should be a thing for immortal souls to sieve through! Who art thou, boy?"

"Bell-boy, sir; ship's-crier; ding, dong, ding! Pip! Pip! Pip! One hundred pounds of clay reward for Pip; five feet high—looks cowardly—quickest known by that! Ding, dong, ding! Who's seen Pip the coward?"

"There can be no hearts above the snow-line. Oh, ye frozen heavens! look down here. Ye did beget this luckless child, and have abandoned him, ye creative libertines. Here, boy; Ahab's cabin shall be Pip's home henceforth, while Ahab lives. Thou touchest my inmost center, boy; thou art tied to me by cords woven of my heart-strings. Come, let's down."

"What's this? here's velvet shark-skin," intently gazing at Ahab's hand, and feeling it. "Ah, now, had poor Pip but felt so kind a thing as this, perhaps he had ne'er been lost! This seems to me, sir, as a man-rope; something that weak souls may hold by. Oh, sir, let old Perth now come and rivet these two hands together; the black one with the white, for I will not let this go."

"Oh, boy, nor will I thee, unless I should thereby drag thee to worse horrors than are here. Come, then, to my cabin. Lo! ye believers in gods all goodness, and in man all ill, lo you! see the omniscient gods oblivious of suffering man; and man, though idiotic, and knowing not what he does, yet full of the sweet things of love and gratitude. Come! I feel prouder leading thee by thy black hand, than though I grasped an Emperor's!"

"There go two daft ones now," muttered the old Manxman. "One daft with strength, the other daft with weakness. But here's the end of the rotten line—all dripping, too. Mend it, eh? I think we had best have a new line altogether. I'll see Mr. Stubb about it."

Chapter CXXVI

THE LIFE-BUOY

STEERING NOW SOUTH-EASTWARD BY AHAB'S LEVELED STEEL, AND HER PROGRESS SOLELY DETERmined by Ahab's level log and line; the *Pequod* held on her path towards the Equator. Making so long a passage through such unfrequented waters, descrying no ships, and ere long, sideways impelled by unvarying trade-winds, over waves monotonously mild; all these seemed the strange calm things preluding some riotous and desperate scene.

At last, when the ship drew near to the outskirts, as it were, of the Equatorial fishing-ground, and in the deep darkness that goes before the dawn, was sailing by a cluster of rocky islets; the watch—then headed by Flask—was startled by a cry so plaintively wild and unearthly—like half-articulated wailings of the ghosts of all Herod's murdered Innocents—that one and all, they started from their reveries, and for the space of some moments stood, or sat, or leaned all transfixedly listening, like the carved Roman slave, while that wild cry remained within hearing. The Christian or civilized part of the crew said it was mermaids, and shuddered; but the pagan harpooneers remained unappalled. Yet the gray Manxman—the oldest mariner of all—declared that the wild thrilling sounds that were heard, were the voices of newly drowned men in the sea.

Below in his hammock, Ahab did not hear of this till gray dawn, when he came to the deck; it was then recounted to him by Flask, not unaccompanied with hinted dark meanings. He hollowly laughed, and thus explained the wonder.

Those rocky islands the ship had passed were the resort of great numbers of seals, and some young seals that had lost their dams, or some dams that had lost their cubs, must have risen nigh the ship and kept company with her, crying and sobbing with their human sort of wail. But this only the more affected some of them, because most mariners cherish a very superstitious feeling about seals, arising not only from their peculiar tones when in distress, but also from the human look of their round heads and semi-intelligent faces, seen peeringly uprising from the water alongside. In the sea, under certain circumstances, seals have more than once been mistaken for men.

But the bodings of the crew were destined to receive a most plausible confirmation in the fate of one of their number that morning. At sun-rise this man went from his hammock to his mast-head at the fore; and whether it was that he was not yet half waked from his sleep (for sailors sometimes go aloft in a transition state), whether it was thus with the man, there is now no telling; but, be that as it may, he had not been long at his perch, when a cry was heard—a cry and a rushing—and looking up, they saw a falling phantom in the air; and looking down, a little tossed heap of white bubbles in the blue of the sea.

The life-buoy—a long slender cask—was dropped from the stern, where it always hung obedient to a cunning spring; but no hand rose to seize it, and the sun having long beat upon this cask it had shrunken, so that it slowly filled, and the parched wood also filled at its every pore; and the studded iron-bound cask followed the sailor to the bottom, as if to yield him his pillow, though in sooth but a hard one.

And thus the first man of the *Pequod* that mounted the mast to look out for the White Whale, on the White Whale's own peculiar ground; that man was swallowed up in the deep. But few, perhaps, thought of that at the time. Indeed, in some sort, they were not grieved at this event, at least as a portent; for they regarded it, not as a foreshadowing of evil in the future, but as the fulfillment of an evil already presaged. They declared that now they knew the reason of those wild shrieks they had heard the night before. But again the old Manxman said nay.

The lost life-buoy was now to be replaced; Starbuck was directed to see to it; but as no cask of sufficient lightness could be found, and as in the feverish eagerness of what seemed the approaching crisis of the voyage, all hands were impatient of any toil but what was directly connected with its final end, whatever that might prove to be; therefore, they were going to leave the ship's stern unprovided with a buoy, when by certain strange signs and innuendoes Queequeg hinted a hint concerning his coffin.

"A life-buoy of a coffin!" cried Starbuck, starting.

"Rather queer, that, I should say," said Stubb.

"It will make a good enough one," said Flask, "the carpenter here can arrange it easily."

"Bring it up; there's nothing else for it," said Starbuck, after a melancholy pause. "Rig it, carpenter; do not look at me so—the coffin, I mean. Dost thou hear me? Rig it."

"And shall I nail down the lid, sir?" moving his hand as with a hammer.

"Ay."

"And shall I caulk the seams, sir?" moving his hand as with a caulking-iron.

"Ay."

"And shall I then pay over the same with pitch, sir?" moving his hand as with a pitch-pot.

"Away! what possesses thee to this? Make a life-buoy of the coffin, and no more.—Mr. Stubb, Mr. Flask, come forward with me."

"He goes off in a huff. The whole he can endure; at the parts he baulks. Now I don't like this. I make a leg for Captain Ahab, and he wears it like a gentleman; but I make a band-box for Queequeg, and he won't put his head into it. Are all my pains to go for nothing with that coffin? And now I'm ordered to make a life-buoy of it. It's like turning an old coat; going to bring the flesh on the other side now. I don't like this cobbling sort of business—I don't like it at all; it's undignified; it's not my place. Let tinkers' brats do tinkerings; we are their betters. I like to take in hand none but clean, virgin, fair-and-square mathematical jobs, something that regularly begins at the beginning, and is at the middle when midway, and comes to an end at the conclusion; not a cobbler's job, that's at an end in the middle, and at the beginning at the end. It's the old woman's tricks to be giving cobbling jobs. Lord! what an affection all old women have for tinkers. I know an old woman of sixty-five who ran away with a bald-headed young tinker once. And that's the reason I never would work for lonely widow old women ashore, when I kept my job-shop in the Vineyard; they might have taken it into their lonely old heads to run off with me. But heigh-ho! there are no caps at sea but snow-caps. Let me see. Nail down the lid; caulk the seams; pay over the same with pitch; batten them down tight, and hang it with the snap-spring over the ship's stern. Were ever such things done before with a coffin? Some superstitious old carpenters, now, would be tied up in the rigging, ere they would do the job. But I'm made of knotty Aroostook hemlock; I don't budge. Cruppered with a coffin! Sailing about with a grave-yard tray! But never mind. We workers in woods make bridal-bedsteads and card-tables, as well as coffins and hearses. We work by the month, or by the job, or by the profit; not for us to ask the why and wherefore of our work, unless it be too confounded cobbling, and then we stash it if we can. Hem! I'll do the job, now, tenderly. I'll have me—let's see—how many in the ship's company, all told? But I've forgotten. Anyway, I'll have me thirty separate, Turk's-headed life-lines, each three feet long hanging all round to the coffin. Then, if the hull go down, there'll be thirty lively fellows all fighting for one coffin, a sight not seen very often beneath the sun! Come hammer, caulking-iron, pitch-pot, and marling-spike! Let's to it."

Chapter CXXVII

THE DECK

The coffin laid upon two line-tubs, between the vice-bench and the open hatchway; the Carpenter caulking its seams; the string of twisted oakum slowly unwinding from a large roll of it placed in the bosom of his frock.—Ahab comes slowly from the cabin-gangway, and hears Pip following him.

BACK LAD; I WILL BE WITH YE AGAIN PRESENTLY. HE GOES! NOT THIS HAND COMPLIES WITH MY humor more genially than that boy.—Middle aisle of a church! What's here?"

"Life-buoy, sir. Mr. Starbuck's orders. Oh, look, sir! Beware the hatchway!"

"Thank ye, man. Thy coffin lies handy to the vault."

"Sir? The hatchway? oh! So it does, sir, so it does."

"Art not thou the leg-maker? Look, did not this stump come from thy shop?"

"I believe it did, sir; does the ferrule stand, sir?"

"Well enough. But art thou not also the undertaker?"

"Ay, sir; I patched up this thing here as a coffin for Queequeg; but they've set me now to turning it into something else."

"Then tell me; art thou not an arrant, all-grasping, intermeddling, monopolizing, heathenish old scamp, to be one day making legs, and the next day coffins to clap them in, and yet again life-buoys out of those same coffins? Thou art as unprincipled as the gods, and as much of a jack-of-all-trades."

"But I do not mean anything, sir. I do as I do."

"The gods again. Hark ye, dost thou not ever sing working about a coffin? The Titans, they say, hummed snatches when chipping out the craters for volcanoes; and the grave-digger in the play sings, spade in hand. Dost thou never?"

"Sing, sir? Do I sing? Oh, I'm indifferent enough, sir, for that; but the reason why the grave-digger made music must have been because there was none in his spade, sir. But the caulking mallet is full of it. Hark to it."

"Ay, and that's because the lid there's a sounding-board; and what in all things makes the sounding-board is this—there's naught beneath. And yet, a coffin with a body in it rings pretty much the same, Carpenter. Hast thou ever helped carry a bier, and heard the coffin knock against the church-yard gate, going in?"

"Faith, sir, I've—"

"Faith? What's that?"

"Why, faith, sir, it's only a sort of exclamation-like—that's all, sir."

"Um, um; go on."

"I was about to say, sir, that—"

"Art thou a silk-worm? Dost thou spin thy own shroud out of thyself? Look at thy bosom! Dispatch! and get these traps out of sight."

"He goes aft. That was sudden, now; but squalls come sudden in hot latitudes. I've heard that the Isle of Albermarle, one of the Gallipagos, is cut by the Equator right in the middle. Seems to me some sort of Equator cuts yon old man, too, right in his middle. He's always under the Line—fiery hot, I tell ye! He's looking this way—come, oakum; quick. Here we go again. This wooden mallet is the cork, and I'm the professor of musical glasses—tap, tap!"

(*Ahab to himself*)

"There's a sight! There's a sound! The grayheaded wood-pecker tapping the hollow tree! Blind and dumb might well be envied now. See! that thing rests on two line-tubs, full of tow-lines. A most malicious wag, that fellow. Rat-tat! So man's seconds tick! Oh! how immaterial are all materials! What things real are there, but imponderable thoughts? Here now's the very dreaded symbol of grim death, by a mere hap, made the expressive sign of the help and hope of most endangered life. A life-buoy of a coffin! Does it go further? Can it be that in some spiritual sense the coffin is, after all, but an immortality-preserver! I'll think of that. But no. So far gone am I in the dark side of earth, that its other side, the theoretic bright one, seems but uncertain twilight to me. Will ye never have done, Carpenter, with that accursed sound? I go below; let me not see that thing here when I return again. Now, then, Pip, we'll talk this over; I do suck most wondrous philosophies from thee! Some unknown conduits from the unknown worlds must empty into thee!"

Chapter CXXVIII

The Pequod Meets the Rachel

NEXT DAY, A LARGE SHIP, THE *RACHEL*, WAS DESCRIED, BEARING DIRECTLY DOWN UPON THE *PEQUOD*, all her spars thickly clustering with men. At the time the *Pequod* was making good speed through the water; but as the broad-winged windward stranger shot nigh to her, the boastful sails all fell together as blank bladders that are burst, and all life fled from the smitten hull.

"Bad news; she brings bad news," muttered the old Manxman. But ere her commander, who, with trumpet to mouth, stood up in his boat; ere he could hopefully hail, Ahab's voice was heard.

"Hast seen the White Whale?"

"Ay, yesterday. Have ye seen a whale-boat adrift?"

Throttling his joy, Ahab negatively answered this unexpected question; and would then have fain boarded the stranger, when the stranger captain himself, having stopped his vessel's way, was seen descending her side. A few keen pulls, and his boat-hook soon clinched the *Pequod*'s main-chains, and he sprang to the deck. Immediately he was recognized by Ahab for a Nantucketer he knew. But no formal salutation was exchanged.

"Where was he?—not killed!—not killed!" cried Ahab, closely advancing. "How was it?"

It seemed that somewhat late on the afternoon of the day previous, while three of the stranger's boats were engaged with a shoal of whales, which had led them some four or five miles from the ship; and while they were yet in swift chase to windward, the white hump and head of Moby-Dick had suddenly loomed up out of the water, not very far to leeward; whereupon, the fourth rigged boat—a reserved one—had been instantly lowered in chase. After a keen sail before the wind, this fourth boat—the swiftest keeled of all—seemed to have succeeded in fastening—at least, as well as the man at the mast-head could tell anything about it. In the distance he saw the diminished dotted boat; and then a swift gleam of bubbling white water; and after that nothing more; whence it was concluded that the stricken whale must have indefinitely run away with his pursuers, as often happens. There was some apprehension, but no positive alarm, as yet. The recall signals were placed in the rigging; darkness came on; and forced to pick up her three far to windward boats—ere going in quest of the fourth one in the precisely opposite direction—the ship had not only been necessitated to leave that boat to its fate till near midnight, but, for the time, to increase her distance from it. But the rest of her crew being at last safe aboard, she crowded all sail—stun-sail on stun-sail—after the missing boat; kindling a fire in her try-pots for a beacon; and every other man aloft on the look-out. But though when she had thus sailed a sufficient distance to gain the presumed place of the absent ones when last seen; though she then paused to lower her spare boats to pull all around her; and not finding anything, had again dashed on; again paused, and lowered her boats; and though she had thus continued doing till daylight; yet not the least glimpse of the missing keel had been seen.

The story told, the stranger Captain immediately went on to reveal his object in boarding the *Pequod*. He desired that ship to unite with his own in the search; by sailing over the sea some four or five miles apart, on parallel lines, and so sweeping a double horizon, as it were.

"I will wager something now," whispered Stubb to Flask, "that someone in that missing boat wore off that Captain's best coat; mayhap, his watch—he's so cursed anxious to get it back. Who ever heard of two pious whale-ships cruising after one missing whale-boat in the height of the whaling season? See, Flask, only see how pale he looks—pale in the very buttons of his eyes—look—it wasn't the coat—it must have been the—"

"My boy, my own boy is among them. For God's sake—I beg, I conjure"—here exclaimed the stranger Captain to Ahab, who thus far had but icily received his petition. "For eight-and-forty hours let me charter your ship—I will gladly pay for it, and roundly pay for it—if there be no other way—for eight-and-forty hours only—only that—you must, oh, you must, and you *shall* do this thing."

"His son!" cried Stubb, "oh, it's his son he's lost! I take back the coat and watch—what says Ahab? We must save that boy."

"He's drowned with the rest of 'em, last night," said the old Manx sailor standing behind them; "I heard; all of ye heard their spirits."

Now, as it shortly turned out, what made this incident of the *Rachel*'s the more melancholy, was the circumstance, that not only was one of the Captain's sons among the number of the missing boat's crew; but among the number of the other boats' crews, at the same time, but on the other hand, separated from the ship during the dark vicissitudes of the chase, there had been still another son; as that for a time, the wretched father was plunged to the bottom of the cruelest perplexity; which was only solved for him by his chief mate's instinctively adopting the ordinary procedure of a whale-ship in such emergencies, that is, when placed between jeopardized but divided boats, always to pick up the majority first. But the captain, for some unknown constitutional reason, had refrained from mentioning all this, and not till forced to it by Ahab's iciness did he allude to his one yet missing boy; a little lad, but twelve years old, whose father with the earnest but unmisgiving hardihood of a Nantucketer's paternal love, had thus early sought to initiate him in the perils and wonders of a vocation almost immemorially the destiny of all his race. Nor does it unfrequently occur, that Nantucket captains will send a son of such tender age away from them, for a protracted three or four years' voyage in some other ship than their own; so that their first knowledge of a whaleman's career shall be unenervated by any chance display of a father's natural but untimely partiality, or undue apprehensiveness and concern.

Meantime, now the stranger was still beseeching his poor boon of Ahab; and Ahab still stood like an anvil, receiving every shock, but without the least quivering of his own.

"I will not go," said the stranger, "till you say *ay* to me. Do to me as you would have me do to you in the like case. For *you* too have a boy, Captain Ahab—though but a child, and nestling safely at home now—a child of your old age too—Yes, yes, you relent; I see it—run, run, men, now, and stand by to square in the yards."

"Avast," cried Ahab—"touch not a rope-yarn"; then in a voice that prolongingly molded every word—"Captain Gardiner, I will not do it. Even now I lose time. Good-bye, good-bye. God bless ye, man, and may I forgive myself, but I must go. Mr. Starbuck, look at the binnacle watch, and in three minutes from this present instant warn off all strangers; then brace forward again, and let the ship sail as before."

Hurriedly turning, with averted face, he descended into his cabin, leaving the strange captain transfixed at this unconditional and utter rejection of his so earnest suit. But starting from his enchantment, Gardiner silently hurried to the side; more fell than stepped into his boat, and returned to his ship.

Soon the two ships diverged their wakes; and long as the strange vessel was in view, she was seen to yaw hither and thither at every dark spot, however small, on the sea. This way and that her yards were swung around; starboard and larboard, she continued to tack; now she beat against a head sea; and again it pushed her before it; while all the while, her masts and yards were thickly clustered with men, as three tall cherry trees, when the boys are cherrying among the boughs.

But by her still halting course and winding, woeful way, you plainly saw that this ship that so wept with spray, still remained without comfort. She was *Rachel,* weeping for her children, because they were not.

Chapter CXXIX

The Cabin

(*Ahab moving to go on deck; Pip catches him by the hand to follow*)

"Lad, lad, I tell thee thou must not follow Ahab now. The hour is coming when Ahab would not scare thee from him, yet would not have thee by him. There is that in thee, poor lad, which I feel too curing to my malady. Like cures like; and for this hunt, my malady becomes my most desired health. Do thou abide below here, where they shall serve thee, as if thou wert the captain. Ay, lad, thou shalt sit here in my own screwed chair; another screw to it, thou must be."

"No, no, no! ye have not a whole body, sir; do ye but use poor me for your one lost leg; only tread upon me, sir; I ask no more, so I remain a part of ye."

"Oh! spite of million villains, this makes me a bigot in the fadeless fidelity of man!—and a black! and crazy!—but methinks like-cures-like applies to him too; he grows so sane again."

"They tell me, sir, that Stubb did once desert poor little Pip, whose drowned bones now show white, for all the blackness of his living skin. But I will never desert ye, sir, as Stubb did him. Sir, I must go with ye."

"If thou speakest thus to me much more, Ahab's purpose keels up in him. I tell thee no; it cannot be."

"Oh good master, master, master!

"Weep so, and I will murder thee! have a care, for Ahab too is mad. Listen, and thou wilt often hear my ivory foot upon the deck, and still know that I am there. And now I quit thee. Thy hand!—Met! True art thou, lad, as the circumference to its center. So: God forever bless thee; and if it come to that—God forever save thee, let what will befall."

(*Ahab goes; Pip steps one step forward*)

"Here he this instant stood, I stand in his air—but I'm alone. Now were even poor Pip here I could endure it, but he's missing. Pip! Pip! Ding, dong, ding! Who's seen Pip? He must be up here; let's try the door. What? neither lock, nor bolt, nor bar; and yet there's no opening it. It must be the spell; he told me to stay here: Ay, and told me this screwed chair was mine. Here, then, I'll seat me, against the transom, in the ship's full middle, all her keel and her three masts before me. Here, our old sailors say, in their black seventy-fours great admirals sometimes sit at table, and lord it over rows of captains and lieutenants. Ha! what's this? epaulets! epaulets! the epaulets all come crowding. Pass round the decanters; glad to see ye; fill up, monsieurs! What an odd feeling, now, when a black boy's host to white men with gold lace upon their coats!—Monsieurs, have ye seen one Pip?—a little negro lad, five feet high, hang-dog look, and cowardly! Jumped from a whale-boat once;—seen him? No! Well then, fill up again, captains, and let's drink shame upon all cowards! I name no names. Shame upon them! Put one foot upon the table. Shame upon all cowards.—Hist! above there, I hear ivory—Oh, master! master! I am indeed down-hearted when you walk over me. But here I'll stay, though this stern strikes rocks; and they bulge through; and oysters come to join me."

Chapter CXXX

THE HAT

AND NOW THAT AT THE PROPER TIME AND PLACE, AFTER SO LONG AND WIDE A PRELIMINARY cruise, Ahab—all other whaling waters swept—seemed to have chased his foe into an ocean-fold, to slay him the more securely there; now, that he found himself hard by the very latitude and longitude where his tormenting wound had been inflicted; now that a vessel had been spoken which on the very day preceding had actually encountered Moby-Dick;—and now that all his successive meetings with various ships contrastingly concurred to show the demoniac indifference with which the White Whale tore his hunters, whether sinning or sinned against; now it was that there lurked a something in the old man's eyes, which it was hardly sufferable for feeble souls to see. As the unsetting polar star, which through the livelong, arctic, six months' night sustains its piercing, steady, central gaze; so Ahab's purpose now fixedly gleamed down upon the constant midnight of the gloomy crew. It domineered above them so, that all their bodings, doubts, misgivings, fears, were fain to hide beneath their souls, and not sprout forth a single spear or leaf.

In this foreshadowing interval too, all humor, forced or natural, vanished. Stubb no more strove to raise a smile; Starbuck no more strove to check one. Alike, joy and sorrow, hope and fear, seemed ground to finest dust, and powdered, for the time, in the clamped mortar of Ahab's iron soul. Like machines, they dumbly moved about the deck, ever conscious that the old man's despot eye was on them.

But did you deeply scan him in his more secret confidential hours; when he thought no glance but one was on him; then you would have seen that even as Ahab's eyes so awed the crew's, the inscrutable Parsee's glance awed his; or somehow, at least, in some wild way, at times affected it. Such an added, gliding strangeness began to invest the thin Fedallah now; such ceaseless shudderings shook him; that the men looked dubious at him; half uncertain, as it seemed, whether indeed he were a mortal substance, or else a tremulous shadow cast upon the deck by some unseen being's body. And that shadow was always hovering there. For not by night, even, had Fedallah ever certainly been known to slumber, or go below. He would stand still for hours: but never sat or leaned; his wan but wondrous eyes did plainly say—We two watchmen never rest.

Nor, at any time, by night or day could the mariners now step upon the deck, unless Ahab was before them; either standing in his pivot-hole, or exactly pacing the planks between two undeviating limits—the main-mast and the mizzen; or else they saw him standing in the cabin-scuttle—his living foot advanced upon the deck, as if to step; his hat slouched heavily over his eyes; so that however motionless he stood, however the days and nights were added on, that he had not swung in his hammock; yet hidden beneath that slouching hat, they could never tell unerringly whether, for all this, his eyes were really closed at times: or whether he was still intently scanning them; no matter, though he stood so in the scuttle for a whole hour on the stretch, and the unheeded night-damp gathered in beads of dew upon that stone-carved coat and hat. The clothes that the night had wet, the next day's sunshine dried upon him; and so, day after day, and night after night; he went no more beneath the planks; whatever he wanted from the cabin that thing he sent for.

He ate in the same open air; that is, his two only meals—breakfast and dinner: supper he never touched; nor reaped his beard; which darkly grew all gnarled, as unearthed roots of trees blown over, which still grow idly on at naked base, though perished in the upper verdure. But though his whole life was now become one watch on deck; and though the Parsee's mystic watch was without intermission as his own; yet these two never seemed to speak—one man to the other—unless at long intervals some passing unmomentous matter made it necessary. Though such a potent spell seemed secretly to join the twain; openly, and to the awe-struck crew, they seemed pole-like asunder. If by day they chanced to speak one word; by night, dumb men were both, so far as concerned the slightest verbal interchange. At times, for longest hours, without a single hail, they stood far parted in the starlight; Ahab in his scuttle, the Parsee by the main-mast; but still fixedly gazing upon each other; as if in the Parsee Ahab saw his forethrown shadow, in Ahab the Parsee his abandoned substance.

And yet, somehow, did Ahab—in his own proper self, as daily, hourly, and every instant, commandingly revealed to his subordinates—Ahab seemed an independent lord; the Parsee but his slave. Still again both seemed yoked together, and an unseen tyrant driving them; the lean shade siding the solid rib. For be this Parsee what he may, all rib and keel was solid Ahab.

At the first faintest glimmering of the dawn, his iron voice was heard from aft—"Man the mast-heads!"—and all through the day, till after sunset and after twilight, the same voice every hour, at the striking of the helmsman's bell, was heard—"What d'ye see?—sharp! sharp!"

But when three or four days had slided by, after meeting the children-seeking *Rachel*; and no spout had yet been seen; the monomaniac old man seemed distrustful of his crew's fidelity; at least, of nearly all except the Pagan harpooneers; he seemed to doubt, even, whether Stubb and Flask might not willingly overlook the sight he sought. But if these suspicions were really his, he sagaciously refrained from verbally expressing them, however his actions might seem to hint them.

"I will have the first sight of the whale myself"—he said. "Ay! Ahab must have the doubloon!" and with his own hands he rigged a nest of basketed bowlines; and sending a hand aloft, with a single sheaved block, to secure to the main-mast-head, he received the two ends of the downward-reeved rope; and attaching one to his basket prepared a pin for the other end, in order to fasten it at the rail. This done, with that end yet in his hand and standing beside the pin, he looked round upon his crew, sweeping from one to the other; pausing his glance long upon Daggoo, Queequeg, Tashtego; but shunning Fedallah; and then settling his firm relying eye upon the chief mate, said—"Take the rope, sir—I give it into thy hands, Starbuck." Then arranging his person in the basket, he gave the word for them to hoist him to his perch, Starbuck being the one who secured the rope at last; and afterwards stood near it. And thus, with one hand clinging round the royal mast, Ahab gazed abroad upon the sea for miles and miles—ahead, astern, this side, and that—within the wide expanded circle commanded at so great a height.

When in working with his hands at some lofty almost isolated place in the rigging, which chances to afford no foothold, the sailor at sea is hoisted up to that spot, and sustained there by the rope; under these circumstances, its fastened end on deck is always given in strict charge to some one man who has the special watch of it. Because in such a wilderness of running rigging, whose various different relations aloft cannot always be infallibly discerned by what is seen of them at the deck; and when the deck-ends of these ropes are being every few minutes cast down from the fastenings, it would be but a natural fatality, if, unprovided with a constant watchman, the hoisted sailor should by some carelessness of the crew be cast adrift and fall all swooping to the sea. So Ahab's proceedings in this matter were not unusual; the only strange thing about them seemed to be, that Starbuck, almost the one only man who had ever ventured to oppose him with anything in the slightest degree approaching to decision—one of those too, whose faithfulness on the look-out he had seemed to doubt somewhat; it was strange, that this was the very man he should select for his watchman; freely giving his whole life into such an otherwise distrusted person's hands.

Now, the first time Ahab was perched aloft; ere he had been there ten minutes; one of those red-billed savage sea-hawks which so often fly incommodiously close round the manned mast-heads of whalemen in these latitudes; one of these birds came wheeling and screaming round his head in a maze of untrackably swift circlings. Then it darted a thousand feet straight up into the air; then spiralized downwards, and went eddying again round his head.

But with his gaze fixed upon the dim and distant horizon, Ahab seemed not to mark this wild bird; nor, indeed, would anyone else have marked it much, it being no uncommon circumstance; only now almost the least heedful eye seemed to see some sort of cunning meaning in almost every sight.

"Your hat, your hat, sir!" suddenly cried the Sicilian seaman, who being posted at the mizzen-mast-head, stood directly behind Ahab, though somewhat lower than his level, and with a deep gulf of air dividing them.

But already the sable wing was before the old man's eyes; the long hooked bill at his head: with a scream, the black hawk darted away with his prize.

An eagle flew thrice round Tarquin's head, removing his cap to replace it, and thereupon Tanaquil, his wife, declared that Tarquin would be king of Rome. But only by the replacing of the cap was that omen accounted good. Ahab's hat was never restored; the wild hawk flew on and on with it; far in advance of the prow: and at last disappeared; while from the point of that disappearance, a minute black spot was dimly discerned, falling from that vast height into the sea.

Chapter CXXXI

The Pequod Meets the Delight

The intense *Pequod* sailed on; the rolling waves and days went by; the life-buoy-coffin still lightly swung; and another ship, most miserably misnamed the *Delight*, was descried. As she drew nigh, all eyes were fixed upon her broad beams, called shears, which, in some whaling-ships, cross the quarter-deck at the height of eight or nine feet; serving to carry the spare, unrigged, or disabled boats.

Upon the stranger's shears were beheld the shattered, white ribs, and some few splintered planks, of what had once been a whale-boat; but you now saw through this wreck, as plainly as you see through the peeled, half-unhinged, and bleaching skeleton of a horse.

"Hast seen the White Whale?"

"Look!" replied the hollow-cheeked captain from his taffrail; and with his trumpet he pointed to the wreck.

"Hast killed him?"

"The harpoon is not yet forged that ever will do that," answered the other, sadly glancing upon a rounded hammock on the deck, whose gathered side some noiseless sailors were busy in sewing together.

"Not forged!" and snatching Perth's leveled iron from the crotch, Ahab held it out, exclaiming—"Look ye, Nantucketer; here in this hand I hold his death! Tempered in blood, and tempered by lightning are these barbs; and I swear to temper them triply in that hot place behind the fin, where the White Whale most feels his accursed life!"

"Then God keep thee, old man—see'st thou that"—pointing to the hammock—"I bury but one of five stout men, who were alive only yesterday; but were dead ere night. Only *that* one I bury; the rest were buried before they died; you sail upon their tomb." Then turning to his crew—"Are ye ready there? place the plank then on the rail, and lift the body; so, then—Oh! God"—advancing towards the hammock with uplifted hands—"may the resurrection and the life—"

"Brace forward! Up helm!" cried Ahab like lightning to his men.

But the suddenly started *Pequod* was not quick enough to escape the sound of the splash that the corpse soon made as it struck the sea; not so quick, indeed, but that some of the flying bubbles might have sprinkled her hull with their ghostly baptism.

As Ahab now glided from the dejected *Delight,* the strange life-buoy hanging at the *Pequod*'s stern came into conspicuous relief.

"Ha! yonder! look yonder, men!" cried a foreboding voice in her wake. "In vain, oh, ye strangers, ye fly our sad burial; ye but turn us your taffrail to show us your coffin!"

Chapter CXXXII

The Symphony

It was a clear steel-blue day. The firmaments of air and sea were hardly separable in that all-pervading azure; only, the pensive air was transparently pure and soft, with a woman's look, and the robust and man-like sea heaved with long, strong, lingering swells, as Samson's chest in his sleep.

Hither, and thither, on high, glided the snow-white wings of small, unspeckled birds; these were the gentle thoughts of the feminine air; but to and fro in the deeps, far down in the bottomless blue, rushed mighty leviathans, sword-fish, and sharks; and these were the strong, troubled, murderous thinkings of the masculine sea.

But though thus contrasting within, the contrast was only in shades and shadows without; those two seemed one; it was only the sex, as it were, that distinguished them.

Aloft, like a royal czar and king, the sun seemed giving this gentle air to this bold and rolling sea; even as bride to groom. And at the girdling line of the horizon, a soft and tremulous motion—most seen here at the Equator—denoted the fond, throbbing trust, the loving alarms, with which the poor bride gave her bosom away.

Tied up and twisted; gnarled and knotted with wrinkles; haggardly firm and unyielding; his eyes glowing like coals, that still glow in the ashes of ruin; untottering Ahab stood forth in the clearness of the morn; lifting his splintered helmet of a brow to the fair girl's forehead of heaven.

Oh, immortal infancy, and innocency of the azure! Invisible winged creatures that frolic all round us! Sweet childhood of air and sky! how oblivious were ye of old Ahab's close-coiled woe! But so have I seen little Miriam and Martha, laughing-eyed elves, heedlessly gambol around their old sire; sporting with the circle of singed locks which grew on the marge of that burned-out crater of his brain.

Slowly crossing the deck from the scuttle, Ahab leaned over the side, and watched how his shadow in the water sank and sank to his gaze, the more and the more that he strove to pierce the profundity. But the lovely aromas in that enchanted air did at last seem to dispel, for a moment, the cankerous thing in his soul. That glad, happy air, that winsome sky, did at last stroke and caress him; the step-mother world, so long cruel—forbidding—now threw affectionate arms round his stubborn neck, and did seem to joyously sob over him, as if over one, that however willful and erring, she could yet find it in her heart to save and to bless. From beneath his slouched hat Ahab dropped a tear into the sea; nor did all the Pacific contain such wealth as that one wee drop.

Starbuck saw the old man; saw him, how he heavily leaned over the side; and he seemed to hear in his own true heart the measureless sobbing that stole out of the center of the serenity around. Careful not to touch him, or be noticed by him, he yet drew near to him, and stood there.

Ahab turned.

"Starbuck!"

"Sir."

"Oh, Starbuck! it is a mild, mild wind, and a mild looking sky. On such a day—very much such a sweetness as this—I struck my first whale—a boy-harpooneer of eighteen! Forty—forty—forty years ago!—ago! Forty years of continual whaling! forty years of privation, and peril, and stormtime! forty years on the pitiless sea! for forty years has Ahab forsaken the peaceful land, for forty years to make war on the horrors of the deep! Ay and yes, Starbuck, out of those forty years I have not spent three ashore. When I think of this life I have led; the desolation of solitude it has been; the masoned, walled-town of a Captain's exclusiveness, which admits but small entrance to any sympathy from the green country without—oh, weariness! heaviness! Guinea-coast slavery of solitary command!—when I think of all this; only half-suspected, not so keenly known to me before—and how for forty years I have fed upon dry salted fare—fit emblem of the dry nourishment of my soul!—when the poorest landsman has had fresh fruit to his daily hand, and broken the world's fresh bread to my moldy crusts—away, whole oceans away, from that young girl-wife I wedded past fifty, and sailed for Cape Horn the next day, leaving but one dent in my marriage pillow—wife? wife?—rather a widow with her husband alive! Ay, I widowed that poor girl when I married her, Starbuck; and then, the madness, the frenzy, the boiling blood and the smoking brow, with which, for a thousand lowerings old Ahab has furiously, foamingly chased his prey—more a demon than a man!—ay, ay! what a forty years' fool—fool—old fool, has old Ahab been! Why this strife of the chase? why weary, and palsy the arm at the oar, and the iron, and the lance? how the richer or better is Ahab now? Behold. Oh, Starbuck! is it not hard, that with this weary load I bear, one poor leg should have been snatched from under me? Here, brush this old hair aside; it blinds me, that I seem to weep. Locks so gray did never grow but from out some ashes! But do I look very old, so very, very old, Starbuck? I feel deadly faint, bowed, and humped, as though I were Adam, staggering beneath the piled centuries since Paradise. God! God! God!—crack my heart!—stave my brain!—mockery!—mockery—bitter, biting mockery of gray hairs, have I lived enough joy to wear ye; and seem and feel thus intolerably old? Close! stand close to me, Starbuck; let me look into a human eye; it is better than to gaze into sea or sky; better than to gaze upon God. By the green land; by the bright hearth-stone! this is the magic glass, man; I see my wife and my child in thine eye. No, no; stay on board, on board!—lower not when I do; when branded Ahab gives chase to Moby-Dick. That hazard shall not be thine. No, no! not with the far away home I see in that eye!"

"Oh, my Captain! my Captain! noble soul! grand old heart, after all! why should anyone give chase to that hated fish! Away with me! let us fly these deadly waters! let us home! Wife and child, too, are Starbuck's—wife and child of his brotherly, sisterly, playfellow youth; even as thine, sir, are the wife and child of thy loving, longing, paternal old age! Away! let us away!—this instant let me alter the course! How cheerily, how hilariously, O my Captain, would we bowl on our way to see old Nantucket again! I think, sir, they have some such mild blue days, even as this, in Nantucket."

"They have, they have. I have seen them—some summer days in the morning. About this time—yes, it is his noon nap now—the boy vivaciously wakes; sits up in bed; and his mother tells him of me, of cannibal old me; how I am abroad upon the deep, but will yet come back to dance him again."

" 'Tis my Mary, my Mary herself! She promised that my boy, every morning, should be carried to the hill to catch the first glimpse of his father's sail! Yes, yes! no more! it is done! we head for Nantucket! Come, my Captain, study out the course, and let us away! See, see! the boy's face from the window; the boy's hand on the hill!"

But Ahab's glance was averted; like a blighted fruit-tree he shook, and cast his last, cindered apple to the soil.

"What is it, what nameless, inscrutable, unearthly thing is it; what cozening, hidden lord and master, and cruel, remorseless emperor commands me; that against all natural lovings and longings, I so keep pushing, and crowding, and jamming myself on all the time; recklessly making me ready to do what in my own proper, natural heart, I durst not so much as dare? Is Ahab, Ahab? Is it I, God, or who, that lifts this arm? But if the great sun move not of himself; but is as an errand-boy in heaven; nor one single star can revolve, but by some invisible power; how then can this one small heart beat; this one small brain think thoughts; unless God does that beating, does that thinking, does that living, and not I. By heaven, man, we are turned round and round in this world, like yonder windlass, and Fate is the handspike. And all the time, lo! that smiling sky, and this unsounded sea! Look! see yon albacore! who put it into him to chase and fang that flying-fish? Where do murderers go, man! Who's to doom, when the judge himself is dragged to the bar? But it is a mild, mild wind, and a mild looking sky; and the air smells now, as if it blew from a far-away meadow; they have been making hay somewhere under the slopes of the Andes, Starbuck, and the mowers are sleeping among the new-mown hay. Sleeping? Ay, toil we how we may, we all sleep at last on the field. Sleep? Ay, and rust amid greenness; as last year's scythes flung down, and left in the half-cut swaths—Starbuck!"

But blanched to a corpse's hue with despair, the Mate had stolen away.

Ahab crossed the deck to gaze over on the other side; but started at two reflected, fixed eyes in the water there. Fedallah was motionlessly leaning over the same rail.

Chapter CXXXIII

THE CHASE—FIRST DAY

THAT NIGHT, IN THE MID-WATCH, WHEN THE OLD MAN—AS HIS WONT AT INTERVALS—STEPPED forth from the scuttle in which he leaned, and went to his pivot-hole, he suddenly thrust out his face fiercely, snuffing up the sea-air as a sagacious ship's dog will, in drawing nigh to some barbarous isle. He declared that a whale must be near. Soon that peculiar odor, sometimes to a great distance given forth by the living sperm whale, was palpable to all the watch; nor was any mariner surprised when, after inspecting the compass, and then the dog-vane, and then ascertaining the precise bearing of the odor as nearly as possible, Ahab rapidly ordered the ship's course to be slightly altered, and the sail to be shortened.

The acute policy dictating these movements was sufficiently vindicated at daybreak, by the sight of a long sleek on the sea directly and lengthwise ahead, smooth as oil, and resembling in the pleated watery wrinkles bordering it, the polished metallic-like marks of some swift tide-rip, at the mouth of a deep, rapid stream.

"Man the mast-heads! Call all hands!"

Thundering with the butts of three clubbed handspikes on the forecastle deck, Daggoo roused the sleepers with such judgment claps that they seemed to exhale from the scuttle, so instantaneously did they appear with their clothes in their hands.

"What d'ye see?" cried Ahab, flattening his face to the sky.

"Nothing, nothing, sir!" was the sound hailing down in reply.

"T'gallant sails!—stun-sails! alow and aloft, and on both sides!"

All sail being set, he now cast loose the life-line, reserved for swaying him to the main-royal-mast-head; and in a few moments they were hoisting him thither, when, while but two thirds of the way aloft, and while peering ahead through the horizontal vacancy between the main-top-sail and top-gallant-sail, he raised a gull-like cry in the air, "There she blows!—there she blows! A hump like a snow-hill! It is Moby-Dick!"

Fired by the cry which seemed simultaneously taken up by the three look-outs, the men on deck rushed to the rigging to behold the famous whale they had so long been pursuing. Ahab had now gained his final perch, some feet above the other look-outs, Tashtego standing just beneath him on the cap of the top-gallant-mast, so that the Indian's head was almost on a level with Ahab's heel. From this height the whale was now seen some mile or so ahead, at every roll of the sea revealing his high sparkling hump, and regularly jetting his silent spout into the air. To the credulous mariners it seemed the same silent spout they had so long ago beheld in the moonlit Atlantic and Indian Oceans.

"And did none of ye see it before?" cried Ahab, hailing the perched men all around him.

"I saw him almost that same instant, sir, that Captain Ahab did, and I cried out," said Tashtego.

"Not the same instant; not the same—no, the doubloon is mine, Fate reserved the doubloon for me. *I* only; none of ye could have raised the White Whale first. There she blows! there she blows!—there she blows! There again!—there again!" he cried, in long-drawn, lingering, methodic tones, attuned to the gradual prolongings of the whale's visible jets. "He's going to sound! In stun-sails! Down top-gallant-sails! Stand by three boats. Mr. Starbuck, remember, stay on board, and keep the ship. Helm there! Luff, luff a point! So; steady, man, steady! There go flukes! No, no; only black water! All ready the boats there? Stand by, stand by! Lower me, Mr. Starbuck; lower, lower—quick, quicker!" and he slid through the air to the deck.

"He is heading straight to leeward, sir," cried Stubb, "right away from us; cannot have seen the ship yet."

"Be dumb, man! Stand by the braces! Hard down the helm!—brace up! Shiver her!—shiver her!—so; well that! Boats, boats!"

Soon all the boats but Starbuck's were dropped; all the boat-sails set—all the paddles plying; with rippling swiftness, shooting to leeward; and Ahab heading the onset. A pale, death-glimmer lit up Fedallah's sunken eyes; a hideous motion gnawed his mouth.

Like noiseless nautilus shells, their light prows sped through the sea; but only slowly they neared the foe. As they neared him, the ocean grew still more smooth; seemed drawing a carpet over its waves; seemed a noon-meadow, so serenely it spread. At length the breathless hunter came so nigh his seemingly unsuspecting prey, that his entire dazzling hump was distinctly visible, sliding along the sea as if an isolated thing, and continually set in a revolving ring of finest, fleecy, greenish foam. He saw the vast, involved wrinkles of the slightly projecting head beyond. Before it, far out on the soft Turkish-rugged waters, went the glistening white shadow from his broad, milky forehead, a musical rippling playfully accompanying the shade; and behind, the blue waters interchangeably flowed over into the moving valley of his steady wake; and on either hand bright bubbles arose and danced by his side. But these were broken again by the light toes of hundreds of gay fowls softly feathering the sea, alternate with their fitful flight; and like to some flag-staff rising from the painted hull of an argosy, the tall but shattered pole of a recent lance projected from the White Whale's back; and at intervals one of the cloud of soft-toed fowls hovering, and to and fro skimming like a canopy over the fish, silently perched and rocked on this pole, the long tail feathers streaming like pennons.

A gentle joyousness—a mighty mildness of repose in swiftness, invested the gliding whale. Not the white bull Jupiter swimming away with ravished Europa clinging to his graceful horns; his lovely, leering eyes sideways intent upon the maid; with smooth bewitching fleetness, rippling straight for the nuptial bower in Crete; not Jove, not that great majesty Supreme! did surpass the glorified White Whale as he so divinely swam.

On each soft side—coincident with the parted swell, that but once leaving him, then flowed so wide away—on each bright side, the whale shed off enticings. No wonder there had been some among the hunters who namelessly transported and allured by all this serenity, had ventured to assail it; but had fatally found that quietude but the vesture of tornadoes. Yet calm, enticing calm, oh, whale! thou glidest on, to all who for the first time eye thee, no matter how many in that same way thou may'st have bejuggled and destroyed before.

And thus, through the serene tranquilities of the tropical sea, among waves whose hand-clappings were suspended by exceeding rapture, Moby-Dick moved on, still withholding from sight the full terrors of his submerged trunk, entirely hiding the wrenched hideousness of his jaw. But soon the fore part of him slowly rose from the water; for an instant his whole marbleized body formed a high arch, like Virginia's Natural Bridge, and warningly waving his bannered flukes in the air, the grand god revealed himself, sounded, and went out of sight. Hoveringly halting, and dipping on the wing, the white sea-fowls longingly lingered over the agitated pool that he left.

With oars apeak, and paddles down, the sheets of their sails adrift, the three boats now stilly floated, awaiting Moby-Dick's reappearance.

"An hour," said Ahab, standing rooted in his boat's stern; and he gazed beyond the whale's place, towards the dim blue spaces and wide wooing vacancies to leeward. It was only an instant; for again his eyes seemed whirling round in his head as he swept the watery circle. The breeze now freshened; the sea began to swell.

"The birds!—the birds!" cried Tashtego.

In long Indian file, as when herons take wing, the white birds were now all flying towards Ahab's boat; and when within a few yards began fluttering over the water there, wheeling round and round, with joyous, expectant cries. Their vision was keener than man's; Ahab could discover no sign in the sea. But suddenly as he peered down and down into its depths, he profoundly saw a white living spot no bigger than a white weasel, with wonderful celerity uprising, and magnifying as it rose, till it turned, and then there were plainly revealed two long crooked rows of white, glistening teeth, floating up from the undiscoverable bottom. It was Moby-Dick's open mouth and scrolled jaw; his vast, shadowed bulk still half blending with the blue of the sea. The glittering mouth yawned beneath the boat like an open-doored marble tomb; and giving one sidelong sweep with his steering oar, Ahab whirled the craft aside from this tremendous apparition. Then, calling upon Fedallah to change places with him, went forward to the bows, and seizing Perth's harpoon, commanded his crew to grasp their oars and stand by to stern.

Now, by reason of this timely spinning round the boat upon its axis, its bow, by anticipation, was made to face the whale's head while yet under water. But as if perceiving this stratagem, Moby-Dick, with that malicious intelligence ascribed to him, sidlingly transplanted himself, as it were, in an instant, shooting his pleated head lengthwise beneath the boat.

Through and through; through every plank and each rib, it thrilled for an instant, the whale obliquely lying on his back, in the manner of a biting shark, slowly and feelingly taking its bows full within his mouth, so that the long, narrow, scrolled lower jaw curled high up into the open air, and one of the teeth caught in a row-lock. The bluish pearl-white of the inside of the jaw was within six inches of Ahab's head, and reached higher than that. In this attitude the White Whale now shook the slight cedar as a mildly cruel cat her mouse. With unastonished eyes Fedallah gazed, and crossed his arms; but the tiger-yellow crew were tumbling over each other's heads to gain the uttermost stern. .

And now, while both elastic gunwales were springing in and out, as the whale dallied with the doomed craft in this devilish way; and from his body being submerged beneath the boat, he could not be darted at from the bows, for the bows were almost inside of him, as it were; and while the other boats involuntarily paused, as before a quick crisis impossible to withstand, then it was that monomaniac Ahab, furious with this tantalizing vicinity of his foe, which placed him all alive and helpless in the very jaws he hated; frenzied with all this, he seized the long bone with his naked hands, and wildly strove to wrench it from its grip. As now he thus vainly strove, the jaw slipped from him; the frail gunwales bent in, collapsed, and snapped, as both jaws, like an enormous shears, sliding further aft, bit the craft completely in twain, and locked themselves fast again in the sea, midway between the two floating wrecks. These floated aside, the broken ends drooping, the crew at the stern-wreck clinging to the gunwales, and striving to hold fast to the oars to lash them across.

At that preluding moment, ere the boat was yet snapped, Ahab, the first to perceive the whale's intent, by the crafty upraising of his head, a movement that loosed his hold for the time; at that moment his hand had made one final effort to push the boat out of the bite. But only slipping further into the whale's mouth, and tilting over sideways as it slipped, the boat had shaken off his hold on the jaw; spilled him out of it, as he leaned to the push; and so he fell flat-faced upon the sea.

Ripplingly withdrawing from his prey, Moby-Dick now lay at a little distance, vertically thrusting his oblong white head up and down in the billows; and at the same time slowly revolving his whole spindled body; so that when his vast wrinkled forehead rose—some twenty or more feet out of the water—the now rising swells, with all their confluent waves, dazzlingly broke against it; vindictively tossing their shivered spray still higher into the air.[1] So, in a gale, the but half baffled Channel billows only recoil from the base of the Eddystone, triumphantly to overleap its summit with their scud.

But soon resuming his horizontal attitude, Moby-Dick swam swiftly round and round the wrecked crew; sideways churning the water in his vengeful wake, as if lashing himself up to still another and more deadly assault. The sight of the splintered boat seemed to madden him, as the blood of grapes and mulberries cast before Antiochus's elephants in the book of *Maccabees*. Meanwhile Ahab half smothered in the foam of the whale's insolent tail, and too much of a cripple to swim—though he could still keep afloat, even in the heart of such a whirlpool as that; helpless Ahab's head was seen, like a tossed bubble which the least chance shock might burst. From the boat's fragmentary stern, Fedallah incuriously and mildly eyed him; the clinging crew, at the other drifting end, could not succor him; more than enough was it for them to look to themselves. For so revolvingly appalling was the White Whale's aspect, and so planetarily swift the ever-contracting circles he made, that he seemed horizontally swooping upon them. And though the other boats, unharmed, still hovered hard by; still they dared not pull into the eddy to strike, lest that should be the signal for the instant destruction of the jeopardized castaways, Ahab and all; nor in that case could they themselves hope to escape. With straining eyes, then, they remained on the outer edge of the direful zone, whose center had now become the old man's head.

Meantime, from the beginning all this had been descried from the ship's mast-heads; and squaring her yards, she had borne down upon the scene; and was now so nigh, that Ahab in the water hailed her;—"Sail on the"—but that moment a breaking sea dashed on him from Moby-

1. This motion is peculiar to the sperm whale. It receives its designation (pitchpoling) from its being likened to that preliminary up-and-down poise of the whale-lance, in the exercise called pitchpoling, previously described. By this motion the whale must best and most comprehensively view whatever objects may be encircling him.

Dick, and whelmed him for the time. But struggling out of it again, and chancing to rise on a towering crest, he shouted—"Sail on the whale!—Drive him off!"

The *Pequod*'s prows were pointed; and breaking up the charmed circle, she effectually parted the White Whale from his victim. As he sullenly swam off, the boats flew to the rescue.

Dragged into Stubb's boat with blood-shot, blinded eyes, the white brine caking in his wrinkles; the long tension of Ahab's bodily strength did crack, and helplessly he yielded to his body's doom for a time, lying all crushed in the bottom of Stubb's boat, like one trodden under foot of herds of elephants. Far inland, nameless wails came from him, as desolate sounds from out ravines.

But this intensity of his physical prostration did but so much the more abbreviate it. In an instant's compass, great hearts sometimes condense to one deep pang, the sum total of those shallow pains kindly diffused through feebler men's whole lives. And so, such hearts, though summary in each one suffering; still, if the gods decree it, in their life-time aggregate a whole age of woe, wholly made up of instantaneous intensities; for even in their pointless centers, those noble natures contain the entire circumferences of inferior souls.

"The harpoon," said Ahab, half-way rising, and draggingly leaning on one bended arm—"is it safe?"

"Ay, sir, for it was not darted; this is it," said Stubb, showing it.

"Lay it before me;—any missing men?"

"One, two, three, four, five;—there were five oars, sir, and here are five men."

"That's good.—Help me, man; I wish to stand. So, so, I see him! there! there! going to leeward still; what a leaping spout!—Hands off from me! The eternal sap runs up in Ahab's bones again! Set the sail; out oars; the helm!"

It is often the case that when a boat is stove, its crew, being picked up by another boat, help to work that second boat; and the chase is thus continued with what is called double-banked oars. It was thus now. But the added power of the boat did not equal the added power of the whale, for he seemed to have treble-banked his every fin; swimming with a velocity which plainly showed, that if now, under these circumstances, pushed on, the chase would prove an indefinitely prolonged, if not a hopeless one; nor could any crew endure for so long a period, such an unintermitted, intense straining at the oar; a thing barely tolerable only in some one brief vicissitude. The ship itself, then, as it sometimes happens, offered the most promising intermediate means of overtaking the chase. Accordingly, the boats now made for her, and were soon swayed up to their cranes—the two parts of the wrecked boat having been previously secured by her—and then hoisting everything to her side, and stacking her canvas high up, and sideways outstretching it with stun-sails, like the double-jointed wings of an albatross; the *Pequod* bore down in the leeward wake of Moby-Dick. At the well known, methodic intervals, the whale's glittering spout was regularly announced from the manned mast-heads; and when he would be reported as just gone down, Ahab would take the time, and then pacing the deck, binnacle-watch in hand, so soon as the last second of the allotted hour expired, his voice was heard.—"Whose is the doubloon now? D'ye see him?" and if the reply was No, sir! straightway he commanded them to lift him to his perch. In this way the day wore on; Ahab, now aloft and motionless; anon, unrestingly pacing the planks.

As he was thus walking, uttering no sound, except to hail the men aloft, or to bid them hoist a sail still higher, or to spread one to a still greater breadth—thus to and fro pacing, beneath his slouched hat, at every turn he passed his own wrecked boat, which had been dropped upon the quarter-deck, and lay there reversed; broken bow to shattered stern. At last he paused before it; and as in an already over-cloudy sky fresh troops of clouds will sometimes sail across, so over the old man's face there now stole some such added gloom as this.

Stubb saw him pause; and perhaps intending, not vainly, though, to evince his own unabated fortitude, and thus keep up a valiant place in his Captain's mind, he advanced, and eyeing the wreck exclaimed—"The thistle the ass refused; it pricked his mouth too keenly, sir, ha! ha!"

"What soulless thing is this that laughs before a wreck? Man, man! did I not know thee brave as fearless fire (and as mechanical) I could swear thou wert a poltroon. Groan nor laugh should be heard before a wreck."

"Ay, sir," said Starbuck drawing near, " 'tis a solemn sight; an omen, and an ill one."

"Omen? omen?—the dictionary! If the gods think to speak outright to man, they will honorably speak outright; not shake their heads, and give an old wives' darkling hint.—Begone! Ye two are the opposite poles of one thing; Starbuck is Stubb reversed, and Stubb is Starbuck; and ye two are all mankind; and Ahab stands alone among the millions of the peopled earth, nor gods nor men his neighbors! Cold, cold—I shiver!—How now? Aloft there! D'ye see him? Sing out for every spout, though he spout ten times a second!"

The day was nearly done; only the hem of his golden robe was rustling. Soon it was almost dark, but the look-out men still remained unset.

"Can't see the spout now, sir;—too dark"—cried a voice from the air.

"How heading when last seen?"

"As before, sir—straight to leeward."

"Good! he will travel slower now 'tis night. Down royals and top-gallant stun-sails, Mr. Starbuck. We must not run over him before morning; he's making a passage now, and may heave-to a while. Helm there! keep her full before the wind!—Aloft! come down!—Mr. Stubb, send a fresh hand to the fore-mast-head, and see it manned till morning."—Then advancing towards the doubloon in the main-mast—"Men, this gold is mine, for I earned it; but I shall let it abide here till the White Whale is dead; and then, whosoever of ye first raises him, upon the day he shall be killed, this gold is that man's; and if on that day I shall again raise him, then, ten times its sum shall be divided among all of ye! Away now! the deck is thine, sir!"

And so saying, he placed himself half-way within the scuttle, and slouching his hat, stood there till dawn, except when at intervals rousing himself to see how the night wore on.

Chapter CXXXIV

THE CHASE—SECOND DAY

At day-break, the three mast-heads were punctually manned afresh.

"D'ye see him?" cried Ahab after allowing a little space for the light to spread.

"See nothing, sir."

"Turn up all hands and make sail! he travels faster than I thought for;—the top-gallant sails!—ay, they should have been kept on her all night. But no matter—'tis but resting for the rush."

Here be it said, that this pertinacious pursuit of one particular whale, continued through day into night, and through night into day is a thing by no means unprecedented in the South Sea fishery. For such is the wonderful skill, prescience of experience, and invincible confidence acquired by some great natural geniuses among the Nantucket commanders; that from the simple observation of a whale when last descried, they will, under certain given circumstances, pretty accurately foretell both the direction in which he will continue to swim for a time, while out of sight, as well as his probable rate of progression during that period. And, in these cases, somewhat as a pilot, when about losing sight of a coast, whose general trending he well knows, and which he desires shortly to return to again, but at some further point; like as this pilot stands by his compass, and takes the precise bearing of the cape at present visible, in order the more certainly to hit aright the remote, unseen headland, eventually to be visited: so does the fisherman, at his compass, with the whale; for after being chased, and diligently marked, through several hours of daylight, then, when night obscures the fish, the creature's future wake through the darkness is almost as established to the sagacious mind of the hunter, as the pilot's coast is to him. So that to this hunter's wondrous skill, the proverbial evanescence of a thing writ in water, a wake, is to all desired purposes well-nigh as reliable as the steadfast land. And as the mighty iron Leviathan of the modern railway is so familiarly known in its every pace, that, with watches in their hands, men time his rate as doctors that of a baby's pulse; and lightly say of it, the up train or the down train will reach such or such a spot, at such or such an hour; even so, almost, there are occasions when these Nantucketers time that other Leviathan of the deep, according to the observed humor of his speed; and say to themselves, so many hours hence this whale will have gone two hundred miles, will have about reached this or that degree of latitude or longitude. But to render this acuteness at all successful in the end, the wind and the sea must be the whaleman's allies; for of what present avail to the becalmed or windbound mariner is the skill that assures him he is exactly ninety-three leagues and a quarter from his port? Inferable from these statements, are many collateral subtle matters touching the chase of whales.

The ship tore on; leaving such a furrow in the sea as when a cannon-ball, missent, becomes a plow-share and turns up the level field.

"By salt and hemp!" cried Stubb, "but this swift motion of the deck creeps up one's legs and tingles at the heart. This ship and I are two brave fellows!—Ha, ha! Someone take me up, and launch me, spine-wise, on the sea—for by live-oaks! my spine's a keel. Ha, ha! we go the gait that leaves no dust behind!"

"There she blows—she blows!—she blows!—right ahead!" was now the mast-head cry.

"Ay, ay!" cried Stubb, "I knew it—ye can't escape—blow on and split your spout, O whale! the mad fiend himself is after ye! blow your trump—blister your lungs!—Ahab will dam off your blood, as a miller shuts his water-gate upon the stream!"

And Stubb did but speak out for well-nigh all that crew. The frenzies of the chase had by this time worked them bubblingly up, like old wine worked anew. Whatever pale fears and forebodings some of them might have felt before; these were not only now kept out of sight through the growing awe of Ahab, but they were broken up, and on all sides routed, as timid prairie hares that scatter before the bounding bison. The hand of Fate had snatched all their souls; and by the stirring perils of the previous day; the rack of the past night's suspense; the fixed, unfearing, blind, reckless way in which their wild craft went plunging towards its flying mark; by all these things, their hearts were bowled along. The wind that made great bellies of their sails, and rushed the vessel on by arms invisible as irresistible; this seemed the symbol of that unseen agency which so enslaved them to the race.

They were one man, not thirty. For as the one ship that held them all; though it was put together of all contrasting things—oak, and maple, and pine wood; iron, and pitch, and hemp—yet all these ran into each other in the one concrete hull, which shot on its way, both balanced and directed by the long central keel; even so, all the individualities of the crew, this man's valor, that man's fear; guilt and guiltiness, all varieties were welded into oneness, and were all directed to that fatal goal which Ahab their one lord and keel did point to.

The rigging lived. The mast-heads, like the tops of tall palms, were outspreadingly tufted with arms and legs. Clinging to a spar with one hand, some reached forth the other with impatient wavings; others, shading their eyes from the vivid sunlight, sat far out on the rocking yards; all the spars in full bearing of mortals, ready and ripe for their fate. Ah! how they still strove through that infinite blueness to seek out the thing that might destroy them!

"Why sing ye not out for him, if ye see him?" cried Ahab, when, after the lapse of some minutes since the first cry, no more had been heard. "Sway me up, men; ye have been deceived; not Moby-Dick casts one odd jet that way, and then disappears."

It was even so; in their headlong eagerness, the men had mistaken some other thing for the whale-spout, as the event itself soon proved; for hardly had Ahab reached his perch; hardly was the rope belayed to its pin on deck, when he struck the key-note to an orchestra, that made the air vibrate as with the combined discharge of rifles. The triumphant halloo of thirty buck-skin lungs was heard, as—much nearer to the ship than the place of the imaginary jet, less than a mile ahead—Moby-Dick bodily burst into view! For not by any calm and indolent spoutings; not by the peaceable gush of that mystic fountain in his head, did the White Whale now reveal his vicinity; but by the far more wondrous phenomenon of breaching. Rising with his utmost velocity from the furthest depths, the Sperm Whale thus booms his entire bulk into the pure element of air, and piling up a mountain of dazzling foam, shows his place to the distance of seven miles and more. In those moments, the torn, enraged waves he shakes off, seem his mane; in some cases, this breaching is his act of defiance.

"There she breaches! there she breaches!" was the cry, as in his immeasurable bravadoes the White Whale tossed himself salmon-like to Heaven. So suddenly seen in the blue plain of the sea, and relieved against the still bluer margin of the sky, the spray that he raised, for the moment, intolerably glittered and glared like a glacier; and stood there gradually fading and fading away from its first sparkling intensity, to the dim mistiness of an advancing shower in a vale.

"Ay, breach your last to the sun, Moby-Dick!" cried Ahab, "thy hour and thy harpoon are at hand!—Down! down all of ye, but one man at the fore. The boats!—stand by!"

Unmindful of the tedious rope-ladders of the shrouds, the men, like shooting stars, slid to the deck, by the isolated back-stays and halyards; while Ahab, less dartingly, but still rapidly was dropped from his perch.

"Lower away," he cried, so soon as he had reached his boat—a spare one, rigged the afternoon previous. "Mr. Starbuck, the ship is thine—keep away from the boats, but keep near them. Lower, all!"

As if to strike a quick terror into them, by this time being the first assailant himself, Moby-Dick had turned, and was now coming for the three crews. Ahab's boat was central; and cheering his men, he told them he would take the whale head-and-head—that is, pull straight up to his forehead—a not uncommon thing; for when within a certain limit, such a course excludes the coming onset from the whale's sidelong vision. But ere that close limit was gained, and while yet all three boats were plain as the ship's three masts to his eye; the White Whale churning himself into furious speed, almost in an instant as it were, rushing among the boats with open jaws, and a lashing tail, offered appalling battle on every side; and heedless of the irons darted at him from every boat, seemed only intent on annihilating each separate plank of which those boats were made. But skillfully maneuvered, incessantly wheeling like trained chargers in the field; the boats for a while eluded him; though, at times, but by a plank's breadth; while all the time, Ahab's unearthly slogan tore every other cry but his to shreds.

But at last in his untraceable evolutions, the White Whale so crossed and recrossed, and in a thousand ways entangled the slack of the three lines now fast to him, that they foreshortened, and, of themselves, warped the devoted boats towards the planted irons in him; though now for a moment the whale drew aside a little, as if to rally for a more tremendous charge. Seizing that opportunity, Ahab first paid out more line: and then was rapidly hauling and jerking in upon it again—hoping that way to disencumber it of some snarls—when lo!—a sight more savage than the embattled teeth of sharks!

Caught and twisted—corkscrewed in the mazes of the line, loose harpoons and lances, with all their bristling barbs and points, came flashing and dripping up to the chocks in the bows of Ahab's boat. Only one thing could be done. Seizing the boat-knife, he critically reached within—through—and then, without—the rays of steel; dragged in the line beyond, passed it, inboard, to the bowsman, and then, twice sundering the rope near the chocks—dropped the intercepted fagot of steel into the sea; and was all fast again. That instant, the White Whale made a sudden rush among the remaining tangles of the other lines; by so doing, irresistibly dragged the more involved boats of Stubb and Flask towards his flukes; dashed them together like two rolling husks on a surf-beaten beach, and then, diving down into the sea, disappeared in a boiling maelstrom, in which, for a space, the odorous cedar chips of the wrecks danced round and round, like the grated nutmeg in a swiftly stirred bowl of punch.

While the two crews were yet circling in the waters, reaching out after the revolving line-tubs, oars, and other floating furniture, while aslope little Flask bobbed up and down like an empty vial, twitching his legs upwards to escape the dreaded jaws of sharks; and Stubb was lustily singing out for someone to ladle him up; and while the old man's line—now parting—admitted of his pulling into the creamy pool to rescue whom he could;—in that wild simultaneousness of a thousand concreted perils—Ahab's yet unstricken boat seemed drawn up towards Heaven by invisible wires—as, arrow-like, shooting perpendicularly from the sea, the White Whale dashed his broad forehead against its bottom, and sent it, turning over and over, into the air; till it fell again—gunwale downwards—and Ahab and his men struggled out from under it, like seals from a sea-side cave.

The first uprising momentum of the whale—modifying its direction as he struck the surface—involuntarily launched him along it, to a little distance from the center of the destruction he had made; and with his back to it, he now lay for a moment slowly feeling with his flukes from side to side; and whenever a stray oar, bit of plank, the least chip or crumb of the boats touched his skin, his tail swiftly drew back, and came sideways smiting the sea. But soon, as if satisfied that his work for that time was done, he pushed his pleated forehead through the ocean, and trailing after him the intertangled lines, continued his leeward way at a traveler's methodic pace.

As before, the attentive ship having descried the whole fight, again came bearing down to the rescue, and dropping a boat, picked up the floating mariners, tubs, oars, and whatever else could be caught at, and safely landed them on her decks. Some sprained shoulders, wrists and ankles; livid contusions; wrenched harpoons and lances; inextricable intricacies of rope; shattered oars and planks; all these were there; but no fatal or even serious ill seemed to have befallen anyone. As with Fedallah the day before, so Ahab was now found grimly clinging to his boat's broken half, which afforded a comparatively easy float; nor did it so exhaust him as the previous day's mishap.

But when he was helped to the deck, all eyes were fastened upon him; as instead of standing by himself he still half-hung upon the shoulder of Starbuck, who had thus far been the foremost to assist him. His ivory leg had been snapped off, leaving but one short sharp splinter.

"Ay, ay, Starbuck, 'tis sweet to lean sometimes, be the leaner who he will; and would old Ahab had leaned oftener than he has."

"The ferrule has not stood, sir," said the carpenter, now coming up; "I put good work into that leg."

"But no bones broken, sir, I hope," said Stubb with true concern.

"Ay! and all splintered to pieces, Stubb!—d'ye see it.—But even with a broken bone, old Ahab is untouched; and I account no living bone of mine one jot more me, than this dead one that's lost. Nor White Whale, nor man, nor fiend, can so much as graze old Ahab in his own proper and inaccessible being. Can any lead touch yonder floor, any mast scrape yonder roof?—Aloft there! which way?"

"Dead to leeward, sir."

"Up helm, then; pile on the sail again, ship keepers! down the rest of the spare boats and rig them—Mr. Starbuck away, and muster the boat's crews."

"Let me first help thee towards the bulwarks, sir."

"Oh, oh, oh! how this splinter gores me now! Accursed fate! that the unconquerable captain in the soul should have such a craven mate!"

"Sir?"

"My body, man, not thee. Give me something for a cane—there, that shivered lance will do. Muster the men. Surely I have not seen him yet. By heaven it cannot be!—missing?—quick! call them all."

The old man's hinted thought was true. Upon mustering the company, the Parsee was not there.

"The Parsee!" cried Stubb—"he must have been caught in—"

"The black vomit wrench thee!—run all of ye above, alow, cabin, forecastle—find him—not gone—not gone!"

But quickly they returned to him with the tidings that the Parsee was nowhere to be found.

"Ay, sir," said Stubb—"caught among the tangles of your line I thought I saw him dragging under."

"*My* line! *my* line? Gone?—gone? What means that little word?—What death-knell rings in it, that old Ahab shakes as if he were the belfry. The harpoon, too!—toss over the litter there—d'ye see it?—the forged iron, men, the White Whale's—no, no, no—blistered fool! this hand did dart it!—'tis in the fish!—Aloft there! Keep him nailed—Quick!—all hands to the rigging of the boats—collect the oars—harpooneers! the irons, the irons!—hoist the royals higher—a pull on all the sheets!—helm there! steady, steady for your life! I'll ten times girdle the unmeasured globe; yea and dive straight through it, but I'll slay him yet!

"Great God! but for one single instant show thyself," cried Starbuck; "never, never wilt thou capture him, old man—In Jesus' name no more of this, that's worse than devil's madness. Two days chased; twice stove to splinters; thy very leg once more snatched from under thee; thy evil shadow gone—all good angels mobbing thee with warnings:—what more wouldst thou have?—Shall we keep chasing this murderous fish till he swamps the last man? Shall we be dragged by him to the bottom of the sea? Shall we be towed by him to the infernal world? Oh, oh—Impiety and blasphemy to hunt him more!"

"Starbuck, of late I've felt strangely moved to thee; ever since that hour we both saw—thou know'st what, in one another's eyes. But in this matter of the whale, be the front of thy face to me as the palm of this hand—a lipless, unfeatured blank. Ahab is forever Ahab, man. This whole act's immutably decreed. 'Twas rehearsed by thee and me a billion years before this ocean rolled. Fool! I am the Fates' lieutenant; I act under orders. Look thou, underling! that thou obeyest mine.—Stand round me, men. Ye see an old man cut down to the stump; leaning on a shivered lance; propped up on a lonely foot. 'Tis Ahab—his body's part; but Ahab's soul's a centipede, that moves upon a hundred legs. I feel strained, half-stranded, as ropes that tow dismasted frigates in a gale; and I may look so. But ere I break, ye'll hear me crack; and till ye hear *that,* know that Ahab's hawser tows his purpose yet. Believe ye, men, in the things called omens? Then laugh aloud, and cry encore! For ere they drown, drowning things will twice rise to the surface; then rise again, to sink forever more. So with Moby-Dick—two days he's floated—to-morrow will be the third. Ay, men, he'll rise once more—but only to spout his last! D'ye feel brave men, brave?"

"As fearless fire," cried Stubb.

"And as mechanical," muttered Ahab. Then as the men went forward, he muttered on: "The things called omens! And yesterday I talked the same to Starbuck there, concerning my broken boat. Oh! how valiantly I seek to drive out of others' hearts what's clinched so fast in mine!—The Parsee—the Parsee!—gone, gone? and he was to go before:—but still was to be seen again ere I could perish—How's that?—There's a riddle now might baffle all the lawyers backed by the ghosts of the whole line of judges:—like a hawk's beak it pecks my brain. *I'll, I'll* solve it, though!"

When dusk descended, the whale was still in sight to leeward.

So once more the sail was shortened, and everything passed nearly as on the previous night; only, the sound of hammers, and the hum of the grind-stone was heard till nearly daylight, as the men toiled by lanterns in the complete and careful rigging of the spare boats and sharpening their fresh weapons for the morrow. Meantime, of the broken keel of Ahab's wrecked craft the carpenter made him another leg; while still as on the night before, slouched Ahab stood fixed within his scuttle; his hid, heliotrope glance anticipatingly gone backward on its dial; sat due eastward for the earliest sun.

Chapter CXXXV

The Chase—Third Day

The morning of the third day dawned fair and fresh, and once more the solitary night-man at the fore-mast-head was relieved by crowds of the daylight look-outs, who dotted every mast and almost every spar.

"D'ye see him?" cried Ahab; but the whale was not yet in sight.

"In his infallible wake, though; but follow that wake, that's all. Helm there; steady, as thou goest, and hast been going. What a lovely day again! were it a new-made world, and made for a summer-house to the angels, and this morning the first of its throwing open to them, a fairer day could not dawn upon that world. Here's food for thought, had Ahab time to think; but Ahab never thinks; he only feels, feels, feels; *that's* tingling enough for mortal man! to think's audacity. God only has that right and privilege. Thinking is, or ought to be, a coolness and a calmness; and our poor hearts throb, and our poor brains beat too much for that. And yet, I've sometimes thought my brain was very calm—frozen calm, this old skull cracks so, like a glass in which the contents turned to ice, and shiver it. And still this hair is growing now; this moment growing, and heat must breed it; but no, it's like that sort of common grass that will grow anywhere, between the earthy clefts of Greenland ice or in Vesuvius lava. How the wild winds blow it; they whip it about me as the torn shreds of split sails lash the tossed ship they cling to. A vile wind that has no doubt blown ere this through prison corridors and cells, and wards of hospitals, and ventilated them, and now comes blowing hither as innocent as fleeces. Out upon it!—it's tainted. Were I the wind, I'd blow no more on such a wicked, miserable world. I'd crawl somewhere to a cave, and slink there. And yet, 'tis a noble and heroic thing, the wind! who ever conquered it? In every fight it has the last and bitterest blow. Run tilting at it, and you but run through it. Ha! a coward wind that strikes stark naked men, but will not stand to receive a single blow. Even Ahab is a braver thing—a nobler thing than *that*. Would now the wind but had a body; but all the things that most exasperate and outrage mortal man, all these things are bodiless, but only bodiless as objects, not as agents. There's a most special, a most cunning, oh, a most malicious difference! And yet, I say again, and swear it now, that there's something all glorious and gracious in the wind. These warm Trade-winds, at least, that in the clear heavens blow straight on, in strong and steadfast, vigorous mildness; and veer not from their mark, however the baser currents of the sea may turn and tack, and mightiest Mississippies of the land swift and swerve about, uncertain where to go at last. And by the eternal Poles! these same Trades that so directly blow my good ship on; these Trades, or something like them—something so unchangeable, and full as strong, blow my keeled soul along! To it! Aloft there! What d'ye see?"

"Nothing, sir."

"Nothing! and noon at hand! The doubloon goes a-begging! See the sun! Ay, ay, it must be so. I've oversailed him. How, got the start? Ay, he's chasing *me* now; not I, *him*—that's bad; I might have known it, too. Fool! the lines—the harpoons he's towing. Ay, ay, I have run him by last night. About! about! Come down, all of ye, but the regular look-outs! Man the braces!"

Steering as she had done, the wind had been somewhat on the *Pequod*'s quarter, so that now being pointed in the reversed direction, the braced ship sailed hard upon the breeze as she rechurned the cream in her own white wake.

"Against the wind he now steers for the open jaw," murmured Starbuck to himself, as he coiled the new-hauled main-brace upon the rail. "God keep us, but already my bones feel damp within me, and from the inside wet my flesh. I misdoubt me that I disobey my God in obeying him!"

"Stand by to sway me up!" cried Ahab, advancing to the hempen basket. "We should meet him soon."

"Ay, ay, sir," and straightway Starbuck did Ahab's bidding, and once more Ahab swung on high.

A whole hour now passed; gold-beaten out to ages. Time itself now held long breaths with keen suspense. But at last, some three points off the weather-bow, Ahab descried the spout again, and instantly from the three mast-heads three shrieks went up as if the tongues of fire had voiced it.

"Forehead to forehead I meet thee, this third time, Moby-Dick! On deck there!—brace sharper up; crowd her into the wind's eye. He's too far off to lower yet, Mr. Starbuck. The sails shake! Stand over that helmsman with a top-maul! So, so; he travels fast, and I must down. But let me have one more good round look aloft here at the sea; there's time for that. An old, old sight, and yet somehow so young; ay, and not changed a wink since I first saw it, a boy, from the sand-hills of Nantucket! The same!—the same!—the same to Noah as to me. There's a soft shower to leeward. Such lovely leewardings! They must lead somewhere—to something else than common land, more palmy than the palms. Leeward! the White Whale goes that way; look to windward, then; the better if the bitterer quarter. But good-bye, good-bye, old mast-head! What's this?—green? ay, tiny mosses in these warped cracks. No such green weather stains on Ahab's head! There's the difference now between man's old age and matter's. But ay, old mast, we both grow old together; sound in our hulls, though, are we not, my ship? Ay minus a leg, that's all. By heaven this dead wood has the better of my live flesh every way. I can't compare with it! and I've known some ships made of dead trees outlast the lives of men made of the most vital stuff of vital fathers. What's that he said? he should still go before me, my pilot; and yet to be seen again? But where? Will I have eyes at the bottom of the sea, supposing I descend those endless stairs? and all night I've been sailing from him, wherever he did sink to. Ay, ay, like many more thou told'st direful truth as touching thyself, O Parsee; but, Ahab, there thy shot fell short. Good-bye, mast-head—keep a good eye upon the whale, the while I'm gone. We'll talk to-morrow, nay, to-night, when the White Whale lies down there, tied by head and tail."

He gave the word; and still gazing round him, was steadily lowered through the cloven blue air to the deck.

In due time the boats were lowered; but as standing in his shallop's stern, Ahab just hovered upon the point of the descent, he waved to the mate—who held one of the tackle-ropes on deck—and bade him pause.

"Starbuck!"

"Sir?"

"For the third time my soul's ship starts upon this voyage, Starbuck."

"Ay, sir, thou wilt have it so."

"Some ships sail from their ports, and ever afterwards are missing, Starbuck!"

"Truth, sir: saddest truth."

"Some men die at ebb tide; some at low water; some at the full of the flood;—and I feel now like a billow that's all one crested comb, Starbuck. I am old;—shake hands with me, man."

Their hands met; their eyes fastened; Starbuck's tears the glue.

"Oh, my captain, my captain!—noble heart—go not—go not!—see, it's a brave man that weeps; how great the agony of the persuasion then!"

"Lower away!"—cried Ahab, tossing the mate's arm from him. "Stand by the crew!"

In an instant the boat was pulling round close under the stern.

"The sharks! the sharks!" cried a voice from the low cabin-window there; "O master, my master, come back!"

But Ahab heard nothing; for his own voice was high-lifted then; and the boat leaped on.

Yet the voice spake true; for scarce had he pushed from the ship, when numbers of sharks, seemingly rising from out the dark waters beneath the hull, maliciously snapped at the blades of the oars, every time they dipped in the water; and in this way accompanied the boat with their bites. It is a thing not uncommonly happening to the whale-boats in those swarming seas; the sharks at times apparently following them in the same prescient way that vultures hover over the banners of marching regiments in the east. But these were the first sharks that had been observed by the *Pequod* since the White Whale had been first descried; and whether it was that Ahab's crew were all such tiger-yellow barbarians, and therefore their flesh more musky to the senses of the sharks—a matter sometimes well known to affect them—however it was, they seemed to follow that one boat without molesting the others.

"Heart of wrought steel!" murmured Starbuck gazing over the side, and following with his eyes the receding boat—"canst thou yet ring boldly to that sight?—lowering thy keel among ravening sharks, and followed by them, open-mouthed to the chase; and this the critical third day?—for when three days flow together in one continuous intense pursuit; be sure the first is the morning, the second the noon, and the third the evening and the end of that thing—be that end what it may. Oh! my God! what is this that shoots through me, and leaves me so deadly calm, yet expectant—fixed at the top of a shudder! Future things swim before me, as in empty outlines and skeletons; all the past is somehow grown dim. Mary, girl! thou fadest in pale glories behind me; boy! I seem to see but thy eyes grown wondrous blue. Strangest problems of life seem clearing; but clouds sweep between—Is my journey's end coming? My legs feel faint; like his who has footed it all day. Feel thy heart—beats it yet? Stir thyself, Starbuck!—stave it off—move, move! speak aloud!—Mast-head there! See ye my boy's hand on the hill?—Crazed;—aloft there!—keep thy keenest eye upon the boats:—mark well the whale!—Ho! again!—drive off that hawk! see! he pecks—he tears the vane"—pointing to the red flag flying at the main-truck—"Ha! he soars away with it!—Where's the old man now? see'st thou that sight, oh Ahab!—shudder, shudder!"

The boats had not gone very far, when by a signal from the mast-heads—a downward pointed arm, Ahab knew that the whale had sounded; but intending to be near him at the next rising, he held on his way a little sideways from the vessel; the becharmed crew maintaining the profoundest silence, as the head-bent waves hammered and hammered against the opposing bow.

"Drive, drive in your nails, oh ye waves! to their uttermost heads drive them in! ye but strike a thing without a lid; and no coffin and no hearse can be mine:—and hemp only can kill me! Ha! ha!"

Suddenly the waters around them slowly swelled in broad circles; then quickly upheaved, as if sideways sliding from a submerged berg of ice, swiftly rising to the surface. A low rumbling sound was heard; a subterraneous hum; and then all held their breaths; as bedraggled with trailing ropes, and harpoons, and lances, a vast form shot lengthwise, but obliquely from the sea. Shrouded in a thin drooping veil of mist, it hovered for a moment in the rainbowed air; and then fell swamping back into the deep. Crushed thirty feet upwards, the waters flashed for an instant like heaps of fountains, then brokenly sank in a shower of flakes, leaving the circling surface creamed like new milk round the marble trunk of the whale.

"Give way!" cried Ahab to the oarsmen, and the boats darted forward to the attack; but maddened by yesterday's fresh irons that corroded in him, Moby-Dick seemed combinedly possessed by all the angels that fell from heaven. The wide tiers of welded tendons over-spreading his broad white forehead, beneath the transparent skin, looked knitted together; as head on, he came churning his tail among the boats; and once more flailed them apart; spilling out the irons and lances from the two mates' boats, and dashing in one side of the upper part of their bows, but leaving Ahab's almost without a scar.

While Daggoo and Queequeg were stopping the strained planks; and as the whale swimming out from them, turned, and showed one entire flank as he shot by them again; at that moment a quick cry went up. Lashed round and round to the fish's back; pinioned in the turns upon turns in which, during the past night, the whale had reeled the involutions of the lines around him, the half torn body of the Parsee was seen; his sable raiment frayed to shreds; his distended eyes turned full upon old Ahab.

The harpoon dropped from his hand.

"Befooled, befooled!"—drawing in a long lean breath—"Ay, Parsee! I see thee again.—Ay, and thou goest before; and this, *this* then is the hearse that thou didst promise. But I hold thee to the last letter of thy word. Where is the second hearse? Away, mates, to the ship! those boats are useless now; repair them if ye can in time, and return to me; if not, Ahab is enough to die—Down, men! the first thing that but offers to jump from this boat I stand in, that thing I harpoon. Ye are not other men, but my arms and my legs; and so obey me.—Where's the whale? gone down again?"

But he looked too nigh the boat; for as if bent upon escaping with the corpse he bore, and as if the particular place of the last encounter had been but a stage in his leeward voyage, Moby-Dick was now again steadily swimming forward; and had almost passed the ship—which thus far had been sailing in the contrary direction to him, though for the present her headway had been stopped. He seemed swimming with his utmost velocity, and now only intent upon pursuing his own straight path in the sea.

"Oh! Ahab," cried Starbuck, "not too late is it, even now, the third day, to desist. See! Moby-Dick seeks thee not. It is thou, thou, that madly seekest him!"

Setting sail to the rising wind, the lonely boat was swiftly impelled to leeward, by both oars and canvas. And at last when Ahab was sliding by the vessel, so near as plainly to distinguish Starbuck's face as he leaned over the rail, he hailed him to turn the vessel about, and follow him, not too swiftly, at a judicious interval. Glancing upwards he saw Tashtego, Queequeg, and Daggoo, eagerly mounting to the three mast-heads; while the oarsmen were rocking in the two staved boats which had but just been hoisted to the side, and were busily at work in repairing them. One after the other, through the port-holes, as he sped, he also caught flying glimpses of Stubb and Flask, busying themselves on deck among bundles of new irons and lances. As he saw all this; as he heard the hammers in the broken boats; far other hammers seemed driving a nail into his heart. But he rallied. And now marking that the vane or flag was gone from the main-mast-head, he shouted to Tashtego, who had just gained that perch, to descend again for another flag, and a hammer and nails, and so nail it to the mast.

Whether fagged by the three days' running chase, and the resistance to his swimming in the knotted hamper he bore; or whether it was some latent deceitfulness and malice in him: whichever was true, the White Whale's way now began to abate, as it seemed, from the boat so rapidly nearing him once more; though indeed the whale's last start had not been so long a one as before. And still as Ahab glided over the waves the unpitying sharks accompanied him; and so pertinaciously stuck to the boat; and so continually bit at the plying oars, that the blades became jagged and crunched, and left small splinters in the sea, at almost every dip.

"Heed them not! those teeth but give new rowlocks to your oars. Pull on! 'tis the better rest, the sharks' jaw than the yielding water."

"But at every bite, sir, the thin blades grow smaller and smaller!"

"They will last long enough! pull on!—But who can tell"—he muttered—"whether these sharks swim to feast on the whale or on Ahab?—But pull on! Ay, all alive, now—we near him. The helm! take the helm! let me pass"—and so saying, two of the oarsmen helped him forward to the bows of the still flying boat.

At length as the craft was cast to one side, and ran ranging along with the White Whale's flank, he seemed strangely oblivious of its advance—as the whale sometimes will—and Ahab was fairly within the smoky mountain mist, which, thrown off from the whale's spout, curled round his great Monadnock hump; he was even thus close to him; when, with body arched back, and both arms lengthwise high-lifted to the poise, he darted his fierce iron, and his far fiercer curse into the hated whale. As both steel and curse sank to the socket, as if sucked into a morass, Moby-Dick sideways writhed; spasmodically rolled his nigh flank against the bow, and, without staving a hole in it, so suddenly canted the boat over, that had it not been for the elevated part of the gunwale to which he then clung, Ahab would once more have been tossed into the sea. As it was, three of the oarsmen—who foreknew not the precise instant of the dart, and were therefore unprepared for its effects—these were flung out; but so fell, that, in an instant two of them clutched the gunwale again, and rising to its level on a combing wave, hurled themselves bodily inboard again; the third man helplessly dropping astern, but still afloat and swimming.

Almost simultaneously, with a mighty volition of ungraduated, instantaneous swiftness, the White Whale darted through the weltering sea. But when Ahab cried out to the steersman to take new turns with the line, and hold it so; and commanded the crew to turn round on their seats, and tow the boat up to the mark; the moment the treacherous line felt that double strain and tug, it snapped in the empty air!

"What breaks in me? Some sinew cracks!—'tis whole again; oars! oars! Burst in upon him!"

Hearing the tremendous rush of the sea-crashing boat, the whale wheeled round to present his blank forehead at bay; but in that evolution, catching sight of the nearing black hull of the ship; seemingly seeing in it the source of all his persecutions; bethinking it—it may be—a larger and nobler foe; of a sudden, he bore down upon its advancing prow, smiting his jaws amid fiery showers of foam.

Ahab staggered; his hand smote his forehead. "I grow blind; hands! stretch out before me that I may yet grope my way. Is't night?"

"The whale! The ship!" cried the cringing oarsmen.

"Oars! oars! Slope downwards to thy depths, O sea, that ere it be forever too late, Ahab may slide this last, last time upon his mark! I see: the ship! the ship! Dash on, my men! will ye not save my ship?"

But as the oarsmen violently forced their boat through the sledge-hammering seas, the before whale-smitten bow-ends of two planks burst through, and in an instant almost, the temporarily disabled boat lay nearly level with the waves; its half wading, splashing crew, trying hard to stop the gap and bale out the pouring water.

Meantime, for that one beholding instant, Tashtego's mast-head hammer remained suspended in his hand; and the red flag, half-wrapping him as with a plaid, then streamed itself straight out from him, as his own forward-flowing heart; while Starbuck and Stubb, standing upon the bowsprit beneath, caught sight of the down-coming monster just as soon as he.

"The whale, the whale! Up helm, up helm! Oh, all ye sweet powers of air, now hug me close! Let not Starbuck die, if die he must, in a woman's fainting fit. Up helm, I say—ye fools, the jaw! the jaw! Is this the end of all my bursting prayers? all my life-long fidelities? Oh, Ahab, Ahab, lo, thy work. Steady! helmsman, steady. Nay, nay! Up helm again! He turns to meet us! Oh, his unappeasable brow drives on towards one, whose duty tells him he cannot depart. My God, stand by me now!"

"Stand not by me, but stand under me, whoever you are that will now help Stubb; for Stubb, too, sticks here. I grin at thee, thou grinning whale! Whoever helped Stubb, or kept Stubb awake, but Stubb's own unwinking eye? And now poor Stubb goes to bed upon a mattress that is all too soft; would it were stuffed with brushwood! I grin at thee, thou grinning whale! Look ye, sun, moon, and stars! I call ye assassins of as good a fellow as ever spouted up his ghost. For all that, I would yet ring glasses with thee, would ye but hand the cup! Oh, oh! oh, oh! thou grinning whale, but there'll be plenty of gulping soon! Why fly ye not, O Ahab! For me, off shoes and jacket to it; let Stubb die in his drawers! A most moldy and over salted death, though;—cherries! cherries! cherries! Oh, Flask, for one red cherry ere we die!"

"Cherries? I only wish that we were where they grow. Oh, Stubb, I hope my poor mother's drawn my part-pay ere this; if not, few coppers will now come to her, for the voyage is up."

From the ship's bows, nearly all the seamen now hung inactive; hammers, bits of plank, lances, and harpoons, mechanically retained in their hands, just as they had darted from their various employments; all their enchanted eyes intent upon the whale, which from side to side strangely vibrating his predestinating head, sent a broad band of overspreading semicircular foam before him as he rushed. Retribution, swift vengeance, eternal malice were in his whole aspect, and spite of all that mortal man could do, the solid white buttress of his forehead smote the ship's starboard bow, till men and timbers reeled. Some fell flat upon their faces. Like dislodged trucks, the heads of the harpooneers aloft shook on their bull-like necks. Through the breach, they heard the waters pour, as mountain torrents down a flume.

"The ship! The hearse!—the second hearse!" cried Ahab from the boat; "its wood could only be American!"

Diving beneath the settling ship, the whale ran quivering along its keel; but turning under water, swiftly shot to the surface again, far off the other bow, but within a few yards of Ahab's boat, where, for a time, he lay quiescent.

"I turn my body from the sun. What ho, Tashtego! Let me hear thy hammer. Oh! ye three unsurrendered spires of mine; thou uncracked keel; the only god-bullied hull; thou firm deck, and haughty helm, and Pole-pointed prow—death-glorious ship! must ye then perish, and without me? Am I cut off from the last fond pride of meanest shipwrecked captains? Oh, lonely death on lonely life! Oh, now I feel my topmost greatness lies in my topmost grief. Ho, ho! from all your furthest bounds, pour ye now in, ye bold billows of my whole foregone life, and top this one piled comber of my death! Towards thee I roll, thou all-destroying but unconquering whale; to the last I grapple with thee; from hell's heart I stab at thee; for hate's sake I spit my last breath at thee. Sink all coffins and all hearses to one common pool! and since neither can be mine, let me then tow to pieces, while still chasing thee, though tied to thee, thou damned whale! *Thus*, I give up the spear!"

The harpoon was darted; the stricken whale flew forward; with igniting velocity the line ran through the groove;—ran foul. Ahab stooped to clear it; he did clear it; but the flying turn caught him round the neck, and voicelessly as Turkish mutes bowstring their victim, he was shot out of the boat, ere the crew knew he was gone. Next instant, the heavy eye-splice in the rope's final end flew out of the stark-empty tub, knocked down an oarsman, and smiting the sea, disappeared in its depths.

For an instant, the tranced boat's crew stood still; then turned. "The ship? Great God, where is the ship?" Soon they through dim, bewildering mediums saw her sidelong fading phantom, as in the gaseous Fata Morgana; only the uppermost masts out of water; while fixed by infatuation, or fidelity, or fate, to their once lofty perches, the pagan harpooneers still maintained their sinking lookouts on the sea. And now, concentric circles seized the lone boat itself, and all its crew, and each floating oar, and every lance-pole, and spinning, animate and inanimate, all round and round in one vortex, carried the smallest chip of the *Pequod* out of sight.

But as the last whelmings intermixingly poured themselves over the sunken head of the Indian at the main-mast, leaving a few inches of the erect spar yet visible, together with long streaming yards of the flag, which calmly undulated, with ironical coincidings, over the destroying billows they almost touched;—at that instant, a red arm and a hammer hovered backwardly uplifted in the open air, in the act of nailing the flag faster and yet faster to the subsiding spar. A sky-hawk that tauntingly had followed the main-truck downwards from its natural home among the stars, pecking at the flag, and incommoding Tashtego there; this bird now chanced to intercept its broad fluttering wings between the hammer and the wood; and simultaneously feeling that ethereal thrill, the submerged savage beneath, in his death-gasp, kept his hammer frozen there; and so the bird of heaven, with archangelic shrieks, and his imperial beak thrust upwards, and his whole captive form folded in the flag of Ahab, went down with his ship, which, like Satan, would not sink to hell till she had dragged a living part of heaven along with her, and helmeted herself with it.

Now small fowls flew screaming over the yet yawning gulf; a sullen white surf beat against its steep sides; then all collapsed, and the great shroud of the sea rolled on as it rolled five thousand years ago.

Epilogue

"AND I ONLY AM ESCAPED ALONE TO TELL THEE"
Job

The drama's done. Why then here does anyone step forth?—Because one did survive the wreck.

It so chanced, that after the Parsee's disappearance, I was he whom the Fates ordained to take the place of Ahab's bowsman, when that bowsman assumed the vacant post; the same, who, when on the last day the three men were tossed from out of the rocking boat was dropped astern. So, floating on the margin of the ensuing scene, and in full sight of it, when the half-spent suction of the sunk ship reached me, I was then, but slowly, drawn towards the closing vortex. When I reached it, it had subsided to a creamy pool. Round and round, then, and ever contracting towards the button-like black bubble at the axis of that slowly wheeling circle, like another Ixion I did revolve. Till, gaining that vital center, the black bubble upward burst; and now, liberated by the reason of its cunning spring, and owing to its great buoyancy, rising with great force, the coffin life-buoy shot lengthwise from the sea, fell over, and floated by my side. Buoyed up by that coffin, for almost one whole day and night, I floated on a soft and dirge-like main. The unharming sharks, they glided by as if with padlocks on their mouths; the savage sea-hawks sailed with sheathed beaks. On the second day, a sail drew near, nearer, and picked me up at last. It was the devious-cruising Rachel, that in her retracing search after her missing children, only found another orphan.

BILLY BUDD, SAILOR
(AN INSIDE NARRATIVE)

Dedicated to
JACK CHASE
Englishman

Wherever that great heart may now be
Here on Earth or harbored in Paradise

Captain of the Maintop
in the year 1843
in the U.S. Frigate
United States

Chapter I

IN THE TIME BEFORE STEAMSHIPS, OR THEN MORE FREQUENTLY THAN NOW, A STROLLER ALONG the docks of any considerable sea-port would occasionally have his attention arrested by a group of bronzed mariners, man-of-war's men or merchant-sailors in holiday attire ashore on liberty. In certain instances they would flank, or, like a body-guard quite surround some superior figure of their own class, moving along with them like Aldebaran among the lesser lights of his constellation. That signal object was the "Handsome Sailor" of the less prosaic time alike of the military and merchant navies. With no perceptible trace of the vainglorious about him, rather with the off-hand unaffectedness of natural regality, he seemed to accept the spontaneous homage of his shipmates.

A somewhat remarkable instance recurs to me. In Liverpool, now half a century ago, I saw under the shadow of the great dingy street-wall of Prince's Dock (an obstruction long since removed) a common sailor, so intensely black that he must needs have been a native African of the unadulterate blood of Ham. A symmetric figure much above the average height. The two ends of a gay silk handkerchief thrown loose about the neck danced upon the displayed ebony of his chest; in his ears were big hoops of gold, and a Scotch Highland bonnet with a tartan band set off his shapely head. It was a hot noon in July; and his face, lustrous with perspiration, beamed with barbaric good humor. In jovial sallies right and left, his white teeth flashing into he rollicked along, the center of a company of his shipmates. These were made up of such an assortment of tribes and complexions as would have well fitted them to be marched up by Anacharsis Cloots before the bar of the first French Assembly as Representatives of the Human Race. At each spontaneous tribute rendered by the wayfarers to this black pagoda of a fellow—the tribute of a pause and stare, and less frequent an exclamation—the motley retinue showed that they took that sort of pride in the evoker of it which the Assyrian priests doubtless showed for their grand sculptured Bull when the faithful prostrated themselves.

To return. If in some cases a bit of a nautical Murat in setting forth his person ashore, the Handsome Sailor of the period in question evinced nothing of the dandified Billy-be-Damn, an amusing character all but extinct now, but occasionally to be encountered, and in a form yet more amusing than the original, at the tiller of the boats on the tempestuous Erie Canal or, more likely, vaporing in the groggeries along the tow-path. Invariably a proficient in his perilous calling, he was also more or less of a mighty boxer or wrestler. It was strength and beauty. Tales of his prowess were recited. Ashore he was the champion; afloat the spokesman; on every suitable occasion always foremost. Close-reefing top-sails in a gale, there he was, astride the weather yard-arm-end, foot in the Flemish horse as "stirrup," both hands tugging at the "earring" as at a bridle, in very much the attitude of young Alexander curbing the fiery Bucephalus. A superb figure, tossed up as by the horns of Taurus against the thunderous sky, cheerily hallooing to the strenuous file along the spar.

The moral nature was seldom out of keeping with the physical make. Indeed, except as toned by the former, the comeliness and power, always attractive in masculine conjunction, hardly could have drawn the sort of honest homage the Handsome Sailor in some examples received from his less gifted associates.

Such a cynosure, at least in aspect, and something such too in nature, though with important variations made apparent as the story proceeds, was welkin-eyed Billy Budd, or Baby Budd, as more familiarly under circumstances hereafter to be given he at last came to be called, aged twenty-one, a foretopman of the British fleet toward the close of the last decade of the eighteenth century. It was not very long prior to the time of the narration that follows that he had entered the King's Service, having been impressed on the Narrow Seas from a homeward-bound English merchantman into a seventy-four outward-bound, H.M.S. *Bellipotent*; which ship, as was not unusual in those hurried days, having been obliged to put to sea short of her proper complement of men. Plump upon Billy at first sight in the gangway the boarding officer Lieutenant Ratcliff pounced, even before the merchantman's crew was formally mustered on the quarter-deck for his deliberate inspection. And him only he elected. For whether it was because the other men when ranged before him showed to ill advantage after Billy, or whether he had some scruples in view of the merchantman being rather short-handed, however it might be, the officer contented himself with his first spontaneous choice. To the surprise of the ship's company, though much to the Lieutenant's satisfaction, Billy made no demur. But, indeed, any demur would have been as idle as the protest of a goldfinch popped into a cage.

Noting this uncomplaining acquiescence, all but cheerful one might say, the shipmates turned a surprised glance of silent reproach at the sailor. The Shipmaster was one of those worthy mortals found in every vocation, even the humbler ones—the sort of person whom everybody agrees in calling "a respectable man." And—nor so strange to report as it may appear to be—though a ploughman of the troubled waters, life-long contending with the intractable elements, there was nothing this honest soul at heart loved better than simple peace and quiet. For the rest, he was fifty or thereabouts, a little inclined to corpulence, a prepossessing face, unwhiskered, and of an agreeable color—a rather full face, humanely intelligent in expression. On a fair day with a fair wind and all going well, a certain musical chime in his voice seemed to be the veritable unobstructed outcome of the innermost man. He had much prudence, much conscientiousness, and there were occasions when these virtues were the cause of overmuch disquietude in him. On a passage, so long as his craft was in any proximity to land, no sleep for Captain Graveling. He took to heart those serious responsibilities not so heavily borne by some shipmasters.

Now while Billy Budd was down in the forecastle getting his kit together, the *Bellipotent*'s Lieutenant, burly and bluff, nowise disconcerted by Captain Graveling's omitting to proffer the customary hospitalities on an occasion so unwelcome to him, an omission simply caused by preoccupation of thought, unceremoniously invited himself into the cabin, and also to a flask from the spirit-locker, a receptacle which his experienced eye instantly discovered. In fact he was one of those sea-dogs in whom all the hardship and peril of naval life in the great prolonged wars of his time never impaired the natural instinct for sensuous enjoyment. His duty he always faithfully did; but duty is sometimes a dry obligation, and he was for irrigating its aridity, whensoever possible, with a fertilizing decoction of strong waters. For the cabin's proprietor there was nothing left but to play the part of the enforced host with whatever grace and alacrity were practicable. As necessary adjuncts to the flask, he silently placed tumbler and water-jug before the irrepressible guest. But excusing himself from partaking just then, he dismally watched the unembarrassed officer deliberately diluting his grog a little, then tossing it off in three swallows, pushing the empty tumbler away, yet not so far as to be beyond easy reach, at the same time settling himself in his seat and smacking his lips with high satisfaction, looking straight at the host.

These proceedings over, the Master broke the silence; and there lurked a rueful reproach in the tone of his voice: "Lieutenant, you are going to take my best man from me, the jewel of 'em."

"Yes, I know," rejoined the other, immediately drawing back the tumbler preliminary to a replenishing; "Yes, I know. Sorry."

"Beg pardon, but you don't understand, Lieutenant. See here now. Before I shipped that young fellow, my forecastle was a rat-pit of quarrels. It was black times, I tell you, aboard the *Rights* here. I was worried to that degree my pipe had no comfort for me. But Billy came; and it was like a Catholic priest striking peace in an Irish shindy. Not that he preached to them or said or did anything in particular; but a virtue went out of him, sugaring the sour ones. They took to him like hornets to treacle; all but the buffer of the gang, the big shaggy chap with the fire-red whiskers. He indeed out of envy, perhaps, of the newcomer, and thinking such a 'sweet and pleasant fellow,' as he mockingly designated him to the others, could hardly have the spirit of a game-cock, must needs bestir himself in trying to get up an ugly row with him. Billy forebore with him and reasoned with him in a pleasant way—he is something like myself, Lieutenant, to whom aught like a quarrel is hateful—but nothing served. So, in the second dog-watch one day the Red Whiskers in presence of the others, under pretence of showing Billy just whence a sirloin steak was cut—for the fellow had once been a butcher—insultingly gave him a dig under the ribs. Quick as lightning Billy let fly his arm. I dare say he never meant to do quite as much as he did, but anyhow he gave the burly fool a terrible drubbing. It took about half a minute, I should think. And, lord bless you, the lubber was astonished at the celerity. And will you believe it, Lieutenant, the Red Whiskers now really loves Billy—loves him, or is the biggest hypocrite that ever I heard of. But they all love him. Some of 'em do his washing, darn his old trousers for him; the carpenter is at odd times making a pretty little chest of drawers for him. Anybody will do anything for Billy Budd; and it's the happy family here. But now, Lieutenant, if that young fellow goes—I know how it will be aboard the *Rights*. Not again very soon shall I, coming up from dinner, lean over the capstan smoking a quiet pipe—no, not very soon again, I think. Ay, Lieutenant, you are going to take away the jewel of 'em; you are going to take away my peacemaker!" And with that the good soul had really some ado in checking a rising sob.

"Well," said the officer who had listened with amused interest to all this, and now waxing merry with his tipple; "Well, blessed are the peacemakers, especially the fighting peacemakers! And such are the seventy-four beauties some of which you see poking their noses out of the port-holes of yonder war-ship lying-to for me," pointing thro' the cabin window at the *Bellipotent*. "But courage! don't look so downhearted, man. Why, I pledge you in advance the royal approbation. Rest assured that His Majesty will be delighted to know that in a time when his hard tack is not sought for by sailors with such avidity as should be; a time also when some shipmasters privily resent the borrowing from them a tar or two for the service; His Majesty, I say, will be delighted to learn that *one* shipmaster at least cheerfully surrenders to the King, the flower of his flock, a sailor who with equal loyalty makes no dissent. But where's my beauty? Ah," looking through the cabin's open door, "Here he comes; and, by Jove—lugging along his chest—Apollo with his portmanteau! My man," stepping out to him, "you can't take that big box aboard a war-ship. The boxes there are mostly shot-boxes. Put your duds in a bag, lad. Boot and saddle for the cavalryman, bag and hammock for the man-of-war's man."

The transfer from chest to bag was made. And, after seeing his man into the cutter and then following him down, the Lieutenant pushed off from the *Rights-of-Man*. That was the merchant-ship's name; tho' by her master and crew abbreviated in sailor fashion into the *Rights*. The hard-headed Dundee owner was a staunch admirer of Thomas Paine whose book in rejoinder to Burke's arraignment of the French Revolution had then been published for some time and had gone everywhere. In christening his vessel after the title of Paine's volume, the man of Dundee was something like his contemporary shipowner, Stephen Girard of Philadelphia, whose sympathies, alike with his native land and its liberal philosophers, he evinced by naming his ships after Voltaire, Diderot, and so forth.

But now, when the boat swept under the merchantman's stern, and officer and oarsmen were noting—some bitterly and others with a grin—the name emblazoned there; just then it was that the new recruit jumped up from the bow where the coxswain had directed him to sit, and waving his hat to his silent shipmates sorrowfully looking over at him from the taffrail, bade the lads a genial good-bye. Then, making a salutation as to the ship herself, "And good-bye to you too, old *Rights-of-Man*."

"Down, Sir!" roared the Lieutenant, instantly assuming all the rigor of his rank, though with difficulty repressing a smile.

To be sure, Billy's action was a terrible breach of naval decorum. But in that decorum he had never been instructed; in consideration of which the Lieutenant would hardly have been so energetic in reproof but for the concluding farewell to the ship. This he rather took as meant to convey a covert sally on the new recruit's part, a sly slur at impressment in general, and that of himself in especial. And yet, more likely, if satire it was in effect, it was hardly so by intention, for Billy, tho' happily endowed with the gayety of high health, youth, and a free heart, was yet by no means of a satirical turn. The will to it and the sinister dexterity were alike wanting. To deal in double meanings and insinuations of any sort was quite foreign to his nature.

As to his enforced enlistment, that he seemed to take pretty much as he was wont to take any vicissitude of weather. Like the animals, though no philosopher, he was, without knowing it, practically a fatalist. And, it may be, that he rather liked this adventurous turn in his affairs, which promised an opening into novel scenes and martial excitements.

Aboard the *Bellipotent* our merchant-sailor was forthwith rated as an able-seaman and assigned to the starboard watch of the fore-top. He was soon at home in the service, not at all disliked for his unpretentious good looks and a sort of genial happy-go-lucky air. No merrier man in his mess: in marked contrast to certain other individuals included like himself among the impressed portion of the ship's company; for these when not actively employed were sometimes, and more particularly in the last dog-watch when the drawing near of twilight induced reverie, apt to fall into a saddish mood which in some partook of sullenness. But they were not so young as our foretopman, and no few of them must have known a hearth of some sort; others may have had wives and children left, too probably, in uncertain circumstances, and hardly any but must have had acknowledged kith and kin, while for Billy, as will shortly be seen, his entire family was practically invested in himself.

Chapter II

THOUGH OUR NEW-MADE FORETOPMAN WAS WELL RECEIVED IN THE TOP AND ON THE GUN decks, hardly here was he that cynosure he had previously been among those minor ship's companies of the merchant marine, with which companies only had he hitherto consorted.

He was young; and despite his all but fully developed frame, in aspect looked even younger than he really was, owing to a lingering adolescent expression in the as yet smooth face, all but feminine in purity of natural complexion, but where, thanks to his seagoing, the lily was quite suppressed and the rose had some ado visibly to flush through the tan.

To one essentially such a novice in the complexities of factitious life, the abrupt transition from his former and simpler sphere to the ampler and more knowing world of a great war-ship; this might well have abashed him had there been any conceit or vanity in his composition. Among her miscellaneous multitude, the *Bellipotent* mustered several individuals who, however inferior in grade, were of no common natural stamp, sailors more signally susceptive of that air which continuous martial discipline and repeated presence in battle can in some degree impart even to the average man. As the Handsome Sailor, Billy Budd's position aboard the seventy-four was something analogous to that of a rustic beauty transplanted from the provinces and brought into competition with the highborn dames of the court. But this change of circumstances he scarce noted. As little did he observe that something about him provoked an ambiguous smile in one or two harder faces among the blue-jackets. Nor less unaware was he of the peculiar favorable effect his person and demeanor had upon the more intelligent gentlemen of the quarter-deck. Nor could this well have been otherwise. Cast in a mould peculiar to the finest physical examples of those Englishmen in whom the Saxon strain would seem not at all to partake of any Norman or other admixture, he showed in face that humane look of reposeful good nature which the Greek sculptor in some instances gave to his heroic strong man, Hercules. But this again was subtly modified by another and pervasive quality. The ear, small and shapely, the arch of the foot, the curve in mouth and nostril, even the indurated hand dyed to the orange-tawny of the toucan's bill, a hand telling alike of the halyards and tar-bucket; but, above all, something in the mobile expression, and every chance attitude and movement, something suggestive of a mother eminently favored by Love and the Graces; all this strangely indicated a lineage in direct contradiction to his lot. The mysteriousness here became less mysterious through a matter-of-fact elicited when Billy, at the capstan, was being formally mustered into the service. Asked by the officer, a small brisk little gentleman, as it chanced among other questions, his place of birth, he replied, "Please, Sir, I don't know."

"Don't know where you were born? Who was your father?"

"God knows, Sir."

Struck by the straightforward simplicity of these replies, the officer next asked, "Do you know anything about your beginning?"

"No, Sir. But I have heard that I was found in a pretty silklined basket hanging one morning from the knocker of a good man's door in Bristol."

"*Found*, say you? Well," throwing back his head and looking up and down the new recruit; "Well, it turns out to have been a pretty good find. Hope they'll find some more like you, my man; the fleet sadly needs them."

Yes, Billy Budd was a foundling, a presumable by-blow, and, evidently, no ignoble one. Noble descent was as evident in him as in a blood horse.

For the rest, with little or no sharpness of faculty or any trace of the wisdom of the serpent, nor yet quite a dove, he possessed that kind and degree of intelligence going along with the unconventional rectitude of a sound human creature, one to whom not yet has been proffered the questionable apple of knowledge. He was illiterate; he could not read, but he could sing, and like the illiterate nightingale was sometimes the composer of his own song.

Of self-consciousness he seemed to have little or none, or about as much as we may reasonably impute to a dog of Saint Bernard's breed.

Habitually living with the elements and knowing little more of the land than as a beach, or, rather, that portion of the terraqueous globe providentially set apart for dance-houses, doxies and tapsters, in short what sailors call a "fiddlers'-green," his simple nature remained unsophisticated by those moral obliquities which are not in every case incompatible with that manufacturable thing known as respectability. But are sailors, frequenters of "fiddlers'-greens," without vices? No; but less often than with landsmen do their vices, so called, partake of crookedness of heart, seeming less to proceed from viciousness than exuberance of vitality after long constraint; frank manifestations in accordance with natural law. By his original constitution aided by the cooperating influences of his lot, Billy in many respects was little more than a sort of upright barbarian, much such perhaps as Adam presumably might have been ere the urbane Serpent wriggled himself into his company.

And here be it submitted that apparently going to corroborate the doctrine of man's fall, a doctrine now popularly ignored, it is observable that where certain virtues pristine and unadulterate peculiarly characterize anybody in the external uniform of civilization, they will upon scrutiny seem not to be derived from custom or convention, but rather to be out of keeping with these, as if indeed exceptionally transmitted from a period prior to Cain's city and citified man. The character marked by such qualities has to an unvitiated taste an untampered-with flavor like that of berries, while the man thoroughly civilized, even in a fair specimen of the breed, has to the same moral palate a questionable smack as of a compounded wine. To any stray inheritor of these primitive qualities found, like Caspar Hauser, wandering dazed in any Christian capital of our time, the good-natured poet's famous invocation, near two thousand years ago, of the good rustic out of his latitude in the Rome of the Cesars, still appropriately holds:

Honest and poor, faithful in word and thought,
What has thee, Fabian, to the city brought?

Though our Handsome Sailor had as much of masculine beauty as one can expect anywhere to see; nevertheless, like the beautiful woman in one of Hawthorne's minor tales, there was just one thing amiss in him. No visible blemish, indeed, as with the lady; no, but an occasional liability to a vocal defect. Though in the hour of elemental uproar or peril he was everything that a sailor should be, yet under sudden provocation of strong heart-feeling, his voice otherwise singularly musical, as if expressive of the harmony within, was apt to develop an organic hesitancy, in fact, more or less of a stutter or even worse. In this particular Billy was a striking instance that the arch interferer, the envious marplot of Eden, still has more or less to do with every human consignment to this planet of earth. In every case, one way or another he is sure to slip in his little card, as much as to remind us—I too have a hand here.

The avowal of such an imperfection in the Handsome Sailor should be evidence not alone that he is not presented as a conventional hero, but also that the story in which he is the main figure is no romance.

Chapter III

At the time of Billy Budd's arbitrary enlistment into the *Bellipotent* that ship was on her way to join the Mediterranean fleet. No long time elapsed before the junction was effected. As one of that fleet the seventy-four participated in its movements, tho' at times, on account of her superior sailing qualities, in the absence of frigates, despatched on separate duty as a scout and at times on less temporary service. But with all this the story has little concernment, restricted as it is to the inner life of one particular ship and the career of an individual sailor.

It was the summer of 1797. In the April of that year had occurred the commotion at Spithead followed in May by a second and yet more serious outbreak in the fleet at the Nore. The latter is known, and without exaggeration in the epithet, as the Great Mutiny. It was indeed a demonstration more menacing to England than the contemporary manifestoes and conquering and proselyting armies of the French Directory. To the British Empire the Nore Mutiny was what a strike in the fire-brigade would be to London threatened by general arson. In a crisis when the kingdom might well have anticipated the famous signal that some years later published along the naval line of battle what it was that upon occasion England expected of Englishmen; *that* was the time when at the mast-heads of the three-deckers and seventy-fours moored in her own roadstead—a fleet, the right arm of a Power then all but the sole free conservative one of the Old World—the blue-jackets, to be numbered by thousands, ran up with huzzas the British colors with the union and cross wiped out; by that cancellation transmuting the flag of founded law and freedom defined, into the enemy's red meteor of unbridled and unbounded revolt. Reasonable discontent growing out of practical grievances in the fleet had been ignited into irrational combustion, as by live cinders blown across the Channel from France in flames.

The event converted into irony for a time those spirited strains of Dibdin—as a song-writer no mean auxiliary to the English Government at the European conjuncture—strains celebrating, among other things, the patriotic devotion of the British tar:

And as for my life, 'tis the King's!

Such an episode in the Island's grand naval story her naval historians naturally abridge; one of them (G.P.R. James) candidly acknowledging that fain would he pass it over did not "impartiality forbid fastidiousness." And yet his mention is less a narration than a reference, having to do hardly at all with details. Nor are these readily to be found in the libraries. Like some other events in every age befalling states everywhere, including America, the Great Mutiny was of such character that national pride along with views of policy would fain shade it off into the historical background. Such events can not be ignored, but there is a considerate way of historically treating them. If a well-constituted individual refrains from blazoning aught amiss or calamitous in his family, a nation in the like circumstance may without reproach be equally discreet.

Though after parleyings between Government and the ringleaders, and concessions by the former as to some glaring abuses, the first uprising—that at Spithead—with difficulty was put down, or matters for the time pacified; yet at the Nore the unforeseen renewal of insurrection on a yet larger scale, and emphasized in the conferences that ensued by demands deemed by the authorities not only inadmissible but aggressively insolent, indicated—if the Red Flag did not sufficiently do so—what was the spirit animating the men. Final suppression, however, there was; but only made possible perhaps by the unswerving loyalty of the marine corps and voluntary resumption of loyalty among influential sections of the crews.

To some extent the Nore Mutiny may be regarded as analogous to the distempering irruption of contagious fever in a frame constitutionally sound, and which anon throws it off.

At all events, of these thousands of mutineers were some of the tars who not so very long afterwards—whether wholly prompted thereto by patriotism, or pugnacious instinct, or by both—helped to win a coronet for Nelson at the Nile, and the naval crown of crowns for him at Trafalgar. To the mutineers those battles, and especially Trafalgar, were a plenary absolution and a grand one: For all that goes to make up scenic naval display, heroic magnificence in arms, those battles, especially Trafalgar, stand unmatched in human annals.

Chapter IV

IN THIS MATTER OF WRITING, RESOLVE AS ONE MAY TO KEEP TO THE MAIN ROAD, SOME BYPATHS have an enticement not readily to be withstood. I am going to err into such a by-path. If the reader will keep me company I shall be glad. At the least we can promise ourselves that pleasure which is wickedly said to be in sinning, for a literary sin the divergence will be.

Very likely it is no new remark that the inventions of our time have at last brought about a change in sea-warfare in degree corresponding to the revolution in all warfare effected by the original introduction from China into Europe of gunpowder. The first European fire-arm, a clumsy contrivance, was, as is well known, scouted by no few of the knights as a base implement, good enough peradventure for weavers too craven to stand up crossing steel with steel in frank fight. But as ashore, knightly valor, tho' shorn of its blazonry, did not cease with the knights, neither on the seas, though nowadays in encounters there a certain kind of displayed gallantry be fallen out of date as hardly applicable under changed circumstances, did the nobler qualities of such naval magnates as Don John of Austria, Doria, Van Tromp, Jean Bart, the long line of British Admirals and the American Decaturs of 1812 become obsolete with their wooden walls.

Nevertheless, to anybody who can hold the Present at its worth without being inappreciative of the Past, it may be forgiven, if to such an one the solitary old hulk at Portsmouth, Nelson's *Victory*, seems to float there, not alone as the decaying monument of a fame incorruptible, but also as a poetic reproach, softened by its picturesqueness, to the *Monitors* and yet mightier hulls of the European ironclads. And this not altogether because such craft are unsightly, unavoidably lacking the symmetry and grand lines of the old battle-ships, but equally for other reasons.

There are some, perhaps, who while not altogether inaccessible to that poetic reproach just alluded to, may yet on behalf of the new order, be disposed to parry it; and this to the extent of iconoclasm, if need be. For example, prompted by the sight of the star inserted in the *Victory*'s quarter-deck designating the spot where the Great Sailor fell, these martial utilitarians may suggest considerations implying that Nelson's ornate publication of his person in battle was not only unnecessary, but not military, nay, savored of foolhardiness and vanity. They may add, too, that at Trafalgar it was in effect nothing less than a challenge to death; and death came; and that but for his bravado the victorious Admiral might possibly have survived the battle; and so, instead of having his sagacious dying injunctions overruled by his immediate successor in command, he himself, when the contest was decided, might have brought his shattered fleet to anchor, a proceeding which might have averted the deplorable loss of life by shipwreck in the elemental tempest that followed the martial one.

Well, should we set aside the more disputable point whether for various reasons it was possible to anchor the fleet, then plausibly enough the Benthamites of war may urge the above. But the *might-have-been* is but boggy ground to build on. And, certainly, in foresight as to the larger issue of an encounter, and anxious preparations for it—buoying the deadly way and mapping it out, as at Copenhagen—few commanders have been so painstakingly circumspect as this same reckless declarer of his person in fight.

Personal prudence even when dictated by quite other than selfish considerations surely is no special virtue in a military man; while an excessive love of glory, impassioning a less burning impulse, the honest sense of duty, is the first. If the name *Wellington* is not so much of a trumpet to the blood as the simpler name *Nelson*, the reason for this may perhaps be inferred from the above. Alfred in his funeral ode on the victor of Waterloo ventures not to call him the greatest soldier of all time, tho' in the same ode he invokes Nelson as "the greatest sailor since our world began."

At Trafalgar, Nelson, on the brink of opening the fight, sat down and wrote his last brief will and testament. If under the presentiment of the most magnificent of all victories to be crowned by his own glorious death, a sort of priestly motive led him to dress his person in the jeweled vouchers of his own shining deeds; if thus to have adorned himself for the altar and the sacrifice were indeed vainglory, then affectation and fustian is each more heroic line in the great epics and dramas, since in such lines the poet but embodies in verse those exaltations of sentiment that a nature like Nelson, the opportunity being given, vitalizes into acts.

Chapter V

YES, THE OUTBREAK AT THE NORE WAS PUT DOWN. BUT NOT EVERY GRIEVANCE WAS REDRESSED. If the contractors, for example, were no longer permitted to ply some practices peculiar to their tribe everywhere, such as providing shoddy cloth, rations not sound, or false in the measure, not the less impressment, for one thing, went on. By custom sanctioned for centuries, and judicially maintained by a Lord Chancellor as late as Mansfield, that mode of manning the fleet, a mode now fallen into a sort of abeyance but never formally renounced, it was not practicable to give up in those years. Its abrogation would have crippled the indispensable fleet, one wholly under canvas, no steam-power, its innumerable sails and thousands of cannon, everything in short, worked by muscle alone; a fleet the more insatiate in demand for men, because then multiplying its ships of all grades against contingencies present and to come of the convulsed Continent.

Discontent foreran the Two Mutinies, and more or less it lurkingly survived them. Hence it was not unreasonable to apprehend some return of trouble, sporadic or general. One instance of such apprehensions: In the same year with this story, Nelson, then Vice-Admiral Sir Horatio, being with the fleet off the Spanish coast, was directed by the Admiral in command to shift his pennant from the *Captain to the Theseus*; and for this reason: that the latter ship having newly arrived on the station from home where it had taken part in the Great Mutiny, danger was apprehended from the temper of the men; and it was thought that an officer like Nelson was the one, not indeed to terrorize the crew into base subjection, but to win them, by force of his mere presence, back to an allegiance if not as enthusiastic as his own, yet as true. So it was that for a time on more than one quarter-deck anxiety did exist. At sea precautionary vigilance was strained against relapse. At short notice an engagement might come on. When it did, the lieutenants assigned to batteries felt it incumbent on them, in some instances, to stand with drawn swords behind the men working the guns.

Chapter VI

But on board the seventy-four in which Billy now swung his hammock, very little in the manner of the men and nothing obvious in the demeanor of the officers would have suggested to an ordinary observer that the Great Mutiny was a recent event. In their general bearing and conduct the commissioned officers of a warship naturally take their tone from the Commander, that is if he have that ascendancy of character that ought to be his.

Captain the Honorable Edward Fairfax Vere, to give his full title, was a bachelor of forty or thereabouts, a sailor of distinction even in a time prolific of renowned seamen. Though allied to the higher nobility, his advancement had not been altogether owing to influences connected with that circumstance. He had seen much service, been in various engagements, always acquitting himself as an officer mindful of the welfare of his men, but never tolerating an infraction of discipline; thoroughly versed in the science of his profession, and intrepid to the verge of temerity, though never injudiciously so. For his gallantry in the West Indian waters as Flag-Lieutenant under Rodney in that Admiral's crowning victory over De Grasse, he was made a Post-Captain.

Ashore in the garb of a civilian, scarce anyone would have taken him for a sailor, more especially that he never garnished unprofessional talk with nautical terms, and grave in his bearing, evinced little appreciation of mere humor. It was not out of keeping with these traits that on a passage when nothing demanded his paramount action, he was the most undemonstrative of men. Any landsman observing this gentleman, not conspicuous by his stature and wearing no pronounced insignia, emerging from his cabin to the open deck, and noting the silent deference of the officers retiring to leeward, might have taken him for the King's guest, a civilian aboard the King's-ship, some highly honorable discreet envoy on his way to an important post. But in fact this unobtrusiveness of demeanor may have proceeded from a certain unaffected modesty of manhood sometimes accompanying a resolute nature, a modesty evinced at all times not calling for pronounced action, and which shown in any rank of life suggests a virtue aristocratic in kind. As with some others engaged in various departments of the world's more heroic activities, Captain Vere, though practical enough upon occasion, would at times betray a certain dreaminess of mood. Standing alone on the weather-side of the quarter-deck, one hand holding by the rigging, he would absently gaze off at the blank sea. At the presentation to him then of some minor matter interrupting the current of his thoughts he would show more or less irascibility; but instantly he would control it.

In the navy he was popularly known by the appellation—Starry Vere. How such a designation happened to fall upon one who, whatever his sterling qualities, was without any brilliant ones was in this wise: A favorite kinsman, Lord Denton, a free-hearted fellow, had been the first to meet and congratulate him upon his return to England from his West Indian cruise; and but the day previous turning over a copy of Andrew Marvell's poems, had lighted, not for the first time however, upon the lines entitled Appleton House, the name of one of the seats of their common ancestor, a hero in the German wars of the seventeenth century, in which poem occur the lines,

This 'tis to have been from the first
In a domestic heaven nursed,
Under the discipline severe
Of Fairfax and the starry Vere."

And so, upon embracing his cousin fresh from Rodney's great victory wherein he had played so gallant a part, brimming over with just family pride in the sailor of their house, he exuberantly exclaimed, "Give ye joy, Ed; give ye joy, my starry Vere!" This got currency, and the novel prefix serving in familiar parlance readily to distinguish the *Bellipotent*'s Captain from another Vere his senior, a distant relative, an officer of like rank in the navy, it remained permanently attached to the surname.

Chapter VII

IN VIEW OF THE PART THAT THE COMMANDER OF THE *BELLIPOTENT* PLAYS IN SCENES SHORTLY TO follow, it may be well to fill out that sketch of his outlined in the previous chapter.

Aside from his qualities as a sea-officer, Captain Vere was an exceptional character. Unlike no few of England's renowned sailors, long and arduous service with signal devotion to it, had not resulted in absorbing and salting the entire man. He had a marked leaning toward everything intellectual. He loved books, never going to sea without a newly replenished library, compact but of the best. The isolated leisure, in some cases so wearisome, falling at intervals to commanders even during a war-cruise, never was tedious to Captain Vere. With nothing of that literary taste which less heeds the thing conveyed than the vehicle, his bias was toward those books to which every serious mind of superior order occupying any active post of authority in the world naturally inclines; books treating of actual men and events no matter of what era—history, biography and unconventional writers, who, free from cant and convention, like Montaigne, honestly and in the spirit of common sense philosophize upon realities. In this line of reading he found confirmation of his own more reasoned thoughts—confirmation which he had vainly sought in social converse, so that as touching most fundamental topics, there had got to be established in him some positive convictions, which he forefelt would abide in him essentially unmodified so long as his intelligent part remained unimpaired. In view of the troubled period in which his lot was cast this was well for him. His settled convictions were as a dyke against those invading waters of novel opinion, social, political and otherwise, which carried away as in a torrent no few minds in those days, minds by nature not inferior to his own. While other members of that aristocracy to which by birth he belonged were incensed at the innovators mainly because their theories were inimical to the privileged classes, not alone Captain Vere disinterestedly opposed them because they seemed to him incapable of embodiment in lasting institutions, but at war with the peace of the world and the true welfare of mankind.

With minds less stored than his and less earnest, some officers of his rank, with whom at times he would necessarily consort, found him lacking in the companionable quality, a dry and bookish gentleman, as they deemed. Upon any chance withdrawal from their company one would be apt to say to another, something like this: "Vere is a noble fellow, Starry Vere. Spite the gazettes, Sir Horatio" (meaning him with the Lord title) "is at bottom scarce a better seaman or fighter. But between you and me now, don't you think there is a queer streak of the pedantic running thro' him? Yes, like the King's yarn in a coil of navy-rope?"

Some apparent ground there was for this sort of confidential criticism; since not only did the Captain's discourse never fall into the jocosely familiar, but in illustrating of any point touching the stirring personages and events of the time he would be as apt to cite some historic character or incident of antiquity as that he would cite from the moderns. He seemed unmindful of the circumstance that to his bluff company such remote allusions, however pertinent they might really be, were altogether alien to men whose reading was mainly confined to the journals. But considerateness in such matters is not easy to natures constituted like Captain Vere's. Their honesty prescribes to them directness, sometimes far-reaching like that of a migratory fowl that in its flight never heeds when it crosses a frontier.

Chapter VIII

THE LIEUTENANTS AND OTHER COMMISSIONED GENTLEMEN FORMING CAPTAIN VERE'S STAFF IT IS not necessary here to particularize, nor needs it to make any mention of any of the warrant-officers. But among the petty-officers was one who having much to do with the story, may as well be forthwith introduced. His portrait I essay, but shall never hit it. This was John Claggart, the Master-at-arms. But that sea-title may to landsmen seem somewhat equivocal. Originally, doubtless, that petty-officer's function was the instruction of the men in the use of arms, sword or cutlass. But very long ago, owing to the advance in gunnery making hand-to-hand encounters less frequent and giving to niter and sulfur the preeminence over steel, that function ceased; the Master-at-arms of a great war-ship becoming a sort of Chief of Police, charged among other matters with the duty of preserving order on the populous lower gun decks.

Claggart was a man about five and thirty, somewhat spare and tall, yet of no ill figure upon the whole. His hand was too small and shapely to have been accustomed to hard toil. The face was a notable one; the features all except the chin cleanly cut as those on a Greek medallion; yet the chin, beardless as Tecumseh's, had something of strange protuberant heaviness in its make that recalled the prints of the Rev. Dr. Titus Oates, the historic deponent with the clerical drawl in the time of Charles II and the fraud of the alleged Popish Plot. It served Claggart in his office that his eye could cast a tutoring glance. His brow was of the sort phrenologically associated with more than average intellect; silken jet curls partly clustering over it, making a foil to the pallor below, a pallor tinged with a faint shade of amber akin to the hue of time-tinted marbles of old. This complexion, singularly contrasting with the red or deeply bronzed visages of the sailors, and in part the result of his official seclusion from the sunlight, tho' it was not exactly displeasing, nevertheless seemed to hint of something defective or abnormal in the constitution and blood. But his general aspect and manner were so suggestive of an education and career incongruous with his naval function that when not actively engaged in it he looked a man of high quality, social and moral, who for reasons of his own was keeping incog. Nothing was known of his former life. It might be that he was an Englishman; and yet there lurked a bit of accent in his speech suggesting that possibly he was not such by birth, but through naturalization in early childhood. Among certain grizzled sea-gossips of the gun decks and forecastle went a rumor perdue that the Master-at-arms was a *chevalier* who had volunteered into the King's Navy by way of compounding for some mysterious swindle whereof he had been arraigned at the King's Bench. The fact that nobody could substantiate this report was, of course, nothing against its secret currency. Such a rumor once started on the gun decks in reference to almost anyone below the rank of a commissioned officer would, during the period assigned to this narrative, have seemed not altogether wanting in credibility to the tarry old wiseacres of a man-of-war crew. And indeed a man of Claggart's accomplishments, without prior nautical experience, entering the navy at mature life, as he did, and necessarily allotted at the start to the lowest grade in it; a man, too, who never made allusion to his previous life ashore; these were circumstances which in the dearth of exact knowledge as to his true antecedents opened to the invidious a vague field for unfavorable surmise.

But the sailors' dog-watch gossip concerning him derived a vague plausibility from the fact that now for some period the British Navy could so little afford to be squeamish in the matter of keeping up the muster-rolls, that not only were press-gangs notoriously abroad both afloat and ashore, but there was little or no secret about another matter, namely that the London police were at liberty to capture any able-bodied suspect, any questionable fellow at large and summarily ship him to dockyard or fleet. Furthermore, even among voluntary enlistments there were instances where the motive thereto partook neither of patriotic impulse nor yet of a random desire to experience a bit of sea-life and martial adventure. Insolvent debtors of minor grade, together with the promiscuous lame ducks of morality found in the Navy a convenient and secure refuge. Secure, because once enlisted aboard a King's-ship, they were as much in sanctuary, as the transgressor of the Middle Ages harboring himself under the shadow of the altar. Such sanctioned irregularities, which for obvious reasons the Government would hardly think to parade at the time, and which consequently, and as affecting the least influential class of mankind, have all but dropped into oblivion, lend color to something for the truth whereof I do not vouch, and hence have some scruple in stating; something I remember having seen in print, though the book I can not recall; but the same thing was personally communicated to me now more than forty years ago by an old pensioner in a cocked hat with whom I had a most interesting talk on the terrace at Greenwich, a Baltimore Negro, a Trafalgar man. It was to this effect: In the case of a war-ship short of hands whose speedy sailing was imperative, the deficient quota in lack of any other way of making it good, would be eked out by draughts culled direct from the jails. For reasons previously suggested it would not perhaps be easy at the present day directly to prove or disprove the allegation. But allowed as a verity, how significant would it be of England's straits at the time, confronted by those wars which like a flight of harpies rose shrieking from the din and dust of the fallen Bastille. That era appears measurably clear to us who look back at it, and but read of it. But to the grandfathers of us graybeards, the more thoughtful of them, the genius of it presented an aspect like that of Camoëns' Spirit of the Cape, an eclipsing menace mysterious and prodigious. Not America was exempt from apprehension. At the height of Napoleon's unexampled conquests, there were Americans who had fought at Bunker Hill who looked forward to the possibility that the Atlantic might prove no barrier against the ultimate schemes of this French upstart from the revolutionary chaos who seemed in act of fulfilling judgment prefigured in the Apocalypse.

But the less credence was to be given to the gun-deck talk touching Claggart, seeing that no man holding his office in a man-of-war can ever hope to be popular with the crew. Besides, in derogatory comments upon anyone against whom they have a grudge, or for any reason or no reason mislike, sailors are much like landsmen; they are apt to exaggerate or romance it.

About as much was really known to the *Bellipotent*'s tars of the Master-at-arms' career before entering the service as an astronomer knows about a comet's travels prior to its first observable appearance in the sky. The verdict of the sea quid-nuncs has been cited only by way of showing what sort of moral impression the man made upon rude uncultivated natures whose conceptions of human wickedness were necessarily of the narrowest, limited to ideas of vulgar rascality—a thief among the swinging hammocks during a night-watch, or the man brokers and land-sharks of the sea-ports.

It was no gossip, however, but fact, that though, as before hinted, Claggart upon his entrance into the navy was, as a novice, assigned to the least honorable section of a man-of-war's crew, embracing the drudgery, he did not long remain there. The superior capacity he immediately evinced, his constitutional sobriety, ingratiating deference to superiors, together with a peculiar ferreting genius manifested on a singular occasion; all this capped by a certain austere patriotism abruptly advanced him to the position of Master-at-arms.

Of this maritime Chief of Police the ship's-corporals, so called, were the immediate subordinates, and compliant ones; and this, as is to be noted in some business departments ashore, almost to a degree inconsistent with entire moral volition. His place put various converging wires of underground influence under the Chief's control, capable when astutely worked thro' his understrappers, of operating to the mysterious discomfort, if nothing worse, of any of the sea-commonalty.

Chapter IX

LIFE IN THE FORE-TOP WELL AGREED WITH BILLY BUDD. THERE, WHEN NOT ACTUALLY ENGAGED on the yards yet higher aloft, the topmen, who as such had been picked out for youth and activity, constituted an aerial club lounging at ease against the smaller stun'sails rolled up into cushions, spinning yarns like the lazy gods, and frequently amused with what was going on in the busy world of the decks below. No wonder then that a young fellow of Billy's disposition was well content in such society. Giving no cause of offence to anybody, he was always alert at a call. So in the merchant service it had been with him. But now such a punctiliousness in duty was shown that his topmates would sometimes good-naturedly laugh at him for it. This heightened alacrity had its cause, namely, the impression made upon him by the first formal gangway-punishment he had ever witnessed, which befell the day following his impressment. It had been incurred by a little fellow, young, a novice, an afterguardsman absent from his assigned post when the ship was being put about; a dereliction resulting in a rather serious hitch to that maneuver, one demanding instantaneous promptitude in letting go and making fast. When Billy saw the culprit's naked back under the scourge gridironed with red welts, and worse; when he marked the dire expression on the liberated man's face as with his woolen shirt flung over him by the executioner he rushed forward from the spot to bury himself in the crowd, Billy was horrified. He resolved that never through remissness would he make himself liable to such a visitation or do or omit aught that might merit even verbal reproof. What then was his surprise and concern when ultimately he found himself getting into petty trouble occasionally about such matters as the stowage of his bag or something amiss in his hammock, matters under the police oversight of the ship's-corporals of the lower decks, and which brought down on him a vague threat from one of them.

So heedful in all things as he was, how could this be? He could not understand it, and it more than vexed him. When he spoke to his young topmates about it they were either lightly incredulous or found something comical in his unconcealed anxiety. "Is it your bag, Billy?" said one. "Well, sew yourself up in it, bully boy, and then you'll be sure to know if anybody meddles with it."

Now there was a veteran aboard who because his years began to disqualify him for more active work had been recently assigned duty as mainmastman in his watch, looking to the gear belayed at the rail roundabout that great spar near the deck. At off-times the Foretopman had picked up some acquaintance with him, and now in his trouble it occurred to him that he might be the sort of person to go to for wise counsel. He was an old Dansker long anglicized in the service, of few words, many wrinkles and some honorable scars. His wizened face, time-tinted and weather-stained to the complexion of an antique parchment, was here and there peppered blue by the chance explosion of a gun-cartridge in action.

He was an *Agamemnon* man; some two years prior to the time of this story having served under Nelson, when but Sir Horatio, in that ship immortal in naval memory, and which, dismantled and in part broken up to her bare ribs, is seen a grand skeleton in Haydon's etching. As one of a boarding-party from the *Agamemnon* he had received a cut slantwise along one temple and cheek, leaving a long scar like a streak of dawn's light falling athwart the dark visage. It was on account of that scar and the affair in which it was known that he had received it, as well as from his blue-peppered complexion, that the Dansker went among the *Bellipotent*'s crew by the name of "Board-her-in-the-smoke."

Now the first time that his small weasel-eyes happened to light on Billy Budd, a certain grim internal merriment set all his ancient wrinkles into antic play. Was it that his eccentric unsentimental old sapience, primitive in its kind, saw or thought it saw something which, in contrast with the war-ship's environment, looked oddly incongruous in the Handsome Sailor? But after slyly studying him at intervals, the old Merlin's equivocal merriment was modified; for now when the twain would meet, it would start in his face a quizzing sort of look, but it would be but momentary and sometimes replaced by an expression of speculative query as to what might eventually befall a nature like that, dropped into a world not without some man-traps and against whose subtleties simple courage, lacking experience and address and without any touch of defensive ugliness, is of little avail; and where such innocence as man is capable of does yet in a moral emergency not always sharpen the faculties or enlighten the will.

However it was, the Dansker in his ascetic way rather took to Billy. Nor was this only because of a certain philosophic interest in such a character. There was another cause. While the old man's eccentricities, sometimes bordering on the ursine, repelled the juniors, Billy, undeterred thereby, revering him as a salt hero, would make advances, never passing the old *Agamemnon* man without a salutation marked by that respect which is seldom lost on the aged however crabbed at times or whatever their station in life.

There was a vein of dry humor, or what not, in the mast-man; and, whether in freak of patriarchal irony touching Billy's youth and athletic frame, or for some other and more recondite reason, from the first in addressing him he always substituted *Baby* for Billy. The Dansker in fact being the originator of the name by which the Foretopman eventually became known aboard ship.

Well then, in his mysterious little difficulty, going in quest of the wrinkled one, Billy found him off duty in a dog-watch ruminating by himself, seated on a shot-box of the upper gun deck, now and then surveying with a somewhat cynical regard certain of the more swaggering promenaders there. Billy recounted his trouble, again wondering how it all happened. The salt seer attentively listened, accompanying the Foretopman's recital with queer twitchings of his wrinkles and problematical little sparkles of his small ferret eyes. Making an end of his story, the Foretopman asked, "And now, Dansker, do tell me what you think of it."

The old man, shoving up the front of his tarpaulin and deliberately rubbing the long slant scar at the point where it entered the thin hair, laconically said, "Baby Budd, *Jemmy Legs*" (meaning the Master-at-arms) "is down on you."

"*Jemmy Legs!*" ejaculated Billy, his welkin eyes expanding; "What for? Why he calls me the sweet and pleasant fellow, they tell me."

"Does he so?" grinned the grizzled one; then said, "Ay, Baby Lad, a sweet voice has Jemmy Legs."

"No, not always. But to me he has. I seldom pass him but there comes a pleasant word."

"And that's because he's down upon you, Baby Budd."

Such reiteration along with the manner of it, incomprehensible to a novice, disturbed Billy almost as much as the mystery for which he had sought explanation. Something less unpleasingly oracular he tried to extract; but the old sea-Chiron, thinking perhaps that for the nonce he had sufficiently instructed his young Achilles, pursed his lips, gathered all his wrinkles together and would commit himself to nothing further.

Years, and those experiences which befall certain shrewder men subordinated life-long to the will of superiors, all this had developed in the Dansker the pithy guarded cynicism that was his leading characteristic.

Chapter X

THE NEXT DAY AN INCIDENT SERVED TO CONFIRM BILLY BUDD IN HIS INCREDULITY AS TO THE Dansker's strange summing-up of the case submitted. The ship at noon, going large before the wind, was rolling on her course, and he, below at dinner and engaged in some sportful talk with the members of his mess, chanced in a sudden lurch to spill the entire contents of his soup-pan upon the new scrubbed deck. Claggart, the Master-at-arms, official rattan in hand, happened to be passing along the battery in a bay of which the mess was lodged, and the greasy liquid streamed just across his path. Stepping over it, he was proceeding on his way without comment, since the matter was nothing to take notice of under the circumstances, when he happened to observe who it was that had done the spilling. His countenance changed. Pausing, he was about to ejaculate something hasty at the sailor, but checked himself, and pointing down to the streaming soup, playfully tapped him from behind with his rattan, saying in a low musical voice peculiar to him at times, "Handsomely done, my lad! And handsome is as handsome did it too!" And with that passed on. Not noted by Billy, as not coming within his view, was the involuntary smile, or rather grimace, that accompanied Claggart's equivocal words. Aridly it drew down the thin corners of his shapely mouth. But everybody taking his remark as meant for humorous, and at which therefore as coming from a superior they were bound to laugh "with counterfeited glee," acted accordingly; and Billy tickled, it may be, by the allusion to his being the handsome sailor, merrily joined in; then addressing his messmates exclaimed, "There now, who says that Jemmy Legs is down on me!"

"And who said he was, Beauty?" demanded one Donald with some surprise. Whereat the Foretopman looked a little foolish, recalling that it was only one person, Board-her-in-the-smoke, who had suggested what to him was the smoky idea that this Master-at-arms was in any peculiar way hostile to him. Meantime that functionary, resuming his path, must have momentarily worn some expression less guarded than that of the bitter smile, and usurping the face from the heart, some distorting expression perhaps; for a drummer-boy heedlessly frolicking along from the opposite direction and chancing to come into light collision with his person was strangely disconcerted by his aspect. Nor was the impression lessened when the official, impulsively giving him a sharp cut with the rattan, vehemently exclaimed, "Look where you go!"

Chapter XI

WHAT WAS THE MATTER WITH THE MASTER-AT-ARMS? AND, BE THE MATTER WHAT IT MIGHT, how could it have direct relation to Billy Budd with whom, prior to the affair of the spilled soup, he had never come into any special contact, official or otherwise? What indeed could the trouble have to do with one so little inclined to give offence as the merchant-ship's peacemaker, even him who in Claggart's own phrase was "the sweet and pleasant young fellow"? Yes, why should Jemmy Legs, to borrow the Dansker's expression, be down on the Handsome Sailor? But, at heart and not for nothing, as the late chance encounter may indicate to the discerning, down on him, secretly down on him, he assuredly was.

Now to invent something touching the more private career of Claggart, something involving Billy Budd, of which something the latter should be wholly ignorant, some romantic incident implying that Claggart's knowledge of the young blue-jacket began at some period anterior to catching sight of him on board the seventy-four-all this, not so difficult to do, might avail in a way more or less interesting to account for whatever of enigma may appear to lurk in the case. But in fact there was nothing of the sort. And yet the cause, necessarily to be assumed as the sole one assignable, is in its very realism as much charged with that prime element of Radcliffian romance, the mysterious, as any that the ingenuity of the author of the *Mysteries of Udolpho* could devise. For what can more partake of the mysterious than an antipathy spontaneous and profound, such as is evoked in certain exceptional mortals by the mere aspect of some other mortal, however harmless he may be, if not called forth by this very harmlessness itself?

Now there can exist no irritating juxtaposition of dissimilar personalities comparable to that which is possible aboard a great war-ship fully manned and at sea. There, every day among all ranks almost every man comes into more or less of contact with almost every other man. Wholly there to avoid even the sight of an aggravating object one must needs give it Jonah's toss or jump overboard himself. Imagine how all this might eventually operate on some peculiar human creature the direct reverse of a saint?

But for the adequate comprehending of Claggart by a normal nature, these hints are insufficient. To pass from a normal nature to him one must cross "the deadly space between." And this is best done by indirection.

Long ago an honest scholar my senior, said to me in reference to one who like himself is now no more, a man so unimpeachably respectable that against him nothing was ever openly said though among the few something was whispered, "Yes, X——is a nut not be cracked by the tap of a lady's fan. You are aware that I am the adherent of no organized religion much less of any philosophy built into a system. Well, for all that, I think that to try and get into X——, enter his labyrinth and get out again, without a clue derived from some source other than what is known as 'knowledge of the world'—that were hardly possible, at least for me."

"Why," said I, "X——, however singular a study to some, is yet human, and knowledge of the world assuredly implies the knowledge of human nature, and in most of its varieties."

"Yes, but a superficial knowledge of it, serving ordinary purposes. But for anything deeper, I am not certain whether to know the world and to know human nature be not two distinct branches of knowledge, which while they may coexist in the same heart, yet either may exist with little or nothing of the other. Nay, in an average man of the world, his constant rubbing with it blunts that fine spiritual insight indispensable to the understanding of the essential in certain exceptional characters, whether evil ones or good. In a matter of some importance I have seen a girl wind an old lawyer about her little finger. Nor was it the dotage of senile love. Nothing of the sort. But he knew law better than he knew the girl's heart. Coke and Blackstone hardly shed so much light into obscure spiritual places as the Hebrew prophets. And who were they? Mostly recluses."

At the time my inexperience was such that I did not quite see the drift of all this. It may be that I see it now. And, indeed, if that lexicon which is based on Holy Writ were any longer popular, one might with less difficulty define and denominate certain phenomenal men. As it is, one must turn to some authority not liable to the charge of being tinctured with the Biblical element.

In a list of definitions included in the authentic translation of Plato, a list attributed to him, occurs this: "Natural Depravity: a depravity according to nature." A definition which tho' savoring of Calvinism, by no means involves Calvin's dogmas as to total mankind. Evidently its intent makes it applicable but to individuals. Not many are the examples of this depravity which the gallows and jail supply. At any rate for notable instances, since these have no vulgar alloy of the brute in them, but invariably are dominated by intellectuality, one must go elsewhere. Civilization, especially if of the austerer sort, is auspicious to it. It folds itself in the mantle of respectability. It has its certain negative virtues serving as silent auxiliaries. It never allows wine to get within its guard. It is not going too far to say that it is without vices or small sins. There is a phenomenal pride in it that excludes them from anything mercenary or avaricious. In short the depravity here meant partakes nothing of the sordid or sensual. It is serious, but free from acerbity. Though no flatterer of mankind it never speaks ill of it.

But the thing which in eminent instances signalizes so exceptional a nature is this: though the man's even temper and discreet bearing would seem to intimate a mind peculiarly subject to the law of reason, not the less in his heart he would seem to riot in complete exemption from that law, having apparently little to do with reason further than to employ it as an ambidexter implement for effecting the irrational. That is to say: Toward the accomplishment of an aim which in wantonness of malignity would seem to partake of the insane, he will direct a cool judgment sagacious and sound. These men are true madmen, and of the most dangerous sort, for their lunacy is not continuous but occasional, evoked by some special object; it is probably secretive, which is as much to say it is self-contained, so that when moreover, most active, it is to the average mind not distinguishable from sanity, and for the reason above suggested that whatever its aims may be—and the aim is never declared—the method and the outward proceeding are always perfectly rational.

Now something such an one was Claggart, in whom was the mania of an evil nature, not engendered by vicious training or corrupting books or licentious living, but born with him and innate, in short "a depravity according to nature."

Dark sayings are these, some will say. But why? Is it because they somewhat savor of Holy Writ in its phrase "mysteries of iniquity?" If they do, such savor was far from being intended, for little will it commend these pages to many a reader of to-day.

The point of the present story turning on the hidden nature of the Master-at-arms has necessitated this chapter. With an added hint or two in connection with the incident at the mess, the resumed narrative must be left to vindicate, as it may, its own credibility.

Chapter XII

THAT CLAGGART'S FIGURE WAS NOT AMISS, AND HIS FACE, SAVE THE CHIN, WELL MOLDED, HAS already been said. Of these favorable points he seemed not insensible, for he was not only neat but careful in his dress. But the form of Billy Budd was heroic; and if his face was without the intellectual look of the pallid Claggart's, not the less was it lit, like his, from within, though from a different source. The bonfire in his heart made luminous the rose-tan in his cheek.

In view of the marked contrast between the persons of the twain, it is more than probable that when the Master-at-arms in the scene last given applied to the sailor the proverb Handsome is as handsome does, he there let escape an ironic inkling, not caught by the young sailors who heard it, as to what it was that had first moved him against Billy, namely, his significant personal beauty.

Now envy and antipathy, passions irreconcilable in reason, nevertheless in fact may spring conjoined like Chang and Eng in one birth. Is Envy then such a monster? Well, though many an arraigned mortal has in hopes of mitigated penalty pleaded guilty to horrible actions, did ever anybody seriously confess to envy? Something there is in it universally felt to be more shameful than even felonious crime. And not only does everybody disown it, but the better sort are inclined to incredulity when it is in earnest imputed to an intelligent man. But since its lodgment is in the heart not the brain, no degree of intellect supplies a guarantee against it. But Claggart's was no vulgar form of the passion. Nor, as directed toward Billy Budd, did it partake of that streak of apprehensive jealousy that marred Saul's visage perturbedly brooding on the comely young David. Claggart's envy struck deeper. If askance he eyed the good looks, cheery health and frank enjoyment of young life in Billy Budd, it was because these went along with a nature that, as Claggart magnetically felt, had in its simplicity never willed malice or experienced the reactionary bite of that serpent. To him, the spirit lodged within Billy, and looking out from his welkin eyes as from windows, that ineffability it was which made the dimple in his dyed cheek, suppled his joints, and dancing in his yellow curls made him preeminently the Handsome Sailor. One person excepted, the Master-at-arms was perhaps the only man in the ship intellectually capable of adequately appreciating the moral phenomenon presented in Billy Budd. And the insight but intensified his passion, which assuming various secret forms within him, at times assumed that of cynic disdain—disdain of innocence. To be nothing more than innocent! Yet in an aesthetic way he saw the charm of it, the courageous free-and-easy temper of it, and fain would have shared it, but he despaired of it.

With no power to annul the elemental evil in him, tho' readily enough he could hide it; apprehending the good, but powerless to be it; a nature like Claggart's surcharged with energy as such natures almost invariably are, what recourse is left to it but to recoil upon itself and like the scorpion for which the Creator alone is responsible, act out to the end the part allotted it.

Chapter XIII

PASSION, AND PASSION IN ITS PROFOUNDEST, IS NOT A THING DEMANDING A PALATIAL STAGE whereon to play its part. Down among the groundlings, among the beggars and rakers of the garbage, profound passion is enacted. And the circumstances that provoke it, however trivial or mean, are no measure of its power. In the present instance the stage is a scrubbed gun deck, and one of the external provocations a man-of-war's-man's spilled soup.

Now when the Master-at-arms noticed whence came that greasy fluid streaming before his feet, he must have taken it—to some extent willfully, perhaps—not for the mere accident it assuredly was, but for the sly escape of a spontaneous feeling on Billy's part more or less answering to the antipathy on his own. In effect a foolish demonstration he must have thought, and very harmless, like the futile kick of a heifer, which yet were the heifer a shod stallion, would not be so harmless. Even so was it that into the gall of Claggart's envy he infused the vitriol of his contempt. But the incident confirmed to him certain tell-tale reports purveyed to his ear by Squeak, one of his more cunning Corporals, a grizzled little man, so nicknamed by the sailors on account of his squeaky voice, and sharp visage ferreting about the dark corners of the lower decks after interlopers, satirically suggesting to them the idea of a rat in a cellar.

From his Chief's employing him as an implicit tool in laying little traps for the worriment of the Foretopman—for it was from the Master-at-arms that the petty persecutions heretofore adverted to had proceeded—the Corporal having naturally enough concluded that his master could have no love for the sailor, made it his business, faithful understrapper that he was, to foment the ill blood by perverting to his Chief certain innocent frolics of the good-natured Foretopman, besides inventing for his mouth sundry contumelious epithets he claimed to have overheard him let fall. The Master-at-arms never suspected the veracity of these reports, more especially as to the epithets, for he well knew how secretly unpopular may become a master-at-arms, at least a master-at-arms of those days zealous in his function, and how the blue-jackets shoot at him in private their raillery and wit; the nickname by which he goes among them (Jemmy Legs) implying under the form of merriment their cherished disrespect and dislike. But in view of the greediness of hate for patrolmen, it hardly needed a purveyor to feed Claggart's passion.

An uncommon prudence is habitual with the subtler depravity, for it has everything to hide. And in case of an injury but suspected, its secretiveness voluntarily cuts it off from enlightenment or disillusion; and, not unreluctantly, action is taken upon surmise as upon certainty. And the retaliation is apt to be in monstrous disproportion to the supposed offence; for when in anybody was revenge in its exactions aught else but an inordinate usurer? But how with Claggart's conscience? For though consciences are unlike as foreheads, every intelligence, not excluding the Scriptural devils who "believe and tremble," has one. But Claggart's conscience being but the lawyer to his will, made ogres of trifles, probably arguing that the motive imputed to Billy in spilling the soup just when he did, together with the epithets alleged, these, if nothing more, made a strong case against him; nay, justified animosity into a sort of retributive righteousness. The Pharisee is the Guy Fawkes prowling in the hid chambers underlying the Claggarts. And they can really form no conception of an unreciprocated malice. Probably, the Master-at-arms' clandestine persecution of Billy was started to try the temper of the man; but it had not developed any quality in him that enmity could make official use of or even pervert into plausible self-justification; so that the occurrence at the mess, petty if it were, was a welcome one to that peculiar conscience assigned to be the private mentor of Claggart. And, for the rest, not improbably it put him upon new experiments.

Chapter XIV

NOT MANY DAYS AFTER THE LAST INCIDENT NARRATED, SOMETHING BEFELL BILLY BUDD THAT more gravelled him than aught that had previously occurred.

It was a warm night for the latitude; and the Foretopman, whose watch at the time was properly below, was dozing on the uppermost deck whither he had ascended from his hot hammock, one of hundreds suspended so closely wedged together over a lower gun deck that there was little or no swing to them. He lay as in the shadow of a hill-side, stretched under the lee of the booms, a piled ridge of spare spars amidships between fore-mast and mainmast and among which the ship's largest boat, the launch, was stowed. Alongside of three other slumberers from below, he lay near that end of the booms which approaches the fore-mast; his station aloft on duty as a foretopman being just over the deckstation of the forecastlemen, entitling him according to usage to make himself more or less at home in that neighborhood.

Presently he was stirred into semi-consciousness by somebody, who must have previously sounded the sleep of the others, touching his shoulder, and then as the Foretopman raised his head, breathing into his ear in a quick whisper, "Slip into the lee forechains, Billy; there is something in the wind. Don't speak. Quick, I will meet you there;" and disappeared.

Now Billy, like sundry other essentially good-natured ones had some of the weaknesses inseparable from essential good-nature; and among these was a reluctance, almost an incapacity of plumply saying no to an abrupt proposition not obviously absurd, on the face of it, nor obviously unfriendly, nor iniquitous. And being of warm blood he had not the phlegm tacitly to negative any proposition by unresponsive inaction. Like his sense of fear, his apprehension as to aught outside of the honest and natural was seldom very quick. Besides, upon the present occasion, the drowse from his sleep still hung upon him.

However it was, he mechanically rose, and sleepily wondering what could be in the wind, betook himself to the designated place, a narrow platform, one of six, outside of the high bulwarks and screened by the great dead-eyes and multiple columned lanyards of the shrouds and back-stays; and, in a great war-ship of that time, of dimensions commensurate with the hull's magnitude; a tarry balcony, in short, overhanging the sea, and so secluded that one mariner of the *Bellipotent*, a non-conformist old tar of a serious turn, made it even in daytime his private oratory.

In this retired nook the stranger soon joined Billy Budd. There was no moon as yet; a haze obscured the star-light. He could not distinctly see the stranger's face. Yet from something in the outline and carriage, Billy took him to be, and correctly, one of the afterguard.

"Hist! Billy," said the man in the same quick cautionary whisper as before; "You were impressed, weren't you? Well, so was I"; and he paused, as to mark the effect. But Billy, not knowing exactly what to make of this, said nothing. Then the other: "We are not the only impressed ones, Billy. There's a gang of us. Couldn't you—help—at a pinch?"

"What do you mean?" demanded Billy, here thoroughly shaking off his drowse.

"Hist, hist!" the hurried whisper now growing husky, "see here;" and the man held up two small objects faintly twinkling in the nightlight; "see, they are yours, Billy, if you'll only—"

But Billy broke in, and in his resentful eagerness to deliver himself his vocal infirmity somewhat intruded: "D-D-Damme, I don't know what you are d-d-driving at, or what you mean, but you had better g-g-go where you belong!" For the moment the fellow, as confounded, did not stir; and Billy springing to his feet, said, "If you d-don't start I'll t-t-toss you back over the r-rail!" There was no mistaking this and the mysterious emissary decamped disappearing in the direction of the main-mast in the shadow of the booms.

"Hallo, what's the matter?" here came growling from a forecastleman awakened from his deck-doze by Billy's raised voice. And as the Foretopman reappeared and was recognized by him; "Ah, Beauty, is it you? Well, something must have been the matter for you st-st-stuttered."

"O," rejoined Billy, now mastering the impediment; "I found an afterguardsman in our part of the ship here and I bid him be off where he belongs."

"And is that all you did about it, Foretopman?" gruffly demanded another, an irascible old fellow of brick-colored visage and hair, and who was known to his associate forecastlemen as Red Pepper; "Such sneaks I should like to marry to the gunner's daughter!" by that expression meaning that he would like to subject them to disciplinary castigation over a gun.

However, Billy's rendering of the matter satisfactorily accounted to these inquirers for the brief commotion, since of all the sections of a ship's company, the forecastlemen, veterans for the most part and bigoted in their sea-prejudices, are the most jealous in resenting territorial encroachments, especially on the part of any of the afterguard, of whom they have but a sorry opinion, chiefly landsmen, never going aloft except to reef or furl the mainsail and in no wise competent to handle a marlinspike or turn in a dead-eye, say.

Chapter XV

THIS INCIDENT SORELY PUZZLED BILLY BUDD. IT WAS AN ENTIRELY NEW EXPERIENCE; THE FIRST time in his life that he had ever been personally approached in underhand intriguing fashion. Prior to this encounter he had known nothing of the afterguardsman, the two men being stationed wide apart, one forward and aloft during his watch, the other on deck and aft.

What could it mean? And could they really be guineas, those two glittering objects the interloper had held up to his eyes? Where could the fellow get guineas? Why even spare buttons are not so plentiful at sea. The more he turned the matter over, the more he was non-plussed, and made uneasy and discomforted. In his disgustful recoil from an overture which tho' he but ill comprehended he instinctively knew must involve evil of some sort, Billy Budd was like a young horse fresh from the pasture suddenly inhaling a vile whiff from some chemical factory, and by repeated snortings tries to get it out of his nostrils and lungs. This frame of mind barred all desire of holding further parley with the fellow, even were it but for the purpose of gaining some enlightenment as to his design in approaching him. And yet he was not without natural curiosity to see how such a visitor in the dark would look in broad day.

He espied him the following afternoon, in his first dog-watch, below, one of the smokers on that forward part of the upper gun deck allotted to the pipe. He recognized him by his general cut and build, more than by his round freckled face and glassy eyes of pale blue, veiled with lashes all but white. And yet Billy was a bit uncertain whether indeed it were he—yonder chap about his own age chatting and laughing in free-hearted way, leaning against a gun; a genial young fellow enough to look at, and something of a rattlebrain, to all appearance. Rather chubby too for a sailor, even an afterguardsman. In short the last man in the world, one would think, to be overburthened with thoughts, especially those perilous thoughts that must needs belong to a conspirator in any serious project, or even to the underling of such a conspirator.

Altho' Billy was not aware of it, the fellow, with a sidelong watchful glance had perceived Billy first, and then noting that Billy was looking at him, thereupon nodded a familiar sort of friendly recognition as to an old acquaintance, without interrupting the talk he was engaged in with the group of smokers. A day or two afterwards, chancing in the evening promenade on a gun deck to pass Billy, he offered a flying word of good-fellowship, as it were, which by its unexpectedness, and equivocalness under the circumstances so embarrassed Billy that he knew not how to respond to it, and let it go unnoticed.

Billy was now left more at a loss than before. The ineffectual speculation into which he was led was so disturbingly alien to him, that he did his best to smother it. It never entered his mind that here was a matter which from its extreme questionableness, it was his duty as a loyal bluejacket to report in the proper quarter. And, probably, had such a step been suggested to him, he would have been deterred from taking it by the thought, one of novice-magnanimity, that it would savor overmuch of the dirty work of a telltale. He kept the thing to himself. Yet upon one occasion, he could not forbear a little disburthening himself to the old Dansker, tempted thereto perhaps by the influence of a balmy night when the ship lay becalmed; the twain, silent for the most part, sitting together on deck, their heads propped against the bulwarks. But it was only a partial and anonymous account that Billy gave, the unfounded scruples above referred to preventing full disclosure to anybody. Upon hearing Billy's version, the sage Dansker seemed to divine more than he was told; and after a little meditation during which his wrinkles were pursed as into a point, quite effacing for the time that quizzing expression his face sometimes wore," Didn't I say so, Baby Budd?"

"Say what?" demanded Billy.

"Why, *Jemmy Legs* is down on you."

"And what," rejoined Billy in amazement, "has *Jemmy Legs* to do with that cracked afterguardsman?"

"Ho, it was an afterguardsman then. A cat's-paw, a cat's-paw!" And with that exclamation, which, whether it had reference to a light puff of air just then coming over the calm sea, or subtler relation to the afterguardsman there is no telling, the old Merlin gave a twisting wrench with his black teeth at his plug of tobacco, vouchsafing no reply to Billy's impetuous question, tho' now repeated, for it was his wont to relapse into grim silence when interrogated in skeptical sort as to any of his sententious oracles, not always very clear ones, rather partaking of that obscurity which invests most Delphic deliverances from any quarter.

Long experience had very likely brought this old man to that bitter prudence which never interferes in aught and never gives advice.

Chapter XVI

YES, DESPITE THE DANSKER'S PITHY INSISTENCE AS TO THE MASTER-AT-ARMS BEING AT THE BOTtom of these strange experiences of Billy on board the *Bellipotent*, the young sailor was ready to ascribe them to almost anybody but the man who, to use Billy's own expression, "always had a pleasant word for him." This is to be wondered at. Yet not so much to be wondered at. In certain matters, some sailors even in mature life remain unsophisticated enough. But a young seafarer of the disposition of our athletic Foretopman, is much of a child-man. And yet a child's utter innocence is but its blank ignorance, and the innocence more or less wanes as intelligence waxes. But in Billy Budd intelligence, such as it was, had advanced, while yet his simplemindedness remained for the most part unaffected. Experience is a teacher indeed; yet did Billy's years make his experience small. Besides, he had none of that intuitive knowledge of the bad which in natures not good or incompletely so foreruns experience, and therefore may pertain, as in some instances it too clearly does pertain, even to youth.

And what could Billy know of man except of man as a mere sailor? And the old-fashioned sailor, the veritable man-before-the-mast, the sailor from boyhood up, he, tho' indeed of the same species as a landsman, is in some respects singularly distinct from him. The sailor is frankness, the landsman is finesse. Life is not a game with the sailor, demanding the long head; no intricate game of chess where few moves are made in straightforwardness, and ends are attained by indirection; an oblique, tedious, barren game hardly worth that poor candle burnt out in playing it.

Yes, as a class, sailors are in character a juvenile race. Even their deviations are marked by juvenility. And this more especially holding true with the sailors of Billy's time. Then, too, certain things which apply to all sailors, do more pointedly operate, here and there, upon the junior one. Every sailor, too, is accustomed to obey orders without debating them; his life afloat is externally ruled for him; he is not brought into that promiscuous commerce with mankind where unobstructed free agency on equal terms—equal superficially, at least—soon teaches one that unless upon occasion he exercise a distrust keen in proportion to the fairness of the appearance, some foul turn may be served him. A ruled undemonstrative distrustfulness is so habitual, not with business-men so much, as with men who know their kind in less shallow relations than business, namely, certain men-of-the-world, that they come at last to employ it all but unconsciously; and some of them would very likely feel real surprise at being charged with it as one of their general characteristics.

Chapter XVII

BUT AFTER THE LITTLE MATTER AT THE MESS BILLY BUDD NO MORE FOUND HIMSELF IN STRANGE trouble at times about his hammock or his clothesbag or what not. While, as to that smile that occasionally sunned him, and the pleasant passing word, these were if not more frequent, yet if anything, more pronounced than before.

But for all that, there were certain other demonstrations now. When Claggart's unobserved glance happened to light on belted Billy rolling along the upper gun deck in the leisure of the second dog-watch, exchanging passing broadsides of fun with other young promenaders in the crowd; that glance would follow the cheerful sea-Hyperion with a settled meditative and melancholy expression, his eyes strangely suffused with incipient feverish tears. Then would Claggart look like the man of sorrows. Yes, and sometimes the melancholy expression would have in it a touch of soft yearning, as if Claggart could even have loved Billy but for fate and ban. But this was an evanescence, and quickly repented of, as it were, by an immitigable look, pinching and shriveling the visage into the momentary semblance of a wrinkled walnut. But sometimes catching sight in advance of the Foretopman coming in his direction, he would, upon their nearing, step aside a little to let him pass, dwelling upon Billy for the moment with the glittering dental satire of a Guise. But upon any abrupt unforeseen encounter a red light would flash forth from his eye like a spark from an anvil in a dusk smithy. That quick fierce light was a strange one, darted from orbs which in repose were of a color nearest approaching a deeper violet, the softest of shades.

Tho' some of these caprices of the pit could not but be observed by their object, yet were they beyond the construing of such a nature. And the thews of Billy were hardly compatible with that sort of sensitive spiritual organization which in some cases instinctively conveys to ignorant innocence an admonition of the proximity of the malign. He thought the Master-at-arms acted in a manner rather queer at times. That was all. But the occasional frank air and pleasant word went for what they purported to be, the young sailor never having heard as yet of the "too fair-spoken man."

Had the Foretopman been conscious of having done or said anything to provoke the ill will of the official, it would have been different with him, and his sight might have been purged if not sharpened. As it was, innocence was his blinder.

So was it with him in yet another matter. Two minor officers—the Armorer and Captain of the Hold, with whom he had never exchanged a word, his position in the ship not bringing him into contact with them; these men now for the first began to cast upon Billy when they chanced to encounter him, that peculiar glance which evidences that the man from whom it comes has been some way tampered with and to the prejudice of him upon whom the glance lights. Never did it occur to Billy as a thing to be noted or a thing suspicious, tho' he well knew the fact, that the Armorer and Captain of the Hold, with the ship's-yeoman, apothecary, and others of that grade, were by naval usage, messmates of the Master-at-arms, men with ears convenient to his confidential tongue.

But the general popularity that our Handsome Sailor's manly forwardness bred upon occasion, and his irresistible good-nature, indicating no mental superiority tending to excite an invidious feeling, this good will on the part of most of his shipmates made him the less to concern himself about such mute aspects toward him as those whereto allusion has just been made, aspects he could not fathom as to infer their whole import.

As to the afterguardsman, tho' Billy for reasons already given necessarily saw little of him, yet when the two did happen to meet, invariably came the fellow's off-hand cheerful recognition, sometimes accompanied by a passing pleasant word or two. Whatever that equivocal young person's original design may really have been, or the design of which he might have been the deputy, certain it was from his manner upon these occasions, that he had wholly dropped it.

It was as if his precocity of crookedness (and every vulgar villain is precocious) had for once deceived him, and the man he had sought to entrap as a simpleton had, through his very simplicity, ignominiously baffled him.

But shrewd ones may opine that it was hardly possible for Billy to refrain from going up to the afterguardsman and bluntly demanding to know his purpose in the initial interview, so abruptly closed in the fore-chains. Shrewd ones may also think it but natural in Billy to set about sounding some of the other impressed men of the ship in order to discover what basis, if any, there was for the emissary's obscure suggestions as to plotting disaffection aboard. Yes, the shrewd may so think. But something more, or rather, something else than mere shrewdness is perhaps needful for the due understanding of such a character as Billy Budd's.

As to Claggart, the monomania in the man—if that indeed it were—as involuntarily disclosed by starts in the manifestations detailed, yet in general covered over by his self-contained and rational demeanor; this, like a subterranean fire was eating its way deeper and deeper in him. Something decisive must come of it.

Chapter XVIII

After the mysterious interview in the fore-chains—the one so abruptly ended there by Billy—nothing especially germane to the story occurred until the events now about to be narrated.

Elsewhere it has been said that in the lack of frigates (of course better sailers than line-of-battle ships) in the English squadron up the Straits at that period, the *Bellipotent* was occasionally employed not only as an available substitute for a scout, but at times on detached service of more important kind. This was not alone because of her sailing qualities, not common in a ship of her rate, but quite as much, probably, that the character of her commander, it was thought, specially adapted him for any duty where under unforeseen difficulties a prompt initiative might have to be taken in some matter demanding knowledge and ability in addition to those qualities implied in good seamanship. It was on an expedition of the latter sort, a somewhat distant one, and when the *Bellipotent* was almost at her furthest remove from the fleet, that in the latter part of an afternoon-watch she unexpectedly came in sight of a ship of the enemy. It proved to be a frigate. The latter perceiving thro' the glass that the weight of men and metal would be heavily against her, invoking her light heels, crowded sail to get away. After a chase urged almost against hope and lasting until about the middle of the first dog-watch, she signally succeeded in effecting her escape.

Not long after the pursuit had been given up, and ere the excitement incident thereto had altogether waned away, the Master-at-arms, ascending from his cavernous sphere, made his appearance cap in hand by the main-mast, respectfully waiting the notice of Captain Vere then solitary walking the weather-side of the quarterdeck, doubtless somewhat chafed at the failure of the pursuit. The spot where Claggart stood was the place allotted to men of lesser grades seeking some more particular interview either with the officer-of-the-deck or the Captain himself. But from the latter it was not often that a sailor or petty-officer of those days would seek a hearing; only some exceptional cause, would, according to established custom, have warranted that.

Presently, just as the Commander absorbed in his reflections was on the point of turning aft in his promenade, he became sensible of Claggart's presence, and saw the doffed cap held in deferential expectancy. Here be it said that Captain Vere's personal knowledge of this petty-officer had only begun at the time of the ship's last sailing from home, Claggart then for the first, in transfer from a ship detained for repairs, supplying on board the *Bellipotent* the place of a previous master-at-arms disabled and ashore.

No sooner did the Commander observe who it was that deferentially stood awaiting his notice, than a peculiar expression came over him. It was not unlike that which uncontrollably will flit across the countenance of one at unawares encountering a person who, though known to him indeed, has hardly been long enough known for thorough knowledge, but something in whose aspect nevertheless now for the first provokes a vaguely repellent distaste. But coming to a stand, and resuming much of his wonted official manner, save that a sort of impatience lurked in the intonation of the opening word, he said, "Well? what is it, Master-at-arms?"

With the air of a subordinate grieved at the necessity of being a messenger of ill tidings, and while conscientiously determined to be frank, yet equally resolved upon shunning overstatement, Claggart, at this invitation or rather summons to disburthen, spoke up. What he said, conveyed in the language of no uneducated man, was to the effect following, if not altogether in these words, namely, that during the chase and preparations for the possible encounter he had seen enough to convince him that at least one sailor aboard was a dangerous character in a ship mustering some who not only had taken a guilty part in the late serious troubles, but others also who, like the man in question, had entered His Majesty's service under another form than enlistment.

At this point Captain Vere with some impatience interrupted him: "Be direct, man; say *impressed men.*"

Claggart made a gesture of subservience, and proceeded. Quite lately he (Claggart) had begun to suspect that on the gun decks some sort of movement prompted by the sailor in question was covertly going on, but he had not thought himself warranted in reporting the suspicion so long as it remained indistinct. But from what he had that afternoon observed in the man referred to, the suspicion of something clandestine going on had advanced to a point less removed from certainty. He deeply felt, he added, the serious responsibility assumed in making a report involving such possible consequences to the individual mainly concerned, besides tending to augment those natural anxieties which every naval commander must feel in view of extraordinary outbreaks so recent as those which, he sorrowfully said it, it needed not to name.

Now at the first broaching of the matter Captain Vere, taken by surprise, could not wholly dissemble his disquietude. But as Claggart went on, the former's aspect changed into restiveness under something in the witness' manner in giving his testimony. However, he refrained from interrupting him. And Claggart, continuing, concluded with this: "God forbid, Your Honor, that the *Bellipotent*'s should be the experience of the—"

"Never mind that!" here peremptorily broke in the superior, his face altering with anger, instinctively divining the ship that the other was about to name, one in which the Nore Mutiny had assumed a singularly tragical character that for a time jeopardized the life of its commander. Under the circumstances he was indignant at the purposed allusion. When the commissioned officers themselves were on all occasions very heedful how they referred to the recent events, for a petty-officer unnecessarily to allude to them in the presence of his Captain, this struck him as a most immodest presumption. Besides, to his quick sense of self-respect, it even looked under the circumstances something like an attempt to alarm him. Nor at first was he without some surprise that one who so far as he had hitherto come under his notice had shown considerable tact in his function should in this particular evince such lack of it.

But these thoughts and kindred dubious ones flitting across his mind were suddenly replaced by an intuitional surmise which, though as yet obscure in form, served practically to affect his reception of the ill tidings. Certain it is, that long versed in everything pertaining to the complicated gun-deck life, which like every other form of life, has its secret mines and dubious side, the side popularly disclaimed, Captain Vere did not permit himself to be unduly disturbed by the general tenor of his subordinate's report.

Furthermore, if in view of recent events prompt action should be taken at the first palpable sign of recurring insubordination, for all that, not judicious would it be, he thought, to keep the idea of lingering disaffection alive by undue forwardness in crediting an informer, even if his own subordinate, and charged among other things with police surveillance of the crew. This feeling would not perhaps have so prevailed with him were it not that upon a prior occasion the patriotic zeal officially evinced by Claggart had somewhat irritated him as appearing rather supersensible and strained. Furthermore, something even in the official's self-possessed and somewhat ostentatious manner in making his specifications strangely reminded him of a bandsman, a perjurous witness in a capital case before a court-martial ashore of which when a lieutenant, he, Captain Vere, had been a member.

Now the peremptory check given to Claggart in the matter of the arrested allusion was quickly followed up by this: "You say that there is at least one dangerous man aboard. Name him."

"William Budd. A foretopman, Your Honor—"

"William Budd," repeated Captain Vere with unfeigned astonishment; "and mean you the man that Lieutenant Ratcliff took from the merchantman not very long ago—the young fellow who seems to be so popular with the men—Billy, the 'Handsome Sailor,' as they call him?"

"The same, Your Honor; but for all his youth and good looks, a deep one. Not for nothing does he insinuate himself into the good will of his shipmates, since at the least all hands will at a pinch say a good word for him at all hazards. Did Lieutenant Ratcliff happen to tell Your Honor of that adroit fling of Budd's, jumping up in the cutter's bow under the merchantman's stern when he was being taken off? It is even masqued by that sort of good-humored air that at heart he resents his impressment. You have but noted his fair cheek. A man-trap may be under his ruddy-tipped daisies."

Now the Handsome Sailor, as a signal figure among the crew, had naturally enough attracted the Captain's attention from the first. Tho' in general not very demonstrative to his officers, he had congratulated Lieutenant Ratcliff upon his good fortune in lighting on such a fine specimen of the *genus homo,* who in the nude might have posed for a statue of young Adam before the Fall. As to Billy's adieu to the ship *Rights-of-Man,* which the boarding lieutenant had indeed reported to him, but in a deferential way more as a good story than aught else, Captain Vere, tho' mistakenly understanding it as a satiric sally, had but thought so much the better of the impressed man for it; as a military sailor, admiring the spirit that could take an arbitrary enlistment so merrily and sensibly. The Foretopman's conduct, too, so far as it had fallen under the Captain's notice, had confirmed the first happy augury, while the new recruit's qualities as a sailor-man seemed to be such that he had thought of recommending him to the executive officer for promotion to a place that would more frequently bring him under his own observation, namely, the captaincy of the mizzentop, replacing there in the starboard watch a man not so young whom partly for that reason he deemed less fitted for the post. Be it parenthesized here that since the mizzentopmen having not to handle such breadths of heavy canvas as the lower sails on the main-mast and fore-mast, a young man if of the right stuff not only seems best adapted to duty there, but in fact is generally selected for the captaincy of that top, and the company under him are light hands and often but striplings. In sum, Captain Vere had from the beginning deemed Billy Budd to be what in the naval parlance of the time was called a "King's bargain," that is to say, for His Britannic Majesty's Navy a capital investment at small outlay or none at all.

After a brief pause during which the reminiscences above mentioned passed vividly through his mind and he weighed the import of Claggart's last suggestion conveyed in the phrase "man-trap under his daisies," and the more he weighed it the less reliance he felt in the informer's good faith, suddenly he turned upon him and in a low voice: "Do you come to me, Master-at-arms, with so foggy a tale? As to Budd, cite me an act or spoken word of his confirmatory of what you in general charge against him. Stay," drawing nearer to him, "heed what you speak. Just now, and in a case like this, there is a yard-arm-end for the false-witness."

"Ah, Your Honor!" sighed Claggart, mildly shaking his shapely head as in sad deprecation of such unmerited severity of tone. Then, bridling—erecting himself as in virtuous self-assertion—he circumstantially alleged certain words and acts, which collectively, if credited, led to presumptions mortally inculpating Budd. And for some of these averments, he added, substantiating proof was not far.

With gray eyes impatient and distrustful essaying to fathom to the bottom Claggart's calm violet ones, Captain Vere again heard him out; then for the moment stood ruminating. The mood he evinced, Claggart—himself for the time liberated from the other's scrutiny—steadily regarded with a look difficult to render—a look curious of the operation of his tactics, a look such as might have been that of the spokesman of the envious children of Jacob deceptively imposing upon the troubled patriarch the blood-dyed coat of young Joseph.

Though something exceptional in the moral quality of Captain Vere made him, in earnest encounter with a fellow-man, a veritable touch-stone of that man's essential nature, yet now as to Claggart and what was really going on in him, his feeling partook less of intuitional conviction than of strong suspicion clogged by strange dubieties. The perplexity he evinced proceeded less from aught touching the man informed against—as Claggart doubtless opined—than from considerations how best to act in regard to the informer. At first indeed he was naturally for summoning that substantiation of his allegations which Claggart said was at hand. But such a proceeding would result in the matter at once getting abroad, which in the present stage of it, he thought, might undesirably affect the ship's company. If Claggart was a false witness—that closed the affair. And therefore before trying the accusation, he would first practically test the accuser; and he thought this could be done in a quiet undemonstrative way.

The measure he determined upon involved a shifting of the scene, a transfer to a place less exposed to observation than the broad quarter-deck. For although the few gun-room officers there at the time had, in due observance of naval etiquette, withdrawn to leeward the moment Captain Vere had begun his promenade on the deck's weather-side; and tho' during the colloquy with Claggart they of course ventured not to diminish the distance; and though throughout the interview Captain Vere's voice was far from high, and Claggart's silvery and low; and the wind in the cordage and the wash of the sea helped the more to put them beyond earshot; nevertheless, the interview's continuance already had attracted observation from some topmen aloft and other sailors in the waist or further forward.

Having determined upon his measures, Captain Vere forthwith took action. Abruptly turning to Claggart he asked, "Master-at-arms, is it now Budd's watch aloft?"

"No, Your Honor."

Whereupon, "Mr. Wilkes!" summoning the nearest midshipman, "tell Albert to come to me." Albert was the Captain's hammock-boy, a sort of sea-valet in whose discretion and fidelity his master had much confidence. The lad appeared.

"You know Budd the Foretopman?"

"I do, Sir."

"Go find him. It is his watch off. Manage to tell him out of earshot that he is wanted aft. Contrive it that he speaks to nobody. Keep him in talk yourself. And not till you get well aft here, not till then let him know that the place where he is wanted is my cabin. You understand. Go. Master-at-arms, show yourself on the decks below, and when you think it time for Albert to be coming with his man, stand by quietly to follow the sailor in."

Chapter XIX

NOW WHEN THE FORETOPMAN FOUND HIMSELF CLOSETED THERE, AS IT WERE, IN THE CABIN with the Captain and Claggart, he was surprised enough. But it was a surprise unaccompanied by apprehension or distrust. To an immature nature essentially honest and humane, forewarning intimations of subtler danger from one's kind come tardily if at all. The only thing that took shape in the young sailor's mind was this: Yes, the Captain, I have always thought, looks kindly upon me. Wonder if he's going to make me his coxswain. I should like that. And maybe now he is going to ask the Master-at-arms about me.

"Shut the door there, sentry," said the Commander; "stand without, and let nobody come in. Now, Master-at-arms, tell this man to his face what you told of him to me"; and stood prepared to scrutinize the mutually confronting visages.

With the measured step and calm collected air of an asylum-physician approaching in the public hall some patient beginning to show indications of a coming paroxysm, Claggart deliberately advanced within short range of Billy, and mesmerically looking him in the eye, briefly recapitulated the accusation.

Not at first did Billy take it in. When he did, the rose-tan of his cheek looked struck as by white leprosy. He stood like one impaled and gagged. Meanwhile the accuser's eyes removing not as yet from the blue dilated ones, underwent a phenomenal change, their wonted rich violet color blurring into a muddy purple. Those lights of human intelligence losing human expression, gelidly protruding like the alien eyes of certain uncatalogued creatures of the deep. The first mesmeric glance was one of serpent fascination; the last was as the hungry lurch of the torpedo-fish.

"Speak, man!" said Captain Vere to the transfixed one, struck by his aspect even more than by Claggart's, "Speak! defend yourself." Which appeal caused but a strange dumb gesturing and gurgling in Billy; amazement at such an accusation so suddenly sprung on inexperienced nonage; this, and, it may be, horror of the accuser, serving to bring out his lurking defect and in this instance for the time intensifying it into a convulsed tongue-tie; while the intent head and entire form straining forward in an agony of ineffectual eagerness to obey the injunction to speak and defend himself, gave an expression to the face like that of a condemned Vestal priestess in the moment of being buried alive, and in the first struggle against suffocation.

Though at the time Captain Vere was quite ignorant of Billy's liability to vocal impediment, he now immediately divined it, since vividly Billy's aspect recalled to him that of a bright young schoolmate of his whom he had once seen struck by much the same startling impotence in the act of eagerly rising in the class to be foremost in response to a testing question put to it by the master. Going close up to the young sailor, and laying a soothing hand on his shoulder, he said, "There is no hurry, my boy. Take your time, take your time." Contrary to the effect intended, these words so fatherly in tone, doubtless touching Billy's heart to the quick, prompted yet more violent efforts at utterance—efforts soon ending for the time in confirming the paralysis, and bringing to his face an expression which was as a crucifixion to behold. The next instant, quick as the flame from a discharged cannon at night, his right arm shot out, and Claggart dropped to the deck. Whether intentionally or but owing to the young athlete's superior height, the blow had taken effect fully upon the forehead, so shapely and intellectual-looking a feature in the Master-at-arms; so that the body fell over lengthwise, like a heavy plank tilted from erectness. A gasp or two, and he lay motionless.

"Fated boy," breathed Captain Vere in tone so low as to be almost a whisper, "what have you done! But here, help me."

The twain raised the felled one from the loins up into a sitting position. The spare form flexibly acquiesced, but inertly. It was like handling a dead snake. They lowered it back. Regaining erectness Captain Vere with one hand covering his face stood to all appearance as impassive as the object at his feet. Was he absorbed in taking in all the bearings of the event and what was best not only now at once to be done, but also in the sequel? Slowly he uncovered his face; and the effect was as if the moon emerging from eclipse should reappear with quite another aspect than that which had gone into hiding. The father in him, manifested towards Billy thus far in the scene, was replaced by the military disciplinarian. In his official tone he bade the Foretopman retire to a state-room aft (pointing it out), and there remain till thence summoned. This order Billy in silence mechanically obeyed. Then going to the cabin-door where it opened on the quarter-deck, Captain Vere said to the sentry without, "Tell somebody to send Albert here." When the lad appeared his master so contrived it that he should not catch sight of the prone one. "Albert," he said to him, "tell the Surgeon I wish to see him. You need not come back till called."

When the Surgeon entered—a self-poised character of that grave sense and experience that hardly anything could take him aback—Captain Vere advanced to meet him, thus unconsciously intercepting his view of Claggart, and interrupting the other's wonted ceremonious salutation, said, "Nay, tell me how it is with yonder man," directing his attention to the prostrate one.

The Surgeon looked, and for all his self-command, somewhat started at the abrupt revelation. On Claggart's always pallid complexion, thick black blood was now oozing from nostril and ear. To the gazer's professional eye it was unmistakably no living man that he saw.

"Is it so then?" said Captain Vere intently watching him. "I thought it. But verify it." Whereupon the customary tests confirmed the Surgeon's first glance, who now looking up in unfeigned concern, cast a look of intense inquisitiveness upon his superior. But Captain Vere, with one hand to his brow, was standing motionless. Suddenly, catching the Surgeon's arm convulsively, he exclaimed, pointing down to the body—"It is the divine judgment on Ananias! Look!"

Disturbed by the excited manner he had never before observed in the *Bellipotent*'s Captain, and as yet wholly ignorant of the affair, the prudent Surgeon nevertheless held his peace, only again looking an earnest interrogation as to what it was that had resulted in such a tragedy.

But Captain Vere was now again motionless standing absorbed in thought. But again starting, he vehemently exclaimed—"Struck dead by an angel of God! Yet the angel must hang!"

At these passionate interjections, mere incoherences to the listener as yet unapprised of the antecedents, the Surgeon was profoundly discomposed. But now as recollecting himself, Captain Vere in less passionate tone briefly related the circumstances leading up to the event. "But come; we must despatch," he added. "me to remove him" (meaning the body) "to yonder compartment," designating one opposite that where the Foretopman remained immured. Anew disturbed by a request that as implying a desire for secrecy, seemed unaccountably strange to him, there was nothing for the subordinate to do but comply.

"Go now," said Captain Vere with something of his wonted manner—"Go now. I shall presently call a drum-head court. Tell the lieutenants what has happened, and tell Mr. Mordant," meaning the Captain of Marines, "and charge them to keep the matter to themselves."

Chapter XX

FULL OF DISQUIETUDE AND MISGIVING THE SURGEON LEFT THE CABIN. WAS CAPTAIN VERE SUDdenly affected in his mind, or was it but a transient excitement, brought about by so strange and extraordinary a happening? As to the drum-head court, it struck the Surgeon as impolitic, if nothing more. The thing to do, he thought, was to place Billy Budd in confinement and in a way dictated by usage, and postpone further action in so extraordinary a case to such time as they should rejoin the squadron, and then refer it to the Admiral. He recalled the unwonted agitation of Captain Vere and his excited exclamations so at variance with his normal manner. Was he unhinged? But assuming that he is, it is not so susceptible of proof. What then can he do? No more trying situation is conceivable than that of an officer subordinate under a Captain whom he suspects to be, not mad indeed, but yet not quite unaffected in his intellect. To argue his order to him would be insolence. To resist him would be mutiny.

In obedience to Captain Vere he communicated what had happened to the lieutenants and Captain of Marines; saying nothing as to the Captain's state. They fully shared his own surprise and concern. Like him too they seemed to think that such a matter should be referred to the Admiral.

Chapter XXI

WHO IN THE RAINBOW CAN DRAW THE LINE WHERE THE VIOLET TINT ENDS AND THE ORANGE tint begins? Distinctly we see the difference of the colors, but where exactly does the one first blendingly enter into the other? So with sanity and insanity. In pronounced cases there is no question about them. But in some supposed cases, in various degrees supposedly less pronounced, to draw the exact line of demarcation few will undertake tho' for a fee some professional experts will. There is nothing namable but that some men will undertake to do it for pay.

Whether Captain Vere, as the Surgeon professionally and privately surmised, was really the sudden victim of any degree of aberration, one must determine for himself by such light as this narrative may afford.

That the unhappy event which has been narrated could not have happened at a worse juncture was but too true. For it was close on the heel of the suppressed insurrections, an aftertime very critical to naval authority, demanding from every English sea-commander two qualities not readily interfusable—prudence and rigor. Moreover there was something crucial in the case.

In the jugglery of circumstances preceding and attending the event on board the *Bellipotent*, and in the light of that martial code whereby it was formally to be judged, innocence and guilt personified in Claggart and Budd in effect changed places. In a legal view the apparent victim of the tragedy was he who had sought to victimize a man blameless; and the indisputable deed of the latter, navally regarded, constituted the most heinous of military crimes. Yet more. The essential right and wrong involved in the matter, the clearer that might be, so much the worse for the responsibility of a loyal sea-commander inasmuch as he was not authorized to determine the matter on that primitive basis.

Small wonder then that the *Bellipotent*'s Captain, though in general a man of rapid decision, felt that circumspectness not less than promptitude was necessary. Until he could decide upon his course, and in each detail; and not only so, but until the concluding measure was upon the point of being enacted, he deemed it advisable, in view of all the circumstances, to guard as much as possible against publicity. Here he may or may not have erred. Certain it is, however, that subsequently in the confidential talk of more than one or two gun-rooms and cabins he was not a little criticized by some officers, a fact imputed by his friends and vehemently by his cousin, Jack Denton, to professional jealousy of Starry Vere. Some imaginative ground for invidious comment there was. The maintenance of secrecy in the matter, the confining all knowledge of it for a time to the place where the homicide occurred, the quarter-deck cabin; in these particulars lurked some resemblance to the policy adopted in those tragedies of the palace which have occurred more than once in the capital founded by Peter the Barbarian.

The case indeed was such that fain would the *Bellipotent*'s Captain have deferred taking any action whatever respecting it further than to keep the Foretopman a close prisoner till the ship rejoined the squadron, and then submitting the matter to the judgement of his Admiral.

But a true military officer is in one particular like a true monk. Not with more of self-abnegation will the latter keep his vows of monastic obedience than the former his vows of allegiance to martial duty.

Feeling that unless quick action was taken on it, the deed of the Foretopman, so soon as it should be known on the gun decks, would tend to awaken any slumbering embers of the Nore among the crew, a sense of the urgency of the case overruled in Captain Vere every other consideration. But tho' a conscientious disciplinarian, he was no lover of authority for mere authority's sake. Very far was he from embracing opportunities for monopolizing to himself the perils of moral responsibility, none at least that could properly be referred to an official superior, or shared with him by his official equals or even subordinates. So thinking, he was glad it would not be at variance with usage to turn the matter over to a summary court of his own officers, reserving to himself as the one on whom the ultimate accountability would rest, the right of maintaining a supervision of it, or formally or informally interposing at need. Accordingly a drum-head court was summarily convened, he electing the individuals composing it, the First Lieutenant, the Captain of Marines, and the Sailing Master.

In associating an officer of marines with the sea-lieutenants in a case having to do with a sailor, the Commander perhaps deviated from general custom. He was prompted thereto by the circumstance that he took that soldier to be a judicious person, thoughtful, and not altogether incapable of grappling with a difficult case unprecedented in his prior experience. Yet even as to him he was not without some latent misgiving, for withal he was an extremely good-natured man, an enjoyer of his dinner, a sound sleeper, and inclined to obesity, a man who tho' he would always maintain his manhood in battle might not prove altogether reliable in a moral dilemma involving aught of the tragic. As to the First Lieutenant and the Sailing Master, Captain Vere could not but be aware that though honest natures, of approved gallantry upon occasion, their intelligence was mostly confined to the matter of active seamanship and the fighting demands of their profession.

The court was held in the same cabin where the unfortunate affair had taken place. This cabin, the Commander's, embraced the entire area under the poopdeck. Aft, and on either side, was a small state-room; the one room temporarily a jail and the other a dead-house, and a yet smaller compartment leaving a space between, expanding forward into a goodly oblong of length coinciding with the ship's beam. A skylight of moderate dimension was overhead and at each end of the oblong space were two sashed port-hole windows easily convertible back into embrasures for short carronades.

All being quickly in readiness, Billy Budd was arraigned, Captain Vere necessarily appearing as the sole witness in the case, and as such, temporarily sinking his rank, though singularly maintaining it in a matter apparently trivial, namely, that he testified from the ship's weather-side, with that object having caused the court to sit on the lee-side. Concisely he narrated all that had led up to the catastrophe, omitting nothing in Claggart's accusation and deposing as to the manner in which the prisoner had received it. At this testimony the three officers glanced with no little surprise at Billy Budd, the last man they would have suspected either of the mutinous design alleged by Claggart or the undeniable deed he himself had done. The First Lieutenant, taking judicial primacy and turning toward the prisoner, said, "Captain Vere has spoken. Is it or is it not as Captain Vere says?"

In response came syllables not so much impeded in the utterance as might have been anticipated. They were these: "Captain Vere tells the truth. It is just as Captain Vere says, but it is not as the Master-at-arms said. I have eaten the King's bread and I am true to the King."

"I believe you, my man," said the witness, his voice indicating a suppressed emotion not otherwise betrayed.

"God will bless you for that, Your Honor!" not without stammering said Billy, and all but broke down. But immediately was recalled to self-control by another question, to which with the same emotional difficulty of utterance he said, "No, there was no malice between us. I never bore malice against the Master-at-arms. I am sorry that he is dead. I did not mean to kill him. Could I have used my tongue I would not have struck him. But he foully lied to my face and in presence of my Captain, and I had to say something, and I could only say it with a blow, God help me!"

In the impulsive above-board manner of the frank one, the court saw confirmed all that was implied in words that just previously had perplexed them, coming as they did from the testifier to the tragedy and promptly following Billy's impassioned disclaimer of mutinous intent—Captain Vere's words, "I believe you, my man."

Next it was asked of him whether he knew of or suspected aught savoring of incipient trouble (meaning mutiny, tho' the explicit term was avoided) going on in any section of the ship's company.

The reply lingered. This was naturally imputed by the court to the same vocal embarrassment which had retarded or obstructed previous answers. But in main it was otherwise here; the question immediately recalling to Billy's mind the interview with the afterguardsman in the fore-chains. But an innate repugnance to playing a part at all approaching that of an informer against one's own shipmates—the same erring sense of uninstructed honor which had stood in the way of his reporting the matter at the time though as a loyal man-of-war-man it was incumbent on him, and failure so to do if charged against him and proven, would have subjected him to the heaviest of penalties; this, with the blind feeling now his, that nothing really was being hatched, prevailed with him. When the answer came it was a negative.

"One question more," said the officer of marines now first speaking and with a troubled earnestness. "You tell us that what the Master-at-arms said against you was a lie. Now why should he have so lied, so maliciously lied, since you declare there was no malice between you?"

At that question unintentionally touching on a spiritual sphere wholly obscure to Billy's thoughts, he was nonplussed, evincing a confusion indeed that some observers, such as can readily be imagined, would have construed into involuntary evidence of hidden guilt. Nevertheless he strove some way to answer, but all at once relinquished the vain endeavor, at the same time turning an appealing glance towards Captain Vere as deeming him his best helper and friend. Captain Vere who had been seated for a time rose to his feet, addressing the interrogator. "The question you put to him comes naturally enough. But how can he rightly answer it? or anybody else? unless indeed it be he who lies within there," designating the compartment where lay the corpse. "But the prone one there will not rise to our summons. In effect, tho', as it seems to me, the point you make is hardly material. Quite aside from any conceivable motive actuating the Master-at-arms, and irrespective of the provocation to the blow, a martial court must needs in the present case confine its attention to the blow's consequence, which consequence justly is to be deemed not otherwise than as the striker's deed."

This utterance, the full significance of which it was not at all likely that Billy took in, nevertheless caused him to turn a wistful interrogative look toward the speaker, a look in its dumb expressiveness not unlike that which a dog of generous breed might turn upon his master seeking in his face some elucidation of a previous gesture ambiguous to the canine intelligence. Nor was the same utterance without marked effect upon the three officers, more especially the soldier. Couched in it seemed to them a meaning unanticipated, involving a prejudgment on the speaker's part. It served to augment a mental disturbance previously evident enough.

The soldier once more spoke; in a tone of suggestive dubiety addressing at once his associates and Captain Vere: "Nobody is present—none of the ship's company, I mean—who might shed lateral light, if any is to be had, upon what remains mysterious in this matter."

"That is thoughtfully put," said Captain Vere; "I see your drift. Ay, there is a mystery; but, to use a Scriptural phrase, it is 'a mystery of iniquity,' a matter for psychologic theologians to discuss. But what has a military court to do with it? Not to add that for us any possible investigation of it is cut off by the lasting tongue-tie of—him—in yonder," again designating the mortuary stateroom. "The prisoner's deed—with that alone we have to do."

To this, and particularly the closing reiteration, the marine soldier knowing not how aptly to reply, sadly abstained from saying aught. The First Lieutenant who at the outset had not unnaturally assumed primacy in the court, now overrulingly instructed by a glance from Captain Vere, a glance more effective than words, resumed that primacy. Turning to the prisoner, "Budd," he said, and scarce in equable tones, "Budd, if you have aught further to say for yourself, say it now."

Upon this the young sailor turned another quick glance toward Captain Vere; then, as taking a hint from that aspect, a hint confirming his own instinct that silence was now best, replied to the Lieutenant, "I have said all, Sir."

The marine—the same who had been the sentinel without the cabin-door at the time that the Foretopman followed by the Master-at-arms, entered it—he, standing by the sailor throughout these judicial proceedings, was now directed to take him back to the after compartment originally assigned to the prisoner and his custodian. As the twain disappeared from view, the three officers as partially liberated from some inward constraint associated with Billy's mere presence, simultaneously stirred in their seats. They exchanged looks of troubled indecision, yet feeling that decide they must and without long delay. As for Captain Vere, he for the time stood unconsciously with his back toward them, apparently in one of his absent fits, gazing out from a sashed port-hole to windward upon the monotonous blank of the twilight sea. But the court's silence continuing, broken only at moments by brief consultations in low earnest tones, this seemed to arm him and energize him. Turning, he to-and-fro paced the cabin athwart; in the returning ascent to windward, climbing the slant deck in the ship's lee roll; without knowing it symbolizing thus in his action a mind resolute to surmount difficulties even if against primitive instincts strong as the wind and the sea. Presently he came to a stand before the three. After scanning their faces he stood less as mustering his thoughts for expression, than as one inly deliberating how best to put them to well-meaning men not intellectually mature, men with whom it was necessary to demonstrate certain principles that were axioms to himself. Similar impatience as to talking is perhaps one reason that deters some minds from addressing any popular assemblies.

When speak he did, something both in the substance of what he said and his manner of saying it, showed the influence of unshared studies modifying and tempering the practical training of an active career. This, along with his phraseology, now and then was suggestive of the grounds whereon rested that imputation of a certain pedantry socially alleged against him by certain naval men of wholly practical cast, captains who nevertheless would frankly concede that His Majesty's Navy mustered no more efficient officer of their grade than Starry Vere.

What he said was to this effect: "Hitherto I have been but the witness, little more; and I should hardly think now to take another tone, that of your coadjutor, for the time, did I not perceive in you—at the crisis too—a troubled hesitancy, proceeding, I doubt not, from the clash of military duty with moral scruple—scruple vitalized by compassion. For the compassion, how can I otherwise than share it? But, mindful of paramount obligations I strive against scruples that may tend to enervate decision. Not, gentlemen, that I hide from myself that the case is an exceptional one. Speculatively regarded, it well might be referred to a jury of casuists. But for us here acting not as casuists or moralists, it is a case practical, and under martial law practically to be dealt with.

"But your scruples: do they move as in a dusk? Challenge them. Make them advance and declare themselves. Come now: do they import something like this? If, mindless of palliating circumstances, we are bound to regard the death of the Master-at-arms as the prisoner's deed, then does that deed constitute a capital crime whereof the penalty is a mortal one? But in natural justice is nothing but the prisoner's overt act to be considered? How can we adjudge to summary and shameful death a fellow-creature innocent before God, and whom we feel to be so? Does that state it aright? You sign sad assent. Well, I too feel that, the full force of that. It is Nature. But do these buttons that we wear attest that our allegiance is to Nature? No, to the King. Though the ocean, which is inviolate Nature primeval, tho' this be the element where we move and have our being as sailors, yet as the King's officers lies our duty in a sphere correspondingly natural? So little is that true, that in receiving our commissions we in the most important regards ceased to be natural free-agents. When war is declared are we the commissioned fighters previously consulted? We fight at command. If our judgments approve the war, that is but coincidence. So in other particulars. So now. For suppose condemnation to follow these present proceedings. Would it be so much we ourselves that would condemn as it would be martial law operating through us? For that law and the rigor of it, we are not responsible. Our avowed responsibility is in this: That however pitilessly that law may operate, we nevertheless adhere to it and administer it.

"But the exceptional in the matter moves the hearts within you. Even so too is mine moved. But let not warm hearts betray heads that should be cool. Ashore in a criminal case will an upright judge allow himself off the bench to be waylaid by some tender kinswoman of the accused seeking to touch him with her tearful plea? Well the heart here denotes the feminine in man is as that piteous woman, and hard tho' it be, she must here be ruled out."

He paused, earnestly studying them for a moment; then resumed.

"But something in your aspect seems to urge that it is not solely the heart that moves in you, but also the conscience, the private conscience. But tell me whether or not, occupying the position we do, private conscience should not yield to that imperial one formulated in the code under which alone we officially proceed?"

Here the three men moved in their seats, less convinced than agitated by the course of an argument troubling but the more the spontaneous conflict within.

Perceiving which, the speaker paused for a moment; then abruptly changing his tone, went on.

"To steady us a bit, let us recur to the facts. In war-time at sea a man-of-war's-man strikes his superior in grade, and the blow kills. Apart from its effect, the blow itself is, according to the Articles of War, a capital crime. Furthermore—"

"Ay, Sir," emotionally broke in the officer of marines, "in one sense it was. But surely Budd purposed neither mutiny nor homicide."

"Surely not, my good man. And before a court less arbitrary and more merciful than a martial one, that plea would largely extenuate. At the Last Assizes it shall acquit. But how here? We proceed under the law of the Mutiny Act. In feature no child can resemble his father more than that Act resembles in spirit the thing from which it derives—War. In His Majesty's service—in this ship indeed—there are Englishmen forced to fight for the King against their will. Against their conscience, for aught we know. Tho' as their fellow-creatures some of us may appreciate their position, yet as navy officers, what reck we of it? Still less recks the enemy. Our impressed men he would fain cut down in the same swath with our volunteers. As regards the enemy's naval conscripts, some of whom may even share our own abhorrence of the regicidal French Directory, it is the same on our side. War looks but to the frontage, the appearance. And the Mutiny Act, War's child, takes after the father. Budd's intent or non-intent is nothing to the purpose.

"But while, put to it by these anxieties in you which I can not but respect, I only repeat myself—while thus strangely we prolong proceedings that should be summary—the enemy may be sighted and an engagement result. We must do; and one of two things must we do—condemn or let go."

"Can we not convict and yet mitigate the penalty?" asked the junior Lieutenant here speaking, and falteringly, for the first.

"Lieutenant, were that clearly lawful for us under the circumstances, consider the consequences of such clemency. The people" (meaning the ship's company) "have native-sense; most of them are familiar with our naval usage and tradition; and how would they take it? Even could you explain to them—which our official position forbids—they, long molded by arbitrary discipline have not that kind of intelligent responsiveness that might qualify them to comprehend and discriminate. No, to the people the Foretopman's deed, however it be worded in the announcement, will be plain homicide committed in a flagrant act of mutiny. What penalty for that should follow, they know. But it does not follow. Why? they will ruminate. You know what sailors are. Will they not revert to the recent outbreak at the Nore? Ay. They know the well-founded alarm—the panic it struck throughout England. Your clement sentence they would account pusillanimous. They would think that we flinch, that we are afraid of them—afraid of practicing a lawful rigor singularly demanded at this juncture lest it should provoke new troubles. What shame to us such a conjecture on their part, and how deadly to discipline. You see then, whither, prompted by duty and the law, I steadfastly drive. But I beseech you, my friends, do not take me amiss. I feel as you do for this unfortunate boy. But did he know our hearts, I take him to be of that generous nature that he would feel even for us on whom in this military necessity so heavy a compulsion is laid."

With that, crossing the deck he resumed his place by the sashed port-hole, tacitly leaving the three to come to a decision. On the cabin's opposite side the troubled court sat silent. Loyal lieges, plain and practical, though at bottom they dissented from some points Captain Vere had put to them, they were without the faculty, hardly had the inclination, to gainsay one whom they felt to be an earnest man, one too not less their superior in mind than in naval rank. But it is not improbable that even such of his words as were not without influence over them, less came home to them than his closing appeal to their instinct as sea-officers in the forethought he threw out as to the practical consequences to discipline, considering the unconfirmed tone of the fleet at the time, should a man-of-war's-man's violent killing at sea of a superior in grade be allowed to pass for aught else than a capital crime demanding prompt infliction of the penalty.

Not unlikely they were brought to something more or less akin to that harassed frame of mind which in the year 1842 actuated the Commander of the U.S. brig-of-war *Somers* to resolve, under the so-called Articles of War, Articles modeled upon the English Mutiny Act, to resolve upon the execution at sea of a midshipman and two petty-officers as mutineers designing the seizure of the brig. Which resolution was carried out though in a time of peace and within not many days' of home. An act vindicated by a naval court of inquiry subsequently convened ashore. History, and here cited without comment. True, the circumstances on board the Somers were different from those on board the *Bellipotent*. But the urgency felt, well-warranted or otherwise, was much the same.

Says a writer whom few know, "Forty years after a battle it is easy for a non-combatant to reason about how it ought to have been fought. It is another thing personally and under fire to direct the fighting while involved in the obscuring smoke of it. Much so with respect to other emergencies involving considerations both practical and moral, and when it is imperative promptly to act. The greater the fog the more it imperils the steamer, and speed is put on tho' at the hazard of running somebody down. Little ween the snug card-players in the cabin of the responsibilities of the sleepless man on the bridge."

In brief, Billy Budd was formally convicted and sentenced to be hung at the yard-arm in the early morning watch, it being now night. Otherwise, as is customary in such cases, the sentence would forthwith have been carried out. In war-time on the field or in the fleet, a mortal punishment decreed by a drum-head court—on the field sometimes decreed by but a nod from the General—follows without delay on the heel of conviction without appeal.

Chapter XXII

It was Captain Vere himself who of his own motion communicated the finding of the court to the prisoner; for that purpose going to the compartment where he was in custody and bidding the marine there to withdraw for the time.

Beyond the communication of the sentence what took place at this interview was never known. But in view of the character of the twain briefly closeted in that state-room, each radically sharing in the rarer qualities of our nature—so rare indeed as to be all but incredible to average minds however much cultivated—some conjectures may be ventured.

It would have been in consonance with the spirit of Captain Vere should he on this occasion have concealed nothing from the condemned one—should he indeed have frankly disclosed to him the part he himself had played in bringing about the decision, at the same time revealing his actuating motives. On Billy's side it is not improbable that such a confession would have been received in much the same spirit that prompted it. Not without a sort of joy indeed he might have appreciated the brave opinion of him implied in his Captain's making such a confidant of him. Nor, as to the sentence itself could he have been insensible that it was imparted to him as to one not afraid to die. Even more may have been. Captain Vere in the end may have developed the passion sometimes latent under an exterior stoical or indifferent. He was old enough to have been Billy's father. The austere devotee of military duty, letting himself melt back into what remains primeval in our formalized humanity, may in the end have caught Billy to his heart even as Abraham may have caught young Isaac on the brink of resolutely offering him up in obedience to the exacting behest. But there is no telling the sacrament, seldom if in any case revealed to the gadding world, wherever under circumstances at all akin to those here attempted to be set forth, two of great Nature's nobler order embrace. There is privacy at the time, inviolable to the survivor, and holy oblivion, the sequel to each diviner magnanimity, providentially covers all at last.

The first to encounter Captain Vere in act of leaving the compartment was the senior Lieutenant. The face he beheld, for the moment one expressive of the agony of the strong, was to that officer, tho' a man of fifty, a startling revelation. That the condemned one suffered less than he who mainly had effected the condemnation was apparently indicated by the former's exclamation in the scene soon perforce to be touched upon.

Chapter XXIII

Of a series of incidents within a brief term rapidly following each other, the adequate narration may take up a term less brief, especially if explanation or comment here and there seem requisite to the better understanding of such incidents. Between the entrance into the cabin of him who never left it alive, and him who when he did leave it left it as one condemned to die; between this and the closeted interview just given, less than an hour and a half had elapsed. It was an interval long enough however to awaken speculations among no few of the ship's company as to what it was that could be detaining in the cabin the Master-at-arms and the sailor; for a rumor that both of them had been seen to enter it and neither of them had been seen to emerge, this rumor had got abroad upon the gun decks and in the tops; the people of a great war-ship being in one respect like villagers taking microscopic note of every outward movement or non-movement going on. When therefore in weather not at all tempestuous all hands were called in the second dog-watch, a summons under such circumstances not usual in those hours, the crew were not wholly unprepared for some announcement extraordinary, one having connection too with the continued absence of the two men from their wonted haunts.

There was a moderate sea at the time; and the moon, newly risen and near to being at its full, silvered the white spar-deck wherever not blotted by the clear-cut shadows horizontally thrown of fixtures and moving men. On either side of the quarter-deck, the marine guard under arms was drawn up; and Captain Vere standing in his place surrounded by all the ward-room officers, addressed his men. In so doing his manner showed neither more nor less than that properly pertaining to his supreme position aboard his own ship. In clear terms and concise he told them what had taken place in the cabin; that the Master-at-arms was dead; that he who had killed him had been already tried by a summary court and condemned to death; and that the execution would take place in the early morning watch. The word mutiny was not named in what he said. He refrained too from making the occasion an opportunity for any preachment as to the maintenance of discipline, thinking perhaps that under existing circumstances in the navy the consequence of violating discipline should be made to speak for itself.

Their Captain's announcement was listened to by the throng of standing sailors in a dumbness like that of a seated congregation of believers in hell listening to the clergyman's announcement of his Calvinistic text.

At the close, however, a confused murmur went up. It began to wax. All but instantly, then, at a sign, it was pierced and suppressed by shrill whistles of the Boatswain and his Mates piping down one watch.

To be prepared for burial Claggart's body was delivered to certain petty-officers of his mess. And here, not to clog the sequel with lateral matters, it may be added that at a suitable hour, the Master-at-arms was committed to the sea with every funeral honor properly belonging to his naval grade.

In this proceeding as in every public one growing out of the tragedy, strict adherence to usage was observed. Nor in any point could it have been at all deviated from, either with respect to Claggart or Billy Budd, without begetting undesirable speculations in the ship's company, sailors, and more particularly men-of-war's-men, being of all men the greatest sticklers for usage. For similar cause, all communication between Captain Vere and the condemned one ended with the closeted interview already given, the latter being now surrendered to the ordinary routine preliminary to the end. This transfer under guard from the Captain's quarters was effected without unusual precautions—at least no visible ones. If possible, not to let the men so much as surmise that their officers anticipate aught amiss from them is the tacit rule in a military ship. And the more that some sort of trouble should really be apprehended the more do the officers keep that apprehension to themselves; tho' not the less unostentatious vigilance may be augmented. In the present instance the sentry placed over the prisoner had strict orders to let no one have communication with him but the Chaplain. And certain unobtrusive measures were taken absolutely to insure this point.

Chapter XXIV

IN A SEVENTY-FOUR OF THE OLD ORDER THE DECK KNOWN AS THE UPPER GUN DECK WAS THE ONE covered over by the spar-deck which last though not without its armament was for the most part exposed to the weather. In general it was at all hours free from hammocks; those of the crew swinging on the lower gun deck, and berth-deck, the latter being not only a dormitory but also the place for the stowing of the sailors' bags, and on both sides lined with the large chests or movable pantries of the many messes of the men.

On the starboard side of the *Bellipotent*'s upper gun deck, behold Billy Budd under sentry, lying prone in irons, in one of the bays formed by the regular spacing of the guns comprising the batteries on either side. All these pieces were of the heavier caliber of that period. Mounted on lumbering wooden carriages they were hampered with cumbersome harness of breechen and strong side-tackles for running them out. Guns and carriages, together with the long rammers and shorter lintstocks lodged in loops overhead—all these, as customary, were painted black; and the heavy hempen breechens, tarred to the same tint, wore the like livery of the undertakers. In contrast with the funereal hue of these surroundings the prone sailor's exterior apparel, white jumper and white duck trousers, each more or less soiled, dimly glimmered in the obscure light of the bay like a patch of discolored snow in early April lingering at some upland cave's black mouth. In effect he is already in his shroud or the garments that shall serve him in lieu of one. Over him, but scarce illuminating him, two battle-lanterns swing from two massive beams of the deck above. Fed with the oil supplied by the war-contractors (whose gains, honest or otherwise, are in every land an anticipated portion of the harvest of death), with flickering splashes of dirty yellow light they pollute the pale moonshine all but ineffectually struggling in obstructed flecks thro' the open ports from which the tompioned cannon protrude. Other lanterns at intervals serve but to bring out somewhat the obscurer bays which, like small confessionals or side-chapels in a cathedral, branch from the long dim-vistaed broad aisle between the two batteries of that covered tier.

Such was the deck where now lay the Handsome Sailor. Through the rose-tan of his complexion, no pallor could have shown. It would have taken days of sequestration from the winds and the sun to have brought about the effacement of that. But the skeleton in the cheekbone at the point of its angle was just beginning delicately to be defined under the warm-tinted skin. In fervid hearts self-contained, some brief experiences devour our human tissue as secret fire in a ship's hold consumes cotton in the bale.

But now lying between the two guns, as nipped in the vice of fate, Billy's agony, mainly proceeding from a generous young heart's virgin experience of the diabolical incarnate and effective in some men—the tension of that agony was over now. It survived not the something healing in the closeted interview with Captain Vere. Without movement, he lay as in a trance. That adolescent expression previously noted as his, taking on something akin to the look of a slumbering child in the cradle when the warm hearth-glow of the still chamber at night plays on the dimples that at whiles mysteriously form in the cheek, silently coming and going there. For now and then in the gyved one's trance a serene happy light born of some wandering reminiscence or dream would diffuse itself over his face, and then wane away only anew to return.

The Chaplain coming to see him and finding him thus, and perceiving no sign that he was conscious of his presence, attentively regarded him for a space, then slipping aside, withdrew for the time, peradventure feeling that even he the minister of Christ, tho' receiving his stipend from Mars, had no consolation to proffer which could result in a peace transcending that which he beheld. But in the small hours he came again. And the prisoner, now awake to his surroundings, noticed his approach, and civilly, all but cheerfully, welcomed him. But it was to little purpose that in the interview following the good man sought to bring Billy Budd to some godly understanding that he must die, and at dawn. True, Billy himself freely referred to his death as a thing close at hand; but it was something in the way that children will refer to death in general, who yet among their other sports will play a funeral with hearse and mourners.

Not that like children Billy was incapable of conceiving what death really is. No, but he was wholly without irrational fear of it, a fear more prevalent in highly civilized communities than those so-called barbarous ones which in all respects stand nearer to unadulterate Nature. And, as elsewhere said, a barbarian Billy radically was; as much so, for all the costume, as his countrymen the British captives, living trophies, made to march in the Roman triumph of Germanicus. Quite as much so as those later barbarians, young men probably, and picked specimens among the earlier British converts to Christianity, at least nominally such, and taken to Rome (as to-day converts from lesser isles of the sea may be taken to London), of whom the Pope of that time, admiring the strangeness of their personal beauty so unlike the Italian stamp, their clear ruddy complexion and curled flaxen locks, exclaimed, "Angles" (meaning *English* the modern derivative) "Angles do you call them? And is it because they look so like angels?" Had it been later in time one would think that the Pope had in mind Fra Angelico's seraphs some of whom, plucking apples in gardens of the Hesperides, have the faint rose-bud complexion of the more beautiful English girls.

If in vain the good Chaplain sought to impress the young barbarian with ideas of death akin to those conveyed in the skull, dial, and cross-bones on old tombstones; equally futile to all appearance were his efforts to bring home to him the thought of salvation and a Savior. Billy listened, but less out of awe or reverence perhaps than from a certain natural politeness; doubtless at bottom regarding all that in much the same way that most mariners of his class take any discourse abstract or out of the common tone of the work-a-day world. And this sailor-way of taking clerical discourse is not wholly unlike the way in which the pioneer of Christianity full of transcendent miracles was received long ago on tropic isles by any superior *savage* so called—a Tahitian say of Captain Cook's time or shortly after that time. Out of natural courtesy he received, but did not appropriate. It was like a gift placed in the palm of an outreached hand upon which the fingers do not close.

But the *Bellipotent*'s Chaplain was a discreet man possessing the good sense of a good heart. So he insisted not in his vocation here. At the instance of Captain Vere, a lieutenant had apprised him of pretty much everything as to Billy; and since he felt that innocence was even a better thing than religion wherewith to go to Judgment, he reluctantly withdrew; but in his emotion not without first performing an act strange enough in an Englishman, and under the circumstances yet more so in any regular priest. Stooping over, he kissed on the fair cheek his fellow-man, a felon in martial law, one who though on the confines of death he felt he could never convert to a dogma; nor for all that did he fear for his future.

Marvel not that having been made acquainted with the young sailor's essential innocence (an irruption of heretic thought hard to suppress) the worthy man lifted not a finger to avert the doom of such a martyr to martial discipline. So to do would not only have been as idle as invoking the desert, but would also have been an audacious transgression of the bounds of his function, one as exactly prescribed to him by military law as that of the boatswain or any other naval officer. Bluntly put, a chaplain is the minister of the Prince of Peace serving in the host of the God of War—Mars. As such, he is as incongruous as a musket would be on the altar at Christmas. Why then is he there? Because he indirectly subserves the purpose attested by the cannon; because too he lends the sanction of the religion of the meek to that which practically is the abrogation of everything but brute Force.

Chapter XXV

THE NIGHT, SO LUMINOUS ON THE SPAR-DECK, BUT OTHERWISE ON THE CAVERNOUS ONES BELOW, levels so like the tiered galleries in a coal-mine—the luminous night passed away. But, like the prophet in the chariot disappearing in heaven and dropping his mantle to Elisha, the withdrawing night transferred its pale robe to the breaking day. A meek shy light appeared in the East, where stretched a diaphanous fleece of white furrowed vapor. That light slowly waxed. Suddenly *eight bells* was struck aft, responded to by one louder metallic stroke from forward. It was four o'clock in the morning. Instantly the silver whistles were heard summoning all hands to witness punishment. Up through the great hatchways rimmed with racks of heavy shot, the watch below came pouring, overspreading with the watch already on deck the space between the main-mast and fore-mast including that occupied by the capacious launch and the black booms tiered on either side of it, boat and booms making a summit of observation for the powder-boys and younger tars. A different group comprising one watch of topmen leaned over the rail of that sea-balcony, no small one in a seventy-four, looking down on the crowd below. Man or boy, none spake but in whisper, and few spake at all. Captain Vere—as before, the central figure among the assembled commissioned officers—stood nigh the break of the poop-deck facing forward. Just below him on the quarter-deck the marines in full equipment were drawn up much as at the scene of the promulgated sentence.

At sea in the old time, the execution by halter of a military sailor was generally from the fore-yard. In the present instance, for special reasons the main-yard was assigned. Under an arm of that lee-yard the prisoner was presently brought up, the Chaplain attending him. It was noted at the time and remarked upon afterwards, that in this final scene the good man evinced little or nothing of the perfunctory. Brief speech indeed he had with the condemned one, but the genuine Gospel was less on his tongue than in his aspect and manner towards him. The final preparations personal to the latter being speedily brought to an end by two boatswain's mates, the consummation impended. Billy stood facing aft. At the penultimate moment, his words, his only ones, words wholly unobstructed in the utterance were these—"God bless Captain Vere!" Syllables so unanticipated coming from one with the ignominious hemp about his neck—a conventional felon's benediction directed aft towards the quarters of honor; syllables too delivered in the clear melody of a singing-bird on the point of launching from the twig, had a phenomenal effect, not unenhanced by the rare personal beauty of the young sailor spiritualized now thro' late experiences so poignantly profound.

Without volition as it were, as if indeed the ship's populace were but the vehicles of some vocal current electric, with one voice from alow and aloft came a resonant sympathetic echo—

"God bless Captain Vere!" And yet at that instant Billy alone must have been in their hearts, even as he was in their eyes.

At the pronounced words and the spontaneous echo that voluminously rebounded them, Captain Vere, either thro' stoic self-control or a sort of momentary paralysis induced by emotional shock, stood erectly rigid as a musket in the ship-armorer's rack.

The hull deliberately recovering from the periodic roll to leeward was just regaining an even keel, when the last signal, a preconcerted dumb one, was given. At the same moment it chanced that the vapory fleece hanging low in the East, was shot thro' with a soft glory as of the fleece of the Lamb of God seen in mystical vision, and simultaneously therewith, watched by the wedged mass of upturned faces, Billy ascended; and, ascending, took the full rose of the dawn.

In the pinioned figure, arrived at the yard-end, to the wonder of all no motion was apparent, none save that created by the ship's motion, in moderate weather so majestic in a great ship ponderously cannoned.

Chapter XXVI

When some days afterward in reference to the singularity just mentioned, the Purser, a rather ruddy rotund person more accurate as an accountant than profound as a philosopher, said at mess to the Surgeon, "What testimony to the force lodged in will-power," the latter—saturnine, spare and tall, one in whom a discreet causticity went along with a manner less genial than polite, replied, "Your pardon, Mr. Purser. In a hanging scientifically conducted—and under special orders I myself directed how Budd's was to be effected—any movement following the completed suspension and originating in the body suspended, such movement indicates mechanical spasm in the muscular system. Hence the absence of that is no more attributable to will-power as you call it than to horse-power—begging your pardon."

"But this muscular spasm you speak of, is not that in a degree more or less invariable in these cases?"

"Assuredly so, Mr. Purser."

"How then, my good sir, do you account for its absence in this instance?"

"Mr. Purser, it is clear that your sense of the singularity in this matter equals not mine. You account for it by what you call will-power, a term not yet included in the lexicon of science. For me I do not, with my present knowledge, pretend to account for it at all. Even should we assume the hypothesis that at the first touch of the halyards the action of Budd's heart, intensified by extraordinary emotion at its climax, abruptly stopt—much like a watch when in carelessly winding it up you strain at the finish, thus snapping the chain—even under that hypothesis, how account for the phenomenon that followed?"

"You admit then that the absence of spasmodic movement was phenomenal."

"It was phenomenal, Mr. Purser, in the sense that it was an appearance the cause of which is not immediately to be assigned."

"But tell me, my dear Sir," pertinaciously continued the other, "was the man's death effected by the halter, or was it a species of euthanasia?"

"*Euthanasia*, Mr. Purser, is something like your *will-power*: I doubt its authenticity as a scientific term—begging your pardon again. It is at once imaginative and metaphysical—in short, Greek. But," abruptly changing his tone, "there is a case in the sick-bay that I do not care to leave to my assistants. Beg your pardon, but excuse me." And rising from the mess he formally withdrew.

Chapter XXVII

THE SILENCE AT THE MOMENT OF EXECUTION AND FOR A MOMENT OR TWO CONTINUING THEREafter, a silence but emphasized by the regular wash of the sea against the hull or the flutter of a sail caused by the helmsman's eyes being tempted astray, this emphasized silence was gradually disturbed by a sound not easily to be verbally rendered. Whoever has heard the freshet-wave of a torrent suddenly swelled by pouring showers in tropical mountains, showers not shared by the plain; whoever has heard the first muffled murmur of its sloping advance through precipitous woods, may form some conception of the sound now heard. The seeming remoteness of its source was because of its murmurous indistinctness since it came from close-by, even from the men massed on the ship's open deck. Being inarticulate, it was dubious in significance further than it seemed to indicate some capricious revulsion of thought or feeling such as mobs ashore are liable to, in the present instance possibly implying a sullen revocation on the men's part of their involuntary echoing of Billy's benediction. But ere the murmur had time to wax into clamor it was met by a strategic command, the more telling that it came with abrupt unexpectedness. "Pipe down the starboard watch, Boatswain, and see that they go."

Shrill as the shriek of the sea-hawk the whistles of the Boatswain and his Mates pierced that ominous low sound, dissipating it; and yielding to the mechanism of discipline, the throng was thinned by one half. For the remainder most of them were set to temporary employments connected with trimming the yards and so forth, business readily to be got up to serve occasion by any officer-of-the-deck.

Now each proceeding that follows a mortal sentence pronounced at sea by a drum-head court is characterized by promptitude not perceptibly merging into hurry, tho' bordering that. The hammock, the one which had been Billy's bed when alive, having already been ballasted with shot and otherwise prepared to serve for his canvas coffin, the last offices of the sea-undertakers, the Sail-Maker's Mates, were now speedily completed. When everything was in readiness a second call for all hands made necessary by the strategic movement before mentioned was sounded and now to witness burial.

The details of this closing formality it needs not to give. But when the tilted plank let slide its freight into the sea, a second strange human murmur was heard, blended now with another inarticulate sound proceeding from certain larger sea-fowl, whose attention having been attracted by the peculiar commotion in the water resulting from the heavy sloped dive of the shotted hammock into the sea, flew screaming to the spot. So near the hull did they come, that the stridor or bony creak of their gaunt double-jointed pinions was audible. As the ship under light airs passed on, leaving the burial-spot astern, they still kept circling it low down with the moving shadow of their outstretched wings and the croaked requiem of their cries.

Upon sailors as superstitious as those of the age preceding ours, men-of-war's-men too who had just beheld the prodigy of repose in the form suspended in air and now foundering in the deeps; to such mariners the action of the sea-fowl, tho' dictated by mere animal greed for prey, was big with no prosaic significance. An uncertain movement began among them, in which some encroachment was made. It was tolerated but for a moment. For suddenly the drum beat to quarters, which familiar sound happening at least twice every day, had upon the present occasion a signal peremptoriness in it. True martial discipline long continued superinduces in average man a sort of impulse of docility whose operation at the official sound of command much resembles in its promptitude the effect of an instinct.

The drum-beat dissolved the multitude, distributing most of them along the batteries of the two covered gun decks. There, as wont, the guns' crews stood by their respective cannon erect and silent. In due course the First Officer, sword under arm and standing in his place on the quarter-deck, formally received the successive reports of the sworded Lieutenants commanding the sections of batteries below; the last of which reports being made, the summed report he delivered with the customary salute to the Commander. All this occupied time, which in the present case, was the object of beating to quarters at an hour prior to the customary one. That such variance from usage was authorized by an officer like Captain Vere, a martinet as some deemed him, was evidence of the necessity for unusual action implied in what he deemed to be temporarily the mood of his men. "With mankind," he would say, "forms, measured forms are everything; and that is the import couched in the story of Orpheus with his lyre spell-binding the wild denizens of the wood." And this he once applied to the disruption of forms going on across the Channel and the consequences thereof.

At this unwonted muster at quarters, all proceeded as at the regular hour. The band on the quarter-deck played a sacred air. After which the Chaplain went thro' the customary morning service. That done, the drum beat the retreat, and toned by music and religious rites subserving the discipline and purpose of war, the men in their wonted orderly manner, dispersed to the places allotted them when not at the guns.

And now it was full day. The fleece of low-hanging vapor had vanished, licked up by the sun that late had so glorified it. And the circumambient air in the clearness of its serenity was like smooth marble in the polished block not yet removed from the marble-dealer's yard.

Chapter XXVIII

THE SYMMETRY OF FORM ATTAINABLE IN PURE FICTION CAN NOT SO READILY BE ACHIEVED IN A narration essentially having less to do with fable than with fact. Truth uncompromisingly told will always have its ragged edges; hence the conclusion of such a narration is apt to be less finished than an architectural finial.

How it fared with the Handsome Sailor during the year of the Great Mutiny has been faithfully given. But tho' properly the story ends with his life, something in way of sequel will not be amiss. Three brief chapters will suffice.

In the general re-christening under the Directory of the craft originally forming the navy of the French monarchy, the *St. Louis* line-of-battle ship was named the *Atheiste*. Such a name, like some other substituted ones in the Revolutionary fleet, while proclaiming the infidel audacity of the ruling power was yet, tho' not so intended to be, the aptest name, if one consider it, ever given to a war-ship; far more so indeed than the *Devastation*, the *Erebus* (the *Hell*) and similar names bestowed upon fighting-ships.

On the return-passage to the English fleet from the detached cruise during which occurred the events already recorded, the *Bellipotent* fell in with the *Atheiste*. An engagement ensued; during which Captain Vere, in the act of putting his ship alongside the enemy with a view of throwing his boarders across her bulwarks, was hit by a musket-ball from a port-hole of the enemy's main cabin. More than disabled he dropped to the deck and was carried below to the same cock-pit where some of his men already lay. The senior Lieutenant took command. Under him the enemy was finally captured and though much crippled was by rare good fortune successfully taken into Gibraltar, an English port not very distant from the scene of the fight. There, Captain Vere with the rest of the wounded was put ashore. He lingered for some days, but the end came. Unhappily he was cut off too early for the Nile and Trafalgar. The spirit that spite its philosophic austerity may yet have indulged in the most secret of all passions, ambition, never attained to the fullness of fame.

Not long before death, while lying under the influence of that magical drug which soothing the physical frame mysteriously operates on the subtler element in man, he was heard to murmur words inexplicable to his attendant—"Billy Budd, Billy Budd." That these were not the accents of remorse, would seem clear from what the attendant said to the *Bellipotent*'s senior officer of marines who, as the most reluctant to condemn of the members of the drum-head court, too well knew, tho' here he kept the knowledge to himself, who Billy Budd was.

Chapter XXIX

SOME FEW WEEKS AFTER THE EXECUTION, AMONG OTHER MATTERS UNDER THE HEAD OF NEWS from the Mediterranean, there appeared in a naval chronicle of the time, an authorized weekly publication, an account of the affair. It was doubtless for the most part written in good faith, tho' the medium, partly rumor, through which the facts must have reached the writer, served to deflect and in part falsify them. The account was as follows:-

"On the tenth of the last month a deplorable occurrence took place on board H.M.S. *Bellipotent*. John Claggart, the ship's Master-at-arms, discovering that some sort of plot was incipient among an inferior section of the ship's company, and that the ringleader was one William Budd; he, Claggart, in the act of arraigning the man before the Captain was vindictively stabbed to the heart by the suddenly drawn sheath-knife of Budd.

"The deed and the implement employed, sufficiently suggest that tho' mustered into the service under an English name the assassin was no Englishman, but one of those aliens adopting English cognomens whom the present extraordinary necessities of the Service have caused to be admitted into it in considerable numbers.

"The enormity of the crime and the extreme depravity of the criminal, appear the greater in view of the character of the victim, a middle-aged man respectable and discreet, belonging to that official grade, the petty-officers, upon whom, as none know better than the commissioned gentlemen, the efficiency of His Majesty's Navy so largely depends. His function was a responsible one, at once onerous & thankless, and his fidelity in it the greater because of his strong patriotic impulse. In this instance as in so many other instances in these days, the character of this unfortunate man signally refutes, if refutation were needed, that peevish saying attributed to the late Dr. Johnson, that patriotism is the last refuge of a scoundrel.

"The criminal paid the penalty of his crime. The promptitude of the punishment has proved salutary. Nothing amiss is now apprehended aboard H.M.S. *Bellipotent*."

The above, appearing in a publication now long ago superannuated and forgotten, is all that hitherto has stood in human record to attest what manner of men respectively were John Claggart and Billy Budd.

Chapter XXX

EVERYTHING IS FOR A TERM REMARKABLE IN NAVIES. ANY TANGIBLE OBJECT ASSOCIATED WITH some striking incident of the service is converted into a monument. The spar from which the Foretopman was suspended, was for some few years kept trace of by the blue-jackets. Their knowledge followed it from ship to dock-yard and again from dock-yard to ship, still pursuing it even when at last reduced to a mere dock-yard boom. To them a chip of it was as a piece of the Cross. Ignorant tho' they were of the secret facts of the tragedy, and not thinking but that the penalty was somehow unavoidably inflicted from the naval point of view, for all that they instinctively felt that Billy was a sort of man as incapable of mutiny as of wilfull murder. They recalled the fresh young image of the Handsome Sailor, that face never deformed by a sneer or subtler vile freak of the heart within. Their impression of him was doubtless deepened by the fact that he was gone, and in a measure mysteriously gone. At the time, on the gun decks of the *Bellipotent*, the general estimate of his nature and its unconscious simplicity eventually found rude utterance from another foretopman, one of his own watch, gifted, as some sailors are, with an artless poetic temperament; the tarry hands made some lines which after circulating among the shipboard crew for a while, finally got rudely printed at Portsmouth as a ballad. The title given to it was the sailor's.

BILLY IN THE DARBIES

Good of the Chaplain to enter Lone Bay
And down on his marrow-bones here and pray
For the likes just o' me, Billy Budd. But look:
Through the port comes the moon-shine astray!
It tips the guard's cutlas and silvers this nook;
But 'twill die in the dawning of Billy's last day.
A jewel-block they'll make of me to-morrow,
Pendant pearl from the yard-arm-end
Like the ear-drop I gave to Bristol Molly—
O, 'tis me, not the sentence they'll suspend.
Ay, Ay, Ay, all is up; and I must up to
Early in the morning, aloft from alow.
On an empty stomach, now, never it would do.
They'll give me a nibble—bit o' biscuit ere I go.
Sure, a messmate will reach me the last parting cup;
But, turning heads away from the hoist and the belay,
Heaven knows who will have the running of me up!
No pipe to those halyards. But aren't it all sham?
A blur's in my eyes; it is dreaming that I am.
A hatchet to my hawser? all adrift to go?
The drum roll to grog, and Billy never know?
But Donald he has promised to stand by the plank;
So I'll shake a friendly hand ere I sink.
But—no! It is dead then I'll be, come to think.
I remember Taff the Welshman when he sank.
And his cheek it was like the budding pink.
But me they'll lash me in hammock, drop me deep.
Fathoms down, fathoms down, how I'll dream fast asleep.
I feel it stealing now. Sentry, are you there?
Just ease this darbies at the wrist, and roll me over fair,
I am sleepy, and the oozy weeds about me twist.

About the Author

HERMAN MELVILLE (1819-1891) WAS BORN IN NEW YORK CITY AND RAISED IN UPSTATE NEW YORK. After holding a number of clerical and teaching jobs, he shipped out on a Pacific-bound whaling ship in 1841. His experiences as a sailor over the next four years—which included desertion, mutiny, a reported stay among cannibals in the Marquesas Islands, and enlistment in the United States Navy—served as raw materials for fiction that he began writing in 1845. His first book, *Typee* (1846), was published as non-fiction but challenged for its authenticity and censored for its controversial content. Over the next four years Melville published four novels—*Omoo* (1847), *Mardi* (1849), *Redburn* (1849), and *White-Jacket* (1850)—all of which featured colorful accounts of travel and seagoing adventure punctuated with provocative commentary on the harshness of the sailor's life. Melville's increasing experimentation with theme and narrative form led him to write *Moby Dick* (1851), a fanciful account of a sea captain's obsessive pursuit of a legendary white whale. Although lauded today as a landmark of literature and one of the most important novels by an American writer, the book was reviewed badly and sold poorly. Poor sales of his next three novels—*Pierre* (1852), *Israel Potter* (1855), and *The Confidence Man* (1857)—convinced Melville to give up writing fiction and concentrate on poetry. He collected most of his short fiction in *The Piazza Tales* (1856) and much of his verse in *Battle-Pieces and Aspects of the War* (1866). Melville served as a customs inspector in New York from 1866 to 1885. His last work of fiction, *Billy Budd, Sailor,* was published posthumously.

THE LIBRARY OF ESSENTIAL WRITERS

JANE AUSTEN *Seven Novels*

CHARLOTTE BRONTË *Four Novels*

LEWIS CARROLL *Complete Works*

JOSEPH CONRAD *Complete Short Stories*

JAMES FENIMORE COOPER *Five Novels*

DANIEL DEFOE *Five Novels*

CHARLES DICKENS *Five Novels*

ALEXANDRE DUMAS *Three Novels*

GEORGE ELIOT *Four Novels*

GUSTAVE FLAUBERT *Five Novels*

E. M. FORSTER *Four Novels*

THOMAS HARDY *Five Novels*

NATHANIEL HAWTHORNE *Five Novels*

ERNEST HEMINGWAY *Four Novels*

O. HENRY *The Fiction*

VICTOR HUGO *Three Novels*

HENRY JAMES *Five Novels*

JACK LONDON *Six Novels*

H.P. LOVECRAFT *The Fiction*

W. SOMERSET MAUGHAM *Five Novels*

HERMAN MELVILLE *Seven Novels*

EDGAR ALLAN POE *Fiction and Poetry*

SAKI *The Fiction*

ROBERT LOUIS STEVENSON *Seven Novels*

BRAM STOKER *Five Novels*

LEO TOLSTOY *Three Novels*

MARK TWAIN *Five Novels*

JULES VERNE *Seven Novels*

H. G. WELLS *Seven Novels*

EDITH WHARTON *Five Novels*

OSCAR WILDE *Collected Works*